Power Generation and the Environment

Power Generation and the Environment

by Anco S. Blazev

THE FAIRMONT PRESS, INC.

CRC Press
Taylor & Francis Group

Library of Congress Cataloging-in-Publication Data

Blazev, Anco S., 1946-
  Power Generation and the Environment / by Anco S. Blazev.
    pages cm
  Includes bibliographical references and index.
    ISBN 0-88173-705-4 (alk. paper) (alk. paper) -- ISBN 0-88173-706-2 (electronic) -- ISBN 978-1-4822-2299-9 (Taylor & Francis distribution : alk. paper) 1. Electric power systems--Environmental aspects. I. Title.

  TD195.E4B58 2014
  363.73'1--dc23

                                                                    2013048309

Published by The Fairmont Press, Inc.
700 Indian Trail
Lilburn, GA 30047
tel: 770-925-9388; fax: 770-381-9865
http://www.fairmontpress.com

Distributed by Taylor & Francis Ltd.
6000 Broken Sound Parkway NW, Suite 300
Boca Raton, FL 33487, USA
E-mail: orders@crcpress.com

Distributed by Taylor & Francis Ltd.
23-25 Blades Court
Deodar Road
London SW15 2NU, UK
E-mail: uk.tandf@thomsonpublishingservices.co.uk

Printed in the United States of America
10 9 8 7 6 5 4 3 2 1

ISBN-0-88173-705-4 (The Fairmont Press, Inc.)
ISBN-978-1-4822-2299-9 (Taylor & Francis Ltd.)

Table of Contents

Chapter 4

Chapter 5

Chapter 6

Chapter 7

Chapter 8

Foreword

At a time when energy and environmental issues dominate the national and international news, about 70% of Americans say they don't know how energy is generated and delivered. A similar number are not familiar with the effects power generation has on the environment and the increasing global warming, all of which are discussed in detail in this text.

This book, therefore, is a *detailed technical analysis* of energy (heat and electric power) generation technologies and operations, and their direct or indirect impact on the environment. We dive deep into the technical details of the planning, design, production, setup, function, operation, and use of the different power generating technologies, processes, and facilities. Then we analyze the direct and hidden costs that the environment and people must pay when using thus generated power.

Power generation is not just a technical matter, although it operates on a highly technical level. The equipment is complex and expensive, and must be dealt with in a reliable, efficient, cost-effective, and safe manner. This requires that management, engineers, technicians, and operators be well trained and well aware of all aspects of the operations.

Because things seldom go smoothly all the time, there are always gaps and problems in power generating technologies—be it conventional (coal, oil, gas), or renewable (solar, wind, bio, geo)—and the related processes and procedures during their cradle-to-grave life span.

In addition to technical aspects, we also analyze all variables in key areas of the power generation industries, including political, regulatory, and socio-economic activities, to unveil some of the misunderstandings and misrepresentations that have been haunting the sector during the last several decades.

Power generation is not a black box, nor is it a necessary evil that we simply put up with, as often misrepresented by interested parties. It is not just an ever-increasing monthly bill that we must blindly accept, nor is it something we are not allowed to understand—God forbid, question.

On the contrary, generated power does not belong to the inventors, designers, operators, or owners of power plants and utilities. It belongs to people like you and me who use it daily and pay for it. However, we have allowed government, utility officials, big business, and the media to keep us in the dark and lead us with misinformation.

Everyone should understand what power generation is about, how the different types of power are produced, distributed, and used, and what happens behind the scenes. Armed with knowledge on the matter, we can make our own conclusions and decisions about the power generation industry, its inner workings, the fair use of power, and our power bills. Then, as we analyze the different technologies, we can translate every aspect of power generation into its effects on the environment.

To help us with that endeavor, in this book we analyze in detail:

1. Fuels the different power generating technologies use,

2. Power generating equipment and facilities design, production and daily function,

3. Actual power generation processes and procedures,

4. Generated power, its distribution, delivery, and use in homes and businesses, and

5. Because all things must come to an end, we take into account the end-of-life decommissioning and disposal of power generating equipment and facilities.

NOTE: We never cease to be amazed how elaborate, expensive, and unpredictable this final activity is, and how often it is (intentionally or unintentionally) underestimated and even ignored in the design, and/or final calculations. This small but very important procedure exemplifies the need for thorough understanding and utmost attention to detail, when dealing with such complex technical issues.

Once we know how power is produced, we can clearly and confidently look at how the environment and humans are affected by all these activities. With this in mind, in this text we hope to achieve our ultimate goal, which is to

1) Present a clear, unbiased, and complete picture of the power generation industry,

2) Superimpose power-generating activities, with all their ramifications, onto the global environmental picture of today,

3) Estimate the results of these activities now, and extrapolate them into the future.

We hope this text will give the reader a good understanding of the way all energy sources work, and the issues they create. This, in turn, will allow us to make informed decisions on how to handle today's *power generation vs. environmental change* debate and how to proceed in the future as engaged and responsible citizens of Mother Earth.

FOR THE READER:

We made a conscious effort to keep the technical aspects of this text at a level that can be understood by a wide audience, from high school students to professionals in various fields. We think we have achieved this goal for most of the book. There are some exceptions on both levels, which were simply unavoidable.

This is not easy to do, especially when dealing with such a great number of highly technical subjects that must be presented concisely and completely, so we are prepared for, and accept, criticism from both sides.

Chapter 1

Energy and the Environment

In the beginning God created the heavens and the earth. The earth was without form and void, and darkness was upon the face of the deep; and the Spirit of God was moving over the face of the waters. And God said, "Let there be light"; and there was light. And God saw that the light was good; and God separated the light from the darkness.

Genesis 1:1-4

For those of us who believe that the Bible is the ultimate truth, things are very clear and quite simple: the Earth was created by an omnipresent and omnipotent power. God put everything in motion and now we are traveling on spaceship Earth, driven by its Designer, to an unknown destination.

We have been given a cursory understanding of life on Earth, but are advised to not dig too deeply into it, for the answer is above our comprehension. We also know that a day is coming when everything and everybody on Earth will perish, but we don't know when that day will be, and how exactly the destruction will proceed. Fire seems to be one of the destruction methods, but we don't know where it will come from—war, natural disaster, or...? We don't know how bad it will be afterward. Yet we are confident that no matter what happens our Driver is solidly in charge, so we can sit back and enjoy the ride.

For those of us who do not take the Bible so literally, things are much more complicated and full of uncertainty. We must look much harder at the facts around us to find meaning and explanation that does not include God. This is not easily done, because the creation is veiled in complex scientific twists and uncertainties. Most environmental events are complex developments that take a long time to reveal themselves, at which point there are still a number of questions remaining in most cases. Often, it is not possible to get a clear picture of many present events, let alone those of our distant past. Similarly, the future is also veiled in uncertainty and mystery. Attempts to predict the future are futile, as has been demonstrated many times.

We do know that we have some, albeit minimal, control over the speed and direction our spaceship is moving, but we have not figured out how and what exactly must be done to gain more or complete control. Since we don't have all the facts, we often complete the picture with suppositions and guesswork which translate into inaccuracies and might lead to bad decisions and big mistakes.

Nevertheless, we must attempt to understand the major environmental events surrounding us, to find solutions to the problems at hand and those to come.

We must act fast though, because there is a real danger that by the time we understand what's going on and take appropriate action, it might be too late to do anything about it. A good example is the real and present danger of climate warming, which might prove exceedingly destructive if not controlled soon. If Earth's temperature were to increase to the point of no return, life would become impossible. We know that things have changed significantly during the last century, and we are now very much aware that we live in a even more rapidly changing environment.

The environmental changes are discussed and debated with an ever increasing passion around the world, because we see clearly the negative effects increasing with every passing day. We are bombarded with bad news about increasingly inclement weather and natural disasters, contaminated soil and water, and even poisons in the air we breath. Is it really that bad? And if it is, why? Is there anything we can do to change things for the better?

These are questions, we will be asking and tackling in this text, while focusing on the role and the environmental effects of power generation.

THE BOOK

This is an environmental book with a twist. The author is a chemical engineer specialized in the area of power generating equipment and its use. In this text, energy sources, materials, equipment, processes and devices are evaluated using the available scientific facts as filtered by the author's experience as an energy engineer.

Environmental effects caused by energy sources and their use are then analyzed, to provide possible solutions to any damage caused by them, again filtered by the author's experience in the field.

Based firmly on the engineering principle that the glass is neither half empty nor half full, but rather representing instead work in progress, we are presenting the facts as we see them. No bias, no overemphasizing of negative or positive effects, or taking sides is intended in this text.

Since our main objective is to lay down the facts of power generation and related environmental effects, we take a close look at the intricate details of all the different types of energy generation sources, materials, equipment, facilities, processes and methods. In each case we start with technical analysis of the key components, focusing on their impact on the environment.

Looking closely at coal, oil, and gas on one hand, and solar, wind and biofuels on the other, we compare what it takes to manufacture and use these different technologies. This will give us a good idea where the environmental problems start and what, if anything, can be done to control their negative effects.

OUR WONDERFUL WORLD

Looking at the early morning sky, we are greeted by Earth's oldest friend, the Sun, which we have known, enjoyed and mostly taken for granted since our childhood. We are well aware that our wellbeing, and in fact our very lives, depends upon its daily presence in the sky, and yet we seldom give it more than a passing thought. However, it never fails us; it is out there shining brightly every day whether or not we see it or care. It is one of the few things in this life on which we can count. But if the Sun's rays were blocked from reaching the Earth for longer than usual, life as we know it would cease.

Thomas Edison recognized and appreciated the power of the Sun almost 100 years ago, saying, "I'd put my money on solar energy...I hope we don't have to wait 'til oil and coal run out before we tackle that." How profound and prophetic this sounds today!

Even then, in 1931 when there were only a few cars on the streets and one or two power plants, he was worried that oil and coal would prevent solar energy from being widely used. And he was right. Coal and oil are still winning the race, and the awesome power of the Sun is kept out of our reach by oil, coal, business enterprises, and political interests.

In our estimate, this situation won't change until the last drop of oil is pumped out of the Earth and the last shovel of coal is thrown into the furnace—regardless of deteriorating environmental conditions. This is capitalism at work, and there is not much we can do about it, except prepare to face the consequences.

Our goal here is to consider and reconsider the role of the different energy sources and their effects, which might help us find ways to clean the environment. Let us take this opportunity to examine the facts more closely, keeping in mind that virtually all energy on Earth has been (and still is), in one way or another, created by "solar" power—the power of light coming from the Sun.

The fundamental energy that sustains human life—food energy—comes from plants using photosynthesis to convert sunlight and CO_2 into living tissue. Even last night's hamburger can be traced back to the grasses and grain eaten by the cows—energy converted into food by the direct and indirect action of sunlight.

The gasoline in our cars comes from petroleum, formed when plants and animals (full of the sunlight's energy from photosynthesis) were submerged underground and transformed over millions of years into hydrocarbons which we extract and burn. Just think of the immense supply of energy stored underground in the form of crude oil, coal and natural gas. This is energy that the Sun provided millions of years ago to life on Earth—energy which has been carefully stored until now, and which we are determined to deplete by the end of the 21st century.

What about wind energy? Well, without the heating rays of the Sun there would be no wind, rain, or other weather fluctuations on Earth. The Sun heats the air, and this results in wind currents which are transformed into wind energy, which can then be captured by wind mills and converted into electricity. What about hydroelectric energy? Without the Sun heating the oceans and drawing up water into the clouds, which then falls as rain in the mountains, there would be no rivers and therefore nothing for us to dam for capturing the energy from falling water. So you see, with very few exceptions, all forms and shapes of energy on Earth are related to solar energy.

Here is an interesting fact to consider: the sunlight that reaches the Earth's surface in one 24-hour period contains enough energy (if converted into usable electricity) to meet the needs of the entire world for one full year. Imagine that! So why are we digging into the depths of the Earth to excavate and pump to the ground dinosaur remains (petroleum, coal and such) to use for fuel and electric energy generation? Why are we exposing human health and life to the dangers of the deep and toxic by-products? Why do we continue making oil-rich nations richer by buying their remaining oil and gas reserves? Why not do what we should have done decades ago: harness the abundant, free and renewable energy of the wind and Sun, thus generating free, clean and renewable energy?

The sooner these renewable energy technologies are perfected, the better life will be for us and future generations. Also, the sooner this is accomplished, the sooner we will be able to begin to reverse the damages of global warming and other disasters.

It has been the dream of mankind through the centuries to be able to capture the bright warm rays of the Sun and harness their power, but our ancestors were limited in their technical abilities. Our generation, however, has the knowledge, experience, materials and equipment to harness a large portion of the light coming down to Earth and to use it as we wish. Nevertheless, we continue to use fossil fuels to transport, cool and warm ourselves. How long will these fossil fuels last? What excuse do we have to postpone the inevitable? What excuse are we going to give the next generations if we fail to address the misuse of fossil fuels?

Most of the energy we use comes from burning coal, and many people die in the process of mining it and breathing its by-products. We still use crude oil as if there were an unlimited supply, pumping millions of gallons daily and saturating the atmosphere with harmful by-products. We still plan the construction of dangerous nuclear power plants to supplement our energy gluttony, and then we hastily hide the toxic waste materials in weird places, leaving future generations to figure out what to do with them. And in the process of doing all this, we waste 99% of the free and clean solar power coming to us.

Just think, 100 square miles of Nevada desert could power the entire USA, and 3% of the world's unused desert lands could power the entire world. A small part of the world's deserts covered with PV modules (or other solar power generating equipment), could power the entire world. Imagine that! We have a chance to use that free sunlight in unprecedented, efficient and cost-effective ways. Why not take full advantage of it now, while we still have time?

As wonderful as this sounds, however, it is no more than utopia. The possibility of powering the world with renewables has been on and off the table so many

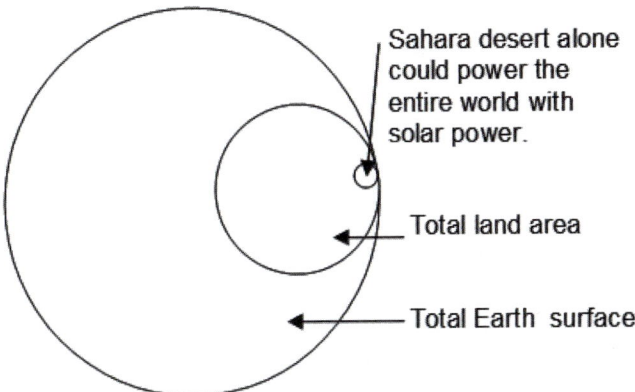

Figure 1-1. How little land is needed to provide power to the entire world. (Not to scale)

times that it is embarrassing to recall. The solar fiasco during the last solar boom-bust cycle of 2007-2012 is further confirmation. No! Things won't change significantly anytime soon. Solar just doesn't fit well in our lives right now; it is not the way we do business in our 21st century society.

Make no mistake, however; solar and wind will be major energy sources someday. It will happen out of necessity 20, 50 or maybe 100 years from now, when the Earth's natural resources have all been depleted. It will happen when the atmosphere is intolerable.

There is not much that average citizens can do to help or speed up things, but we have the obligation to understand the situation thoroughly and facilitate the move towards more reasonable energy policies and practices where we can.

We must find a balance between using dirty coal and clean solar energies. We must figure out a way to clean the dirty coal power generation process, while improving the efficiency and reliability of wind and solar generators. We must figure out a better way of dealing with dwindling oil supplies, and replace them with renewables.

It is time to start talking about reduction of energy use, instead of pushing for more production of fossil fuels. These are tasks that must be undertaken in the very near future, or the next generations are doomed to energy-poor existence and an unhealthy environment. Energy is life, and we have no right to deprive them of that basic commodity.

Because we are talking about power and energy in this text, and since it is such an important issue, we need to take a close look at all types, shapes, and forms. Our goal is to understand everything we can about energy and power. We will then superimpose that understanding onto the roles the different types of energies play in our lives, connecting their effects to environmental changes that are shaping our lives...and those of future generations.

LET THERE BE ENERGY...

Energy, in the form of light, is recorded in the Bible as the initiation of the world as we know it. It was the beginning—the big bang—that scientists now view as an extremely violent one, packed with dense and incomprehensible types and amounts of energy.

Today, we have tools that allow us to look far back in time...but only to a point, because the beginning of our world is too far distant for even these powerful tools to see some significant parts. Nevertheless, what can be seen surely looks like the aftermath of an enormous explosion.

Regardless of weather we adhere to the Biblical record or not, there was a big bang of some kind. We will not dwell on who started it, nor when and how it exactly started (10 thousand, or 10 billion years ago). Instead we need to understand what happened immediately after that glorious moment. We will focus on it and the energy in its different forms at that time, and attempt to describe some of the important roles it played then, and plays even now, in our universe.

So let's go back to the very beginning of our universe, and look at the role of energy there. We will then follow it, as its form and role change through time to the present. Then we can try to extrapolate into the future.

In the Beginning, There Was Energy...

Again, for Biblical scholars, "In the beginning God created the heavens and the Earth." He said, "let there be light," and there was light. End of discussion! Our well-informed secular world, however, requires more data and more proof than that. We also need some of those data to run our advanced technological society. So, here we are, trying to explain what happened billions of years ago and how energy, the way we know it, started its life on Earth.

Not being astronomers we must believe what we have been told by the professional astronomers, and other scientists dedicated to this matter, and filter the information through our common senses and scientific knowledge. What we are told is that the Universe at its birth was a tightly packed mass of basic, and still not fully understood, particles of elementary, primordial character. This mass was compressed to unimaginable density.

Imagine a large container full of this high concentration of energy, a billion or quadrillion times denser and heavier than water. This mass was tightly packed and pressurized close to the bursting point of the container, the strength of which we cannot even imagine. This highly pressurized cooking vessel ("cosmic egg," Isaac Asimov called it) was filled to the brim with all the matter and all of the energy of our universe, in a form and shape that we can only describe as out of this world.

We don't know where this pressure cooker came from. We don't know who made it, who put it there, when or why. Those who believe in God believe that it is God who made it and placed it at that precise place and time with the single goal of creating the universe.

Those who don't believe in God are not sure, and prefer to think that Cosmic Chaos (or Lady Luck) reigned then and controlled events. Either way, this is irrelevant now, so we will not dwell on it. Instead, we will concentrate on what happened after the vessel was in place, because that is what brought energy and life to Earth.

From Einstein's theories on matter and energy we know that matter can be converted to energy, and because energy can never be created nor destroyed, that highly pressurized pressure vessel at the beginning of time contained (packed incomprehensively densely into it) all the energy ingredients needed for the existence of the entire universe.

We agreed that energy can be neither created nor destroyed, since it is one of the building blocks of the physical universe, so we call this condition the first law of thermodynamics, also known as the law of conservation of energy, which simply states that: In a closed system, energy can be neither created nor destroyed.

We also remember that the primordial pressure cooker was a closed system, with the mass in it isolated and self-contained within the "walls" of the vessel. So when the universe popped out of it, it was (and still is) a closed system, in which energy can neither be lost nor created—only changed in form. Thus, we base all our assumptions and calculations on these facts. Thus assuming that our universe is a closed system, the law is in full force and applies to all activities on Earth too.

Since the Universe is a closed system, the amount of energy in it remains constant. The different energies in it, however, can and do change their form, shape and quantity. In the primordial pressure cooker energy was present in several forms, represented by

1)   The mass of the original elementary particles,

2)   Their motion as they continuously collided under the immense pressure of the forces that drew them together in the container, and

3)   The immense radiation that filled the space between them all.

We see that some forms of energy are active and constantly in motion, so we call this "kinetic energy." It is energy always on the move, which is totally different from the other type of energy which we call "potential energy," or stored energy (to be used eventually).

Kinetic energy is the energy represented by heat, where the atoms and molecules are constantly in motion. A moving car has enough kinetic energy to do the work needed to run the distance, and also do serious damage if it strikes a another object. Radiation also involves the constant, non-stop, motion of waves in their never-ending kinetic energy state.

Potential energy, or stored energy, is energy at rest. It is contained within an object or space, waiting to be used, and in most cases it can be stored in a number of ways, shapes and forms. A bowling ball sitting on a table has potential energy stored in it, which can be released by dropping the ball to the floor, where it could do some work (hopefully not on Spot's head). Similarly, water held behind a hydro dam can generate electrical power when released through a turbine.

THE BIG BANG

Back to our primordial pressure cooker. Regardless of how it really happened—by intelligent or chaotic force—the primordial pressure cooker was loaded, placed in the right place and awaiting the right time. It was packed with so much energy of different types, and with the immense pressure and temperature inside its walls increasing even more, it became increasingly unstable.

All unstable energy systems tend to drift toward stability, the transition to which can be expressed in many forms. Just like a pressure cooker that is left too long over a very high flame, our primordial cooker exceeded its manufacturer's limits and finally blew apart—in search of a more stable state. Lo and behold, our universe was born and started its eternal journey in a stable, albeit somewhat incomprehensible manner. After thousands of years on Earth, humans with their limited intelligence and sophisticated tools are still wondering what this cosmic soup we live in, called Universe, is all about.

This bring us back to the moment of the big bang.

Day 1, The Initial Moment

The explosion, about 14 billion years ago, that blew the primordial pressure cooker apart must have been awesome and far above anything we can comprehend. We cannot even imagine the loud noise and blinding brilliance that surely accompanied it. It was surely the biggest bang there ever was. In that instant, the matter and energy that filled the pressure cooker vessel spilled out and started to expand at great speed. The pressure was released and the temperature in the vessel was dropping. In a split second everything changed, and a number of events occurred in rapid sequence.

The mystery particles flying out of the vessel started changing during the release, due to sudden and great changes in pressure and temperature. They evolved quickly, as the energy in and around them shifted back and forth, thus forming their neutrons in the excess-energy process of primordial nucleo-synthesis.

The scientists, who specialize in these things, believe that this process may have taken place just moments after the big bang. It is also responsible for the formation of a heavier isotope of hydrogen known as deuterium (H-2 or D), as well as the more stable helium isotopes He-3 and He-4, and the lithium isotopes Li-6 and Li-7. Also, some unstable, or radioactive, isotopes were also produced during that time, such as tritium H-3; beryllium (Be-7 and Be-8). These unstable isotopes then either decayed over time, or fused with other nuclei to make one of the more stable isotopes we encounter today.

In More Detail

As the universe expanded, it was also cooling. Because free neutrons and protons are less stable than helium nuclei, they have a strong tendency to form helium-4. That, however, requires the intermediate step of forming deuterium. Before the nucleo-synthesis process initiation, the temperature was high enough for many photons to have energy greater than the binding energy of deuterium; therefore, any deuterium that is formed is immediately destroyed (a situation known as the deuterium bottleneck).

So, the formation of helium-4 was delayed until the universe became cool enough to form deuterium (at about $T = 0.1$ MeV), when there was a sudden burst and many other elements were formed. Then, shortly after the bang moment, the Universe became too cool for further nuclear fusion, and the nucleo-synthesis process slowed down and finally stopped altogether. At this point, the elemental abundances were nearly fixed, only changing as some of the radioactive products of the big bang moment (such as tritium) decay.

The big bang nucleo-synthesis process was short lived—only a few minutes, or maybe even seconds. Some say that it lasted exactly 17 minutes (or a period from 3 to about 20 minutes from the time-zero of the big bang to the beginning of space expansion), and while this is possible, we doubt that any of the specialists were there to clock the time, so we will reserve some doubt. Considering the nature and speed of chemical and radio-active reactions, we rather doubt that they could have lasted more than a few seconds. But then, we weren't there either, so we'll let the specialists win this debate.

Still, this was a great moment, with a true nucle-ar fusion reaction, accompanied by a number of other explosions, actions and counteractions, all of immense dimensions. It must have been a spectacular light and sound show...and then there was darkness and silence!

Even as the main process stopped, things were still cooking in the big digester, the Universe, while it was settling down after this incredible violent-birth experi-ence. The pressure, temperature and density of the parti-cles that formed the Universe fell below critical reaction limits, so the chemical reactions and physical changes slowed down, and some stopped. Although this cooling cycle was a short process, it is most important, because it prevented elements heavier than beryllium from form-ing while at the same time allowing unburned light ele-ments, such as deuterium, to exist.

Another important characteristic of the process, according to the same specialists, is that it took place in immense area. It was widespread, and encompassed the entire Universe as we know it today. This is another hard thing to imagine, since it takes thousands of light years to go from one end of the Universe to the other, so we'll just add this to the list of unanswered questions.

Because free neutrons are short-lived, and as the matter expanded fast, they changed into protons and electrons. At this early stage of the expansion, the neu-trons and the newly formed protons were still close enough together for the short-range nuclear force to operate, so neutrons and protons combined to form hy-drogen atoms. In the atom, the neutron is stable, so they were preserved.

The important thing here is that stable constituents of matter were formed at the time of the explosion. They continued their evolution slowly, some turning into ele-ments and matter that we are familiar with today.

The Energy Component

Energy was changing from form to form during the expansion period. Heat energy was converted to the mechanical kinetic energy of motion of the outward-rushing atoms. Equally important was the conversion of matter into energy; as each neutron changed into a pro-ton and an electron, the total mass decreased and energy was released according to the now famous formula $E = mc^2$. As electrons and protons combined into hydrogen atoms, more energy was released.

Another critical energy conversion at the time was the continuous conversion of the kinetic energy of the explosion process into gravitational potential energy. At that moment, the cosmic vessel mass spread out into space, working against the pull of gravity, similar to stretching invisible springs that connect matter.

Most of the energy of the universe still resides in the gravitation field of all that dispersed mass, in those "stretched springs" so to speak. We need to add this to the list of unanswered questions, because we couldn't find "invisible spring" specialists to clarify how this gravity thing works.

Actually we know very well how it behaves by the bruises on our knees, but not what makes it behave that way. And it appears that not much real progress has been made in this area, since Newton noticed gravity several centuries ago, when an apple fell on his head. The springs are still invisible to even the most famous of physicians and mathematicians.

Nevertheless, we all agree that gravitation energy is what holds the Universe together. When the Universe begins to collapse someday, as some say it will, its entire matter will come crashing back in on itself in the form of mass and energy, possibly forming a new pressure cooker, which will grow increasingly unstable as need-ed to explode again, forming the next universe. This is another idea that defies our senses and stretches our imagination to the max.

NOTE: Advances in the field of quantum mechanics confirm time after time how little we know about the very basics of our universe and even life on Earth. We know how particles (photons, electrons, etc.) behave, but we are having a hard time describing why they do what they do. Most scientists write papers and establish theories, but they still can't figure the very basics, such as gravity, quantum entanglement, and many other phe-nomena which we live with daily.

Some Time Later...The Celestial Bodies

The big bang happened about 14-15 billion years ago. The explosion, the first stages of the expansion of the matter and energy of the blown apart primordial pressure cooker, the formation of protons and electrons, and many other events happened very quickly. Some say minutes, but it could've been hours days, weeks or months.

As time passed, changes continued, but at a slower pace. During the next several million years, the still-expanding hydrogen gas cloud filled large regions of space, and eventually, as it reached a more stable energy state, it started to condense in places, for reasons not completely understood. This process was the beginning of the formation of our solar system, estimated to have begun 4.5 billion years ago.

The process, according to the specialists, started with the gravitational collapse of a small part of a giant gas cloud, mixed with residue and particles. The cloud consisted mostly of hydrogen and other gasses, with small amounts of different types of matter, including oxygen, silicon, and carbon.

Because of gravity, the gas cloud wanted to concentrate in one place, but when the gas got closer to the axis of rotation, it started to rotate faster around that axis, just like an ice skater rotates faster around her axis when she pulls in her arms. The fast rotation of the gas meant that it could not all be concentrated in one place, and what happened instead is that the gas concentrated in a flat disk (like a pancake) with most of the material in the center.

The material in the center concentrated more until it got so hot and dense that it could start generating energy through nuclear fusion of the hydrogen in its mix. At that moment, the Sun became a star. The rest of the material clumped together and formed the planets, including the Earth.

Only the very light elements, hydrogen, helium, and some lithium, were formed during the big bang. Heavier elements such as carbon, oxygen, nitrogen, and silicon were formed later—either during the cooling of the initial matter, or much later inside the newly formed stars.

When some of the early stars exploded as supernovas, the heavier elements got mixed with the hydrogen gas that was still floating around, so these elements also ended up in our solar system. Carbon, calcium, and other elements that are essential parts of our bodies; the silicon, iron, and oxygen atoms that form most of the Earth; the oxygen atoms that are needed to form water; the nitrogen and oxygen atoms that form most of the Earth's atmosphere—all of these atoms were formed inside very, very hot stars a long time ago. The hydrogen atoms that are part of our lives are even older, since they were formed in the big bang.

Our Home

Our solar system was formed at that time, and has evolved considerably since then. Many moons have been formed from circling discs of gas and dust around their parent planets, while other moons are thought to have formed independently and later been captured by their planets. Still others, as the Earth's Moon, may be the result of giant collisions. Collisions between bodies have occurred continually up to the present day and have been central to the evolution of the Solar System.

The positions of the planets often shifted, and planets have switched places. This planetary migration is now thought to have been responsible for much of the Solar System's early evolution.

In the next 5-6 billion years, the specialists say, the Sun will cool and expand outward many times its current diameter, thus becoming a red giant. It will then cast off its outer layers as a planetary nebula, which will leave behind a stellar residue known as a white dwarf. That will mark a drastic change in the Solar System, and end of all life on Earth.

It is also possible—even before that—for the Earth's core to start cooling down. Albeit slow, its temperature will eventually drop to the point where the Earth's surface will be covered with ice, and life might cease.

In the even more distant future, the gravity of the passing stars will gradually reduce the Sun's retinue of planets. Some planets will be destroyed, others ejected into interstellar space. Ultimately, over the course of trillions of years, it is likely that the Sun will be left with none of the original bodies in orbit around it.

NOTE: We have presented a plausible theory of how things happened in our universe and on our Earth. We were not there to certify the legitimacy of this narration, but we need a foundation to build upon, so here we are.

Of course, there are many other theories of the origins of the Universe and our world's creation mechanisms, some of which are more plausible than others. Most scientific theories are based on long-time studies, research and observation made by knowledgeable scientists. Scientific explanations are based on facts that are well researched, and though they all have gaps and holes in them, they all contain seeds of truth that we can to draw upon.

Some of the More Plausible Scientific Theories about Earth's Origin

The Tidal Theory was developed by Sir James Jeans; an English mathematician and physicist. According to it, the Earth was formed from materials pulled out from the Sun. While the Sun existed alone at first, there came a time when another star passed very near the Sun. The movement created big tides that tore away some of the gas in the Sun's outer layer. Eventually, the gas massed together and formed bodies that became planets.

The *Nebular Theory* claims that the Sun and the planets were formed at the same time from a great cloud of dust and gas floating in space. This material collapsed because of gravity and became a mass. As time passed, the smaller mass began to rotate and formed a disc. The rotation caused a bulge in the disc and as the rotation went on the bulge became hotter and hotter until it produced enough energy to shine. This became the Sun while the other smaller bodies around it became the planets.

The *Solar Disruption Theory* says that the Sun almost collided with another star in space causing some parts of the Sun to burst. The torn pieces became the planets in space.

The *Planetissimal Theory* is quite similar to the Solar Disruption Theory in that the theory agrees that the planets are formed when the Sun and another star almost collided in space which caused the Sun to burst out some hot materials that became parts of the star passing near the Sun. As the Sun continued to spew out materials, these became the planets and other objects in space.

The *Dynamic Encounter Theory* claims that the world came from the molten materials from the Sun when it collided with the comet.

The *Condensation Theory* envisions a time when the stars came from a mass of hydrogen gas and atomic dust. The stars burst out pieces that became planets.

The *Big Bang Theory* is the most accepted, and is the one we described in more detail above. According to it, the world came from an extremely hard and charged cosmic egg. When the cosmic mix burst into pieces, many of these were formed into planets and other heavenly bodies.

All these theories are very helpful in explaining and expanding some aspects of our understanding of the world's formation, if one wants to get that deep into it. We will use our limited knowledge in these and other matters, to focus our attention on the present state-of-affairs in our world, and specifically on the facts surrounding energy sources, types of energy generation, and energy use.

The Sun's Energy

During the big bang, the protons of the matter in the primordial mix became close enough together during a collision for the short-range nuclear forces to take over. These strong nuclear forces then pulled the two protons together to fuse them into a new nucleus. When this happened, when fusion took place, not only was the original kinetic energy of the colliding protons released, but some of the mass of the particles themselves was converted into energy. Such a reaction between nuclear particles is called a "thermonuclear reaction" because it is triggered by high temperature.

The sequence of nuclear reactions that provides the enormous energy of a star, such as our Sun, is a multistep process, the net accomplishment of which is to convert four hydrogen nuclei (protons) into a helium nucleus. The helium nucleus is slightly less massive than the total of the four protons. This extra mass is converted into energy—mostly heat and light.

It is these thermonuclear reactions that account for the enormous energy of our Sun. They turned on when gravitational contraction produced sufficient heat. This new source of energy so increased the outward pressure in the Sun's interior that gravitational contraction was halted and the Sun stayed at its present size.

Our star was probably not formed of the primordial hydrogen from the big bang, which occurred 14 billion years ago, since the Sun is only about 4.5 billion years old. It was instead, and most probably formed out of hydrogen gas enriched with elemental debris from earlier stars that had exploded at the end of several cycles of more complicated nuclear reactions, in which not only helium, but heavier elements, had been formed. From this richer matter around the early Sun, the various planets, including Earth, were probably formed.

The Sun has enormous potential energy storage and exhibits amazingly great kinetic energy every second. It is emitting energy at an enormous rate, where approximately 4.5 million tons of mass per second are reacted and converted into energy. While this is a lot of mass and energy, it is very little compared with the overall mass of the Sun and its energy supply. It has been estimated that would take over 50 billion years to use up just 50% of the Sun's energy.

Sunlight arrives on Earth at a measured power of about 1,000 W/m^3. Its rays have different lengths and frequencies, which determine their unique behavior within the solar spectrum.

Figure 1-2. The Sun is what powers everything on Earth.

The different wavelengths of the solar spectrum have different energies, with the most important to us humans being in the 400 to 700 nm range, which is actually the visible part of the sunlight. Some wavelengths, like UV and IR, which are at both ends of the solar spectrum, are invisible and even harmful to humans and some materials.

The most amazing, almost unbelievable fact is that Sun's energy is radiated into space in all directions—it is not focused on Earth, as some of us might imagine. Nope, we are not the center of the Universe; the Sun is. And as such, at the great distance of 93 million miles from Earth, it spread its energy in the form of light and heat all around its periphery to places that are as distant as infinity.

What a waste of energy, you may say. And we'd agree in general, but we should not complain, because any more than what we get now would burn us alive. As a matter of fact, here on Earth we get only a very small portion of the Sun's overall energy, because the Earth is only a small dot—a golf ball size—compared with the

football stadium size of the Sun. It's even smaller when the circumference of the sun's rays is considered.

As such, we get much less than a billionth of the Sun's radiation. So, from the 4.5 million tons of mass converted into energy every second, we get approximately 4 lbs. This 4 lbs the Sun's power, however, is enough to keep life on Earth going and provides a comfortable climate over most of the Earth surface.

Again, the amount of sunlight we receive in one day equals the amount of energy that all of humanity uses in a year. So the solar energy flowing to Earth dwarfs all other energy sources known to man. We measure it in terms of kilowatts (kW), or megawatts (MW) of power.

It takes sunlight (photons) about 8 minutes to reach the Earth's surface. Some of it is reflected back into space (30%), some is absorbed and reradiated (47%), some is used in evaporation, precipitation and wind/waves creation, while some provides for photosynthesis of plants.

The Sun sends us nearly 173 trillion kW of energy at any single moment of the day. If we could capture and convert enough of it into useful energy, we could eliminate most of the problems related to energy scarcity, environmental pollution, and climate change. Because this is not possible under the economic status-quo and the state of the art of energy generating technologies, we are afflicted with energy dependence and environmental maladies.

Fossils Then...

In the middle part of the Late Paleozoic Era, 250-300 million years ago, plants emerged from the oceans, and the tropical marshlands were covered by vegetation of different types. Giant forests of ferns, horsetails, and mosses grew in enormous wooded areas, while human life was still a work in progress. Human genes were just beginning their evolution in some of the creatures in the newly formed jungles and oceans.

The Sun's abundant energy was used in the life

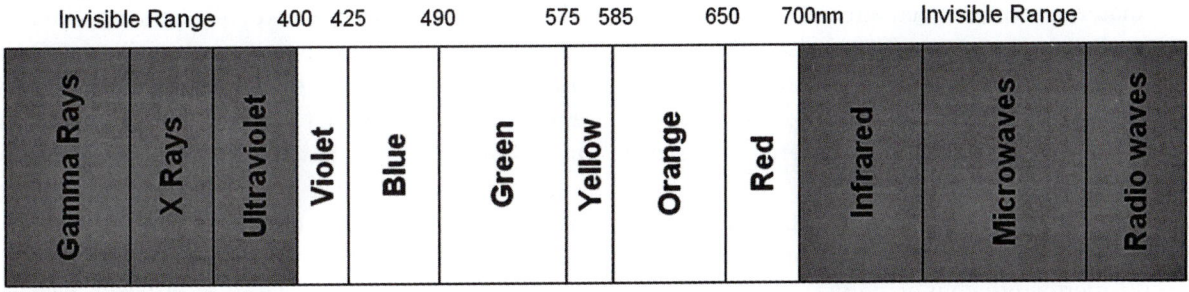

Visible range of the solar spectrum

Figure 1-3. The solar spectrum

processes of the huge fern trees and other vegetation. The radiant energy of sunlight was converted into chemical potential energy, the third great form of potential energy (and the source of life and energy on Earth).

The Energy Storage

In the energy-converting process of photosynthesis, the energy of sunlight was used by plants to break up molecules of carbon dioxide (CO_2) and water (H_2O) and to rearrange their atoms into carbohydrates (sugars and starches). Oxygen was produced as a byproduct.

A form of potential energy storage was created. The carbohydrates formed with the help of the Sun's energy are either food or fuel, depending on the use we make of them. The jungle of 300 million years ago grew in a fertile environment and much of the world at that time had an almost tropical climate, wet and warm. The atmosphere was also rich in CO_2, which was carried up from the depths of the Earth by many active volcanoes and hot springs.

The huge trees grew and died, falling into the shallow waters from which they had emerged initially. Large disasters killed more trees and animals with time, covering more plants and dead animals with water or dirt. Some of their remains decayed, while others were buried deeper into the soil, where oxygen-requiring bacteria could not destroy them completely.

Over tens of thousands of years, huge amounts of this un-decayed plant material built up into the spongy mass we call peat. In peat, the anaerobic bacteria (those that do not require oxygen) broke down the carbohydrates without forming CO_2. Pressure and accompanying heat caused by the overbearing material drove off some of the water, oxygen, nitrogen, and miscellaneous products so that the percentage of carbon was increased. These chemical changes and the increases in density also increased the potential energy per pound of the buried material.

More and more of the water, nitrogen, oxygen, and other materials were driven out so that the percentage of carbon content increased—from an original 50% by weight up to 80%. The energy density, energy per pound, was significantly increased also. The peat was now compacted into a hard, black mineral, and a coal basin was formed.

Through similar processes, we get crude oil and natural gas deposits all over the world. These are packed with energy, which is actually sunlight collected and converted into living matter thousands of years ago, and which is available to us today.

Fossils Today...

The fossil sources (coal, oil, natural gas) contain stored chemical potential energy. This is one of the five primary forms of energy available to our industrious species. Of the others, one is also a potential or stored form—nuclear potential energy—and the other three are kinetic forms (in our broad definition): solar energy, geothermal energy, and tidal energy.

These five forms provide all the energy resource available to our beloved "Spaceship Earth." Three of them, chemical potential energy (fossils), nuclear energy, and geothermal energy, are stored and ready for use. Solar energy comes from the "mother ship," so to speak, our Sun, while tidal energy is a kinetic energy stored in the rotation of Earth and its moon, and also affected (albeit to a much smaller extent) by the rotation of both of these around the Sun.

The fossils—in all their forms—have been, and still are, the major energy source in our world. We have been using them for a long time at an ever increasing rate, and there is no slowing down. We simply don't seem bothered by the fact that very soon—as soon as 20-30 years from today—many of them will be depleted.

As we burn through the fossils, we are also (and even more importantly) destroying the energy and physicochemical balance of the Earth. Once gone, the fossils will not return—ever! The conversion process (vegetation and animals decaying to fossils) is so slow, and requires such special conditions, that the combination of these simply cannot be reproduced—ever.

The sad truth is that the "fossil fuels" that were buried deep in the ground millions and billions of years ago are all we have now. They are all we will ever have. There are no new "fossil fuel" reserves in development stages that we know of, nor are there any expected to be created.

Yet, within several short decades we have extracted most of what took Mother Nature millions of years to create. This precious gift, which future generations see no trace of (at the rate we are consuming it), will be completely gone within the next 50-100 years. What then?

If this were not bad enough, burning fossils in such huge amounts is creating great environmental pollution and climate change that we (or future generations) may not survive. We may have already caused so much damage to the Earth that it would be unlikely to return to normal even if we stopped all fossil-related activities today.

With the ever increasing population growth, and the accompanying demand for better life (which requires lots of energy) we don't expect slowing down of these activities. Yes, there is a lot of talk about it, but as a matter of fact, as of 2012, the U.S. and many other countries (China, India and others) have turned back to fossil fuels for most of their energy needs. Drill, baby, drill is echoing all over the world. Climate change? Oh, yeah, but it can wait...

TODAY'S ENERGY BASICS

What is energy? Generally speaking, energy is what makes everything move, change, grow and even exist. More specifically, translated from Greek energy means "activity and/or operation." It is a quantity that exists, but is indirectly observed, for it is invisible and immeasurable in its purest form.

In practical terms, it is represented as the ability of a physical system to do work on other physical systems or on itself.

Work is defined as force acting through a distance (a length of space), where energy is always equivalent to the ability to exert pulls or pushes against the basic forces of nature, along a path of a certain length.

The important facts here are that:

1. Potential energy remains an "indirectly observed" entity while any of its two main constituents "force" and "distance" are missing. This type of energy is called potential, because it has the potential to do work, but does not until activated by its components force and distance, and

2. Kinetic energy is a "visible," or measurable entity when both of the variables (force and distance) are present. In this case the potential energy has been "activated" and has become kinetic energy. Then it does work and can be observed and measured.

Two other very important conditions to remember about energy:

1. Energy that is visible and measurable in an object, or a person, can be identified with, and measured by, its mass, and

2. Energy cannot be created or destroyed.

Finally, in this text we observe and measure the impact of energy—including power generation and use—on the environment, and where we distinguish three different types of energy (or electric power) generating systems:

1. Conventional energy generators, such as coal, oil, and natural gas, also called fossils,

2. Renewable energy generators, such as solar, wind, and bio-fuels, and

3. A third category of energy generators, which don't fit in the above systems, or are hanging on the fringes, includes nuclear, geo, and hydro power generators.

Energy at Work

Energy is measured in joules, but in many fields other units, such as kilowatt-hours and kilocalories, are used too. All of these units translate to units of work, which are always defined in terms of forces and the distances through which the forces act. In the electric field we use the word power to replace energy, but for all practical purposes they are one and the same.

When ordinary material particles are changed into energy (such as energy of motion, or radiation), the mass of the system does not change through the transformation process. However, there may be mechanistic limits as to how much of the matter in an object may be changed into other types of energy and thus into work, on other systems. Energy, like mass, is a scalar physical quantity.

A system can also transfer energy to another system by simply transferring matter to it (since matter is equivalent to energy, in accordance with its mass). However, when energy is transferred by means other than matter-transfer, the transfer produces changes in the second system, as a result of work done on it.

This work manifests itself as the effect of force(s) applied through distances within the target system. For example, a system can emit energy to another by transferring (radiating) electromagnetic energy, but this creates forces upon the particles that absorb the radiation. Similarly, a system may transfer energy to another by physically impacting it, but in that case the energy of motion in an object, called kinetic energy, results in forces acting over distances (new energy) to appear in another object that is struck.

Transfer of thermal energy by heat occurs by both of these mechanisms; heat can be transferred by electromagnetic radiation, or by physical contact in which direct particle-particle impacts transfer kinetic energy.

Energy may be stored in systems without being present as matter, or as kinetic or electro-magnetic energy. Stored energy is created whenever a particle has been moved through a field it interacts with (requiring a force to do so), but the energy to accomplish this is stored as a new position of the particles in the field. This is a configuration that must be "held" or fixed by a different type of force; otherwise, the new configuration would resolve itself by the field pushing or pulling the particle back toward its previous position.

Potential energy is that which has been "stored" by force-fields and particles that have been forced into a new physical configuration in the field by doing work on them with another system. A simple example of potential energy is the work needed to lift up an object in a gravity field, to a support.

Each of the basic forces of nature is associated with a different type of potential energy, and all types of potential energy (like all other types of energy) appear as system mass, whenever present. For example, a compressed spring will be slightly more massive than before it was compressed. Likewise, whenever energy is transferred between systems by any mechanism, an associated mass is transferred with it.

Any form of energy may be transformed into another form. For example, all types of potential energy are converted into kinetic energy when the objects are given freedom to move to a different position (as for example, when an object falls off a support). When energy is in a form other than thermal energy, it may be transformed with good or even perfect efficiency, to any other type of energy, including electricity or production of new particles of matter. With thermal energy, however, there are often limits to the efficiency of the conversion to other forms of energy, as described by the second law of thermodynamics.

In all such energy transformation processes, the total energy remains the same, and a transfer of energy from one system to another, results in a loss to compensate for any gain.

Although the total energy of a system does not change with time, its value may depend on the frame of reference. For example, a seated passenger in a moving airplane has zero kinetic energy relative to the airplane, but non-zero kinetic energy (and higher total energy) relative to the Earth.

Types of Energy

The concept of energy and its transformations is useful in explaining and predicting most natural phenomena. The direction of transformations in energy (what kind of energy is transformed to what other kind) is often described by entropy (equal energy spread among all available degrees of freedom) considerations, as in practice all energy transformations are permitted

on a small scale, but certain larger transformations are not permitted because it is statistically unlikely that energy or matter will randomly move into more concentrated forms or smaller spaces.

Energy Applications

Energy, in all its forms and variations is widely used in the sciences. For example:

1. *In physics*, energy is considered a quantity that exists, but is indirectly observed (or invisible and immeasurable in its purest form. It comes to life, and is measurable when its other components (force and distance) are considered. In that case energy becomes work, and can be measured as a physical entity. The work then could be observed, measured and expressed as variables of heat, electric power, mass, speed, etc.

    For example, photons traveling from the Sun through space have potential energy stored, which upon impact onto a solar panel is released and converted into heat (heating the panels) and electricity, which can be extracted and used.

2. *In chemistry*, energy is an attribute of a substance as a consequence of its atomic, molecular or aggregate structure. Since a chemical transformation is accompanied by a change in one or more of these kinds of structures, it is invariably accompanied by an increase or decrease of energy in the substances involved. Some energy is transferred between the surroundings and the reactants of the reaction in the form of heat or light; thus, the products of a reaction may have more or less energy than the reactants.

    Chemical reactions are invariably not possible unless the reactants overcome an energy barrier known as the activation energy. The speed of a chemical reaction (at given temperature T) is related to the activation energy E, by the Boltzmann's population factor $e-E/kT$, which represents the probability of a molecule to have energy greater than or equal to E at the given temperature T. This exponential dependence of a reaction rate on temperature is known as the Arrhenius equation. The activation energy necessary for a chemical reaction can be in the form of thermal energy.

3. *In biology*, energy is an attribute of all biological systems from the biosphere to the smallest living organism. Within an organism it is responsible for growth and development of a biological cell or an

organelle of a biological organism. Energy is thus often said to be stored by cells in the structures of molecules of substances such as carbohydrates (including sugars), lipids, and proteins, which release energy when reacted with oxygen in respiration. In human terms, the human equivalent (H-e) (Human energy conversion) indicates, for a given amount of energy expenditure, the relative quantity of energy needed for human metabolism, assuming an average human energy expenditure of 12,500 kJ per day and a basal metabolic rate of 80 watts.

For example, if our bodies run (on average) at 80 watts, then a light bulb running at 100 watts is running at 1.25 human equivalents (100 ÷ 80) i.e. 1.25 H-e. For a difficult task of only a few seconds' duration, a person can put out thousands of watts, many times the 746 watts in one official horsepower. For tasks lasting a few minutes, a fit human can generate perhaps 1,000 watts. For an activity that must be sustained for an hour, output drops to around 300; for an activity kept up all day, 150 watts is about the maximum. The human equivalent assists understanding of energy flows in physical and biological systems by expressing energy units in human terms: it provides a "feel" for the use of a given amount of energy.

4. *In geology,* continental drift, mountain ranges, volcanoes, and earthquakes are phenomena that can be explained in terms of energy transformations in the Earth's interior, while meteorological phenomena like wind, rain, hail, snow, lightning, tornadoes and hurricanes, are all a result of energy transformations brought about by solar energy on the atmosphere of the planet Earth.

     For example, an erupting volcano releases its energy to create land slides or start fires, phenomena related to release of the thermal and mechanical energies stored in it through the millennia

5. *In cosmology and astronomy* the phenomena of stars, nova, supernova, quasars and gamma ray bursts are the universe's highest-output energy transformations of matter. All stellar phenomena (including solar activity) are driven by various kinds of energy transformations.

     Energy in such transformations is either from gravitational collapse of matter (usually molecular hydrogen) into various classes of astronomical objects (stars, black holes, etc.), or from nuclear fusion of lighter elements, primarily hydrogen.

For the purposes of this book, the term "energy" is used with the understanding that it is contained in fuels which generate energy or electric power. The energy contained in these fuels is converted from one form to another—usually from potential to kinetic—by burning coal, oil, or natural gas. The chemical energy contained in these is converted into mechanical movement of and changes in their particles, which results in heat. Thus produced heat boils water into a stem, which drives steam turbines and generators that produce another form of energy, electric power, which can be measured and used to power our lives.

Similarly, energy (electric power) can also be generated by collecting sunlight, or wind energy and converting them into a flow of useful electrons, which can be used as electric energy (power).

In more practical terms, energy is all around us and can be observed and measured in its different forms as depicted in Figure 1-4.

Energy Conversions

Energy in the Universe is sometimes quickly and easily changed from one state (or type) into another. At times the conversion process is not that quick, or easy,

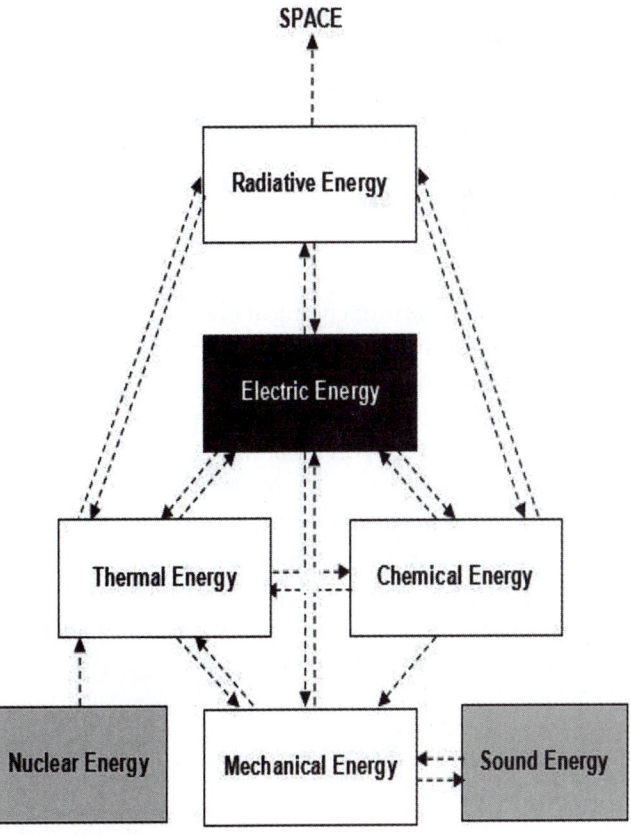

Figure 1-4. Universal energy conversion diagram

depending on the types of materials and processes involved. Here are some examples of the major energy conversion cycles:

1. Radiative to/from thermal energy conversion:
   Incandescence is an example of radiative to thermal energy conversion.
   The solar collector is an example of thermal to radiative energy conversion.

2. Radiative to/from chemical energy conversion:
   Photosynthesis is an example of radiative to chemical energy conversion.
   Chemi-luminescence is an example of chemical to radiative energy conversion.

3. Radiative to/from electric energy conversion:
   The solar (PV) cell is an example of radiative to electric energy conversion.
   The fluorescent light is an example of electric to radiative energy conversion.

4. Thermal to/from electrical energy conversion:
   The thermo-cell is an example of thermal to electric energy conversion.
   The electrical resistance of wires is an example of electric to thermal energy conversion.

5. Thermal to/from mechanical energy conversion:
   Heated steam is used to turn the turbines in power stations.
   The mechanical energy from rubbing two sticks together is converted into heat.

6. Thermal to/from chemical energy conversion:
   Endothermic reactions are examples of thermal to chemical energy conversion.
   Exothermic reactions are examples of chemical to thermal energy conversion.

7. Chemical to/from electric energy conversion:
   The car battery is an example of chemical to electric energy conversion.
   Electrolysis is an example of electric to chemical energy conversion.

8. Chemical to mechanical energy conversion process is observed in human muscles, where the chemical energy stored in the body is converted into mechanical, as needed to activate the different body muscles.

9. Mechanical to/from electric energy conversion:
   The car alternator is an example of mechanical to electric energy conversion.
   The electric car engine is an example of electric to mechanical energy conversion.

10. Mechanical to/from thermal energy conversion:
    Automobile brakes are an example of mechanical to thermal energy conversion.
    The locomotive is an example of thermal to mechanical energy conversion.

11. Mechanical to/from sound energy conversion:
    A running car engine is an example of mechanical to sound energy conversion.
    Ella Fitzgerald breaking a glass with the high pitch in her voice is an example of sound to mechanical energy conversion.

12. Nuclear energy stored in nuclear materials is converted to thermal energy in nuclear power plants, and the resulting heat is used to generate electricity.

Energy transformations in the universe over time are characterized by various kinds of potential energy that has been available since the big bang, and is later being "released" (transformed to more active types of energy such as kinetic or radiant), when a triggering mechanism is available.

Familiar examples of such processes include nuclear decay, in which energy is released that was originally "stored" in heavy isotopes (such as uranium and thorium), by nucleosynthesis, a process ultimately using the gravitational potential energy released from the gravitational collapse of supernovae, to store energy in the creation of these heavy elements before they were incorporated into the solar system and the Earth. This energy is triggered and released in nuclear fission bombs. In a slower process, radioactive decay of these atoms in the core of the Earth releases heat.

This thermal energy drives plate tectonics and may lift mountains, via orogenesis. This slow lifting represents a kind of gravitational potential energy storage of the thermal energy, which may be later released to active kinetic energy in landslides, after a triggering event. Earthquakes also release stored elastic potential energy in rocks, a store that has been produced ultimately from the same radioactive heat sources. Thus, according to present understanding, familiar events such as landslides and Earthquakes release energy that has been stored as potential energy in the Earth's gravitational field or elastic strain (mechanical potential energy) in rocks. Prior to this, they represent release of energy that has been stored in heavy atoms since the collapse of long-destroyed supernova stars created these atoms.

In another similar chain of transformations beginning at the dawn of the universe, nuclear fusion of hydrogen in the Sun releases another store of potential energy which was created at the time of the big bang. At that time, according to theory, space expanded and the universe cooled too rapidly for hydrogen to completely fuse into heavier elements.

This means that hydrogen represents a store of potential energy that can be released by fusion. Such a fusion process is triggered by heat and pressure generated from gravitational collapse of hydrogen clouds when they produce stars, and some of the fusion energy is then transformed into sunlight. Such sunlight from our Sun may again be stored as gravitational potential energy after it strikes the Earth. For example, water evaporates from oceans and is deposited upon mountains where, after being released at a hydroelectric dam, it can be used to drive turbines or generators to produce electricity.

Sunlight also drives many weather phenomena, save those generated by volcanic events. An example of a solar-mediated weather event is a hurricane, which occurs when large unstable areas of warm ocean, heated over months, suddenly give up some of their thermal energy to power a few days of violent air movement.

Sunlight is also captured by plants as chemical potential energy in photosynthesis, when carbon dioxide and water (two low-energy compounds) are converted into the high-energy compounds carbohydrates, lipids, and proteins. Plants also release oxygen during photosynthesis, which is utilized by living organisms as an electron acceptor, to release the energy of carbohydrates, lipids, and proteins.

Release of the energy stored during photosynthesis as heat or light may be triggered suddenly by a spark, in a forest fire, or it may be made available more slowly for animal or human metabolism, when these molecules are ingested, and catabolism is triggered by enzyme action.

Through all of these transformation chains, potential energy stored at the time of the big bang is later released by intermediate events, sometimes being stored in a number of ways over time between releases, as more active energy. In all these events, one kind of energy is converted to other types of energy, including heat.

There are several major types of energy that we need to take a close look at, especially those that can be used to generate power on Earth:

A.   Energy can be divided into three major categories:
1. Gravitational energy

This is the energy (or force) that attracts all objects, humans and animals to the Earth's center. Without it, objects would not be able to stay grounded and would most likely be floating around in space.

2. Electromagnetic energy

This is the energy emitted and absorbed by charged particles. It exhibits wave-like behavior as it travels through space. It has both electric and magnetic field components in equal proportions and force. In a vacuum it moves at the speed of light. Sunlight is a type of electromagnetic energy.

3. Nuclear energy

This is the energy that is hidden in the atoms and molecules of the elements and substances that make up this world. This energy plays a major role in chemical and other reactions on the molecular level.

B.   We can also divide energy, as briefly mentioned before, into two important types, according to their state and the work they do or intend to do:
1. Potential energy is any energy that is stored and is idle; waiting to be released.

A good example of potential energy is a large tank of water perched on a tall hill. The water in the tank is stored and idle, but has "potential" to do some work if and when released, at which point it will obtain kinetic energy. But until then its energy is "potential," or idle.

2. Kinetic energy is energy in action. It is what moves things.

Any object that is in motion has some amount of kinetic energy. The amount of kinetic energy at a certain time can be expressed as power.

C.   Other major types of energy are:
1. Mechanical energy

This is the energy that is needed to move, bend, break and otherwise change material objects. Slamming a hammer onto a piece of metal, or breaking a twig require mechanical energy.

2. Chemical energy

Reacting different substances (chemicals) in order to obtain a new, or modified, substance requires chemical energy.

D. In the physical and more practical aspects of our lives, there are several forms of energy, the main ones of which are:

— Physical energy is the energy that moves things.
— Chemical energy includes a number of energy types that drive chemical reactions.
— Electrical energy makes our electrical appliances work.
— Thermal energy, or heat, is used to elevate the temperature of objects.
— Biomass energy is generated by plants.
— Heat energy comes from burning coal and other fuels.
— Geothermal energy comes from hot springs deep in the ground.
— Solar energy comes from the Sun and can be converted into heat or electricity.
— Hydro power is obtained from water turning a wheel, which generates energy.
— Ocean energy is the energy generated by ocean waves and tides.
— Nuclear energy generates heat through nuclear reactions.
— Wind energy makes the wings of a wind mill rotate to generate electricity.
— Transportation energy facilitates moving large loads.
— Magnetic energy is created by permanent magnets or electromagnets.
— Sound energy is created by increasing noise levels.
— Cosmic energy includes the different types of energy contained in the Universe.

Let's take a look at some of the major types that would help us clarify the concepts of energy and its use on Earth:

Physical Energy

Energy in the physical realm it is invisible and immeasurable in its purest form. When another component is added to it, however, such as force, mass, distance, speed, etc., it comes to life, and is very easily measurable. In conjunction with its other components (force and distance) it is truly a physical entity that we use in our daily lives.

As a physical work, energy can be observed, measured and expressed as heat, electric power, mass, speed, and other variables.

For example, a large body of water sitting behind the secure walls of a dam contains energy which is hid-den from view while the water is just sitting in the lake reservoir. The energy is released immediately when the intake gate is opened and the water is allowed to run down the penstocks. At its destination, it hits the turbine blades with a great force to generate electricity.

The water hitting the turbines converts the potential energy stored in the lake into kinetic energy (work) and eventually into electric power, which is measured in kilowatts (kW) and megawatts (MW) of electric power.

Chemical Energy

Energy can be changed by rearranging the atoms in a molecule or by combining free atoms, at which point chemical energy becomes available. The reverse of the photosynthesis process that created the huge forests discussed earlier is a good example of that process. When the carbon, hydrogen, and oxygen molecules in carbohydrates and sugars (as in the fossils) are oxidized, either by burning or by the process of digestion, CO_2 and H_2O are formed, and energy is released (such as when burning fossil fuels). Free carbon (in coal, or oil) combines with oxygen during the burning process to form CO_2 and release heat energy too.

Chemical energy can also be generated when strips of lead (Pb) are dipped into sulfuric acid (H_2SO_4), where the Pb replaces the H_2 in the H_2SO_4 to form $PbSO_4$ and H_2O (like in a lead battery). This process goes in reverse during charging, and releases energy during discharge, which can be used to generate electrons in a wire connected between the electrodes. The electrons are then extracted in a form of electric current. This is the process of conversion of chemical potential energy into electrical energy, as takes place in a car battery. Many other combinations of metals, liquids, and gases can be arranged and forced to release energy in a similar way.

Chemical potential energy is one of the most important forms of energy known to man, because it is the energy of fossil fuels. The largest amount of our electric energy comes from fossil fuels, so as they become more expensive to burn, and in shorter supply, we must find other ways to generate electric energy.

Solar Energy

We now know how solar energy is created at the Sun, where immense amounts of matter are converted to light and heat via fusion reactions of hydrogen converted to helium. Sunlight travels 93 million miles to Earth in a matter of minutes, and arrives at our atmosphere as radiant energy contained in particles called photons. This is pure energy, riding on its own electromagnetic fields through space. The photons also contain potential energy which can be released upon impact.

Radiant energy (the photons) has properties that are wavelike, but at the same time it has particle-like properties. These wavelike, particle-like units are delivered in discrete chunks that have two distinct properties, wavelength and frequency.

The wavelength is measured by the distance between the peaks of the waves, while the frequency is the speed of its vibration, which, in turn determines its energy. The higher the frequency of the photons, the greater the amount of energy they carry. For example, X-ray photons are vibrating at very high frequencies, and carry enough energy to do physical damage to body tissues and organs. Radio waves, however, vibrate several times slower, and do no damage.

Sunlight radiation waves have a wide range of vibrations, and carry enough energy to cause chemical changes in molecules they encounter along the way. Most of the incoming radiation is visible light, and life forms have developed in response to those wavelengths. The reflected or converted solar radiation leaves Earth as the much longer infrared (IR, or heat) radiation.

Radiation Energy

Radiant energy interacts with matter by 1) reflection from surfaces it encounters on its way; 2) absorption, where it sets molecules or atoms into vibration, which could cause re-radiation in the same or at longer wavelengths; 3) absorption and then dissipation within a substance as heat; and 4) absorption and production of a chemical change.

Heat absorbed by land provides the major heat input into the lower atmosphere. It is this converted solar energy that provides the kinetic energy for the great trade winds and all the other winds of the "atmospheric engine." Windmills are driven, indirectly, by solar energy which creates wind conditions. The combination of unequal heating, the Earth's gravity, and the spin about its axis are responsible for the atmospheric and oceanic motion.

Much of the solar technology depends on this radiant-to-heat energy conversion. Solar collectors for space and water heating, and other solar collectors rely on this interaction.

Radiant energy absorbed by the ocean and converted to heat ultimately provides humankind with another useful form of energy. When water molecules become hot enough, they can escape from the liquid. This is the process we call evaporation. This water vapor is then lifted by rising heated air and is carried by the winds until it falls as rain. By this lifting of great masses of wa-

ter away from the surface of the Earth, some of the solar energy is turned to gravitational potential energy.

Some amount of this gravitational potential energy is converted to mechanical energy when water is forced to run through a turbine on its way back to the sea. Thus, hydropower is a second indirect consequence of solar energy.

The selective absorption of radiant energy in the atmosphere (interaction 2 above) also has important consequences. Without the absorption at the top of the atmosphere of most of the ultraviolet radiation and other short-wavelength radiation, life on Earth would be impossible. If this energetic radiation were not stopped by the thin layer of ozone there, no living thing could exist in the sunlight.

Nuclear Energy

The nuclear energy we discuss here is the energy that is stored in the nuclei of atoms and can be released by rearrangements of the protons and neutrons in it. An example of this energy comes from thermonuclear reactions such as in the Sun (fusion) as well as the atom bomb (fission).

In fusion reactions, the lighter elements (with nucleus made up of a few protons and neutrons) can combine to make heavier ones, during which process a great amount of energy is released, as four protons fuse to make a helium nucleus, which contains two protons and two neutrons. Since the helium nucleus has less mass than the combined mass of the four protons, the mass difference is converted to energy.

Energy can be released in fission nuclear reactions too, by elements with a heavy nucleus, such as uranium. This nucleus can be split into two medium-mass nuclei, releasing a lot of energy. The two medium-mass nuclei have less mass than the original uranium, and in this reaction the missing mass is also converted into energy.

For our everyday energy generating purposes we must be able to control nuclear reactions. While we have learned how to control fission nuclear reactions, which are used in our many nuclear power plants, we still don't know how to efficiently initiate and safely control fission nuclear reactions. This challenge will be left to the next generations. No doubt they will resolve it, since it might be the only choice for energy production they'll have by then.

Gravitational Energy

Energy is contained in and released during the moon's travel around the Earth. Potential energy, in the form of gravitational energy, is stored in the space between the Earth, moon and Sun. At the same time, all three bodies have a lot of kinetic energy due to their rotation around each other and around their own axes.

Some of this energy is converted into mechanical energy in the form of ocean waves and tides. Tides are formed as a result of the gravitational push-pull mechanism of the moon, and to a lesser extent by the Sun. Since the oceans' surface is flexible, the waters beneath it can move up and down according to the moon's position. The converted energy causes the rise and fall of the tides, while some is dissipated as heat energy through friction.

The possibility of converting waves and tidal energy into useful electric energy has been on the agenda for many decades. Turbines can be turned by letting seawater run through them as it comes and goes in and out with the tides, or up and down with the waves. Such projects are feasible in a number of places, but technical difficulties and expense have not allowed their wide deployment.

Nevertheless, we believe this is another unexplored, yet very plausible alternative for future generations.

Geothermal Energy

Geothermal energy is one of the most interesting and elegant solutions to energy generation. The nucleus of the Earth consists of molten lava, and some of the heat leaks through cracks in the Earth's core and crust, escaping to the surface by forming hot springs, geysers, or volcanoes. This is free heat in its most basic form—lots of it and ready to use.

The Earth's heat can be captured as hot water, steam, or high-pressure steam. Different energy generators are used in each case, with the overall result of using this free energy to generate useful electric energy. In some parts of the world, the hot water or gasses are used to heat homes, or in commercial applications, but these are exceptions.

Geologists are not exactly sure how the Earth's molten core was formed, but we know that the inner heat is maintained by the slow decay of radioactive materials in it. The concentration of radioactive material in the Earth is small, yet enough to balance the heat loss through the surface.

However, as we remove significant amounts of the radioactive materials in the Earth's crust, and use more and more of its heat, it remains to be seen if geothermal energy would be renewable energy for very long. Increasing the use of geothermal energy complicates the environmental picture, and seems to be a double-edged

Figure 1-5. Geothermal energy wells

sword, so we must be careful using it.

The next generation will be forced to take a closer look at the inner and outer heat energy balance of the Earth and decide if this energy source can be expanded.

Wind Energy

Wind power is another form of solar energy, where billions of photons arriving from the sun hit the Earth's surface and the air around it and the energy in them is converted into mechanical and heat energy. The heated air molecules start rising up. When enough air is warmed and moved up, an air current is created. This current interacts with other environmental elements and surface structures, creating turbulence. Increased turbulence gives rise to wind currents, which can travel at high speeds across great distances.

Wind energy is a major electric power generator in the world now. Large-scale wind farms provide a significant portion of the global commercial electric power.

Cosmic Energy

There is a lot of radiation in the Universe that bombards everything in its path. Celestial bodies such as stars, gas giants, and black holes are the best examples of massive radiation. Stars, planets, and black holes are continuously producing high energy radiation, which in most cases comes from nuclear fusion. The combining of separate atoms produces high levels of energy that are dispersed into space in the full electromagnetic spectrum. Gas giants can also produce large fields of radiation. This is because most gas giants are celestial bodies that failed to fully become stars, not having sufficient mass to complete fusion.

There is also radiation from the universe as a whole, which is called cosmic microwave background radiation. Luckily, each of the cosmic radiation sources is far beyond the Earth's atmosphere. Unfortunately, to be useful to people, cosmic energy must be captured and controlled, something we are simply unable to do at this point.

Nevertheless, cosmic energy is available in immense quantities in high space, so the next generations will be charged with the task of figuring out how capture it.

Other Effects

The atmosphere does not absorb very much radiation from visible wavelengths, since it is transparent to them. When this radiant energy is absorbed at the Earth's surface, however, it is reradiated at longer wavelengths, in the infrared region.

CO_2 and other gasses act as a barrier which traps some of the wavelengths, helping to keep the Earth warmer at night. Without this effect, the Earth would radiate back out into space most of the energy gathered during the day, and the nights would be very cold. Instead, the absorbed energy is reradiated so that about half of it comes back to Earth.

This "green house effect" is quite sensitive to the content, the type, and the amount of gasses in the barrier layer. We'll discuss it in more detail in the following chapters.

The process of photosynthesis is another interaction that provides not only food and fossil fuels, but also the resource of biomass in general—life-giving wood, water, grains, etc.

Photovoltaic reactions are another example of this interaction. In the text below, we will take a very close look at this process, as well as some of the new ways to get usable energy from sunlight in general.

A number of other effects are important, when painting a full picture of the energy cycles. Some of these are the shielding action of ozone (O_3), where it is formed when photons strike O_2 molecules on top of the atmospheric layer to make an additional layer of O_3 that is beneficial to the Earth's environment. O_3 is also produced in the lower atmosphere by a similar reaction, but there it is harmful to humans.

The Energy Laws

We know that energy in a closed system, such as our universe, can be neither created nor destroyed, since it is one of the building blocks of the physical universe. We call this condition the first law of thermodynamics, which is also known as the "law of conservation of energy," and which states that:

*In a closed system, energy can be
neither created nor destroyed.*

We must remember that the ultimate closed system is the Universe, which is isolated and self-contained, so we must base all our assumptions and calculations on these facts.

None of the energy here on Earth can be destroyed, or created. It can only be converted from one form to another. In a steam turbine, for example, the many energy transfers and conversion processes are to or from heat energy, but the overall energy balance is preserved.

Even more amazing is the fact that at the end of a long chain of energy conversions (i.e., radiant energy conversion to chemical energy in plants' photosynthesis process), the burning of the resulting biomass usually ends up in heat energy (and other energy forms) which is equal to the sum of all other energies involved in the process.

This is preliminary evidence of another and even more important law, called the second law of thermodynamics, which also rules energy conversions. It is evidenced in the conversion of the stored chemical energy in coal to electricity through the operations in an electric power plant. A full description of the process is given below.

In coal power plant operations there are many instances of the conversion of different energy forms into heat energy. Basically all of the chemical energy in coal can be converted to heat energy. On the other hand, all of the electrical energy carried through a wire at the end of the power plant conversion process can be converted back to heat energy as well (just like in electric hot water heaters).

The problem occurs when we try to convert heat energy back to mechanical energy. This type of conversion is controlled and limited by different laws of nature. It is here that the second law of thermodynamics is illustrated best and can be stated in several ways. For example:

*No device can operate in a cycle (like an engine),
extracting energy from some source,
and converting it* completely *into mechanical energy.*

So, we can rephrase the first law as, "You can't get

something for nothing," while the second law would chime in to complete the energy cycle by stating, "You can't even get all you see or think you can get."

The second law provides broad and far-reaching consequences. It not only categorically denies the possibility of converting more than a fraction of the energy in the dam water or the steam into work (as in the steam turbine), but it also assures us that the energy that escapes in the form of heat at all other conversion points (as waste heat, or waste mechanical energy) can never be completely reclaimed for work.

This might seem confusing, but it simply means that the second law claims that in any transfer of energy or conversion of one to another form, the energy becomes less useful after every step and sometimes with every second. It is not lost, but rather converted into other forms that have other functions—not necessarily the form we expected, or wanted.

Power, Work, and Heat

Matter can have energy in many different forms. The three major forms of potential energy are gravitational, nuclear, and electrical. The kinetic or transient forms of energy are the mechanical forms of mass in motion, moving along straight or curved paths, and its other forms, heat and radiation.

Energy in its potential form is latent; it is there but it isn't going anywhere, or doing anything. To use energy to move something, change the temperature of a substance, provide light or some other form of radiation, etc., the potential energy must be converted into a kinetic form, which is then expressed as power.

There are many energy conversion mechanisms. Burning (oxidation) is a major conversion mechanism for fuels and chemical processes. We have already mentioned a number of processes and devices (i.e., steam turbines) that convert the energy contained in a substance into mechanical energy (power), while electrical generators convert mechanical energy into electrical power.

Energy is also transferred from one place to another. Heat energy heats a substance and changes its form or state (melting ice). It can also move, or lift it, by means of a physical contact with steam (as in a steam turbine), or with wind (as in a wind turbine).

Energy is transferred from its potential form into kinetic form as work (mechanical energy), heat, or radiation. The practical energy exchange and the corresponding changes of state, or transformation into another type of energy, are best represented by the variables of power, work and heat.

Power

In the real world, power is the rate at which energy is transferred, used, or transformed. The unit of power is the joule per second (J/s), known as the watt (in honor of James Watt, the 18th-century developer of the steam engine). For example, the rate at which a light bulb transforms electrical energy into heat and light is measured in watts—the more wattage, the more power, or the more electrical energy is used per unit time.

Energy transfer can be used to do work, so power is also the rate at which this work is performed. The same amount of work is done when carrying a load up a flight of stairs whether the person carrying it walks or runs, but more power is expended during running because the work is done in a shorter amount of time.

The output power of an electric motor is the product of the torque the motor generates and the angular velocity of its output shaft. The power expended to move a vehicle is the product of the traction force of the wheels and the velocity of the vehicle.

The average power P_{avg} over a period of time is given by the formula

$$P_{avg} = \frac{\Delta W}{\Delta t}$$

where:
ΔW is the amount of work performed
Δt is the period or time of duration

This is the average amount of work done or energy converted per unit of time. The average power is often simply called "power" when the context makes it clear. The instantaneous power is then the limiting value of the average power as the time interval Δt approaches zero.

$$P = \lim_{\Delta t \to 0}{}^{*} Pavg = \lim_{\Delta t \to 0} \frac{\Delta W}{\Delta t} = \frac{dW}{dt}$$

In the case of constant power P, the amount of work performed during a period of duration T is given by:

$$W = PT$$

In the context of energy conversion it is more customary to use the symbol E rather than W.

The basic unit for power is the Watt, which subdivisions shown in Table 1-1.

Table 1-1. Power denominations and equivalents

Units		Equivalent to power in:
Picowatt	$pW = 10^{-12}W$	human cell
Nanowatt	$nW = 10^{-9}W$	microchip
Microwatt	$mW = 10^{-6}W$	quartz wrist watch
Milliwatt	$mW = 10^{-3}W$	laser beam in a CD player
Watt	W	light bulb, home appliances
Kilowatt	$kW = 10^3W$	propelling engines in general
Megawatt	$MW = 10^6W$	power of train engines and power plants in general
Gigawatt	$GW = 10^9W$	large hydropower plant's capacity, average power consumption in a country
Terawatt	$TW = 10^{12}W$	average world power consumption, global annual energy production by photosynthesis in the world
Petawatt	$PW = 10^{15}W$	solar power received by the Earth

The integral of power over time defines the work done. Because this integral depends on the trajectory of the point of application of the force and torque, this calculation of work is said to be "path dependent."

NOTE: Although in theory there is a significant difference between energy and power, at times we use them interchangeably, realizing that this might cause some learnèd folks headache and confusion. We do emphasize, however, that energy is a measure of the potential to do work, while power is the expression of that work.

For example, we say, "the Sun's energy is converted into electric power by the PV effect." Both the incoming solar energy and the generated electric power are measurable entities, but are in different forms and shapes. Nevertheless, we can replace power with energy as the end result, thus saying, "the Sun's energy is converted into electric energy by the PV effect." While theoretically incorrect, electric energy is a popular term, which is more convenient for use at times.

Force

Force is an act that causes an object to undergo a change in any of its possible conditions—its movement, direction, shape, or structure. Force is what causes an object with a certain mass to start moving. It can also cause it to change its velocity if it is already moving, or to accelerate. In simple terms, this could be described as push and pull.

In physics, Newton's second law is used to clarify that the net force acting upon an object is equal to the rate at which its momentum changes. Or, acceleration of an object is directly proportional to the net force acting on it, is in the direction of the net force, and is inversely proportional the mass of the object.

So, force has both magnitude and direction, making it a vector quantity. It can be measured with the SI unit of newtons (N) and represented by the symbol F.

Mathematically, force in motion is expressed as:

$$\vec{F} = m\vec{a}$$

where

m   is the mass

a   is the acceleration

$\rightarrow$ implies a vector quantity with both magnitude and direction

Force also includes the concepts of thrust and drag (increase and decrease in the velocity of an object respectively), and torque (or change in rotational speed of an object).

Force acting in an un-uniform way on parts of a physical body causes mechanical stress, which can also move or deform the body. Force, or mechanical stress in a liquid or gas causes change in its pressure, volume, and temperature.

Force is also a defining variable in calculating the amount of work done by and/or within a system.

Gravitational Force

Gravitational force, or gravity, is a natural phenomenon, where physical bodies attract each other with a force proportional to their masses. It is the invisible force that keeps our solar system together, where the Sun's large mass attracts all celestial bodies, making them rotate around it. Gravity is also responsible for the moon's rotation around the Earth, which in turn create tides, natural convection, and a number of other phenomena.

It is also the force that gives weight to objects and people on Earth. It keeps them on the Earth's surface, instead of floating somewhere in space, and causes them to fall to the ground when elevated above the surface and dropped.

Gravitational force acts upon all objects—small and large. Gravity itself is very small, and since the mass of the object has a lot to do with the overall interaction, we can notice the gravitational force of large bodies, like the Earth, moon and Sun. This is also why smaller objects are attracted by larger ones, as is the case of the Earth being attracted by the Sun and forced to rotate around it *ad infinitum*. It is also why all objects and people on Earth are attracted by it and stick to its surface like little pins onto a large magnet.

Gravity is the force that causes dispersed matter to coalesce, and coalesced matter to remain intact. This accounts for the existence of planets, stars, galaxies on one hand, and most of the microscopic and macroscopic objects around us, on the other.

Mass vs. Weight

This might be a good time to point out that although we use mass and weight interchangeably, there is a big difference between them. While mass represents only the amount of matter (stuff) that is contained in an object, weight also takes into account its gravitational state and the related forces acting upon it.

As an example, a bowling ball with a weight of 10 kg has that much mass in its structure as it sits idle. As a matter of fact, the true name for mass is slug. Really! But by adding the gravity variable to the concept of the idle mass of the bowling ball, we get its actual weight, which is also its potential energy. Since the gravity acceleration constant is 9.8 m/s^2, that multiplied by the 10 kg of the ball, we get 98 kg·m/s^2.

Our bowling ball with 10 kg of mass, therefore, actually weighs 98 N (newtons) on Earth. This is useful to know, because when we get to the moon someday, our 10 kg bowling ball will actually be 1/6 as heavy, and will weigh only 11.3 N, or 1/6th of its Earth weight. This way we can distinguish between 10 kg mass on Earth and 10 kg mass on the moon, and thus make accurate calculations between events on places with different gravitational forces.

In more practical terms, the bowling ball with 10 kg mass will weigh more (albeit not that much more) at the bottom of the Grand Canyon, than on top of Mount Everest. This is because at the bottom of the Grand Canyon it is 4-5 miles closer to the Earth's center than on top of Mount Everest.

Work

Work is defined as the act of transferring energy that is accomplished by the application of a force over a distance. For example, a car engine performs work by propelling the car. Pumping water up into a tank and the water's effect when flowing back down are both forms of work.

NOTE: The difference between work and power is that: a) Work is the act of energy transfer, while b) Power is the rate of that same energy transfer process. A steam turbine does work (spinning) when hit by the steam blast, which determines the rate of electric power it will generate.

We can distinguish two kinds of work, processing and storage. In processing work, the initial energy is completely converted to kinetic energy. In this case, matter is moved about, changed, and rearranged.

In storage work, some potential energy is converted to kinetic and then reconverted to potential energy. The automobile is doing processing work when running down the highway, while the pumped water in a dammed lake is an example of storage work.

In all these examples work is accomplished by the application of a force, a push or a pull. The force may not be obvious, but we know that it is there when we see the evidence of the work done. Work is done by one part of a system on another part of the same or a different system. It is a measure of the change of energy in a part of the system.

Work is done by that part of a system which exerts a force. Work is done on that part of a system on which a force acts. Work is often also done against a force.

Processing work is done against resisting forces such as friction or air resistance. It is also done against inertial forces, the resistance of mass to being accelerated or decelerated.

The important part is that work is a measure of the change in energy when energy is transferred from one part of a system to another by the action of a force.

Units of Work and Mechanical Energy

Work is defined as force times a distance. In SI units the work unit is newtons times meters or joules. A force of one newton operating over a distance of one meter produces one joule of work.

$$1 \text{ N} \times 1 \text{ m} = 1 \text{ J}$$

In the English system, the force is measured in pounds and the distance in feet, so the unit of work is the foot-pound (ft-lb).

$$1 \text{ ft} \times 1 \text{ lb} = 1 \text{ ft-lb}$$

This unit is important in the engineering practice, but it is not used much in energy calculations.

Work is the act of energy change. According to the first law of thermodynamics, the change in total internal energy of a system equals the added heat minus the work performed by the system.

$$\delta E = \delta Q - \delta W$$

Also, from Newton's second law for rigid bodies it can be shown that work on an object is equal to the change in kinetic energy of that object,

$$W = \Delta KE$$

The work of forces generated by a potential function is known as potential energy and the forces are said to be conservative. Therefore work on an object moving in a conservative force field is equal to minus the change of potential energy of the object,

$$W = -\Delta PE$$

This shows that work is the energy associated with the action of a force, therefore having the physical dimensions and units of energy.

The work energy principle applies to mechanical, chemical, and electrical types of work.

Heat

By definition, heat is the form of energy that flows between two bodies due to their temperature differential. Heat is basically energy always in transit between a warmer and cooler body, such as hot gases in the power plant furnace turning the water in the boiler to hot steam. This phenomena is due to the higher energy of the hotter molecules. It is also called "internal energy" and can have many forms.

Internal energy is in fact the energy stored in a system at a molecular level. It has no practical way of measurement, so it is usually calculated by measuring macroscopic variables, such as volume, temperature, pressure and composition. It cannot be absolutely calculated as a function, and is only used in relation to an initial state of reference.

Heat energy, as internal energy, is also described in terms of a random motion. It can be a more complicated vibratory motion of the molecules or atoms of the substance and thus a mixture of kinetic and potential energy. A broader definition of internal energy includes all forms of energy a substance can have at a certain time and state.

Heat Types

Heat comes in different types and forms. Some of the major types are:

1. *Conduction*—During heating, the "hotter" molecules flow towards and collide with the "cooler" ones and immediately transfer energy to them. Thus, some energy leaves the hotter substance (or part of it), thus leaving it with less energy—or cooling it—as it enters the cooler substance and warming it. This is the process of heat conduction.

2. *Convection*—The other two mechanisms of heat transfer are convection and radiation. In convection, matter actually moves while carrying heat energy with it, as when hot water rises from the bottom of a kettle on a hot stove.

3. *Radiation* process is when heat energy is changed into the electromagnetic form (light, infrared, etc.) and is carried away. In all these types of energy transfers, however, the net flow of energy must still be from a hot body to cooler surroundings.

One very important substance in the heat process is the gas that is generated in most cases during heating. It is the hot gas, such as the steam in the steam engine, or the hot gases in a burning coal furnace, that do the actual work. Gas is also the simplest state of matter to understand, so its most important properties can be deduced from a model that treats the gas as a substance made up of identical, non-interacting (no forces other than contact forces between them) spheres. These spheres collide elastically with each other, with the container walls, or with other matter, and transfer their energy during impact.

In a simple gas, the most important form of internal energy is this random molecular or atomic motion of the heat energy. The hotter a substance is, the more energy its molecules contain. The hotter it is, the faster its molecules move, because the kinetic energy of motion increases with the velocity or speed of the moving matter. Heat energy, therefore, in the broad definition that we are using here, is related to the average kinetic energy of the moving molecules of the substance.

Heat is often created by combustion of matter, and is defined as a chemical exothermic reaction in which oxygen is combined with some other element, releasing heat in the process. Because natural fuels, such as coal, oils, natural gas, and biomass contain carbon, the combustion or oxidation of the carbon molecules occurs during the reaction.

$C + O_2 = CO_2 + 94.03$ kcal of heat.

Carbon has an atomic weight of 12, so during burning 7.8 kcal per gram of carbon are produced.

Natural fuels also contain hydrogen, the combustion, or oxidation of which is $H_2 + O = H_2O + 68.37$ kcal. Each gram of hydrogen produces 34.2 kcal of heat, which is four times the heat produced by the same amount of carbon. Some natural fuels are partially oxygenated, which means they contain oxygen in their molecule, so they normally lose part of the energy that they could produce during combustion.

Figure 1-6 shows the heat content, in kilocalories and Btus, obtained when burning just one gram of these natural fuels. The data tell us that natural gas has the highest heat value (heat energy released during burning). Natural gas is the only natural fuel sold in a gas form, and one gram of liquid natural gas (LNG) creates a lot of gas.

Heat source	Heat (kcal/g)	Btu
Natural gas	13.2	52.4
Oil	10.0	39.7
Fat	9.1	36.1
Coal	7.8	31.0
Ethyl alcohol	7.1	28.2
Proteins	5.7	22.6
Sugars	4.1	16.3
Wood	3.3	13.1

Figure 1-6. Heat content of natural fuels

Wood, on the other hand, has a fairly high heat content, but in its natural, freshly cut, form it contains 50-80% water. Burning such wood lowers its heat value significantly, because a lot of the heat is used to boil and evaporate the water content. Oven dry wood, which is sold at a premium, has a much higher heat value—close to that of coal—but the drying process requires a lot of energy, which in effect reduces the overall heat value of the final product and increases its price significantly.

Another form of energy is that generated and used by humans and animals. Fats, proteins, sugars and starches are contained in most of the foods we eat. When we ingest and burn those, they are converted into CO_2 and water, and generate energy which we can use for our bodily functions. The conversion process is different, but the final result is energy that can be measured.

The SI heat energy unit is the calorie (cal) or kilocalorie (kcal), or the amount of heat energy needed to raise the temperature of 1 kg of water (at a specific temperature and pressure), by 1°C (degree Celsius). It is also the traditional measure of the energy value of foods.

In the English system, the amount of water is measured in pounds (lbs) and the temperature rise in degrees Fahrenheit (°F), while the heat energy is measured in British thermal units (Btu.)

1 Btu added to 1 lb of water at standard temperature and pressure will raise its temperature by 1°F.

Energy Measurement Units

The energy value of fuels such as coal and oil is usually given in Btus. As a result, most of the energy data in English-speaking countries are presented in Btus. The calorie, watt, horsepower, ton of oil equivalent, and joule units are used also in some scientific measurements and for simplicity in some conversions and calculations.

Table 1-2. Key energy conversion units

Unit	Measure
1 joule (J)	1 N.m
	1 kg.m/s^2
	0.2388 cal
	9.4782^{-4} Btu
	2.7778^{-4} Wh
	10^7 ergs
1 calorie	4.1868 J
1 kWh	3.6×10^{13} ergs
	3600 kJ
	860 kcal
	8.6^{-5} toe *
1 toe *	10^{10} cal
	41.8 GJ
	11.63 MWh
	1.28 tons coal equivalent
	39.68 million Btu
1 million Btu	1.0551 GJ
	2.52^{-2} toe
	0.2931 MWh
1 Watt	1 J/s
1 HP	746 W
1 GWh	86 toe

*toe = tons of oil equivalent

Since energy in motion is work, the SI units are the same. The basic units joule (J), named after Sir James Prescott Joule, are derived from his hands-on experiments and calculations on the mechanical equivalent of heat energy. Basically, 1 joule is equal to 1 newton-meter and can be expressed as:

$$1\,J = 1\,kg\left(\frac{m}{S}\right)^2 = 1\,\frac{kg \cdot m^2}{s^2}$$

where

    kg   is in kilograms
    m   is in meters, and
    s   is in seconds

The US units for both energy and work are: the foot-pound force (or 1.3558 J), the British thermal unit (Btu, or about 1055 J), and the horsepower-hour (or 2.6845 MJ).

The unit used to represent everyday electricity, as in utility bills, is the kilowatt-hour (kWh), where one kWh is equivalent to 1,000 Watts used during one hour, or about 3600 kJ. Another useful unit is that of kilowatt-hours per year (kWh/yr), which is actually the average electric energy (power) consumption, or the average rate at which energy is used during the period of one year.

Exothermic and Endothermic Heat Processes

In thermodynamics (the science of heat), the term exothermic, from the Greek *outside heating*, describes a process that releases energy from the system, usually in the form of heat, but also in the form of light (e.g., a spark, flame, or explosion). It can also produce electricity (as in a battery), or sound (such as when burning hydrogen). Explosions are some of the most violent and most noticeable exothermic reactions.

Exothermic refers to a transformation of energy in which a system releases energy (heat) to the surroundings: $Q < 0$, when the transformation occurs at constant pressure, $\Delta H < 0$, and constant volume $\Delta U < 0$.

In a closed system that does not give off heat to the surroundings, such as water boiling in a pressure cooker, the exothermic process results in an increase in internal temperature, and in this case in rise of pressure as well.

The opposite of an exothermic process is an endothermic process, one that absorbs energy in the form of heat as needed to complete a reaction or work activity.

In chemical reactions, the heat that is absorbed is in the form of electromagnetic energy. The loss of kinetic energy via reacting electrons causes light energy to be released. This amount of light is equivalent in energy to the stabilization energy that is needed to complete the chemical reaction, i.e. the bond energy. The light that is released can be absorbed by other molecules in solution to give rise to molecular vibrations or rotations, resulting in heat generation, and in the end represents an exothermic reaction which has negative enthalpy (DH < 0), see *enthalpy* below.

In endothermic reactions, in order for the process to be completed, energy is absorbed to place an electron in a higher energy state, such that the electron can associate with another atom to form another chemical complex, thus completing the process. The loss of energy within solution is absorbed by the endothermic reaction and therefore is a loss of heat. Therefore in an exothermic reaction the energy needed for the reaction to occur is less than the total energy released, and the system enthalpy at that point is positive (DH > 0), see *enthalpy* below.

Enthalpy

Enthalpy is another important variable, which is basically a measure of the total energy (or thermodynamic potential) of a thermodynamic system. It includes the internal energy, which is the energy required to create a system, and the amount of energy required to make room for it by displacing its environment and establishing its volume and pressure. This can be figuratively seen reflected in the behavior of water vapor in a water boiler. As the vapor goes through the boiler's piping, it carries its energy to another place—be it a space heater or a steam turbine. At this point there are no transfers of energy and no chemical reactions. It is simply a physical transport of a heated mass to a point of use.

The total enthalpy, H, of a system cannot be measured directly. Thus, change in enthalpy, ΔH, is a more useful quantity than its absolute value. The change ΔH is positive in endothermic reactions, and negative in heat-releasing exothermic processes. ΔH of a system is equal to the sum of non-mechanical work done on it and the heat supplied to it.

Enthalpy is the preferred expression of the energy changes in chemical, biological, and physical measurements, because it simplifies the description of different energy transfer mechanisms. A change in enthalpy takes into account the energy transferred to the environment through the expansion of the system under study.

Supposing a closed system, we then see the system's enthalpy combining the internal energy of the vapor and variations of pressure and volume. As with internal energy, it does not have an absolute value and only its variations (DH) can be calculated in relation to a state of reference.

In exothermic reactions, those that generate heat, the enthalpy is negative (DH < 0). A practical example is the formation of water from hydrogen combustion. In an endothermic reaction, in turn, there is heat absorption, and thus with positive enthalpy (DH > 0). A practical example is that of water that vaporizes at the base of a waterfall. It turns into a gas with heat absorption generated by the kinetic energy of the falling water at the moment of impact.

Energy consumed as heat during a chemical transformation under constant pressure may be defined as reaction enthalpy and may be measured by a device called a calorimeter, or calculated by the difference between the formation heats of products and of chemical reagents. However, understanding and interpreting the reaction heat (enthalpy) for a particular transformation requires understanding how chemical energy accumulates in matter.

Enthalpy is also measures by the joule, and/or the other units (Btu, calorie, etc.) as discussed above.

Energy Disorder

There is a tendency in all energy conversions to change from some order to increasing disorder. Looking at hot water molecules in a boiling water tank and steam column, we can see them constantly colliding with each other and with the walls of the container, and moving chaotically in all directions. Their motion is totally randomized, and we draw the conclusion that it is disordered, with no apparent preference for moving in one direction over another. Heat energy is a disordered type of energy, so the water molecules in the steam move randomly.

On the other hand, there are examples of well ordered forms of energy. One of these is the flow of electric current in a wire, or water running in a pipe. Under ideal conditions (no resistance in the wire and no roughness in the pipe walls) the electrons and molecules are lined up and moving in perfect order.

In the reality, both of these cases have some disordered motion. The electrons in the wires and the water molecules in the pipe would be bumping into the walls or bouncing in various directions, but in both cases, ordered motion is evident and is superimposed over the disorder.

As time goes on, the order gets more disordered. In the wire example, the wire becomes heated, resistance increases and the electron flow becomes much harder and almost random, until it is used in an electric light or motor, where it is converted into much more disordered heat, light, or mechanical work states of energy.

The water in the pipe cannot remain in that state forever, and usually ends up splashing in a sink, where the molecules enter a totally disordered state and bounce whichever way gravity or impact directs them.

In all cases, state of disorder is easier to achieve, thus it is more probable under most circumstances. The process usually goes from order to disorder, and not the other way around.

Entropy

In both examples above (the electrical wire and the water pipe) the application of work provides the orderly motion. An electric impulse forced the electrons to move, and a gravitational force pulled the water molecules to line up and flow in an orderly manner. In both cases the orderly state eventually changes.

Electricity is eventually converted into more disordered heat energy; piped water eventually runs into a basin. Disorder seems more probable to exist than order, and the probability of this happening is the key to understanding the broader statement of the second law of thermodynamics.

The evidence that order is less probable than disorder is all around us. Disorder is more probable than order. If a sample of matter is in an ordered state, spontaneous change will take it in the direction of disorder.

In all changes of state within a closed system the total energy remains unchanged. That is a statement of the first law of thermodynamics. But something changes in the system, and it has to do with order and disorder in the state of the system. We call that something "entropy."

The entropy of the state of a system is a measure of the probability of its occurrence. States of low probability have low entropy; states of high probability have high entropy. With this definition, we see from the previous examples that in any transfer or conversion of energy, because the spontaneous direction of the change of slate of a closed system is from a less to a more probable state, the entropy of the system must increase. That is also a broader statement needed to describe the second law of thermodynamics.

In any energy transfer or conversion within a closed system, the entropy (or disorder) of that system increases. Energy conversions can proceed so that the entropy of a part of a system is decreased too, i.e. charging a storage battery, or freezing ice cubes. In each of these examples, order has been won from disorder and entropy has decreased during the input of energy.

If the total system is considered, however, the total effect has been an increase in disorder. To charge a battery we must provide energy above and beyond that necessary to re-form the chemical combinations in the battery plates. Some of this low-entropy electrical energy (ordered state) is changed into high-entropy heat energy (disordered state) in the current-carrying wires and in the output devices.

In freezing ice, we increase the order and thus decrease the entropy of the water in the ice cube trays by removing heat from it. The heat energy removed, however, must flow into a substance (the expanded Freon gas) that is at a much lower temperature than its surroundings. Thus, the entropy and the disorder of the gas is increased.

Another way of stating the consequence of the second law of thermodynamics is to say that all energy transfers or conversions are irreversible. They will go spontaneously in the direction of increasing entropy (disorder). They will not go spontaneously toward a state of lower entropy (order). Thus, all the losses we described in the power plant conversions are necessary to fulfill the laws of nature. Some of them can be minimized, but none of them can be eliminated. Entropy must increase, and it always does.

The New Energy Economy

Today, the low-entropy (perhaps the lowest possible) forms of energy (the fossils) and being steadily depleted. They lie there in their primordial state of rest until we dig or pump them out. Then they jump from a state of lowest (dormant) entropy to enter (albeit temporarily) into a state of highest entropy. During the burning they also change their physical state, from that of liquid or solid to gas and residue. Since there is no way to return to their original state of low entropy, they are gone up in smoke.

When we use the fossils, we do not use up only their energy—we deplete the entire usefulness of the energy contained in them. This is the significance of the present-day energy crisis. Burning and eliminating a large part of the fossils is destroying the state of low entropy that formed over millennia and converting it into the highest form of entropy.

During the golden age of fossil fuels (1920-1970) we didn't worry about any of this because useful fossil energy was plentiful and cheap. We thought it would last forever, and used it carelessly. Large 8-cylinder cars were the norm, and we drove them just for fun and because we could.

We still waste, but now we are more aware that the time has come to begin the practice of "the new economy"—the conservation of our precious low-entropy energy forms. We only delay the inevitable with half-way measures and lots of talk. The high gas-pump prices are a constant reminder of the new reality.

The second law of thermodynamics tells us that because entropy increases in any transfer or conversion of energy, we should try to find energy transfer and/or conversion mechanisms (and products) in which the entropy of the source and the end use are as close as possible, thus minimizing the entropy increase. This is still a form of delaying the inevitable, but at least it will buy us more time to find some alternative energy sources for the short term.

This new way of thinking and living will lead us to a new way to measure efficiency in terms of "increased entropy." In the long run, the entropy of the universe will increase no matter what we do. Entropy is the "arrow of time" which increases the chaos level in the direction of the future.

In any actual decision about energy use, of course, we have other things besides the entropy increase to consider. We must take into account the present cost and environmental impacts, for instance. Although we have considered these in the past, we have not paid much attention to the entropy involved. This may be just the right time to begin considering it as a reliable measurement.

We must begin to apply this concept as a type of new thermodynamic economy, making certain that each use of low entropy is for a necessary end and is accomplished with as small an increase in entropy as possible.

Below we take a close look at the concept of energy efficiency, to gain a measure of our success in practicing this new kind of economy as we strive to increase the efficiency of energy generating systems.

Energy and Power

The terms "energy" and "power" are essentially synonyms, although most scientists and engineers prefer to distinguish between them, depending on the conditions in each case. Technically speaking, power is not the same as energy. Energy is the potential of doing work, but power is the rate at which energy is converted and work is performed. This is the energy we can then express and measure in units of power, such as Watt, kW MW, GW, etc. in the electric industry.

As mentioned before, energy is invisible and immeasurable until its components activate it. For example, energy sits in our car's gas tank until it is pumped into the engine and forced to do work, at which point we feel the power of the fuel moving the car. The power at that point can be measured in units of horsepower in the engine torque, feet per second in road speed, or degrees Celsius in the engine cylinders.

By the same token, a hydroelectric plant generates power by allowing the water above the dam to pass through turbines. It actually converts the water's potential energy into kinetic energy and ultimately into electric energy. So, the amount of electric energy that is generated per unit of time is the electric power generated.

Still, in everyday discussions, the concepts of electric energy and electric power are interchangeable, simply because they refer to the same activity—a flow of energized electrons on their way to do work. So we also will use the terms of electric energy and electric power interchangeably and somewhat indiscriminately.

NOTE: In this text we use the terms power and energy interchangeably in many places, simply because they are so similar in their practical applications. In the power generating industry, it would be proper to say that energy is converted from one form to another, during which process power is generated and used. So we say that there is a lot of energy flowing and stored in the power grid, and we don't need to quantify it. Then we say that the energy in the power grid can be used to generate (electric) power, which can be measured as a certain quantity (in MW, GW, etc.).

Energy Transfers

The transfer of energy between a "system" and adjacent regions is expressed as work. One example is mechanical work, which in the simplest of cases is expressed in the following equation:

$$\Delta E = W \text{ (if there are no other energy-transfer processes involved.)}$$

where
  ΔE is the amount of energy transferred, and
  W represents the work done on the system.

In this case the ΔE is the difference of the energy before and after the transfer. For example, burning a log generates 100 Btus of heat. ΔE here would be 100 Btu, because we started from zero.

Energy transfer can be split into several categories:

$$\Delta E = W + Q$$

where
  Q represents the heat flow into the system.

There are other ways in which an open system can gain or lose energy. In chemical systems, energy can be added to a system by means of adding substances with different chemical potentials which are then extracted (both of these process are illustrated by fueling an auto, a system which gains in energy without addition of either work or heat). Winding a clock would be adding energy to a mechanical system (the spring).

These terms may be added to the above equation, or they can generally be subsumed into a quantity called "energy addition term, E," which refers to any type of energy carried over the surface of a control volume or system volume.

As an example, the kinetic energy of a stream of particles entering a system, or energy from a laser beam adds to system energy, without being either work done or heat added, in the classic senses.

$$\Delta E = W + Q = E$$

where
  E represents other additional energy not covered by work done on a system, or heat added to it.

Energy is also transferred from potential energy, E_p, to kinetic energy E_k and then back to potential energy constantly. This is referred to as conservation of energy, although there are always losses in transfer processes.

In a closed system, energy cannot be created or destroyed; therefore, the initial energy and the final energy will be equal to each other. In this case the "losses" would be counted as energy that is transferred into other types of energy, but yet remains in the system.

This transfer can be represented by:

$$E_{pi} + E_{ki} = E_{pF} + E_{kF}$$

where:
  E_{pi} is initial potential energy
  E_k is initial kinetic energy
  E_{pF} is final potential energy
  E_{kF} is final kinetic energy

The equation can then be simplified further since

$$E_p = mgh$$

where
  E_p is potential energy

m   is mass
g   is gravity, and
h   is height

and

$$E_k = 1/2mv^2$$

where
E_k is kinetic energy
m   is mass, and
v   is velocity

Then the total amount of energy can be found by adding

$$E_p + E_k = E_{total}$$

Efficiency of energy conversion

There are rare instances in which energy (or the fuel it is contained in) is used without conversion, such as heating buildings with geothermal power (steam coming from the Earth's core). In most other instances, energy is converted from one form to another, as needed for more efficient or more convenient delivery and use. In some cases, several conversions are necessary before we obtain energy where we want it and in the way we want it.

For example, nuclear energy generated by radioactive elements (chemical energy) in a nuclear plant is converted into steam (heat energy), which then turns a turbine and a generator (mechanical energy) to generate flow of electrons in the wires (electric energy—the final product) which can be used whenever and wherever we need it.

Each energy conversion type and cycle has advantages and disadvantages, with accompanying losses of energy during different steps of the transfer process. The losses can be related to the efficiency of the conversion process.

The key measurement of efficiency is the number which we assign to the successful completion of these conversions. In the case of geothermal power it is 100% complete and successful, because no conversion takes place, thus there are no measurable losses before the actual application.

Coal, on the other hand, must be processed and burned before it can generate any useful energy. A lot of energy is used during these operations, and then more efficiency is lost during the burning process.

As another example, solar energy (sunlight) is converted into electricity, but not before 80 percent or more of it has been lost to inefficiencies in the equipment and related processes.

The efficiency of the different fuels is different, and is determined by their heat value and burning properties, as in Table 1-3.

Table 1-3. Energy generated by different fuels

Natural Gas	1,030 Btu/cu ft
Propane	2,500 Btu/cu ft
Methane	1,000 Btu/cu ft
Landfill gas	500 Btu/cu ft
Butane	3,200 Btu/cu ft
Kerosene	135,000 Btu/gal
Biodiesel oil	120,000 Btu/gal
Gasoline	125,000 Btu/gal
Anthracite coal	26,000,000 Btu/ton
Bituminous coal	24,000,000 Btu/ton
Electricity	3,412 Btu/kW
Softwood	15,000,000 Btu/cord
Hardwood	20,000,000 Btu/cord
Corn, shelled	15,000,000 Btu/ton

In more practical terms, we can generate 1 kW/h of electric energy by burning:
0.00052 tons, or 1.03 pounds, of coal
0.01003 Mcf (1,000 cubic feet) of natural gas, or
0.0016 barrels of fuel oil

Or, the number of kW/h generated per unit of fuel used is:

2,000 kWh per ton of coal, or 0.1 kWh per pound of coal
100 kWh per Mcf (1,000 cubic feet) of natural gas, or 610 kWh per barrel, or 14.5 kWh per gallon, of fuel oil

Obviously, the different fuels have different energy (or heat) value, which determines the efficiency of the burning process too. It all depends on the type and quality of the different fuels, so the fuel's state (gas, liquid, or solid) and heat values must be considered, in order to choose the proper fuel for each power plant design.

Energy conversion efficiency also greatly depends on the completeness and usefulness of the output as compared to the input. For example, part of the heat produced from burning a fuel in a furnace may become waste heat, so the process would not be 100% efficient. The furnace is an energy converter, and the burning process is an example of an energy transformation in which the efficiency is measured by:

$$\eta = \frac{P_{out}}{P_{in}}$$

where:

P_{out} is the energy that is produced
        (energy kcal produced)

P_{in} is the energy input (coal kcal burned)

Efficiency is a technical or physical term, which can be translated as degree of usefulness of an energy conversion process. It can also be expressed in terms of effectiveness/efficacy—related terms used in some engineering calculations.

Energy conversion efficiency is usually expressed in numbers between 0 and 1.0, or in percentage 0 to 100% with the maximum being 1.0 or 100%. 100% is assigned only to the perpetual motion machine, so efficiency of 0.95, or 95% would be considered an efficiency ceiling.

Examples of the measurement of efficiency:

Pump	$= [(kg{\cdot}m^2/s^2)/(kWh)]$
Turbine	$= [(kg{\cdot}m^2/s^2)/(kg{\cdot}m^2/s^2)]$
Engine	$= [(kW)]/(kg/s) \times (kJ/kg)]$
Steam gen.	$= [(kg/s) \times (kJ/kg)/(kg/s) \times (kJ/kg)]$
Boiler	$= [(kg/s) \times (kJ/kg)/(kg/s) \times (kJ/kg)]$

where

    kg   is in kilograms
    kW   is in kilowatts
  kWh   is in kilowatt/hours
     m   is in meters
    kJ   is in kilojoules

In some exceptions, effectiveness measures can exceed 1.0, or 100%, but these are used for heat pumps and other devices that move heat rather than convert it.

The efficiency of power generating stations varies according to fuel and technology used. For example, a wind power generating station could be 50% efficient. This means that half of the energy of the incoming wind was converted into useful power.

Similarly, a 15% efficient solar module means that 85% of the solar energy coming in at 1,000W/m² is wasted—either by reflection, or conversion to waste heat, or it is simply not converted due to the cell's inefficiency.

If our solar module produces 150 Watts of power when exposed to 1,000 Watts of solar power, then its efficiency in this case would be:

Table 1-4. Efficiency of energy convertors

Item	Efficiency %
Solar cells	2-43
Light bulb	5-10
Photosynthesis	5-10
Fluorescents	8-16
Human muscle	14--27
Sodium lamps	15-29
LEDs	up to 35
Gas turbine	up to 40
Steam turbine	30-40
Gas engine	40-50
Heat pump	20-30
Refrigerators	40-50
Wind turbine	up to 59
Fuel cell	up to 85
Water turbine	up to 90
Electric motors	70-99
Electric heaters	99+

$$\eta = \frac{P_{out}}{P_{in}} = \frac{150 \text{ W}}{1,000 \text{ W}} = 15\% \ (0.15)$$

But there is another variable that must be considered when calculating the efficiency of power plants. It is the capacity factor, which denotes the overall capacity of the plant or solar module to produce power during a certain time period.

Capacity Factors

The capacity factor of a power plant is the ratio of the actual output of a power plant over a period of time and its potential output if it had operated at full nameplate capacity the entire time. The name plate is the maximum possible output, or the output determined by the manufacturer.

To calculate the capacity factor, we take the total amount of energy the plant produced during a period of time and divide it by the nameplate capacity.

As an example, a large solar power plant rated at 1,000 MWp (megawatt peak) produces 648,000 MW/h (megawatt hours) in a month. The number of MW/h that would have been produced had the plant been operating at full capacity is determined by multiplying the plant's nameplate (maximum) capacity by the number of hours in the time period. 1,000 MW × 30 days × 24 hours/day is 720,000 MW/h.

The capacity factor is then determined by dividing the actual output by the maximum possible output. In this case, the capacity factor is 0.9 (90%)

$$Cf = \frac{200,000 \text{ MW/h}}{1,000 \text{ MWp} \times 30 \text{ days} \times 24 \text{ hrs/day}} = 0.28$$

This particular power plant has a capacity factor of 0.28, or 28%, which is actually quite good for a solar power plant today. It is low, compared to fossil fuel plants which operate at 80-90% capacity, because solar power cannot be generated at night or during cloudy or rainy weather.

The capacity factor is different from the availability factor, which is the actual operating time minus repairs and such. It is also different from firm capacity and from efficiency, which we reviewed above. The capacity factors vary greatly depending on the type of fuel used, the technology, and the design of the plant.

Energy Use

Energy comes in different forms, and is not easy to measure. Still, we need to have a good idea of what it is and what it does, in order to be able to comprehend and compare its different states and properties.

Table 1-5 gives a list of energy use in different areas and under different conditions:

Table 1-5. Comparative energy use.

Energy Use	Btu	kW/h
Human daily activity	6000	1.8
Gallon of gasoline	10^5	30
Mfc of natural gas	3×10^5	90
Lightning bolt	10^6	300
Barrel fuel oil	2×10^6	600
Making one car	10^7	3,000
Ton of coal*	2×10^7	6,000
Rocket launch	10^9	300,000
Boiling lake Michigan	10^{13}	3×10^9
H bomb	10^{14}	3×10^{10}
World energy use	10^{17}	3×10^{13}
Photosynthesis, annual	10^{19}	3×10^{15}
Solar energy, annual**	10^{23}	3×10^{19}
Earth rotation	10^{25}	3×10^{21}

*The theoretical heat content in coal is in the 3,000-6,000 kWh per ton range. When burned, converted into steam and then into rotational energy of the turbine blades, however, coal's energy efficiency drops significantly, so that in practice we get approximately 2,000-3,000 kWh electric energy from each ton of coal—depending on the type of coal and the efficiency of the power plant's equipment.

** Solar, wind, hydro and biofuels energy is difficult to present in conventional energy terms and even harder to compare with conventional fuels. Their importance in world energy generation is gradually increasing, however, so in the following chapters we will review in great detail their contribution to the world energy balance, as well as the environmental consequences of their production and use.

Overall energy use in the U.S. can be presented approximately as:

Table 1-6. Energy use in the U.S.

Energy Use	%
Space heating	15
Water heating	5
Cooking	2
Air conditioning	5
Refrigeration	2
Raw materials	7
Process steam	6
Direct heat	8
Electric motors	5
Cars	13
Trucks	6
Airplanes	2
Trains	1
Other	23

POWER GENERATION

Power generation starts with production of energy sources, such as coal, oil, natural gas, nuclear materials, and biomass materials, which we also call fuels. We can divide these as follows:

1. *Primary* energy sources include coal, oil, natural gas, solar, wind, water falls, tidal, biomass and geothermal. These are called primary because they are found in nature and can be used in some way to generate power (heat and/or electricity).

2. *Secondary* energy sources include electricity and hydrogen and are not found in nature, but instead are obtained by a conversion of the primary energy sources, i.e., burning coal to generate electricity, or using solar energy to decompose water for hydrogen production. Refined fuels, such as gasoline and diesel are also secondary sources, because they are obtained by processing a primary fuel, crude oil.

A second classification of energy sources:

1. *Non-renewable* energy sources include coal, oil, natural gas, and nuclear. They are non-renewable because the quantity of their deposits in the Earth's crust are limited, slow to replace and will be eventually exhausted at the present rate of use.

NOTE: Some of the non-renewable energy sources (coal, oil, and natural gas) are also called fossil fuels, because they were made in primordial times by anaerobic decomposition of fossils (vegetation and animals).

2. *Renewable* energy sources include solar, wind, hydro, tidal, biomass and geothermal. As the name suggests, these are constantly renewed by natural processes and will never be exhausted under normal use. Exceptions are hydro and biomass, because they depend on other (natural and man-made) conditions that might limit their supply.

A third classification of energy sources:

1. *Commercial* energy sources are these that are usually sold or traded as entity (like selling a ton of coal), or their equivalents (such as selling one kilowatt of electricity made by burning coal).

    NOTE: At a cost of $100/bbl in the complex 2012 world energy, economic, and financial situations, the energy-related commercial (monetary) global transactions were estimated at about $2.0 trillion annually.

2. *Non-commercial* energy sources are those that are freely obtained, such as sunlight and water. They can be freely used as is, for example for solar cooking using the Sun's heat, or turning a water wheel at a stream to power an irrigation pump. Although they don't have a commercial value in their "as is" form—mostly because the oil companies have not figured out how to patent them yet—they can, nevertheless, be used commercially.

These primary energy sources (fuels) are used extensively in the actual processes of generating energy (as in electric energy, or heat) for use in our daily lives. These are complex, expensive and often dirty and dangerous processes. There are usually a number of steps needed to get the different types of energy sources ready for generating secondary energy, like electricity or gasoline.

First, we must access the raw materials, from which the fuels are derived. These are mined, dug out, pumped, or otherwise removed from where they have been sitting for millions of years undisturbed. These places are usually deep under ground or even deeper under the oceans.

Once we get them out, we must prepare them for

transport, refining, further transport, storage, and finally use to generate heat or electricity. This is usually done by burning the raw materials in a power plant to produce the final product—electric energy, or heat.

The Energy Generating Materials (Fuels)

All power plants use some type of fuel, be it primary, or secondary, renewable or not. Fossil fuels (coal, oil, and natural gas) account for more than 90% of the total amount of materials used in energy generation. They have been and still are the most important primary energy generating sources in the world. The rest of the total power generation is contributed by hydropower, nuclear energy, and in much smaller amounts by solar, wind, and geothermal power.

Firewood, which is also used in enormous quantities worldwide, falls in a different category altogether and we will review it as such.

Solar energy has a special place here, because it has been involved in the creation of most of the primary and secondary fuels since the beginning of time. This is another complex process, which requires another book to review. For our purposes, we will consider solar power generation only, which is the actual production of energy by photovoltaic or thermal solar conversion devices.

Obviously, coal rules in the power generation sector! Still. The other fuel types are creeping up in use, but coal is still on top, and is foreseen to be there for a very long time.

Another widely used energy source is raw wood used as firewood by millions in developing countries. Many of these people simply have no other choice. Due

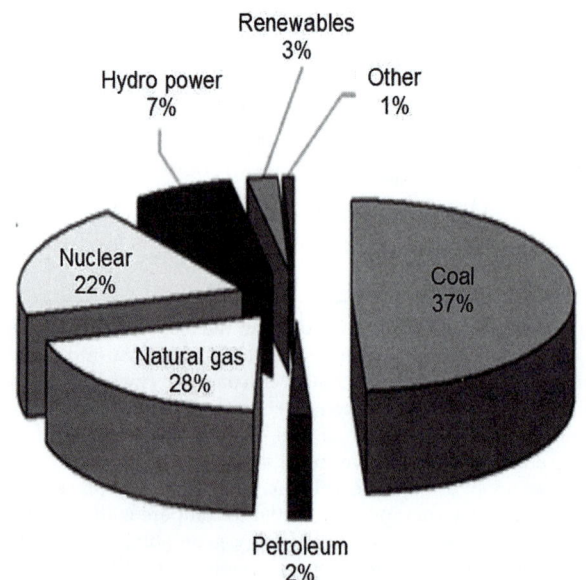

Figure 1-7. Power generation in the U.S.

to their poverty or isolation from civilization, they have access only to one fuel source—firewood—which is abundant and free in most cases.

The amount of firewood used worldwide is staggering. While the greatest use is by people in developing countries, many in developed countries use firewood, but for different reasons, and the amount of wood used is much lower.

Firewood

Until the middle of the 19th century, the major source of energy was wood—the same energy source that has been used since the beginning of time. Even when coal became a major energy source, firewood was still prevalent, mostly due to its unlimited supply. It accounted for more than 90% of U.S. energy generation, mostly for home heating and cooking.

An average of 18 cords (stacks 4 x 4 x 8 feet) of wood per year were needed to heat an American house in the mid 1800s—the heat energy equivalent of 2.5 times the amount used to warm a typical home today. This is mostly due to the inefficiency of the old fireplaces, which had less than a 10% efficiency rating, and which consumed three quarters of all wood used at the time. Stoves are about four times as efficient, but were not popular in the Americas at that time for convenience reasons. Wood stoves became fashionable in North America in the mid 20th century, and wood consumption increased with time.

Wood also powered the growing industries of the 19th century. This included steamships and trains running on wood fire, burning nearly 8 million cords of wood a year. The iron and steel industry were the major industrial users of wood, although there was a twist. Most of the energy for iron smelting came from charcoal, which was made out of 1.5 million cords of wood per year.

The charcoal used in iron smelting totaled some 700,000 to 750,000 tons. This compares to an estimated 750,000 tons of charcoal used each year in backyard barbeques in this country.

Charcoal is still important worldwide. Brazil uses charcoal in 45% of its iron smelting—3.6 million tons of charcoal are used in Brazil annually—and consumption is increasing. Charcoal is also a major fuel in less developed countries such as Ghana and Kenya, where 250,000-300,000 tons are used annually.

Firewood stoves are fashionable today, and are selling at a rate of 200,000 per year in the United States. Over 50 million cords of firewood are used annually for home heating alone, and wood and wood residue pro-

vide almost 2 quads of total energy per year, most of it in the wood products and paper industries. In these industries, "biofuels" served about half of the total energy needs.

Consumption of fuel wood in this country reached a peak of almost 150 million cords in 1870, since at that time wood was the primary fuel. In comparison, the 100 million cords used today in the US account for only a few percent of the total primary energy input.

Even if the use of wood and biomass increases to a maximum, the total annual potential of biomass energy generation, could provide only about 1/4 of the U.S. primary energy input.

The situation is different in developing countries, of course. Firewood is, and will long remain, a primary fuel, especially in rural areas.

The gasses, which are produced during wood fuel burning are serious pollutants, and account for a large portion of the world's environmental and climate change problems. We will take a close look at these in the next chapter.

Coal

Coal is the energy engine of the world. During the last two centuries, the U.S. coal industry has grown. By the mid-19th century, the superiority of coal over wood burning was noted. The growing scarcity of firewood in some parts of the country caused the first great replacement fuel cycle, which established coal as the fuel of the past century.

Anthracite is a type of coal, which contains almost 100% carbon. This quality, and the fact that it is cleaner-burning made it most popular at first. By the end of the century, however, bituminous coal with lower carbon content but comparable heat value, took its place as the preferred fuel. Until then, more than half of the coal came from the great "Pittsburgh seam," which lay exposed along the rivers above the city.

The first turnover was dramatic; wood had fallen from 90% of the energy input in 1850 to 20% by the end of the century, while coal grew to 70% use during the same time. One of the reasons for the swiftness of the replacement was the rich seams of coal in the East, where high population density and industrial concentration created an energy demand that the vanishing forests could not satisfy. Changes in industry and transportation fed the demand for coal.

NOTE: Before 1900 less than 800 Mt of hard coals and lignites accounted for about 95% of the world's total annual primary energy supply, according to TPES. Coal production went up and down during that part of the century, but doubled by 1949, to nearly 1.3 Gt of hard coals, and about 350 Mt of lignites, mostly because of the expansion of traditional manual mining of underground. By 1988 the world produced and consumed 4.9 Gt, with 3.6 Gt of hard coal and 1.3 Gt of lignites. Forty percent of the coal at the time came from Eastern Germany and Russia, and was of very low quality.

U.S. coal increased to the point that it not only energized our own industry, heated our homes, and powered our trains, but it enabled us to become a major exporter as well. During the early peak in coal production, in 1918, 678 million tons were taken from the ground, and 27 million tons were exported overseas. During the wartime peak of the 1944-1945, 688 million tons of coal were mined, while exports amounted to 94 million tons. This amounted to nearly half of the world's coal production at the time.

U.S. coal exports grew again as production increased during the early 1980s, when it reached a new peak of approximately 800 million tons annually, with some 100 million tons of exports. At that time, however, the world's coal production was four times larger than that of the U.S.

Coal's customers changed as radically as the peaks and valleys of its production. In the early 20th century, industrial and home heating accounted for 60%, while railroads consumed 20% of the coal burned. Electric utilities consumed only 8%. By the mid-20th century, the rail's share had been cut to 15%, industry's share was 40%, and 20% was used for home and commercial heating.

The number of electric power plants grew at the time too, so they consumed 15% of all coal produced in the country. Then the use of coal changed even more drastically. Diesel-powered railroads consumed only 2%, and the retail coal market shrank to less than 10%. Industry, where natural gas and oil competed strongly, used only 36% of the total. Most of the rest, well over 50%, was consumed by the electric utilities.

By the 1980s the electric utilities' share had climbed to 82% of the total coal consumed in the U.S. Less than 1% was used for heating. In 2011, 90% of the coal produced in the U.S. was used by the nation's electric power generators.

Recent estimates place the total amount of coal in the Earth's crust at over 20 trillion tons, but only 1.0 trillion is economically exploitable for now, meaning that the rest won't be easy or cheap to mine, if at all. This also means that we here in the US, at the present rate of use, have about 150 years of coal burning left.

There are reports and claims of vast coal supplies in the U.S. and abroad, which would be able to fuel the global economies for 150 years or more. Several other studies suggest, however, that coal may not be nearly as abundant as once believed. A 2007 National Academy of Sciences report concluded that a more realistic number is about 100 years, or less, if coal consumption were to grow beyond the current rate.

Even more disturbingly, data from EIA show that the total heat content of U.S. coal has been declining since the late 1990s while production levels have been steady. This means that coal grades are dropping, so that the actual energy we get from domestic coal is less, and the waste from coal burning is increasing.

Worldwide reserves are probably half of what is currently stated simply because, just as with oil reserves, coal reserve estimates have been steadily dropping, down to what is actually minable, and not necessarily to what might be available.

In 2007 the Germany's Energy Watch Group suggested that China, which has some of the largest coal resources in the world, has supposedly already mined more than 20% of the existing coal in the country. Keeping in mind that China's industrial revolution is only a couple of decades old, and that coal use has been increasing steadily, it is easy to see that China could run out of coal by the end of this century. What then?

In the U.S., the electric utilities still dominate the coal market, with coal gasification, new coal converting technologies, carbon sequestration and conversion to natural gas taking over the industry. These new developments make the future of coal uncertain. New and large natural gas reserves are found and exploited daily, and new renewable technologies are taking over—all of them trying to replace coal in critical power-generation operations.

The new trend of converting coal-burning plants to natural gas is another fast-growing phenomena which would aid and extend the energy transition, thus allowing us (and future generations) to adapt to the dwindling global energy resources and find new, more sustainable ways to generate and use energy.

Crude Oil

Petroleum products are produced by the refining of oil-based fossils, which were created millions of years ago by decomposition of organic materials. These oil-based fossils, however, are in liquid form, and are much younger than coal.

They are usually found in sedimentary basins, but the exact fossilization mechanism is still under research and a subject of many heated debates (where lots of waste energy is released).

During their initial formation, fossils consist of large and very complex organic (hydrocarbon) molecules. At that stage they are very similar to those in many living cells, and not surprisingly, since they were formed by the transformation of living cells (vegetation, animals, etc.) into fossils.

During their "gestation" period, which also consists of millions of years, they are subjected to extreme temperatures and pressures. Under these conditions, and with time, their molecules "crack" into lighter and more mobile ones, creating different types and qualities of oils.

When extracted and refined, these oils reproduce the natural cracking process, and when done in a controlled way, different preferred fuels such as light oils, gasoline, jet fuel, etc. are obtained.

Oil and gas migrate through the rock layers toward the Earth's surface, and some reach the surface and produce oil pools and gas flares that are the first evidence of the presence of these fuels. However, most crude oil is trapped in rock-solid, impermeable formations, where it forms the pools that are explored and pumped out.

Presently, gasoline is the major product of refinery operations, followed by the distillation of fuel oil used in furnaces and the residual fuel oil that industry and utilities burn. Kerosene for jet fuel is also important.

The switch from coal to petroleum products, during the second of the fuel cycles, saw coal go from 76% of total consumption in 1910 to less than 30% by 1955. During the same time, petroleum products increased their share from 10% to 65%. Production doubled about every eight years. Oil has improved our lives significantly, but it is a problem that we have become dependent on imports, with a peak of 3.21 billion barrels in 1977. At times during that year, crude oil imports accounted for half of the total input to U.S. refineries.

In 2011, the U.S. imported 8.7 million barrels of oil daily—close to the 1977 figure. In 2006 oil imports peaked at 12.2 million barrels per day, which is equal to 4.5 billion barrels annually. These are amazing numbers, so one must wonder how much longer can we do this?

In 2000 USGS estimated that the entire global supply of oil is approximately 3.0 trillion barrels, of which 24% has already been pumped out and used, while 29% has been discovered. While this suggests that there is still a lot of oil left in the Earth's crust, it is getting much harder and more expensive to extract.

It has been estimated that the average global production in existing oilfields is declining by about 4% annually. This means that if no new fields, or new capacities are added, the world will run out of oil in 25 years. That also means that the industry is forced to develop new oil production capacity constantly. The size of each of these developments is enormous—equivalent to the current capacity of the North Sea oil field, which is one of the largest ever. In order to grow production, the oil industry must exceed this amount. This, however, is unlikely to happen due to increasing difficulties with extraction.

There is also talk about lots of oil in the tar sands in Canada, heavy oil in Venezuela and oil shale in Colorado and other places. While these are real and feasible sources of oil, they represent the most difficult to extract types. The easy oil is mostly gone, and what we must deal with now is increasingly difficult oil types that will prove to be a great challenge to the oil industry. This will certainly result in price increases.

High-cost and capital-intensive production methods will slow down the rate of production; they will be slow to ramp up and difficult to maintain. These types of hydrocarbons must be heavily processed at high cost, using enormous amounts of energy, so they are much more expensive.

So, yes, we have a lot of oil, and oil-like substances left in the Earth's crust, but they are becoming difficult to reach, so the oil industry must figure determine a way to obtain enough oil at an acceptable price. Basically, the big issue for the 21st century is the rate of production, regardless of the size of the resource.

Oil is a convenient-to-use fuel, and we cannot even imagine life without it, as it has become crucial to the economic development of the U.S. and most other countries. The abundance of inexpensive supplies from the Middle East since World War II has hooked mankind on oil. This has led to a number of negative effects—with environmental changes and global warming as the main issues we are now forced to address.

Reducing dependence on petroleum imports is a major goal of the U.S. government, and it seems that recently the decision to proceed full-speed with an increase in domestic oil and natural gas production is seen as a solution. Perhaps, but for how long, and then what? These are questions we try to answer in this text.

Still, oil is a big business; it is the evil we can't do with or without, so we have learned to endure it. Time is running out, however, so at the very least, we need to take a close look at our personal use of oil, and get involved in the campaign to reduce oil use in our daily lives. This is one thing we surely can do on a personal level, in addition to electing government officials who will help us in the battle to reduce oil use.

Natural Gas

Natural gas was the most popular fuel in this country in the beginning of the 20th century, increasing from about 5% of the market in 1925 to a peak of 33% in 1970, then dropping to 26% in 1982. Natural gas is a normal component of petroleum production, and comes through the same formation process.

Natural gas contains mostly methane (CH_4), a simple hydrocarbon, and smaller amounts of heavier and more complex hydrocarbon chains. Some of these can be liquefied at atmospheric pressure, and are known as natural gas liquids (NGL). One of them is a natural gasoline that is usually added to refined gasoline. The fuels sold as bottled gas, such as propane and butane, are also NGLs.

In the near past, the difficulty of storage and shipment of gas products resulted in much of it being burned at the well. Over 90% of the natural gas produced in Oklahoma, Texas, and California in the early 1900s was burned or vented in the atmosphere. Finally a pipeline network connected the rich Southwestern and Western fields with the populations of the Midwest and East, and large underground storage systems (some of them in natural caverns) were built. At that time natural gas began to compete with other fuels, and many American homes and businesses were equipped with gas lines and meters, as it became an energy source equal to electricity.

The biggest boost came from two federally financed pipelines: the "Big Inch," a 24-inch diameter pipeline, 1250 miles long, and the "Little Big Inch," 20 inches in diameter and 1475 miles long. These pipelines were built during the submarine threat of World War II to connect the Southwestern oil fields to the East Coast.

From 1935 to 1955, total pipeline mileage increased from 167,400 miles to 448,770 miles, about a third of which are long-distance transmission lines. The estimated extent of pipelines in 1980 was 1,029,800 miles, of which 263,500 miles were transmission lines and 688,500 miles distribution lines. These distribution pipelines are calling themselves to our attention more and more through leaks and explosions, a new environmental hazard.

In 2000, USGS estimated that there are 15.4 quadrillion cubic feet of natural gas in the world (or the energy equivalent of about 2.5 trillion barrels of oil), of which 11% has been pumped out and used, while over 31% has been discovered. Recently, there were a number of additional large natural gas supplies discovered in North America, which brings the total amount of available gas to an equivalent of over 2.25 trillion barrels of oil, or a guaranteed minimum 100-year supply.

But that was then. Figures were based on rates of consumption in 2000. Natural gas has now been promoted to a much more important role—that of a "transition fuel," which will power our society with the least environmental damage and lowest possible cost, while we find ways to deploy renewable and other clean energy types.

This means that the rate of production of natural gas will increase in parallel with growth of population and commerce. Replacing coal and oil is a big job, and natural gas is tasked with it. Simple calculations show that at just 2% annual growth, the previously suggested 100-year U.S. domestic natural gas supply will be exhausted in about 50 years.

The picture gets much worse if the rate of gas production rises to meet the economic growth expected by the middle of the 21st century. With an estimated 3% growth rate, exhaustion is expected in just over 45 years, while a 5% production growth rate will cause exhaustion of national gas supplies in just over 35 years.

The good news is that predictions for the U.S. are for a gas production growth rate of just 0.4 percent per year through 2035, so this would extend the natural gas time line significantly. Also, there were some major gas reserves discovered lately, increasing the gas supply estimate significantly.

The bad news is that according to a U.S. Geological Survey assessment of recoverable natural gas in one of the largest of the shale deposits, the Marcellus Shale, the deposit was reduced from the previously estimated 410 tcf to just 84 tcf—almost an 80% reduction. If this is a sign of things to come, then this may not be the only estimate that must be corrected.

Also, the 100-year gas supply estimates were done before natural gas was promoted as a "transition fuel" (the fuel that will take us into the 22nd century). This is a great task, so all estimates must be recalculated from that vintage point.

Additional, equally serious questions arise about gas production and use:

1. Can the natural gas of the future be efficiently and economically recovered?

2. Will the obvious, often hidden, physical and chemical damages caused by gas exploration (fracking mainly) irrevocably damage the local environment and some of us in the process?

NOTE: Raw natural gas (methane gas) is over 25 times more potent and dangerous than carbon dioxide as a greenhouse gas. It is released into the environment during the entire life cycle of natural gas production and use—from the first drilling, through delivery and actual use. Shale gas, which is the source of the future, is much worse in this respect—releasing even more greenhouse gasses during production and use.

We cannot predict the natural gas future either, but we see it burning bright (no pun intended) at least for awhile, which will help a lot. Natural gas is a clean-burning fuel, so the environment will take a breath of relief at least for the duration—assuming that the fracking issues are resolved. Otherwise, those might just put an end to the expectations.

In conclusion, natural gas has become a premium fuel. It provides (or did until the removal of federal price controls) cheap Btus; it is clean and requires a very simple furnace. It has become very popular in both residential and industrial heating and has made inroads into the electric utility market.

The popularity of natural gas as a fuel is undeniable. It is used in all sectors, and recently increasingly so in some methane-powered truck and automobile fleets. In addition, wide use in the residential market, accounted for 40 percent of natural gas consumption until recently. Natural gas is not only making inroads into the markets of coal and oil, but is challenging electricity production in some areas like space heating, where it has the advantage of efficiency (60-70% efficiency).

It needs only one single conversion, rather than the several conversions (as in coal and oil electricity production) that reduce the efficiency of electrical heating to below 30%.

The fuel cell, a technology under development, would give gas an even greater efficiency advantage. Gas also has an advantage in the economy of transportation, which is growing quickly as well.

Summary

Energy is the force that created and moves the world. The first energy conversion process, burning firewood, was developed and managed successfully 100,000 years ago by our predecessors. It provided warmth and made their food more digestible. It eventually led to their industrial progress.

Wood being a primary source of solar energy conversion was used extensively until the mid-19th century. After that, coal became the fuel that provided most energy and contributed most to the development of the European and American civilizations. Coal was what people used to warm their homes, and what turned the wheels of transportation and industry, replacing wood,

which is an inconvenient and low-energy fuel.

By the end of the nineteenth century the first of the great replacement cycles was under way, and coal was providing 90 percent of this country's primary energy. It was abundant in the industrialized East, and had more Btus per pound than wood. Coal became the fuel for the fledgling steel industry and for the trains that ran on the steel rails. This went on until 1950, when oil pushed coal out of the picture.

Oil was an even more convenient fuel, especially to transport and to use in vehicles. It offered much more energy (Btus) per pound. It replaced coal in the railroads and pushed the nation into the automobile age, which we still embrace. By 1970, oil and oil products provided 75% of the nation's energy, with coal less than 20%. But coal found its niche with the electric utility industry and made an impressive comeback. It is now the fuel of choice in most electric power generating stations.

Natural gas was wasted early on by burning it at the oil wells, but became the fuel of choice for home heating and industrial furnaces when gas pipelines were constructed to the Midwest and the East in the US.

US gas production peaked in 1970, and use increased. Most oil was, and still is, imported. In 1977, imported crude oil was almost 50% of the total oil used, and almost 25% of our total primary energy consumption. Oil imports continued to increase through the years to over 60% total crude oil imports from 80 countries.

Slowly but surely, the United States and much of the world built a fossil fuels-dependent society. This period, however, is coming to an end, because the fossils have problems, and we are now looking for other energy sources.

No one knows the future, but we know now that there is a problem that needs to be addressed and solved. We are presently in the "addressing" stage. It is an important stage, because in order to solve a problem, one must recognize that there is a problem.

We are just now agreeing that there is a problem, and that we need to address it fully. That is the goal of this book. Herein, we intend to present a complete and unadulterated account of the different energy sources, their technical characteristics, and their effects on socio-political and environmental aspects of life in the U.S. and the world.

Solutions will come only after we have reached an agreement, for which we need to get prepared by completely understanding the issues at hand—the other key goal of this book.

The fossil fuel industry and utilities executives have their agenda, geared to sell their products. Period.

Everything else is secondary. Any talk about environment, climate changes, environmental disasters etc., is secondary. Such talk is often in conflict with their interests, so we must view everything they say and do with a grain of salt. This is not to say that these are bad people, but in a capitalist society everyone must defend their own turf—especially if it is what they rely on to make a living. It truly is their turf we are invading and their livelihood we are attacking with such talk, so we must be considerate and proceed carefully.

Government officials, politicians, regulators and utilities officials have agendas too. Although their intentions are good, results from the latest energy markets development show that there are complex interactions and numerous interwoven interests that are not easily understood—making issues even more complicated and difficult to solve.

U.S. energy policy has been, "Drill, Baby, drill," and recently it was modified to, "Good to the Last Drop." This means a huge windfall for oil and gas producers, and to a certain extent coal producers. Of course, we hear about the benefits of these fuels and miraculous benefits to our society.

We must recognize that, no matter what we think about all of this, we depend on coal, oil and gas in our daily lives. They are the evil that we cannot do without. As such, we must treat them with respect and do our best to work towards solutions—for the sake of our children and their children.

The immediate issue is that our industrial society—now and for the foreseeable future—depends on fossil fuels. The continuous input of high-grade energy resources is critical to our progress, and if they decline, the system will falter. As a matter of fact, we saw the effects of high oil prices (during the 2008 price hikes) and constrained oil supplies, and the way they affected the markets and suppressed economic activity, pressuring our already fragile financial system. High oil prices were the straw that broke the camel's back and marked the start of the great 2008-2012 economic slow down in the U.S. and the world.

We are at the peak of our technological development. Future, more efficient, cheaper, and cleaner fossil fuel technologies, although feasible, are not very likely. We should not rely on a technological miracle anytime soon. The known trends and data tell us clearly that we should wait no longer, but start looking into more reliable and promising renewable energy technologies—new ways to use energy at home and in industry.

The transition to renewables is inescapable. It must happen, since there is no other way in the long run. The question is whether we, as a responsible society, will do it now, or let somebody in the distant future take care of it.

Do we have a feasible plan for a rapid transition to renewable energy technologies, and new ways to use energy? Without one, global energy chaos will prevail, as will the economic ups and downs, as we go from one energy- or environment-induced crisis to another. That is neither a good way for responsible people to behave in the face of the inevitable, nor a good way to account to future generations.

CONVENTIONAL POWER GENERATORS

For the purposes of this writing, and especially when we refer to electric power generation, we will intermingle the words "energy" and "power," simply because they mean the same in most practical situations. We will, however, remind the esteemed reader that "power" is not the same as "energy," since *energy* is a state without quantity or measurements, while power is the rate at which energy is converted. Get it? Energy cannot be rated even if it is there. It is just there. So, power could be thought of as energy in motion, and now in a measurable form.

NOTE: As a further clarification on the subject, when we talk about electric power generation or use, we are talking about either a) or b):

a)   Energy contained in the cycles, such as the energy potential of water behind the dam walls, or the potential energy of the incoming sunlight before hitting the solar panel's surface. These are examples of energy that is available and waiting to be released.

b)   The "rate" energy is produced or used, in measurable denominations such as Btus, kilowatts (kW), or kilowatt-hours (kWh), after the water has been released from its dam storage and let run down the penstock into the turbine. These are measurable quantities of energy in action. They represent energy which is alive and in the midst of doing some work, and thus it can be measured in power units.

In either case, the energy we refer to when discussing power generation and use (electric or heat) is energy and power all in one, which is the reason we do not make much of a distinction between these words in this text, unless absolutely necessary.

Electric energy powers 90% of the developed world, including most residential and commercial applications. It is produced primarily by means of burning fossils (coal, oil, and natural gas), nuclear reactions, hydro power, and lately through the renewable energy generators, solar, wind and bio-fuels.

We will review these energy sources in great technical detail in the following chapters, to understand completely their structure and operation. We will then translate into practical terms, the types and amount of environmental damage these cause now, or are capable of causing during their entire cradle-to-grave life span.

Electric power, using fossil fuels, is generated via several major methods which involve burning them and converting them, thus producing energy (heat or mechanical) into electricity.

The key energy conversion and power generation methods follow.

Fossils Burning

Fossil fuels (coal, crude oil, and natural gas) are used to generate electricity, usually by burning them to convert their potential energy into heat. This heat is used to boil water into steam, which then turns its energy into mechanical energy by turning a steam turbine and a generator, which finally generates electricity.

Coal Burning

After coal is mined, it is transported to a coal burning power plant by trains, barges, and trucks. A conveyor belt carries the coal to a pulverizer, where it is ground to a fine powder, similar in consistency to talcum powder.

The powdered coal is then blown into a combustion chamber of a boiler, where it is burned at around 1,400°C. Surrounding the walls of the boiler room are pipes filled with water. Because of the intense heat, the water vaporizes into superheated high-pressure steam.

The steam passes through a turbine (which is similar to a large propeller) connected to a generator. The incoming steam causes the turbine to rotate at high speeds, which in turn rotates the generator rotor.

The rotation creates a magnetic field inside the wound wire in the stator coils in the generator. This action creates, and pushes, an electric current through the wire coils out of the power plant and into the transmission lines.

After the steam passes through the turbine chamber, it is cooled down in cooling towers and is then returned to the water/steam cycle.

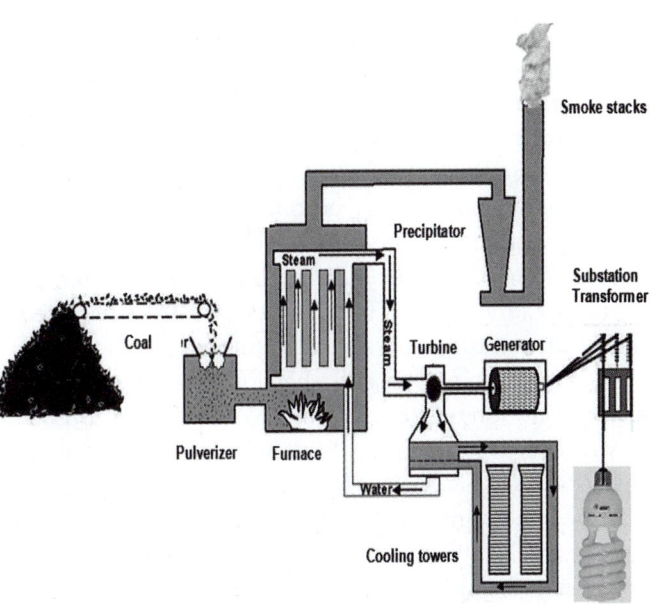

Figure 1-8. Coal burning power plant

The Heat-to-electricity Conversion Process

The first step of energy conversion takes place in the furnace where coal is burned. Most of the potential energy in coal is converted to heat energy. Only those carbon atoms that don't join up with two oxygen atoms and form CO_2, carbon dioxide, are not effectively used. This wasted raw energy goes up the stack as carbon or as partially burned carbon (carbon monoxide, CO). Inside the furnace the usable energy is in the form of the thermal energy of hot combustion gases, CO_2, and a host of other chemical combinations formed when coal is completely burned.

But some of the heat energy is lost as friction and other process inefficiencies, while some goes up in smoke through the smokestack. But the smokestack is essential for efficient burning process, for its draft pulls oxygen into the furnace. It also carries away some of the unburnable pollutants, together with nearly 10% of the total heat energy generated by the coal's burning.

The 90% that remains in the furnace is absorbed by the pipes lining the furnace walls in which water is converted into high-pressure, high-temperature steam. The steam is then transported through insulated pipes to the turbine, but because insulation is never perfect, some of the steam's heat travels out from the pipe, through the insulation, warms the air around it, and is also lost.

The high-pressure steam is directed to the steam turbine and sets it spinning. This conversion of heat energy (in the steam) to mechanical energy (in the spinning turbine propeller) lowers both the pressure and the temperature of the steam, as energy is transferred from it to the spinning turbine.

In most cases, a number of turbines are arranged in a row of multiple stages. Each one in the sequence is designed to work with lower-pressure steam, as the steam moves down the line.

Finally the pressure becomes too low to be useful and the steam is now ready to be exhausted. Much energy, 50-60% of the total, still remains in it and its temperature has fallen from 700°C to about 100°C. The steam then exits the turbine's area and enters the condenser.

At this point the steam has lost most of its energy, and can no longer be used for any work functions, but is still hot enough to need cooling down for return to the process cycle. Water from a river or lake is usually pumped through coils in the condenser to cool down the steam. As it's cooled, the steam changes state from gaseous to liquid. It thus condenses back to warm water, which is then pumped back to the furnace boiler. The cooling water, which is now also warm can be discharged back into the river or lake where it came from, or is recycled after post-cooling treatment (expensive process).

The turbine is connected to an electrical generator and its mechanical energy (spinning generator rotor) is converted into electrical energy. Some energy is lost here too due to friction of the spinning parts and electrical resistance. As the electric current runs through the various conductors in the generator and out through wires to the transmission lines, it heats these wires, and the heat is lost to the environment.

In each of these conversion steps we can see significant loss of energy from the flow. Almost all of this energy escaped in the form of waste heat—by either direct transition into the surrounding air, or by mechanical friction. There is a significant "heat tax" on any type of energy conversion. This loss of energy is actually a loss of the final output. The lost energy still exists, but is now in different forms and outside the system. It is lost forever, as far as the related process is concerned.

Energy losses in these conversions fall into several categories. In the furnace, steam pipes, turbine and generator, the amount of loss is subject to some control. We can control the speed and quality of some of the different steps of the process by, for example, blowing more air into the furnace to improve burning, letting the hot gases heat water as they go up the smokestack, doubling the insulation in the steam pipes, using oil to reduce friction, and increasing the conduction effectiveness of the wires to reduce their heating. By doing this we can significantly reduce the "heat lax" at these conversions.

One major loss that is different, however, and over which we have no control is that at the condenser. As long as the steam is hot, it contains energy, and there is no practical way to get the temperature of the exhaust steam below that of its surroundings (the air or the cooling water from the river). While the other losses are limited only by human ingenuity and a willingness to spend money to improve the equipment, the loss at the condenser is obligatory, controlled by the laws nature. We can only sit and watch...and waste water in cooling the hot steam.

The heat-to-electric process of steam turbines suffers from a number of inefficiencies, the largest of which is the need for cooling the low-temperature steam, to convert it back to water, for use to create more steam. In addition to heat loss, we also waste a lot of water to evaporation.

NOTE: Imagine a large turbine set operating at a solar thermal (CSP) power plant in the desert. Yes, CSP solar plants also heat water to generate steam and run it through turbines, just like described above. But where is the cooling water going to come from in the desert? And since each turbine uses millions of gallons of water annually, the immediate question is, how could we justify using, and wasting, so much water in the desert? We will take a closer look at this phenomena in the following chapters.

Yes, steam turbines create great waste, but this is the state of the art (amazingly primitive), so until a new way is found, lots of calories and millions of gallons of water will be lost for cooling the steam in coal, gas and solar power plants.

Instead of coal dust, oil and natural gas can be used in a similar way to generate electricity. Oil, in the form of gasoline or diesel, or natural gas in its gaseous form are injected into the furnace where they are burnt in a similar way and to similarly high temperature to generate steam. The rest of the process—including the energy and water wasted to cool the used steam—is identical.

There were over 2,300 coal burning power stations worldwide in 2012. Of those, 620 were in China and 550 in the U.S. In addition to electricity, coal burning power plants also generate over 2.0 billion tons of CO_2 every year in the U.S. alone. Extrapolating this number to a global level, we see that coal burning is a major polluter, generating over 8.0 billion tons of CO_2.

We will take closer look at these numbers in the following chapters, so this is just an introduction to the enormous effect coal burning has on our environment.

Waste Materials and Pollutants

Several by-products, including solids and gases, are created in the electricity generation process, when using coal as a fuel. A substance called "clinker" or bottom ash (glassy particles of melted coal ash) settles at the base of the furnace. This material is periodically removed and disposed of. Fly ash, the noncombustible minerals found in coal (including ash, dust, soot, and cinders) travels upward with gaseous by-products. Fly ash can be captured in an electrostatic precipitator and then transported by pipes to a holding pond, where it settles. Over 98 percent of all waste solids are captured in the plant.

Gaseous by-products include carbon dioxide (CO_2), sulfur oxides (SO_x), and nitrogen oxides (NO_x). These are air polluters, or green house gasses (GHGs) that are held responsible for the present-day climate warming.

Sulfur oxides can be controlled with the installation of scrubbers at coal-fired power plants. Scrubbers allow high-sulfur coals to be used because they remove sulfur dioxides out of the gas stream in the stacks (a process called desulfurization).

Scrubbers work by spraying limestone slurry directly in the path of the materials leaving the boiler chamber. The limestone reacts with the sulfur in the gases within the stacks. The combination of carbonate (limestone) and sulfur forms the mineral gypsum. Gypsum is a solid, which falls to the bottom of the stacks, where it can be collected—many tons of it. Gypsum created in this process can be used to make drywall, bowling balls, and for other practical uses.

Nitrogen oxides are managed by careful control of the furnace temperature, while current technology is also available to control carbon dioxide emissions. Using high-efficiency coals (such as those found in Kentucky) also helps reduce the CO_2 output without much equipment modification.

Coal is also used in industrial processes to heat commercial boilers and ovens. Cement production (the biggest worldwide industrial use of coal), glass, ceramic, and paper industries all use large amounts of coal. In some North American states, industrial process heating accounts for 10% of the annual coal usage, all of which contributes to high levels of GHG emissions.

Similarly polluting are the other fossil fuels—oil and natural gas. Though natural gas does not pollute much during burning, it is a great polluter during its fracking, transport and storage process steps.

Natural Gas Power Generation

Natural gas also can be burned to generate steam to power a turbine-generator set to generate electric power. The process is similar to that described in coal burning above, and is preferred now because it emits fewer gasses. As a matter of fact, there is a trend today of converting power plants from coal-burning to gas-burning.

Gas/Diesel Engine Powered Generator

Gas and diesel engine generator sets are often used for power generation in peaker plants, and for remote communities' power generation. In addition, emergency (standby) power systems may use reciprocating internal combustion engines operated by fuel oil or natural gas. Standby generators may serve as emergency power for a factory or data center, or may also be operated in parallel with the local utility system to reduce peak power demand charge from the utility.

Gas or diesel engines can produce strong torque at relatively low rotational speeds, which is generally desirable when driving an alternator, but diesel fuel in long-term storage can be subject to problems resulting from water accumulation and chemical decomposition. Rarely used generator sets may correspondingly be installed as natural gas or LPG to minimize the fuel system maintenance requirements.

Spark-ignition internal combustion engines operating on gasoline (petrol), propane, or LPG are commonly used as portable temporary power sources for construction work, emergency power, or recreational purposes.

Reciprocating external combustion engines such as the Stirling engine can be run on a variety of fossil fuels, as well as renewable fuels or industrial waste heat, but installations of Stirling engines for electric power production are relatively uncommon.

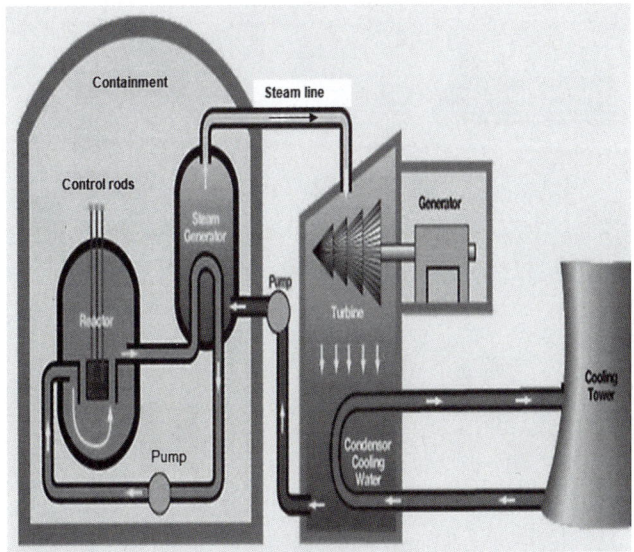

Figure 1-9. Nuclear power plant

There are 1021 oil-burning power plants world-wide, of which over 740 are operated in the United States. Imagine the amount of oil that goes through these oil guzzlers on a daily basis.

Nuclear Power Generation

Other methods of energy generation consist of capturing the energy of nuclear reactions in nuclear power plants, or falling water in hydroelectric power plants, and converting it into electricity.

Hydro Power Generation

Hydroelectric power is produced by the force of falling water, which is determined by the mass, height and speed of the water flow. In the past, flowing or falling water was channeled through a water wheel, making it spin, thus providing mechanical power for activities such as turning grinding wheels.

Today, the most important use of water power is storing it behind a high dam, where it builds a lot of potential energy waiting to be released. When the water is allowed to flow down the penstock pipes into the spinning turbine blades, it releases the potential energy, converting it to kinetic, and in more practical terms, mechanical, energy when it strikes the turbine blades.

The turbine's axle is attached to the rotor of a large electromagnet which spins and generates current in stationary coils of wire arranged around it. The current is fed into a transformer and conditioning devices where the voltage is increased for long-distance transmission over power lines.

There are many energy losses in this energy conversion process. To start with, the sunlight falling on

the lake behind the dam converts many tons of water into vapor, which evaporates in the atmosphere. When the water starts going down the penstock its potential (storage) energy is converted into kinetic energy, with some losses along the way due to friction with the walls of the pipes. Thus acquired kinetic energy is converted into mechanical energy when the water hits the turbine blades and makes them turn.

The turbine bearings cause some resistance and some of the mechanical energy acting upon them is converted into heat. There are also losses in the wires from the generator to the transformer and to the point of use, where the electrical energy traveling in them encounters resistivity and part of it is converted into heat energy.

NOTE: We include nuclear and hydro in the class of "conventional" energy sources because:

1. Nuclear energy depends on the availability of materials (uranium and other radioactive ores) which are in limited quantities and are estimated to last no more than 150 years, so they cannot be called renewable.

   Nuclear poses great danger, as seen in a number of nuclear accidents around the world, so with such great potential to damage the environment and life we cannot call it clean, green, or safe.

2. Hydro energy generation depends on the amount of snowfall at a certain periods, and rainwater running into the lake. Since these amounts are unpredictable, and are heavily dependent on climate conditions, we cannot call them renewable, nor can we rely on them fully under the increasing environmental uncertainties. Also, the number of hydropower plants around the world is reaching its limit and not many more plants can be built.

Damming causes extensive damage in up- and downstream areas. Entire populations have been moved in some cases, and the extent of the damage over millions of acres of good land is questionable in the long run. Because of that, hydro (although quite clean and safe during operation) cannot be called truly green, clean, and safe in its entirety.

THE RENEWABLE ENERGIES

Capturing the energy of solar, wind, bio-fuels, and geothermal sources, and converting it to electricity is considered renewable, green, clean and safe operation.

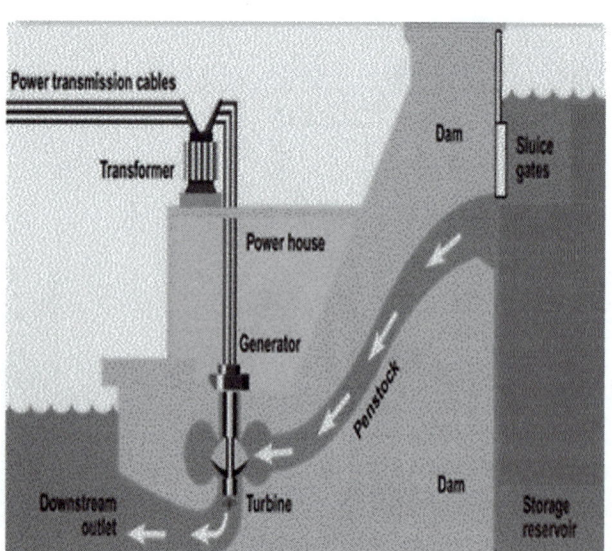

Figure 1-10. Hydro power generation

These energy sources and the related technologies are called renewable because the respective sources have been renewed constantly and because we don't see any reason to fear their depletion.

They are also considered green, clean, and safe because as compared with conventional energy sources, they do not emit a significant amount of GHGs, liquid, or solid waste during operation. There is some pollution during the production cycle of the equipment needed for their conversion into useful energy. Additional pollution is generated during the installation and decommissioning of the equipment in the power plants as well, and we take a close look at all these events later on in this text.

Let's look at these promising energy sources.

Solar Energy

Why solar energy? The answer seems obvious, but solar energy conversion equipment has been around for over half a century without showing much progress until recently. What's the catch? We will take a brief look at solar energy generation here, leaving the more detailed portion of the answer for the following chapters.

Solar energy, and its energy components, radiant light and heat in the form of photons, are generated during the fusion reactions on the Sun's surface. The part that arrives on Earth has been used by humans since ancient times, initially for heating water and drying fruits and vegetables.

Present-day solar energy technologies include solar heating, solar photovoltaics, solar thermal electricity and solar architecture. These disciplines are considered promising in solving our energy problems, and are expected to contribute to solving some of the urgent environmental problems as well.

Solar technologies can be divided into passive and active solar devices, according to the way they capture, convert and distribute solar energy.

An example of passive solar technique is a building that is designed and oriented to use the available sunlight most efficiently, to save the maximum amount of energy needed for heating and cooling the living spaces in the building. By selecting proper materials with favorable thermal mass and light dispersing properties, and by designing living and working spaces that naturally circulate air within the building, we can maintain comfortable living temperatures with minimum outside energy input.

Active solar techniques include the use of photovoltaic (PV) modules and solar thermal collectors to harness the energy and eventually convert it to electricity.

An example of an active solar technology is a solar water heater mounted on a housetop. It consists of a heating plate with pipes, where water running through pipes gets heated and can then be used for residential and commercial purposes.

The main component in the PV modules is the solar cell. It can be made by special processing of silicon material, or some other semiconductor materials like Ga, As, Ge and others. Sometimes the solar cells are made by depositing other types of semiconductor materials on a piece of glass. In all cases, the resulting product (solar cells) cannot be used by themselves, so they are encapsulated in a special package called a PV module.

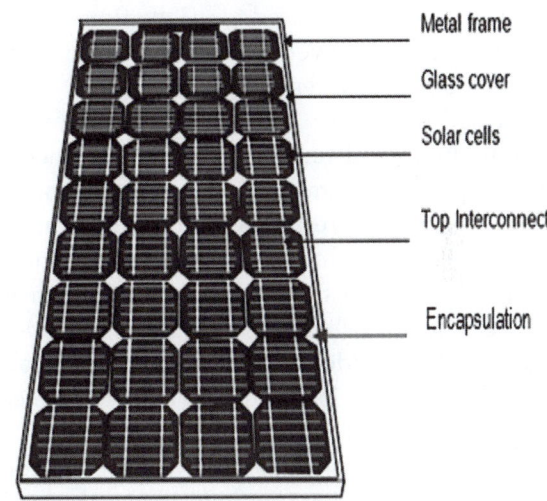

Figure 1-11. PV module (panel)

When sunlight hits the solar cell surface, the photons (radiation energy) energize the electrons to the point where they exit the device via wires attached to it. In this case the radiation energy of the photons is converted directly into electric energy. This is the photovoltaic (PV) type of solar energy conversion

Here we also have a number of significant energy losses. To start with, when the sunlight strikes a surface—any surface—part of it gets reflected and part of it gets converted to heat. Only 10-20%, of the sunlight is converted to electricity by the available solar conversion devices. We have further losses in the electric wires, in the inverters and transformers.

The design and manufacturing processes of the solar cells and modules are quite complex, so we will take a closer look at these in the following chapters.

On the commercial side of things we use PV modules and systems to generate electric energy by direct conversion of sunlight to electricity. We can also use solar thermal conversion technologies for indirect conversion, where water is heated to high temperatures and then run through a steam turbine (just like in the coal power plants discussed above). The steam energy spins the turbine propellers, which in turn spin a generator to produce electric energy.

There are a number of other solar technologies, such as thin film PV, thermal solar collectors and other solar energy generators, which we will look at closely in the following chapters.

Wind Energy

Wind power generation is defined as the conversion of wind energy into mechanical energy and then into electric power, which can then be used as needed. Wind turbines have been used for a long time to directly provide mechanical power, such as rotating a grinding wheel and pumping water.

A large wind farm may consist of several hundred individual wind turbines which are connected to the electric power transmission network. Offshore wind farms can harness more frequent and powerful winds than are available to land-based installations and have less visual impact on the landscape, but construction costs are considerably higher. Small onshore wind facilities are used to provide electricity to isolated locations, and utility companies increasingly buy surplus electricity produced by small domestic wind turbines.

A wind turbine is the basic device used to convert wind's kinetic energy into mechanical and then electric energy, a process known as wind power. If the mechanical energy is used to produce electricity, the device may be called a wind turbine or wind power plant. If the me-

Figure 1-12. Wind turbines

chanical energy is used to drive machinery, such as for grinding grain or pumping water, the device is called a windmill or wind pump.

A generator attached to the blades of the wind turbine spins the rotor of an electric power generator, and the generated electricity is transferred to the point of use through electric wires.

The energy losses in the wind-to-electricity conversion processes in wind turbines are significant. First, a major part of the incoming wind power is lost by the inefficiency of the blades. Only 30-40% of it is converted into mechanical energy that is used to rotate the blades. Some energy is lost also during the rotation of the blades and the generator, due to the friction in the axle bearings, where it is converted into heat. And the ever present resistivity in the electrical wires robs us of some additional energy, which is also converted into heat.

Today's wind turbines are manufactured in a wide range of sizes and types with vertical and horizontal axis of rotation of the blades. Large wind farms consist of several dozen to hundreds of individual wind turbines which are connected to the electric power transmission network. Offshore wind farms harness more frequent and more powerful winds than those at land-based installations, but construction costs are higher.

We will take a closer look at the wind turbines, and their use in wind power generation in the following chapters.

Bio-energy

Bio-energy is energy generated by materials obtained from biological sources. Biomass is any organic material which has stored sunlight in the form of chemical energy. As a fuel, biomass might refer to wood, wood waste, straw, manure, sugarcane, and many other byproducts from a variety of agricultural processes.

In a practical sense bio-energy is a synonym to biofuel, which is derived from biological sources. In its broader sense it is referred to as biomass (the biological material actually used as biofuel) as well as for the production of biofuels like bio-alcohols and bio-diesel. Bio-energy basically encompasses a number of social, economic, scientific and technical fields associated with using biological sources for generating energy.

There is some confusion in terminology, where the word bio-energy is used in Europe, while biofuel is used in North America to mean the same. In both cases, some clarification must be given as of the type of bio-technology and its use, to get a clear picture of the final product and its use.

The energy conversion process here consists of

converting the chemical energy contained in the vegetation into heat, light, electricity and other forms of energy. There are many types and sizes of bio-energy conversion equipment, but in most cases direct generation of heat is the most efficient energy product from any type of bio-mass.

Liquids and gaseous fuels generated from bio-mass are more convenient to use, but a lot of energy is wasted in their production process. Lately, the generation of gasses is becoming very important and a lot of effort is spent in that area. Energy losses in these processes are confined mainly to the production cycle, during the burning process where some heat is lost in the surrounding environment as well.

The major, and most practical, bio-fuels today are bio-*ethanol*, bio-*diesel* and bio-*gas*.

- Bio-ethanol is a man-made alcohol, which is usually made by fermentation of carbohydrates containing vegetation. It is produced by sugar or starch crops such as corn or sugarcane. Cellulosic biomass, contained in non-food vegetation like trees and grasses can also be developed as a feedstock for ethanol production. Ethanol can be used in its pure form as a fuel for vehicles, but in most cases it is used as a gasoline additive to increase octane and improve vehicle emissions. Bio-ethanol is used in great quantities in the USA and Brazil.

- Biodiesel is also made from vegetables containing oils, and from animal fats. Biodiesel can be used as a fuel for vehicles in its pure form, but it is usually used as a diesel additive to reduce levels of particulates, carbon monoxide, and hydrocarbons from diesel-powered vehicles. Biodiesel is produced from oils or fats using trans-esterification. It is a common type of biofuel in Europe, but is finding its place in US energy markets as well.

- Bio-gas can be produced by breakdown of different types of organic matter in the absence of oxygen. Dead plants and animal material, animal feces, and kitchen waste can be converted into a gas that can be used as fuel. Man-made bio-gas is produced by the anaerobic digestion or fermentation of biodegradable materials such as biomass, manure, sewage, municipal waste, green waste, plant material, and crops. Biogas comprises primarily methane (CH_4) and carbon dioxide (CO_2) and may have small amounts of hydrogen sulphide (H_2S), moisture and siloxanes. Biogas can be used also as a fuel for heating and cooking purposes, or in anaerobic digesters where it is typically used in a gas engine to generate electric or heat power.

NOTE: Although biomass and its products can be considered renewable forms of energy, we must remember that biomass comes from agricultural vegetation or animals, so its quantity is variable and sometimes (like in extreme draughts) simply unavailable.

Nevertheless, global biomass production is a truly renewable resource—something we can count on every day. As with all other fuels, its production and use must be done in a systematic fashion, so we don't end up with another disaster like the ethanol overproduction and global food crops deficiency of 2008-2010. Mad cow disease outbreaks around that time also remind us that biomass is a fragile, variable and unreliable energy source, so we need to be very careful when planning its production and use in the 21st century.

ELECTRIC POWER DISTRIBUTION

Thus far we discussed the different energy sources and the way electric energy is generated. Once generated, the electric power must be delivered to homes, offices and factories. Power distribution in the US is done by the national power grid, as reflected in Figure 1-13.

The Basics

The economic significance of generating, transmitting, distributing and using electricity today is staggering. It is one of the largest and most capital-intensive sectors of the economy. Total asset value is estimated to exceed $800 billion, with approximately 60% invested in power plants, 30% in distribution facilities, and 10% in transmission facilities.

Annual electric revenues—the nation's electric bill—are about $247 billion, paid by America's 131 million electricity customers, which includes nearly every business and household. The average price paid is about 8-15 cents per kilowatt-hour, although prices vary from state to state depending on local regulations, generation costs, and customer mix.

There are more than 3,100 electric utilities in the US:

- 213 stockholder-owned utilities provide power to about 73% of the customers.

- 2,000 public utilities run by state and local government agencies provide power to about 15% of the customers.

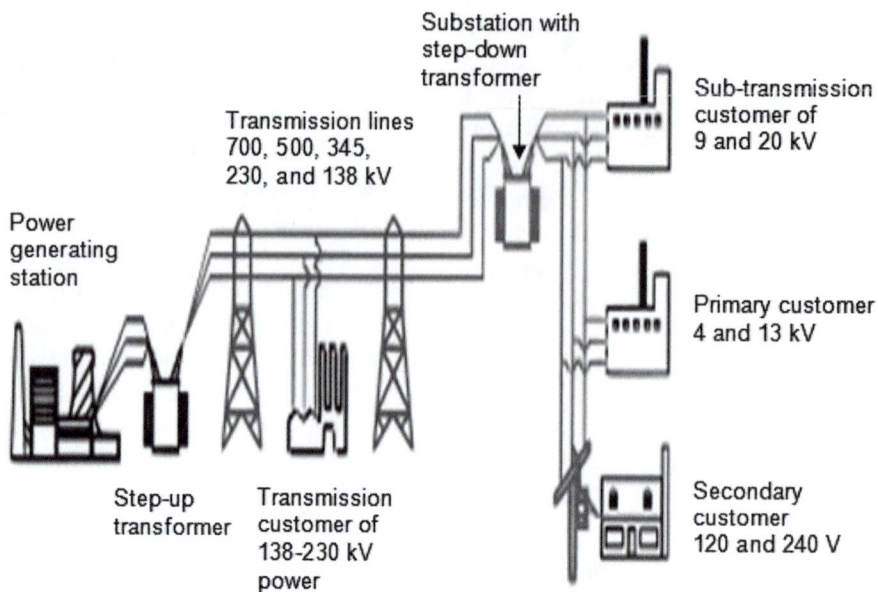

Figure 1-13. Power generation, transmission and distribution

- 930 electric cooperatives provide power to about 12% of the customers.

Additionally, there are nearly 2,100 non-utility power producers, including both independent power companies and customer-owned distributed energy facilities.

The bulk power system consists of three independent networks: Eastern Interconnection, Western Interconnection, and the Texas Interconnection. These networks incorporate international connections with Canada and Mexico as well. Overall reliability planning and coordination is provided by the North American Electric Reliability Council, a nonprofit organization formed in 1968 in response to the Northeast blackout of 1965.

Power Generation

America operates a fleet of about 10,000 power plants, mostly thermal (coal and diesel) with average efficiency of around 33%. Efficiency has not changed much since 1960 because of slow turnover of the capital stock and the inherent inefficiency of central power generation that cannot recycle heat. Nuclear and hydro plants are more efficient, but much more expensive.

Power plants are generally long-lived investments, with the majority of existing US capacity 30 years old or older. They can be divided into:

a.   Baseload power plants, which are run all the time to meet minimum power needs;

b.   Peaking power plants, which are run only to meet power needs at maximum load (known as peak load); and

c.   Intermediate power plants, which fall between the two and are used to meet intermediate and emergency power loads.

The roughly 5,600 distributed energy facilities typically combine heat and power generation and achieve efficiencies of 40% to 55%, accounting for about 6% of US power capacity in 2001 and several times more today.

A shift in ownership is occurring from regulated utilities to competitive suppliers. The share of installed capacity provided by competitive suppliers has increased from about 10% in 1997 to about 35% today. Recent data suggest, however, that this trend is slowing down. Also, cleaner and more fuel-efficient power generation technologies are becoming available. These include combined cycle combustion turbines, wind energy systems, advanced nuclear power plant designs, clean coal power systems, and distributed energy technologies such as photovoltaics and combined heat and power systems.

Because of the expected near-term retirement of many aging plants in the existing fleet, growth of the information economy, economic growth, and the forecast growth in electricity demand, America faces a significant need for new electric power generation. In this transition, local market conditions will dictate fuel and technology choices for investment decisions, capital markets will provide the financing, and federal and state policies will affect siting and permitting. It is an enormous challenge that will require a large commitment of technological, financial and human resources in the years ahead.

Power Transmission

Adequate electric generation in the US is hindered by bottlenecks in the transmission system, which interfere with reliable, efficient, and affordable delivery of electric power to customers. America operates about 157,000 miles of high voltage (>230 kV) electric transmission lines.

Construction of transmission facilities has decreased about 30%, and annual investment in new transmission facilities has declined over the last 25 years. The result is grid congestion, which can mean higher electricity costs because customers cannot get access to lower-cost electricity supplies, and because of higher line losses. Transmission and distribution losses are related to how heavily the system is loaded. Transmission and distribution losses in the U.S. were about 5% in 1970, grew to 9.5% in 2001, and are even higher today, due to heavier utilization and more frequent congestion.

Congested transmission paths or "bottlenecks" now affect many parts of the grid across the country. In addition, it is estimated that power outages and power quality disturbances cost the economy up to $150-200 billion annually. These costs could soar if outages or disturbances become more frequent or longer in duration. There are also operational problems in maintaining voltage levels.

America's electric transmission problems are also affected by the new structure of the increasingly competitive bulk power market. Based on a sample of the nation's transmission grid, the number of transactions has increased substantially recently. For example, annual transactions on the Tennessee Valley Authority's transmission system numbered less than 20,000 in 1996. They exceed 250,000 today, a volume the system was not originally designed to handle. Actions by transmission operators to curtail transactions for economic reasons and to maintain reliability (according to procedures developed by the North American Electric Reliability Council) grew from about 300 in 1998 to over 1,000 in 2000 and are much higher today.

Additionally, significant impediments interfere with solving the country's electric transmission problems. These include opposition and litigations by different groups against the construction of new facilities,

uncertainty about cost recovery for investors, confusion over whose responsibility it is to build and maintain, and jurisdiction and government agency overlap for siting and permitting. Competing land uses, especially in urban areas, leads to opposition and litigation against new construction facilities.

In Figure 1-13, we get a glimpse into the complexity of the generation-transmission-distribution scheme of electric power transfer. The generator (coal or nuclear power plant) might be miles away from the point of use (POU)—residential or industrial customer.

The power generated at the power plant is sent to a step-up transformer (substation), where it must be transformed into higher voltage, as needed for long distance transfer. Some of this power is used by larger users who have their own sub-stations for power in their facilities. The rest of the power (most of it) is transported via the national power grid to step-down substations all over the country, where it is converted to lower voltage and is sent via the distribution power lines for use by residential and commercial customers, who also have their own sub-stations or transformers for converting the power to the exact voltage they can use.

Power Distribution

The "handoff" from electric transmission to electric distribution usually occurs at the substation. America's fleet of substations takes power from transmission-level voltages and distributes it to hundreds of thousands of miles of lower voltage distribution lines. The distribution system is generally considered to begin at the substation and end at the customer's meter. Beyond the meter lies the customer's electric system, which consists of wires, equipment, and appliances—an increased number of which involve computerized controls and electronics operating on DC.

There are two types of distribution networks in the U.S., radial or interconnected.

a. A radial network leaves the power generating station for its final destination with no connection to any other supply in the network. This is typical of long rural lines with isolated load areas.

b. An interconnected network is generally found in more urban areas and will have multiple connections to other points of supply. These points of connection are normally open but allow various configurations by the operating utility by closing and opening switches.

The distribution system supports retail electricity markets. State or local government agencies are heavily involved in the electric distribution business, regulating prices and rates of return for shareholder-owned distribution utilities. Also, in 2,000 localities across the country, state and local government agencies operate their own distribution utilities, as do over 900 rural electric cooperative utilities. Virtually all of the distribution systems operate as franchise monopolies as established by state law.

The greatest challenge facing electric distribution is that of responding to rapidly changing customer needs for electricity; i.e., increased use of information technologies, computers, and consumer electronics has lowered the tolerance for outages, fluctuations in voltages and frequency levels, and other power quality disturbances. In addition, rising interest in distributed generation and electric storage devices is adding new requirements for interconnection and safe operation of electric distribution systems.

Finally, a wide array of information technology is entering the market and could revolutionize the electric distribution business. For example, having the ability to monitor and influence each customer's usage, in real time (part of the smart grid solution), could enable distribution operators to better match supply with demand, thus boosting asset utilization, improving service quality, and lowering costs. More complete integration of distributed energy and demand-side management resources into the distribution system could enable customers to implement their own tailored solutions, thus boosting profitability and quality of life.

THE ENVIRONMENT

We know so much about energy—what it is, how it is generated and used. Now we must integrate this knowledge with our understanding of how global energy generation (the production of electricity) effects the environment.

Figure 1-14 shows graphically that there is some pollution taking place during several steps of the fossils' lifecycle. The pollution type and quantity varies with the types of fuels used, but it is significant in all cases. So, it must be taken into account when discussing the effects and cost of power generation with the different energy sources.

Figure 1-15 shows that there is some, albeit much less, pollution taking place at different steps of the renewables' life cycle. Although insignificant at a first

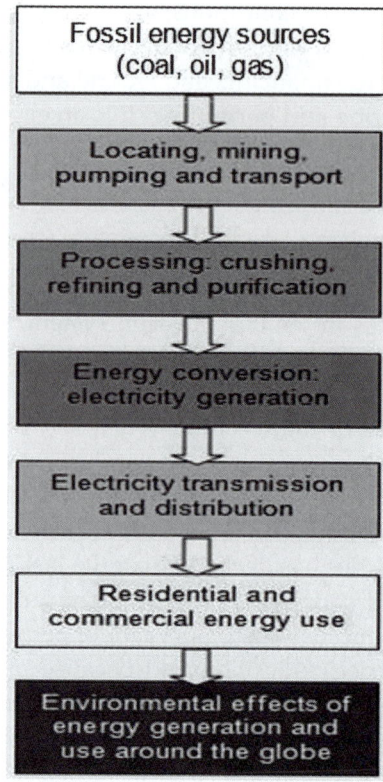

Figure 1-14. Lifecycle of the fossil fuels

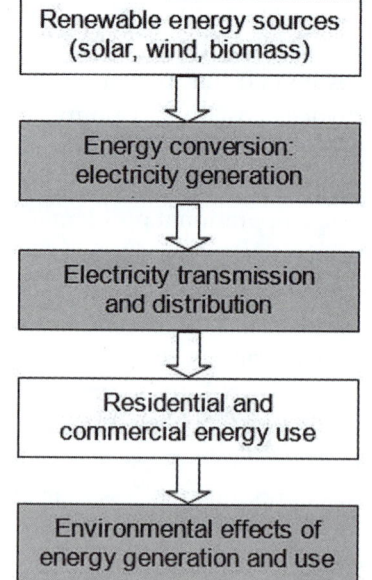

Figure 1-15. Lifecycle of the renewables

glance, the pollution cannot, and should not, be ignored because of the extremely large scale of development expected with these technologies in the future.

There is no doubt that energy generators of all kinds emit some waste gasses, liquids and solids during different stages of their cradle-to-grave life span. The fossils, however, emit many times the amount emitted during the life time of the renewables.

One doesn't have to be a specialist to see, smell and hear the pollution escaping from a coal-fired power plant. Standing near a coal power plant you can see the smoke and water vapor rising in the atmosphere, and smell the hot gasses on their way up. There are also millions of gallons of hot water produced during the cooling cycle, as well as other liquids produced at different steps of the process. Thousands of tons of ash are produced as a byproduct of burning coal, and those are deposited on large ships, and transported elsewhere for disposal.

In addition, there are many other polluting activities that cannot be observed or smelled during the power plant's life time. In all cases, large quantities of gasses containing carbon are being emitted, causing serious environmental issues.

In nature, carbon is a vital part of life and can be found in the form of different hydrocarbons in plants and animals, in the near-surface soils, and in fossil fuels buried deep underground. As an environmental killer, carbons can be found in the CO_2 in the atmosphere, or dissolved in the oceans. Some of it occurs naturally, but a lot (some say most) of it was man-made mostly during the burning of fossils and biomass.

Prior to the Industrial Revolution starting in 1850, the Earth's atmosphere contained approximately 280 parts per million (ppm) of carbon dioxide, which is close to the 574 gigatons (Gt) of carbon contained in the global atmosphere. Today the concentration is 390 ppm, which corresponds to 800 Gt of carbon in the global atmosphere. This is an almost 30% increase of CO_2, adding 226 Gt of carbon to our atmosphere, and this increase is held responsible for an almost 1.0 degree C increase of the average global temperature during the last 150 years.

Most of the increase, however, is thought to have happened during the last 50 years, due to human activities such as coal and oil burning. Because the burning won't stop anytime soon, we expect a further increase in CO_2 to raise the global temperature by 4 degree C, having catastrophic consequences to the world as we know it. Rising sea levels inundating coastal cities worldwide and scorching temperatures converting farm lands to deserts are only some of the maladies awaiting future generations.

We will take much closer look at the human activities related to energy generation in the following chapters, so here we will give just a broad overview of environmental issues, in preparation for the forthcoming deep dive into the subject.

The Natural Environment

Our environment is basically the space in which we live and work. It encompasses all living and non-living things occurring naturally on Earth. The concept of environment includes the presence, activities and interaction of all living species, and their impact on the their surroundings and the globe as a whole.

Our natural environment can be distinguished by several components:

a. *The complete natural systems* that function without any human intervention are the different types of vegetation, microorganisms, animals, soil, atmosphere, and natural phenomena that occur within these systems.

b. *The natural resources* and the physical phenomena that exist and operate without human intervention are air, water, climate, energy, radiation, and magnetism.

There is a difference between the natural environment vs. man-made, and it involves areas and components that are influenced one way or another by human intervention. Absolutely natural environment—that which is 100% unaffected by man's activities—can be found on very few places on Earth today because man has spread his activities so far that even the highest mountains and deeper oceans bare traces of them. So, it is more likely that we'd find some combination of natural and man-made segments in the Earth's environment. The term "natural environment," therefore, is usually used as a synonym for animal habitat.

Scientists recognize four different environmental spheres on Earth: the lithosphere (rock formations), the hydrosphere (water formations), the atmosphere (air space), and the biosphere (life forms). Cryosphere corresponds to ice formations as a distinct and somewhat separate portion of the hydrosphere, and pedosphere corresponds to soil as another active and intermixed sphere.

Earth science, or geoscience, is an all-encompassing term for all sciences related to the study and of the planet Earth. The four major disciplines in Earth sciences are geography, geology, geophysics and geodesy. These major disciplines use a mix of physics, chemistry, biology, chronology and mathematics to analyze and build a qualitative and quantitative understanding of the Earth's spheres.

Earth's Atmosphere

The Earth is surrounded by the atmosphere, which consists of different layers composed of different gasses which play different roles, the most important of which is to protect the planet and enable life on it. The atmosphere located close to the Earth's surface is the most dense part of the system. It consists of 79% nitrogen and just under 21% oxygen; the small amount remaining is composed of carbon dioxide and other gasses. This is just enough to support all forms of life on Earth.

There are several distinct layers of the Earth. Let's look at each, from closest to the farthest away.

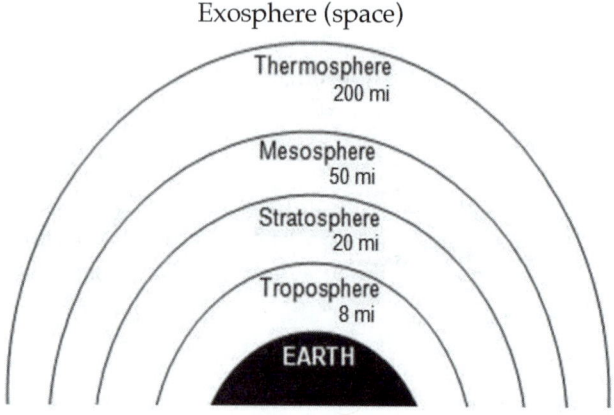

Exosphere (space)

Thermosphere
200 mi

Mesosphere
50 mi

Stratosphere
20 mi

Troposphere
8 mi

EARTH

Figure 1-16. Earth's atmosphere

Troposphere is the layer of the atmosphere that is closest to the Earth's surface. It is the densest and is where weather occurs. It begins at the surface of the Earth and extends out to about 4-12 miles. The temperature of the troposphere decreases with height. This layer is known as the lower atmosphere. The troposphere is composed primarily of nitrogen and oxygen, or approximately 99% of the gas in the atmosphere—the air we breath

The key components of the troposphere are:

Nitrogen	78.084%
Oxygen	20.95%
Argon	0.934%
Water vapor	0.75%
Carbon dioxide	0.036%
Neon	0.0018%
Helium	0.0005%
Methane	0.00017%
Hydrogen	0.00005%
Nitrous oxide	0.00003%
Ozone	0.000004%

There are also traces of krypton, xenon, carbon monoxide, sulfur dioxide, nitrogen dioxide, hydrogen sulfide, and others.

Stratosphere is the layer directly above the troposphere, and it is where the temperature drops at a level slightly below freezing. On the upper edge of the stratosphere is located the very important ozone layer, which keeps the UV balance on Earth, and which if damaged can contribute to great climate changes.

Mesosphere is where the air is especially thin and molecules are spaced great distances apart. The temperature in the mesosphere is very low and reaches close to –180°F. The stratosphere and the mesosphere are the middle atmosphere.

Thermosphere (also called ionosphere) is several hundred miles above the Earth's surface. Its temperature increases with height and can rise to as high as 3,600°F. Nonetheless, the air would feel cold because the hot molecules are so far apart. This layer is known as the upper atmosphere.

Exosphere is the uppermost layer of the Earth's atmosphere, which extends from the top of the thermosphere into space. It is the last layer that separates us from space. This layer has very few atmospheric molecules, which tend to escape into space. The structure and behavior of the ionosphere is influenced by the solar wind—charged particle emitted by the Sun—which depends on the level of solar activity. This interaction then affects the atmospheric layers and life on Earth.

Between each layer of the atmosphere is a boundary which is also called "pauses." Above the troposphere is the tropo-pause; above the stratosphere is the strato-pause; above the mesosphere is the meso-pause; and above the thermosphere is the thermo-pause. At these "pauses," temperature and other exchanges between the different atmospheric layers occur.

The troposphere is, of course, the most important to life on Earth, since it is where we live without life-support equipment, but the integrity of the other layers is also important, for they do influence each other. Our emphasis in this text is mainly on the behavior of, and the events in, the troposphere. It is the layer that life depends on, and it is also the one that is most affected by human activities.

For the purposes of discussing the effects on our environment of energy generation and use, we will take look closely at changes in structure and behavior of the different environmental spheres. The air, climate, oceans, mountains, lakes, rivers, population centers, etc. are affected one way or another by our presence and activities in their environment. The largest effect, and one that we are most interested in, is that on our atmosphere—the global climate and local weather systems.

Disclaimer: The author does not belong to any environmental organization, and does not participate in any environmental movements or activities. This text represents facts collected from different reliable (in our opinion) sources that have been carefully sorted and filtered through the impartial eye of a scientist with long experience in power generation and use.

The resulting combination of facts and issues is carefully balanced to present the intimate details of the present-day power generation vs. environment reality in its totality. Counter-opinions and theories to the key issues have been supplied as needed and when possible, to provide a complete and balanced picture of power-related environmental issues.

Major Pollutants

There is a lot of talk today about the different pollutants, but very few people know how these are created, and even more importantly; what exactly they do to harm the environment and the life forms in it. We will take a closely at these in the next chapters, but for now it suffices to present a brief description of the major pollutants:

The major pollutants, emitted during energy generation processes, as well as their effects on humans, are:

Sulfur dioxide, SO₂, is formed during the combustion of coal and oil byproducts and a number of industrial processes using sulfur and its salts. The presence of sulfur in fuels forms sulfates (SO_4). Its effect on humans is represented by respiratory distress, lack of air, harmed pulmonary function, increase in susceptibility to infections and diseases of the lower respiratory tract, chronic pulmonary diseases and pulmonary fibrosis. It is especially harmful to children,

Carbon dioxide, CO₂, is formed during incomplete burning of fossil fuels and biomass, such as fuel wood. In large amounts it interferes with blood oxygen and causes chronic anoxia. Again, children are affected most seriously.

Nitrous oxides, NOₓ, are formed by a number of fuels containing nitrogen in their molecule. It causes eye and nose irritation, respiratory tract diseases, lung damage, decreased pulmonary function, and heart stress.

Particular matter, PM, is formed during incomplete burning of fossil fuels and burning of biomass, causing irritation, altered immunological response, systematic toxicity, decreased pulmonary function, and heart stress.

There are serious concerns about large amounts of pollutants in some regions of the world, and people in the affected areas must be well informed as what types and quantities of pollutants are dangerous and how to protect themselves.

While the types of pollutants are well defined and understood, there is still confusion as to the amounts of these in the air. There are two arenas in which to tally these:

a) The total pollutants load, which is the total emitted by the power plant stacks for a given period of time. A major part of this is usually dissipated into the upper atmosphere or carried away.

b) The concentration of pollutants in a given amount of the lower atmosphere and especially the local air we breathe. These amounts are given in parts per million (ppm), or as flow measured in cubic meters per hour. We compare these numbers with those specified by the World Health Organization to find out if the area is negatively affected.

The big problem here is that our "local" air is not isolated and is affected by activities far away and even across the world. Because of that we must be aware of, and take into account, global events that might affect our local environment.

Major Pollution Effects

The major effects of the pollutants, are reflected in a number of environmental phenomena, some of which are:

*   Ozone (O₃) pollution is formed during photochemical reactions, by the action of sunlight on gasoline and other gaseous hydrocarbons (HCs) in the air. The behavior of the resulting O₃ depends on a number of factors such as climate; i.e., wind might blow the cloud of O₃ miles away where the resulting ozone pollution is unexpected and cannot be explained.

Remember that while O₃ is harmful and toxic in the lower atmosphere (the troposphere), when it is up in the stratosphere, it envelops the Earth in a blanket, which is an essential part of controlling the climate and life on Earth by filtering some of the harmful UV light in sunlight.

We all have heard of the "ozone hole" (a big hole in the ozone blanket) which creates a number of problems, the largest being the resulting global warming. The hole is caused by the chemical reaction with CFCs and other man-made polluters.

• Acid rain is pollution caused by the reaction of pollutants in the air with rain drops on their way down to Earth. The drops become acidic from contact with pollutants, causing significant damage to buildings, vegetation, and most things they fall on. The pollutants can also react with ground water to form equally damaging acids.

In broader terms, acid rain is a mixture of wet and dry deposition of pollutants falling from the atmosphere. These usually contain abnormally high amounts of nitric and sulfuric acids. Acid rain formation result from both natural sources, such as volcanoes and decaying vegetation, and man-made sources, primarily emissions of sulfur dioxide (SO_2) and nitrogen oxides (NO_x) which result from fossil fuel combustion.

Because in the U.S. 75% of all SO_2 and 25% of all NO_x come from fossil burning for electric power generation, serious acid rain occurs when these gases react with water, oxygen, and other chemicals in the air or the ground, to form various acidic compounds around the areas of their production. The result is a mild solution of sulfuric acid and nitric acid. When sulfur dioxide and nitrogen oxides are released from power plants and other sources, prevailing winds blow these compounds across state and national borders, sometimes over hundreds of miles.

— Wet deposition refers to acid rain, fog, and snow. If the acid chemicals in the air are blown into areas where the weather is wet, the acids can fall to the ground in the form of rain, snow, fog, or mist. As this acidic water flows over and through the ground, it affects a variety of plants and animals. The strength of the effects depends on several factors, including how acidic the water is; the chemistry and buffering capacity of the soils involved; and the types of fish, trees, and other living things that rely on the water.

— Dry deposition occurs mostly in areas where the weather is dry, and the acidic chemicals may become incorporated into dust or smoke, falling to the ground dry and sticking to the ground, buildings, homes, cars, and trees. Dry deposited gases and particles can be washed from these surfaces by rainstorms, leading to increased runoff. This runoff water makes the resulting mixture more acidic. About half of the acidity in the atmosphere falls back to Earth through dry deposition.

Most of these acidic dry deposits are also products of fossil fuels burning for electric power generation.

There are estimates that over 100 million tons of SO_2 come from fossil fuel burning plants, 3.0 million tons from fuel wood and forest burning, and over 8.0 million tons from volcanoes.

The end-products of fossil fuel burning, SO_2 and NO_x, may be taken very far away from the emission point by the wind. This causes acid rain in places far from the primary pollution source—a regional problem that may cross national boundaries.

The anthropogenic emissions of these precursors have systematically decreased in OECD countries, but have increased elsewhere, particularly in Asia. The anthropogenic SO_2 and NO_x, flows are concentrated in a few industrial regions.

Frequently, local areas are affected by a considerable amount of pollution originated elsewhere; for example, 90% of the sulfur precipitation in Switzerland in recent years came from other countries and only 10% was produced in the country itself. A severe problem now occurs all around Asia, where the fast industrial expansion requires large amounts of energy, especially from coal and oil, and where different countries are affected disproportionately. A large increase in acidic deposition in Asia is expected in the coming decades, especially in regions close to heavy industrial and power generating activities.

• *Pollution of seas* and trans-boundary water bodies occurs when large-area oil and other leakages in international waters could cause regional water pollution, in turn contaminating underground aquifers and life forms with toxins.

• *Persistent organic pollutants (POPs)* and radioactive waste is accumulation of heavy metals, such as mercury emitted by coal burning plants, entering the food chain. Man-made toxic compounds (such as PCBs found in electric equipment fluids, and radioactive substances from nuclear plant leakages are serious global polluters, and are also blamed for loss of biodiversity, changes in the oceans, and increased desertification.

• *GHG pollution*, or greenhouse effect, is caused by greenhouse gasses (GHG), mostly carbon dioxide and methane, which actually balance the Earth's climate when in the right proportions, by controlling the amount of heat. When their concentration increases, however, as has been happening lately, they contribute to climate warming by trapping too much heat.

The average carbon dioxide concentration has increased by 30% since the 1800s, while the methane concentration has increased more than 200% during the same time. There is also about a 20% increase of nitrous oxide for this period.

This all leads to changes in our surroundings and in the weather, the most significant of which is an average global temperature increase of about 1.0 degree C. There is a real physical danger from melting glaciers and polar ice caps, rising ocean levels, excessive flooding, storms, and other abnormalities.

GHG gasses are produced mainly during the burning of fossil fuels for electric power generation. There is no doubt that something must be done, but what, when, how, and by whom?

Pollution Areas

We see a number of different types of environmental changes today, so for clarity, we will look at the different effects per geographic and socio-economic region. Because a major part of the environmental changes are a result of air and other types of pollution (most of which comes from energy generation), we also divide the environment into local, regional and global areas.

Local Pollution

Local pollution is the gas, liquid, or solid pollution emitted and contained in a single, usually small, area. This might be the area around a coal burning power plant, or a gas station.

Urban Air Pollution

Emissions of sulfur dioxide (SO_2), carbon monoxide (CO_2), nitrogen oxides (NO_x,) and particulate matter (PM) in fossil fuels burning, especially oil and coal are the predominant pollutions in some local areas. Evaporative emissions of hydrocarbons (HCs) and other volatile organic compounds (VOCs) by solvents and fuel transfer operations are also of concern, as are formation of low-altitude ozone (O_3) by the solar light action on NO_x and HCs.

Emissions of heavy metals such as lead (Pb), cadmium (Cd), mercury (Hg) and other toxic and carcinogenic substances of the dioxins and furans types are emitted when burning coal, oils and solid wastes.

"Occupational" Air Pollution

Emissions of PM and CO by the use of solid fuels (biomass and coal) for heating and cooking in indoor environments in some underdeveloped countries, as well as toxic emissions from industrial and manufacturing processes fall under this category.

Exposure of workers in certain professional categories to intense air pollution, as well as pollution of superficial water bodies (rivers, lakes, estuaries) can affect life forms. Leakages of oil and use of fertilizers and pesticides in agricultural activities are occupational hazards too.

Groundwater contamination is caused by landfill leachate, and industrial or commercial activities, such as leaking underground tanks at gas filling stations. Similar damage is done by abandoned industrial and mining operations, some of which lack appropriate decommissioning as needed for proper final cleanup, isolation and storage, and recovery. There are also environmental accidents and emergencies of different types and magnitudes that are classified as occupational pollution.

Regional

Regional pollution is the gas, liquid, or solid pollution emitted and contained in much larger areas, such as a town, or entire geographic area, such as the Gulf of Mexico.

Global

Global pollution is the gas, liquid, or solid pollution emitted and contained anywhere in the world that affects the global environment, weather or climate.

Global environmental damage is caused also by deforestation for producing fuel wood and charcoal, land clearing for agriculture, coastal and marine degradation due to oil leakages into the sea, CO_2 emissions causing acidification of the oceans, etc.

Air Quality Standards

The contents of different gasses and particles in the air we breath determines its quality, or suitability to support healthy lives. To provide some control of the polluting components in the ambient air, the US government has established standards. These standards determine the maximum amount of pollutants in the air in our homes and work places.

EPA has set National Ambient Air Quality Standards for six principal pollutants, which are called "criteria" pollutants, as listed in Table 1-7. Units of measure for the standards are parts per million (ppm) by volume, parts per billion (ppb) by volume, and micrograms per cubic meter of air ($\mu g/m^3$).

The Clean Air Act identifies two types of national ambient air quality standards. Primary standards provide public health protection, including protecting the health of "sensitive" populations such as asthmatics,

Table 1-7. National Ambient Air Quality Standards

Pollutant [final rule cite]		Primary/ Secondary	Averaging Time	Level	Form
Carbon Monoxide [76 FR 54294, Aug 31, 2011]		primary	8-hour	9 ppm	Not to be exceeded more than once per year
			1-hour	35 ppm	
Lead [73 FR 66964, Nov 12, 2008]		primary and secondary	Rolling 3 month average	0.15 µg/m³ [1]	Not to be exceeded
Nitrogen Dioxide [75 FR 6474, Feb 9, 2010] [61 FR 52852, Oct 8, 1996]		primary	1-hour	100 ppb	98th percentile, averaged over 3 years
		primary and secondary	Annual	53 ppb [2]	Annual Mean
Ozone [73 FR 16436, Mar 27, 2008]		primary and secondary	8-hour	0.075 ppm [3]	Annual fourth-highest daily maximum 8-hr concentration, averaged over 3 years
Particle Pollution Dec 14, 2012	PM2.5	primary	Annual	12 µg/m³	annual mean, averaged over 3 years
		secondary	Annual	15 µg/m³	annual mean, averaged over 3 years
		primary and secondary	24-hour	35 µg/m³	98th percentile, averaged over 3 years
	PM10	primary and secondary	24-hour	150 µg/m³	Not to be exceeded more than once per year on average over 3 years
Sulfur Dioxide [75 FR 35520, Jun 22, 2010] [38 FR 25678, Sept 14, 1973]		primary	1-hour	75 ppb [4]	99th percentile of 1-hour daily maximum concentrations, averaged over 3 years
		secondary	3-hour	0.5 ppm	Not to be exceeded more than once per year

children, and the elderly. Secondary standards provide public welfare protection, including protection against decreased visibility and damage to animals, crops, vegetation, and buildings.

There are also standards for the amount of air pollutants emitted by power plants and industrial enterprises. Most air toxins originate from manmade sources such as power plants, vehicles, factories and refineries, as well as indoor sources such as cooking and cleaning.

"Major" pollution sources are those that emit 10 or more tons per year of any of the listed toxic air pollutants, or 25 or more tons per year of a mixture of air toxins. These sources may release air toxins from equipment leaks, when materials are transferred from one location to another, or during discharge through emission stacks or vents.

"Area" pollution sources are smaller-size facilities that release lesser quantities of toxic pollutants into the air—less than 10 tons per year of a single air toxin, or less than 25 tons per year of a combination of air toxins. Emissions from individual area sources are often rela-

tively small, but when viewed collectively, they are of great concern. Especially when large numbers of these small sources are located in heavily populated areas.

The U.S. EPA periodically publishes a list of "source categories," indicating whether the sources are considered to be "major" or "area" sources, and sets air pollution standards for all major sources of air toxins. Some area sources that are of particular concern are included as well. We will take a closer look at these sources and the related standards in the following chapters.

Notes and References
1. U.S. Energy Information Administration. http://www.eia.gov/naturalgas/
2. National Hydropower Association. http://www.hydro.org/
3. World Coal Association http://www.worldcoal.org/coal/uses-of-coal/coal-electricity/
4. Ambient Air Quality Standards. http://www.epa.gov/air/criteria.html
5. *Photovoltaics for Commercial and Utilities Power Generation*, Anco S. Blazev. The Fairmont Press, 2011
6. *Solar Technologies for the 21st Century*, Anco S. Blazev. The Fairmont Press, 2013

Chapter 2

Fossil Energy Sources

*Like some ghastly cannibal cult, we subsist on the
dead bodies of our ancestors and distant relatives (the fossils).*
Dr. Carl Sagan

In this chapter we will take a close look at the most common energy generation—that produced by conventional energy sources, the fossil fuels (coal, crude oil, and natural gas). In the next chapter we will take a similarly close look at less-conventional energy sources, nuclear and hydropower, and then at the renewables (or alternative) energy sources (solar, wind, etc). We will also analyze the environmental impact of the different energy sources, as related to their production, transport, and use.

We learned about energy and power and their use in Chapter 1, so here we just need to review the key points of the subject, and discuss the major types of energy.

Practical Energy Types

In practice, with energy generation processes we are concerned with the energy properties of all physical energy types:

1. Radiative energy
2. Electric energy
3. Thermal energy
4. Chemical energy
5. Nuclear energy
6. Mechanical energy, and
7. Sound energy

These types of energy play a part in energy conversion processes, so we are most concerned with them.

Here are some examples of the major energy conversion cycles:

1. Radiative to/from thermal energy conversion:
   — Incandescence is an example of radiative to thermal energy conversion.
   — The solar collector is an example of thermal to radiative energy conversion.
2. Radiative to/from chemical energy conversion:
   — Photosynthesis is an example of radiative to chemical energy conversion.

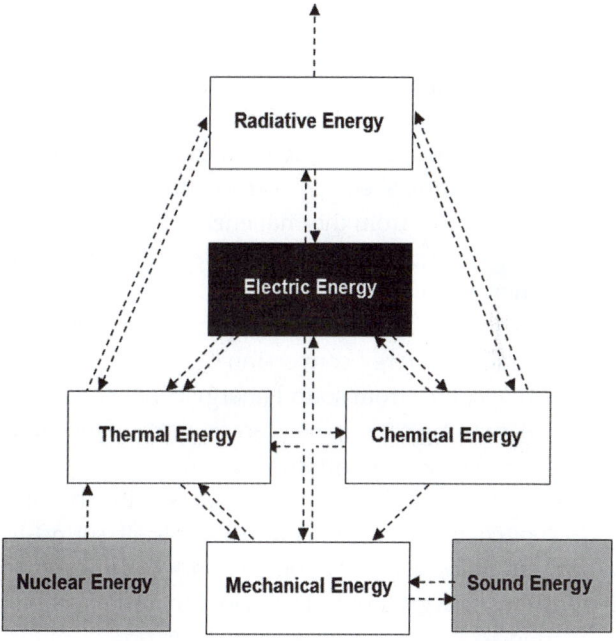

Figure 2-1. The energy conversion cycles

   — Chemi-luminescence is an example of chemical to radiative energy conversion.
3. Radiative to/from electric energy conversion:
   — The solar (PV) cell is an example of radiative to electric energy conversion.
   — The fluorescent light is an example of electric to radiative energy conversion.
4. Thermal to/from electrical energy conversion:
   — The thermo-cell is an example of thermal to electric energy conversion.
   — The electrical resistance of wires is an example of electric to thermal energy conversion.
5. Thermal to/from mechanical energy conversion:
   — Heated steam is used to turn the turbines in power stations.
   — The mechanical energy from rubbing two sticks together is converted into heat.
6. Thermal to/from chemical energy conversion:

— Endothermic reactions are examples of thermal to chemical energy conversion.
— Exothermic reactions are examples of chemical to thermal energy conversion.

7. Chemical to/from electric energy conversion:
   — The car battery is an example of chemical to electric energy conversion.
   — Electrolysis is an example of electric to chemical energy conversion.

8. Chemical to mechanical energy conversion process is observed in human muscles, where the chemical energy stored in the body is converted into mechanical, as needed to activate the different body muscles.

9. Mechanical to/from electric energy conversion:
   — The car alternator is an example of mechanical to electric energy conversion.
   — The electric car engine is an example of electric to mechanical energy conversion.

10. Mechanical to/from thermal energy conversion:
    — The car brakes are an example of mechanical to thermal energy conversion.
    — The locomotive is an example of thermal to mechanical energy conversion.

11. Mechanical to/from sound energy conversion:
    — A running car engine is an example of mechanical to sound energy conversion.
    — Ella Fitzgerald breaking a glass with the high pitch in her voice is an example of sound-to-mechanical energy conversion.

12. Nuclear energy, stored in nuclear materials, is converted to thermal energy in nuclear power plants, and the resulting heat is used to generate electricity.

So how does all this relate to the energy generation we are reviewing? The relation is found in the production, transport, storage, processing, burning, and use of the energy sources. We'll review conventional energy sources, the fossil fuels—coal, oil, and natural gas. Nuclear power is on the borderline of the fossils category, simply because it was produced from ores found deep in the Earth, where they were created billions of years ago in limited quantity. Because of that they cannot be called renewables.

Different types of energy conversion take place in many steps of the energy generation process. For example, the chemical energy in the fossils is converted into heat energy during the burning process, then into mechanical energy by turning the turbine blades, and finally into electric energy in the generator. We will take a closer look at these steps and the energy states during these steps. We will also attempt to connect these to the environmental effects created during their production and use.

For the purposes of this text, we will divide the conventional energy sources in several categories:

1. Wood fuels
2. Fossil fuels
   — coal
   — crude oil (hereafter called oil)
   — natural gas
3. Nuclear energy
4. Hydro energy

These are different from the non-conventional, or alternative, energy sources (solar, wind, biomass, and geothermal) for a number of technical and socio-economic reasons, the details of which we will discuss later on.

NOTE: The term "renewable energy sources" applies to the energy sources that are truly renewable, and which use does not affect their quantity or availability. Some of the conventional energy sources (hydro power, for example) are on the renewables borderline because they are finite, their quantities vary, and because we are close to reaching the limits of their further expansion.

Power Generation

Generating electric power and heat are important elements of the global economy and an equally important part of our daily lives. Those of us living in developed countries are so accustomed to flipping the wall switch, fully expecting bright light to flood the room, or turning the ignition keys of our cars, absolutely sure that the engine will start within a split second. This is not the case in many developing countries, where the rooms (if there is are walls) don't have a light switch, and cars are only for the privileged few. Yet, people in these countries also depend, one way or another, on conventional energy sources.

Energy generation is the mark of a civilization that has great plans and depends on energy to achieve them. Its history is brief and very dynamic, and even now—150 years since the Industrial Revolution—it is still evolving as fast as ever.

The major conventional energy generating technologies today use coal, oil and natural gas to produce electricity and heat. These contain different amounts of energy, thus their different prices and applications.

The approximate values of some fossil fuels units are indicated in Table 2-1.

The different fuels have varying energy values, and can be used in numerous ways. Sometimes the convenience of use is more important than the energy values. For example, coal was the preferred fuel for train engines

Table 2-1. Energy values of different fuels

Fuel type	Energy value
1 US gallon gasoline =	115,000 Btu
	121 MJ
	32 MJ/liter
1 boe (barrel of oil equivalent) =	42.0 US gal.
	6.1 GJ
	5.8 million Btu
	1,700 kWh
1 metric ton gasoline =	8.5 barrels
	43.5 GJ
1 US gallon diesel =	130,500 Btu
1 metric ton coal =	30 GJ anthracite
	20 GJ lignite
1 cubic meter natural gas =	35 MJ
	32,840 Btu

during the first part of the 20th century, but because it is very bulky and dirty it was replaced by diesel fuel. So, although diesel fuel is very expensive today, as compared with coal, it is still in use because of its convenience.

Coal still leads the fuels used for power generation in the U.S. and will remain as the preferred fuel for generating electricity in many areas of the U.S. and the world. Today, however, it is slowly being replaced by its more convenient and much cleaner cousin, natural gas.

Coal has done a good job of powering our economy, but times are changing, and it is time to consider the long-term ramifications of coal use.

Figure 2-3 shows the sign of the times. Natural gas is pushing the other fuels out, and coal is an endangered species. What happens in California is soon repeated in

most other states, so it won't be too long before we see similar scenarios in other states.

As Figure 2-4 shows, coal is still hanging in, and its production price is still the lowest among the competing fuels. Although we are painfully aware of the damages coal is causing to the environment, its low price as a fuel for power generation is indisputable, and in many cases coal wins on that basis alone.

**Energy Generation and
Its Impacts on the Environment**

While energy generation is an absolute necessity for economic development and a comfortable life, we pay for it not only with money, but with our health and welfare. The conventional energy sources (the fossils) are serious polluters causing serious damage to the environment and all life in it.

No matter what, we cannot live without fossil fuels. Not yet. And since they will be with us for a long time,

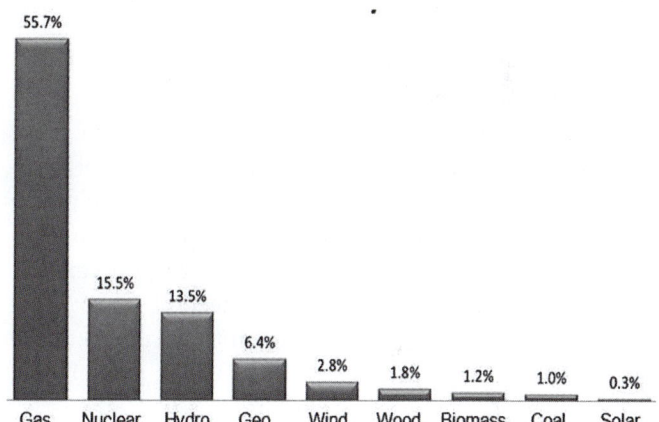

Figure 2-3. California energy generation

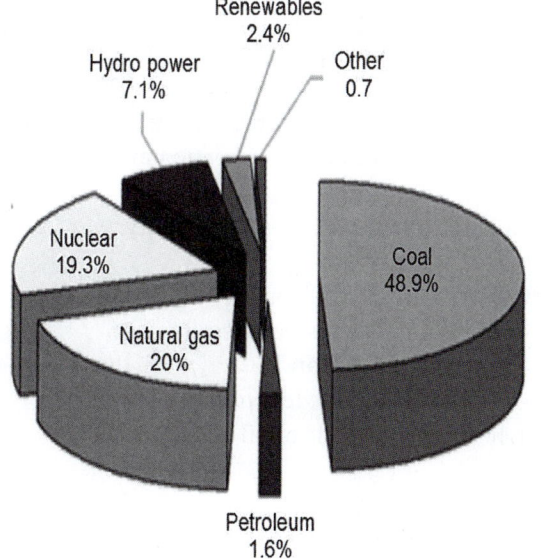

Figure 2-2. Power generation in the U.S.

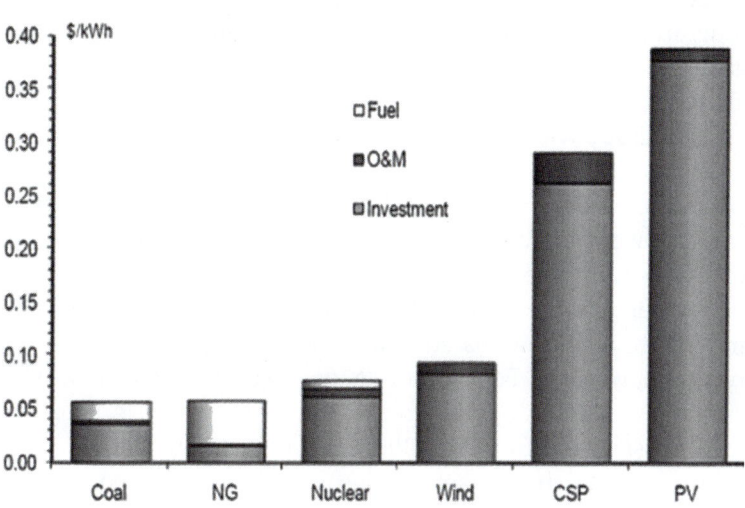

Figure 2-4. Energy cost per kW/h.

we are obligated to learn ALL we can about them, including their operation and how they harm us. From that, we might understand how to change the negative effects, to improve the environment's and our own chance of survival.

With that purpose in mind, we will take a detailed look at conventional energy sources—through their cradle-to-grave lifespan. We will start with the very beginning of the process; from the initial extraction of the raw materials, their transport, storage, refining, and burning, to generating electricity. We will look carefully at the facilities in which the fuels are produced, transported, refined, burned, and transformed into electricity. We will look closely at how electricity is transmitted, distributed, and used.

This detailed study will take us to the depths of the coal mines, and the oil and natural gas wells. We will visit the miners, and gas and oil workers, and will learn all we can about the process of mining, oil pumping and natural gas fracking. Then we will go into the power plants to see what happens there, after which we will follow the flow of electricity to its point of use.

Each step of the process will be evaluated from technical, socio-economic, and environmental points of view. Environmental conclusions will be made in terms of overall damage done to the surroundings at each step of the process for each conventional fuel. Appropriate suggestions for further study, or suggestions for improvement, will be made whenever possible and needed.

So join us in this long journey into the depth of the conventional (fossil) fuels world.

Background

Conventional energy sources (fossil fuels—coal, crude oil, and natural gas) have been with us for a long time, and are still a major part of the electric and heat generation industries. Nuclear and hydro power generators also provide a large part of our electricity, and though we are not happy with the damage some of them cause, we need them.

Fossil fuels (crude coal, oil, and natural gas) are the major power generators in the U.S. and most other countries. They provide the major baseload power which is the power a utility must maintain at all times as a very minimum, and which is absolutely needed for uninterrupted power use. For that alone, we owe the fossils a sincere *thank you*.

Fossils were formed millions of year ago by natural processes such as anaerobic decomposition of buried dead organisms. The age of these in some cases exceeds 650 million years, which means that they need a lot of

time to become fuels, and will not be replaced anytime soon.

Coal, oil and natural gas are found in reservoirs, where they have been locked within rock formations together or separately for millions of years. Natural gas can be also found in the form of methane clathrates on ocean floors or in permafrost. Crude oil is usually found in dedicated reservoirs with quality varying from place to place and at great depth. Coal is found in veins, some of which are close to the surface, but those deep underground are hard to reach and extract.

Fossil fuels have a high carbon content and range from volatile materials with low carbon vs. hydrogen ratios like methane (the major constituent of natural gas), to liquid petroleum, to nonvolatile materials composed of almost pure carbon, like coal.

Fossil fuels contain a wide range of organic, or hydrocarbon, compounds, which vary in the different fuels and fuel mixtures. The specific content, or mixture of hydrocarbons determines the fuels' characteristic properties. The different physical and chemical properties (boiling point, melting point, heat content, density, viscosity, etc.) determine their application and use.

Some fossil fuels contain only very low boiling, gaseous components, like natural gas which is gas under normal temperature and pressure, but can be liquefied under high pressure. Gasoline and diesel are byproducts obtained during different stages of the crude oil distillation processes, and contain much higher boiling-point components.

Fuels Use

Coal, oil, and natural gas account for over 80% of the entire global energy production today. Extrapolated in millions tons of oil equivalent (mtoe), this represents 35% coal, 20% oil, and 25% natural gas. Lately (2010-2012) new fossil reserves were discovered in the US, Canada and abroad, so these quantities and ratios are changing slowly.

Annual production levels until recently were broken down to:

905 billion metric tons of coal,
    or 4,416 billion barrels of oil equivalent.
1,200 billion barrels oil, and
6,183–6,381 trillion cubic feet natural gas,
    or 1,161 billion barrels of oil equivalent

Daily production averaged:
16,761,260 metric tons of coal,
    or 52,000,000 barrels of oil equivalent per day,
84,000,000 barrels of oil per day, and

104,435 billion cubic feet of natural gas,
or 19,000,000 barrels of oil equivalent per day.

NOTE: Natural gas was once burned off as an un-needed byproduct of petroleum production, but is now considered a very valuable, convenient and inexpensive resource. Heavy crude oil, which is much more viscous than conventional crude oil, and tar sands, where bitumen is found mixed with sand and clay, are becoming more important as sources of fossil fuel. Oil shale and similar materials are sedimentary rocks containing kerogen, a complex mixture of high-molecular weight organic compounds which yield synthetic crude oil when heated (pyrolized). These materials have yet to be exploited commercially.

Present-day estimates of remaining world supplies:

a)   100-150 years of coal reserves (some estimates say 250 years, but we could dispute these claims in light of the quickly expanding use of coal in some large countries like China and India),

b)   45-60 years of crude oil, and

c)   75-100 years of natural gas reserves.

These estimates assume that the product could be produced at a constant level for that number of years and that all of the proved reserves could be recovered. In reality, however, consumption of all three resources is expected to increase during the mid-21st century, which means that the resources will be used up much faster.

At some point, the production of each resource will reach a maximum value, after which production will decline until it is no longer economically feasible or physically possible. We have seen a glimpse of this, where oil wells must be drilled much deeper, and the resulting oil quality is inferior.

Changes in technology, prices, or political policy are factors that can lead to significant deviations from these estimates, but all indicators point to increased shortages and higher prices of all fossil fuels by the end of the 21st century.

Alternative fuels are one of the best solutions, and are a subject of intense debate worldwide. Their future, however, depends on political and economic decisions that for the most part do not take into consideration the decline of fossil production or the extensive environmental damage they cause.

Fossil fuels are considered non-renewable energy resources because reserves are being depleted much fast-er than new ones can form. The production and use of fossil fuels also raises growing environmental concerns. A global movement toward the use of renewable energy is under way to help meet increased energy needs and clean the environment.

The global burning of fossil fuels produces around 21.3 gigatons of carbon dioxide (CO_2) per year, while natural processes can absorb only about half of that amount. This basically represents a net increase of 10.65 billion tons of CO_2 per year—and every year—in the Earth's atmosphere. These amounts of pollutants are estimated to increase over time, as developing countries ramp up their coal- and gas-fired power plants.

CO_2, SO_2, and NO_x are greenhouse gases emitted by power plants and vehicles. These gases contribute to environmental damage and global warming by causing the average surface temperature of the Earth to rise. This surface warming, the vast majority of climate scientists agree, will cause major adverse effects to the Earth and its inhabitants in the future, if it is not stopped.

NOTE: Firewood used for energy generation in underdeveloped counties is a major, (possibly even larger) contributor to the fuel mix and related environmental problems. Its negative effect on the environment, however, has been largely ignored, and no serious action has been outlined to reduce it.

Data of present contributions of the other (non-fossil) energy sources show hydroelectric and geothermal power at ~6%, and nuclear at ~8%. The renewables (solar, tidal, wind, wood, and biomass) amount to a grand total of ~1%.

Before the 2008 economic crisis, world energy consumption was growing about 2.5% per year. It is slower now, and with that and other significant changes, the energy balance is changing in favor of using natural gas as a major fuel for power generation. The other fuels and energy technologies are putting up a fight, but it would be hard for any of them to beat natural gas, at least in the short term.

Environmental Concerns in Brief

The U.S., with its 5% of the world's population, uses more than 25% of the world's supply of fossil fuels. On average, Americans are causing at least 5 times more waste than the average person in the developed countries. This is 100 times the waste of those in undeveloped or underdeveloped countries.

Take a look at the recycle bins in U.S. neighborhoods. The paper, aluminum, glass and other materials in these are a reminder of how much stuff we consume and how much of it is wasted. There are millions of recycle bins all over the country, the contents of which if put in one place would make a medium-size mountain…every week.

Still, the mountain of recycling materials is just a drop in the ocean as far as our environment is concerned. More than 90% of greenhouse gas (GHG) emissions come from the combustion of fossil fuels, which also produces other air pollutants, such as nitrogen oxides, sulfur dioxide, volatile organic compounds and heavy metals. Again, most of these are generated in the US and the developed countries.

Electricity generation is the largest contribution to gas and other emissions that are associated with nearly all air quality issues. Nitrogen oxides and sulfur dioxide emissions contribute to smog, acid rain, and the formation of fine particulate matter, as well as mercury emissions. Fossil fuel-fired electric power plants also emit carbon dioxide, which may contribute to climate change.

The impact of all these pollutants on water, habitat, and species is significant. Hydro dams, although clean power generators, also have numerous negative effects on water bodies and biodiversity.

Combustion of fossil fuels generates sulfuric, carbonic, and nitric acids which fall to Earth as acid rain, impacting both natural areas and the manmade structures. Monuments and sculptures made from marble and limestone are particularly vulnerable, as the acids dissolve calcium carbonate.

In addition, fossil fuels contain radioactive materials, mainly uranium and thorium, which are released into the atmosphere. In 2000, about 12,000 tons of thorium and 5,000 tons of uranium were released worldwide from burning coal. It is estimated that during 1982, US coal burning released 155 times as much radioactivity into the atmosphere as the Three Mile Island incident.

Burning coal also generates large amounts of solid waste, in the form of bottom ash and fly ash. These materials are used in a wide variety of applications, and in all cases generate polluting particles.

The process of producing (mining, and fracking mainly), transport, processing, and distributing fossil fuels also creates environmental concerns. Coal mining methods, particularly mountaintop removal and strip mining, have negative environmental impacts, and offshore oil drilling poses a hazard to aquatic organisms. Oil refineries have a great negative impact on the environmental, including air and water pollution during normal operation or through accidents. Transportation of coal via diesel-powered trains, tanker ships, trucks, etc., requires the combustion of great amounts of fossil fuels.

Environmental regulations use a variety of approaches to limit these emissions, such as command-and-control (which mandates the amount of pollution or the technology used), economic incentives, or voluntary programs.

An example of such regulation in the US is the EPA implementing policies to reduce airborne mercury emissions. Under regulations issued in 2005, coal-fired power plants must reduce their emissions by 70% by 2018.

In economic terms, pollution from fossil fuels is regarded as a negative externality. Taxation is considered one way to make societal costs explicit, in order to "internalize" the cost of pollution. This aims to make fossil fuels more expensive, thereby reducing their use and the amount of pollution associated with them, along with raising the funds necessary to counteract these factors.

Energy and Environment Timeline

It is easy to see in Figure 2-5 that as things are going—and there is no change in sight—fossils will be depleted by the end of this century (and some of them even sooner), while energy use increases with the increase in Earth's population. As the demand for energy increases, more coal, oil, and gas are burned, in turn creating more and new environmental issues.

Burning coal, oil, and gas gives us comfort, technical and economic progress, while at the same time causing global warming and other harmful effects which are posing great threats to the environment. The dangers seem to be growing greater for the future as we intensify coal, oil and gas burning.

What are the plusses and minuses of these process and their consequences? This is what we aim to look at in detail in this text.

Now we will take a very close look at the major energy sources—coal, crude oil, natural gas, and nuclear power—and the related processes of their location, extraction, transport, refining, burning, energy transformation, and use.

THE FOSSIL FUELS

Coal, crude oil, and natural gas are the primary energy sources, used in over 85% of energy generation in the world. There are other fossil products, such as peat and bitumen that are also used for power generation, consumer goods, and other applications such as paving roads, but coal, oil and natural gas are by far the dominant fossil fuels today.

Coal consists largely of carbon, although lower grades contain significant quantities of hydrocarbons and other contaminants such as sulfur and mercury.

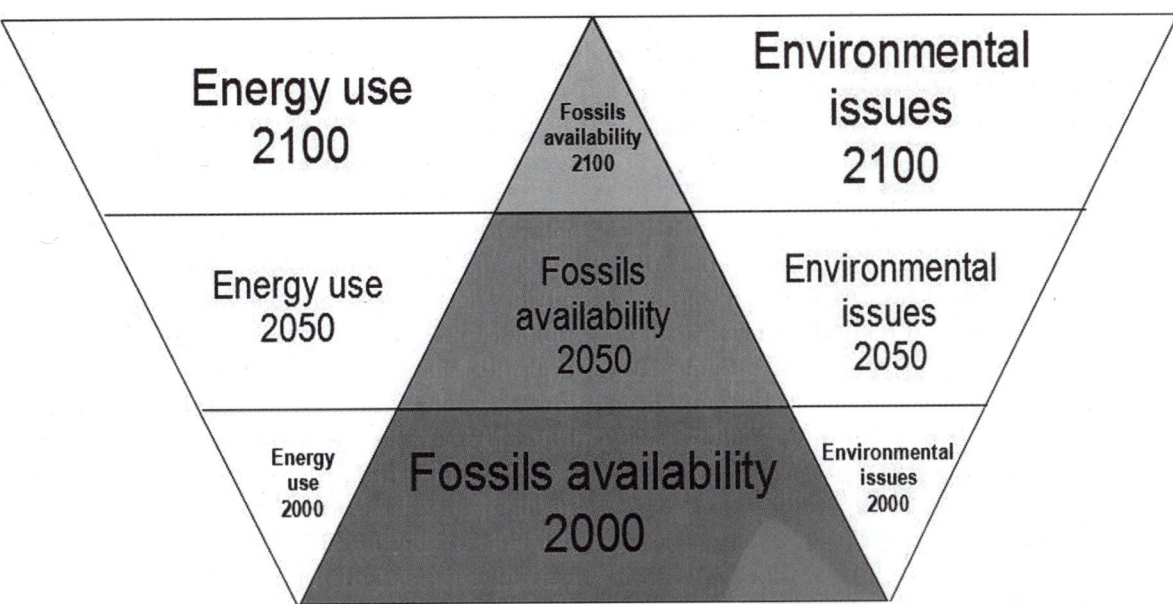

Figure 2-5. Energy use and supply vs. environmental issues of the 21st century

Petroleum is even more complex as a chemical mix of different substances. The liquid component of the oil reserves is crude oil, which contains typically about 85% carbon by weight and a mix of different hydrocarbons with small amounts of sulfur, oxygen, and nitrogen mixed in. The exact composition of the oil reserves varies with location, as well as the age and the conditions of its formation.

Natural gas is the simplest from a chemical standpoint, because it contains one major gas (methane) and the rest is a mixture of different hydrocarbons and impurities in different proportions. The ratio of gas to liquid in coal and oil reserves is very important. The gaseous component of petroleum (natural gas) consists largely of methane, which is the simplest organic hydrocarbon. Other light, gaseous hydrocarbon molecules are also present in the gas mixture.

An important thing to remember here is that we don't burn all the products that are made from coal, crude oil, or natural gas. About 7% of crude oil, for example, is turned into consumer goods, road making products, lubricants, and petrochemical feedstocks. The feedstocks are important derivatives that go into making a vast array of the products we use today. Without these, there would be no plastics, some medicines, inks, insecticides, pesticides, toothpaste, perfumes, fertilizers, lipstick, paints, and food preservatives, just to mention a few. The remarkable thing is that we have build our lives around these, so that a shortage of any would bring serious problems. Just imagine fields without fertilizers...no insecticides. Or imagine a life without plastics, or where they cost 100

times the present value. Impossible? Yes, possible, for this is what will happen 50-100 years from today when the fossils are gone.

We foresee a future, as oil supplies dwindle, where plastics and some of the above mentioned commodities would become scarce and as precious and expensive as gold. This should, and will, eventually give us all the more incentive to look elsewhere for our energy sources. Or would it?

We clearly see future generations looking back, scratching their heads and asking incredulously, "Did they actually burn all this precious stuff?"

Historical Use

Coal has been used as a fuel, mostly for personal use—cooking, heating, etc.—for over 2,000 years. Other uses were also known as early as 1,000 BC, where the Chinese were using coal to smelt copper, and coal cinders from 400 BC Roman-occupied Britain show traces of other use, but the written record of coal use dates back to the 13th century.

From the 17th century on, coal was a major heating fuel in England, and there are a number of famous buildings that are blackened from coal smoke. The Industrial Revolution in Europe made coal a driving force, and the steam engine put coal on a pedestal. By the mid-1800s, coal mining was well underway in the Eastern United States too, supplying coal for industrial uses and steam locomotives that were crossing the country on the newly developed railroads.

Since in some locations liquid crude oil seeps naturally to Earth's surface, it was known and used for a variety of purposes, including medicinally, as early as 5000 BC. Later, oil became a weapon, when Persians and Arab tribes used it quite successfully in oil-soaked arrows and other incendiary weapons. Oil use increased in the 19th century, when it was used for lighting and heating.

In the mid-1800s the first commercial oil well was drilled in Pennsylvania, where oil was struck at 70 feet below ground, and the rest is history. Today, oil is by far the largest and most important natural resource of modern society.

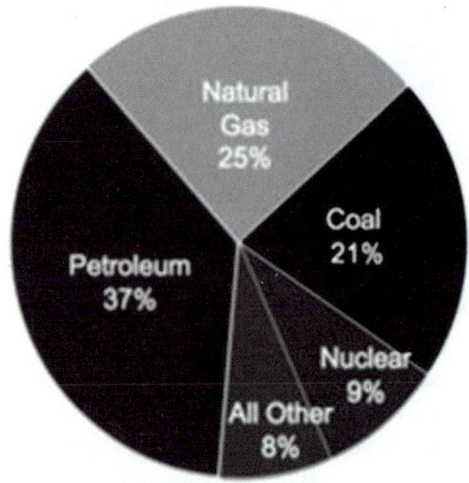

Figure 2-6. Use of fossil fuels in the U.S.

Natural gas use is a new phenomena that has taken a new form and risen to unimaginable levels lately. There was very little use of it in the distant past, and as a matter of fact, until recently, it was simply vented, or burned at oil well sites in a process known as flaring. Flaring is now mostly illegal, and today natural gas is treated with due respect and quickly turned into cash.

Today natural gas is an increasingly important energy resource. With a number of new and very large gas-deposit discoveries, and the improvement of horizontal drilling and fracking processes, it will become even more so with time. Gas rules the U.S. energy markets, and no doubt it will continue to for a long time.

The Fossil Energy Science in Brief

When we burn fossil fuels, the carbon in them reacts with atmospheric oxygen to create carbon compounds, during which process a lot of heat and smoke are generated. In a coal-burning process, the heat released in the burning process sustains the combustion. We can use the generated heat for heating our homes, and generating electricity.

The bad part is that because fossil fuels consist largely of hydrocarbons, the combustion process produces a lot of carbon dioxide (CO_2) gas and some water vapor (H_2O). Both are nontoxic, common substances, which are present in the atmosphere, but when their quantities increase above certain limits, they become harmful climate-changing greenhouse gases. CO_2 is possibly the most dangerous greenhouse gas, and is blamed for serious environmental damage and climate warming.

Herein lies the dilemma: we need heat and electricity from the fossils, but we don't need their toxic greenhouse gasses. Since these go hand in hand, and we cannot have one without the other, we have a big problem that needs quick resolution. So we need to gain a complete understanding about what we are dealing with.

Different fossil fuels have different chemical compositions, thus different combustion processes, which result in differing amounts of CO_2 emission. Since coal consists of simple molecules, which are mostly carbon, CO_2 is the main product of coal burning. Sure enough, coal burning power plants are the major emitter of CO_2 gasses.

NOTE: Although carbon emissions—and CO_2 gas especially—from coal-burning is a major global environmental problem, CO_2 is not an incidental by-product of coal fuel combustion. It is actually exactly what we want and need to produce when burning coal. This is because CO_2 represents the lowest possible energy state of carbon in the Earth's atmosphere. By generating large amounts of CO_2, we've achieved our purpose of efficient extraction of the maximum possible amount of energy from the coal we burn for energy. This is also the major point in the present-day dilemma of energy generation. Can't live with it; can't live without it.

Crude oil has a different, much larger and much more complex molecule. It consists of long hydrocarbon molecule chains, which contain twice as many hydrogen atoms as carbon atoms. Because of that, when oil burns, most of the released energy comes from the formation of H_2O so, for a given amount of energy, less CO_2 is emitted—less than that emitted by an equal amount of coal.

Finally, natural gas is largely methane gas (CH_4), so it contains even more hydrogen and produces much less CO_2—almost two times less CO_2 for an equal quantity of coal.

NOTE: Our calculations show—considering the average efficiency and other coal-to-electricity conversion factors and variables—that an average coal-burning power plant emits CO_2 at a rate of approximately 500 lbs. per second. Got that? Every second there are 500 pounds of CO_2 billowing from the plant's stacks. This is staggering 40 million lbs. of CO_2 emitted daily or close to 16 billion lbs. annually. From just one plant. Multiply that by the thousands of such plants worldwide and you'll see the magnitude of the problem.

Now, a similar size natural gas-burning power plant has better conversion efficiency and less carbon, so it will emit half the amount of CO_2 of the coal-burning unit. Even then, it emits 8 billion lbs. of CO_2 annually—too much to ignore. When multiplied by the thousands of similar power plants around the world, we can clearly see dense clouds of GHGs saturating our atmosphere and changing our climate.

Also, studies have shown that the fracking process, as used today emits large amounts of gasses, raw methane being one of them, which are even worse than CO_2 as far as their GHG content and overall effect on the global climate are concerned. So we must wonder if in this case we are not jumping from the frying pan into the fire.

Still, there is a drive today to shift from coal and oil to natural gas. It is presumed that this switch to a cleaner fuel would slow the process of anthropogenic climate change in the long term. We think that it might slow it down some in the short term, but it cannot stay the inevitable harmful effects, simply because it too produces greenhouse gasses, during both its production and burning processes.

In summary, fossil fuels are the primary energy source in the US and most other countries. We use them in every area of our lives, while at the same time we complain of the increasing cost of the energy they provide, and the pollution they create. Well, as the old folks say, "You cannot have your cake and eat it too." So instead of complaining, we must get serious about understanding the different fossil and renewable technologies and find ways to use them while preserving the energy balance and the environment now, as we search for alternatives.

That is exactly the goal of this text—to present the technical, logistics and economic details of all energy generating technologies, showing their good and bad sides. Having a view of the complete picture is a good start. It will allow us to recognize the problems and help us look for solutions. Whining and complaining won't do! Smart thinking and hard work are needed, if we are to stop the destruction of the world as we know it, while gaining energy independence.

Here we take a close look at the fossils and the related materials, equipment, and processes used during their life cycle; as needed to understand their function and the environmental effects of their production and use. We'll start with coal—the fossil fuel that is used the most, and is the most controversial.

COAL

Coal deserves a very, very close look, because it is the fuel that is most responsible for comforting us with warm homes and limitless electricity, and for killing us with smog and pollution. Sorting out our demands from our responsibilities will not be an easy task.

In the beginning...

How were beds of coal created in such a convenient-to-mine way? What forces were responsible for their creation, and support their existence? One theory claims that many centuries ago strange forces made a number of weird things to happen very quickly. The skies became cloudy and the air very moist so that even the sun's rays had a hard time going through the mush, according to this theory. The weather was very warm, and the crust of the earth was still new and not as thick as we know it now. Enormous amounts of heat were coming from the Earth's core, where nuclear reactions were going wild, contributing energy to the flesh and vegetation cooker on the surface of the Earth.

The vegetation and trees grew wildly in the moist air, and very large plants, trees and animals developed at the time. Vegetation 40 to 50 feet high and huge trees were the norm and grew extremely fast, especially in swamps.

When time came for them to die, others took their place within weeks. Dead leaves and trees fell and heaped up all over the place. Stumps stood up for awhile, decaying slowly, and every year the soft, black, decaying mass of vegetation and animal carcasses grew deeper and deeper.

The crust of the fairly new Earth was still very thin and pliable, so it bent and wrinkled easily. Some swampy places rose up, and some sank, so that water rushed over them, pressing down on the deposits with great pressure, while sweeping in sand and clay.

Under normal conditions, the carbon in wood burns completely, with only a pile of ashes left as a reminder. But if you cover the wood pile before lighting it, and make sure that only a little oxygen reaches it after it is lit, it will smolder slowly with much of the carbon left in it in a form of charcoal.

When wood decays, the process is similar to the smoldering, where carbon reacts with small amounts of oxygen in the air to create charcoal—provided that not much oxygen reaches the decaying mass.

And this is the big difference between the forests of today where leaves and trees fall and decay in the open air with nothing remaining. In the times when coal was forming, the water and soil covering the vegetation and dead animals restricted air access to the decaying mass, so that much of the carbon was left to form our useful coal deposits. High heat and pressure from above and below finished the job.

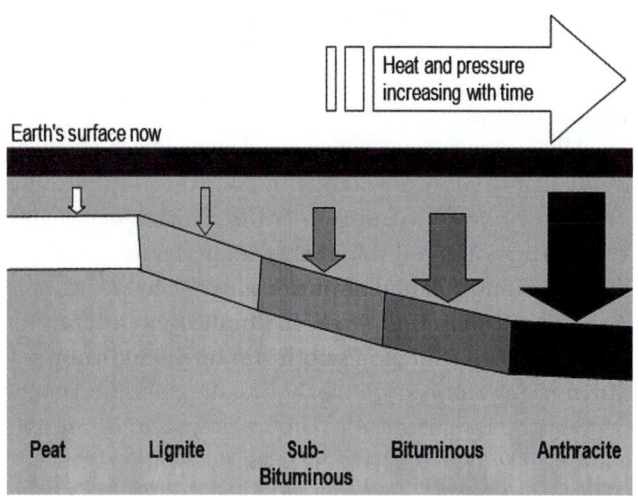

Figure 2-7. Coal formation over time.

Anthracite is the oldest coal. Formed so long ago and given a chance to mature, it is the highest quality coal and has the highest heat content.

Some of the layers, or strata, of coal are 50 or 60 feet thick, while some are very thin. Most, however, have a layer of sandstone or dark-gray shale on top, which was created by the sand and mud which covered the decaying mass. This layer, as the lid of a pressure cooker, sealed the mass under and kept the heat and pressure in until the process was completed.

The Earth's crust was thin, and it wrinkled under the weight of the mass; the pressure cooker lid was cracked open slightly. This brought some of the strata of coal to the surface, which we now find as surface coal deposits. These deposits are mined today in surface (or pit) mines.

Some of the mass, however, travelled (together with its pressure cooker lid) deep underground, as if trying to hide. Today we can easily find it, but must dig long, deep shafts to get to it. This is where miners go every day to do their dirty and dangerous job of digging the coal and taking it to the surface to be shipped to coal-burning power plants to make electricity for our comfort.

Sixty percent of U.S. coal is scraped and ripped out from the earth in surface mines. The rest is dug out from underground mines. Coal companies often remove entire mountaintops to expose the coal below, which is then easily excavated and loaded on trucks and railroad cars for transport to power plants. Underground mines consist of large and very long holes dug deep into the

ground, where miners descend every day into deep shafts to scrape and load coal on carts and transport it to the surface.

Just think how long it took Nature to create this precious, albeit limited, gift. It took billions of years to get coal ready for use, but it took us only a century to dig out and burn 80% of it. Did they really burn that precious stuff...?

Carbon

Carbon is a miracle element. It is in the structure of all living things. Without carbon there would be no life on Earth. It is also the main constituent of coal, and although it has a fairly simple physical structure, it is a chemically complex element in the way it behaves and in the never-ending versatility of its use. It is found in many different compounds; it is in the food we eat, the clothes we wear, our cosmetics and the gasoline that fuels our cars.

Carbon is the sixth most abundant element in the universe, and is number one in usefulness. It is a very special element because it plays an essential role not only in thousands of products, but it is the dominant component in the chemistry of life. Life as we know it cannot exist without carbon. All living matter is made of carbon with other elements added to it. Amazing... Carbon was known in ancient times, when it was manufactured by burning organic material for making charcoal.

There are four known allotopes of carbon: amorphous, graphite, diamond and fullerene. A new (fifth) allotrope of carbon was recently found. It is a spongy solid that is extremely lightweight and, very unusually, attracted to magnets. This new magnetic addition to the carbon family, nanofoam, may someday find important medical applications that might change our lives in a drastic way. That is, if there is any carbon left at the pace we are burning it.

Carbon has four electrons in its valence shell (the outer shell), or the energy shell, which plays a major role

Figure 2-8. The carbon atom

in chemical reactions, and which in this case can hold a maximum of eight electrons. Each carbon atom, therefore, can share electrons with up to four different atoms (carbon or other elements), since carbon can combine with other elements as well as with itself. This allows carbon to form an amazing number of different compounds of varying size and shape.

Carbon alone forms the familiar substances graphite and diamond. Both are made only of carbon atoms. Graphite is very soft and slippery, while diamond is the hardest substance known to man, and although both are made only of carbon atoms what gives them different properties is the different ways the carbon atoms form bonds with each other in the different materials.

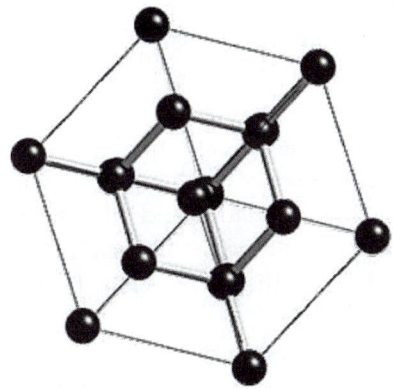

Figure 2-9. Diamond structure

In the diamond structure, the carbon atoms are arranged very symmetrically and are compacted very closely together, so that they cannot move at all. This gives diamonds their very special physical and chemical properties—exceptional shine, hardness and inertness—not to mention great value, for they are rare and hard to find and mine. Cutting and polishing the extremely hard raw diamonds increases their price even more.

Carbon's key physical and chemical properties are:

Atomic Number	6
Atomic Mass	12.011
Melting Point	6422°F
Boiling Point	6917°F)
Density	2.267 g/cu.cm.
Velocity of sound	18350/m s^{-1}
Hardness Scale:	0.5 Mohs
Stable Isomers:	2

Carbon Uses

Carbon on Earth is most abundant in coal, which is usually burned to generate electric power. Besides that,

there are thousands of other uses and products of which carbon is a part. Some of the major uses of coal are:

- Graphite combined with clays form the "lead" used in pencils.
- Diamonds are used for decorative purposes, and also as drill bits.
- Carbon is added to iron to make steel products.
- Carbon is used for control rods in nuclear reactors.
- Graphite carbon in a powdered, caked form is used as charcoal for cooking, artwork and other uses.
- Charcoal pills are used in medicine in pill or powder form to adsorb toxins or poisons from the digestive system.
- Carbon compounds are used in a great number of medical preparations.
- Basically, all compounds in the so-called organic chemistry branch are carbon based. This includes coal, crude oil, natural gas, and all their derivatives.

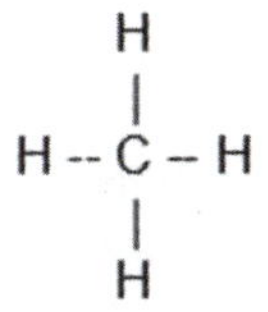

$$H \atop | $$
$$H -\!- C - H$$
$$| \atop H$$

Figure 2-10. Methane molecule

The simplest carbon based molecule is that of methane, which is the major component in natural gas. Crude oil and coal have much more complex molecules. By adding more hydrogen atoms we can change the methane molecule to others—ethane, hexane, octane, propane, etc.

Adding oxygen and other atoms would take us to the depths of the organic chemistry compounds, which are too deep and complex for our purposes, but which are the origins of most life matter and many things (plastics, cosmetics, and such) around us.

Coal Types

Coal is a mixture with carbon, hydrogen, oxygen, nitrogen and sulfur atoms combined in its molecule. It is a complex mixture, and the numbers vary, but basically speaking it can be expressed as $C_{100}H_{73}O_8NS$. What this means is that for every 100 atoms of carbon in the coal molecule, there are 73 atoms of hydrogen, 8 oxygen, one nitrogen and one sulfur atom. The distribution of the atoms and links to each other are too complex for this text. Only organic chemists understand completely the exact structure and the relations within, so we will leave this task to them.

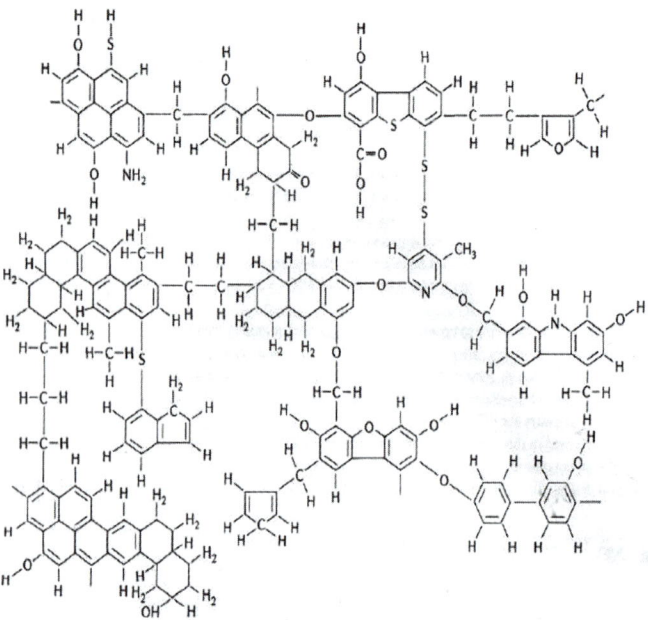

Figure 2-11. Segment of a coal molecule.

For our purposes it suffices to say that coal and crude oil chemical structures consist of a large number of different molecules (different for each type of product), consisting mostly of carbon, hydrogen and oxygen. The molecules are interlocked into long chains, which, in addition to the quantity of hydrogen and oxygen atoms, determine the overall properties and qualities of the different types of coal.

Although the different type of coal have somewhat similar formulas, they have different qualities, which are determined by the arrangement of the atoms in the molecules, which varies with location, and is usually an indication of the time and way they were formed.

One important thing to remember here is that some coals have more hydrogen and oxygen atoms in their molecules than others, which determine their qualities. Basically speaking, coals that were formed in the more recent past tend to have more hydrogen and oxygen atoms in their molecules. They are also of lower commercial quality because of their lesser heating value.

So, depending on these variables we now have several types of coal, as follow:

Peat is actually a precursor of coal, or coal that is in the maturing stages. It has commercial value as a fuel in some regions. In its dehydrated form it is used as an absorbent for oil spills on land and water. It can also be used as a conditioner for agricultural soils, enabling them to retain and slowly release water.

Lignite, or brown coal, is the lowest quality coal, used almost exclusively as fuel for electric power genera-

tion. Jet coal, a compact form of lignite, can be used in artwork, and when polished it can be used for ornamental work.

Sub-bituminous coal has properties that range from those of lignite to those of bituminous coal. It is used primarily as fuel for steam-electric power generation and is an important source of light aromatic hydrocarbons for the chemical synthesis industry.

Bituminous coal is a dense sedimentary rock. It is black or dark brown in color, and has characteristic bands of bright and dull material. It is used primarily as fuel in steam-electric power generation, with substantial quantities used for heat and power applications in manufacturing. It is also used to make coke.

Steam coal has a quality value between bituminous coal and anthracite. In the recent past, it was used as a fuel for steam locomotives, where it is known as sea-coal. It was also used as a fuel for domestic water heating, cooking, etc.

Anthracite is the highest quality coal. It is hard, glossy black coal that is used primarily for residential and commercial space heating and other needs. It may be divided further into a) metamorphically altered bituminous coal, and b) petrified oil, such as from the deposits in Pennsylvania.

Graphite is a different type of coal, which is hard to ignite and is not used as fuel. Instead, it has found use in commercial materials, such as pencils and lately as a solid (powder) lubricant.

NOTE: Peat and lignite have a lot of hydrogen and oxygen atoms in their molecules. They are somewhat soft and have lower heating value. On the other extreme, anthracite has very little hydrogen and oxygen, so it is hard and has the greatest heating value of the coals we use commercially today.

Lignite, for example has 50-65% volatiles (water and other liquids), including 6% hydrogen and 20% oxygen, while anthracite has only 10% volatiles, 3.5% hydrogen and 2.5% oxygen.

Coal Properties

There are four types or ranks: lignite or brown coal, bituminous or black coal, anthracite and graphite. Each of these has a certain set of physical characteristics which are expressed by moisture, volatile content (in terms of aliphatic or aromatic hydrocarbons), and carbon content in the coal.

A closer look at coal's properties:

The most important property of coal is its energy content, expressed in Btu/lb, or the heat that a pound of coal can generate.

Coal Grade	(Btu/lb)
Anthracite	12910
Semi-anthracite	13770
Low-volatile bituminous	14340
Medium-volatile bituminous	13840
High-volatile bituminous A	13090
High-volatile bituminous B	12130
Sub-bituminous B	9150
Sub-bituminous C	8940
Litnite	6900

Figure 2-12. Heating values of coal

The energy or fuel content is the amount of potential energy contained in the coal that can be easily converted into actual heating ability. This heating ability (or heating value) is the factor that determines what coal is going to be used for, how much, and at what price. Anthracite and its sub-categories are the most valuable from that perspective and bring the highest price per unit as compared with most of the other coal types.

Another way of evaluating the heat content in coal is looking at its calorific value Q, which is the actual heat liberated by its complete combustion at different oxygen levels. The Q value is determined experimentally by using special test equipment such as calorimeters.

The approximate formula for determining Q at an oxygen content of less than 10% is:

$$Q = 337C + 1442(H - O/8) + 93S$$

Where:

C is the mass percent of carbon in the coal sample,
H is the mass percent of hydrogen,
O is the mass percent of oxygen, and
S is the mass percent of sulfur.

Q in this case is given in kilojoules per kilogram.

Moisture is one of the most important properties of coal, which determines in part its commercial value. All coals contain some amount of moisture. External moisture is known as adventitious moisture and is readily evaporated during mining and transport. Moisture that is held within the coal itself is known as inherent moisture and is analyzed.

Moisture may occur in four possible forms within coal: a) surface moisture is water held on the surface of the coal particles, b) hydroscopic moisture is water held by capillary action within the microfractures of the coal pieces, c) decomposition moisture is water held within

the coal's decomposed organic compounds, and d) mineral moisture is water which comprises part of the crystal structure of hydrous silicates such as clays.

Volatile matter are all other components of coal, except for moisture, which can be freed (evaporated) at high temperatures in the absence of air. These are usually a mixture of short- and long-chain hydrocarbons, aromatic hydrocarbons, and usually some sulfur. The volatile matter of coal is determined under rigidly controlled standards. In Europe this involves heating the coal sample to 1650 ±10°F in a muffle furnace. Procedures in the US involve heating the coal samples to 1740 ± 45°F in a vertical platinum crucible and weighing the before and after samples. The difference is the volatile matter.

Fixed carbon is the carbon found in the material which is left after all volatile materials have been evaporated. This is different from the ultimate carbon content of the coal, because some carbon is lost with the volatiles. Fixed carbon is an estimate of the amount of coke that will be yielded from this type of coal. Fixed carbon is determined by removing the mass of volatiles determined by the volatility test from the original mass of the coal sample.

Ash is the non-combustible residue which is left after coal is burned. It is the bulk mineral matter left behind after all carbon, oxygen, sulfur and water have been evaporated during combustion. Ash content is determined by burning the coal thoroughly and the remaining ash material is weighed and expressed as a percentage of the original weight.

Coal is sorted and classified by rank, which is basically a measure of the process of its formation and present state. It represents the amount of alteration (the amount of heat and pressure) that the coal has undergone during its formation. The increase in rank describes an increase in temperature and pressure which results in the coal's having a lower volatile content, therefore increased carbon content. That also determines its heat content, which in turn determines its commercial value, with anthracite having the highest heating and commercial value.

Coal is also classified according to the content of its contaminants, sulfur, phosphorous, volatile and ash contents, which generally vary and which determine its rank as well. Consecutive stages in the evolution of rank, from an initial peat stage, are brown coal (or lignite), sub-bituminous coal, bituminous coal, and anthracite.

Coking coal is used in the steel making industry where the coal requires specific qualities such as low sulfur and phosphorous contents. Approximately 630 kg of coal are used for every ton of steel produced. Electricity generation normally uses lignite (thermal) coal, which is ground to a fine powder prior to combustion.

The classification of coal is generally based on the content of volatiles. However, the exact classification varies between countries.

Class	Volatile matter weight in %
Anthracites	< 6.1
Dry steam coals	9.1 - 13.5
Cooking steam coal	15.1 - 17.0
Low volatile steam coal	19.1 - 19.5
Prime cooking coal	19.6 - 32.0
Heat altered coal	19.6 - 32.0
Strong coking coal	32.1 - 36.0
Medium coking coal	32.1 - 36.0
Weak coking coal	32.1
Very weak coking coal	32.1 - 36.0
Non-coking coal	32.1 - 36.0

Figure 2-13. Coal types per volatile matter content

Coal is classified into four general categories or "ranks." They range from lignite through sub-bituminous and bituminous to anthracite, reflecting the progressive response of individual deposits of coal to increasing heat and pressure. The carbon content of coal supplies most of its heating value, but other factors also influence the amount of energy it contains per unit of weight.

NOTE: The amount of energy in coal is expressed in British thermal units per pound. A Btu is the amount of heat required to raise the temperature of one pound of water one degree Fahrenheit.

About 90 percent of the coal in the U.S. falls in the bituminous and sub-bituminous categories, which rank below anthracite and, for the most part, contain less energy per unit of weight. Bituminous coal predominates in the Eastern and Midwest coal fields, while sub-bituminous coal is generally found in the Western states and Alaska.

Lignite ranks the lowest and is the youngest of the coals. Most lignite is mined in Texas, but large deposits also are found in Montana, North Dakota, and some Gulf Coast states.

Coal types are determined and priced by their carbon and energy content during testing procedures. The different coal types are expanded on below.

Anthracite

Anthracite is coal with the highest carbon content, between 86 and 98 percent, with a heat value of nearly 15,000 Btus per pound. Most frequently associated with home heating, anthracite is a very small segment of the

U.S. coal market. There are 7.3 billion tons of anthracite reserves in the United States, found mostly in 11 northeastern counties in Pennsylvania.

Steam Coal

Steam coal is a grade between bituminous coal and anthracite, which was widely used as a fuel for steam locomotives in the past. In this specialized use, it is sometimes known as "sea-coal" in the US. Small steam coal, or dry small steam nuts, was used as a fuel for domestic water heating in the past as well. Today steam coal is used in a number of applications that can afford its somewhat higher cost.

Bituminous Coal

The most plentiful form of coal in the United States, bituminous coal is used primarily to generate electricity and make coke for the steel industry. The fastest growing market for coal, though still a small one, is supplying heat for industrial processes. Bituminous coal has a carbon content ranging from 45 to 86 percent carbon and a heat value of 10,500 to 15,500 Btus per pound.

Sub-bituminous Coal

Sub-bituminous coal is the type of coal used most extensively in coal-fired power plants, so it deserves a closer look. It is also called black lignite, and has a dark brown to black color. Its qualities (and heating value) are between lignite and bituminous coal according to the coal classification used in the United States and Canada. In many other countries sub-bituminous coal is considered to be a brown coal and is used for domestic and commercial heating and cooking purposes.

Sub-bituminous coal contains 42 to 52% carbon (on a dry, ash-free basis), and its heat (calorific) values ranges between 19 and 26 MJ per kilogram, or about 8,200 to 11,200 Btus per pound. It is also characterized by greater compaction than lignite and has greater brightness and luster. The lower quality, woody-like structure lignite is not found in sub-bituminous coal, which exhibits alternating dull and bright maceral bands composed of vitrinite in patterns similar to those found in bituminous coals. Some sub-bituminous coal is macroscopically indistinguishable from bituminous coal.

There are reliable estimates that nearly half of the world's proven coal reserves are made up of sub-bituminous coal and lignite. There are large deposits of these coal types in Australia, Brazil, Canada, China, Russia, Ukraine, Germany, other European countries, and the United States.

Most sub-bituminous coal is considered to be relatively young from a geological point of view, dating from the Mesozoic and Cenozoic eras, or about 250 million years ago. Although age is important, the quality of coal is determined primarily by the pressure and temperature reached during the "cooking" cycle.

Sub-bituminous coal usually also contains less water, around 10 to 25% and is harder than lignite. This makes it more valuable and easier to transport, store, and use.

One important characteristic of great importance to the energy generation sector is the fact that although sub-bituminous coal has lower heat value than bituminous coal, it is lower in sulfur content, usually less than 1 percent, so it is preferred in some cases. Since it has a lower heat value, however, more sub-bituminous coal must be burned to obtain an equal amount of energy.

Recently, a number of coal-fired power generating plants have switched from burning bituminous coal to sub-bituminous coal and lignite. The main reason is the relatively low sulfur content.

Lignite

Lignite is a geologically young coal which has the lowest carbon content, 25-35 percent, and a heat value ranging between 4,000 and 8,300 Btus per pound. Sometimes called brown coal, it too is mainly used for electric power generation, but its low energy content makes it less desirable than any of the other types.

Peat

Peat is a fairly young coal, actually considered to be a precursor of coal. It has some industrial uses as a fuel for some special applications. One of the wide applications is its dehydrated form. Since dehydrated peat is a highly effective absorbent, it is used in great quantities for fuel and oil spills on land and water. It is also used as a conditioner for soil to make it more able to retain and slowly release water.

Graphite

Graphite is technically the highest rank of coal with the highest carbon content, but its physical structure and chemical properties make it difficult to ignite and it is not commonly used as fuel. It is mostly used for making pencils, electrodes and, when powdered, it is widely used in lubricants.

OTHER USES OF COAL

In addition to its wide use in electric power generation, and domestic heating and cooking, coal has a number of different applications. Some of these uses follow.

Sea Coal

Finely ground bituminous coal, known in this application as sea coal, is a constituent of foundry sand. While the molten metal is in the mold, the coal burns slowly, releasing reducing gases at pressure, thereby preventing the metal from penetrating the pores of the sand. It is also contained in "mould wash," a paste or liquid with the same function applied to the mould before casting.

Sea coal can be mixed with the clay lining (the "bod") used for the bottom of a cupola furnace. When heated, the coal decomposes and the bod becomes slightly friable, easing the process of breaking open holes for tapping the molten metal.

Chemicals Production

Coal is used extensively as feedstock to produce chemicals using processes which require substantial quantities of water, and which release a number of toxic gasses and liquids. Because of that, presently most of the coal-to-chemical production is concentrated in China, where environmental regulation and water management policies are weak to non-existent.

In coal-to-chemical production, synthesis gas (syngas), which is a gaseous mixture of primarily carbon monoxide and hydrogen gas is produced by gasification of coal. The syngas can then be used as a chemical building block in a number of chemical processes, such as making methanol or acetyls.

Ammonia and urea are significant products of coal-to-chemicals for use in fertilizers. The syngas composition, or the ratio of hydrogen to carbon monoxide, is important for some downstream processes, so a water-gas shift reactor is sometimes used to change this balance.

Coking Coal

Coking coal (coke) is a solid carbonaceous residue derived from low-ash, low-sulfur bituminous coal from which the volatile constituents are driven off by baking in an oven in the absence of oxygen at $1,832°F$ in order to fuse the fixed carbon and residual ash together.

Coke from coal is grey, hard, and porous and has a heating value of 24.8 million Btu/ton (29.6 MJ/kg). Some coke-making processes produce valuable byproducts, including coal tar, ammonia, light oils, and coal gas.

Metallurgical coke is used as a fuel and as a reducing agent in smelting iron ore in a blast furnace. The result is pig iron and is too rich in dissolved carbon, so it must be treated further to make steel. The coking coal is low in sulfur and phosphorus, so those do not migrate into the metal to deteriorate its properties.

The coke is also strong enough to resist the weight

of overburden in the blast furnace, which is why coking coal is so important in making steel using the conventional route. An alternative route is direct reduced iron, where any carbonaceous fuel can be used to make sponge or pelletized iron.

Petroleum coke is the solid residue obtained in oil refining, which resembles coke, but contains too many impurities to be useful in metallurgical applications.

Gasification

Coal gasification can be used to produce syngas, which is basically a mixture of carbon monoxide (CO) and hydrogen (H_2) gas. This syngas can then be converted into transportation fuels such as gasoline and diesel, through the Fischer-Tropsch process. This technology is currently used by the Sasol chemical company of South Africa to make motor vehicle fuels from coal and natural gas. Alternatively, the hydrogen obtained from gasification can be used for various purposes, such as powering a hydrogen economy, making ammonia, or upgrading fossil fuels.

During gasification, the coal is mixed with oxygen and steam while also being heated and pressurized. During the reaction, oxygen and water molecules oxidize the coal into carbon monoxide (CO), while also releasing hydrogen gas (H_2).

This process has been conducted in both underground coal mines and in the production of town gas.

$$C \text{ (as Coal)} + O_2 + H_2O \rightarrow H_2 + CO$$

If the refiner wants to produce gasoline, the syngas is collected at this state and routed into a Fischer-Tropsch reaction. If hydrogen is the desired end product, however, the syngas is fed into the water gas shift reaction, where more hydrogen is liberated.

$$CO + H_2O \rightarrow CO_2 + H_2$$

In the past, coal was converted to make coal gas (town gas), which was piped to customers to burn for illumination, heating, and cooking.

Liquefaction

Coal can also be converted into synthetic fuels equivalent to gasoline or diesel by several different processes. In the direct liquefaction processes, coal is either hydrogenated or carbonized. Hydrogenation processes are the Bergius process, the SRC-I and SRC-II (Solvent Refined Coal) processes and the NUS Corporation hydrogenation process. In the process of low-temperature carbonization, coal is coked at temperatures between 680 and 1,380°F. These temperatures optimize the production of coal tars richer in lighter hydrocarbons than normal coal tar. The coal tar is then further processed into fuels.

Alternatively, coal can be converted into a gas first, and then into a liquid, by using the Fischer-Tropsch process. Coal liquefaction methods involve carbon dioxide (CO_2) emissions in the conversion process. If coal liquefaction is done without employing either carbon capture and storage (CCS) technologies or biomass blending, the result is lifecycle greenhouse gas footprints that are generally greater than those released in the extraction and refinement of liquid fuel production from crude oil.

If CCS technologies are employed, reductions of 5-12% can be achieved in coal-to-liquid (CTL) plants and up to a 75% reduction is achievable when co-gasifying coal with commercially demonstrated levels of biomass (30% biomass by weight) in coal/biomass-to-liquids plants. For future synthetic fuel projects, carbon dioxide sequestration is proposed to avoid releasing CO_2 into the atmosphere. Sequestration adds to the cost of production. Currently, all US and at least one Chinese synthetic fuel projects, include sequestration in their process designs.

Refined Coal

Refined coal is the product of a coal-upgrading technology that removes moisture and certain pollutants from lower-rank coals such as sub-bituminous and lignite (brown) coals. It is one form of several pre-combustion treatments and processes for coal that alter coal's characteristics before it is burned.

The goals of pre-combustion coal technologies are to increase efficiency and reduce emissions when the coal is burned. Depending on the situation, pre-combustion technology can be used in place of or as a supplement to post-combustion technologies to control emissions from coal-fueled boilers.

Coal Mining

The most economical method of coal extraction from coal seams depends on the depth and quality of the seams, the geology, and environmental factors. Coal mining processes are differentiated by whether they operate on the surface or underground.

Presently surface and underground mining are the most common methods used to dig coal out of the ground. Surface mining is cleaner and safer than underground mining, but it causes serious visual and environmental damages. Underground mining is equally harmful to the environment, but the scars and damage are much less visible in most cases. It is also the most dangerous human undertaking on Earth.

Technical and economic feasibility of coal mining are evaluated based on the following criteria: regional geologic conditions; overburden characteristics; coal seam continuity, thickness, structure, quality, and depth; strength of materials above and below the seam for roof and floor conditions; topography (especially altitude and slope); climate; land ownership as it affects the availability of land for mining and access; surface drainage patterns; ground water conditions; availability of labor and materials; coal purchaser requirements in terms of tonnage, quality, and destination; and capital investment requirements.

Basically speaking, coal that can be found at depths of 180 to 300 ft (50 to 100 m) is usually mined in underground mines, but in some cases surface mining techniques can be used. For example, some western U.S. coal that occurs at depths in excess of 200 ft (60 m) is mined by the open pit method, due to the thickness of the seam 60-90 feet (20-30 m).

Coals deposits below 300 ft (100 m) are usually mined in underground mines. Although there are open pit mining operations working on coal seams up to 1000-1500 feet (300-450 m) below ground level, for instance in some regions in Germany, they are exceptions.

Surface, or strip, mining is usually preferred for extracting coal that is less than 200 feet under the surface. So, today we have two distinct methods of mining coal: surface, or strip, mining and underground mining.

Below we will take a close look at cradle-to-grave coal mining and burning operations. When we say from the "cradle," we include the cradle too, because it also had to be manufactured and used, and those processes also have some impact.

The cradle-to-grave coal mining, cleaning, transport and burning process basically consists of:

Mine planning
- Locating, testing and exploring the coal reserves in the proposed mine location
- Estimating the construction, operating cost and related issues
- Applying for and obtaining the necessary federal, state and local permits

Mine design
- Mine area design
- Equipment design
- Process design

Mine construction
- Mine construction
- Surface facilities
- Infrastructure

Daily operations
- Coal digging and surface transport
- Coal preparation and waste treatment
- Coal and waste transport

Mine decommissioning and land reclamation
- Mine shut down and evacuation
- Mine reconstruction
- Surface land reclamation

In addition, a major portion of mined coal is transported to a coal-fired power plant to be burned in furnaces. The heat of these furnaces is used to boil water and generate steam, which is run through turbines attached to electricity generators. Thus generated electric power is sent into the national grid for use at residences and businesses.

Let's start with a close look at coal mine development and operation.

Surface, or Strip, Mining

When coal seams are near the surface, it may be economical to extract the coal using open cut (also referred to as open cast, open pit, or strip) mining methods. Open cast coal mining recovers a greater proportion of the coal deposit than underground methods, as more of the coal seams in the strata may be exploited. Large open cast mines can cover an area of many square kilometers and use very large pieces of equipment. This equipment can include draglines which operate by removing the overburden, power shovels, large trucks which transport overburden and coal, bucket wheel excavators, and conveyors.

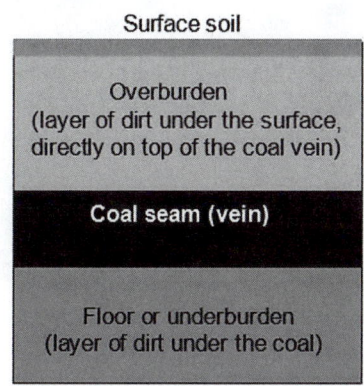

Figure 2-14. Coal deposit, cross section

In surface mining, explosives are used to break through the surface soil and the overburden of the mining area. The overburden is then removed by draglines or by power shovels and trucks. Once the coal seam is exposed, it is drilled, fractured and thoroughly mined in strips. The coal is then loaded onto large trucks or conveyors for transport to either the coal preparation plant or directly to where it will be used.

Most open cast mines in the United States extract bituminous coal. In Australia and South Africa open cast mining is used for both thermal and metallurgical coals. In New South Wales open casting for steam coal and anthracite is practiced. Surface mining accounts for around 80 percent of production in Australia, while in the US it is used for about 67 percent of production. Globally, about 40 percent of coal production involves surface mining.

Surface mining is the most widely spread mining method, with the most obvious—in your face—environmental damages. Underground mining has its problems too, but they are hidden and harder to observe.

Underground Mining

Most coal seams are deep underground, and since opencast mining is impractical, underground mining is used instead. It accounts for about 60% of world coal production. Underground mining offers a number of totally different challenges to extracting coal from the Earth. Since coal is very deep in some locations, and strip mining would not work there, deep holes (shafts) are dug into the ground down to the level of the coal veins. Miners are lowered down into the hole, where they dig the coal and bring it to the surface.

Figure 2-15. Underground mining operations

Let's follow the miners in their daily work. They arrive in early morning at the shaft's opening and get into an elevator which lowers them down hundreds, sometimes thousands, of feet underground. The cage stops at the bottom of the mine shaft, and the minors spill out to their assigned places for the daily toil.

Some of them dig with picks, some drill holes, some drive coal trains, but all are covered with, and breath, great amounts of black coal dust. Most miners wear tiny lamps on their caps, since it is dark in there and not many lamps are allowed. Today, large machines do most of the digging and loading, but manual work in different areas of the mine operation is still a major part of the miners' daily effort.

Looking around you'll see a low ceiling, usually held up by pillars of wood and coal. It is noisy and dusty in there. From time to time, the noise accelerates and an approaching light signals the coal train, pulling many cars loaded with coal. It soon rushes back with empty cars, taking them back to be refilled. Explosions thunder at times, when new veins are to be exploited.

There are small rooms and larger chambers everywhere you go. They were created by digging out the coal and taking it up to the surface. You can only imagine the amount of earth and rock above the ceilings of these rooms; hundreds of feet in thickness. And you also start imagining what would happen, if the roof in one of these rooms caves in. The rooms are usually small enough to not allow caving of the roofs, but you never know. Stuff happens…

NOTE: In many cases the "room-and-pillar" mining methods are used, where "pillars" of coal are created by digging the coal around the columns or pillars that serve as supports for the rooms' ceilings. This method accounts for a significant portion of the total mineral production in the United States. Well in excess of $6 billion worth of mineral commodities are produced each year by this method. A substantial portion ($3.55 billion) of coal production still comes from room-and-pillar mining.

Coal mines experience large-scale, catastrophic pillar collapses, if and when the strength of a pillar in a room-and-pillar mine is exceeded. When one pillar collapses, the load that it supported will be transferred to neighboring pillars. The additional load on these pillars may lead to increased stress of their structures and the ceiling above them.

This mechanism of pillar overloading, load transfer, and continuing pillar failures can lead to the rapid collapse of very large areas of a mine. In some cases, only a few pillars might fail; however, in extreme cases, hundreds, even thousands, of pillars can fail.

This kind of failure has many names, such as: progressive pillar failure, massive pillar collapse, domino-type failure, or pillar run. A special term, "cascading pillar failure" or CPF has been coined to describe and study these rapid pillar collapses. There are over 21 instances of large-scale pillar collapses in room-and-pillar mines, mainly in the United States, in the recent past.

There are many other dangers of underground mining, which we will review in the next chapters.

COAL MINES

Large scale-industrial process operations are expensive, and most of them cause significant environmental damage which must be taken into consideration and calculated in terms of economic and health issues. Coal mining is no exception.

When all costs are considered, the process of locating coal, obtaining permits, designing a mine structure (facilities, equipment, process, and labor), hiring and training engineers and technicians, and a mine's daily operation and maintenance is overwhelming and expensive. Also, number of steps in the overall mining process cause significant air, soil or water table damage.

Let's take a close look at the entire cradle to grave, mining process and estimate the cost, and the environmental and other damages at each step of the process.

The cradle-to-grave coal mining, cleaning, transport and burning process consists of number of consecutive steps, which vary in type and magnitude from state to state and from country to country.

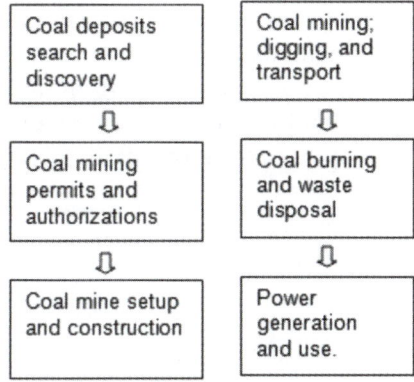

Figure 2-16. Cradle-to-grave coal power generation

In more detail, the mine development process consists of:

Mine planning
- Testing and exploring coal reserves in the proposed mine location

- Estimating the cost of construction, operation and related issues
- Obtaining the necessary federal, state and local permits

Mine design
- Mine area design
- Equipment design
- Process design

Mine construction
- Mine construction
- Surface facilities
- Infrastructure

Daily operations
- Coal digging and surface transport
- Coal preparation and waste treatment
- Coal and waste transport

Mine decommissioning and land reclamation
- Mine shut down and evacuation
- Mine reconstruction
- Surface land reclamation

Now we'll look at the business end of coal mining's life cycle.

Surface Mine Development

The development of a coal mine includes the design and construction of the facilities, which might include access roads, utility line connections and, of course, the mine itself. A railroad spur may need to be designed and built as well, depending on the amount of coal produced and where it is to be used. Coal types with excessive impurities require a preparation plant. In some cases (usually at large mines) the coal preparation is done on-site, but in most cases (smaller mines) the coal is loaded on train cars and shipped to a central plant, where it is processed prior to shipping to the power plant or large industrial customer.

Preliminary Mine Design Considerations

Coal mine sites vary in type and size, but typically involve large land areas, especially when surface mining methods are used. Coal seams vary in size, depth and quality, and mining methods are chosen on the basis of physical feasibility, economic viability and safety. The size of the mining operation will depend on the site characteristics, the coal reserve, and the mining method.

For coal mined by surface methods, the mine plant

should be located off the outcrop (as in a visible exposure of coal deposits on a hill), if possible.

The mine plant itself consists of coal handling and storage facilities, offices, shops and laboratories, equipment storage buildings, and waste disposal areas.

Access to coal deposits at a surface operation involves the use of large equipment such as bucket-wheel excavators, draglines, and shovels to remove overburden from the coal so extraction can begin. As mining progresses, development consists mainly of extending paved roads and power lines, and constructing new roads for access to the coal deposit.

The mined coal typically goes on a conveyor belt and on small cars to a preparation plant that is usually located close to the mining site. At the plant, the coal gets cleaned and otherwise processed to remove dirt, rocks, ashes, sulfur, and other unwanted materials. After that the coal is sorted by quality and size, according to the customer's needs. This increases the heating value of the coal.

Once the coal is processed, it is shipped typically by rail, but also by truck or barge or even a coal-slurry pipeline, to the coal burning power plant. Transportation methods depend on the distance to be traveled, as well as the access to existing transportation systems.

Coal is delivered to coal-fired power plants and burned to boil water. The steam produced is injected in steam turbines that turn generators to produce electricity. The electricity is sent into the transmission system that consists of electric transmission lines, towers, substations and other components. Coal accounts for over 50% of the electricity produced in the US.

The process, however, starts with finding the coal seam, or vein.

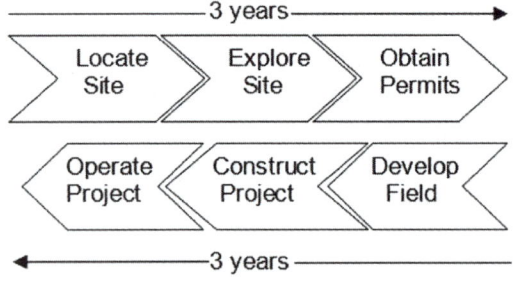

Figure 2-17. Project timeline

Coal Reserves Locating, Tests and Estimates

Before a coal mine can be planned and built, a number of tests and surveys must be conducted to estimate the type and quantity of coal in a particular location. Then engineering and financial estimates must be made to ensure the project's technical and economical

feasibility. The environmental aspects of the entire cradle-to-grave process are plugged in as well, to complete the picture.

These activities include historical research, mapping, drilling (to obtain geological samples), and geophysical exploration. The latter include a number of field and lab tests, such as aerial photography, airborne geophysical surveys (magnetic, radiometric, and electromagnetic); on-the-ground geophysical surveys (drill-hole logging; electrical, magnetic, electromagnetic, radiometric, gravimetric, and refraction-seismic surveys; induced polarization surveys using exposed electrodes). Field surveys for identifying cultural resources, paleontological resources, and ecological resources (habitats, species, etc.) in the project area should also be conducted during this phase.

Reclamation of exploratory areas that will not be part of the project area would occur during this phase as well.

A number of engineering disciplines and scientific methods are applied when evaluating all activities related to mine design and to estimating its technological and economic potential. As major parts of the process, the cradle-to-grave cost and environmental impact are considered during every step.

Finally, the obtained data on the different aspects of the potential mine are provided to the mine engineers, managers and investors as needed to make decisions on the plant design and financing. Some of the information needed for such decisions is as follows.

A. Geology

Complete geological information on the soil, overburden and coal deposits, obtained from historical data and from the preliminary exploration steps is needed. This includes the overall geological structure and the relevant physical properties of the proposed mine, thickness and variability of the different layers, and the quality and quantity of the coal seams—all vital information.

B. Geometry and Geography

Planning calls for a complete picture of the location, its climate and earthquake zoning, as well as the size shape, continuity, attitude, and drainage patterns of the different layers.

C. Hydrology

A complete picture of the permeability and porosity of the overburden and coal layers, as well as location of the aquifers is needed.

D. Toxicology

Planning demands a complete picture of the present hazardous, toxic, reactive, and radioactive species on the surface and in the ground. Additionally, best and worst case scenarios must be developed for dealing with industrial accidents and hazmat situations during operation, as well as during the mine's decommissioning and land reclamation stages.

MINE PLANNING

The process of strip mining is quite simple. It basically consists of a) carefully clearing the topsoil (mountaintop removal in some cases) and stockpiling it for reclamation, b) removing the overburden and stockpiling it for the same reasons, and c) mining of the coal seam.

The coal is removed from the ground layers by a number of methods, depending on type of formation etc. It is then loaded on dump trucks or a conveyor belt for transport to the preparation plant. There it is processed as required by the customer, and loaded on railroad cars for transport to the coal burning power plant.

As the mining of the surface seam moves forward, the mined area is simultaneously reclaimed by replacing and recontouring the overburden and replacing the topsoil.

In open-pit mines, mining begins by drilling and blasting waste rock and clearing the overburden and debris to expose the coal seam. The coal is removed one layer (bench) at a time, forming terraces. The mined bench continues to get wider as mining continues, and goes deeper with each bench.

In order to determine the technical and economic feasibility of the mine, a number of pieces of information are needed:

A. Market analysis

Data on potential customers, contract agreements, size and location of the markets, etc. needed to figure out the size and other peculiarities of the potential markets.

B. Transportation

Size and type of loads, property access, elevation of the mine and the customer sites, road system, etc.

C. Utilities

Availability and distance to electric power and substations, location, right-of-way and the related costs for new transmission lines.

D. Water

Type, quantity, and quality of potable and process water, and source location, type, and the cost of aqueducts, etc.

E. Labor

Local availability, type and quality, rates and trends, and the local labor history.

Surface Mine Planning and Design

The planning and design stages of a large size surface or pit mine in the U.S. is a complex and specialized undertaking, with many variables. The information collected in the evaluation stage, as well as all available project-related information, is reviewed as a first step, to develop the most appropriate extraction plan for the particular mine.

Figure 2-18. Surface mine

Various mining methods and equipment set combinations and permutations are considered by the team of mining engineers, geologists, environmentalists, and economists. After the technology, process and equipment sets are determined, economic and market analyses are performed of the best case scenario, to determine project viability from a financial point of view.

The preliminary mine plan usually goes through a number of iterations, which finally result in a technically feasible and economical operating plan, subject to the specific contractual, legal, environmental, and other constraints of the specific property and the related equipment and operating procedures.

This is a long and complex process which, together with obtaining the necessary permits, etc., could take 10-15 years, or more, in addition to millions of dollars of related expenses.

Here are some of the long and complex steps in this process:

A. Environmental impact package
- Initial site evaluation
- Scope of work program
- Environmental impact report
- Environmental monitoring program
- Reclamation bonds

B. Coal mining package
- Lease or buyout rights acquisition
- Mapping the area
- Site drilling and sample analysis
- Coal type and quantity evaluation
- Drilling coal samples and analysis
- Development drilling and sample analysis

C. Land rights
- Land requirements, surface land and minerals ownership, oil and gas wells location and ownership, etc.

D. Taxes and royalties
- Federal, state and local taxation, royalties payments, zoning, and operating and reclamation requirements

E. Process design and equipment set planning
- Concept mine design
- Mining process design
- Equipment selection and ordering
- Economic evaluation
- Overall mining plan development

F. NEPA procedures
- Lead EIS agency communications
- EIS draft and reviews
- EIS hearing and federal review
- CEQ filing and approvals

G. Permits
- Surface drilling rights acquisition
- Federal permits
- USFS land use
- State water use and mining
- State industrial siting
- Local permits

H. Mining preparation
- Stripping equipment setup
- Loaders and conveyors setup
- Support equipment setup
- Labor hiring and training
- Production ramp-up procedures
- Full production specs and documentation

A quick look at these steps reveals that:

1.   The environmental studies of the proposed site, combined with post-test monitoring, are a major part of the process and could take over 10 years.

2.   The initial process design and equipment ordering are strictly engineering disciplines, the completion of which could take 2-3 years.

3.   The design and construction of the site facilities and support structures are specialized tasks that would also take 2-3 years.

4.   Completing the National Environmental Policy Act (NEPA) requirements and related procedures would take 5-6 years.

5.   The necessary federal, state, local, tribal and other permits and negotiations would take the project well over the 10-year mark, and might even extend it *ad infinitum*.

6.   If all goes well with the above tasks and sub-projects, and if their design and implementation are well coordinated and properly executed, initial setup and limited coal production could be started around year 10 to 12. Most of the tasks and sub-projects mentioned above can be conducted in parallel, saving time.

NOTE: There are a number of complex details that go into the mine process design and equipment selection that are particular for individual sites, and some might be considered exceptional. Some of these are:

a.   *Equipment limitations*
       In many cases the size and type of equipment limits the full exploration of coal seams. Land instability might also limit the activities in some areas. Some of these limitations cannot be foreseen, and so they must be dealt with by planning on eventual equipment or strategy changes in order to obtain the maximum amount of coal from the area.

b.   *Mining losses*
       As in any process, mining also suffers losses during full operation. The most common loss-

es are those in the top, bottom, and rib coal layers. These are losses in which the loaders, for any number of reasons, cannot grab all the coal from the top, bottom and the sides of the coal seam. There are also fly rock losses from blasting, and transportation losses from dump trucks and conveyor belts. These are so-called barrier losses, and can amount to over 5% of a mine's gross, which is significant and which must be taken into consideration in the preliminary designs.

7. When a green light is given, a year or more will be needed for final setup, operators' training, and ramping up of the production cycle. Another year will be needed to establish the final, full production cycle and all its steps, specs, procedures, training, and the related documentation. Then the mine is in full production until there is no longer enough coal to dig out at full speed.

8. When the coal deposits in the mine seams diminish, mine production volume will be reduced. This requires special, albeit temporary measures, which eventually lead to reduced profits. Eventually the mine is shut down, and special procedures must be followed to accomplish that process successfully and safely.

9. After shutdown of mining operations, the mine area must be reconstructed as closely as possible to its original state. This is seldom possible, so there a number of mines that have been simply abandoned, while others are partially reconstructed.

NOTE: As part of the permitting process, new mine constructions in the US are required to purchase Reclamation Bonds, as required by the Bureau of Land Management (BLM) and various state environmental agencies. These are long-term surety obligations, which are like insurance that the site will be returned to its original condition upon termination of mining operations. Once issued, the bonds cannot be canceled. Adequate performance can be highly subjective, and bond losses can be large.

Surface Mine Operation

Surface mining (strip mining) is used where large coal deposits are near the surface. This coal can be reached and extracted easily by digging deep trenches and loading it directly on large trucks. This method has

its advantages; it is much safer and efficient than underground mining. However, it has its disadvantages; it damages the Earth's surface and changes the environment and life in it for miles around.

Surface mining is simply working on the surface of a mountain or a hill, where huge machines, called power shovels, scoop large amounts of soil just above the coal seam. The seam (also called overburden) is then dug out by the same machines in similarly large quantities.

This technique has vast economic advantages since manual labor is replaced by machines. Some of these power shovels have buckets that hold over 200 cubic yards, or more than 300 tons with each scoop, which is enough to fill 15-20 regular dump trucks.

This level of mechanization and automation of strip-mined coal is responsible for the low price of coal, which is estimated at almost two times lower cost than coal mined underground. The gap is increasing due to increasing labor costs and new mine safety regulations for underground mines.

There are several types of surface mining:

1) Area mining (the preferred technique in most areas)
2) Open pit mining (used on very thick coal seams)
3) Contour mining (used in mostly hilly terrain)
4) Auger mining (usually accompanies contour mining)

1. *Area mining* is a surface mining method where the overburden is removed in mile-long, 100-foot-wide strips. Holes are drilled in the exposed coal seam, filled with explosives and blasted. The coal is scooped and loaded onto dump trucks or conveyors for transport to the coal preparation (or wash) plant.

Once this strip is empty of coal, the process is repeated with a new strip being created next to it. At the same time, but with some delay, a parallel trench is dug close to the first trench and the overburden from it (the new trench) is dumped in the old trench as the machines move forward simultaneously.

The coal from the new trench is also removed, and a third parallel trench is dug. This process is repeated until all the coal of the surface is removed.

If the vein is deep enough, the process might be taken to a deeper level. The depth at which coal can be profitably reached has been increasing as the equipment has become larger. The maximum overburden that could be handled at first was about 70 feet, but it increased to 125 feet with time, and now it is close to 200 feet.

The equipment used in strip mining depends on

local geological conditions. For example, to remove overburden that is loose or unconsolidated, a bucket wheel excavator might be used as the most efficient and productive piece of equipment.

Some area mines may be productive for more than 50 years.

The problem of the area mining method is that flat farmland is replaced by a series of ridges and gullies, which brings the usefulness of the land and its value for crops, recreation, or anything else, to practically zero. Elaborate reclamation processes can be used to restore the land to its original shape and quality, but this is a very expensive undertaking.

Area mining is widespread in the Midwest, and the huge coal reserves in Montana, Wyoming, the Dakotas, and the Southwest. About 1/3 of the estimated 440 billion tons of U.S. coal reserves lies in beds that are less than 100 feet below the surface, thus suitable for strip mining.

2.   *Open pit mining* is similar to area mining except that larger and often deeper trenches of up to 1000 feet wide, are usually dug out. This method is used on thick beds of coal, and similarly when the coal is removed from the first trench, it is filled with overburden from the second trench. The land is left in a similarly useless shape and quality for any practical purpose.

3.   *Contour mining* is used in mountainous coal deposits, and consists of removing overburden from the seam in a pattern following the contours along a ridge or around a hillside. It is most commonly used in areas with rolling to steep terrain. It is quite different from area strip mining and is much more destructive.

The process begins with the power shovel cutting at the area where the coal seam reaches the surface. The resulting overburden is pushed down the mountainside and the coal is removed in long strips, in a way very similar to paring an apple.

The haul-back or lateral movement method is widely used and consists of an initial cut with the overburden (or spoil) deposited down slope or at some other site. Spoil from the second cut usually refills the first. A ridge of undisturbed natural material 15 to 20 ft (5-6 m) wide is often intentionally left at the outer edge of the mined area. This barrier adds stability to the reclaimed slope by preventing spoil from slumping or sliding downhill.

The shovel moves toward the center of the mountain, as each cut removes more overburden. A wall over 100 feet high is created and is too thick to remove, so an auger is used at that time to drill out more coal.

The overburden is stacked on the edge or thrown down the slope, and this is what causes the major damage to the surrounding area. The loose soil in an area with no trees or grass to anchor it is easily eroded and washed down the hill and into streams below. Heavily travelled access roads, with heavy dump trucks and other equipment roaring up and down day and night, add even more to the erosion and overall area damage.

But erosion is not the only problem. Loose boulders and landslides are responsible for even more permanent damage. Entire towns in Wales and Virginia have been buried by such landslides.

The remaining high walls circle the mountains, making them useless and inaccessible. There are over a million such disturbed acres in the U.S., with an additional 30,000 acres added every year. Most of this land remains unreclaimed.

Adding insult to injury, rainwater floods the abandoned coal seams and reacts with the sulfur-containing pyrites and other minerals in them. Leachate, a corrosive and destructive pollutant such as sulfuric acid is formed in many areas and runs down the hills killing all vegetation. It then runs into the streams where it kills aquatic life with increased acidity.

Mine drainage also contributes to increased amounts of sediments, sulfates, iron, and hardness in the streams and lakes, changing their environment and affecting the life forms in them.

Surveys in some post-contour stripping areas in the U.S. show that about 5% percent of the hillsides had a pH less than 3 (highly acidic), and 80% with pH of 3-5—which is also unacceptable. Over 6000 miles of Appalachian streams are affected by acid mine drainage, and over 11,000 miles of streams are affected by other mine pollutants as well.

The limitations on contour strip mining are economic and technical. When the operation reaches a predetermined stripping ratio (tons of overburden/tons of coal), it becomes unprofitable. Also, depending on the equipment used, it may not be technically feasible to reach a certain height of high wall. Producing more coal with the auger method is possible today.

4.   *Auger mining* is a method for coal extraction by boring into a coal seam at the base of strata exposed by excavation. Augering is usually associated with contour strip-mining, recovering coal for a limited depth (up to 1,000 feet) beyond which stripping becomes uneconomical because the seam of coal lies so far beneath the sur-

face. It is also limited to horizontal or slightly pitched seams that have been exposed by geologic erosion.

In this process, auger drills mounted with cutter heads cut and fracture through both overburden and coal, operating very similar to a drill machine. The augering differs from other types of coal cutting machines such as continuous miners in that it tends to exploit the lower tensile strength of coal rather than trying to over compensate for its high compressive strength.

The power of the auger as well as the diameter of the cutterhead are the two features that govern an auger drill's performance. The greater the power of the machine, the greater the depth of the coal seam into which it is able to bore, producing a higher rate of coal.

Auger drills used in auger mining can range from 60 to 200 feet (18 to 61 m) in length, and two to seven feet (0.6 to 2.1 m) in diameter. The cutter head on the auger bores a number of openings into the seam, similar to how a wood drill produces wood shavings. The coal is then extracted and transported up to the surface.

As the depth of the bored hole is extended, coal production is most likely to decrease. The auger drill will continue to penetrate into a high wall until the maximum torque of an auger is reached, usually at a depth of 492 feet (150 m). Once the coal arrives at the surface, it is lifted up to a dump truck for hauling by a conveyor or front end loader.

Recent auger drill technology has led to the introduction of a new type of auger drilling machine called the thin-seam miner (TSM). It is actually a type of continuous miner that can cut an entry up to 8 feet (2.4 m) wide and up to 5 feet (1.5 m) high into a coal seam situated under a high wall in surface mines.

One of the drawbacks of this method is that once the cutter head enters the coal seam, the operator is unable to view the cutting action directly and must rely more on a sense of feel for the machine, as needed to control it, and its performance, as well as to detect potential problems.

5. *Mountaintop removal mining* is a surface mining method that relies on the removal of entire mountaintops, in order to expose large coal seams. Mountaintop removal is a combination of area and contour strip mining methods. In areas with rolling or steep terrain with a coal seam occurring near the top of a ridge or hill, the entire top is removed in a series of parallel cuts, and the overburden is deposited in nearby valleys and hollows.

This method usually leaves ridges and hill tops as flattened plateaus. The process is highly controversial since it creates drastic changes in local topography. It is accompanied by the creation of head-of-hollow-fills, or filling in valleys with mining debris; it covers streams and disrupts ecosystems.

In preparation for filling the overburden disposal area, vegetation and soil are removed and a rock drain is constructed down the middle of the area to be filled, thus replacing natural drainage. Upon completion of the fill the underdrain forms a continuous water runoff system from the upper end of the valley to the lower end of the fill. Typical head-of-hollow fills are graded and terraced to create permanently stable slopes.

In all cases, the change of many acres of the local area is dramatic and permanent.

Pre-burning Treatment

The mined coal is loaded on cars and transported to an elevator. The cars are then hoisted to the surface, where the coal is dumped. Once on the surface, the coal is piled in great piles, awaiting its turn in the preparation process. The preparation work is done in large buildings, called breakers, which reach heights of 150 feet or more. Here the coal is taken to the top of the breaker by a conveyor belt system and undergoes several transformation on its way down.

The coal is crushed between rollers, and is then sifted over sorting screens. The smaller pieces fall through and are sold as a lower quality coal. There are screens that sort different shapes and sizes of coal, as required by the customers.

One efficient way of sorting coal is by putting it and the accompanying slate into moving water. The slate is heavier than the coal, and sinks in the water, while the coal floats on the surface and can easily be separated and carried away.

The different sizes and types of coal have different names. For example, an "egg" must be between 2 inches, and 2-5/8 inches in diameter; a "nut" is usually between 3/4 and 1-1/8 inches; and a "pea" is between one 1/2 and 3/4 of an inch.

From here coal is loaded on large train cars that comprise a long train, called a "unit." A unit can have 100 or more cars and is usually sent on a non-stop trip to the power plant. We will take a close look at what happens at the power plant later on in this text.

Underground Mine Development

Until recently mining was a fully manual job, where miners cut into the walls and ceilings of the rooms with special pickaxes. They reached as far as the pickaxe would reach, and then a hole was bored into the top of the coal, and a cartridge of dynamite was exploded to release a ton or two of coal. The coal was then shoveled into a car and pushed out of the room to join the long string of cars going to the surface. The digging and exploding work continued all day long.

Today, miners cut and dig the coal with machines that are as sophisticated and safe as the state of the art and economics allow. The machines grind the coal, and leave a deep cut all along the side of the room. Then another group of miners bore holes in the walls for the blasting. The holes are made with powerful, compressed air-driven drills, and dynamite charges are placed in the holes. After the explosions are set off, and the dust has settled, the coal is loaded manually or with machines into the cars. Then it is taken to the surface and made ready for market.

Modern, fully automated operations are the most efficient and safest in deep mining. This type of mining is done along the seam with machines, and pillars and timbers are left standing to support the mine roof.

When the seam mining is complete, for reasons of geology formations or economics, a supplementary version of the room and pillar mining (second mining) takes over. It consists of removal of the coal in the support pillars in the dugout, thus recovering the maximum amount of coal possible from the seam.

Modern methods for coal pillar sections removal use remote-controlled equipment, which includes large hydraulic machines that are used to support the roof during the pillar removal process. The mobile roof supports look like a large dining-room table with hydraulic jacks for legs. After the coal pillars are removed, the legs of the table are shortened and it is withdrawn to a safe area.

This efficient and safe method is used to prevent cave-ins until the miners and their equipment have left a work area, because the unsupported roof of the room usually collapses when the roof supports are removed.

If the coal is to be mined by underground methods, the mine plant is constructed near the main portal or entrance.

Access to coal deposits at an underground operation is provided by drifts, slopes, or shafts. The coal bed is developed for further operations by driving entries. Although terminology varies, the following system of entries is universal in the industry.

Main entries are extensions of access openings and often run several miles in one direction. Three or more parallel entries, 12 to 22 feet wide and 40 to 100 feet between centers, are driven in a given direction and connected at intervals by crosscuts to provide proper air circulation. These are the major routes of underground transport and access, and serve for the life of the mine.

Panel entries are driven from the main entries, resulting in a subdivision of the coal bed into blocks or panels having dimensions that may be as much as 1 by 1/2 mile. Panel entries serve as routes from the main entries to the working places, and for air circulation. Although coal is removed during the driving of the main and panel entries, the production cycle begins upon completion of the panel entries.

Underground Mine Planning and Design

The main activities during planning and design of mine construction and during operation phases of either surface or underground mining are focused on the efficient and safe function of the proposed mine as well as any auxiliary facility (e.g., shaft construction) and coal transport system (e.g., access roads, rail lines, pipelines, conveyor systems).

As with the surface mine, we need to go through a number of steps, some of which are:

1. Coal mine
   - Planning and design
   - Permitting
   - Land preparation
   - Facilities construction
   - Equipment purchase, delivery and installation

2. Daily operations
   — Coal digging
   — Onsite transport
   — Coal preparation (on-site)

3. Coal transport
   - Loading
   - Unit train transport
   - Unloading

4. Coal preparation (off-site)
   - Sorting
   - Washing
   - Treating

5. Coal burning power plants
   - Unloading
   - Pulverizing
   - Steam generation
   - Power generation
   - Gasses, ash and cooling water disposal

6. End of life decommissioning and waste disposal
- Mine or plant shut down and disabling
- Equipment disassembly and demolition
- Facilities demolition
- Waste disposal
- Land decontamination and reconstruction

Here, as in the surface mine, we need to go through the different steps of site location, testing, and exploration. Then many months and thousands of dollars will be spent obtaining the necessary federal, state and local permits and approvals. Design of the actual mine, the mining equipment, and the support infrastructure (buildings, roads, railroad, etc.) follow. When all these tasks are completed, the miners go to work.

The Mining Process

The process of underground mining includes cutting into the coal deposit and removing it from the coal face via room-and-pillar methods using a continuous mining machine, or through longwall methods using a longwall cutting machine. In either method, once the coal is removed, the supports or pillars can be removed and the roof of the mine is allowed to collapse. The mined area is then abandoned and later on reconstructed, if possible.

Underground mine planning and design is a unique engineering discipline. It involves the development of infrastructure and working conditions that are very sophisticated, highly specialized, and quite different from other industrial processes.

This type of mine design consists of the three basic engineering phases, conceptual, preliminary, and final design. While the second and third steps are common for many industrial processes, the development of the conceptual design is different for mining and is the key to the success of the entire operation. An error in interpreting the results from preliminary tests, for example, could lead the entire process in the wrong direction, cause technical and financial difficulties, and even disaster.

The goal of underground mine planning and design is integrated with mine systems design, with the final result being efficient and safe extraction of coal. The coal is then prepared to desired market requirements, at a minimum cost, while meeting social, legal and regulatory constraints.

A number of engineering disciplines are needed for successful mine planning and design process. Mining is a complex undertaking, so proper planning leads to the correct selection and implementation of all subsystems. Proper design, by the same token, ensures the implementation of traditional engineering subsystems.

An underground mining operation is a system which, due to the diversity of the technological processes, facilities, personal skills, and large capital investment, must consider and coordinate the behavior of, and interactions between the different subsystems.

Advances in several fields used in mining operations have the potential for making a significant impact on mining. These, therefore, must be taken into account during the planning and design process as well.

The First Steps

The initial process of evaluation and exploration of the particular area considered for underground mining is similar to that used for surface mining, although the objectives and the results are different.

After this step, the planning and design process is also similar to that of surface mining. Here are some of the long and complex steps in this process:

A. Environmental impact package
- Initial site evaluation
- Scope of work program
- Environmental impact report
- Environmental monitoring program
- Reclamation bonds

B. Coal mining package
- Lease or buyout rights acquisition
- Mapping the area
- Site drilling and sample analysis
- Coal type and quantity evaluation
- Drilling coal samples and analysis
- Development drilling and sample analysis

C. Land rights
- Land development and operational requirements
- Surface land and minerals ownership
- Oil, gas, and water wells location and ownership

D. Taxes and royalties
- Federal, state and local taxation
- Zoning, operating, and reclamation requirements
- Royalties, payments

E. Process design and equipment set planning
- Concept mine design
- Mining process design
- Equipment selection and ordering
- Economic evaluation
- Overall mining plan development

F. NEPA procedures
- Lead EIS agency communications
- EIS draft and reviews
- EIS hearing and federal review
- CEQ filing and approvals

G. Permits
- Surface drilling rights acquisition
- Federal permits
- USFS land use
- State water use and mining
- State industrial siting
- Local permits

H. Mining preparation
- Stripping equipment setup
- Loaders and conveyors setup
- Support equipment setup
- Labor hiring and training
- Production ramp-up procedures
- Full production specs and documentation

Baseline Assessment

This is an essential process, and encompasses the evaluation of all available data, prior to starting the actual planning efforts. This is a comprehensive review of all available information gathered through historical materials and by actual site tests. This includes the review of all geographic, geologic, environmental, technical, economic, and other data available. Supposedly, the data contain enough historical and present-day information for proper planning and mine design.

Preliminary Planning

Most plans start with a feasibility study—an overview of the project, making reasonable assumptions and estimates of the physical and other key operating factors of the mine. The intent is to figure out as quickly as possible if the project justifies further effort.

A life-of-mine plan must be developed to determine the reserve's type and size, and other mining parameters, including the costs of site reclamation. Reclamation costs are often great, so those could put the project's feasibly in question.

Regulatory and Legal Factors

The planning process must also review the state of current regulatory affairs. These play a significant role in the overall mining operation, and these must be faced in the very beginning and attacked in a proactive manner, rather than addressing them after the fact.

Each sub-system and step of the process is subject to compliance, and often needs to be submitted to the various agencies for inspection and approval. At a minimum, these may include mine layout, strata and roof control plan, shaft ventilation plan, fan stoppage plan, medical and emergency evacuation plan, fire control evacuation plan, and escape route plan.

It is of utmost importance to ensure that the latest regulations, policies, and proposed rulemaking have been incorporated.

Geologic/Geotechnical Factors

The most important part of the data collection is the information on the coal deposits. Coal variability can be mathematically defined, if enough accurate information is available.

Exploration permits are needed to start the data collection, and must be first on the plan schedule.

Understanding the regional geology and features of the deposit are of utmost importance. Potentially adverse geologic conditions, such as faults, wants, rolls, low cover, or water inflow must be located and well defined. Seam or horizon conditions are important also.

A thorough review of the land lease is needed to determine the requirements and compliance provisions, which may be excessive for a profitable and safe mine operation.

Reserves Data

A complete and accurate coal reserves inventory is needed. Since composing the geological model is a free interpretation of the available data, it depends heavily on the experience of the geologists working on it. Exploration efforts do not rely on actual core recovery, but on indirect conclusions.

Changes in the data interpretation are usually made as new data come in, and might change the entire geologic model. Geophysical logging, core photography, and petrographic identification are used with the most success. There are different approaches for geologic modeling: accepting the geology and developing the plan around it, or considering the geologic model incomplete and incorporating flexibility in the planning for potential changes.

The evaluation and calculation of the coal reserve is one of the most crucial factors to the long-term success of a mine. The reserve type, magnitude, grade, depth, inclination, geometry, etc. are key to proper mine design.

There are a number of methods applied in proper estimation of the variables and the overall mine design characteristics. Mathematical methods are of utmost importance. This involves taking data, such as drilled samples, and extrapolating the data into blocks or grids to make the appropriate calculations. Mapping, determining reserve classification, leasehold boundaries, etc. are required for the final calculations. The data are then processed via different mathematical techniques, such as polygonal, inverse distance weighing, and others.

Geographic and Economic Factors

Geographic factors include the location, transportation infrastructure, type, size, and skill level of the local work force, private and public facilities available locally, local climate, local power availability, etc.

Economic factors include the local political and tax environment, government stability (if a foreign country), socio-economic conditions, and availability of support networks. Economics usually favor starting with the "lowest hanging fruit" approach, which in this case means extraction of the best-grade material, or starting with the lowest mining cost areas. While this approach might maximize the return on investment in the short term and shorten the payback period, it might also create a compromise in the mine's design and operation.

Environmental Factors

Environmental data gathering is very important from feasibility and economic points of view. Because of that, sometimes as much as 5 years' data are necessary, especially if an environmental impact statement is required. The minimum necessary baseline environmental data required for planning include a) topsoil, subsoil, and overburden analysis, b) hydrologic studies, c) vegetation and land use surveys, d) air quality analyses, e) wildlife surveys, and f) archeological survey.

Tasks, such as core holes sealing and site reclamation, and their impacts on the local environment, must be considered and included in the planning stages. Some of the impacts are aesthetics, noise, air quality, vibration, water discharge and runoff, subsidence, and process wastes. Surface and groundwater quality during operation and through the remedial and treatment stages must be developed to meet supply and discharge standards.

Planning is basically responsible for environmental protection, from the initial exploration to final reclamation. It is to alleviate or mitigate potential impacts of mining to a) minimize the cost of environmental protection by proper steps in the overall design, thus eliminating remedial measures, and b) minimize negative publicity or poor public relations which may have severe economic consequences.

Technical Factors

From an engineering point of view, the technical aspects of mining operation planning and design are the most extensive and detailed. Data from regulatory, geologic, and environmental analysis must be evaluated and translated into technical specifications. This information is used to determine which process to use, and then to outline and develop each step.

The layout of the mine is determined by the size and shape of the coal deposits, and these features are used to calculate the mine reserves and determine the best way to extract them. Access to the reserves can be by vertical shafts, inclined slopes and drifts, or horizontal entries, and the production levels will determine the number and size of the access openings made.

The technical parameters will form the conceptual basis for the plan, from which the detailed plan will be drawn. The larger and more extensive the area, the more complicated the plan.

Each item and step of mine construction and the production process are defined by the available key assumptions, the physical factors, the equipment, mine facilities and infrastructure, and transportation. These are detailed as much as possible in the beginning, and then modified as each item is executed, according to the new data and the "best-fit" technical models.

Equipment

The type and size of coal deposits, including their hardness, will determine the types of equipment to use. The seam and working height, mining dilution limits, production rates, and property extent, ventilation, size constraints, regulations, and floor pressures may impact the choice of equipment. For example, a large flat-lying coal seam may allow the use of longwall mining equipment. Floor condition plays a big part in the equipment type. Equipment productivity is also a factor that might prove essential in the final decision.

Maintenance, equipment overhaul and replacement schedules must be developed accordingly, to ensure continuous production. Transportation of the product may be by rail, truck or a combination.

Transportation

Movement of materials, personnel, and equipment into and out of a mine is a critical part of mine operation. Workers must reach their designated work area in an expeditious manner. Supplies must get to their points of use before need becomes critical. The equipment itself must be transported through the mine to the working area. Then the coal must be transported from the working face to the processing facility.

A smooth flow of people and materials is critical to the efficient operation of a mine, so the various transport vehicles and pathways must be properly selected for efficient operation.

Underground Mining Operation

Upon obtaining the necessary permits, and a series of inspections and modifications, the mine is ready for exploitation. There are basically several methods of underground mining:

1. *Room and pillar mining* consists of coal deposits that are mined by cutting a network of rooms into the coal seam. Pillars of coal are left behind to hold up the roof. The pillars can make up to 30-40% of the total coal in the seam, as needed to provide space for head and floor coal.

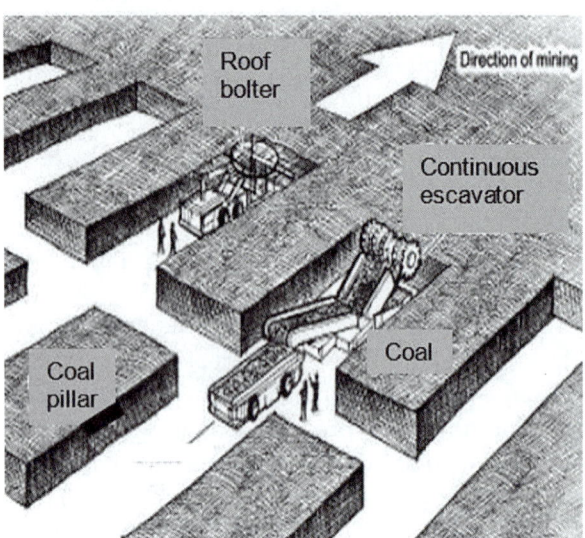

Figure 2-19. Room and pillar mining operation

There is evidence from recent open cast excavations that 18th century operators used a variety of room and pillar techniques to remove 92% of the *in situ* coal. The coal in the pillars can be extracted at a later stage by the retreat mining method, where a large machine with a self-supporting roof digs out the coal in the pillars and lets the roof collapse, as it pulls out of the area.

2. *Longwall mining* accounts for about 50% of underground production. The longwall method utilizes a large machine, Shearer, with a cutting face of 1,000 feet (300 m) or more. It is a sophisticated machine with a rotating drum that moves mechanically back and forth

across a wide coal seam. The loosened coal falls onto a pan line that takes the coal to the conveyor belt for removal from the work area. Longwall systems have their own hydraulic roof supports which provide safety, and can advance with the machine as mining progresses.

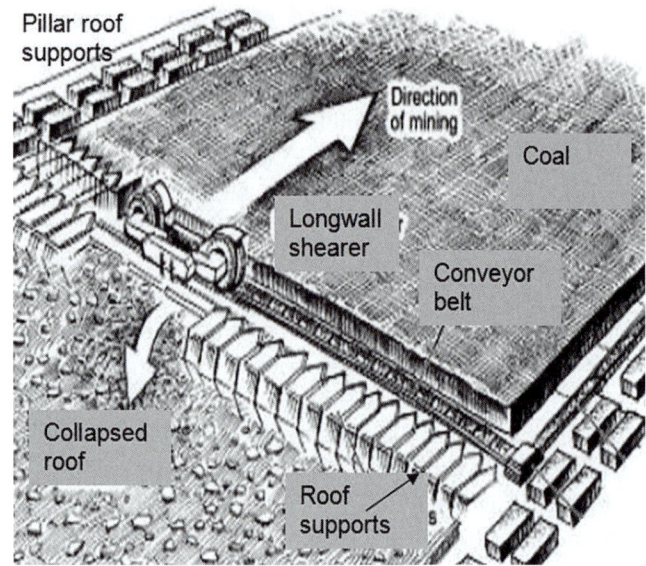

Figure 2-20. Longwall mining operations

As the longwall mining equipment moves forward, overlying rock that is no longer supported by coal is allowed to fall behind the operation in a controlled manner. Sensors detect how much coal remains in the seam, while robotic controls enhance the efficiency of the process. Longwall systems allow a 60-100% coal recovery rate when surrounding geology allows the use of this method. Once the coal is removed from approximately 75% of a section, the roof is allowed to collapse in a safe manner.

3. *Continuous mining* utilizes a continuous-miner machine with a large rotating steel drum equipped with tungsten carbide teeth that scrape coal from the seam. Operating in a "room and pillar" (also known as "board and pillar") system—where the mine is divided into a series of 20- to 30-foot (5-10 m) "rooms" or work areas cut into the coal bed—it can mine as much as five tons of coal a minute, more than a non-mechanized mine of the 1920s would produce in an entire day. Continuous miners account for about 45 percent of underground coal production.

Conveyors transport the removed coal from the seam. Remote-controlled continuous miners are used to work in a variety of difficult seams and conditions, and robotic versions controlled by computers are becoming increasingly common. Continuous mining is truly a misnomer, as room and pillar coal mining is very cyclical. In the US, one can generally cut 20 ft or 6 meters (or a bit more with MSHA permission) (12 meters or roughly 40 ft in South Africa before the continuous miner goes out and the roof is supported by the roof bolter), after which, the face must be serviced, before it can be advanced again.

During servicing, the continuous miner moves to another face. Some continuous miners can bolt and dust the face (two major components of servicing) while cutting coal, while a trained crew may be able to advance ventilation, to truly earn the "continuous" label. However, very few mines are able to achieve it. Most continuous mining machines in use in the US lack the ability to bolt and dust. This may be partly because incorporation of bolting makes the machines wider, and therefore, less maneuverable.

4.   *Blast mining*, or conventional mining, is an older practice that uses explosives such as dynamite to break up the coal seam, after which the coal is gathered and loaded onto shuttle cars or conveyors for removal to a central loading area. This process consists of a series of operations that begins with "cutting" the coal bed so it will break easily when blasted with explosives. This type of mining accounts for less than 5% of total underground production in the US today.

5.   *Shortwall mining* is a method currently accounting for less than 1% of deep coal production. It involves the use of a continuous mining machine with movable roof supports, similar to those used in the longwall method. The continuous miner shears coal panels 150 to 200 feet (40 to 60 m) wide and more than a half-mile (1 km) long, keeping in mind the local geological strata and other factors.

6.   *Retreat mining* is a method in which the pillars, or coal ribs, used to hold up the mine roof are extracted, allowing the mine roof to collapse as the mining works back towards the entrance. This is one of the most dangerous forms of mining, owing to the unpredictability of ceiling behavior, and possibility of collapse, which could crush or trap miners.

In all cases, and no matter what type of mining is used, underground mining is complex, expensive and dangerous work, where experience counts. That often determines the difference between loss and profit—even life and death.

Coal Preparation Plant

Coal straight from the ground, known as run of mine (ROM) coal, often contains unwanted impurities such as rock and dirt and comes in a mixture of different-sized fragments. However, coal users need coal of a consistent quality, so coal preparation—also known as coal beneficiation or coal washing—or other treatment of ROM coal is performed to ensure consistent quality and to enhance its suitability for particular end uses.

Crushing and cleaning of mine-run coal is also referred to as beneficiation or preparation. Often, crushing and sizing is all that is required, but many coal seams, especially those in eastern and mid-western states, contain enough impurities to necessitate further cleaning. Whether the cleaning process is wet or dry, it is commonly referred to as *washing*.

The dry washing method uses high-pressure, pulsating airflow to blow dust from the coal. Wet washing starts with breaking and screening the coal to remove the large, hard pieces of impurities. Larger material is usually treated using "dense medium separation," where the coal is separated from other impurities by floating in a tank containing a liquid of specific gravity, usually a suspension of finely ground magnetite.

As the coal is lighter, it floats and can be separated off, while heavier rock and other impurities sink and are removed as waste. The smaller size fractions are treated in a number of ways, usually based on differences in mass, such as in centrifuges. A centrifuge is a machine which turns a container around very quickly, causing solids and liquids inside it to separate.

Equipment can include any of the following: jigs, screens, landers, heavy-medium cyclones, tricone separators, concentrating tables, froth flotation, cells, filters, and driers.

Additional cleaning depends on the amount, size, and nature of impurity, how it is dispersed in the coal, and how the coal is to be used. The treatment depends on the properties of the coal and its intended use. It may require only simple crushing or it may need to go through a complex treatment process to reduce impurities.

Alternative preparation/washing methods use the different surface properties of coal and waste. In "froth flotation," coal particles are removed in a froth produced by blowing air into a water bath containing chemical reagents. The bubbles attract the coal but not the waste and are skimmed off to recover the coal fines. Recent technological developments have helped increase the recovery of ultra fine coal material.

Coal Transport

After the coal is dug out from the ground and taken up to the surface, it is processed per consumer specifications of size, cleanliness, etc. before being shipped to the customer for burning. Transportation is a major step in the overall coal production process.

The coal transport system will depend on site-specific and project-specific factors and could be a conveyor system running from within the mine site to the coal preparation plant or a rail system. A system of haul roads is also likely to be present. Transporting coal off-site may be accomplished by rail, truck, barge, or some combination thereof. A coal-slurry pipeline also may be used to send coal off-site.

Usually, coal transport includes, loading on railroad cars and moving to a central point for preparation and upgrading (cleaning, sorting, refining), and loading and shipping to a power plant where it is burned for electricity generation.

A brief look at the coal transportation system shows that:

- Coal mines are growing larger and their production increases exponentially. There were 316 mines in the mid-1970s with an annual output of above 500,000 tons. These large mining complexes execute all coal preparation operations onsite. From there the coal moves, usually by train, to the end use site—utility power plant or a large industrial consumer.

- Most of the 4325 coal mines in the U.S., however, produce less than 50,000 tons per year. It is impractical, and economically unfeasible to process the coal at the smaller mines, so it is usually trucked to a central processing facility. On arrival, it is unloaded, cleaned, sorted to customer specs before shipping to the point of use (POU).

- Most of the coal in the U.S. is shipped by "unit train." These are special train compositions, containing 100 or more coal hopper cars. Unit trains shuttle back and forth non-stop between large coal mines and coal-fired power plants, and sometimes on dedicated railroads lines.

- The typical coal train is 100-120 hopper cars long, with each of the cars holding 100-115 tons. This is almost a mile of coal, which can feed a large coal burning power plant operation for about a day, or two maximum. The larger surface mines load two or three unit trains of coal a day.

- There are approximately 80 trains leaving Wyoming mines every day, or about 26,000 trains annually. This is 26,000 miles of coal, or more than the circumference of the earth. If the unit trains from the other coal producing states are added, they can be wrapped around the Earth several times.

Figure 2-21. Unit trains

There is a trend of building "mine mouth" plants, to avoid transportation costs. These power plants are built and operated right at, or very close to the mines, because the coal is cheap at the mine (about $5 per ton). The transportation makes 60-80% of the total cost of coal. Environmental and capital expense considerations, however, make this practice unprofitable in some locations, such as the West Coast.

There are several large complexes in the Four Corners area (where Colorado, New Mexico, Arizona, and Utah join) and in the Dakotas and Montana, which are good examples of mine mouth plants.

Coal can be shipped by barge on the nation's inland waterways, or by ocean freighters, to coal's export customers. A huge transoceanic coal export facility is located at Norfolk, Virginia. Coal is currently shipped also from sea ports of Baltimore, Philadelphia, New York City, New Orleans, and Los Angeles.

Coal can be shipped by another water method, via *slurry pipelines*. In this method, a mixture of powdered coal and water is mixed at the mine and pumped through a long, large-diameter, pipeline to the coal burning power plant. An example of that was the 273-mile-long pipeline from the Peabody mine on the "Black Mesa" in Arizona to the 1500-MW Mohave power plant near Page, Arizona. The Black Mesa slurry pipeline delivered about 8 tons of coal per minute along with 2700 gallons or 11 tons of water. At the plant the coal was dried and burned.

NOTE: This slurry pipeline is an example of lack of consideration for the natural resources and the local environment. Built on Native American tribal land in the harshest and driest desert on Earth, it used 2700 gallons of water a minute, or close to 4 million gallons per day. This is 1.5 billion gallons—an entire lake—taken from one area of the desert and pumped to another, where it was discharged as waste water after the coal was filtered out.

Tapping the Navajo Aquifer depleted the main source of potable groundwater for the Navajo and Hopi tribes, causing a severe decline in potable water and contamination of water sources. Did no one consider the consequences?

Similar slurry pipelines are proposed for the North Central coal fields of the Dakotas, Montana, and Wyoming to feed the power plants of the Midwest (Chicago, St. Louis, etc). Although studies show that slurry transport is less expensive than rail—after the pipeline is installed—environmental and economic controversies have so far frustrated pipeline projects.

Transportation Cost

The cost of transport via unit train today is approximately $0.020 per ton/mile, or 1,000 mile trip would cost approximately $20.00 per ton of coal transported from the mine to the power plant. This multiplied by 100 tons per car and 100 cars per unit train gives us the grand total of $200,000, which is the amount a large-scale power plant pays every day for coal transport alone. Remember that coal started with a humble price of $5 per ton at some mines.

The transportation cost is even higher when considering other methods, such as barges and trucks. This, compared with the cost of mining the coal, which is approximately $5-15 per ton in the U.S. (but much higher in other countries), is a true highway robbery. There is, however, no way around it; if you want it you must ship it—except in the case of "mine mouth" versions, where the power plant is located at the mine site, so the coal goes directly into the furnace to be converted into electricity.

There is a loss of power during the transmission of the generated electric power from the remote power station to the populated centers, but this is a small price to pay, compared with shipping millions of tons of coal cross-country.

Land Reclamation

Land reclamation is the preferred post-strip mining method for bringing land back to original conditions. It is expensive, however, and at a cost of about $10,000 per acre, it would cost $2-3 billion to reclaim all damaged land in the U.S. This is not likely to happen anytime soon.

Still, there are examples of great success in this area. In the Rhineland, Germany, coal fields they store both the topsoil and the subsoil, and later replace it in the empty coal trenches. The land is fully refilled, graded and then fertilized and seeded. Drains carry the water away before it can form sulfuric acid and the acid in the leachate is sometimes neutralized with limestone.

The acid can be also neutralized with ashes, which are a serious solid waste from coal burning. However, using these ashes to fill the trenches and neutralize the leachate acidity would be practical only at mine mouth plants. Transport of large quantities of ashes to mines that are far away from the power plant would be prohibitively expensive.

In other cases, sewage sludge and even liquid sewage from the water reclamation plants can be spread over strip-mined areas to help restore the fertility and soil texture. The land then can be revegetated and slowly returned to its original state.

The U.S.'s most difficult reclamation is in the north central regions, where grassy ranch land is being destroyed in large numbers. Restoring this arid land to usable status would be almost economically impossible. As confirmation, no coal company has ever had its reclamation performance bond returned in Montana.

Meeting the requirements of federal surface mining controls adds to the cost of coal. The cost of reclaiming Western surface mines is $1000-$5000 per acre. A more useful comparison is provided by the additional cost per million Btu (MBtu) of energy obtained from coal. In mid-1981 coal energy was available to electric utilities at an average cost of about $1.50 per MBtu. It is estimated that federally mandated reclamation adds about $0.02/MBtu to Western coal—where the seams are deep, but the energy content is relatively low, about $0.05/MBtu to Midwestern coal and $0.11/MBtu to Appalachian coal.

Existing requirements cost an additional $0.10 MBtu for Appalachian coal. Added to these costs is a tax (equivalent to $0.02/MBtu) assessed on the coal companies for the reclamation of abandoned strip-mined land. Thus, the highest total of additions, Appalachia's $0.23/MBtu, raises the cost of coal to the utility, and ultimately of electricity to the consumer, by over 15%.

About 1.1 million acres of coal mined land currently need reclamation, and new land is being disturbed at a rate of about 65,000 acres/year. Reclamation laws need careful enforcement to keep up with the draglines.

Typical activities during the decommissioning and site reclamation phase include removing infrastructure, such as structures, conveyors, and rail lines; filling in the mined area or shafts; recontouring the surface; and revegetation. Potential impacts from these activities are presented below, by the type of affected resource. Depending on the mining method, some reclamation activities occur while the coal mining continues, such as in strip mining.

The following potential impacts may result from decommissioning and site reclamation:

Acoustics (Noise) sources during decommissioning would be similar to those during construction and mining, and would include equipment (rollers, bulldozers, and diesel engines) and vehicular traffic. Whether the noise levels exceed guidelines established by the U.S. Environmental Protection Agency (EPA) or local ordinances would depend on the distance to the nearest residence. If near a residential area, noise levels could exceed the EPA guideline, but would be intermittent and occur for a limited time.

Air Quality, affecting global climate change and carbon footprint during decommissioning activities includes vehicle tailpipe emissions; diesel emissions from large construction equipment and generators; and fugitive dust from many sources such as backfilling, dumping, restoration of disturbed areas (grading, seeding, planting), and truck and equipment traffic. Permitting would be required (as during construction and mining), and therefore these emissions would not likely exceed air quality standards or impact climate change.

Cultural Resources would be unlikely to be affected during decommissioning because these resources would have been removed professionally prior to mining, or would have been already disturbed or destroyed by prior activities. Collection of artifacts could be a problem if access roads were left in place and the area was not monitored.

Visual impact of the coal mine would be mitigated if the site were restored to its preconstruction state. However, despite the physical removal of any surface facilities, the impact of a scarred landscape on an area would likely remain.

Ecological Resources impacted by the decommissioning activities would be similar in nature to impacts from construction and mining, with a reduction or elimination of blasting activities. Negligible to no reduction in wildlife habitat would be expected, and injury and mortality rates of vegetation and wildlife could be lower than they would be during mining. Impacts resulting from acid mine drainage could continue if not properly managed. Restoration of the mine site would reduce habitat fragmentation. Following site reclamation, the ecological resources at the project site could return to preproject conditions.

Environmental Justice could result from significant impacts to any resource areas, and when these impacts disproportionately affect the populations. Issues that could be of concern during decommissioning are noise, air quality, water quality, loss of employment and income, and visual impacts from the project site.

Hazardous Materials and Waste Management of industrial wastes, such as lubricating oils, hydraulic fluids, coolants, solvents, and cleaning agents would be treated similarly to wastes generated during mining activities (that is, put in containers, characterized and labeled, possibly stored briefly, and transported by a licensed hauler to an appropriate permitted off-site disposal facility). Impacts could result if these wastes were not properly handled and were released to the environment. Additional solid and industrial waste would be generated during the dismantling of any ancillary facilities. Much of the solid material from dismantling facilities could be recycled and sold as scrap or used in road building or bank re-stabilization projects; the remaining nonhazardous waste would be sent to permitted disposal facilities.

Human Health and Safety are potential impacts to worker and public health and safety during the decommissioning and reclamation of a coal mine, and would be similar to those from any construction-type project with earthmoving, crushing, large equipment, and transportation of overweight and oversized materials. Added risk may be involved with the reclamation of underground mines due to the potential for mine subsidence. In addition, health and safety issues include working in potential weather extremes and possible contact with natural hazards, such as uneven terrain and dangerous plants, animals, or insects.

Land Use, upon decommissioning of the mine site and rectifying the impacts from coal mining, would be largely reversed and made ready for use. Future subsidence of underground mines could be a long-term issue. Open pit mines could have lasting land-use impacts; the land may be irreversibly altered if reclamation to pre-development condition is not possible. Alternate land uses may be established.

Paleontological Resources during decommissioning activities would not be impacted, because these resources would have been removed professionally prior to mining, or would have been already disturbed or destroyed by prior activities. Fossil collection could be a problem if access roads were left in place and the area was no longer periodically monitored.

Socioeconomic impacts of decommissioning of the mine and reclamation would include those resulting from the cessation of mining activities, including job loss and revenue loss, and also the creation of new jobs for workers during reclamation activities and the associated income and taxes paid. Indirect impacts would occur from both the loss of economic development created by the loss of mining jobs and new economic development that would include things such as new jobs at businesses that support the reclamation workforce or that provide project materials and associated income and taxes. No adverse effect to property values is anticipated as a result of decommissioning. Site reclamation could result in economic values of residential properties adjacent to the coal mine becoming equivalent to similarly developed residential areas that were not affected by the coal mine. The loss of royalty and tax revenue could adversely impact the local and regional economies.

Soils and Geologic Resources (including Seismicity/Geo Hazards) activities during the decommissioning/reclamation phase, include removal of access and on-site roads and heavy vehicle traffic. Surface disturbance, heavy equipment traffic, and changes to surface runoff patterns can cause soil erosion. Impacts of soil erosion include soil nutrient loss and reduced water quality in nearby surface water bodies. Disturbed areas would be contoured and revegetated to minimize the potential for soil erosion.

Transportation impact is reflected in short-term increase in the use of local roadways, occurring during the reclamation period. Heavy equipment would remain at the site until reclamation is completed. Overweight and oversized loads, when removing the heavy equipment, could cause temporary disruptions to local traffic.

Visual Resources during decommissioning would be similar to those from construction and mining. Restoring a decommissioned site to preproject conditions would entail recontouring, grading, scarifying, seeding and planting, and perhaps stabilizing disturbed surfaces. Newly disturbed soils would create visual contrasts that would persist at least several seasons before revegetation would begin to disguise past activity. Restoration to preproject conditions may take much longer. Invasive species may colonize newly and recently reclaimed areas. Non-native plants that are not locally adapted could produce contrasts of color, form, texture, and line.

Water Resources (surface water and groundwater) might be trucked in from off-site or obtained from local groundwater wells or nearby surface water bodies, depending on availability. It would be used for dust control for road traffic and mine filling and for consumptive use by the decommissioning/site reclamation crew.

Water Quality could be affected by continued acid mine drainage if not effectively managed. Mining activities cause soil erosion, leading to leaching, oxidation and release of chemicals into the water, discharges of waste or sanitary water, and pesticide applications. Upon completion of decommissioning, disturbed areas would be contoured and revegetated to minimize the potential for soil erosion and water-quality-related impacts.

Water Flow would be affected by withdrawals made for water use, wastewater and storm water discharges, and the diversion of surface water flow for access road reclamation or stormwater control systems. The interaction between surface water and groundwater could also be affected if the two resources are hydrologically connected, potentially resulting in unwanted dewatering or recharging of any of these water resources.

Mine Development

Federal legal requirements apply to specific activities associated with coal mining. A number of federal laws, regulations, and Executive Orders apply to coal mining activities. For the most part, state laws and regulations do not apply to coal mining on tribal lands.

The extent to which federal requirements apply to specific coal mine projects depends upon the nature of the project, its location, and size. In addition, the requirements for one project and location are usually different from those applicable to other projects, in different areas and under other regulatory programs.

NOTE: here we only list the laws and regulations

that affect mining operations, to give the reader an idea of the complexities surrounding this subject. We take a close look at some of the related laws and regulations in the following chapters.

The federal requirements that may apply to specific activities associated with coal mining are:

- The National Environmental Policy Act, which addresses all environmental issues

- Cultural Resources are addressed by the:
  — American Indian Religious Freedom Act
  — Antiquities Act
  — Archaeological and Historic Preservation Act
  — Archaeological Resources Protection Act
  — Executive Order 11593: Protection and Enhancement of the Cultural Environment
  — Executive Order 13007: Indian Sacred Sites
  — Executive Order 13175: Consultation and Coordination with Indian Tribal Governments
  — Executive Order 13287: Preserve America
  — Historic Sites, Buildings, and Antiquities Act (Historic Sites Act)
  — Illegal Trafficking in Native American Human Remains and Cultural Items
  — National Historic Preservation Act
  — Native American Graves Protection and Repatriation Act
  — Theft and Destruction of Government Property

- Ecological Resources issues are addressed by the:
  — Bald and Golden Eagle Protection Act
  — Clean Water Act
  — Endangered Species Act
  — Executive Order 11988: Floodplain Management
  — Executive Order 11990: Protection of Wetlands
  — Executive Order 12996: Management and General Public Use of the National Wildlife Refuge System
  — Executive Order 13112: Invasive Species
  — Executive Order 13186: Responsibilities of Federal Agencies to Protect Migratory Birds
  — Federal Insecticide, Fungicide, and Rodenticide Act
  — Fish and Wildlife Coordination Act
  — Migratory Bird Treaty Act
  — National Wildlife Refuge System Administration Act
  — Noxious Weed Act
  — Rivers and Harbors Act
  — Wild Free-Roaming Horses and Burros Act

- Energy Resource Development issues are addressed by the:
  — Surface Mining Control and Reclamation Act
  — Tribal Energy Resource Agreements
- Environmental justice issues are addressed by the Executive Order 12898: Federal Actions to Address Environmental Justice in Minority Populations and Low-Income Populations
- Hazardous Materials & Waste Management issues are addressed by the:
  — Comprehensive Environmental Response, Compensation, and Liability Act
  — Emergency Planning & Community Right-to-Know Act
  — Executive Order 12856: Federal Compliance With Right-to-Know Laws and Pollution Prevention Requirements
  — Federal Insecticide, Fungicide, and Rodenticide Act
  — Hazardous Materials Transportation Act
  — Pollution Prevention Act
  — Resource Conservation and Recovery Act
  — Toxic Substances Control Act
- Health & Safety issues are addressed by the:
  — Emergency Planning & Community Right-to-Know Act
  — Executive Order 13045: Protection of Children From Environmental Health Risks and Safety Risks
  — Federal Mine Safety and Health Act
  — Occupational Safety & Health Act
  — Acoustics (Noise), via the Noise Control Act
  — Air Quality, via the Clean Air Act
- Land use issues are addressed by the:
  — Air Commerce and Safety Act
  — Farmland Protection and Policy Act
  — Federal Land Policy and Management Act
  — National Trails System Act
  — Rivers and Harbors Act
  — Soil and Water Resources Conservation Act
  — Surface Mining Control and Reclamation Act
  — Wild and Scenic Rivers Act
  — Wilderness Act
- Paleontological Resources are addressed by the:
  — Antiquities Act
  — Paleontological Resources Preservation
  — Theft and Destruction of Government Property
- Soils & Geological Resources issues are addressed by the:
  — Farmland Protection and Policy Act
  — Soil and Water Resources Conservation Act

- Water Quality issues are addressed by the:
  — Clean Water Act
  — Safe Drinking Water Act
- Transportation issues of mining operations are not addressed by any law or regulation
- Visual resources issues of mining operations are not addressed by any law or regulation
- Socioeconomic issues of mining operations are not addressed by any law or regulation

A long list it is. And the issues it covers are of utmost importance, so we will cover these in the following chapters.

Case Study

In the text below—a real case—we will take a close look at the development of a large coal mining operation in China. It has initial capacity of 30 MT/a (mega ton per annum), which was approved by the regulators and government bodies in 2010 and implemented shortly thereafter. The project was developed as follows:

Initial Evaluation and Exploration

The initial process of evaluation and exploration, conducted by a team of specialists, concluded that the geological conditions of this site are excellent for large-scale mine development. The coal-containing stratum is of the Jurassic period, with upper coverage of soils dating back to the Quaternary and Cretaceous Age.

The main coal containing stratum is B1 coal seam of Middle Jurassic Xishanyao group. The stratum inclination is gentle, only 1-3°, and the maximum partial inclination is 6°. There are no significant faults in the area.

The coal seam was qualified as that of the non-caking type coal, which has low ash, low sulfur, and low phosphorus content, while exhibiting high calorific value.

The hydrological condition of the site is a mixture of category two and type one. The three aquifers in the upper coverage of the coal seam are all fissure aquifers with small water inflow into the colliery.

There is a low gas outflow, with moderate risk of coal dust explosion, or natural fire. The ground temperature is normal. The ground is Gobi desert type, with no human residents or fertile land on the property or close by.

The seismic basic intensity is grade VI. At the south boundary of the mine field are the railway and highway for the coalfield transportation needs.

Mine Planning

In the planning of this mine area, the principles of centralization and large-scale production were determined by, and adapted to, the anticipated geological conditions. A face length of high output and high efficiency of 200-300 m, and maximum length of 350-400 m was determined. The mining distance could go to 4000-6000 m.

According to this development trend, and to fully utilize advanced mining technology, after review of multiple proposals the coal field was designed according to the principles of most efficient, large size, large area, and large reserves mining operation, as follow:

South-North length of the coalfield is 12.3-13.5 km, while East-West width is about 12 km. The entire mining area is 155.8 km², with coal reserves estimated at 10.47 billion tons, and recoverable reserves estimated at 4.96 billion tons. This does not include the industrial type coal area of approximately 2.57 billion tons, as well as a number of coal pillars and other possible losses during the construction and operation of the mine.

Assuming that the "reserve factor" of the coal reserves is 1.4, and the annual output is 30 MT, then the coal reserves will last 118 years. If the annual output increases to 40 MT anytime in the future, then the total service of the mine life will drop to 88 years. At 50 MT annual production, the field would produce coal for a total of about 58 years.

If production started at 30 MT, then several years later was increased to 40 MT, and later on to 50 MT, then the life of the plant would be an extrapolation of the times and volumes, in a range between 70 and 90 years.

In all cases, the wide mining area and the large coal quantity guarantee stable, long-term, large-scale production at high throughput.

Equipment

The advanced integrated automation and mechanization of the coal mining process is the core of the colliery production, ensuring efficient and safe operation. The high production levels require the development and implementation of specialized and efficient coal mining equipment and processes.

There are more and more working mines with annual output of tens of million of tons today. The specialized thick coal seam worked with integrated automation equipment for mining via roof caving process (China's own innovation) is developing and improving fast.

Recently, a record of integrated mechanization mining of a single face with a length of 300m and annual output of 6 million tons was established. In recent years, several Chinese collieries showed great improvement in integrated automation mechanization. For example, at one of the main coal seams with 913m thickness, two integrated automated mining teams with roof caving working faces and related advancing face were implemented, with total colliery's annual output of 17.68 million tons.

At another mine with a main working face of 300m, and length of 1600m, the maximum daily output was 54,000 MT, the maximum monthly output was 1.18 MT, and the annual output was 10.38 MT.

When comparing these collieries, it becomes obvious that we can easily reach the goal of annual output of 15-17 MT by adopting such advanced integrated mechanization mining methods as the roof caving and layering mining techniques.

The final work parameters of the equipment and the processes will be determined according to the actual operating conditions of the working face, when put into production. Applying integrated mechanization of the roof caving process will reduce the layering numbers and will increase the efficiency of the mining operations.

Process Design

Proper and efficient exploitation is the key to success in a large coal mine design. After considering and researching various operation modes, we adopted the combination of area division exploitation and integrated exploitation in the development of the final coalfield.

AREA DIVISION EXPLOITATION

There is a railway on the south boundary of the coalfield. To the north of the industrial protection area is the approved development area, with south-north width of 9 km, and east-west length of 12 km. The coalfield is divided into two main sub-areas, south sub-area and north sub-area.

Each sub-area has its own tunnels, auxiliary shaft and ventilation shaft. Each sub-area is divided into east and west wings along the shaft line; each wing is a panel area with one working face. Each working face can maintain stable and continual production for the duration.

This colliery basically maintains 4 working faces, which are each in completely independent panel areas. Each working face can produce 7.5 MT annually under the present working conditions, bringing the total annual capacity of the coal mine to about 30 MT.

It can be assumed that after some period of operation, each working face can increase production capacity from 7.5 to about 10 MT annually. If demanded by

changing market conditions, the colliery's production capacity can be increased further to reach 40, and even 50 MT annually. In such a case, the industrial coal area planned at the south part of the coal field will need to be exploited, to maximize output.

Present and future levels of production can be achieved by the implementation of automated equipment and efficient mining techniques, which will be developed and implemented as new conditions require. The new design parameters will ensure high efficiency, high throughput and safety of all aspects of the coal mine operations, because:

a.   Each working face is in a large-scale panel area available for decades of continuous exploitation,

b.   Each tunnel system of the two sub-areas is completely independent.

c.   Two wings have one working face respectively. This guarantees the air supply/ventilation and the high efficiency of the production. It also provides the possibility of stage construction, as needed for upgrades, subject to market demand.

d.   The conveyor system is quite simple and yet efficient. There are few link nods, so that after the coal is mined from the working face, it can pass the roadway of the panel area, and be continually transported above ground via the belt conveyor from the main shaft.

The auxiliary transportation system is of the vertical type with up and down movement, through the two separate sub-area auxiliary shafts.

INTEGRATED EXPLOITATION MODE

The colliery depth is about 500 m, which was serviced by a vertical shaft in the past. A main inclined shaft, equipped with a belt conveyor for hoisting the coal is best for this mine's purposes. Its hoisting capacity is greater, it is safer, and could handle potential production increases. It provides continuous transportation of coal from the working face to the surface with high efficiency and low cost. The equipment, its setup and maintenance are easier and cheaper than that needed for the hoisting equipment of the vertical shaft.

Since the production capacity is very great, two large-scale belt conveyors are respectively set in the two inclined shafts. The main inclined shaft was also equipped with a railway.

At first, one main inclined shaft was built for Phase 1, with 15 MT annual production, and serves sub-area 1. Phase 2 of the project will add another main inclined shaft in the same area.

At the bottom of the shaft, a main transport roadway is built up to sub-area 2. Two belt inclined shafts share a mutual connection in the shaft bottom. The two belts can separately handle the coal transportation of each sub-area, and can also be used as a backup system for each other, if needed.

The final design is a large coal mine with an integrated exploitation mode, consisting of main inclined shafts, auxiliary vertical shafts, and ventilation shafts. The above-ground and underground systems such as mining, coal flow, auxiliary transport, and ventilation of this large coal mine are simplified to the greatest extent. The safety of this reliable and highly efficient mining operation is guaranteed as well.

Advanced Design Details

When designing advanced mining technology, the reasonable exploitation and advanced mining *modus operandi* are guaranteed by implementing the latest of advanced equipment and processes, such as conveyors, hoisting, transportation, ventilation, and safety and communication systems.

Coal Transportation and Hoisting

The mine adopted and implemented belt conveyor transportation. Nearly 30 years' experience proves that the belt conveyor continual transportation and hoisting is the optimal coal transportation mode, and it is extremely efficient and cheap for any large-scale coal mine.

The belt conveyor is widely adopted in underground coal mining and transportation. After comparing the conditions of the 500 m vertical depth under which the inclined shaft belt conveyor is used to hoist the coal, the belt conveyor was determined to be best for efficient, continuous transportation.

During the design and selection of the main inclined shaft belt conveyor for hoisting the coal, was taken into account that the production capacity of 30 MT/ year is a significant load and might be increased to 40 MT.

1. *Auxiliary transportation*

    In the past, the underground auxiliary transportation for the vertical shafts of coal mines at great depth was done by a tracked mine car. Recently, mining operations adopted trackless transportation as auxiliary

transportation with great success.

This method has been promoted and used in colliery design at fairly gentle coal seam inclination. The auxiliary shaft is fitted with a large cage (8.2 m long and 3.8 m wide), and equipped with a counter weight. The general purpose equipment and other loads can be directly put into/out of the cage via the trackless car, and delivered to the work site without trans-shipment (for loads below 8 t total weight).

2. *Ventilation and safety*
    a. The ventilation system of this colliery is simple and reliable. Each sub-area has an independent ventilation system. Each sub-area is divided into two separate wings; where each wing is a panel area with one production working face. The fresh air is delivered to shaft bottom via the auxiliary shaft of the sub-area, through the auxiliary transportation roadway of one wing. Here it directly enters the intake airway and the return airway of the working face; then the air is delivered from the return air roadway of one wing to the ventilation shaft and then discharged to the outside. The exhausting fan is a powerful axial flow fan with excellent performance.
    b. Safety is of utmost importance in coal mine production. The perfect safety measures are established per the "Requirement of Safety Regulations of Coal Mines," which encompass gas prevention, fire control, flood prevention, and other safety measures.

The main safety systems in this mine are designed and implemented as per the latest requirements and as needed to ensure the maximum safety of the colliery operators. To prevent natural fire disaster, the colliery implemented the experience of a high output working face of other working mines in the area. This includes the use of anti-fire mortar tank and working face nitrogen filling, which are effectively combined to prevent natural fire disasters.

Surface Services

This is a large mine, so it has elaborate surface facilities. These include on-site coal preparation plant and a power plant. Since the main shaft is near the power plant, the surface facilities, offices, ground production system and coal storage facilities are combined.

Some coal is sent to the preparation plant for treatment and is then loaded on railroad cars. Part of the coal production, which needs external treatment is transported by rubber belt conveyor directly from the mine to a storage area and then to the railway for loading on trains to be transported to the external plant for further processing.

Communications and Integrated Automation

The integrated communication, information, and control system of the coal mine is based on a computer network run by an industrial Ethernet system. The backbone of the network uses an optical fiber network, fed by the servers and extending to the different mine locations. The subsystem is integrated into a digital monitoring platform to effectively process the data that forms the digital coal mine control system.

The colliery management and supervisory personnel perform real time monitoring and control of production, all business operations, management, environmental and safety procedures. The goal of the integrated monitoring, management and control systems is to coordinate activities to make production more efficient, cost effective, and safe.

The integrated automatic system adopts modern control, computer, communication, and graphic display technology to monitor and control all underground mining operations, including the main face activities, coal flow, transportation system, ground production system, main inclined shaft belt conveyor system, auxiliary shaft hoist system, ventilator system, main drainage pump, exhaust fans, and air compressor.

This setup guarantees the overall production coordination, improves production efficiency, ensures product quality, improves labor conditions and safety, and increases the overall economic benefit of the mine.

Conclusions

The main characteristics of this large mine example are centralization of the production cycle, automation of mining and excavation processes, a simplified exploitation system, coal transportation continuity, simplification of auxiliary transportation, automation of main equipment, mechanization of auxiliary production, simplification of the ground layout, and advanced management communications with emphasis on safety and environmental protection.

During the design work, the basic principles of forward looking coal mine design were followed. These are based on the reality and available technologies of today, and take into account the trends of tomorrow. The design is also focused on integration and innovation of mining technologies to provide the most efficient and

safe operation.

The new and advanced technology achievements and experiences in mining are gradually absorbed and combined within such coal mine designs in China and followed in other countries as well, thus ensuring maximum efficiency, cost-effectiveness and safety of the respective mining operations.

Coal Production

Coal is a big business worldwide—very big. With nearly 25% of the world's reserves located in the U.S., it will remain big business in this country for a long, long time.

In the United States, coal is found in great quantities in several regions, such as the Appalachian region in the states of PA, OH, WV, KY, TN, and AL; the Midwest region in the states of IL, IN, and KY; the Gulf Coast region in the states of TX, LA, AR, and MS; and in the West in the states of UT, CO, AZ, NM, WY, SD, ND, and MT.

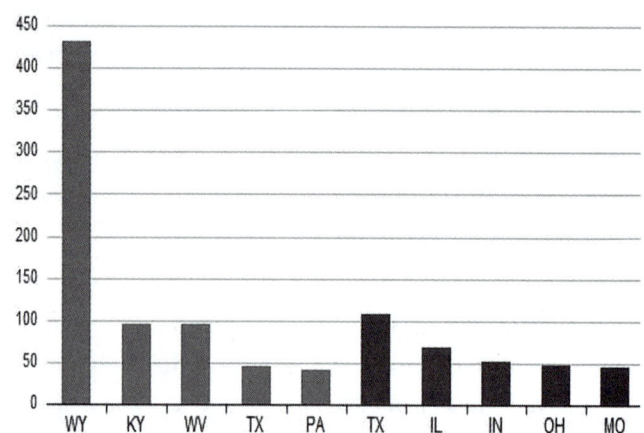

Figure 2-22. Coal producing states (in millions of tons)

Different types of coal can be found in different areas, as follow: lignite is found in the states of MT, TX, and ND; sub-bituminous coal is found in the states of MT and WY; bituminous coal is found in the states of IL, KY, and WV; and anthracite is found in the state of PA

To begin with, we need to emphasize that there are different types and quality of coal, which determine the design and operation of the coal mine, as well as the use of the coal produced at each mine. Coal varies in composition from deposit to deposit, and sometimes within the same deposit.

There are four major and very different types of coal. Each of these is characterized by differences in appearance, but more importantly in energy output. These are determined by the different pressure, heat, and time the coal reserves have endured.

The types of coal:

1. *Lignite* is a brownish-black coal with high moisture and ash content, which has the lowest heating value of the four types. It is considered an "immature" coal that is still soft. It is used for generating electricity.

2. *Sub-bituminous coal* is a dull black coal with a higher heating value than lignite and is used principally for electricity and space heating.

3. *Bituminous coal* is the most common type in the United States, accounting for over 50% of the demonstrated reserve base. It is the most commonly used type of coal for electric power generation in the U.S. It is a dark, hard coal that has a higher heating value than lignite and sub-bituminous coal, but a lower heating value than anthracite.

4. *Anthracite* is also known as "hard coal" that was formed from bituminous coal under increased pressures in rock strata during the creation of mountain ranges. In the United States, it is located primarily in the Appalachian region of Pennsylvania. It is very hard and shiny. This type of coal is the most compact and therefore, has the highest energy content of the four levels of coal. It is used for space heating and generating electricity. It makes up only 1.5% of the demonstrated reserve base for coal in the United States.

There were 1,325 mines in the U.S. in 2011, with total coal production of roughly 1.1 billion short tons. Production in the western region, which includes Wyoming, totaled 587.6 million short tons.

The average number of employees in U.S. coal mines at the same time was 91,611. Domestic coal consumption of metallurgical coal by the coking industry was 21.4 million short tons. The average sales price of coal was $41.01 per short ton.

Approximately 25% of the world's recoverable coal deposits are in the US (approximately 270 billion tons), with Russia following at 176 billion tons, except that most of the deposits are in areas that are very difficult to mine.

There are estimates of over 1.0 trillion tons of coal available globally, equivalent to over 120 years of current production and 100% of the world total, with the largest reserves located in the US, Russia, China, Australia and India.

The major coal producers today are China, the USA, India, Australia, Russia, Indonesia and South Africa. Global coal production lately has been in the 7-7.5 billion tons annually. China accounts for nearly 50% of world's coal consumption, followed by the US, India, Japan and Russia as major coal consuming nations.

Coal is still the primary energy source for a number of countries worldwide, and provides between 25% and 28% of the world's primary energy. Coal is the main fuel for the generation of electricity as the price of coal is cheap compared to other fuels. Unfortunately, it is also the highest polluting source of electricity.

Other major uses of coal are in the production of steel and synthetic fuels. Coal generates over $1.0 trillion annual revenue, which is rapidly growing.

Coal Use

The primary use of coal is to generate electricity or heat. Bituminous coal is also used to produce coke for making steel and other industrial process heating. Coal gasification and coal liquefaction (coal-to-liquids) are used also to produce synthetic fuels.

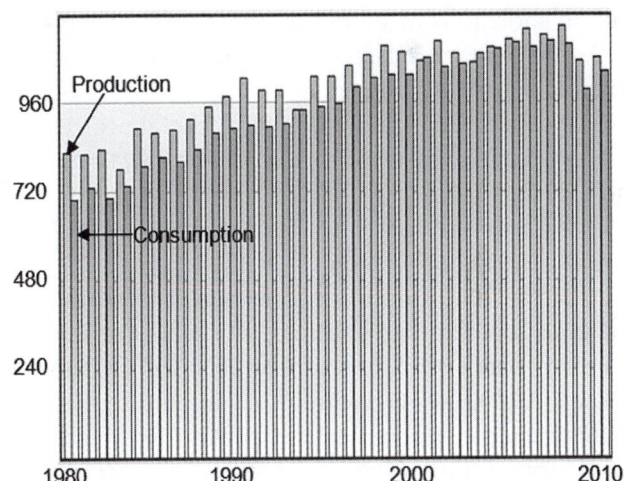

Figure 2-23. U.S. coal production and use (in millions of tons/year)

Obviously, we produce almost all the coal we need for internal use. Only 4-5% of the coal mined in the United States is exported, mostly for making steel.

Coal is mined commercially in over 50 countries. Over 7,036 Mt/yr of hard coal is currently produced, a substantial increase over the past 25 years. In 2006, the world production of brown coal and lignite was slightly over 1,000 tons, with Germany the world's largest brown coal producer at 194.4 Mt, and China second at 100.6 Mt.

Coal production has grown fastest in Asia, while Europe has declined. Table 2-2 illustrates the top coal mining nations in 2010 (in millions of tons).

Table 2-2. Global coal production and use.

Country	Annual production	% of world production	% of world use
China	3,050	39.4	38.6
US	960	19.3	18.4
India	557	6.8	7.7
Australia	415	6.6	1.7
S. Africa	250	4.7	3.0
Russia	310	4.9	3.6
Indonesia	250	4.7	3.2
Poland	150	2.2	1.9
Kazakhstan	125	1.8	1.1
Japan	—	—	3.9
S. Korea	—	—	1.8

Most coal production is used in the country of origin, but some of it is being exported. U.S. coal production in 2011 increased slightly from 2010, driven by export demand, to roughly 1.1 billion short tons, but declined 0.7 percent in the western region.

Productive capacity of coal mines increased by 2.5 million short tons to 1.3 billion short tons. At the same time, the average number of employees in U.S. coal mines increased 6.3 percent to 91,611.

Domestic coal consumption of metallurgical coal by the coking industry rose 1.6 percent to 21.4 million short tons.

The average sales price of coal increased 15.2 percent to $41.01 per short ton.

Global coal production is expected to reach 7,000 Mt/yr in 2030 (update required, world coal production is already past 7,000 Mt/yr and by 2030 will probably be closer to 13,000 Mt/yr), with China accounting for most of this increase. Steam coal production is projected to reach around 5,200 Mt/yr; coking coal 620 Mt/yr; and brown coal 1,200 Mt/yr.

Coal reserves are available in almost every country worldwide, with recoverable reserves in around 70 countries. At current production levels, proven coal reserves are estimated to last 147 years. However, production levels are by no means level, are in fact increasing, and some estimates are that peak coal could arrive in many countries such as China and America by around 2030.

Coal reserves are usually stated as either:

1) "Resources," which consist of the "measured + indicated + inferred = resources," and then, a smaller number, often only 10-20% of "resources";

2) "Run of Mine" (ROM) reserves; and

3) "Marketable reserves," which may be only 60% of ROM reserves.

The standards for reserves are set by stock exchanges, in consultation with industry associations. For example in ASEAN countries reserves standards follow the Australasian Joint Ore Reserves Committee Code used by the Australian Securities Exchange.

Major Coal Mines

Demand for coal is increasing by the day. There are presently nearly 1,200 proposed coal plant projects in 59 countries around the globe, with most targeted for the Pacific market. China and India top the list with over 800 coal fired plants planned for implementation in the next several years.

While new coal-fired plant construction has slowed somewhat and is under increasing fire in the U.S., the rest of the world is poised to go all-in with a dirty coal future. The expert conclusion is that coal demand could rise by 20% by 2035.

This will increase coal mining activities proportionately, and we expect that the US will be a major player in this new game by increasing coal exports. The top coal mining nations (in millions of tons) are shown in Table 2-3.

Table 2-3. Coal mining, 2010

Country	Mining
China	3,050
United States	973
India	557
Australia	409
South Africa	250
Russia	298
Indonesia	252
Poland	135
Kazakhstan	101
Colombia	72

While most coal production is used in the country of origin, only around 15% of hard coal production is exported. Global coal production is expected to reach 13,000 Mt/yr in 2030. Steam coal production is projected to reach around 5,200 Mt/yr; coking coal 620 Mt/yr; and brown coal 1,200 Mt/yr.

Of the 1,325 mines in the U.S. in 2011, the largest are shown in Table 2-4.

Table 2-4. Major U.S. mines

Mine	Type	State	Annual
North Antelope	Surface	WY	98,279,377
Black Thunder	Surface	WY	81,079,043
Cordero Mine	Surface	WY	39,380,964
Antelope Coal Mine	Surface	WY	33,975,524
Jacobs Ranch Mine	Surface	WY	29,021,485
Belle Ayr Mine	Surface	WY	28,395,952
Enlow Fork Mine	Underground	PA	11,092,684
Bailey Mine	Underground	PA	10,232,360
Mcelroy Mine	Underground	VA	9,863,588
Foidel Creek Mine	Underground	CO	7,827,079

Coal mining produced over 1.1 billion tons in 2011, with northeastern Wyoming contributing the largest amount produced in any state in the US. It also presently produces more coal than any other region in the world.

Cost of Mining Operations

Underground mining currently accounts for about 60% of world coal production, although surface mining is prevalent in some regions of the US and other countries. For example, surface mining accounts for around 80% of production in Australia, while in the USA it represents about 67% of production.

The cradle-to-grave mining operation is an expensive undertaking. The cost of a large mine, from concept to exploitation, is hundreds of millions of dollars.

1. Site location, exploration and data collection alone are major tasks, consisting of many sub-tasks and involving numerous professionals and specialized firms.

2. Construction of surface facilities, local infrastructure, and mine structure comprise another grand undertaking, worth millions of dollars and involving hundreds of people.

3. Equipment procurement and installation require considerable effort and expense.

4. Mine exploitation is, of course, the main goal of this undertaking, and its day-to-day operations bring a continuous stream of expensive tasks and sub-projects.

5. Mine decommissioning and land reclamation are also major and equally expensive undertakings.

The initial process of mine location, development and construction is estimated at about $150 million per million tons of annual production—or—a 5 million tons per annum coal mine would have an initial cost estimate of $750 million. This is the amount of money needed to begin operations, if everything goes well.

The cost of mining operations is an equally expensive and complex process. The cost of underground coal mines and coal cleaning in the eastern USA ranges from $15 to $45 per ton of clean coal (in 2010 dollars). The overall weighted average cost per ton of clean coal is $25. So, 5 million tons of annual production spends about $125 million annually for daily operations. The retail value of coal depends on the type, quality, quantity, the season, and the location of the order. Due to increasing transport charges, taxes, broker fees, etc., the retail prices could be twice the cost of mining, or more.

Labor

As in any industry, labor pay in the mines is different from person to person and from mine to mine. Labor remuneration in the mines is categorized according to the level of expertise and experience. It is also dependent on mine location. Different states have different pay scales. Of course, underground workers are paid higher wages, due to the increased level of difficulty and danger, which requires additional training and expertise. Table 2-5 shows some labor pay rates.

Table 2-5. Labor rates in different states

Worker	Pay $/hour
Laborer—surface mine	7.00-22.00
Laborer—underground mine	14.00-27.00
Mill equipment operator	12.00-30.00
Stationary equipment operator	19.00-26.00
Mechanic—surface mine	11.00-30.00
Electrician—underground mine	14.00-32.00
Equipment operator	11.00-32.00
Production truck driver	9.00-28.00
Heavy equipment operator	9.00-30.00

Miners are not the best paid workers in the world. Considering the dangers, the dirt and misery in underground mines, and the other hazards these people are exposed to on a daily basis. They might be the most underpaid workers in the world.

Equipment

Mine operations require a number of specialized pieces of equipment, as needed for digging, loading and transporting coal from the mining site to the surface and beyond. Some examples are shown in Table 2-6.

Table 2-6. Mining equipment specs and prices

Equipment	Specifications	Weight in lbs.	Cost in $
Dragline	55 cu yd bucket, 250 ft. dump height	16 million	$100 million
Shovel, hydraulic	5.2 cu yd bucket 23.6 ft (7.2 m) dump height	131,000	$925,000
Loader, wheel	9.0 cu yd bucket, 12'1" dump height	114,000	$720,000
Truck, rear-dump	60 ton, 46 cu yd, mechanical drive	22,000	$120,000
Drill, rotary (crawler)	5.13" to 7.88" hole, 25 ft drill length	30,000	$600,000
Tractor, crawler (dozer)	13.7' maximum blade width	39,100	$300,000
Grader, road	14 ft blade width	52,200	$450,000
Truck, water	5,000 gallon water tank	20,000	$255,000
Truck, service	Off-road tire service truck	15,000	$55,000
Truck, shot loader	1,000 per minute capacity	15,000	$75,000

Mining equipment is usually very, very large, and not cheap. When all additional expenses related to equipment transport, assembly, maintenance, disassembly, EOL disposal, etc. are added, we get many more billions of dollars spent on mining equipment (after the initial purchase) through its long life in the mines.

Figure 2-24. Mining equipment...try it for size.

Coal Prices

Coal prices vary from state to state, from mine to mine, and also depend heavily on the seasons and the overall market conditions.

These are only examples of the purchase costs of coal from mines in different U.S. states. The price would vary according to quality of coal, location, transport charges, and other fees. Compare these prices with the average cost of $15 per ton in 1950.

The official estimates show coal prices in the $40-60 per short ton (2,000 lbs.). At the same time, Powder River Basin coal costs only $8.75 per ton. The variation is due to the quality of coal and the amount of heat as measured in Btus generated.

Table 2-7. Average sales price of coal (in $/ton)

STATE	Under-ground	Surface mine
Alabama	100.17	108.71
Illinois	51.43	46.60
Indiana	51.77	44.91
Illinois	51.43	46.60
Indiana	51.77	44.91
Kentucky Total	63.38	64.01
East Kentucky	78.63	70.86
West Kentucky	47.87	38.93
Ohio	47.86	43.41
Pennsylvania	78.67	82.89
Tennessee	66.27	77.27
West Virginia	89.40	77.39
Northern W. VA	60.91	65.74
Southern W. VA	114.25	78.15

Figure 2-25 shows the relative prices of the fossil fuels during the energy crisis of 2008-2012. The fluctuating prices were driven by rising crude oil prices, and the related uncertainties with its production. Recently, natural gas is shaping up as the fossil fuel of choice in the U.S., which is once again changing the balance of the energy markets.

New hydrofracking technology opened new possibilities, and now enormous gas reserves are being exploited and a lot of natural gas is flowing around the country. This is bringing a number of new trends in energy production and use. Coal plants are being converted to natural gas, and other changes are expected in order to fully utilize the newly abundant energy source.

NOTE: While we can clearly see the price fluctuations in Figure 2-25, the actual dollar-per-unit comparison is very difficult to do for a number of reasons. First, the physical properties of the different energy sources are so different—oil is liquid, coal is solid and natural gas is gaseous. Then, their heating values are quite different, and to top it off, the official market prices are expressed in different units; oil is given in $ per barrel (42 gallons), while the price of coal is in $ per ton (1,000 kilograms), and that of natural gas in $ per thousand cubic meters.

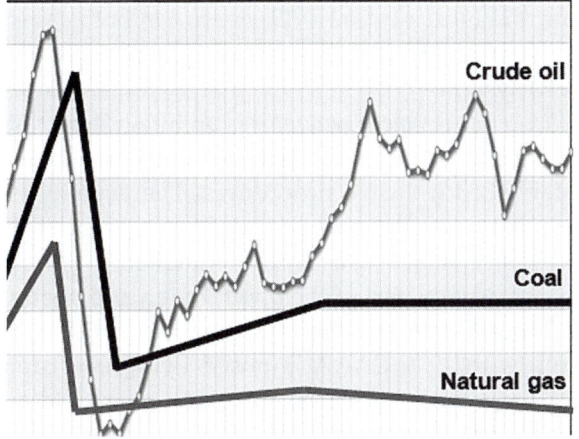

Figure 2-25. U.S. fossil fuels, comparative prices in US$

If we equate the energy of the different sources to that of crude oil (42 gallons), which contains approximately 1.7 MWh of power, we see that 1,000 m³ natural gas contains 10.5 MWh of energy, while 1 ton of coal contains 6.5 MWh energy equivalent.

This information reveals that a $90 barrel of oil contains only 1/4 of the energy contained in $60 ton of coal, and 1/6 of the energy contained in 1,000 cubic feet natural gas worth $40.

That's not all. The above numbers are the theoretical content of energy, while the actual amount of electricity, or heat, produced when burning the different sources will depend on a number of additional factors, such as the type and efficiency of the equipment and the quality of the input material.

Basically, the prices reflect not only the actual energy value of the energy sources, but other factors, such as convenience of use. So, in order to get the real value in dollars of each energy source, we must know the actual application, its location, the type of process and equipment to be used, and a number of other factors that might play a role in determining the best value.

COAL FIRED POWERED PLANTS

Coal produced in the U.S. and most other countries is used primarily for burning in power plants for electric power generation. Since this is a huge industry (and expanding in some countries like China and India) coal burning in coal-fired power plants is considered as the most serious contributor to air pollution, leading to human illness, environmental damage and climate change.

This process is evident as we go through the entire cradle-to-grave lifespan of a coal-burning power plant and see where the problems start and end. The entire life-span cycle of a coal-fired power plant consists of several phases, as follow:

Plant site and structure planning and design
- Locating, testing and exploring the proposed power plant location
- Engineering design of plant facilities, equipment and process
- Estimating the construction and operating cost and the related tasks
- Applying for and obtaining the necessary federal, state and local permits

Plant construction and setup
- Plant building construction
- Plant equipment procurement and setup
- Labor training

Power plant daily operation
- Coal unloading and transport
- Coal burning and energy generation
- Coal waste disposal
- Electric energy distribution

Power plant decommissioning and land reclamation
- Plant shut down and disassembly
- Plant waste disposal
- Surface land reclamation

Planning and Design

In a coal-burning power plant the chemical energy stored in coal is converted into thermal energy (steam), which is converted into mechanical energy by turning a turbine. The energy of the turbine turns a generator, which produces electrical energy. Multiple generating units may be built at each power plant, for more efficient use of land, natural resources and labor.

The development of a coal-burning power plant is a complex and expensive process. It begins with the planning and design of the plant, starting with the main power plant building, including the main power generating unit, and related equipment and processes. Facilities and equipment must be designed to guaranty long-term efficient, profitable and safe operation of the plant.

The coal-burning power plant planning process starts with the need for electric power. A utility company decides that it needs more power, and a new power plant needs to be built. The executives decide what type of fuel will be used. If there is a coal mine nearby, and/or if a railroad node is available to transport large quantities of coal, then a decision is made to use coal for fuel, necessitating the design and construction of a coal-burning power plant.

Then a search is undertaken for an appropriate location for the plant buildings and infrastructure. The plant must be located close to railroad tracks, yet far enough from population centers. A water source must be located nearby (a well, or enough underground water) for the cooling cycle. Access to roads and electrical distribution lines must be considered.

When the location is chosen, environmental tests and analyses are conducted for state and federal permits. The permitting stage might take months and years, and construction can be started only upon obtaining the necessary permits.

The technical aspects of the coal burning power plant equipment and process design includes:

The coal handling system—designed to provide the equipment required for the entire cycle of unloading, conveying, preparing, and storing the coal delivered to the plant. The scope of the coal handling system includes everything from the transport vehicles to storage areas. This includes the operation of the trestle bottom dumper and coal receiving hoppers, including the slide gate valves on the outlet of the coal storage silos.

The steam generator design—the most critical part of the planning and design effort. The coal-burning power plant is usually designed to operate non-stop as a base-load unit for the majority of its life, with some weekly cycling the last few years.

The heat and mass balance of the main plant steam power cycle is of utmost importance to planning and design. As an example, a plant using a 2500 psi and 1000°F single reheat steam power cycle has a high-pressure turbine that uses 2,734,000 lb/h steam at 2415 psi and 1000°F. The cold reheat flow is 2,425,653 lb/h of steam at 600 psi and 630°F, which is reheated to 1000°F before entering the intermediate-pressure turbine. These are extremely high pressures and temperature regimes, so the proper heat and mass balance (steam generated vs. coal burned) is critical. So, the proper design requires the effort of a lot of experienced engineers with the appropriate tools.

The limestone handling and reagent preparation system is designed to receive, store, convey, and grind the limestone delivered to the plant. The scope of the system is from the storage pile up to the limestone feed system. The system is designed to support long-term operation, and roadways, turnarounds, and unloading hoppers are usually included in the overall plant design as well.

Dry scrubber, using electrostatic charge or other dry technology, can be used instead of limestone in the combustor for sulfur capture. NO_x control in both cases can be accomplished by a selective non-catalytic reduction (SNCR) system.

The electric power generator is an integral part of the system, so its design and operation are done according to established industry procedures. The generators are large units, usually made in the US or Germany. Their maintenance is critical as well, so detailed O&M procedures are usually part of the plant design and operation.

The pollution emission systems and controls must comply with 1990 CAAA imposed two-phase capping of SO_2 emissions in the U.S. For a new greenfield plant, the reduction of SO_2 emissions that would be required depends on possessions or availability of SO_2 allowances by the utility, and on local site conditions. In many cases, Prevention of Significant Deterioration (PSD) regulations will apply, requiring that Best Available Control Technology (BACT) be used. BACT is applied separately for each site, and results in different values for varying sites.

The flue gas desulfurization (FGD) system is part of the pollution emission control system. It is designed to scrub the boiler exhaust gases to remove at least 90% of the SO_2 gas in these, prior to release to the environment. The FGD system design includes the outlet of the induced draft fans to the stack inlet. The system is designed to support long-term operation with minimum maintenance.

The ash handling system is designed to provide the equipment required for conveying, preparing, storing, and disposing of the fly ash and bottom ash produced on a daily basis by the boiler. This includes the precipitator hoppers, air heater hopper collectors, and bottom ash hoppers to the ash pond (for bottom ash) and truck filling stations (for fly ash). The system is designed to support long-term operation with minimum maintenance

The support facilities and infrastructure are a major element of the design process. Proper design of buildings, roads and a rail spur within the plant fence line is of great importance, since thousands of tons of coal are needed to run the plant every day. The rail spur design includes coal receiving and handling, crushing, storing, drying and shipping. There is also a limestone leg of the spur that includes facilities for receiving, crushing, storing, and feeding the fresh limestone needed for the operation.

The waste disposal system is dedicated to solid waste disposal, flue gas desulfurization, wastewater treatment and related equipment, as needed for an efficient, safe facility capable of a full 30-year life cycle.

Figure 2-26. Coal fired power plant

Standard *operation and maintenance* and safety procedures, the replacement of critical parts and major equipment overhaul, and personnel training are important parts of daily operations and must be taken into account with plant design.

The U.S. power regulations are based on equipment manufactured in the United States, Germany, or England, all of which comes with the standard manufacturer's warranties. Power plant designs are usually based on a referenced design approach to engineering and construction, where all facilities, process equipment and procedures are designed and procured in accordance with the applicable codes and standards, such as ASME, ANSI, IEEE, NFPA, CAA, state regulations. OSHA codes are all adhered to in the design.

The coal power plant planning and design process is a lengthy one, as outlined in Table 2-8.

Construction of the Power Plant

The construction of the coal plant and support facilities is begun immediately after the design and permitting processes are completed. In some cases, permitting and construction processes can be undertaken in parallel, but in most cases permitting and related steps are full of uncertainty, so proceeding with construction

Table 2-8. Power plant planning and design

Task	Time
Plant planning	1 year
Land acquisition	
Environmental studies	
Plant design	1 year
Engineering	
Construction	
Permits	3 years
Local	
State	
Federal	
Construction	2 years
Buildings	
Equipment setup	

might result in great financial loss.

There are several methods of power plant design and construction, the most popular being stick and modular.

Stick-built design power plants incorporate conventional design and construction from the ground up. In this case, each area and piece of equipment is designed and installed as a separate entity in a predetermined sequence of events.

Modular design and construction uses modules of shop assemblies, sub-assemblies, and full-scale modular packages. By maximizing the use of modular design and construction, significant cost and schedule savings can be realized. This method, however, is not widely accepted, and so most power plants are constructed with the old, stick-built method. Plant construction process consists of:

- Land clearing and preparation
- Support structures and infrastructure construction
- Plant building construction
- Plant equipment procurement and setup
- Labor training

The overall construction process is also a very a lengthy one, as outlined in Table 2-9.

Here again, the different steps can be taken in parallel, the proper execution of which requires exceptional planning and management.

Daily Operations
Power Plant Daily Operation
- Coal unloading and transport
- Coal preparation and burning
- Energy generation

Table 2-9. Power plant construction

Plant construction	1 year
Land preparation	
Facilities buildup	
Equipment procurement	1 year
Capital equipment	
Support equipment	
Equipment install	
Materials procurement	1 year
Raw materials	
Consumables	
Labor	1 year
Hiring	
Training	
Plant startup	6 months
Initial tests	
Certification	

- Coal waste disposal
- Energy distribution

A coal-fired power plant operates primarily by burning coal to generate electricity. There are a number of different steps which allow this process to proceed. Coal cannot be efficiently burned in its natural form, because it comes in large chunks, which make the combustion process inefficient.

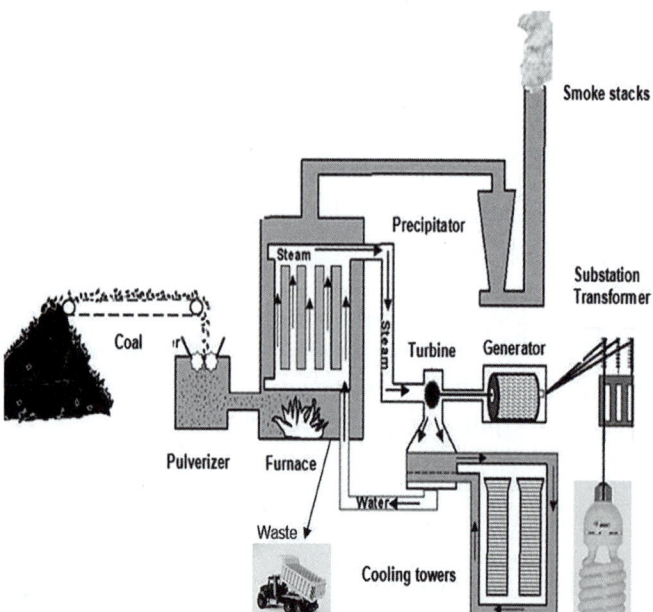

Figure 2-27. Coal burning power plant

Instead, the coal must be pulverized into extremely small particles, as fine as baby powder in most cases. The powder is then mixed with hot air, and the mixture is blown into a furnace called a "firebox." Here the coal powder is burned in suspension and before being able

to settle on the bottom or the walls of the furnace. This space burning results in the most complete combustion of the coal, which produces the hottest flame and heat which can be obtained from coal.

There are also rows of pipes in the furnace walls, through which flows water. The heat from the burning coal heats the water quickly and turns it into a high-temperature (1,000°F) and high-pressure (3,000 PSI) steam. The superheated steam is injected into the blades of a turbine, where the extreme pressure is enough to turn the turbine blades fast. When the turbine blades turn fast enough, they engage a generator, which produces electric power by rotating magnets on its axles into wire coils. Thus generated electric power is sent to a transformer in the substation, where it is conditioned and sent into the transmission lines for use at a distant location.

After the steam exits the turbine compartment, it is sent into a condenser in the basement of a power plant, where the steam is cooled by running it between rows of pipes in which flows cool water that which can be returned to the boiler where the entire process is repeated. The cooling water, on exiting the condenser, is very hot and could be used for heating in industrial processes, or is discharged into a local river, lake, or the ocean.

The daily operation of the different stages of coal burning and power generation are complex, but are standardized operations, where the personnel is highly skilled, and where the execution of the different steps is controlled and documented at all times, with safety as a priority.

Power Plant Decommissioning and Land Restoration

After several decades of exploration, mines usually go dry and must be shut down. In most cases, there is still some coal left in the ground, but its extraction is too difficult and expensive, so the mine must be shut down and the land returned to its original state. Sometimes it is, but very often this does not happen.

The major steps in the coal burning power plant decommissioning and reclamation are:

- Plant shut down and disassembly
- Turbine and generator dismantling and removal
- Smoke stack demolition and dismantling
- Rigging and removal of support equipment
- Construction and equipment waste disposal
- Surface land decontamination and reclamation

The decommissioning effort usually starts with disassembly and removal of key electro-mechanical components, including breaker boxes, transformers, conduit, wring, and other electrical components. The rest of the equipment, furnace components, piping, turbine rotor and blading, generators, static exciters, frequency changers, heat exchangers, and other related mechanical equipment is disassembled and removed from the facility as well.

This effort might also involve selective dismantling and rigging of some power equipment pieces, which are in good condition and could be reused or sold. When all equipment has been removed from a facility, the buildings are demolished and the waste, together with the demolished equipment, is loaded on dump trucks for removal and disposal.

Last, but not least, the land that was occupied by the plant must be decontaminated, leveled, and/or otherwise brought to its original state. This, too, is usually a very complex, lengthy, and expensive undertaking.

All decommissioning, rigging and dismantling work is done in accordance to all safety rules and regulations and is quite labor intensive and expensive as well.

Coal Power Plant Costs

The overall cost for the planning, design and construction of a power plant in the US is approximately $1,500 per kW installed, so a 500 MWp coal-burning power plant would cost about $750 million in 2010 dollars. This includes all steps of the concept-to-implementation process. Of course, running the plant is a different matter that requires additional expense for materials, power, labor, etc.

We need to emphasize here that because the expense of starting and operating a coal-fired power plant is so great, only very large companies or governments can undertake and complete the task. Lately, even they cannot get the necessary permits, for a number of reasons, in addition to the trend of using natural gas instead of coal. As a matter of fact a number of the existing coal-fired power plants are being converted to gas.

On top of that, the cost of construction has been sky rocketing. For example, the cost to build a new 300 MW coal-fired power plant in Wisconsin, which would generate enough power to supply 150,000 homes, is now projected to cost $1.1 billion if it is built in southwestern Wisconsin and $1.2 billion if it is built in Ohio. Only several months back, the projected cost of this plant was $850-$950 million, but the cost of building power plants has risen quickly lately, as the prices of steel, concrete and other materials have escalated.

Pollution Footprint of Coal Power Plant Equipment

Similar to the mining process, a number of large and small pieces of equipment are used during power plant construction and operation. Starting with plant design and construction, we see pollution taking place in the shape of exhaust from large trucks, and heavy plumes of smoke from large ground-leveling bulldozers.

Plant equipment arrives on trains and trucks. All this machinery was made somewhere on the planet some time in the past, where and when their manufacturing processes and transport created a significant pollution footprint. As in the case of mining, we would assign 5-10% of the manufacturing and transport of power plant equipment to the initial construction step (A).

The main pieces of equipment, boilers, turbines, generators, etc. arrive in wooden boxes or on enormous trailers or rail cars. These are assembled with the help of other equipment and put to work after creating another set of pollution tracks (B).

Many smaller items include tools and consumables for personal or specialized operations, shovels, helmets, computers, boots, shoes, overalls, first aid kits, goggles, etc. All these were also made somewhere around the world, sometime in the past, and transported to the mine. During their manufacturing processes and transport, they also left a significant pollution footprint (C).

To complete the pollution footprint picture, we must add the people involved in the entire process—engineers and technicians involved in the equipment manufacture, transport, installation, setup, and operation. These people drive cars and use air transportation, leaving another significant set of pollution footprints (D).

So, the total pollution footprint of the power plant's equipment cradle-to-grave process is expressed by:

$$P_f = A + B + C + D$$

where

P_f is the total pollution footprint

A   is the equipment manufacturing and transport to the mine

B   is equipment assembly, test and installation at the mine

C   is the manufacturing and transport to the mine of tools and consumables, and

D   is the pollution footprint of the equipment personnel during the design and setup phases.

Combining the pollution footprint of A (the plant equipment manufacturing and transport) with B (plant equipment assembly, test and installation), adding C (the manufacturing and transport of the tools and consumables), plus D (the pollution footprint of the equipment personnel) gives us the environmental footprint of the plant equipment before even starting the plant operations.

Here again, this footprint is significant! It stretches from one part of the country to the other...and around the world.

In order to put a value on it we must take inventory of all items delivered to the plant, and needed for its design, construction and operation. We must take a close look at the manufacturing of a boiler, a turbine, or a generator, as well as a number of other pieces of equipment used at the plants.

These are also very large pieces of equipment that require hundreds and thousands of tons of metals to create. Each of these began as an iron ore dug from a mine somewhere in the world, and then transported to a smelter. The molten metal was shaped in various forms and shipped to various parts manufacturers, who drilled, welded and otherwise constructed the parts for these vehicles.

Remember, we are talking about huge pieces of metal—some as big as an entire building. These parts are then packed and loaded on railroad cars or trucks to be shipped to the assembly facility. The parts of a large dump truck or a dragline might require a dozen railroad cars for transport. At the assembly plant they are assembled into major components, or entire units. After another loading and unloading operation, they finally arrive at the plant for final assembly, installation, and testing. This is a long process.

Putting a dollar value on this process would be too complex for our purposes, so suffice it to say that the pollution effects of these steps are significant. We will take a second, closer look at these processes and their environmental effects in the following chapters.

Upon starting the power plant's operation, the equipment continues to generate secondary pollution. Spare parts for these monsters are periodically arriving from the parts manufacturers, after leaving their own trail of footprints. Again, we will revisit these activities and their environmental effects, and attempt to assign a dollar figure to them in the following chapters.

After 20-30 years of non-stop operation, the power plant is finally declared obsolete, at which point it must be shut down and decommissioned. Decommissioning and land reclamation are major, expensive, and polluting undertakings as well. The equipment and materials used during the decommissioning and waste disposal process create additional air and ground pollution which is not to be ignored.

Additional, specialized equipment and personnel (environmental specialists and inspectors), are usually brought in to assist with and coordinate the effort. With them, more pollution footprints are left at the already exhausted mine.

When the final tally is made, a significant part of the emissions and overall pollution can be attributed to the plant's equipment and support personnel. This number is significant and we will go through the calculations in the next chapters as well.

Air, Liquid and Solid Pollution

The coal mining, transport, and burning process consists of several steps, each of which generates air, liquid, and solid pollution.

Air pollution is generated at all stages, from mine site development, through mine operation, and during processing and transport of coal. Most of the air pollution throughout coal's entire life cycle, however, is emitted during its burning power plants.

Coal-fired power plants have been blamed for emitting most of the GHG pollutants that are causing environmental problems, including global warming.

Liquid pollution is also a big problem all through the coal mining process and burning cycle. Mines and processing facilities use huge amounts of water which is dumped after use. The waste water is stored in large polls and often finds its way into the local water table or other bodies of water.

Coal-fired plants also use a lot of water for cooling the steam prior to being reused, a process which contaminates local water supplies and increases their temperature.

Solid pollution is also a problem during coal production and use, because the process demands movement of large amounts of coal, generating a lot of dust and solid waste. Removal of large amounts of soil from surface mines, the overburden, is part of the mining process that is accompanied with the generation of a lot of dust and soil waste. Depending on the nature, attitude, and grade of the deposits, often much more waste soil is removed from the surface mine than the total quantity of ore mined there.

Solid waste is classified as either *sterile* or *mineralized*, and the movement and stacking (or dumping) of this material forms a major part of the mine planning process. When the mineralized package is determined by an economic cut-off, the soil waste is dumped separately (if it contains some minerals) with the intention of harvesting those, if that becomes economically viable.

Civil engineering design parameters are used in the design of the waste dumps, and special conditions apply to high-rainfall areas, e.g. Brazil or Venezuela, or where the dumps are created in seismically active areas like Chile, Peru, and parts of Canada.

Coal-fired power plants also generate immense amounts of ash and solid waste during the coal-burning process, and that is stored in mountainous heaps on-site or transported for disposal off-site.

All in all, coal production, processing, transport, and burning are dirty endeavors in which large quantities of toxic gasses, liquids, and solids are emitted, spilled, piled up and otherwise left behind. All of these must be taken into account when discussing the coal process.

We take a very close at the environmental impacts of coal production and use in the next chapters.

CRUDE OIL

Crude oil is second to none in its importance as a transportation and power generation fuel. Our dependence on its magical properties is unprecedented, but unfortunately we have burned most of what Nature took millions of years to create, so now we must be very careful how we use crude oil.

In present-day terms, underuse of crude oil would mean significantly slowing down economic development in many countries, while overuse would exhaust the already depleted supply and force us into an era of oil-less existence. It's a catch-22.

In the beginning...

Immediately after the big bang there were no coal, oil, or natural gas deposits on Earth. These were formed through millions of years by complex and very lengthy processes. We saw above how coal was created during the time oil and natural gas were also created. These processes also took millions of years to complete, and as a matter of fact they are not fully completed yet. This can be evidenced by the different coal layers, which show different stages of coal development—from peat (the most recent) to anthracite (the oldest).

Oil and natural gas formation processes, in most cases, were somewhat different from that of coal. Coal's beginning started in the much shallower and warmer oceans, where dead animals, vegetation, and other organic matter was continuously falling into the waters.

The bulk of the organic matter were tiny, surface dwelling organisms called plankton, which includes several animal species (zooplankton) and plant species (phytoplankton). Phytoplankton uses photosynthesis to capture the solar energy that is the basis of marine food chains.

The organic materials sank to the floor eventually, to join with the inorganic matter, consisting of sand and dirt, carried in by the rivers and land runoff. The different materials mixed together on the ocean floor, resulting in a thick layer of sediments.

As the water level increased, the pressure of the overlying water compacted the sediments. A number of natural processes, such as crystallization and cementation of inorganic minerals eventually converted the soft sediments into solid material.

Over time, the ocean-floor sediments were buried deeper and deeper, and the water became deeper, so the sediment layers were subjected to ever-increasing, extremely high pressures and temperatures. This resulted in the formation of the layered solids, under the ocean floor, called sedimentary rock.

During the long exposure to high pressure and elevated temperature, organic material in the sedimentary layers got cooked, much like in a pressure cookers, but at much higher pressure and temperature, and for much longer.

Initially, the sediments cooked to a waxy substance called kerogen. Kerogen, as in tar and shale oil deposits, is similar to the peat segment of the coal formation process and represents the not-yet completed process of conversion to crude oil. Like peat, it has different (inferior heating) properties than the respective final products, crude oil and coal. As time passed and the cooking processes continued, the sediment was eventually converted into a combination of organic liquids and gases which we call petroleum.

NOTE: Although the term petroleum is usually used for liquids (i.e., crude oil) alone, officially petroleum refers to both liquids and gases. So when we talk about petroleum, we do refer to a group of fossils which contain both crude oil and natural gas.

Petroleum contains some of the energy (sunlight) that was captured many years ago by the plankton on the ocean surface. This energy is what we need badly today, and on which our comfort and progress depend. Because of that, we now extract millions of gallons from the large petroleum deposits formed by the migration and pooling of oils and gases into large underground reservoirs.

There are also small petroleum deposits in many sedimentary rock formations around the world, but extracting them is technologically difficult and economically unfeasible in the present state of the art.

Remember, when we talk about petroleum, we do refer to a group of fossils which contains both crude oil and natural gas. Below we will take a close look at present-day crude oil production and use, followed by natural gas.

In the Recent Past...

We know that oil in large deposits comes mainly from strata of coarse sandstone, formed by sand deposited by water ages ago. We've also noticed that there is no oil in flat strata, so we must deduce that the oil flowed from the sediment layers into the sandstone strata, where it is held like in a sponge and has remained through the millennia.

After the initial explosion and the following overheating at the very beginning, Earth's mass grew cooler and went though a number of processes such as folding, during which horizontal movements press inward and move rock layers upward into a fold or anticline; and faulting, where the layers of rock crack, and one side shifts upward or downward; and pinching out, where a layer of impermeable rock is squeezed upward into the reservoir rock.

While undergoing all these different processes the Earth's surface layer, the crust, twisted and wrinkled, so that oil and gas is now found in the large sandstone wrinkles, with gas on top and oil on the bottom. If cracks develop in the strata, oil would usually run toward a lower level.

Trapped gas is usually under pressure and is constantly looking for a way out. If we know where it is, we could easily drill to it and pipe it for use in a house or business. Not long ago, near Niagara Falls there was a gas deposit that constantly released gas, until somebody drove a pipe down and lit the gas. The flame was 3-4 feet high and was visible from far away.

The presence of gas is often an indication that there is oil underneath too. This is how the first colonists discovered petroleum in New York, but they didn't know what to do with it. Native Americans in the area used oil in the local springs as medicine. They also soaked their blankets with oil on the surface and then wrung them out to sell the oil.

Later, the first "gusher" was discovered by accident, when workmen drilled 500 feet down and a high pressure stream of crude oil burst forth, hurling tools and people high into the air. They just let the oil gush out, since they didn't know how to stop it or what to do with it.

A large gusher in Lakeview, California, spewed 50,000 barrels of oil a day to a height of 350 feet. The steady oil column sprayed the countryside for more than a mile's diameter. The oil flowed away as a river, and no one could stop it or store it. Finally a large storage tank was built around the well with stones and sand bags.

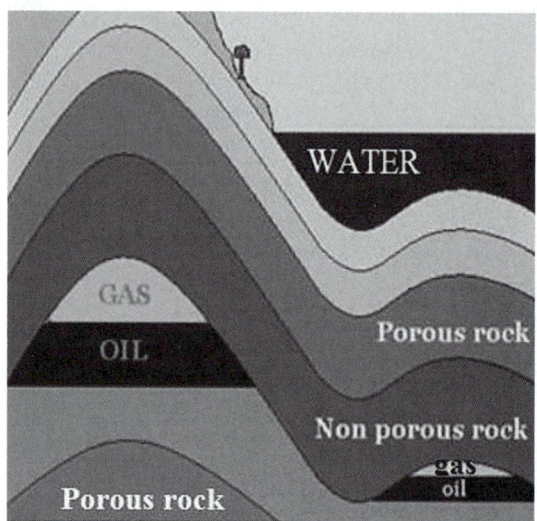

Figure 2-28. Crude oil deposits

The high pressure with which oil rises is sometimes due to the pressure of natural gas in the deposit. This is confirmed by the fact that the pressure is reduced with time, after the oil is pumped out for awhile.

So in the past, the landowner who thought there was oil in his ground, would build a derrick over it with the intention of collecting the oil and selling it. The derrick usually consisted of four wooden or metal beams, 30-100 feet high, firmly held together by crossbeams. It was positioned over the spot where the oil well was to be dug. An engine house nearby provided power for the drilling machine.

An iron pipe eight or ten inches in diameter was driven slowly down in the ground until it came to the oil-containing rock. At this point regular drilling operations began.

A pulley mounted on top of the derrick held a heavy-duty rope to one end of which were attached the drilling tools. The drilling tools went down in the pipe and drilled a hole in the rock day and night. While the drill was busy making the hole, a sand pump sucked out water and loose bits of stone from the drilling hole.

As soon as the drill reached the bottom of the strata, the sides of the bore hole were cased to keep water out, and drilling continued. Then the drill penetrated the oil-bearing sandstone and if there was oil in it, it gushed out.

Often, however, drill as they might, oil was nowhere to be found. That was because although it was under there somewhere (and near the surface in places), more often than not it was as deep as 1,000-5,000 feet. To reach these depths, specialized equipment and advanced procedures are needed.

This is where the modern oil drilling industry comes in. Today's drilling rigs, with their sophisticated tools, computerized controls and GPS navigation can find and reach oil and gas many thousands of feet beneath the surface—on land or sea.

Recently a more sophisticated and efficient method of horizontal drilling is promising extraction from depths and locations that were impossible to even imagine several short years back.

Crude Oil Properties

Crude oil is actually mixtures of many (dozens and even hundreds) of different species of organic chemical compounds, most of which are classified as hydrocarbons—or chemicals that contain both carbon (C) and hydrogen (H).

Some of these are paraffins, naphthenes, aromatics, or combinations of these, such as alkyl naphthenes and aromatics, and the polycyclic compounds. Mercaptan, thiophene and others are also present in high concentration as well. And there are olefins, which usually are not present in crude oil, but are formed during decomposition of the crude oil components during high temperature distillation processes.

To complete the soup, a number of other chemicals, some of which are inorganic (not carbon and hydrogen containing) are found in raw crude oils. Sulfur in the form of free (elemental) sulfur (S) and hydrogen sulfide (H_2S) are the most troublesome byproducts of the oil refining process. They cause corrosion and produce sulfur dioxide (SO_2), which is toxic and creates acid rain when burned. The other major sulfur compound, H_2S is a vicious poison, which paralyzes the olfactory nerves so that its victim is unaware of its presence and can choke to death.

On the other hand, the petroleum industry produces large quantities of sulfur by converting the H_2S byproduct to elemental sulfur, which is quite useful in other industries. A lot of nitrogen is produced also, and can be captured and used in other applications.

Salts, such as chlorides, sulfates, and carbonates (compounds of sodium, calcium, and magnesium) are found in crude oil in liquid or small particles, which are expressed in pounds of salt (NaCl equivalent) per thousand barrels of crude.

These salts cause corrosion and deposits in heating and heat-transfer equipment by adhering to the surfaces of boilers and pipes. Even worse, in the presence of H_2S and H_2O they are extremely corrosive, and can damage metal equipment, even stainless steel.

Very importantly, crude oil and all its organic components are highly flammable. Their different boiling points are shown in Table 2-10.

Table 2-10. Crude oil fractions

Compound	Boil °F	MW
LPG	−44-31	44-58
Gasoline	31-400	100-110
Jet fuel	380-520	160-190
Diesel fuel	520-650	245
Gas oil	650-800	320
Residuals	800-1000	—
Vacuum gas	800-1000	430
Crude coke	2,000	2,500

where:
 Boil is the boiling point in degree F, and
 MW is the molecular weight of the different compounds

It can be easily seen that the boiling point increases as the compounds get heavier—as their MW increases.

Most crude oil compounds can be ignited at different temperatures, for which we use a standard, called auto-ignition temperature (AIT) for comparative purposes. AIT is basically a measure of the temperature at which a vapor from a particular compound will ignite spontaneously (in the absence of a flame). For example, gasoline or naphtha could ignite spontaneously on coming into contact with a 600°F surface.

The specific gravity of crude oil and petroleum products is generally expressed as degrees API (American Petroleum Institute), which is defined by the following equation:

$$API = \left(\frac{141.5}{S.G.} \right) - 131.5$$

where:
S.G. is the specific gravity, which is the ratio of the density of the material at 60°F to the density of water at that same temperature. For example, the gravity of water at 60°F is 10° API.

Classification

American Petroleum Institute's inverted scale for denoting the "lightness" or "heaviness" of crude oils and other liquid hydrocarbons (calibrated in API degrees, or degrees API), is used universally to expresses a crude's relative density in an inverse measure. The lighter the crude, the higher the API gravity, and vice versa, because the lighter the crude, the higher its market value.

Oil with API greater than 30° is termed light; between 22° and 30°, medium; below 22°, heavy; and below 10°, extra heavy.

Asphalt on average has an API gravity of 8°, while Brent Crude's is 35.5°, and gasoline's is 50°.

Crudes can be classified as "light" or "heavy," a characteristic which refers to the oil's relative density based on the American Petroleum Institute (API) gravity. This measurement reflects how light or heavy a crude oil is compared to water. If an oil's API gravity is greater than 10, it is lighter than water and will float. If an oil's API gravity is less than 10, it is heavier than water and will sink.

Light crude oil is defined as having an API gravity higher than 31.1°API. Medium oil is defined as having an API gravity between 22.3°API and 31.1°API. Heavy oil is defined as having an API gravity below 22.3°API.

Lighter crudes are easier and less expensive to produce. They generally have a higher percentage of light hydrocarbons that can be recovered with simple distillation at a refinery. Heavy crudes can't be produced, transported, and refined by conventional methods because they have high concentrations of sulfur and several metals, particularly nickel and vanadium. Heavy crudes have a density approaching or even exceeding that of water. Heavy crude oils are also known as "tar sands" because of their high bitumen (tar) content.

Crude oils are also measured and qualified by their sulfur content. Crude oils with low sulfur content are classified as "sweet." Those with a higher sulfur content are classified as "sour." Sulfur content is generally considered an undesirable characteristic with respect to both processing and end-product quality. Sweet crudes are usually more desirable and valuable than sour crudes.

Toxicity

Toxicity of crude oil and their derivatives refers to how harmful they might be to humans and other living organisms. Generally, the lighter the oil the more toxic it is considered. EPA has classified crude oils in four categories that reflect how the oils would behave in a spill and its aftermath:

Class A crude oils are light and highly liquid. These clear and volatile oils can spread quickly on impervious surfaces and on water. Their odor is strong and they evaporate quickly, emitting volatiles. Usually flammable, these oils also penetrate porous surfaces such as dirt and sand and may remain in areas into which they have seeped. Humans, fish, and other biota face danger of toxicity to Class A oils. These high-quality light crudes

and the products produced from them are in this class.

Class B oils are considered less toxic than Class A. These oils are generally non-sticky but feel waxy or oily. The warmer it gets, the more likely Class B oils can be to soak into surfaces, and they can be hard to remove. When volatile components of Class B oils evaporate, the result can be a Class C or D residue. Class B includes medium to heavy oils.

Class C oils are heavy, tarry oils (which include residual fuel oils and medium to heavy crudes) that are slow to penetrate into porous solids and are not highly toxic. However, Class C oils are difficult to flush away with water and can sink in water, so they can smother or drown wildlife.

Class D are non-fluid, thick oils, comparatively non-toxic, and don't seep into porous surfaces. Mostly black or dark brown, Class D oils tend to dissolve and cover surfaces when they get hot, which makes cleanup more difficult. Heavy crude oils, such as the bitumen found in tar sands, fall into this class.

Crude Oil Production

According to OPEC, at the end of 2011, the world's proven crude oil reserves stood at 1,481,526 million barrels, of which 1,199,707 million barrels, or 81 percent, was in OPEC member countries. The picture is changing, however, and a number of non-OPEC member countries are increasing their production levels due to new technologies and processes.

Table 2-11. Global oil production and use, 2011.

Country	% of world production	% of world use
Saudi Arabia	13.1	2.4
Russia	12.3	3.3
USA	8.0	24.1
China	4.7	9.0
Canada	3.9	2.5
Iran	5.4	1.1
Mexico	4.7	1.4
Venezuela	3.7	1.0
Kuwait	3.4	1.0
Norway	3.3	1.0

What do we need to find and extract crude oil?

In general terms, the cradle-to-grave oil production and use process consists of:

- Oil search and location
- Proposed area survey
- Environmental studies

- Oil rights and agreements
- Permits and legal issues
- Drill area preparation
- Drilling rig construction
- Daily O&M operations
- Oil transport
- Oil use (burning)
- Decommissioning and area reconstruction

We'll take a close look at all of these steps, to determine the total energy cost and environmental impact of the cradle-to-grave oil production and use process.

Oil Search and Locating

The first step of the oil extraction process is locating significant oil deposits, that are worth the time and expense of extracting the oil. Geologists employed by oil companies or under contract from private firms are the ones that look for and find oil. Their efforts are focused on founding the signs and indications of an oil deposit. These could be a source rock, reservoir rock, and entrapment.

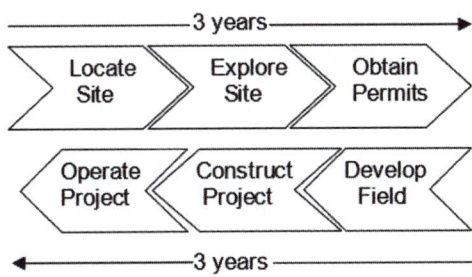

Figure 2-29. Project timeline

In the past, geologists had to read the surface features, surface rock and soil types, and then drilled small core samples to confirm their suspicions. A variety of other methods were applied too. Sensitive gravity meters were used to measure small deviations in the Earth's gravitational field, which could be translated into gaps of oil deposits. Magnetometers were also used to measure changes in the Earth's magnetic field that might be caused by flowing oil. Detecting the smell of escaping gas by sensitive electronic sniffers was another good way, but most commonly, seismology was used. In this method, shock waves are created and travel through the rock layers where some are reflected by the different materials.

Such a shock wave is created by a compressed-air gun which shoots pulses of air into the water (for exploration over water), or a thumper truck that slams heavy plates into the ground (for exploration over land), or by explosives that are detonated after being drilled into the ground (for exploration on land) or thrown overboard (for exploration in water)

The waves reflected back to the surface travel at different speeds, depending on the type or density of rock layers through which they must pass. Sensitive microphones or vibration detectors pick up the reflections (hydrophones over water, seismometers over land) and seismologists interpret the readings for signs of oil and gas traps. Once a prospective oil strike is found, the location is marked using GPS coordinates on land or marker buoys on water.

Today satellite images and other sophisticated, computerized technologies do most of the work of detecting, interpreting and locating oil deposits.

Oil drilling can be separated as land and off-shore drilling. Land drilling is done on solid ground, while off-shore drilling is done miles from the shore, and sometimes at great depths.

Oil Drilling

Once the oil has been located and the drilling site has been selected, the area must be surveyed, to determine its exact boundaries. Environmental impact studies are conducted as well in most cases.

If everything checks out and the decision is made to proceed with drilling at a site, then the legal work starts. Lease agreements, or land titles, rights-of-way, legal jurisdiction and other conditions must be determined and met.

After the legal issues are settled, the crew prepares the land, in land drilling cases. The land is cleared and leveled for derrick erection, and pumping equipment and support structures are put in place. Access roads also need to be constructed for transporting of equipment and products to and from the oil well.

A lot of water is used during the drilling process, so a source of water must be located nearby. A water well must be drilled in many cases prior to initiating oil drilling. In isolated cases watertank trucks are used instead.

A reserve pit must be dug nearby as well, to deposit rock cuttings and drilling mud during the drilling process. The pit is a temporary structure, which is usually lined with heavy plastic to prevent ground contamination and related cleanup expense. In an ecologically sensitive area, such as a marsh or wilderness, a pit might not be allowed, so the waste materials must be disposed of by trucking them offsite.

The next step is to dig several holes in the place of the oil rig and the main hole, and a rectangular pit, or cellar, is dug around the drilling hole area. This is needed to provide a work space around the hole for workers and drilling accessories.

The main hole drilling can be then started, first with a small drill truck, since the top part of the hole is larger and shallower than the main portion. The drill hole is then lined with a large-diameter metal pipe, and additional holes are dug off to the side for temporary equipment storage.

The main rig components can be set up now, starting with the power system, which usually is a diesel engine coupled with a generator, to provide electric power for drilling processes. The components of the mechanical system, a hoisting system and a turntable, are set up next. The hoisting setup is used for lifting heavy loads and consists of a mechanical winch with a large steel cable spool, a block-and-tackle pulley, and a receiving storage reel for the cable. The turntable, a part of the drilling mechanism, is installed next.

The main part of the drilling mechanism is the rotating equipment, which consists of a swivel—a large handle that holds the weight of the drill string and allows it to rotate. It also makes a pressure-tight seal on the hole. A kelly is a four- or six-sided pipe that transfers rotary motion to the turntable and drill string, while the turntable drives the rotating motion using power from the electric motors. The drill string consists of a drill pipe (connected sections of about 30 feet) and drill collars consisting of larger-diameter, heavier pipe that fits around the drill pipe and places weight on the drill bit.

A special drill bit that actually cuts up the rock is mounted at the end of the drill. These come in many shapes and materials, such as tungsten carbide steel and diamond. Drill bits are usually specifically designed for the different drilling tasks and rock formations. Finally, the casing is a large-diameter concrete pipe that lines the drill hole and prevents it from collapsing and leaking. It also allows the drilling mud that is pumped into the smaller drill pipe to circulate to the surface.

An oil rig or derrick constructed in this manner is tall enough to allow new sections of drill pipe to be added to the drilling apparatus as drilling progresses and the drill bit goes further down into the ground. A blowout preventer is added to prevent explosions. It consists of several high-pressure valves that seal the high-pressure drill lines and relieve pressure when necessary to prevent a blowout. This prevents uncontrolled gushing of gas or oil to the surface and eliminates fires.

When activated, the circulation system pumps the drilling mud through the kelly, the rotary table, the drill pipes and collars. A mixture of water, clay, and other

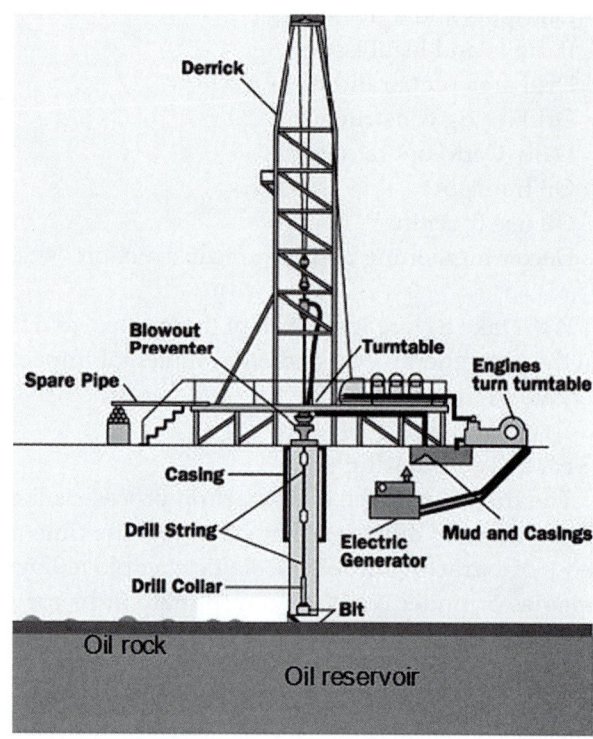

Figure 2-30. Land oil drilling rig

material and chemicals is pumped down in the drill hole and used to carry rock cuttings from the drill bit to the surface.

The pump sucks mud from the mud pits and pumps it to the drilling apparatus and down the hole. Pipes and hoses connect the pump to the drilling apparatus, while the mud-return line returns mud from the hole to the surface and into a shale shaker which separates rock cuttings from the mud.

The shale slide pumps send the waste rock cuttings into the reserve pit, where these are separated from the mud. The cleaned mud is sent into a mud pit to be mixed and recycled in a mud-mixing hopper for another use.

Drilling starts by lowering the drill bit into the ground and rotating it. The drill bit is stopped when it is very close to hitting the oil deposit. Technical and safety checks are completed at this point, and a surface hole is then drilled from the starter hole to a pre-set depth, just above the oil deposit. The surface hole is lined with a casing pipe, which is cemented in place in the center of the hole, to prevent it from collapsing in on itself. The casing pipe is centered by spacers around the outside to keep it centered in the hole. The cement is allowed to harden and is then tested for hardness, alignment and a proper seal.

Drilling in the main hole continues for awhile, and then stops again for the new surface hole area to be lined and cemented. Then the drilling continues further down, repeating the lining and cementing of the surface hole until the rock cuttings in the mud show oil sand, which is a signal that the well's final depth is very near.

Now the drilling mechanism is removed from the hole and a number of tests are performed to confirm the presence of oil. These tests are done by lowering sensors into the main drill hole. Some of tests are well logging, measuring the rock formations, drill-stem testing for measuring the pressures in the hole, and core samples for taking samples of rock to look for characteristics of oil deposit bedrock.

If the tests look good, the hole is drilled further until oil flows into the casing in a controlled manner. A perforating gun is lowered into the well to the depth of the oil deposits and using explosive charges to create holes in the casing through which oil can flow. A smaller-diameter pipe is then run in the hole as a conduit for the oil and gas to flow up through the well and to the surface.

A packer is then run down the outside of the tubing and is allowed to expand to form a seal around the outside of the tubing. A multi-valve structure called a Christmas tree is mounted on the top of the tubing and is cemented to the top of the casing. It allows control of the flow of oil from the bottom of the well to the surface.

The flow of oil into the well is started by acids pumped down into the well and out the perforations. Thus dissolved channels in the limestone allow oil into the well. If the rock is sandstone, then a specially blended fluid containing a mixture of sand, walnut shells, and aluminum pellets is pumped down the well. The pressure makes small fractures in the sandstone that allow oil to flow into the well, while the mixture holds these fractures open.

At this point the oil rig is removed from the site and a set of production equipment is installed for continuous extraction of the oil. Several methods are used for this. The pump system uses an electric motor to drive a gear box that moves a lever. The lever pushes and pulls the pump rod, attached to a pump. The up-and-down action creates a suction that draws oil up through the well.

If the oil is too heavy to flow freely, an enhanced oil recovery method is used, where a second hole is drilled into the oil reservoir, and steam is injected into it under pressure. The heat thins the oil and the pressure helps push it up the well.

Offshore Oil Drilling

While oil extracted by the above methods is done on solid ground, much more complex and dangerous ef-

forts are needed to extract oil from under the deep waters of rivers, lakes and oceans. If it is done correctly it can also be efficient, safe and profitable, but if things go wrong, the results can be deadly for the workers and devastating for the surrounding environment. We only need to mention Deep Horizon to get a feel of the consequences from such a scenario.

The search, location, and exploration of potential oil deposits is similar to those described for land use. When all preliminaries are completed, a mobile offshore drilling unit (MODU) is brought in and installed over the potential oil deposit. They are then used to dig the initial well and sometimes are converted into production rigs. More often, however, MODU rigs are replaced by permanent oil production rigs for long-term oil extraction.

Figure 2-31. Offshore oil rig

There are several different types of MODUs: a submersible MODU is used in shallow and calm waters. It is a barge supported on the sea floor, and on the deck are steel posts that extend above the water line. A drilling platform rests on top of the steel posts and is used to drill the oil hole, similar to the methods described above.

A *jackup* MODU is a rig that sits on the deck of a floating barge, which is towed to the drilling site. The jackup is set up can be used in depths of up to 525 feet, by extending its legs down to the sea floor and resting them there without penetrating the floor. The jackup is then ratcheted up so that the platform is kept above the water level to keep it safe from high waves. Drilling can commence in a similar fashion as described above.

Drill ships are special ships designed for deep-water oil drilling. They are equipped with a drilling rig mounted on the top deck, with a drill setup operating through a hole in the hull. Once the drilling starts, the ship uses a combination of anchors and propellers to maneuver as needed to correct for waves and currents.

Semi-submersible drilling rigs float on the surface of the ocean on top of huge, submerged pontoons, using propulsion systems to navigate to drilling sites and to maneuver over the hole. Computers control the anchor chain tension and engine power to correct for waves and currents.

During the drilling process, a blowout preventer (BOP) is installed at the ocean floor. It is equipped with a pair of hydraulically powered clamps that close off the pipe to the rig in the case of a blowout.

When the hole is drilled and ready for production, the well is sealed by a pair of plugs. The bottom plug sits near the oil deposit and drilling mud or seawater keeps it in place, while the top plug is placed to cap the oil well. Then the well is hooked to a production rig which operates in a similar way to the land-based oil rigs.

OIL TRANSPORT

All oil must be transported from the point of production to the point of use. After crude oil is pumped from the ground, its next step is transportation to a refinery where the desired end products are generated. It gets to the refinery by pipeline typically, but the pipeline may either be connected to the well or filled at a tanker port. There are other modes of transport as well.

The transport of oil is big business. The world's tank ship fleet numbers more than 5000. On any given day as much as 750 million barrels of crude oil and products may be in tankers on the world's oceans. The U.S. pipeline system totals about 223,000 miles. From the refineries, gasoline, fuel oil, and so on, go by truck or train tank car to wholesalers or large consumers. The U.S. tank truck fleet numbers about 160,000, and the number of rail tank cars is over 165,000.

The different oil transport methods include pipelines, marine vessels, tank trucks, and rail tank cars to transport crude oils, compressed and liquefied hydrocarbon gases, liquid petroleum products and other chemicals from their point of origin to pipeline terminals, refineries, distributors and consumers.

Following is a closer look at the main components of this important chapter of in oil's cradle-to-grave life cycle.

Pipelines

At one time or another all crude oils, natural gas, liquefied natural gas, liquefied petroleum gas (LPG) and petroleum products flow through some type of pipeline from the well to a refinery, gas plant, terminal, or consumer.

There are aboveground, underwater and underground pipelines, varying in size from several inches to several feet in diameter. These pipelines move vast amounts of crude oil, natural gas, LHGs and liquid petroleum products across the US and most other countries.

The first successful crude-oil pipeline, a 2-inch-diameter wrought iron pipe, 6 miles long with a capacity of about 800 barrels a day, was built in Pennsylvania in 1865. During WWII large pipe networks were built in the US, to move oil from coast to coast. A large pipeline project, planned to deliver Canadian syncrude oil to Gulf Coast refineries is stalled in the permitting and political debate stages.

Figure 2-32. The Alaska pipeline

The lower 48 states receive 1.5 to 1.6 million barrels of oil per day, courtesy of the Alaskan pipeline. This pipeline, 789 miles of 48-inch steel pipe, curving up and down and around hills and valleys, carries great quantities of oil from the rich North Slope field to the port of Valdez in southern Alaska. Here the oil is loaded on tankers for shipment south. The Alaskan pipeline was built in controversy which is still unresolved and is a subject of high-level debates and legal battles.

Today, liquid petroleum products are moved long distances through pipelines at speeds of up to 6 miles per hour, assisted by large pumps and compressors along the way, at intervals ranging from 60 miles to 200 miles. Pipeline pumping pressures and flow rates are controlled throughout the system to maintain a constant movement of product within the pipeline. Sensors, control mechanisms and safety devices are installed along the length of the major pipelines to prevent spills, fires, and other possible disasters.

Pipelines run from the frozen tundra of Alaska and Siberia to the hot deserts of the Middle East, across rivers, lakes, seas, swamps and forests, over and through mountains and under cities and towns. There is a network of over 95,000 miles of petroleum product pipelines in the United States. This network delivers finished petroleum products to the end customers. It is separate from the network of crude oil pipelines, and balances the demand and supply conditions in each region.

The initial construction of pipelines is difficult and expensive, but once they are built, properly maintained and operated, they provide one of the safest and most economical means of transporting these products.

Types of Pipelines

There are four basic types of pipelines in the oil and gas industry— flow lines, gathering lines, crude trunk pipelines and petroleum product trunk pipelines.

Flow lines move crude oil or natural gas from producing wells to producing field storage tanks and reservoirs. Flow lines may vary in size from 5 cm in diameter in older, lower-pressure fields with only a few wells, to much larger lines in multi-well, high-pressure fields. Offshore platforms use flow lines to move crude and gas from wells to the platform storage and loading facility. Lease lines carry all of the oil produced on a single lease to a storage tank.

Gathering and feeder lines collect oil and gas from several locations for delivery to central accumulating points, such as from field crude oil tanks and gas plants to marine docks. Feeder lines collect oil and gas from several locations for delivery directly into trunk lines, such as moving crude oil from offshore platforms to on-shore crude trunk pipelines. Gathering lines and feeder lines are typically larger in diameter than flow lines.

Crude trunk pipelines move natural gas and crude oil long distances, from producing areas or marine docks to refineries and from refineries to storage and distribution facilities by 1- to 3-m-diameter or larger trunk pipelines.

Petroleum product trunk pipelines move liquid petroleum products such as gasoline and fuel oil from refineries to terminals and from marine and pipeline terminals to distribution terminals. Product pipelines may also distribute products from terminals to bulk plants and consumer storage facilities, and occasionally from refineries direct to consumers. Product pipelines are used to move LPG from refineries to distributor storage facilities or large industrial users.

Batch Shipments and Interface

Although pipelines originally were used to move only crude oil, they evolved into carrying all types and grades of liquid petroleum products. Because petroleum products are transported by pipelines in successive batches, there is co-mingling or mixing of the products at the interfaces. The product intermix is controlled by one of three methods: downgrading (derating), using liquid and solid spacers for separation or reprocessing the intermix.

Radioactive tracers, color dyes and spacers may be placed into the pipeline to identify where the interfaces occur. Radioactive sensors, visual observation, or gravity tests are conducted at the receiving facility to identify different pipeline batches.

Petroleum products are normally transported through pipelines in batch sequences with compatible crude oils or products adjoining. One way to maintaining product quality and integrity, downgrading or derating, is by lowering the interface between the two batches to the level of the least affected product. For example, a batch of high-octane premium gasoline is typically shipped immediately before or after a batch of lower-octane regular gasoline. The small quantity of the two products which has intermixed will be downgraded to the lower octane rating regular gasoline.

When shipping gasoline before or after diesel fuel, a small amount of diesel interface is allowed to blend into the gasoline, rather than blending gasoline into the diesel fuel, which could lower its flashpoint. Batch interfaces are typically detected by visual observation, gravitometers or sampling.

Liquid and solid spacers or cleaning pigs may be used to physically separate and identify different batches of products. The solid spacers are detected by a radioactive signal and diverted from the pipeline into a special receiver at the terminal when the batch changes from one product to another. Liquid separators may be water or another product that does not co-mingle with either of the batches it is separating and is later removed and reprocessed. Kerosene, which is downgraded (derated) to another product in storage or is recycled, can also be used to separate batches.

A third method of controlling the interface, often used at the refinery ends of pipelines, is to return the interface to be reprocessed. Products and interfaces which have been contaminated with water may also be returned for reprocessing.

Marine Transport

The majority of the world's crude oil is transported by tankers from producing areas such as the Middle

East and Africa to refineries in consumer areas such as Europe, Japan and the United States. Oil products were originally transported in large barrels on cargo ships. The first tanker ship, which was built in 1886, carried about 2,300 SDWT (2,240 pounds per ton) of oil. Today's supertankers can be over 300 m long and carry almost 200 times as much oil.

Gathering and feeder pipelines often end at marine terminals or offshore platform loading facilities, where the crude oil is loaded into tankers or barges for transport to crude trunk pipelines or refineries. Petroleum products also are transported from refineries to distribution terminals by tanker and barge. After delivering their cargoes, the vessels return in ballast to loading facilities to repeat the sequence.

Marine Vessels

Oil tankers and barges are vessels designed with the engines and quarters at the rear of the vessel and the remainder of the vessel divided into special compartments (tanks) to carry crude oil and liquid petroleum products in bulk. Cargo pumps are located in pump rooms, and forced ventilation and inerting systems are provided to reduce the risk of fires and explosions in pump rooms and cargo compartments. Modern oil tankers and barges are built with double hulls and other safety features required by the United States Oil Pollution Act of 1990 and the International Maritime Organization (IMO) tanker safety standards. Some new ship designs extend double hulls up the sides of the tankers to provide additional protection. Generally, large tankers carry crude oil, and small tankers and barges carry petroleum products.

Oil tankers are smaller vessels, which in addition to ocean travel can navigate restricted passages such as the Suez and Panama Canals, shallow coastal waters and estuaries. Large oil tankers, which range from 25,000 to 160,000 SDWTs, usually carry crude oil or heavy residual products. Smaller oil tankers, under 25,000 SDWT, usually carry gasoline, fuel oils and lubricants.

Barges carrying oil products operate mainly in coastal and inland waterways and rivers, alone or in groups of two or more, and are either self-propelled or moved by tugboat. They may carry crude oil to refineries, but more often are used as an inexpensive means of transporting petroleum products from refineries to distribution terminals. Barges are also used to off-load cargo from tankers offshore whose draft or size does not allow them to come to the dock.

Supertankers are the least expensive means of long-distance shipment of oil and oil products. These modern ocean-going vessels are huge floating oil tanks that make their slow cumbersome way from the giant oil fields of the Mideast to ports in the industrial countries. As there are no supertanker ports in this country, they are usually unloaded off-shore into smaller tankers. Supertankers are huge. The largest ones presently in service have a DWT (deadweight tonnage, i.e., cargo and fuel capacity) of more than 546,000 tons. They are up to 400 meters long (the length of about five football fields laid end to end) and can carry about 40 million barrels of oil.

Ultra-large and very large crude carriers (ULCCs and VLCCs) are restricted by their size and draft to specific routes of travel. ULCCs are vessels whose capacity is over 300,000 SDWTs, and VLCCs have capacities ranging from 160,000 to 300,000 SDWTs. Most large crude carriers are not owned by oil companies, but are chartered from transportation companies which specialize in operating them.

Their "draft" or how deep they sit in the water is very important for their navigation. A fully loaded draft of over 90 feet prevents such a large ship from going into any of the U.S. ports. Our deepest port, Los Angeles, cannot handle ships of more than 100,000 deadweight tons. As a result, supertankers now unload offshore in the Caribbean and transfer their cargo to smaller tankers for delivery to the United States.

This off-shore transfer method consumes a lot of additional energy and money, and for this purpose an alternative LOOP facility was built. LOOP is the Louisiana Offshore Oil Port (LOOP), which is a deepwater port in the Gulf of Mexico off the coast of Louisiana, near the town of Port Fourchon. It provides offloading and temporary storage services for crude oil transported on some of the largest tankers in the world, since most of them cannot enter US ports.

LOOP presently handles 13% of the nation's oil imports, or about 1.2 million barrels a day. It is connected by a pipeline to the refineries, thus feeding 50% of the U.S. refining capacity.

Tankers offload at LOOP by pumping crude oil through hoses connected to a single point mooring (SPM) base. Three SPMs are located 8,000 feet from the marine terminal. The SPMs are designed to handle ships of up to 700,000 deadweight tons. The crude oil then moves to the marine terminal via a 56-inch diameter submarine pipeline.

The marine terminal consists of a control platform and a pumping platform. The control platform is equipped with a helicopter pad, living quarters, control room, vessel traffic control station, offices and life support equipment. The pumping platform contains four 7,000-hp pumps, power generators, metering and laboratory facilities. Crude oil is handled only on the pumping platform where it is measured, sampled, and boosted to shore through a 48-inch-diameter pipeline.

Railroad Tank Cars

Railroad tank cars are constructed of carbon steel or aluminium and may be pressurized or unpressurized. Modern tank cars can hold up to 171,000 liters of compressed gas at pressures up to 600 psi. Non-pressure tank cars have evolved from the small wooden tank cars of the late 1800s to jumbo tank cars which transport as much as 1.31 million liters of product at pressures up to 100 psi.

Non-pressure tank cars may be individual units with one or multiple compartments, or a string of interconnected tank cars called a tank train. Tank cars are loaded individually, and entire tank trains can be loaded and unloaded from a single point. Both pressure and non-pressure tank cars may be heated, cooled, insulated and thermally protected against fire, depending on their service and the products transported.

All railroad tank cars have top- or bottom-liquid or vapor valves for loading and unloading, and hatch entries for cleaning. They are also equipped with devices intended to prevent the increase of internal pressure when exposed to abnormal conditions. These devices include safety relief valves held in place by a spring which can open to relieve pressure and then close, safety vents with rupture discs that burst open to relieve pressure but cannot reclose, or a combination of the two devices.

A vacuum relief valve is provided for non-pressure tank cars to prevent vacuum formation when unloading from the bottom. Both pressure and non-pressure tank cars have protective housings on top surrounding the loading connections, sample lines, thermometer wells and gauging devices. Platforms for loaders may or may not be provided on top of cars.

Older non-pressure tank cars may have one or more expansion domes. Fittings are provided on the bottom of tank cars for unloading or cleaning. Head shields are provided on the ends of tank cars to prevent puncture of the shell by the coupler of another car during derailments.

Tank Trucks

Petroleum products and crude oil tank trucks are typically constructed of carbon steel, aluminium or a plasticized fiberglass material, and vary in size from 1,900-l tank wagons to jumbo 53,200-l tankers. The capacity of tank trucks is governed by regulatory agencies, and usually is dependent upon highway and bridge capacity limitations and the allowable weight per axle or total amount of product allowed.

There are pressurized and non-pressurized tank trucks, which may be non-insulated or insulated depending on their service and the products transported. Pressurized tank trucks are usually single-compartment, and non-pressurized tank trucks may have single or multiple compartments. Regardless of the number of compartments on a tank truck, each compartment must be treated individually, with its own loading, unloading and safety-relief devices. Compartments may be separated by single or double walls. Regulations may require that incompatible products and flammable and combustible liquids carried in different compartments on the same vehicle be separated by double walls. When pressure testing compartments, the space between the walls should also be tested for liquid or vapor.

Tank trucks have either hatches which open for top loading, valves for closed top- or bottom-loading and unloading, or both. All compartments have hatch entries for cleaning and are equipped with safety relief devices to mitigate internal pressure when exposed to abnormal conditions. These devices include safety relief valves held in place by a spring which can open to relieve pressure and then close, and hatches on non-pressure tanks which pop open if the relief valves fail and rupture discs on pressurized tank trucks.

A vacuum relief valve is provided for each non-pressurized tank truck compartment to prevent vacuum when unloading from the bottom. Non-pressurized tank trucks have railings on top to protect the hatches, relief valves, and vapor recovery system in case of a rollover. Tank trucks are usually equipped with breakaway, self-closing devices installed on compartment bottom loading and unloading pipes and fittings to prevent spills in case of damage in a rollover or collision.

Oil Storage Tanks

There are different types of vertical and horizontal aboveground atmospheric and pressure storage tanks in tank farms, which contain crude oil, petroleum feedstocks, intermediate stocks or finished petroleum products. Their size, shape, design, configuration, and operation depend on the amount and type of products stored and company or regulatory requirements. Aboveground vertical tanks may be provided with double bottoms to prevent leakage onto the ground and cathodic protection to minimize corrosion. Horizontal tanks may be constructed with double walls or placed in vaults to contain any leakage.

Atmospheric cone roof tanks are aboveground, horizontal or vertical, covered, cylindrical atmospheric vessels. Cone roof tanks have external stairways or ladders and platforms, and weak roof-to-shell seams, vents, scuppers or overflow outlets; they may have appurtenances such as gauging tubes, foam piping and chambers, overflow sensing and signaling systems, automatic gauging systems and so on.

When volatile crude oil and flammable liquid petroleum products are stored in cone roof tanks there is an opportunity for the vapor space to be within the flammable range. Although the space between the top of the product and the tank roof is normally vapor rich, an atmosphere in the flammable range can occur when product is first put into an empty tank or as air enters the tank through vents or pressure/vacuum valves when product is withdrawn and as the tank breathes during temperature changes. Cone roof tanks may be connected to vapor recovery systems.

Conservation tanks are a type of cone roof tank with an upper and lower section separated by a flexible membrane designed to contain any vapor produced when the product warms and expands due to exposure to sunlight and to return the vapor to the tank when it cools and condenses at night. Conservation tanks are typically used to store aviation gasoline and similar products.

Atmospheric floating roof tanks are aboveground, vertical, open top or covered cylindrical atmospheric vessels that are equipped with floating roofs. The primary purpose of the floating roof is to minimize the vapor space between the top of the product and the bottom of the floating roof so that it is always vapor rich, thus precluding the chance of a vapor-air mixture in the flammable range. All floating roof tanks have external stairways or ladders and platforms, adjustable stairways or ladders for access to the floating roof from the platform, and may have appurtenances such as shunts which electrically bond the roof to the shell, gauging tubes, foam piping and chambers, overflow sensing and signaling systems, automatic gauging systems and so on. Seals or boots are provided around the perimeter of floating roofs to prevent product or vapor from escaping and collecting on the roof or in the space above the roof.

Floating roofs have legs which may be set in high or low positions depending on the type of operation. Legs are normally maintained in the low position so that the greatest possible amount of product can be withdrawn from the tank without creating a vapor space between the top of the product and the bottom of the floating roof. As tanks are brought out of service prior to entry for inspection, maintenance, repair or cleaning, there is

a need to adjust the roof legs into the high position to allow room to work under the roof once the tank is empty. When the tank is returned to service, the legs are readjusted into the low position after it is filled with product.

Aboveground floating roof storage tanks are further classified as external floating roof tanks, internal floating roof tanks or covered external floating roof tanks.

External (open top) floating roof tanks are those with floating covers installed on open-top storage tanks. External floating roofs are usually constructed of steel and provided with pontoons or other means of flotation. They are equipped with roof drains to remove water, boots or seals to prevent vapor releases, and adjustable stairways to reach the roof from the top of the tank regardless of its position. They may also have secondary seals to minimize release of vapor to the atmosphere, weather shields to protect the seals, and foam dams to contain foam in the seal area in case of a fire or seal leak. Entry onto external floating roofs for gauging, maintenance or other activities may be considered confined-space entry, depending on the level of the roof below the top of the tank, the products contained in the tank, and government regulations and company policy.

Internal floating roof tanks usually are cone roof tanks which have been converted by installing buoyant decks, rafts or internal floating covers inside the tank. Internal floating roofs are typically constructed of various types of sheet metal, aluminum, plastic or metal-covered plastic expanded foam, and their construction may be of the pontoon or pan type, solid buoyant material, or a combination of these. Internal floating roofs are provided with perimeter seals to prevent vapor from escaping into the portion of the tank between the top of the floating roof and the exterior roof. Pressure/vacuum valves or vents are usually provided at the top of the tank to control any hydrocarbon vapors which may accumulate in the space above the internal floater. Internal floating roof tanks have ladders installed for access from the cone roof to the floating roof. Entry onto internal floating roofs for any purpose should be considered confined-space entry.

Covered (external) floating roof tanks are basically external floating roof tanks that have been retrofitted with a geodesic dome, snow cap, or similar semi-fixed cover or roof so that the floating roof is no longer open to the atmosphere. Newly constructed covered external floating roof tanks may incorporate typical floating roofs designed for internal floating roof tanks. Entry into covered external floating roofs for gauging, maintenance or other activities may be considered confined-space entry, depending on the construction of the dome or cover, the level of the roof below the top of the tank, the products contained in the tank, and government regulations and company policy.

Tank Farms

Tank farms are groupings of storage tanks at producing fields; refineries; marine, pipeline and distribution terminals; and bulk plants which store crude oil and petroleum products. Within tank farms, individual tanks or groups of two or more tanks are usually surrounded by enclosures called berms, dykes or fire walls. These tank farm enclosures may vary in construction and height, from 45-cm earth berms around piping and pumps inside dykes to concrete walls that are taller than the tanks they surround.

Dykes may be built of earth, clay or other materials; they are covered with gravel, limestone or sea shells to control erosion; they vary in height and are wide enough for vehicles to drive along the top. The primary functions of these enclosures are to contain, direct and divert rainwater, physically separate tanks to prevent the spread of fire from one area to another, and to contain a spill, release, leak or overflow from a tank, pump or pipe within the area.

Dyke enclosures may be required by regulation or company policy to be sized and maintained to hold a specific amount of product. For example, a dyke enclosure may need to contain at least 110% of the capacity of the largest tank therein, allowing for the volume displaced by the other tanks and the amount of product remaining in the largest tank after hydrostatic equilibrium is reached. Dyke enclosures may also be required to be constructed with impervious clay or plastic liners to prevent spilled or released product from contaminating soil or groundwater.

CRUDE OIL PROCESSING

Crude oil is the stuff that comes from the ground when a crude oil deposit is found. It is unprocessed oil which is also known as petroleum, or fossil fuel. This is because it was made naturally, from decaying plants and animals (or fossils) living in ancient seas millions of years ago. In most cases, crude oil is found under the oceans, or in places which were once sea beds.

Crude oils vary in color, from clear to tar-black, and their viscosity varies from water-like, to molasses-like, to almost solid. Crude oil is extremely valuable material. It is for making many different substances, all of which contain hydrocarbons.

NOTE: Hydrocarbons are organic materials that contain hydrogen and carbon in their molecules which come in various lengths and structures, from straight chains, to branching chains, to rings.

The two most important characteristics of the fossil fuels are:

- Their high energy content. Many of the things derived from crude oil (like gasoline, diesel fuel and paraffin wax) have large energy content. Hydrocarbon chains are very versatile and can also take on many different forms. The smallest hydrocarbon is methane (CH_4), which is a gas that is lighter than air. Longer chains with five or more carbons are liquids, like gasoline and diesel. Very long chains are solids, like wax or tar.

- Via special chemical reactions we can react and cross-link hydrocarbon chains to obtain consumer goods—anything from synthetic rubber, to nylon and different types of plastics.

The major classes of hydrocarbon types in crude oils include:

— *Paraffins* with the general formula CnH_2n+2, where n is a whole number, usually from 1 to 20. These are straight-or branched-chain molecules which can be gasses or liquids at room temperature depending upon the molecules. Some of these are methane, ethane, propane, butane, isobutane, pentane, hexane—all of which are gasses at room temperature.

— *Aromatics* with general formula C_6H_5 are ringed structures with one or more rings. Each ring contains six carbon atoms, with alternating double and single bonds between the carbons. These hydrocarbons are typically liquids, like benzene and napthalene.

— *Napthenes or Cycloalkanes* with the general formula CnH_{2n}, where n is a whole number usually from 1 to 20, are also ringed structures with one or more rings. Their rings contain only single bonds between the carbon atoms. These compounds are typically liquids at room temperature, like cyclohexane and methyl cyclopentane.

— *Alkenes* with the general formula CnH_{2n}, where n is a whole number usually from 1 to 20, are linear or branched chain molecules containing one carbon-carbon double-bond. These hydrocarbon materials can be liquid or gas, such as ethylene, butene and isobutene.

— *Dienes and Alkynes* with the general formula CnH_2n-2, where n is a whole number usually from 1 to 20, are linear or branched chain molecules, containing two carbon-carbon double-bonds. These hydrocarbons can be liquid or gas, such as acetylene and butadienes.

Now that we know what's in crude oil, let's see what we can make from it.

Types of Oil Products

Crude oil contains hundreds of different hydrocarbons and impurities, all mixed together and in varying proportions. To be useful, the different fractions must be separated by the type of hydrocarbons and impurities. This is done by refining the oil.

Because different hydrocarbon chain lengths have progressively higher boiling points, they can be separated by distillation. This is what happens in an oil refinery—in one part of the process, crude oil is heated and the different chains are pulled out by their vaporization temperatures. Each chain length has a special property that makes it useful in a different way.

There are great diversities in crude oil, which is why refining it is so important in our society. Following is a list of some key products that can be refined from crude oil.

- *Petroleum gas* is used for heating, cooking, and making a number of plastics. It contains small alkanes (1 to 4 carbon atoms), commonly known by the names methane, ethane, propane, butane with a boiling range of less than 104°F/40°C. These are often liquefied under pressure to create LPG (liquefied petroleum gas).

- *Naphtha or Ligroin* is an intermediate product that will be further processed to make gasoline. It is a mix of 5 to 9 carbon atom alkanes with a boiling range of 140 to 2120°F.

- *Gasoline* is a liquid motor fuel, which is a mix of alkanes and cycloalkanes, containing 5 to 12 carbon atoms. Its boiling range is 104 to 4010°F.

- *Kerosene* is fuel for jet engines and tractors and is also used as a starting material for making other products. It is a liquid mix of alkanes, containing 10 to 18 carbons, and aromatics. Its boiling range is 350 to 6170°F.

- *Gas oil or diesel distillate* is used for diesel fuel and heating oil, as well as a starting material for making other products. It is a liquid mix of alkanes, containing 12 or more carbon atoms. The boiling range is 482 to 6620°F.

- *Lubricating oil* is used for motor oil, grease and other lubricants. It is a liquid long chain, containing 20 to 50 carbon atoms, alkanes, cycloalkanes, and aromatics. Its boiling range is 572 to 7000°F.

- *Heavy gas or fuel oil* is used for industrial fuel, as well as for a starting material to make other products. It is a liquid long chain, containing 20 to 70 carbon atoms, alkanes, cycloalkanes, and aromatics. Its boiling range is 700 to 11120°F.

- *Residuals* are materials like coke, asphalt, tar and waxes. They are also used as a starting material for making other products. These materials are usually solid multiple-ringed compounds with 70 or more carbon atoms. Their boiling range is greater than 11,120°F.

All these products have different sizes and boiling ranges, which is very the basis for their refining. They can be easily separated by heating, boiling and condensing each fraction, as we will see below.

As seen in Figure 2-33, most of the oil fractions produced from each barrel of crude oil are fuels (gasoline, diesel and such) intended to be burned in a number of applications, while about 7-8% of the crude oil is turned into road-making products, lubricants, and other petrochemical feedstocks.

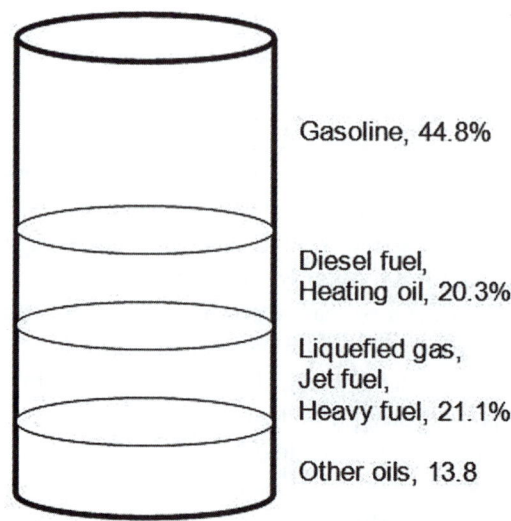

Gasoline, 44.8%

Diesel fuel,
Heating oil, 20.3%

Liquefied gas,
Jet fuel,
Heavy fuel, 21.1%

Other oils, 13.8

Figure 2-33. Crude oil products

A smaller amount of the crude is converted into oil derivatives, many of which go into making a vast array of the commonplace products we use today. Plastics are of the largest quantity of these products, followed by medicines, contact lenses, insecticides, toothpastes, cosmetics, fertilizers, paint, food preservatives, and much more.

This precious commodity is being burned with no trace left, except for the climate-warming gasses. What will future generations think of us?

The Oil Refinery

We refine crude oil to produce a variety of fuel products, ranging from the heaviest oils for use in industrial boilers, to fuel oil used in home heating, diesel oil that powers most trucks and some cars, jet aircraft fuel, gasoline for automobiles. Each of these products contains a mix of different molecules, so no single chemical formula describes a given fuel. Molecules typically found in gasoline, for example, include heptane, octane, nonane, and decane. These molecules consist of long chains of carbon with attached hydrogen molecules.

Higher grades of gasoline have a greater ratio of octane to heptane which makes them burn better in high-performance engines. This is the origin of the term high octane at the gas pump. The energy content of refined fuels varies somewhat, but a rough figure is about 45 MJ/kg for any product derived from crude oil.

Figure 2-34. Oil refinery

Oil refineries are huge developments encompassing entire cities of buildings, towers, piping, electrical substations, wires, storage tanks, railroad stations and ports. Refinery activity can be summed up as constantly loading and unloading, processing and re-processing oil products in gaseous, liquid and solid form.

Refining is an energy-intensive process; some 8% of total U.S. energy consumption is used to run oil refineries. The actual quantitative breakdown of the different fractions produced in a refinery varies with demand. For example, the percentage of crude oil refined into heavier fuel oil for heating increases significantly in the winter months.

The Oil Refining Process

The crude oil is pumped from the storage tanks by charge pumps located at one of the oil storage tanks. Each of them can pump 350 gallons of oil per minute at 240 PSI outlet pressure. The crude is then mixed with "make-up water," which is fresh water pumped from a well into an automated water desalination system, to purify it prior to the mixing. After mixing with the make-up water, the crude is pumped through two heat exchangers, connected in series and mounted about 20 feet above the ground, in close proximity to the crude distillation tower.

The crude goes through the tubes of the heat exchangers and gets heated to over 400°F by indirect contact with the hot liquids coming from different stages of the process. It is then pumped into a condenser unit to separate one of the low-boiling fractions contained in the oil product.

Then the crude is mixed with more make-up water to form a water-in-oil emulsion. Salts, of the type of magnesium chloride and calcium chloride, are in this emulsion and must be removed. The goal is to obtain a salt concentration of less than 1 pound of salt per 1000 barrels of crude. This is achieved by an electrostatic device and by adding demulsifying chemicals in the mix.

Thus purified crude is then pumped into the Atmospheric distillation unit where the crude oil is distilled (separated) into low boiling point fractions. It is then pumped into a vacuum distillation unit, which distills the higher boiling point fractions remaining after the atmospheric distillation.

The most important processes take place in the distillation column, or vacuum distillation units. This is a method of separating the different fractions by reducing the pressure in the vessel, which together with the high temperature of the oil causes evaporation of the volatile liquids. Vacuum distillation can be used also without heating the mixture, but in that case the high boiling point fractions will not be separated.

Some of the fractions go through a naphtha hydrotreater unit where hydrogen gas is used to de-sul-

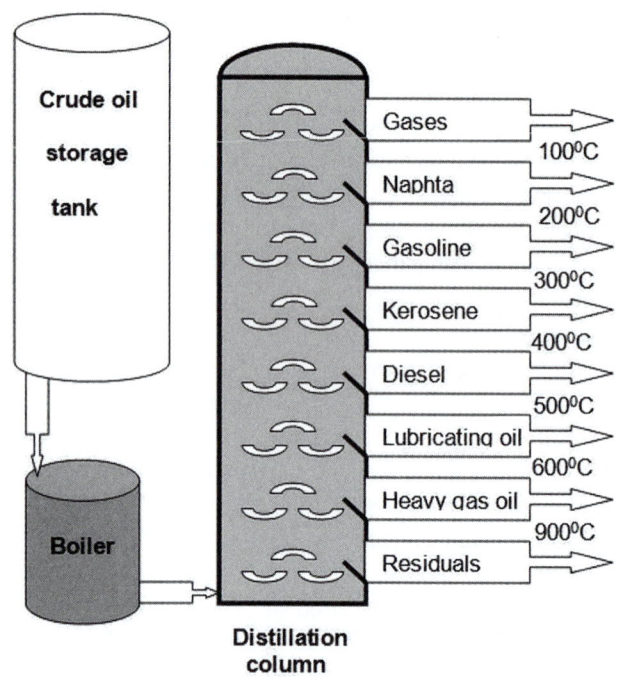

Figure 2-35. Distillation of the different oil fractions

furize the naphtha fraction left over from the previous atmospheric distillation. The naphtha is then hydro-treated to separate other fractions and impurities, before sending it to a Catalytic Reformer unit, where the naphtha fractions are converted into higher octane products. Hydrogen is released during the catalyst reaction and is used either in the hydrotreating or the hydrocracking process.

The different fractions go through various additional steps and pieces of equipment, such as fluid catalytic crackers, hydrocrackers, visbreaking, merox, coking, alkylation units, dimerization, isomeration, steam reforming, amine gas treater, claus unit, and other units and steps during the long, complex refining process.

The final products, obtained and separated during the steps, are petroleum-based products that can be grouped into light distillates (LPG, gasoline, naphtha), middle distillates (kerosene and diesel), heavy distillates (misc. products), and residuum (heavy fuel oil, lubricating oils, wax, asphalt).

In more practical terms, the refinery produces liquefied petroleum gas, gasoline, naphtha, kerosene, jet aircraft fuel mixes, diesel fuel, fuel oils, lubricating oils, paraffin wax, asphalt and tar, petroleum coke, and sulfur. A number of gasses, like propane and others, are also produced.

All products are stored and eventually shipped for use to different customers and industries.

Refinery Logistics

During World War II, the US Department of Defense established the "Petroleum Administration for Defense Districts" (PADD) to control and facilitate oil allocation. At first, the refineries processed crude oil and distributed petroleum products for use in the local district, but soon it was necessary to construct the Virginia and Colonial product pipelines, linking the Gulf Coast with the northeast United States, which led to a network of crude oil and petroleum product pipelines that interlinks the PADDs, making them interdependent.

PADD 1, the East Coast refineries, process crude oil shipped from all over the world, while PADD 2 (Midwest) and PADD 4 (Rocky Mountains) depend on crude oil produced and moved by pipeline from Canada and the Gulf Coast. PADD 3 (Gulf Coast) is the largest refining region, and obtains crude oil from the Gulf Coast outer continental shelf, Mexico, Venezuela, and the rest of the world. PADD 5 (West Coast) gets crude oil delivered by tankers from Alaska and California oil wells, and imports.

A large pipeline project, planned to deliver Canadian syncrude oil to Gulf Coast refineries is stalled in the permitting and political debate stages.

The US refineries increased in number and capacity through the century, reaching a peak around 2005, when US and world demand for gasoline was increasing by the day. Then, due to the economic crisis, the US gasoline consumption declined by almost 9 million barrels in 2008, and another 10 million barrels in 2009. Amazingly, the US imported 81 million barrels in 2009, while the production of ethanol peaked at over 256 million barrels, with nearly 4.6 million barrels of ethanol imports. It's complicated, the decision makers would say, no doubt!

Market volatility increased and led to record high crude oil prices, peaking at $150/bbl in 2008. Oil companies' and related parties' profit margins rose accordingly during the period. As a result, US refineries are now faced with the possibility of long-term decrease in fuel demand, which is forcing them to cut costs, reduce capacity, and even close some facilities.

In the golden year of 2000, there were 158 fully operational refineries in the US and its territories. Now we have about 124 refineries that process crude oil into fuels, and 13 that produce lubricating oils and asphalt. Their production volumes go up and down according to supply and demand ratios and other political and economic factors, but for all practical purposes they are working full-time with short shutdowns for maintenance and upgrades.

The number of refineries is declining, but their efficiency is increasing, as is their operable refining capacity. From 16.5 million barrels/day total capacity a decade ago, it is now over 18 million barrels/day. Amazing number...

Since we are concerned mainly with energy generation in this text, we will take a close look at how crude oil is used in the energy sector.

Oil-fired Power Plant

Oil-fired power plants are powered directly by unrefined crude oil, or more often by some of its derivatives. The oil-fuel is transported to the power plants by ship, pipelines, truck or train, where several methods can be used to generate electricity from the oil.

One way is to burn the oil in boilers to produce heat and steam, which is used by a steam turbine to generate electricity. Another common method is to inject the oil into combustion turbines, which are similar in operation to jet engines.

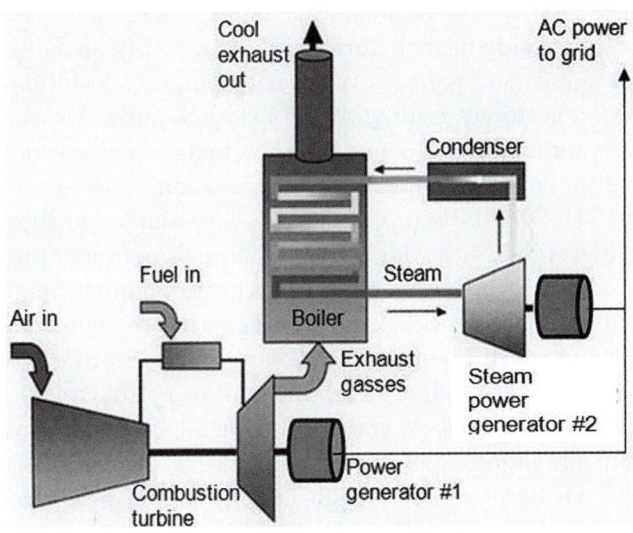

Figure 2-36. Combined cycle power plant

A more efficient method is the combined cycle technology, where oil is burned in a combustion turbine, but the hot exhaust gasses are then used to make steam and drive a steam turbine and generator to generate electricity. This technology is much more efficient because it uses the same fuel source twice. What makes this setup efficient is that the waste steam generated in the combustion turbines is sent to a boiler to generate steam, which drives the turbine and generator sets.

Another use of crude oil derivatives (gasoline and diesel) is to fuel internal combustion engines, which then drive the turbine-gen sets to generate electricity.

Saudi Arabia's Shoaiba is one of the largest oil-fired power plants in the world. Following completion of stage 1 in 2003, stage 2 consisting of six additional 400 MW units was completed, bringing the total output of the plant's stage 1 and 2 to 4400 MW.

Stage 3 was completed recently, adding 1.2 GW of electric power generation, bringing the total power generation to 5.6 GW. The plant uses oil furnaces to burn crude oil and generate steam, which drives the steam turbines and generators to produce electric power.

This monster crude-oil-wasting plant alone provides over 40% of the western region's current power requirements, and is a world record breaker in terms of size for an oil-fired plant. During the construction of stage 2, several records were broken in terms of construction and commissioning time for a steam power plant.

A multi-stage flash distillation water desalination plant was constructed as part of the plant complex. It has a desalination capacity of 50 million cubic meters of water per year. A second desalination plant with a capacity of 50 million cubic meters of water per year was constructed later. The clever feature of this setup is that the waste steam generated in the power plant turbines is sent to the desalination plant to be used to heat sea water. This provides cheap clean water, while at the same time cools the steam before reuse, thus reducing the waste heat cooling losses.

Gas-fired power plants life-span cycle consists of several phases, very similar to those of a coal-fired power plant:

Plant site and structure planning and design
- Locating, testing and exploring the proposed power plant location
- Engineering design of plant facilities, equipment and process
- Estimating the construction and operating cost and the related tasks
- Applying for and obtaining the necessary federal, state and local permits

Plant construction and setup
- Plant building construction
- Plant equipment procurement and setup
- Labor training

Power plant daily operation
- Petroleum fuel oil delivery
- Oil burning and energy generation
- Electric power distribution

Power plant decommissioning and land reclamation
- Plant shutdown and disassembly
- Plant waste disposal
- Surface land reclamation

Since the steps are very similar to those used for coal-fired plants' construction and use, we refer the reader to the section on COAL for more details.

Practical Uses of Crude Oil

Great quantities of crude oil are used for energy generation, as described herein, but it is used in many other areas as well. Some of these uses consume huge amounts, while generating equally huge amounts of air pollution.

The most obvious culprits are cars, trucks used in transportation, and heating oil used for residential and industrial heating and other purposes.

Cars and Trucks

The world transportation sector consumes more oil than all other sources combined. In the U.S. alone more than 13 million barrels of oil-equivalent are used every day. This is roughly two-thirds of total U.S. oil use.

Crude oil products (gasoline, diesel, and jet fuels) account for more than 95% of all the energy used for transportation in the U.S. Oil products power virtually every mile we drive, and we drive a lot of miles in our gas guzzling cars and trucks.

Also, millions of gallons of oil are used every year for motor oil and lubricating oils and greases. There are more than 250 million cars and trucks on U.S. roads today, traveling a whopping 3 trillion miles annually. This is enough miles for one car to make more than 14,000 round-trip voyages to the sun.

The U.S. transportation system requires about 5 billion barrels of crude oil to meet the needs of all cars and trucks on the road. At the same time, the number of vehicles and miles driven are expected to rise.

Oil companies and a handful of foreign countries benefit from this trend, while we all lose out. There's a better, cleaner way to power America's transportation system. By increasing the use of clean biofuels, and creating the next generation of advanced vehicles that no longer rely exclusively on oil, we can decrease our reliance on petroleum for fuel. By improving the fuel efficiency of our cars and trucks, we can dramatically reduce the amount of oil we need in the first place.

Clean vehicle and fuel technologies are discussed, and some implemented, but much more work is needed to reduce the amount of oil we use for transportation.

If we act now, we can cut America's projected crude oil used for transportation in half during the next 20 years. This would save us billions of dollars at the gas pump, slash oil consumption, and move us toward a cleaner environment and a safer transportation future. Yes, this is just a pipe dream for now... and until crude oil hits $250/bbl.

What *is* $250/bbl? Based on the 2008 gas price hike, we estimate $8-10/gal. Such an abrupt and unforeseen price jump would bring uncontrolled chaos to the energy system. The transportation sector would begin to shut down. Unless prices were quickly lowered to about $150/bbl, the economy would be in a state of free fall.

Heating Oil

Home and business oil-fired furnaces are major users of heating oil, which is derived from refining crude oil. Home oil heating is widely used in developed countries, especially during the winter months.

Heating oil is usually delivered by tank truck to residential, commercial and municipal buildings and stored in above-ground storage tanks. These are located either outside near the building, or in empty areas like basements and garages. When used in larger quantities, the oil is stored in underground storage tanks. Heating oil is sometimes used as a fuel in industrial applications, and for small or remote power generation.

Heating oil's properties are very similar to those of diesel fuel, and consist of a mixture of petroleum-derived hydrocarbons in the 14- to 20-carbon atom range. During oil distillation, heating oil condenses at between 482 and 662°F. It condenses at a lower temperature than the heavy (C20+) hydrocarbons such as petroleum jelly, bitumen, candle wax, and lubricating oil, but it condenses at a higher temperature than kerosene, or over 500°F.

Heating oil has a high heating value, producing 138,500 Btus per gallon, which is close to the same heat per unit mass of diesel fuel and is known in the U.S. as No. 2 heating oil. It must conform to ASTM standard D396, which is somewhat different from that of diesel and kerosene.

Heating oil is widely used during the winter months in parts of the United States and Canada where natural gas is not available and propane is priced higher. The northeastern United States and Canada are the most likely users of oil from Irving Oil's refinery in Saint John, New Brunswick, which is the largest oil refinery in Canada.

In addition to the toxic gases emitted during the burning process, leaks from tanks and piping are a well known environmental concern. Various federal and state regulations are in place regarding the proper transportation, storage and burning of heating oil, which is classified as a hazardous material by U.S. federal regulators.

With about 4% of the U.S. total consumption of crude oil going into heating oil, this is a significant issue, which is on the radar of environmentalists, awaiting prompt resolution.

Consumable Products

Transportation fuels and heating oil are only some of the many products derived from petroleum. Americans consume petroleum products at a rate of 3½ gallons of oil and more than 250 cubic feet of natural gas per day—each person!

The problem in Figure 2-37 is obvious; we use three times more oil than we produce. The effect is also obvious; we are spending a lot of money to support foreign suppliers, instead of using the money to build our own economy. This unjustifiable imbalance has been going on for almost a century, during which time we made several nations very rich, consuming most of the oil which took the Earth billions of years to create. How long can uncontrolled pumping and burning of a limited resource continue?

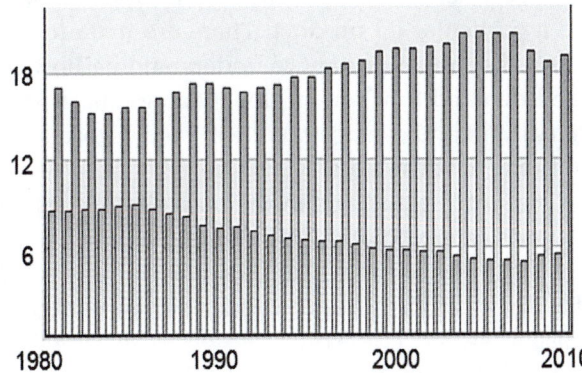

Figure 2-37. U.S. oil production and use (in millions of bbls/ day)

Petroleum is not only used only as a fuel. One 42-gallon barrel of oil creates 19.4 gallons of gasoline and 9-10 gallons of diesel and heating oil. The rest (over half of the total content) is used to make things like:

- Ammonia, anesthetics, antifreeze, antihistamines, antiseptics, artificial limbs, artificial turf, aspirin, awnings...
- Balloons, ballpoint pens, bandages, basketballs, bearing grease, bicycle tires, boats...
- Cameras, candles, car battery cases, car enamel, car tires, cassettes, caulking, CD players, CDs & DVDs,

clothes, clothesline, cold cream, combs, cortisone, crayons, curtains...
- Dashboards, denture adhesive, dentures, deodorant, detergents, die, diesel fuel, dishes, dishwasher parts, dresses, drinking cups, dyes...
- Electric blankets, electrician's tape, enamel, epoxy, eyeglasses...
- Fan belts, faucet washers, fertilizers, fishing boots, fishing lures, fishing rods, floor wax, folding doors, food preservatives, football cleats, football helmets, footballs ...
- Gasoline, glycerin, golf bags, golf balls, guitar strings...
- Hair coloring, hair curlers, hand lotion, heart valves, house paint...
- Ice chests, ice cube trays, ink, insect repellent, insecticides...
- Life jackets, linings, linoleum, lipstick, luggage...
- Model cars, mops, motor oil, motorcycle helmets, photo film...
- Nail polish, nylon rope...
- Oil filters, oils and lubricants...
- Paint, paint, brushes, paint rollers, panty hose, parachutes, percolators, perfumes, petroleum jelly, pillows, plastic wood, purses, putty...
- Refrigerants, refrigerators, roller skates, roofing, rubber cement, rubbing alcohol...
- Safety glasses, shag rugs, shampoo, shaving cream, shoe polish, shoes, shower curtains, skis, slacks, soap, soft contact lenses, solvents, speakers, sports car bodies, sun glasses, surfboards, sweaters, synthetic rubber...
- Telephones, tennis rackets, tents, toilet seats, tool boxes, tool racks, toothbrushes, toothpaste, transparent tape, trash bags, TV cabinets...
- Umbrellas, upholstery...
- Vaporizers, vitamin capsules...
- Water pipes, wheels...
- Yarn, and many, many more.

This is only a small fraction of products made from petroleum—only 150 of the more than 6000 different items made from this miraculous liquid. Our lives are so wrapped in it that it is absolutely impossible to even imagine living without it. Just think...no gas for the car, no heat for the house, no plastic bags, no cosmetics...

And yet, this is exactly what is going to happen by the mid 21st century when most petroleum deposits in the ground will be pumped up, refined, used and otherwise wasted. Just think...

Cost of Petroleum Production

Like all other industries, oil rigs and refineries use a lot of expensive equipment and employ a large number of specialized engineers and technicians. The cost of equipment and labor adds to the already high prices of the raw materials, which in turn keeps the price of the final products high.

Too, there is a significant cost for transporting crude oil from the oil rigs, some of which are thousands of miles away (in the Middle East, South America and Asia). Shipping, which is done mostly by huge ocean cruising oil tankers, is a complex and expensive proposition. The cost of new oil tankers is a major expense that is increasing due to increased requirements and the rising cost of materials, energy and labor involved in construction. Tankers in the 32,000-45,000 DWT, 80,000-105,000 DWT, and 250,000-280,000 DWT cost approximately $18, $22, and $47 million respectively.

Oil tankers are often sold and bought second-hand too. In 2005, 27.3 million DWT worth of used oil tankers were sold. As an example, in 2006, First Olsen paid $76.5 million for *Knock Sheen*, a 159,899 DWT tanker.

After refining, oil products are again loaded on trucks and trains for transport to end users at power plants, gas stations, manufacturing facilities, etc.

All this loading, unloading and wheeling hundreds and thousands of miles is expensive, since it depends on fossils as well. When the price of oil goes up, the cost of transportation goes up—another catch-22.

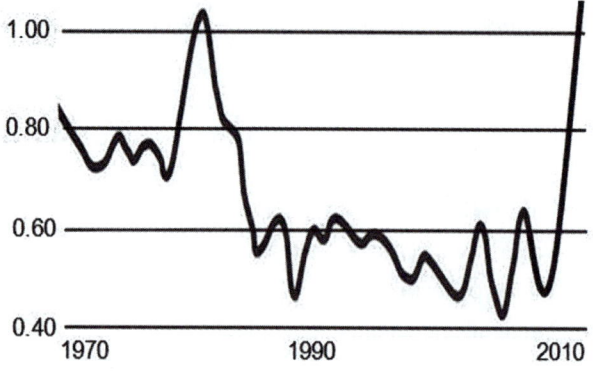

Figure 2-38. Historical oil refining and distribution prices (in $/gallon)

The approximate breakdown of the costs of materials and services required to produce and sell oil products is as follows:

74% Cost of the crude oil
11% Taxes
10% Refining costs

5% Distribution and marketing

As an example, when paying $100 for a barrel (42 gallons) of crude oil, the cost for a gallon of gasoline is about $2.38. At a gas pump the price will go up to $4.00 per gallon, where 44 cents goes to pay for taxes and 20 cents for distribution and marketing.

This leaves $3.36 for the oil company, which pays for the cost of the gallon of crude oil itself ($2.38) and the 40 cents to refine it into gasoline. This leaves $0.58 profit per gallon of gasoline for the oil company. In reality, the reported profit-margin is in the 30 to 60 cents per gallon range.

As crude oil prices go up, fuel consumption goes down and oil companies find it harder to pass the increases to the customers, so they do often lose money.

Global Oil Markets

The global oil market is the most important of the world energy markets because of oil's dominant role as an energy source. Oil is a commodity, as any other, but much more important than most. Contracts for its supply are usually traded through commodity exchanges, and are designed to efficiently and fairly allocate resources between those who supply and those who demand a particular oil product. There are two economic concepts that are important to understanding how supply and demand function in global energy markets: the marginal unit and elasticity. We will take a close look at these in the next chapters.

One of the standards in the marketplace has been West Texas Intermediate (WTI) crude oil, which is high quality crude oil with a 39.6° API gravity. It is considered a "light" crude oil, and with a 0.24% sulfur content it is also a "sweet" crude oil.

North Sea Brent crude oil, at 38-39° API gravity is also a light sweet crude oil, but with higher sulfur content than WTI, which makes it a global standard for other types of crude oil grades and is widely used to determine the global crude oil prices. Brent is typically refined in Northwest Europe, and it is also exported to the U.S. Gulf and East Coast.

Gasoline, diesel and other petroleum products' prices vary according to issues such as supply and demand, political situations, etc. One major factor in the pricing of fuels is also the pricing of crude oil futures contracts traded on the New York Mercantile Exchange (NYMEX) and the Tokyo Commodity Exchange (TOCOM).

Crude oil futures are standardized, exchange-traded contracts in which the contract buyer agrees to take delivery from the seller of a specific quantity of crude oil (in 1000 barrel lots at NYMEX and 50,000 liter lots at TOCOM) at a predetermined price on a future delivery date. So traders and producers' traders buy and sell virtual oil, as part of their daily business.

What drives the oil markets crazy is speculators and risk-taking moves by large traders. When speculators think that oil prices are going up for some reason, as happened in 2008, they continue to outbid each other, driving prices of the actual crude oil higher and higher. We saw an increase to over $150/bbl in 2008, which was explainable only by the speculators' betting on the prices increasing indefinitely.

Stupid and unfair? Maybe, but this is capitalism, so everyone is afforded the right to make a quick buck, and speculators will continue driving the energy markets.

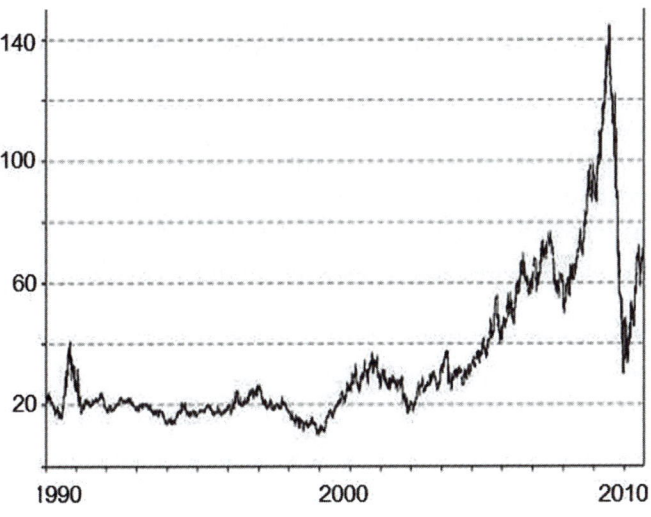

Figure 2-39. Crude oil prices (in $/bbl)

No wonder we are panicking. Look at the jump in oil prices to near $150/bbl in 2008 and the resulting repercussions from 2007-2009. For a short period in 2008, diesel at a truck stop near Bakersfield, CA, rose to $6.95 a gallon—a U.S. record of sorts. Filling a 50-gallon diesel tank came to $350. The same tank only a year or two earlier was filled for $75 at the same gas station. We did panic!

Of course, this is nothing new to most European and Asian drivers, since gas and diesel prices there have been at least twice as high as those in the U.S. for a long time. There are various reasons for the high fuel prices, but one thing is certain: things won't get any better… ever. On the contrary, they will only get worse as oil prices continue rising.

Because of the simple dynamics of capitalist enterprise, the supply and demand ratio's increasing demand

(as in China and India), and reduced supplies (due to depletion of major deposit sites), prices are inevitably headed up. We could face some big surprises in the near future when oil-producing nations would not hesitate to initiate another embargo, just because they can.

Figure 2-40 is a rough representation of the relation between crude oil production and demand vs. price. Excluding the glitch in 2008, the general trend has been increased demand, production and prices. The big difference in the future is the projected production levels and gradually increasing prices.

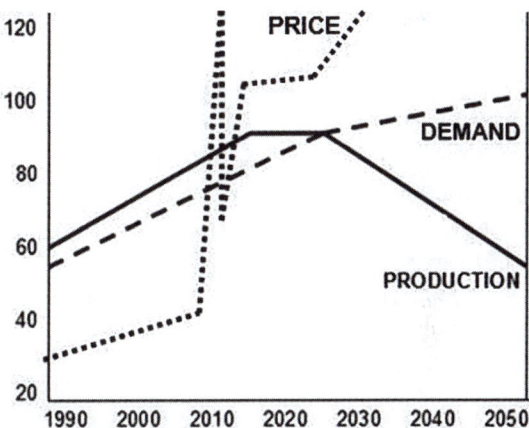

Figure 2-40. Crude oil price, demand, and production (in $/bbl)

Demand and price will continue to increase, while global crude oil production will decrease sharply, due to well depletion and increasing technical difficulties. The availability of other energy sources, such as natural gas and renewables like solar and wind, will contribute to high oil prices by the mid-21st century.

Decommissioning Oil Rigs

After 20-30 years of non-stop operation, aging rigs and depleted oil deposits are no longer reliable for safe operation. At that time, oil rigs go into the last phase of their lifespan—the decommissioning process. Decommissioning of oil rigs is a complex and expensive effort. It can cost $5-$10 million per rig in the shallow water of the Gulf of Mexico (GOM), and several times that much for decommissioning deep-water rigs.

The U.S. Department of the Interior, Bureau of Ocean Energy Management, Regulation, and Enforcement (BOEMRE) Gulf of Mexico's OCS Region, issued a new decommissioning regulation in September 2010, which further tightens the requirements and increases the costs. The new NTL 2010-G05 requires wells that have not been used for the last five years to be classified as permanently abandoned, temporarily abandoned, or zonally isolated by Oct. 15, 2013.

If wells are zonally isolated, operators have 2 additional years to permanently or temporarily abandon the wellhead. Platforms and supporting infrastructure that have been idle for five or more years must be removed within 5 years as of the same date. This means that the new NTL, on top of the typical volume of decommissioning work in the GOM, will increase demand for contractors and, in turn, expenses.

There are 10 steps to the decommissioning process:

- Project Management
- Engineering and Planning
- Permitting and Regulatory Compliance
- Platform Preparation
- Well Plugging and Abandonment
- Conductor Removal
- Mobilization and Demobilization of Derrick Barges
- Platform Removal
- Pipeline and Power Cable Decommissioning
- Materials Disposal
- Site Clearance and final test

Project management, engineering and planning for decommissioning an offshore rig usually starts three years before the well runs dry. The process involves review of contractual obligations, engineering analysis, operational planning and contracting. Due to the limited number of derrick barges, many operators contract these vessels two to three years in advance. In addition, much of the decommissioning process requires contractors who specialize in a specific part of the process. Most operators contract out the project management, cutting, civil engineering, and diving services.

Permitting and regulatory compliance consists of obtaining permits to decommission an offshore rig and can take up to three years to complete. Often, operators will contract a local consulting firm to ensure that all permits are in order prior to decommissioning. Local consulting firms are familiar with the regulatory framework of their region.

An execution plan is one of the first steps in the process. Included in this plan is environmental information and field surveys of the project site. The plan describes a schedule of decommissioning activities and the equipment and labor required to carry out the operation. An execution plan is required to secure permits from federal, state, and local regulatory agencies. BOEMRE will also analyze the environmental impact of the project and recommend ways to eliminate or minimize those impacts.

Federal agencies often involved in decommissioning projects include BOEMRE, National Marine Fisheries Service, US Army Corps of Engineers, US Fish and Wildlife Service, National Oceanic and Atmospheric Administration, US Environmental Protection Agency, US Coast Guard, and the US Department of Transportation, Office of Pipeline Safety.

Platform Preparation

To prepare a platform for decommissioning, tanks, processing equipment and piping must be flushed and cleaned, and residual hydrocarbons must be disposed of. Platform equipment must be removed, which includes cutting pipe and cables between deck modules, separating the modules, installing padeyes to lift the modules, and reinforcing the structure. Underwater, workers prepare the jacket facilities for removal, which includes removing marine growth.

Well Plugging and Abandonment

Plugging and abandonment is one of the major costs of a decommissioning project and can be broken into several stages.

The planning phase of well plugging includes:

- Data collection
- Preliminary inspection
- Selection of abandonment methods
- Submittal of an application for BOEMRE approval

In the GOM, the rigless method, which was developed in the 1980s, is primarily used for plugging and abandonment jobs. The rigless method uses a load spreader on top of a conductor, which provides a base to launch tools, equipment and plugs downhole.

Actual well abandonment involves:

- Well entry preparations
- Use of a slick line unit
- Filling the well with fluid
- Removal of downhole equipment
- Cleaning out the wellbore
- Plugging open-hole and perforated intervals(s) at the bottom of the well
- Plugging casing stubs
- Plugging of annular space
- Placement of a surface plug
- Placement of fluid between plugs

Plugs must be tagged to ensure proper placement or pressure-tested to verify integrity.

According to BOEMRE, all platform components including conductor casings must be removed to at least 15 ft below the ocean floor or to a depth approved by the regional supervisor based on the type of structure or ocean-bottom conditions.

To remove conductor casing, operators can chose one of three procedures:

- Severing, which requires the use of explosive, mechanical or abrasive cutting

- Pulling/sectioning, which uses the casing jacks to raise the conductors that are unscrewed or cut into 40-ft-long segments.

- Offloading, which utilizes a rental crane to lay down each conductor casing segment in a platform staging area, offloading sections to a boat, and offloading at a port. The conductors are then transported to an onshore disposal site.

Mobilization/Demobilization and Platform Removal

Mobilization and demobilization of derrick barges is a key component in platform removal. According to BOEMRE, platforms, templates and pilings must be removed to at least 15 ft below the mudline.

First, the topsides are taken apart and lifted onto the derrick barge. Topsides can be removed all in one piece, in groups of modules, reverse order of installation, or in small pieces.

When removing topsides in one piece, the derrick barge must have sufficient lifting capacity. This option is best used for small platforms. Also keep in mind the size and the crane capacity at the offloading site. If the offloading site can't accommodate the platform in one piece, then a different removal option is required.

Removing combined modules requires fewer lifts, thus is a time-saving option. However, the modules must be in the right position and have a combined weight under the crane and derrick barge capacity. Dismantling the topsides in reverse order to that in which they were installed, whether installed as modules or as individual structural components, is another removal option and the most common.

Topside can also be cut into small pieces and removed with platform cranes, temporary deck-mounted cranes, or other small (less expensive) cranes. However, this method takes the most time to complete the job, so any cost savings incurred using a smaller derrick barge will likely be offset by the dayrate.

Removing the jacket is the second and most costly step in the demolition process. First, divers using explosives, mechanical means, torches or abrasive technology make the bottom cuts on the piles 15 ft below the mudline. Then the jacket is removed either in small pieces or as a single lift. A single lift is possible only for small structures in less than 200 ft of water. Heavy lifting equipment is required for the jacket removal as well, but a derrick barge is not necessary. Less expensive support equipment can do the job.

Pipeline and power cable decommissioning can be done in place if they do not interfere with navigation or commercial fishing operations or pose an environmental hazard. However, if BOEMRE rules that it is a hazard during the technical and environmental review of the permitting process, it must be removed.

The first step to pipeline decommissioning in place requires flushing it with water followed by disconnecting it from the platform and filling it with seawater. The open end is plugged, buried 3 ft below the seafloor, and covered with concrete.

Site Clearance and Materials Disposal

Clearance and disposal of platform materials is used to ensure that all materials are refurbished and reused, scrapped, recycled or disposed of in specified landfills.

To ensure proper site clearance, operators need to follow a four-step site clearance procedure.

- A pre-decommissioning survey maps the location and quantity of debris, pipelines, power cables, and natural marine environments.

- A post-decommissioning survey identifies debris left behind during the removal process and notes any environmental damage.

- ROVs and divers are deployed to further identify and remove any debris that could interfere with other uses of the area.

- Test trawling verifies that the area is free of any potential obstructions.

In Summary

Above we took a fairly close look at crude oil production, transport, and use. There is much more to it, of course, but we feel that this is just enough to give us a good understanding of the technological and logistic complexities involved in the crude oil lifespan.

Now, let's take a close look at oil's first cousin, natural gas.

Environmental Impact of Oil Production

Constructing and installing an oil rig and pumping millions of barrels of oil requires many pieces of large equipment. Building a oil-fired power station also requires large pieces of equipment, in addition to huge amounts of concrete, steel, and many other materials. All these materials are made with the help of fossil fuels—lots of them. During the production and transport of these materials a lot of gaseous, liquid and particulate pollution was generated as well, including huge amounts of CO_2 pollution.

It has been estimated that the steel and concrete production and transport for the construction of a 1 GW power station have a carbon footprint of roughly 300,000 tons of CO_2. Spreading the CO_2 over a 25-year reactor life we come up with almost 1.5 grams of CO_2 emitted per each kWh of electricity generated.

According to industry estimates, the total carbon footprint of an oil-fired power plant (including construction, fuel processing, decommissioning, etc.) is about 40 grams of CO_2 per kWh.

Pollution Footprint of Oil-fired Plant Equipment

Similar to the mining process, a number of large and small pieces of equipment are used during oil rig and oil-fired power plant construction and operation. Starting with the well and plant design and construction, we see pollution taking place in the shape of ground-leveling bulldozers with heavy plumes of smoke, and large trucks moving earth around.

Then oil rig and power plant equipment pieces arrive on trains and trucks. All this machinery was made someplace where and when their manufacturing processes and transport created a significant pollution footprint.

Just as in the mining case, we would assign 5-10% of the manufacturing and transport of oil-well and power plant equipment to the initial construction step.

(A) The main pieces of equipment, rig structure, boilers, turbines, generators, etc. arrive in wooden boxes or on enormous trailers or railroad cars. These pieces are assembled with the help of other equipment and put to work after creating another set of pollution problems.

(B) In addition, there are many other items and small pieces of equipment, tools and consumables for personal or specialized operations. These are shovels, helmets, computers, boots, shoes, overalls, first aid kits, goggles, etc. These were also made elsewhere and transported to the mine, leaving a significant pollution footprint.

(C) To complete the pollution footprint picture, we must add the footprint of the people involved in the entire process—engineers and technicians involved in the equipment manufacturing, transport, installation, setup, and operation. These people drive cars and travel by air, leaving more pollution.

(D) So, the total pollution footprint of the power plant's equipment cradle-to-grave process is expressed by:

$$P_f = A + B + C + D$$

where

P_f is the total pollution footprint;

A   is the equipment manufacturing and transport to the well and power plant;

B   is equipment assembly, test and installation at the well and power plant;

C   is the manufacturing and transport to the power plant of tools and consumables; and

D   is the pollution footprint of the equipment personnel during the design and setup phases.

Combining the pollution footprint of A (the plant equipment manufacture and transport) with B (plant equipment assembly, test and installation), adding C (manufacture and transport of tools and consumables), plus D (the pollution footprint of the equipment personnel) gives us the environmental footprint of plant equipment *before* even starting plant operations.

Here again, the pollution footprint is significant, to be sure! It goes reaches deep and wide from one part of the country to the other…and from one end of the world to the other.

To put a value on it, we must take inventory of all items delivered to the plant and needed for its design, construction and operation. We must look closely at the manufacturing of oil rig and power plant components, rig structure, boiler, steam turbine, generator, and a number of other pieces of equipment.

These are also very large pieces of equipment, and it takes hundreds and thousands of tons of metals to make them. Each of these started as an iron ore, dug out from a mine and transported to a smelter. The molten metal was shaped in different forms and shipped to the different parts manufacturers, who constructed parts for these vehicles.

Again, remember that we are talking about huge pieces of metal—some as big as an entire building. These parts are then packed and loaded on railroad cars or trucks to be shipped to the assembly facility. The parts of a large dump truck or a dragline might require a dozen railroad cars for transport. The parts are then sent to the assembly plant, where they are assembled into major components, or entire units. After one more loading and unloading operation, they finally arrive at the plant for final assembly, installation and testing, before being put to work.

This is a long and winding process, with many stop and go, loading and unloading steps. Putting a dollar value on all of this would be too complex a procedure for our purposes, so it suffices to say that the pollution effects during and after these steps are significant.

We will take an even closer look at these steps and their environmental effects in the following chapters.

Upon starting a well or power plant operation, the production equipment continues to generate secondary pollution. Spare parts for these monsters periodically arrive from the parts manufacturers, after leaving their pollution footprint all over the place. We will attempt to assign a number—quantity of air and land pollution—and a related dollar amount to these activities and their environmental effects in the following chapters.

After 20-30 years of non-stop operation, the oil well and the oil-fired power plant are finally declared obsolete, at which point they must be shut down and decommissioned. Decommissioning and land reclamation are major, expensive and polluting undertakings as well. The equipment and materials used during the decommissioning and waste disposal process create additional air and ground pollution which is not to be ignored.

Additional specialized equipment and personnel (environmental specialists and inspectors) are usually brought in to coordinate the effort. With that, more pollution footprints are left at the already exhausted mine.

When the final tally is made, a significant part of the emissions and overall pollution are to be attributed to wells' and plants' equipment and support personnel. This number is significant too, and we will go through the calculations in the next chapters as well.

NATURAL GAS

Natural gas occurs naturally, and its pure form is a mixture of several gasses consisting primarily of methane mixed with other hydrocarbons, such as carbon dioxide, nitrogen and hydrogen sulfide. Natural gas is an important energy source, which we use extensively (and lately increasingly) to provide electricity, for heating our homes and for industrial purposes. It is also used as fuel for vehicles and as a chemical feedstock in the manufacture of plastics and other commercially important organic chemicals.

Natural gas deposits are usually found deep underground in rock formations, or on top of oil and coal beds, where it is in the form of methane clathrates.

In the beginning...

Natural gas, like coal and oil, was created millions of years ago when large quantities of plants and animals were buried amidst sand and rock deposits deep underground. The events that led to the death of such large quantities of life vary, but the important thing is that layers of mud, sand, rock, plants, and huge amounts of animal matter built up, while the heat and pressure in their deep graves underground increased, slowly turning the once-living matter into fossils— coal, oil and natural gas.

Another theory states that the Earth was made up of primordial materials that combined in space billions of years ago when the basic structure of our Earth evolved. These materials are still buried far below the earth's crust where they have been trapped for 4.5 billion years, some of them slowly turning into coal, oil, and natural gas.

No one really knows exactly when and how this all happened, since no one was there to record the events. And since all this happened so long ago, we simply lack the tools and ability to understand and analyze the situation in detail. Nevertheless, we must at least consider the theories provided by the specialists, and it is very likely that there is more than just one mechanism responsible for the formation of fossil fuels.

What we know for certain is that the formation of natural gas was driven primarily by three main physical-chemical processes, those of thermogenic, biogenic, and abiogenic natural gas formation.

1. Thermogenic methane is formed from organic particles that are covered in mud and other sediment. Over time, more sediment, mud and other debris are piled on top of the organic matter. This sediment and debris put a great deal of pressure on the organic matter, compressing it. This compression, combined with high temperatures found deep underground, breaks down the carbon bonds in the organic matter. As we scan deeper under the earth's crust, the temperature gets higher. At low temperatures (shallower deposits) more oil is produced than natural gas. At higher temperatures, however, more natural gas is created than oil. That is why natural gas is usually associated with oil in deposits that are 1 to 2 miles below the earth's crust. Deeper deposits, very far underground, usually contain primarily natural gas, and in many cases, pure methane.

2.   Biogenic natural gas formation is done through the transformation of organic matter by tiny microorganisms. This type of methane is referred to as biogenic methane. Methanogens, tiny methane-producing microorganisms, chemically break down organic matter to produce methane. These microorganisms are commonly found in areas near the surface of the earth that are void of oxygen. These microorganisms also live in the intestines of most animals, including humans. Formation of methane in this manner usually takes place close to the surface of the earth, and the methane produced is usually lost into the atmosphere. In certain circumstances, however, methane can be trapped underground, recoverable as natural gas. An example of biogenic methane is landfill gas. Waste-containing landfills produce a relatively large amount of natural gas from the decomposition of the waste materials that they contain. New technologies are allowing this gas to be harvested, adding to the supply of natural gas.

3.   Abiogenic natural gas formation processes start extremely deep beneath the earth's crust, in the presence of hydrogen-rich gases and carbon molecules. As these gases gradually rise towards the surface of the earth, they may interact with minerals that also exist underground, in the absence of oxygen. This interaction may result in a reaction, forming elements and compounds that are found in the atmosphere (including nitrogen, oxygen, carbon dioxide, argon, and water). If these gases are under very high pressure as they move toward the surface of the earth, they are likely to form methane

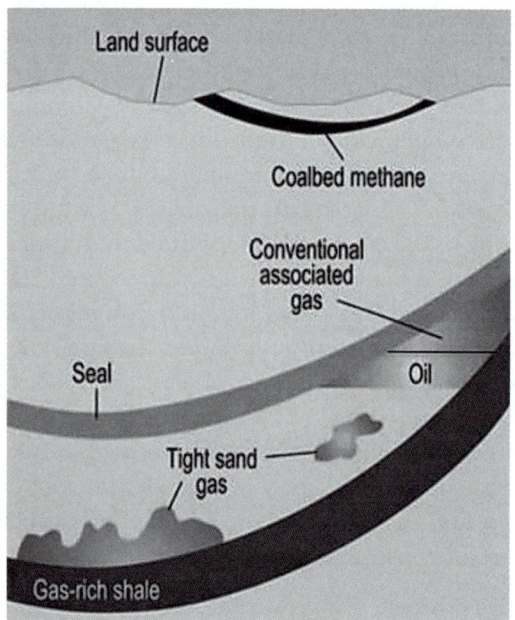

Figure 2-41. Natural gas deposits

deposits, similar to thermogenic methane.

Natural gas in its "as is" state is not very useful, for it contains mixtures of other gasses, moisture, and other contaminants that are impractical and even dangerous for use. So it must be processed to remove inorganic impurities and water. Thus purified gas meets the customers' specifications for use as marketable natural gas that is safe for use in normal domestic and commercial applications.

The by-products of natural processing include chemicals such as ethane, propane, butanes, pentanes, and higher molecular weight hydrocarbons. Hydrogen sulfide is another major byproduct which can be converted into and sold as pure sulfur. There are also carbon dioxide, water vapor, and sometimes helium and nitrogen gasses in the "as is from the wellhead" natural gas mixture.

NOTE: Natural gas is informally referred to simply as gas, especially when used in conjunction with the other fossil energy sources, coal and oil, and this is how we are referring to it sometimes in this text as well.

There are several products that are similar to natural gas, but should not be confused with it. Some of these are town gas, biogas, landfill gas and methane hydrate.

Town gas a synthetically produced mixture of methane and other gases, which contains the highly toxic carbon monoxide. Town gas is produced by treating coal chemically, and can be used the same way as natural gas. This technology is not economically competitive with other sources of fuel gas today, but there are still some specific cases where it is the best option, and it may be even more so in the future.

There were town "gashouses" in the eastern US in the late 19th and early 20th centuries, which were simple by-product coke furnaces, where bituminous coal was burned in air-tight chambers. The gas driven off from the coal—the town gas—was collected and distributed through networks of pipes to residences and other buildings where it was used for cooking and lighting.

The coal tar (or asphalt) that collected in the bottoms of the gashouse ovens was often used for roofing and other water-proofing purposes. When mixed with sand and gravel, it was used for paving streets. These methods were replaced by natural gas heating by the end of the 20th century.

Biogases are methane-rich gases produced by the anaerobic decay of non-fossil organic matter (biomass), and are also called natural biogas. Biogas was formed mostly in swamps, marshes, and landfills. It is also found in sewage sludge and cow manure where the conversion is done by way of anaerobic digesters or enteric fermentation, as is the case with cattle-based biogas.

Landfill gas is a type of methane gas which, as the name suggests, is formed in landfills by the decomposition of organic matter. Landfill gas is already used in some areas, but its use could be greatly expanded. Landfill gas is a type of biogas, but biogas usually refers to gas produced from organic material that has not been mixed with other waste, so landfill gas has its own place.

Methane hydrate is a type of gas that is formed on the bottom of oceans and other water bodies. It is simply molecules of methane trapped into ice (water) pockets, which must be heated to release the methane. We will take a very close look at this type of gas in this text, because there are huge amounts of it locked in the ocean floor and in permafrosts, which hold the promise of becoming primary energy sources of the distant future.

When methane from any source is released directly into the atmosphere, it is considered a pollutant, because it is oxidized by the oxygen in the air, producing carbon dioxide. This is a dangerous process that, considering the great amount of gas used today, has severe environmental consequences.

The conversion to carbon dioxide is a very slow process. Methane gas has a half life of seven years, which means that of 1,000 kg of methane emitted today, 500 kg will have broken down to carbon dioxide and water after seven years. This also means that methane released in the atmosphere today will be slowly but consistently damaging the environment by releasing carbon dioxide at a slow rate for a long time.

Nomenclature

Since we will be talking about natural gas in more detail, and because it has its own measurements, terms and nomenclature, we'd like to familiarize the reader with them for future use:

Natural gas measurement units
Volume units:

CCF	one hundred cubic feet
Mcf	one thousand cubic feet of natural gas
Mmcf	one million cubic feet of natural gas
Bcf	one billion cubic feet of natural gas
Tcf	one trillion cubic feet of natural gas
Mmcf/d	millions of cubic feet of gas per day

Energy equivalents:

Boe	barrels of oil equivalent* (6,000 ft³ natural gas)
Mboe	one thousand barrels of oil equivalent
Mmboe	one million barrels of oil equivalent
Mmcfe	one million cubic feet of natural gas equivalent
Bcfe	one billion cubic feet of natural gas equivalent
Tcfe	one trillion cubic feet of natural gas equivalent

---

*NOTE: The energy contained in one barrel of crude oil equals that in 6,000 cubic feet of natural gas.

General Heat Measurement Units

Btu: British thermal unit, or the amount of energy required to raise the temperature of one pound of water by one degree Fahrenheit.
—One Btu is equivalent to 252 calories, 0.293 watt-hours or 1,055 joules.

Calorie: The energy needed to increase the temperature of 1 gram of water by 1°C at standard atmospheric pressure.
—One calorie is equal to 4.18400 joules.

Joule: A derived unit of energy, work, or amount of heat in the International System of Units.
—One Joule is equal to the energy expended (or work done) in applying a force of one newton through a distance of one meter (1 newton meter or N·m), or in passing an electric current of one ampere through a resistance of one ohm for one second.

Types of Natural Gas

There are several different types of commercially available natural gas, some of which are as follow:

Pipe natural gas or natural gas that is transported via pipeline, is known in commercial terms as sale gas. Sale gas is mainly composed of methane. It is transmitted to customers to be used as fuel at power generation and industrial plants. It is not used for residential purposes, but instead 24% of the energy consumed in the US comes from natural gas, and its share is increasing as new deposits are discovered and exploited.

Coalbed methane is basically a type of natural gas that is extracted from coal beds. Coal seams that contain some coalbed methane and are isolated from other fluid units are also called coalbed methane reservoirs. By analysis and comparison of the typical coalbed methane reservoirs, these can be divided into hydrodynamic sealing coalbed methane reservoirs, and self-sealing coalbed methane reservoirs.

Currently, hydrodynamic sealing reservoirs are the main target for coalbed methane exploration and development, since self-sealing reservoirs are unsuitable for profitable coalbed methane extraction.

Natural Gas for Vehicles (NGV) is the form of natural gas used as fuel for vehicles. NGV is purified natural gas, primarily composed of pure methane, which is transported through a pipeline, or via truck (under pressure) to gas stations. At the gas stations, low pressure gas will be compressed and stored at high pressure (3000-3600 PSI), and can be then injected into the vehicles' gas tanks.

Liquefied Natural Gas (LNG) is natural gas that is liquefied by lowering its temperature to –160°C. At this temperature it becomes liquid and is 600 times smaller in volume. It is then stored at atmospheric pressure in specially designed vessels (tanker trucks, railroad cars, or cargo ships) and transported to end users. The cost of waterway transport today is most convenient for distribution to many areas of the world, and could be less than transportation through pipeline.

Cooking gas (LPG) has a commercial name of liquefied petroleum gas or LPG which is a product from the oil refineries, or the gas separation plants. LPG is a mixture of several hydrocarbon gases, with propane and butane as the major constituents. LPG can be in any ratio or purely propane or butane. LPG is sold in pressurized bottles and can be used as fuel in homes, industry and transportation. Natural gas is not used directly for domestic cooking and heating purposes.

Natural Gas Properties

Natural gas is a nearly odorless and colorless gas that accumulates in the upper parts of oil and gas wells. Raw natural gas is a mixture of methane (55-98%), higher hydrocarbons (primarily ethane), and noncombustible gases. Some other constituents, principally water vapor, hydrogen sulfide, helium, and other petroleum gases are present in different ratios. These must be removed from the mix prior to distribution and use by the public.

Natural gas fuels typically contain a mixture of a number of gasses, as shown in Table 2-11.

Table 2-11. Natural gas components

Gas species	Content
Methane, CH_4	70 to 96%
Ethane, C_2H_6	1 to 14%
Propane, C_3H_8	up to 4%
Butane, C_4H_{10}	up to 2%
Pentane, C_5H_{12}	up to 0.5%
Hexane, C_6H_{14}	up to 2%
Carbon dioxide, CO_2	up to 2%
Oxygen, O_2	up to 1.2%
Nitrogen, N_2	4 to 17%

Some of the practical natural gas measurements are as follow:

1 cubic foot (CF) natural gas averages 1,000 Btus
A typical *Gas Quality Spec* allows 950 to 1,100 Btus per CF
1 hundred cubic feet (CCF) average 100,000 Btus
1 CCF is about 1 therm
1 Therm averages 100,000 Btus
1 dekatherm (10 therms) averages 1,000,000 Btus
1 MCF (10 CCF) = 1,000 CF = 1,000,000 Btus

The composition of natural gas depends on its location and source. Commercial gas is usually a mixture of gas drawn from various sources, so its composition can vary slightly. Nevertheless, a fairly constant heating value is usually maintained for control and safety. Heating values of natural gases vary from 900 to 1,200 Btu/ft³; but the usual commercial range is 1,000 to 1,050 Btu/ft³ at sea level.

For safety purposes, odorants (such as mercaptans) are added to natural gas and LPG to give them noticeable odors.

NOTE: Propane is not natural gas. It is a different, albeit similar, gas (a byproduct) that is produced during natural gas processing and crude oil refining. It has different properties, and its heating value is approximately 10% lower than natural gas (methane). There is up to 4% propane in the commercial natural gas used today.

Natural gas is:
- Very safe as it is lighter than air, and when leaked it will float up and dissipate quickly.
- Ready to use as it is in gas form.
- Its ignition point is 593 degree C.
- The concentration at which natural gas would ignite or explode is 5-15% gas in air.
- Colorless and odorless, and burns completely, without emissions of soot or sulfur. Storage tanks are usually not needed for storing natural gas.

LPG is:
- Less safe, as it is heavier than air, and when leaked it will pool on the ground.
- A liquid, so it needs to be converted to gas.
- Colorless and odorless, but odor is normally added for safety reason.
- It burns completely, without emissions of soot or sulfur.
- Storage tanks and advance ordering are needed in most cases.
- Its ignition point is lower than natural gas; 410-580 degree C*

- The concentration at which LPG gas would ignite or explode is 2.0-9.5% gas in 100% air ratio.

NOTE: The great variation of ignition points in LPG is due to the fact that there are a number of different petroleum compounds in it, each of which has a different ignition point. Basically, LPG is more dangerous to use than natural gas. It is easier to ignite or explode LPG gas than natural gas, since its ignition point is significantly lower. Also, LPG is heavier than air, so it tends to settle down and concentrate in corners, where it could explode in the presence of a spark, or open flame.

NATURAL GAS PRODUCTION

Natural gas is becoming a major, if not predominating, energy source in the U.S. and a number of other countries. Its importance is increasing with the discovery of new gas reservoirs and with the quick development of new and more efficient production techniques, such as hydrofracking, all of which contributes to abundant and cheap gas production.

We will take a close look at the equipment, mechanisms, and processes of natural gas in this text. We will also discuss the advantages and disadvantages of producing and using natural gas, as well as the environmental impact of the related activities.

The different gas production processes and the steps in each could be summarized as follow:

Natural Gas Well Location and Development

Natural gas cradle-to-grave process is quite similar to that of oil production. The key process steps in gas production are:

- Gas deposits search and location
- Proposed area survey
- Environmental studies
- Gas rights and agreements
- Permits and legal issues
- Drill area preparation
- Drilling rig construction
- Daily O&M operations
- Gas transport
- Gas use (burning)
- Decommissioning and area reconstruction

Well Site Search and Location

The practice of locating natural gas and petroleum deposits has been transformed dramatically in the last 20 years with the advent of extremely advanced, ingenious technology. In the early days of the industry, the only way to locate underground petroleum and natural gas deposits was to search for surface evidence of these underground formations.

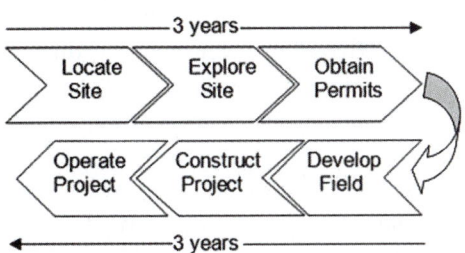

Figure 2-42. Gas well development

In the past, those searching for natural gas deposits were forced to scour the earth, looking for seepages of oil or gas emitted from underground before they had any clue that there were deposits underneath. However, because such a low proportion of petroleum and natural gas deposits actually seeps to the surface, was a very inefficient and difficult exploration process. As the demand for fossil fuel energy has increased dramatically, so has the necessity for more accurate methods of locating these deposits.

Technology has allowed for a remarkable increase in the success rate of locating natural gas reservoirs. Today, geologists and geophysicists use advanced technologies and their knowledge of the properties of underground natural gas deposits to gather data that can later be interpreted and used to make educated guesses as to where natural gas deposits exist and how large they might be. However, the process of exploring for natural gas and petroleum deposits is still characteristically an uncertain one, due to the complexity and difficulties related to finding deposits that are hundreds and thousands of feet below ground.

Exploration for natural gas typically begins with geologists examining the surface structure of the earth, using various equipment to determine where it is geologically likely that petroleum or gas deposits exist. By surveying and mapping the surface and sub-surface characteristics of a certain area, the geologist can extrapolate which areas are most likely to contain a petroleum or natural gas reservoir. The geologist uses techniques that range from outcroppings of rocks (on flatland or in valleys and gorges) to geologic information obtained from rock cuttings and samples from the digging of irrigation ditches, water wells, and other oil and gas wells.

This information is combined and processed to make decisions on the fluid content, porosity, permeability, age, and formation sequence of the rocks beneath the surface of a particular area.

Once the geologists have identified an area where it is geologically possible for a natural gas or petroleum formation to exist, further tests can be performed to gain more detailed data about the potential reservoir. These tests allow for the more accurate mapping of underground formations, most notably those formations that are commonly associated with natural gas and petroleum reservoirs.

Seismology is one of the greatest tools used to locate oil deposits. It refers to the study of how energy, in the form of seismic waves, moves through the Earth's crust and interacts differently with various types of underground formations.

Onshore seismology involves artificially creating seismic waves, in the form of small explosions, the sound reflections of which are then picked up by sensitive pieces of equipment called "geophones" that are embedded in the ground. The data picked up by these geophones are then transmitted to a seismic computer which records the data for further interpretation by geophysicists and petroleum reservoir engineers.

Recently a new, non-explosive technology is used, which consists of a large heavy-wheeled or tracked-vehicle carrying special equipment designed to create a large impact or series of vibrations. These impacts or vibrations create seismic waves similar to those created by dynamite explosions. The signal is then used to locate deposits.

Offshore seismology uses a slightly different method of seismic exploration, but instead of trucks and geophones, equipment on a ship is used to pick up seismic data, and hydrophones are used to pick up seismic waves under water. These hydrophones are towed behind the ship in various configurations depending on the needs of the geophysicist. Instead of using dynamite or impacts on the seabed floor, the seismic ship uses a large air gun, which releases bursts of compressed air under water, creating seismic waves that can travel through the Earth's crust and generate the seismic reflections that are necessary.

There are also other techniques for locating oil deposits today, such as: a) *magnetometers*, which detect the magnetic properties of underground formations, which are then measured to generate geological and geophysical data; b) *gravimeters*, which measure and record the difference in the Earth's gravitational field to figure out what is underground; and c) *exploratory wells* which are used to dig deep into the Earth's crust to allow geologists to study the composition of the underground rock layers in detail.

Well Site Development

Once a potential natural gas deposit has been located by a survey team, the team of drilling experts takes over. Their job is to dig down to the natural gas deposit site and figure out a way to extract it. Natural gas deposits, like those of oil, can be both onshore and offshore.

Although the process of digging deep into the Earth's crust to find deposits of natural gas that may or may not actually exist seems daunting, the industry has developed a number of innovations and techniques that both decrease the cost and increase the efficiency of drilling for natural gas.

Determining to drill a well depends on many factors, including the economic potential of the hoped-for natural gas reservoir. It costs a great deal of money for exploration and production companies to search and drill for natural gas, and there is always the inherent risk that no gas will be found.

Figure 2-43. Natural gas drilling site

The exact placement of the drill site depends on many factors, including the nature of the potential formation to be drilled, the characteristics of the subsurface geology, and the depth and size of the target deposit. After the geophysical team identifies the optimal location for a well, it is necessary for the drilling company to ensure that it completes all the necessary steps to legally drill in that area. This usually involves securing permits for drilling operations, establishment of a legal arrangement to allow the natural gas company to extract and sell the resources under a given area of land, and a design for gathering lines that will connect the well to the pipeline.

There are a variety of potential owners of the land and mineral rights of a given area. To learn more about permitting, leasing, and royalties associated with the extraction of natural gas, visit the regulation section of our website.

If a new well does in fact come in contact with natural gas deposits, it is developed to allow for the extraction of this gas, and is termed a "development" or "productive" well. At this point, with the well drilled and hydrocarbons present, the well may be completed to facilitate its production of natural gas.

However, if the exploration team was incorrect in its estimation of the existence of a marketable quantity of natural gas at a well site, the well is termed a "dry well," and production does not proceed.

On-shore Drilling

There are several types of onshore drilling.

Percussion, or cable tool drilling consists of repeatedly dropping a heavy metal bit into the ground, eventually breaking through rock and punching a hole through to the desired depth. The bit, usually a blunt, chisel shaped instrument, can vary with the type of rock that is being drilled. Water is used in the well hole to combine with all of the drill cuttings, and is periodically bailed out of the well when this "mud" interferes with the effectiveness of the drill bit.

The *"springpole"* technique, used in the early 1800s, consisted of a flexible pole (usually a tree trunk) anchored at one end, and laying across a fulcrum, much like a diving board. The flexible pole, or springpole, would have a heavy bit attached at the loose end. In order to get the bit to strike the ground, workers would use their own body weight to bend the pole toward the ground, allowing the bit to strike rock. The tension in the pole would spring the bit free if it became stuck in the ground.

Many improvements have been made since these early percussion rigs. In fact, it was from cable tool drilling that one of the most important drilling advancements was made. In 1806, David and Joseph Ruffner were using the springpole technique to drill a well in West Virginia. To prevent their well from collapsing, they used hollow tree trunks to reinforce the sides of the well, and to keep water and mud from entering the well as they dug. They are credited as the first drillers to use a casing in their well—an advancement that made drilling much more efficient.

Innovations, such as the use of steam power in cable tool drilling, greatly increased the efficiency and range of percussion drilling. Conventional man-powered cable tool rigs were generally used to drill wells 200 feet or less, while steam powered cable tool rigs,

consisting of the familiar derrick design, had an average drilling depth of 400 to 500 feet. The deepest known well dug with cable tool drilling was completed in 1953, when the New York Natural Gas Corporation drilled a well to a depth of 11,145 feet.

Horizontal drilling is flexible in that it allows for the extraction of natural gas that had previously not been accessible. Although on the surface it resembles a vertical well, beneath the surface, the well inclines so that it runs parallel to the natural gas formation. These legs can go in different directions at different depths and can be more than one mile long horizontally, in addition to the vertical well that can be thousands of feet below the surface. Horizontal drilling allows one surface well to branch out underground and tap many different natural gas resources. It also allows the well to make contact with larger areas within productive formations.

NOTE: The terms directional and horizontal drilling are often used interchangeably, although directional drilling usually refers to drilling at a slight angle to increase contact with the resource, while horizontal drilling is a type of directional drilling which often uses a technique known as hydraulic fracturing to extract natural gas from geologic formations by fracturing them.

Well Casing

Installing well casing is an important part of the drilling and well completion process. Well casing consists of a series of metal tubes installed in the freshly drilled hole. Casing strengthens the sides of the well hole, ensures that no oil or natural gas seeps out of the well hole as it is brought to the surface, and keeps other fluids or gases from seeping into the formation through the well.

A good deal of planning is necessary to ensure that the proper casing for each well is installed. The type of casing used depends on the subsurface characteristics of the well, including the diameter of the well and the pressures and temperatures experienced throughout the well. The diameter of the well hole depends on the size of the drill bit used. In most wells, the diameter of the well hole decreases, the deeper it is drilled, leading to a type of conical shape that must be taken into account when installing casing.

There are five different types of well casing: conductor casing, surface casing, intermediate casing, liner string, and production casing. They are used during the different cycles of the well drilling process, and are designed to provide a complete, efficient and safe well structure.

Well Completion

Once the casing is complete, the well is ready for production of natural gas. At this point, a decision is made on the characteristics of the intake portion of the well in the targeted formation. This process is called well completion, and the different types of well completions include: open hole completion, conventional perforated completion, sand exclusion completion, permanent completion, multiple zone completion, and drain hole completion. The use of any type of completion depends on the characteristics and location of the hydrocarbon formation to be mined. For example, an open hole completion is used when the surface is not in danger of collapse (cave in). In this case, the pipe end that is above ground is left as is, open without any protective hardware.

The type of completion used depends on the particular characteristics and location of the formation to be exploited.

The Wellhead

The wellhead consists of pieces of equipment mounted at the opening of the well, which are used to control the extraction of oil or gas from the underground formation. It prevents leaking of oil or natural gas out of the well, and it prevents blowouts caused by high pressure. Formations that are under high pressure typically require wellheads that can withstand a great upward pressure from the escaping gases and liquids. These wellheads must be able to withstand pressures of up to 20,000 psi.

Figure 2-44. Gas well head

The wellhead consists of three components: the casing head, which consists of heavy fittings that provide a seal between the casing and the surface; the tubing head, which provides a seal between the tubing, which is run inside the casing and the surface; and the Christmas tree, which is the piece of equipment that fits on top of the casing and tubing heads, and contains tubes and valves that control the flow of hydrocarbons and other fluids out of the well.

Well Treatment

In most cases, in the beginning of the exploitation of a new well, the pressure of the deposit is enough to expel the gas to the surface. With time, however, the pressure in the deposit will diminish and the gas or oil must be pumped out.

Well treatment is another method of ensuring the efficient flow of gas from a formation. Its use is increasing with the use of fracking techniques. This method consists of injecting acid, water, or gases into the well to open up the formation (fracking) and allow the petroleum to flow through it easily.

Acidizing a well consists of injecting acid (usually hydrochloric acid) into the well. In limestone or carbonate formations, the acid dissolves portions of the rock in the formation, opening up existing spaces to allow for the flow of petroleum.

Fracturing consists of injecting a fluid into the well, the pressure of which "cracks" or opens up fractures already present in the formation. In addition to the fluid being injected, "propping agents" are also used. These propping agents can consist of sand, glass beads, epoxy, or silica sand, and serve to prop open the newly widened fissures in the formation.

Hydraulic fracturing involves the injection of water into the formation, while CO_2 fracturing uses gaseous carbon dioxide. Fracturing and acidizing as well as lifting equipment may all be used on the same well to increase permeability, widening the pores of the formation.

Hydraulic Fracturing

Hydraulic fracturing is a process that is used widely lately since it makes it feasible to produce oil and natural gas from certain underground rock formations that are not productive under any other conditions. Since the gas is tightly bound within the rock's structure it is in effect sealed into it and cannot be extracted unless the rock is broken.

To produce oil or gas, a well is drilled to an underground rock formation that contains oil or gas which can flow through the rock itself by moving from one pore or crack to the next, through interconnections between the pores. A rock through which such fluids flow easily has high permeability. If the rock is solid, and the interconnections between pores and cracks are too narrow and too few, the rock will have low permeability. In that case, the oil or gas will not flow out easily. It is not economical to produce oil or gas from such formations with conventional methods.

Production from low permeability formations

has become economical lately, thanks to the new fracking technology, which creates cracks or fractures in the rock so that oil or gas can flow through the fractures instead of flowing only through interconnections between pores.

Fracturing wells started in the US in the 1860s, not very long after the first oil well was drilled in Pennsylvania in 1859. The earliest method of fracturing was explosive fracturing, where an explosive charge—called a "torpedo"—was dropped into a well and detonated. The explosion would fracture the surrounding rock, and usually provided a higher rate of production.

In the late 1940s, hydraulic fracturing was developed, where water is pumped into a rock formation at extremely high pressure. At high pressures, rocks fracture, and water moves into the fractures, forcing them to open even more. The water displaces the gas, which then escapes to the surface.

To prevent the fractures from closing when the high-pressure water is withdrawn, companies use "proppants" to prop them open. Proppants are small particles—typically sand—though small ceramic particles or sintered bauxite are sometimes used. The proppants are mixed into the fracturing water before it is pumped into the formation that will be fractured.

As the water moves into fractures, it carries proppants along with it. When the water is removed at the end of the fracturing process, the proppants stay behind, preventing the fractures from closing. For oil or gas to travel through the fractures, it must travel through the proppant particles, but this is not a problem because the proppants have high permeability.

By creating new pathways, hydraulic fracturing can exponentially increase oil and gas flow to the well. For example, a single fracture job can increase the pathways available for fluid migration in a formation by as much as 270 times in a vertical well, and much more in a horizontal well.

Usually about 99.5% of the fracturing fluid consists of water and proppants, but operators also add various other substances, including biocides to inhibit microbial growth and corrosion inhibitors to protect the well's piping. They also add other chemicals to assist the hydraulic fracturing process in other ways.

There are estimates of more than a million fracking wells being drilled and exploited in the US, since the process was commercially developed in the late 1940s. In addition to being used in low permeability rock formations, hydraulic fracturing is used in coalbeds to facilitate the production of coalbed methane.

Horizontal Drilling vs. Vertical Drilling

In traditional drilling, a well is drilled more or less vertically downward. When the target formation is reached, drilling continues for some distance into the target formation. The operator then uses a special tool to create perforations in a portion of the wellbore that is within the target formation. Oil or gas can then flow into the well through the perforations.

The longer the length of perforated pipe, the faster oil or gas can flow into the well, but with vertical drilling the length of pipe that can be perforated is limited by the vertical height of the target rock formation.

On the other hand, a formation that may be only a couple of hundred feet or less in height might extend horizontally for miles. Horizontal drilling takes advantage of this. In horizontal drilling, the operator drills vertically downward toward the target formation, then turns the drill bit to drill in a horizontal direction. The drilling might then proceed horizontally for a mile or so within the target formation, providing a long horizontal "leg" that can be perforated.

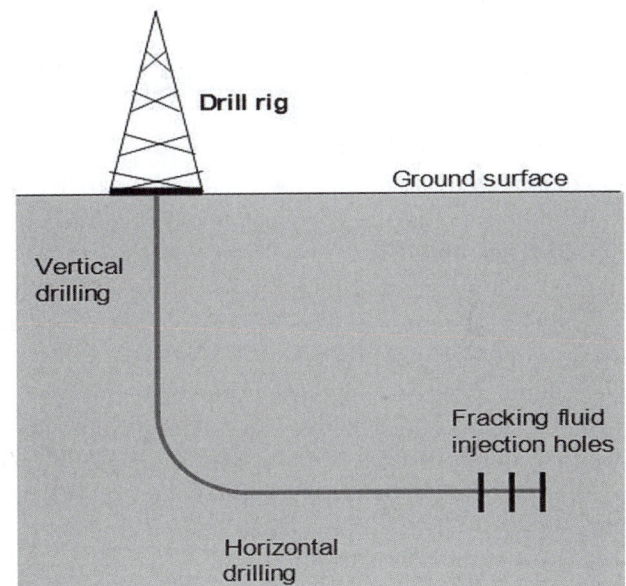

Figure 2-45. Horizontal (directional) drilling and fracking

Hydraulic fracturing makes it feasible to produce oil and gas from shale and other low-permeability formations from which production would otherwise not be feasible. Such production and the activity associated with it are beneficial for several reasons.

First, the activity has substantial economic benefits. Economists have estimated that shale gas development has created more than 200,000 jobs—direct and indirect—in the United States. Some of the new jobs are in the oil and gas industry itself, while other jobs are with companies that supply products, materials or services to the oil and gas industry. These include companies that mine the sand or manufacture the ceramic particles used as proppants; transport water, sand, and equipment to drilling sites; manufacture the high-pressure pumps used in fracturing; operate pipelines; perform construction; and operate the hotels, restaurants and caterers that house and feed workers.

State and local governments benefit from increased tax revenue, and sometimes mineral royalty revenue. In northwest Louisiana, where Haynesville Shale is located, some local governments have seen their sales tax revenue double over the course of a few years, enabling those governments to pay cash for the construction of numerous capital improvements, even while state and local governments elsewhere are struggling. State and local governments in other areas, including Texas, Pennsylvania, and North Dakota, also have benefitted.

Second, the increased production of oil and gas bolster our national security by reducing our country's dependence on imported oil and gas, some of which comes from areas that are politically unstable.

Third, hydraulic fracturing can have environmental benefits because it is often used to facilitate production of natural gas, which is the cleanest-burning of all fossil fuels. For a given amount of energy production, the combustion of natural gas produces only half as much carbon dioxide as coal, and about one-third less than oil. The combustion of natural gas also produces smaller amounts of other pollutants.

NOTE: The glass in this case is always half empty or half full. Depending on your point of view and your personal interests. Fracking has produced the most controversial issues and debates on very important socioeconomic and political subjects to date. On one hand we are happy that we now have plenty of clean, affordable natural gas, which can replace coal-burning, thus killing two birds with one stone—providing cheap energy and cleaning the environment at the same time.

On the other hand, however, there are documented reports of environmental disasters caused by large-area fracking wells—water table contamination, ground cave-ins, earthquakes, toxic gas emission, etc. People and animals have been hurt by the liquid and gas emissions, and property values have been decreased because of it as well.

A short-term solution to the controversy is to a) open the communication channels between producers and locals, and b) accelerate the R&D and testing of new proppants and chemicals for use in fracking.

Off-shore Gas Drilling

Offshore drilling for natural gas is usually done on anchored or fixed platforms that are dozens to hundreds of miles away from the coastline. This creates challenges that just don't exist when drilling onshore, although the actual drilling processes are very similar. The key difference is that with offshore drilling, the sea floor can be hundreds or thousands of feet below sea level. An artificial, manmade drilling platform must be constructed to support the drilling equipment on the surface. This is not an easy undertaking. There are many different types of such platforms, depending on the type of well to be drilled. The most important factor is depth of the underwater drilling target.

A *subsea drilling template* is a piece of equipment that connects the underwater well site (the actual hole in the ocean floor that leads to the gas deposits) to the drilling platform on the surface of the ocean. It consists of an open steel box with multiple holes in it, dependent on the number of wells to be drilled.

The subsea drilling template resembles a cookie cutter that is placed over the well site on the ocean floor, exactly where the hole(s) will be drilled. A shallow hole is then dug and the drilling template is cemented into place, secured to the ocean floor and connected with cables to the drilling platform above. This setup provides accurate drilling, while at the same time allowing the platform to move on the ocean surface, as it will inevitably be affected by waves and currents.

A *blowout preventer* is installed on the sea floor next, to prevent any oil or gas from seeping out into the water. Remember the malfunction of the blowout preventer of BP's Deep Water Horizon in 2010, and you'll get a good idea of how important this piece of equipment is.

On top of the blowout preventer, a special "marine riser" is raised to the drilling platform above. It houses the drill bit and drill-string. It is flexible enough, via slip and ball joints, to accommodate the shifting of the drilling platform.

Types of Offshore Gas Drilling Rigs

The actual design of the platform and the rest of the equipment vary, so that ultimately there are several types of offshore drilling rigs, as follow:

Drilling barges are usually used for drilling in inland water bodies—lakes, swamps, rivers and canals. Drilling barges are large, floating platforms which must be towed by tugboat from location to location. Suitable for still, shallow waters, drilling barges are not able to withstand the water movement of large open-water situations.

Drillships are large ships designed to carry out drilling operations. These boats are specially designed to carry drilling platforms out to deep-sea locations. A typical drillship will have, in addition to all of the equipment normally found on a large ocean ship, a drilling platform and derrick located in the center of its deck. In addition, drillships contain a hole (or "moonpool"), extending right through the ship, down through the hull, which allows for the drill string to extend down into the water.

Drillships are often used to drill in very deep water, which can be turbulent. They use what is known as "dynamic positioning" systems. They are equipped with electric motors on the underside of the ship's hull, capable of propelling the ship in any direction. These motors are integrated into the ship's computer system, which uses satellite positioning technology, in conjunction with sensors located on the drilling template, to ensure that the ship is directly above the drill site at all times.

Jack-up rigs are similar to drilling barges, with one difference. Once a jack-up rig is towed to the drilling site, three or four "legs" are lowered until they rest on the sea bottom. This allows the working platform to rest above the surface of the water, as opposed to a floating barge. However, jack-up rigs are suitable for shallower waters, as extending these legs down too deeply would be impractical. These rigs are typically safer to operate than drilling barges, as their working platform is elevated above the water level.

Moveable drilling rigs are two basic types of offshore drilling rigs: those that can be moved from place to place, allowing for drilling in multiple locations, and those rigs that are permanently placed. Moveable rigs are often used for exploratory purposes because they are much cheaper to use than permanent platforms. Once large deposits of hydrocarbons have been found, a permanent platform is built to allow their extraction. The sections below describe a number of different types of moveable offshore platforms.

Submersible rigs consist of platforms with two hulls positioned on top of one another. The upper hull contains the living quarters for the crew, as well as the actual drilling platform. The lower hull works much like the outer hull in a submarine, so that when the platform is being moved from one place to another, the lower hull is filled with air, thus making the entire rig buoyant. When the rig is positioned over the drill site, the air is let out of the lower hull, and the rig submerses to the sea floor. This type of rig has the advantage of mobility in the water, but its use is limited to shallow-water areas.

Semisubmersible rigs are the most common type of offshore drilling rigs, combining the advantages of submersible rigs with the ability to drill in deep water. A semisubmersible rig works on the same principle as a submersible rig: through the "inflating" and "deflating" of its lower hull. The main difference with a semisubmersible rig, however, is that when the air is let out of the lower hull, the rig does not submerge to the sea floor. Instead, the rig is partially submerged, but still floats above the drill site. When drilling, the lower hull, filled with water, provides stability to the rig.

Semisubmersible rigs are held in place by huge anchors, each weighing upwards of 10 tons. These anchors, combined with the submerged portion of the rig, ensure that the platform is stable and safe enough to be used in turbulent offshore waters. Semisubmersible rigs can be used to drill in much deeper water than their submersible cousins.

Gas Production Platforms

There are several types of production platforms on which the entire extraction and production cycles are conducted by a number of methods. Generally, offshore production platforms are very expensive, semi-permanent structures used when exploiting large, commercially viable natural gas or petroleum deposits, and on which the entire gas extraction and production processes are conducted.

Some of the largest offshore platforms are located in the North Sea, where because of almost constant inclement weather, structures able to withstand high winds and large waves are necessary. A typical permanent platform in the North Sea must be able to withstand wind speeds of over 90 knots (103 mph), and waves over 60 feet high. Correspondingly, these platforms are among the largest structures built by man.

Types of Offshore Production Rigs

There are a number of different types of temporary or permanent offshore platforms, each useful for a particular depth range. The major types are as follow:

Compliant Towers consist of a narrow tower attached to a foundation on the seafloor and extending up to the platform. The support tower is flexible, however, vs. the rigid legs of a fixed platform. The flexibility of the support system allows the rig to operate in deep water, since it is capable of "absorbing" surface waves and currents, and yet it is strong enough to withstand even hurricanes.

Fixed Platforms are usually found in shallower water, where they are attached to the sea floor via "legs" constructed with concrete and steel. The legs extend down from the platform, and are fixed to the seafloor with piles. Large platforms mounted on heavy-duty concrete legs structures are so heavy that they are not attached to the seafloor, and the entire rig relies on its weight for stability.

There are many possible designs for these fixed, permanent platforms. The main advantage of these types of platforms is their stability. As they are attached to the sea floor there is limited exposure to movement due to wind and water forces. The limitation here, of course, is depth, for it is simply not economical to build very long legs.

Floating Production Systems are essentially semisubmersible drilling rigs, or ships, like those used for drilling, except that these contain both drilling and production equipment. Surface platforms are kept steady via large, heavy anchors attached to the ocean floor. They can also be fixed in place via the dynamic positioning system used by drillships. The wellhead of this setup is attached to the seafloor once the drilling is completed, rather than being attached up to the platform. The extracted petroleum is transported via risers from this wellhead to the production facilities on the semisubmersible platform. These production systems can operate in water depths of up to 6,000 feet.

Seastar Platforms are like miniature tension leg platforms. The platform consists of a floating rig, much like the semisubmersible type discussed above. A lower hull is filled with water when drilling, which increases the stability of the platform against wind and water movement. In addition to this semisubmersible rig, however, Seastar platforms also incorporate the tension leg system employed in larger platforms. Tension legs are long, hollow tendons that extend from the seafloor to the floating platform. These legs are kept under constant tension, and do not allow for any up or down movement of the platform. However, their flexibility does allow for side-to-side motion, which allows the platform to withstand the force of the ocean and wind without breaking the legs off. Seastar platforms are typically used for smaller deep-water reservoirs, when it is not economical to build a larger platform. They can operate in water depths of up to 3,500 feet.

Spar Platforms are among the largest offshore platforms in use. These huge platforms consist of a large cylinder supporting a typical fixed rig platform. The cylinder does not extend all the way to the seafloor, but instead is tethered to the bottom by a series of cables and lines. The large cylinder serves to stabilize the platform in the water, and allows for movement to absorb the force of potential hurricanes. The first Spar platform in the Gulf of Mexico was installed in September of 1996. Its cylinder measured 770 feet long and was 70 feet in diameter, and the platform operated in 1,930 feet of water.

Subsea Production Systems are wells located on the sea floor, as opposed to the surface. The gas or oil is extracted at the seafloor, and then "tied-back" to an already existing production platform. The well is drilled by a moveable rig, but instead of building a production platform for that well, the extracted natural gas and oil are transported by riser or undersea pipeline to a nearby production platform. This allows one strategically-placed production platform to service many wells over a reasonably large area. Subsea systems are typically in use at depths of 7,000 feet or more.

Tension leg platforms are larger versions of the Seastar platform. The long, flexible legs are attached to the sea floor, and run up to the platform itself. As with the Seastar platform, these legs allow for significant side-to-side movement (up to 20 feet), with little vertical movement. Tension leg platforms can operate at around 7,000 feet.

NATURAL GAS REFINING AND PROCESSING

A number techniques are used in the process of creating pipeline-quality natural gas, depending on the source and makeup of the wellhead production stream. Several of the steps of the usual process may be integrated into one operation, or be performed in a different order, while some are not required at all. The usual stages of gas processing/treatment are:

- Gas-oil Separation
- Condensate Separation
- Dehydration
- Contaminants Removal
- Nitrogen Extraction
- Methane Separation
- Fractionation

In more detail:
- *Gas-Oil Separation* is needed in some cases, where a multi-stage gas-oil separation process is used to separate the gas stream from the crude oil. These gas-oil separators are usually closed cylindrical shells, horizontally mounted with inlets at one end, an outlet at the top for removal of gas, and an outlet at the bottom for removal of oil. Separation is accomplished by alternately heating and cooling (by compression) the flow stream through

multiple steps. Some water and condensate, if present, will also be extracted as the process proceeds.

• *Condensate Separation* is used to remove condensates from the gas stream at the wellhead with mechanical separators. Most often the gas flow into the separator comes directly from the wellhead, since the gas-oil separation process is not needed. The gas stream enters the processing plant at high pressure (600 pounds per square inch gauge [psig] or greater) through an inlet slug catcher where free water is removed from the gas and then directed to a condensate separator. Extracted condensate is routed to on-site storage tanks.

• *Dehydration Process* is needed to eliminate water which may cause the formation of hydrates. Hydrates form when a gas or liquid containing free water experiences specific temperature/pressure conditions. Dehydration is the removal of this water from the produced natural gas and is accomplished by several methods. Ethylene glycol (glycol injection) systems are used as an absorption* mechanism to remove water and other solids from the gas stream. Alternatively, adsorption* dehydration may be used, utilizing dry-bed dehydrator towers, which contain desiccants such as silica gel and activated alumina, to perform the extraction.

• *Contaminants Removal* is needed to remove contaminates from the gas. This includes the elimination of hydrogen sulfide, carbon dioxide, water vapor, helium, and oxygen. The most commonly used technique is to first direct the flow though a tower containing an amine solution. Amines absorb sulfur compounds from natural gas and can be reused repeatedly. After desulphurization, the gas flow is directed to the next section which contains a series of filter tubes. As the velocity of the stream reduces in the unit, primary separation of remaining contaminants occurs due to gravity. As gas flows through the tubes, separation of smaller particles occurs and they combine into larger particles which flow to the lower section of the unit. Further, as the gas stream continues through the series of tubes, a centrifugal force is generated which further removes any remaining water and small solid particulate matter.

---

*Adsorption is the binding of molecules or particles to the surface of a material, while absorption is the filling of the pores in a solid. The binding to the surface is usually weak with adsorption and, therefore, easily reversible.

• *Nitrogen Extraction* is performed after the hydrogen sulfide and carbon dioxide are processed to acceptable levels, and the stream is routed to a nitrogen rejection unit (NRU), where it is further dehydrated using molecular sieve beds. In the NRU, the gas stream makes a series of passes through a column and a brazed aluminum plate fin heat exchanger. Using thermodynamics, the nitrogen is cryogenically separated and vented. Another type of NRU unit separates methane and heavier hydrocarbons from nitrogen using an absorbent* solvent. The absorbed methane and heavier hydrocarbons are flashed off from the solvent by reducing the pressure on the processing stream in multiple gas decompression steps. The liquid from the flash regeneration step is returned to the top of the methane absorber as lean solvent. Helium, if any, can be extracted from the gas stream in a pressure swing adsorption (PSA) unit.

• *Methane Separation* is the process of demethanizing the gas stream and can occur as a separate operation in the gas plant or as part of the NRU operation. Cryogenic processing and absorption methods are some of the ways to separate methane from NGLs.

a. The cryogenic method is better at extraction of the lighter liquids, such as ethane, than is the alternative absorption method. Essentially, cryogenic processing consists of lowering the temperature of the gas stream to around –120 degrees Fahrenheit. While there are several ways to perform this function, the turbo expander process is most effective, using external refrigerants to chill the gas stream. The quick drop in temperature that the expander is capable of producing condenses the hydrocarbons in the gas stream, but maintains methane in its gaseous form.

b. The absorption* method, on the other hand, uses a "lean" absorbing oil to separate the methane from the NGLs. While the gas stream is passed through an absorption tower, the absorption oil soaks up a large amount of the NGLs. The "enriched" absorption oil, now containing NGLs, exits the tower at the bottom. This oil is fed into distillers where the blend is heated to above the boiling point of the NGLs while the oil remains fluid. The oil is recycled while the NGLs are cooled and directed to a fractionator tower. Another absorption method that is often used is the refrigerated oil absorption method where the lean oil is chilled rather than heated, a feature that enhances recovery rates somewhat.

• *Fractionation* is the process of separating the various NGLs present in the remaining gas stream, using the varying boiling points of the individual hydrocarbons in the stream (by now virtually all NGLs). The process occurs in stages as the gas stream rises through several towers where heating units raise the temperature of the stream, causing the various liquids to separate and exit into specific holding tanks.

The Process Flow

There are a great many ways in which to configure the various steps in the processing and refining of raw natural gas. The usual process flow can be described as follows:

To start with, the raw natural gas is pumped up from a well or a group of adjacent wells. It is then processed on-site usually, for removal of free liquid water and natural gas condensate. The condensate is trucked to a petroleum refinery and the water is disposed of as wastewater.

Processing raw natural gas yields several byproducts, such as natural gas condensate, sulfur, ethane, and natural gas liquids (NGL), such as propane, butanes and C5+ (commonly used term for pentanes plus higher molecular weight hydrocarbons). All these fractions must be separated and otherwise treated in separate streams, until the final product is pure enough.

The somewhat cleaned raw gas is sent from the wellhead via pipeline to a gas processing plant where it is treated first to remove the acid creating gases; hydrogen sulfide and carbon dioxide, using Amine gas treating. Polymeric membranes can be used also to dehydrate and separate the carbon dioxide and hydrogen sulfide from the natural gas stream.

Thus removed acid gases are sent to a sulfur recovery unit, where they are converted into elemental sulfur, using the Claus process in most cases. The residual gas from the Claus process is processed in a tail gas treating unit (TGTU) to recover and recycle residual sulfur-containing compounds. The final residual gas from the TGTU is incinerated, so that the carbon dioxide in the raw natural gas ends up in the incinerator flue gas stack and is disposed by venting in the atmosphere.

Removal of water vapor from the gas is an impor-

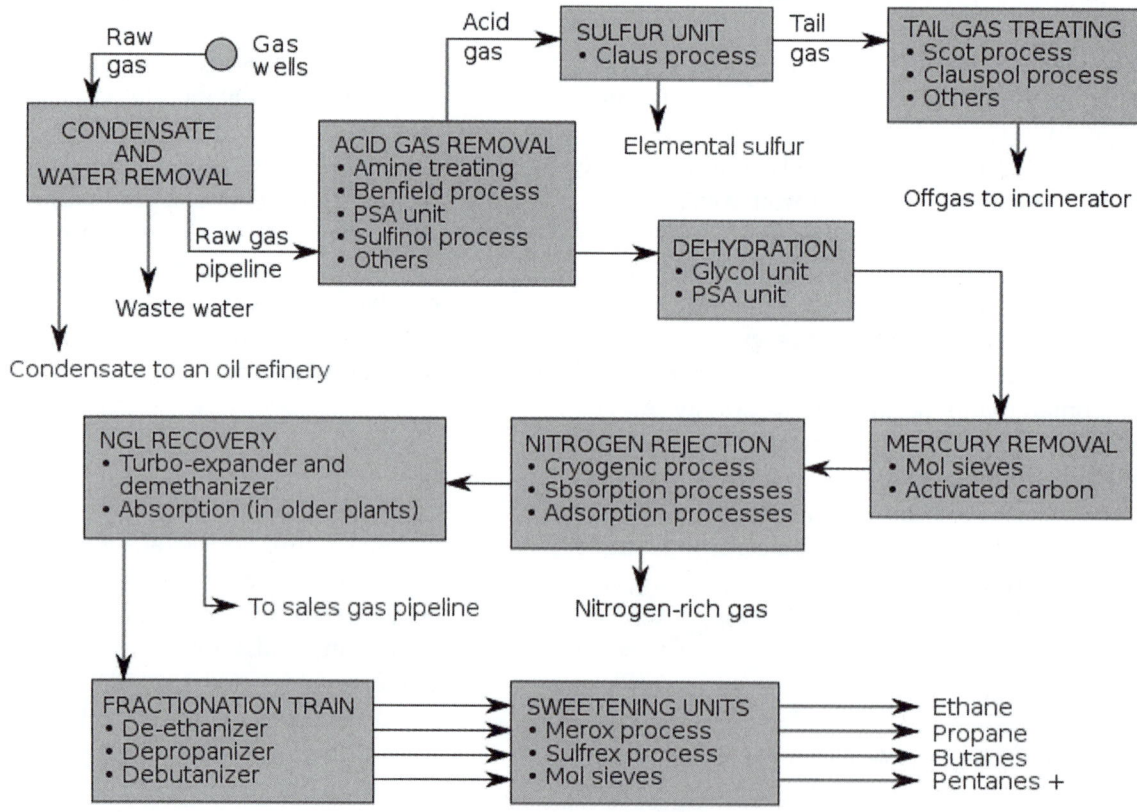

Figure 2-46. Natural gas processing (refining) plant

tant step, which is done by using either regenerable absorption in liquid triethylene glycol (TEG), also called glycol dehydration, or by using a pressure swing adsorption (PSA) unit using a solid adsorbent.

Mercury is then removed by using adsorption processes using activated carbon or regenerable molecular sieves.

Nitrogen is removed next and rejected using one of these processes:

— Cryogenic process, using low temperature distillation.
— Absorption process, using lean oil or a special solvent as the absorbent, or
— Adsorption process, using activated carbon or molecular sieves as the adsorbent.

The natural gas liquids (NGL) are recovered next, via cryogenic low-temperature distillation process involving expansion of the gas through a turbo-expander, followed by distillation in a de-methanizing fractionating column. Lean oil absorption process can be used here also, rather than the cryogenic turbo-expander process. The residue gas from the NGL recovery section is the final, purified "sales" gas which is pipelined to end-user markets.

The recovered NGL stream is processed through a fractionation train consisting of three distillation towers in series: a de-ethanizer, a de-propanizer and a debutanizer. The overhead product from the de-ethanizer is ethane and the bottoms are fed to the de-propanizer.

The overhead product from the depropanizer is propane and the bottoms are fed to the debutanizer. The overhead product from the debutanizer is a mixture of normal and iso-butane, and the bottoms product is a C5+ mixture.

The recovered streams of propane, butanes and C5+ are each "sweetened" in a Merox process unit to convert undesirable mercaptans into disulfides and, along with the recovered ethane, are the final NGL by-products from the gas processing plant.

NOTE: There are important differences between the drilling and production methods for shale gas vs. coal bed methane (CBM), known as coal seam gas, as follow:

1. Shale strata (at 1,000m to 3,000m) are typically much deeper than coal deposits (100m to 1,000m). This reduces the likelihood that gas, fracking fluids and produced water could migrate from the shale formation to contaminate the water table.

2. Coal deposits are much more porous than shale rock. Nearly all shales require hydraulic fracturing to extract gas, whereas only a portion of coal deposits require fracturing. In Queensland, Australia, for example, only 10%-40% of CBM wells are estimated to ultimately require fracturing.

3. Shale is much denser than coal, requiring greater energy to fracture (25,000-35,000 horsepower, compared with 4,000-5,000 horsepower to fracture coal seams). Therefore, more and more powerful equipment is required to fracture shale layers than to fracture coal deposits.

4. Water must generally be pumped out of coal deposits to extract natural gas, while it must be pumped into shale to fracture the deposit and extract natural gas. Therefore, coal gas projects potentially put less immediate strain on surface water resources. However, they also have greater subsurface water risks insofar as water from adjacent aquifers could migrate into coal formations as reservoir pressures decline.

For both coal and shale gas wells, water produced from the well (also known as "produced water" or "gray water") is saline and toxic in high concentrations, requiring similar types of handling, special treatment and disposal.

Natural Gas Transport

Transporting natural gas from the wellhead to the final customer involves several physical transfers of custody and multiple processing steps. A natural gas pipeline system begins at the gas producing well or field. Once the gas leaves the well, a pipeline gathering system directs the flow either to a natural gas processing plant or directly to the mainline transmission grid, depending upon the initial quality of the wellhead product.

The processing plant produces pipeline-quality natural gas. This gas is then transported by pipeline to consumers or is put into underground storage for future use. Storage helps to maintain pipeline system operational integrity and to meet customer requirements during peak-usage periods.

Transporting natural gas from wellhead to market involves a number of pieces of equipment, a series of processes, and an array of physical facilities. The list of these is long, but the key pieces are:

Gathering Lines are small-diameter pipelines which move natural gas from the wellhead to the natural gas processing plant or to an interconnection with a larger mainline pipeline.

Mainline Transmission System is a wide-diameter, long-distance pipeline transport natural gas from the producing area to market areas.

Processing Plant is the operation that extracts natural gas liquids and impurities from the natural gas stream. The gas is then sent to the customers via mainline pipelines.

Market Hubs/Centers are locations where pipelines intersect and flows are transferred.

Underground Storage Facilities is where natural gas is stored. These could be depleted oil and gas reservoirs, aquifers, and salt caverns, where the gas is pumped in for future use.

Peak Shaving is a system design methodology permitting a natural gas pipeline to meet short-term surges in customer demands with minimal infrastructure. Peaks can be handled by using gas from storage or by short-term line-packing.

LNG Transport

LNG is shipped as a cryogenic gas in insulated tank trucks and rail pressure tank cars. Pressure tank trucks and rail tank cars for LNG transport have a stainless steel inner reservoir suspended in an outer reservoir of carbon steel. The annular space is a vacuum filled with insulation to maintain low temperatures during shipment. To prevent gas from igniting back to the tanks, they are equipped with two independent, remotely controlled fail-safe emergency shut-off valves on the filling and discharge lines and have gauges on both the inside and outside reservoirs.

LPG is transported on land in specially designed rail tank cars (up to 130 m^3 capacity) or tank trucks (up to 40 m^3 capacity). Tank trucks and rail tank cars for LPG transport are typically un-insulated steel cylinders with spherical bottoms, equipped with gauges, thermometers, two safety relief valves, a gas level meter and maximum fill indicator and baffles.

Rail tank cars transporting LNG or LPG should not be overloaded, since they may sit on a siding for some period of time and be exposed to high ambient temperatures, which could cause overpressure and venting. Bond wires and grounding cables are provided at rail and tank truck loading racks to help neutralize and dissipate static electricity. They should be connected before operations commence and not disconnected until operations are complete and all valves are closed. Truck and rail loading facilities are typically protected by fire water-spray or mist systems and fire extinguishers.

NATURAL GAS PRODUCTION AND USE

Lately, natural gas production has been headed sky high, and there is no stopping it— hail or high water. The use of natural gas as fuel for electricity generation is climbing faster than the other fossil fuels combined. Other uses of natural gas, such as in the production of different chemicals, are also finding wider acceptance worldwide, so we foresee an even larger expansion of natural gas drilling and production in the near future.

Because we know for sure that there are problems related to natural gas drilling, extraction and use, we need to know all about it, and take the necessary precautionary and regulatory measures. Ignorance or denial will not work! Educated reasoning and decisive action might help us prevent a major disaster.

Table 2-12. Global natural gas production and use, 2009.

Country	% of world production	% of world use
Russia	21.3	15.1
USA	18.5	22.0
Canada	6.5	3.4
Iran	3.7	3.7
Norway	3.0	3.0
Algeria	2.9	2.9
U.K.	2.8	3.2
Saudi Arabia	2.6	2.6
Netherlands	2.2	2.2
Ukraine	—	2.3
Japan	—	3.0

Natural Gas Use

Natural gas is the fuel of the future. It powers large numbers of chemical and refining processes in the U.S. It is also the fuel of choice for our electric power generating network, and is a major feedstock for hydrogen production, hydrocracking, hydro-desulfurization, ammonia and other chemicals production.

Natural gas is also used for making syngas, methanol, and its derivatives—MTBE, formaldehyde, and acetic acid. The condensate derivatives, ethane and propane, are used as an advantageous raw material in a number of processes and products. Via ethylene and propylene, natural gas is also used in much of the organic chemicals production industries today.

The main uses of natural gas, however, are as a fuel for personal and commercial transport vehicles and electricity generation.

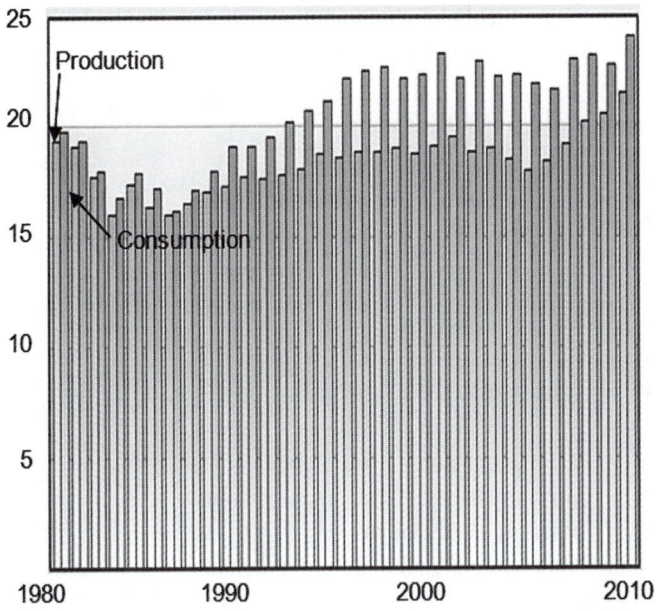

Figure 2-47. US natural gas production and use (in trillion ft³)

Transportation Use

Within the last decade, the industry began to count the natural gas plant liquids (NGPL) as part of our energy supply, and there is increasing talk about using some of these as vehicle fuel. NGPLs are hydrocarbons, other than methane, that are separated from raw natural gas at a processing plant. These include ethane, propane, butane and pentane in variable amounts.

For example, some major natural gas sources contain 11 percent ethane, 5 percent propane, 2 percent butane and about 2 percent of natural gasoline or drip gas (a low-octane fuel used mostly as a solvent.) Other natural gas sources contain much higher percentage of methane and correspondingly smaller percentages of NGPL—7 percent ethane, 4 percent propane, 1 percent butane, and other components including carbon dioxide and pentanes.

In these, and most other cases, ethane makes up about half of the NGPL, propane makes up about a quarter, butane makes up 5-10 percent of NGPL.

Please note that NGPL products come from natural gas, where only propane and butane can be used as vehicle fuel, but they are a small component (25-35%) of the total NGPL volume. Most of the volume of NGPL cannot easily be used as vehicle fuel.

It is therefore doubtful that either propane or butane could become major vehicles fuels since they make up only a small fraction of the total natural gas volume, and are limited in supply by the quality and amount of natural gas extracted.

Some NGPLs are also used as feedstocks for chemical production, just as petroleum is. Nevertheless, the likelihood is small that NGPLs would significantly displace crude oil in this market, as it is currently configured. So, NGPLs will most likely be used as a fuel in gas-fired power plants and other heat-producing applications.

POWER GENERATION

Natural gas is a major fuel for electric power generation that is becoming more important by the day.

The U.S. produces a significant amount of natural gas, which is increasing exponentially as we speak. Some of that amount is exported, while most of the rest is used for power generation.

Figure 2-48 shows that natural gas provides over half of the electric power used in California. While there are a lot of discussions, disagreements, and even fights over the renewable energies, natural gas is quietly taking the driver's seat of the California energy industry. Gas usage is also growing in many other states due to its abundance, low price, and environmental friendliness.

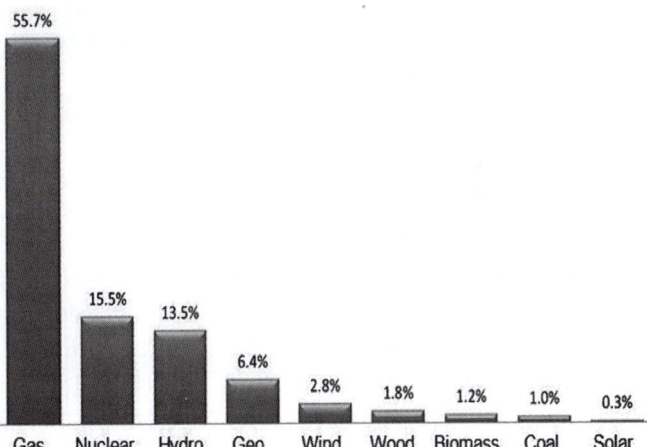

Figure 2-48. California electricity generation, 2010

We reviewed drilling and extraction procedures and some of the uses, so we will now take a close look at the natural gas use as a fuel for electricity generation.

The Gas-fired Power Plant

Natural gas-fired power plants are similar to their oil-fired cousins. The only difference is the fuel, which is in gas form and is fed via gas pipe in the most efficient setup—that of combined cycle power generator. In it, the gas is fed into the first section (the combustion turbine) where it is burned (as in a jet engine) to turn the turbine blades. The turbine in turn rotates the rotor of a generator, and the produced electricity is sent into the grid.

The exhaust heat from the combustion turbine is sent into a boiler, where water is heated and turned into steam. The steam is sent into a second turbine, which turns and rotates the rotor of a second generator. The additional electricity is sent into the grid as well (see Figure 2-36).

We've seen lately a large-scale conversion of coal-fired plants into gas-fired. The main reasons for this are a) natural gas emits less GHG, and b) natural gas benefits from less strict regulations. A compromise between coal- and gas-fired plants is mixed fuel power generation.

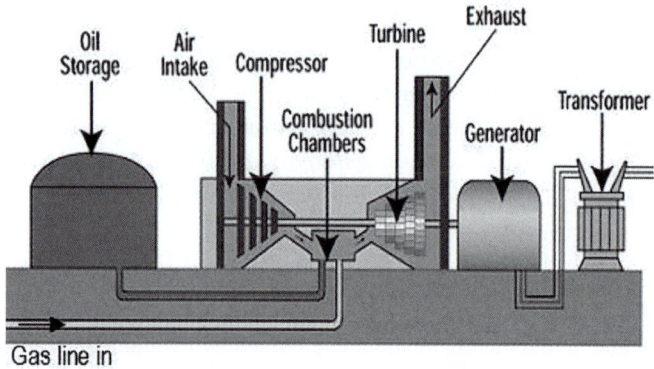

Figure 2-49. Mixed fuel gas power plant

In this setup, dual fuel (oil and gas) is fed into a turbine, where both fuels burn simultaneously to rotate the turbine and the generator's rotor, which generates electricity. This setup is convenient since allows versatility, and also benefits from lower emissions, in addition to more lenient regulations.

Gas Power Plant Construction and Operation

The gas-fired power plant life-span cycle consists of several phases, very similar to those of coal- and oil-fired power plants, as follow:

Plant site and structure planning and design
- Locating, testing and exploring the proposed power plant location
- Engineering design of plant facilities, equipment and process
- Estimating construction and operating cost and related tasks

- Applying for and obtaining the necessary federal, state and local permits

Plant construction and setup
- Plant building construction
- Plant equipment procurement and setup
- Labor training

Power plant daily operation
- Gas delivery
- Gas burning and energy generation
- Electric power distribution

Power plant decommissioning and land reclamation
- Plant shutdown and disassembly
- Plant waste disposal
- Surface land reclamation

Since the steps are very similar to those used for coal-fired plants construction and use, we refer the reader to the section on COAL for more details.

Natural Gas Cost

Natural gas prices have varied through the years, driven by the overall energy markets and local political and socio-economic conditions.

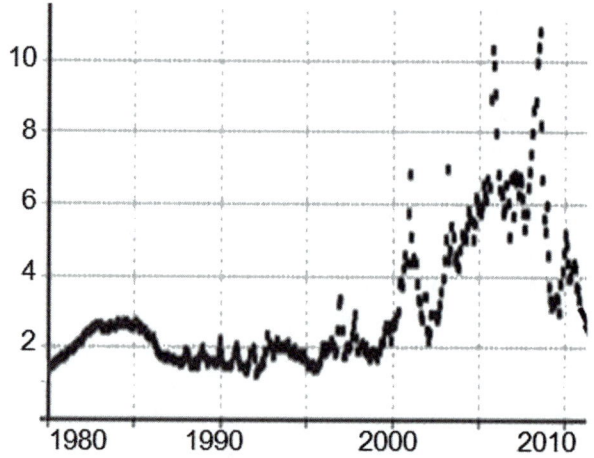

Figure 2-50. Natural gas cost of production (in \$/thousand ft³)

Large gas reserve finds and better extraction technologies have already begun pushing gas production costs lower than they were in previous years, as shown in Figure 2-52. Nevertheless, there are many other factors influencing the production cost of natural gas. A major one is the fact that unlike crude oil, where the spigot can be turned off when needed, natural gas has no spigot. Once turned on, it cannot be turned off. That creates the necessity of identifying long-term markets and contracting purchasers long before a well is exploited. This makes the gas prices somewhat stable, and at least much more stable than oil.

Enron lobbied for the linking of gas price to oil prices, even though gas competes with and is replacing mostly coal. But this suited the Texan lobby, as the state produced large quantities of both oil and gas. Oil prices soared only after the Middle-East formed a cartel in the 1970s (the OPEC embargo). That too suited Texas oil men.

Even today, there are charges of price rigging, which both the US and the EU are investigating. One example is Qatar, who had been selling LNG to the East Coast of the US at $15 per million metric British thermal unit (MMBtu), when in actuality the average price was $3. Someone was trying to push prices higher, as often happens with energy sources.

Everything about natural gas changed with the hydrofracked shale gas, and by 2010 the world had over 200 trillion cubic meters of natural gas available in addition to the existing reserves. But with more shale gas being found everyday, especially in China, which has more than the combined reserves of the US and Canada put together, shale gas could exceed other energy reserves, which might bring prices even lower than expected. The biggest shale gas production centers are in Australia, China and Russia.

Figure 2-51 shows that the cost of power generation using natural gas (NG) equals that of coal, as far as the entire cradle-to-grave production and power generation cycles are concerned. The price of gas fuel itself is still higher than coal, but that is compensated for by the other costs of using coal. As the price of fuel gas is decreasing, in the very near future it will become the cheapest and one of the cleanest fuels in the world—un-

til it is depleted or until large-scale environmental disasters (due to hydrofracking anomalies) stop it in its tracks.

The Future of Natural Gas

Natural gas is a versatile fuel—or better said, it can be used in a number of versatile electricity generation setups. It is becoming increasingly important, because it is well suited for numerous applications such as cogeneration, gas turbines, steam turbines, and for a combined use in association with renewable energy sources such as wind or solar. Lately it is also finding increasing use for alimenting peak-load power stations functioning in tandem with hydroelectric plants—wide use of a plentiful fuel on our way to energy independence, no doubt!

Most grid-peaking power plants and some off-grid engine generators use natural gas for multiple reasons. Particularly high efficiencies can be achieved through combining gas turbines with a steam turbine in combined cycle mode. Natural gas burns more cleanly than other hydrocarbon fuels, such as oil and coal, and produces less carbon dioxide per unit of energy released. For an equivalent amount of heat, burning natural gas produces about 30% less carbon dioxide than burning petroleum and about 45 percent less than burning coal.

Coal-fired electric power generation emits around 2,000 pounds of carbon dioxide for every megawatt hour generated, which is almost double the carbon dioxide released by a natural gas-fired electric plant for the same power generation. Because of the higher carbon efficiency of natural gas generation, as the fuel mix in the US reduces coal and increases natural gas generation, carbon dioxide emissions have unexpectedly fallen. Those measured in the first quarter of 2012 were the lowest on record for the first quarter of any year since 1992. Of course, there are other factors that affect emissions, so we will be watching future developments.

Combined cycle power generation using natural gas is currently the cleanest available source of power using hydrocarbon fuels, and this technology is widely and increasingly used, as natural gas can be obtained easily and at increasingly reduced costs. Locally produced electricity and heat using a natural gas powered combined heat and power plant (CHP or cogeneration plant) is considered energy efficient and a rapid way to cut carbon emissions.

In May 2013 a number of energy-related organizations reported that gas prices will continue to ease, and some countries are expecting their gas import bills to fall by half, mostly thanks to lower shale gas pricing and extraordinary availability. During the same time, the

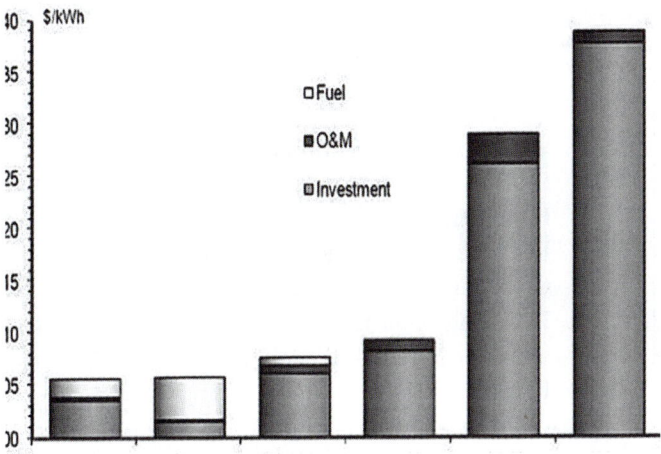

Figure 2-51. Energy generation cost (in $/kW/h)

International Energy Agency issued a warning that any attempt to push gas prices up beyond $5/MMBtu could prompt the US to step up use of coal, after years of cutting back on its consumption in favor of cleaner-burning gas. So we now have a theoretical ceiling on gas prices. How long it will last, and what is next for natural gas remains to be seen.

End-of-life Decommissioning

Decommissioning gas rigs is a complex and expensive effort. There are 10 steps to the decommissioning process:

- Project management
- Engineering and planning
- Permitting and regulatory compliance
- Platform preparation
- Well plugging and abandonment
- Conductor removal
- Mobilization and demobilization of derrick barges
- Platform removal
- Pipeline and power cable decommissioning
- Materials disposal
- Site clearance and final test

Project Management, engineering and planning for decommissioning an offshore rig usually starts three years before the well runs dry. The process involves review of contractual obligations, engineering analysis, operational planning, and contracting, Due to the limited number of derrick barges, many operators contract these vessels two to three years in advance. In addition, much of the decommissioning process requires contractors who specialize in a specific part of the process. Most operators contract out the project management, cutting civil engineering and diving services.

Permitting and Regulatory Compliance consists of obtaining permits to decommission an offshore rig and can take up to three years to complete. Often, operators will contract a local consulting firm to ensure that all permits are in order prior to decommissioning. Local consulting firms are familiar with the regulatory framework of their region.

An execution plan is one of the first steps in the process. Included in this plan is environmental information and field surveys of the project site. The plan describes a schedule of decommissioning activities and the equipment and labor required to carry out the operation. An execution plan is required to secure permits from federal, state, and local regulatory agencies. BOEMRE

will also analyze the environmental impacts of the project and recommend ways to eliminate or minimize those impacts.

Federal agencies often involved in decommissioning projects include BOEMRE, National Marine Fisheries Service, US Army Corps of Engineers, US Fish and Wildlife Service, National Oceanic and Atmospheric Administration, US Environmental Protection Agency, US Coast Guard, and the US Department of Transportation, Office of Pipeline Safety.

Platform Preparation starts with the preparation of tanks, processing equipment, and piping that needs to be flushed and cleaned. Residual hydrocarbons must be disposed of; platform equipment must be removed (which includes cutting pipe and cables between deck modules, separating the modules, installing padeyes to lift the modules); and reinforcing the structure. Underwater, workers prepare the jacket facilities for removal, which includes removing marine growth.

Well Plugging and Abandonment

Plugging and abandonment is one of the major costs of a decommissioning project and can be broken into two phases. The planning phase of well plugging includes:

— Data collection
— Preliminary inspection
— Selection of abandonment methods
— Submittal of an application for BOEMRE approval

In the GOM, the rigless method, which was developed in the 1980s, is used primarily for plugging and abandonment jobs. The rigless method uses a load spreader on top of a conductor, providing a base to launch tools, equipment and plugs downhole.

Well abandonment involves:
— Well entry preparations
— Use of a slick line unit
— Filling the well with fluid
— Removal of downhole equipment
— Cleaning out the wellbore
— Plugging open-hole and perforated intervals(s) at the bottom of the well
— Plugging casing stubs
— Plugging of annular space
— Placement of a surface plug
— Placement of fluid between plugs

To remove conductor casing, operators can chose one of three procedures:

— *Severing* requires the use of explosive, mechanical or abrasive cutting
— *Pulling, or sectioning* uses the casing jacks to raise the conductors that are unscrewed or cut into 40-ft-long segments.
— Offloading utilizes a rental crane to lay down each conductor casing segment in a platform staging area, to offload sections to a boat and for offloading at a port. The conductors are then transported to an onshore disposal site.

Mobilization/Demobilization and Platform Removal of derrick barges is a key component in platform removal. According to BOEMRE, platforms, templates, and pilings must be removed to at least 15 ft below the mud line.

First, the topsides are taken apart and lifted onto the derrick barge. Topsides can be removed all in one piece, in groups of modules, reverse order of installation, or in small pieces.

If removing topsides in one piece, the derrick barge must have sufficient lifting capacity. This option is best used for small platforms. Also the crane size and capacity at the offloading site are very important. If the offloading site can't accommodate the platform in one piece, then a different removal option is required.

Removing combined modules requires fewer lifts, thus is a time-saving option. However, the modules must be in the right position and have a combined weight under the crane and derrick barge capacity. Dismantling the topsides in reverse order in which they were installed, whether installed as modules or as individual structural components, is another removal option and the most common.

Topsides can also be cut into small pieces and removed with platform cranes, temporary deck-mounted cranes, or other small (less expensive) cranes. However, this method takes the most time, so any cost savings incurred using a smaller derrick barge will likely be offset by the dayrate.

Removing the jacket is the second step in the demolition process and the most costly. First, divers using explosives, mechanical means, torches or abrasive technology make the bottom cuts on the piles 15 ft below the mudline. Then the jacket is removed either in small pieces or as a single lift. A single lift is possible only for small structures in less than 200 ft of water. Heavy lifting equipment is required for the jacket removal as well, but a derrick barge is not necessary. Less expensive support equipment can do the job.

Pipeline and Power Cable Decommissioning can be done in place if they do not interfere with navigation or commercial fishing operations or pose an environmental hazard. However, if BOEMRE rules that it is a hazard during the technical and environmental review, during the permitting process, it must be removed.

The first step to pipeline decommissioning in place requires flushing it with water, followed by disconnecting it from the platform and filling it with seawater. The open end is plugged and buried 3 ft below the seafloor and covered with concrete.

Materials Disposal and Site Clearance ensures that all platform materials are removed to be refurbished, reused, scrapped and recycled or disposed of in specified landfills. To ensure proper site clearance, operators need to follow a site clearance procedure consisting of:
— Pre-decommissioning survey maps the location and quantity of debris, pipelines, power cables, and natural marine environments.
— Post-decommissioning survey identifies debris left behind during the removal process and notes any environmental damage.

If the rig is off-shore then:
— ROVs and divers target are deployed to further identify and remove any debris that could interfere with other uses of the area.
— Test trawling verifies that the area is free of any potential obstructions.

This is a long, complex process, full of safety hazards. It is imperative that each step of the process be executed properly, efficiently, and safely. One misstep, one hesitation, and the entire project is in jeopardy.

Here we need to mention also the complex and expensive process of decommissioning gas-fired power plants, which is quite similar to that used for decommissioning coal- and oil-fired power plants. The costs and environmental impact of these operations are serious, so they need to be kept in mind when analyzing the entire cradle-to-grave cycle of gas production and use.

Gas Production Equipment Environmental Impact

A number of large and small pieces of equipment are used during gas drilling, production, and use. Starting with the gas rig and power plant design and construction, we see pollution taking place in the shape of heavy plumes of smoke from large trucks and bull-dozers all around the gas site. There are also trains and trucks used for transporting the production equipment to the site, the exhausts of which are significant.

Don't forget that all this machinery was made somewhere, sometime in the past, where and when their manufacturing processes and transport created a significant pollution footprint as well. Since most of these pieces of equipment are used only temporarily, we cannot assign the entire footprint to them, so we would consider assigning 5-10% of it to the manufacture and transport of gas rigging and power plant equipment (A).

The equipment arrives in wooden crates on enormous trailers or railroad cars. The different pieces are assembled with the help of other equipment and put to work after creating another set of pollution problems (B).

In addition, there are many other items and small pieces of equipment, tools and consumables—some for personal use, and some for specialized operations. These are shovels, helmets, computers, power drills, boots, shoes, overalls, goggles, first aid kits, chemicals… the list is long. All of these were also made sometime in the past, and transported to the gas site. During their manufacture and transport, they also left a significant pollution footprint. (C).

To complete the pollution footprint picture, we must add the footprint of the people involved in the entire process—engineers and technicians involved in equipment manufacturing, transport, installation, setup, and operation. These people drive cars, or travel by air, trains and busses, all of which leave another significant set of pollution footprints (D).

So, the total cradle-to-grave pollution footprint of the well drilling and exploitation equipment is expressed by:

$$P_f = A + B + C + D$$

where

P$_f$ is the total pollution footprint
A   is the gas rigging equipment manufacturing and transport to the drill site
B   is gas production equipment assembly, testing and installation at the drill site
C   is the manufacturing and transport of tools and consumables to the new well
D   is the pollution footprint of the equipment personnel during the design, setup, drilling, and production phases of the operation.

Combining the pollution footprints of A (equipment manufacturing and transport), B (production equipment assembly, test and installation), C (manufacturing and transport of tools and consumables), and D (pollution footprint of equipment personnel) gives us the environmental footprint of the gas rigging and production equipment before even starting drilling operations.

This pollution footprint is significant, to be sure! It goes deep and wide, stretching from one part of the world to the other.

To put a value on it, we must take inventory of all items delivered to the site, as needed for its design, construction and operation. We must take a close look at the manufacturing of a gas rig, a bulldozer, a dump truck and a number of other pieces of equipment used at the gas well site.

Keep in mind that some of these pieces are quite large, and that it takes many tons of metals to make them. Each of these pieces started as an iron or aluminum ore dug from a mine, and which was transported to a smelter. The molten metal was then shaped in different forms and shipped to various parts manufacturers, who drilled, welded and otherwise constructed parts for the equipment.

Again, remember that we are talking about huge pieces of metal—some of the gas well pipes are 20-30 feet long, and longer. One single bolt from the gas rig might be over a foot long, and the drill bore might need 5,000 feet of large- and small-diameter tubing for casing.

After the equipment is manufactured, which is usually an energy-intensive and polluting process, these parts are packed and loaded on railroad cars or trucks to be shipped to the assembly plant where they are assembled into major components, or entire vehicles. After one more loading and unloading operation, they finally arrive at the gas well site, or the power plant, for final assembly and testing, before being put to work.

This is a long and winding process with many loading and unloading steps, all of which require a lot of energy and generate a lot of toxic gasses.

Putting a dollar value to all this would be too complex for our purposes, so it suffices to say that the energy use and pollution effects during and after these steps are significant. We will take a closer look at these steps and their environmental effects in the following chapters.

Production Equipment Environmental Impact

Now, we have started the drilling operation and see another set of pollution footprints. Again…it is significant. As an example, at the remote gas rig, a number of large diesel generators provide power for drilling operations and personnel accommodations. During an average work day and under a full load, these will burn 1,000 gallons of diesel.

Several bulldozers, water carriers, and dump trucks are serving the rig during the drilling of the gas well. They also burn a lot of fuel in their never-ending runs, so the entire area is fogged with dust and soaked in diesel fumes and lubricating oils, leaving their pollution imprint day after day, hour after hour—for the duration! This does not include the harm done to the land, which is a different but no less serious type of environmental damage.

Spare parts for equipment periodically arrive from the parts manufacturers, after leaving their footprint.

There are a number of activities that require the use of different equipment during the 20-30 years of non-stop operation of the gas well, until it is finally declared exhausted. At this point the well must be shut down and decommissioned. Decommissioning and land reclamation are major, expensive, and polluting undertakings. The equipment and materials used during the decommissioning and waste disposal process create additional air and ground pollution which is not to be ignored.

Specialized equipment and personnel (environmental specialists and inspectors) are usually brought in to coordinate the effort. Some equipment must be disassembled and disposed of as hazardous waste, so it is loaded on trucks and transported to a landfill. With that, more pollution footprints are left at the already exhausted well site.

When the final tally is made, a significant part of the emissions and overall pollution are to be attributed to the gas drilling and production equipment and that of the support personnel. This number is significant and we will go through the calculations in the next chapters as well.

Externalized Cost of Gas Drilling, Processing, and Use

Natural gas is the new priority of many governments because of its low cost and abundance. Low prices and abundance, however, cannot change the fact that gas drilling is a hazardous operation, from both environmental and human health points of view. Although safety is paramount in gas drilling and production operations (especially in the US), there are still problems which often result in accidents and injuries—even in the US. In addition to the large accidents that make news, there are smaller ones daily, in which people get hurt or sick as a result of the effects of gas drilling and related operations.

The damages could be classified as:

- Burn injuries occur at the site of a gas drilling operation, where the victims are likely to suffer burn injuries from gas or chemicals, accompanied pain, suffering and loss of limbs or life.

- Chemical spills and leaks of toxic chemicals can cause injury to people close to a spill by direct exposure, or contact or inhalation of fumes, which could lead to chemical burns and respiratory illness. If the water supply becomes contaminated, it could lead to long-term health problems such as cancer.

- Drill site fires at oil and gas rigs are a constant threat. The source could be negligence, lack of experience, or defective equipment, but the consequences can be grave.

- Explosions could occur too, although the oil and natural gas industry is tightly regulated to ensure the safety of workers. An explosion in a gas drilling rig is a major event that could hurt and kill people, so precautions are the norm, but even then, accidents do happen.

- Gas field accidents—small and large—are not unheard of. They are rare, but when they do happen, those affected can be badly injured and even killed.

- Gas truck accidents are exceedingly dangerous, given the combustible nature of the cargo. Injuries can vary from broken bones to severe burns and death when a tank is ignited.

- Property damage happens during gas drilling accidents. Homeowners and individuals who live close to a drilling rig could be indirectly hurt by damage to their property, caused by fire, chemical spill or air contamination. Groundwater contamination is one of the most pervasive forms of property damage from gas drilling today.

- Toxic vapors and chemical exposure might cause damages that appear immediately or are not evident for months or years. Common examples include chemical burns, respiratory complications, and various forms of cancer related to contaminated air or water at the drill site. In these cases, gas rigs and processing workers, as well as local people, are sickened by pollution from the gas emissions and liquids escaping from the work sites.

Hydrofracking is a main cause of contamination of soil and the water table, where fish and wild life are poisoned by harsh chemicals dumped intentionally or unintentionally into their habitat.

The externalized costs of gas production and use are estimated to be in the billions. Since the gas drilling business is growing daily, estimates vary, but it seems that soon costs will be even larger than those of coal and oil.

As a result (what we call "externalities"), future generations will be heavily impacted by global warming from the exhaust gases and liquid wastes that gas drilling, production and use spew into the air and spill into the soil.

We will take a much closer look at these statistics and the reasons for these discrepancies in following chapters. We would like to emphasize here that the complex, expensive and dangerous gas drilling, exploitation and use (burning by power generators or cars) have some components that are very complex and difficult to understand, let alone estimate accurately.

In all cases, we must be aware of the problems, while keeping in mind that gas is a necessary evil. We also need to treat gas and the people who work in the industry with respect and admiration, because their efforts and sacrifices make our lives comfortable and prosperous.

THE FOSSIL ALTERNATIVES

Our fossils are headed toward extinction. The depletion rate is high, and while we are not sure what time line each fossil fuel will follow, we guess that the practical use of oil will end around year 2050. Gas, which will become the predominant fuel after that, will be mostly depleted by 2075, and coal will run its course by 2100.

Give or take 25-50 years, we are looking at a fossilless existence sometime during the next century. This is hard to imagine, given the present dependence on these. Unless the alternative energy technologies are fully developed, or new energy forms are found and quickly implemented, the world will sink in darkness and misery.

From our vantage point we see no great developments in the area of fossil replacement, so renewables (solar and wind, plus new fuels and processes) are the only hope for a fossil fuel alternative after 2100. One of the most promising is the mega-tons of *methane hydrate* still resting deep in the Earth's bosom. Future genera-

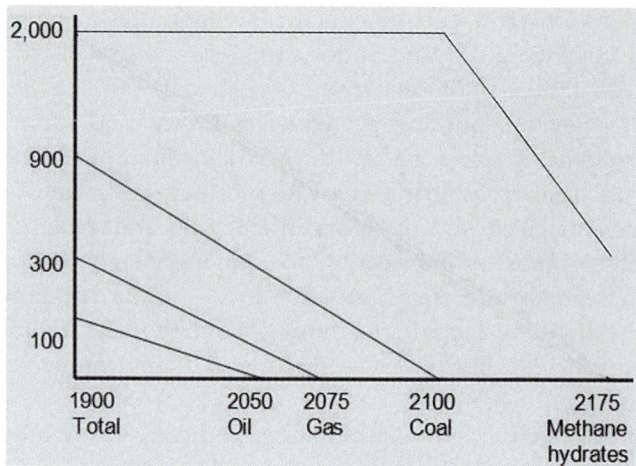

Figure 2-52. Fossil reserves; billions of tons of fossils vs. depletion time

tions must find a way to extract, refine and use this energy source, or get ready for a fossil-less future.

And speaking of methane hydrates…

Methane Hydrates

Methane hydrates are the best kept secret in the energy industry. They are well known by many scientists, but some people are too shy, while others are too scared to take them out of the closet—and there are some good reasons for that. The science behind this awesome energy source is complex and overwhelming, while the logistics are even more so. Since the fossils still reign (and pay the bills) most of the professionals prefer to stay on the sidelines.

Nevertheless, some of those who are involved in the energy field claim that methane hydrates are the energy source of the future, while some say they are an expensive exercise in futility, and yet others warn us that it is the most dangerous effort ever to be undertaken. All this fuss about a single, and otherwise humble, compound, composed of methane (CH_4)— the simplest of all hydrocarbon molecules—buried deep under the ocean floor and in the permafrost.

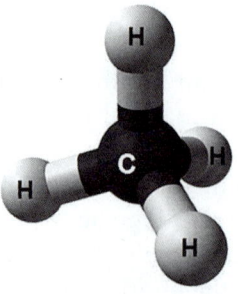

Figure 2-53. Methane

Methane consists of a single carbon atom bonded to four hydrogen atoms. There is nothing special about methane, for it is the primary component of natural gas, which we know well and use all the time. We know now how natural gas was formed, where it is found and how to extract it. These deposits are the traditional natural gas wells we tap into most often, extracting the gas through controversial hydraulic fracturing (fracking) techniques.

The Basics

Methane hydrates are somewhat different than the other fossils. They were also formed long ago, and in a similar fashion, except that during its slow migration to the Earth's surface, methane gas encountered cold water while still in a high-pressure environment. This usually happened close to the ocean floor and in permafrost areas. The most significant known deposits are found in the permafrost of Siberia and Northern Canada.

The cold water and high pressure in the permafrost, or the ocean depth, combined with spending a long time under this environment, changed the structure of methane gas so that its chemical composition is quite different. It can be envisioned as small balls of ice (frozen water, which gives it the hydrate denomination) with the methane molecules trapped inside the ice balls. See Figure 2-54.

Figure 2-54. Methane hydrate

Methane hydrate is a somewhat different type of methane or natural gas. It is chemically and physically the same compound, with the only difference being that its molecules have been trapped and enclosed in ice. The ice forms a tight ball around each molecule, or a group of molecules, thus immobilizing the methane

gas in them, so it no longer acts as gas. It is, instead, a prisoner in a frozen watery grave, where it will remain for a long time—at least until the ice cover is broken or melted, and the methane is released. Then it acts like normal methane gas and goes on its way.

The estimates of potential methane hydrate deposits in the world's ocean floors are significant—several times larger than all fossils together. While there are no clear estimates of the total quantity, there is a reliable indication that it is more than all of the other fossil fuels on Earth.

To extract methane from its ice trap it must be treated by a) heating, to melt the ice around it, or b) reducing the pressure it is under in the icy grave, which would have the same effect.

Both processes are, unfortunately, extremely expensive and well beyond existing technological capabilities. Heating frozen permafrost layers, in addition to being a gigantic undertaking, is unthinkable because the energy (heat) needed for that would significantly exceed the total energy value of the extracted methane. Lowering the pressure in the methane hydrate deposits seems more reasonable, but we don't have the needed technology presently. Maybe in several decades we will become more desperate and focus on it. For now, only a few experimental wells to tap into methane hydrate deposits are currently underway in the U.S., Russia, Canada, and Japan.

NOTE: Obtaining large quantities of fuel from the methane hydrates on the ocean floors is a new development, but since there is no practical and reliable extraction method, it is not included in the calculations of global fossil reserves. Too, the potential effects this new fuel might have on greenhouse gas emission projections are also unknown and hence not entered in the overall global environmental calculation.

So, our task in the near future is to consider in detail the pros and cons of large quantities methane pumped from the ocean depths. We must be well aware of what we are dealing with, and calculate its potential for a) helping us achieve the holy grail of global energy balance, b) complicate environmental conditions with excess GHG emissions, or c) bringing us a disaster of unthinkable proportions by exploding or shifting the land in large areas.

To begin with, we have no doubt that if and when we figure out efficient ways to extract methane from the permafrost, it will provide us with a long-term (at least a century) of cheap and fairly clean energy. But the problems, as we glanced at above, are numerous, and some must be addressed immediately.

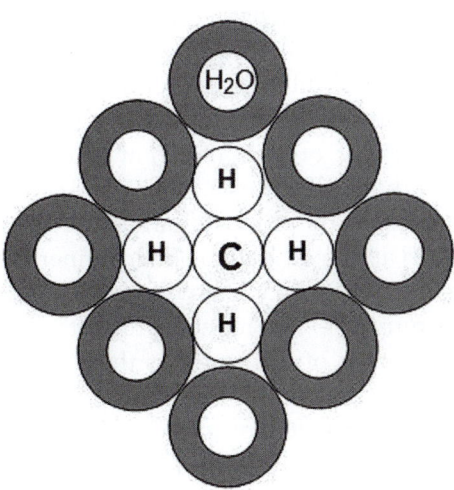

Figure 2-54. Methane hydrate

The Issues

1. An immediate problem arises from the fact that as the oceans warm, due to overall global warming, the trapped methane hydrates deposits will warm up and start releasing methane in an uncontrolled way. Any activities in those deposits might accelerate the melting and methane release process.

2. Raw methane gas is one of the worst environmental polluters, for it is over 40 times more efficient than CO_2 as a green house gas, so a significant release would increase global temperatures which would, in turn, melt more methane hydrate. The vicious cycle will expand as it feeds on itself and accelerates the release of even more methane....

3. Although we see a great opportunity in methane hydrate deposits, short of miraculous technical breakthroughs and global developments, any of the possible technical solutions would require a lot of time and money to develop. Methane hydrate deposits are usually deep in the oceans, at a minimum of 1,000 feet and up to miles in depth, so this would be the technological challenge of the century.

4. Finally, it will take time for the oil companies and governments to agree on property rights and methods of exploitation. This, in many cases, will require global consensus on how to proceed, lots of money for R&D, and equipment and production sites development—all of which requires sustained efforts on all levels.

As politicians and governments cannot agree on the simplest things today, it would be unreasonable to expect any serious action in the short term. So the great methane hydrates deposits will need to wait for future generations to get to them, which we are sure they will do, after we burn all the fossils during this century.

We will take a closer look at this unusual and promising energy source in the next chapters.

Tar Sands

Tar or oil sands, also called bituminous sands, are a type of fossil (petroleum) deposit. These are usually loose sandy areas, or sandstone saturated with a viscous form of petroleum, or bitumen, which has the odor, color, and other properties of tar. It is so thick, sticky, and viscous that it does not flow at room temperature; it is as thick as molasses. Instead, it must be heated or diluted with lighter oils to become liquid.

Tar deposits differ in the degree by which they have been degraded from the original conventional oils by bacteria, and the tar oil in these usually has a viscosity greater than 10,000 centipoises, and a gravity of less than 10° API. Since tar is very thick and mixed with sand, it is extracted mostly by strip mining of the sandy deposits. The tar oil is then forced to flow into wells by reducing it through techniques such as injecting steam, solvents and hot air into the sands.

These processes use much more water and energy than conventional oil extraction, although most of the conventional oil fields also use a lot of water and energy during daily operations. This process generates 12% more greenhouse gas per barrel of final product than the "production" of conventional oil.

Natural tar deposits are located in many countries, but in particular are found in extremely large quantities in Canada. Other large reserves are located in Kazakhstan and Russia. Total natural bitumen reserves are estimated at 249.67 billion barrels (39.694×10^9 m^3) globally, of which 176.8 billion barrels (28.11×10^9 m^3), or 70.8%, are in Canada. However, it is estimated that approximately 80-90% of Canada's oil sands are too deep below the surface to use open-pit mining. Instead, several *in-situ* techniques have been developed to extract these.

The oil sands in the Orinoco Belt in Venezuela are sometimes described as tar sands, but they are not bituminous. Instead, they fall in the category of heavy or extra-heavy oil, since their viscosity is even lower. Oil sands reserves are considered as part of the world's oil reserves, but higher costs and technological issues limit their use.

Shale Oil

Shale oil, also known as kerogen oil or oil-shale oil, is an unconventional oil produced from oil shale, which is sedimentary rock filled with kerogen. It can be processed by pyrolysis, hydrogenation, or thermal dissolution to convert the organic matter within the kerogen rock into synthetic oil and gas.

The resulting oil products can be used as a fuel or can be refined and upgraded to obtain refinery feedstock by adding hydrogen and removing impurities such as sulfur and nitrogen. The refined products can then be used for a number of purposes, as those derived from crude oil.

There are estimates of almost a billion barrels of shale oil in the world, or almost half of the available crude oil reserves. A major part of the shale reserves, estimated at over 2 trillion barrels, are in the US. Other countries, like Estonia, Brazil and China, also have significant shale oil reserves. Technical issues and high costs are hindering expansion of shale oil, so we estimate that it will be the last of the fossils to go.

In summary, our fossils have been, and still are, very good to us. They have powered our lives faithfully for a long time, and have provided economic prosperity to many countries. Their future, however, looks bleak.

In less than a century, we dug out, pumped out and burned most of what took nature millions of years to make. We can't help but imagine the puzzled look on students' faces in the year 2222, when they are told that their ancestors wasted selfishly ALL of their fossil inheritance.

We would not be surprised also if the people of the next century or two will have never seen or used coal, oil, or natural gas. These commodities will be as distant and foreign to them as dinosaurs are to us. If they manage to survive without them, they will certainly have found a way to lead a fossil-less life. This is certain because present generations have no intention of slowing down their aggressive use of fossils. Man will not stop until the last chunk of coal, the last drop of oil, and the last cubic foot of gas are extracted and burned.

The generations to be most affected by the lack of fossils are those following closely behind us, because they must live in the transitional period. It is hard to imagine how they will address transportation and comfort during that period of fuel shortages and extreme price increases. How will they survive extreme weather conditions? How will they meet their basic needs for food and water? How?

Notes and References

1. Fossils. http://www.sciencedaily.com/articles/f/fossil_fuel.htm
2. Fossil fuels. http://www.darvill.clara.net/altenerg/fossil.htm#how
3. Fossil fuel. http://www.sciencedaily.com/articles/f/fossil_fuel.htm
4. U.S. Energy Information Administration. http://www.eia.gov/coal/
5. World Coal Organization. http://www.worldcoal.org/
6. Coal is Dirty. http://www.coal-is-dirty.com/
7. Natural Gas.Org. http://naturalgas.org/
8. U.S. Energy Information Administration. http://www.eia.gov/naturalgas/
9. OPEC. http://www.opec.org/opec_web/en/press_room/180.htm
10. U.S. Energy Information Administration. http://www.eia.gov/petroleum/
11. Crude Oil. http://toxtown.nlm.nih.gov/text_version/chemicals.php?id=73
12. USGS. http://woodshole.er.usgs.gov/project-pages/hydrates/
13. The National Methane Hydrate R&D Program. http://www.netl.doe.gov/technologies/oil-gas/FutureSupply/Methane-Hydrates/maincontent.htm
14. *Photovoltaics for Commercial and Utilities Power Generation*, Anco S. Blazev. The Fairmont Press, 2011
15. *Solar Technologies for the 21st Century*, Anco S. Blazev. The Fairmont Press, 2013

Appendix A
History of Energy

1903 First coal-powered thermo-power plant starts in Chicago, IL.

1904 Einstein's theory of relativity is discovered. Mass, energy and speed of light ($E = mc^2$).
New York opens the first underground railway.

1905 Hermann Nernst stipulates the 3rd Law of Thermodynamics.

1908 Henry Ford starts mass production of his Model T.

1930 Oil tanker spills oil in Point Reyes, US. This is the first oil spill on record.

1933 Crude oil deposits are discovered in Saudi Arabia.

1935 Fluorescent light bulb is developed in Germany and simultaneously in the US.
PCBs (polychlorinated biphenyls) production is initiated.

1936 Hoover Dam hydropower plant generates over 1000MW.

1942 The first controlled nuclear fission executed successfully by Enrico Fermi, Chicago, IL.

1944 The first nuclear reactor starts operation in Richland, WA.

1950 Heavy smog damage to vegetation reported in Berkeley, CA.

1951 The first thermonuclear power generator starts in Idaho Falls, ID.

1952 Smog, caused by coal burning kills 4,700 in London.

1957 The first nuclear thermo-power plant starts operation in Shippingport, PA.
Colorado Rocky Flats nuclear plant leaks plutonium into the atmosphere.

1960 Iraq, Iran, Kuwait, Saudi Arabia and Venezuela form OPEC.
The first law for controlling vehicular emissions is established in California.

1962 Ms. Rachel Carson publishes *Silent Spring* on the effects of pesticides in the environment.

1966 First superconductor engine is developed and tested.

Oil is found in Alaska.

1967   Oil tanker *Torrey Canyon* spills; countries do not count on international laws to punish tanker owners.

1968   In Europe, a movement concerned with the environmental problems in the participants' countries and globally is started, designated the Rome Club. The participants, experts in different areas of human knowledge, gather in Rome to discuss current and future crises for humanity.

1968   Nuclear Non-Proliferation Treaty NPT.
        International Conference promoted by UNESCO on the Rational Use and Conservation of Biosphere Resources.

1969   Brussels Convention imposes objective responsibility for accidents and spillage on the signing countries. The owner of the oil tanker is made responsible, which leads to the establishment of a fund for compensations with indemnity caps destined to the victim state.
        President Nixon, signs the National Environment Policy, which forces the government to assess its projects.
        In 2002, the Bush administration states that the law does not go beyond its territorial waters.
        Patrick Moore founds the NGO Greenpeace, which coordinates actions against nuclear tests in the Aleutian Islands.
        Windscale, England, nuclear plant leaks radioactive iodine and polonium.

1970   Aswan Hydropower Plant, Egypt, starts operating after the transference of archaeological monuments.
        — Commercial solar photocells generate power.
        — Oil found in the North Sea by British Petroleum (BP); the area became one of the world's major producers.
        — Clean Air Act of USA is established to control air pollution, makes the adoption of catalytic converters in automobiles compulsory.
        — The US Environmental Protection Agency (EPA) is established. The California Environmental Quality Act makes it compulsory for entrepreneurs to produce an Environmental Impact Report for new projects.

1971   Denmark establishes the first Ministry for the Environment.
        Ramsar International Convention on Wetlands, Iran. 1972 Club of Rome publishes the report "The Limits to Growth," calling attention to the

fact that humanity would compulsorily have a limit of growth with the economic model then used, based on exacerbated consumption and highly concentrated on a few nations.

1972   The United Nations Conference on the Human Environment is held in Stockholm, Sweden. Delegates from developing countries advocate their right to economic growth opportunities at any cost. At the end, the ideal form of environmental planning is proclaimed to be that which associated ecological prudence with pro-development actions.

1973   First oil crisis caused by OPEC, which quadrupled its price in a year; until 1974 the Arab countries ban exports to the US in retaliation for their support of Israel, starting a world economic crisis.
        The construction of the great Alaskan pipeline is started.

1974   First remediation program for areas where nuclear tests had been conducted (Los Alamos, NM).
        — The International Energy Agency is established in Paris to coordinate oil distribution.
        International Energy Agency is established in Paris to coordinate oil distribution.
        The last nuclear plant in the U.S. is built and starts operation.

1976   The largest oil field in the world is discovered in Mexico.
        International community bans the use of environmental modification techniques such as cloud seeding and defoliating (agent orange).
        — Liberian oil tanker *Argo Merchant* spills in the North Atlantic.

1977   Law enacted in the US for remediating abandoned mines.

1978   223,000 tons of oil spill from oil tanker *Amoco Cadiz* on the French coast.
        Iran revolution starts the second oil crisis; prices double.
        223,000 tons of oil spill from oil tanker *Amoco Cadiz* on the French coast.

1979   Nuclear accident in the Three Mile Island Plant (PA) leads to halting new projects.
        — Accident between the *Atlantic Empress* and another supertanker on the Tobago coast, the largest disaster ever recorded; 278,000 tons of oil spilled into the sea.

1980   Iraq invades Iran in a dispute for the strategic outflow in the Shatt al-Arab area.
        Oil exploitation forbidden in ecological reserves

in Alaska (withdrawn in 2002).

1981 Amendment to the Law of Endangered Species allows the destruction of certain habitats, while others are preserved.

Shell, Exxon and Texaco employees inform on the spillage of MTBE (methyl tri butyl ether) in filling stations, contaminating the underground water in the US.

1982 Montego Bay UN Convention on the Law of the Sea consolidates uses and proposes resolution of disputes on spillages by an international court, with headquarters in Germany; agreement establishes civil responsibilities, extra-contractual and personal.

— First decommissioning of an operating nuclear plant (Shippingport, US).

1983 The third largest accident involving ships: *Castillo de Bellver*, South Africa coast; 252,000 tons of oil.

1984 In Brazil, the large Itaipu and Tucuruí hydropower plants start operating.

Ninety-three deaths and 2500 homeless due to the burst of a Petrobrás pipeline in the Vila Socó favela, Cubatão, Brazil.

— US seeks a permanent deposit for nuclear wastes.

1986 Nuclear accident in the Chernobyl nuclear plant, USSR; reactor burns for ten days and emits 200 times more radiation than the atomic bombs of Hiroshima and Nagasaki; radioactive clouds reach Europe; US $ 130 billion estimated damages.

— In Brazil, Angra 1 nuclear power plant starts operating. At the same time, a deep well revested with concrete, supposedly for testing explosions, is found at an aeronautics base at the Cachimbo Range, in the south of Pará.

— EPA announces that 35 percent of the US underground gasoline tanks leak.

1987 The first permanent deposit of radioactive wastes (Yucca Mountain, NV) is designated.

— Lebanese militia "Free Forces" allow storage of toxic waste from Italy, Germany, Canada and Belgium, contaminating 70 percent of the water sources in the country.

— Earthquake in Ecuador destroys the major oil pipeline in the country.

— Montreal Protocol for protecting the ozone layer gradually eliminates chlorofluorocarbons (CFCs) production and use, as well as other substances. Acceptance by governments (156 ratifications in the first year) and industries (which found markets for replace-

ments) contributes to the success of the international treaty.

1989 *Exxon Valdez* disaster in Alaska becomes the largest oil spill in US waters.

1990 Congress passes act to stimulate development of hydrogen power.

1994 US begins importing more petroleum than it produces.

1996 Solar Two plant demonstrates low-cost method of storing solar energy.

1996 Hydrogen Future Act of 1996 is passed to further expand hydrogen power development.

1997 EV1 Electric Car is made available to the public. The lease program and EV1 are later dismantled by GM…reasons and outcome unknown.

2003 President Bush unveils the Hydrogen Fuel Initiative to promote hydrogen fuel cell development

— Plans announced to build FutureGen, the world's first zero emissions coal power plant.

2005 US House prevents drilling for oil in the Arctic National Wildlife Refuge.

2007 IPCC Report concludes climate change is happening and is mostly human caused.

2008 First commercial cellulosic ethanol plant goes into production in Wyoming.

2008 National Biofuel Action Plan unveiled.

2008 Worst coal ash spill in US history, Kingston, TN.

2009 American Recovery and Reinvestment Act of 2009 contains billions of dollars for renewable energy and energy efficiency developments.

— First framework for wind energy development on the US outer continental shelf announced.

— President Obama issues presidential directive to USDA to expand access to biofuels. $786.5 million in biofuels funding was announced.

— US announces $467 million in Recovery Act funding for solar energy and geothermal energy development.

— US invests $3.4 billion to modernize the power grid.

2010 BP Deep Horizon oil rig explodes and causes largest oil spill in US history.

2011 Earthquake off coast of Japan damages six nuclear reactors at Fukushima Dai-ichi. The nuclear crisis reaches level 7, the highest level of nuclear danger possible.

2011 Solyndra declares bankruptcy after receiving $528 million in federal loan guarantees.

Other solar companies fail after spending millions

of federal money, which results in a major embarrassment for the Obama administration and revision of the solar energy plans.

2012   US Nuclear Regulatory Commission (NRC) approves new nuclear power plants for first time
since 1978.

Two new nuclear reactors to be built in Georgia.

— EPA announces the first Clean Air Act Standard
for carbon pollution from new power plants.

— EPA issues first ever Clean Air Rules for natural gas produced by fracking.

2013   California commercial solar plants pump record
1.5 GW electricity into the grid. Almost that much
is generated by the residential solar installations at
the same time.

Chapter 3

The Other Energy Sources
(Nuclear, hydro, hydrogen, ocean, geo- and bio-energy)

There are many ways to look at the upcoming energy crisis.
The only way to solve it is through serious and
persistent use of our imagination and ingenuity.
Anco Blazev

In this chapter we discuss several energy sources which are used presently, and which will be used for a long time to come for reliable and affordable electric power and transportation fuels. These are nuclear, hydro, hydrogen, fuel cells, wave and tidal power, geo- and bio-energy sources.

We put these in a separate chapter because due to their unique advantages and disadvantages they just don't fit in the known energy categories; they are not fossils, and do not fit perfectly in the renewables category. Due to their importance and complexity, however, these energy sources deserve a special place of their own, and a more thorough discussion of their attributes as energy generators and fuels now and in the future.

As with the other energy sources, we will review their environmental effects, which are significant.

NUCLEAR POWER

Nuclear power is the Cinderella of the energy industry. Some love, some envy, and some even hate her… but no one knows what to do about her without damaging their own case. Nuclear power is mysterious, and just whispering the word *nuclear* we hear an awesome thunder with a foreign-sounding echo which evokes respect and even fear in every human being.

It is the synonym of unlimited power, extreme danger, and uncontrollable damage, if released by accident. Like it or not, just saying the word nuclear inevitably reminds us of Hiroshima… Chernobyl… Fukushima; all symbols of its fierce power and frightful widespread devastation.

Like the Genie in the bottle, when controlled nuclear energy can bring miracles, but when released by accident, it brings merciless devastation. On the loose, it does not hesitate to kill everything in its path—no excuses, no exceptions, no mercy.

There are awful signs of nuclear power damage around the world, and there will be many more before we find another form of large quantity electric power generation as useful, but safer. For now we have no choice; if we want to continue living in comfort. We need this beast, which has provide us with reliable and cheap electric power anytime we want and as much as we want. We just need to tame and befriend this necessary evil to the best of our ability to use it safely.

This is not an easy chore for our feeble understanding of this unlimited power. It pushes our technical capabilities to the max, and we all are always on our toes, afraid that we might make a mistake to which the beast would respond with unspeakable fury, wide-spread destruction, and deadly devastation.

Nevertheless, we are fully engaged in the nuclear power generation game and although many countries are making serious efforts to reduce their dependence on nuclear power, it will not happen that easily, or anytime soon.

As a matter of fact, we need nuclear power more than ever, because we know we are running out of fossils. Letting nuclear go now, and before we have lined up transitional energy sources, will cause unimaginable hardships. So, at least for the foreseeable future we must use it, deal with it, and try to avoid surprises.

Germany and Japan tried to reduce and even eliminate nuclear power, but are now reconsidering. Just recently, both countries, whose governments were scared to death after the Fukushima disaster and shut down most of their nuclear plants, changed their minds and are back to full steam ahead with nuclear power in their respective countries.

The U.S. was not impressed, let alone scared, by the Fukushima events, most likely thinking that such a thing cannot happen here, just because we are the mighty US of A. Sure enough, in 2012 the nuclear industry watchdog, the U.S. Nuclear Regulatory Commission, approved applications for several new nuclear power plants for first time since 1978. So, at least two new nuclear reactors will be built in Georgia in the near future.

Are these the last power plants to be built in the U.S., or just a new wave of nuclear power increase? Is this the beginning of the nuclear renaissance we have been talking about for decades?

Let's see what nuclear power offers in terms of convenient and plentiful energy generation vs. cost, safety, and environmental damage.

Something amazing to keep in mind when comparing nuclear power generation and fuel efficiency with the different competing energy generating fuels and technologies:

- One kilogram (2.2 lbs.) of nuclear-grade uranium contains the energy equivalent of 30-50 tons, or 30,000-50,000 kilograms (66,000-110,000 lbs.) of coal, which is about half a railroad car full of coal.

- One kilogram of uranium-235 can theoretically produce about 45 MWh of electric energy, assuming complete fission.

Nuclear fuels contain tremendous amounts of power, which if properly used and controlled generates a lot of electricity. If not properly controlled, however, they could do a lot of damage. A lot!

Table 3-1 shows the energy content of different materials that can be used as fuel for different applications, including power generation. The incredible energy content of uranium, resulting in a 1:50,000 ratio as compared with the energy content of coal is an enormous advantage for nuclear power generation. It offers the convenience of handling smaller amounts of raw material; a truck load of uranium would produce power for many months vs. an endless line of coal cars being loaded and unloaded 24/7 at the mines and coal-fired plants respectively.

Once the nuclear fuel is spent, only one truckload of nuclear waste is driven away from the nuclear plant—this vs. several hundred train cars being loaded with ash and soot at the coal-fired power plant to be dumped at a distant, hazardous dump site. Sure enough, the truckful of nuclear waste presents a number of dangers too, but

Table 3-1. Energy content of fuels

Firewood (dry)	10-16 MJ/kg
Brown coal (lignite)	<10 MJ/kg
Black coal (low quality)	10-25 MJ/kg
Black coal (high quality)	25-30 MJ/kg
Natural gas	38 MJ/m^3
Crude oil	45-50 MJ/kg
Uranium (nuclear grade)	500,000 MJ/kg

a smaller package is always preferred to a large-scale waste site.

More importantly, from an environmental point of view, is the fact that uranium does not produce any harmful gasses or liquids, such as the thousands of tons of toxic smoke, ash, and soot produced at the coal-fired plants—not to mention the acres of liquid and solid waste contamination around coal-fired plants and at the remote dump sites.

The big disadvantage to nuclear power is the fact that the disposal of nuclear waste is still an unresolved issue, as is the greater risk of nuclear accidents. Since there is no perfect solution or compromise at this point, we need to carefully pick and choose our energy future, keeping in mind that in all cases there will be problems that we must be familiar with to make the right decisions.

In the Beginning...

There are a number of theories of the creation and availability of uranium and other nuclear (radioactive) materials on Earth. Some of these claim that these materials were produced in one or more supernovae, exploding stars in which the radiated energy increases several billion times within, as a result of the catastrophic collapse of the star's core. Such events are hard to describe exactly, because of the enormity and complexity of the different energies generated and released for the duration.

Supernovae events are extremely luminous and noisy, and cause a burst of radiation that often briefly outshines an entire galaxy, before fading from view over several weeks or months. During this short interval a supernova can radiate as much energy as the Sun is expected to emit over its entire life span.

The initial explosion expels much or all of a star's material at high velocity of up to 20,000 miles per second, thus driving a shock wave into the surrounding interstellar medium. This shock wave sweeps up an expanding shell of gas and dust called a supernova remnant, accompanied by a flood of free neutrons. The main process that leads to the creation of uranium and other radioactive isotopes can be explained by the rapid capture of these free neutrons on seed nuclei at rates greater than disintegration through radioactivity during the explosive supernovae event.

For the sake of simplification, we will assume that the Earth's uranium and some of the other radioactive materials we find here were produced through similar processes in one or more supernovae, which must have occurred billions of years ago.

This is a crude oversimplification, since there were many other extraordinary events with even more spectacular effects around the time of the Big Bang and shortly thereafter. There is evidence that more than ten separate and distinctly different stellar sources were involved in the genesis of the solar system material. Thus the relative abundance of U-235 and U-238 at the time of formation of the solar system is most likely as a result of the explosive debris of many supernovae and the related interactions.

In any case, the final result of these events is that we now have large deposits of uranium and other radioactive materials here on Earth that allow us to extract and use them for generating electric power via nuclear power reactors.

The average abundance of uranium in meteorites is about 0.008 parts per million (ppm, or gram/ton), the abundance of uranium in the Earth's "primitive mantle" (prior to the extraction of the continental crust) is 0.021 ppm. Allowing for the extraction of a core-forming iron-nickel alloy with no uranium (because of the characteristic of uranium which makes it combine more readily with minerals in crustal rocks rather than iron-rich ones), this still represents a roughly two-fold enrichment in the materials forming the proto-Earth compared with average meteoritic materials.

The present-day abundance of uranium in the "depleted" mantle exposed on the ocean floor is about 0.004 ppm. The continental crust, on the other hand, is relatively enriched in uranium at some 1.4 ppm. This represents a 70-fold enrichment compared with the primitive mantle. In fact, the uranium lost from the "depleted" oceanic mantle is mostly sequestered in the continental crust.

The processes which transferred uranium from the mantle to the continental crust are complex and consist of many consequent steps over a long time period, but for the past 2 billion years they have involved:

a.) Formation of oceanic crust and lithosphere through melting of the mantle at mid-ocean ridges.

b.) Migration of this oceanic lithosphere laterally to a site of plate consumption (this is marked at the surface by a deep-sea trench).

c.) Production of fluids and magmas from the down-going (subducted) lithospheric plate and overriding mantle "wedge" in these subduction zones.

d.) Transfer of these fluids/melts to the surface in zones of "island arcs" (such as the Pacific's Ring of Fire).

e.) Production of continental crust from these island arc protoliths, through re-melting, granite formation and intra-crustal recycling.

All through this crust-forming cycle, the lithophile character of uranium is manifested in the constancy of the potassium-to-uranium ratio in the rock range from peridotite to granite. Keeping track of how uranium is distributed in the Earth, we see the abundance and isotopic characteristics of lead (a relative of U-235 and U-238) as a useful parameter.

There is a relatively low abundance of lead in the Earth's mantle and a high uranium-to-lead ratio, compared with meteorites, which can be explained by lead's volatile nature and its tendency to combine with iron. Thus lead is being lost during terrestrial accretion and core separation.

One of the consequences of these high ratios is the comparatively high radiogenic/non-radiogenic content of Pb-207/Pb-204, and conversely Pb-206/Pb-204 in the Earth's crust and mantle compared with meteorites or the Earth's core.

NOTE: Pb-207 is the final stable decay product of U-235, and Pb-206 is that of U-238, while Pb-204 is non-radiogenic.

Nuclear Fuels

Materials that can sustain a chain nuclear reaction and produce a nuclear explosion are known as fissile materials, such as uranium. Some examples of the nuclear fuels are ^{233}U, ^{235}U, ^{239}Pu, ^{237}Np, and ^{243}Am. Energy is released when heavy elements like thorium, uranium, or plutonium undergo fission, during which process the heavy nuclide with atomic mass of 235 for ^{235}U, is split into two lighter nuclides like ^{90}Sr, or ^{137}Cs, several neutrons, and occasionally a hydrogen atom.

Uranium is the preferred fuel for most nuclear reactors, and presently generates over 16% of all electricity worldwide. This makes it an important fuel, and a key chemical element, which also played an important role in the evolution of the Earth.

Uranium Properties

Uranium is a very heavy and hard, silvery-white metallic chemical element, of the rare earth/actinides series in the periodic table. Its chemical symbol is U, and corresponds to atomic number 92. Each uranium atom has 146 neutrons, 92 protons and 92 electrons in its atom. 6 of the electrons are in the outer shell and are its valence electrons. It has a high melting point, of 2070°F.

U is malleable, ductile, slightly paramagnetic, strongly electropositive and is a poor electrical conductor. It has very high density, being approximately 70% denser than lead and only slightly less dense than gold. Unlike gold, it reacts readily with almost all nonmetallic elements and their compounds, with reactivity increasing with temperature.

Hydrochloric and nitric acids dissolve uranium, but non-oxidizing acids (other than hydrochloric acid) attack the element very slowly. When finely ground, it can react with cold water, where, and in air it gets coated with a dark layer of uranium oxide. Because of that, uranium in ores is extracted chemically and converted into uranium dioxide or other chemical forms usable in industry.

Uranium metal has three allotropic forms:

α   (orthorhombic) stable up to 660°C
β   (tetragonal) stable from 660°C to 760°C
γ   (body-centered cubic) from 760°C to melting point. This is the most malleable and ductile state.

Fission Properties

Upon bombardment with slow neutrons, the uranium-235 isotope divides into two smaller nuclei, releasing nuclear energy (which was used for the binding) and more neutrons.

Uranium has the ability to absorb thermal neutrons, during which time the reaction may go one of two ways:

1. Over 80% of the time, it will fission, or
2. 18% of the time it will not fission, and will instead emit gamma radiation, thus yielding U-236.

If too many neutrons are absorbed by other uranium-235 nuclei, a nuclear chain reaction occurs. If not controlled, the chain reaction could result in a burst of heat, and under some special circumstances it gets so violent that it could explode. The size of the explosion would depend on the type and quantity of nuclear material involved.

Such a chain reaction is initiated in a nuclear reactor, but it is strictly controlled and slowed down by a neutron poison which absorbs some of the free neutrons that cause acceleration of the reaction. The neutron poison (or better said neutron absorber) could be made of a number of materials that are part of reactor's control rods.

The main use of uranium in the civilian sector is to fuel nuclear power plants. One kilogram of uranium-235 can theoretically produce about 45,000 kWh of electric energy, assuming complete fission. This is as much energy as is contained in 10,000 kg oil, or 14,000 kg coal. This is a tremendous amount of power, which, if properly controlled, could be harnessed to generate a lot of electricity. If not properly controlled, however, it could do a lot of damage.

Commercial nuclear power plants use fuel that is typically enriched to around 3% uranium-235. The *CANDU* and Magnox reactor designs are the only commercial reactors capable of using unenriched uranium fuel. Fuel used for United States Navy reactors is typically highly enriched in uranium-235 (the exact values of this fuel are classified).

In the military, uranium is used in nuclear reactors to power ships and submarines. It is also used for making atomic bombs. Fifteen pounds of uranium-235 is all that is needed to make a small atomic bomb with huge destructive powers. The first nuclear bomb used in war, the Little Boy, was based on uranium fission, while the very first nuclear explosive (The Gadget) and the bomb that destroyed Nagasaki (Fat Man) were plutonium-based bombs.

The Isotopes

Naturally occurring uranium ores contain one or more of the three U isotopes, uranium 234, 235 and 238. All three isotopes are radioactive, but only one of them, uranium 235 with 143 neutrons, is fissionable and can be used in the generation of nuclear power.

Pure uranium is slightly radioactive and has the second highest atomic weight of the primordially occurring elements, lighter only than plutonium. Its density is about 70% higher than that of lead, but not as dense as gold or tungsten. It occurs naturally in low concentrations of a few parts per million in soil, rock and water, and is commercially extracted from uranium-bearing minerals such as *uraninite*.

Uranium atoms decay slowly by emitting an alpha particle. The half-life of uranium-238 is about 4.47 billion years, and that of uranium-235 is 704 million years, which makes them useful in dating the age of the Earth.

The uranium nuclear fuel is usually based on the metal oxides of uranium metal. The oxides are used rather than the pure metal itself simply because the ox-

Table 3-2. Uranium isotopes

Isotope	Half Life
U-230	20.8 days
U-231	4.2 days
U-232	70.0 years
U-233	159000.0 years
U-234	247000.0 years
U-235	$7.0004 \times E8$ years
U-236	$2.34 \times E7$ years
U-237	6.75 days
U-238	$4.47 \times E9$ years
U-239	23.5 minutes
U-240	14.1 hours

ide melting point is much higher than that of the metal, thus they are safer in case of reactor overheating and meltdown. Another benefit of the oxides is that they cannot burn, being already in the final oxidized state of matter of the uranium metal. This is another important operational and safety consideration.

Uranium Nuclear Fuel

Uranium is found in a number of places around the world, since it is as common as some more common metals, such as tin and germanium. As a matter of fact, Uranium is a constituent of most rocks, dirt, and of the oceans—albeit in very small quantities. And this is a problem, because mining is economically feasible only in deposits of somewhat larger concentrations of uranium. Estimates today show that, at the present rate of use, there are enough uranium deposits to last about 100 years.

Today, uranium is economically recovered at a price of $100 per 150/kg. This higher level of assured resources is normal for most minerals, and a significant (expected) price increase as well as improved methodologies could create a correspondingly high increase in extractable resources over time.

Nuclear Fuel Use

All power plants require the use of large quantities of different fuels. Nuclear plants are no exception and need a constant large supply of high-quality fuel. The most common fissile nuclear fuels, used in today's fission nuclear power plants, are uranium-235 (^{235}U) and plutonium-239 (^{239}Pu). These materials have the highest energy density (contain the most Btus per given mass) of all practical fuel sources in use today.

To be used in a controlled manner as a nuclear fuel, enriched uranium typically is formed into small (ap-

proximately 1.0″ x 0.5″) pellets. These pellets are usually arranged into long rods, and the rods are tied together into bundles. Several of these bundles are submerged in water inside a pressure vessel, where the water acts as a coolant.

If the bundles are left unattended the uranium fission would accelerate beyond control and would eventually overheat the bundles, evaporate the water and melt the containment vessel. To prevent such uncontrolled conditions and overheating, control rods made of a material that absorbs neutrons are inserted between the rods in the uranium bundle. The control rods are attached to a special mechanism that can raise or lower them very accurately. By raising and lowering the control rods allow operators to control the rate of the nuclear reaction.

For the uranium core to produce more heat, the control rods are lifted out of the uranium bundle, which reduces the surface of the control rods, so that they absorb fewer neutrons. To reduce the generated heat, the control rods are lowered into the uranium bundle to absorb more neutrons. The lower the rods, the more neutrons absorbed, producing less power. If the rods are lowered completely into the uranium bundle, then all neutrons are absorbed and the entire reaction stops. This is how a nuclear reactor can be shut down for maintenance, or in the event of an accident.

The type, quality and use of radioactive materials is regulated by the federal Nuclear Regulatory Commission (NRC), as well as different state regulating agencies.

Plutonium Nuclear Fuel

The second most used fissile isotope is plutonium-239. It can also fission on absorbing a thermal neutron, with the end product being plutonium-240 (Pu-240). Pu-240 makes up a large proportion of reactor-grade plutonium used today—plutonium recycled from spent fuel that was originally made with enriched natural uranium and then used once in a light water reactor (LWR).

NOTE: Current light water reactors (LWR) make relatively inefficient use of nuclear fuel by fissioning only the very rare and expensive uranium-235 isotope. Nuclear reprocessing can make this waste reusable, and more efficient reactor designs allow better use of the available resources.

Pu-240 decays with a half-life of 6561 years into U-236. In a closed nuclear fuel cycle, most Pu-240 will be fissioned (after more than one neutron capture) before it decays. However, Pu-240 discarded as nuclear waste will decay over thousands of years.

Recently, several countries have experimented with using thorium as a substitute nuclear fuel in nuclear reactors. The growing interest in a thorium fuel cycle is due to its abundance in some areas (3-4 times more abundant than uranium), its safety benefits, and absence of non-fertile isotopes.

Thorium Nuclear Fuel

Thorium is a naturally occurring radioactive chemical element with the symbol Th and atomic number 90. In nature, virtually all thorium is found as Th-232, which has a half-life of about 14.05 billion years. Other isotopes of thorium are short-lived intermediates in the decay chains of higher elements and found only in trace amounts. Thorium is mostly refined from monazite sands as a by-product of extracting rare earth metals.

Thorium undergoes a complete combustion in specialized nuclear reactors, vs. only 1% for standard uranium reactors using natural uranium. Thorium reactors are popular in India and will become more popular worldwide when the global supplies of uranium ore are near depletion.

Thorium reactors generate 3.6 billion kWh of heat per ton of thorium at 40% efficiency, which means that a 1 GW reactor uses about 6 tons of thorium per year. Worldwide thorium resources are estimated at 2 million tons, so the thorium supply (theoretically) could power the world for several centuries.

India's three-stage nuclear power program is possibly the most famous, well funded, and advanced thorium nuclear process development effort.

Other Nuclear Fuels

Uranium dioxide (UO_2) nuclear fuel is a black solid material, which is prepared by reacting uranyl nitrate with ammonia to form a solid (ammonium uranate). It is then heated (calcined) to form U_3O_8 that can then be converted by heating in an argon/hydrogen mixture at 700°C to form UO_2. Thus obtained UO_2 is mixed with an organic binder and pressed into pellets, which are then fired at a high temperature again in an argon/hydrogen gas mixture to sinter the pellets into a solid material with few pores.

Mixed oxide, or MOX, nuclear fuel, is a blend of plutonium and natural or depleted uranium which behaves similarly to the enriched uranium feed, for which most nuclear reactors were designed. MOX fuel is an alternative to low-enriched uranium (LEU) fuel used in the light water reactors (LWR) which are used in global nuclear power generation.

Metal nuclear fuels have much higher heat conductivity than oxide fuels, but cannot withstand high temperatures. Metal fuels have the highest fissile atom density, and are normally alloyed, made with pure uranium metal. Uranium alloys include uranium aluminum, uranium zirconium, uranium silicon, uranium molybdenum, and uranium zirconium hydride. Any of these can be made with plutonium and other actinides as part of a closed nuclear fuel cycle. Metal fuels have been used in water reactors and liquid metal fast breeder reactors such as EBR-II.

TRIGA nuclear fuel is used in TRIGA (training, research, isotopes, general atomics) reactors, which use uranium-zirconium-hydride (UZrH) fuel, which has a built-in safety, where as the temperature of the core increases, the fuel reactivity decreases. This pretty much eliminates the possibility of a meltdown. Most cores that use this fuel are "high-leakage" cores where the excess leaked neutrons can be utilized for research. TRIGA fuel was originally designed to use highly enriched uranium; however, in 1978 the U.S. Department of Energy launched its Reduced Enrichment for Research Test Reactors program which promoted reactor conversion to low-enriched uranium fuel. Thirty-five TRIGA reactors have been installed across the USA. Thirty-five more have been installed in other countries.

Actinide nuclear fuel is a by-product of fast neutron reactors, where minor actinides produced by neutron capture of uranium and plutonium can be used as fuel. Metal actinide fuel is typically an alloy of zirconium, uranium, plutonium and the minor actinides. It can be made inherently safe, as thermal expansion of the metal alloy will increase neutron leakage.

NOTE: The minor actinides include neptunium, americium, curium, berkelium, californium, einsteinium, and fermium. The most important isotopes in spent nuclear fuel are neptunium-237, americium-241, americium-243, curium-242 through -248, and californium-249 through -252.

Ceramic Nuclear Fuels

Ceramic nuclear fuels, in addition to the oxides, also have high heat conductivities and melting points, but they are more prone to swelling than oxide fuels and are not understood as well.

Uranium nitride (UN) is used in NASA reactor designs, because it has a better thermal conductivity than UO_2 which it has a very high melting point. UN fuel's disadvantage is that a large amount of 14C would be generated from the nitrogen by the (n,p) reaction. As the nitrogen required for such a fuel would be so expensive, it is likely that the fuel would need to be reprocessed by a pyro method to enable the 15N to be recovered. It is likely that, if the fuel were processed and dissolved in nitric acid, the nitrogen enriched with 15N would be diluted with the common 14N.

Uranium carbide was used in the form of pin-type fuel elements for liquid metal fast breeder reactors during their intense study during the '60s and '70s. Recently there has been a revived interest in uranium carbide in the form of plate fuel and most notably micro fuel particles (such as TRISO particles).

The high thermal conductivity and high melting point makes uranium carbide an attractive fuel. In addition, because of the absence of oxygen in this fuel, as well as the ability to complement a ceramic coating, uranium carbide could be the ideal fuel candidate for certain Generation IV reactors such as the gas-cooled fast reactor.

Liquid Nuclear Fuels

Liquid nuclear fuels are basically liquids that contain some percentage of dissolved nuclear fuel. Liquid-fueled reactors generally have large negative feedback mechanisms and therefore are particularly stable designs. Liquid fuels have the disadvantage of being easily dispersible in the event of an accident, such as a leak in the primary system.

Molten salts nuclear fuels have nuclear fuel dissolved directly in the molten salt coolant. Molten salt-fueled reactors, such as the liquid fluoride thorium reactor (LFTR), are different than molten salt-cooled reactors that do not dissolve nuclear fuel in the coolant.

Molten salt fuels were used in the LFTR known as the "molten salt reactor experiment," as well as other liquid core reactor experiments. The liquid fuel for the molten salt reactor was a mixture of lithium, beryllium, thorium and uranium fluorides: $LiF-BeF2-ThF4-UF4$ (72-16-12-0.4 mol%). It had a peak operating temperature of 705°C in the experiment, but could have operated at much higher temperatures, since the boiling point of the molten salt was in excess of 1400°C.

Aqueous solutions of uranyl salts are used in the aqueous homogeneous reactors (AHRs) in a solution of uranyl sulfate, or other uranium salt, in water. Historically, AHRs have all been small research reactors, not large power reactors. An AHR, known as the Medical Isotope Production System is being considered for production of medical isotopes.

Types, Forms and Shapes of Nuclear Fuel

During production, the final uranium dioxide (UO_2) product, in the form of a fine powder, is compact-ed into cylindrical pellets and sintered at high temperatures. The objective is to produce ceramic nuclear fuel pellets with a high density and well defined physical properties and chemical composition.

The pellets are exposed to grinding to give them uniform and precise cylindrical shape. Thus obtained fuel pellets are then stacked into metallic tubes. The metal tubes type and shape depends on the design of the reactor. Stainless steel used in the past is now replaced by zirconium alloy which is highly corrosion-resistant and has low neutron absorption.

The metal tubes with the fuel pellets inside (fuel rods) are sealed, and grouped into fuel assemblies which comprise the core of a power reactor. The outer layer of the fuel rods (cladding) is made of a corrosion-resistant material with a low-absorption cross section for thermal neutrons, and protects the tubes from reacting with the surrounding media. Cladding also prevents radioactive fission fragments from escaping the fuel into the coolant and contaminating it.

The fuel rod assemblies are then shipped to the nuclear power plant for installation in the reactors. Since there are a number of different types of reactors, fuel rod assemblies are also different in type and size.

The major fuel rod assembly types are:

Pressurized water reactor (PWR) nuclear fuel assemblies consist of cylindrical rods put into bundles. Here, uranium oxide ceramic is formed into pellets and inserted into the Zircaloy tubes that are bundled together. The tubes are about 1 cm in diameter, and the fuel cladding gap is filled with helium gas to improve the conduction of heat from the fuel to the cladding.

There are about 179-264 fuel rods per fuel bundle and about 121 to 193 fuel bundles are loaded into a reactor core. Generally, the fuel bundles consist of fuel rods bundled 14×14 to 17×17. PWR fuel bundles are about 4 meters long. In PWR fuel bundles, control rods are inserted through the top directly into the fuel bundle. The fuel bundles usually are enriched several percent in 235U.

The uranium oxide is dried before inserting into the tubes to try to eliminate moisture in the ceramic fuel that can lead to corrosion and hydrogen embitterment. The Zircaloy tubes are pressurized with helium to try to minimize pellet-cladding interaction which can lead to fuel rod failure over long periods.

Boiling water reactor nuclear fuel, as the name suggests is used in boiling water reactors (BWR). It is similar to PWR fuel, except that the bundles are "canned" by means of a thin metal tube surrounding each bundle.

This is primarily done to prevent local density variations from affecting the neutronics and thermal hydraulics of the reactor core.

Modern BWR fuel bundles consist of either 91, 92, or 96 fuel rods per assembly, depending on the manufacturer and reactor type. The reactor core contains a total of 368 assemblies for the smallest and 800 assemblies for the largest US-based BWR reactors. Each fuel rod is back filled with helium to a pressure of about three atmospheres.

CANada Deuterium Uranium (CANDU) nuclear fuel bundles are about a half meter long and 10 cm in diameter. They consist of sintered (UO_2) pellets in zirconium alloy tubes, welded to zirconium alloy endplates. Each bundle weighs about 20 kg, and a typical core loading is on the order of 4500-6500 bundles, depending on the design. Modern types typically have 37 identical fuel pins radially arranged about the long axis of the bundle, but in the past several different configurations and numbers of pins have been used.

The *CANDU FLEXible fuelling (CANFLEX)* nuclear fuel bundle has 43 fuel elements, with two element sizes. It is also about 10 cm (4 inches) in diameter, 0.5 m (20 in) long and weighs about 20 kg (44 lb) and replaces the 37-pin standard bundle. It has been designed specifically to increase fuel performance by utilizing two different pin diameters. Current CANDU designs do not need enriched uranium to achieve criticality (due to their more efficient heavy water moderator); however, some newer concepts call for low enrichment to help reduce the size of the reactors.

There are also a number of less common nuclear fuels, such as:

Magnox nuclear fuel is used in reactors which are pressurized, carbon dioxide cooled, and graphite-moderated using natural, unreached uranium as fuel and magnox alloy as fuel cladding

Tristructural-isotropic (TRISO) nuclear fuel is a type of micro fuel particle. It consists of a fuel kernel composed of uranium compounds (UOX, UC, or UCO) in the center, coated with four layers of three isotropic materials. The four layers are a porous buffer layer made of carbon, followed by a dense inner layer of pyrolytic carbon (PyC), followed by a ceramic layer of silicon carbide SiC to retain fission products at elevated temperatures and to give the TRISO particle more structural integrity, followed by a dense outer layer of PyC.

Quad-structural-isotropic (QUADRISO) nuclear fuel particles consist of europium oxide, erbium oxide or carbide layers surrounding the fuel kernel of ordinary TRISO particles, which helps to better manage the excess reactivity.

RBMK nuclear fuel was used in Soviet-designed and built RBMK type reactors. This is a low enriched uranium oxide fuel. The fuel elements in a RBMK are 3 m long each, and two of these sit back-to-back on each fuel channel pressure tube. Reprocessed uranium from spent Russian VVER reactor fuel is used to fabricate RBMK fuel. As a result of the Chernobyl accident, the enrichment of nuclear fuel was changed from 2.0% to 2.4%, to compensate for control rod modifications and the introduction of additional absorbers

CerMet nuclear fuel consists of ceramic fuel particles (usually uranium oxide) embedded in a metal matrix. It is thought that this type of fuel is what is used in United States Navy reactors. This fuel has high heat transport characteristics and can withstand a large amount of expansion.

Plate type nuclear fuel is commonly composed of enriched uranium sandwiched between metal cladding. It is used in several research reactors where a high neutron flux is desired, for uses such as material irradiation studies or isotope production without the high temperatures seen in ceramic, cylindrical fuel.

Sodium bonded nuclear fuel consists of fuel that has liquid sodium in the gap between the fuel pellet and the cladding. The sodium bonding is used to reduce the temperature of the fuel. It is often used for sodium-cooled, liquid, metal-fast reactors and has been used in EBR-I, EBR-II, and the FFTF type reactors. The fuel pellets may be metallic or ceramic.

Whatever type, form, and shape the fuel pellets, rods and bundles might be, these are loaded in special canisters and transported to the nuclear plant to be loaded in the reactors and used to generate steam and electricity for several months. When the fuel is exhausted, the reactor is shut down, and the fuel bundles are removed and taken to temporary storage. New bundles are loaded in the reactor and the power generating cycles starts anew.

The Nuclear Fuel Cycle

As Figure 3-1 shows, the life of the nuclear fuel starts and ends underground. Uranium is dug out from underground uranium mines, transported to processing facilities and then to the nuclear plants to be used. When most of its energy is extracted and converted into electricity, it is then transported as radioactive waste and deposited in long-term underground storage facilities. Actually, this is how it should be. Presently a number of underground spent-fuel storage facilities are works in progress, so thousands of tons of spent nuclear fuel are stuck in temporary storage.

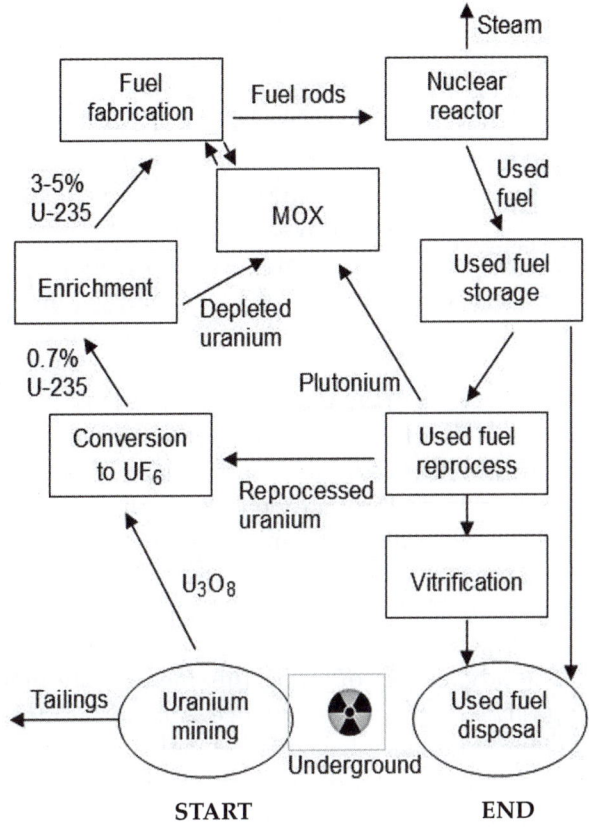

Figure 3-1. Nuclear fuel cycle

Put together, the actions of mining, transporting, refining, purifying, using, recycling, reprocessing, reusing, and ultimately disposing of nuclear fuel materials make up the nuclear fuel cycle.

Let's start with the first step of the process; uranium ore mining.

Uranium Ore Mining

Uranium is found in seams under the Earth's surface, just like coal, and is dug out of these just like coal, but uranium mining is one of the dirtiest and most dangerous jobs in the mining industry…if not in the world. Here, in addition to the other dangers related to surface and underground mining, the miners digging radioactive ores are exposed to high levels of radiation.

Uranium deposits are usually in sedimentary rocks that include those in sandstone (in Canada and Western U.S. Precambrian unconformities, located in Canada), phosphate, Precambrian quartz-pebble conglomerate, collapse breccia pipes (Arizona Breccia Pipe Uranium Mineralization), and calcrete.

Sandstone uranium deposits are generally of two types; roll-front type deposits occur at the boundary between the up dip and oxidized part of a sandstone body and the deeper down dip reduced part of a sandstone body. Peneconcordant sandstone uranium deposits, also called Colorado Plateau-type deposits, most often occur within generally oxidized sandstone bodies, often in localized reduced zones, such as in association with carbonized wood in the sandstone.

Precambrian quartz-pebble conglomerate-type uranium deposits occur only in rocks older than two billion years. The conglomerates also contain pyrite. These deposits have been mined in the Blind River-Elliot Lake district of Ontario, Canada, and from the gold-bearing Witwatersrand conglomerates of South Africa.

Hydrothermal uranium deposits encompass the vein-type uranium ores. Igneous deposits include *nepheline syenite* intrusives found at *Ilimaussaq, Greenland*; the disseminated uranium deposit at *Rossing*, Namibia; and uranium-bearing *pegmatites*. Disseminated deposits are also found in the states of Washington and Alaska in the US.

The worldwide production of uranium in 2009 amounted to 50,572 tons. Kazakhstan, Canada, and Australia are the top three producers and together account for 63% of world uranium production. Other important uranium producing countries in excess of 1000 tons per year are Namibia, Russia, Niger, Uzbekistan, and the United States.

Known uranium ore resources that can be mined at about current costs are estimated to be sufficient to produce fuel for about a century, based on current consumption rates.

India and several other countries have large deposits of thorium. India is sitting on more than 30% of the world's thorium reserves, so they are trying desperately to develop thorium-fueled reactors.

Uranium Ore Mining

The goal of uranium mining is to locate and extract uranium ore suitable for nuclear fuel from the ground. Like coal mining, uranium is mined via open pit (surface mining), or underground.

In *surface mining*, the overburden is removed from the surface by drilling into and blasting the topsoil to expose the ore layers. The ore is then mined by conventional blasting and excavation, with the help of large loaders and dump trucks. The big difference here is that the entire area is contaminated by different levels of nuclear radiation. Because of that, special precautions are taken to protect all life forms in the locale. Miners wear special clothing and safety equipment and spend most of the work day in enclosed, air conditioned cabins to limit the exposure to radiation.

The entire area is carefully monitored and special precautions are taken to limit the radiation levels and reduce its spreading in the environment. For example, large quantities of water are used all through the operation to suppress airborne dust, preventing it from leaving the immediate mine area.

Underground mining is another story. Here the workers are exposed to high levels of radiation from the rocks and from radon gas in tight quarters. Uranium is often mined in association with copper, gold, silver and other ores. Once the ore body has been identified, a shaft is sunk close to the ore veins, crosscuts are driven horizontally at various levels, usually every 100-150 meters, and tunnels are driven along the ore veins from the crosscuts. Drive tunnels, or raises, are driven through the deposit from level to level to the stopes, where the ore is mined from the veins.

The "cut and fill" or open stoping method used today consists of removal of the ore and refilling the space left behind with waste rock, sand and cement. The "shrinkage" method is used when sufficient broken ore is removed via the chutes below to allow miners working from the top of the pile to drill and blast the next layer to be broken off. This eventually leaves a large hole in the mine body.

Another method, known as room and pillar (similar to that used in coal mining) is used for thinner, flatter ore bodies. In this method, the ore body is first divided into blocks by intersecting drives, removing the ore in some sections, then systematically removing the blocks one by one, but always leaving enough ore for roof support.

Heap leaching is another type of mining, which is suitable for oxide-type ore deposits. Here, dilute sulfuric acid is used to extract the uranium from the ore. In this method, bulldozers level large areas of land with a small gradient, after which workers layer the area with thick plastic. Sometimes clay, silt or sand is placed beneath the plastic liner for additional protection.

The ore is crushed, piled in heaps in the plastic container, sprayed with the leaching agent, and left to react for 1-3 months. The leaching agent breaks the uranium bonds with the rocks around it and dissolves them. The solution filters down along the gradient into collecting pools. As different heaps will yield different concentrations the solution is pumped to a mixing plant that is carefully monitored. The properly balanced solution is then sent to a processing plant where the uranium

is separated from the sulfuric acid. This method allows only about 70% of the uranium content to be extracted.

Heap leaching has a number of advantages. It is more convenient and significantly cheaper than traditional milling processes, so lower grade ore can be economically mined.

In-situ Leaching is very similar to the heap leaching technique, but here the ore doesn't even need removal from the mine shafts. *In-situ* leaching (ISL), also known as *in-situ* recovery (ISR) in North America, involves leaving the ore untouched where it is in the ground. The recovery of the minerals from it is done by flooding the shafts with acid, dissolving the uranium and pumping the solution to the surface where the uranium can be recovered.

In most cases, native groundwater in the ore body is used. It is fortified with complexing agents and in some cases by the addition of an oxidant. This chemical mix is pumped through the underground ore body, to dissolve and recover the minerals in it by leaching. Once the pregnant solution is returned to the surface, it is sent to a processing plant to separate and recover the uranium in it.

The advantages of using this method are many; there is little surface disturbance and no tailings or waste rock generated. This method, however, poses the greatest environmental damage, so special precautions are taken prior to issuing permits.

The oxidant used in most cases is hydrogen peroxide and the complexing agent is sulfuric acid. Some mines do not employ an oxidant but use much higher acid concentrations in the circulating solutions instead. ISL mines in the US use an alkali leach, instead of acids, due to the presence of significant quantities of acid-consuming minerals such as gypsum and limestone in the host aquifers. The high carbonate minerals' presence dictates the alkali leach use vs. the more efficient acid leach.

Worldwide production of uranium ore is around 50,000 tons annually. Kazakhstan, Canada, and Australia are the top three producers, accounting for over 603% of the total worldwide uranium production. Over 1000 tons per year are also produced by Namibia, Russia, Niger, Uzbekistan, and the United States.

Presently known uranium ore resources, at the present-day rate of use, are estimated to last over a century.

Uranium Ore Processing

In nature, uranium is found as uranium-238 (99.2742%) and uranium-235 (0.7204%). All U-based isotopes are radioactive, and pose serious health danger if improperly handled.

At the mine, the uranium ore is loaded on special trucks or trains and transported to a processing facility. Here the ore is first crushed to a fine powder by crushers and grinders. The "pulped" ore is further processed by a treatment with concentrated acid, alkaline, and/or peroxide solutions, which dissolve and extract the uranium from the mix.

The resulting solution is further refined, filtered and dried to yield the final product called yellowcake, or urania, which is actually brown or black in color. The yellowcake name is a remainder of the color and texture of the final product in the past, when it was considered to be ammonium or sodium di-uranate, and was quite un-uniform and unstable, depending on the refining process conditions. The natural uranium "yellowcake" is sold on the uranium market as U_3O_8. The yellowcake can then be processed into UO_2, for making fuel rods.

Yellowcake is a coarse powder which has a pungent odor, is insoluble in water and contains about 80% uranium oxide (U_3O_8), which melts at approximately 5212.4°F. It contains, among other things; uranyl hydroxide, uranyl sulfate, sodium para-uranate, uranyl peroxide, and some uranium oxides.

Today yellowcake's quality is tightly controlled to contain about 90% triuranium octoxide (U_3O_8) by weight. It is produced by all countries in which uranium ore is mined. It is used predominantly in the preparation of uranium fuel for nuclear reactors, for which it is smelted into purified UO_2 for use in fuel rods for pressurized heavy-water reactors and other systems that use natural unenriched uranium.

Purified pure uranium metal (not UO_2) can be enriched in the isotope U-235, by combining the pure uranium metal with fluorine to form uranium hexafluoride gas (UF_6). The gas is then processed via gaseous diffusion, or through a gas centrifuge, where it undergoes isotope separation. This process produces low-enriched uranium containing up to 20% U-235, or the type used in most large civilian electric-power reactors.

Further processing produces highly enriched uranium, containing over 20% U-235, which is used in smaller reactors to power naval warships and submarines. Even further processing can yield weapons-grade uranium which contains over 90% U-235 and is used for making nuclear weapons.

Since the end of the Cold War in 1990, there is a worldwide surplus of highly enriched uranium, and it is often diluted for use in some nuclear reactors.

Isotope Enrichment

Isotope separation is designed to concentrate (enrich) the fissionable uranium-235 for nuclear weapons and most nuclear power plants, except for gas-cooled reactors and pressurized heavy-water reactors. Most neutrons released by a fissioning atom of uranium-235 must impact other uranium-235 atoms to sustain the nuclear chain reaction. The concentration and amount of uranium-235 needed to achieve this is called a "critical mass."

To be considered "enriched," the uranium-235 fraction should be between 3% and 5%. This process produces huge quantities of uranium that are depleted of uranium-235 and have a correspondingly increased fraction of uranium-238, called depleted uranium (DU).

To be considered "depleted," the uranium-235 isotope concentration should be no more than 0.3%. The price of uranium has risen since 2001, so enrichment tailings containing more than 0.35% uranium-235 are being considered for re-enrichment, driving the price of depleted uranium hexafluoride.

The gas centrifuge process, where gaseous uranium hexafluoride (UF_6) is separated by the difference in molecular weight between $^{235}UF_6$ and $^{238}UF_6$ using high-speed centrifuges, is the cheapest and leading enrichment process. The gaseous diffusion process had been the leading method for enrichment for a long time. Here, uranium hexafluoride is repeatedly diffused through a silver-zinc membrane, and the different isotopes of uranium are separated by diffusion rate (uranium 238 is heavier, so diffuses more slowly than uranium-235). Today, gas diffusion is becoming an obsolete technology that is steadily replaced by later technologies, as diffusion plants reach their ends of life.

The molecular laser isotope separation method employs a laser beam of precise energy to sever the bond between uranium-235 and fluorine. This leaves uranium-238 bonded to fluorine and allows uranium-235 metal to precipitate from the solution.

An alternative laser method of enrichment is known as atomic vapor laser isotope separation (AVLIS) and employs visible tunable lasers such as dye lasers.

The uranium enrichment facilities are usually designed, built, and operated under strict security, to which very few outsiders have access. Because of that, we will limit our discussion on uranium processing and handling to the very minimum.

Recovery from Seawater

Uranium ore reserves are limited and estimated to last about 80-100 years, thus nuclear power is not a renewable energy source. Because of that, there are efforts to extract uranium, and other materials suitable for nuclear fuel, from other sources. Rocks like granite contain minute amounts of uranium and have been considered, but the process is cumbersome and very expensive.

Extracting uranium from seawater seems more doable, and there are a number of efforts in that area. The uranium concentration in seawater varies, but averages about 3.3 mg uranium per cubic meter of seawater. This is a very small amount by all means, but the quantity of this resource is huge, so even a small portion of the uranium in seawater could provide fuel for nuclear power generation for a long time.

A number of methods have been tried to extract uranium from seawater, including using a uranium-specific nonwoven fabric as an absorbent. In one case, the total amount of uranium recovered from three collection boxes containing 350 kg of fabric was >1 kg of yellowcake after 240 days of submersion in the ocean, which brings the cost of uranium to over $150/lb.

A new absorbent material, called HiCap, was developed in 2012 which outperformed previous best adsorbents five to seven times. HiCap also effectively removes toxic metals from water, so it might have a dual use. It is possible that this and other efforts will bring the cost of uranium from seawater down to acceptable levels, thus significantly extending the time we can use nuclear power for generating electricity.

The major cost of nuclear power is in the construction and operation of the power station, so the fuel's contribution to the overall cost of the electricity produced is relatively small. Because of that, even a large fuel price escalation will have relatively small effect on the price of generated electric power.

For example, doubling the uranium market price would increase the fuel cost for a light water reactor by 26% and the electricity cost about 7%, whereas doubling the price of natural gas would typically add 70% to the price of electricity from that source.

If the price becomes very high in the distant future, then extraction from sources such as seawater and other materials containing traces of uranium might become economically feasible.

Ore and Nuclear Fuel Transport

Uranium transport is a complex issue that involves a number of sophisticated equipment pieces and procedures. Unlike the other fuels which can be dumped on any old truck, when uranium ore from the mines, or spent nuclear fuel from the plant are transported, special equipment and procedures are always used. No exceptions!

These special precautions are needed because uranium and its products are radioactive, and people must be protected. Additionally, uranium presents security issues, so transport must be done in such a manner as to prevent its falling in the hands of terrorists and rogue nations.

Uranium ore is transported from the mines to the milling plant to produce yellowcake. The yellowcake is then transported to the enrichment facility to make UF_6 which is transported to the fuel fabrication plant, where the final nuclear fuel is produced. Thus enriched UF_6 (nuclear fuel) is finally transported to the power plant to be used for generating electricity.

Once used, the nuclear fuel is transported to a used-fuel storage facility, from where it is transported to a nuclear waste disposal site or to a reprocessing facility. From the reprocessing plant, the transportation cycle repeats.

There are an estimated 20 million shipments of radioactive material from one place to another every year. These vary from a single small package, or a number of packages sent from one location to another, to large containers. Radioactive materials are used in many other areas (not nuclear fuel related), such as medicine, agriculture, research, manufacturing, non-destructive testing and minerals exploration. As a matter of fact, only 5% of these annual shipments are fuel-cycle related.

The shipment of any radioactive material is governed by international regulations for the transport of radioactive materials, established as far back as 1961. These regulations control shipment of radioactive material in a manner that is independent of the material's intended application.

Nuclear fuel processing facilities are located in various parts of the world, and materials of many kinds are transported between them. Many of these are similar to materials used in other industrial activities. However, the nuclear industry's fuel and waste materials are radioactive, and it is these "nuclear materials" about which there is most public concern.

In the USA, only one percent of the 300 million packages of hazardous material shipped each year contains radioactive materials. Of this, about 250,000 contain radioactive wastes from US nuclear power plants, and 50 to 100 packages contain actual used fuel.

The Nuclear Reaction

There are two types of nuclear reactions; fission and fusion. Presently fusion nuclear reactions are in a development stages, and only fission is used in nuclear power plants, so it is fission that we will consider in more detail in this text.

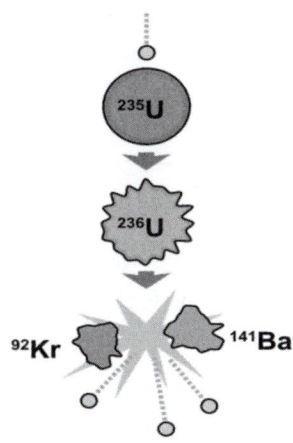

Figure 3-2. Nuclear fission

During uranium fission reaction, see Figure 3-2, neutrons are captured by the nucleus of the U-235 atoms and are absorbed within it. This briefly turns the nucleus into a highly excited U-236 atom, and very quickly it splits into two lighter atoms; Ba-141 and Kr-92, plus two or three neutrons. The number of ejected neutrons depends on the conditions under which the U-235 atom splits. This process (neutron capturing and splitting) is very fast and energetic.

The decay of a single U-235 atom releases approximately 200 million electron volts (MeV). Since there are billions of atoms undergoing this reaction in a uranium fuel source, the energy release is enormous. For example, the energy released by just a pound of highly enriched uranium undergoing a fission reaction is equal to the energy released by over a million gallons of gasoline burning.

In addition to energy (heat) released during the splitting of the atoms, a large amount of gamma radiation (radiation made of high-energy photons) is released as well. The two atoms that result from the fission of each atom, go on their own way releasing beta radiation (super-fast electrons) and gamma radiation of their own as well. These particles are what creates the radioactivity of nuclear fuels, and it is they that make nuclear accidents so very dangerous.

For all this to work most efficiently, uranium used for nuclear fuel must be enriched to contain 2 to 3 percent additional U-235. Three-percent enrichment is sufficient for nuclear power plants, but weapons-grade uranium requires at least 90% U-235.

NOTE: It is important to point out that one neutron impinging onto the U-235 nucleus creates three neutrons, which can in turn impinge on three other U-235 nuclei, thus propagating and escalating the reaction *ad infinitum*. This is why nuclear reactions must be controlled to avoid overheating of the vessel.

The fission process is accompanied by large amounts of kinetic (heat) energy that is generated during the U-236 fission. If a large amount of U-235 is bombarded by neutrons in a containment vessel (as that in a nuclear power plant), an enormous amount of heat can be generated and consequently used to make electricity.

Nuclear Radiation

Nuclear radiation is defined as the energy and matter released during radioactive decay of nuclear elements and fuels. Nuclear radiation can take the following two principle forms:

Particulate radiation consists of actual subatomic particles being emitted from the nucleus of the atom.

Electromagnetic radiation is the energy emitted in wave form that possesses both electrical and magnetic characteristics.

The two types of particulate radiation are a result of alpha and beta decay. Electromagnetic radiation is a result of gamma decay.

Alpha (α) *particles* are typically ejected from heavy uranium or other atoms, which have excess to neutrons.

For example:

$$^{-238}U \rightarrow {}^{-234}Th + \alpha \text{ particle}$$

Alpha particles are massive, relatively slow moving, with a short travel length (mean free path) before losing their energy. At the end of the travel path they pick up two elections and become stable helium atoms. Alpha particles are stopped within a few millimeters of travel in water, or human tissue.

Beta (β) *radiation* originates at the shell of the atoms as a free electron (a negatively charged particle). Beta particles have energies ranging from a few keV to several MeV. The emission of a beta particle (with its negative charge) results in converting a neutron into a proton, which effectively raises the atomic number of the affected element by 1, but at the same time keeps the atomic mass unchanged.

For example:

$$^{-239}U + \beta \text{ particle} = {}^{-239}Pu$$

Here we see uranium emitting a beta particle, which is then converted into plutonium.

Gamma (γ) *radiation* is a photon (electromagnetic wave, not a particle), which originates in the nucleus. The gamma emission transfers energy without changing mass or charge. The fission of U-235 produces 2 or 3 neutrons each with several MeV. Since they have no charge, they can pass through matter, unless they collide with other nuclei. In case of collision with a proton (hydrogen ion), the energy is shared with the proton.

An example of gamma rays production is:

$$^{60}Co \rightarrow {}^{60}Ni^* + e^- + \gamma \text{ radiation}$$

$$^{60}Ni^* \rightarrow {}^{60}Ni + 2\gamma \text{ radiation}$$

In this case, ^{60}Co decays into excited ^{60}Ni during beta decay and emits an electron and gamma radiation. The excited 60Ni then drops down to its ground energy state, emitting two gamma rays in the process.

High energy gamma waves have mean free paths in water of over three feet. Anti-gamma radiation shielding of about 20 feet of water, or 4-6 feet of cement slab, are required for human safety.

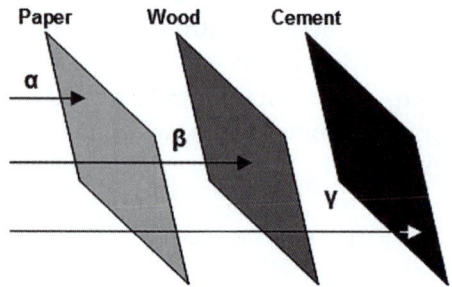

Figure 3-3. α, β, γ particles penetration potential

Neutron radiation arises from nuclear fission, such as the fission of U-235, which produces 2 or 3 neutrons each with several MeV. Since the protons have no charge, they pass through matter, unless they collide with other nuclei. If they strike a proton, such as a hydrogen ion, the energy is equally shared. If a neutron strikes heavy nuclei it may be deflected with little energy loss, or it may be absorbed and incorporated into the heavier nuclei, as in the collision with a U-238 nuclei:

$$^{-238}U + \text{neutron} = {}^{-239}U$$

This results in a chain reaction of dangerous nuclear (neutron) radiation. Neutrons are electrically neutral, more penetrating than any other radiation, and could be more harmful over great areas.

NUCLEAR POWER PLANTS

A nuclear power plant is similar in design to a conventional power plant in which electricity is generated by the combustion of coal, oil, or natural gas. The only important difference between these is the source of energy from which the electricity is generated—fossil fuel in a conventional power plant and a nuclear material in a nuclear power plant.

The core of a nuclear power plant is where the nuclear reaction happens and where the heat is generated. It is in fact called just that—the reactor core. It contains a fissionable fuel, uranium or plutonium, from which energy is released. The fuel is fabricated in the form of long, thin, cylindrical fuel rods, bundled together in groups called "fuel assemblies."

When uranium or plutonium atoms in the fuel fission (are activated), they release energy, which ultimately is used to boil water and produce the steam needed to generate electricity.

The reactor core is surrounded by a large dome-shaped structure, made of concrete and reinforced steel. It is called a "containment" building, which purpose is to shield and prevent radioactive materials from escaping from the reactor core during operation and in case of an accident.

Along with the fuel rods, long and thin cylindrical control rods (made out of boron or cadmium) are placed in the core. They have the ability to absorb neutrons very efficiently, so that the position of the control rods with regard to the fuel rods determines the rate at which fission occurs within the reactor core.

When the control rods are completely inserted into the core, they block the fuel rods so that large numbers of neutrons are absorbed, and the fission reaction can be stopped. If the controls rods are removed completely, however, very large numbers of neutrons would become available, and fission would occur at a very rapid rate. The reaction might eventually accelerate to such a degree that could melt the core materials, and radioactive materials would be released.

The reactor core is not capable of exploding, since the mass of fissionable material in it is never large enough to permit uncontrolled chain reaction. A core meltdown is, however, an extremely serious event, as shown by the core meltdown at Chernobyl in 1986.

Control rods, then, are what control the reaction and the generated heat. They are moved up or down to raise or decrease the reaction rate, and the temperature of the heated liquid varies with that. Basically, successful operation of a nuclear power plant depends on the exact control of the control rods, to release enough energy to heat the water, but no more than that. Of course, there are many other operational and safety controls that ensure the proper and safe operation of a nuclear power plant, as we will see below.

Once the nuclear reaction is under control, heat is generated in the reactor core, and water of some other (heat transfer) liquid is run via pipes in the core. Thus heated liquid is used to drive a turbine. The turbine in turn runs an electric generator, which generates electrical energy.

There are two major methods of transferring heat from the reactor core to the steam generator. These are the boiling water system and the pressurized water system. In the boiling water system, water circulating around the reactor core is allowed to come to the boiling point. Thus generated steam is sent via pipes to the turbine where an electric generator attached to it generates electric power.

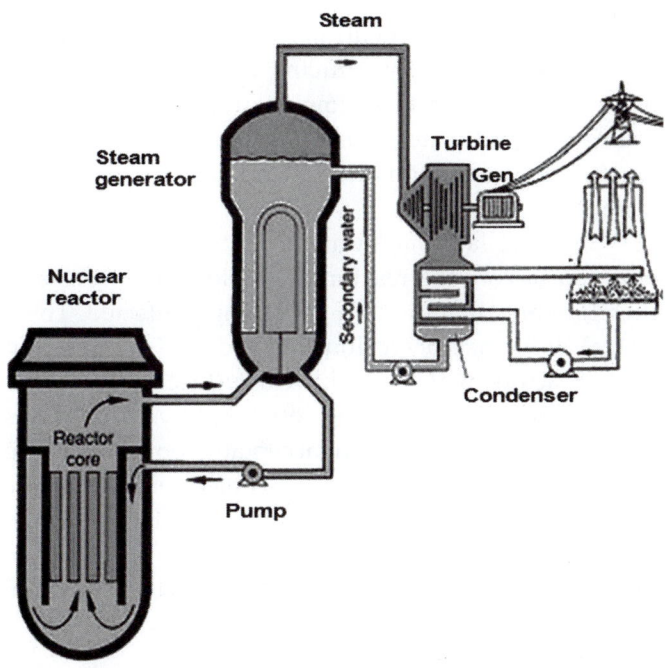

Figure 3-4. Nuclear power plant with pressurized system

In the pressurized water system, the water in the reactor core is kept in pipes and under pressure, to prevent it from boiling. The super-heated water is then transferred through pipes to the external building where it is used to heat water in a second system, causing that water to boil.

Each type of nuclear power plant has its technical advantages and disadvantages. Today, about two-thirds of all nuclear power plants in the United States use pressurized water systems, and the other third use boiling water systems.

In addition to the type of water heating, the nuclear reactors used in nuclear power plants can be classified as breeder and fusion reactors.

Breeder Reactors

A seemingly illogical concept, that any reactor can make more fuel than it consumes, is actually the reaction that occurs between uranium-238 and neutrons in a nuclear reactor core. Strange, but fact. Since uranium-238 is not fissionable, only the uranium-235 atoms in a fuel rod undergo fission. Uranium-238, however, does react with neutrons to produce an isotope of the next heavier element in the periodic table, plutonium-239 (Pu-239), which is one of the isotopes that can undergo fission. It can also be removed from the "waste" products of the nuclear reactor, reprocessed, and used as fuel in another nuclear reactor.

A breeder reactor then is a nuclear reactor capable of generating more fissile material than it consumes because of its neutron interractions and economy, which is high enough to breed fissile fuel from fertile material like uranium-238 or thorium-232.

Breeder reactors were considered for use in the past because of their superior fuel economy compared to light water reactors. That changed after the 1960s, as more uranium reserves were found, and new methods of uranium enrichment were used to reduce fuel costs. Today, breeder reactors are again of research interest, since they offer means of controlling nuclear waste, thus closing the nuclear fuel cycle.

Breeder Reactor Types

There are a number of breeder reactors, since a "breeder" is simply a reactor designed for very high neutron economy with an associated conversion rate higher than 1.0. So, in principal, almost any reactor design could possibly be modified in some way to become a breeder.

The evolution of the light water reactor (LWR) is a good example. LWR is a heavily moderated thermal design, into the "super fast reactor" concept, using light water in an extremely low-density super-critical form to increase the neutron economy high enough to allow breeding.

There are many types of breeder reactors possible, such as water-cooled, molten-salt cooled, and liquid-metal cooled designs that can be fueled by uranium, plutonium, minor actinides, or thorium, and may also be designed for alternative operations, such as creating more fissile fuel, long-term steady-state operation, or active burning of nuclear wastes.

We can divide the reactor designs into two broad categories based on their neutron spectrum: a) those designed to utilize primarily uranium and transuranics, and b) those designed to use thorium.

The fast breeder reactor or FBR uses fast (unmoderated) neutrons to breed fissile plutonium and possibly higher transuranics from fertile uranium-238. The fast spectrum is flexible enough that it can also breed fissile uranium-233 from thorium.

The thermal breeder reactor uses thermal spectrum (moderated) neutrons to breed fissile uranium-233 from thorium (thorium fuel cycle). Due to the behavior of the various nuclear fuels, a thermal breeder is thought commercially feasible only with thorium fuel, which avoids the buildup of the heavier transuranics.

Following are the major types of nuclear reactors.

Fast Breeder Reactors

Recently all large-scale fast breeder (FBR-based) reactors in power plants have been of the liquid metal fast breeder (LMFBR) reactors type, which is distinguished from the rest by the fact that it uses liquid (molten) sodium for heat transfer and cooling.

There are two basic designs of LMFBR reactors:

1. *Loop type*, in which the primary coolant is circulated through primary heat exchangers outside the reactor tank (but inside the biological shield due to radioactive sodium-24 in the primary coolant), and

2. *Pool type*, in which the primary heat exchangers and pumps are immersed in the reactor tank.

All current fast neutron reactor designs use liquid metal as the primary coolant to transfer heat from the core to steam used to power the electricity generating turbines. FBRs have been built cooled by liquid metals other than sodium. Some early FBRs used mercury, other experimental reactors have used a sodium-potassium alloy (NaK.)

Both have the advantage that they are liquids at room temperature, which is convenient for experimental rigs but less important for pilot or full-scale power stations. Lead and lead-bismuth alloy have also been used.

The new Generation IV FBR reactor types still in development are: gas-cooled fast reactor (GFR) which is cooled by helium; sodium-cooled fast reactor (SFR) which is based on the existing liquid metal FBR (LMFBR); integral fast reactor designs; and lead-cooled fast reactor (LFR) which is based on Soviet naval propulsion units.

FBRs usually use a mixed oxide fuel core of up to 20% plutonium dioxide (PuO_2) and at least 80% uranium dioxide (UO_2). Another fuel option is metal alloys, typically a blend of uranium, plutonium, and zirconium (used because it is "transparent" to neutrons). Enriched uranium can also be used on its own.

In many designs, the core is surrounded in a blanket of tubes containing non-fissile uranium-238 which, by capturing fast neutrons from the reaction in the core, is converted to fissile plutonium-239 (as is some of the uranium in the core), which is then reprocessed and used as nuclear fuel.

Other FBR designs rely on the geometry of the fuel itself (which also contains uranium-238), arranged to attain sufficient fast neutron capture.

The plutonium-239 (or the fissile uranium-235) fission cross-section is much smaller in a fast spectrum than in a thermal spectrum, as is the ratio between the $^{239}Pu/^{235}U$ fission cross-section and the ^{238}U absorption cross-section. This increases the concentration of $^{239}Pu/^{235}U$ needed to sustain a chain reaction, as well as the ratio of breeding to fission.

On the other hand, a fast reactor needs no moderator to slow down the neutrons at all, taking advantage of the fast neutrons producing a greater number of neutrons per fission than slow neutrons. For this reason ordinary liquid water, being a moderator as well as a neutron absorber, is an undesirable primary coolant for fast reactors.

Because large amounts of water in the core are required to cool the reactor, the yield of neutrons and therefore breeding of ^{239}Pu are strongly affected. Theoretical work has been done on reduced moderation water reactors, which may have a sufficiently fast spectrum to provide a breeding ratio slightly over 1. This would likely result in an unacceptable power derating and high costs in a liquid-water-cooled reactor, but the supercritical water coolant of the SCWR has sufficient heat capacity to allow adequate cooling with less water, making a fast-spectrum water-cooled reactor a practical possibility.

Thermal Breeder Reactors

Thermal breeder reactors operate on the principle of neutron absorption by fertile isotopes in a thermal spectrum. These reactions also produce more fissile fuel than they consume. Their absorption cross-section is an important factor in choosing fertile material for the core, so the fact that Th-232 breeds U-233, through neutron absorption and successive beta decays with higher neutron absorption cross-section than U-238, is an overriding factor for using thorium in thermal breeders.

Adding low-enriched uranium provides another safety advantage to thorium fuel because the lower-absorption cross-section for epithermal neutrons in pure Th-232 reduces the negative power coefficient in case of a power transient. Too much uranium in the fuel, however, might result in a higher concentration of plutonium produced by the fertile isotope U-238.

In a thermal breeder reactor, the low-enriched fuel reaches high burn-up and achieves higher Pu-240/Pu-239 ratio for the fuel. The blanket with half the size of the driver also breeds only reactor-grade plutonium in lower quantity.

Advanced heavy water reactor (AHWR) is one of the few large-scale reactors that use thorium, and is presently developed for use in India and other countries with large thorium reserves, and which lack significant uranium deposits

The Shippingport Atomic Power Station, a 60 MWe reactor, was a light-water thorium breeder which began operating in August 1977 and was brought to full power by the end of that year, after testing. It used pellets made of thorium dioxide and uranium-233 oxide; initially the U233 content of the pellets was 5-6% in the seed region, 1.5-3% in the blanket region and none in the reflector region. It operated at 236 MWt, generating 60 MWe and ultimately produced over 2.1 billion kilowatt hours of electricity. After five years, the core was removed and found to contain nearly 1.4% more fissile material than when it was installed, demonstrating that breeding from thorium had occurred.

The liquid fluoride thorium reactor (LFTR) can also be developed as a thorium thermal breeder. LFTRs have many advantages, such as inherent safety (due to their strong negative temperature coefficient of reactivity and their ability to drain their liquid fuel into a passively cooled and non-critical configuration), no need to manufacture precise fuel rods, and the possibility of relatively simple continual reprocessing of the liquid fuel.

This concept was first investigated at the Oak Ridge National Laboratory Molten-Salt Reactor Experiment in the 1960s. It has recently been the subject of renewed interest worldwide. Japan, China, the UK, as well as private US, Czech and Australian companies have expressed intent to develop and commercialize the technology.

Fusion Reactors

Fusion reactors are still a dream that might power the future someday. Fusion (vs. fission, which was described above) reactions are the ultimate nuclear reactions in which two small particles, such as two hydrogen atoms, are combined or "fused" to form one larger particle, releasing enormous energy in the process.

The fusion process is the mirror image of fission. Here two nuclei must be brought close enough and fused together to create a different and heavier nucleus

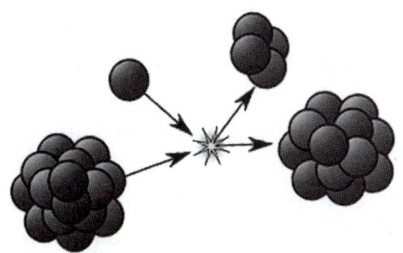

Figure 3-5. Fusion reaction

as a result. This can be done by overcoming the electrostatic repulsion by the attractive nuclear force, which is stronger at close distances. A lot of energy is required to overcome the electrostatic force barrier between the nucleus and initiate the fusion process.

If the nucleus is sufficiently heated to the point of being plasma, the fusion reaction may occur due to collisions with extreme thermal kinetic energies of the particles. This process is called thermonuclear fusion and is the only one that can be used for obtaining fusion energy for practical purposes. Fusion reactors presently are experimental types of nuclear reactors, built on the principle of controlled nuclear fusion reactions as the source of energy.

The amount of energy produced in fusion reactions is far greater than that obtained from fission reactions, since fusion reactions are the mechanisms by which stars (including the Sun) produce energy. The Sun's fusion reactions, which give us all the energy we need here on Earth, are maintained by 620 million metric tons of hydrogen being fused every single second in the Sun's core.

Equally enormous energy produced during any fusion process is a fundamental problem, as far as the materials used for construction of fusion reactors and their containment are concerned. Thus far, there are no known materials that can contain the excessive heat generated during a fusion reaction.

Case study: National Ignition Facility (NIF)
Lawrence Livermore National Labs in Livermore, CA

The author was part of a team serving NIF during the last stages of the construction of the large, laser-based, inertial confinement fusion (ICF) research system. It is the largest and most energy consuming and releasing laser setup ever.

Using 192 powerful lasers focused on a very small target (2mm in diameter), the ICF system aims to create a nuclear *fusion* reaction within the target, which would then generate an enormous amount of heat. This is the theory behind this monstrous, multi-billion dollar project, and it seems to be convincing enough for Congress to authorize that much money for a single project with unknown outcome.

NIF's ultimate mission was to achieve *fusion* ignition with high energy gain, which would help to study the behavior of matter in nuclear weapons and reactions, and hopefully build a fusion reactor someday.

NIF construction began in 1997, but management problems and technical delays slowed progress and the facility was completed five years behind schedule in 2009. It was also four or five times more expensive than the originally budgeted $1.1 billion.

After a number of tests, on July 5, 2012, the NIF laser system pointed its 192 beams at the small target and delivered more than 500 trillion terawatts watts (TW) of peak power and 1.85 megajoules (MJ) of ultraviolet laser light to the target. All this power was discharged into the miniscule, 2-mm-diameter target.

> To give the reader an idea of what 500 TW of electric power is, it is approximately 1,000 times more power than the United States uses at any instant in time. At the same time, 1.85 MJ of energy is about 100 times what any other laser can produce.

Figure 3-6. NIF's laser bay

That's a great achievement, no doubt. A lot of research will be done at NIF in the future to further advance US nuclear power generation and weapons technologies. The initial idea to create a fusion reaction is still a mirage, and many more billions of dollars will be needed to implode the pea-size target and release its enormous energy.

Even if achieved someday, it is only the beginning. More billions of dollars will be needed to design a commercial reactor that could withstand the enormous temperature, and the accompanying problems, created during the fusion of a sizeable chunk of fusionable material.

As demonstrated by NIF's 500 TW laser blast, we need as much energy as the entire country uses now to initiate the fusion reaction in a small ~2-mm-diameter target. With that and everything else we know about fusion in mind, there a number of unanswered questions:

1. How much energy could be produced by a 2 mm target during its fusion process, and how long would it last?

2. How much of the energy released by the target can be captured and used?

3. Is it possible to use larger targets for practical power generation with the NIF setup?

4. How much energy is needed for the fusion of a 4 mm target? 4 cm? 4 feet?

5. How big a target and how much power do we need to produce 1 GW of electric power via fusion reaction?

6. What would be the maximum practical amount of energy generated by a larger target?

7. Could the fusion reaction of a larger target be controlled?

8. What materials would be used to build the vessels needed to contain the enormous heat generated during thermonuclear fusion of larger targets?

9. Would a practical fusion power plant be as safe, or safer, than today's fission power plant of the same size?

Judging from how things stand today, there is a lot of work to be done before fusion becomes a practical nuclear power generator, and many more billions of dollars will be spent by NIF and others on tests, equipment modifications, and upgrades.

One doesn't need to be a laser or nuclear scientist to see that NIF is the model T of the fusion industry, and that a lot of time is needed to build a practical, functioning and safe fusion reactor on Earth. Because the initial efforts were abandoned, even more time will pass before fusion technology replaces present-day fission reactors. For now we will keep our fingers crossed for the NIF scientists and the future of fusion nuclear power in general.

Nuclear Plants Construction

Nuclear power plant (using fission nuclear processes for now) design and construction is a complex and expensive undertaking. It differs from coal- or gas-burning power plants by the different (nuclear) fuel it uses and the special requirements for efficient and safe use of that fuel. Safe here must be underlined, emphasized, and over-emphasized, for the entire future of nuclear energy depends on safe operation.

That makes a big difference in designing and building the front end of the plant (the nuclear reactors), while the rest (steam generation, turbines and electric generators) and other support infrastructure and equipment are quite similar in design to that of coal- and gas-fired power plants.

Figure 3-7. Nuclear power plant under construction

The fission nuclear plant consists of a number of key elements, each of a high level of complexity, and most of a very large size.

For example:

Reactor Pressure Vessels (RPV) are large pieces of equipment, over 20 feet inside diameter by 90 feet high, and can weigh up to 1,200 tons. For example, each GEN III+ unit has one RPV and one RPV head, so with everything included, the total weight of the entire unit is well over 2,000 tons.

Steam Generators are nearly 80 feet tall with an 18-foot-diameter upper section and a 14-foot-diameter lower section, and weigh about 730 tons. Moisture separator reheaters are up to 100 feet long and 13 feet in diameter. Each moisture separator reheater weighs around 440 tons. For example each GEN III+ unit uses either two steam generators or two to four moisture separator reheaters.

Control Rod Drives and Fuel Elements are key elements of a nuclear power plant and consist of 200 accurate fine-motion control rod drives per reactor. Over 1,000 fuel elements are used per reactor.

Steam Turbine Generators (STG) and condensers are about 1,500 MVA and have low pressure (LP) turbine with last-stage blades that are about 52 inches long. The high pressure steam turbine weighs over 500 tons. Several low pressure rotors are used, each weighing about 250 tons. The generator stator weighs 500 tons and the generator rotor another 250 tons. The STG condenser's lower sections each weigh over 650 tons with dimensions of 57 x 31 x 34 feet. Each STG has up to three condensers.

Pumps are used to move liquids and gasses around the plant. There are ten reactor coolant pumps, two turbine-driven feedwater pumps and two motor-driven feedwater pumps for each reactor. Each unit also has several very large (>400HP) safety-related pumps, and over 100 smaller pumps. Some reactors have "passive safety" features and do not require that many safety-related pumps.

Valves are used to control the flow of liquids and gasses around the nuclear power plant. Each reactor unit has over 2,000 valves. Over 1,000 motor operated valves (MOVs) and air operated valves (AOVs) are used in each unit, with 700 valves of 3" size and larger. For example, different GEN III+ units have a total of 9,000-18,000 valves, with over 2,000 values used in the reactors alone.

Class 1E Switchgear and Equipment are used to assist the power plant operations and usually consist of two or three medium-voltage switchgear panels, three 5MW emergency diesel generators, nine 480V motor control centers, four 125VDC uninterruptible power supply systems, and three 120VAC uninterruptible power supply systems. Some reactors have "passive safety" features and do not require many, if any, emergency diesel generators.

Control Equipment is used to control the power plant operations, and consists of 2,000-3,500 instruments, digital plant control systems, main control panels, reactor protection panels, local panels, and a plant simulator.

This short review reveals that thousands of tons of metals and other materials are used to make the different components of a nuclear power plant. These materials are processed one way or another, then machined before assembly and delivery to the plant.

Some of the plant equipment pieces used in the

construction of nuclear reactors and the other plant components are prefabricated. There are 500-600 prefabricated modules used in the assembly of each reactor, half of which are fabricated by third-party contractors, usually at their own offsite facilities. These units include electro-mechanical equipment modules, piping, pipe supports, valves, controls and measurement instrumentation, tubing, conduit, cable tray, junction boxes, structural bases, and structural supports.

The maximum size of a module or sub-assembly fabricated off-site is 12 x 12 x 80 feet, to allow shipment by rail or truck. Larger structural and equipment modules are assembled onsite from scratch or from multiple sub-assemblies.

Over 250 reinforcing steel modules and piping assemblies and over 140 mechanical equipment modules are required for each plant of the most modularized design. In addition over 60 structural modules and 20 electrical equipment modules are required for each unit. The largest structural modules consist of numerous factory preassembled sub-modules that weigh up to 800 tons. Some of the structural modules include leave-in-place formwork for concrete placement.

Upon delivery of the different parts and components, they undergo final assembly onsite and are mounted in place, to complete plant construction.

Construction Labor

From the first shovel to initial plant testing, construction work requires hundreds, sometimes thousands, of engineers, technicians and general labor personnel. The construction labor force is usually temporary and is different for different power plant designs. The construction labor, and on-site labor support personnel includes craft supervision, warehouse personnel, clerical staff, security personnel, quality control inspectors, EPC contractors, engineers, schedulers, start-up personnel, and the ever-present Nuclear Regulatory Commission inspection staff.

All these people are highly trained and have specific daily tasks and overall goals. The labor force is divided into groups according to their specialty and work location. All jobs and tasks are managed, monitored and inspected.

Each unit site requires 130-150 administrators, engineers, and loss-control personnel during the peak construction period. This does not include the work of supervision, quality control and system start-up personnel associated with vendors and subcontractors since these are different specialized groups that are counted separately.

During the construction phases, 40-50 quality control inspectors are assigned to different areas of the plant. At the same time, NRC is also represented by 10-20 NRC inspectors on-site and at different off-site locations during construction, start-up, and testing periods. This is in addition to over 60 highly trained specialists onsite during the critical start-up phases.

EPC contractors are involved and are usually in charge of plant construction. They need a staff of over 100 specialists at each unit site during different phases of construction. This includes project managers, engineers, schedulers, and other specialized and clerical personnel.

Usually the plant owner is represented by an operating and maintenance (O&M) staff of 200 specialists who support the commissioning, start-up, and maintenance of unit systems during the construction and start-up phases. The O&M staff amount to over 650 for a single unit and 400 for the second unit of a twin unit plant, during normal plant operation.

Most of the permanent plant O&M personnel and plant management, engineering, and security staff are also present onsite during the construction period, but are not included in most labor efforts. They undergo hands-on training for the duration, instead.

Craft labor and on-site labor supporting construction and start-up during the peak construction period totals 2,400 people of different occupations and specialties. Basically, 800 onsite managers and specialists support 1600 personnel during daily labor activities for the duration of plant construction and start-up. Some of these people are gradually transferred to, or interchangeably used in, the construction of other units.

A five-year nuclear power plant construction schedule includes 12 to 18 months for site preparation, 36 to 42 months for construction from first concrete to fuel load, and 6 to 12 months for commissioning and testing.

There are 8-10 million man hours of craft-labor estimated for the construction of one unit of an average nuclear plant in the United States. Peak-construction craft labor is estimated at 1,500-1,700 personnel working on each unit.

Most construction schedules have 12 to 18 months between the commercial operation dates of units in multiple-unit plants. The cost of the consecutive units within the staggered 12-18-month construction period is usually significantly lower than the construction of the first unit for several reasons.

There are preliminary estimates that additional GEN III+ units will be built after 2014, at the rate of eight units under construction at any time. By staggering the construction effort, two units would be entering commercial operation every year. This would require a substantial number of sustained total labor force during the deployment period.

Nuclear plant design, engineering, equipment set, construction, testing and initial start-up are some of the world's most complex, sophisticated, efficient and safe operations. The same is true for the plants' O&M procedures, which are a model of precision and accuracy that simply cannot even be achieved in most other industrial operations.

The Construction Process

On top of the regular permits and authorizations needed for the construction and operation of coal, oil and gas power plants, nuclear power plants require additional analyses, permits, certifications, and licensing. These are needed to comply with safety rules and regulations specific to the nuclear industry, as required by local, state and federal authorities. It is a complex and expensive process.

A nuclear power plant cradle-to-grave process includes:

- Nuclear plant site search
- Proposed area survey
- Environmental studies
- Local rights and agreements
- Federal and state permits and legal work
- Plant site preparation
- Plant construction
- Initial tests, certification, and ramp-up
- Daily plant O&M operations
- Fresh and spent fuel transport and storage
- EOL decommissioning and area reconstruction

The difficulties in every step of the way are enormous, which is the reason there have not been any new nuclear plants built in the US since the mid 1970s. Problems start with locating an area to construct a nuclear plant. Locals usually evoke their NIMBY rights. Not in my backyard demonstrations of local activists and neighbors accompany any plans for nuclear plant construction. We have seen these around the country since the beginning of nuclear power generation, and the movement is not going away.

Obtaining the needed local, state and federal permits, certifications and authorizations is another enormous task. Due to changes in regulations and technologies, it is almost impossible to complete the permitting

process. Many nuclear plant plans are on hold for this reason alone.

Once a site is chosen, and the opposition is kept at a safe distance, the area survey and analysis can start. These consist of the usual geological analysis and historical data collection to determine if the site can support large structures, deep excavations, roads and infrastructure for construction activities.

Several stages of environmental tests and studies are conducted, to determine the present environmental conditions, and as needed for the required reports. A long chain of events in the never-ending permitting and licensing processes follow.

Once the necessary permits and licenses have been issued, plant construction proceeds in a fashion similar to that of coal, oil, and gas-fired power plants.

Since no new plants have been built in the U.S. since 1974, we are unclear how the construction of new plants will be planned and executed. Most of them are now stuck in the permitting and licensing stages, so we must wait and see how the situation develops.

NUCLEAR PLANT OPERATION

A nuclear power plant is a 24/7, 365 days a year operation. It never sleeps, and is only shut down from time to time for refueling, and for major scheduled maintenance. Sometimes it is shut down in emergencies to prevent accidents, which in many cases is a complex undertaking that requires skilled operators and some luck.

In all cases, a nuclear power plant is fully staffed by O&M personnel around the clock, regardless of the condition or stage it is in.

Each unit has a shift supervisor, several control room operators, and additional auxiliary operators whose job is to operate the equipment. Multi-unit power plants do have a general shift manager who is responsible for the entire site.

During normal operation, the operators perform many tasks, such as supporting O&M activities, testing safety and emergency equipment, performing minor maintenance, and processing radioactive liquids and gases.

During refueling, which is conducted at least every 2 years, O&M personnel handle the old fuel removal, and transfer new fuel into the reactor, following carefully designed and strictly supervised fuel replacement and safety procedures.

The shift manager and supervisors are highly

trained and licensed by the national regulatory agency. Mid- and high-level managers and supervisors are licensed as senior reactor operator, for which they have undergone special training and tests, to show superb accident assessment, supervisory, and team management abilities. They spend a lot of time working in plant simulators, where real-life situations can be reproduced, followed by written and oral tests. In addition, supervisory personnel usually have many years of hands-on experience as plant operators or engineers, prior to assuming the higher responsibility.

Control room operators are licensed as reactor operators by NRC, and are in charge of and control different areas of the plant from the control room. For example, while one operator watches and controls the operating parameters of the turbine, generator, circulating water and related systems, another is in charge of the reactor, reactor cooling, and emergency systems.

Figure 3-8. Nuclear power plant control room

The different plant systems are usually controlled from different areas of the control board in the room, but the operators communicate with each other and make coordinated decisions, with plant efficiency and safety as a priority.

Operators also are trained on simulators where they learn their basic duties in addition to practicing activities that they would be rarely required to perform. Plant startups, shutdowns, and emergencies are included in simulator training, and are needed to provide operators with the maximum understanding and comfort level of managing the plant under all possible situations.

In addition, plant personnel undergoe constant on-the-job training and re-qualification, via plant simulator training and testing, to maintain their skills and demonstrate competence.

NOTE: The plant simulator is a functional (but not operational) copy of the control room, with an exact copy of all gauges, alarms, controls, etc. that function for the real plant. It is driven by computers and can be programmed to simulate any possible situation—from a refueling to a critical accident. It is an integral part of plant operation and, in addition to operator training, it allows process improvements and provides solutions for unusual situations, ultimately optimizing the plant's efficiency and safety.

Spent Nuclear Fuel

Three percent of spent-fuels mass consists of fission products of ^{235}U and ^{239}Pu, which comprise the radioactive waste. These can be processed and separated further for various industrial and medical uses. Fission products include the second transition metals row, Zr, Mo, Tc, Ru, Rh, Pd, Ag, and the next in the periodic table, I, Xe, Cs, Ba, La, Ce, and Nd.

Many fission waste products are either non-radioactive or only short-lived radioisotopes, while a considerable number of these are medium- to long-lived radioisotopes such as ^{90}Sr, ^{137}Cs, ^{99}Tc and ^{129}I.

Fission waste products can modify the thermal properties of the uranium dioxide, where the lanthanide oxides tend to lower the thermal conductivity of the fuel, while the metallic nanoparticles slightly increase its thermal conductivity.

Different types of nuclear fuels produce different kinds of spent nuclear fuel (nuclear waste). Spent low-enriched uranium nuclear fuel, for example, is a type of a nanomaterial. In the uranium oxide spent fuel, intense temperature gradients cause fission products to migrate. The zirconium tends to move to the center of the fuel pellet where the temperature is highest, while the lower-boiling fission products move to the edge of the pellet. The pellet is likely to contain a lot of small bubble-like pores which form during the fission cycle. Fission xenon migrates to these voids, and some of it decays to form cesium, C-137 (^{137}Cs), so many of the bubbles contain a large concentration of ^{137}Cs.

In MOX, the xenon tends to diffuse out of the plutonium-rich areas of the fuel, and it is then trapped in the surrounding uranium dioxide, while the neodymium is not very mobile. Metallic particles of an alloy of Mo-Tc-Ru-Pd also tend to form in the fuel, while other solids form at the boundary between the uranium dioxide grains. The majority of fission products remain in the uranium dioxide as solid solutions.

Successful efforts have been led to segregate the rare isotopes in fission waste including the "fission platinoids," Ru, Rh, Pd, and Ag, as a way of offsetting the cost of reprocessing. Although this is possible, it is no economical enough, so it is not done commercially.

In all cases, spent nuclear fuel has only two possible paths: stored as a waste or ship for reprocessing. Reprocessing is uneconomical in most cases, but some fuels are showing promise, so efforts in recycling, reprocessing, and reusing spent nuclear fuels will continue and intensify.

Most spent nuclear fuels, however, are stored in large onsite water pools at the nuclear plant, where they are left to cool down for a long time. Eventually the cooled fuel rods and bundles are transferred into special canisters and shipped to an offsite storage facility.

Decommissioning of Nuclear Plants

Decommissioning costs of nuclear plants are very high, and significantly different than those of other power plants. This is due to the complexity of the technology, and also because of the added serious danger of nuclear radiation at every step of the way. This means that the demolition crew must be well trained in and thoroughly familiar with radioactive components and materials. Every action could result in the unexpected release of radiation, which could be damaging and even fatal.

Decommissioning involves a number of administrative and technical actions, including inspection, clean-up of radioactivity, demolition of the plant, and removal and disposal of components. There are contaminated materials, parts and components that must be handled with utmost care.

Engineering services and labor used in decommissioning of nuclear plants can be described by specialized services, starting with concrete and metal cutting and removal, including:

- Man access cuts
- Equipment hatch enlargement
- Containment wall penetrations
- Dog house cutting for SGRPs
- Elevated platform removals
- Fuel pool and canal segmentation
- Fuel transfer canal segmentation

There are a number of tasks performed by experienced professionals during decommissioning of a nuclear power reactor, such as:

- CRDM cutting
- Reactor nozzle cutting
- Heat exchanger cutting
- Ion guide tube removals
- Monitoring line cutting
- Steel plate stabilizer cutting
- Carbon containment liner cutting

Hands-on demolition services experience is needed here, but it must be supplemented by a thorough understanding of nuclear plant components and their function. Only a well-trained, committed workforce attuned to personal radiation and toxic materials exposure and waste minimization awareness could be allowed in such an undertaking. Anything less might result in environmental and personal damage and even death.

Decommissioning costs represent 5-10 percent of the initial capital cost of a nuclear power plant, but when discounted, they contribute only a few percent to the investment cost and even less to the generation cost. For example, in the US, decommissioning costs average 0.1-0.2 cent/kWh, which is about 5 percent of the cost of the electricity produced.

Decommissioning and land remediation is a complex and expensive undertaking. The dismantling could cost from $5 million to $10 million. Handling and removal of the fuel could cost another $5-10 million. The entire decommissioning could be in the range of $25 million to $1 billion. In some cases there is an additional charge for upkeep of the area, which could be up to $10 million annually.

One can only hope that all these costs were foreseen and estimated in the overall operating budget of the plant.

Once a nuclear facility is decommissioned properly, there is no longer danger of radioactivity. After official inspection and certification, the area is released from regulatory control, and the owner of the plant is no longer responsible for the nuclear safety of the area.

Nuclear Renaissance

A pending nuclear renaissance—still using fission reactors—has been in the news lately, describing ways for a possible return to the nuclear power industry's glory days. Global economics and rising fossil fuel prices would be the drivers, while rising concerns about greenhouse gas emission limits and global warming would provide the support for the nuclear progress.

Unfortunately, there are a number of unresolved issues on the way to a full nuclear renaissance. Some issues slowing down the progress are:

1. Serious delays in permitting and siting of new power plants,
2. Unfavorable economics and safety record as com-

pared to other sources of energy,

3.   Industrial bottlenecks and personnel shortages in the nuclear sector, and

4.   Uncertainty about what to do with nuclear waste and spent nuclear fuel,

5.   The fear of additional nuclear accidents, such as Chernobyl,

6.   Lingering national security issues related to nuclear plants, fuels, and weapons,

7.   The increasing threat of nuclear terrorism, and

8.   The increasing threat of nuclear weapons proliferation.

Memories of the nuclear accidents at Fukushima I Nuclear Power Plant, Chernobyl, Three Mile Island and other nuclear facilities linger in people's minds and restrict the introduction of new nuclear programs around the world. These recent developments raise serious questions about the future of nuclear power, and the nuclear renaissance is on hold for now, with a nuclear reversal underway.

Germany led the nuclear reversal trend when, following the 2012 Fukushima nuclear disaster, they decided to shut down all nuclear power plants by 2020, while reviewing the safety of the nuclear energy in general. Several countries followed their example to a certain degree. Several new nuclear reactors planned for construction in European countries (which were headed toward nuclear renaissance) have been delayed or cancelled.

There are estimates that 30 nuclear plants may be closed worldwide in the near future. Those located in seismic zones or close to national boundaries are the most likely to shut down first. Switzerland, Israel, Malaysia, Thailand, United Kingdom, Italy and the Philippines are all reviewing the safety of nuclear power programs as well. At the same time Australia, Austria, Denmark, Greece, Ireland, Latvia, Lichtenstein, Luxembourg, Portugal, Israel, Malaysia, New Zealand, and Norway remain unshakably opposed to nuclear power.

A hundred older reactors will need to be decommissioned by 2025, and many nuclear power programs are running over-budget and out of time. Indonesia and Vietnam are the exception and are still planning to build nuclear power plants in the near future.

China has 27 new nuclear reactors under construction. A number of new nuclear power plants are being built in South Korea, India, and Russia as well. Still, the International Energy Agency reduced its estimate of additional nuclear generating capacity built by 2035 by more than 50 percent.

Even a pro-nuclear country like France is planning to close at least two reactors to demonstrate political action and restore the public acceptability of nuclear power. As a confirmation of the upcoming debacle, Siemens (one of the giants in the industry) decided to withdraw entirely from the nuclear industry.

In the U.S., Exelon Corporation, the nation's largest nuclear operator, threw in the towel on a planned twin-reactor project in Victoria County, TX, in the face of fierce opposition from people who claim that there is not enough water in the area and that the ground was subject to subsidence that could wreck a cooling pond. The Nuclear Regulatory Commission might have approved the site over these objections, but Exelon admitted that the economics were not favorable, so it would be better to give up on the project.

At the same time, a panel of administrative law judges ruled that Électricité de France (EDF) could not proceed with a plant in Maryland, Calvert Cliffs. That plant was originally a joint venture between Constellation Energy, which owned the adjacent Calvert Cliffs 1 & 2, and the French EDF. Two years ago the Unistar consortium fell apart when it could not obtain a loan guarantee from the Department of Energy on terms acceptable to Constellation, which was later on bought by Exelon. Two new nuclear plants, each with two reactors, are underway, one in Georgia and one in South Carolina, but permitting and financial issues make us believe that no groundbreaking seem likely anytime soon.

A Show-stopper

There are still problems with units 2 and 3 of San Onofre nuclear power plant in Southern California which were shut down in January 2012 after it was discovered that a generator might have been tampered with. Engine coolant was also found seeping in the oil system of the backup diesel generator.

Technicians later found excessive wear on hundreds of tubes in units 2 and 3, which had been taken offline earlier for maintenance. The problems center on damage to alloy tubing in four steam generators that were installed during a $670 million overhaul in 2009 and 2010. These and other abnormalities forced the plant shutdown.

Although these issues pose no direct safety risk, the bad news of abnormalities at the nuclear plant, and record-keeping errors stretching back to 1985, are another blow to San Onofre's reputation, which will cost over $300 million in additional repairs and other costs.

Figure 3-9. San Onofre nuclear plant, San Clemente, CA.

A year and a half later, the plant was still shut down due to safety issues. California Edison proposed in the summer of 2013 to run the plant at reduced power to avoid the safety issues. This haphazard solution for nuclear power plant operation is a worrisome development and an indication that U.S. utilities are getting careless about the safety of nuclear power. All California needs right now is a nuclear disaster such as Chernobyl at its San Diego coast line.

Gregory Jaczko, ex-chair of the U.S. Nuclear Regulatory Commission expressed doubts about Edison's proposal to restart the San Onofre nuclear plant at 70 percent power. "When you're operating at a reduced power level, it indicates a lack of confidence," said Jaczko. "It raises a lot of questions." Yes, there are lots of questions.

The abnormalities at nuclear plants lately cast the shadow of a doubt on the future of all global nuclear energy too, since it is apparent that even the most technologically advanced countries (Japan and the U.S.) cannot ensure the safety of their nuclear power generators. The second thoughts about using nuclear power on a large scale are overwhelming, and will surely have long-lasting consequences, and might even signal a major shift away from nuclear power for the most part—similar to the decision of the German government to shut down all nuclear plants by 2020. If that happens, the other energy sources and technologies like renewables, gas and coal will benefit most. Such a drastic development, however, will eventually put additional upward pressure on the price of energy.

As always, nations with limited local energy resources will suffer most. Deprived of nuclear power, the developing economies will have a hard time maintaining the increasing demand for electricity to keep up with their economic growth.

THE ISSUES

No new nuclear plants have been built in the US since the 1980s. Ground hasn't been broken for a new nuclear power plant in the U.S. for more than 30 years, although more than 20 companies have announced plans to build new nuclear plants, both regulated and unregulated. But planning is one thing...so the ultimate question is how many will actually be built?

The engineering design plans are less than 50% complete for most U.S. conforming designs, with some entrants less than 20% complete. Millions of engineering man-hours are required before cost estimates become reliable enough to allow original equipment manufacturer (OEM) and engineering, procurement and construction (EPC) contract-cost negotiations to fully define cost and performance risk parameters across all parties.

While simplified nuclear steam supply system (NSSS) designs and innovations in modular construction suggest the potential to build plants more economically, a confluence of largely uncontrollable forces are pushing preliminary factor cost estimates upward. These include commodity price escalation, engineering, and craft labor shortages and manufacturing and shipping constraints.

Combined with uncertainties about executing engineering and construction, overnight cost estimates (that exclude the costs of escalation and financing) for proposed plants are increasing, and the range of estimates is wide—between $3,000 a kilowatt and $5,500/kW, depending on a number of factors, including the date of the estimate. Cost variability, and consequently financing uncertainty, threatens the overall economic attractiveness of nuclear development.

Technological Problems

Add to the complexity and money waste, most of the new designs being proposed for nuclear power plants lack proven track records of efficient and safe operation, since there is limited experience with some of the new designs.

For example, the Advanced Boiling Water Reactor (ABWR) design had some problems in the past, so a number of new design variants have been considered as improvements. The power outputs of the new designs vary from 600 to 1800 MWe, with the most developed design being the ABWR-II, which started as an enlarged 1718 MWe ABWR. It was intended to make nuclear power generation more competitive in the late 2010s, but unfortunately, none of these designs has been properly lab and long-term field tested. So the question of their usability, efficiency and safety still remains to be answered.

Another example: the EPR (European Pressurized Reactor, or Evolutionary Power Reactor, now simply named EPR) design, which was supposed to be completed and ready for construction in the early 2000s, remains unfinished. The design has numerous flaws.

The EPR is the first reactor design proposed to be controlled by fully computerized systems both during normal operation and during accidents. The original design for the computer systems has been found to violate just about every basic principle of nuclear safety, and many regulators are requiring an analogue back-up system. Using several complex software systems to control a nuclear power plant introduces an enormous amount of potential errors and unpredictable interactions.

No approved design of the control systems exists as yet, even though lots of work has been done on this system for years. In addition, some EPR components are proposed to use off-the-shelf computer systems that do not comply with nuclear safety standards. The EPR design is not equipped to deal with a sustained blackout of the power supply to the reactor's emergency systems, a crucial design defect that caused the Fukushima nuclear disasters in March 2011. The EPR reactor's emergency diesel generators are insufficient to power many crucial subsystems needed to cool down the reactor. If the diesel generators malfunction, the reactor is designed to prevent a meltdown of the reactor and the nuclear waste ponds for only 24 hours before risking meltdown.

In Fukushima, the blackout lasted 11 days. Once cooling is lost, an accident can proceed fast: in the Fukushima reactors, fuel was completely molten 11 hours after the meltdown started.

So, lots of work is still needed.

Global Competition

Increased estimated costs for today's new generation of nuclear plants are due in large part to fierce worldwide competition for the resources and manufacturing capacity needed in the design and construction of new power plants. This competition has led to double-digit annual increases in the costs of key power plant commodities such as steel, copper and concrete.

Worldwide demand is also straining the limited capacity of EPC (Engineering, Procurement, and Construction) firms and equipment manufacturers. The limited number of manufacturers and suppliers could cause bottlenecks in construction if, as expected, there are multiple orders for new power plants in the U.S. and abroad.

For example, there are only two companies that have the heavy forging capacity to create the largest equipment/components in new nuclear plants—Japan Steel Works and Creusot Forge in France. The demand for heavy forgings will be significant because the nuclear industry will be waiting in line for the material, alongside the petrochemical industry and new refineries.

Twenty years ago there were about 400 suppliers of nuclear plant components and 900 so-called nuclear stamp, or N-stamp, certifications from the American Society of Mechanical Engineers. Today there are fewer than 80 suppliers in the U.S. and fewer than 200 N-stamp certifications.

It appears that there will be a great reliance on overseas companies to manufacture plant systems and components, so the NRC would need to inspect the quality of the manufacturing programs in foreign firms to ensure that substandard materials or equipment don't end up installed in plants. This would require more time to inspect foreign-made components than it would to check quality control of U.S.-manufactured components. The heavy reliance on overseas suppliers will also lead to cost increases due to the continuing weakness of the U.S. dollar relative to other currencies.

Standardization would be very helpful in this area, for it will force all global manufacturers and providers of commodities and services to operate in a uniform and reliable manner. This, however, is far in the future, so for now we must do things the old and proven ways.

There are many difficulties in front of the U.S. nuclear industry, in addition to the technical issues. Political uncertainty, regulatory changes, environmental pressure, and other such factors are overwhelming the industry, and it needs to come up with proper response, if it is to progress in the 21st century.

Nuclear Plants Standardization

Presently, nuclear plants construction and operation is much like a well hidden black box. There are good reasons for this, but these reasons combined are hindering the progress of the nuclear industry.

Because of the black-box mentality, we now have a multiplicity of specialized and customized reactor designs, governed by different regulatory approaches and licensing requirements. As in many other cases, this lack of uniformity in equipment and procedures has the effect of increasing cost and uncertainty of operations, and is far from being optimally conducive to nuclear plant efficiency and safety.

Also affected are investment and political decisions, which depend on the level of risk manageability. Future standardization, resulting in transparent and predictable licensing processes and oversight, would contribute significantly to a stable investment framework and contribute to a rapid, efficient and orderly expansion of nuclear power worldwide.

The concept of standardization need not cover every single detail in a nuclear plants' operation. To begin with, all that is needed is sufficient standardization to:

1. Enable the owner to prepare standardized specifications for the procurement of new plant equipment, and

2. Establish standardized regulations in determining the adequacy of a nuclear facility's safety.

This would limit the degree of individual nuclear power plant adaptation, but would allow enough flexibility to meet site-specific conditions and other local factors.

In more detail, nuclear plant standardization would mean taking the nuclear power plant's equipment and procedures out of the black box and making them uniform.

This effort would eventually lead to:

*   Developing much higher levels of detail for standard reactor designs, where special reactor designs will be the exception rather than the rule, and will need special, and different requirements;

*   Harmonizing the nuclear industry's standards and requirements, focusing on convergence of codes and standards applicable to key components affecting efficiency and safety;

*   Clarifying and expanding the existing feedback-sharing among utilities and the participating parties, during power plant construction and operation;

*   Enhancing the cooperation between vendor and utilities by establishing efficient mechanisms for long-term design knowledge management, such as training materials, operator certification, and plant operation procedures;

*   Information and expertise sharing among governments, vendors and regulators, which will eventually lead to wide adaptation of the standards.

There are presently efforts to identify the differences and develop international codes and standards in different areas, such as mechanical codes and instrumentation and control (I&C). Organizations like ASME and AFCEN, and IEEE and IEC are fully involved in this effort, and some general utility requirements for new reactor designs have been developed already by EPRI-URD in the US and EUR in Europe.

In addition, a number of multinational regulatory initiatives have been created, such as the Multinational Design Evaluation Program (MDEP) with its main objective as establishing convergent reference regulatory practices.

Regional initiatives have also been taken by regulators and utilities, such as the Western European Regulators' Association (WENRA) and the European Nuclear Installations Safety Standards (ENISS) initiative in Europe). WENRA has established common reference levels for reactor safety to be implemented in member countries, which will lead to further harmonization.

The International Atomic Energy Agency (IAEA's) Integrated Regulatory Review Service (IRRS) provides reviews of national regulatory systems to identify and spread best practices in licensing and oversight. It also provides a reference point for states seeking to establish a nuclear infrastructure. IAEA Safety Standards specify safety requirements and guides representing best/good practices, which are increasingly used as a reference for review of national safety standards and as a benchmark for harmonization in all countries utilizing nuclear energy for peaceful purposes.

There is much more work to be done in the standardization area, though, and the steps taken thus far are the baby steps that are needed to develop a strong and safe international nuclear power generating industry. Nuclear power is a viable, efficient and clean energy source, which is badly needed to support our life style and industrial progress, so we need to support and expand these efforts.

Nuclear Waste Transport

Waste nuclear fuel and its transport, storage, and disposal in particular have been of most concern to all involved—from the power plant owners to the investors and the customers. Because of that, special attention is paid to the technology and procedures used in this process.

Low-level Radiation Fuels

Low-level and intermediate-level wastes (LLW and ILW respectively) are generated throughout the nuclear fuel cycle and from the production of radioisotopes used in medicine, industry and other areas. The transport of these wastes is commonplace, and they are safely transported to waste treatment facilities and storage sites.

Low-level radioactive wastes are a variety of materials that emit low levels of radiation, slightly above normal background levels. They often consist of solid materials, such as clothing, tools, or contaminated soil. Low-level waste is transported from its origin to waste treatment sites, or to an intermediate or final storage facility.

A variety of radio-nuclides give low-level waste its radioactive character. However, the radiation levels from these materials are very low and the packaging used for the transport of low-level waste does not require special shielding.

Low-level wastes are transported in drums, often after being compacted to reduce their total volume. The drums commonly used contain up to 200 liters of material. Typically, 36 standard, 200-liter drums go into a 6-meter transport container. Low-level wastes are moved by road, rail, and internationally by sea. However, most low-level waste is only transported within the country where it is produced.

The composition of intermediate-level wastes is broad, but they require shielding. Much ILW comes from nuclear power plants and reprocessing facilities. Intermediate-level wastes are taken from their source to an interim storage site, a final storage site (as in Sweden), or a waste treatment facility. They are transported by road, rail and sea.

The radioactivity level of intermediate-level waste is higher than low-level wastes. The classification of radioactive wastes is decided for disposal purposes, not on transport grounds. The transport of intermediate-level wastes take into account any specific properties of the material, and requires shielding.

In the US there had been 9,000 road shipments of defense-related trans-uranic wastes for permanent disposal in the deep geological repository near Carlsbad, NM, by October 2010, without any major accident or any release of radioactivity. Almost half the shipments were from the Idaho National Laboratory. The repository, known as the Waste Isolation Pilot Plant (WIPP), is about 700 meters deep in a Permian salt formation.

High-level Radiation Fuels

Used fuel unloaded from a nuclear power reactor contains 96% uranium, 1% plutonium, and 3% fission products (from the nuclear reaction), and trans-uranics. It emits high levels of both radiation and heat, so it is stored in water pools adjacent to the reactor to allow the

initial heat and radiation levels to decrease. Typically, used fuel is stored on-site for at least five months before it can be transported, although it may be stored there long-term.

From the reactor site, used fuel is transported by road, rail or sea to either an interim storage site or a reprocessing plant where it will be reprocessed.

Used fuel assemblies are shipped in Type B casks which are shielded with steel, or a combination of steel and lead, and can weigh up to 110 tons when empty. A typical transport cask holds up to 6 tons of used fuel.

Since 1971 there have been some 7,000 shipments of used fuel (over 80,000 tons) over millions of miles with no property damage or personal injury, no breach of containment, and very low dose rate to the personnel involved (e.g. 0.33 mSv/yr per operator at La Hague). This includes 40,000 tons of used fuel shipped to Areva's La Hague reprocessing plant, at least 30,000 tons of mostly UK used fuel shipped to UK's Sellafield reprocessing plant, 7,140 t used fuel in 160 shipments from Japan to Europe by sea (see below) and 4,500 tons of used fuel shipped around the Swedish coast.

Some 300 sea voyages have been made carrying used nuclear fuel or separated high-level waste over a distance of more than 6 million miles. The major company involved has transported over 4,000 100-ton casks each carrying 8,000 tons of used fuel or separated high-level wastes. A quarter of these have been through the Panama Canal.

In Sweden, more than 80 large transport casks are shipped annually to a central interim waste storage facility called CLAB. Each 80 ton cask has steel walls 30 cm thick and holds 17 BWR or 7 PWR fuel assemblies. The used fuel is shipped to CLAB after it has been stored for about a year at the reactor, during which time heat and radioactivity diminish considerably. Some 4,500 tons of used fuel had been shipped around the coast to CLAB by the end of 2007.

Shipments of used fuel from Japan to Europe for reprocessing used 94-tonne Type B casks, each holding a number of fuel assemblies (e.g. 12 PWR assemblies, total 6 tons, with each cask 6.1 meters long, 2.5 meters diameter, and with 25 cm thick forged steel walls). More than 160 of these shipments took place from 1969 to the 1990s, involving more than 4,000 casks, and moving several thousand tons of highly radioactive used fuel—4,200 tons to the UK and 2,940 tons to France. Within Europe, used fuel in casks has often been carried on normal ferries e.g. across the English Channel.

Following reprocessing, plutonium is transported as an oxide powder since this is its most stable form. Plutonium oxide is transported in several different types of sealed packages, and each can contain several kilograms of material.

Risk of exposure is reduced by the design of the package, limiting the amount within and the number of packages carried on a transport vessel. Special physical protection measures apply to plutonium consignments too.

A typical transport consists of one truck carrying one protected shipping container. The container holds a number of packages with a total weight varying from 80 to 200 kg of plutonium oxide. A sea shipment may consist of several containers, each of them holding between 80 to 200 kg of plutonium in sealed packages.

Nuclear Waste Recycling

One of most plausible solutions to reducing nuclear waste is recycling it. To this purpose, in 2000 the US and Russia signed a bilateral agreement, committing to eliminate 34 metric tons of surplus military plutonium produced during the Cold War by recycling it as fuel for civil nuclear applications. In 2008, the Department of Energy made an agreement with a joint venture created by the AREVA and SHAW groups for the construction of a MOX fuel production plant.

The effort consists of two parts:

1. Construction and operation of a pit disassembly and conversion facility (PDCF), where nuclear warheads are dismantled and where the recovered metal is converted into plutonium oxide, and

2. Construction and operation of a fuel fabrication plant, mixed-oxide (MOX) fuel fabrication facility (MFFF), where plutonium oxide is mixed with uranium oxide to make MOX assemblies.

The 600,000 ft^2 MFFF plant is currently under construction at the Savannah River Site near Aiken, SC, and is on track to be completed by its target date of 2016. Its purpose is to reduce the surplus weapons grade plutonium and provide fuel for commercial plants. If successful, the MOX process might be the ultimate answer both politically and environmentally for a safer nuclear power industry.

It is estimated that when the MFFF operation is complete, enough electricity could be generated to power all households in South Carolina for up to 20 years. The project is overseen by the National Nuclear Security Administration (NNSA), via third-party contractors.

In addition, there will be a waste solidification building, and a pit disassembly and conversion unit that are pivotal in the attempt to shrink the waste plutonium mountain.

At the MFFF facility, surplus plutonium will be processed and blended with depleted uranium oxide to make mixed oxide fuel that will be used as new fuel for nuclear plants.

The waste solidification building and the pit disassembly and conversion unit are vital cogs in the wheel of using the plutonium as a resource. The waste unit is forecast to treat 150,000 gallons of transuranic waste, and approximately 600,000 gallons of low-level radioactive waste from the MFFF and pit disassembly buildings.

NOTE: As an additional benefit to national and international security, once the MOX fuel has been irradiated by the commercial reactors, the plutonium can no longer be used for nuclear weapons activity. Most importantly, MOX facilities would provide environmental safety for future generations by converting potentially dangerous radioactive materials into safe commercial nuclear fuel.

Nuclear Waste Storage

Ideally, a nuclear power plant runs at the maximum allowed power level from one refueling to the next. It must be shut down for several hours, or days, during each refueling, and then restarted and brought up to the maximum power output.

Used nuclear fuel, which is removed from the reactor after a year or two of service, is a solid material that must be stored safely, usually at nuclear plant sites. This temporary storage is only one component of an integrated *used fuel management system* in use at all nuclear plants, addressing all facets of storing, recycling and disposal.

The *integrated used fuel management approach* mandates that used nuclear fuel will remain safely stored at nuclear power plants for the near term, with safety as the key word. Hopefully, the government will find a way to recycle it eventually, and place the unusable end product in a deep, long-term repository.

Low-level wastes are byproduct remaining from uses of a wide range of radioactive materials produced during electricity generation, medical diagnosis and treatment, and various other medical processes. These could be liquids or solids, and are treated in a number of ways prior to disposal as hazardous waste, burning, or storage in temporary containers.

Recycling of waste nuclear fuels is a program of the federal government, which includes plans to develop

Figure 3-10. Airtight containers for nuclear waste storage

advanced recycling technologies to take full advantage of the unused energy in used fuel, and to also reduce the amount and toxicity level of byproducts requiring disposal.

Transportation of waste nuclear fuel is the responsibility of the U.S. Department of Energy, which will transport used nuclear fuel to the repository by rail and road, inside massive, sealed containers that have undergone safety and durability testing.

Repository for long-term storage is under review, and under any used fuel management scenario, disposal of high-level radioactive byproducts in a permanent geologic repository is necessary.

NOTE: The criticality of nuclear waste storage is reflected in the roughly 53 million gallons of nuclear waste stored in 177 large underground tanks at DOE's Hanford Nuclear Reservation in Washington State. Of these, 149 are more than 40 years beyond their expected 25-year design life. One-third of them are known or suspected to be leaking, releasing roughly 1 million gallons of waste to Hanford's surrounding soils.

Hanford lacks the storage capacity to retrieve the waste from these tanks until the waste treatment and disposal process is underway. Washington's $12.3 billion Waste Treatment Plant (WTP) continues to be designed and constructed to meet standards specific to the Yucca Mountain facility. Design and engineering for the WTP is 78% complete and construction is 48% complete.

In 2002, Congress designated Yucca Mountain as the nation's sole current repository site for deep geologic disposal of high-level radioactive waste and spent nuclear fuel. At that time, the Secretary of Energy concluded that, "The amount and quality of research the DOE has invested…done by top-flight people…is nothing short of staggering…I am convinced that the product of over 20 years, millions of hours, and four billion dollars of this research provides a sound scientific basis for concluding the site can perform safely."

Congress then directed DOE to file a license application for the Yucca Mountain site with the Nuclear Regulatory Commission (NRC) and thereby commence a formal evaluation and licensing process overseen by the NRC.

But…in January 2010, President Obama, Secretary Chu, and DOE determined that they would withdraw with prejudice the application submitted by DOE to the NRC for a license to construct a permanent repository at Yucca Mountain, NV, for high-level nuclear waste and spent nuclear fuel.

Also that month, President Obama, Secretary Chu, and DOE chose to unilaterally and irrevocably terminate the Yucca Mountain repository process mandated by the Nuclear Waste Policy Act, 42 U.S.C. §§ 10101-10270. Several law suites were filed as a result, but these will take years to resolve, during which time the US has no place to store its large pile of nuclear waste produced during power generation and nuclear weapons production.

In Finland, a radical solution is planned to build an enormous bunker for permanent storage of the dangerous radioactive waste. It consists of burying the stuff deep underground, sealing the depository and throwing the key away. Literally. The intent is to keep everyone—including future civilizations—away by hiding the nuclear waste somewhere so unremarkable and unpleasant that nobody would ever think to go there, let alone dig into it.

On Olkiluoto Island, just off Finland's southwest coast, the underground facility known as Onkalo will hold all of the country's 5,500 tons of nuclear waste—all that is expected to be produced by the end of the century. It is designed to keep that waste secure for at least 100,000 years, taking measures and counting on making humans forget that Onkalo was ever there.

Onkalo is intended to permanently and safely store high-level waste (HLW) which consists of spent nuclear fuel and some equally dangerous decay products. This residue emits dangerous types and levels of radiation for tens of thousands of years. Over 300,000 tons of this stuff now exist around the world and about 12,000 more tons are produced annually. It is also expected that numbers will increase significantly in the years to come.

Onkalo boasts a maze of deep underground bunkers carved from impermeable rock, in geologically stable zones, where the waste can be redundantly sealed and then permanently buried.

At a $3 billion price tag thus far, Onkalo will start accepting nuclear waste in 2020, while construction of new tunnels will continue as needed until the facility is shut down and sealed forever.

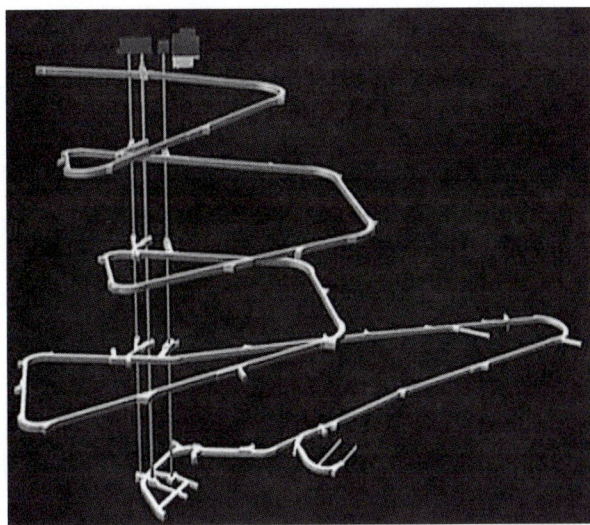

Figure 3-11. Onkalo' maze of underground tunnels

Will this grandiose plan work? Who knows? It is too big, expensive, complex, and ambitious to be properly assessed with the available information, so we just have to wait and see.

Abandoned Uranium Mines

Finally, we need to mention this important issue, which has caused problems for the locals for decades. The uranium mining industry began in the 1940s primarily to produce uranium for weapons and later for nuclear fuel. Although there are about 4,000 mines with documented production, a database compiled by EPA, with information provided by other federal, state, and tribal agencies, includes 15,000 mine locations with uranium-related activities in 14 western states. Most of those locations are found in Colorado, Utah, New Mexico, Arizona, and Wyoming, with about 75% of those on federal and tribal lands.

The majority of these sites were conventional (open pit and underground) mines. The mining of uranium ores by both underground and surface methods produces large amounts of bulk waste material, including bore hole drill cuttings, excavated top soil, barren overburden rock, weakly uranium-enriched waste rock, and subgrade ores (or protore).

At some abandoned mine sites, ore enriched with uranium was left on-site when prices fell, while transfer stations at some distance from remote mines may contain residual radioactive soil and rock without any visible facilities to mark their location.

While most pose minimal radiation risk to the public, since exposure is most likely to be short and intermittent (e.g., visitation, recreation), they may pose other physical safety risks.

No single national AML program exists; rather, several authorities and multiple departments and agencies address AML sites as part of broader programs. Similarly, funding for remediation projects is spread among separate appropriations for participating departments and agencies. Federal and state agencies are doing more than ever before to display their spatial data and exchange information. Data from the former U.S. Bureau of Mines and the U.S. Geological Survey provide the foundation of most mine inventories.

There is a "polluter pays" principle that requires the federal government, where possible, to compel responsible parties to clean up their sites or help cover the costs. Priorities focus on water quality and sites involving release or potential release of hazardous substances. The enforcement of this policy is partial, and little information exists on its compliance by the coal industry, as evidenced by the large number of abandoned mines. No one is held responsible for the environmental damage, human health issues, and other consequences, resulting from abandoned mines.

Basically, the uranium mining industry leaves its dangerous mark everywhere, even after operations have ceased; abandoned underground and surface mines are the longest lasting and least controlled damage to the environment and those in it.

Although there are signs of revival of the movement to secure abandoned mines, we do not see it reviving anytime soon. So it will fall to future generations to clean up our mess—abandoned uranium mines included.

NUCLEAR POWER USE

The benefits of using nuclear power are obvious, so a lot of it is produced and routed into the national power grid and distributed to residences and commercial applications on 24/7 basis.

Nuclear power in the United States is generated by 104 commercial reactors, of which 69 are pressurized water reactors (PWR) and 35 are boiling water reactors (BWR). These operate at 65 nuclear power plants spread strategically around the country and produce a total of over 800 TWh of electricity. This represents about 20% of the total electrical generation, making the U.S. the world's largest supplier of commercial nuclear power.

Nuclear power provides about 5.7% of the world's energy and 13% of the world's electricity generated by 437 operational nuclear power reactors in 31 countries.

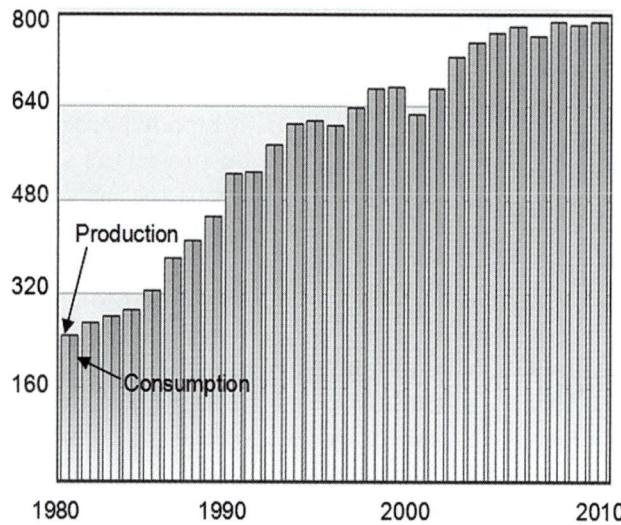

Figure 3-12. U.S. nuclear power production and use (in billion kWh)

There are also approximately 140 naval vessels using nuclear propulsion in operation, powered by 180 reactors.

In 2012 there were 68 nuclear power reactors under construction in 15 countries around the world, 28 of which are in China. The newest nuclear power reactor was connected to the electrical grid in February 2013 in Hongyanhe Nuclear Power Plant, China.

In the US, two new Generation III reactors are under construction at Vogtle—the first after a 34-year period of stagnation in the US nuclear power industry. One big problem we face today is that most nuclear plants are old. The first reactors were built in the 1960s and 1970s, but after the Three Mile Island accident in 1979, and following years of changing economics, many nuclear projects were discontinued and plans for others were canceled. There has been no new nuclear plant built in the United States since 1974, although a number of reactors started before 1974 have been completed since then.

Because of that, the licenses of almost half the present 104 power reactors in the US have expired, and they have been given extensions to 60 years, instead of the original 30 years useful operation design. Plans to build a dozen new power reactors are under consideration and negotiations.

Talk about "nuclear renaissance" has been on the increase in the last several years, and the construction of several new reactors began in the early 2010s. However, as a result of the 2011 Japanese nuclear accident, and the persisting global economic crisis, most of the newly planned nuclear plant projects were canceled. Now, only five new reactors are expected to enter service by 2020.

China and Nuclear Power

In comparison, China is in the midst of an energy revolution, led by a strong nuclear renaissance. China is quickly becoming self-sufficient in reactor design and construction, as well as in other aspects of the fuel cycle. It is quickly shaping up as the emerging giant of the nuclear industry. Newly planned nuclear plants in China include some of the world's most advanced reactors, which will give a five- or six-fold increase in nuclear capacity to 58 GWe by 2020, then possibly 200 GWe by 2030, and 400 GWe by 2050.

The Chinese made AP1000 reactor units have substantially lower costs, which is mostly due to significantly lower labor rates. For example, the cost for the first two AP1000 units under construction in China was $5.3 billion. An additional four AP1000 reactors constructed in China were estimated to cost a total of $8 billion, or about $2,000 per kW installed capacity.

Construction costs in China are expected to fall even further once full-scale mass production is underway. Another domestic CAP1400 reactor design, based on the AP1000 model, is due to start construction in 2013 with a scheduled completion in 2017. Once the CAP1400 design has been installed and proven, work is scheduled for a CAP1700 design with a target construction cost of $1000 per kW installed.

Mainland China presently has 16 nuclear power reactors in operation, 27 under construction, and even more in planning stages, or about to begin construction. This includes China's most ambitious nuclear project, started in the fall of 2012, when China resumed construction on a "fourth generation" nuclear power plant. It was actually started in 2011, but the construction was suspended in the wake of the 2011 Fukushima disaster.

The Shidao Bay nuclear plant in Rongcheng, a city in eastern China's Shandong province, resumed in November, 2012, and is planned to be China's biggest nuclear project. The 6.6 GW reactors will be cooled by high-temperature gas and will also become the world's first successfully commercialized 4th generation nuclear technology, designed as the safest and most cost effective plant in the world.

Official plans, however, do not specify the level of safety of this overgrown giant. Nuclear safety information, like all important information in communist China, is kept secret for as long as possible. Human life is undervalued in China, and quality is not always up to par, so we would not be surprised if we see some of the greatest nuclear accidents there in the future.

Is China going to bring the nuclear industry out

of its slumber, or would it bring us a Fukushima on steroids instead?

ENVIRONMENTAL IMPACT

Building a nuclear power plant requires huge amounts of concrete, steel, and many other materials. All these materials are made with the help of fossil fuels—lots of them. During the production and transport of these materials a lot of gas, liquid and particulate pollution is generated as well, including huge amounts of CO_2 pollution.

There is also much large and expensive equipment delivered and installed at a new nuclear plant. This equipment is also made out of metals and plastics, processing a lot of energy, and emitting a lot of pollution during manufacturing and transport to the power plant.

It has been estimated that the steel and concrete production and transport for the construction of a 1 GW nuclear power station have a carbon footprint of roughly 300,000 tons CO_2. Spreading the CO_2 over a 25-year reactor life, we come up with almost 1.5 grams of CO_2 emitted per kWh of electricity generated.

According to industry estimates, the total carbon footprint of a nuclear power plant, including construction, fuel processing, and decommissioning is about 40 grams of CO_2 per kWh. This is exactly 10 times less than the fossil-fuel average of 400 grams of CO_2 emissions per kWh generation. Still, considering that a typical 1 GW nuclear power plant generates 1,000,000 kWh every hour, this is the equivalent of 40,000 kilograms (or 88,000 lbs.) of CO_2 every hour.

Pollution Footprint of Plant Equipment

Similar to the mining process, many pieces of equipment are used during nuclear power plant construction and operation. Starting with the plant's design and construction, we see pollution taking place in the shape of ground leveling and digging by large bulldozers and trucks with heavy plumes of smoke.

The plant's equipment arrives on trains and trucks—all manufactured, transported, and having left a significant pollution footprint.

Just as in the case of mining, we would assign 5-10% of the manufacturing and transport of power plant equipment to the initial construction step (A). The main pieces of equipment, boilers, turbines, generators, etc. arrive in wooden boxes or behind enormous trailers or railroad cars. These are assembled with the help of other equipment and put to work after creating another set of pollution problems (B). In addition, there are many other items and small pieces of equipment, tools and consumables for personal or specialized operations. These are shovels, helmets, computers, boots, shoes, overalls, first aid kits, goggles, etc. All these were also manufactured and transported, leaving a significant pollution footprint.(C). To complete the pollution footprint, we must the people involved in the entire process—engineers and technicians involved in the equipment manufacturing, transport, installation, setup, and operation. Their use of transportation, goods and services leaves yet another set of pollution footprints (D).

So, the total pollution footprint of the power plant's equipment cradle-to-grave process is expressed by:

$$P_f = A + B + C + D$$

where

P$_f$ is the total pollution footprint

A is the equipment manufacturing and transport to the power plant

B is equipment assembly, test and installation at the power plant

C is the manufacturing and transport to the power plant of tools and consumables, and

D is the pollution footprint of the equipment personnel during the design and setup phases.

Combining the pollution footprint of A (plant equipment manufacture and transport) with B (plant equipment assembly, test and installation), and adding C (the manufacture and transport of tools and consumables), plus D (the pollution footprint of personnel) gives us the environmental footprint of the plant equipment before even starting plant operations.

Here again, the pollution footprint is significant and reaches far. To put a value on it, we must take inventory of all items delivered to the plant and needed for its design, construction and operation. We must take a close look at the manufacturing of a nuclear reactor, boiler, turbine, or generator, as well as a number of other pieces of equipment used at the plants.

These are also very large pieces of equipment, and it takes hundreds and thousands of tons of metals to make them. Each of these started as an iron ore, dug out from a mine and transported to a smelter. The molten metal was shaped in different forms and shipped to various parts manufacturers who drilled, welded and otherwise constructed parts for these vehicles.

Again, we are talking about huge pieces of metal—some as big as an entire building. These parts are then packed and loaded on railroad cars or trucks to be shipped to the assembly facility. The parts of a large dump truck or a dragline might require a dozen railroad cars for transport. The parts are then sent to the assembly plant, where they are assembled into major components or entire units. After one more loading and unloading, they arrive at the plant for final assembly, installation, and testing, before being put to work.

This is a long, winding process, starting and stopping, loading and unloading, with many energy-consuming steps. Putting a dollar value on this would be too complex for our purposes, so it suffices to say that the pollution effects during and after all these steps are significant. We will take a closer look at these steps and their environmental effects in the following chapters.

On starting the power plant operation, the equipment continues to generate secondary pollution. Spare parts for these monsters periodically arrive from the parts manufacturers, after leaving their pollution footprint hither and yon. We will attempt to assign a number—quantity of air and land pollution—and a related dollar amount to these activities and their environmental effects in the following chapters.

After 20-30 years of non-stop operation, the power plant is finally declared obsolete, and it must be shut down and decommissioned. Decommissioning and land reclamation are major, expensive, and polluting undertakings as well. The equipment and materials used during the decommissioning and waste disposal process create additional air and ground pollution which is not to be ignored.

Additional specialized equipment and personnel (environmental specialists and inspectors) are usually brought in to assist or coordinate the effort. With that, more pollution footprints are left at the already exhausted mine.

When the final tally is made, a significant part of the emissions and overall pollution are to be attributed to the plant's equipment and support personnel. We will go through these calculations in the next chapters as well.

External Costs

A major European study, ExternE, reports the external costs of various fuel cycles, focusing on coal and nuclear. It shows that in clear cash terms nuclear energy incurs about one tenth the costs of coal.

The *external* costs are defined as those actually incurred in relation to health issues and environmental damage. These costs are quantifiable, but are presently not built into the cost of the electricity. If these costs

were in fact included, the EU price of electricity from coal would double and that from gas would increase 30%. Even these costs do not include the external costs of accidents, global warming and other factors.

NOTE: In the nuclear plant case, things are complicated further by a very important factor that is not included in the external costs. It is the external cost of environmental damage and pain and suffering caused by nuclear plant accidents. These costs are hard to even estimate, let alone put a definitive number on the effects. How do you estimate the cost of damages caused by the Chernobyl accident. Or Fukushima?

These accidents caused complete devastation of large land masses and their flora and fauna as well as their water. Unlike other accidents caused by power generators, nuclear radiation lasts a long time, so an area is rendered useless for many, many years, if not forever.

The most un-reconcilable damage is the thousands of animals and people who have been made ill or killed. How do we estimate the cost of human lives or the pain and suffering of more than a million after Chernobyl.

If these enormous costs are somehow compiled and spread over the entire global nuclear industry, it may in fact prove to be the most expensive energy source in use today.

HYDRO POWER

Water is the liquid gold of the Earth, and it has been abundant over much of the world. Unfortunately, the type of water that is necessary for human consumption and other practical uses—including hydropower—is limited and becoming more so each year.

The reduction of water quality and quantity in many places is becoming critical, and, of course, there are large areas that simply have no water. Our liquid gold is becoming more scarce and expensive, raising a number of questions as to its use for power generation in general, because most power plants use a lot of water for cooling.

Hydropower power plants use more water than any others, since water is the fuel—the energy source. Although it is not totally wasted, a lot is diverted, evaporated, and otherwise made unavailable for human use.

Still, we depend on hydropower to supply a major portion of our electric power. Because for the most part we have already built the hydropower infrastructure, we just need to make sure that we use it efficiently. The first step is to assure that we have a clear understanding of the advantages and disadvantages of hydropower—a must in the process of making rational decisions.

Introduction

Hydropower, refers to the potential energy contained in water (dams, rivers, and streams). The energy contained in ocean waters is a subject of a different technology which we review later on in this chapter.

Hydropower is energy created by the hydrologic cycle, which is ultimately driven by the sun, making it an indirect form of solar energy. Energy contained in sunlight evaporates water from the oceans and deposits it on land in the form of rain and snow, thus forming and maintaining thousands of streams, rivers, and lakes.

Some rain water is absorbed by the ground, while the part that is not absorbed runs off the land and into the ocean by means of streams and rivers. Some of the water in the long journey to the ocean is lost to evaporation, irrigation, refilling the water table etc., while the water reaching the ocean repeats the evaporation cycle.

> Believe it or not, the water that fuels hydro-power generation—which uses the largest amount of water of all power generators—is not considered (officially) a renewable power source. To remedy that, the issue was recently brought up before the US Congress for a vote.
>
> Water's renewability is debatable, regardless of the Congressional decision, for there are many ways to look at global water production, storage, preservation, and use, including the damage and waste that come with these activities.

Most often, hydroelectric plants are built along rivers, where they generate power by releasing water stored behind concrete dams built across the river to turn water turbines. The power plants capture the energy released by water falling through a turbine which converts the water's energy into mechanical power. The mechanical energy of the rotating turbines drives generators to produce electricity.

Hydropower from dams accounts for approximately 75% of the nation's total renewable electricity generation, making it the leading renewable energy source of power. The annual hydropower output is equivalent to the energy produced from burning 200 million barrels of heating oil. There are estimates that more than 200 million tons of CO_2 emissions are avoided in the U.S. annually because of hydropower generation (as compared with coal, oil, and gas power generation).

Hydropower turbines are capable of converting more than 90% of available energy into electricity, mak-

ing it the most efficient form of electricity generation. By comparison, fossil fuel plants are only about 50% efficient.

In addition to providing low-cost electricity, multi-purpose dams provide water for irrigation, wildlife, recreation, barge transportation, and flood control benefits.

NOTE: While significant CO_2 emission reduction and 90% efficiency at the last leg of the hydropower generation cycle are undeniable facts, there are serious inefficiencies, pollution, and environmental damage throughout the cycle that must be taken into account when comparing the different technologies. We will take a close look at these here and in the following chapters.

Hydropower plants range in size from large power plants that supply many consumers with electricity, to small and micro plants operated for individual needs or to sell power to utilities.

Hydropower plants vary in size, but according to the U.S. DOE:

1. Large hydropower plants are facilities that have a capacity of more than 30 megawatts.
2. Small Hydropower plants are facilities that have a capacity of 100 kilowatts to 30 megawatts, and
3. Micro hydropower plants are facilities with capacities of up to 100 kilowatts.

NOTE: A small or micro-hydroelectric power system is usually designed to produce enough electricity for a home, farm, ranch, or a small village. In some cases the excess power is sold to the local utility.

The types of hydropower we will be discussing herein are:
1. Dam
2. River
3. Ocean
4. Storage

Dam Hydropower

Dams on rivers and streams have been around for a long time, and are still present and in use in almost all regions of the globe. They have played a key role in the development of human activities, and are now used for irrigation, water supply, flood control, electric power generation, and improvement of navigation. They also provide recreation, such as fishing and swimming, and become refuges for fish and birds, and they slow down streams and rivers so that the water does not carry away soil, thereby preventing erosion.

During the last two centuries, dams have also

played a key role in producing large-scale power and electricity. Hydropower is the only renewable resource currently used on a large scale to generate electricity.

Hydroelectric plants range in size from several kW to many GW. For example, the Three Gorges Dam on the Yangtze river, the largest hydroelectric dam in the world, has installed capacity of over 20 GW, which is nearly twice the power of the next largest hydropower plant, the Brazil-Paraguay Itaipu dam, at 14 GW.

There are about 35,000 large dams in existence today. Their importance for boosting economic development has increased in recent decades, most significantly in developing countries.

Since there is no more room (or river water) for large dams, hydropower development in most countries is now focused on building smaller dams, on refurbishing and upgrading existing hydroelectric plants, and on retrofitting dams constructed for other purposes.

The feasibility of small hydropower plants depends on the availability of a back-up source of electricity, since most of the smaller plants often do not have a reservoir for storage, thus depending on the variable river flow. Large- and intermediate-scale dams, however, will continue to be very important in developing countries, in Russia and China, and in some industrialized nations, such as Canada.

Hydro Power Generation

Hydroelectric power plants produce electricity by using a power source (water in this case) to turn a turbine, which then spins an electric generator that produces electricity. While a coal- or gas-fired power plant uses steam to turn the turbine blades, the hydroelectric plant uses falling water to turn the turbine and generate electricity. The results are the same; electric power flows from the facility into the grid. A distinguishable exception in the case of a coal-fired plant is the significant emission of toxic gasses, liquid and solid waste, in addition to the electrical flow.

Hydroelectric power is generated by the gravitational force of falling water, so the capacity to produce energy is dependent on both the amount of flow and the height from which it falls. The water behind the dam accumulates huge amounts of potential energy which is transformed into mechanical energy when the water rushes down the sluice and strikes the turbine's rotary blades.

The power available from falling water can be calculated from the flow rate and density of water, the height of fall, and the local acceleration due to gravity, as follows:

$$P = \eta \rho Q g h$$

where

    P is power generated by falling water in watts
    η is the dimensionless efficiency of the turbine
    ρ is the density of water in kilograms per cubic meter
    Q is the flow in cubic meters per second
    g is the acceleration due to gravity
    h is the height difference between inlet and outlet

The turbine's rotation spins electromagnets which generate current in stationary coils of wire. Finally, the current is put through a transformer where the voltage is increased for long-distance transmission over power lines.

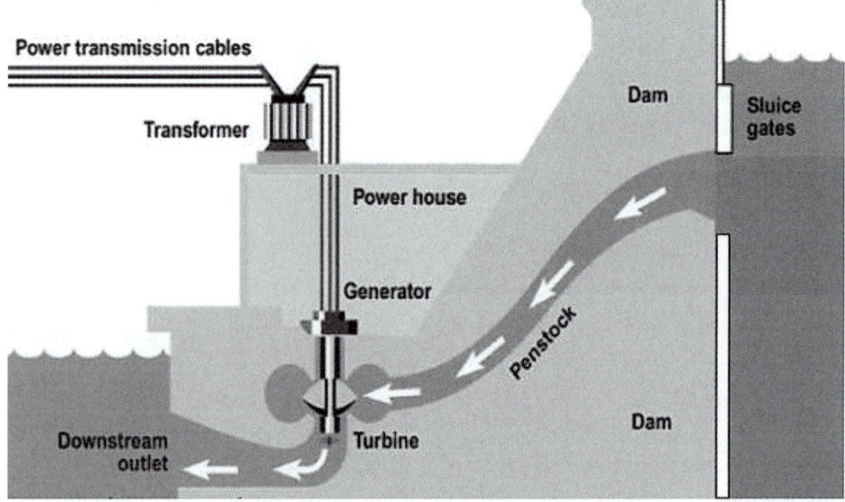

Figure 3-13. Hydroelectric power plant at a dam

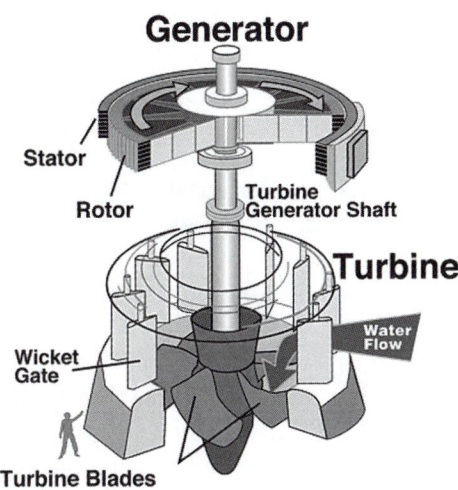

Figure 3-14. Turbine-generator set

Types of Hydropower Turbines

Impulse Turbine

The impulse turbine generally uses the velocity of the water to move the runner, and discharges to atmospheric pressure. The water stream hits each bucket on the runner. There is no suction on the down side of the turbine, and the water flows out the bottom of the turbine housing after hitting the runner. An impulse turbine is generally suitable for high-head, low-flow applications.

Pelton Wheel has one or more free jets discharging water into an aerated space and impinging on the buckets of a runner. Draft tubes are not required for impulse turbine since the runner must be located above the maximum tailwater to permit operation at atmospheric pressure.

Turgo Wheel is a variation on the Pelton and is made exclusively by Gilkes in England. The Turgo runner is a cast wheel whose shape generally resembles a fan blade that is closed on the outer edges. The water stream is applied on one side, goes across the blades and exits on the other side.

Cross-flow turbine is drum-shaped and uses an elongated, rectangular-section nozzle directed against curved vanes on a cylindrically shaped runner. It resembles a "squirrel cage" blower. The cross-flow turbine allows the water to flow through the blades twice. The first pass is when the water flows from the outside of the blades to the inside; the second pass is from the inside back out. A guide vane at the entrance to the turbine directs the flow to a limited portion of the runner. The cross-flow was developed to accommodate larger water flows and lower heads than the Pelton.

Reaction Turbine

A reaction turbine develops power from the combined action of pressure and moving water. The runner is placed directly in the water stream flowing over the blades rather than striking each individually. Reaction turbines are generally used for sites with lower head and higher flows than impulse turbines.

Propelle turbine generally has a runner with three to six blades in which the water contacts all of the blades constantly. Picture a boat propeller running in a pipe. Through the pipe, the pressure is constant; if it isn't, the runner would be out of balance. The pitch of the blades may be fixed or adjustable. The major components besides the runner are a scroll case, wicket gates, and a draft tube. There are several different types of propeller turbines:

Bulb turbine is where turbine and generator are a sealed unit placed directly in the water stream.

Straflo turbine uses a generator that is attached directly to the perimeter of the turbine.

Tube turbine uses a penstock that bends just before or after the runner, allowing a straight-line connection to the generator.

Kaplan turbine uses blades and the wicket gates that are adjustable, allowing for a wider range of operation.

Francis Turbine

Francis turbines have a runner with fixed buckets (vanes), usually nine or more. Water is introduced just above the runner and all around it and then falls through, causing it to spin. Besides the runner, the other major components are the scroll case, wicket gates, and draft tube.

Kinetic energy turbines, also called free-flow turbines, generate electricity from the kinetic energy present in flowing water rather than the potential energy from the head. The systems may operate in rivers, manmade channels, tidal waters, or ocean currents. Kinetic systems utilize the water stream's natural pathway. They do not require the diversion of water through manmade channels, riverbeds, or pipes, although they might have applications in such conduits. Kinetic systems do not require large civil works; however, they can use existing structures such as bridges, tailraces and channels.

TYPES OF HYDROELECTRIC PLANTS

Hydropower plants can be small, medium and large in size. Below we will take a close look at the different types hydropower plants.

Large Hydropower Plants

Building a hydropower plant on a large dam is a huge undertaking of national proportions. It cannot be done by one company alone. Instead, a number of companies, under the direction and supervision of government bodies are usually involved in the project.

As an example, we will take a look at the construction of Hoover Dam on the Arizona-Nevada border. It was approved by the U.S. Congress and executed under the direction of the Bureau of Reclamation. A decision on the massive concrete arch-gravity dam structure was made and the design was overseen by the bureau's chief design engineer, John L. Savage.

The bureau issued bid documents available to interested parties, where the government was to provide the materials, but the contractor was to prepare the site and build the dam. The dam was described in minute detail, covering 100 pages of text and 76 drawings. A $2 million bid bond by the contractors accompanied each bid, and the winner posted a $5 million performance bond, allowing him seven years to build the dam, or else.

There were three valid bids, and a bid of $48,890,955 was the lowest. It was amazingly only within $24,000 of the confidential government estimate of what the dam would cost to build. The best bid was also $5 million dollars lower than the next lowest bid.

An entire city was built in the desert near the dam site, which is still there as we know it today as Boulder City, Nevada. There was also a special railroad line constructed to join Boulder City to Las Vegas for transport of people and materials.

The dam building began by diverting the Colorado River away from the construction site. Four diversion tunnels (56 ft in diameter and nearly 3 mi total length) were drilled through the canyon walls, on both sides of the proposed dam structure. This work had to completed quickly in late fall and winter, when the water level in the river was low enough.

When the tunnels were completed, they had to be lined with concrete, using Gantry cranes running on rails through the entire length of each tunnel. Then the sidewalls were poured, using movable sections of steel forms, to create a 3-ft-thick concrete lining.

The river was then diverted into the two Arizona tunnels, by exploding the temporary cofferdam protecting the Arizona tunnels, while at the same time dumping rubble into the river until its natural course was blocked and it started flowing through the two tunnels. The tunnels on the Nevada side were kept in case of high-water floods. On completion of the dam, the entrances to the diversion tunnels were sealed at the opening and halfway through the tunnels with large concrete plugs, while the downstream halves of the tunnels following the inner plugs are now the main bodies of the spillway tunnels.

Two cofferdams were constructed to facilitate the river's diversion, each 96 ft high, and 750 feet thick at the base, which is actually thicker than the dam base. Each contained 650,000 cubic yards of rock material and cement.

The site was then drained of water and the accumulated erosion soils and other loose materials in the riverbed were dredged until sound bedrock was reached for the dam foundation. This requiired the excavation and removal off-site of over 1,500,000 cubic yards of river bed material. Since the dam was an arch-gravity type, the side walls of the canyon would bear the force of the impounded lake. The side walls of the surrounding rock channel were excavated too, to reach virgin rock for the load-bearing side walls and eliminate water seepage.

The dam foundation was reinforced with grout and holes were driven into the walls and base of the canyon, as deep as 150 feet into the rock, and all cavities were filled with grout, to stabilize the rock. This would also prevent water from seeping past the dam through the canyon rock and limit the upward pressure of water seeping under the dam.

After the dam base and sides were secured the pouring of concrete into the dam structure was initiated. This is complex undertaking in such an enormous structure, because concrete heats and contracts for a long time while it cures. The potential for uneven cooling and contraction of concrete is a serious problem, so to avoid a long curing process, the dam was built in sections. The ground where the dam was to rise was marked with rectangles, and concrete blocks in columns were poured. These were 50 ft square and 5 ft. high, strengthened by a series of 1-inch steel pipes through which first cool river water, then ice-cold water from a refrigeration plant was run.

Once each individual block had cured and had stopped contracting, the pipes were filled with grout. Grout was also used to fill the hairline spaces between columns, which were grooved to increase the strength of the joints.

Huge steel buckets (7 ft high by 7 ft in diameter, and weighing 18 tons when full), suspended from aerial cableways above the construction site, were used to pour the concrete for each block. The concrete was prepared at two large concrete plants on the Nevada side, and delivered to the site in special railcars. A team of men worked the newly poured cement in each block throughout the form until achieving the desired uniformity.

A total of 3,250,000 cubic yards of concrete was used in the dam. An additional 1,110,000 cubic yards of concrete were used for the construction of the power plant and other works. More than 582 miles of cooling pipes were placed within the concrete. It is estimated that there is enough concrete in the Hoover Dam and the surrounding structures and infrastructure to pave a two-lane highway from San Francisco to New York.

Although the dam was completed in 1935, concrete cores removed from the dam for testing in 1995 showed that the concrete has continued to slowly gain strength. It was also confirmed that the dam is composed of a durable concrete having a compressive strength exceeding the range typically found in normal mass concrete. Hoover Dam concrete is not subject to Alkali-Silica Reaction (ASR) as the Hoover Dam builders happened to use nonreactive aggregate, unlike that at downstream Parker Dam, where ASR has caused measurable deterioration.

The huge monolithic dam is 660 ft. thick at the very bottom and gets thinner as it goes up, ending with a 45-ft.-wide road, connecting Nevada and Arizona. It has a convex face towards the water level above the dam. It was estimated that the curving arch would transmit the water's force into the abutments of the rock walls of the canyon.

Following an upgrade in 1993, the total gross power rating of the Hoover hydropower plant, including two 2.4 MW Pelton turbine-generators that power Hoover Dam's own operations, is a maximum capacity of 2.1 GW. The annual power generation varies, according to water conditions and other factors. The maximum annual generation of 10.3 TWh/y was recorded in 1984, and the minimum was 2.6 TWh in 1956. The average has been about 4.2 TWh/year.

The dam reservoir has been very low since around 2005, and although still far from minimum level, it is watched closely and preventative measures are planned.

The upstream picture is much more impressive and even dramatic. In the Arizona/Nevada desert, 250 square miles (160,000 acres, or 28,537,000 acre/feet) were permanently flooded, radically changing the local environment. Good or bad, this change must be taken seriously and evaluated for what it is, which what we will do in the next chapters.

Labor

Working on dam and power plant construction was a dangerous and exhausting job. An average of 5,000 people were involved in the daily dam construction. The most dangerous job was that of the "high scalers." These were people who climbed down the canyon walls every day and were suspended from the top of the canyon with ropes. Suspended on the vertical rock wall, they removed loose rock with jackhammers and dynamite.

There were falling rocks and other debris that hurt and killed workers. One high scaler was able to save a government inspector, who lost his grip on a safety line and began tumbling down a slope towards a certain death, when the high scaler intercepted him, risking his

Figure 3-15. Upstream side of Hoover dam before filling the reservoir

Figure 3-16. Downstream of Hoover dam.

own life, and pulling him to safety.

The workers were under severe time constraints too, because the concrete pour was due, and sometimes they negligently ignored seepage and cavities in the wall. As a result, many holes were incompletely filled. This eventually caused unacceptable leaks in the completed dam, and the bureau decided to fix the problem by drilling new holes from inspection galleries inside the dam into the surrounding bedrock. This work was done in secrecy, and at additional cost, taking over nine years to complete after the dam was already in full operation.

Although there are myths that men were caught in the pour and are entombed in the dam to this day, each bucket only deepened the concrete in a form by an inch, and Six Companies engineers would not have permitted a flaw caused by the presence of a human body.

Nevertheless, there were over 110 deaths during the construction of Hoover Dam. One of the first victims was a surveyor who drowned in 1922, while looking for an ideal spot for the dam. Incidently, his son was the last man to die working on the dam's construction, 13 years to the day later. Ninety-six of the deaths occurred during construction at the site, and 91 of these were contracted employees. The rest were helpers and visitors.

In addition to the official fatalities due to accidents and incidents, there were a number of deaths due to illness, such as pneumonia. There were allegations, however, that this diagnosis was a cover for death from carbon monoxide poisoning of people overexposed to fumes from gasoline-fueled equipment in the diversion tunnels. The diagnosis was used by the contractor to avoid paying compensation claims.

River Hydropower

Hydropower plants based on the *run of the river* generate electricity on a smaller scale by simply using the water flow of a local stream or river. One way to generate electricity is to channel a certain amount of water through a pipe from the rive to a turbine at the outlet. The water flow makes the turbine blades spin, which in turn spins a generator to produce electricity. This method is preferred to damming the river because it is much cheaper and causes much less environmental damage than flooding large areas for dams.

Electricity can also be generated from turbines installed directly in the river. While this seems a most practical and economic way to use water flow, this method has not yet been commercially used, although there are a number of tests underway in the U.S. and Europe.

The problem here is that the water flow is usually low, so the power generator relies solely on the density and mass of the running water. The slow speed significantly limits the amount of generated electricity, but it does reduce the risk to aquatic life.

River dams of the *run of the river* type are the new trend in hydropower generation. One of the most remarkable examples is the joint Romanian-Yugoslavian mega hydro project that started operation in 1972 on the river Danube. The first version, Iron Gate I dam, had two dams with power plants each containing 6 turbines at approximately 1.0 GW power generation. Iron Gate II dam extension followed in the late 1990s by an upgrade and 10% increase of the total power. Two additional smaller power plants are still to be built as well.

Construction of these dams created a large reservoir on the Danube shoreline, and raised the water level of the river near the dam by 35 meters. Six villages (a total population of 17,000) were evacuated, and they, together with the local Orşova island, were flooded. The locals were relocated, and the settlements have been lost forever to the Danube. Dam construction had a major impact on the local environment, especially on the fauna. The spawning routes of several species of sturgeon were permanently interrupted.

The good news is that during post-dam construction, the geo-morphological, archaeological and cultural historical artifacts of the Iron Gates have been under protection by both nations. In Serbia the Dzerdap National Park was created in 1974 on 245.59 sq mi., and in Romania, the Porţile de Fier National Park was created in 2001, with 446.55 sq mi., both officially protected territories.

There are a number of similar examples of river hydropower, but a lot of work remains on this technique before its efficiency and cost-effectiveness can be assessed and it finds wider commercial applications.

Small Hydropower Plants

Building a small hydropower plant on an existing lake, spillway or river, is a straightforward process, much like any other power plant would go through, with normal channels of development. The only difference here is that there is no fuel to be procured and transported, or waste or byproducts to be stored and disposed of. Emissions coming from the hydropower power during full operation are close to nil too.

A typical cradle-to-grave development process for a small hydropower plant includes:

• Hydropower plant site search
• Proposed area survey

- Environmental studies
- Local rights and agreements
- Permits and legal issues
- Plant site preparation
- Plant construction
- Daily plant O&M operations
- Decommissioning and area reconstruction

All these steps must be considered to obtain a complete picture of the project and assess properly its technical and financial feasibility. As with all power plants, the survey, environmental studies and permitting processes are complex undertakings, in need of expert personnel. They might take months, but most likely years, of intense work and negotiations with local and federal authorities and regulators.

After all studies have been completed, and the necessary permits secured, construction of the plant can begin. Here again, we see large pieces of equipment moving in, leveling the site, and digging holes in the ground. Cement trucks dump their loads in the foundation, and construction workers erect the buildings and complete the other elements of the plant infrastructure.

In most cases, small- to medium-size hydropower plants are built in remote locations—far away from populated centers and the power grid. A substation must be built nearby to transform the generated electricity into voltage suitable for transmission to a connection point in the national power grid or to remote customers. Rights-of-way for transmission lines are needed, which is another great obstacle in building remote power plants.

After all the work has been completed, the power plant goes through a series of start-up, testing and certification procedures. If everything checks out as fit, the plant is switched into full operation, starts sending electricity to the grid, and normal O&M procedures take place on a daily, usually 24/7, basis.

Case Study

In the 1980s the author was part of a team contracted for the design and implementation of small hydropower plants in Eastern Europe. The permitting and financing of the projects was the greatest hurdle and had to be considered first. Due to the complexity of these procedures, several sites were rejected. Another set of potential sites was rejected because of their remoteness which made connecting to any customers or the grid impossible (or prohibitively expensive). The remote sites also bore the risk of vandalism, which was not justifiable from the investors' point of view.

After the preliminary evaluation of dozens of proposed sites, only two were approved for development, and only one was eligible for government support. So the team focused on the proposed site located on a large stream in a mountain region, 1.5 miles away from a large resort—the customer.

The stream is full and water flow is fast 8 months of the year, while for the other 4 months the level and flow vary. The stream freezes occasionally for 2-3 months in the winter, and the turbine is frozen and shut down.

The hydropower plant site was proposed at a natural curve on a hill where the stream zigzags for about a mile, as in Figure 3-17. An intake at the top of the curved section was to be built and the water diverted from the natural stream. A catch box at the mouth of the intake was to filter out floating debris and fish, using an array of bars to keep large debris out, and a large mesh screen to remove smaller objects. An inspection gate was installed to divert the water for inspection and for maintenance of the box.

A large bore cement pipeline was run ¼ mile from the intake to the turbine building. This was a major challenge, due to the mountainous terrain. An electro-mechanical control was installed in the turbine building to regulate the speed of the turbine and the electric generator attached to it. Thus generated power was sent to a transformer and then to the main breakers of the building for use on demand.

The power plant was rated at 150 kW and was equipped with a German turbine/gen set. The plant operation was quite simple, and consisted of periodic cleaning and inspection of the catch box, and normal periodic maintenance of the turbine/gen stack.

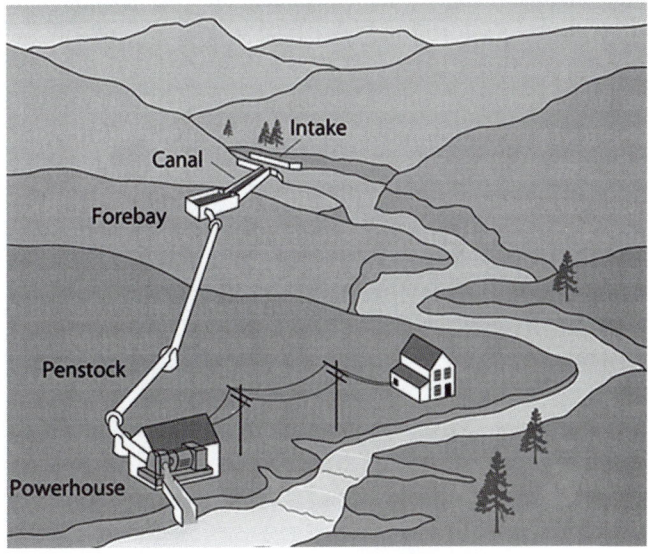

Figure 3-17. Small hydropower plant

The only anticipated long-term problem was the availability of water in the stream during the low flow months in summer and the freeze in the winter. Late-night use of power at the resort was drastically reduced, and since the power grid was far away, the turbine was idling several hours every night. The team could not come up with a solution for using the excess power generated during the nighttime.

The total cost from concept to final inspection was about $1.2 million, or $8,000/kW. This somewhat higher cost was due to extensive work needed for the ¼ mile pipe in the mountainous terrain.

Pumped Storage Hydropower

There are several types of storage hydropower.

Pumped water storage is basically storing water and reusing water for peak electricity demand. Demand for electricity is not "flat" and constant. Demand goes up and down during the day, and overnight there is less need for electricity in homes, businesses, and other facilities. For example, in Phoenix, AZ, on an August day, the demand for electricity to run millions of air conditioners is huge, but by midnight, it is drastically reduced.

Some hydroelectric plants use "pumped storage" to generate power on demand anytime of day by reusing the same water more than once.

Pumped energy storage is a method of keeping water in reserve for peak period power demands by pumping water that has already flowed through the turbines back up a storage pool above the powerplant *at a time when customer demand for energy is low*, such as during the middle of the night. The water is then allowed to flow back through the turbine-generators *at times when customer demand is high*, like at noon on a hot August day in Arizona. This reduces the heavy load placed on the electric system at peak hours, when the air conditioners are cranked up.

The reservoir acts much like a battery, storing

Figure 3-18. Pumped energy storage.

power in the form of water when demands are low and producing maximum power during daily and seasonal peak periods. An advantage of pumped storage is that hydroelectric generating units are able to start up quickly and make rapid adjustments in output. They operate efficiently when used for one hour or several hours. Because pumped storage reservoirs are relatively small, construction costs are generally low compared with conventional hydropower facilities.

Compressed air hydro is used when a plentiful head of water can be made to generate compressed air directly without moving parts. In these designs, a falling column of water is purposely mixed with air bubbles generated through turbulence at the high-level intake. This is allowed to fall down a shaft into a subterranean, high-roofed chamber where the now-compressed air separates from the water and becomes trapped. The falling water column maintains compression of the air in the top of the chamber, while an outlet submerged below the water level in the chamber allows water to flow back to the surface at a slightly lower level than the intake. A separate outlet in the roof of the chamber supplies the compressed air to the surface. A facility on this principle was built on the Montreal River at Ragged Shutes near Cobalt, Ontario, in 1910 and supplied about 4.5 MW electric power to nearby mines.

Another method of compressed air storage uses excess electric energy during low power demand hours to run compressors, which compress air in special storage tanks. During high power demand hours, the compressed air can be released to run turbines connected to generators. This power is sent into the grid to reduce the need for power generated by peaking power plants.

Compressed air storage suffers from low efficiency (less than 50%), so there are designs to improve the efficiency by using a mist of water sprayed into the air storage tanks, which absorb and store the heat generated from the compression (and release it on expansion). This allows the improved system to achieve a 80-90% thermodynamic efficiency, and a total 70% overall efficiency.

Ocean Hydropower

The potential energy stored in the world's oceans is huge. Calculating the energy stored in ocean tides, currents and waves, we come up with a very large number, and conclude that even if a small part of this energy can be captured and used, we won't have to worry about energy crises or global warming.

Alas, the key components here, *capture and use*, are still in the early stages of planning and development.

Capturing ocean energy won't be easy, for its powers are many and awesome. Powerful storms devastate everything in their way, wild waves can crush mechanical devices, and corrosion could eat through any material man has available today.

Nevertheless, the energy is there, we need it, and since it is human nature to try the impossible, we will be trying for as long as needed to capture this untamed giant and use its endless energy sources.

Ocean energy occurs in the form of tides, waves, currents, and heat. Tidal energy resources are modest on a global basis, and tapping them involves building major dams on inlets and estuaries that are prized for other purposes, so few tidal energy facilities have been developed. Harnessing waves and currents on a significant scale will involve designing turbine structures that are large, inexpensive, and can operate for long periods under the physical stresses and corrosive forces of ocean environments. For the most part, such systems are at the research stage today.

The largest but most experimental form of ocean energy is ocean thermal energy conversion, which taps heat stored in the ocean to generate electricity. This process runs warm surface seawater through several different types of systems that use the water's stored heat to turn a turbine, then cool the resulting steam or vapor with cold deep-seawater.

Making this conversion work affordably on a large scale is technologically very difficult because it requires large structures and physical challenges associated with working in the ocean environment. It works most effectively in regions where there are large temperature differences between surface and deeper waters, mainly in the tropics. If ocean thermal energy conversion can be commercialized at some point, however, it could become an enormous new energy source.

We will take a closer look at the ocean energy technologies later on in this text.

HYDROELECTRIC POWER USE

Hydro power generation is probably the oldest method of producing power. We can even imagine the amazement of the first caveman who noticed that moving stream water can do work. Then we figured out how to make the water spin a wheel that crushed grain, feeding the entire village with little effort. This must have been one of the first mass-service capitalist enterprises.

People have used moving water in increasing sophistication to facilitate their work throughout history, while presently people make use of moving water mainly to produce electricity.

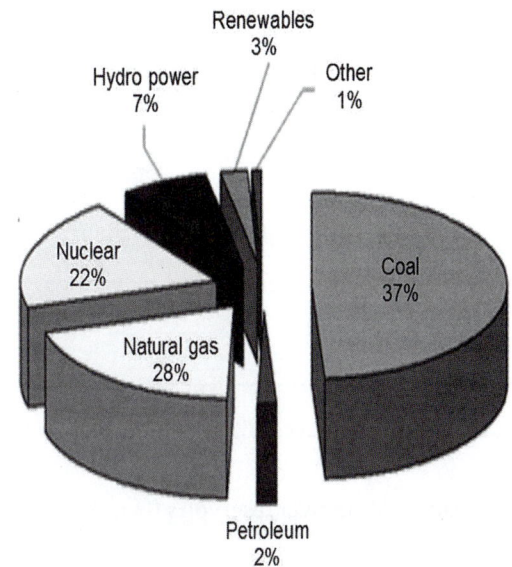

Figure 3-19. Power generation in the U.S.

Most energy in the United States is produced by fossil-fuel and nuclear power plants, and only 7% of total power is produced by hydroelectric plants. Most of the hydropower comes from huge power generators placed inside dams.

A great limitation of this type of generation is the fact that there is no more room to build new hydropower plants. On top of that, even the available water is in short supply. Frequent draughts and other natural events make hydropower's reliability questionable for the long run.

Most U.S. states use some type of hydroelectric power, but states with low topographical relief, such as Florida and Kansas, produce very little hydroelectric power. Some states, such as Arizona, Idaho, Washington, and Oregon use hydroelectricity as the main power source. As a matter of fact, most of Idaho's electric power comes from hydroelectric plants.

In 2006, Texas had only 23 dams with hydroelectric power plants out of the state's hundreds of medium to large dams built for purposes other than power generation. The 23 dams have a total generating capacity of 673 MW, but the amount of electricity they actually produce annually is well below their maximum generation potential. This is due to water level and demand variations, and other factors that reduce the plants' up-time and efficiency.

For example, in 2004 Texas hydropower plants operated at an average 22% capacity factor, and in 2006 the

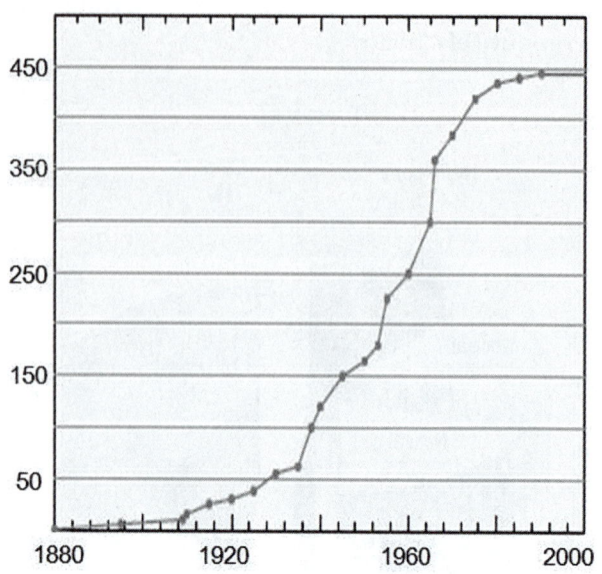

Figure 3-20. U.S. hydropower reservoirs (in million acre-feet)

capacity factor averaged only 11 percent. Hydropower production is limited most drastically by droughts or other factors that affect surface water flows.

Officially, there are six types of hydropower plants in the U.S.:

- Municipal and other non-federal public
- Private utility
- Private, non-utility
- Industrial
- Federal
- Cooperative

There are 2,388 licensed U.S. hydroelectric plants, assigned to one or more of the six owner classes. These plants represent the bulk of the U.S. hydroelectric capacity of approximately 75 GW in 1996. Of these, 69% of the plants are owned by private owners, as follow: private utility 31%, and private non-utility 27%, while industrial hydropower plants represent 9%, and cooperative 2%.

Table 3-3. Large U.S. dams

Dam name	Year built	MW
Grand Coulee	1942	6,809
Chief Joseph Dam	1958	2,620
Robert Moses Niagara	1961	2,515
John Day Dam	1949	2,160
Bath County PSP	1985	2,100
Hoover Dam	1936	2,080
The Dalles Dam	1981	2,038

Nearly 75% of the total capacity is owned by federal and public owners, as follow: federal 51% and public 22%. Different federal agencies are considered owners of different dams and hydro plants. Since an owner may own plants in more than one owner class (e.g., private non-utility and industrial) the total number is referred to as "presence" rather than owners.

The total number of owners, therefore, is 1,134, while the total number of presences is 1,152. As with the distribution of the plant population by owner class, the distribution of the plant ownership shows that approximately 70% of the plant ownership is in the private sector.

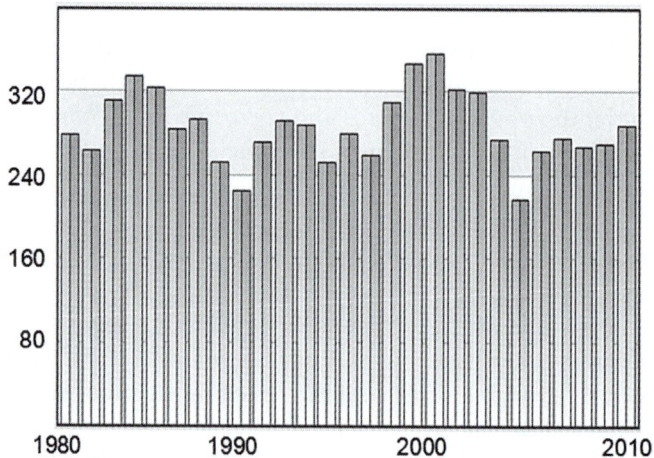

Figure 3-21. U.S. hydropower production and use (in billion kWh)

No doubt, we use all the hydropower we generate since it is clean and cheap, and we want more too. Hydroelectric power is the best and cheapest power available. It is clean and reliable (to a point), and is totally clean at the customer end. So the question is why don't we use more of it to produce a lot (or all) of the electric power we need? The answer is quite simple—there is just not enough of it, and no more can be produced due to lack of hydro resources.

Hydropower is good, but the beginnings of each hydropower plant on a dammed river are bad and even ugly. This is due mainly to the fact that lots of water and a lot of land are needed to build a dam and create a large lake (reservoir) at the expense of the local environment and the people living in it. The local environment covered by the lake is lost forever, and once flooded it cannot be restored to its original condition.

Large dam hydropower projects also require a lot of money, time, construction materials and effort. Today, most of the good locations for large dams and hydro plants have been taken, so only smaller plants can be built.

While in the early part of the 20th century hydroelectric plants supplied about half of the nation's power, that number is down to about 7% today and falling, as gas and nuclear use increases. The only possible trend for the future is to build small-scale hydro plants on rivers and streams that can generate electricity for single communities.

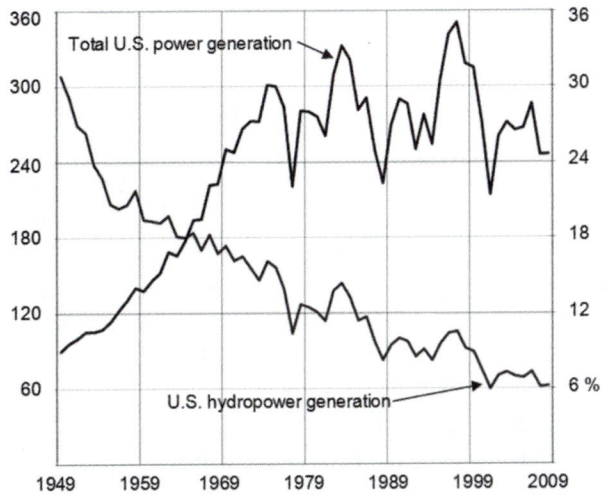

Figure 3-22. Percent U.S. total power vs. hydropower generation (in GW)

Worldwide Hydropower

Worldwide hydropower represents about 20% of total global electricity production. Hydro power supplies more than 50 percent of national electricity in about 65 countries, more than 80 percent in 32 countries and almost all of the electricity in 13 countries.

China has been building large hydroelectric facilities in the last decade and now leads the world in hydroelectricity use. Canada and Brazil follow. In many countries it is the most important widely used renewable energy source. In addition to large hydro dams, which are no longer an option in most countries, hydropower is produced by using the power of large rivers and natural drops in elevation.

While large-scale hydropower is almost fully developed in developed countries, underdeveloped countries have untapped hydro resources which are still abundant in Latin America, Central Africa, India and China.

The world's total technically feasible hydropower (the amount of hydropower that can be achieved if no other conditions were considered) is estimated at ap-

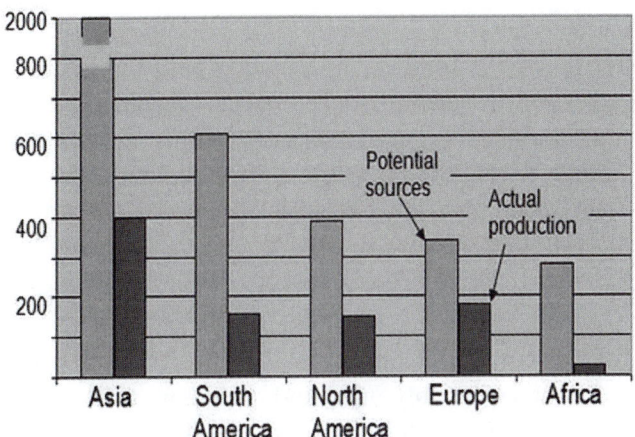

Figure 3-23. Global hydropower availability (in GW, 2010)

proximately 15,000 TWh/year, of which about 8,000 TWh/year is currently considered economically feasible for development. This is about 700 GW (or about 2600 TWh/year) already in operation, with an additional 100+ GW under construction. Most of the remaining potential is in Africa, Asia and Latin America.

Table 3-4. World-wide hydropower potential

Continent	Technically feasible potential	Economically feasible potential
Africa	1750 TWh/year	1000 TWh/year
Asia	6800 TWh/year	3600 TWh/year
N. America	1660 TWh/year	1000 TWh/year
S. America	2665 TWh/year	1600 TWh/year

Although there are significant (potential) hydropower resources, using them is not that easy. A number of countries, such as China India, Iran and Turkey, are undertaking large-scale hydro development programs, and there are projects under construction in about 80 countries. According to the recent world surveys, a number of countries see hydropower as the key to their future economic development. Some of these are: Sudan, Rwanda, Mali, Benin, Ghana, Liberia, Guinea, Myanmar, Bhutan, Cambodia, Armenia, Kyrgyzstan, Cuba, Costa Rica, and Guyana.

Characteristics of Hydropower

Hydropower has its own up and downsides. The major benefits are:

- The water resources are widely spread around the world. Potential exists in about 150 countries, and about 70 percent of the economically feasible potential remains to be developed. This is mostly in developing countries.

- It is a proven and well advanced technology (more than a century of experience), with modern power-plants providing the most efficient energy conversion process (>90 percent), which is also an important environmental benefit.

- The production of peak load energy from hydro-power allows for the best use to be made of base load power from other less flexible electricity sources, notably wind and solar power. Its fast response time enables it to meet sudden fluctuations in demand.

- It has the lowest operating costs and longest plant life, compared with other large-scale generating options. Once the initial investment has been made in the necessary civil works, the plant's life can be extended economically with relatively cheap maintenance and periodic replacement of electromechanical equipment. Typically a hydro plant in service for 40-50 years can have its operating life doubled.

- The "fuel" (water) is renewable, and is not subject to fluctuations in market. Countries with ample reserves of fossil fuels, such as Iran and Venezuela, have opted for a large-scale program of hydro development, recognizing environmental benefits. Hydro also represents energy independence for many countries.

NOTE: Can water used for energy generation be considered a renewable resource? This question is becoming a focal point in U.S. politics. A resolution in Congress calls for officially recognizing it as such, but its destiny is uncertain.

Benefits of Hydropower

Hydropower provides unique benefits, rarely found in other sources of energy. These benefits can be the electricity itself, or those associated with reservoir development. Despite recent debates, few would disclaim that the net environmental benefits of hydropower are far superior to fossil-based generation. In 1997, for example, it was calculated that hydropower saved GHG emissions equivalent to all the cars on the planet (in terms of avoided fossil fuel generation).

While development of all the remaining hydroelectric potential could not hope to cover total future world demand for electricity, implementation of even half of this potential could have enormous environmental ben-

efits in terms of avoided generation by fossil fuels.

Carefully planned hydropower development can also make a vast contribution to improving living standards in the developing world (Asia, Africa, Latin America), where the greatest potential still exists. Approximately 2 billion people in rural areas of developing countries are still without an electricity supply.

As the most important of the clean, renewable energy options, hydropower is a benefit of a multipurpose water resources development project. As hydro schemes are generally integrated within multipurpose development schemes, they can often help subsidize other vital functions of a project.

Typically, construction of a dam and its associated reservoir results in a number of benefits associated with human well-being, such as secure water supply, irrigation for food production and flood control, and societal benefits such as increased recreational opportunities, improved navigation, the development of fisheries, and cottage industries. This is not the case for any other source of energy.

Electrical System Benefits

Hydropower, as an energy supply, also provides unique benefits to an electrical system. First, when stored in large quantities in the reservoir behind a dam, it is immediately available for use when required. Second, the energy source can be adjusted to meet demand instantaneously.

These benefits are part of a large family of benefits, known as ancillary services. They include:

- *Spinning reserve*—the ability to run at a zero load while synchronized to the electric system. When loads increase, additional power can be loaded rapidly into the system to meet demand. Hydropower can provide this service while not consuming additional fuel, thereby assuring minimal emissions.

- *Non-spinning reserve*—the ability to enter load into an electrical system from a source not on-line. While other energy sources can also provide non-spinning reserve, hydropower's quick start capability is unparalleled, taking just a few minutes, compared with as much as 30 minutes for other turbines and hours for steam generation.

- *Regulation and frequency response*—the ability to meet moment-to-moment fluctuations in system power requirements. When a system is unable to respond properly to load changes its frequency changes, resulting not just in a loss of power, but potential damage to electrical equipment connected to the system, especially computer systems. Hydropower's fast response characteristic makes it especially valuable in providing dependable regulation and frequency.

- *Voltage support*—the ability to control reactive power, thereby assuring that power will flow from generation to load.

- *Black start capability*—the ability to start generation without an outside source of power. This service allows system operators to provide auxiliary power to more complex generation sources that could take hours or even days to restart. Systems having available hydroelectric generation are able to restore service more rapidly than those dependent solely on thermal generation.

Avoided Emissions

Today 85 percent of the primary energy consumption is fossil (coal, oil and gas) or traditional (wood), with associated large-scale emissions to the atmosphere of greenhouse gases—carbon dioxide from combustion, and methane from processing coal and natural gas. It is well recognized at the international level that this is leading to major climatic changes, and will therefore also have consequences on the hydrological system (the water supply, agriculture, and sea level).

Recent research in North America confirms that the GHG emission factor for hydro plants in boreal ecosystems is typically 30-60 times less than factors for fossil fuel generation. Studies have also shown that development of even half of the world's economically feasible hydropower potential could reduce GHG emissions by about 13 percent, and the impact on avoided sulfur dioxide (SO_2) emissions (the main cause of acid rain) and nitrous oxide emissions is even greater.

Taking into account the fuel required to build hydropower stations, a coal-fired plant can emit 1000 times more SO_2 than hydropower systems. The magnitude of the impact of *particulate* emissions from fossil fuel is now also becoming recognized, particularly in connection with respiratory disease. A recent estimate of the environmental cost of this form of pollution is put at US$100-500/t/year.

Research is continuing on emissions, and it is recognized that more research is needed, particularly regarding tropical reservoirs. A theoretical calculation has been done for the case of Tucurui in Brazil, including

"worst case" assumptions concerning the decomposition of flooded biomass (that 100 percent of the biomass would decompose over 100 years, and that 20 percent of biomass carbon would be emitted as methane). Even if this were the case, the emission factor for Tucurui would be 213 g CO_2 equivalent per kWh, a factor five times lower than that for coal. In addition, the on-going upgrading of the Tucurui plant, with a near doubling of its capacity, without added flooding, will decrease significantly the GHG output per kWh of the plant.

As an example of pollution from fossil-fuel generation, in China 23 million tons of SO_2 are discharged into the atmosphere each year by thermal power plants, causing 40 percent of the total land area to be seriously affected by acid rain. The resulting damage to crops, forests, materials and human health was calculated, in 1995, to be more than US$13 billion. In North America the consumption of coal is at the same level.

Comparing Options

Compared with hydropower, thermal plants take less time to design, obtain approval, build and recover investment. However, they have higher operating costs, typically shorter operating lives (about 25 years), are important sources of air, water and soil pollution and greenhouse gases, and provide fewer opportunities for economic spin-offs.

Other renewable sources of power (solar, wind, etc.) are valuable options in addition to hydropower in specific contexts, but even if major efforts were made to develop them, they will not be able to produce large amounts of energy in the coming decades, or offer the same level of service, as they are intermittent sources requiring back-up supply. In assessing life cycle costs, hydropower consistently compares favorably with virtually all other forms of energy generation.

Cost of Hydropower Plants

The actual cost of a hydropower plant design and construction are astronomical. While the Hoover Dam's construction in 1936 was estimated at less than $50 million ($838 million today), the total cost of the Three Gorges dam in 2012 is estimated at $28 billion.

Large dams are things of the past, however, so now we can talk only about smaller dams and power plants. These are much cheaper, but still in the billions of dollars range. The cost of the proposed Marvin Nichols reservoir in northeast Texas, for example, has been estimated at $2.2 billion, with no power plant included. It would flood 30,000 acres of rare bottomland hardwood forest, and another 42,000 acres of mixed forest, family farms, and ranches along the Sulphur River in northeast Texas.

The other thing to consider, always, is the external cost of the generated power. The suffering of relocated families is heard in the residents' outcry, as is their concerned for wildlife habitat and local water quality. Long-lasting bad memories and negative publicity surround most hydro projects.

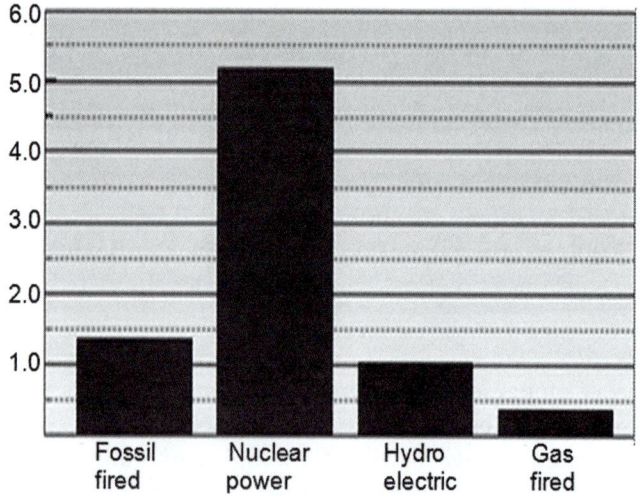

Figure 3-24. Power plants construction costs (in $/watt)

The actual cost of power plant construction (as related to the amount of produced power) varies from plant to plant. The main variable in the power generation cycle is always the size of the plant, since it could take as many people to operate and maintain a small one-unit generator as it would to operate and maintain two larger generators. This means that the cost of operation and maintenance per kilowatt produced would be maybe twice as high for the smaller plant.

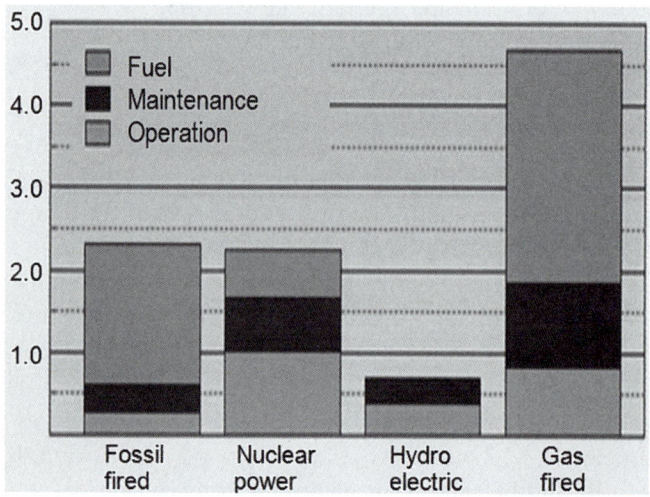

Figure 3-25. Power generation expenses in cents/kWh

A number of other variables also affect the final cost of the generated energy. The type, availability, quantity, and price of the fuels used in different power plants are critical components. Hydropower plants are the only power plants that have no allowance for fuel because water is free (if the external effects are not considered).

As water is becoming a precious commodity, this issue is becoming more important, and we will eventually be assigning a price to the water used by hydro-power plants.

Maintenance and operation variables are also significant and must be considered. Again, hydropower requires little daily maintenance, and only scheduled periodic maintenance and replacement of turbines and other components add cost.

Operational costs of hydropower plants are also quite low, so the entire fuel-maintenance-operation regime is quite stable, efficient and cheap—provided there is enough water.

Here are estimates of small hydropower plant costs and production expenses:

Capital cost	$1700-2300/kW
Operation cost	0.4¢/kW
Maintenance cost	0.3¢/kW
Operating life:	50+ years
Capacity factor:	50-60%
Average size:	30 MW
Large size:	over 1.0 GW

In general, the larger the hydroelectric plant, the cheaper the cost per kilowatt to produce the electricity. When compared to other means of producing electricity, hydroelectric production costs run about one third those of either fossil-fueled (coal or oil) or nuclear power plants, and less than one fourth those of gas turbine electricity production. The main contributing factor for the difference in this cost of production is the fuel costs for the other means of producing electricity.

The original plant cost for a small hydroelectric plant is somewhat cheaper than either fossil fuel or nuclear plants (not including the support infrastructure—water reservoir, etc.). On the other hand, gas turbine plants are the cheapest to build but the most expensive to operate.

As long as there is sufficient water to run the turbines, electricity can be produced very cheaply. Compared even to mature nuclear plants, hydropower costs less than half as much to produce, at under a penny per kWh. The power is transmitted to the national power grid and sold to the wholesale and retail markets at the same prices as electricity generated by other means, complete with premiums for peak demand production. This means a significant profit for the middle man and the utilities.

In summary, hydropower is a great energy source, which will continue to provide a major part of the world's energy, but there is the unanswered issue of water availability. It must be properly addressed and resolved once and forever, if we are to rely on hydropower in the 21st century.

Environmental Impact

Any infrastructure development inevitably involves a certain degree of change. That change can be quite significant, as is the case of new dam construction. A new dam requires the impounding and inundation of a large area for a water reservoir. This always creates certain social and physical changes up- and downstream.

There are difficult ethical issues. On top of the list is ensuring that the rights of people and communities affected by a new project are respected.

Social Aspects

As with other forms of economic activity, hydropower projects can have both positive and negative social aspects. Social costs are reflected in transformation of large land areas, displacement of people living in the reservoir area, and effects on the lifestyle of people living downstream.

Relocating people from the reservoir area is, undoubtedly, the most challenging social aspect of hydropower. This usually leads to significant concerns regarding local culture, religious beliefs, and the effects of submerging homes and burial sites.

There is no good way to handle this, so compromises are commonly used. The countries in Asia and Latin America, where resettlement is a major issue, have developed comprehensive strategies for compensation and support for people who are impacted.

We should keep in mind that other power generating technologies also cause significant resettlement. For example, coal mining and processing, and coal ash disposal sites, also displace communities. Also, the long-term GHG-induced climate change may eventually cause the greatest population migrations, as sea levels rise.

Social effects of hydro schemes are variable and project-specific. If anticipated and tackled early in the planning stage, negative impacts for locals can be addressed in a positive manner, or in avoided altogether.

When these impacts cannot be avoided or mitigated, compensation measures can be implemented.

During the construction phase of a hydro scheme (often several years) there may be a large workforce, and access roads can lead to a sudden influx of outside labor and the development of new economic activities, with resulting tensions, if populations in the area are unprepared. Issues of resettlement, sustainable livelihoods, cultural impacts and flood control must be addressed.

Effective mitigation measures can be implemented if local authorities and project promoters acknowledge and address these issues. On the positive side, the additional economic activities create new employment opportunities.

During the operational stage, the hydro project may represent a significant source of revenue for local communities. Access roads, local availability of electricity and other activities associated with the reservoir are all possible sources of sustainable economic and social development. Clearly, there must be cooperation between proponents, authorities, political leaders and communities, and long-term benefits must be directed to affected communities.

Socially acceptable hydropower means that any proposal for a project must be discussed with stakeholders and adapted to their needs, and that successful negotiations must be concluded with affected local communities for a project to move ahead.

From a social point of view, the relative success or failure of a hydro project is determined by integrating social considerations early into the project design.

Of course there are negative effects on wildlife in the area. Both up- and downstream fish, birds and other wildlife are affected by the landscape changes. Since these changes are permanent, changes in wildlife habits and patterns are irreversible too.

Case Study

In 1970, the Indian government built the huge Farakka Barrage dam on the Ganges River. Located on the border with Bangladesh, the gated dam has had devastating effects on the environment and the population of both the Indian state of West Bengal and neighboring Bangladesh.

The dam is controlled by the Indian side and has been creating its own environment, with regular floods in the summer and prolonged droughts in winter months. The negative effects are felt mostly downstream in Bangladesh, where the locals are forced to live in flooded houses part of the time and without water the rest of the time.

Through the years, the dam forced the Ganges river to shift almost six miles eastward, eroding several villages in the process. Factories, sugar mills, hospitals, and government buildings were flooded by the river. The Ganges' fast shift, however, made land that was once underwater reappear on the other side of the river bank. The land shift has created a territory dispute, so neither West Bengal nor Bangladesh recognizes thousands of displaced villagers.

The Farakka barrage was built at the narrowest point on the Ganges to divert water to Calcutta to the south and flush out the silt that was clogging up its port. But scientists say the project was ill-conceived from the start. Water upstream from the dam carried massive amounts of silt, dropping it directly behind the dam. The buildup—almost 700 million tons annually—has clogged the dam's gates and raised the river bed more than 20 feet, forcing the river to change its course.

With that process, the river is swallowing villages and buildings one day and bringing devastating droughts the next. This man-made disaster has created a large-scale humanitarian crisis.

It is not only large dams that have such profound negative effects. A recent five-year study concluded that for certain environmental impacts the cumulative damage caused by *small river dams* is even worse than that caused by large dams.

According to researchers, hydropower may be renewable, but there are serious questions about the sustainability of the overall process with its far-reaching rammifications to streams, wildlife and communities.

Small hydropower projects are often located in poor areas of the world which get no benefit from them because the small hydropower stations are almost always connected to the national grid, with the electricity being sent outside the local area. Locals are left to endure the results from construction and operation, which can be profound.

There are already 750,000 small (under 50 MW) dams in China alone, and about one new dam is built every day, according to the study. The ecological concerns these projects raise, especially in areas of biological diversity have been ignored until now, but are surfacing slowly as the number of hydropower projects increases.

Per megawatt of energy produced, small tributary dams sometimes have negative environmental impacts that are greater than large, main stem dams. Small dams can have significant impacts on habitat loss when some or the entire river flow is diverted into channels or pipes, leaving large sections of a river with no water at all.

Fish, wildlife, water quality and riparian zones are all affected by water diversion, and changes in nearby land use and habitat fragmentation can lead to further species loss. The cumulative effect on habitat diversity can be 100 times larger for small dams as compared to large dams.

China and other countries encourage more construction of small dams, but because they are usually built in remote areas inhabited by poor people, there is much less oversight and governance during the construction, operation and monitoring of small hydropower projects.

As a result, mitigation actions and governance structures that would limit social and environmental impacts of small hydropower stations are not adequately implemented. These conclusions are relevant to national energy policies in many nations or regions, and the locals are left to bear the brunt of the negative effects.

Large hydropower projects are usually well designed, organized, and managed, which is not the case with small hydropower projects, many of which are constructed and operate under the radar of the media and the regulators. There is much less control during the lifetime of the project and lots of bad things can happen unnoticed.

According to the study, the overwhelming result of all this is that the negative biophysical and social impacts of small hydropower exceed those of large hydropower, especially when the local habitat and hydrologic changes are concerned.

Equipment Impact

Building a hydro dam and hydro power plant requires huge amounts of concrete, steel, and other materials and equipment, which are made with the help of tons of fossil fuels. During the production and transport of this equipment, a lot of gaseous liquid and particulate pollution was generated as well, including huge amounts of CO_2.

Pollution Footprint of Plant Equipment

Similar to the mining process, starting with the plant's design and construction, we see pollution spewing from bulldozers and large trucks. Millions of tons of equipment, cement, sand, rocks, and water are delivered to the site on trucks and trains for dam construction. Then power plant equipment arrives. It, too, has a left a footprint in the wake of its creation and manufacture.

Just like in the mining case, we would assign 5-10% of the manufacturing and transport of power plant equipment to the initial construction step (A). The main pieces of equipment arrive on back of enormous trailers or rail cars. These are assembled with the help of other equipment and put to work, leaving more pollution (B). In addition, many other items are delivered, such as smaller equipment, tools and consumables. These have left their marks as well (C). To complete the pollution footprint picture, we add the people involved, their use of transportation, and the provision of their basic needs (D).

So, the total pollution footprint of the power plant's equipment cradle-to-grave process is expressed by:

$$P_f = A + B + C + D$$

where

 P_f is the total pollution footprint

A is equipment manufacture and transport to the power plant

B is equipment assembly, test and installation at the power plant

C is the manufacture and transport to the power plant of tools and consumables, and

D is the pollution footprint of the equipment personnel during the design and setup phases.

Combining the pollution footprint of A (the plant equipment manufacturing and transport) with B (plant equipment assembly, test and installation), adding C (the manufacture and transport of the tools and consumables), plus D (the pollution footprint of the equipment personnel) gives us the environmental footprint of the plant equipment before even starting plant operation.

Here again, the pollution footprint is significant and far-reaching.

To put a value on it we must take inventory of all items employed in the design, construction and operation processes, considering their raw materials, manufacture and handing. Putting a dollar value to all of it would be too complex for our purposes, so it suffices to say that the pollution effects during and after all these steps are significant.

We will take a second, closer look at these steps and their environmental effects in the following chapters.

Upon starting power plant operation, equipment begins to generate secondary pollution in the form of spare parts for monsters-size pieces of equipment which are periodically arriving from the manufacturers, after leaving their pollution footprint all over the place. We will attempt to assign a number—quantity of air and land pollution—and a related dollar value to these activities and their environmental effects later on.

After 20-30 years of non-stop operation, the dam might still be good, but the power plant is finally declared obsolete and must be shut down and decommissioned, or rebuilt. The decommissioning or rebuilding of a hydropower plant is an expensive and polluting undertaking. The equipment and materials used during this process create additional air and ground pollution which is not to be ignored.

Specialized equipment and personnel (environmental specialists and inspectors), are usually brought in to assist and/or coordinate the effort. With that more pollution footprints are left at the already exhausted mine.

When the final tally is made, a significant part of the emissions and overall pollution are to be attributed to the plant's equipment and support personnel. We will look at the calculations of this number in the next chapters as well.

HYDROGEN ENERGY

In its as-is form, hydrogen flowing free in the mixture of other gasses in the air around us is actually only a potential energy source. It must be extracted from the air (or somehow created from other materials), collected and otherwise processed and stored, before it can be classified and used as an energy source suitable for power generation or fueling transportation vehicles.

For our purposes (power generation) it could be classified as energy storage technology, more than anything else. By storing the excess energy from wind and solar power generators, for use at a later hour or date, hydrogen could become very important in making those energy sources more viable. It is their variability due to fluctuation with solar and wind availability that keeps them from being more practical.

Hydrogen could be generated using excess power produced at solar and wind power plants, stored and burned to produce electricity in times of low power generation (when no sun or wind are available) and at night.

The problem with using hydrogen today for everyday purposes is that it costs about $6-8 to produce one kilogram of hydrogen, which contains about the same energy content as one gallon of gasoline. Once produced in large quantity, sometime in the future, the price would go down significantly. At that point, combining hydrogen with free oxygen in fuel cells would make an extraordinarily convenient green form of power since there is a lot of energy produced by this reaction and the waste byproduct is pure water.

For this to work efficiently on a large scale, however, will require excavating larger reserves of Platinum-group metals to build the requisite number of fuel cells. The United States Geological Survey today estimates the total global reserves of platinum that can be mined are roughly 100 million kilograms, which is just enough to fit the 4 billion automobiles world-wide with fuel cells at the current 22.6 grams platinum needed per hydrogen-powered vehicle.

And then, there would be no more platinum...

If platinum is depleted we will have to move mining operations off the planet, to mine the richer platinum reserves found in near-earth asteroids, or the lunar highlands where there is evidence of much higher densities of platinum and platinum group metals (cobalt, nickel, ruthenium, rhodium, palladium, osmium, iridium).

It might become a reality when future generations run out of fossils, nuclear plants become more harmful than helpful, and water is no longer available for hydro-power generation.

Hydrogen Production

There are a few ways to produce free hydrogen gas suitable for practical use as a fuel. This could be done by:

1. Electrolysis of water,
2. High temperature pyrolysis of natural gas, or
3. Steam reforming or hydrocarbons from petroleum or coal.

A true hydrogen economy of our clean-energy future depends on water electrolysis as the most promising from an environmental point of view, because when fossil fuels are burned to free hydrogen, they contribute to greenhouse gas emissions. Or we could await the arrival of more widespread use of nuclear fission or fusion processes or solar powered electrolysis for hydrogen to become a realistic energy source.

> Using special catalysts created by MIT chemists, sunlight can turn water into hydrogen. If the process can scale up, it could make solar power a dominant source of energy. But there are still many issues to be resolved, mostly related to the type and quantity of solar power to be used, the conversion of hydrogen gas into liquid, as well as its storage and transport.
>
> In addition to the technical issues at hand, the hydrogen conversion process requires expensive equipment and processes, as well as a lot of energy, so it remains to be seen how far this technology can go in the present state of the art.

Background

Over the last century, technology has developed at an amazingly fast pace, as has global population which has grown from about 1.0 billion persons in 1800, to 3.0 billion in 1960 and over 6.0 billion at the beginning of the 21st century. With it, the demand for energy has also increased proportionatey in most places and in ridiculous disproportion in others—such as the US—where people use several times more energy than they need.

For the last century, we have been relying mostly on fossil fuels—coal, oil, and natural gas—that are not renewable natural resources. Global demand for energy is increasing by the day and is expected to double by the middle of this century. By then, the world's oil resources will be exhausted, while gas and coal reserves will be substantially depleted. Three or four of the present generations will have consumed natural reserves that took over 100 million years to generate.

As far as using natural resources is concerned, all of humanity is living on borrowed time. We are burning fossil fuels equivalent to 9.0 billion gallons of oil per day. With every day, the Earth contains less and less coal, oil, and natural gas, while the environment bares the scars of our race to eliminate the natural resources.

The fiddler will be recompensed, and it will be the following generations who will pay. Forget about using oil to burn, they'll be lucky to have oil to make the necessities of life, which we take for granted today, such as cheap plastics, clothing, medications, cosmetics etc. And the only benefit from this would be a significant decrease in pollution. We wonder if the future generations will thank us for that.

Life without abundant and cheap energy of the types we have today would be full of hardships and misery. We hope future generations will be more responsible, and will find ways to develop more reliable and sustainable energy sources, and learn how to conserve energy so that it lasts longer.

A hydrogen-based economy of the post 21st century meets some of these expectations and requirements. It might be the main source of energy for power generation and transport during the next several centuries.

Solar Hydrogen (Most Possible) Future

Mass hydrogen production is one of the possible ways to reduce the use of natural resources and stop the rampant air, water and soil pollution. Hydrogen is a nontoxic, clean-burning fuel which can be produced from water and sunlight. Thus produced "solar hydrogen" can be used in every application where conventional fuels are used today—including all residential, industrial and transport applications.

Solar hydrogen is basically hydrogen gas produced by using solar energy (as a primary energy source) or one of its derivative, renewable forms (secondary energy source), such as wind, ocean waves, falling water, and biomass. Hydrogen can then be used on-site when and as needed, or it can be transported for use anywhere—in the world.

By replacing fossil fuels with solar hydrogen, we can move from an unsustainable, dirty, and wealth-depleting economy, to a clean, environmentally friendly, sustainable, wealth-enhancing one.

Another great benefit that accompanies the production of solar hydrogen is the generation of mass quantities of oxygen as a byproduct of the water molecule splitting process. There are other benefits too, as we will see below.

Solar energy, albeit abundant in many areas of the world is inconveniently remote and inaccessible in large quantities. It is also variable, so we cannot count on it alone for providing reliable power. Generating hydrogen by splitting water via solar energy generated at large-scale solar fields in the high deserts, and storing it for use as a primary energy source when solar is unavailable, might be one of the most promising solutions to the issues at hand.

Hydrogen is an efficient fuel. It is carbon-free and is converted back into pure water during the combustion process. This means that we start with water, use the sunlight to split it and generate hydrogen during the day, store it and then burn the hydrogen at night to generate heat and electricity, which process produces water…again.

This is an almost perfect closed-loop system—a type of practical perpetuum mobile machine, using only the free sun's energy to assist in the never ending and very efficient water-to-hydrogen conversion process, where very little energy and water are lost and where the action never stops…as long as the sun shines and the wind blows.

The overall water-to-hydrogen-to-heat-to-electricity process goes something like this:

1. During the day:

2. During the night:

$$2H_2 + O_2 = 2H_2O + \text{heat} \rightarrow \text{electricity}$$

The generated water, together with the sunlight used for splitting it are the only materials and fuel needed to generate and store hydrogen, which could be used later to generate power. This is clean and abundant energy in a carbon-free, natural and renewable cycle. Unlike the other fuels, hydrogen can be liquefied and transported over long distances without the presence of expensive transmission or pipelines, and the losses and other hassles associated with those.

It can be also stored, unlike electricity, and transported over long distances to any location on the globe and to areas that need it most. Hydrogen also can be stored in large quantity in underground reservoirs or in containers to be used as needed by industrial enterprises, in households, power stations, cars and aviation.

Upon combustion, hydrogen produces heat and clean water. Two pounds of hydrogen release about 120,000 Btu heat, or as much as one gallon of gasoline. Or, 10 million tons of hydrogen per year can fuel 25 to 30 million hydrogen fueled cars, or power 6 to 8 million homes. Keep in mind that 10 million tons of hydrogen could be easily generated in the Arizona or Nevada deserts, where sunlight is as abundant as sand.

The practical implementation and application of new hydrogen-based economy, however, is not simple, or cheap. To provide the US transportation system with hydrogen fuel we will need:

- 250,000 small neighborhood-based hydrogen electrolysis generators to fuel cars and trucks, plus

- 20,000 interstate hydrogen vehicle refueling stations for passenger and commercial vehicles refueling.

This means replacing and/or retrofitting most of the existing gas stations with new high pressure storage tanks, compressors, pumps, and equipment needed to serve hydrogen powered vehicles. This would come at an enormous expense, in addition to a number of other serious problems during the transition period

The production of 10 million tons of hydrogen annually, as needed to run the hydrogen based U.S. transportation sector, would require:

- 35 coal/biomass gasification plants, similar to today's large coal-fired plants,

- 25 large nuclear plants making only hydrogen, and

- 15 medium-size power plants, using oil and natural gas in multi-fuel gasifiers and reformers.

Or it all can be done by using solar and wind energy. The huge unused desert areas in Arizona, New Mexico, Utah, Texas, and Nevada offer unlimited solar energy, which can be easily captured and converted into gaseous and liquid hydrogen for the U.S. and abroad.

How do we generate hydrogen using solar power? What problems might be encountered going that route?

Other Hydrogen Production Methods

Hydrogen is one of the most abundant elements in the universe, for it is locked in the gas mixtures and in the molecules of most organic and some inorganic materials. However, it does not exist naturally as gas or liquid in large quantities or in any significant concentrations. Hydrogen, therefore, must be produced from other compounds such as air, water, biomass, or fossil fuels.

Various methods of production have unique needs in terms of energy sources (e.g., heat, light, electricity), all of which generate unique by-products and emissions.

Following are some of the conventional hydrogen generation methods under consideration and development today.

- Hydrogen generation by steam methane reforming constitutes 95% of the hydrogen produced in the United States today. This is a process of reacting natural gas or other light hydrocarbons catalytically with steam to produce a mixture of hydrogen and carbon dioxide. The mixture is then separated to produce high-purity hydrogen. This method is the most energy-efficient commercialized technology currently available, and is most cost-effective when applied to large, constant loads. However, it uses ever more expensive and depleting natural resources, and produces large quantities of carbon dioxide, which must be sequestered, or otherwise dealth with.

- Partial oxidation of fossil fuels in large gasifiers is another method of thermal hydrogen production. It is done by the reaction of conventional fuels with a limited supply of oxygen to produce a hydrogen mixture, which is then purified. This process can be applied to a wide range of hydrocarbon fuels including natural gas, heavy oils, solid biomass, and coal. Large amounts of carbon dioxide are produced during this cycle as well.

- Hydrogen can also be produced by using electricity in electrolyzers to extract it from water. We call this process "splitting water." Thermal dissociation of water using concentrated solar energy is another approach for practical hydrogen generation.

These methods are not as efficient or cost effective as using fossil fuels in steam methane reforming and partial oxidation, but are most promising for the near future due to a number of factors discussed above. They also allow more distributed hydrogen generation and use, and open possibilities for using electricity made from renewable resources. The primary byproducts of the water-to-hydrogen conversion process are oxygen and small amounts of carbon dioxide (as a byproduct from electricity generation). The byproduct of burning hydrogen is pure water.

Methods for producing hydrogen without using fossils (solar and wind) are most interesting, due to the obvious avoidance of depleted natural resources and without much environmental contamination. Some of these methods are our best hope for efficient and safe 21st century power generation. Although components of these systems are still in development phases, these technologies are our best hope in the 21st century, because hydrogen generated by solar energy (thermal or electrical) induced water splitting is capable of replacing fossil fuels, ultimately bringing us energy independence and a cleaner environment.

These fossil-free solar hydrogen generation approaches include:

- Splitting (electrolysis) of water using electricity generated from solar energy or a other energy sources (wind, hydro etc.),

- Thermo-chemical reactions that release hydrogen from water or biomass,

- Thermal dissociation of water using concentrated solar power (CSP); and

- Microbial activity that releases hydrogen from organic compounds and biomass.

During burning, hydrogen readily reacts with oxygen in an highly exothermic reaction (energy is released—heat in this case), producing pure water as a result of the reaction and as a unique byproduct, which could be used in a number of applications—including re-use in the hydrogen generation process:

$$2H_2(g) + O_2(g) = 2H_2O(l) + 572 \text{ kJ (heat)}$$

In reality, fuel cells of this type use air rather than pure oxygen, and as a consequence a small amount of nitrogen oxides are formed as exhaust products (since there is a lot of nitrogen in air). PEM and SOFC (high temperature) fuel cells, the most efficient H_2 technologies today, emit trace amounts of nitrogen oxide (NO_x) gasses, while others might emit more.

Hydrogen must be generated by extracting it from hydrogen sources, and unfortunately today most of the commercially produced H_2 gas comes from fossils, which process contributes to the overall CO_2 emissions and to global warming.

Once available, however, H_2 is an excellent fuel that can replace hydrocarbons with numerous advantages, including a specific heat capacity three times higher than that of our best fossil fuel (natural gas, or methane).

NOTE: Fossil fuels have high-energy content and their power densities (the rate of energy production per unit of the earth's area these come from) are approximately 102 W per m², while in contrast their energy production is well below 1 W per m², which is a horrible efficiency ratio.

At the same time, densities of electricity produced by PV generation are over 40 W per m² at peak power when using some highly efficient PV technologies (i.e. CPV and HCPV trackers).

One of the big problems of PV technologies is their variability—no sunlight at night, or on rainy days means no electricity generation during those times. Also, when a cloud covers the sky, PV power is drastically reduced, and all this contributes to increase reluctance on the part of users to rely on solar power.

So, the best solution is generating H_2 gas and storing it to reduce or eliminate the variability. H_2 is an excellent option for storing excess energy during the day, for use at night and on cloudy days. Several methods rely on the two main solar energy technologies which are photovoltaics (PV) and concentrated solar power (CSP).

Water Electrolysis

This is the water electrolysis using electrical current generated by PV of CSP power fields, where:

$$H_2O + 2F = H_2 + \tfrac{1}{2}O_2$$

where

F is the Faraday constant, measuring 1 mol of electricity.

Once available in gaseous or liquid form, H_2 can be used to generate electricity by the reverse of reaction:

$$H_2 + \tfrac{1}{2}O_2 = H_2O + 2F \text{(energy)}$$

This is in fact the process that occurs in an $H_2 - O_2$ fuel cell, which can work as a fuel cell, or as an electrolyzer, depending on the operating conditions. The process is able to create any amount of hydrogen, as needed to power a house or commercial building. Hydrogen can also be used to power cars and boats with internal combustion engines, providing similar power density with added safety.

NOTE: Although hydrogen is highly flammable, it is 14.4 times lighter than air, rising at 20m/s^{-1} rate, so if ignited the flame tends to shoot up vertically, while gasoline and diesel are heavy and tend to run and accumulate under vehicles, where they can explode or spread and feed a fire.

The energy needed for the electrolysis can be provided by a number of sources. Presently CSP is the energy of choice for generating large quantities of H_2 from water. The preferred process includes catalytic thermo-chemical processes that make use of the intense heat or electricity generated by the solar radiation to create a large surplus of hydrogen suitable for storage and later use. The entire process is entirely renewable, using abundant energy sources and raw materials: solar energy and water, respectively, without generation of any appreciable CO_2 emissions.

Theoretically, the product yield of the water splitting reaction is 100% efficient since no electrical energy is wasted. Because the cost of water is negligible, this process is quite cheap too. The economics of the process are driven mostly by the cost of electricity.

Small amounts of electrolyte (usually KOH, or NaOH) are dissolved in water to enhance conductivity and thus the overall rate of the process of water electrolysis. A 30 percent KOH solution at 80°C (alkaline electrolysis) is used, and the electrolyte can be recovered and re-used time after time. Such electrolysis systems make use of a ceramic micro-porous separator (diaphragm), whereas the electrodes are usually made of nickel, with Pt coated cathode and MgO_2 coated anode.

The reactions during electrolysis are:

$$2H_2O + 2e = H_2 + 2OH \text{ (cathode)}$$
$$2OH = \tfrac{1}{2}O_2 + H_2O + 2e \text{ (anode)}$$

Typically, a commercial alkaline electrolyzer produces H_2 by consuming 4.49 kW h/m³ of electricity with

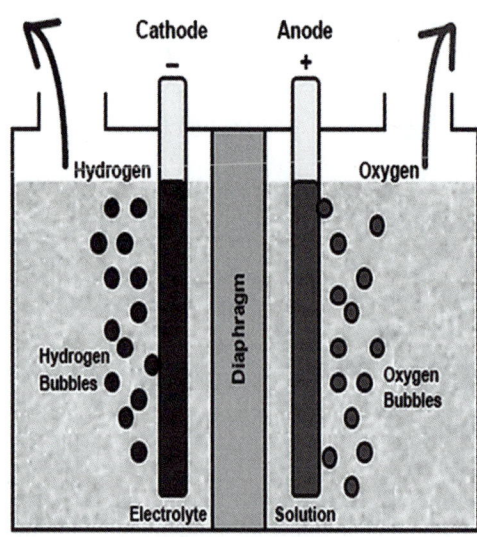

Figure 3-26. Hydrogen electrolysis apparatus

current yield and hydrogen purity both close to 100%. The fuel cell makes it possible to use the solar power made available as H_2 when the (weather) conditions are optimal and to store the excess power so that it can be made available for later use as required.

Extracted from water using photovoltaics and electrolysis, H_2 is oxidized in the fuel cell and the only emission is clean water, completing a zero emission energy production cycle.

The necessary investment for the hydrogen infrastructure gains more economic profitability with an increasing number of cells.

Today, when solar panels generate more electricity than a home is using, the excess is simply fed back into the grid, essentially subtracting from the homeowner's utility bill. In an off-grid application, the excess is put into batteries, but fuel cells are more versatile and their price is rapidly declining.

Existing electrolyzers are expensive, hence, the challenge is devising a system that is efficient enough to make energy inexpensively. In general, PV electricity should be used as such, for electricity is the highest quality energy available, but this will require the introduction of a new generation of batteries able to recharge rapidly with large amounts of energy.

Yet, the idea to use PV energy to crack water molecules into hydrogen and oxygen and later in a fuel cell to make electricity when the sun is not shining is plausible. The concept is a closed-loop system in which hydrogen oxidized with air in the fuel cell creates water, which is captured and used again.

Thermo-chemical Water Splitting

Achieving our energy independence will require large-scale alternative energy generation, where solar-based H_2O splitting could play a deciding role. This process requires practical technology in terms of quantity and cost. The thermo-chemical redox-cycle process using simple and robust materials is capable of that.

This process is a thermal reaction that requires an energy input in a multichannel ceramic honeycomb reactor resembling the familiar catalytic converter of automobiles, coated with active water-splitting materials. The system is heated by concentrated solar radiation using a set of mirrors to concentrate the solar energy, increasing the temperature in the reactor.

In the first step of water-splitting, the activated redox reagent (usually the reduced state of a metal oxide) is oxidized by taking oxygen from water, and with the help of high-temperature heat produces hydrogen, according to the reaction:

$$MOx \text{ (reduced)} + H_2O \rightarrow MOx \text{ (oxidized} + H_2$$

During the second step the oxidized state of the reagent is reduced, to be used again (regeneration), delivering some of the oxygen of its lattice according to the reaction:

$$MOx \text{ (oxidized)} \rightarrow / MOx \text{ (reduced)} + O_2$$

The metal oxide (such as mixed iron oxide) in this case acts as a redox system which is fixed on the surface of a porous absorber. At the beginning, the metal oxide is present in a reduced form. By adding water vapor at 800°C, oxygen is abstracted from the water molecules and hydrogen is produced. When the metal oxide system is saturated, or fully oxidized, it is heated for regeneration at 1100°C to 1200°C in an oxygen-lean atmosphere.

Oxygen is exhausted from the redox system using nitrogen as a flushing gas. The product gas passes through heat exchangers and is cooled down before residual water is separated.

The receiver surface is divided into several square apertures; two apertures make up one receiver pair. One aperture is applied for the dissociation of the water vapor, while the other is used for the regeneration of the redox system. Thus, hydrogen can be produced continuously by alternating the reaction steps.

One advantage here is the production of pure hydrogen and the removal of oxygen in separate steps, avoiding the need for high-temperature separation and the chance of explosive mixture formation. The active redox material is in fact capable of water-splitting and regeneration, so that complete operation (water splitting and redox material regeneration) is achieved in a closed solar reactor.

Iodine-sulfur Thermo-chemical Water Splitting

Another promising approach for hydrogen production is the iodine–sulfur (IS) thermo-chemical water splitting cycle. Here, high temperature is needed to start and maintain the reaction, which consists of three sections:

1. Bunsen section,
2. Hydrogen–Iodide (HI) section, and
3. Sulfuric acid section

This complex process is initiated in the Bunsen section, where under the effects of high heat influx, assisted by the action of sulfur dioxide SO_2 and iodine I_2, excess water and heat are added to keep the exothermic and spontaneous character of the reaction.

Once started, the reaction must be kept exothermic, and when it is stabilized, excess iodine is added to help the mixture split into two immiscible aqueous phases. This is achieved via the so-called spontaneous liquid-liquid (L-L) phase separation process, during which sulfuric acid and poly-hydroiodic acid (HIx) phases are obtained.

The lighter sulfuric acid phase is fed to the sulfuric acid, H_2SO_4 decomposition section, where it is concentrated, while at the same time it is thermally decomposed to sulfur trioxide, SO_3 and water, H_2O.

Increasing the temperature dissociates the sulfur trioxide, which is readily divided into oxygen, O_2 and sulfur dioxide SO_2.

Thus obtained O_2 can be used as a byproduct of the reaction when needed, while the SO_2 and H_2 must be recooled and recycled back to the Bunsen section and stored for further use.

At the same time, the heavier HIx phase is sent to the HI decomposition section, where the hydrogen iodide, HI is separated from the mixture and is exposed to high heat, where it is thermally decomposed into H_2 and I_2. The resulting H_2 gas is the final product of this process, and is stored for future use. The accompanying I_2 and H_2 are also cooled, recycled.

NOTE: Using waste heat from solar (CSP) installations to maintain the H_2 generation reaction has been proposed. We see this as one way to both provide much needed cooling for the CSP plant steam, and provide heat to maintain the exothermic nature of the H_2 generation reaction.

One problem with this approach is that the volume and heat content of the CSP plant's steam varies with the weather conditions. Inconsistent steam volume or heat content would hinder the proper maintenance of the H_2 generating reaction. CSP plants with energy storage, however, might be able to resolve this problem and provide constant quality steam using the stored heat as a source.

There are other ways to generate hydrogen as well, so future generations will have a great choice of equipment and processes.

The Challenges

Despite the advantages, water electrolysis and hydrogen/oxygen fuel cell technology still face enormous challenges. For instance, the electrodes used in water electrolysis are currently coated with platinum, which is not a sustainable resource and is quite expensive.

Researchers are currently investigating the employment of nanomaterials with a large reduction on the amount of precious metal needed. Indeed, the main advantage of these materials is that they are far cheaper and more abundant compared to expensive metals such as platinum.

Another problem is the intermittent nature of PV electricity (or solar heat), due to interruptions like nighttime and clouds. These anomalies create several problems for the H_2 generation process, mostly expressed as:

1. The process activity would decrease in time of cloud activity, and

2. Shutdown of H_2 generation process is unacceptable, with numerous consequences such as the initiation of Ni dissolution at the cathode, as it is driven to more positive potentials by short-circuit with the anode.

These shortcomings can be alleviated by using stored heat or electricity as energy sources. The Ni cathodes could be activated by coating them with a thin layer of more active and more stable materials.

One great problem to be considered is the fact that lots of electrical or thermal energy is required to break the $H_2 - O_2$ bond in water molecules, to free the hydrogen in it.

The simple reaction,

$$2H_2O \text{ (liquid)} = 2H_2 \text{ (gas)} + O_2 \text{ (gas)},$$

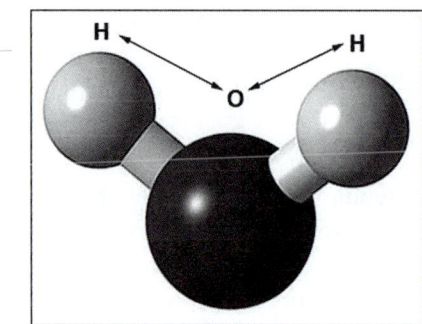

Figure 3-27. Water molecule

requires almost 3 time more energy (electric power or heat) than it can generate by burning thus obtained hydrogen. It is not a good account of energy efficiency, but the usefulness of hydrogen electrolysis comes when no other ways of storing energy, produced by other sources, are available. Photovoltaics, thermal solar and wind power generators will benefit tremendously when the hydrogen technology is fully developed and implemented in large-scale power generation fields.

The Hydrosol Project

The Hydrosol project was designed and proposed by a group of EU scientists and has won a number of prestigious awards as a practical way to generate a large amount of clean energy, including energy storage (for nighttime use) and transport of energy (hydrogen) to remote locations.

The Hydrosol process consists of an innovative solar thermo-chemical reactor for the production of hydrogen from water splitting, resembling the familiar catalytic converter of automobiles.

The reactor contains no moving parts and is constructed from special ceramic multi-channelled monoliths that absorb solar radiation. The monolith channels are coated with active water-splitting nanomaterials capable of splitting water vapor passing through the reactor by trapping its oxygen and leaving as product pure hydrogen in the effluent gas stream.

In a next step, the oxygen trapping material is solar-aided regenerated (i.e. releases the oxygen absorbed) and a cyclic operation is established on a single, closed reactor/receiver system. The integration of solar energy concentration systems with systems capable of splitting water will have an immense impact on energy economics worldwide, as it is a promising route to affordable, renewable solar hydrogen with virtually zero CO_2 emissions.

The uniqueness of the HYDROSOL approach is based on coating nano-materials with very high water-splitting activity and regeneration (produced by novel materials and processes such as aerosol & combustion synthesis) on special ceramic reactors with high capacity for solar heat absorption.

The production of solar hydrogen offers opportunities to many poor regions of the world which have a large solar potential. Producing solar hydrogen will create new opportunities for countries of southern Europe that can become local producers of energy as well.

With traditional energy sources diminishing, interest in alternative energy generation and storage is increasing. After nuclear energy, Hydrogen is considered by many to be the next link in the evolution of energy.

Hydrogen Economy

There is a concept that we need to clarify here, for it is extremely important. Presently we use a lot of fossil fuels and are not making much effort to determine what will happen when these are gone. When there are no more fossils, life as we know it will simply stop. Cars, trains, and planes will be parked for good. Power plants and factories will be shut down and an energy starved world will start a steady decline into poverty which would degenerate into chaos and crime.

We must strive to implement an effective transitional energy management plan with the decline of each of our fossil fuel sources. When crude oil is depleted, the transportation system could be converted to natural gas. By the time natural gas is depleted the transportation system would be ready to run on liquid hydrogen.

Such an endeavor would allow fuel for the critical transportation modes for the duration, and as a consequence there would be no economic penalties. The power generation sector should be able to transition from one available fuel to another, until it reaches the state of complete reliance on renewable energy sources, such as solar, wind, ocean, bio- and geo-power generators.

Facilitating the *energy transition* period is what we must be thinking about and working toward now, and this is where hydrogen has a major role to play:

1. Hydrogen promises smooth transition from the existing dirty and unsustainable energy systems of power generation, storage and transport, to clean, efficient, renewable energy.

2. Hydrogen energy generation, storage and transport systems are fully developed today and do not need special materials or processes but can be implemented immediately…if and when economically feasible.

3. The use of hydrogen as an energy source is ecologically safe, because there is virtually no pollution generated in the process, unlike most conventional energy generators and their supply chains.

4. Solar hydrogen generated power could be quite cheap (around 8-10 cents/kWh), if and when implemented on a large industrial scale.

5. Hydrogen is a convenient renewable energy source which can be stored and distributed all over the world, including Third World countries where such implementation is badly needed now and will be more so in the future.

Hydrogen can be cost competitive with gasoline. This estimate is based on the use of solar thermal energy to generate hydrogen, mass production of the necessary equipment, and subsidies equivalent to those provided to the oil, coal, and utility industries. Large-scale production could deliver hydrogen at under $1 per GGE. Given the low cost of producing electrical power from some power generators (i.e. hydroelectric dams), the use of this electricity to produce hydrogen by electrolysis would cost less than that needed to produce gasoline and diesel.

Hydrogen holds the world's record for burning faster than any other fuel and at leaner (lower) fuel-to-air ratios than those of the hydrocarbon fuels. These characteristics allow engines that burn hydrogen to operate more efficiently and much cleaner than those that depend on fossil fuels.

Virtually every existing engine application from lawn mowers to automobiles and locomotives can be fueled with hydrogen, and benefits include more power and longer engine life. But perhaps the most astonishing benefit of burning hydrogen in a conventional engine is what we might call minus emissions—that is, the exhaust pipe releases cleaner air than that which enters the engine. Atmospheric levels of carbon monoxide, tire particles, hydrocarbons, pollen, and diesel soot are reduced as air is cleaned by the hydrogen flame and in the exhaust system. The pollutants are substantially converted into harmless gases, and particles are trapped in the exhaust. This is a great benefit to the environment, where billions of cars, trucks, boats, trains, and planes would be traveling around the globe cleaning the air as they go, instead of polluting it. What a beautiful vision of a clean future...

Kits for high-efficiency combustion of hydrogen can be retrofitted on most engines in the global fleet of motor vehicles even now. Ordinary engines that have been converted to operate on hydrogen show no sign of metal embrittlement or other degradation after decades of pollution-free service. Engine oil stays clean, spark plugs last much longer, and degradation as measured by corrosion and wear on piston rings and bearings is greatly reduced. These vehicles can therefore last longer, run better, and clean the air. Transitioning will facilitate the distribution of hydrogen for the advent of fuel cells on a commercial scale.

Solar hydrogen can make any country energy-independent and pollution-free as far into the future as the sun will shine. For example, a small portion of the U.S. deserts can produce enough solar hydrogen to supply all the energy needs of the whole continent. Currently, Canada, Germany, Japan, Saudi Arabia, and Russia lead the world in developing plans to employ solar hydrogen. Several major auto manufacturers have experimental fleets of hydrogen-powered vehicles.

If solar hydrogen is used on a large enough scale to provide energy-intensive goods and services to the world's population, it will facilitate wealth addition as opposed to wealth depletion that results from burning fossil resources.

The harder we work on implementing a solar-hydrogen economy, the more goods and security everyone can have, resulting in a lower rate of inflation and less reason for conflict worldwide. These circumstances can create a global incentive to work for higher sustainable living standards, for both present and future generations.

Of course, there are serious barriers in the way. Capitalism imposes its own rules, and those usually do not consider the well-being of all, much less that of future generations. So, we see the new hydrogen economy mostly as a dream.

Practical Hydrogen Economy

A quote in the media from an unknown source: "With most hydrogen today being produced from hydrocarbons, the cost per unit of energy delivered through hydrogen is higher than the cost of the same unit of energy from the hydrocarbon itself." Duh! Why are you wasting fossils to produce clean energy sources? Is that the best use for that precious commodity? Isn't this the right time to start eliminating fossils from our energy vocabulary all together?

Energy economy powered by solar hydrogen requires complete control of the production, storage, distribution, and utilization of hydrogen, as well as the production of electricity from all renewable energy sources.

A practical, efficient, and cost-effective renewable economy, based on solar, wind, and hydrogen power generation could be achieved by:

1. Establishing renewable power fields, where generators convert solar energy and its derivatives, such as wind, falling water, wave motion, and biomass resources into electricity and hydrogen to be used as storage of energy or for transport to be used at remote locations.

2. Surplus hydrogen, and that for night power generation, could be stored in depleted natural-gas and oil wells and similar geological formations.

3. Existing infrastructure of electricity grids, natural gas pipelines, highways, and rails to distribute hydrogen and electricity from renewable resources could be used without much modification and expense.

4. Installation of kits that enable the current internal combustion engines of motor vehicles to operate with directly injected hydrogen, landfill gas, or gasoline. A vehicle converted to operate on hydrogen cleans the air through which it travels.

5. Introduction of automobiles that run on hydrogen-based fuel cells, to replace the wasteful and dirty internal combustion engines.

6. Installation of reversible electrolyzers and fuel cells in homes and businesses, where these could produce electricity during off-peak hours, to be converted to storable hydrogen. Thus stored hydrogen can be used to make electricity at peak hours.

DOE Hydrogen Roadmap

The US Department of Energy (DOE) has fully appreciated and evaluated the need for a new hydrogen-based economy, and has made some attempts to outline and implement the steps. Some of the conclusions and decisions—albeit focusing on the generation, storage and transport of hydrogen for fueling cars—follow.

Hydrogen Production, Challenges

Multiple challenges must be overcome to achieve the vision of secure, abundant, inexpensive and clean hydrogen production with low carbon emissions.

In 2011 DOE set the following goals in the U.S. hydrogen development program:

Hydrogen Production

Reduce the cost of hydrogen production to <$2.00/gge (gallon of gasoline equivalent), or $2.00-$4.00/gge delivered and dispensed. This cost is independent of the technology pathway and takes into consideration a range of assumptions for fuel cell electric vehicles (FCEVs) to be competitive with hybrid electric vehicles (HEVs). Those considerations include a range of gasoline prices and fuel economies. Technologies are being researched to achieve this goal in timeframes appropriate to their current states of development.

•   By 2020, reduce the cost of distributed production of hydrogen from biomass-derived renewable liquids to <$2.30/gge (≤$4.00 delivered and dispensed).

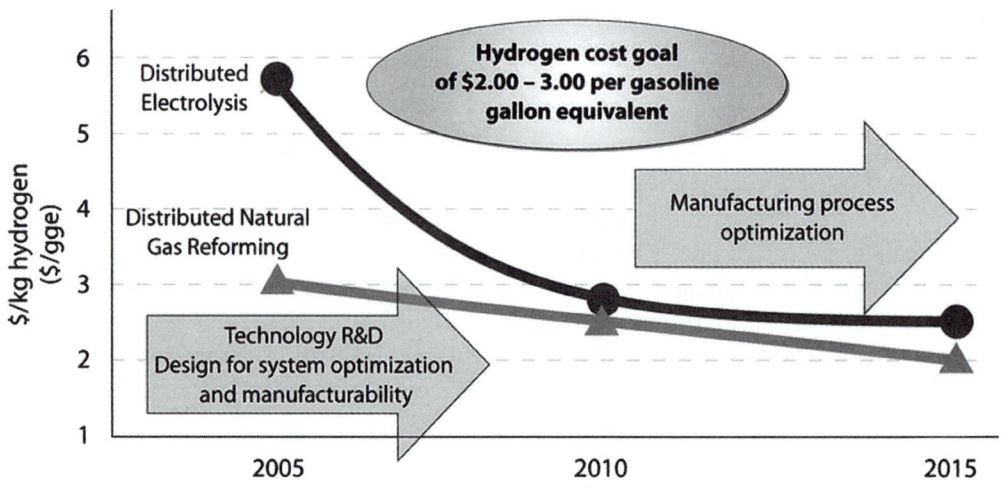

Figure 3-28. Hydrogen production 2005-2015

- By 2020, reduce the cost of distributed production of hydrogen from water electrolysis to <$2.30/gge (≤$4.00 delivered and dispensed).

- By 2015, reduce the cost of central production of hydrogen from water electrolysis using renewable power to $3.00/gge at plant gate. By 2020, reduce the cost of central production of hydrogen from water electrolysis using renewable power to ≤$2.00/gge at plant gate.

- By 2020, reduce the cost of hydrogen produced from biomass gasification to ≤$2.00/gge at the plant gate.

- By 2015, verify the potential for solar thermo-chemical (STCH) cycles for hydrogen production to be competitive in the long term, and by 2020, develop this technology to produce hydrogen with a projected cost of $3.00/gge at the plant gate.

Hydrogen Delivery

Develop technologies that reduce the costs of delivering hydrogen to a level at which its use as an energy carrier in fuel cell applications is competitive with alternative transportation and power generation technologies.

- By 2012, identify optimized delivery pathways that meet an as-dispensed hydrogen cost of <$4/gge (~$1.00/100 standard cubic feet [scf], including the average cost of hydrogen at current production facilities) for the emerging fuel cell powered material handling equipment (MHE) market.

- By 2014, reduce the cost of hydrogen delivery from the point of production to the point of use for fuel cell powered MHE to <$3/gge (~$0.75/100 scf).

- By 2015, reduce the cost of hydrogen delivery from the point of production to the point of use for emerging regional consumer and fleet vehicle markets to <$4/gge.

- By 2020, reduce the cost of hydrogen delivery from the point of production to the point of use in consumer vehicles to <$2/gge.

Hydrogen Storage
- Develop and demonstrate viable hydrogen storage technologies for transportation, stationary, and portable power applications.

- By 2017, develop and verify onboard hydrogen storage systems achieving 1.8 kWh/kg (5.5 wt.%), 1.3 kWh/L (0.040 kg hydrogen/L).

- Ultimate full-fleet target of 2.5 kWh/kg system (7.5 wt.% hydrogen) and 2.3 kWh/L (0.070 kg hydrogen/L).

- The system cost targets for 2017 and the ultimate full fleet system target are under review by the U.S. DRIVE Partnership (Driving Research and Innovation for Vehicle efficiency and Energy sustainability).

Hydrogen Safety

Develop and implement practices and procedures for the safe conduct of DOE-funded hydrogen and fuel cell projects. Provide the scientific and technical basis for requirements in critical RCS to enable full deployment of hydrogen and fuel cell technologies in all market sectors.

- Develop and validate test measurement protocols and methods to support and facilitate international harmonization of codes and standards for high pressure tanks by 2013.

- Conduct materials R&D to provide the technical underpinning to enable fault tolerant system designs for use with hydrogen infrastructure rollout by 2015.

- Conduct a quantitative risk assessment study to address indoor refueling requirements to be adopted by code developing organizations, e.g., National Fire Protection Association (NFPA) and International Code Council, by 2015.

- Support and facilitate development and promulgation of essential codes and standards by 2015 to enable widespread deployment and market entry of hydrogen and fuel cell technologies and completion of all essential domestic and international RCS by 2020.

- Ensure that best safety practices underlie research, technology development, and market deployment activities supported through DOE-funded projects.

- Conduct R&D to provide critical data and information needed to define requirements in developing codes and standards.

- Develop and enable widespread sharing of safety-related information resources and lessons learned with first responders, authorities having jurisdiction (AHJs), and other key stakeholders.

In Summary

Hydrogen production costs are high relative to conventional fuels. With most hydrogen currently produced from hydrocarbons, the cost per unit of energy delivered through hydrogen is higher than the cost of the same unit of energy from the hydrocarbon itself. This is especially the case when the comparison is made at the point of sale to the customer, as delivery costs for hydrogen are also higher than for hydrocarbons.

The large-scale, well-developed production and delivery infrastructures for natural gas, oil, coal, and electricity keep energy prices low and set a tough price point for hydrogen to meet.

Low demand inhibits development of production capacity. Although there is a healthy, growing market for hydrogen in refineries and chemical plants, there is little demand for hydrogen as an energy carrier. Demand growth will depend on the development and implementation of hydrogen storage and conversion devices, and on a demand pull from products such as hydrogen-powered cars and electric generators.

Without demand for high-quality hydrogen in the merchant energy carrier market, there is little incentive for industry to completely develop, optimize, and implement existing and new technologies.

Current technologies produce large quantities of carbon dioxide and are not optimized for making hydrogen as an energy carrier. Existing production technologies can produce vast amounts of hydrogen from hydrocarbons but emit large amounts of carbon dioxide into the atmosphere. Existing commercial production methods (such as steam methane reformation, multi-fuel gasification, and electrolysis) require technical improvements to reduce costs, improve efficiencies, and produce inexpensive, high-purity hydrogen with little or no carbon emissions.

Advanced hydrogen production methods need development. While wind, solar, and geothermal resources can produce hydrogen electrolytically, and biomass can produce hydrogen directly, other advanced methods for producing hydrogen from renewable and sustainable energy sources without generating carbon dioxide are still in early research and development phases.

Processes such as nuclear thermo-chemical water splitting, photo-electrochemical electrolysis, and biological methods require long-term, focused efforts to move toward commercial readiness. Renewable technologies, such as solar, wind, and geothermal need further development for hydrogen production to be more cost-competitive from these sources.

Public-private production demonstrations are essential. Stakeholders need a basic understanding of the different sources of hydrogen production before they will be willing to embrace the concepts. Demonstrations are the best way to gain the needed confidence. The large scale of some production processes, however, makes them particularly difficult and expensive to demonstrate.

Potential of Solar Hydrogen Generation and Use

H_2 Generation

The most developed and most promising technologies for large-scale electricity generation are solar photovoltaic, solar thermal, and wind power generation. These technologies are so sufficiently developed and field tested that they are becoming household terms. They are also becoming technologically and economically feasible. For example, an installed 100 MWp photovoltaic power plant situated in a desert area with yearly insolation of 2300 kWh/m, and 15% efficiency of conversion into hydrogen would have a collector surface of about $1/2$ km^2 and would produce yearly 0.5×10^9 m^3 of hydrogen gas, which can be burned to generate electricity or power cars.

New, more efficient solar technologies, like multi-junction solar cells and efficient CSP receivers, are capable of bringing the sunlight-to-AC power efficiencies up to 30%, and expected over 50% in the near future. This would reduce equipment and labor costs, as well as material and land requirements.

Calculating hydrogen power generation efficiency is tricky, and a number of factors must be considered in the calculation process.

$$r = \frac{\rho E 100}{P}$$

where

r	=	efficiency in %
ρ	=	H_2 density, normal conditions (0.08988 kg/m^3)
E	=	H_2 specific energy (about 40 kWh/kg)
P	=	power consumed per volume of extracted
H_2	=	mass in kWh/Nm^3 (3.6 kWh/Nm^3 for 100% efficient H_2 generator)

The energy of hydrogen electrolysis (the process of converting water into hydrogen) is estimated at 50-80%, depending on the method and equipment used. A lot of outside electricity is used to initiate and maintain this process, so when input of energy is considered, the overall fuel-to-grid efficiency drops to about 30-40%.

The EU's electricity consumption could be met with the European yearly insolation of about 1000 kWh/m^2/y and 15% conversion efficiency, while using less than 1% of Europe's land surface. However, it doesn't make much sense to use cloud-covered Europe for such mass energy production. A much better alternative would be using the sunny African desert—especially in North Africa—which could produce all the energy Europe needs and much more.

This is a grand undertaking, yes, but it represents a smart investment in the future, which will benefit European nations, and provide African countries with opportunities they need.

The yearly insolation in Africa's deserts is approximately 2000 kWh/m^2, so a surface area of less than 1% of the Sahara desert land mass would be required by the solar collector field to meet Europe's entire electricity consumption.

There are already underwater cables crossing the Mediterranean Sea to deliver high voltage DC power to sub-stations in France, Spain, Germany, and Italy for conversion to AC and distribution to the other EU nations, and it is easy to see more.

Some of the energy produced by the solar fields in Africa (approximately 1/4) can be converted to LH_2 and delivered in conventional transport vehicles to power stations in the above-mentioned EU countries for conversion into electricity and distribution in the EU power network.

Where *will* the Europeans of the 22nd century get their energy? From the Soviet Union's natural gas pipelines? From waning Saudi Arabian oil wells?

The continental USA has a similar problem, although the situation here is somewhat different. Ours and Canada's oil and gas deposits will take us farther down the path of unsustainable, wasteful and dirty carbon economy. Smarter and more sustainable ways must be found.

So, large-scale solar power generation in the North African deserts, assisted by hydrogen generation and energy storage, appears to be the most efficient, versatile, and cost-effective alternative energy technology available today. For cloudy Europe, that is. The U.S. will follow, but probably much later!

Storage and Distribution

Once generated, hydrogen can be stored in its gaseous form, but it is more convenient to convert it into a liquid form. In this state, hydrogen can be transported, stored and burned either as free hydrogen or linked to other molecules like ammonia (NH_3), methanol (CH_3OH), methylcyclohexane (C_7H_{14}), or in a solid, such as a metal hydride.

Although liquid hydrogen (LH_2) has the highest energy density, it is disadvantaged by the energy required for conversion to liquid and keeping it at a very low temperature of 20 K. Approximately 30% of hydrogen's combustion energy is used by powerful compressors to pressurize and liquefy it.

Generating large quantities of LH_2 is a relatively new process that benefits from long experience borrowed from the space sector. Its transport is directly adaptable to existing technologies since the storage techniques of hydrogen as a gas are similar to those of natural gas. It can be stored in storage tanks or underground in confined aquifers, or in abandoned natural gas reservoirs. There are losses from underground reservoirs, but most rock formations are sealed by water in their capillary pores, so that the nature and properties of the contained gas have no effect on the overall leakage.

Transportation/distribution of LH_2 can be done easily and conveniently by pipelines, and in pressurized or cryogenic containers. A gaseous hydrogen pipeline system of some hundred kilometers and a vacuum-jacketed LH_2-system of some hundred meters are in operation today, including the Kennedy Space Center, so there is enough experience to design and operate a large system. The finances for doing that are significant and unavailable.

Another storage method is to convert (combine) LH_2 into Methylcyclohexane which is liquid at ambient pressure and temperature, so it can be stored in its as-is state (its consistency and specific weight are similar to diesel fuel). It could also be transported via the normal petroleum product carriers. This is important for a smooth energy-system infrastructure transition from crude oil to hydrogen…sometime in the distant future

Another form to which LH_2 lends itself for storage and transport is solid. Converting hydrogen gas into solid, rechargeable metal hydrides offers favorable volumetric hydrogen packing, although the weight of the non-saturated compound needed for storage of hydrogen is rather high. In an energy transition period, hydrogen can be mixed with natural gas; and as a matter of fact the "town gas" that was used in the past contained 50-60% hydrogen.

Environmental Effects of Hydrogen Generation

Although much cleaner than the fossils, the environmental effects of hydrogen production (via electro-cells), delivery (via pipes), storage (in underground caverns, or pressurized tanks), and power generation (by direct burning, via fuel cells, or other means) is measurable and at times significant.

The initial production of hydrogen via wind, solar, geothermal, biomass, or any other advanced methods, proceeds mostly without generating carbon dioxide, or any other harmful gasses or liquids. This is not to say that the entire process is absolutely clean, because it is not.

All energy sources used in hydrogen gas production have their own environmental imprint, as discussed in the previous chapters, so just by using them we are contributing to the complexity of the already complex environmental picture. A lot of energy is needed to free hydrogen from water molecules, and a lot of equipment must be manufactured, installed and used in the process...

We need to add here the impact of the solar and wind power equipment (which we discussed in detail in the previous chapter). This is in addition to the pollution created by the hydrogen gas generating and burning equipment (electrolyzers, fuel cells, and such).

The electrolytic cells equipment for mass production of hydrogen is made of different—usually expensive—materials and is of significant size too. These systems are contained in quartz or stainless steel vessels, with a ceramic micro-porous separator (diaphragm) in the middle, while the electrodes are usually made of nickel, with Pt coated cathode, and MgO_2 coated anode.

Where did it all come from? The metals were mined and refined in some third world country, then transported, machined, or otherwise processed per spec into the needed materials. The finished parts were shipped to the hydrogen producing plant for final assembly. This is exotic, expensive stuff that also requires a lot of energy (mostly fossil) to produce, manufacture, and transport. All these processes are accompanied by serious pollution as well and generate a lot of pollution, including carbon dioxide, particles, gas, liquid, and soil pollutants.

Once hydrogen gas is generated, it must be transported to a storage or liquefying facility, using steel pipes laid on or in the ground. Sometimes the hydrogen is sent into underground storage for later use, but more often it is sent to a compressor setup to be pressurized and liquefied in special cylinders. Thus filled cylinders are loaded on trucks or trains to be transported to the user location, which may be hundreds or thousands of miles away.

A lot of pollution was generated during all these steps.

FUEL CELLS

Hydrogen is a carbon-free fuel with excellent combustion properties. This makes it a clean, universal fuel for use in industry, households, power stations, road vehicles, boats, trains, and aviation. The hard part is producing it, but once that is resolved (using solar, wind etc. renewable energy in the future), using hydrogen will provide a number of benefits.

The specific properties of hydrogen induce new end-use equipment, processes and techniques that can be used for a number of practical applications.

Fuel Cells Operation and Use

The key element of efficient, future electricity generation is the fuel cell, for which hydrogen is the best fuel. Since these devices transform chemical energy directly into electric energy, hydrogen generation is not subjected to Carnot cycle limitations. It is also done silently without moving parts and with high efficiency.

Efficiencies of future fuel cells (like molten carbonate cells operating at 600-800°C with total energy efficiencies of 60-80% with waste heat at 600°C) make the fuel cell concept a potential candidate for use in power stations, and for air and road transport and space vehicles.

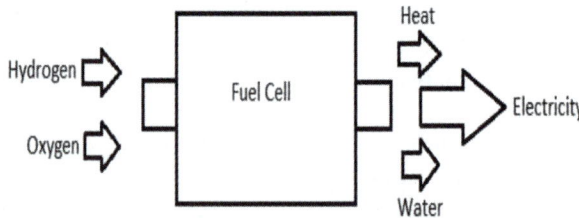

Figure 3-29. Fuel cell process

Advances in catalyst and electrode technology and cost reductions will need to be made, however, before fuel cells can be seriously considered for general use. Still, several power plants have already been established using different fuels (which is one of the great advantages of fuel cells.)

Catalytic Burners

Having lower ignition energy than some conventional fuels, including natural gas, hydrogen burns smokelessly when in contact with a suitable catalytic surface. Its burning temperature is quite low too—between 100 and 400°C. This makes it preferred technology for generating low-temperature heat in residential space heaters, cooking devices and industrial dryers and heaters.

Catalytic combustion has the advantages of higher safety levels and very high efficiency (up to 99%) with negligible emissions of nitrogen oxides.

Liquid Hydrogen Technologies

Super/hypersonic aviation and direct use in jet engines at super/hypersonic speeds could be advantageously—if not necessarily—powered with liquid hydrogen in the future because of its:

a. Higher (three-fold) gravimetric heating value compared with kerosene, and

b. Cooling capacity, which can be used to cool critical parts (turbine inlet rim, wing leading edges, passenger cabins, etc.), since LH_2 cryogenic storage temperature is approximately -252 C.

As an added benefit, cooling of the wing skin induces laminar flow, considerably reducing drag by up to (theoretically) 30%.

Automotive Vehicles

The main problem with hydrogen utilization in vehicles is storage due to its low volumetric energy content, which is about one-third that of gasoline. Even liquid hydrogen is far less dense than hydrocarbon fuels. Three different storage technologies are actually available and more or less mature: gaseous hydrogen in pressure vessels, cryogenic liquid hydrogen and hydrogen chemically bonded in metal and liquid hydrides (methyl-cyclohexane).

The low ignition energy of hydrogen and its wide ignition range of hydrogen/air mixtures make gas turbines as well as piston engines adaptable for hydrogen combustion. Ignition within a wide range of non-stoichiometric air/fuel mixture permits combustion with a high amount of excess air and thus full and load operation with low nitrogen oxides emission.

Many vehicles with hydride storage have been built and operated by Daimler Benz and others through the years, although the operation of the necessary infrastructure, re-fueling, and service must be addressed first. Because it is a major issue which will take a lot of time and money to resolve, the rest of the technology will lag for a long while.

A number of liquid hydrogen cars have been built and operated by BMW and DFVLR (Deutsche Forschungs-und Versuchsanstalt fur Luft-und Raumfahrt). Trucks with the methylcyclohexane technology have been built and operated by the Paul Scherrer Institute in Switzerland.

It should be emphasized that the problems of the necessary infrastructure development are at least as heavy as the development of the different components.

Hydrogen Homesteads

In the energy transition period, gaseous hydrogen can be utilized in existing natural gas pipelines of natural gas fueled appliances in homes and in industry, bearing in mind, however, that such a pipe system would not be optimized for use of hydrogen. Hydrogen has a volumetric heating value of approximately one-third that of natural gas, requiring a three times higher flow rate and compressor power at given pipe diameter and energy flow to keep the system under pressure (50-70 bar).

Fuel cells are by far most useful for large-scale power generation, which is the subject of this text, so we will take a close look at them.

Fuel Cells Design

Fuel cells convert the chemical energy contained in hydrogen (or other fuels) into electricity through a chemical reaction with oxygen or another oxidizing agent. Hydrogen is used most often, but other hydrocarbons such as natural gas and alcohols (methanol and others) can be used as well. Fuel cells are not energy storage devices, but rather energy conversion devices. They convert the chemical energy in the fuels into electrical energy. Therefore, they require a constant source of fuel and oxygen (or other catalyst) to run. They would generate electricity continually as long as fuel and catalysts are supplied, and the cell is in good operating order.

In addition to electricity, fuel cells produce water, heat and, depending on the fuel source, very small amounts of nitrogen dioxide and other emissions. The energy efficiency of a fuel cell is generally between 40-60%, or up to 85% if waste heat is captured for use.

The function of fuel cells, regardless of type and size, is based on the same principle; a sandwich consisting of three key and adjacent components (segments): anode, electrolyte, and cathode, as can be seen in Figure 3-30. There are two major chemical reactions occurring at the two interfaces between the three different segments. During these reactions, incoming fuel (hydrogen) is used and consumed, and at the end of the reactions, water or carbon dioxide are produced and emitted. Electric current is created during this process as well, and can be sent into the grid, or used to directly power electrical devices.

Fuel Cell Function

Fuel cell reactions proceed as follow. The fuel (usually hydrogen) is oxidized at the anode under the influence of the electric current applied to it, and a special catalyst is mixed in. Here the hydrogen molecule is basically split into a positively charged ion and a negatively charged electron. The electrolyte, in the middle of the sandwich, is a special chemical that is specifically designed so that free ions can pass through it, but the electrons are filtered and cannot go through. Thus separated electrons are free to travel on their own, and are then extracted from the cell through a metal wire. This creates electric current, the strength of which depends on the speed of reaction and number of molecules taking part in it.

The ions that pass through the electrolyte reach the other end of the cell—the cathode. If the wire from the anode is plugged into the cathode, the ions are reunited with the free electrons and the two react with a third chemical, usually oxygen, to create water or carbon dioxide. At the same time, electric current generated at the anode, and flowing through the load, will reach the cathode to complete the electrical circuit.

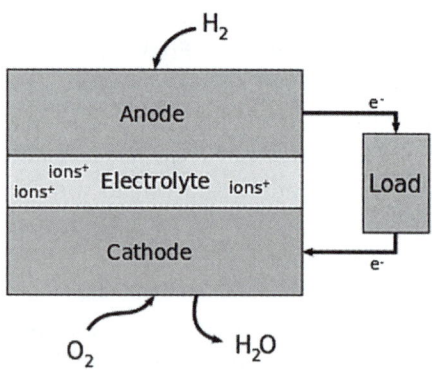

Figure 3-30. A block diagram of a fuel cell

The most important design feature in a fuel cell is the electrolyte composition, which usually defines the type of fuel cell. The type of fuel that is most commonly used is hydrogen. The anode catalyst, which breaks down the fuel into electrons and ions is usually made up of very fine platinum powder. The cathode catalyst, which turns the ions into waste chemicals like water or carbon dioxide, are made of nickel but can be also made

of a nanomaterial-based catalyst material.

A single, typical fuel cell produces a voltage from 0.6 V to 0.7 V at full rated power and load conditions. Usually, the voltage decreases as the current increases, due to activation loss. There is ohmic loss and voltage drop due to resistance of the cell components and interconnects, and there is mass transport loss resulting in depletion of reactants at catalyst sites under high loads. These cause loss of voltage.

Since the amount of energy generated by a single fuel cell is low, a number of these are usually connected together, if higher voltage and current generation is required. If connected in series, the cell yields higher voltage, and when in parallel the current is higher. Stacking several cells together is called a fuel cell stack. Increasing the cell surface area allows stronger current from each cell.

Types of Fuel Cells

There are many types of fuel cells, the main difference among them being the type and composition of the *electrolyte* layer. Fuel cells are usually classified by the type of electrolyte they use, and each type comes in a variety of sizes. Other distinguishing elements are the composition, shape and size of the cell components, which would also determine its type and application.

We will review several of the major, and most promising fuel cell designs: a) phosphoric acid fuel cells, b) proton exchange membrane fuel cells, c) solid oxide fuel cells, and d) molten carbonate fuels cells.

Phosphoric Acid Fuel Cells

Phosphoric acid fuel cells (PAFC) use liquid phosphoric acid as an electrolyte, and due to their simple and practical construction, they were the first fuel cells to be commercialized in the 1970s. Their quality and efficiency have improved significantly and have made them a good candidate for stationary power generating applications.

The chemical reactions for a PAFC system can be expressed as follow:

Anode reaction: $2H_2 \rightarrow 4H+ + 4e^-$
Cathode reaction: $O_2(g) + 4H+ + 4e^- \rightarrow 2H_2O$
Overall cell reaction: $2 H_2 + O_2 \rightarrow 2H_2O$

The electrolyte here is highly concentrated liquid phosphoric acid (H_3PO_4), which is saturated in a silicon carbide material (SiC). The electrode is made out of carbon paper coated with a finely dispersed platinum catalyst. The normal operating temperature range is

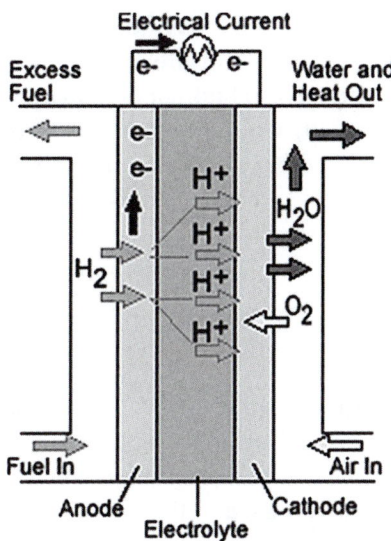

Figure 3-31. PAFC fuel cell

about 150 to 210°C, at which point the expelled water is converted into steam and can be used for air and/or water heating.

NOTE: Generating both hot air and water is known as combined heat and power process, which increases its practical efficiency up to 70%.

At lower temperatures phosphoric acid is a poor ionic conductor, and serious CO poisoning of the platinum electro-catalyst in the anode can occur. Nevertheless, these cells are much less sensitive to CO than PEFCs and AFCs.

PAFCs are also CO_2- and CO-tolerant (of concentration of about 1.5 percent). This broadens the choice of fuels they can use, which includes gasoline if the sulfur is removed prior to injecting into the fuel cell. A major disadvantage is the low power density of the cell, and the aggressive (corrosive acid) electrolyte in its structure.

PAFC have been used mostly for stationary power generators with output in the 100-400 kW range and for powering large vehicles such as buses.

The best known manufacturers of PAFC fuel cells are UTC Power, and Fuji Electric. India's DRDO is developing PAFC for air-independent propulsion in their Scorpène class submarines, and the Indian Navy has requested a fully operational PAFC system for implementation by 2014.

Proton Exchange Membrane Fuel Cells

The proton exchange membrane fuel cell (PEMFC) design is based on a proton-conducting polymer membrane, as the electrolyte between the anode and cathode.

Initially, this design was called *solid polymer electrolyte fuel cell* (SPEFC), before the key proton exchange mechanism was well understood.

The chemical reaction in this cell starts on the anode side, where hydrogen diffuses to the anode catalyst where it later dissociates into protons and electrons. The protons often react with oxidants which become multi-facilitated proton membranes, which allow the protons to pass through the membrane to the cathode. The membrane (which at this point is electrically insulating) does not allow electrons to pass through, so they are directed into an external circuit through wires, which can be connected to the grid, or used directly to power appliances and other electrical devices.

If a wire is connected from the anode to the cathode, the cathode catalyst (oxygen) reacts with the incoming electrons which have traveled through the external circuit, and the available protons, thus forming pure water.

Other hydrocarbon fuels which can be used in this type of fuel cell include diesel, methanol, and chemical hydrides. In all cases, the waste products from types of fuel cells are CO_2 and H_2O.

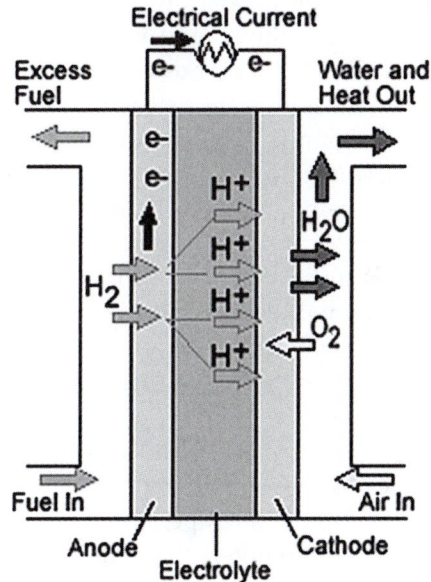

Figure 3-32. PEM fuel cell

A high temperature PEMFC consists of a bipolar plate electrode, with included in-milled gas channel structure. It is fabricated from conductive composites, enhanced with carbon-containing materials (graphite, carbon black, carbon fiber, and carbon nanotubes) for more conductivity. The membrane is made out of porous carbon paper.

The key components of a PEMFC are a) bipolar plate, b) electrode, c) catalyst, d) membrane, and e) wires and necessary hardware. These can be made out of different materials. For example, the bipolar plates can be made of materials such as metal, coated metal, graphite, flexible graphite, C-C composite, and carbon–polymer composites.

The membrane electrode assembly (MEA) is the heart of the PEMFC, and is usually made of a proton exchange membrane sandwiched between two catalyst coated carbon papers.

Platinum or similar types of noble metals are usually used for catalysts in PEMFC devices, while the electrolyte could be a polymer membrane.

Water and air management in PEMFCs is critical. The membrane must be hydrated, which requires water to be evaporated at precisely the same rate that it is produced—not an easy task. The problem is that if water is evaporated too quickly, the membrane dries and the resistance across it increases. This will eventually crack it, creating a gas "short circuit," where hydrogen and oxygen combine directly. This unwanted process generates heat capable of damaging the fuel cell.

On the other hand, if the water is evaporated too slowly, the electrode floods, preventing the reactants from reaching the catalyst, and usually stopping the reaction. Electro-osmotic pumps can be developed and used to control the flow, since a steady ratio between the reactant and oxygen is necessary to keep the fuel cell operating efficiently.

Temperature management is critical in this type of fuel cell, since a constant temperature must be maintained throughout the cell to prevent destruction of the cell through thermal loading. This is not easy, because the particularly challenging $2H_2 + O_2 \rightarrow 2H_2O$ reaction is exothermic and generates a large quantity of heat within the fuel cell.

Durability, or service life, and special requirements for some types of cells require more than 40,000 hours of reliable operation at a temperature of −31 to +104°F. At the same time, automotive fuel cells require at least a 5,000-hour lifespan, which is equivalent to 150,000 miles operation under extreme temperatures. Unfortunately, the service life of present-day PEM fuel cells is about 7,000 hours under normal cycling conditions. Another problem is the requirement that car engines must be able to start reliably at −22°F, and have a high power-to-volume ratio of typically 2.5 kW per liter, which is a problem with the present PEMFC's state of the art.

Another problem is that some non-PEDOT cathodes have very limited carbon monoxide tolerance, which narrows down the area of their applications.

The cost of this type of fuel cell in volume production (projected to 500,000 units per year) was estimated at $49 per kilowatt, while the goal is $35 per kilowatt. This almost 25% cost reduction is needed for PEM fuel cells to compete with current market technologies, including gasoline engines. Companies working on this effort are Ballard Power Systems and Monash University, Melbourne.

Solid Oxide Fuel Cell

Solid oxide fuel cells (SOFC) use a solid material, most commonly a ceramic material, such as yttria-stabilized zirconia (YSZ), instead of an electrolyte. SOFCs do not have any liquids, and they have no limitations as to their size or shape, so they are often manufactured as rolled tubes. However, they require much higher operating temperatures in the 800-1000°C range, but can be run on a variety of fuels, including natural gas.

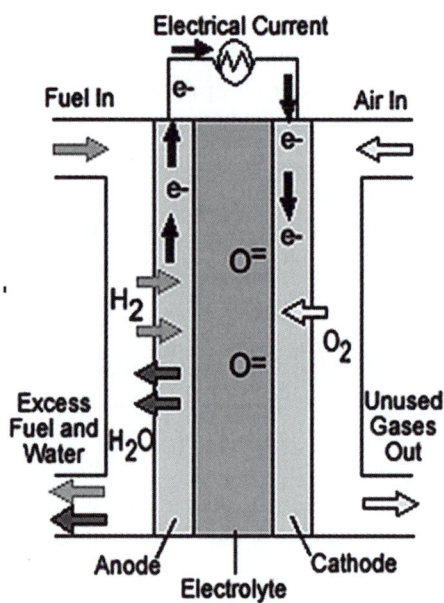

Figure 3-33. SOFC fuel cell

The chemical reactions for an SOFC system can be expressed as follows:

Anode Reaction: $2H_2 + 2O^{2-} \rightarrow 2H_2O + 4e^-$
Cathode Reaction: $O_2 + 4e^- \rightarrow 2O^{2-}$
Overall Cell Reaction: $2H_2 + O_2 \rightarrow 2H_2O$

During the SOFCs' operating process, the negatively charged oxygen ions travel from the cathode to the anode. This is opposite to the case with other fuel cells, where positively charged hydrogen ions usually travel from the anode to the cathode. Here, oxygen gas fed through the cathode reacts with electrons to create oxygen ions, which then travel through the electrolyte to react with hydrogen gas at the anode. This reaction at the anode produces electricity and water as by-products.

Carbon dioxide is usually a by-product, depending on the fuel, but in all cases, the carbon emissions from an SOFC system are less than those from a fossil fuel combustion plant. SOFC systems can run on fuels other than pure hydrogen gas, but since hydrogen is necessary for the reactions listed above, all fuels must contain hydrogen atoms. The fuel also must be converted into pure hydrogen gas for proper cell operation.

SOFCs are capable of internally reforming light hydrocarbons such as methane (natural gas), propane and butane. Heavier hydrocarbons including gasoline, diesel fuel, jet fuel and biofuels can serve as fuels in a SOFC system, but in these cases, an external reformer is required.

Another advantage of these systems is that waste heat from SOFC operations can be captured and reused, thus increasing the theoretical overall efficiency of the devices to as high as 80%-85%.

The major disadvantage of using SOFC systems is their very high operating temperatures. Also, carbon dust builds up on the anode with time, slowing down the internal reforming process. The "carbon coking" issue can also be resolved by using copper-based cermet (heat-resistant materials made of ceramic and metal), which reduces coking and the loss of performance.

NOTE: The high operating temperature is largely due to the physical properties of the YSZ electrolyte, since as temperature decreases, so does the ionic conductivity of YSZ. So, to obtain optimum performance of the fuel cell, a high operating temperature is required. Some SOFC manufacturers have developed methods of reducing the operating temperature of their SOFC system to 500-600°C. This can be done by replacing the YSZ electrolyte with a CGO (cerium gadolinium oxide) electrolyte. The lower operating temperature allows using stainless steel instead of ceramic, as the cell substrate, which reduces cost and start-up time of the system.

Another serious disadvantage of SOFC systems is the long start-up time needed to reach operating temperature. This makes them less useful for mobile, temporary, and low-temperature applications. Nevertheless, the high operating temperature eliminates the need for expensive precious metal catalysts, like platinum, reducing the initial cost.

Molten Carbonate Fuel Cell

Molten carbonate fuel cells (MCFCs) also require very high operating temperature, over 650°C, similar to SOFCs. Here lithium potassium carbonate salt used as an electrolyte liquefies at the high temperatures, thus allowing free movement of charges (negative carbonate ions) within the cell.

MCFCs are also capable of converting some fossil fuels to a hydrogen-rich gas in the anode, eliminating the need of an external hydrogen generator, while the reforming process creates CO_2 emissions. MCFC-compatible fuels include natural gas, biogas and gas produced from coal. The hydrogen in the gas reacts with carbonate ions from the electrolyte to produce water, carbon dioxide, electrons and small amounts of other chemicals.

The electrons travel through an external circuit creating electricity and return to the cathode. There, oxygen from the air and carbon dioxide recycled from the anode react with the electrons to form carbonate ions that replenish the electrolyte, completing the circuit.

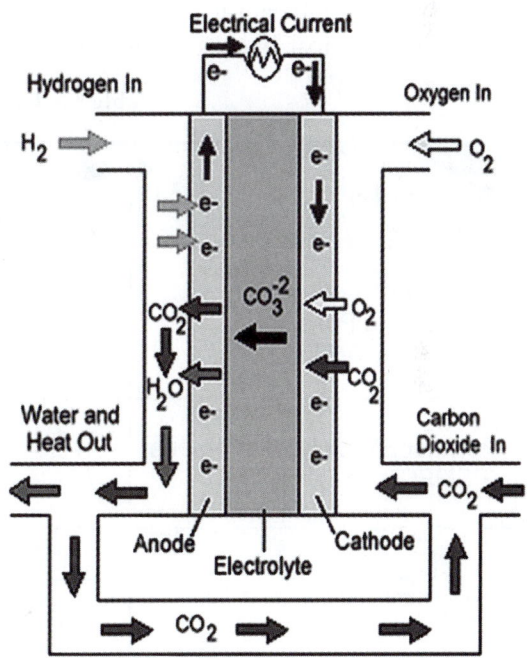

Figure 3-34. Molten carbonate fuel cell

The chemical reactions for an MCFC system can be expressed as follow:

Anode Reaction: $\quad CO_3^{2-} + H_2 \rightarrow H_2O + CO_2 + 2e-$
Cathode Reaction: $\quad CO_2 + \frac{1}{2}O_2 + 2e- \rightarrow CO_3^{2-}$
Overall Cell
Reaction: $\quad H_2 + \frac{1}{2}O_2 \rightarrow H_2O$

MCFCs hold several advantages over other fuel cell technologies, including their resistance to impurities. The main one is that they are not prone to "carbon coking," which is carbon build-up on the anode that results in reduced performance by slowing down the internal fuel reforming process. Therefore, carbon-rich fuels like gases made from coal are compatible with the system. The Department of Energy claims that coal itself might even be a fuel option in the future, assuming the system can be made resistant to impurities such as sulfur and particulates that result from converting coal into hydrogen.

MCFCs also have relatively high efficiencies. They can reach a fuel-to-electricity efficiency of 50%, considerably higher than the 37-42% efficiency of a phosphoric acid fuel cell plant. Efficiencies can be as high as 65% when the fuel cell is paired with a turbine, and 85% if heat is captured and used in a combined heat and power (CHP) system.

MCFC disadvantages include slow start-up times because of their high operating temperature. This makes MCFC systems not suitable for mobile applications, and this technology will most likely be used for stationary fuel cell purposes.

Another serious problem here is the cells' short life span. The high temperature and carbonate electrolyte lead to corrosion of the anode and cathode materials with time.

These factors accelerate the degradation of MCFC components, decreasing durability and cell life. Researchers are exploring corrosion-resistant materials for components as well as fuel cell designs that may increase cell life without decreasing performance. One company working on this type of fuel cell is FuelCell Energy.

Generally, the fuel cell market is also growing at a healthy pace and, according to insiders, the stationary fuel cell market is predicted to reach 40-50 GW by 2020.

Vehicles Use

Fuel cells are important for use in vehicles, where presently their *tank-to-wheel* (TTW) efficiency is greater than 45% at low loads, and about 36% during a normal driving cycle load.

NOTE: The comparable value for a diesel vehicle is 22%, and Honda has a demonstration fuel cell electric

Table 3-5. Fuel cell types and applications

Fuel Cell Type	Temperature Electrolyte / Charge Carrier	Applications
Phosphoric Acid (PAFC) and Polymer / Phosphoric Acid	150–200° C	Distributed power Transportation
	H_3PO_4, Polymer/H_3PO_4 / H^+	
Polymer Electrolyte Membrane (PEMFC)	50–100° C	Distributed power Portable power Transportation
	Perfluorosulfonic acid / H^+	
Direct Methanol (DMFC)	50–100° C	Portable Power
	Perfluorosulfonic acid / H^+	
Alkaline (AFC)	25–75° C, 100–250° C	Portable Power Backup Power
	Alkaline polymer, KOH / OH^-	
Molten Carbonate (MCFC)	600–700° C	Distributed power
	$(Li,K,Na)_2CO_3$ / CO_3^{2-}	
Solid Oxide (SOFC)	500–1000° C	Electric utility Distributed power APUs
	Yttria–Stabilized Zirconia $(Zr_{.92}Y_{.08}O_2)$ / O^{2-}	

Table 3-6. Working parameters and specifics of leading fuel cell types

Cell type	Maximum Power, kW	%Cell efficiency
Direct formic acid	0.05	—
Alkaline fuel cell	100	60-70
Direct methanol fuel	1	20-30
Reformed methanol	100	50-60
Proton exchange membrane	500	50-70
RFC-Redox	10,000	—
Phosphoric acid	10,000	55
Molten carbonate	100,000	55
Tubular solid oxide	100,000	60-65
Direct carbon	—	80
Planar solid oxide	100,000	60-65
Magnesium-air	100,000	90

vehicle, the Honda FCX Clarity, with a 60% tank-to-wheel efficiency.

The problem with this approach is that there are serious energy losses due to fuel production, transportation, and storage. Here we talk about power plant to wheel (PPW) energy conversion and efficiency; i.e., fuel cell vehicles running on compressed hydrogen have a power-plant-to-wheel efficiency of 22% if the hydrogen is stored as high-pressure gas, and 17% if it is stored as liquid hydrogen.

Fuel cells cannot store energy like a battery, except as hydrogen, but in some applications, such as stand-alone power plants based on discontinuous sources such as solar or wind power, they are combined with electrolyzers and storage systems to form an energy storage system.

Most hydrogen, however, is produced by steam methane reforming, so most hydrogen production emits carbon dioxide. The overall efficiency (electricity to hydrogen and back to electricity) of such plants (known as *round-trip efficiency*), using pure hydrogen and pure oxygen, can be from 35 to 50 percent, depending on gas density and other conditions. While a much cheaper lead-acid battery might return about 90%, the electrolyzer/fuel cell system can store indefinite quantities of hydrogen, and is therefore better suited for long-term storage.

Solid-oxide fuel cells produce exothermic heat from the recombination of the oxygen and hydrogen. The ceramic can be as hot as 800°Celsius. This heat is captured and used to heat water in a micro-combined heat and power (m-CHP) application. When the heat is captured, total efficiency can reach 80-90% at the unit, but does not consider production and distribution losses. CHP units are being developed today for the European home market.

Generally, while fuel cells are efficient relative to combustion engines, they are not as efficient as batteries, due primarily to the inefficiency of the oxygen reduction reaction, or the oxygen evolution reaction, should the hydrogen be formed by electrolysis of water. They make the most sense for operation disconnected from the grid or when fuel can be provided continuously.

For applications that require frequent and relatively rapid start-ups, where zero emissions are a requirement (as in enclosed spaces such as warehouses), in operations where hydrogen is considered an acceptable reactant, and if exchanging batteries is inconvenient, PEM fuel cells are an attractive choice.

Industrial Applications

In the last ten years, the hydrogen topic has raised several questions, such as the claim that hydrogen is an economically viable fuel for transportation because of the cost and greenhouse gases generated during production, the low energy content per volume and weight of the container, the cost of the fuel cells, and the cost of the infrastructure.

The price of solar electricity in the last 3 years has fallen to such an extent, and the pace of innovation in both fields of solar energy has been so intense, that a number of unexpected practical hydrogen-based applications have emerged.

For example, Enel, Italy, started operation of a 12 MW H_2-powered electricity plant in Venice recently. The plant is fueled by hydrogen by-products from local petrochemical industries. The turbines were specially designed to resist embrittlement from hydrogen, but the only emission of hydrogen combustion is water.

In 2009 the Austrian companies Fronius, Bitter and Frauscher successfully presented Riviera 600, the first electric boat powered by solar hydrogen fuel cells. The concept is that of a self-contained energy supply provided by hydrogen simply obtained by photovoltaic electrolysis of water.

The team "Future Project Hydrogen" has created budget calculations for the generation of hydrogen on-site by use of photovoltaics under the premises of 10 boats for commercial use, for example, within a boat rental. With a range of 80 kilometers with a full hydrogen tank and having been awarded a safety certificate by Germany's T€ UV, the boat is 6 m long, 2.2 m wide and weighs 1400 kg. Its 4 kW continuous-power electric motor has twice the range of conventional battery-powered boats. The 47% efficiency of the noise free fuel cell engine should be compared to the 18%-20% efficiency of a conventional (steel) internal combustion engine.

The main economic advantage compared with conventional electric boats is the fact that no time must be spent charging the batteries. For conventional electric boats, 6-8 h of charging gives just 4-6 h of use. The hydrogen-powered electric boat requires only the time that it takes to change the cartridge—5 min. The boat's fueling system consists of a 20 kg cartridge that can be charged with up to 0.7 kg of hydrogen kept at 350 bar. Refueling is done using a standard filler coupling plus a simple exchange of an empty cartridge for a full one.

For example, all three companies involved in the "Future Project Hydrogen" are based close to each other in Austria. Scientific and technical advice was provided by the Technical University of Graz, whereas the project was realized with support of the European Union regional programs and further funding from one of Austria's regions. The first 600 Riviera boat is commercialized at 150,000 V, with the first exemplars to be delivered to customers in early 2010.

The renewable energy filling ("Clean Power") recharging station makes use of PV modules integrated in a $250m^2$ flat roof, and connected to an electrolytic cell. Even at Austria's cold latitudes the station is capable of affording an annual yield of 823 kg hydrogen, equivalent to 1100 cartridges with a 27,200 kW h energy content—enough hydrogen to run a boat for 80,000 km. Its installation is simple thanks to the "container construction" design and can be carried out quickly at many different locations.

The station comprises an electricity power charger, hydrogen and payment units. For comparison, storing power in batteries over long periods of time is linked to huge losses due to self-discharge (5-10% per month), while the energy density is a fraction of that for hydrogen, which means that by storing energy in the summer in a battery of the same capacity, one would have no more energy available in winter.

Another example shows photovoltaic renewable hydrogen in the world's first underground pipeline supplying H_2 to customers in the Italian city of Arezzo. At present, the pipeline serves 4 companies and the HydroL Ab with a main channel of around 600 m where the whole network is around 1 km. Four goldsmith companies use it for industrial and energy needs via four 5 kW fuel cells and two 1 kW fuel cells at the HydroLAb, the laboratory for hydrogen and renewable energies.

The aim was to set up a completely off-grid testing lab for technologies in the renewable energy sector, collecting data to test solar energy technologies linked with hydrogen production and use. Hence, solar panels provide electricity, solar thermal vacuum tube panels provide heat for room heating and feed a 5 kW solar cooling machine to get zero emission air conditioning in summer.

Waste water is completely recycled through a special remediation dry technique and rain is collected and stored. The technologies implemented are continuously monitored, with the aim of further optimization in view of widespread commercial application in the building industry.

This is either the humble beginning of a promising technology or the end of a good idea that was not properly funded and developed. Time will tell.

DOE Fuel Cell Roadmap

The US Department of Energy (DOE) has fully appreciated and evaluated the need for a new hydrogen-based economy, and has made some attempts to outline and implement the steps. Some of the conclusions and decisions—albeit focusing on the generation, storage and transport of hydrogen for fueling cars—follow.

In 2011 DOE set the following goals in the U.S. hydrogen development program:

Fuel Cell Development

Develop and demonstrate fuel cell power system technologies for transportation, stationary and portable power applications.

- By 2015, develop a fuel cell system for portable power (<250 W) with an energy density of 900 Wh/L.

- By 2017, develop a 60% peak-efficient, 5,000 hour durable, direct hydrogen fuel cell power system for transportation at a cost of $30/kW.

- By 2020, develop distributed generation and micro-CHP fuel cell systems (5 kW) operating on natural gas or LPG that achieve 45% electrical efficiency and 60,000 hours durability at an equipment cost of $1500/kW.

- By 2020, develop medium-scale CHP fuel cell systems (100 kW–3 MW) that achieve 50% electrical efficiency, 90% CHP efficiency, and 80,000 hours durability at a cost of $1,500/kW for operation on natural gas, and $2,100/kW when configured for operation on biogas.

- By 2020, develop a fuel cell system for auxiliary power units (1-10 kW) with a specific power of 45 W/kg and a power density of 40W/L at a cost of $1000/kW.

Fuel Cell Production

Research, develop, and demonstrate technologies and processes that reduce the cost of manufacturing hydrogen production, delivery, storage, and fuel cell systems.

Objectives

- Develop manufacturing techniques to reduce the cost of automotive fuel cell stacks at high volume (500,000 units/year) from the 2008 value of $38/kW2 to $21/kW by 2017.

- Develop fabrication and assembly processes to produce compressed hydrogen storage systems that cost 12% less than the current high-volume value of $18/kWh for widespread commercialization of hydrogen fuel cell vehicles across most light duty platforms by 2017.

- Support efforts to reduce the cost of manufacturing components and systems to produce hydrogen at $2-$4/gge (2007 dollars) (untaxed, delivered, and dispensed) in 2020.

Fuel Cell Education

The education sub-program's objectives are closely coordinated with technology demonstration and validation, safety, codes and standards, and early market deployment and associated market transformation activities, as well as state and regional-based hydrogen and fuel cell outreach programs—as part of a comprehensive strategy to transform success in demonstrating and deploying technologies into success in the broader marketplace. Specific objectives include the following:

- Increase the acceptance of the use of hydrogen and fuel cell technologies as part of a clean energy portfolio of energy efficiency and renewable energy technologies in federal, state, and local government investments, and private sector investments.

- Decrease "soft costs" associated with the deployment and early adoption of hydrogen and fuel cell technologies in multiple applications (e.g., insurance, permitting, uniform codes and standards) through education, outreach, and training of "second generation" clean energy professionals.

- Increase general knowledge and awareness of the benefits of the use of hydrogen and fuel cell technologies in multiple applications among the key target audiences.

- Increase awareness of the potential full range of fuel cell and hydrogen applications (e.g., not just light-duty vehicles and buses).

Market Transformation

The sub-program's goal is to enable and accelerate expansion of hydrogen and fuel cell system use by lowering the life cycle costs of hydrogen and fuel cell power and by identifying and reducing the barriers impeding full technology commercialization.

- Conduct market transformation deployment projects to enable life cycle cost and performance of fuel-cell powered lift trucks and emergency back-up power systems to be on a par with conventional technologies by 2020.

- Establish baseline energy efficiency and reliability performance metrics for commercially available emergency backup, material handling, and light commercial/residential power systems and provide feedback to component suppliers regarding cost reduction opportunities by 2013.

- Develop and launch energy efficiency and reliability certification programs. This can be achieved, for example, by including fuel cell stationary power systems in the Environmental Protection Agency's (EPA) Energy Star rating program by 2015.

- Develop and publish a best practices procurement guide for federal agencies by 2012.

- Test emerging approaches to grid management using renewable hydrogen storage and fuel cell systems in coordination with the U.S. Department of Energy (DOE) Office of Electricity Delivery and Energy Reliability by 2014.

- Advance the knowledge and expertise of waste-to-energy stationary fuel cells, shipboard auxiliary power unit applications, and aviation applications through targeted testing and evaluation efforts in coordination with the Technology Validation sub-program and in partnership with the U.S. Department of Defense (DOD), the U.S. Navy, the U.S. Army, and civilian agencies such as the U.S. Department of Agriculture (USDA) and the Federal Aviation Administration (FAA) by conducting design requirements planning for aircraft APUs by 2012, shipboard APUs by 2013, and waste-to-energy fuel cells by 2014.

- Identify lessons learned from promulgated policies and regulations and promote the development of the most effective and applicable incentives for hydrogen and fuel cell technologies by 2016.

Environmental Effects of Fuel Cells

Fuel cells are thought of as more environmentally friendly than most other electricity generating technologies. In the end, they are. The produced power is free of pollutants, resulting in only pure, clean water as a byproduct.

Because of that, fuel cell power plants qualify under several environmental certifications established by the government, such as the Leadership in Energy and Environmental Design (LEED) program and Renewable Energy Standards (RES). DFC power plants also have been designated as "Ultra-Clean" by the California Air Resources Board (CARB), and exceed all 2007 CARB standards. FuelCell Energy's power plants eliminate emissions generated by fossil-fuel-based backup generators.

Another benefit of fuel cell technology is the fuel flexibility and diversity. In addition to hydrogen, renewable biogas produced by industrial facilities, agricultural plants and wastewater treatment facilities can be used. Fuel cell power plants can harness the methane in this byproduct and use the gas to power the system in lieu of hydrogen, or natural gas, making it a renewable energy source. In many places where digester gas production volume is variable, fuel cell plants can operate with automatic blending with natural gas or other fuels.

The front end of the process shows that the environmental effects of the initial production and transport of fuel cells components and parts—as in all power generating technologies—is related to large gas emissions and has significant environmental impact.

The fuel cells equipment itself has left a large imprint on the environment well before it was put into production; the fuel cell equipment for large-scale electrical generation is made of different—usually expensive materials—of significant size. These are large vessels made of stainless steel, ceramics and other corrosion-resistant materials. The electrodes are made of different metals, usually containing significant amounts of platinum. The catalyst also contains platinum in powder form, thinly coated onto carbon paper or cloth. The backing layers, flow fields, and current collectors are usually made of a porous carbon paper or carbon cloth, about as thick as 4 to 12 sheets of paper.

Again, acquisition of the materials—mined and refined, transported, machined, or otherwise processed, then shipped and assembled—leaves a marked footprint.

Raw Hydrogen Gas Emissions

The good news is that 100% efficient system of producing, storing and transporting hydrogen (theoretically speaking) leads to no unwanted emissions of any gases or liquids. But such a system does not exist, nor is it practically possible for it would be exceedingly expensive. In reality, around 20% of the hydrogen would be expected to escape into the atmosphere during the different steps.

This leads us to the wicked side of fuel cells operation. Scientists estimate that if hydrogen fuel cells replace all of today's combustion technologies, the escaping hydrogen would double or triple the total hydrogen in the atmosphere. This would have a great impact on environmental dynamics, for this excess of hydrogen would be oxidize in the stratosphere, causing unpredictable and uncontrollable cooling of the stratosphere region, which in turn would create more clouds.

What these clouds would do is uncertain, but the potential of doing harm is there, and the numbers are too large to ignore. At the very least, excess clouds would delay the breakup of the polar vortex at the north and south poles, thus increasing the holes in the ozone layer, making them larger and longer lasting. Estimates show that the extra hydrogen would cause as much as an 8% rise in ozone depletion at the North Pole and up to 7% at the South Pole.

Another unknown effect of hydrogen production and use, yet a very important one, is the possibility of excess hydrogen absorption into the surface waters and topsoil. It is conceivable that this process could compensate for all new anthropogenic emissions.

Although these possibilities depend on a number of additional (some unknown) factors and quantities, they must be researched and well understood, before a large quantity of free hydrogen gas is released into the atmosphere.

TIDAL AND WAVE POWER

The world's oceans contain immeasurable amounts of never ending, renewable, and clean (potential) power. The key here is potential, because although the energy is there for the taking, taking it is not easy. Nevertheless, there are many efforts underway—large and small—to capture and use this energy.

There are three basic sources of ocean energy: tides, waves, and thermal sources.

Tidal Energy

Tidal energy is a form of ocean energy. When tides come into the shore, they can be trapped in reservoirs behind dams. Then when the tide drops, the water behind the dam can be let out just like in a regular hydroelectric power plant.

For this to work well, however, a large increase in tides' height is necessary. An increase of 16 feet between low and high tide is the minimum needed for significant power generation. There are only a few places around the world where such large tide changes can be found, and some power plants are already operating using this idea. One plant in France makes enough energy from tides to power 240,000 homes.

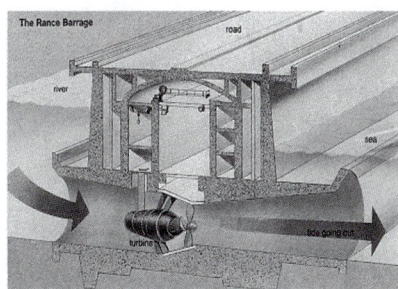

Figure 3-35. Ocean tidal engine

More practical for small applications is the tidal power generation depicted in Figure 3-36. Here the tidal waves are directed into a channel, where they speed one way when the tide comes and back the other way when the tide goes out. A turbine is located in the channel and its blades turn with the tides coming in and out. The rotational energy is converted into electricity by an electrical generator and is used in the power grid or for directly powering electrical devices.

Wave Energy

Kinetic energy (movement) exists in the ocean's moving waves and can be used to power a turbine, which in turn can generate electric power.

In Figure 3-35 the wave rises into a chamber, where the rising water forces the air out of the chamber. The moving air spins a turbine which can turn a generator. When the wave goes down, air flows through the turbine and back into the chamber through doors that are

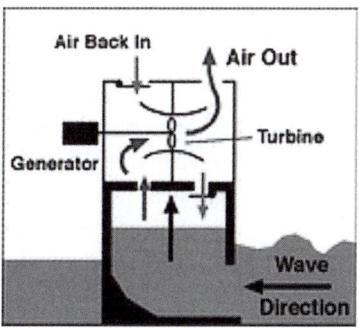

Figure 3-36. Ocean wave engine

normally closed.

This is only one type of wave-energy system. Others actually use the up and down motion of the wave to power a piston that moves up and down inside a cylinder. That piston can also turn a generator. Most wave-energy systems today are very small for the purpose of investigating their work function and future possibilities. Many of them can be used to power a warning buoy or a small lighthouse. Larger systems in the future could supply power to harbors and coastal towns.

Ocean Thermal Energy

The final ocean energy idea uses temperature differences in the ocean. If you ever swam in the ocean and dove deep below the surface, you would have noticed that the water gets colder the deeper you go. It's warmer on the surface because sunlight warms it. Below the surface, the ocean gets very cold. That's why scuba divers wear wetsuits when they dive down deep. Wetsuits trap their body heat to keep them warm.

Power plants can be built that use this difference in temperature to make energy, but a temperature difference of at least 38°Fahrenheit is needed between the warmer surface water and the colder deep ocean water.

Cold seawater is an integral part of each of the three types of ocean thermal systems, closed-, open-, and hybrid-cycle. To operate, the cold seawater must be brought to the surface. The primary approaches are active pumping and desalination. Desalinating seawater near the sea floor lowers its density, causing it to rise to the surface.

The alternative to costly pipes to bring condensing cold water to the surface is to pump vaporized low-boiling-point fluid into the depths to be condensed, thus reducing pumping volumes and technical and environmental problems, and lowering costs.

There are several types of ocean thermal energy systems.

Closed-cycle System

Closed-cycle systems use fluid with a low boiling point, such as ammonia, to power a turbine to generate electricity. Warm surface seawater is pumped through a heat exchanger to vaporize the fluid. The expanding vapor turns the turbo-generator. Cold water, pumped through a second heat exchanger, condenses the vapor into a liquid, which is then recycled through the system.

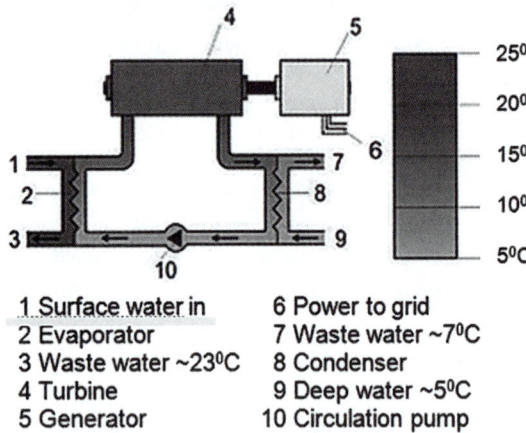

1 Surface water in   6 Power to grid
2 Evaporator   7 Waste water ~7°C
3 Waste water ~23°C   8 Condenser
4 Turbine   9 Deep water ~5°C
5 Generator   10 Circulation pump

Figure 3-37. Closed cycle thermal system

The first mini-ocean thermal experiment in 1979 achieved the first successful at-sea production of net electrical power from a closed-cycle thermal system. The mini-ocean thermal energy generating vessel was moored 1.5 miles (2.4 km) off the Hawaiian coast and produced enough net electricity to illuminate the ship's light bulbs and run its computers and television.

Open-cycle System

Open-cycle ocean thermal energy generators use warm surface water directly to make electricity. Placing warm seawater in a low-pressure container causes it to boil. In some schemes, the expanding steam drives a low-pressure turbine attached to an electrical generator. The steam, which has left its salt and other contaminants in the low-pressure container, is pure fresh water. It is condensed into a liquid by exposure to cold temperatures from deep-ocean water. This method produces desalinized fresh water, suitable for drinking or irrigation.

In other schemes, the rising steam is used in a gas lift technique of lifting water to significant heights. Depending on the embodiment, such steam lift pump techniques generate power from a hydroelectric turbine either before or after the pump is used.

The first vertical-spout evaporator to convert warm seawater into low-pressure steam for open-cycle plants was developed in 1984. Conversion efficiencies were as

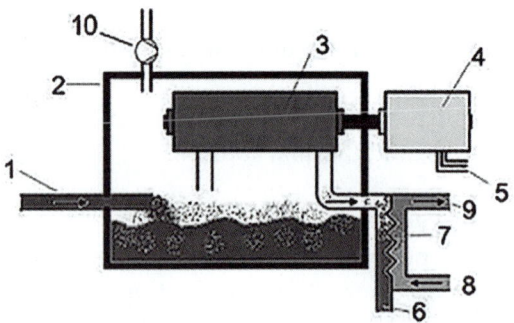

1 Surface water   6 Desalinated water
2 Vacuum chamber   7 Condenser
3 Turbine   8 Deep water ~5°C
4 Generator   9 Waste water ~7°C
5 Power to grid   10 Vacuum pump

Figure 3-38. Open cycle OTEC system

high as 97% for seawater-to-steam conversion (overall efficiency using a vertical-spout evaporator would still only be a few percent). In May 1993, an open-cycle ocean thermal plant at Keahole Point, Hawaii, produced 50,000 watts of electricity during a net power-producing experiment. This broke the record of 40 kW set by a Japanese system in 1982.

Hybrid Thermal Cycle Systems

A hybrid cycle combines the features of the closed- and open-cycle systems. In a hybrid system, warm seawater enters a vacuum chamber and is flash-evaporated, similar to the open-cycle evaporation process. The steam vaporizes the ammonia working fluid of a closed-cycle loop on the other side of an ammonia vaporizer. The vaporized fluid then drives a turbine to produce electricity. The steam condenses within the heat exchanger and could be used for desalination of sea water at the same time.

Ocean thermal energy conversion systems are being used in Japan and in Hawaii in some demonstration and small-scale projects.

Environmental Effects of Tidal Power Generation

The power generation via tidal and wave power generating devices usually proceeds without generating carbon dioxide, or any other harmful gasses or liquids. But as the number of wave and tidal projects in the world's oceans increases, attention is focusing on the negative effect power that generating devices might have on marine life.

Ocean Environment

Any man-made equipment placed in the oceans creates some sort of interference with the marine environment. At the very least, the metals would have some chemical reactions, while the moving parts would affect it in another way.

For example, the presence of any electro-mechanical devices in the world's oceans would introduce:

* Static and dynamic effects,
* Chemical effects,
* Acoustic effects,
* Electromagnetic effects,
* Energy changes and removal, and
* Many cumulative effects.

This would result in some interference with:
* Near and far-field physical environment,
* Habitat,
* Invertebrates,
* Migratory fish,
* Resident fish,
* Marine mammals,
* Sea birds, and
* General ecosystem interactions.

Figure 3-39. Ocean power generation

Noise, electromagnetic fields, and mechanical damage are suspected to affect marine life. Noise, for example, is known to confuse marine mammals, causing them stress and loss of orientation. Other marine species—turtles, crabs, sharks, skates, salmon and other fish—rely on Earth's magnetic fields for migrating and searching for food. The wave, tidal and hydrokinetic power devices, and the cables that bring the electricity they generate to shore, produce similar electromagnetic fields, which might confuse migratory sea creatures.

One known fact is that fish swimming close to these devices might get hurt or killed by the moving parts—propellers, pistons, turbines, etc. Precautions must be taken to avoid collisions, by installing special devices that emit noise to alert potential victims. It is not clear what other effects such a noise makers would have.

We really don't know if animals would be affected by all this or not. There's surprisingly little comprehensive research to tell us.

Beyond those concerns, ocean power generating technologies are as clean as a whistle. They emit no emissions, and they cause no damage to the environment during operation.

Up front, however, there are problems. Large-scale power generating equipment from tidal and wave motion consists of very large pieces of metal, ceramics and plastics. Initial production of the components would leave its mark. The equipment itself would be made of different—usually expensive—materials. These components would be made of stainless steel, ceramics and other exotic and expensive materials.

Here again, the metals were mined and refined, transported, machined and processed before being shipped to the tidal or wave power generating plant for final assembly. All of these processes left harmful gasses and liquids along the way.

Considerable amount of disturbance to the ocean floor would be caused during exploration and installation phases, with large pieces of equipment brought in to dig deep holes in the ocean floor for the support structures. Large amounts of cement and other materials would be dumped in these holes to fix the structures in place.

During these activities, all marine life in the area would be killed or chased away. Clearly, the larger the project, the more damage would be inflicted to the ocean environment and life in it.

GEOTHERMAL POWER

The term *geothermal* is from the Greek words geo (earth) and therme (heat), which put together mean earth's heat. This is exactly what geothermal power generation is—using the earth's interior, which is naturally and eternally very hot. This heat, geothermal energy, originates from the Earth's creation over 6 billion years ago. At the center of the Earth—more than 4,000 miles deep—ferocious thermo-nuclear reactions are at play, and the temperatures reach over 9,000°F.

Like any heated body, the heat in the Earth's core is continuously emitted and flows towards cooler bodies in the surroundings. In this case, the heat flows outward towards the surface, heating the rocks and earth as it cools on its way up.

The nearby layer of rock, the *mantle, is heated red hot,* and when temperatures and pressures become high enough, some mantle rock melts, becoming magma. During this process the magma becomes less dense and lighter than the surrounding rock and rises upward. This motion, or convection, makes it move slowly up toward the earth's crust, still hot but cooling down with every inch.

If and when the hot magma reaches the surface, via volcanic explosions or through cracks in the ground, it flows down the hills like molten metal, which we know as lava. Most often, however, the magma remains contained in pools well below earth's crust. The pools of magma are heating nearby rocks and water in the water table or rainwater seepage. The rocks can get very hot—nearly 1000°F—and can keep the nearby water very hot too.

Some of the heated water flows up to the surface through cracks, where it forms *hot springs or geysers*. Most often, however, it stays in pools deep underground where, trapped in cracks and porous rock, it forms natural formations called *geothermal reservoirs*.

Geothermal Electricity Generation

Here we have a totally different type of energy ready to be extracted and used. People have used the hot water on the Earth's surface for just relaxing and therapeutic activities since the beginning of time. But now, this free energy is used in other, much more creative and practical ways, mostly for heating buildings, and generating electric power.

The process of generating electricity from geothermal reservoirs is quite simple. We simply drill deep

wells into the hot geothermal reservoirs, pump the water to the surface and use it (and the *geothermal power* in it) to make steam. Thus produced steam is sent into a turbine, where it provides the force to spin the *turbine blades* and the *generator*, which produces electricity. The used and cooled geothermal water exiting the turbine is then returned down the *injection well* into the reservoir to be reheated, and the cycle can be repeated *ad infinitum*.

There are three kinds of *geothermal power plants*, depending on the temperatures and pressures of the underground geothermal reservoir, which can be divided as follow:

Dry Steam Reservoir

A "dry" steam reservoir produces a lot of steam but very little water. The steam is piped directly into a *dry steam power plant* to provide the force to spin the turbine generator. The largest dry steam field in the world is The Geysers, about 90 miles north of San Francisco. Production of electricity started at The Geysers in 1960, at what has become the most successful alternative energy project in history.

Hot Water Reservoir

A geothermal reservoir that produces mostly hot water is called a "hot water reservoir" and is used in a "flash" power plant. Water ranging in temperature from 300-700°F is brought up to the surface through the production well where, upon being released from the pressure of the deep reservoir, some of the water flashes into steam in a "separator." The steam then powers the turbines.

Binary Systems

A reservoir with temperatures between 250-360°F is not hot enough to flash enough steam but can still be used to produce electricity in a "binary" power plant. In a binary system the geothermal water is passed through a heat exchanger, where its heat is transferred into a second (binary) liquid, such as isopentane, that boils at a lower temperature than water. When heated, the binary liquid flashes to vapor which, like steam, expands across and spins the turbine blades. The vapor is then re-condensed to a liquid and is reused repeatedly. In this closed-loop cycle, there are no emissions to the air.

Worldwide there are about 10 GW of geothermal power generated in over 20 countries, of which about 1/3 are generated in the U.S.—equivalent to not burning over 60 million barrels of oil each year. The geothermal electricity generation is most prevalent where Earth's

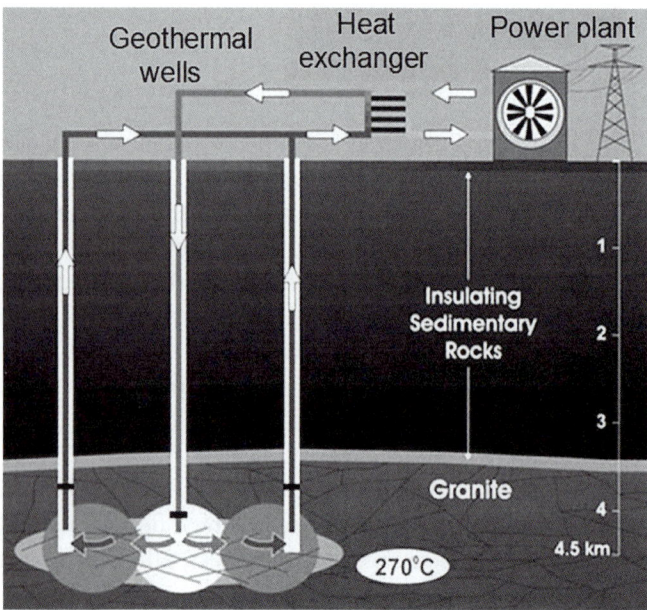

Figure 3-40. Geothermal power generation

large oceanic and crustal plates collide and one slides beneath another. These are called subduction zones, with the best example being the Ring of Fire bordering the Pacific Ocean, the South American Andes, Central America, Mexico, the Cascade Range of the U.S. and Canada, the Aleutian Range of Alaska, the Kamchatka Peninsula of Russia, Japan, the Philippines, Indonesia and New Zealand.

Active geothermal energy sources are also found where these plates are sliding apart, such as in Iceland, the rift valleys of Africa, the mid-Atlantic Ridge and the Basin and Range Province in the U.S. There are also places called "hot spots," which are fixed points in the mantle that continually propel magma to the surface. In these cases the plate is continually moving across the hot spot, forming strings of volcanoes, such as the chain of Hawaiian Islands.

The countries currently producing the most electricity from geothermal reservoirs are the United States, New Zealand, Italy, Iceland, Mexico, the Philippines, Indonesia and Japan, but geothermal energy is also being used in many other countries.

Other Uses of Geothermal Energy

Geothermal power can be used even when the water is not hot enough for applications other than generating steam and electricity. The main non-electric ways to use low temperature geothermal energy are through direct use and geothermal heat pumps.

Direct Use

Geothermal waters ranging from 50°F to over 300°F, are used directly from the earth in domestic and industrial applications, such as soothing aching muscles in hot springs, and health spas (balneology); growing flowers and vegetables in greenhouses (agriculture); growing fish, shrimp, abalone and alligators to maturity (aquaculture); pasteurizing milk, drying onions and lumber, and washing wool (industrial).

Space heating of individual buildings and entire population centers is the most common and oldest direct use of nature's hot water. Geothermal *district heating* systems pump geothermal water through a *heat exchanger*, where it transfers its heat to clean city water that is piped to buildings in the district. There, a second heat exchanger transfers the heat to the building's heating system. The geothermal water is injected down a well and back into the reservoir to be heated and used again.

The first modern district heating system was developed in Boise, Idaho. In the western U.S. there are 271 communities with geothermal resources available

for this use. Modern district heating systems also serve homes in Russia, China, France, Sweden, Hungary, Romania, and Japan. The world's largest district heating system is in Reykjavik, Iceland. Since it started using geothermal energy as its main source of heat, previously polluted Reykjavik has become one of the cleanest cities in the world.

Geothermal heat is being used in some creative ways. For example, in Klamath Falls, Oregon, geothermal water is piped under roads and sidewalks to keep them from icing over in freezing weather. In New Mexico and other places, rows of pipes carrying geothermal water have been installed under soil, where flowers or vegetables are growing. This ensures that the ground does not freeze, providing a longer growing season and overall faster growth of agricultural products that are not protected by the shelter and warmth of a greenhouse.

Geothermal Heat Pumps

We all know that deeper into the ground the temperature is relatively stable compared to surface air temperature. Using this free energy, geothermal heat pumps (GHPs) take advantage of the stable earth temperature (about 45-58°F) just a few feet below the surface. This heat can be used to keep indoor temperatures comfortable in homes and businesses.

The GHPs simply pump and circulate water or other liquids through pipes buried in a continuous loop (either horizontally or vertically) underground, next to a building to be heated.

Depending on the weather, the system is used for heating or cooling.

Heating

Earth's heat (the difference between the earth's temperature and the colder temperature of the air) is transferred through the buried pipes into the circulating liquid and then transferred again into the building.

Cooling

During hot weather, the continually circulating fluid in the pipes "picks up" heat from the building—helping to cool it—and transfers it into the earth.

GHPs use very little electricity and are very easy on the environment. In the U.S., the temperature inside more than 300,000 homes, schools and offices is kept comfortable by these energy saving systems, and hundreds of thousands more are used worldwide. The U.S. Environmental Protection Agency has rated GHPs among the most efficient of heating and cooling technologies.

Shallow ground heat is one of the most cost-effective from an initial-capital point of view. The earth's temperature a few feet below the ground surface is relatively constant everywhere in the world (about 45-58°F), while the air temperature can change from summer to winter extremes. Shallow ground temperatures are not dependent upon tectonic plate activity or other unique geologic processes, thus geothermal heat pumps can be used cheaply to help heat and cool homes anywhere.

In summary, thousands more megawatts of power could be developed from already-identified hydrothermal resources. With *improvements in technology*, much more power will become available. Usable geothermal resources will not be limited to the "shallow" hydrothermal reservoirs at the crustal plate boundaries. Much of the world is underlain (3-6 miles down) by hot dry rock which in most cases contains no water but packs a lot of heat. The U.S., Japan, England, France, Germany and Belgium are experimenting with piping water into this deep hot rock to create more hydrothermal resources for use in geothermal power plants. As drilling technology improves, allowing us to drill much deeper, geothermal energy from hot dry rock could be available anywhere. At such time, we will be able to tap the true potential of the enormous heat resources of the earth's crust.

Advantages of Using Geothermal Energy

There are a lot of advantages to using geothermal heat for making electricity and for cooling/heating homes and businesses. Geothermal power plants, like wind and solar power plants, do not burn fuels to make steam to turn the turbines. Generating electricity with geothermal energy helps to conserve nonrenewable fossil fuels, and by decreasing the use of these fuels, we reduce emissions that harm our atmosphere. There is no smoky air around geothermal power plants, and in fact some are built in the middle of farm lands and forests, and share land with cattle and wildlife.

For over ten years, Lake County, California, home to five geothermal electric power plants, has been the first and only county in the U.S. to meet the most stringent governmental air quality standards in the U.S.

The land area required for geothermal power plants is smaller (per megawatt) than for almost every other type of power plant. Geothermal installations don't require damming of rivers or harvesting of forests—and there are no mine shafts, tunnels, open pits, waste heaps or oil spills.

Geothermal power plants are designed to run 24 hours a day, all year, providing consistent and more reliable power than any other technology. A geothermal power plant sits right on top of its fuel source, so there is no need for mining, processing, or transport operations. It is resistant to interruptions of power generation due to weather, natural disasters or political rifts that can interrupt mining, processing and transportation of fuels. Geothermal "fuel"—unlike the sun and the wind—is always on, the economic benefits remain in the region, and no fuel price shocks are expected.

Geothermal power plants can have modular designs, with additional units installed in increments when needed to fit growing demand for electricity.

Finally, geothermal projects, with all their benefits could help developing countries grow their energy system efficiently and without pollution. Installations in remote locations can raise the standard of living and quality of life by bringing electricity to people far from "electrified" population centers.

If this is such a wonderful energy source, why is it not used more frequently around the world? Unavailability of equipment and experienced staff, and infrastructure issues are some of the reasons. All of these hinder efficient location, installation and operation of geothermal plants across the globe. Not enough skilled manpower and availability of suitable-to-build locations (in addition to funding barriers) have been identified as the most serious problems in adopting geothermal energy globally.

Getting geothermal energy requires installation of power plants and other expensive equipment as needed to pump hot water up from deep within the earth and convert it into useful electric power. All this requires a huge one-time investment, a certified installer and the relocation of experienced staff to the plant. Then, great expense is incurred for adding the power-delivery infrastructure. This alone often makes the entire project prohibitively expensive and limits its financing opportunities.

Geothermal energy is only practical in regions with hot rocks below the earth which can produce steam over a long period of time. To identify such places, great research is required. This initial investment is significant, and only a few can afford it, since it increases the total expense in setting up a geothermal power plant.

There is also the potential of a higher level of corrosion at some sites, due to dissolved minerals in the water used in the pipes and in the power plant. This might increase maintenance costs significantly and reduce profits accordingly.

Since geothermal sites penetrate miles below the Earth's surface, the drill holes and hot rock reservoirs often contain toxic gases which can escape to the surface, and there is a fear of toxic substances being released into the local atmosphere. The toxic gasses can also travel deep within the earth and contaminate the water table, all of which is a liability to the investors and owners.

There is also a danger that geothermal sites can run out of steam over time due to drop in temperature, shifts in the Earth's layers, or if too much water is injected to cool the rocks. Since these are unpredictable events in most cases, the risk of financial loss for investors is high.

Geothermal Power Generation

The United States leads the world in geothermal electricity production with about 3.0 GW of installed capacity generated at 77 geothermal power plants. The largest concentration of geothermal power plants is located at The Geysers geothermal field in California. The Philippines is the second highest producer of geothermal power, with close to 2.0 GW of capacity, or nearly 20% of the country's electricity generation.

There are at least 1.5 million geothermal wells is Texas alone, most of them small and on private lands. The state looks like a Swiss cheese from that point of view. How many more holes can be drilled, and their use is uncertain, but geothermal power is increasing in importance, so expect to hear more good news about geothermal power in Texas in the coming years.

There are nearly 11 GW of geothermal power generated in 24 countries today, which generate over 65 GWh of electricity annually. This is about 20% increase in geothermal power online capacity since 2005, and is expected to grow to nearly 20 GW by 2020. There are a number of projects presently under consideration, often in areas previously assumed to have little geothermal value, so these numbers seem plausible.

Several countries, El Salvador, Kenya, the Philippines, Iceland, and Costa Rica presently generate more than 15% of their electricity from geothermal sources.

Enhanced geothermal systems several kilometers in depth are operational in France and Germany and some are being developed or evaluated in several other countries. The advance of these types of systems might bring geothermal power to places where it was not considered possible until recently.

NOTE: Iceland has one of the best and most productive geothermal installations in the world. The total potential for electricity production from the high-temperature geothermal fields in Iceland is estimated at about 1500 TWh, which translates in energy generation to 15 TWh per year over a 100-year period. Electricity production capacity from geothermal fields presently is only about 1/10 of that, or 1.3 TWh per year.

Does this mean that Iceland has a 1,000-year supply of geothermal energy at the present level of use? Maybe… It all depends on many factors, some of which are not under the control of the Icelanders, and some of which might change the picture entirely and very quickly if and when Nature decides to intervene.

Cost of Geothermal Power Generation

The cost of geothermal power installations includes:

- Planning and design
- Exploration
- Permitting
- Well drilling
- Power plant construction
- Power plant operation and maintenance
- Site decommissioning

The cost of building a geothermal power plant heavily weighs toward the initial expenses. This is different from other power plants, where fuel supplies, transport and disposal are major factors. Here, well drilling and pipeline construction start the entire process, followed by resource analysis of the drilling information. Next is design of the actual plant, if the drilling information shows favorable conditions for geo-power generation (a large quantity of high-temperature rocks at a reasonable depth).

Power plant construction is usually completed concurrent with final field development. The initial cost for the field and power plant is around $2500 per installed kW for large installations (over 1 MW installed capacity) in the U.S. It is somewhat higher—$3000 to $5000/kW—for a smaller power plant and in other countries that need to import expertise and technology.

Operating and maintenance costs range from $0.01 to $0.03 per kWh. Most geothermal power plants can run at greater than 90% availability, which means they are fully operational (and at 100% capacity) 90% of the time. This is remarkable, and should be entered as best of all power generators.

Running at higher availability of 97% or 98%, however, can increase maintenance costs, so only higher-priced electricity justifies running the plant 98% of the time as needed to recover the higher maintenance costs.

Recent reports suggest that geothermal power may actually be cheaper than all other fuels, including coal. The U.S. stimulus package that includes $28 billion in direct subsidies for renewable energy and an additional $13 billion for research and development, gave renew-

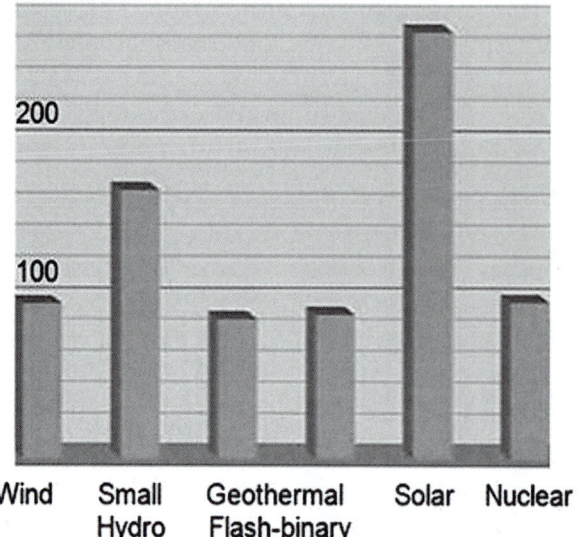

Figure 3-41. LCOE cost in $/MWh of generated electricity

able energy sources—geothermal power included—a shot in the arm, so we expect some great things to happen soon in this area of the energy industry.

Estimates from Credit Suisse estimate geothermal power costs at 3.6 cents per kilowatt-hour, versus 5.5 cents per kilowatt-hour for coal. This, however, does not include the risks and a number of assumptions that must be made when considering a new geothermal power plant. Still, the basics are there, starting with the tax incentives which save about 1.9 cents per kilowatt-hour, but they won't last, even though the stimulus bill extended them through 2013.

Table 3-7. Installation cost of conventional geothermal power plant (in $.kW installed)

Stage	$/kW	%
Exploration	14	0.4
Permitting	50	1.4
Steam Gathering	250	6.8
Exploratory Drilling	169	4.6
Production Drilling	1,367	37.5
Plant & Construction	1,700	46.6
Transmission	100	2.7
TOTAL	3,650	

The development of geothermal energy requires the consideration and evaluation of a number of factors, such as site (geography), geology, reservoir size, geothermal temperature, and plant type. The majority of the overall cost is typically attributed to construction of the power plant, due to the high cost of raw materials including steel. The second highest cost-intensive

processes are the exploratory and production drilling stages, which combined are as much as the plant construction.

Geothermal power production is relatively capital-intensive with high first-cost and risk, but it has fairly low operating and maintenance (O&M) costs and a high capacity factor. This makes it one of the most economical baseload power generation options available. A number of factors contribute to the cost of developing a geothermal power plant, with the power conversion technology having some, but not great effect on the final cost.

Low-temperature reservoirs typically use binary power plants, while moderate- to high-temperature reservoirs employ dry steam or flash steam plants, based on whether the production wells produce primarily steam or water, respectively. The different technologies show similar construction costs and O&M expenses.

One thing to keep in mind is that the significant up-front capital requirements, pervasive resource and development uncertainty, and long project lead times bring greater risk-related mark-up, as compared to other renewable and traditional energy alternatives. These factors, combined with current economic conditions, mean private firms seeking to develop geothermal projects may face greater difficulties in obtaining the requisite capital for exploration and development. Industry analysts suggest that although financing is still available, the terms will be less attractive to investors and developers.

Most cost estimates rely on the *levelized cost of energy* (LCOE), which represents the total cost to produce a given unit of energy, usually in $/MWh. This figure assumes that the money to build a new geothermal plant is available at reasonable interest rates.

That is not the case today. Although there is interest in geothermal energy generation, the general consensus is that it's difficult to get to and that it's expensive to produce. Therefore, only very low-risk and outstandingly profitable projects can get even credit card interest rates, according to insiders. This means that the up-front costs are too high for a profitable project. So, utilities and other companies prefer to spend their money on lower front-end costs, like natural gas powered plants, which are cheap to build but relatively expensive to operate in the long run, due to the cost of fuel needed to run them.

Natural gas LCOE is averaged at $0.052 per kWh (vs. $0.036/kWh for geothermal power) but is finding greater use because it can be deployed anywhere. This is a great advantage over most other location-specific technologies, including geothermal power.

Only 13 U.S. states have identified significant geothermal resources, which severely limits its usefulness, since it is not possible to transport it like gas or oil. Nevertheless, there are estimates that the U.S. has over 30 GW of geothermal energy supplies that could be exploited using today's technology. These supplies are also estimated to last indefinitely, but this has not been verified.

Environmental Effects of Geothermal Power Generation

The environmental problems caused by building a geothermal energy plant start while looking for a suitable site. During exploration, researchers do a land survey, which may take several years to complete. To extract profitable heat, they must find certain hot spots within the Earth's crust, which are most often around volcanos and fault lines. But who wants to build their geothermal energy plant next to a volcano? So they search for similar conditions elsewhere.

Some areas may have sufficient hot rocks to supply hot water to a power station, but many are in harsh areas of the world, near the poles or in high mountains. The search can continue for a long time, digging, drilling, damaging.

Of course, some damage to the local environment occurs during construction of the facility; large pieces of equipment are brought in to level the ground and drill deep holes. Lots of pipes is delivered and laid in the exploration and production holes.

During the well drilling and operation stages toxic gasses can escape from the site, since it is hard to control what's happening deep under the surface. Things also change down there, so although there were no problems today, tomorrow things can change and toxic gas leakage can occur. Gasses can escape into the local environment or penetrate deep into the ground and contaminate the water table.

Another danger of geothermal energy is the likelihood of recurring earthquakes. People who live in areas of production report that there are increasing numbers of earthquakes there. Although they are low-level quakes, no stronger than magnitude 4, they are damaging homes and foundations.

Increased volcanic activities could bring the eruption of an old or a new volcano during hot rock drilling. Such an eruption could devastate the local flora and fauna in an instant. Of course, this is not as dangerous as a nuclear power plant explosion, but those unfortunate to be nearby during an eruption will pay dearly.

Finally, after years of generating power in many cases the site "cools down" and production stops. Then more environmental damage is incurred by the shutting down and decommissioning of the power plant—all is at the expense of the local environment.

The good news is that generally, a geothermal site—unlike coal mines, gas and oil fields—can be restored to near-perfect (original) condition.

NOTE: Most importantly, looking at the larger picture, we can easily see that injecting large amounts of cold water into any hot body (including the Earth) day after day has limits—quantity and time limits. Where these limits lie is uncertain, but we should not be as naïve as to think that we can continue doing this indefinitely, and even increase the volume of cold water injected in the Earth's hot rocks, without any negative effects sometime in the future.

Like any other technology, when geothermal is applied in small quantities—as it is today—it cannot do much harm for a very long time. When deployed on a large scale, however, things will surely change and negative effects will follow...as they always do in such cases!

It is a great mistake to take examples of old, small, good and reliable production geothermal wells and extrapolate the results to large- and very large-scale power generation. This is like comparing apples and oranges... or worse!

The energy in the Earth's core is huge, no doubt, but it is not unlimited. Cooling it down by ceaselessly pumping in lots of cold water might be the dumbest and most dangerous thing we've ever done. It is like permanently cutting the branch we are sitting on, just to warm up our hands temporarily. This is why we do not consider geo-thermal power a renewable power. It is renewable while it lasts, but then it is gone, which happens eventually at each location. How renewable is that?

BIO-ENERGY SOURCES

This category is most controversial, because although bio materials are a plentiful and renewable energy source, they are related to resource overuse and abuse, where the demand outstrips the supply in many cases. Also, serious greenhouse gas (GHG) emissions are produced by burning large quantities of bio-materials (wood and other vegetation).

The major components of the bio-energy sources are biomass (natural woods, vegetation, and agricultural crops), and bio-fuels and their sub-components, as we will see below.

Bioenergy, in the general meaning of the term, is

renewable energy that is contained and can be extracted from materials created by natural biological sources. In more specific terms, biomass is any organic material which has stored sunlight in the form of chemical energy.

As a fuel it may include wood, wood waste, straw, manure, sugarcane, and many other byproducts from a variety of agricultural processes. By 2010, there were 35GW of globally installed bioenergy capacity for electricity generation, of which 7GW were in the United States.

In its most narrow sense it is a synonym for biofuel, which is fuel derived from biological sources. In its broader sense it includes biomass, the biological material used as a biofuel, as well as the social, economic, scientific and technical fields associated with using biological sources for energy. This is a common misconception, as bioenergy is the energy extracted from the biomass. The biomass is the fuel and the bioenergy is the energy contained in the fuel.

NOTE: There is confusion about the words *bioenergy vs. biofuel*, the latter of which is used in North America to mean both biomass and biofuels. The major difference between these is that biomass is natural organic matter, which is used as is. It is usually burned directly, without any processing, or any modifications. Biofuels, and their sub-components, on the other hand, are usually derived from processing biomass and other organic or inorganic materials.

Biomass is mostly naturally grown, or with little human assistance, while biofuels need 100% human intervention, a lot of equipment and energy, and complex processes.

BIOMASS

Biomass is the common name for all organic materials classed as renewable energy sources such as wood, crops, and all types of animal, vegetable and other biological wastes. Biomass is a type of renewable energy source, and while it is replenished by nature in most cases, when used it is by no means green or clean, as far as the environment and the fight against climate change are concerned.

The amount of energy released when a given unit of fuel is combusted is referred to as the energy content of that fuel. For example, the energy content of wood is generally in the range of 6 to 18 megajoules per kg (MJ/kg) of wood, depending on the moisture content of the wood.

Freshly cut wood could have as much as 60% moisture and would have a relative low energy content (e.g., 6 MJ/kg), whereas oven-dried wood with close to zero moisture content could have up to 18 MJ/kg. An average commonly used value for wood is 15 MJ/kg. The energy content in some types of biomass are approximately:

Table 3-8. Energy content in different fuels

Fuel	Energy
Crude oil	42 MJ/kg
Coal	27 MJ/kg
Natural gas	18 MJ/kg
Paper	17 MJ/kg
Dung (dry)	16 MJ/kg
Straw (dry)	15 MJ/kg
Wood	14 MJ/kg
Domestic waste	9 MJ/kg
Grass (fresh cut)	4 MJ/kg

NOTE: 1kW electricity = 3.6 MJ energy

The biomass production rate in terms of the quantity of biomass that can be grown on a parcel of land per unit time, which is generally given as kilograms of biomass per hectare per year (kg/ha/yr) varies greatly depending on the crop, soil type, availability of water, and moisture content of the crop.

Some representative yields of biomass products in kilogram/hectare/year are:

Wood	20,000 kg/ha/yr.
Wheat, rice, and sorghum	15,000 kg/ha/yr.
Sugar cane	35,000 kg/ha/yr.

****NOTE**: 1 hectare is 10,000 m^2 or about 2.5 acres.

For liquid biofuels, the energy content is usually given in terms of megajoules per liter (MJ/L). Representative values for the energy content of crops grown for biofuels are:

Gasoline	35 MJ/L
Sunflower oil	33 MJ/L
Castor oil	33 MJ/L

The biomass production rate for plants to be grown for biofuels, given as liters per hectare or L/ha varies greatly. Some representative values for plants grown as biofuels are:

Sunflower	952 L/ha
Soybean	446 L/ha
Castor oil	1,413 L/ha

Examples

Assuming one crop per year, a hectare of castor beans would produce the equivalent of approximately 1,400 L of gasoline.

Given an average yield of 15,000 kg/ha/yr, and an energy content of 15 MJ/kg, the amount of thermal energy that can be expected to be available from cultivated wood production would be about 225,000 MJ/ha/yr, which would be about the same amount of energy contained in approximately 7.5 tons of coal.

The biomass power generating industry in the United States consists of approximately 11 GW of summer operating capacity actively supplying power to the grid, which produces about 1.4 percent of the U.S. electricity supply.

The 140 MW New Hope Power Partnership is the largest biomass power plant in North America. It uses mainly sugar cane fiber (bagasse), and recycled urban wood as fuel to generate enough power for large industrial operations and to supply electricity for nearly 60,000 homes.

The power generation reduces the import of 1 million barrels of oil annually and, by recycling sugar cane and wood waste, preserves landfill space in urban communities in Florida.

We will now take a close look at the different types of biomass and bio-fuels.

Solid Biomass

Biomass is the common name for organic materials used as renewable energy sources such as wood, crops, and waste. Solid biomass includes a number of natural and man-made products, such as wood, sawdust, grass trimmings, domestic refuse, charcoal, agricultural waste, nonfood energy crops, and dried manure.

Biomass is not to be confused with biofuels, which are a product of the organic material in the biomass. Biomass, then, refers only to the organic matter which can be used as a renewable energy source in a number of different ways.

Raw biomass in a suitable to use form such as firewood can burn directly in a stove or furnace, as needed to provide heat or generate steam. When raw biomass is in a different form, such as sawdust, wood chips, grass, urban waste wood, or agricultural residues, the typical process is to process it to increase the density of the as-is biomass.

This process sometimes includes grinding to an appropriate particulate size to produce hogfuel which, depending on the densification type, can be from 1 to 3 cm in size, and which is then concentrated into a fuel product. The current processes produce wood pellets, cubes, or pucks of condensed biomass materials. The pellet process is common in Europe, and is typically a pure wood product. The other types of densification used in commercial operations are larger in size, and are compatible with a broad range of input feedstocks. The resulting densified fuel is easier to transport and feed into thermal generation systems such as boilers.

Table 3-9. Comparative value of biofuels

Bio Fuel	Energy content (MJ/kg)
Coal	28
Commercial wastes	16
Domestic refuse	9
Dung, dried	16
Biogas	55
Newspaper	17
Oil waste	42
Straw, harvested, baled	15
Sugar cane residues	17
Wood, green	6
Wood, air-dried	15
Wood, oven-dried	18

One of the advantages of solid biomass fuel is that it is often a byproduct, residue or waste-product of other processes such as farming, animal husbandry, and forestry. This means that this type of fuel does not compete for resources with food production, although this is not always the case as we saw in 2008 with the ethanol production in the U.S.

More specifically, different biomass materials contain different energy levels. Some examples are as follow:

1 ton dry wood	= 18 GJ = 5 MWh = 500 liters oil = 500 m³ natural gas
1 ton air-dry wood fuel	= 11 GJ = 3 MWh
1 m³ wood chip (.7 ton)	= 3.6 GJ = 1.0 MWh

1 barrel of crude oil   = 6.1 GJ = 1.7 MWh, =
1 barrel of crude oil   = 1.7 m³ wood chip = 0.5 m³ dry wood

There are a number of materials that qualify as sold biomass. Below, we will take a look at several of these materials, and their use as energy sources.

Although biomass is classed as a renewable energy source, it is by no means good for the environment and the fight against climate change. To produce energy from biomass, organic matter must be burned. This releases carbon dioxide into the air, unlike the use of solar, wind, and other renewable energy sources. Although the processing of biomass emits carbon dioxide, it is classed as a carbon neutral fuel, due to the total cradle-to-grave carbon cycle of the biomass. The carbon cycle means that while the crop grows it will absorb carbon dioxide, releasing it back into the atmosphere when burned. Nevertheless, in practice lots of carbon dioxide is emitted when burning biomass. Firewood is one example of this negative effect on the environment.

FIREWOOD

Until the middle of the 19th century, the major sources of energy were coal and firewood. Firewood is one of the oldest energy sources. Even when coal became a major energy source, firewood was next in line, mostly due to its unlimited supply. It accounted for over 90% of U.S. energy generation, mostly for home heating and cooking.

An average of 18 cords (stack of 4 x 4 x 8 feet) of wood per year were needed to heat an American house in the mid 1800s. This is quite a waste of energy, since it is the heat energy equivalent of 2.5 times the amount of heat energy used to warm a typical home today. This is mostly due to the inefficiency of the old fireplaces, which had less than 10% efficiency rating, and which swallowed three quarters of all wood used at the time (approximately 75 million cords). Stoves are about four times as efficient, but were not popular in the Americas at that time for convenience reasons. Wood stoves became fashionable in North America in the mid 20th century, and wood consumption increased.

Wood also powered the growing industries of the 19th century. This included steamships and trains and consumed nearly 8 million cords of wood a year. The iron and steel industries were the major industrial users of wood, although there was a twist. Most of the energy for iron smelting came from charcoal, which was made out of 1.5 million cords of wood per year.

The charcoal used in iron smelting totaled 700,000 to 750,000 tons. Today, outdoor chefs at backyard barbeques in the U.S. use an estimated 750,000 tons of charcoal annually.

Charcoal is still important worldwide. Brazil uses charcoal in 45% of its iron smelting. Annually, 3.6 million tons of charcoal are used in Brazil, and consumption is increasing. Charcoal is also a major fuel in less developed countries such as Ghana and Kenya, where 250,000-300,000 tons are used every year.

Firewood stoves are fashionable today, and are selling at a rate of 200,000 per year in the United States. Over 50 million cords of firewood were used annually for home heating alone in 2012, while wood and wood residue provided almost 2 quads of total energy that year, most of it *used* in the wood products manufacturing and paper making industries. In these industries, "biofuels" met about half of the total energy needs too.

Consumption of fuel wood in this country reached a peak of almost 150 million cords in 1870, since at that time wood was the primary fuel. In comparison, the 100 million cords used today in the U.S. account for only a few percent of the total primary energy input.

Even if the use of wood and biomass increases to a maximum, the total annual potential of biomass energy generation could provide only about 1/4 of the U.S. primary energy input.

Firewood Pollution

Finally, we must point to the amazing fact that firewood is the world's energy source (in terms of number of people affected and Btus used daily) that creates the most pollution. Yes, brushes, branches, twigs and stumps of trees that are burned by millions of people in the developed and developing countries.

While wood burning in developed countries is mostly by choice, over 600 million people in Sub-Sa-

Figure 3-42. Daily supply of firewood.

haran Africa, 800 million in India, 500 million in China and 100 million in South America use firewood for their daily needs, out of necessity.

Deadwood is collected around roadways and forests, and many live trees are cut for this purpose as well. As time goes on, the deadwood is used, and more and more trees are cut from the forest, thus helping in the propagation of the deforestation phenomena in some parts of the world.

Consumption of firewood is estimated at approximately 800 kg. per person per year. This comes to only 2-3 lbs. per person per day, but it is a large amount of wood—especially in areas that have been cleared of trees and vegetation for years. This creates great problems, including deforestation and tensions, especially in the more densely populated areas in a number of countries.

Let's assume for the purposes of this rough calculation that 500 kg. firewood are used per person annually by approximately 2 billion poor people worldwide. Firewood has energy content equivalent to 0.35 tons of oil per ton of firewood, and assuming that firewood stoves and fire pits burn at maximum 15% efficiency, we can conclude that to replace the firewood used worldwide, we would need over 150 million tons of oil a year.

This is nearly a quarter of U.S. oil consumption, which means that the 300 million U.S. inhabitants use 4 times the amount of oil used by all 2 billion poor around the world. Or, the U.S. uses more than 20 times more energy per person than the entire developing world.

Firewood is also used in large quantities in the rural areas of developing countries. The 1973 oil crisis brought out an entire firewood burning industry in the U.S., complete with the most efficient wood burning stoves and processes. There are also many fireplaces in the U.S. cities that use natural wood to heat houses during the cold months.

Firewood use in developed countries is not of necessity. It is a type of luxury, or convenience. Cuddling with a book by a roaring wood fire is part of the American dream, and people very seldom pass the opportunity. Firewood use has increased lately, so now there are many winter days with local wood burning bans, due to increased particulate or CO_2 pollution.

Of course, with every wood fire there is smoke. Lots of it. Toxic gasses, sometimes in enclosed quarters, poison the inhabitants and cause a number of health problems.

Believe it or not, wood burning is one of the largest energy generators and largest polluters in the world. It is the least known and discussed subject in the energy field, and is also one that most energy principles prefer

to ignore. It is of no consequence to them or their business, and there is not much they can do about it, so why bother? And because of that, the entire issue has fallen between the cracks and become a non-issue.

The majority of the wood-burning people represent the poorest segment of the world's population, and since there are not much business opportunities in this area, their wood burning is left alone and will continue this way for a long time.

It is hard to say if the extensive wood use is creating a problem big enough to classify wood burning as a non-renewable energy. We hesitate to call it renewable, simply because it leads to uncontrollable and extensive destruction of forests and vegetation in entire regions. Plus it is simply not something we should encourage. Instead, we should find a way to replace it with a more sustainable and less damaging energy system.

One simple 100 Watt solar panel installed on a hut's roof might solve the energy problems of an entire Sub-Saharan family. A hundred PV modules in the village might prevent a hundred from wasting time gathering wood 2-3 hours every morning. This will save a lot of wood and will eliminate a lot of smoke emission in the process.

Multiplied by the millions of wood-burning families, this might save millions of tons of wood, and that many toxic gasses from being released in the atmosphere. Doing this would be the greatest environmental success ever! But this is not going to happen anytime soon, mainly because of indifference.

NOTE: Flying over some areas of Asia or Africa at night, one can easily see hundreds and thousands of fires on the ground below. Even large cities, like Taipei, Beijing and others are marked by the fires and plums of smoke coming from their suburbs at night.

Large areas of bare land, where there were once forests and woodlands, can be seen for miles at a time in certain areas too. These bare areas create additional problems such as soil erosion, and are becoming increasingly troublesome in a number of countries.

Wood burning cannot be eliminated completely, for it has some useful purposes, but providing alternative energy sources for people in places such as India and Sub-Saharan Africa, who are forced to burn wood daily, would help their development and contribute significantly to cleaning the environment from harmful gasses and the related effects.

Sawdust

Sawdust, or wood dust, is a byproduct of cutting, grinding, drilling, sanding, or otherwise pulverizing wood, and is therefore composed of fine particles of wood. It is also a byproduct of certain animals, birds and insects which invade wood, such as the woodpecker and carpenter ant. It can present a hazard in manufacturing industries, especially in terms of its flammability. Sawdust is the main component of particleboard.

A major use of sawdust is for particleboard; coarse sawdust may be used for wood pulp. Sawdust has a variety of other practical uses, including serving as a mulch, as an alternative to clay cat litter, or as a fuel. Until the advent of refrigeration, it was often used in icehouses to keep ice frozen during the summer. It has been used in artistic displays, and as scatter. It is also sometimes used to soak up liquid spills, allowing the spill to be easily collected or swept aside. As such, it was formerly common on barroom floors, and used to make Cutler's resin. Mixed with water and frozen, it forms pykrete, a slow-melting, much stronger form of ice.

Sawdust is also used in the manufacture of charcoal briquettes, the invention of which is credited to Henry Ford who made some from the wood scraps and sawdust produced by his automobile factories.

Burning sawdust to generate electricity is not very common, but still occurs in special situations, mostly in developing countries.

In addition to the pollution problems described above, sawdust burners at sawmills generate a lot of toxic gasses. Sawdust also may be stored in large outdoor piles causing harmful leachates into local water systems, thus creating an environmental hazard. This problem has become serious for small sawyers and environmental agencies, putting them in a deadlock.

Questions about the science behind the determination of sawdust being an environmental hazard remain for sawmill operators (though this is mainly with finer particles), who compare wood residuals to dead trees in a forest. Technical advisors have reviewed some of the environmental studies, but say most lack standardized methodology or evidence of a direct impact on wildlife. They don't take into account large drainage areas, so the amount of material that is getting into the water from the site in relation to the total drainage area is minuscule.

Other scientists have a different view, saying "dilution is the solution to pollution," but this argument is no longer accepted in environmental science. The decomposition of a tree in a forest is similar to the impact of sawdust, but the difference is of scale. Sawmills may be storing thousands of cubic meters of wood residues in one place, so the issue becomes one of concentration.

Of greater concern are substances such as lignins and fatty acids that protect trees from predators while they are alive, but can leach into water and poison wildlife. Those types of things remain in the tree and, as the tree decays, they are slowly broken down. But when sawyers are processing a large volume of wood and large concentrations of these materials permeate into the runoff, the toxicity they cause is harmful to a broad range of organisms.

Domestic and Agricultural Refuse

Also called garbage, domestic refuse is a waste type consisting of everyday items that are discarded by the public and end up in the municipal dumps, where they rot and emit all kinds of gasses. Grass, leaves, brush and branches from backyard maintenance comprise a significant amount of domestic waste, and also end up in municipal dumps, adding to the emissions.

Agricultural waste consisting of dead vegetation and small animals is added in large amounts to the pollution emitters on a daily basis. Manure, of course is an inevitable result of large animal herding, and can be found in large amounts in the fields and in the cow and pig feeding farms.

Large parts of thus generated refuse can be used for biogas generation, but some must be disposed of in municipal dump sites, landfills, and land spreading (in special circumstances).

In many cases, the municipal solid waste can be used to generate energy. Several technologies have been developed that make the processing of solid waste for energy generation cleaner and more economical than ever before. This includes landfill gas capture, combustion, pyrolysis, gasification, and plasma arc gasification methods.

Older waste incineration plants emit high levels of pollutants, recently new technologies have significantly reduced this type of pollution. For example, EPA regulations in 1995 and 2000 under the Clean Air Act reduced emissions of dioxins from waste-to-energy facilities by more than 99% from 1990 levels. At the same time, mercury emissions have been reduced by over 90%. These improvements allowed waste-to-energy sources to have less environmental impact than almost any other source of electricity.

Agricultural refuse, mostly in the form of manure and feed scraps, is mostly organic matter that can be used as organic fertilizer in agriculture, where it contributes to the fertility of the soil by adding organic matter and nutrients.

Large quantities of manure can be also processed in digesters to produce methane gas, in a process similar to that of producing biogas.

Table 3-10. Husbandry biofuels potential

Animal	Manure		Biogas	
	Kg/day	MJ/day	m³/day	MJ/day
Cows	40	62	1.2	26
Hens	0.19	0.9	0.18	3.8
Pigs	2.3	6.2	0.18	3.8

Charcoal

Charcoal is a type of man-made fuel, made from wood or vegetation and animal matter, via special processes, where wood is burned in a controlled presence of oxygen. The main reason for producing this type of fuel is to convert unusable materials (even waste materials) into useful fuels that are easy to transport and use.

Charcoal is soft, brittle, and lightweight, with a dark grey to black appearance very similar to coal. It consists mainly of carbon and ash, which remain after the water and other volatile compounds are removed from the raw materials. Its combustion properties are also close to those of coal.

In the past, charcoal was produced by piling wood logs, or other combustible materials, in a conical pile which was covered to restrict contact with the air. A small opening at the base was used to control the intake of air, which was directed through a central air shaft serving as a flue. The fire was started at the bottom of the flue, and allowed to gradually spread upwards—a process which took days at a time to complete.

Slow combustion is the key to producing quality charcoal. Small-scale production yields 50% by volume, or 25% by weight, of charcoal, which produces heat equivalent to the heat produced by the starting materials. Today charcoal is produced by a special carbonization process, where small pieces of wood, sawdust, or other waste materials are burned under controlled conditions in cast iron retorts, which produce charcoal of different quality and for different purposes.

When charcoal is made at 300°C it is brown, soft, friable, and readily inflames at 380°C. When it is made at higher temperatures it is hard and brittle, and does not fire until heated to about 700°C. Charcoal production is extensively practiced for the recovery of byproducts that have some useful heat content, such as tree branches, wood shavings and sawdust.

There was massive production of charcoal during the last several centuries, which supported a large industry employing hundreds of thousands of workers in Central Europe and the UK. Thousands of acres of forest were cut, creating major deforestation in those areas.

Large wooded areas were cut and regrown cyclically, to provide a steady supply of charcoal. Over-exploitation, lack of new supplies, and increased demand for charcoal created a supply and demand imbalance, which facilitated the switch to coal and later to fossil fuels for domestic and industrial use.

Biochar

Biochar is charcoal which is used for particular purposes, especially as a soil amendment. It is a possible source of carbon sequestration as it produces negative carbon dioxide emissions, so it has the potential to help mitigate climate change via carbon sequestration.

When mixed with soils, biochar can increase soil fertility, increase agricultural productivity and provide protection against some foliar and soil-borne diseases. A stable, solid, rich in carbon material, biochar can endure in the soil for thousands of years.

Biochar made from agricultural waste can substitute wood charcoal. As wood stock becomes scarce, this alternative is gaining ground. In some parts of Africa, for example, biomass briquettes are being marketed as an alternative to charcoal to prevent deforestation associated with charcoal production.

Bagasse

Bagasse is the dry, fibrous matter that remains after crushing sugarcane, blue agave, or sorghum stalks, and extracting their juice. It is mostly used in the production of biofuel, paper products, and some special building materials. Sugarcane and other plants are taken to a processing plant, where the juice contained in them is extracted for use in foods.

Sucrose accounts for little more than 30% of the chemical energy stored in the mature sugarcane plant, while about 35% is in the leaves and stem tips, which are left in the fields during harvest. Another 35% of the energy in the plant is in the fibrous material (bagasse) left over from crushing and pressing the sugarcane stalks, which can then be used for making fuel gas.

Bagasse is often used as a primary fuel source for sugar mills, where it is burned in large quantity to produce enough heat to run an entire sugar mill. The energy in biogas can be also used to provide both heat energy used in the mill, and electricity which is typically sent into the electricity grid. This allows the plants to be energetically self-sufficient and even sell surplus electricity to utilities.

An average sugar- or ethanol-producing plant could produce 500 MW electricity for self-use, and 100 MW for sale. The sale of power is expected to boom as new regulations force the utilities to pay "fair price." This type of power is also especially valuable to utilities because it is produced mainly in the dry season when hydroelectric dams, and the electricity produced by them are running low.

Estimates of the potential power generation from bagasse in Brazil range from 1,000 to 9,000 MW depending on technology. Higher estimates assume gasification of biomass, replacement of current low-pressure steam boilers and turbines by high-pressure ones, and use of harvest trash currently left behind in the fields.

Presently, it is economically viable to extract about 288 MJ of electricity from the residues of one ton of sugarcane, of which about 180 MJ are used in the plant itself. Thus a medium-size distillery processing 1 million tons of sugarcane per year could sell about 5 MW of surplus electricity. At current prices, it would earn $18 million from sugar and ethanol sales, and about $1 million from surplus electricity sales. Not bad.

With advanced boiler and turbine technology, the electricity yield could be increased to 648 MJ per ton of sugarcane, but current electricity prices do not justify the necessary investment. Presently the World Bank would only finance investments in bagasse power generation if the price were at least $0.068/kWh.

In many other countries (such as Australia), sugar factories significantly contribute "green" power to the electricity supply. In the U.S., for example, Florida Crystals Corporation, one of America's largest sugar companies, owns and operates the largest biomass power plant in North America. The 140 MW facility uses bagasse and urban wood waste as fuel to generate enough energy to power its large milling and refining operations as well as supply enough renewable electricity for nearly 60,000 homes.

Researchers are also working with cellulosic ethanol, to optimize the extraction of ethanol from sugarcane bagasse and other plants viable on an industrial scale. The cellulose-rich bagasse is being widely investigated for its potential for producing commercial quantities of cellulosic ethanol. For example, Verenium Corporation is building a cellulosic ethanol plant based on cellulosic byproducts like bagasse in Jennings, Louisiana.

Bagasse is being sold for use as a fuel (replacing heavy fuel oil) in various other industries too, including citrus juice concentrate, vegetable oil, ceramics, and tire recycling. The state of São Paulo, Brazil, uses 2 million tons, saving about $35 million in fuel oil imports.

Bagasse burning is environmentally friendly compared to other fuels like oil and coal. Its ash content is only 2.5%, vs. 30-50% of coal-fired power plants, and it

also contains very little sulfur. Since it burns at relatively low temperatures, it produces little nitrous oxides, which has a dual effect of reducing some of the worst pollutants (acid rain especially), and allowing to introduce ways to reduce nitrous oxides generation (which is not possible at high sulfur levels).

The resulting CO_2 emissions are equal to the amount of CO_2 that the sugarcane burned in the power plant absorbed from the atmosphere during its growing phase, which makes the process of cogeneration greenhouse gas-neutral.

All in all, sugarcane and bagasse are shaping as an integral part of our energy future.

Environmental Impacts of Biomass and Biomass Power Generation

The organic matter in biomass products must be burned or processed, and these processes release carbon dioxide and other gasses into the air, unlike solar, wind, and other renewable energy sources. Although the processing of biomass emits carbon dioxide, it is still classed as a carbon neutral fuel—which is even better than wind and solar. This is due to the carbon cycle, which means that while the crop grows it will absorb carbon dioxide, releasing it back into the atmosphere when burned. CO_2 in plus CO_2 out equals zero, or near zero.

The only problem is that in most cases biomass is grown in one place and burned in another. This creates zones of environmental damage at the burning or processing sites. This and other factors contribute to the conclusion that the use of biomass is actually a serious contributor to climate change.

Although biomass is a carbon neutral fuel, other, somewhat unrelated, factors play a significant role, and can disturb this aspect. For example, biomass can contribute to global warming as a result of "carbon leakage." Deforestation is a cause of carbon leakage, as we are reducing the world's carbon absorption capacity and disturbing the natural equilibrium of carbon dioxide between the atmosphere, biosphere, geosphere, and hydrosphere.

There is also the different types of energy and the related pollution taking place during the planting, maintaining, harvesting, transporting, and processing of the crops. With renewable energy sources such as solar, wind, and geothermal, the only carbon based energy used will be to manufacture, transport, and construct the system. And the amounts are fairly low.

So, keeping in mind that biomass is still much cleaner than the use of fossil fuels to provide energy, it is not perfect in that respect, and improvements and even new alternatives must be sought. The major culprit is the use of biomass, which in all cases involves burning, which emits considerable amounts of pollutants, such as particulates and polycyclic aromatic hydrocarbons.

Even modern pellet boilers generate more pollutants than oil or natural gas boilers. Pellets made from agricultural residues are usually much worse than wood pellets, producing much larger emissions of dioxins and chlorophenols.

Nevertheless, estimates show that biomass fuels (when considering the entire growing-to-burning process) has significantly less impact on the environment than fossil based fuels, due to the CO_2 in/CO_2 out concept. But we must keep in mind that power generation with these fuels emits significant amounts of greenhouse gases (GHGs), mainly CO_2. Sequestering CO_2 from the power plant flue gas can significantly reduce the released GHGs, but the CO_2 capture and sequestration consumes additional energy, thus lowering the plant's fuel-to-electricity efficiency. To compensate for this, more fossil fuel must be procured and consumed to make up for lost capacity, which in turn produces more harmful gasses—another catch-22.

Taking this into consideration, the global warming potential (GWP), which is a combination of CO_2, methane (CH_4), and nitrous oxide (N_2O) emissions, and the energy balance of the system need to be examined using a life cycle assessment. This takes into account the upstream processes which remain constant after CO_2 sequestration, as well as the steps required for additional power generation.

For example, black carbon—a pollutant created by incomplete combustion of fossil fuels and biomass—is possibly the second largest contributor to global warming. A recent study of the giant brown haze that periodically covers large areas in South Asia determined that it had been principally produced by biomass burning and to a lesser extent by fossil-fuel burning. Researchers measured a significant concentration of carbon, which is associated with recent plant life rather than with fossil fuels.

Forest-based biomass has recently come under fire from a number of environmental organizations, including Greenpeace and the Natural Resources Defense Council, for the harmful impacts it can have on forests and the climate. Greenpeace recently released a report entitled "Fueling a BioMess, which outlines their concerns about forest-based biomass.

Because any part of the tree can be burned, the harvesting of trees for energy production encourages whole-tree harvesting, which removes more nutrients and soil cover than regular harvesting, and can be harmful to the long-term health of the forest. In some jurisdictions, forest biomass is increasingly consisting of elements essential to functioning forest ecosystems, including standing trees, naturally disturbed forests, and remains of traditional logging operations that were previously left in the forest.

Recent scientific research indicates that it can take many decades for the carbon released by burning biomass to be recaptured by re-growing trees, and even longer in low productivity areas. Also, logging operations may disturb forest soils and cause them to release stored carbon. In light of the pressing need to reduce greenhouse gas emissions in the short term to mitigate the effects of climate change, a number of environmental groups are opposing the large-scale use of forest biomass in energy production.

Finally, there is one serious issue that needs to be resolved. It is the location of the different phases of the seed-to-burn of plant and animal life cycles. While the fields and the forests that are used for making the biomass is green, clean, and safe places, the actual processes of transport, burning and otherwise using the fuels are polluting—seriously at times. How do we assign a value to the contribution and the damage in the different areas?

Sometimes money is paid (carbon tax) for excessive pollution and the related damages to those who are hurt by it, but is it possible, or fair, to assign a monetary value to environmental damage and human suffering? These cases are not accidents, so can they be considered as planned and premeditated violation of environmental and human safety laws?

BIOFUELS

Biofuels are types of fuel derived from biomass and other organic raw materials. Biofuels can be divided into solid, liquid and gas fuels.

- Solid biofuels are usually found in nature, and include wood, sawdust, grass trimmings, domestic refuse, charcoal, agricultural waste, nonfood energy crops, and dried manure. Solid biomass processes are used worldwide to make wood pellets, cubes, or pucks, which are most common in Europe, and are typically a pure wood product processed in some form and shape for commercial distribution and use.

Other types of densification produce larger size products, as compared to a pellet, and are compatible with a broad range of input feedstocks. The resulting densified biofuels (in the form of logs and other shapes) are easier to transport and feed into thermal generation systems, such as boilers and cooking stoves.

- *Liquid biofuels* include bioethanol, biodiesel, and organic compounds in liquid form that have a high heat value. These fuels are produced from different raw biomass materials using special processes.

- *Gaseous biofuels* are often byproducts from the processing of solid or liquid biofuels. These include a number of bio-gasses that can be burned onsite or delivered to other locations for burning.

Liquid and gas based biofuels, which can be divided into:

- *First-generation biofuels* are made from the sugars and vegetable oils found in energy crops (sugarcane, soy, corn, etc.), which can be easily extracted using conventional technology.

These are also called conventional biofuels, and include well-established processes that are already producing biofuels on a commercial scale. These biofuels, commonly referred to as first-generation, include sugar- and starch-based ethanol, oil-crop based biodiesel and straight vegetable oil, as well as biogas derived through anaerobic digestion. Typical feedstocks used in these processes include sugarcane and sugar beet, starch-bearing grains like corn and wheat, oil crops like rape (canola), soybean and oil palm, and in some cases animal fats and used cooking oils.

- *Second- and third-generation* biofuels are made from ligno-cellulosic biomass or woody crops, and agricultural residues or waste, which makes it harder and more expensive to extract the required fuel.

These are also called advanced biofuels, and are basically conversion technologies which are still in R&D, pilot or demonstration phase. They could be of the second- or third-generation biofuels, and some are ready for reclassification to the first generation category.

These include hydro-treated vegetable oil (HVO), which is based on animal fat and plant oil, as well as biofuels based on ligno-cellulosic biomass, such as cellulosic-ethanol, biomass-to-liquids (BtL)-diesel and bio-synthetic gas (bio-SG).

This category also includes novel technologies that are mainly in the R&D and pilot stage, such as algae-based biofuels and the conversion of sugar into diesel-type biofuels using biological or chemical catalysts. The lines between the second- and third-generation technologies are fading, as the state of the art changes and provides more options.

Recently the boundaries between the biofuels of the first, second and third generations have been getting hazier, with many gaps and overlaps contributing to the confusion. In some cases the same fuel might be classified differently, depending on technology specifics and its level of maturity, as well as its heating value, GHG emission balance, and the feedstock used in making the distinction.

In a more practical manner the biofuels could be divided into the following categories.

1. Commercially available biofuels today are:
   a. Ethanol from sugarcane and corn
   b. Biodiesel, via trans-esterification, and
   c. Biogas, via anaerobic digestion (biogas)
2. Biofuels in early commercial stages today are:
   a. Hydro-treated vegetable oils
   b. Bio-methanol
   c. Bio-gas reforming (H_2 gas)
3. Biofuels in demonstration stages today are:
   a. Cellulosic ethanol
   b. BtL diesel from gasification
   c. Biobutanol and DME,
   d. Pyrolysis-based fuels, and
   e. Bio-SG (biogas)
4. Biofuels in some type of R&D stage are:
   a. Biodiesel from microalgae,
   b. Furanics (novel biofuel),
   c. Hydrogen, novel bio-generation
   d. Sugar based hydrocarbons, and
   e. Gasification with reforming (H_2 gas)

For the purposes of this text, we will review the biofuels that have the most practical value. To start with, we'll take a look at some of the biofuels currently in use:

- Bioethanol
- Biobutanol
- Biodiesel
- Bioethers
- Biogas
- Syngas

Biofuels made from processing biomass are considered much cleaner than petrol/diesel alternatives. Theoretically they could be considered carbon neutral, since the biomass they were made from absorbs roughly the same amount of carbon dioxide during growth as when burned. While this is true, the fact that vegetation is grown in one place, processed as biofuels in another, and burned at a third contributes to the regional inequality of global pollution. The air in the agricultural fields is usually clean, while that at the processing plants and the burning site it is badly contaminated.

On top of that, biofuels are responsible for other environmental inequalities. In many cases, large areas of forest are cut down to make space for the plantation of biofuel suitable crops. This deforestation not only harms the carbon cycle, but also harms surrounding peoples who live off the forest.

Many environmentalists argue that biofuel is a disaster in the making, and doesn't offer a significant positive long-term environmental impact. No doubt, biofuels have some drawbacks, which—together with the benefits—must be thoroughly understood, carefully evaluated, and efficiently and safely implemented in the global energy future.

Biofuels can contribute to global warming as a result of "carbon leakage," an example of which is large-scale deforestation taking place in some areas of the world. It is a cause of carbon leakage, as we are reducing the world's carbon absorption capacity and disturbing the natural equilibrium of carbon dioxide between the atmosphere, biosphere, geosphere, and hydrosphere.

We must also take into account the energy involved during the planting, maintaining, harvesting, transporting, and manufacturing of the crops. And let's not forget the mountains of fertilizer, pestisides, and and other chemicals that are used during the crop planting and growing cycles.

Water usage is another troublesome issue, especially with large-scale biofuel crops growing in desert-like areas. These crops require significant amounts of water several months at a time, year after year. Water is becoming a precious commodity in many areas, so it remains to be seen how much can be dedicated to growing biofuel crops.

Then, the processes involved in biofuels production are energy guzzling operations, which also emit large amounts of GHGs.

Some of these processes are:

- *Hydrothermal processing* is a chemical process where biomass can be processed in a liquid media (typically water) under pressure and at temperatures between 300-400°C. The reaction yields oils and residual solids that have a low water content, and a lower oxygen content than oils from fast pyrolysis. Upgrading of the so-called "bio-crude" is similar to that of pyrolysis oil.

- *Pyrolysis* oil can be produced by fast pyrolysis, a process involving rapidly heating the biomass to temperatures between 400-600°C, followed by rapid cooling. Through this process, thermally unstable biomass compounds are converted to a liquid product. The obtained pyrolysis oil is more suitable for long-distance transport than for instance straw or wood chips.

As a byproduct, bio-char is produced that can be used as solid fuel, or applied on land as a measure of carbon sequestration and soil fertilization. The oil can be processed in ways similar to crude oil, and several research efforts are underway to upgrade pyrolysis oil to advanced biofuels.

- Dimethylether (DME) is another biofuel that can be produced from methanol through the process of catalytic dehydration, or it can be produced from syngas through gasifying ligno-cellulosic and other biomass feedstocks. Production of DME from gasification of biomass is in the demonstration stage, and the first plant started production in September 2010 in Sweden (Chemrec, 2010). DME is the simplest ether and can be used as a substitute for propane in liquefied petroleum gas (LPG) used as fuel, and it is a promising fuel in diesel engines, due to its high cetane number.

- Biobutanol is used as a fuel in a number of applications, including unmodified internal combustion engines. It has a greater energy density (29.2 MJ/l) and is more similar to gasoline than ethanol, and could thus be distributed through existing gasoline infrastructure.

Biobutanol can be produced by fermentation of sugar via the acetone-butanol-ethanol (ABE) process using bacteria such as Clastridium acetobutylicum. Demonstration plants are operating in Germany and the US, and others are under construction. Biobutanol can be produced from the same starch and sugar feedstocks that are used for conventional ethanol. In addition, sugars can also be derived from lignocellulosic biomass, using the same biochemical conversion steps required for advanced ethanol production. This underlines the need for enhanced research into the biochemical conversion of biomass to sugars.

• *Solar bio-fuels* are produced by processing biomass into syngas using heat generated by a concentrating solar plant, thus potentially improving conversion efficiency and providing higher GHG emission savings. More demonstration plants and further research are needed to make the process more efficient and allow for commercial-scale operation.

In Brazil, 25% ethanol is added to all gasoline mixes, resulting in E25 fuel mixture. Millions of flex-vehicles in Brazil can also run on pure ethanol, E100. As a matter of fact, Brazil has been running on ethanol since the 1970s, and why this practice is not widely implemented in other countries—including the U.S.—is a mystery, which we have been trying to uncover for decades. It seems to be the trees that prevent us from seeing the forest...

Ethanol can be produced by fermenting biomass (types of vegetation and agricultural crops), or from burned by a reacting ethylene with steam. The so-called

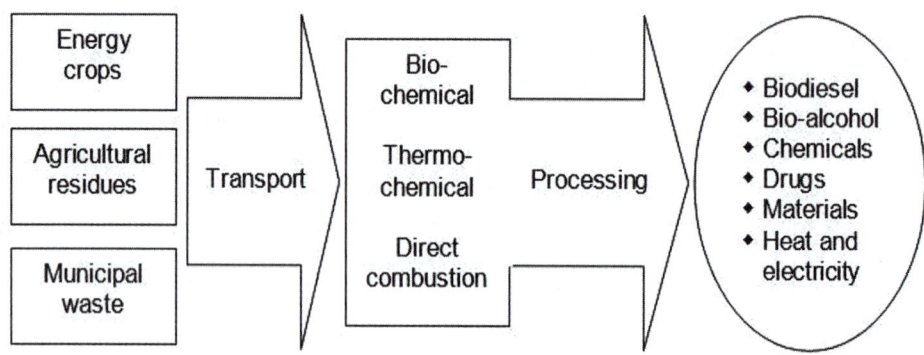

Figure 3-43. The bio-mass cradle-to-grave process

We will now take a close look at the key biofuels, remembering that some of them are well established and widely used, while others are still in R&D or small-scale production phases.

Bioethanol

Bioethanol, ethanol, or ethyl alcohol (C2H5OH), is a clear colorless liquid. It is biodegradable, low in toxicity and causes little environmental pollution if spilt. When burning, ethanol produces carbon dioxide and water. Bioethanol is actually ethanol, but produced from bio materials; instead of from burned. It is the fuel substitute mixed with gasoline and used for passenger and commercial vehicles.

Ethanol is a high-octane fuel and has replaced lead as an octane enhancer in petrol. Ethanol oxygenates the gasoline fuel mixture so it burns more completely and reduces polluting emissions. Ethanol fuel blends are widely sold in some states, mostly in the summer months, with the most common mix being 10% ethanol and 90% petrol, also called E10. Vehicle engines run well on this mixture, without the need of any modifications. Some hybrid vehicles can operate on as much as 85% ethanol and 15% gasoline blends, called E85.

energy crops are the main sources of sugar required to produce bioethanol commercially. These crops are grown specifically for bioethanol production and include sugar cane, corn, maize and wheat crops, waste straw, willow and popular trees, sawdust, reed canary grass, cord grasses, jerusalem artichoke, myscanthus and sorghum plants. Solid municipal wastes are another possible source of ethanol fuel stock, but these are still in the R&D stages.

Bioethanol is produced from biomass by the hydrolysis and sugar fermentation processes of biomass wastes which contain a complex mixture of carbohydrate polymers from the plant cell walls known as cellulose, hemicellulose and lignin. It is also produced from the energy crops, containing starch, or other carbohydrates.

To break these into sugars, the raw materials are treated with acids or enzymes. This initially reduces the size of the feedstock and opens up the plant structure, making it more susceptible to the fermentation process.

NOTE: Some biomass types contain mostly cellulose $(C_6H_{10}O_5)n$, while the most used energy crops contain starch $(C_6H_{10}O_5)n$. Note that the chemical formulas of cellulose and starch are basically the same, but that

Table 3-11. Ethanol production

	Ethanol Yield	
Material	A	B
Cassava roots	0.18	0.05 - 0.4
Maize grain	0.36	0.03 - 0.2
Sugar cane stalks	0.07	0.04 - 1.2
Sweet potato roots	0.12	0.1 - 0.5
Wood products	0.16	0.02 - 0.4

where

    A   is kilograms of material needed to produce one liter ethanol, and

    B   is square meters of land needed to produce one liter ethanol

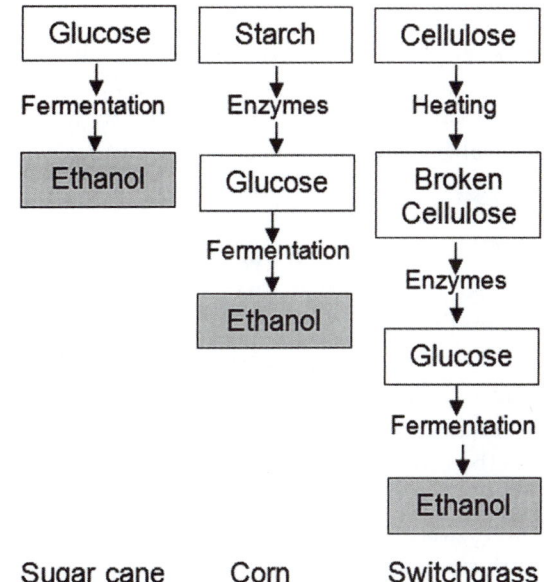

Figure 3-44. Bioethanol processing from different biomass materials

their behavior is totally different. Starch lends easily to chemical treatment when converted into sugars, while cellulose requires much more aggressive and expensive processing. This is because corn's molecule is actually one long chain of glucose molecules held together loosely, so adding enzymes is all that is needed to break the chains and separate the individual glucose molecules (sugar).

Also note in Table 3-11 that it takes much less sugar cane (0.07 kg) to produce 1 liter of ethanol, verses 0.16 kg wood needed to produce the same amount of ethanol. This is mostly due to the fact that cellulosic materials (wood is composed mostly of cellulose) contain less glucose.

Cellulose is made of similar long chains of glucose molecules, but the bonds between these are what make the big difference. The bonds (links) holding glucose molecules together in the chain are very different in orientation and behavior, and so fewer enzymes are capable of breaking down the long chains in the cellulose molecule.

Enzymes work as a lock-and-key system, where each enzyme is effective exclusively with a particular molecule, so the right enzyme is needed to build or degrade an organic molecule biologically.

Sugarcane, sugar beets and several other energy crops, on the other hand, are quite unique in that they contain pure sugars in their molecule, which are very easily extracted by mechanical or chemical treatment.

As can be seen in Figure 3-44, the processing of sugar cane is much simpler and cheaper than that of cellulosic materials, such as Switchgrass, which is becoming a favorite. In any case, the goal is to convert the raw biomaterials into sugar—whatever it takes.

Cellulose and starch components are hydrolyzed

(broken down) by enzymes or dilute acids into sucrose (type of sugar) in a solution. With time and with the help of heat and yeasts, the mass is then fermented into ethanol. Lignin and other waste products in the biomass are normally separated, and some are burned as a fuel for the ethanol production plants boilers.

There are three main commercial methods of extracting sugars from biomass and fuel crops: a) concentrated acid hydrolysis, b) dilute acid hydrolysis, and c) enzymatic hydrolysis.

Concentrated Acid Hydrolysis

The Arkanol process works by adding 70-77% sulfuric acid to the biomass that has been dried to a 10% moisture content. The acid is added in the ratio of 1.25 acid to 1 biomass and the temperature is controlled to 50°C. Water is then added to dilute the acid to 20-30% and the mixture is again heated to 100°C for 1 hour. The gel produced from this mixture is then pressed to release an acid sugar mixture and a chromatographic column is used to separate the acid and sugar mixture. The sugar mixture is then fermented with the help of enzymes or acids and the resulting dilute alcohol is distilled to pure bioethanol.

Dilute Acid Hydrolysis

The dilute acid hydrolysis process is one of the oldest, simplest and most efficient methods of producing ethanol from biomass. Dilute acid is used to hydrolyze the biomass to sucrose. The first stage uses 0.7% sulfuric acid at 190°C to hydrolyze the hemicellulose present in the biomass. The second stage is optimized to yield the more resistant cellulose fraction. This is achieved by using 0.4% sulfuric acid at 215°C. The liquid hydrolates are then neutralized and recovered from the process.

Enzymatic Hydrolysis

In this process, instead of using acid to hydrolyse the biomass into sucrose, enzymes are employed to break down the biomass in a similar way. However this process is very expensive, and is still in R&D and in early stages of development.

Bioethanol in the U.S. is produced mostly from corn, via the following processes:

Wet Milling Process

In this process, the corn kernels are first steeped in warm water (thus the name) to break down the skin and soften the kernel and the proteins, to release the starch locked in. The corn is then milled in a mechanical mill, where germ, fiber and starch are produced. The germ is extracted and used for the production of corn oil, while the starch fraction is centrifuged and then left for saccharification which produces a wet cake of gluten material.

The ethanol is extracted from the gluten by a fractional distillation process. The wet milling process is used in large-scale bioethanol production plants, which annually produce hundreds of millions of gallons of ethanol.

Dry Milling Process

The dry milling process involves cleaning and breaking down the corn kernel into fine particles using a hammer mill process. This creates a powder with a course flour-like consistency. The powder contains the corn germ, starch and fiber. To produce a sugar solution, the mixture is then hydrolysed or broken down into sucrose sugars using enzymes or a dilute acid. The mixture is then cooled, and yeast is added to ferment the mixture into ethanol. The dry milling process is used in lower volume factories, which on average produce less than 50 million gallons of ethanol annually.

Bioethanol from sugarcane is the easiest to process, since the sugarcane contains free sugars, which only need to be squeezed out from the stalks and fermented into alcohol.

Sugar Fermentation Process

The hydrolysis process breaks down the cellulosic part of the biomass or corn into sugar solutions that can then be fermented into ethanol. Yeast is added to the

solution which is then heated. The yeast contains an enzyme called invertase, which acts as a catalyst and helps to convert the sucrose sugars into glucose and fructose (both $C_6H_{10}O_5$).

The chemical reaction is:

$$C_{12}H_{22}O_{11} + H_2O = C_6H_{12}O_6 + C_6H_{12}O_6$$
$$\text{Sucrose} \quad \text{Water} \qquad \text{Fructose} \quad \text{Glucose}$$

The fructose and glucose are produced in the presence of invertase (a catalyst).

These sugars then react with another enzyme called zymase, which is also contained in the yeast, to produce ethanol and carbon dioxide.

The chemical reaction of this process is:

$$C_6H_{12}O_6 = 2C_2H_5OH + 2CO_2$$
$$\text{Sugars} \qquad \text{Ethanol}$$

The fermentation process takes around three days to complete and is carried out at a temperature of between 250°C and 300°C. All that must be done after that is separate the alcohol from the mixture.

Fractional Distillation Process

Ethanol produced from the fermentation process described above contains a significant quantity of water which must be removed. This is achieved by using the fractional distillation process. The distillation process works by boiling the water and ethanol mixture. Since ethanol has a lower boiling point (78.3°C) than water (100°C), it reaches a vapor state before the water and can be condensed and separated.

Since bioethanol is a primary source of biofuels in North America, many organizations are conducting research in that area. The National Corn-to-Ethanol Research Center (NCERC) is a research division of Southern Illinois University Edwardsville dedicated solely to ethanol-based biofuel research projects. On the federal level, the USDA conducts a large amount of research regarding ethanol production in the United States. Much of this research is targeted toward the effect of ethanol production on domestic food markets. A division of the U.S. Department of Energy, the National Renewable Energy Laboratory (NREL), has also conducted various ethanol research projects, mainly in the area of cellulosic ethanol.

Glucose (a simple sugar) is created in the plant by photosynthesis.

$$6CO_2 + 6H_2O + \text{light} \rightarrow C_6H_{12}O_6 + 6O_2$$

During ethanol fermentation, glucose is decomposed into ethanol and carbon dioxide.

$$C_6H_{12}O_6 \rightarrow 2C_2H_5OH + 2CO_2 + heat$$

During combustion ethanol reacts with oxygen to produce carbon dioxide, water, and heat:

$$C_2H_5OH + 3O_2 \rightarrow 2CO_2 + 3H_2O + heat$$

After doubling the combustion reaction, because two molecules of ethanol are produced for each glucose molecule, and adding all three reactions together, there are equal numbers of each type of atom on each side of the equation, and the net reaction for the overall production and consumption of ethanol is simply: light $\rightarrow$ heat.

The heat of the combustion of ethanol is used to drive the piston in the engine by expanding heated gases. It can be said that sunlight is used to run the engine, as is the case with any combustion-based energy source (as sunlight is the only way energy is added to the planet).

Glucose itself is not the only substance in the plant that is fermented. The simple sugar fructose also undergoes fermentation. Three other compounds in the plant can be fermented after breaking them up by hydrolysis into the glucose or fructose molecules that compose them. Starch and cellulose are molecules that are strings of glucose molecules, and sucrose (ordinary table sugar) is a molecule of glucose bonded to a molecule of fructose. The energy to create fructose in the plant ultimately comes from the metabolism of glucose created by photosynthesis, so sunlight also provides the energy generated by the fermentation of these other molecules.

Ethanol may also be produced industrially from ethylene. The addition of water to the double bond converts ethene to ethanol:

$$C_2H_4 + H_2O \rightarrow C_2H_5OH$$

This is done in the presence of an acid which catalyzes the reaction but is not consumed. The ethene is produced from petroleum by steam cracking.

When burning in a pure-oxygen environment, ethanol produces large amounts of CO_2 and H_2O.

$$C_2H_5OH + 3O_2 \rightarrow 2CO_2 + 3H_2O$$

When ethanol is burned in the atmosphere rather than in pure oxygen, however, much different and dangerous chemical reactions take place, since there are different gasses in the atmospheric, such as nitrogen (N_2).

$$C_2H_5OH + 5O_2 + N_2 \rightarrow 2CO_2 + 2NO_2 + 3H_2O$$

While burning in this air mixture, ethanol produces a lot of nitrous oxides (major air pollutants), actually 300 times more dangerous than CO_2. This makes burning large quantities of alcohol a very dangerous affair, as far as the environment and global warming in particular are concerned.

It appears that equal amounts of CO_2 and NO_2 gasses are generated during the bioethanol burning process, and these gasses produce unwanted environmental effects.

Example: Starting with, let's say 100 lbs. of starch or cellulosic materials, we get about 120 lbs. of glucose after adding the enzymes to the mixture. After fermentation we measure about 60 lbs. of bioethanol and 60 lbs. of CO_2.

Note that there is almost as much CO_2 produced during this process as there is ethanol. Still, the process is considered CO_2 neutral, because the CO_2 released during the conversion process was actually absorbed by the plants during their growth in the fields.

Because the nitrogen in the air is also oxidized during the ethanol burning process, we now have 30 lbs. of CO_2 and 30 lbs. of NO_2. Considering the fact that NO_2 is 300 times more damaging than CO_2, we arrive at the conclusion that thus burned alcohol does at least 150 times more damage than burning an equal amount of other fuels that produce only CO_2. This is not good…

Another problem, related environmental issues is the actual location where the different operations take place. The CO_2 in question was absorbed in the fields where the biomass was grown—usually several hundred miles away from the processing plants. During their growth, the plants absorbed a lot of CO_2, while at the same time releasing a lot of oxygen, thus making the air clean and fresh in that location. Of course, there is no any trace of NO_2 in these fields.

Looking ahead to the place where bioethanol is burned by vehicles in large populated centers (where the entire amount of CO_2 stored in the biomass plus an equal amount of NO_2 are released), both of those pollute the air at that location. In Los Angeles, or Beijing, on a late summer afternoon, you can see and smell a lot of these polluting gasses. At times you cannot see more than a few feet ahead or take a deep breath because of the dense smog, some of which is caused by ethanol burning.

The effects of this local gas pollution imbalance are open to debate, as is the entire effect of CO_2 on the global environment, but it is a proven fact that some areas have totally different air quality than others.

It is possible to minimize the CO_2 and NO_2 emissions, and significantly improve the greenhouse gas profile of ethanol, but we need to deal squarely with the importance issue. It is a serious one and should not be ignored. Basically, we have a good thing in bioethanol that comes with some bad consequences which we must address efficiently.

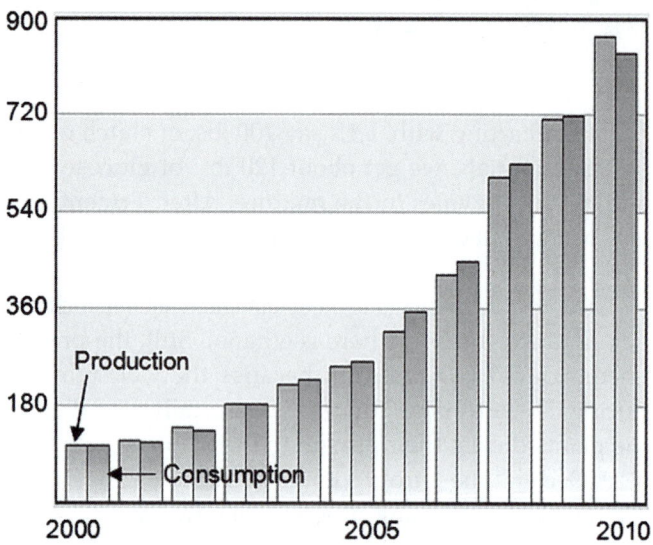

Figure 3-45. U.S. Bio-ethanol production and use (in thousand barrels/day)

Case study 1. Sacramento bio-ethanol production and power cogeneration plant.

The Sacramento ethanol and power generation plant was one of the first attempts for large-scale bio-ethanol production from cellulosic materials in the U.S. It was initiated around 1992, but it took 2 years to obtain construction permits. At the time, it was not only the first commercial cellulosic biomass-to-ethanol plant, but was also a key part of the solution to the rice straw disposal problem facing California's rice-growing industry in the face of regulations banning most field burning of such agricultural residues. This process would eliminate the post-harvest open field burning of rice straw on some 40,000 acres, approximately 15 percent of the total Sacramento Valley rice under cultivation.

This was a win-win situation, no doubt…at least on paper. In practice, things are much more difficult—from political, regulatory, and technical points of view. The plant was to be built on 90 acres and was to convert over 400 tons per day of rice straw and other cellulosic agricultural residue into approximately 35,000 gallons per day of fuel-grade ethanol, using patented concen-

trated acid hydrolysis technology. This is 12 million gallons bio-ethanol obtained by processing 132,000 tons of rice-straw per year. Thus produced bio-ethanol would be used in tandem with natural gas to generate about 150 MW electricity as a base-load power plant.

The plant was essentially two separate yet linked projects with different owners united by a contractual arrangement, sharing a site and various operational synergies, including process heat and power supplied to the ethanol plant by the cogeneration plant, shared water supply and waste disposal provisions, etc. It's complicated…

Partnership issues flared up, delayed the project and finally caused the permit to expire. Five years later, the owner applied for a new permit which was granted in 2000. The struggles continued, but the plant was never built. Plant construction did not go forward mostly due to complexities with the joint venture and multiple parties, who could not divide the pie to everyone's satisfaction. The technological approach was also unproven and somewhat too advanced for the time, which complicated things further.

Nevertheless, a number of lessons (albeit expensive) were learned from this experience. It was an early test case of the California regulatory process for permitting a bio-refinery facility, where bio-alcohol production would be combined with electricity generation. As such, the project could be considered as a partial success story.

Some of the successfully executed tasks and lessons learned were:

•   Extensive environmental analysis was conducted and complex mitigation measures considered on a full range of issues, including air quality, water supply and water quality, hydrology, and biological resources. Issuance of an air quality permit for the entire project was based on emission offsets to be obtained via the discontinuation of rice straw burning resulting from the use of rice straw as the ethanol plant feedstock.

•   Flood plain concerns resulted in modifications to the facility site plan. Original plans to use groundwater wells were changed to the use of surface water; water supply arrangements included mitigation measures at the Sacramento River water intake to protect salmon. Various other mitigation measures were adopted involving several different endangered species found on the site.

•   The unique features of the project, combining rice straw to ethanol production and electricity cogeneration, posed a number of considerations not previously encountered in the California regulatory proceedings.

- Reliability, or lack thereof, of the unproven cellulosic ethanol production process affected both the cogeneration performance and emission offset viability of the power plant. Various issues associated with the feedstock supply plan based on the yet-to-be-demonstrated use of rice straw were addressed as well.

Case Study 2. Gridley Ethanol Plant

The Gridley Ethanol Project was another attempt, designed as a potential solution to the rice straw disposal problem in the Sacramento Valley region of California, which became acute with legislative mandates to significantly reduce the amount of rice straw burning after the fall rice harvest.

The Rice Straw Burning Reduction Act of 1991 (AB 1378) mandated a reduction in rice straw burning by the year 2000 to no more than 25% of the planted acreage. The California rice straw burning phase-down has proceeded as required by the statute, with growers burning less than the statutory limitations. Other open-field burning laws and regulations further limit the actual rice straw acreage burned annually.

Despite the ongoing reduction of rice straw burning, no alternative market or disposal option sufficient to handle the quantities of rice straw being produced was available at the time. As a result, very large volumes of this material continue to accumulate without a viable market alternative to dispose of the rice straw. This could eventually render useless thousands of acres of rice lands, since in these hard clay-pan soils, no other crops have been successful. Production of bio-ethanol from rice straw was seen as a potential solution.

The original concept of the Gridley plant involved application of an unproven enzymatic hydrolysis process to produce ethanol. Lignin remaining from the hydrolysis process was to be utilized as combustion fuel for firing the facility's boiler for the production of steam and electricity to be used onsite, with excess steam potentially used by adjacent facilities. Excess electricity would be supplied to the municipal utility or sold to the grid.

Planning of the Gridley plant began in 1994 and was authorized in 1996 by NREL. Phase 1 started with initial screening of the technical and economic feasibility of a commercial rice straw-to-ethanol facility in the Gridley area. Phase II was to acquire financial and site

commitments, perform pilot plant studies of the technology at NREL, prepare a preliminary engineering package, evaluate the economics and risks, and finally to prepare an implementation plan to commercialize the process. Phase II was to lead to a "go/no go" decision regarding the construction of the plants.

Here again, there were many partners, but in 1997 the original conversion technology developer withdrew from the project. Since Phase I tasks had been completed and a rice straw-to-ethanol facility appeared feasible, a new partner was chosen to provide the conversion technology, which was basically also acid hydrolysis and fermentation, with lignin as a co-product.

During the progress of Phases I and II, it was determined that project economics with the then-current state of conversion technology would be enhanced by converting the bio-ethanol production plant into a cogeneration facility. It was then to be sited next to an existing biomass power plant in the region, which uses orchard prunings and forest wastes as feedstock. This co-location would reduce the costs and improve the efficiency of both the power plant and the proposed ethanol facility.

Construction of the new plant was projected to commence in early 2002 with operations to begin in late 2003. The collection and processing of rice straw became a paramount consideration, since infrastructure to harvest rice straw for use in the plant was virtually nonexistent. Processing (grinding) of the rice straw for use as feedstock presented technical challenges due to its high silica content.

Rice straw supply studies indicated that the rice straw would cost over \$30.00/bone dry ton (BDT) to be delivered to the facility. This did not include the grinding and processing of the rice straw at the facility. To produce 23 million gallons of ethanol would require 300,000 dry tons of rice straw (some of which could be provided by orchard and forest wood wastes).

On top of that, there were environmental permitting and impact assessment studies indicating potentially higher costs than originally anticipated. Wastewater from the plant would need to be discharged to the local municipal wastewater treatment plant, which alone would cost several million dollars. Also, to discharge to the wastewater plant, an expensive wastewater pretreatment adding several million dollars to the operating cost, would be necessary, and additional air emission control equipment would be needed to complete the environmental safety not previously anticipated.

This, combined with the technical uncertainties of the two-stage dilute sulfuric acid conversion technology, led a conclusion that the acid hydrolysis technology was not financially viable for use. A decision was made to investigate the use of a gasification technology to create syngas that could be converted to ethanol or other fuels. This evaluation, done in 2002, indicated that switching from the dilute sulfuric acid process to a gasification process could have the a number of advantages, such as increased yields of ethanol, with associated reductions in feedstock and other operating costs per gallon of ethanol produced; lower capital investment cost; fewer air emissions and wastewater effluents; and reduced feedstock requirements, which better fit the initial needs of the area for disposing of a critical mass of rice straw.

The plant was also to be moved again to its original location, due to a new industrial site availablity, shorter transportation hauling distances from the rice fields, significantly reduced wastewater disposal costs, and available infrastructure to better support the proposed facility.

NREL continued to finance and support the plant and its new gasification technology. A pilot facility was used for a proof-of-concept. The results were encouraging, and the Gridley plant was able to get funding from the U.S. Department of Energy. In December 2006 the plant management issued a Request for Proposals to construct and operate a thermo-chemical conversion system using rice straw to produce bio-ethanol and electricity.

The plant was awarded a CEC grant in April 2007 to demonstrate an integrated biofuels and energy production system. The project was geared to support the construction, demonstration and validation of a cost effective and energy efficient biomass conversion system. But conflicts among the partners, shifting locations, and changing processing technologies took their toll, and when the farmers refused to participate due to high transportation costs, the plant was put on hold—indefinitely and after millions of taxpayer dollars spent in the process.

In summary, there were a great number of failed bio-ethanol conversion plants in the U.S. during the last 2-3 decades too, but nevertheless, in the summer of 2013 there were 211 operational bio-ethanol plants in the U.S., producing the grand total of 13.5 billion gallons of bio-ethanol every year, mostly from corn.

What the future holds for bio-ethanol is anyone's guess, but we venture say that it won't go much further for awhile—and until natural gas prices are so low. It will, however, be the fuel of choice for electricity generation and transportation in the distant future, when oil and gas are gone. Make no mistake about it!

Biobutanol

Biobutanol is a type of 4-carbon alcohol that is produced from a number of biomass feedstocks via fermentation. A large variety of biomass types can be used in this process; corn grain, corn stovers, and many other feedstocks. Like in other processes, these are processed into sugars, and the special microbes of the *Clostridium acetobutylicum* species, are introduced to the sugars, which are then broken down into various alcohols, including butanol.

Biobutanol can be produced by fermentation of sugar via the acetone-butanol-ethanol (ABE) process using bacteria such as *Clastridium acetobutylicum*. It can also be made using Ralstonia eutropha H16, which process requires the use of an electro-bioreactor, and the additional input of carbon dioxide and electricity.

The difference from ethanol production is primarily in the fermentation of the feedstock and minor changes in the distillation setup and process parameters. The feedstocks are the same as for ethanol: energy crops such as sugar beets, sugar cane, corn grain, wheat and cassava, prospective non-food energy crops such as switchgrass and even guayule in North America, as well as agricultural byproducts such as straw and corn stalks.

Sugars can also be derived from ligno-cellulosic biomass, using the same biochemical conversion steps required for advanced ethanol production. According to industry experts, existing bioethanol plants can cost-effectively be retrofitted to biobutanol production.

Unfortunately, high alcohol concentration makes the butanol mixture toxic to these microorganisms. This condition made the fermentation process expensive and impractical when compared to the petroleum costs.

New technological advances have improved the efficiency and reduced the cost of the fermentation process. Today, genetically engineered processes are making it possible for the most efficient microbes to withstand even the highest alcohol concentrations. This allows large quantities of biobutanol to be produced commercially.

As with the case of bioethanol, biobutanol can be prepared easier and directly from a ready source of sugar, such as sugarcane, but production from crop wastes and energy grass is possible too. It can also be made entirely with solar energy, from algae, called Solalgal Fuel, or special diatom materials.

Butanol has a total of four different isomers, but only three are used commercially: n-butanol, isobutanol, tertbutanol. They all have multiple uses in industrial and consumer products. The market for n-butanol and isobutanol is over 7 billion lbs annually, and biobutanol producers already have a captive market.

N-butanol finds applications as production intermediate for a number of chemicals, such as butyl acrylate, butyl acetate, dibutyl phthalate, and also as extractant for antibiotics, hormones, and vitamins. It is also an ingredient in perfumes, degreasers, repellents, and cleaning solutions.

Iso-butanol finds applications as paint solvent, ink ingredient, gasoline additive, derivative ester precursor, viscosity reducer in paint, automotive polish, and paint cleaner additive.

Tert-butanol finds application as; perfume ingredient, gasoline octane booster, paint remover ingredient, and solvent, as well as a synthesis intermediate of methyl tert-butyl ether (MTBE), ethyl tert-butyl ether (ETBE), amd tert-butyl hydroperoxide (TBHP).

Biobutanol has a greater energy density (29.2 MJ/l) and is more similar to gasoline than ethanol, so it is used in internal combustion engines, primarily as a gasoline additive, or a fuel blend with gasoline. The energy content of biobutanol is only 10% less than that of regular gasoline, while the energy density of ethanol is over 40% lower. Biobutanol is also more chemically similar to gasoline than ethanol, so it can be integrated into regular internal combustion engines much easier than ethanol.

Biobutanol has the potential to reduce the carbon emissions by 85% as compared to gasoline, which makes it a superior alternative to gasoline and to the gasoline-ethanol blended fuels. It can also be produced from feedstocks which do not compete with food. For example, algae biomass and waste wood particles can be converted to biobutanol, with the advantage that some of these require only a 10th of the land resource needed to grow corn.

Still, most of these achievements are in small-scale or R&D lab settings for now. Because of that, the commercial future of biobutanol is...still in the future.

Table 3-12. Energy content of key fuels

Fuel	Energy density	Air-fuel ratio	Specific energy
Gasoline and biogasoline	32 MJ/L	14.6	2.9 MJ/kg air
Butanol fuel	29.2 MJ/L	11.1	3.2 MJ/kg air
Ethanol fuel	19.6 MJ/L	9.0	3.0 MJ/kg air
Methanol fuel	16 MJ/L	6.4	3.1 MJ/kg air

Biodiesel

Biodiesel is a substance of pure or somewhat modified vegetable oil, or animal based fat, that is used to power diesel engines. It has a technical definition of mono-alkyl (methyl, propyl, or ethyl) ester of long-chain fatty acids, which are produced from vegetable oils or animal fats. Soybean methyl ester is one of the pure biodiesel varieties. It is made from soybeans, has an average molecular weight of 292.2 and is comprised of: Palmitic acid $C_{15}H_{31}CO_2CH_3$, Stearic acid $C_{17}H_{35}CO_2CH_3$, Oleic acid $C_{17}H_{33}CO_2CH_3$, Linoleic acid $CH_3(CH_2)_4CH=CHCH_2CH = CH(CH_2)_7CO_2CH_3$, and Linoleic acid $CH_3(CH_2CH=CH)_3(CH_2)_7CO_2CH_3$.

Since biodiesel is used to power expensive diesel engines in passenger and commercial cars and trucks, it has to meet the strictest quality specifications of ASTM D 6751, and must be compatible in any blend with petroleum diesel fuels.

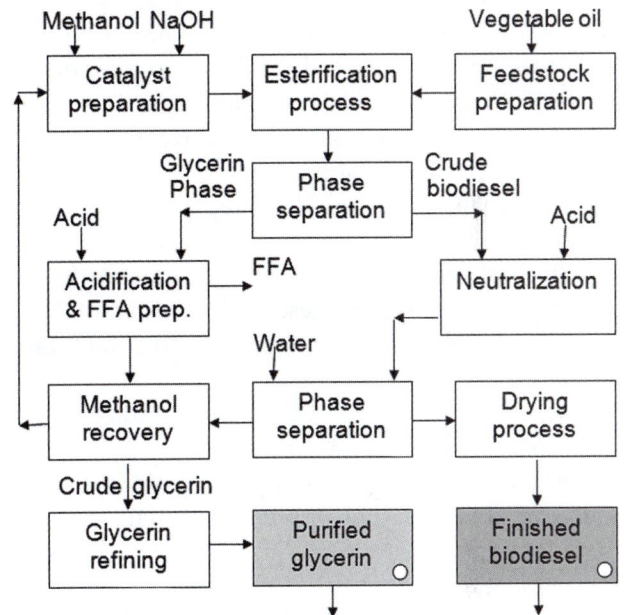

Figure 3-46. Biodiesel production process

Biodiesel is typically made by chemically reacting (trans-esterification) of vegetable oil or animal fat feedstock, lipids, vegetable oil, and animal fat (tallow) with an alcohol producing fatty acid esters.

Recycled oil is processed to remove impurities such as dirt, charred food, and water from cooking, storage, and handling. Virgin oils are refined to commercial grade purity (not to a food-grade level). A degumming process step is used when needed to remove phospholipids and other plant matter via different refinement processes.

Excess water is removed to prevent triglycerides from hydrolysis during base-catalyzed trans-esterification processes, thus preventing the formation of salts in the fatty acids (soaps) instead of producing biodiesel.

The acids present in the oil are either esterified into biodiesel, esterified into glycerides, or removed through neutralization with bases.

Trans-esterified biodiesel is a mix of mono-alkyl esters of long-chain fatty acids, with the most common form being methanol converted to sodium methoxide to produce methyl esters. These are commonly referred to as fatty acid methyl ester, or FAME.

Methanol is used to produce fatty acid ethyl ester, or FAEE biodiesel, but other alcohols such as isopropanol and butanol can also be used. Using alcohols of higher molecular weights improves the cold flow properties of the resulting ester, at the cost of a less efficient trans-esterification reaction.

A lipid trans-esterification production process is used to convert the base oil to the desired esters. Any free fatty acids (FFAs) in the base oil are either converted to soap and removed from the process, or they are esterified, which yields more biodiesel, via an acidic catalyst. After this processing, unlike straight vegetable oil, biodiesel has combustion properties very similar to those of petroleum diesel, and can replace it in most current uses.

Glycerol is a by-product of the trans-esterification process, where 1 ton of biodiesel also produces 100 kg of glycerol. Crude glycerol contains 20% water and catalyst residues and has no practical use today. Research is underway to find use for it as a chemical building block in some products such as epoxy resins.

Biodiesel is considered environmentally friendly, because its ozone (smog) forming potential, as well as its CO_2 particulate, and total hydrocarbons content are about 50% less than that of conventional diesel fuels. Sulfur emissions are essentially eliminated with pure biodiesel, and so are the unburned hydrocarbons, carbon monoxide, and particulate matter, all of which are typical for standard diesel fuels.

The bad news is that NO_x emissions from B100 biodiesel are 10% higher than those from standard diesel which—as we saw above—is 300 times worse for the environment than same amount of CO_2. This is a serious issue that needs to be resolved, if biodiesel is to become accepted as an environmentally safe alternative to petrodiesel.

The good news is that biodiesel's lack of sulfur content allows the use of NO_x control technologies that cannot be used with conventional diesel engines. There are also some additives developed lately that can reduce NO_x emissions in biodiesel blends.

Basically, biodiesels reduce the health risks associated with standard diesel fuels. Biodiesel emissions show decreased levels of polycyclic aromatic hydrocarbons (PAH) and nitrated polycyclic aromatic hydrocarbons (nPAH), which have been identified as potential cancer causing compounds. In Health Effects testing, PAH compounds were reduced by 75 to 85%, while benzo(a)anthracene was reduced by roughly 50%. Targeted nPAH compounds were also reduced dramatically with biodiesel, with 2-nitrofluorene and 1-nitropyrene reduced by 90%, while the rest of the nPAH compounds are reduced to minute (trace) levels.

Biodiesel is extensively used in European and other countries around the world. Pure biodiesel, used in standard diesel engines, is different from waste oils (used for cooking) that are sometimes used to fuel converted diesel engines. Note the term converted, because using waste vegetable oil in a standard diesel engine would cause damage that might require expensive repairs.

Biodiesel can be used pure, or blended with petrodiesel. It can be also used as a low carbon alternative to heating oil. Blends of biodiesel and conventional hydrocarbon-based diesel are most commonly used in the retail diesel market.

The "B" factor system is usually used to reflect the amount of biodiesel in the respective fuel mix, as follows: 100% biodiesel is labeled B100, 20% biodiesel in 80% petrodiesel is labeled B20, 5% biodiesel in 95% petrodiesel is labeled B5, and 2% biodiesel in 98% petrodiesel is labeled B2.

Blends of 20% biodiesel and lower are used in standard diesel equipment with only minor modifications, but in some cases it can violate the manufacturer's warranty. Biodiesel used in its pure form (B100) usually requires major engine modifications.

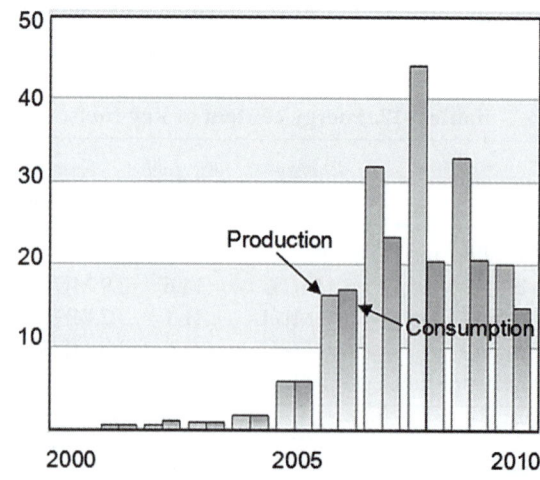

Figure 3-47. U.S. Biodiesel production and use (in thousand barrels/day

Advanced Biodiesel

Several processes are under development that aim to produce fuels with properties very similar to diesel and kerosene. These fuels will be blendable with fossil fuels in any proportion, can use the same infrastructure and should be fully compatible with engines in heavy-duty vehicles. Advanced biodiesel and bio-kerosene will become increasingly important to reach this roadmap's targets since demand for low-carbon fuels with high energy density is expected to increase significantly in the long term.

Advanced biodiesel includes:

- Hydrotreated vegetable oil (HVO) is produced by hydrogenating vegetable oils or animal fats. The first large-scale plants have been opened in Finland and Singapore, but the process has not yet been fully commercialized.

- Biomass-to-liquids (BtL) diesel, also referred to as Fischer-Tropsch diesel, is produced by a two-step process in which biomass is converted to a syngas rich in hydrogen and carbon monoxide. After cleaning, the syngas is catalytically converted through Fischer-Tropsch (FT) synthesis into broad range hydrocarbon liquids, including synthetic diesel and bio-kerosene.

Advanced biodiesel is not widely available at present, but could become fully commercialized in the near future, since a number of producers have pilot and demonstration projects underway.

Biodiesel has great potential as a plentiful, clean and cheap fuel. With more improvements, it might be one of the energy sources that will carry us through the energy transition gap of the 21st and 22nd centuries.

Bio-ethers

Bio-ether is a derivative from bioethanol, which is obtained from the distillation of energy crops and sugar beet. The best known and widely used fuel ethers are MTBE (methyl-tertiary-butyl-ether) and ETBE (ethyl-tertiary-butyl-ether).

Bio-ethers are a class of ethers that are produced from biomass materials, energy crops, and such. They are classified as organic compounds that are characterized by an oxygen atom bonded to two alkyl or aryl groups. Ethers are similar in structure to alcohols, and both ethers and alcohols are similar in structure to water.

The difference here is that in the alcohol molecule, one hydrogen atom of a water molecule is replaced by

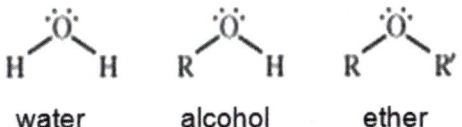

water　　alcohol　　ether

Figure 3-48. Chemical formulas of basic fuels

an alkyl group, while in the ether molecule, both hydrogen atoms are replaced by either an alkyl or aryl groups.

In the presence of acid, two molecules of an alcohol may lose water to form an ether. In practice, however, this bimolecular dehydration to form an ether competes with uni-molecular dehydration to give an alkene. Bimolecular dehydration produces useful yields of ethers only with simple, primary alkyl groups such as those in dimethyl ether and diethyl ether. Dehydration is used commercially to produce diethyl ether.

The most practical method for making ethers is Williamson ether synthesis, which uses an alkoxide ion to attack an alkyl halide, substituting the alkoxy (−O−R) group for the halide. The alkyl halide must be unhindered (usually primary), or elimination will compete with the desired substitution.

Fuel ethers can be produced from a mixture of both petrochemical and agricultural feedstocks. In all cases, the building blocks for fuel ethers are isobutylene or isoamylenes compounds, reacted with methanol or ethanol.

A complete bio-chemical process involves using bio-ethanol, which is derived by a fermenting process from wheat, sugar beet and other agricultural products, and is the major feedstock for the production of ETBE or TAEE (tert-amyl-ethyl-ether).

Bio-methanol, which is also derived from biomass, is the second feedstock used in the production of MTBE or TAME (tert-amyl-methyl-ether).

Isobutylene is yet another feedstock used in both MTBE and ETBE production, but it is derived from fossils, natural gas, or as a byproduct of petroleum refining.

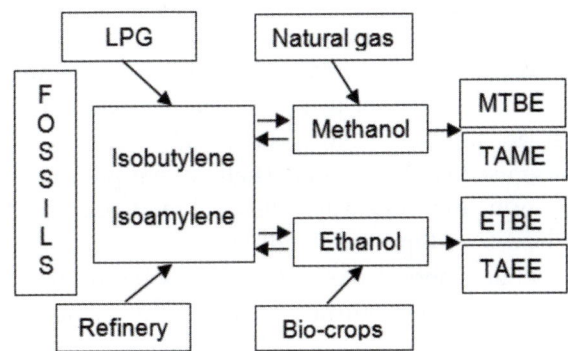

Figure 3-49. Bioether production scheme

Similarly, isoamylenes used in the production of TAME or TAEE are byproducts of petroleum refining.

Bioether production facilities are typically located close to a refinery with a fluid catalytic cracker unit, or in a chemical plant with a steam cracker. Large-scale "stand alone" units are also in operation lately, but these are based mostly on fossils using either butane isomerisation/dehydrogenation technology (where both the butane and the methanol are derived from natural gas), or by dehydration of tertiary butyl alcohols.

Ethers are pleasant-smelling, colorless liquids. They are less dense than alcohol and are less soluble in water. Ethers are relatively unreactive and have lower boiling points than their cousins, the alcohols. They are used widely as solvents for fats, oils, waxes, perfumes, resins, dyes, gums, and many hydrocarbons. Vapors of certain ethers are used as insecticides, miticides, and fumigants for soil.

Ethyl ether is used as a volatile starting fluid for diesel engines and gasoline engines in cold weather. Dimethyl ether is used as a spray propellant and refrigerant. Methyl t-butyl ether (MTBE) is a gasoline additive that boosts the octane number and reduces the amount of nitrogen-oxide pollutants in the exhaust. Its chemical formula is CH_3CH_2–O–CH_3CH_3.

Bioethers are one of the biofuels of choice today in Europe, with over three quarters of all bioethanol being used as bio-ether (ETBE). European energy policy is promoting the use of bio-fuels for transportation. Bioethers and bioalcohols are used as blending agents for enhancing the octane number. By changing the properties of common fuels, they make gasoline work harder, help the engine last longer and reduce air pollution. Development of renewable fuels needs both knowledge of new thermodynamic data and improvement of clean energy technologies. In this context, the use of ethanol of vegetable origin in its manufacturing process increases the interest of ETBE or bio-ETBE as an oxygenated additive.

Used Cooking Oil

A lot of oil of vegetable and animal origin is used for cooking in restaurants and fast food chains around the world. Options for disposal of used cooking oil and grease are limited in most places. Disposal is difficult, because used cooking oil is usually in a liquid, or semi-solid, form, and most waste disposal regulations restrict the disposal of liquids in landfills.

Other disposal methods can also be problematic. For example, open burning of used cooking oil causes black smoke, which is prohibited. Using it as fuel in most standard heating systems will cause black smoke

and soot too, and may even damage the system. Pouring used cooking oil down the drain can clog pipes and damage wastewater or septic systems, and so it is a major no-no.

So, in addition to using it in pet food preparations, one of the best ways of disposing of and actually using cooking oil is to burn it in some approved incinerators. Another way is to use it as a fuel in modified diesel engines. Since the modifications and the supply might be questionable, the best way is to refine it into biodiesl for use in standard diesel engines.

For example, McDonald's UK is recycling 100% of its used cooking oil for biodiesel to be used as fuel in fuel delivery trucks. This is an emission savings of more than 3,500 tons of CO_2, or the equivalent of 1,500 cars being removed from the road each year.

In the USA, McDonald's is implementing a bulk cooking oil delivery and retrieval program, which includes collection of waste cooking oil in a separate tank, which is periodically taken back to a distribution facility where it is sold for re-use to a variety of vendors, including biodiesel companies. Nearly 9,000 U.S. McDonald restaurants are enrolled in this program, and additional franchises are being converted for this service.

This means that the average participating U.S. restaurant recycles nearly 1,500 gallons of used cooking oil per year, together with eliminating large amounts of plastic and corrugated paper packaging. This eliminates the pollution created during the manufacture of packaging, and keeps additional packaging waste from going into the landfill.

Today, there are small, portable, biodiesel generators which can process used cooking oil into biodiesel. These can be used at home, or commercially, and can produce 20 to 200 gallons of biodiesel per day.

Additionally, there are recipes for home-made biodiesel, in which vegetable oil (including used cooking oil) is mixed with sodium hydroxide and methanol in a blender. After blending, the mixture is left to separate, and the top layer can be used as biodiesel. The quality of the biodiesel from this simple process is questionable, and the process cannot be used for large-scale fuel production.

One problem is that biodiesel has a limited shelf life. Some oils contain the antioxidant tocopherol, or vitamin E (e.g., rapeseed oil), and they remain usable longer than biodiesel from other types of vegetable oils. Biodiesel's stability can diminish after a week or two, and is usually unusable after 1-2 months. Higher temperature also negatively affects fuel stability by denaturing it.

BIOGAS

Biogas is a type of gas-fuel produced by the breakdown of organic matter (biomass and other organic materials) in the absence of oxygen. It is considered a renewable energy source, which can be produced from regionally available raw materials and recycled vegetation and animal waste, all of which makes it environmentally friendly and CO_2 neutral.

Anaerobic digestion or fermentation of biodegradable materials used in bio-gas production such as manure, sewage, municipal waste, green waste, plant material, and many crops, also has the advantage of reducing the overall amount of final waste from these materials. Biogas generated from digestion is comprised primarily of ~60% methane (CH_4), 30% carbon dioxide (CO_2), with small amounts of nitrogen (N_2), hydrogen (H_2), oxygen (O_2), hydrogen sulfide (H_2S), moisture, and siloxanes.

Biogas is most often produced as landfill gas (LFG) or digested gas in biogas plants. These are simple anaerobic (oxygen-free) digesters, designed to treat farm wastes or energy crops such as maize silage. Some can process biodegradable wastes including sewage sludge and food waste into biogas as well.

The process requires an air-tight tank, where the biomass waste is digested, or transferred, into methane gas, thus producing renewable energy that can be used for heating, electricity, and many other operations, including fuel for car and truck engines.

Large-scale *landfill* gas is produced by wet organic waste decomposing under anaerobic conditions, where it is covered and mechanically compressed by the weight of the material that is deposited above. This material prevents oxygen exposure thus allowing anaerobic microbes to thrive, and the gas builds up with time. It is slowly released into the atmosphere if the landfill site has not been engineered to capture the gas, or in containers for later use if the design allows.

Table 3-13. Approximate content of household wastes

Material	Typical weight %
Ash	25
Carbon	25
Water	20
Oxygen	18
Hydrogen	3
Chlorine	0.7
Nitrogen	0.6
Sulfur	0.003

Landfill gas is hazardous because:

1. It is explosive when mixed with oxygen. Even a small amount, about 5% methane, can create an explosion;

2. Methane from landfill gas is 20 times more potent as a greenhouse gas than carbon dioxide, so if landfill gas is allowed to escape into the atmosphere, it contributes to global warming; and

3. Landfill gas contains volatile organic compounds (VOCs) which contribute to the formation of photochemical smog—another bad environmental polluter.

In most cases, a thus produced gas mixture is not good enough for use as fuel gas for car engines and other machinery because H_2S in it is corrosive enough to destroy the internal components of a car engine or power plant. So this raw biogas must be purified to remove the contaminants. When the contaminants are scrubbed out, more methane per unit volume of gas is available for burning, and less harmful gasses are released.

There are several methods of refining and upgrading biogas:

a. water washing,
b. pressure swing absorption,
c. selexol absorption, and
d. amine gas treating.

The most practical of these is water washing, where high pressure gas flows into a process column in which the carbon dioxide and other impurities are removed by cascading water running counter-flow to the gas. This method produces over 98% pure methane, but some 2% of the total methane content is lost in the system. It also takes about 5% of the total energy content in the gas to run the scrubbers.

Thus produced upgraded biogas can be compressed, like natural gas, used to power cars and trucks, and to fuel a number of important applications, or almost anywhere natural gas is used. Biogas, for example, has the potential to replace around 15-20% of vehicle fuel in some European countries, and since it also qualifies for renewable energy subsidies in some of these countries, interest in it is increasing.

Another major use for biogas is the so-called gas-grid injection, where biogas is mixed into the natural gas distribution grid network. This way, gas is delivered to customers where it can be used in domestic or commercial power generation (heat or electricity). One thing to note here is the fact that the typical energy losses in natural gas transmission systems are in the 1-2% range, while the energy losses from a large electrical system range from 5-8%.

The difference is that methane gas, which is usually lost in the natural gas distribution system, is many times more environmentally damaging than any of the losses in the electrical system. This leads us to the conclusion that we need to separate the energy conversion efficiency losses from the actual physical loss of physical materials in the energy generation networks.

Syngas

Syngas is a mixture of carbon monoxide, hydrogen and other hydrocarbons, which is produced by partial combustion of biomass. It is emitted during processes such as the making of charcoal, where the biomass combustion is done with a controlled amount of oxygen. The gasification process usually proceeds at temperatures greater than 700°C, but due to insufficient oxygen, it does not convert the biomass completely to carbon dioxide and water. Instead, it removes enough of these to convert the raw biomass into a lighter combustible fuel, accompanied by release of syngas.

The resulting gas mixture, syngas, is more efficient than direct combustion of the original biomass, since more of the energy contained in it is extracted and contained in the resulting biogas.

The wood gas generator is a wood-fueled gasification reactor, that can feed directly an internal combustion engine. It can also be used to produce methanol, DME and hydrogen, or converted via the Fischer-Tropsch process to produce a diesel substitute. A mixture of alcohols used for blending into gasoline can be produced too.

Lower-temperature gasification, as that used normally for co-producing biochar, results in syngas polluted with tar. After refining, syngas may be burned directly in internal combustion engines, turbines or high-temperature fuel cells.

There are a number of biogases available commercially, depending on the raw materials and processes used in their production. They all, however, have similar composition and energy value, and all must be refined and otherwise processed for convenient storage, transport and use.

A number of other biogases are in R&D mode, or are produced on a small commercial scale. These are the second- and third-generation biogases, which we will review below.

Second-generation (Advanced) Biofuels

Second-generation biofuels are made from lignocellulosic biomass or woody crops, agricultural residues or waste, which makes it harder and more expensive to extract the required fuel. These are produced from biomass materials, which are available in large quantity for mass biofuel production, and whose impact on GHG emissions, on biodiversity and land use are well known and acceptable.

Most second-generation biofuels are under development in university, private and government labs and facilities. For example, Cellulosic ethanol, Algae fuel, biohydrogen, biomethanol, DMF, BioDME, Fischer-Tropsch diesel, biohydrogen diesel, mixed alcohols, and wood diesel are prime examples of these fuels.

Cellulosic ethanol production uses nonfood crops or inedible waste products and does not divert food away from the animal or human food chain. Lignocellulose is the "woody" structural material of plants. This feedstock is abundant and diverse, and in some cases (like citrus peels or sawdust) it is in itself a significant disposal problem.

Producing ethanol from cellulose is a difficult technical issue. In nature, ruminant livestock (such as cattle) eat grass and then use slow enzymatic digestive processes to break it into glucose (sugar). In cellulosic ethanol laboratories, various experimental processes are being developed to do the same thing; then the sugars released can be fermented to make ethanol fuel. In 2009, scientists reported development of 15 new highly stable fungal enzyme catalysts (using "synthetic biology") that efficiently break down cellulose into sugars at high temperatures, adding to the 10 previously known.

The use of high temperatures has been identified as an important factor in improving the overall economic feasibility of the biofuel industry, and the identification of enzymes that are stable and can operate efficiently at extreme temperatures is an area of active research. In addition, research conducted at Delft University of Technology by Jack Pronk has shown that elephant yeast, when slightly modified, can also produce ethanol from inedible ground sources such as straw.

The recent discovery of the fungus *Gliocladium roseum* points toward the production of so-called mycodiesel from cellulose. This organism (recently discovered in rainforests of northern Patagonia) has the unique capability of converting cellulose into medium-length hydrocarbons typically found in diesel fuel. Scientists also work on experimental recombinant DNA genetic engineering organisms that could increase biofuel potential.

Scientists working with the New Zealand company Lanzatech have developed a technology to use industrial waste gases such as carbon monoxide from steel mills, as a feedstock for a microbial fermentation process to produce ethanol. In October 2011, Virgin Atlantic announced it was joining with Lanzatech to commission a demonstration plant in Shanghai that would produce an aviation fuel from waste gases from steel production.

Scientists working in Minnesota have developed co-cultures of *Shewanella* and *Synechococcus* that produce long-chain hydrocarbons directly from water, carbon dioxide, and sunlight. The technology has received ARPA-E funding.

NOTE: The conversion of cellulosic matter into alcohol has been an effort of global proportions since the 1970s. The author had a chance to work at a South American cellulose pilot plant in those days, experimenting with Brazilian jungle biomass. The results were promising, but the processes were never efficient, nor the final product profitable enough, for commercial application.

Fast-forwarding 30 years, we still have problems with producing bioethanol from cellulosic materials. As a matter of fact, this was confirmed recently by the Appeals Court, which ruled in 2013 that the EPA's blending targets for the advanced biofuel cellulosic ethanol were simply not feasible. The EPA had demanded that between 2010 and 2012, 20 million gallons of cellulosic ethanol be produced, but to date almost no cellulosic ethanol has been blended into commercial fuel, and cellulosic ethanol startups have been unable to provide significant stock to blenders.

The EPA claims it has the authority to enforce blends based on the 2007 Energy Act passed under the Bush Administration, which promoted biofuels (and corn ethanol) growth. But the Appeals court rejected that argument calling the decision to enforce targets on refiners—customers of the fuel producers—rather than the producers themselves as a bizarre and unprecedented government effort. Wow!

Apparently, although significant technological advances of late have introduced improvements, a steady, fully efficient, and profitable large-scale commercial cellulosic bioethanol conversion process is still in the distant future.

Algae Biofuel

Algal biofuel is a fuel derived from processing bio-materials as an alternative to fossil fuel. This process uses different types of algae as its raw materials. There is an ongoing effort by several companies and government agencies to develop the process to reduce capital cost and operating expense as needed to make algae fuel production commercially viable.

Algae materials release significant amounts of CO_2 when burned, but that amount is compensated by the CO_2 taken out of the atmosphere during the algae growing process. The world food crisis is increasing the interest in algae-culture in the production of vegetable oils and biofuels on land unsuitable for agricultural crops.

Algal fuels can be grown with minimal impact on freshwater resources, and some can even be produced by using ocean and wastewater. Most algae products are biodegradable and harmless to the environment in any form and shape.

Algae cost more per unit mass, about ~$5000/ton, mostly due to high capital and operating costs. This is compensated by the fact that they can yield up to 100 times more fuel per unit area than most other crops. There are estimates that for algae fuel to replace all petroleum fuel used in the United States, it would require 15,000 square miles of land.

As with many other potential energy sources, these estimates remain on paper and far from any sizeable commercial application. And like the other renewables, biofuels production relies heavily on government support in form of grants, and tax and production tax credits. This shows the immaturity of this technology, and as promising it sounds, we still have to wait awhile to see it compete shoulder-to-shoulder with the big guys—coal, oil and gas—and even with the renewables (solar, wind, and geothermal).

In the 80s and 90s, U.S. scientists experimented with algae as a biofuels source. Estimates for replacement of all fuel used in cars and trucks with algae biofuels promise huge increases.

Algae grown in ponds of wastewater treatment plants can then be harvested and processed into biofuels and ethanol. After all the hoopla, the project died off, and the potential of harvesting oil for biofuels from waste pond algae is still far from any practical, large-scale commercial application.

One great advantage, in addition to its projected high yield, is that algae-culture, unlike crop-based biofuels, does not interfere with food production, which led to the crop-ethanol demise in 2008-2009. This is because no agricultural products can be grown in municipal waste plants, so algae does not require farmland or fresh water for its growth.

A number of companies are looking into algae bioreactors for various purposes, including scaling up biofuels production to commercial levels; but again, the work is still confined to small test sites and university labs.

In recent years, several novel biofuel conversion routes have been announced, such as the conversion of sugars into synthetic diesel fuels. These include: a) use of a micro-organisms (yeast, heterotrophic algae or cyanobacteria that turn sugar into alkanes), b) transformation of a variety of water-soluble sugars into hydrogen and chemical intermediates using aqueous phase reforming, and then into alkanes via a catalytic process, and c) use of modified yeasts to convert sugars into hydrocarbons that can be hydrogenated to synthetic diesel. Unfortunately, these processes, as promising as they sound, have not been able to produce commercial products.

Bio-synthetic Gas

Bio-SG (or biomethane) is actually methane derived from biomass via thermal processes. The first demonstration plant producing biomethane thermochemically out of solid biomass started operation in late 2008 in Güssing, Austria, and another plant is operating in Gothenburg, Sweden.

With the increased use of natural gas vehicles (NGV) during the last decade, their share is reaching over 25% and more of the total vehicle fleet in some countries like Armenia and Pakistan. These vehicles can also be run on biomethane, derived from anaerobic digestion or gasification of biomass.

Several routes to fuels and additives at different commercialization stages are available, including hydrothermal processing, pyrolysis oil, dimethylether (DME), biobutanol, and "solar" fuels (produced with the help of solar as energy input).

Biofuels Production and Use

Biofuels are increasing in volume and importance as the financial and energy crisis grow, and as the environmental issues take front stage. Biofuels are considered by some as the solution to all of these problems (to one extent or another), so their use has increased from almost zero 20 years ago, to over 3.0% of the total road transport fuel use in some European countries. For example, in the UK 400 million gallons of biofuels are produced and sold annually.

At the same time, the U.S. produces over 5 billion gallons of ethanol, and about 2 billion gallons of biodiesel. Brazil also produces over 5 billion gallons of ethanol, and China follows with 1 billion. India is next with 500 million, followed by Germany, France, and Russia with about 200 million each, and Canada and South Africa with about 100 million each annually. Many other countries also produce biofuels, but in much smaller volume.

It is expected that by 2020 over 10% of the energy used in road and rail transport in European countries will come from renewable sources. This is equivalent to replacing 4.3 million tons of fossil oil each year. Conventional biofuels are likely to produce between 3.7 and 6.6% of the energy needed in road and rail transport, while advanced biofuels could meet up to 4.3% of the UK's renewable transport fuel target by 2020.

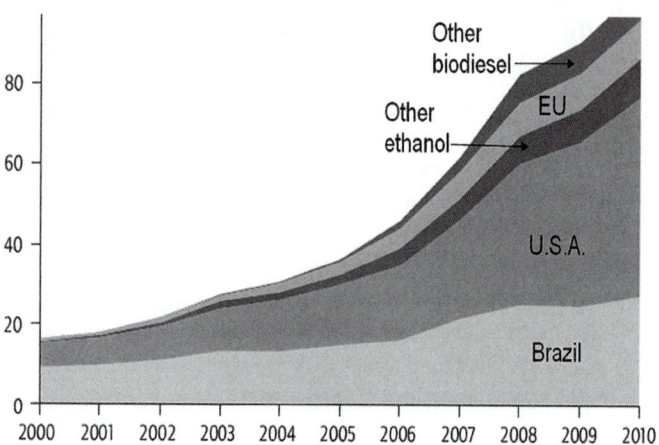

Figure 3-50. Global biofuels production in billion liters

The world leaders in biofuel development and use are Brazil, the United States, France, Sweden and Germany. At the same time Russia, which has over 20% of world's forests is one of the largest biomass (solid biofuels) suppliers, and is also looking into the possibility of increasing its share of biofuels production.

Table 3-14. Total fuel use in 2050 (estimate)

Fuel types	2050
Biofuels	27%
Diesel	23
Gasoline	13
Jet fuel	13
Electricity	13
Hydrogen	7
Heavy fuel oil	2
CNG, LPG	2

The transport sector is the largest consumer of fuels—fossil and biofuels—and will most likely remain in the lead for the foreseeable future. It is expected that biofuels in 2050 will be used mostly for road transport too (over 50%), with 25% used for jet fuel, and the rest for shipping and other commercial purposes.

International organizations, such as IEA Bioenergy, were established by the OECD International Energy

Agency (IEA), to improve the cooperation and information exchange between countries with bioenergy programs, and assist in the research, development and deployment of biofuels. The UN International Biofuels Forum, formed by Brazil, China, India, Pakistan, South Africa, the United States and the European Commission has similar agenda and goals.

Table 3-15. Global bioethanol production (in million liters)

Area	2008	2010	2012
N. America	36,000	51,600	54,600
S. America	24,500	26,000	21,300
Europe	2,900	4,250	5,000
Asia/Pacific	2,750	3,100	4,000
Africa	65	130	235
World total	66,000	85,000	85,000

The global bioethanol industry continues to be a bright spot in the world economy, and continues to grow. It is supporting nearly 1.5 million jobs and contributes over $300 billion to global economy. The future looks bright for biofuels, and bioethanol in particular.

Cost of Bio-energy Sources

The diversity of raw materials and processes for making biofuels is staggering. We can divide the sector into biomass and biofuels, although there is some intermingling possible.

Biomass Costs

Biomass can be subdivided into wood products from forests, and other (crops, waste materials etc.). Forest wood for use as an energy generator and other

purposes can be subdivided into:

a. Direct use of wood (as forest tree trunks and branches), and

b. Wood and wood processing byproducts.

As shown in Table 3-16, a number of products use wood and wood byproducts. Putting a value on each product and use is beyond the scope of this text, but in all cases the price of products and their uses are determined by the market supply and demand dynamics. The availability of the wood products also has a determining role in the final price structure.

The harvesting and marketing of forest biomass in Kenya, for example, would be different from that in Sweden. In Kenya there are no laws, or significant enforcement of wood products harvesting and sale. Because of that, wood harvesting and use in forests and fields is basically free for the locals, but is sold at a certain minimal price in the large cities.

In Sweden, on the other hand, the wood harvesting process is heavily regulated and enforced, which determines the market price, which varies with location and the seasons. No doubt, market prices of wood products in Sweden are much higher than those in Kenya.

The price of biomass products is also determined by their specific heat value in relation to their mass. For example, wood pellets are the densest wood product with the highest heating value per ton of material. On the other side of the spectrum, wood shavings are the least dense material and although the heat value per ton is almost as good as that of the wood pellets, it will take almost 4 times the volume to generate equal heat value.

Table 3-16. Biomass origins and uses

Forest biomass				
Wood			Residues from wood based industry	
Forest residues	Stem wood	Whole trees	Dry residues	Wet residues
Pretreatment				
Solid biofuels				
Wood chips			Pellets	Residues
Bio-heating and bio-electricity systems				
District heat & power	Micro grids		Central heat & power	Stove

Table 3-17.
Bulk weight and heating values of biomass products

Wood products	Bulk weight of dry matter in ton/m³	Heating value in in MW/h per ton dry matter
Pellets	0.70	4.80
Wood chips	0.45	4.70
Forest residues	0.40	4.40
Stem wood	0.45	4.40
Sawdust	0.40	3.00
Shavings	0.25	4.40

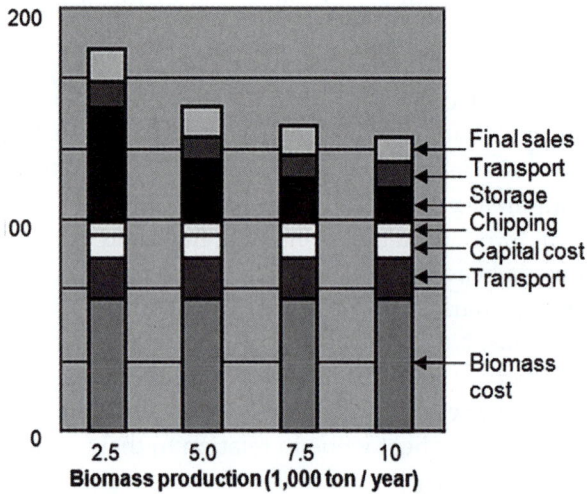

Figure 3-51. Biomass production steps (in $/1,000 tons/year)

Obviously, the price will be different for pure vs. contaminated biomass, while hazardous biomass will have a totally different price schedule, which might be on the negative side.

Table 3-18. Average yield from different energy crops per unit area

Crop	Liters per hectare
Sugarcane	4,900
Sugar beet	4,000
Palm oil	3,600
Cellulose	3,100
Corn	2,600
Rapeseed	1,700
Soy beans	700

The price of different energy crops also depends on the type and location. For example the price of a ton of sugarcane would be different from that of a ton of corn, and very different from a ton of bagasse. One of the reasons for this is the fact that sugarcane yields almost twice the amount of fuel from a hectare than corn, and 5 times that of soy beans. The cost of the land and amount of effort is reduced by the fact that sugarcane requires less land to produce equivalent energy.

Another important factor to consider in the price formation of energy crops used for biofuels is the ease of processing. Sugarcane is the easiest and cheapest to process into biofuel because it is pure sugar, which requires fewer process steps. This would raise its price significantly, as compared to the rest.

Due to the scarcity of wood and wood products in many places, import-export activities have increased during the last decade. Typical CIF prices for sea transport, including loading costs, ocean freight and insurance, are in the range of 100 to 120 Euros per ton for wood pellets with heating value around 17 GJ/ton.

At this price, wood pellets are imported in the EU from Canada, the United States, the Baltic States and Russia. Large scale in freight volumes from 10,000 to 50,000 tons make wood products' import profitable, since the cost for ocean fright is estimated to $7.5/MWh.

Average international prices for common biofuels in 2007 are shown in Table 3-19.

The production of biofuels also varies significantly with location and raw materials types and availability. A municipal waste biogas generating plant would have a different price tag and production cost than an algae biofuel power plant.

As an example, a production plant of 200,000 tons

As shown in Figure 3-51, the cost of biomass materials depends on a number of factors, based on materials and labor conditions. In addition to the major cost of the biomass material in the field, storage and transportation costs affect the price. The further from the source the processing facility and the power plant are, the higher the cost of transport. This increases the cost of the final product as well.

Another factor in determining price is the biomass quality, especially that destined for the generation of bioenergy. The European Committee of Standardization (CEN) is working on standards for fuels and has established three main categories for biomass quality: a) *Pure biomass*, which comprises pure wood and other biomass; b) *Contaminated biomass*, which is fuel that cannot be burned without meeting the demands of waste combustion set by the EU or the Norwegian government; and c) *Hazardous biomass*, e.g., CCA impregnated wood, which can only be burned using a special combustion and cleansing technology.

Table 3-19. Average prices (in $/ton)

Bio-crude	167
Corn oil	802
Cottonseed oil	782
Crude palm oil	543
Maize	179
Peanut oil	891
Poultry fat	256
Rapeseed oil	824
Soybean oil	771
Sugar	223
Tea seed oil	514
Waste oil	224
Wheat	215
Yellow grease	412

of biodiesel per year has been estimated at approximately $500 million, or approximately $2,500 per produced ton. $150 million of the total is for the construction of an oxygen generating facility. So if the plant is located near an oxygen generator, the construction costs would be significantly reduced.

The production cost of biodiesel has been estimated at $500-$600 per ton of diesel, or about $0.60-0.70 per liter of petro-diesel equivalent.

Environmental Effects of Bio-energy Sources

It could be argued that biofuel is a product of solar energy, as the sun is needed to grow the biomass crops which can then be manufactured into usable fuel. It is also true that biofuels are carbon-neutral, simply because the CO_2 emitted during their burning was absorbed during their growth cycle. It is also undeniable that the use of biofuels can help reduce the costs associated with the purchasing of mainstream fuels such as petrol and diesel.

Although *biofuel* sounds like a modern-day invention, we have used this type of fuel since the discovery of fire. If firewood can be classed as a biofuel, as wood is a biomass product, then biofuels are the oldest type of energy used for domestic and industrial applications. It is the material that was burned to released energy in the form of heat since man walked on this Earth. The types of biofuels mentioned above (biodiesel, biogas, etc.) relate to the modern-day uses of biomass as a fuel energy source.

We should not get carried away and exaggerate the importance of biomass and biofuels as future energy sources. To provide biofuel for every car, truck, bus, plane, boat, and factory across the globe would require a colossal amount of land to be used for the cultivation of renewable biomass crops. This would also result in the deforestation of the world, as a direct result of biomass cultivation getting out of hand.

Electric cars powered from the electricity generated by renewable energy sources would be the best option; however, implementing this on a global scale will be a very challenging task. Instead, we need to be looking into all possible methods for powering vehicles and machinery to reduce the future impacts that biofuel, or single technology usage may pose on the environment.

Biofuel Production Issues

Presently there are a number of technical, social, economic, and environmental issues related to the production and use of biofuels. Most of these have been discussed in the media and the scientific journals and include: the effect of moderating oil prices, the food vs. biofuels debate, poverty reduction potential, carbon emissions levels, sustainable biofuel production, deforestation and soil erosion, loss of biodiversity, impact on water resources, as well as energy balance and efficiency, to mention a few.

Scientists warn that not all biofuels perform equally in terms of their impact on climate, energy security, and ecosystems, and suggest that environmental and social impacts need to be assessed throughout the entire life-cycle, prior to making a decision as to which biofuel to use, when and where.

We are well aware of the current issues with biofuel production and use, but the fast development of new biofuel crops and second-generation biofuels are introducing a new variable which at times circumvents the common knowledge. The trend today points to the development of biofuel crops that require less land and use fewer resources than current biofuel crops do.

Algae, as a source for biofuels is one of the solutions, since it uses unprofitable land and wastewater from different industries. Different algae are able to grow in wastewater, which does not affect the land or freshwater needed to produce current food and fuel crops. Also, algae are not part of the human food chain, so do not take away food resources from humans.

Nevertheless, the effects of the biofuel industry on food and the environment in general are still being debated. A recent study shows that biofuel production accounted for up to a 30% increase in food prices in 2008. Market-driven expansion of ethanol in the US increased corn prices by more than 20% in 2009, as compared with the prices of ethanol production at 2004 levels. This changed the direction of the basic research, forcing the development of biofuel crops and technologies that will reduce the impact of a growing biofuel industry on food production and cost.

This prompted some drastic reactions, such as the 2012 decision of the United States House Committee on Armed Services to put language into the 2013 National Defense Authorization Act that would prevent the Pentagon from purchasing biofuels that offered improved performance for combat aircraft.

Developing biofuel crops that are optimized for the local climate and market is the best solution to this problem. Using specific local biofuel crops, voids the need to transport fossil fuels from faraway places for processing and use. The problem is that many areas of the globe are unsuitable for producing the most efficient energy crops, which require large amounts of water and nutrient-rich soil.

So biofuel crops, such as corn, sugarcane and others are impractical in these places and must be grown in different regions. That complicates the picture, and creates a several-fold imbalance, where rich nations produce the crops to be used by poor nations. It also creates an environmental imbalance, where CO_2 absorbed in one part of the world is released in another.

ENVIRONMENTAL EFFECTS

After all the praises of the benefits of biomass and biofuels, we must also take a close look at the negative effects these have on the environment and other aspects of our daily lives.

In-out Energy (Energy Ratio)

Biomass is undoubtedly a renewable source of energy, although its renewable nature is heavily dependent on weather, economic, and socio-political conditions. Its seed-to-energy cycle inevitably involves the consumption of some fossil fuels at one or another point in the cycle. How much is used depends on the type of biomass and the production methods, but it usually includes fuels consumed by farm machinery in land preparation, planting, tending, irrigation, harvesting, storage, and transport. There are also great quantities of fossil feedstocks for chemical products such as herbicides, pesticides, and fertilizers used during the growth cycle. And, of course, a lot of energy is required for plowing, seeding, growing, harvesting, and processing the bioenergy crop into a usable biofuel.

Energy requirements are generally higher for some crops because that need greater use of machinery and a higher level of water and chemical inputs (fertilizers and such). For many energy crops, the energy ratio, or the amount of useful bioenergy the particular crop can produce, compared to the fossil fuel consumed for feedstock production, could be very high.

Table 3-20 shows that hydropower is the most energy efficient power generator, producing 250 units of electric power for each unit of fossil fuel input. Biomass produces 30 units, while biofuel crops produce only 5 units of energy for each unit of fossil fuels used during their life-cycle.

Table 3-20. Energy ratios for different technologies

Technology	Ratio
Hydropower	250
Wind power	35
Biomass waste	30
Bio-fuel crops	5
Nuclear	15
Coal	5
Solar PV	5
Natural gas	5
Fuel cells	3
Crude oil	3

Some crops, such as poplar, sorghum, and switchgrass grown in temperate climates have energy ratios of up to 30. This simply means that each Btu used in the bio-crop cycle generates up to 30 Btus of energy from the respective biomass crops. In tropical climates with good rainfall, these ratios could be considerably higher, because of higher yields and less labor and energy-intensive agricultural practices.

The energy ratios are much lower for crops that require much labor and mechanization, or yield a relatively small proportion of usable bioenergy feedstock per unit of plant matter produced. Some oil crops (like soybean), however, could have an energy ratio close to 1, which means that the amount of energy this crop produces is equal to the energy it required during its entire seed-to fuel life cycle. For some crops, and in some cases, the energy ratio is so low that we need to think twice about using them as energy sources.

Another factor to consider in the energy ratio estimates is the pollution created during production, transport, and processing of the crops. In most cases, cultivation of bio-crops requires heavy machinery which uses a lot of fossil fuels and emits a lot of GHGs. After harvesting, the crops are loaded on large trucks or trains to be delivered to the processing facility. Even if the processing facility is a mile away, which is rarely the case, the crops still must be loaded on vehicles and transported to the intake elevator.

At the processing facility, more energy is used

during the different steps of the conversion process and more polluting gasses, liquids and solids are generated. In all cases, massive amounts of fossil fuels are burned, which further reduces the energy in/energy out ratio. Of course, significant pollution is created in this process as well.

Emissions

Bioenergy is hailed as carbon neutral, and although at first glance this is so, this generalization needs a closer look. Carbon emissions from biofuels can be reduced by:

1. Providing energy that can displace fossil fuel energy, and
2. Changing the amount of sequestered carbon.

The net carbon benefit is calculated by comparing the reality with what would have happened if fossils were used instead. The amount and type of fossil fuel that would otherwise have been consumed, as well as the land use that would otherwise occurred must be entered into the calculations.

The relative carbon intensity must be assessed on the basis of the emissions associated with the biofuel crop production and the efficiency of the energy technology in which the biofuel is used.

As can be seen in Table 3-21, all biomass materials have fairly large carbon content. In most cases, the carbon is released in one or another form, but most likely as CO and CO_2 during the digestion, burning, or otherwise processing of these materials.

Table 3-21. Carbon content in biomass materials

Type of Material	Carbon-Nitrogen Ratio
Alfalfa hay	18: 1
Bagasse	150: 1
Cichen manure	25: 1
Clover	2.7: 1
Cow dung	25: 1
Cow urine	0.8: 1
Grass clippings	12: 1
Kitchen refuse	10: 1
Lucerne	2: 1
Pig droppings	20: 1
Pig urine	6: 1
Potato tops	25: 1
Sawdust	200: 1
Seaweed	80: 1
Straw	200: 1
Sewage sludge	13: 1
Silage liquor	11: 1

Table 3-22 shows natural gas having the highest efficiency, or 45% of its energy input is converted into electric power. Biomass averages 20% efficiency, or only 20% of the available energy contained in it (and everything else considered) can be converted into useful electric power. At the same time, diesel power generators seem to be the most polluting, while biomass is the cleanest, assuming that the bioenergy crop is harvested in a carbon-neutral manner, or that there is no carbon net change in the crop fields or soil over the course of the complete crop growth and harvesting cycle.

Table 3-22.
Efficiency and CO_2 emissions of different fuels (per kWh)

Technology	% Efficiency	Gr. CO_2 emitted
Diesel generator	20%	1,320
Coal steam cycle	33%	1,000
LNG combined cycle	45%	410
Biogas digester and diesel generator	18%	220
Biomass steam cycle	22%	100
Biomass gasifier and gas turbine	35%	60

In practice, the carbon in the land and the soil changes significantly, depending on how the biomass is produced and what would have happened in other cases. Taking as an example clearing the jungle forests, which leaves a bare land for growing energy crops, we see that the bare site has lost its carbon-reducing value and cannot be readily regenerated. The carbon emissions from site preparation alone (trucks, bulldozers, etc.) could exceed the savings from biofuel use, and could be greater than the carbon emissions from a fossil-fuel cycle generating same amount of power.

Justification for the land clearing activities, from an environmental perspective, is that long-term use of biofuels produced at the cleared land will compensate for the increase of CO_2 at the initial stages. This is a frequently used model for the production of energy and non-energy biomass, under which millions of acres have been deforested around the world. The overall global effect of this massive land clearing is yet to be discerned, let alone precisely calculated and extrapolated into the future.

Clearing large areas of natural forests, some of which are used for energy crops planting, means that the CO_2 sequestered in the natural forest will be released eventually during burning of the biomass materials at an amount that depends on the type of the forest. A rough figure of 300 metric tons of carbon per hectare (tC/ha) has been suggested, which is a significant but reasonable number.

As biomass feedstock is grown and harvested in cycles, carbon will be held on the land, partly compensating for the carbon released when the natural forest was cut down. Averaged over a growth cycle, a typical amount of carbon sequestered on the land might be 30 tC/ha, so this leaves an unaccounted for 270 tC/ha balance.

If the purpose of a bioenergy crop in this case is to displace fossil fuels to reduce carbon emissions, it will achieve this (by compensating for this 270 tC/ha difference derived from the above estimate) over a period of roughly 40-45 years. When environmental and social considerations (preserving habitat and protecting watersheds), are taken into account, the total of all considerations might increase the number of years and even outweigh carbon saving benefits.

If bioenergy crops are developed on unproductive land (degraded or abandoned land), then that land and the local environment could benefit from eventual re-vegetation. The degraded land is most likely carbon-starved, so the crop field will store some CO_2 and other below-ground biomass in the soil. This would compensate for some of the initial carbon emissions.

So, the overall effect of using wasteland for energy crops shows definite benefits in

a.)   providing immediate measurable carbon and other local ecosystem benefits, and

b.)   displacing fossil fuels for power generation in the long run.

Soil

Biomass crops are very similar to other crops, as far as managing soil, water, agrochemicals, and biodiversity are concerned. Following good crop managing practices, while taking into consideration the specific technical and environmental challenges, is the key to success.

One difference worth noting is that biomass plants are often harvested completely. They are usually chopped down to the roots, and sometimes are harvested with the roots. This leaves little organic matter or plant nutrients in the soil of the harvested field. This would create soil problems especially in the developing world where the soil depends on recycling crop wastes and manure, rather than on the use of expensive fertilizers. In such cases, biomass production could contribute to dramatic deterioration in soil quality.

To maintain soil quality, clever farmers keep sufficient plant matter on the land for the soil's sake, at the expense of reduced crop yields. As another alternative,

farmers might allow some nutrient-rich parts of the plant, like small branches, twigs, and leaves to decompose in the field. Some feedstock nutrient content can be recovered from the conversion facility in the form of ash or sludge and trucked back to the fields to be used for soil improvement, instead of being put in a landfill. But this is an expensive undertaking and is rarely used.

Hydrology

Bioenergy crops usually consume more water than many food crops, and some energy crops like sugarcane consume immense amounts of water, creating problems with local irrigation systems and wells. Sugarcane and other thirsty crops are known to lower the water table, or reduce stream flow, making local irrigation systems less reliable.

An amazing fact to remember is that three quarters of our fresh water, which is only 5 percent of the Earth's total water supply, is used for crops and animal raising. For this reason alone, many agricultural communities have resisted the introduction of some energy crops and tree plantations.

A number of practices, such as growing tree crops without undergrowth, or planting species that do not generate adequate litter, reduce the ability of rainfall to replenish groundwater supplies, thus increasing the local water overconsumption.

Water scarcity and the desertification of our agricultural lands are proceeding at a frightening pace. Irrigation, for example is quickly depleting our Ogallala Aquifer on the Great Plains. The annual water consumption is about 1.3 trillion gallons faster than it can be replenished by rainfall.

Biodiversity

All farm crops have significant effects on the local ecosystem by enhancing or suppressing the biodiversity of the region. Energy crops have a similar effect, but provide even more biodiversity, which is closer to a natural habitat than other crops. By enhancing biodiversity some gaps between fragments of natural habitat can be filled. For this purpose, in Brazil for example, environmental regulations require 25% of the plantation area to be left in natural vegetation. This helps to preserve biodiversity and provides other ecosystem benefits, where bioenergy crops can also serve as corridors between adjacent natural habitat areas for the benefit of all wildlife.

Energy crops, like many industrial crops, have been escaping from the cultivated area and growing uncontrollably in the natural areas at the expense of the local species. There are many such examples, where crops in various regions have reproduced widely beyond plantations to harm the local species. Growing energy crops at the same field for extended periods of time (monoculture) could have the effect of an incubator for pests or disease, which can then spread into natural habitats.

Meat Production

A lot of water, fuels, and other resources are used to grow meat for human consumption. Watering and cleaning the animals and their facilities consumes huge amounts of water, which usually ends up in a stinky cesspool nearby.

Raising one pound of meat requires 2,000 gallons of water and produces 58 times more greenhouse gasses than growing 1 pound of potatoes. It takes 7,000 pounds of grain to feed the animals that produce 1,000 pounds of meat. It takes sixteen times more energy (mostly fossil generated) to produce six ounces of meat than to produce a cup of broccoli, a cup of vegetables, or a cup of rice. These are significant numbers that deserve our attention and understanding

Each year, ten billion bushels of corn are grown in the U.S. alone, 60 percent of which is used to feed cows and other livestock. The meat of these animals is the major ingredient in processed and fast foods, which in turn are the major cause of obesity and diabetes.

Beef meat also produces a lot of greenhouse gases, because of the methane and nitric oxide produced by cow flatulence. Grains and grass ferment in cows' stomachs and produce large amounts of methane gas, which is one of the largest contributors to global warming. That gas must go somewhere...

If each person eliminated one processed-meat meal per week, this would be the equivalent of taking half a million cars off the road. But the Exxons and BPs of the meat industry would not allow that. When the USDA suggested "Meatless Mondays," the National Cattleman's Beef Association lobbied the government to retract their recommendation. So, for now, there is no Meatless Monday.

In Summary

Solid biomass use around the world is projected to continue at present levels at least for the foreseeable future. The negative effects of that use are well known, but there is little that can be done to reduce them due to the fact that the major use of solid biomass (in form of firewood) is for providing basic, and often the only, human comforts, which cannot be denied to the needy people of the world.

Liquid and gaseous biofuels fuels' production is expected to rise significantly in the future. Biofuels derived from organic matter will play an ever increasing important role in providing fuel and reducing CO_2 emissions in the transport sector, thus enhancing our energy security and helping to clean the environment.

Biofuels could provide 20% of total transport fuel by 2025 and 30% by 2050. They would play a particularly significant role in the replacement of diesel, kerosene and jet fuel.

Sustainably produced and efficiently used biofuels could avoid the generation of around 2.1 gigatonnes (Gt) of CO_2 emissions per year. For this to happen, however, most conventional biofuel technologies need to improve conversion efficiency, cost and especially their overall sustainability.

Advanced biofuels must be deployed on a large scale, which requires additional and quite substantial investment in their future development and demonstration. Special attention to and support for commercial-scale advanced biofuel plants are a must to the timely success of advanced biofuels.

Support policies should be developed that focus on incentivizing the most promising and efficient biofuels in terms of GHG avoidance. Policy framework must ensure that food security and biodiversity are not compromised and that expansion efforts result only in social impacts.

Sustainable land-use management and proper certification schemes, together with support measures that promote "low-risk" feedstocks and efficient processing technologies, are the key factors in ensuring fast and efficient development of large-scale biofuels production.

Meeting the biofuel demand by 2050 would require around 65 exajoules of biofuel feedstock, occupying around 100 million hectares. This is in direct competition with the need for land and feedstocks to meet the rapidly growing demand for food and fiber around the world. An additional 80 exajoules of biomass will be needed by 2050 for generating heat and power. The required 145 exajoules of total biomass for biofuels, heat and electricity from residues and wastes, along with sustainably grown energy crops could be achieved only by the implementation of sound policy framework and by the application of efficient equipment and processes.

Trade in biomass and biofuels will become increasingly important as well, especially in the effort to supply biomass to areas with very high levels of production and/or consumption. Scale expansion and efficiency improvements will reduce biofuel production costs over time. In a low-cost scenario, most biofuels could be competitive with fossil fuels by 2030. In a scenario in which production costs are strongly coupled to oil prices, they would remain slightly more expensive than fossil fuels.

The total biofuel production costs from 2010 to 2050 are estimated in the range of $11 trillion to $13 trillion, while the marginal savings or additional costs compared to the use of gasoline/diesel are in the range of only ±1% of total costs for all transport fuels.

The United States produces 48 billion liters of biofuels annually. Of this amount only 20 million are produced from cellulosic materials (trees, grass, corn stalks, etc.) There are an estimated 150 billion liters of bio-ethanol to be produced by 2025, 60 billion liters of which would be from cellulosic-ethanol.

Increased biofuels production, transport and use will also generate millions of jobs around the world, which will contribute to economic growth in a number of developing countries.

NOTE: The author was part of an R&D team in a South American government R&D lab, which specialized in the production of cellulosic bio-products (paper and biofuels). The results of this effort, after several years of intense work, led to the conclusion that it is technologically feasible to produce cheap bio-ethanol and other bio-fuels, as demonstrated recently by some companies.

There is a big problem, however, with the huge amount of water, energy and chemicals used in these types of processes, making the energy input-output balance questionable. Also, there are huge amounts of waste products generated during the processing of raw biomass. Rivers of chemicals must be prepared, used, and disposed of at the projected levels of production.

More importantly, since the useful content of the cellulosic materials is extremely low, the remaining waste comprises 90-95 percent of the raw materials input. This means that very large quantities of raw materials are hauled in, processed at a great expense of energy and chemicals, and then dried and stored in large storage bins, or hauled away again as waste.

This is a large amount of solid waste product that is basically useless for any type of human or animal use. If production increases to the estimated levels, we will eventually have mountains of waste cellulosic materials. Some of the wastes could be burned for heat generation at biofuel processing plants, but the huge amount of smoke, soot, and GHGs would make this process one of the dirtiest and therefore objectionable from an environmental point of view.

There are a number of difficult problems—especially at the large scale of production anticipated in the next several decades. Biofuels, however, are a very promising and important part of our energy future, so solutions must be found.

So, bio-energy crops are needed, no doubt, and if properly done can produce significant social and environmental benefits. Proper crop management can help us gain energy independence sooner, and could also provide excellent carbon reduction at increased energy production ratios. This in turn would result in reduction in pollution and greenhouse gas emissions.

The key to success here is the implementation of balanced soil and crop management techniques which must be adapted to local conditions. This way greater crop efficiency and environmental benefits could be achieved. Land selection is critical too, where the best case scenario is to use land that is abandoned or in some way is in degradation. Energy crops compete for land with food production, livestock grazing, and firewood gathering practices, so engaging and educating the local communities in the proper development and use of energy crops is another key to success.

Lots of uncertainties lay ahead, and lots of battles will be fought on different fronts, but one thing is for sure: energy crops have an important role to play in our energy and environmental futures. Still, as we saw during the uncontrolled boom-bust of 2007-2008, they can also create large-scale problems.

Using the lessons of the past, we must make sure that future energy crop growing and processing methodologies are properly designed, and implemented in a manner that would benefit the environment and those who are affected.

Notes and References

1. Nuclear Energy Institute, http://www.nei.org/
2. U.S. EIA, http://www.eia.gov/nuclear/
3. National Hydropower Association, http://www.hydro.org/
4. Idaho National Laboratory, http://hydropower.inel.gov/
5. DOE Hydrogen Roadmap http://www.netl.doe.gov/technologies/hydrogen_clean_fuels/refshelf/The%20National%20Hydrogen%20Roadmap.pdf
6. DOE, Fuel Cell Technologies Program Multi-Year Research, Development and Demonstration Plan, 2012
7. Energy Resources, http://www.darvill.clara.net/altenerg/tidal.htm
8. Geothermal Education Office, http://geothermal.marin.org/pwrheat.html
9. U.S. DOE, http://www1.eere.energy.gov/geothermal/
10. U.S. DOE, http://www1.eere.energy.gov/biomass/index.html
11. U.S. IEA, *Sustainable Production of Second-Generation Biofuels. Potential and perspectives in major economies and developing countries, OECD/IEA, Paris, www.iea.org/papers/2010/second_generation_biofuels.pdf*
12. U.S. IEA, *Energy Technology Perspectives 2010*, OECD/IEA, Paris.
13. *Photovoltaics for Commercial and Utilities Power Generation*, Anco S Blazev. The Fairmont Press, 2011
14. *Solar Technologies for the 21st Century*, Anco S Blazev. The Fairmont Press, 2013

Appendix A

Periodic Table of the Elements

Group 1																	Group 18
1 H hydrogen [1.007–1.009]																	2 He helium 4.003
3 Li lithium [6.938–6.997]	4 Be beryllium 9.012											5 B boron [10.80–10.83]	6 C carbon [12.00–12.02]	7 N nitrogen [14.00–14.01]	8 O oxygen [15.99–16.00]	9 F fluorine 19.00	10 Ne neon 20.18
11 Na sodium 22.99	12 Mg magnesium 24.31											13 Al aluminium 26.98	14 Si silicon [28.08–28.09]	15 P phosphorus 30.97	16 S sulfur [32.05–32.08]	17 Cl chlorine [35.44–35.46]	18 Ar argon 39.95
19 K potassium 39.10	20 Ca calcium 40.08	21 Sc scandium 44.96	22 Ti titanium 47.87	23 V vanadium 50.94	24 Cr chromium 52.00	25 Mn manganese 54.94	26 Fe iron 55.85	27 Co cobalt 58.93	28 Ni nickel 58.69	29 Cu copper 63.55	30 Zn zinc 65.38	31 Ga gallium 69.72	32 Ge germanium 72.63	33 As arsenic 74.92	34 Se selenium 78.96	35 Br bromine 79.90	36 Kr krypton 83.80
37 Rb rubidium 85.47	38 Sr strontium 87.62	39 Y yttrium 88.91	40 Zr zirconium 91.22	41 Nb niobium 92.91	42 Mo molybdenum 95.96	43 Tc technetium (98)	44 Ru ruthenium 101.1	45 Rh rhodium 102.9	46 Pd palladium 106.4	47 Ag silver 107.9	48 Cd cadmium 112.4	49 In indium 114.8	50 Sn tin 118.7	51 Sb antimony 121.8	52 Te tellurium 127.6	53 I iodine 126.9	54 Xe xenon 131.3
55 Cs caesium 132.9	56 Ba barium 137.3	57–71 lanthanoids	72 Hf hafnium 178.5	73 Ta tantalum 180.9	74 W tungsten 183.8	75 Re rhenium 186.2	76 Os osmium 190.2	77 Ir iridium 192.2	78 Pt platinum 195.1	79 Au gold 197.0	80 Hg mercury 200.6	81 Tl thallium [204.3–204.4]	82 Pb lead 207.2	83 Bi bismuth 209.0	84 Po polonium (209)	85 At astatine (210)	86 Rn radon (222)
87 Fr francium (223)	88 Ra radium (226)	89–103 actinoids	104 Rf rutherfordium (261)	105 Db dubnium (262)	106 Sg seaborgium (266)	107 Bh bohrium (264)	108 Hs hassium (277)	109 Mt meitnerium (268)	110 Ds darmstadtium (271)	111 Rg roentgenium (272)	112 Cn copernicium (285)	113 Uut ununtrium (284)	114 Uuq ununquadium (289)	115 Uup ununpentium (288)	116 Uuh ununhexium (292)	117 Uus ununseptium (294)	118 Uuo ununoctium (294)

57 La lanthanum 138.9	58 Ce cerium 140.1	59 Pr praseodymium 140.9	60 Nd neodymium 144.2	61 Pm promethium (145)	62 Sm samarium 150.4	63 Eu europium 152.0	64 Gd gadolinium 157.3	65 Tb terbium 158.9	66 Dy dysprosium 162.5	67 Ho holmium 164.9	68 Er erbium 167.3	69 Tm thulium 168.9	70 Yb ytterbium 173.1	71 Lu lutetium 175.0
89 Ac actinium (227)	90 Th thorium 232.0	91 Pa protactinium 231.0	92 U uranium 238.0	93 Np neptunium (237)	94 Pu plutonium (244)	95 Am americium (243)	96 Cm curium (247)	97 Bk berkelium (247)	98 Cf californium (251)	99 Es einsteinium (252)	100 Fm fermium (257)	101 Md mendelevium (258)	102 No nobelium (259)	103 Lr lawrencium (262)

Element Categories: actinoids, alkali metals, metalloids, alkaline metals, nonmetals, other metals, halogens, transition metals, noble gases, lanthanoids, unknown elements

Natural Occurrence: primordial, from decay, synthetic

Appendix B
History of US Nuclear Energy

The first research facility established in the United States was the National Reactor Testing Station (NRTS), located at Arco, Idaho (population about 1,000), 40 miles east of Idaho Falls. Over succeeding years, the NRTS became the center of most basic and applied research on nuclear power production.

Studies have been carried out there both by federal agencies, such as the Argonne National Laboratory, as well as by a host of private companies, including General Electric, Westinghouse, General Atomics, Aerojet General, and Combustion Engineering. The facility's name has undergone a number of changes since its founding in 1949, and it is now known as the Idaho National Engineering and Environmental Laboratory (INEEL), representing a significant change in the laboratory's overall goals and activities.

The first project undertaken at NRTS was the design and testing of a breeder reactor. A breeder reactor, discussed below, is one that generates more fuel than it consumes during its operation. At the time the project was initiated, many scientists and government officials had high hopes that breeder reactors might become an efficient source of nuclear power that would also be capable of generating new nuclear fuel—hopes that would never be realized. NRTS also carried out research on nuclear reactors for use in submarines in response to Admiral Hyman Rickover's campaign to build underwater vessels powered by nuclear energy.

Other nuclear projects that have been carried out at NRTS include research on reactor cooling systems, materials research for fusion reactors, development of radioactive isotopes, and studies of new and advanced types of nuclear reactors.

By the end of the 1990s, a total of 52 reactors had been constructed and operated at NRTS for studies on these subjects. Today, the amount of research on nuclear power reactors conducted is greatly reduced, and studies on nuclear waste disposal problems have assumed a much more important role in the facility's activities.

One minor milestone was achieved at the station

on December 20, 1951, when Experimental Breeder Reactor I (EBRI) produced the first electrical power from nuclear energy, providing enough electricity to light four light bulbs. Four years later, on July 17, 1955, Arco became the first town anywhere to obtain its electricity from nuclear energy, energy provided by an experimental boiling water reactor called BORAX HI.

NRTS was also the site of one of the worst nuclear accidents in history, one of only two incidents in which human lives were lost in a nuclear facility in the United States. (The other accident in which lives were lost occurred at the Surry Nuclear Power Plant, near Norfolk, Virginia, on December 9, 1986.)

On January 3, 1961, three technicians began routine maintenance operations of the reactor core of the experimental SL-1 (Stationary Low Power) reactor. The men accidentally raised the reactor's control rods too far, allowing the nuclear chain reaction to go out of control. The reactor almost immediately caught fire, releasing radioactive material to the room in which the reactor was located. Two of the men were killed immediately, and the third died shortly after the accident.

The bodies of the three men were so radioactive that they had to be treated as if they were a form of nuclear waste and had to be buried in special sites designed to hold such materials. The reactor site itself was so radioactive that it could not be entirely decontaminated and repaired for 18 months.

The Breeder Reactor's History

The possibility of building breeder reactors was an especially attractive idea to the United States and other nations in the 1950s because of the relatively limited supply of uranium-235. Uranium is not a particularly abundant element, and the extraction of uranium-235 (the fissionable isotope) from uranium-238 (the non-fissionable isotope) is a difficult, tune-consuming, and expensive task. In the 1950s and 1960s, nuclear engineers hoped that they could find a faster, less expensive, and more reliable method of obtaining the fuel they needed from which to make nuclear weapons and operate nuclear power plants.

Breeder reactors seemed to be the ideal solution to that challenge. By the early 1960s, the Atomic Energy Commission had invested about a half billion dollars in breeder reactor research. For a time, engineers' hopes for breeder reactors appeared to be well-founded.

The first commercial breeder reactor, the Fermi I plant at Laguna Beach, Michigan, outside Detroit, began operation in 1966. The plant was in operation for only a few months, however, before an accident occurred. On October 5 of that year, for reasons that plant technicians did not then understand, the core temperature suddenly began to rise, forcing operators to shut down the plant's operations. It took nearly a year for engineers to discover the cause of the malfunction, a piece of metal had come loose and blocked the cooling system.

Uncertainty about conditions leading to the metal fracture forced the plant's owner, Detroit Edison, to maintain the reactor on a stand-by status for nearly three years. Then, in 1969, the AEC gave Detroit Edison permission to restart the reactor. The plant operated normally for only a few months before another accident occurred in May 1970. The problem forcing the shutdown this time was quickly solved, and the plant restarted two months later. By then, however, Detroit Edison had begun to have second thoughts about the cost of operating Fermi I and the chances of further accidents.

At the same time, the AEC had not yet issued permission for reopening the plant. As a result, Detroit Edison decided to close Fermi I permanently in 1972, leaving behind one of the most disastrous economic records in the history of nuclear power plants. Fermi I's fate was not a sufficient warning for enthusiasts of breeder reactors in the United States and around the world.

In the same year that Detroit Edison closed down its reactor (1972), the AEC announced an ambitious program to build two experimental breeder reactors. The first of these was to be a liquid-metal fast breeder reactor to be constructed at Clinch River, Tennessee. The term liquid metal refers to the fact that such reactors were to use molten sodium metal as a coolant rather than the water used in most other types of reactors.

The second project was designated as the Fast Flux Test Facility (FFTF), to be built at the AEC's research station at Hanford, Washington. The Clinch River project was to be a cooperative program between the federal government and private industry, with the latter having pledged about one-third of the estimated half-billion-dollar cost of the experiment. Doubts about the project were expressed even before it was begun, with critics pointing out that its success depended upon unrealistically large increases in the demand for electrical power in the future and the virtual complete loss of uranium supplies.

Neither of these events occurred, and, in fact, the cost of uranium continued to drop, from a high of about $100 per kilogram in 1960 to about $50 per kilogram only a decade later. (The price has since leveled off at about $15 per pound [$33 per kilogram].)

In addition, operators of the experimental plant encountered far more problems with the design and operation of the breeder reactor than they had anticipated. As a result, the project was canceled by Congress in 1983. At that point, $1.6 billion had already been invested in the project, about $240 million of which had come from industrial sources.

The Hanford project fared no better. Construction on the facility began in December 1970, and the reactor first went into operation in February 1980. When Congress decided to close down the Clinch River project in 1983, however, it also decided to change the focus of the FFTF facility, putting the testing of fusion materials, the production of radioactive isotopes, testing for foreign governments, weapons research, and other projects above the development of a domestic breeder reactor.

By 1990, Congress decided to discontinue funding for even these kinds of research, and two years later, dismantling of the FFTF began.

The U.S. experience has been repeated in a number of other nations. France, Germany, Great Britain, Japan, Kazakhstan, and Russia have all built large breeder reactors, operated them for a period of 3-20 years, and eventually shut them down as having been unsuccessful methods of generating electrical power and producing plutonium. Today, there are no commercial breeder reactors operating in the world.

The Fusion Reactor

Fusion reaction is the dream nuclear scientists have been chasing for over half a century. Fusion reactions generate so much energy that they would vaporize any known form of matter with which they come into contact. The question then becomes how might one construct a fusion reactor that would not itself be destroyed by the energy produced within it?

One possible solution to this problem was suggested in the 1950s by two Soviet physicists, Igor Tamm and Andrei Sakharov. The device they designed became known as a tokamak, the Russian word for "toroidal chamber." A toroid is a geometric figure with the shape of a doughnut. The key element in a tokamak is a very strong magnetic field that acts as a container within which a fusion reaction can occur. The problem of trapping the fusion reaction within a confined space is solved, then, not by using a form of matter, but a form of energy.

During the 1950s, the Soviets built a number of experimental tokamaks to test the design suggested by Tamm and Sakharov. Over time, interest in fusion reactors of this design had spread to other nations and, by the early 1990s, three large tokamak machines had been constructed outside the Soviet Union (and later Russia),

each at a cost of more than a billion U.S. dollars. They were the Tokamak Fusion Test Reactor (TFTR) at Princeton University, the Joint European Torus at Culham in the United Kingdom, and the Japan Tokamak 60 in Naka City, Japan. In addition, a number of smaller tokamaks had been constructed in Brazil, France, Germany, Japan, Russia, and the United States.

The primary challenge in commercializing fusion reactors has been building a machine that generates more energy than it consumes. Fusion reactions involve the combination of like-charged particles, a process that requires enormous amounts of energy. In stars, such reactions occur only because temperatures are so high (a few million degrees), accounting for the name by which such reactions are sometimes known: thermonuclear reactions.

The first experiment in which a tokamak generated more energy than it consumed occurred at the Princeton facility on December 9, 1993. On that occasion, the TFTR produced a power output of 3 million watts for a period of one second. Nearly a year later, on November 2, 1994, the same reactor attained a maximum power output of 10.7 million watts, but again for no more than a few seconds. In spite of the Princeton successes, the future of tokamak research at all three centers was not bright. It had taken three decades to realize the modest successes achieved at Princeton in 1993 and 1994, and government funding agencies began to raise serious questions as to how long they should continue supporting fusion research.

In response, the United States, Russia, and other nations began to explore the possibility of creating a single large research center that could serve as the focus of fusion studies around the world. The product of that discussion was the creation of the International Thermonuclear Experimental Reactor (ITER) project, under the auspices of the United Nations Atomic Energy Agency. ITER consists of scientists and engineers from China, Europe, Japan, Korea, Russia, and the United States, working together to demonstrate the feasibility of fusion reactions as a source of commercial power.

The ITER was officially launched in 1985 and was formally agreed to and funded in 2006. The initial cost estimate was $12.8 billion, with projected construction completion by 2018. The first tokamak assembly would be completed a year later, and torus pumpdown would be initiated soon after. The first plasma ignition is planned by 2020, followed by the start of the deuterium-tritium operation in 2027.

A different approach used in the NIF fusion project at Lawrence Livermore National Lab (see above) failed to start and maintain a fusion reaction in a small target bombarded by the world's most powerful lasers. After a decade of effort and many billions of dollars spent on building the laser facility, this recent setback brings the entire hope for nuclear fusion reaction using lasers back to where it started—design, planning, and spending additional billions of dollars in future stages.

Even if NIF, ITER, or anyone else succeeds to demonstrate a fusion reaction on a small scale, a full-size practical fusion reactor is even further away. This is because the energy and temperatures in a commercial fusion nuclear reactor would be so high—something like 200 million degrees F or more—that no materials, equipment, or processes available today would be able to contain and control the awesome power of this out-of-this-world reaction.

Here again, we will leave it to the future generations to solve this interesting and potentially very useful issue at their leisure. If and when they succeed to initiate and maintain a commercial size fusion nuclear reaction, however, the energy future would be secured for many centuries.

Chapter 4

Renewable Energy Sources

The renewable energy sources are not fully utilized only because the oil companies haven't figured out how to patent the sun and wind yet.
—Anco Blazev

This chapter is dedicated to the two major renewable sources—solar and wind—since they are the most important part of the global energy supply now. They also promise to become even more important in the near future, and that makes them eligible for a more detailed look and analysis.

Solar and wind power generation came to life for the first time in the U.S. after the Arab oil embargo in the 1970s. Their glory days at that time, however, were numbered, and they were put back in the closet soon after the conflict was resolved. They were brought out of the closet several times after that too, when different political and economic winds blew them out temporarily, only to be shoved back in the corner, time after time. So they have been coming and going through the years, according to the whims of the political winds and big business interests.

During the 2007-2012 renewable boom-bust cycle, however, something extraordinary happened. Solar and wind were given a very high priority by a number of wealthy governments, which fueled by a huge influx of money in the form of subsidies and incentives allowed the construction of many small and large solar and wind power plants in the U.S., Europe, Asia, and Australia. Recently, Africa has been joining the race mostly on paper, but we will be surprised if we don't see some great achievements there in the near future.

This unprecedented and unexpected development caught (even the most optimistic supporters) by surprise and showed that solar and wind technologies are a serious force. Given a chance, they will mature soon enough to stand on their own feet. They're almost there now!

Unfortunately, the rapid success during 2007-2011 was followed by a quick decline during 2011-2013, when hundreds of solar and wind companies went out of business. The remaining companies generating many mega-watts of solar and wind power daily make it clear that solar and wind are not going back in the closet. Ever!

Nevertheless, there are a number of unresolved issues related to these technologies, as well as a lot of controversies on different levels of their cradle-to-grave lifecycle. This, with ever-increasing competition, is not going to make things easier for them, but it is expected in capitalist society. Because solar and wind are relatively new technologies, as compared to their older cousins, the fossil fuels, they need to prove as quickly as possible that they can compete successfully with them.

Competition is a tricky game and can get ugly, with many important and influential people operating on both sides of the issues. So, we will start the discussion about the renewable energy sources—solar and wind—by looking at both sides of the energy and environmental spectrum.

The Energy Debate

When it comes to power generation via renewable energy sources, such as solar and wind, the debating parties are cleanly divided in two groups of activists:

a) those who are strongly against, and
b) those who are strongly pro renewables.

There is a third group consisting of a substantial number of people who don't care about or do not understand the issues, but their presence does not affect developments much, so we will ignore them for now.

This third group, however (especially the billions of energy-deprived people in developing countries) is an important part of the growing energy and environmental crisis because those people are slowly waking up from their energy stupor and ignorance.

Slowly becoming aware of their rights and recognizing the injustice bestowed upon them by the developed countries throughout the 20th century, they will very likely play an important role in the energy and environmental debates and battles of the near future.

As can be seen in Figure 4-1, on the left side we have the defenders of renewable energy sources, which can be classified as follow:

- *The renewables extremists* are people, companies, and groups who believe, and vehemently insist, that renewables are the only reasonable solution to our energy and environmental problems. They claim that using any other energy sources is leading us and future generations to a complete and irreversible doom. Their one-sided and at times misguided activities do more harm than good to the renewables cause.

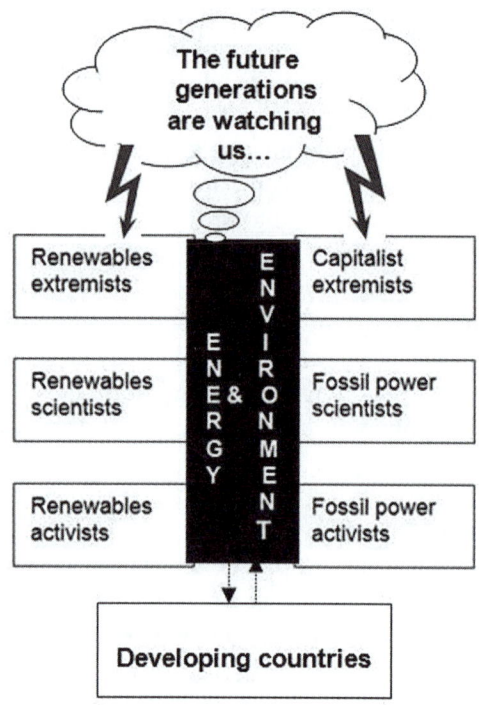

Figure 4-1. The energy and environment battlefield

- *The renewables scientists* are the brains of the industry and those who lead its technological development. They are responsible for developing new renewable technologies, and for improving the efficiency, reducing the cost, and optimizing the quality of the existing ones.

- *The renewables activists*, which sometimes include both groups mentioned above—the renewables extremists and scientists—are the muscle and

face of the movement. The group is driven by the principle, "Enough of fossils; they are killing us, so it is time to replace them once and for all with renewables." This group publishes magazines and articles, gets engaged in debates and public demonstrations, and organize protests against fossil and nuclear projects and companies they consider damaging to their cause and the environment.

On the other side of the energy and environment related issues we have interested groups led by the sub-group of capitalist extremists and opportunists.

- *The capitalist extremists* group usually includes the people who have the most to gain or lose from the matter at hand. Actually, most often it is their representatives that we see on the front lines, since the beneficiaries are rich people and companies who don't like to get their hands dirty. Oil and gas companies, utilities, and their investors come to mind here. This sub-group is most damaging to the progress of renewables, and sometimes defends actions that cannot be defended—such as oil spills, excess smoke pollution, and other fossil-created disasters.

- *The fossil power scientists* are the brain of this group, They are well funded and go to work every day serving their overlords. Their findings are very often manipulated to suit the owner's whims and needs. The findings and results presented by scientists employed with oil and gas companies are often biased, which is understandable. They are protecting their jobs and their bosses' interests. We saw similar scenarios during the asbestos and nicotine debacles of the previous decades, so we know what to look for.

- *The fossil power activists* are the lobbyists and large companies' representatives and spokesmen, who are paid to say and do everything possible to protect the interests of their bosses. This group also sometimes includes people from the above two groups—the capitalist extremists and fossil power scientists. Some of these people have done more harm than good to the renewables industry and society on the whole.

Fossil power supporters often site a number of issues with renewable technologies. Some of their complaints are:

- Uncertainty with long-term renewable energy costs.

- The need for government and other subsidies.

- Variability, due to dependence on weather patterns (sun and wind availability).

- Uncertainty about efficiency, performance and longevity (not enough track record).

- More work needed to optimize materials, processes and final product.

- Standardization is lacking, and best practices procedures are not optimized.

- Lack of scalability of the production process.

- Permitting issues related to land, ROW, and connectivity.

- Too diffused—needs a lot of materials and land for unit of power.

- Solar does not work at night and wind is weak during the day.

- Solar does not work in cloudy locations, and in many northern countries.

While at first glance there is some truth to all these claims and accusations, the simple explanation to all these concerns is that the renewables are too new—not fully developed, tested, explored, and not well understood—so they need some time to mature. In the meantime, expectations must be temporarily lowered in most cases.

We cannot expect a 2-year-old toddler to become an Olympic level athlete overnight just because we want him to. Given a chance, and proper training, he might become one. Similarly, solar, wind, and the other renewables must be given a chance—today, tomorrow and for a number of years—to mature and develop into equal competitors to their older and more experienced cousins, the fossils.

On the bottom of Figure 4-1 we see the developing countries, home to the world's poorest people. Some of these countries are quickly becoming the most active battleground of the pertinent energy and environmental issues. The battle there and around the world is intensifying, but it is becoming obvious that this is one of those cases where nobody wins…unless the fighting stops and all countries join hands in solving the issues.

The battle between the renewables (solar and wind) and the conventional fuels (fossils, nuclear, and hydro power) is more than 50 years old, but since 2007 it has become an open fight. The battle lines are clearly drawn now, with no feasible solution in sight.

One thing we must remember, however, is that the fossils have passed their prime, and no matter how much we like them and want them to stick around, their end is near. There will be no more crude oil by 2050, no more natural gas soon thereafter, and coal will be gone too by the end of the century. Give or take 10-20 years after that, it will be all over with the fossils. And then what…?

At that time nuclear and hydropower maxed up with renewables would be the only energy sources standing with unlimited potential to grow. Thus, they all need our respect and support.

THE RENEWABLES

In the previous chapters we took a close look at the fossil energy sources, coal, oil and natural gas, as well as some of their alternatives, shale, tar and methane hydrates. Then we analyzed the details of the nuclear, hydro, and other promising power generating technologies of the 21st century and beyond.

In this chapter, we complete the picture by presenting the technical specifics and environmental advantages (and a few disadvantages) of the truly renewable energy technologies—solar and wind. Although we hear a lot about them in the media, the number and complexity of the topics warrants a very close look, to fully understand the specifics of these versatile and promising energy sources.

Their importance as energy sources for powering our energy independent future requires a thorough understanding of their materials, structure, manufacturing processes, function, and field operation. A full understanding of the environmental damages they cause during their cradle-to-grave life cycle is also needed if we are to paint a complete picture of their usefulness.

Renewable energy resources shown in Figure 4-2 include solar, wind, biomass, geothermal, ocean thermal, wave action, and tidal action power generation. Obviously a sharp rise in the early 1990s is clear indication of their rising importance, but overall they are still small potatoes as compared with the total U.S. power generation.

Renewables provide only 3% of the total energy generation in the U.S. Solar and wind power generation represents only 0.2% of the total energy used in the country, so it will be a long, long time before these catch up with the fossils.

The major reason for this lag is that the renewables lack the power density and continuity offered by fossil fuels. They also require a lot of land. Thousands of acres

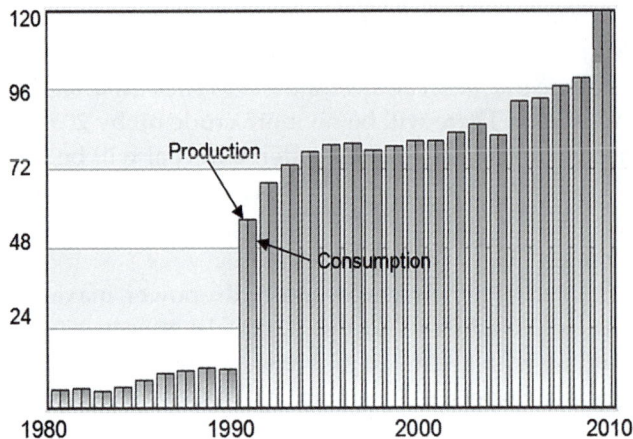

Figure 4-2. U.S. renewables generation and use (in billion kWh)

of land are needed to provide several megawatts of solar or wind power, and then (and this is the worst part) they are variable and unpredictable power generators. Sun and wind have a bad habit of going away at a whim, and the entire power plant dies. The juice stops coming out for hours—even days.

On top of that, solar and wind plants are usually most efficient in remote locations—deserts for solar, and mountains for wind. These are often inhospitable areas that present problems of their own. The long distance to substations and end users poses another set of serious problems, such as permitting, rights-of-way, and higher cost of transmission.

It is obvious that the renewables are still a very small part of U.S. power generation. It is also becoming exceedingly clear from the events of the latest renewable energy boom-bust cycle (2007-2012) that it will be

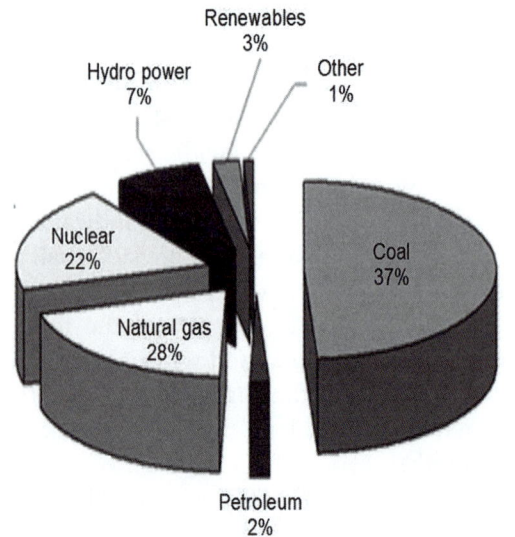

Figure 4-3. Power generation in the U.S.

a long time before the renewables are given a chance to compete shoulder-to-shoulder with fossil fuels.

The fast ramp-up of natural gas exploration and use lately will further delay the full implementation of solar and wind in U.S. energy markets, but unlike previous boom-bust cycles, the renewables are here to stay and grow…slowly for now.

The renewable energy sources and subjects we discuss in this chapter are solar, wind, hybrids, and energy storage. We dedicated a special chapter to these, because they seem to be the most serious competitors on the energy markets today, and will be even more so in the future.

Let's start with the most versatile and promising renewable energy source, solar energy.

SOLAR ENERGY

Solar energy is the foundation of life! There is nothing on this Earth that is not touched, and in one way or another affected, by sunlight. Solar, wind, hydropower, and the fossils all owe their energy and very existence to the sunlight that they absorbed today, yesterday, last year, or a billion years ago.

We humans depend on sunlight to provide the basic necessities of life too, and would be much better off if we knew more about it, and if we were able to use its benefits properly and efficiently.

Sunlight Basics and Key Concepts

Life on Earth, and everything else on it, depends on the sun's energy to provide warmth and light. The sun is a large star at the center of our solar system, approximately 93 million miles away, but its life-giving energy arrives on Earth every day. We don't see it from the clouds some days, but make no mistake—it is always there, providing the same generous amount of energy, regardless of whether we see it or not, and regardless of whether we care or not.

The exact distance between the Sun and the Earth is crucial to maintaining life. The Earth's orbit and its very appropriate distance from the sun are responsible for providing climate conducive for life to exist here. The other planets are either too close (thus too hot), or too far away (and too cold) for organic life as we know it to exist. The Earth also has been blessed with an appropriate atmosphere, which contains enough oxygen, carbon dioxide, and water to maintain life—things the other celestial bodies lack.

All life-maintaining elements are in the right proportion, form and shape needed for life to flourish on Earth. These are also in a very delicate balance, so any changes or modifications to this precise balance would be detrimental to life on Earth. We humans have some understanding of the basic elements of life, but their sheer number and complexity, as well as all possible combinations and their variability, do not allow us to gain complete understanding, let alone obtain control over them all.

Sunlight' frequency and intensity are precise and major and delicate variables; responsible for keeping humans, animals, and vegetation alive and thriving on the Earth' surface. Any changes in these variables—even minute—would have a great impact on the Earth and all life on it.

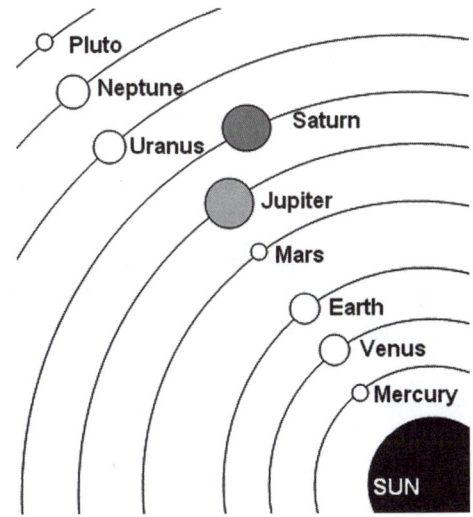

Figure 4-4. The sun and the planets in the solar system

Sunlight essentially consists of a range of energy bands, which we generally refer to as the solar spectrum. We can see some of these bands, but most are invisible to the human eye. We can also feel some of these when they impact our skin and are perceived as heat. So,

sunlight is radiation of the electromagnetic type, with what we see and feel being only a small part of its entire spectrum of energy particles on their respective energy levels and different potential for practical use.

From our perspective, we think of visible light as the most important component of the solar spectrum, because we can see it. The infrared part of the solar spectrum is also noticeable since we feel it as heat. However, these are just small parts of the entire light (sunlight) spectrum, and they are clearly distinguished by their different wavelengths and respective properties.

As the study of light has advanced, physicists have found that while it is usually best to consider light as energy traveling through space as a wave, in some situations light behaves as if it were made up of tiny "packets" of energy or "particles" that have no mass and always travel at the same speed, which we call the speed of light. When light is discussed in this manner the packets of energy are called photons, which is the term we will use in this text.

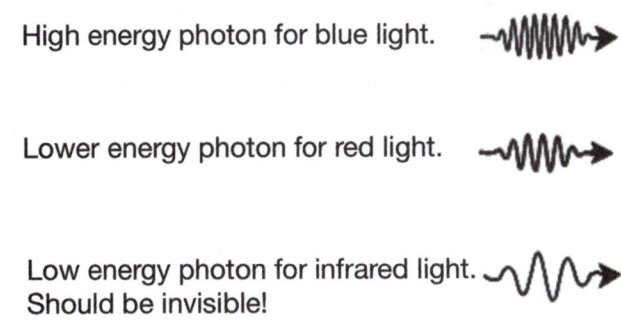

Figure 4-5. Paths of sunlight energy particles (photons) (1)

The Solar Spectrum

The *solar spectrum* is basically the range of energy coming from the sun. It is subdivided into sections and classifications based on the wavelengths of the particular energies.

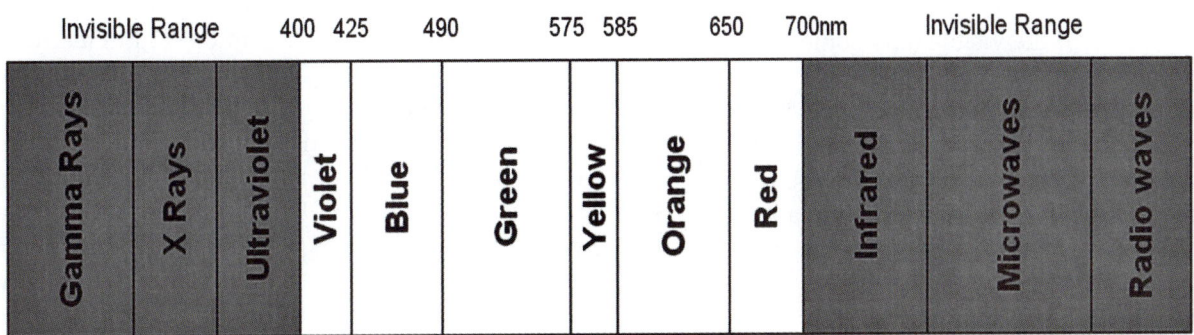

Visible range of the solar spectrum

Figure 4-6. The solar spectrum

The key components of the solar spectrum that are critical for solar devices' operation are as follow:

1. Ultraviolet (UV) radiation:

This part of the spectrum accounts for less than 10% of the energy from the sun that reaches the Earth's surface. Most ultraviolet energy is filtered out by our atmosphere. Ultraviolet energy is divided into three parts:

a. Ultraviolet C or (UVC) spans the range of 100 to 280 nm. The term ultraviolet refers to the fact that the radiation is at a higher frequency than violet light (and hence invisible to the human eye). Due to absorption by the atmosphere, very little UVC reaches the Earth's surface. This spectrum of radiation has germicidal properties and its property of killing bacteria and viruses is used in germicidal lamps.

b. Ultraviolet B or (UVB) range spans 280 to 315 nm. This part of the spectrum is of interest to us because these are the rays that cause our skin to tan and burn, and our bodies to produce vitamin D. It is also absorbed by the atmosphere; along with UVC it is responsible for the photochemical reactions leading to the production of the ozone layer.

c. Ultraviolet A or (UVA) range spans 315 to 400 nm. This part of the spectrum also has rays that cause our skin to tan, although it has been traditionally held as less damaging to the DNA (does not cause skin burns) and hence is used in tanning beds and UVA therapy for psoriasis.

2. Visible radiation

Most of the energy reaching the Earth's surface from the sun is in the visible (and some in the infrared) part of the spectrum. The visible radiation spans 400 to 700 nm. As the name suggests, it is this range that is visible to the naked eye. This is also the part of the spectrum that is most useful to power generation, since it is readily captured by PV equipment and turned into electricity.

3. Infrared (IR) radiation

The infrared range spans 700 nm to 106 nm. It is responsible for an important part of the electromagnetic radiation that reaches the Earth. This is the part of the spectrum that heats water in solar thermal technologies which is then used for heating or to generate electricity. IR radiation is considered "parasitic" energy in most PV technologies, since it heats and overheats the PV cells and modules, thus rendering them inefficient and even causing them to fail.

The different wavelengths of the solar spectrum have different energies, with the most useful for the photovoltaic conversion being these in the 400 to 700 nm range. The UV and IR wavelengths are harmful to PV devices, because they deteriorate the materials (UV light) and generate heat within the PV cells and modules (IR light).

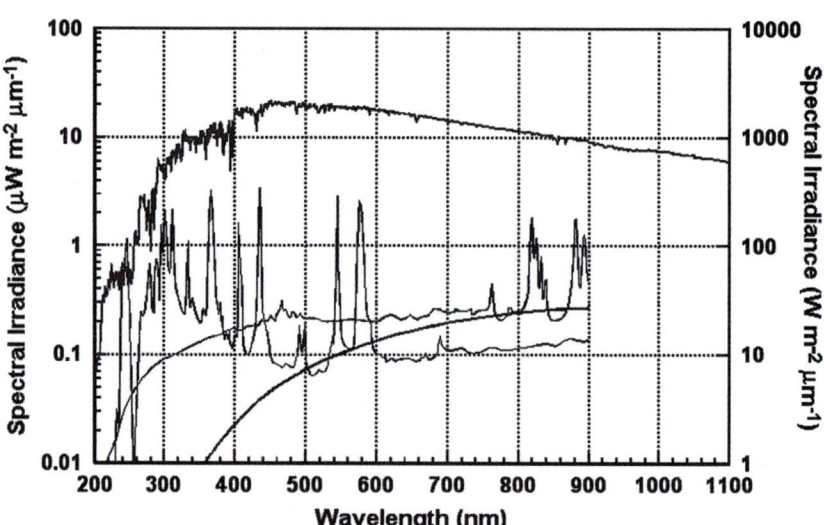

Figure 4-7. The sun's energy

The lowest wavelength of the solar spectrum, that of gamma rays, is around 10 picometers (1×10^{-12}m, or smaller than an atom) while the highest, that of radio waves, is measured in hundreds of meters. Both are undetectable by solar cells and do not play any role in the photovoltaic energy conversion process.

NOTE: If the reader is interested in learning more about the nature of light, we recommend an excellent book on the subject, *QED: The Strange Theory of Light and Matter*, by Richard Feynman, where QED stands for *quantum electro-dynamics*. In it Feynman lays down the basics of light and its interactions with matter in a very clear and entertaining way. Feynman cautions the audience that they may not understand what he will be saying, not because of technical difficulty, but because they may be unable to believe or accept it. "The theory of quantum electrodynamics describes Nature as absurd from the point of view of common sense. And it fully agrees with experiment. So I hope you can accept Nature as She is—absurd."

For all practical purposes, most PV cells capture only certain limited wavelength ranges of the solar spectrum, but some PV technologies, using special non-silicon substrates and multi-junction solar cells are capable of capturing most of the wavelengths, including UV and IR radiation, falling upon them and efficiently converting them into electric energy. We consider these devices the precursor of the PV technologies of the future, since they would be able to use fully the incoming sunlight, and at the same time withstand the excess desert insolation and heat.

Factors Influencing Solar Power Reaching the Earth

Now that we have examined the solar spectrum and have discussed its properties, let's move on to see how much of that energy can be captured and converted into electric energy by our PV devices. These are the properties and characteristics of the sunlight that are very important for calculating and designing PV projects.

Sunlight travels from the sun to Earth in approximately 8 minutes, and while it loses some of its energy during this journey, most of it arrives here safe and sound and ready to serve us. Measured at the top of the atmosphere, we find the highest power density reaching up to 1,367 W/m². That is to say that if we could mount a PV module that was a square meter in an area 200 miles above the Earth's surface, and if that PV module were 100% efficient (which is not possible as yet), we would be able to generate 1,367 W DC electric power from it. The problem of how to transport the produced electricity back to Earth is a separate issue for which we have no answer at this time.

Several factors used to characterize sunlight and measure its properties are: (1)

Spectral Radiance

The spectral irradiance as a function of photon wavelength (or energy), denoted by F, is the most common way of characterizing a light source (sunlight in our case). It gives the power density at a particular wavelength. The units of spectral irradiance are in Wm^{-2} μm^{-1}. The Wm^{-2} term is the power density at the wavelength $\lambda(\mu m)$. Therefore, the m^{-2} refers to the surface area of the light emitter and the μm^{-1} refers to the wavelength of interest.

In the analysis of solar cells, the photon flux is often needed as well as the spectral irradiance. The spectral irradiance can be determined from the photon flux by converting the photon flux at a given wavelength to W/m^2. The result is then divided by the given wavelength, as shown in the equation below.

$$F(\lambda) = \phi E \; \frac{1}{\Delta\lambda}, \quad \text{or}$$

$$F(\lambda) = \phi q \; \frac{1.24}{\lambda(\mu m)} \; * \; \frac{1}{\Delta\lambda(\mu m)}$$

where:

F is the spectral irradiance in Wm^{-2} μm^{-1};

ϕ is the photon flux in # photons m^{-2} sec^{-1};

E and λ are the energy and wavelength of the photon in eV and μm respectively; and

q is a constant

Photon Energy

Sunlight consists of many photons traveling together as a photon flux. Each photon in the flux is characterized by either a wavelength, denoted by λ or equivalently energy denoted by E. There is an inverse relationship between the energy of a photon (E) and the wavelength of the light (λ) given by the equation:

$$E = \frac{hc}{\lambda}$$

where:

h is Planck's constant and

c is the speed of light.

The above inverse relationship means that light consisting of high energy photons (such as "blue" light) has a short wavelength. Light consisting of low energy photons (such as "red" light) has a long wavelength. When dealing with "particles" such as photons or electrons, a commonly used unit of energy is the electron-volt (eV) rather than the Joule (J). An electron volt is the energy required to raise an electron through 1 volt, thus 1 eV = 1.602 x 10⁻¹⁹ J.

By expressing the equation for photon energy in terms of eV and μm we arrive at a commonly used expression which relates the energy and wavelength of a photon, as shown in the following equation:

$$E = \frac{1.24}{\lambda \mu m}$$

The exact value of 1×10^6 (hc/q) is 1.2398 but the approximation 1.24 is sufficient for most purposes.

Photon Flux

The photon flux (and its quality and quantity) determine the intensity of the sunlight reaching our PV devices. The photon flux is defined as the number of photons per second per unit area:

$$\phi = \frac{\# \text{ photons}}{\sec \text{ m}^2}$$

The photon flux is important in determining the number of electrons which are generated, and hence the current produced from a solar cell. As the photon flux does not give information about the energy (or wavelength) of the photons, the energy or wavelength of the photons in the light source must also be specified. At a given wavelength, the combination of the photon wavelength or energy and the photon flux at that wavelength can be used to calculate the power density for photons at the particular wavelength.

Power Density

The power density is calculated by multiplying the photon flux by the energy of a single photon. Since the photon flux gives the number of photons striking a surface in a given time, multiplying by the energy of the photons comprising the photon flux gives the energy striking a surface per unit time, which is equivalent to a power density. To determine the power density in units of W/m^2, the energy of the photons must be in Joules. The equation is:

$$H\left(\frac{W}{m^2}\right) = \phi * \frac{hc}{\lambda}\,(J) = \phi q\,\frac{1.24}{\lambda(\mu m)}$$

where:

ϕ is the photon flux.

One implication of the above equations is that the photon flux of high energy (or short wavelength) photons needed to give a certain radiant power density will be lower than the photon flux of low energy (or long wavelength) photons required to give the same radiant power density. In the animation, the radiant power density incident on the surface is the same for both the blue and red light, but fewer blue photons are needed since each one has more energy.

The total power density emitted from a light source (sunlight in this case) can be calculated by integrating the spectral irradiance over all wavelengths or

energies of interest. However, a closed form equation for the spectral irradiance for a light source often does not exist. Instead the measured spectral irradiance must be multiplied by a wavelength range over which it was measured, and then calculated over all wavelengths. The following equation can be used to calculate the total power density emitted from a light source.

$$H = \int_o^x F(\lambda)\Delta\lambda = \sum_{i=0}^{x} F(\lambda)\alpha\lambda$$

where:

H is the total power density emitted from the light source in $W\,m^{-2}$;

$F(\lambda)$ is the spectral irradiance in units of Wm^{-2} μm^{-1}; and

$d\lambda$ or $\Delta\lambda$ is the wavelength.

As the sunlight travels down and gets close to Earth, it must travel through the atmosphere where it collides with dust and water vapor particles, thus losing some of its power. So, on a perfectly clear day on the equator we could measure up to $1{,}110\ W/m^2$ (down from $1{,}367\ W/m^2$ measured above the atmosphere). In the Arizona desert we measure $900-1100\ W/m^2$ on a clear summer day—not bad for generating useful power from a piece of otherwise "useless" desert land during the daylight periods, when we need it most, especially during the summer months.

Clouds, fog and dust will rob some of the power that sunlight is trying to deliver to Earth, but even then most PV modules will be able to convert some of that energy reaching their surface to electric power (10-90%, depending on the cloud cover density). Although that is a greatly reduced amount, it is still enough to produce a lot of usable energy. Ask the German people, where under mostly cloudy conditions the number of PV installations has risen at an unbelievably high pace lately, and continues to rise.

The curvature of the Earth also influences the amount of energy that strikes its surface at any given location. The intensity of the sunlight is greater in the area of the equator between the tropics, and it loses intensity towards the South and North Poles. This is because the sunlight, due to the Earth's curvature, must travel much greater distance at a sharper angle through the atmosphere before reaching the Earth's surface.

In addition, since the Earth is tilted on its axis, the time of year also influences the amount of energy which strikes its surface at different locations and times. So, the important characteristics of incident solar energy are:

1. The spectral content of the incident light (visible, UV or IR light content),
2. The average radiant power density of sunlight (W/m^2) at the location,
3. The angle at which the incident solar radiation strikes a PV module,
4. The seasonal sunlight energy (summer vs. winter), and the local variations, and
5. The atmospheric and weather conditions (clouds, fog, smog, etc.).

All these properties and characteristics of sunlight are very important for calculating and designing PV projects, and are used extensively by design engineers and installers alike, thus making them integral parts of the proper execution of any solar project. We will take a much more detailed look these parameters in the text below.

Solar Energy Characteristics and Use

To produce electricity, sunlight must be captured and converted into thermal or electric energy suitable for human consumption. As we discussed in the previous section, sun energy races toward the Earth at a very high speed, and if its path were not obstructed by space junk or clouds and dust in the atmosphere, it would arrive to us at full power.

We call this "beam" or "direct" radiation. Arriving "directly" from the sun, it is most powerful and measures around 1367 W/m^2 just above our atmosphere. Its power drops after crossing the atmosphere to approximately 900-1,100 W/m^2 as measured at noon in the deserts during the summer months, and much less than that in other parts of the globe and during different seasons of the year.

When the sunlight hits clouds, dust, or man-made gasses in the air, it gets scattered and we call that "diffused" radiation. Diffused radiation has properties very different from direct radiation. It contains less energy, and thus PV modules will produce less power under diffused radiation—in some cases much less. Particularly, concentrating thermal or PV equipment is affected by this diffusion, and this will cause it to lose its focus and operate well below its maximum efficiency rating, if at all, under extreme conditions.

Sunlight hitting the Earth is reflected from its surface, and we call this effect "albedo." Different materials have different reflecting properties, but most do reflect and some reflect a lot. Take fresh snow, for example. It will reflect almost 80% of the light falling on its surface. Water, on the other hand, absorbs most of the sunlight, instead, and gets heated in the process. Thus, reflected sunlight can be captured by our PV modules installed nearby as well. The albedo always has an effect on PV module performance, so it should be taken into consideration, especially in areas with snow cover or other highly reflective ground surface cover.

As we discussed in the previous section, another factor that affects the amount of energy available for conversion into electricity is the distance the sunlight travels once it enters the Earth's atmosphere. At certain times of the day and year, the sun seems to be overhead at a 90-degree angle to the Earth's surface, and this is when sunlight travels the shortest path and is the strongest. We call this Air Mass = 1 (or AM 1). AM 0 is measured above the atmosphere and is much stronger than AM 1.

In the early morning and later afternoon, the sun is at a sharper angle and sunlight travels a longer path through the atmosphere, so the angle decreases (approaching 45 degrees), the sunlight has a longer path to travel, and the AM number increases: AM 1.15, 1.5 etc. depending on the angle. The sharper the angle of the sun's rays, the larger the AM number and the objects' shadows. AM 1.5 is measured at an angle close to 45 degrees.

The air mass number can be determined by the formula:

$$AM = \sqrt{1 + \left(\frac{s}{h}\right)^2}$$

where:

h is the object's height, and
s is its shadow length.

The revolution of the Earth around the sun and its rotation on its axis produces seasonal and daily effects, which vary by location on the globe. This location is measured on the world map in terms of longitude (east-west direction), and latitude (south-north direction). The intersection of these provides us with a precise point on the map.

All these components taken together represent what we call "global radiation," which is a very important factor in the proper design, installation and operation of solar energy generating systems. Solar professionals need to be very familiar with it, if a properly designed PV system is their goal.

The solar spectrum components and the quantity of sunlight traveling to Earth at any moment are constant, with only slight variations. The sunlight reaching the Earth's atmosphere (but before entering) is represented by AM 0 in Figure 4-8 and is a constant with some very small and predictable variations. When the sunlight hits the atmosphere it becomes a variable, depending mostly on the contents of the atmosphere, the seasons, weather, and the time of day. Thus the amount of sunlight is a variable, which is mostly out of our control, but which we must take into consideration when working with PV equipment.

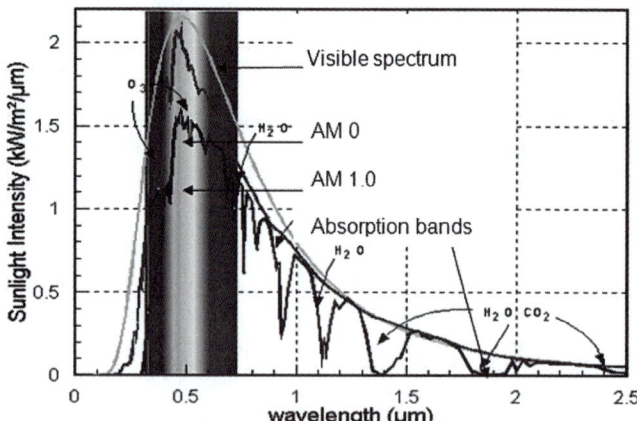

Figure 4-8. Sunlight wavelength vs. power measurements. (1)

Water in the atmosphere (clouds), dust, CO_2 and other gasses absorb radiation, thus diminishing the amount and level of energy that makes it to Earth. So the amount of water vapor and CO_2 (of which there is a lot in the atmosphere) in the sunlight's path will determine how much energy will reach the Earth's surface.

The influence of all these variables is significant and must be well understood and taken into consideration in our solar calculations and designs, if we are to optimize the performance of our PV devices. There is not much we can do about these variables, for they obey higher orders, so we call them "fixed" variables. We can, however, work around them and build and use renewable energy technologies that are best suited for local conditions.

Major variables over which we have no control are the local weather conditions—clouds, rain, snow, fog, smog, dust, humidity, etc. These must also be well understood and looked at very carefully, when designing, installing and operating solar energy generating systems—thermal or photovoltaic. We cannot control the weather, dust, smog and other natural phenomena, but we can study historical weather data and anticipate behaviors, to compensate for the effects, thus obtaining the best possible results at a given location with the

highest possible power output.

Ideally, large-scale solar power plants should be installed in locations with the least cloud, fog and humidity levels. However, since there is no place with perfectly clear skies all through the year, we must provide for the clouds and other effects of weather, estimate their influence, and design the systems accordingly.

There are variables which we can and should control such as the position of trees, buildings, smoggy factories, dusty fields, and other obstructions which will diminish system performance. Tall trees, buildings, etc. near a power field will reduce the output, so they must be avoided, removed, or trimmed. Air pollution generated by industrial activities can hinder the performance of PV devices, so it must be considered. The effects of smog and fog from nearby populated centers or large bodies of water must be also considered and calculated as accurately as possible.

Other variables worthy of mention, due to their effects on power output of PV devices, are the air and ground temperature. Our Earth provides a marvelous thermodynamic balance, where the temperature increase due to incoming sunlight during the day is balanced by the outgoing heat during the cool of night, so that balance is maintained. During the summer months, however, the balance in some areas, like the deserts, is temporarily altered.

The air and ground can get extremely hot during the day, heating solar energy generating equipment to levels it cannot easily handle. The glass and metal structures of the solar power fields could reach temperatures well over the operating limits of the PV devices in them (temperatures near 200°F have been measured), thus causing drastic power output decrease and outright electro-mechanical failure.

Prolonged exposure to extreme heat can cause deterioration, damage and even destruction to most present-day photovoltaic devices, which is why serious consideration must be given to the structure and proper use of these devices in extreme climates. Their function and behavior must be well understood and proven, well before the design stages and definitely before installing and exposing them to harsh deserts and other extreme climate conditions.

Finally, we must also understand and take into consideration the environmental consequences of our efforts. Installing acres upon acres of solar collectors (thermal or PV) in the deserts, for example, could have serious effects on the delicate ecosystems of these lands. Unfortunately, there are not enough data yet to predict these effects.

There may be some positive effects too—the structures will provide shade which could cool the ground in summer months. However the Earth has a delicate and even fragile environmental balance, and we have learned during the past several decades that every action people take for their own comfort and convenience has an effect on the environment—and usually not for the better. So, covering a large land mass with any solar technology will have an effect, which we must evaluate and consider before acting.

Always, all variables must be considered and their impacts incorporated into system design.

How does all this translates to the concept of solar energy? Let's take a close look at a 100 Wp solar panel from an energy point of view.

1. A solar panel sitting ***idle at night or under heavy clouds*** has no energy to offer, only the potential to create energy at the right time. In the absence of sunlight, the only energy related to a solar module results from the gravity and mechanical stresses acting upon it, so it is as useless a paperweight. It cannot do any work, because there is no energy and no force. It also has no power, and it cannot produce any power in the dark.

2. A solar panel in full sunshine, but ***not connected to an outside load*** has potential energy, but no force or power, and is not producing work. It has ***potential*** energy. It is ready to do work, ready to show its force and power, but is sitting idle, like a loaded spring anxiously awaiting to be released.

3. A solar panel sitting under full sunshine, ***connected to an outside load*** is a fully operational device. It is like the spring that has been compressed and then released, springing into action, releasing energy and

creating power. Its potential energy is converted into kinetic energy, and now things start happening. The energy (electrical action) is represented by force (that of the electrons moving around the electrical circuit). This electricity can be measured directly as power (electric power), as the amount of current at the specific voltage at the moment.

So, our 100 Wp solar panel is now generating 100 Watts of DC electric power, which can be used to light a light bulb, run an electric motor, or heat the heating elements of a heater. More often than not, it will be connected to the grid where it will send the generated electricity.

Today, the solar revolution is on a scale much larger than ever, so solar is finally here to stay and prosper. Or is it…? We will review the different possibilities in this text too.

Solar energy comes in two basic useful forms; heat and light. Manmade solar energy equipment is designed and manufactured to use the sun's heat, light, or both in converting them into convenient heat or electricity.

Solar energy equipment which uses the heat (IR) portion of the solar spectrum is called *solar thermal*, while equipment that uses the light (photons) is called *photovoltaics*. Solar energy equipment that uses both heat and light is called *hybrid*, and we will review all these types, beginning with solar thermal power generators.

SOLAR THERMAL POWER GENERATION

The major solar power generating technologies suitable for commercial and utilities applications today, and presumably for the rest of the 21st century are shown in Figure 4-9.

The list of major solar technologies is as follows:

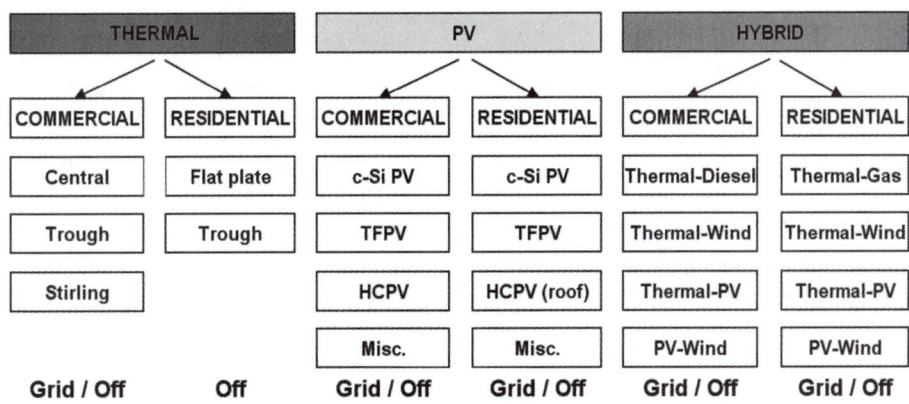

Figure 4-9. Major solar technologies and their uses

1. Solar thermal technologies:
    a   The flat plate water heater
    b. The Stirling engine dish
    c. Parabolic troughs,
    d. Power towers, and
    e. New and exotic solar thermal technologies

2. Solar photovoltaics technologies
    a. Crystalline silicon PV modules,
    b. Thin film PV modules
    c. HCPV trackers, and
    d. New and exotic PV technologies

3. Solar hybrids
    a. PV-CSP hybrid
    b. PV-wind hybrid
    c. PV-hot water hybrid
    d. PV-natural gas hybrid
    e. PV-diesel hybrid
    f. …and more.

Solar thermal equipment, as the name suggests, is used to operate in the thermal (heat) zone of the solar spectrum, and to generate thermal effects, which usually result in heating water or other liquids for use in residential or commercial applications.

A focused beam of light can be also generated and used directly to heat water or objects, and for cooking. In its most useful form, solar thermal is used to concentrate sunlight on receivers (pipes with liquids running through). The hot liquids are pumped into a boiler where they generate steam that can be used to turn a turbine. A generator connected to the turbine then generates electricity that can be sent into the power grid.

*Definition of Solar Thermal and
Solar Thermo-electric Technologies*

Solar thermal equipment uses sunlight to convert its energy directly into heat which is then used for heating or for electric power generation. The heat can be used for heating homes or as a heat source in commercial processes. Most often, however, the heat is converted into electric power which is then sent into the electric grid.

The conversion of sunlight to heat is a straightforward process, while the conversion of heat to electricity is somewhat more complex and requires expensive equipment and large installations to make it cost effective. This conversion is usually done at the so-called "utility scale power plants," using concentrated solar power (CSP) equipment which is the technology of

choice today.

There are currently four different types of solar thermal systems. The first type, *flat plate water heater* solar thermal energy generator, is in its own category, because it generates heat only and is the simplest and cheapest of the bunch. It can be mounted on the roofs of houses and businesses and is used only to heat water (or other liquids) to a moderate temperature. This technology has been successfully used by commercial operations, such as restaurants, laundromats, canning facilities, etc. for several decades.

Smaller size, roof-mounted, parabolic troughs were also popular in the southwest USA in the 1980s, and are making a slow comeback today, while generally speaking, the major CSP technologies are large, ground-mounted, grid-connected systems.

The other types of thermal solar systems, *Stirling engine*, *parabolic trough* and *power tower* are in the category of concentrated solar power (CSP) technologies, because they do capture the sunlight and concentrate (focus) it onto a receiver. The heat is then normally used to make electricity by several different methods which we will review below as well.

CSP technologies require direct (clear sky) sunlight for efficient operation, as needed for the optics to reflect and concentrate the reflected light onto a receiver which converts it into heat. The heat can be used for heating or for electricity generation. Relatively flat land is best for CSP systems, with slopes not exceeding 3 percent being recommended in most cases. The area of land required depends on the type of solar plant, but on average it is about 5-6 acres per produced megawatt (MW) of electric energy. So, cost-effective utility scale CSP power plants are 100 MW in size or larger, requiring a minimum of 500-600 acres of land for each installed 100 MWp. This large land base requirement involves significant surface disturbance (digging, land leveling and other modifications) with associated potential impact on a variety of resources on public and private lands.

These types of facilities also require roads, water source, wind protection, security fencing and such for their safe and efficient operation. The generated electricity is sold to the local utilities under a power purchase agreement (PPA), or other long-term power sale agreements.

There are a number of thermal solar energy converting technologies, and we will review the major ones, focusing on those which we consider most likely to take a major part in, and have the largest impact on, the commercial and utilities type power generation development and use in the 21st century.

In this chapter we present a quick review of solar thermal technologies, then take a much closer look at the competing PV technologies in the following chapters.

The key solar thermal technologies used today are discussed below.

Flat Plate Solar Water Heater

Flat plate water heating systems are used in residential, commercial and industrial applications, primarily for heating water in laundromats, restaurants, public parks, car washes, and canning and bottling facilities. These heating systems could be used practically anyplace where low-temperature hot water is needed during the day. Adding a storage tank could provide water for use during the night and on cloudy days. In all cases, they are truly "thermal" systems designed to provide hot water.

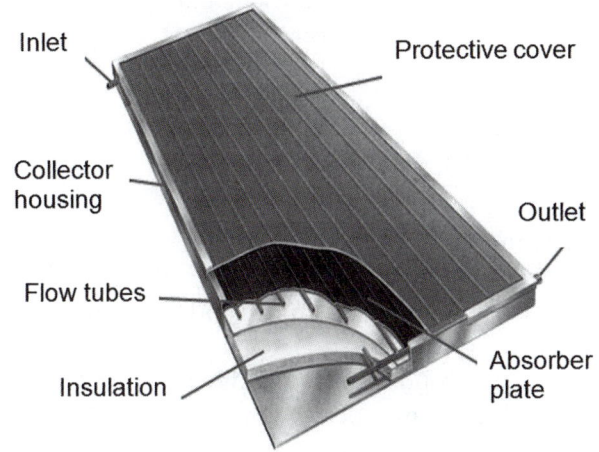

Figure 4-10. Flat plate solar water heater

These are the simplest and cheapest energy conversion devices today, consisting of a frame into which a heat exchanger plate (or some modification of) is mounted. Water runs through the flow tubes in the heat exchanger plate and absorbs the sunlight energy, thus heating the plate and the water (or other heat-absorbing liquid) running through it.

The heat exchanger is protected by a cover glass, which also protects the inner workings of the unit from the outside cold and wind.

The materials, as well as the manufacturing, installation and operation procedures are straightforward and relatively inexpensive. The return on investment (ROI) is one of the highest in the industry, if the systems are properly designed, installed and operated.

There are also a number of incentives today which make it even more feasible and desirable to own and operate such a renewable energy system.

CSP TECHNOLOGIES

Concentrated solar power (CSP) is a thermal technology that, installed in large-scale power fields has a wide use today in generating electric power. It is also one of the most efficient power generating technologies at present.

The sun's energy falling on the Earth's surface for just 60 minutes is equivalent to the entire annual global energy consumption. From that fact alone we can easily conclude that the potential for getting free energy from the sun is virtually unlimited. The deployment of concentrating solar thermal power (CSP) technologies is a good example of our attempts to capture that potential.

CSP's capacity is expected to increase exponentially over the next several years. Worldwide installed CSP capacity estimates vary widely from 20-35 GW by 2025 and reaching 500-1000 GW by 2050. These estimates might be too optimistic, especially in light of the developments of late, reflected in decrease of government subsidies, water shortages and the growing trend of conversion of CSP to PV power plants. Some restrictions in the EU, such as the law passed recently in Spain which reduced government subsidies for solar energy, will have a profound effect on the CSP industry as a whole. We do believe that it will grow as the needs and the energy markets of developing countries continue to expand, but the pace of this growth is uncertain.

CSP technology is facing increasing challenges from PV competitors who have leveraged PV's declining costs and adaptability, to create a large global market. CSP will have trouble competing directly with PV on a cost per kWh basis in the near future but might be able to occupy niche markets with its ability to provide more stable power by providing after-hours energy via on-site thermal storage. The need for cooling water is a great problem facing the CSP industry. PV doesn't have this problem and is taking full advantage of this fact presently.

We estimate that the total solar power (CSP and PV) produced around the world will continue to grow exponentially, but anything can happen at any time to alter the growth pattern one way or another. Technology types, proper design, manufacturing, installation and operation have a lot to do with it, but other—even greater and unrelated—forces will be shaping the overall future of solar energy generation. These forces are future demand and supply balance, material prices, energy costs, financing options, land availability and permitting, transmission and interconnection, socio-economic, political, and a number of other factors that contribute to the complexity and the degree of difficulty in deploying solar power generating equipment.

We will now concentrate on the three major types of thermo-electric (CSP) systems presently used; Stirling dish, the parabolic trough, and the power tower.

These three technologies have one thing in common: they all use trackers and optics of some type to optimize their efficiency in capturing sunlight and converting it into useful heat energy.

Because these systems usually concentrate the sunlight, to generate higher temperatures, they are called concentrating solar power (CSP) systems. They also require a lot of land that needs to be relatively flat, with slopes not exceeding three percent, to accommodate the solar collectors. The area of land required depends on the type of plant, but it is about five acres per installed megawatt (MW).

It is anticipated that a commercial scale CSP facility of any type, would be in the range of 100 MW or larger and require in excess of 500 acres, plus whatever else is needed for their installation and proper infrastructure. The large size is needed for financial justification of the large expense in support equipment (power plant and other facilities).

Unlike solar photovoltaic technologies which use semiconductors to convert sunlight directly into electricity, CSP plants generate electricity by converting sunlight into heat first. Much like a reflective mirror, their reflectors focus sunlight onto a receiver. The heat absorbed by the receiver is used to move an engine piston (Sterling engine), or generate steam that drives a turbine to produce electricity (parabolic troughs and power tower). Power generation after sunset is possible also by storing excess heat in large, insulated tanks filled with molten salt during the day and using it at night.

Since CSP plants require high levels of direct solar radiation to operate efficiently, deserts make ideal locations. As a matter of fact, these types of systems cannot operate efficiently in any other environment.

A study by Ausra, a solar energy company based in California, indicates that more than 90% of fossil fuel-generated electricity in the U.S. and the majority of U.S. oil usage for transportation could be eliminated by using solar thermal power plants and will cost less than it would cost to continue importing oil. The land requirement for the CSP plants would be roughly 15,000 square miles in the SW USA deserts, or the equivalent of 15% of the land area of Nevada. While this may sound like a large tract of land, in the long run CSP plants use less land per equivalent electrical output than large hydro-

electric dams when flooded and wasted land is included and less than coal plants when factoring in the land used for mining and waste disposal.

Another study, published in *Scientific American*, proposes using CSP and PV plants to produce 69% of U.S. electricity and 35% of total U.S. energy including transportation by 2050. This, in this author's opinion, is possible but only if the political winds blow much harder in the solar direction than they are today, and when fossil fuels become critically low, and too expensive. None of this will happen soon, so 2050 might be a bit too early. We'd suggest 2100 as the time when drastic changes in the energy landscape in favor of renewables will become a full-blown reality.

Today the major CSP technologies are:

1. The Stirling engine-dish tracker
2. The parabolic trough tracker, and
3. The power tower (central receiver)

We will discuss each of these below, focusing on their technological advancements and use in large-scale solar installations.

The Stirling Engine

One of the most elegant and flexible solar thermal power conversion technologies today is the Stirling engine dish system. It consists of mirrors mounted on a frame which is continuously tracking the sun all through the day. The mirrors focus the reflected sunlight onto the receiver of the Stirling engine mechanism which is activated by the heat and turns on a shaft, connected to the rotor of an electric generator similar to that of the alternator of your car. The generator rotor turns with the engine shaft and generates electric power while the sun is shining and the receiver is hot enough to activate the engine and rotate the shaft.

A Stirling engine system is actually a solar electricity generator because the heat produced by the mirrors attached to it is converted into electric energy on the spot, so small installations of a few units are possible. That is just not practical with the other CSP technologies. The Stirling engine needs cooling just like a car engine, for more efficient operation, to cool the engine walls, bearings and other moving parts.

The mirror(s) are mounted on a metal frame which is driven by two motor-gear assemblies (x-y drives), programmed to move the frame in such a fashion that it follows the sun's movement precisely all day long, thus providing accurate focusing of the sunlight onto the heating plate of the Stirling engine. When the plate

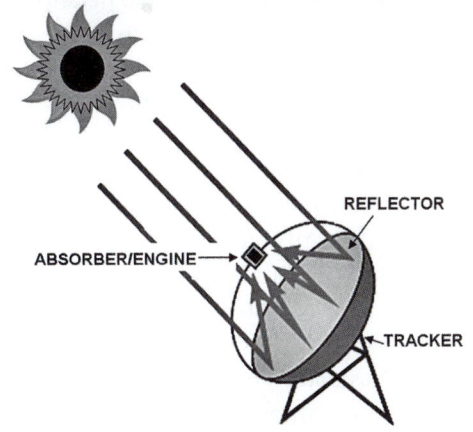

Figure 4-11. Stirling engine dish

gets hot enough, the air in one of the cylinders in it is compressed and forces the piston in it to move up. This action forces the piston in the other cylinder (which is simultaneously cooled) to move down. Eventually, the compression in the second cylinder increases to the point that its piston is forced to go back, thus forcing the piston in the first cylinder to assume its initial position. The cycle repeats over and over while there is enough heat to maintain the process.

The Stirling engine function, under ideal operating conditions, can be represented by four cycles, or *thermodynamic process segments*, of interaction between the working gases, the heat exchanger, pistons and the cylinder walls.

The Stirling engine is a very ingenious and efficient piston engine, without the noise and exhaust of internal combustion engines. As a matter of fact, it can be classified as an "external combustion" engine. The gasses inside the cylinders are not exhausted, so there is no pollution, and there are few moving parts with very little noise, so it can be used virtually anywhere.

Since its invention in 1816 by the Scottish inventor Dr. Robert Stirling, the Stirling engine has been consid-

ered and proposed for use in many different applications. Presently it is used in some specialized applications, where quiet and clean (no exhaust) operation is required. Some fancy and special purpose submarines and vessels use Stirling engines part of the time under special conditions.

Unfortunately, mass-market application of the Stirling engine is not found as yet, although many scientists and inventors are working on it. Its use in solar power generating equipment might be a good start in that direction. There are currently a number of installations using this technology, but most of them are smaller, demo-type systems. No large CSP power plant using Stirling engine technology is in operation today, and, in fact two of the largest (and maybe only) Stirling engine power plants planned for installation in the California deserts were cancelled recently (2010 and 2011). With that, the future of Stirling solar technology remains uncertain.

The Parabolic Trough

Parabolic trough solar systems consist of a frame in a parabolic trough shape in which glass, metal or plastic reflectors are mounted to focus the sun's energy onto a receiver pipe running above and in parallel to the trough's length. The receiver pipe, or heat collection element (HCE), is centered at the focal point of the reflectors and is heated by the reflected sunlight to very high temperatures. Liquid of some sort is pumped through the receiver pipe and is heated in the process.

Parabolic trough power plants, also called solar electric generating systems (SEGS), represent the most mature CSP technology, with the most installed capacity of all CSP technologies. The first SEGS solar trough plant started operating in 1984, with the last one coming on line in 1991. Altogether, nine such plants were built, SEGS I–VII at Kramer Junction and VIII and IX at Harper Lake and Barstow respectively. In February 2005, all but two (I and II) of the Kramer Junction SEGS plants were acquired by FPL Energy and Carlyle/Riverstone and are still operating.

A natural gas system added to the plant "hybridizes" it and contributes up to 25% of the output. This feature also allows operation later at night or on cloudy days to meet grid requirements. FPL now runs these systems, making it the largest solar power generator in the United States. All of the power generated from the SEGS projects is sold to Southern California Edison under long-term contracts negotiated by Luz back in the 1980s.

There are a number of such plants operating around the world and many others are planned.

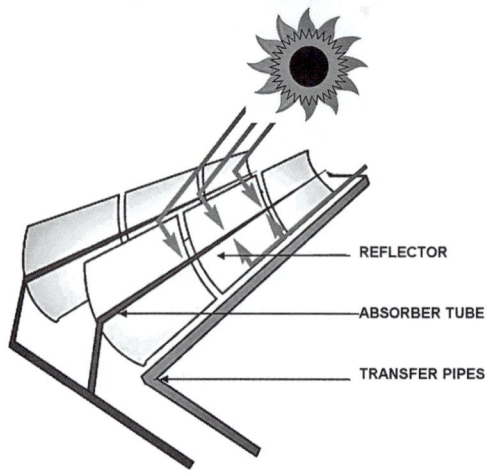

Figure 4-12. Parabolic trough technology

The HCE of the parabolic trough units is usually composed of a metal pipe with a glass tube surrounding it, and with the space between these evacuated to provide low thermal losses from the pipe. The pipe is coated with a material that improves the absorption of solar energy. Several improvements have been made or are underway to improve performance, the most significant of which is the seal between the glass and the pipe, which seal has not been as reliable as desired and development of better seal materials/seal configuration is still underway.

Parabolic troughs can focus the sunlight many times its normal intensity on the receiver pipe, where heat transfer fluid (HTF—usually mineral or synthetic oil) flowing through the pipe is heated. This heated fluid is then used to generate steam which powers a turbine that drives an electric generator. The collectors are aligned on an east-west axis and the trough is rotated north-south, following the sun to maximize the sun's energy input to the receiver tube.

One advantage of CSP systems is their ability to

generate power after the sun has gone down. In these cases, the HTF fluid going through the receiver pipe is routed through a thermal storage system which permits the plant to keep operating for several hours after sunset while the electrical demand is still relatively high. The thermal storage system consists of a "hot" storage tank equipped with heat exchanger where HTF circulates and gives up a portion of its heat to heat the storage solution in the tank during the day.

At night, the hot storage solution flows through the same heat exchanger heating up HTF which is sent to the steam turbines for generating power. The cooled-down storage solution flows from the heat exchanger to a "cold" storage tank where it stays until daytime when it is reheated and returned to the "hot" storage tank. And the cycle is repeated every night.

Linear Fresnel Reflector

Linear Fresnel reflector (LFR) systems are similar to the parabolic trough, but use an array of nearly flat Fresnel reflectors instead. These reflectors concentrate solar radiation onto elevated inverted linear receivers. Water, or other liquid, flows through the receivers and is converted into steam. This system is also line-concentrating with the advantages of low costs for structural support and reflectors, fixed fluid joints, a receiver separated from the reflector system and long focal lengths that allow the use of flat mirrors.

LFR technology is seen as a potentially lower-cost alternative to trough technology for the production of solar process heat. Planned commercial applications are estimated at a size from 50 to 200 MW. Linear Fresnel applications are mostly at the experimental stage for now. Companies working in the field claim higher efficiency and lower costs per kWh than its direct competitor, parabolic trough, due to the high density of mirrors. The Fresnel mirror is available at little more than €7 per m². According to Ausra, this technology can generate electricity for €0.10 per kWh now and under €0.08 per kWh within next 3 years.

The Fraunhofer Institute has contributed greatly in making the key components such as the absorber pipe, the secondary reflectors, primary reflector array and their control ready for operation. Based on theoretical investigations and the specific conditions found in sunny climates, Fraunhofer researchers have calculated that the electricity production costs will not rise above €0.12 per kWh.

The linear Fresnel CSP technology derives its name from a type of optical system that uses a multiplicity of small flat optical faces, invented by the French physicist

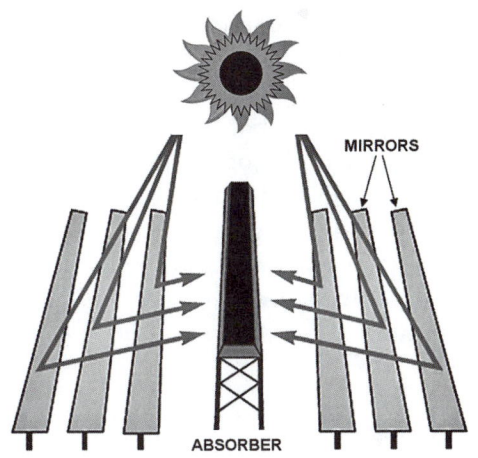

Figure 4-13. Linear Fresnel plant

Augustin-Jean Fresnel who, while Commissioner for Lighthouses, invented the segmented lighthouse lens. Flat moving reflectors follow the path of the sun and reflect its radiation to the fixed pipe receivers above. Molten salt or other operating liquid powers a steam turbine, or is stored for night use.

The technology itself is simple; the biggest challenge is setting mirrors to track the sun and reflect rays effectively. Flat mirrors are much cheaper to produce than parabolic ones, so this is a bonus.

Another advantage of the compact linear Fresnel reflector CLFR is that it allows for a greater density of reflectors in the array. In addition, Fresnel technology is less sensitive to wind loads and allows parallel land use to a large extent.

The LFR technology is more competitive economically due to:

*   More effective land use than rival technologies;
*   Low visual impact on landscape;
*   Lower infrastructure costs due to its design;
*   Lighter base, less steel, flat (not curved) mirrors.

The Power Tower

The power tower (or central receiver) power generation uses methods of collection and concentration of solar power based on a large number of sun-tracking mirrors (heliostats) reflecting the incident sunshine to a receiver (boiler) mounted on the top of a high tower, usually in the middle of the collection field. Eighty to 95 percent of the reflected energy is absorbed into the working fluid which is pumped up the tower and into the receiver. The heated fluid (or steam) returns down the tower and is fed into a thermal electrical power plant, steam turbine, or an industrial process that uses the heat.

The difference between the central receiver concept of collecting solar energy and the trough or dish collectors discussed previously, is that in this case all of the solar energy to be collected in the entire field is transmitted optically to a relatively small central collection region rather than being piped around a field as hot fluid. Because of this, central receiver systems are characterized by large power levels (100 to 500 MW) and higher temperatures (540 to 840°C) of the working fluids which allows the creation of high quality superheated steam which is more efficient for electricity generation.

Power tower technology for generating electricity has been demonstrated in the Solar One pilot power plant at Barstow, CA, since 1982. This system consists of 1818 heliostats, each with a reflective area of 39.9 m² (430 ft²) covering 291,000 m² (72 acres) of land. The receiver is located at the top of a 90.8 m (298 ft) high tower and produces steam at 516°C (960°F) at a maximum rate of 42 MW (142 MBtu/h).

The reflecting element of a heliostat is typically a thin, back (second) surface, low-iron glass mirror. This

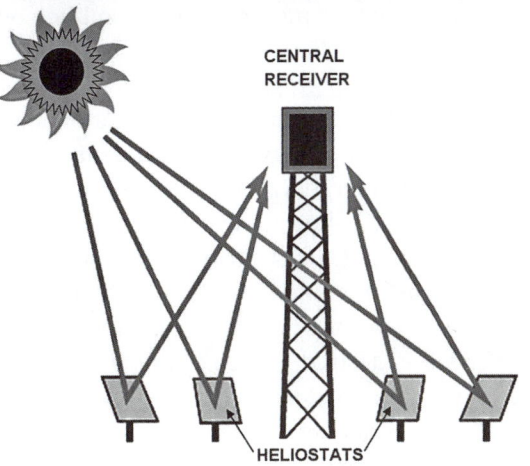

Figure 4-14. Power tower power plant

heliostat is composed of several mirror module panels rather than a single large mirror. The thin glass mirrors are supported by a substrate backing, to form a slightly concave mirror surface. Individual panels on the heliostat are also canted toward a point on the receiver. The heliostat focal length is approximately equal to the distance from the receiver to the farthest heliostat. Subsequent "tuning" and optimization of the closer mirrors is done upon installation.

Another heliostat design concept, not so widely developed, uses a thin reflective plastic membrane stretched over a hoop. This design must be protected from the weather but requires considerably less expenditure in supports and the mechanical drive mechanism because of its light weight. Membrane renewal and cleaning appear to be important considerations with this design. In all cases, the reflective surface is mounted on a pedestal that permits movement about the azimuth and elevation axis. Movement about each axis is provided by a fractional-horsepower motor through a gearbox drive. These motors receive signals from a central control computer that accurately points the reflective surface toward halfway between the sun and the receiver.

System design and evaluation for a central receiver application is performed in a manner similar to that when other types of collectors are used. Basically, the thermal output of the solar field is found by calculating collection efficiency and multiplying this by the solar irradiance falling on the collector (heliostat) field, minus some optical, transmission and other losses.

The major components of a power tower system follow.

Tracking and Positioning Systems

The heliostats must follow the sun all day to focus the sunlight on the tower receiver. This is achieved by means of two electric motor-drive assemblies on each unit. To keep parasitic energy low, fractional horsepower motors with high gear rations are used to move the heliostat about its azimuth and elevation axes. This produces a powerful, slow, steady and accurate tracking motion. Under emergency conditions, however, rapid movement of the heliostats to a safe or stow position is an important design criterion. A typical minimum speed requirement would be that the entire field defocus to less than 3 percent of the receiver flux in 2 minutes. Higher speed is desired in case of impending disasters, such as high wind, hail and such, to protect the mirrors from mechanical damage.

Since it is currently considered best to stow the heliostats face-down during high wind, hail storms, and at night, an acceptable time to travel to this position from any other position would be a maximum of 15 minutes. The requirement for inverted stow is being questioned since it requires that the bottom half of the mirror surface be designed with an open slot so that it can pass through the pedestal. This space reduces not only the reflective surface area for a given overall heliostat dimension, but also the structural rigidity of the mirror rack. However, face-down stow does keep the mirror surface cleaner and safer.

Receiver

The receiver, placed at the top of a tower, is located at a point where reflected energy from the heliostats can be intercepted most efficiently. The receiver absorbs the energy being reflected from the heliostat field and transfers it into a heat transfer fluid. Taking a closer look at the receivers, we see that there are two basic types of receivers, external and cavity receivers.

External receivers normally consist of panels of many small (20-56 mm) vertical tubes welded side-by-side to approximate a cylinder. The bottoms and tops of the vertical tubes are connected to headers that supply heat transfer fluid to the bottom of each tube and collect the heated fluid from the top of the tubes. The tubes are made of Incoloy 800 and are coated on the exterior with high-absorption black paint.

External receivers typically have a height-to-diameter ratio of 1:1 to 2:1. The area of the receiver is kept to a minimum to reduce heat loss. The lower limit is determined by the maximum operating temperature of the tubes and hence the heat removal capability of the heat transfer fluid.

Cavity receivers are an attempt to reduce heat loss from the receiver by placing the flux-absorbing surface inside an insulated cavity, thereby reducing the convective heat losses from the absorber. The flux from the heliostat field is reflected through an aperture onto absorbing surfaces forming the walls of the cavity. Typical designs have an aperture area of about one-third to one-half of the internal absorbing surface area.

Cavity receivers are limited to an acceptance angle of 60 to 120 degrees. Therefore, either multiple cavities are placed adjacent to each other, or the heliostat field is limited to the view of the cavity aperture. The aperture size is minimized to reduce convection and radiation losses without blocking out too much of the solar flux arriving at the receiver. The aperture is typically sized to about the same dimensions as the sun's reflected image from the farthest heliostat, giving a spillage of 1-4%.

Heat transfer fluids vary, so the choice of fluid to be

pumped through the receiver is determined by the application. The primary choice criterion is the maximum operating temperature of the system followed closely by the cost-effectiveness of the system and safety considerations. The heat transfer fluids with the lowest operating temperature capabilities are heat transfer oils. Both hydrocarbon and synthetic-based oils may be used, but their maximum temperature is around 425°C (797°F). However, their vapor pressure is low at these temperatures, thus allowing their use for thermal energy storage. Below temperatures of about –10°C (14°F), heat must be supplied to make most of these oils flow. Oils have the major drawback of being flammable and thus require special safety systems when used at high temperatures. Heat transfer oils cost about $0.77/kg ($0.35/lb).

Water has been studied for many central receiver applications and is the heat transfer fluid used in many power tower plants. Maximum temperature applications are around 540°C (1000°F) where the pressure must be about 10 MPa (1450 psi) to produce a high boiling temperature. Freeze protection must be provided for ambient temperatures less than 0°C (32°F). The water used in the receiver must be highly deionized to prevent scale buildup on the inner walls of the receiver heat transfer surfaces. However, its cost is lower than that of other heat transfer fluids. Use of water as a high-temperature storage medium is difficult because of the high pressures involved.

Nitrate salt mixtures can be used as both a heat transfer fluid and a storage medium at temperatures of up to 565°C (1050°F). However, most mixtures currently being considered freeze at temperatures around 140 to 220°C (285 to 430°F) and thus must be heated when the system is shut down. These mixtures have good storage potential because of their high volumetric heat capacity. The cost of nitrate salt mixtures is around $0.33/kg ($0.15/lb), making them an attractive heat transfer fluid candidate.

Liquid sodium can also be used as both a heat transfer fluid and storage medium, with a maximum operating temperature of 600°C (1112°F). Because sodium is liquid at this temperature, its vapor pressure is low. However, it solidifies at 980°C (208°F), thereby requiring heating on shutdown. The cost of sodium-based systems is higher than the nitrate salt systems since sodium costs about $0.88/kg ($0.40/lb).

For high-temperature applications such as Brayton cycles, the use of air or helium as the heat transfer fluid and operating temperatures of around 850°C (1560°F) at 12 atm. pressure are being proposed. Although the cost of these gases would be low, they cannot be used

for storage and require very large diameter piping and expensive compressors to transport them through the system.

CSP Technologies' Future

The dark areas in Figure 4-15 show where the EU community is planning to install a large number of wind, CSP, and PV power plants. CSP technologies will take a major part in this effort which will bring the CSP industry to a new and much higher level by 2020. This, in addition to plans for many additional GWs of CSP installations in the US and Asia, is a very exciting development which paints a bright picture for the future of CSP technology as a world-class electric power generator.

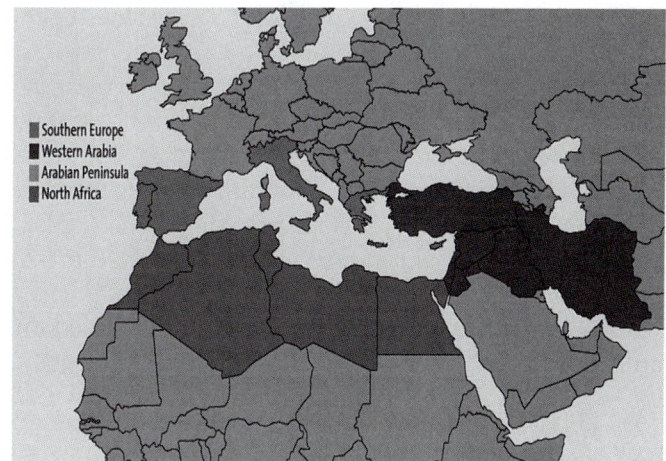

Figure 4-15. Future applications of CSP technologies

We have witnessed the successful development of the CSP industry and have seen the estimates placing it at the top of large-scale power generation. Technological developments and changing socio-economic and political climates make it hard to predict what will happen, but we know that CSP technology is here to stay and will grow steadily.

Now we'll look at the other branch of solar power generating technology; solar photovoltaics. CSP equipment first converts sunlight into heat, which is then used to heat houses or generate electricity. Photovoltaic (PV) power generating equipment, on the other hand, is designed and built to capture and convert sunlight *directly* into electricity.

PV TECHNOLOGIES

Photovoltaic (PV) energy is the energy created by sunlight in devices that are designed to capture and convert it into useful electric energy. Thus generated electric power is in the form of direct current (DC).

Introduction

Photovoltaic (PV) power generation is the most promising area of the renewable energy industry. This is due mostly to the versatility of the basic PV power generator—the solar cell and module. There are many types of solar cells and panels that can be made in different shapes and forms to fit different applications. These can then be installed and used in very small to very large power fields.

In addition, PV power has an advantage over wind power, hydropower, geo-power, and solar thermal power, since these require large turbines and electric generators with many moving parts. The turbines operate at very high temperature, and require a lot of cooling water. They are also noisy, dirty, and require significant maintenance and costly replacements.

In contrast, PV power generators (solar cells, modules, and systems) are quiet, clean, and have no moving parts (unless mounted on trackers). They generate DC electric power that can be used as is, or converted to AC for use in the power grid.

The major components of PV power generation are: PV cells, PV modules, PV arrays, and PV systems.

1. An individual PV (solar) cell is usually a small device, about 4 to 6 inches square, typically producing about 2-3 watts of power each. There are other sizes and shapes for different use. The cells can be made out of silicon, or different thin films deposited on glass, as we will see later in this text.

2. PV modules are used to boost the power output of the PV cells. In the modules, the cells are connected together to form electric circuits that can produce 100-200 Watts and more of DC power.

3. A PV module alone cannot produce enough power for most practical uses. Because of that they are also connected with each other to form even larger units called arrays. Each array can generate 10-100 kW or more of electric power.

4. The arrays can be interconnected to produce even more power. When several arrays are interconnected and the resulting power output is sent to a battery or inverter, then we have a PV system (see note), which can be built to meet almost any electric power need, small or large.

NOTE: PV systems also include structures to support and point them toward the sun, as well as other components that take the direct-current electricity produced by modules and "condition" that electricity, usually by converting it to alternate-current electricity. These additional items are referred to as the balance of system (BOS) components.

Combining modules with BOS components creates an entire PV system. This system is usually everything needed to meet a particular energy demand, such as powering a water pump, the appliances and lights in a home—the electrical requirements of a community. Very often a PV system is designed, built, and operated to provide a large amount of electricity to the national grid.

The most common commercially available PV products today are crystalline silicon (c-Si) solar cells and modules, and thin film (TF) cells and modules.

As seen in Figure 4-16, there are a number of PV technologies which we will look at in the text below, but in this chapter we will focus on crystalline silicon (c-Si) based materials, wafers, solar cells and modules. We will do this in some detail, because c-Si technology is the most mature and most widely used PV technology today, which dominates the PV markets by far now, and is expected to do so in the foreseeable future.

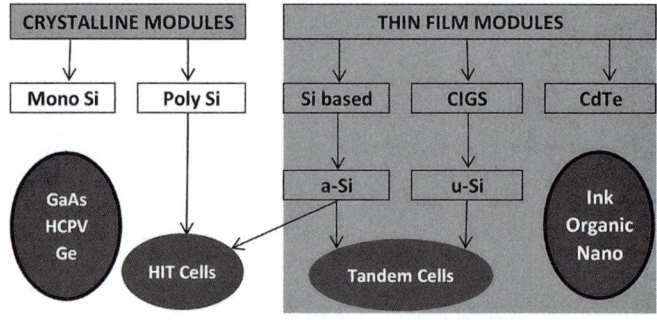

Figure 4-16. Major PV technologies

SILICON PV TECHNOLOGY

Silicon PV is a branch of the solar PV technology which deals with the design, manufacturing, and use of photovoltaic materials, processes, and devices based on the properties of silicon semiconductor material to capture and convert sunlight into electricity.

A number of variations of the materials and properties are in use today, so we will start from the very beginning of the cradle-to-grave lifetime cycle of the silicon devices, which basically consists of:

- Silicon raw material production
  - Mining silicate sands
  - Melting the sands into metallurgical grade (MG) silicon
  - Refining MG silicon into solar grade (SG) silicon
  - Sorting and testing the final SG silicon material

- Solar wafers manufacturing
  - Mono- and poly-crystalline silicon ingots production
  - Slicing the ingots into wafers
  - Testing and sorting
  - Preparing the wafers for processing into solar cells

- Solar cells manufacturing
  - Wafer surface preparation
  - p-n junction creation
  - Metallization
  - Testing and sorting

- Solar modules manufacturing
  - Layout of components
  - Interconnecting the solar cells
  - Lamination
  - Final testing and sorting

In more detail:

SG Silicon Production

Silicon is found in large quantities in nature in the form of sand, or silicon oxide (SiO_2), which actually forms 1/3 of the Earth's crust. Most sand, however, contains so much dirt (like the sand in the deserts) that it is useless for all practical purposes. Silicon is environmentally friendly material, and its waste does not pose any special problems. It can be easily melted, shaped and formed into mono-crystalline or poly-crystalline ingots and wafers. Devices made from silicon can operate at up to 125°C air temperatures (with some loss of efficiency), which allows the use of silicon based semiconductor devices and solar cells even in harsh environments, with some exceptions and restrictions.

The purity of silicon used in semiconductor devices is (at a minimum) 99.99999999%, and somewhat less when used for solar cells. Today's manufacturing operations use 99.999% to 99.9999% pure silicon. The actual number of 9s is used to refer to silicon's quality; i.e., 4 nines, 6 nines etc., and determines the final quality, performance and longevity of the solar cells. Since it is impossible to change the initial silicon material's quality

at a later stage, it is critical that a high quality production starts with high quality (minimum impurities) silicon material.

The basic process for making silicon for manufacturing c-Si PV cells is as follows:

- High purity silica sand found in large quantities in several areas around the world is dug out, sifted and transported for further processing. This process is very similar to the coal surface mining operations we reviewed in the previous chapters, so we won't spend much time on it.

- Mountains of sand are loaded in huge furnaces, where it is melted for removal of the oxygen in the silica molecule through a reaction with carbon (coal or charcoal) added to the mix while heating it to 1500-2000°C in huge electrode-arc type furnaces.

$$SiO_2 + C \rightarrow Si + CO_2$$
$$siO_2 + 2C \rightarrow Si + 2CO$$

- The molten MG Si material is usually treated further for impurities removal by the addition of different additives:

$$SiO_2 + 2SiC + additives \rightarrow 3Si + 2CO$$

The resulting silicon material is metallurgical grade (MG) silicon, still containing a lot of impurities—well over 2-3%—and as such it cannot be used for solar cell manufacturing. At this state it is good for use as an additive in the metallurgical industry only. Additional purification must take place if it is to be used for solar cells, and even more purification is needed if it is to be used in the production of semiconductor devices.

After solidification, the chunks of MG silicon are crushed and shipped to a processing plant for refining, to bring its quality to that needed for manufacturing efficient and reliable solar cells.

- At the refining facility, the MG silicon chunks are reacted with hydrochloric acid (HCl) to make silicon-containing gases:

$$Si + 4HCl \rightarrow SiCl_4 + 2H_2$$
and/or
$$Si + 3HCl \rightarrow SiHCl_3 + H_2$$

The process chemicals go through the distillation and purification processes to obtain and isolate the main silicon-containing gas $SiHCl_3$ trichlorosilane (TCS) which is then purified and sent for preparation of solar grade (SG) silicon material.

The TCS gas is processed in plasma reactors and solidified in the shape of large ingots of SG multi-silicon (poly) as follow:

$$SiCl_4 + 2Zn \rightarrow Si + 2ZnCl_2 \text{ (DuPont process)}$$

or

$$2SiHCl_3 \rightarrow Si + 2HCl + SiCl_3 \text{ (Siemens process)}$$

or

$$4HSiCl_3 \rightarrow 3SiCl_4 + SiH_4, \text{ where } SiH_4 \rightarrow$$
$$Si + 2H_2 \text{ (REC process)}$$

The final product from the refining process is chunks of solar grade (SG) silicon, which are much purer than the MG silicon, but are still not good enough for making solar cells.

- At this point the chunks are crushed, packed and shipped to be melted into high purity doped ingots from which solar wafers will be sliced and processed into solar cells.

Silicon Material Quality

The quality of the SG grade silicon material is extremely important, because it will determine the final quality of the solar cells made from it.

Basically, SG silicon must be pure enough, and the type and quantity of each impurity must be known and controlled, because excess impurities of some types will invariably result in lower efficiency and potentially shorter life span of the cells made from it. This in turn will shorten the life of the PV modules in the field, so a deep understanding of the differences and strict adhesion to quality control procedures by manufacturers is paramount for ensuring the quality of the final product.

Table 4-1 offers a close look at the types and amounts of impurities contained in semiconductor grade silicon (left column), vs. those in MG silicon (right column), and reveals huge differences which translate into drastic differences in quality. Semiconductor grade Si is several times purer than MG Si, which means that a lot of energy, time and effort must be spent on complex processes, to purify it to this degree. Solar grade (SG) c-Si could also benefit from such high purity as that of the semiconductor grade silicon, but the benefits do not justify the steep price increase. Because of that, SG Si is somewhat less pure than its semiconductor grade cousin and is somewhere between the MG and semiconductor grade silicon quality in Table 4-1.

Table 4-1. Quality of different silicon types

Chemical Impurity	Semiconductor Grade Si (ppm)	MG-Si (ppm)
B	4.157	14.548
C	14.264	107.565
O	17.554	66.706
Mg	<0.001	8.204
Al	<0.005	520.458
Si	Matrix	Matrix
P	6.801	21.762
S	<0.044	0.096
K	<0.007	<0.036
Ca	<0.007	44.849
Ti	<0.001	47.526
V	<0.001	143.345
Cr	<0.001	19.985
Mn	<0.001	19.938
Fe	<0.005	553.211
Co	<0.002	0.763
Ni	<0.002	22.012
Cu	<0.001	1.724
Zn	<0.002	0.077
As	<0.002	0.007
Sr	<0.0003	0.353
Zr	<0.0003	2.063
Mo	<0.001	0.790
I	<0.0002	<0.001
Ba	<0.0002	0.266
W	<0.0003	0.024

Some of the impurities play a much larger role in the final quality of solar cells and modules, so when we say that 6 nines SG silicon is suitable for solar cell manufacturing we must also qualify the actual types and amounts of the different impurities; i.e., if the amount of some harmful metal impurities is too high, the final product might be of questionable quality as well.

Once the SG silicon has passed the final tests, it is ready to be melted and shaped into ingots, and then sliced into mono- or poly-crystalline wafers suitable for making silicon solar cells.

Silicon Wafers

The properties and manufacturing process of solar grade wafers, which are used for making solar cells can be divided into two major groups: mono-crystalline and multi-crystalline (poly) silicon solar wafers and cells.

The major types of silicon solar cells are mono-crystalline, also called single crystalline, and multi-crystalline (poly). Figure 4-17a is a graphic representation of silicon material processed by "pulling" as a single crystal (mono-crystalline) material via the so-called Czochralski process, while 4-17b is silicon wafer produced by melting silicon chunks in a crucible, thus the imperfections can be easily seen.

a) Mono-crystalline silicon wafer

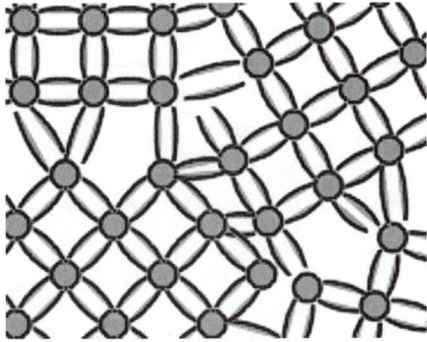

b) Multi-crystalline silicon wafer

Figure 4-17. Silicon wafers

Mono-crystalline Silicon Wafers

Mono-crystalline silicon (also called mono-silicon, single-crystal, mc-Si, or sc-Si) wafers are produced by melting purified solar grade (SG) silicon in special furnaces, called *ingot pullers*, where a long, cylindrical silicon ingot is "pulled" up from the melt as a single crystal silicon. This process of mono-silicon production is known as the Czochralski (CZ) method. The CZ ingot, 4-, 5-, or 6-inch diameter, is sliced into thin wafers which are then processed into solar cells.

This and similar mono-silicon ingot production methods (like float zone, or FZ) are sophisticated and expensive processes, so the single crystal wafers and cells tend to be more efficient and more expensive than their close relative, the polycrystalline solar wafers and solar cells. The efficiency increase is due to the uniform structure of the single crystal materials which facilitates the photoelectric effect and provides a good level of reliability and longevity.

mc-Si wafers are cut from cylindrical ingots and then squared, a process which creates substantial waste of silicon material. Their uneven shape also leaves unused gaps in the PV modules' surface which lowers their overall efficiency.

Like most other types of solar cells, these also suffer from a reduction in output at temperatures over 25°C. A significant drop of output can be expected, especially at very high (desert) temperatures, but the drop is actually much lower than that of poly-crystalline silicon cells and some other types of solar cells. For this and other reasons we consider mono-crystalline silicon cells to be the most efficient and reliable PV devices available today.

Mono-crystalline solar panels are first-generation solar technology and have been around a long time, providing evidence of their durability and longevity. Several of the early mc-Si PV modules installed in the 1970s are still producing electricity, albeit at reduced output levels, and some have even withstood the rigors of space travel.

NOTE: Mono-silicon materials and processes are well understood, since they have been used for over half a century in the semiconductor industry. Manufacturers of solar wafers, cells and modules benefit tremendously from the wealth of knowledge and practical experience of semiconductor manufacturers, and in some cases work together with them to advance the state of the art. This is a great advantage over most other types of solar cells and modules which must be developed without specialized outside help.

Multi-crystalline Silicon (poly) Wafers

Multi-crystalline silicon (poly) material is produced by melting solar grade (SG) silicon in a large cube-like crucible. The solidified cube of poly material is split into 4-, 5-, or 6-inch-wide and 18- to 36-inch-long bars which are then sliced into thin wafers. Since it is not "pulled" as a single-crystal but rather as randomly mixed columns, the resulting material and the wafers sliced from it, look non-uniform with visible boundaries in the bulk which play a significant role in the solar cells' performance.

Large randomly oriented grains (in asymmetric rows and columns) crisscross the silicon bulk giving the poly wafers their distinguished and esthetically pleasing multi-color look. This segmentation, on the other hand, significantly reduces the efficiency of the solar cells made from it. The segmentation (grains) can be thought of as separate pieces of single crystal silicon, scattered randomly in the bulk and separated from each other by boundaries.

These are actual physical and electrical barriers which create obstacles in the operation of these types of solar cells. The boundaries prevent electrons and holes from freely moving across, and contribute to the recombination process, which minimizes the photoelectric effect, thus reducing the efficiency of the solar cells.

The grains are usually so large that they extend all through the wafers when cut from the solidified silicon block. The incorporation of hydrogen during device processing plays an important role in passivating the inter-grain boundaries, which contributes to improving the efficiency and operating stability of the solar cells. Other techniques are also used to boost the efficiency and reliability of poly-silicon solar cells, but they increase the cost of the final product, so their use is limited according to specific needs.

The grain boundaries create a number of effects manifested as sub-grain boundaries, slip deformations, and twinning. These are basically additional lower level boundaries in the form of single dislocations or web of dislocations with different orientation, Burger's vectors and similar abnormalities, all of which complicate the photoelectric process, reduce the efficiency of the solar cells, and contribute to latent failure mechanisms.

Advantages of using multi-crystalline growth over the Czochralski (single crystal silicon) method include:

a. Lower capital costs,

b. Higher throughput,

c. Less sensitivity to the quality of the silicon feedstock used, and

d. Higher packing density of cells to make a module because of the initial square or rectangular shape of the material prior to final wafering and processing.

Silicon Wafers Manufacturing Process

Silicon solar wafers are made out of solar grade (SG) silicon, via melting the chunks and "pulling" or "casting" the molten material, thus creating mono, or poly Si materials respectively. The resulting material is cooled down and sliced into very thin, 200-300 microns (0.007"-.0.012") slices (wafers). These wafers are then processed into solar cells.

The solar wafers manufacturing process sequence below was used by Alpha Solarco, Inc., during the late 1990s at their solar cells manufacturing facility in Phoenix, Arizona. Variations of this process are used presently.

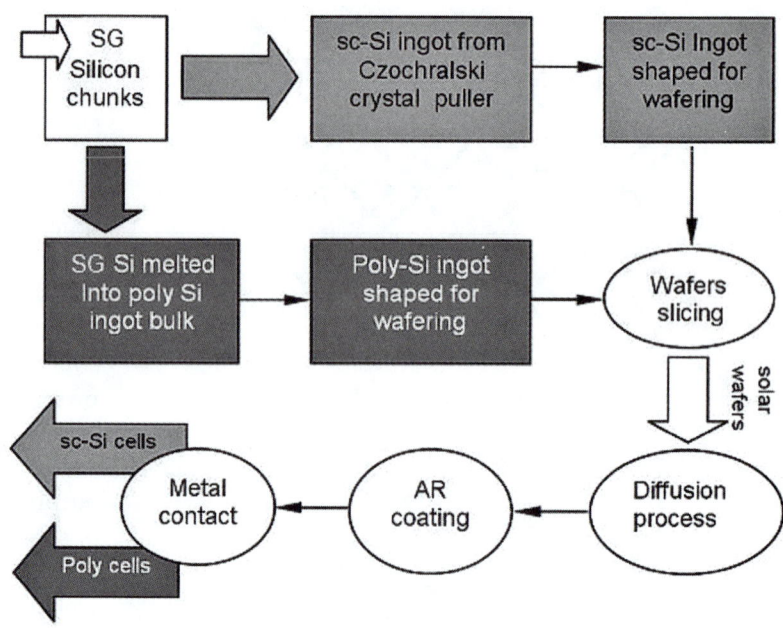

Figure 4-18. Si solar wafers manufacturing process

Multi-crystalline (Poly) Silicon Wafers Manufacturing Process

The polysilicon wafers manufacturing sequence is as follow:

1. *Sorting, Inspection and Cleaning the SG Silicon*

Silicon chunks, purchased directly from the manufacturers or indirectly from dealers, are received, documented, inspected, sorted by size, and tested for resistivity, metal and other contaminants.

2. *Bulk Silicon Cleaning and Surface Prep*

The sorted Si chunks which pass the initial QC procedures are sent into the wet chemistry room for cleaning with detergents and etching with acids. This is needed in order to remove all dirt, oils and impurities from the material's surface. The chunks are then rinsed, dried and taken to the wafer process room for melting in the poly Si ingot HEM (heat exchange method) furnace.

3. *Prepare Ingot Crucible*

The HEM furnace uses a special crucible to melt the silicon in. Before loading the crucible, its inner surface is spray coated with a proprietary solution. This eliminates possible chemical reactions between the silicon material and the silica crucible in the HEM furnace at high temperatures. After application of the coating, the crucible is baked in a kiln for 24 hours to dry the sprayed solution. It is then ready for loading in the HEM furnace.

4. *Load HEM Furnace*

Assemble graphite support plates around the sides of the crucible before loading it into the furnace. Load crucible by adding 80 KG of silicon meltstock and calculated amount of dopant (Boron salt). After loading, clean exterior of furnace, control module, and area adjacent to furnace from any residue or overspray.

5. *Grow Ingot*

Apply vacuum to furnace and backfill with Argon gas. Re-apply vacuum to ensure that all moisture has been eliminated inside the furnace chamber. The control instrumentation on the HEM furnace is designed to automatically control the ingot growth process. No manual intervention is allowed during the entire process, except in emergency.

6. *Cool and Remove Ingot*

Ingot is annealed prior to cool down. Annealing is achieved by maintaining a furnace temperature slightly below the melting temperature of silicon. Stress relief of the ingot is achieved over a 12-hour period. Ingot is then removed from the crucible and ready for cutting. Cutting is done in two steps, block sawing and wafer slicing.

7. *Block Sawing*

After growing an ingot, its surfaces must be shaved square using a special ingot saw. The smooth squared block of silicon is then sectioned into bars that measure 10 cm x 10 cm or as desired and variable length. Some additional proprietary processing of the ingot sides follows. It is intended to reduce some of the surface damage of the ingot and the resulting wafers.

8. *Wafer Slicing*

Wire saws are used to slice the wafers from the bars. Each bar is attached to a glass sheet with a proprietary epoxy adhesive which is dried a minimum of 24 hours. This glass/silicon bar is then attached to a metal work piece (holder) and placed under the cutting wires of the wire saw. The cutting oil and abrasive mix must be prepared and properly mixed in the mixer of the slurry tank at the bottom of the wire saw. Wafers are sliced to the desired thickness and removed from the wire saw with the holder.

9. *Pre-cleaning*

After slicing, the wafers are separated from the holder and loaded into cassettes. They are then taken to a special degreasing area for gross removal of surface contamination, prior to cleaning. Cutting oils and abrasive residues left on the wafers' surfaces from the slicing process are properly and thoroughly removed via proprietary cleaning formulations. The wafers are stored in a water tank to keep them wet.

10. *Wafers Uniformity Test*

Some wafers are taken out of the batch, cleaned thoroughly and tested at five different locations on the surface of each wafer to ensure that the desired degree of thickness uniformity and resistivity has been achieved by the slicing process. Additional inspection and testing procedures are carried out to ensure the quality of the wafers prior to processing into solar cells.

11. *Wafer Storage*

The wafers are loaded in cassettes for ease of handling during the rest of the processing sequence. The cassettes loaded with wafers are stored in water tanks where they are kept until taken for final cleaning.

12. *Process Controls and Quality Control*

Special instrumentation and procedures are used at each process step to ensure proper processing and to check tight adherence to the specs.

13. *DI Water System*

A special deionized (DI) water generating station is used to make DI water for rinsing the wafers. Proper rinsing of the silicon material (chunks) and the resulting wafers is accomplished, leaving the wafers with clean surfaces.

14. *Clean Room*

The critical steps of the solar cells wafer and cells manufacturing process are executed in a specially designed area, called a "clean room." It is built and operated to keep any environmental disturbances such as wind, humidity, heat and cold, particles, etc. isolated from the work environment. Special HEPA filters deliver purified and deionized air, and this way the solar cells are processed under near-ideal conditions and without any outside contamination.

Mono-crystalline Silicon Wafers

The monocrystalline silicon wafers' manufacturing sequence is similar to the above, except that the ingot furnace is quite different:

1. Clean the ingot puller furnace and process crucible.

2. Fill crucible with silicon material and add exact amount of doping chemical. **NOTE**: Crucible surface tends to dissolve, so it must be made of pure silica and kept at maximum cleanliness possible.

3. Melt the silicon chunks in the crucible and keep the temperature close to the melting point. **NOTE**: Convection in the silicon melt is suppressed by correct application of magnetic fields around the crucible. The strength and duration of these fields is a proprietary know-how.

4. Insert the silicon seed crystal into the melt and stabilize the temperature.

5. Start withdrawing the seed crystal slowly by rotating the seed crystal and the crucible. **NOTE**: This process step is proprietary for each operation, but basically, fast withdrawal during the initial stages is needed to reduce the diameter of the growing crystal a few mm. This is needed to ensure that most seed-crystal induced dislocations will be removed.

6. The withdrawal rate must be decreased now to increase the ingot diameter slightly above the desired size. **NOTE**: The impurity concentration (including dopants and oxygen) in the melt will change due to segregation, and the resulting crystal properties will change too, usually by increasing impurities concentration from top to bottom of the ingot. The temperature profile will vary at this stage and must be adjusted. The homogeneity of the crystal depends on the correct temperature and speed of rotation and withdrawal regimes. These parameters are also proprietary, and not much free information can be found.

7. When almost all silicon has left the crucible, the ingot is complete. **NOTE**: Some molten silicon must be left in the crucible, because it is where the impurities are concentrated due to their low segregation coefficients.

8. Pull the ingot out, but beware because the thermal shock introduces temperature gradients which cause stress gradient, and dislocations are nucleated into the crystal. **NOTE**: The new dislocations will interact with previous dislocations, causing serious damage. The withdrawal rate at this point is critical and is usually gradually increased. This

leads to a reduced diameter in cone-like shape of the tail end of the ingot.

9. Remove the ingot slowly and place it on a suitable clean surface for cooling.

10. Shape the ingot on a special lathe to give it more uniform surface and bring it to the exact outside diameter—4, 5 or 6″ diameter.

11. Inspect and test the ingot for mechanical defects and chemical impurities.

12. Clean and slice it into wafers of the desired thickness.

13. Inspect, test, sort and pack the wafers.

The resulting mono-crystalline silicon wafers are used for in-house solar cells manufacturing, or are shipped to solar cells and modules manufacturing facilities around the world.

The best quality PV modules made from multi-crystalline silicon generally have efficiencies 3-6% less than those made of mono-crystalline silicon and cost approximately 15-25% less to produce.

Silicon Solar Cell Manufacturing Process

Solar cells have been mass manufactured since the 1950s, starting with 1.0″ diameter silicon wafers and 2-3% efficiencies. The energy crisis of the 1970s shifted the attention of the US government and public to PV technologies which allowed the quick development of more efficient solar cells and modules, and the related production equipment and process. Still, the progress was seriously hindered by technological issues such as the small size of the silicon wafers, lack of adequate processing equipment and unresolved issues at the different process steps.

Today there are almost unlimited combinations of different materials, equipment options, processing sequences and techniques which allow cost-effective and efficient manufacturing of solar cells and modules. The manufacturers keep most of their process specifics secret, but the overall equipment configuration, process scheme, and different procedures are unchanged since the 1970s.

Process Considerations

Keeping all functional and operational parameters of the solar cells in mind, design engineers must consider a large number of process and application factors to come up with a practical, efficient, reliable and profitable final product with long lifetime.

Some of the main considerations are as follow:

1. The solar cell's material is of primary consideration. Its electro-mechanical and chemical properties, impurities, availability, price, ease and cost of processing factors are thoroughly evaluated and compared with competing materials and technologies. Starting with high quality silicon, and considering all process materials and related issues is the first and most important job of the design team.

2. Actual solar cell structure and process sequence design considerations include:
   a. Evaluating the quality of cleaning, texturizing, doping, edge etch chemicals, gasses, and related equipment and process steps specs.
   b. Optical losses calculations and AR coating type and process specs.
   c. Selection of materials and processes for metallization of the front and back contacts.
   d. Quality control specs and inspection procedures for all process steps.
   e. In-process and final tests and sorting procedures selection.

3. The actual solar cells and modules manufacturing process is done best by using the most appropriate combination of materials, process equipment, chemicals and other consumables. Adequate knowledge and understanding of the cradle-to-grave process steps is paramount. We need to know all there is to know about:
   a. Silicon making, and ingot pulling or casting
   b. Slicing ingot into wafers, testing and sorting
   c. Wafer surface cleaning and texturing
   d. Diffusion chemicals and processes
   e. Edge isolation (wet chem. or plasma etch)
   f. Anti-reflection coatings and processes
   g. Metallization of front and rear contacts
   h. Testing and sorting of finished solar cells
   i. Stringing and encapsulation of solar cells into PV modules
   j. Final test and packing for shipping

There are a number of different manufacturing, test and quality control procedures, specifications, and instructions that accompany these steps, each of which must be perfectly designed and executed.

Mono-crystalline Silicon Solar Cell Manufacturing Sequence

The basic c-Si solar processing sequence, as used in the late 1990s by an associate company is outlined below. This process, or a variation of it, is used by most world class c-Si PV cells and modules manufacturers today. The major steps are as follow:

Wafers Inspection and Sorting

Wafers are placed on inspection tables and are inspected visually and with optical equipment. Any wafers with visible mechanical defects are rejected. The wafers are then tested with a 4-point probe, and are sorted according to their resistivity. Wafers, or wafer samples are sent to an outside lab for metal and organic contamination analysis. Results from these tests determine the level of quality of the finished cells.

Wafers Cleaning and Etch

The wafers that pass all initial inspections and tests go to the wet cleaning line and are chemically processed in special chemicals where they are cleaned and etched to remove damage and oxide formed on the surface. The wafers are then rinsed with de-ionized (DI) water and dried via spin dryer.

Surface Etch (Chemical Etch)

This process is used only on single-crystal silicon with 1-0-0 orientation. (Polycrystalline wafers cannot be textured, because the different strings of silicon have different orientation and the resulting surface is only partially and unevenly textured, if at all.) A controlled chemical solution (composition, concentration, temperature and time) etches the pyramid-like structures in the wafer surface and the surface takes on a dark-gray appearance. The pyramids blend into each other and block excess light reflection. Each pyramid is approximately 4-10 microns high. This step has critical process parameters. The wafers are then rinsed, spin-dried, and stored in special containers for processing.

NOTE: In a variation of this process, wafers are loaded in a fixture two-by-two with the backs of each pair touching, so that the pyramid structure is formed only on their front surfaces.

Diffusion for P-N Junction Formation

The clean wafers are oven dried, placed in the diffusion furnace at 900-950°C in reactive carrier gasses to impregnate the wafers. $POCl_3$ gas is used for n-type diffusion, which diffuses phosphorous atoms in the wafer's surfaces. This creates a p-n junction in the lightly boron-doped wafers.

NOTE: This method is easier to control and has more uniform distribution of dopant than using the spray-on diffusion liquid and belt furnace diffusion process used by many companies today. This step has critical process parameters, so any compromise will be reflected in the cells' overall performance and longevity. In a variation of this process, wafers are loaded in a fixture two-by-two with the backs of each pair touching, so that the diffusion layer is formed only, or mostly, on their front surfaces. This facilitates the processing of the back surface later on.

Mass production solar cell operations use a different method in which the wafers are sprayed with a dopant chemical and run through a conveyor belt type furnace, where the dopant is diffused in the wafers' surface. Both methods have advantages and disadvantages.

Plasma Etch for Removal of Edge Layer (diffusion etc.)

The diffusion process implants P dopant in the wafers' side edges, causing an electrical short circuit between the top and bottom (negative and positive) surfaces of the cell, so it is necessary to remove the dopant with a wet chemistry or plasma etch. Wafers are coin-stacked and etched for a brief period in an RF plasma etch reactor; only the edges of the wafer are exposed to the plasma which removes the diffusion coating.

Wafers are then etched gently in a bath of dilute hydrofluoric acid to remove any oxides formed during the plasma etch step, rinsed with DI water, and finally spin dried.

Anti-reflective Coating

AR coating is deposited on the front surface of the wafers. The purpose of the AR coating is to reducing the amount of sunlight reflected from the finished cell surface. The AR coating is deposited via chemical vapor deposition (CVD) or by spraying the chemicals on the wafers and then baking. Both methods achieve similar outcome of enhancing the solar cells' output and giving them the distinctive dark blue color (for poly solar cells).

NOTE: Different manufacturers deposit and fire the AR coating using different process parameters and sequence order. This is an important process, nevertheless, so its proper design and execution will determine the final, most important aesthetic and performance aspects of the cells.

Printing (Metallization)

Several screen printing steps are used to apply the metallization on the front and back of the wafers. First,

silver paste is printed on the top surface which then becomes the front metal pattern (top contacts, or fingers). The paste is dried and the wafers are flipped for printing the back surface with aluminum paste. After drying, silver paste is printed in special slots in the dried aluminum and the wafers are then transported into the firing furnace.

Metal Firing

Metalized on both sides, wafers are run slowly through an IR-heated furnace where the metal pastes on the top and bottom sides of the wafers diffuse into the substrate, to make an electric contact with the p-n junction and the back surface. This step has critical process parameters.

NOTE: The firing of the front contacts is a very delicate process, where time and temperature are controlled to achieve the desired depth of penetration of the metal into the silicon surface. The depth of penetration determines the electro-mechanical properties of the finished cell. Specially designed automated printing-firing equipment is available for more precise and consistent process control.

Inspection and Quality Control

Solar wafers and cells are inspected and tested at several stages of the process sequence. This is done by eye inspection, using magnification and other instrumentation. Electrical tests are also performed at some steps of the process. The final inspection is the most important step and must be performed by well trained and experienced operators.

Cell Flash Testing and Sorting

A certain percent of the completed wafers are placed on a test stand in the solar simulator and are illuminated for a period of time. I/V curve is generated for each cell and the output data are used to sort the cells into groups according to the I/V curve characteristics, prior to soldering and lamination into modules.

Cell Storage

The cells are finally loaded into cassettes, or coin-stacked (with protective material in between) and packed for ease of handling, transportation, or storage prior to laminating into solar modules or shipping to another location.

c-Si Solar Cells Structure and Function

Crystalline silicon (c-Si) solar cells are relatively simple in design at first glance, but their physical and chemical composition, structure, and electrical properties are quite complex.

We will take a closer look at the c-Si solar cell's structure to get a good understanding of the different aspects of its function. We will also review the major issues and failure mechanisms related to its manufacturing, installation and operation.

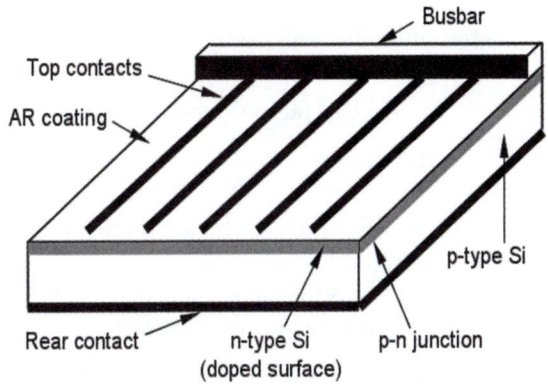

Figure 4-19. Silicon solar cell

The p-n Junction

The p-n junction is the engine of the silicon solar cells. It is an integral part of the solar cell operation, since it is where the photoelectric process starts and where the electric current is generated, so let's take a close look at it.

Figure 4-20 shows a cross section of a solar cell with its top surface (N-type region) on the right-hand side and the bottom (P-type region) on the left. The p-n junction is in the middle and represents an electro-chemical boundary between the P and N regions. The N region and the resulting p-n junction are created during the diffusion process by doping the N side (usually the top of the wafer) with phosphorous or other

such element, thus saturating a very shallow area (less than a micron) below the top surface of the cell with phosphorous atoms. These atoms have excess electrons, which are loosely attached and are readily knocked out to facilitate the electric power generation, if and when energized by sunlight.

The p-n junction is located at the border line between the phosphorus saturated area and the original silicon bulk (P type region) which was very lightly doped with boron (or similar chemical atoms) during the final silicon ingot melting process. The P region will provide the holes (+ charge) when the electron-hole pairs are broken by the incoming sunlight and the electrons extracted during the photoelectric effect.

When at rest, the p-n junction and the areas around it are static with no meaningful activities in or across them. When photons from sunlight with proper energy levels impinge onto the solar cell surface, they penetrate the cell material and impact onto the electrons (in the electron-hole pairs) thus transferring energy to them and breaking the electron-hole pairs. This creates free electrons (–) which start moving around, while the holes (+) from the corresponding electron-hole pairs are mostly left in their original place. Thin areas on both sides of the p-n junction, called the "depletion" region effectively separate the holes from the electrons which are forced towards the N-type region and are finally extracted from the cell as electric current.

The constant movement of electrons back and forth across the p-n junction and through the layers is quite complex, but the final and practical result of it is the creation of DC electric current which flows in an outside circuit attached to the cell. A large part of the electrons do leave the cell through the metal fingers and bars on the N-type side (usually on top of the solar cell), and if we close the circuit, electric current will flow through it.

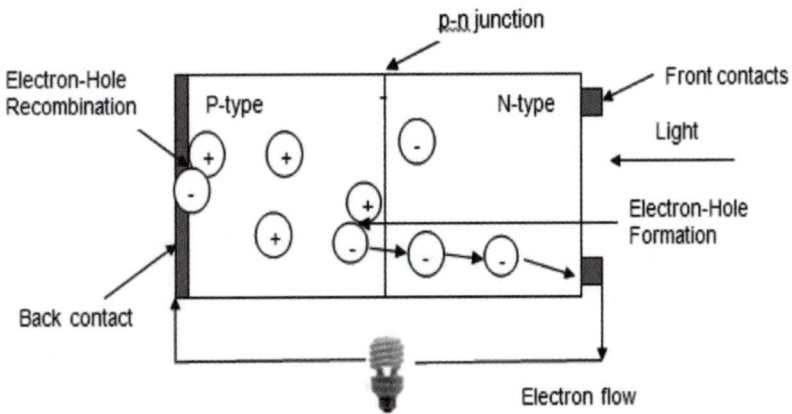

Figure 4-20. The p-n junction function

The electrons in the outside circuit will re-enter the cell via the back side metallization on the P-type side of the cell. Here they will recombine with excess holes in the region and the process repeats indefinitely, or at least while there is enough sunlight to keep it going.

The electron flow provides the current (I) in Amperes and the cell's electric field creates a potential, or voltage (V) in Volts. With both current and voltage above zero we have power (P) in Watts, which is a product of the two and which is what we use to define the PV cells and modules power output.

$$P_{Watts} = I_{Amperes} * V_{Volts}$$

When an external load (such as an electric bulb or a battery) is connected between the front and back contacts of the cell, DC electricity flows through the cell and the external circuit, and powers the load connected to the closed external circuit.

NOTE: Remember that the actual electric current of the external circuit flows in the opposite direction of the electron flow.

Power Generation

Solar cells are characterized by the power they generate, which is at maximum when the current and voltage are at their maximum levels. This can happen only when the cell is fully operational (no defects), and receives maximum solar insolation.

$$P_{max} = I_{max} * V_{max}$$

With these terms at zero, the conditions

$$V = Voc/I = 0 \text{ and } V = 0/I = Isc$$

also represent zero power.

A combination of maximum current and maximum voltage maximizes the generated power and is called the "maximum power point" (MPP).

$$MPP = I_{max} * V_{max}$$

So the MPP of a solar cell with 3.0 A current and 0.5 V voltage would be 1.5 W. A 100 pc. PV module made out of these solar cells connected in series would generate 150 Wp under full solar insolation of 1000 W/m²

The solar conversion efficiency η of a PV cell or module is used most commonly to express and compare performance.

The efficiency is given by:

$$\eta = Voc * Isc * FF/P$$

Where:

Voc is the open circuit voltage (the voltage generated when the load resistance is infinite, or there is no resistance),

Isc is the short circuit current (the current generated when the load resistance is zero,

FF is the fill-factor, calculated as follows:

$$FF\% = \frac{I_{max} * V_{max} \text{ (actual measurements)}}{MPP \text{ (maximum obtainable power)}}$$

This is simply the ratio of the actual measurements (Voc and Isc generated by the cell under the specific testing conditions) divided by the maximum power the cell can generate. In other words, the efficiency is basically the ratio of the amount of power a solar cell or module could produce vs. the total amount of power contained in the incoming sunlight and how efficiently the cell converts it into electric power.

So, if a PV module with 1.0 m² active surface area is rated at 15% efficiency which is average for c-Si PV modules, we can quickly deduct that it theoretically could produce 150 Watts DC power under 1000 W/m² solar insolation (its maximum power). So if it generates 50 V and 3 A, then its FF will be 1. If it produces 50 V and only 2 A (or 100 W), then its FF will be (50 * 2)/150 W, or FF = 0.67.

It's a mouthful of concepts, but a good simplified description of the major practical effects of solar power generation which are the foundation of solar cells' and modules' ability to convert sunlight into useful DC power.

Table 4-2. Typical silicon solar cell specifications

Silicon Solar Cell Specifications	
Material:	Mono-Crystalline Silicon
Size:	4" diameter
Voltage:	0.55V
Current:	0.275-0.33 A
Voltage (load):	0.484V
Current (load):	0.250-0.275 A
Light Level:	1 Full Sun, based on STC (standard test conditions)
STC:	1,000 W/m², 250C temp.
Heat Effect:	0.5% efficiency drop/0C
Degradation:	1% drop of output per year

Note that:

- The voltage output is a constant 0.5-06V per unit, regardless of the type and size of the silicon solar cells.
- The amperage will vary depending on the type and size of the cell; i.e., mono-Si solar cells have 5-10% higher amperage output.
- Elevated cell temperature affects all solar cells (not just silicon) and causes drop in power output according to the type of the cell; i.e., poly-crystalline-Si solar cells exhibit higher drop of efficiency as compared to their first cousins, mono-crystalline Si solar cells.
- All solar cells (not just silicon) lose efficiency with time due to material degradation; i.e., poly-crystalline solar cells are less reliable and tend to degrade more and faster than the mono-crystalline type.

Solar Cell Types

We looked at silicon material and wafer types above, so we just need to remind the reader that the category "crystalline silicon," c-silicon, or c-Si is the general designation of all types of crystalline silicon-based products, including c-Si wafers, solar cells and PV modules. The major types of silicon solar cells follow.

CRYSTALLINE Si	THIN FILMS	OTHER
Mono-Crystalline	Amorphous Si	GaAs
Multi-Crystalline	Epitaxial Si	InP
Micro-Crystalline	CdTe	Other III-V
Super c-Si	CIGS	Germanium
Si Ribbon	Organic/Polymer	CPV Cells

Figure 4-21. Types of solar cells

Mono-crystalline Solar Cells

Single crystal silicon, also called mono-crystalline, mono-silicon, or mono-Si, or mc-Si, or sc-Si is a type of silicon that was grown by the very special and expensive Czochralski (or CZ) method, or via the float zone (FZ) method. Both methods use similar equipment and production methods and end up with the best, most efficient, and much superior silicon material for semiconductor and solar cells device manufacturing.

Solar cells and panels made out of CZ or FZ silicon material have the highest efficiency and longevity of all silicon based PV devices, primarily due to the uniform, stable and predictable nature of the bulk material.

Multi-crystalline Silicon PV Cells

Multi-crystalline silicon is the most widely used silicon material. It is most often called "poly," "poly-silicon," or "polycrystalline" silicon (which is what we will call it in this text too) because it consists of many (poly) strings instead of one single crystal.

Poly is made by melting and casting silicon chunks into large blocks, splitting the blocks into smaller rectangular blocks and slicing these into thin, square-shaped wafers.

Poly-crystalline Silicon Solar Cells

Poly crystalline (note the difference between poly- and multi-crystalline) silicon, which is also called poly silicon, or poly, or pc-Si, is actually a thin film of silicon, deposited via CVD, or LPCVD processes on semiconductor type wafers, to be used as a gate material in MOSFET transistors and CMOS microchips. The solar industry uses similar equipment and processes to deposit very thin layers of silicon (pc-Si and a-Si) onto polysilicon or other substrates. The resulting devices are of lower efficiency, as compared to sc-Si or mc-Si.

NOTE: There is a confusion created by the term "poly" as it is used widely to identify PV cells modules made out of multi-crystalline silicon, instead of its actual use in the semiconductor thin film. Since we cannot change the decades-long use of the term "poly" in the solar industry to identify multi-crystalline silicon products, we will continue using it too with a certain degree of caution and with due clarification when needed.

Amorphous Silicon Solar Cells

Amorphous silicon, also called thin film silicon, alpha silicon, or a-Si, is used in p-i-n type solar cells. Typical a-Si modules include front side glass, TCO film, thin film silicon, back contact, polyvinyl butyral (PVB) encapsulant and back side glass. a-Si has been used to power calculators for some time now, mostly because it is easily and cheaply deposited on any substrate.

Micro-crystalline Silicon Solar Cells

Micro crystalline silicon, also called nano-crystalline silicon, uc-Si, or nc-Si, is a form of silicon in its allotropic form, very similar to a-Si. nc-Si has small grains of crystalline silicon within the amorphous phase, and if grown properly can have higher electron mobility due to the presence of the silicon crystallites. It also shows increased absorption in the red and infrared wavelengths.

Super Mono-crystalline Silicon

This is a new purer type of silicon with more perfect crystalline structure, which exhibits reduced phonon-phonon and phonon-electron interactions. This phenomenon increases certain transport properties, resulting in 60% better room temperature thermal conductivity than natural silicon.

In this text we will focus on mono and poly-crystalline silicon solar cells and modules, their structure, function and the related properties and issues.

CRYSTALLINE-SI PV MODULES

A PV module consists of a number of interconnected solar cells (typically 36 to 72 connected in series for battery charging), and many more for large-scale applications. Individual solar cells are soldered in strings and encapsulated into a single, hopefully long-lasting unit simply because PV modules cannot be disassembled for repairs. The main purpose for encapsulating a set of electrically connected solar cells into a module is to protect them from the harsh environment in which they are going to operate.

Solar cells are relatively thin and fragile and are prone to mechanical damage due to vibration or impact unless well protected. In addition, the metal grid on the top and bottom surfaces of the solar cells, the wires interconnecting the individual solar cells, as well as the soldered junctions can be corroded by moisture or water vapor entering the module, if the protecting materials are damaged or absent. So the encapsulation: a) provides a manageable package that can be installed in the field, b) prevents mechanical damage to the solar cells, and c) prevents water or water vapor from penetrating the module and corroding the electrical contacts and junctions.

Many different types of PV modules exist, and the module structure is often different for different types of solar cells or for different applications. For example, amorphous silicon, and other thin film solar cells are often encapsulated in a flexible array, while crystalline silicon solar cells are usually mounted in rigid metal frames with a glass front surface. Module lifetimes and warranties on bulk silicon PV modules are often 20-25 years, which assumes robust and durable encapsulation of the PV modules. Failing encapsulation will cause performance degradation and failure with time.

Most PV bulk silicon PV modules consist of:

- Glass top surface, which protects the top of the module.
- Top encapsulant, which protects the top side of the solar cells.
- String of PV cells, which provide the DC power.
- Back encapsulant, which protects the back side of the solar cells.
- Back cover, which protects the back of the module.
- Metal frame, which is wrapped around the outer edge of the modules to protect the sides of the module.

In most modules, the top surface is glass, but plastics are used in some cases. The top encapsulant is usually EVA (ethyl vinyl acetate), while the back encapsulant layer is usually Tedlar, or a number of similar plastic and thermo-plastic materials.

Typical module components are:

Cover Glass

The cover of the front surface of a PV module is usually glass with high transmission in the wavelengths which can be used by the solar cells, usually in the range of 350 nm to 1200 nm. In addition, the reflection from the front surface should be low too. While theoretically the reflection could be reduced by applying an anti-reflection coating to the glass surface, in practice these coatings are not robust enough to withstand some of the

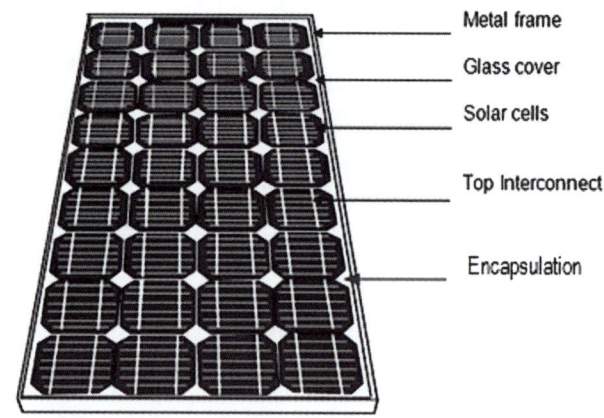

Figure 4-22. Standard silicon PV module, top view

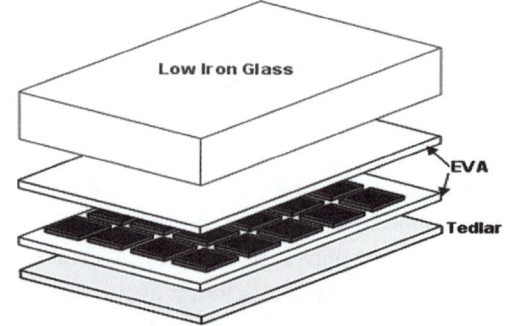

Figure 4-23. Standard silicon PV Module, side view

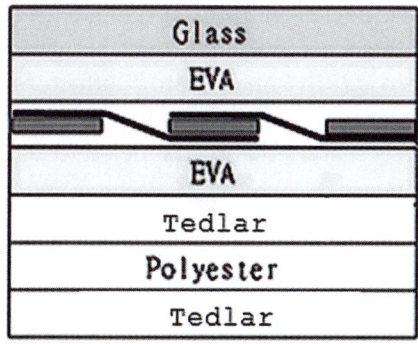

Figure 4-24. PV Modules cross section

conditions in which most PV systems are used.

An alternative technique used to reduce reflection is to "roughen" or texture the top glass surface. In this case dust and dirt are very likely to adhere to the top surface and less likely to be dislodged by wind or rain. These glass surfaces are not "self-cleaning" and the advantages of reduced reflection are quickly outweighed by losses incurred due to increased top surface soiling. Texturing the inside of the glass is also practiced by some manufacturers, but there are some disadvantages in doing this as well, so the proper glass must be selected according to the module type and designation.

In addition, the top surface should have good safety properties and good impact resistance, should be stable under prolonged UV exposure and should have a low thermal resistivity. There are several choices for a top surface material including acrylic, polymers and glass. Tempered, low iron-content glass is most commonly used as it is low cost, strong, stable, highly transparent, mostly impervious to water and gases, and has good self-cleaning properties. This type of glass is the most stable and trouble-free component of the entire module assembly. It doesn't deteriorate easily regardless of the harshness of the elements, and unless it is broken, it will withstand the test of time for 25-30 years largely unaffected. Once the glass is broken, however, the module must be removed or put on a special maintenance schedule.

Encapsulant

The top encapsulant is a transparent, plastic, material used to provide adhesion between the solar cells, the top surface and the rear surface of the PV module. The encapsulant should remain chemically stable at elevated temperatures and high UV exposure. It should also be optically transparent and should have a low thermal resistance. EVA (ethyl vinyl acetate) is the most commonly used encapsulant material. EVA comes in thin

sheets which are inserted between the solar cells and the top surface and the rear surface. This sandwich is then heated to 150°C to polymerize the EVA and permanently bond the module together. Thus formed, the structure cannot be disassembled without destroying the bond, and with that the encapsulated components.

EVA is responsible for protecting the cells from moisture and reactive species entering the module. Long exposure to UV and IR radiation tends to damage the EVA and it becomes yellow, which reduces its transmittance and reduces the module efficiency. Cracks and pores created in it under long exposure will allow the elements to enter the module and destroy the cells.

The back side encapsulant can be made of different materials that provide good mechanical, and electrical resistance, to keep water out and prevent short circuiting the cells' interconnects by touching the back cover. Tedlar sheet is placed under the cell strings in some modules to provide the needed protection.

Cell Strings

A number of solar cells are interconnected and sealed (laminated) between plastic materials, which insulate them from each other, from the interconnecting wires and from the elements. The cells can be arranged and wired in a number of ways, one of which is shown in Figure 4-25.

Thus generated DC power is extracted from the module via two wires protruding from the module and routed into a junction (or terminal) box which is fitted with connectors for quick interconnect within the other array components.

Back Cover

Most c-Si modules have a thin sheet of aluminum for the back cover, which is screwed into the frame, with the terminal box attached to it. A key character-

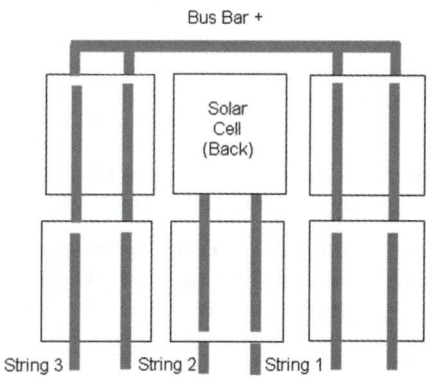

Figure 4-25. Cell stringing

istic of the back cover is that it must have low thermal resistance and that it must prevent the ingress of water or water vapor. In most modules, a thin polymer sheet, typically Tedlar, is used as the rear surface, which provides electrical and environmental protection for the solar cells.

Some PV modules, known as bifacial modules, are designed to accept light from either the front or the rear of the solar cell. In bifacial modules both the front and the rear must be optically transparent, so glass is the preferred material for these.

NOTE: The c-Si module's standard configuration is solid and strong enough to withstand transportation bumps, handling, and high winds during operation. Nevertheless, it is not intended to be used for support, or to be stepped on as some installers do. Even if the glass doesn't break in such case, the weight and impact puts enough stress on the cells to cause micro-cracks and other interruptions, which eventually grow into much bigger problems.

Side Frame

A final structural component of the module is the edging or framing, which provides additional mechanical strength and isolation from the elements. Module edges are sealed by the encapsulant layers in it and by additional adhesive materials for additional protection against the elements. An aluminum frame is then fastened around the edges of the module. The frame structure should be free of projections or pockets which could trap water, dust or other foreign matter.

PV Module Design Considerations

There are a large number of variables to keep in mind when designing or evaluating PV modules. Some of these are listed below.

Cell Packing Density

The packing density of solar cells in a PV module refers to the area of the module that is covered with solar cells compared to that which is blank (between the cells). The packing density affects the output power of the module as well as its operating temperature. The packing density depends on the shape of the solar cells used. For example, single crystalline solar cells are round or semi-square, while multi-crystalline silicon wafers are usually square. Therefore, if single-crystalline solar cells are not cut squarely, the packing density of the resulting module will be lower than that of a multi-crystalline module, because of excess wasted space between the cells.

Sparsely packed cells in a module with a white rear surface can also provide marginal increases in output via the "zero depth concentrator" effect. Some of the light striking regions of the module between cells and cell contacts is scattered and channeled to active regions of the module.

Power Output

While the voltage from the PV module is determined mostly by the number of solar cells, the current from the module depends primarily on the size of the solar cells and also on their efficiency. At AM 1.5 and under optimum tilt conditions, the current density from a commercial solar cell is approximately 30 to 36 mA/cm^2. Single-crystal solar cells are often 100cm^2, giving a total current of about 3.5 A from each cell.

Poly-crystalline silicon modules have comparatively larger size individual solar cells but a lower current density. However, there is a large variation in the size of poly-crystalline silicon solar cells, and therefore the current will vary. Current from a module is not affected by temperature in the same way that voltage is, but instead depends heavily on the tilt angle of the module and the sunlight intensity reaching its surface.

If all the solar cells in a module have identical electrical characteristics, and they all experience the same insolation and temperature, then all the cells will be operating at exactly the same current and voltage. In this case, the IV curve of the PV module has the same shape as that of the individual cells, except that the voltage and current are increased proportionally to the number of cells in the module. If one single cell in the module, however, has different electrical characteristics (i.e. higher resistivity) then the entire module is affected, and will most likely underperform down to the level of the failing cell. The different cell might also overheat and fail under the increased load, thus making the entire module fail.

Because not all cells are made equal and do not perform exactly the same, they should be tested and sorted before stringing and encapsulating into finished PV modules.

This is a tricky operation, because cells tested under "normal" or "standard" test conditions in-house, often perform totally differently in the field. This anomaly could be caused by difference in materials quality and/or improper process execution. In all cases, the established manufacturers who have long experience with solar cells, testing and field applications, have proven ways to sort and assemble the cells to eliminate or reduce this type of field problem.

Always, proper design calculations and tests must be executed, to create an efficient cell and module design.

The equation for the module power under normal operating conditions used to evaluate the different cells and modules is:

$$I_T = M * I_L - M * I_0 \left[\exp\left(\frac{q\frac{V_t}{N}}{nkT} \right) - 1 \right]$$

where:

I_T is the total current from the circuit;
N is the number of cells in series;
M is the number of cells in parallel;
V_T is the total voltage from the circuit;
I_0 is the saturation current from a single solar cell;
I_L is the short-circuit current from a single solar cell;
n is the ideality factor of a single solar cell; and
q, k, and T are respective constants

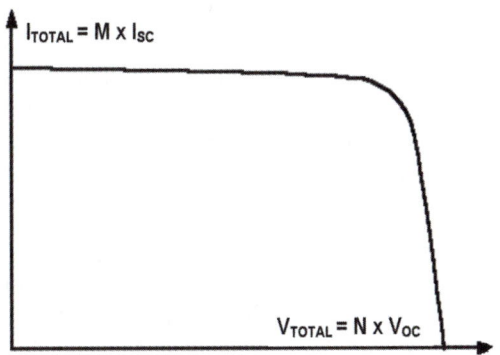

Figure 4-26.
I-V curve for N cells in series x M cells in parallel.

This formula can also be used to predict the behavior of different cells in modules in the field. The situation changes drastically under not-so-normal field conditions, such as operation under high desert sunlight. Although there are formulas to calculate the temperature effect (as discussed in more detail in this writing), experience shows that elevated temperatures and humidity create havoc through individual cells affecting them differently and causing them to behave differently over time. This in turn results in unpredictable behaviors of the affected modules, and these anomalies often lead to reduced power output and short lifetime.

Mismatch of Series Connected Cells

As most PV modules are series-connected, series mismatches are the most common type of mismatch encountered. Of the two simplest types of mismatch

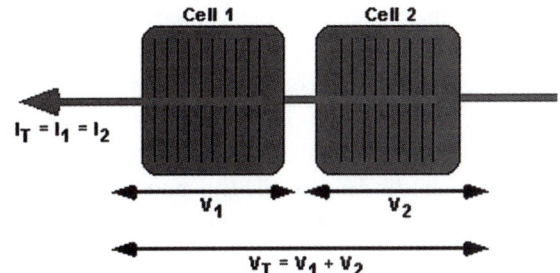

Figure 4-27. Cells in series

considered (mismatch in short-circuit current or in open-circuit voltage), a mismatch in the short-circuit current is more common, as it can easily be caused by shading part of the module. This type of mismatch is also the most severe.

For two cells connected in series, the current through the two cells is the same. The total voltage produced is the sum of the individual cell voltages. Since the current must be the same, a mismatch in current means that the total current from the configuration is equal to the lowest current.

Open circuit voltage mismatch—A mismatch in the open-circuit voltage of series-connected cells is a relatively benign form of mismatch. So, at short circuit current, the overall current from the PV module is unaffected. At the maximum power point, the overall power is reduced because the poor cell is generating less power. As the two cells are connected in series, the current through the two solar cells is the same, and the overall voltage is found by adding the two voltages at a particular current.

Short-circuit current mismatch—A mismatch in the short-circuit current of series connected solar cells can, depending on the operating point of the module and the degree of mismatch, have a drastic impact on the PV module. As shown in Figure 4-27, at open-circuit, the impact of a reduced short-circuit current is relatively minor. There is a minor change in the open-circuit voltage due to the logarithmic dependence of open-circuit voltage on short-circuit current. However, as the current through the two cells must be the same, the overall current from the combination cannot exceed that of the poor cell.

Therefore, the current from the combination cannot exceed the short-circuit current of the poor cell. At low voltages where this condition is likely to occur, the extra current-generating capability of the good cells is not dissipated in each individual cell (as would normally occur at short circuit), but instead is dissipated in the poor cell.

Overall, in a series-connected configuration with current mismatch, severe power reductions are experienced if the poor cell produces less current than the maximum power current of the good cells. Also, if the combination is operated at short circuit or low voltages, the high power dissipation in the poor cell can cause irreversible damage to the module.

Hot-spot Heating

This condition occurs when there is one low-current solar cell in a string of at least several high short-circuit current solar cells, as shown in Figure 4-28.

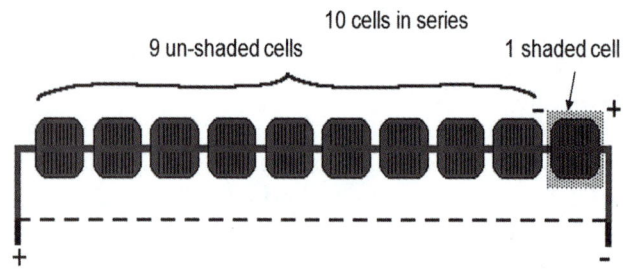

Figure 4-28. Cell shading

If the terminals of the module are connected (module Isc), the power from all unshaded cells is dissipated across the shaded cell, and might result in overheating.

One shaded cell in a string reduces the current through the good cells, causing the good cells to produce higher voltages that can often reverse bias the bad cell. If the operating current of the overall series string approaches the short-circuit current of the "bad" cell, the overall current becomes limited by the bad cell. The extra current produced by the good cells then forward biases the good solar cells. If the series string is short circuited, then the forward bias across all of these cells reverses the bias of the shaded cell. Hot-spot heating occurs when a large number of series connected cells cause a large reverse bias across the shaded cell, leading to large dissipation of power in the poor cell.

Essentially the entire generating capacity of all the good cells is dissipated in the poor cell. The enormous power dissipation occurring in a small area results in local overheating, or "hot-spots," which in turn leads to destructive effects, such as cell or glass cracking, melting of solder or degradation of the solar cell.

Bypass Diodes

The destructive effects of hot-spot heating may be circumvented through the use of a bypass diode. A bypass diode is connected in parallel, but with opposite polarity, to a solar cell. Under normal operation, each

solar cell will be forward biased and therefore the bypass diode will be reverse biased and will effectively be an open circuit. However, if a solar cell is reverse biased due to a mismatch in short-circuit current between several series connected cells, then the bypass diode conducts, thereby allowing the current from the good solar cells to flow in the external circuit rather than forward biasing each good cell.

The maximum reverse bias across the poor cell is reduced to about a single diode drop, thus limiting the current and preventing hot-spot heating. In practice, however, one bypass diode per solar cell is generally too expensive, and instead bypass diodes are usually placed across groups of solar cells. The voltage across the shaded or low-current solar cell is equal to the forward bias voltage of the other series cells which share the same bypass diode plus the voltage of the bypass diode.

The voltage across the unshaded solar cells depends on the degree of shading on the low-current cell. For example, if the cell is completely shaded, then the unshaded solar cells will be forward biased by their short circuit current and the voltage will be about 0.6V. If the poor cell is only partially shaded, some of the current from the good cells can flow through the circuit, and the remainder is used to forward bias each solar cell junction, causing a lower forward bias voltage across each cell.

The maximum power dissipation in the shaded cell is approximately equal to the generating capability of all cells in the group. The maximum group size per diode, without causing damage, is about 15 cells/bypass diode, for silicon cells. For a normal 36-cell module, therefore, 2 bypass diodes are used to ensure the module will not be vulnerable to "hot-spot" damage.

Within Module Heat Generation

A PV module exposed to sunlight generates heat as well as electricity. For a typical commercial PV module operating at its maximum power point, only 10 to 15% of the incident sunlight is converted into electricity, with much of the remainder being converted into heat.

Factors which affect the heating of the module are:

a. <u>Reflection from the top surface.</u>
Light reflected from the front surface of the module does not contribute to the electrical power generated. Such light is considered an electrical loss mechanism which needs to be minimized. Neither does reflected light contribute to heating of the PV module. The maximum temperature rise of the module is therefore calculated as the incident power multiplied by the reflection.

For typical PV modules with a glass top surface, the reflected light contains about 4% of the incident energy.

b.   Electrical operating point.

The operating point and efficiency of the solar cell determine the fraction of the light absorbed by the solar cell that is converted into electricity. If the solar cell is operating at short-circuit current or at open-circuit voltage, then it is generating no electricity and hence all the power absorbed by the solar cell is converted into heat.

c.   Absorption of sunlight in areas not
     covered by solar cells.

The amount of light absorbed by the parts of the module other than the solar cells will also contribute to the heating of the module. How much light is absorbed and how much is reflected is determined by the color and material of the rear backing layer of the module.

d.   Absorption of low-energy (infrared) light.

The amount of light absorbed by the parts of the module other than the solar cells will also contribute to the heating of the module. How much light is absorbed and how much is reflected is determined by the color and material of the rear backing layer of the module.

e.   Packing density of the solar cells.

Solar cells are specifically designed to be efficient absorbers of solar radiation. The cells will generate significant amounts of heat, usually higher than the module encapsulation and rear backing layer. Therefore, a higher packing factor of solar cells increases the generated heat per unit area.

Nominal Operating Cell Temperature (NOCT)

A PV module will generally be rated at 25°C under 1 kW/m². However, when operating in the field, they typically operate at higher temperatures and at somewhat lower insolation conditions. To determine the power output of the solar cell, it is important to determine the expected operating temperature of the PV module.

The nominal operating cell temperature (NOCT) is defined as the temperature reached by open circuited cells in a module under the conditions listed below:

a.   Irradiance on cell surface = 800 W/m²
b.   Air temperature = 20°C
c.   Wind velocity = 1 m/s
d.   Mounting = open back side.

The equations for solar radiation and temperature difference between the module and air show that both conduction and convective losses are linear with incident solar insolation for a given wind speed, provided that the thermal resistance and heat transfer coefficient do not vary strongly with temperature. The best case includes aluminum fins at the rear of the module for cooling which reduces the thermal resistance and increases the surface area for convection.

$$T_{cell} = T_{air} + \frac{NOCT - 20}{80} * S$$

where:
   S is the insolation in mW/cm²

Thermal Expansion and Stress

Thermal expansion is another important temperature effect which must be taken into account when modules are designed.

The spacing between cells tries to increase an amount δ given by:

$$\delta = (\alpha_G C - \alpha_c D)\Delta T$$

where:
   $\alpha_G \alpha_c$ are the expansion coefficients of the glass and
             the cell respectively;
   D   is the cell width; and
   C   is the cell center to center distance.

Typically, interconnections between cells are looped to minimize cyclic stress. Double interconnects are used to protect against the probability of fatigue failure caused by such stress.

In addition to interconnect stresses, all module interfaces are subject to temperature-related cyclic stress which may eventually lead to delamination.

Other Module Design and Evaluation Considerations

A bulk silicon PV module consists of multiple individual solar cells connected nearly always in series to increase the power and voltage to the desired level. The voltage of a PV module is usually chosen to be compatible with a 12V battery, if used for automotive or battery charging purposes, and any other voltage and current combination as needed for each particular application. An individual silicon solar cell has a voltage around 0.6V under 25°C and AM1.5 illumination.

Take into account the expected reduction in PV module voltage due to temperature and the fact that a battery may require 15V or more to charge the modules containing 36 solar cells in series. This gives an open-circuit voltage of about 18-21V under standard test conditions, and an operating voltage at maximum power and operating temperature of about 17 or 18V.

The remaining excess voltage is included to account for voltage drops caused by other elements of the PV system, including operation away from maximum power point and reductions in sunlight intensity.

The same principle is in effect for modules used in commercial or large-scale PV installations. These, however, contain a much larger number of cells in order to generate higher voltage—in the 150-300Wp range. These modules are also much larger in size to accommodate the greater number of cells.

A number of additional factors are considered when designing or evaluating different modules for different applications. The source and quality of the materials and components used in building the PV modules in question must be addressed, although this is easier said than done.

Taking a close look at the certification documents may provide a good estimate of the modules' performance and longevity. We also recommend discussing some of the certification test points with the manufacturers.

Practical PV Modules Characteristics

This is a list of practical factors and issues related to PV modules selection, purchase and use. (2)

There are a lot of modules to choose from, but there is also uncertainty about the survival of many PV module manufacturers because of the large supply-versus-demand imbalance that currently exists, along with the challenge for many manufacturers to produce their products at today's cheap module pricing. These factors—combined with the usual considerations, such as module output ratings, power tolerance, efficiency, and pricing, along with new inverter, mounting, and module-level electronics options—make module selection more complex.

This is a list of top considerations that will be helpful for any array design exercise. Additionally, a module selection example is provided, given our potential roof space and energy generation goals.

- *Power tolerance* is a measurement of how close a module's actual output will be to its rated output under standard test conditions (STC: cell temperature = 77°F and irradiance = 1,000 watts/m²). For example, if a 200-watt module has a power toler-

ance of +/-3%, its actual output (under STC conditions) can vary from 194 W to 206 W. Some modules have a positive-only (such as "+5/-0") power tolerance, which means that these modules should be able to produce at least rated power under STC, and possibly more.

- *PVUSA test conditions* (PTC) calculate module output using an ambient air temperature of 68°F (at 1,000 watt/m² irradiance), which typically causes cell temperatures to be about 113°F to 122°F (36°F to 45°F higher than STC).

  PTC-to-STC ratios specify module power output for settings that more closely represent real-world conditions, which makes them lower than STC ratings. The STC temperature of 77°F for a module's cells is often not a very realistic temperature for these dark cells exposed to direct sunlight; their temperature will commonly be much higher. As cell temperature increases, voltage drops, which reduces module power output.

  However, modules are sold based on their STC-rated power output rather than by PTC ratings, making it more difficult to compare realistic performance between modules. A PTC-to-STC ratio is included in the table for all modules. The closer the PTC rating is to STC, the higher the module output is under more common conditions. For example, if a "200-watt" module has a PTC-to-STC ratio of 0.9 or better, then its PTC rating should be 180 W or higher; if the ratio is 0.85, then its PTC rating will be only 170 W. Although that difference may seem negligible, when you add the power for an entire array, it can be significant.

- *Module voltage and string inverter input window* need to be considered for any grid-tied PV project that uses a string inverter. Each module has a specific maximum power point and open-circuit voltage, and each site has specific temperature ranges it will experience, which will determine the actual voltage at which each module will operate.

  Additionally, each inverter has its own input voltage limitations, which will dictate string size for module models being considered. Many string inverter manufacturers have online sizing calculators to help find string configurations that work for each PV module, considering local climate.

- *Power density* of a module is dependent on module efficiency and is given in watts per square foot. The greater the density, the more power the array can generate per square foot. But higher module efficiency also means more dollars per watt, so before you assume you need a high-efficiency module, check the amount of space you have compared to the total power you want.

- *Module dimensions* need to be considered, especially if you're working with limited mounting space but trying to maximize array capacity. Often, you'll need to compare layouts, including both portrait and landscape configurations, to find the appropriate array layout for a rooftop. When using a string inverter, layout options may need to consider the required number of modules in series (and the number of parallel strings) to make sure the array layout is compatible with the inverter's input and output limitations.

- *PV manufacturer location* can be an important factor. First, some production-based incentives, such as Washington state's RE System Cost Recovery program, pay a higher per-kWh incentive for systems with locally manufactured equipment. Systems funded by the American Recovery and Reinvestment Act (ARRA) and installed on public buildings must use domestically manufactured modules (or foreign modules that use 100% domestic cells). The less distance a module must travel to its ultimate destination, the less embodied energy that module has. Finally, many people want to support local manufacturing jobs over foreign jobs and imports.

- *Module frames and back-sheets* are important to mounting technique and aesthetics. Options include frameless modules, module frames with mounting grooves for rail-less mounting, modules that allow some light to pass through (popular for awning systems), and dark back-sheets (black), which provide a more uniform look within the array.

    PV wire leads are required for ungrounded arrays. Transformerless inverters are becoming increasingly popular because of increased inverter efficiency and enhanced safety. However, they do require the array to be ungrounded, and the modules selected must have "PV-wire" cables for these installations. (PV-wire has specific benefits over standard USE-2 conductors including thicker insulation, higher voltage ratings, better UV resistance and flexibility in extreme cold.)

- *Warranty* is important, and while most PV manufacturers offer 25-year power output warranties, material warranties can range from 2 to 10 years. A warranty is only helpful if the company offering it sticks around to service a future claim. With the PV manufacturing industry undergoing so much change right now, and many companies merging or exiting the market, some manufacturers are offering noncancellable warranties serviced by third-party insurance companies.

- *Cost* is always a factor, and budget can dictate the array you ultimately purchase. Module pricing has been on a downward trend over the last few years. A brief online search shows many modules are available for $1.50 per W, some even below $1. Online module shopping, seeking the cheapest deal instead of buying from a local module supplier/installer, has drawbacks. While the array may cost less upfront, you may be without support should problems arise. In certain areas, installing a grid-tied system without a licensed installer means forfeiting some incentives. While the modules table lists more than 900 modules, no matter whether you buy online or through your local PV installer, available options will be limited to those modules currently offered by that supplier.

- *Compromises Are Inevitable.* Weighing all of these factors can be a time-consuming process that inevitably ends in compromise. Each system designer or homeowner will need to establish their own priorities.

c-Si PV Module Manufacturing

A number of potential issues are encountered during the cell and module manufacturing processes, all of which must be taken into consideration, if we are to have reliably performing PV cells and modules, lasting 25-30 years.

The major issues to keep in mind when designing or planning to use c-Si PV modules are:

1. Quality of silicon material, chemicals and consumables
2. Cell type and design parameters
3. Quality of the cells' manufacturing equipment and process
4. Module type and design parameters

5. Modules' manufacturing equipment and process
6. Possible cell malfunctions within this type and make of module
7. Possible module malfunctions within the particular array

Once the materials—PV cells, laminates, glass, back cover, wiring etc.—have been received and gathered at the module production site, the module is assembled in the sequence shown in Figure 4-29.

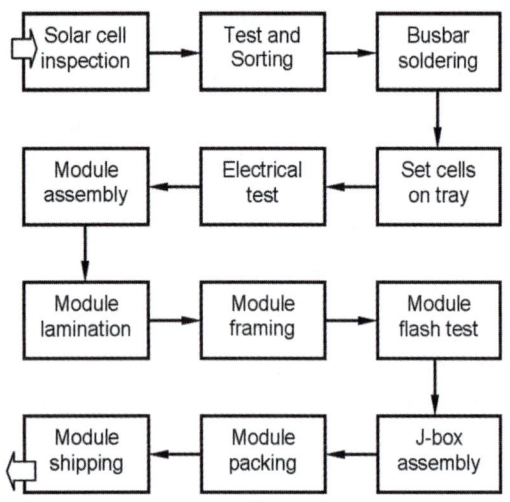

Figure 4-29. PV module assembly sequence

Cell Sorting, Arranging and Soldering

Finished solar cells are flash tested and sorted by their I-V characteristics and power output. Cells that pass the test are placed in bins according to their performance and stored or taken to the module assembly area.

Wiring and Assembly

Cells are connected in a series circuit manually, or by a semi-automated soldering machine using solder coated metal ribbon (usually two in parallel) soldered to the top of one cell and to the bottom of the next cell. This process forms a string of cells which could be as long as desired but usually it is shaped to fit in the respective PV modules tray. Electrical continuity and resistivity tests are performed on some modules to make sure that the bonds are good. "Pull" tests are done sometimes, to check the mechanical strength of the bonds. Thus, connected cells make a complete circuit (string), which is ready for lamination into a completed module.

Lamination

A lay-up for lamination is prepared with clean top glass, and EVA film, and strings of wired cells are placed on it. Sometimes the backing materials (Tedlar and back cover) are placed on top too, forming a complete module. Several lay-ups, each consisting of the above components are lined up in a large cabinet called a laminator. Using silicone vacuum blankets, the batch of lay-ups is heated and vacuum laminated at one time. After cooling, the modules are ready for use.

This method of laminating is much cheaper than laminating one or two units at a time. The excess lamination is trimmed and terminal wiring is attached. In most cases, an aluminum extruded frame is assembled around the material and the unit is ready for shipping.

Basically, module laminators consist of a large-area heated metal platen mounted in a cabinet-like vacuum chamber. The top of the cabinet opens for loading and unloading modules. A flexible diaphragm is attached to the top of the chamber, and a set of valves allows the space above the diaphragm to be evacuated during the initial pump step and backfilled with room air during the press step. A pin lift mechanism is sometimes used to lift modules above the heated platen during the initial pump step, but most standard modules don't require it.

Temperature uniformities of ±5°C at the lamination point are sufficient for obtaining good laminations with acceptable gel content and adhesion across the module. While more uniform temperatures are available from some laminator suppliers, there is no real benefit to the module manufacturer.

Laminators are available with two types of cover opening systems: clamshell and vertical post. In the clamshell design, the cover is mounted on a hinge at the back of the laminator, which opens like the hood of a car. This leaves the laminator wide open on three sides, making it easy for an operator to load and unload modules manually. Automated belt-fed laminators, on the other hand, use the vertical post method, which lifts the cover horizontally above the process chamber.

Because the cover does not need to travel much for belt loading, the chamber opening and closing times, and resulting process steps (heating and vacuum pump down) are reduced. As a result, most high throughput module lines use belt-fed laminators with vertical cover lifts.

NOTE: Fully automated cell assembly and lamination lines exist today, but most low- to mid-volume assembly operations, especially those in Asia, still prefer manual lay-up and stringing operations, combined with low-throughput clamshell type laminators. This is due mostly to the availability of cheap labor, though automating labor-intensive processes is no guaranty of a high quality product.

Modules Flash Testing and Sorting

After completing the assembly process by adding edge sealers, side frame, terminal box, etc., the modules are placed on a test stand in the solar simulator (flasher) and are illuminated with a special type of light that resembles the solar spectrum at STC, for a period of time. The temperature of the modules is kept at 25°C during the test by active or passive cooling. I-V curve is then generated for each module. The output data are used to identify, sort and label the modules according to their output. The modules that pass the test are packed and shipped to the customers.

Table 4-3. Example of Si PV modules specs

Specs \ Power	20 Watt	30 Watt	45 Watt
Dimension, mm L x W x H	656x306 x18	680x426 x18	665x537 x30
Dimension, in L x W x H	25.8x12.04 x0.7	26.8x16.8 x0.7	26.1x21.1 x1.18
Voc, V	21.2V	21.6V	21.9V
Vmp, V	16.8V	17.2V	17.6V
Isc, A	1.32A	1.93A	2.7A
Imp, A	1.19A	1.74A	2.56A
Pm (at STC), Wp	20Wp	30Wp	45Wp

Types of PV Modules

PV modules come in different makes, types, shapes, sizes and designations, but their ultimate purpose is to produce DC power. The more electricity a PV module generates from a given active surface area, the more efficient it is. Different types of modules, using different solar cells, materials and manufacturing techniques have different efficiencies and longevity, but for the most part:

1. The efficiency of the solar cells in each module determines its overall efficiency. One not-so-efficient cell can reduce the efficiency of an entire module. In fact, one "bad" cell can ruin the performance of an entire array of modules—or at least lower the output significantly. The cell's slow degradation will also affect the module's performance over time.

2. The proper structure of the module, and in particular its ability to keep the elements from penetrating inside and attacking the cell components, determines its durability, degree of accelerated degradation and overall longevity.

This is why product quality and quality control procedures during the entire production process are such important aspects of PV cells and modules manufacturing and use.

Efficiency

PV modules come in different types and sizes. The efficiency of the different types of modules is one of the most understood and discussed properties (Table 4-4).

Clearly, sc-Si is the most efficient of the single junction PV cells for all practical purposes (III-V semiconductor cells are usually of the multi-junction type). It is, in our opinion, also most reliable for long-term use as well, simply because its structure is simple, its crystal is perfect and not as easily affected by different electromechanical abnormalities.

Table 4-4. Performance of different cells and PV modules

Solar cell material	Cell efficiency η_z (laboratory) (%)	Cell efficiency η_z (production) (%)	Module efficiency η_M (series production) (%)
Monocrystalline silicon	24.7	21.5	16.9
Polycrystalline silicon	20.3	16.5	14.2
Ribbon silicon	19.7	14	13.1
Crystalline thin-film silicon	19.2	9.5	7.9
Amorphous silicon[a]	13.0	10.5	7.5
Micromorphous silicon[a]	12.0	10.7	9.1
CIS	19.5	14.0	11.0
Cadmium telluride	16.5	10.0	9.0
III-V semiconductor	39.0[b]	27.4	27.0
Dye-sensitized call	12.0	7.0	5.0[c]
Hybrid HIT solar cell	21	18.5	16.8

Polysilicon, however, is most widely used, mostly because of its pleasant aesthetics, ease of manufacturing, and lower cost, even though its efficiency is lower and the imperfections of its crystal bring some unwanted effects in the long run as well.

Generally, we must be aware of the behavior patterns, variables, performance and longevity issues of the different types of PV cells and modules, if we are to design and build efficient and long-lasting PV power plants.

Key Module Issues—Detailed Technical Discussion

Keeping in mind all possible behavior conditions and the problems discussed above, we will now look at the possible problems at each process step of PV cells and modules manufacturing. These issues can be traced to materials, equipment, processes and labor-related problems, and are usually demonstrated during testing or long-term exposure to the elements.

We will examine possible defects and failures which can occur during the final module test or, more importantly, during long-term exposure to harsh climatic conditions.

So, the key issues and all possible effects caused by long-term on-sun exposure following the PV module elements are detailed below and shown in Figure 4-30.

ONE—Glass Cover (Top Cover)

The cover glass is basically designed to provide protection to the fragile solar cells and module components from mechanical damage, such as vibration, impact, etc., as well as to prevent the elements (rain, moisture, dust) from entering the module. If the glass itself is stressed, cracked and broken during processing, handling, transport, installation and operation stages, then the insides of the module might already be damaged as well. Subsequent damage could occur in such cases, by means of mechanical stress and chemical destruction of the cells and other active components.

This is even more important for thin film PV modules because the active layers are deposited directly on the front or back covers, thus any stress or breakage of the glass will directly, and immediately, affect the performance and longevity of the damaged modules. The advantage of c-Si PV modules in this area is that the EVA layer is enveloping the active components (solar cells), so that even if the top or bottom covers are damaged, the EVA envelope is given a chance to protect the cells from an invasion of the elements and chemical attack.

Modules with damaged cover glass—be it cracked or with hazy appearance—should not be installed and must be removed from service immediately. Repairing damaged glass is not an option in most cases, so the entire module must be properly disposed of, or sent back to the manufacturer for credit or for replacement. Periodic testing of the voltage/current output of modules with partially cracked cover glass, if acceptable at all, should be part of the PM schedule.

NOTE: In all cases damaged modules should be handled with utmost care.

Cover glass surface soiling is another serious issue during normal operation. Rain and dust will deposit layers of contaminants and water spots on the surface, which will prevent sunlight from reaching the solar cells underneath. With time the layers might grow so thick that very little light goes through them, significantly reducing the output of the modules. Washing the top surface with a soapy water solution, followed by proper rinsing with DI water will restore the modules' efficiency, so it should be part of the PM schedule and carefully executed. This, however, is an expensive undertaking, especially in the deserts. Periodic use of water and chemicals also causes concerns with water table contamination, which must be kept in mind when deciding on a PV power field location and O&M procedures.

TWO—EVA Encapsulant Deterioration and Delamination

The layer of plastic encapsulation (EVA usually) and the cover glass are in intimate contact and partially bonded. These two, however, have different elasticity, and coefficients of expansion and friction. With long-time exposure to the elements (heating, freezing, excess UV radiation, mechanical stress, fatigue) the EVA plastic will eventually change. Its physical and chemical properties change slowly and we can see it turning a yellowish color. Yellowing of the EVA results in reduction of its transmissivity and causes a decrease of power output.

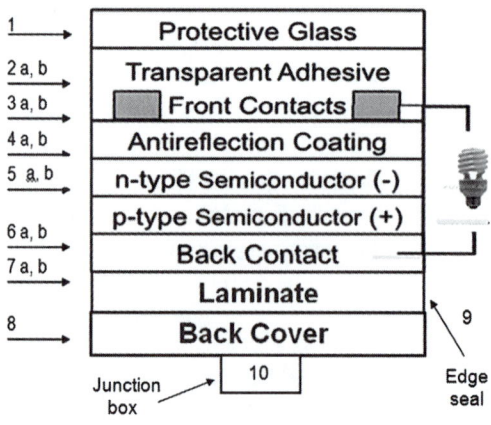

Figure 4-30. Standard silicon PV module cross section

Yellowing is one of the few changes occurring in the modules that can be observed with the naked eye and which gives us a clear indication of the changes within the module. As the changes continue, air bubbles, cracks, pits and cavities could form in the EVA material, which could cause it to separate from the top glass. This contributes further to increasing optical losses due to reflection and poor transmission, ultimately resulting in serious performance deterioration. Once the EVA material damage and the accompanying delamination processes have started they cannot be stopped. At this point the damaged modules are suspect and must be put under periodic observation as part of the O&M schedule.

EVA Delamination from the AR Layer

Some of the above-mentioned damage and defects in the EVA material will also affect the adhesion of the EVA material to the AR coating to which it is bonded. EVA delamination from the glass and AR coating surface is caused by the never-ending UV bombardment, expansion and contraction of the layers, and the resulting friction between them. This action might result in an air gap which would cause a second optical barrier, further decreasing the power output from the affected cells.

The newly created gaps and cracks might allow moisture, air and reactive gasses to enter the module and attack the other modules' components.

Changes at the EVA-AR film interface (air gap, color change, cracking, etc.) are another of the few visually observable changes in PV modules. Depending on the type of cells (mono- or polycrystalline) and type of AR coating (many different formulations are available), the visual effects might change the cell's surface color from black to faded black, and from dark blue to light blue (respectively), as well as a number of shades in between.

THREE — Top Contacts and Interfaces

The top contacts (fingers) consist of silver metal with metal ribbons soldered on top of the contacts to provide connection to the other cells and to the outside circuit. This creates several separate contact points (interfaces) as follow:

a. Silicon to silver metal of the top contact,
b. Silver metal to the soldered metal strip, and
c. Soldered metal strip to the EVA encapsulant.

The different interfaces provide good adhesion to their components and are quite stable under normal operating conditions. In abnormal situations, however,

such as excess heat, overcurrent conditions, mechanical or thermal stress, and/or exposure to the elements (water vapor, chemicals and reactive gasses), the metals undergo serious changes which are usually initiated in the interfaces. The damage could increase with time and cause significant changes in the contacts' structure. In all cases these events will result in electrical changes or failures (high resistivity or open circuit). Interrupting the contact with the adjacent cells will lead to a failure of the module.

In some cases, one or more of the affected contact layers might burn, chemically disintegrate, or undergo other destructive processes, which could cause the device to fail partially, or completely, in which case the entire solar module might stop generating power. In all cases, there will be noticeable reduction in power from the module, due to mismatch caused by the affected solar cell(s).

Top Contact Adhesion into the Silicon Substrate

Under normal operating conditions, the adhesion between the front contacts (silver metal) and the silicon material which they are fused into is good enough to keep them together and properly conducting electricity for the life of the module. Abnormally, however, mechanical stress, excess heat, and moisture and air penetrating into the module, could affect the front contacts. Mechanical forces could induce stress in the materials and their interfaces, while ingress of water and chemicals might corrode and separate them from the substrate.

These processes would negatively affect the bond at the interface between these key components (silicon substrate and silver contact). In such cases:

a. The diffusion area might be affected and undergo internal changes which might affect the cell's performance, and/or

b. The resistivity at the affected area might increase, which could result in overheating, and eventually a breakdown (open circuit), caused by partial or complete separation of the contact from the substrate.

These phenomena could bring partial or total failure of the solar cell and/or the entire module.

FOUR — AR Coating Surface Damage

A number of distractive mechanisms on the cell's surface, caused by mechanical stress and chemical attacks could affect the AR layer. These changes could occur under different operating conditions and cause the AR coating top surface to change mechanically or chemically. This could cause a change in the AR layer's optical properties, decreasing the cell's efficiency.

In addition, blistering of large areas of the AR coating might also stress the cell and the top contacts, causing further increase of resistance and heat generation. Overheating could damage the contacts and/or their interface. The warped AR surface might also reflect some of the incoming sunlight at a greater rate than designed. Always, the final result is reduction in affected cells' efficiency.

These effects (AR layer delamination, blistering etc.) also result in color change of the AR coating which represents another of the few visually observable changes in the solar cell and module. Depending on the type of cells (mono- or polycrystalline) and type of AR coating, the visual effects might change the cell's surface appearance to different variations of the original colors.

AR Coating Adhesion to the Substrate

The anti-reflection coating (AR) is a fairly thin film of inorganic material—TiO_2, Si_3N_4 and such—which is very thin, semi-transparent and fragile under certain conditions. Very thin and lightly bonded to the cell surface, it is easily damaged by mechanical and chemical means. There are several mechanisms that can contribute to changes of the AR layer and its adhesion to the substrate. One is contamination of the silicon substrate surface prior to AR coating, which would result in poor adhesion over time. The surface contamination could be caused by insufficient cleaning and rinsing, improper handling, or an out-of-spec process during the AR coating deposition. All of these inadequacies would compromise the adhesion integrity of the thin AR film to the silicon substrate.

If the AR layer is not fully adhered to the silicon substrate, there would be physical and optical gaps which would cause excess reflection and/or obstruct sunlight transmission into the cell. Combinations of these conditions will contribute greatly to reduction of the cell's efficiency.

Further, and more seriously, changes in the AR film properties could occur quicker if the damaged area is exposed to the elements via moisture and air leaking into the module (see above). The adhesion forces in the interface between the AR film and the substrate in such cases would weaken even more under the outside attacks, and the AR film might disintegrate or separate from the surface, amplifying the negative effects.

Most changes in the AR coating's adhesion and other changes of its properties are also visible on the module's surface, but equally impossible to correct. When these changes occur, future cell/module behavior is impossible to predict without destructive tests, so the module must be checked periodically as part of the O&M schedule.

NOTE: All visually observable changes mentioned above start, and might even continue, as microscopic imperfections which eventually grow bigger and more visible. A trained eye is needed to observe the changes in many cases.

FIVE—P-N Junction and Diffusion Process Issues

The p-n junction is the most critical area of solar cells' function. It has the greatest impact on cell/module efficiency, performance and longevity. The p-n junction is formed by diffusing (injecting) a specified concentration of foreign atoms in the silicon bulk, which then initiate and drive the photoelectric effect. Unacceptable amounts of impurities in the bulk silicon, such as Fe, Cu, K, Na and any other contaminants in the process chemicals and gasses will affect the diffusion concentration and depth, ultimately changing the behavior of the p-n junction. Changes in the concentration of the foreign atoms in the junction, due to parasitic effects during its field operation would produce similar results.

If the wafer surface was not properly prepared, cleaned and rinsed, or if the diffusion process was not properly executed (time, gas concentration and temperature), the p-n junction might not be stable enough. Thus affected solar cells might operate well in the beginning, but eventually the diffusion layer will start changing (decreased concentration and diffusing further into the substrate) causing a drop in output. These effects sometimes occur months or years after the module has been in operation and are called "latent" effects. They are most dangerous for the large-scale power plant's long-term success, because if they happen after the warranty period has expired, and if the failures are great enough, they might cause serious technical and financial difficulties.

The most common negative field effect of the p-n junction is change in the diffusion depth (and the resulting dopant concentration reduction at the junction) over time. While this phenomenon is well understood and the p-n formation parameters are controlled during the manufacturing sequence, certain material and process conditions force greater changes, over time, than allowed by design. In such cases, the cells start losing power quicker than expected and eventually fail altogether.

Diffusion processes techniques vary from manufacturer to manufacturer. Some use the old-fashioned, but most reliable, diffusion furnace process, where the wafers are placed into a glass tube and heated to over 1000°C in a controlled environment. Doping gases are passed through the tube and by precise control of temperature, process time and gas volume, precise deposition concentration and depth are obtained. A high-volume, but less precise, diffusion process has been widely used lately. It consists of spraying or printing the dopant liquid on the wafer surface and then baking it in a conveyor belt type of furnace. This process has more uncontrollable variables and is basically inferior from process control and product quality points of view than the old diffusion furnace method. Nevertheless, it is cheaper and faster, thus we will see it more and more in the future. And due to its less-than-precise and not-so-easy-to-control process parameters, we expect to see more issues with diffusion and p-n junction changes in the field as well.

Diffusion layer depth and concentration changes cannot be visually detected, nor can they be measured under field conditions, so at this point we are looking at a black box and relying on the manufacturer's experience and his properly and efficiently executed quality control procedures.

P-N Junction Field Performance

So, what if the diffusion process were less than perfect? First, and most important, if the materials and process specs were even slightly out of control, the solar cells and modules would show low efficiently during the final tests. After sorting, the less efficient would go into the group of "cheaper" cells and modules to be shipped to a customer who hopes they will work well. But if the diffusion process were somewhat out of spec, thus the reason for the lower quality of some cells, then there would be a good chance that the affected cells and modules might deteriorate much more quickly than the rest.

Exposure to extreme temperature is especially testy, and is the reason for many malfunctions and failures encountered in c-Si modules. It is possible for the species in the diffusion layer to start migrating into the bulk under abnormal conditions brought upon by extreme temperature regimes and/or any imperfections in the silicon material close to the p-n junction area. These will accelerate the changes in the electrical characteristics of the cells, thus causing additional efficiency decrease.

In summary, as soon as the newly processed solar cells are flash-tested they are ready for encapsulation into a module. Provided that the materials are of high quality and all process steps have been properly executed, the p-n junction and the cells will operate properly for a long time. But if we had materials quality problems or the diffusion process were not properly executed, then we might be looking for a surprise in our power field, over time.

NOTE: Here we need to mention the great effect of silicon bulk material on the efficiency and other properties of the solar cells that were made from it. We now know that the quality of the solar wafers determines the quality of the solar cells made from them. The silicon wafers are made from 99.9999% pure solar grade silicon material. Even at that purity, however, a slight increase in one of the harmful contaminants (usually metals) might have serious effects on the solar cells' field performance and longevity. Over time, and when operating at extreme temperatures, parasitic metals could start diffusing through the cell and alter p-n junction properties, with the diffusion speed increasing.

SIX—Rear Contact Damage

The rear contact also consists of several interfaces: a) silicon bulk to aluminum BSF; b) silicon to silver back contact, and; c) silver to soldered metal band.

This metal structure and its interfaces are exposed to the same electro-mechanical, thermal and chemical attacks and changes as the front contacts we reviewed above. Although these are somewhat more protected from and less affected by the UV and IR radiation than the front contacts, their long-term quality is as critical. Any elemental impurities, chemical contaminants, mechanical damage, such as cracks, pits and other imperfections in the structure will have profound effects on the cell's efficiency and longevity.

The quality of the metal deposition is of great importance here too, because if it is defective in any way (high resistivity, cracks and pores, poor adhesion, oxidation at the interface, etc.), it will cause overheating, delamination and ultimately reduced efficiency of the cell, and even total failure. Nevertheless, the rear contacts are much less problematic and affect the cells' function less than the front contacts, but failure of the encapsulants and edge sealers could damage them seriously enough to cause performance degradation and failures.

Rear Contact Adhesion

In case of poor contact quality due to process control inadequacies (time, temperature, or metal quality), the metal film can partially separate from the substrate, eventually leading to decreased efficiency due to higher resistivity and overheating.

Excess overheating at the back surface might contribute to further erosion and delamination of the metal film and total failure of the cell and module.

SEVEN—Laminate Issues

Laminate materials (EVA, PET, PVB, Tedlar, etc.) are organic (plastic) materials, which have been in use and remain basically unchanged in composition and use, for more than 30 years. Also unchanged is their vulnerability to exposure to the elements, where EVA and other organic compounds in the module do undergo mechanical and chemical changes and degradation over time.

Continuous expansion during hot days and shrinking during freezing nights, extreme IR and UV bombardment, and chemicals' ingress will affect the EVA and other organic (plastic) materials. This will eventually result in mechanical changes—discoloration, mechanical stress and disintegration of the lamination materials—creating cracks, bubbles, pits, voids, etc.

Ingress of moisture and gasses into the module via the above formed cracks and voids will contribute further to the degradation process by decomposing the module materials (solar cells, wiring, contacts etc.).

Rear Laminate

The laminate structure on the back of the module usually consists of the EVA envelope with thin Tedlar and/or other plastic materials backing, laid onto the rear metal cover. The rear EVA-on-Tedlar structure is protected from the elements (UV and IR radiation) so it lasts much longer without damage. Its yellowing and even delamination from the back cover don't have such dramatic effects on module performance.

The adhesion of the EVA envelope to the back of the cells, however, can be affected with time. Excess heating, freezing, and moisture penetrating from the sides might eventually debilitate the adhesion to the solar cells. In that case, moisture and air penetrating the laminate material and reaching the solar cells will cause rapid oxidation of the back surface metallization (aluminum and silver metals), which will also affect the interface between these metals and the back surface of the solar cell. This deterioration of the cells' adhesion at interface might cause increased resistivity and overheating, and eventually delamination of the metal contacts from the substrate, which would cause performance issues and eventually failure of the affected cells and modules.

EIGHT—Rear Cover and Frame

The purpose of the frame and back cover (aluminum sheet or glass plate) is to protect the module's insides from attack by the elements. It is highly unlikely for the frame and back cover to degrade significantly with time under normal use, but a severe mechanical or chemical attack could compromise its integrity, forming cracks and voids which might allow moisture and air to penetrate the module. At that point, any of the above-described events might cause the cells and module to decrease in efficiency or fail.

NINE—Side Edge Seal

c-Si PV modules usually have side protection as an extension of their edge protection. Ingress of harmful elements into the module is usually initiated through the sides (the edge seal) and could be slowed by a well-installed and sealed metal frame around the edges. A lot of effort is dedicated to finding better sealing materials, and assembly processes have improved significantly as a result. Edge sealing—its effects and weaknesses—are well understood. No matter how good the sealing materials are, however, they are made of plastic (organic) materials which are affected by the elements—IR and UV radiation and environmental chemicals. Thirty years under the blistering Arizona desert sun would challenge any organic material or compound.

Edge seals are prone to accelerated changes with time which usually lead to the formation of voids, cracks, pores, and bubbles. These imperfections eventually allow moisture and air to penetrate the modules and cause damage as described time after time above. Therefore, new types of frames and edge seal protection should be developed to provide additional protection.

NOTE: Edge seal quality and protection issues are even more important for some thin film PV modules which are frameless. The modules consist of two glass plates with no sides, so that the edge seal is exposed to the elements. This makes the thin films inside the modules more vulnerable to the elements, which could be detrimental to their performance and longevity.

TEN—Junction Box

The junction box is just that—a small box where the wiring "junction" or connection is made. It is a metal container intended for easy, safe, and reliable electrical connections. It is also intended to conceal those from the elements and prevent tampering. The box is attached to the back cover of the module by means of screws and/or glue and contains connectors for wires coming from the module and those connecting it to the external circuitry.

Corrosion of the contacts in the boxes is the most frequent problem encountered during long-term operation in harsh climates. This might cause increased resistance, reduce output power and eventually result in fire or an open circuit. This problem, however, is the only one that can be fixed by replacing the defective parts without tearing the module apart.

Summary

As a summary of issues affecting solar cells and modules performance and longevity, if we represent the actual efficiency and longevity of a solar module using the above described conditions and issues, we get:

$$\eta a = \eta t - (1 + 2a + 2b + 3a + 3b + 4a + 4b + 5a + 5b + 6a + 6b + 7a + 7b + 8 + 9 + 10)$$

$$La = Lt - (1 + 2a + 2b + 3a + 3b + 4a + 4b + 5a + 5b + 6a + 6b + 7a + 7b + 8 + 9 + 10)$$

Where:

ηa is the actual field efficiency of the module

ηt is the theoretical (optimum) efficiency of the module, and

La is the actual longevity of the module

Lt is the theoretical (optimum) longevity of the module

Numbers 1 through 10 are the sequence of conditions and issues discussed above.

It is impossible to predict, let alone put a numerical value on most of the conditions and issues in 1 through 10 above, so these formulas are good only to show roughly the qualitative dependence of the efficiency and longevity of the modules to the members of this long chain of events and how they could affect (usually in a negative way) the cells and modules during their long-term on-sun operation.

As we can clearly see, any discrepancy in the chain of ten events can only reduce the efficiency and/or longevity of the cells and modules, according to the seriousness of the deviation. Or as we mentioned, "The highest quality of the finished device is determined by the lowest quality of any process step," or event in this case.

Applying the related manufacturing process steps, sub-steps and procedures to the each of the members (1-10) of the above formula will result in a long string of variables (literally hundreds of them). Each of these additional sub-routines and variables would have an equally negative effect on the modules' performance and longevity, if not properly executed.

This is why quality of materials, quality of design, and process control, combined with know-how and ex-

perience are so important in ensuring acceptable quality of the final product. This is not impossible, but we fear that very few people are fully aware of the complexity of these matters. Our hope is that now, with all the issues on the table, we will be able to start an open discussion about their resolution. Standardization of materials quality and process controls is the ultimate solution to the issues at hand, so until that occurs we must use great care when designing and evaluating solar cells and modules for large-scale power generation, especially in harsh climates.

PV MODULES CERTIFICATION AND FIELD TESTS

Testing PV modules before installation in the field for long-term operation is a necessary step, but the results are not always indicative of actual lifetime field performance. Many modules qualified and certified as required, and operating for several years in the field, have been found malfunctioning after the abuse of Mother Nature.

Once the solar modules are manufactured, one of the best batches goes to US or European labs for testing and final certification. This is a very important test, which determines the future of this set of modules, and possibly that of the company that manufactures them.

Thus, selected modules undergo standard test procedures. Some pass the testing program, but start deteriorating prematurely and at times fail completely. Sometimes they fail at the pre-test and pre-certification stages—even before the testing procedure has started.

Pre-test Failures

Let's look at an unusual trend of failures, which were discovered even before the actual testing was began. These failures tell us a lot about the manufacturer and don't give us much confidence in their products. See for yourself:

According to Intertek, a certified test facility in California, a number of test modules fail this pre-test screening. Here are five typical reasons why PV modules coming for testing at their facility fail initial inspection—even before the testing can be started. The reasons are shocking, for a supposedly hi-tech business, such as PV cells and module manufacturing operations (7):

1. Inappropriate/incomplete installation instructions.

2. Models provided for testing do not accurately rep-

resent the entire production model scheme being listed (largest module must be submitted for test).

3. Testing requested without prior construction evaluation being performed.

4. Complete bill of materials with ratings and certification information not provided prior to start of the project.

5. Lack of back-sheet panel RTI rating.

According to the author's extensive experience with engineering and quality control operations in the world's semiconductor and solar industries, this phenomena is quite unusual from a quality control point of view. It also points to weaknesses in the overall management systems of the manufacturers in question.

Keep in mind also that the above listed failures are among the very few that can be readily recognized—before the modules are packed, shipped and installed in the field. How, then, will we catch the possible failures of the thousands of modules we need for our 100 MWp power plant, during and after installation in the field?

This is a question that we must answer in the daily quest for PV products needed for large-scale installations. How do we make sure that the modules we are ordering don't fall in this category?

The quick answer is:

1. Take your time to thoroughly check all engineering and quality control procedures used during the processing of your batch of PV modules. The manufacturer must provide some of this information. If not, then go to someone who will.

2. Find out as much as you can about the "sand-to-module" history of the product, before placing a large order.

3. Even better, have a team of qualified engineers visit the manufacturer and inspect the process line your modules go through. This is a difficult task, but short of that, you are working with a black box that may or may not work properly. The choice is yours.

Performance Tests and Failure Rates

The PV modules that pass the pre-test inspection at the certification lab are then put through a real test and undergo procedures such as damp heat, UV exposure, heat and freeze, mechanical strength and other tests that require 3-6 months or more for completion. To make sure the modules will pass the certification tests and to save time and money, manufacturers run similar tests at their facilities before sending the modules for certification; i.e., current standards require approximately 1000 hours of exposure to damp heat, but some manufacturers extend this procedure 2-3 times in their in-house tests, to ensure that the modules perform adequately.

Long test procedures result in the delayed introduction of materials to the PV market; however, many companies, in an attempt to "accelerate" the aging process, utilize alternative test procedures. For example, HAST (highly accelerated stress test) has become popular among PV modules and components manufacturers. The HAST procedure provides some useful, albeit superficial test results. It needs to be standardized and correlated with damp heat and outdoor performance, before it can be relied on for providing meaningful and acceptable test results.

So, modules that pass manufacturers' in-house tests are sent to a qualified test and certification lab (usually in the US or EU) for final testing and certification. At the lab they are put through a series of tests to determine their efficiency, overall performance, and longevity.

During 1997-2009, TUV Rheinland ptl in Tempe, AZ, recorded the results from a series of such tests with several thousand PV modules from a number of different major PV module manufacturers. These results were published in *Photovoltaics International*, May 2010, clearly outlining the test failures and related issues, as shown in Figure 4-31. (5)

In general, the tested PV modules' quality during 2005-2007 was absolutely unacceptable. Quality has improved in some areas during the last several years, but it is still much lower than the best possible and profitable for use. Even higher degradation and failure rates are possible in extreme climate areas, which might lead to lower power output and profits.

An added uncertainty here is the fact that there were significantly less failures (30% less in some cases) during 1997-2005 which number increased during 2005-2007 and then decreased again later. This teeter-totter of failures can be contributed to a number of factors, such as changes in the quality of raw materials and the influx of solar cells and modules manufacturing facilities around the world. It also might be related to the world demand for PV modules, which forced manufacturers to speed up the production process beyond their ability to maintain and control quality.

The overall conclusion here is that the PV industry is immature at best and has not found its "legs" as

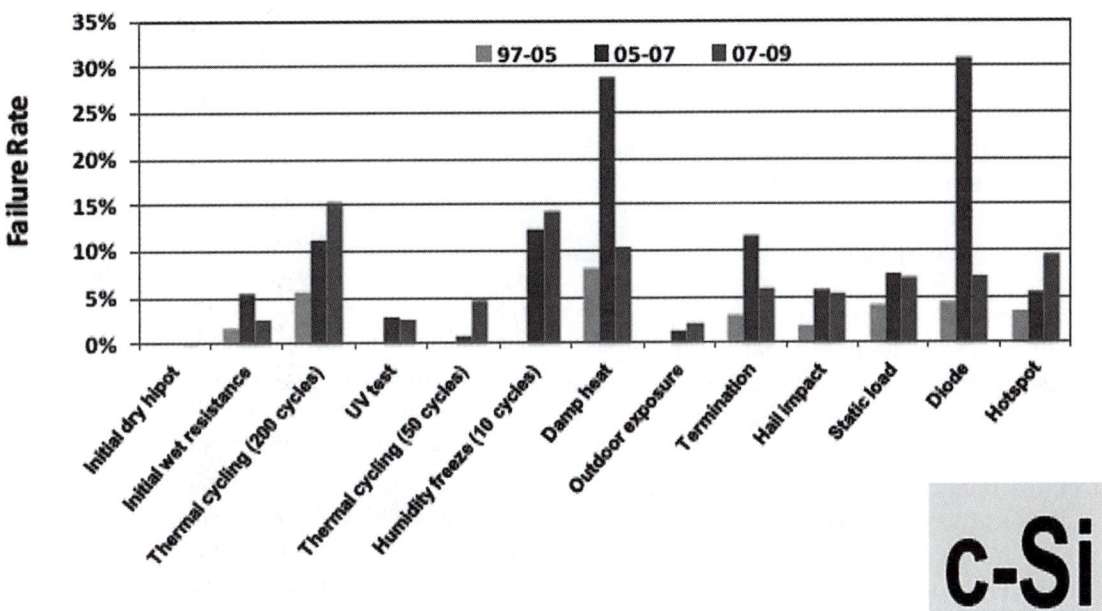

Qualification Testing of 3169 c-Si Modules at TUV Rheinland PTL (1997-2009)

Figure 4-31. c-Si modules tests 1997-2009 (5)

A. Crystalline silicon PV modules (extrapolated from Figure 4-31)

3%	failed at the first wet resistance test (down from 5% in 2007)
16%	failed after 200 thermal cycles* (up from 12% in 2007)
3%	failed UV test
5%	failed after 50 thermal cycles (up from 1% in 2007)
14%	failed after 10 humidity freeze cycles (up from 12% in 2007)
11%	failed damp test (down from 28% in 2007)
2%	failed outdoor exposure test.
6%	failed termination test (down from 2% in 2007)
5%	failed hail impact test
7%	failed static load test
7%	failed diode test (down from 31% in 2007)
9%	failed hotspot test (up from 6% in 2007)

*(200 thermal cycles represent 200 days on-sun operation, while 30 years of thermal cycling = ~10,000 cycles).

**10 humidity freeze cycles represent only part of an Arizona winter season worth of freeze cycles, while 30 years would consist of over 1,000 cycles, and many more in northern states.

yet. This also means that the quality issues need to be brought out in the open and elevated to the highest possible levels of engineering. We know how to do this, so it is just a matter of time.

Conclusions and Recommendations

Some of the conclusions and recommendations of the TUV Rheinland test center team, in regard to these tests and their results are as follow:

• Considering 10-25 years of warranty provided for PV modules, failure rates in qualification testing are still unacceptably high.

• The top 4 failure rates for c-Si modules were related to damp heat, thermal cycling, humidity freeze and diode tests.

• The top 4 failure rates for thin-film modules were related to damp heat, thermal cycling, humidity freeze and static load tests.

• New manufacturers have higher influence on the failure rates of c-Si modules, whereas they have lower influence on the failure rates of thin-film modules. Encouragingly, overall failure rates for both technologies have decreased for the 2007-2009 period as compared to the 2005-2007 period.

- To pass full qualification testing, these top 4 tests are recommended as a minimum, before initiating full qualification testing by the module manufacturers.

- To differentiate among manufacturers who all have qualification certificates, these top 4 tests may be recommended as a minimum, before purchase decisions are made by consumers/system integrators.

- To initiate long-term lifetime reliability or test-to-failure testing, these top 4 tests may be considered as minimum key tests by researchers.

We need to remember always that the above tests, and the conclusions thereof, reflect only a fraction of the time and stress these modules will experience during 20-30 years of non-stop exposure to the sun and the elements. The most critical, but not so stable component of the modules—the EVA encapsulant—is easily affected by heat, freeze, UV radiation, etc. Once it is damaged, cells are in danger of degradation and premature failure.

Dr. Dauskardt, Stanford University (16) concludes:

1. Delamination can occur between EVA and the front surface of the solar cells.

2. More frequent in hot and humid climates.

3. Exposure to atmospheric water and/or ultraviolet radiation leads to EVA decomposition to produce acetic acid, lowering the pH and increasing corrosion.

4. EVA, $T_g \sim -15°C$ so lower temperatures may result in "ductile-to-brittle" transition in adhesive/cohesive properties.

This is self-explanatory: Poor performance and failures cannot be avoided, but need to be calculated, and plans for their elimination (or reduction) need to be made in any plant design. We'd only dare suggest bringing the issues—especially when large-scale PV installations are concerned—to the attention of cell and module manufacturers to look for solutions with their help.

A partnership between manufacturers, installers, investors and customers is the best way to ensure their long-term efficiency, longevity and profitability of the large PV projects.

Field Tests

There is a difference between results from laboratory tests, as above, and what happens under actual field conditions. Results depend on the types of modules used and weather conditions in the test field, so keep in mind that:

1. The results from tests under the extreme heat in the Arizona desert sun or the high humidity in Southern Florida will be drastically different from those under the cloudy skies of Portland, ME, or Berlin, Germany, and that,

2. In all cases, failures and degradations increase after 15-30 years of non-stop operation under climate conditions of extreme heat or humidity.

The field tests in Table 4-5 show the average annual degradation of different PV modules from different manufacturers. Most of the results from c-Si PV modules are actually quite encouraging, but notice also that most of the manufacturers whose products show good results are reputable, well-established companies who have been in the solar business for a while now and have figured out how to make a high-quality product. In contrast, most new manufacturers have not had a chance to work out the process bugs and/or conduct long-term field tests, to prove the reliability of their products.

The field test results prove that c-Si technology, if properly made and used, can be a viable and reliable energy source and that some of the major and well-established manufacturers have achieved reliability. Keep in mind, however, that most of the above tests (except one) have been conducted 10-11 years max, so the conclusions reflect only a fraction of the time, stress and abuse all PV modules will experience.

Also keep in mind that age and extreme climate conditions have detrimental effects. We need to always assume that power degradation after 20-30 years will increase somewhat, and might progress catastrophically in some cases.

Conclusions

Crystalline silicon technologies have a long track record of success. The encouraging aspect of their performance is that there are documented tests and long-term installations with a flawless record. The overwhelming conclusion from all available documentation, including our own tests through the years, is that the quality, performance and longevity of c-Si PV modules and systems is directly related to the quality of materials, equipment,

Table 4-5. Field test results (15)

Manufacturer	Module Type	Exposure (years)	Degradation Rate (% per year)	Measured at System Level?	Ref.
ARCO Solar	ASI 16-2300 (x-Si)	23	-0.4	N	2
ARCO Solar	M-75 (x-Si)	11	-0.4	N	3
[not given]	[not given] (a-Si)	4	-1.5	Y	4
Eurosolare	M-SI 36 MS (poly-Si)	11	-0.4	Y	5
AEG	PQ40 (poly-Si)	12	-5.0	N	6
BP Solar	BP555 (x-Si)	1	+0.2	N	7
Siemens Solar	SM50H (x-Si)	1	+0.2	N	7
Atersa	A60 (x-Si)	1	-0.8	N	7
Isofoton	I110 (x-Si)	1	-0.8	N	7
Kyocera	KC70 (poly-Si)	1	-0.2	N	7
Atersa	APX90 (poly-Si)	1	-0.3	N	7
Photowatt	PW750 (poly-Si)	1	-1.1	N	7
BP Solar	MSX64 (poly-Si)	1	0.0	N	7
Shell Solar	RSM70 (poly-Si)	1	-0.3	N	7
Würth Solar	WS11007 (CIS)	1	-2.9	N	7
USSC	SHR-17 (a-Si)	6	-1.0	Y	8
Siemens Solar	M55 (x-Si)	10	-1.2	Y	9
[not given]	[not given] (CdTe)	8	-1.3	Y	9
Siemens Solar	M10 (x-Si)	5	-0.9	N	10
Siemens Solar	Pro 1 JF (x-Si)	5	-0.8	N	10
Solarex	MSX10 (poly-Si)	5	-0.7	N	10
Solarex	MSX20 (poly-Si)	5	-0.5	N	10

processes in their construction, as well as the performance of the people involved in their manufacture.

Basically, well-established, reputable companies do have the ability and experience to produce a world-class product which functions per the manufacturer's specs. At the same time, a number of newcomers and low-cost manufacturers are working hard at getting their manufacturing and customer support processes streamlined, and we expect that many of them will be successful.

c-Si PV technology could be successfully used in many areas of the world, but we'd like to caution the reader that it is not the ultimate solution to the energy crisis, as some portray it. It is useful, but only in certain geographic areas and special situations. Due to their large temperature coefficient and humidity dependence, we'd suggest that c-Si PV modules could be used without limitations or restrictions in areas with moderate temperatures and humidity. Their use in large-scale power plants in extreme climate areas, such as deserts and humid areas, however, is not well proven.

More research is needed to understand the phenomena at hand, accompanied by appropriate long-term tests which must be conducted to verify the c-Si modules' performance and longevity under these conditions.

So, cost and efficiency goals are almost reached, and the work in these areas continues to set new records.

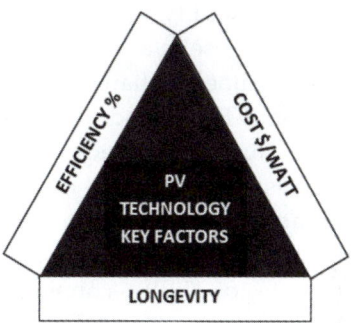

Figure 4-32. Key PV modules parameters

Durability and longevity, however, are not so clearly defined. Some tests show good results, including field tests done under normal conditions. The above-mentioned extreme climates do and will present a serious problem to all PV technologies—c-Si included.

The emphasis should be on longevity, and must be resolved well before we embark on deploying mega plants in US deserts and humid areas. Since these areas are the most promising for large-scale PV installations, this must be a priority for manufacturers, customers, installers, investors and operators alike.

The other major brand of solar cells and modules, which are quite different from the silicon counterparts, are the so-called thin film photovoltaics. They have grown significantly in importance lately, so they also deserve a detailed review and analysis.

THIN FILM PHOTOVOLTAICS

Thin film photovoltaic (TFPV) technologies are a relatively new branch of the solar industry, which has grown much faster in popularity and size than the other PV technologies during the last several years. Since the active layers in TFPV cells and modules are deposited in the form of thin films, via thin film deposition methods, we refer to them as "thin film" PV products.

Thin films of special photovoltaic materials can produce solar cells or modules with relatively high conversion efficiencies, while at the same time using much less semiconductor material than c-Si cells. In addition, thin film equipment and manufacturing methods allow efficient, cheap, fully automated mass production which is the reason for their success lately.

This, however, comes at the expense of reduced efficiency (average 6-9%), which is not expected to increase much in the future (in mass production mode). On the other end of the efficiency spectrum, multi-layer thin film CPV cells have reached efficiencies over 40% and are getting higher by the day with theoretical efficiency limits in the 80% range.

Due to their versatility, TFPV products have become very popular for use in a number of applications. Recently they have gained a share in large-scale installations as well. Some TFPV modules also show better efficiency under reduced solar radiation than the c-Si competition. This is very useful in many regions with cloudy climates, and could account to their quick rise in European and other world energy markets.

The major types of TFPV technologies considered for commercial and large-scale installations are:

1. Cadmium telluride thin films
2. CIGS thin films
3. Amorphous silicon thin films
4. Silicon ribbon
5. Epitaxial silicon thin films
6. Light absorbing dyes thin films
7. Organic/polymer thin films
8. Ink thin films
9. Nano-crystalline cells
10. Indium phosphide
11. Single-junction III-V cells
12. Multi-junction cells
    a. Gallium arsenide based cells
    b. Germanium based cells
    c. CPV solar cells

Thin Films PV Structure

As the name implies, "thin films" are just that; very thin films (layers) of organic or inorganic materials. Thin film PV (TFPV) modules consist of several very thin layers (thin films) of different materials piled up on top of each other, to form a structure that is suitable for trapping and converting sunlight into electricity. The thickness of each film is usually several microns (1 micron is 0.001mm, or 0.0004 inch). Visualize the thickness of a human hair (avg. 100 microns) and you'll get a good idea of what 100 microns is—50-100 times the thickness of an individual thin film.

Now visualize layering these super-thin films until there are 8 or 10. This is how TFPV structures are made and it is what they look like. A better visualization might be using a piece of Scotch tape as an example. Standard Scotch tape is ~0.060mm thick, or 60 microns, which is at least 10-20 times thicker than most thin films. Yes, the entire thin film structure—all different layers combined in your TFPV modules is many times thinner than a Scotch tape strip, and the different layers (different chemical compounds) are even thinner. They are stacked on top of each other, held together by weak electro-mechanical forces of complex nature and behavior. We'll take a closer look at these forces and the related interactions in this text.

Thin films of any type and size are affected by chemical, mechanical, thermodynamic and electric forces and changes in, between, and around them. TFPV structures also depend heavily on the surrounding materials, glass, laminates, etc., and components in the PV module for protection. It's a complex picture, yes, but well understood by design and process engineers and research scientists, thanks to the broad experience we've gained from the semiconductor industry which is based on thin films and processes.

NOTE: Remember this picture, because we will revisit it later on in this chapter, to explain the behavior of thin films in TFPV modules under different environmental conditions.

Thin Film Manufacturing Process

So let's see how these thin films and TFPV modules are made today:

Thin Film Deposition Processes

Thin film PV cells and modules manufacturing processes, similar to thin film processes used in the semiconductor industry, are well controlled. The level of process control depends only on the quality requirements and budget restrictions. The actual thin films deposition is usually done on a substrate (glass, plastic or such) which has been thoroughly inspected, cleaned and otherwise properly prepared for the deposition step.

a. Substrate preparation is a key factor in maintaining process control, and determines the overall quality, performance and longevity of the final product. Basically, dirty substrate will not only produce defective product, but will also contaminate the equipment, forcing lengthy and expensive clean-up procedures. Pre-deposition cleaning of large glass substrates (panes) is done in automated washers, where brushes, soap and/or high pressure water solutions remove all particles and organic material from both surfaces. The glass panes are then rinsed with DI water and dried with forced air and heat applied to both surfaces. This step is also critical, because moisture retained on the large surfaces is a great enemy of vacuum/plasma processes and could seriously affect product quality.

b. The substrate is then placed in a large vacuum chamber (usually on a horizontal or vertical conveyor belt that moves the material along the process path), where powerful vacuum pumps suck out all the air, to clear any mechanical (dust) and chemical contaminants (reactive gasses and water). The substrates are then usually heated, to remove any residual moisture and to heat the surface close to the temperature of the deposited species, reducing potential thermal disequilibrium and stress of the thin films to be deposited on it. Argon gas-based DC or RF plasma is ignited and maintained at a proper pressure and power density during the process, facilitating the deposition process and the related reactions.

c. The material to be deposited as thin film is then evaporated (by actually melting the material and directing the resulting vapor clouds onto the deposit surface), or it is sputtered (by dislodging small clusters of the material via high voltage-generated ion bombardment) onto the substrate. These processes are also called chemical vapor deposition (CVD) and physical vapor deposition (PVD), respectively.

In both cases thin film material particles impinge on and adhere to the heated substrate surface on impact. The strength of the adhesion between film and substrate, or between the individual films, depends on the design and execution quality of the entire process sequence—quality of all materials, cleanliness of substrate and chamber interior, vacuum integrity, actual process temperature, forward and reverse plasma and substrate bias power levels, time duration, partial and total gas pressures, speed, and other process variables.

d. Coated substrate with the films deposited on top of it is taken out of the chamber and exposed to a number of additional operations, such as wet chemistry treatment, rinsing, drying, annealing, and wire attachment. The above CVD, PVD and wet chem processes are repeated several times for some devices, following strict process and quality control procedures all through the sequence. Upon completion of the PV structure creation, the substrate with the deposited thin films is joined to similar substrate (glass usually) with the help of adhesives and encapsulants. Thus, TFPV modules are tested, sorted and packaged for shipment to lucky customers.

Process and Device Issues

No process is perfect, and a defect could be generated at any step of the manufacturing process, including the tightly controlled thin film deposition processes in the semiconductor fabs. Starting with the basics, materials selection is paramount for obtaining quality product. "Garbage in, garbage out," goes the saying. So the quality of the substrates, process chemicals and gasses, and all consumables must meet and exceed specifications—not a simple task. The different pieces of process equipment must be well taken care of, tuned and qualified periodically, to make sure they are in good shape and operating within spec.

a. Step one of the thin film process is cleaning substrate materials. Contaminated cleaning materials or equipment or improper procedures will render the glass surface unsuitable for proper adhesion of deposited films. Cleaning the substrate with poorly selected chemicals, or shoddy procedures, might even introduce fatal impurities, such as Cu, K, Na, Fe metal ions, and phosphates. These impurities would eventually start their own demolition processes from within the thin film structure enclosed in the PV module, reducing its efficiency and longevity.

Dirt, particles, fingerprints, residual moisture, and strong electrostatic charge on the glass surface entering the vacuum chamber will have a profound, usually negative, effect on process integrity and final product quality. These are only few of the things to watch for at this stage of the process.

b. The plasma deposition process could also introduce impurities and defects in film structures if improper parameters or dirty hardware are used. Impurities in carrier gasses, contaminated vacuum chamber walls, back-streaming vacuum pumps, unplanned drops or increases of total or partial pressure, air leaks, process time or belt speed discrepancies are process abnormalities which could introduce other impurities or create defects with immediate or latent problems.

c. Out-of-spec process materials and consumables could be blamed for many process failures. Poor quality substrates, contaminated gasses and chemicals (overlooked during incoming quality control procedures) could cause slight or very great defects in the finished product. But most often, it is the process itself that creates problems in thin film manufacturing.

Generally, there are a number of known, unknown, controlled and uncontrolled manufacturing process factors and variables in most thin film deposition sequences:

a. Human error is the #1 variable in high-volume thin film manufacturing. People tend to cut corners, improvise, push the wrong buttons, rush through operation, maintenance and inspection steps, etc. These kinds of workplace behaviors cause defects of unpredictable proportions and consequences. Handling substrate materials and consumables, as well as operating the complex process equipment requires highly trained engineers, technicians and operators, who in many cases have bad habits that are hard to break even with the best of training.

b. Equipment quality and malfunctions are #2 on the list of process-related variables in sophisticated thin film manufacturing operations. Thin film process equipment is complex in its design, operation and maintenance. Most production equipment made now is of good quality, but even the best equipment can malfunction and create headaches.

Key components and process control instrumentation slowly drift out of spec over time, and product quality could vary from batch to batch. One serious drift in the multi-step process could cause serious defects in a batch. Anomalies during processing also occur unexpectedly and quickly; if not handled promptly and properly they could cause quality problems.

c. Poor quality supplies, materials and chemicals purchased from third-party manufacturers are another serious problem that we encounter in the thin film process. Since high volume operations use a lot of outsourced materials, the incoming quality is hard to verify 100% of the time, so any problem at the third-party vendor's plant will have negative effects in the final PV product quality.

A number of additional factors and variables affect the quality of thin film PV modules, but it suffices to say that the TFPV manufacturing process consists of dozens of different materials and complex process steps, each of which must be immaculately designed, planned, executed and controlled. Basically, the lowest quality of any process step (or material) in the process sequence determines the highest quality of the final product. One mishandled step, or one bottle of contaminated chemical or gas, could lead to rejection of a batch of modules, or worse—to their failure in the field, where things get very expensive...and embarrassing.

TFPV Functional Considerations

Even though the electro-mechanical and chemical properties of PV thin films are thoroughly studied and well understood, improper design and manufacturing procedures are still encountered at times. We already discussed the TFPV manufacturing process and the related issues, so now we'll take a closer look at the behavior of thin films in TFPV modules. (Refer to Figure 4-33.)

Remember our discussion at the beginning of this chapter that thin films are 1 micron thin, or thinner, and that this is less than 1/100 the thickness of human hair. Recall, too, that the entire thin film structure in TFPV modules is several times thinner than a piece of Scotch tape.

Some of these thin films are so thin in places that you could actually count the molecules across the film thickness, if you had a way to do that. And as you look at thin film very closely, you'll see all kinds of imperfections as well; interruptions, distortions, breaks, cracks, splits, slips, pits, voids, bubbles, lose particles, and all kinds of other sub-structures in/on the thin film structure. In other words, the films, although they look perfectly smooth and uniform to the naked eye, are anything but.

And you will also notice in Figure 4-33 a clear delineation between the films—the boundary (interface) between each pair. These are very special areas, which play a huge role in the performance of the PV devices made out of these films. They are also the weakest points in most thin film structures, because it is where the electrical resistivity, mechanical stress and chemical degradation are usually initiated, stored, executed and amplified. These boundaries represent the time and place where the process was interrupted and switched from one material deposition to another, and/or from one deposition step to another. This involves moving the substrate, which could be accompanied by longer than specified delays, switching gasses, changing vacuum and plasma power levels, and a number of additional inter-step process modifications.

Figure 4-33. Cross section of a typical TFPV structure

The inter-step changes do cause momentary out-of-control conditions which could cause a number of process and product abnormalities such as contamination of the surface by carrier gases or pump oil, and temporary process destabilization (total and partial pressures, gas mixing, power fluctuations, temperature imbalance, etc.). All the combinations of possible process abnormalities and extraordinary scenarios are too much to discuss here, but you get the idea; this is a most complex set of parameters and conditions that must be executed perfectly all the time at all process steps, to obtain the best quality of final product. For the purposes of this writing, however, we'll just agree that the inter-layer boundaries (interfaces) are extremely critical areas which have different properties than the parent materials.

These areas are more fragile, so there is a limit as to how much abuse they can handle during long-term field operation.

Each material pair and its interface in the thin film stack has different properties. The thin films have well defined mechanical, chemical, electric and thermal stress limits. Equally so, the interfaces have different properties, depending on the critical de-bonding energy and chemical inertness levels specific for each interface between two different thin film materials.

How much mechanical stress, heat, electrical charge, chemical reactivity or combination of these will be needed to cause delamination, adhesion problems, mechanical, electrical or chemical changes and/or disintegration of the bond between the materials, and eventually the materials themselves?

Amazingly, the energy levels and forces acting in these areas are very small, relative to the mass of the materials and strength of the films; i.e., Van der Wall (VDW) =/~0.001-0.4 eV/bond, H-bonds =/~0.11- 0.44 eV/bond, SiO_2 cracking in water E =/~1.39 eV/bond. So, without getting into much detail, just looking at such extremely small numbers, one can deduct that it doesn't take much effort to damage an interface which will affect the entire thin film structure.

Additionally, in most cases, many of these forces are acting together—on and off many times daily for the duration (30 years or more) of the module's on-sun operation. Worst of all, once these destructive processes have started, they cannot be stopped. As a matter of fact, things usually only get worse with every daily cycle, and can accelerate quickly.

Now we'll take a closer look at the major destructive processes acting upon thin film PV structures.

Mechanical Stress—
Thin Films and Boundaries Disintegration

Thin film modules are exposed to mechanical stress from the moment they leave the production line. Never-ending vibration, hitting, rubbing, pushing, pressing and squeezing of the modules affect the layers in the thin film structure. Stress is induced during handling, packing, transport (long truck and train rides are the worst), installation (careless handling during installation is a major problem) and operation (high winds, hail and storms are some of the worst enemies). Each of these actions and interactions increases the mechanical stress in the film structure.

Because of the films' non-uniformity, and the different coefficients of expansion of the different adjacent films, there is a lot of stress and friction within each film and among the adjacent films. As with other materials stuck together, they will be slipping and sliding, expanding and contracting, forever bending, pulling, pushing and tugging against each other and the materials around them—whether thin films, encapsulants, glass, or other.

In most cases these activities will produce some usually unpredictable changes. The question is what and how bad will these changes be? Stress, cracks, voids and general weakening of the thin film system is expected with time, followed at times by partial or full disintegration of the films, depending on operating conditions. Results from these changes would be expressed as gradual loss of power, intermittent power, and finally complete failure.

Electrical and Heat Stress

Generation of electric energy is the primary purpose of any PV module. The photoelectric process and the accompanying extraction and transmission of electrons (electric current) through the different thin film layers, their interfaces and contacts is usually accompanied by heat generation. Parasitic (excess) heat is generated when the resistivity of the materials increases, which inevitably happens when the internal temperature of the module goes up—and it starts going up from the second the sun hits the module. The higher the sun, the more electricity is generated, and the higher the resistivity goes.

On a bright sunny day in the desert, the module interior could see temperatures as high as 180°F, or more. The heat build-up is a combination of the simultaneous increase of air temperatures and internal resistivity of the thin films and their interfaces. This heat is not enough to damage or destroy the films, since each one can withstand much higher temperatures. The excess heat, however, forces the materials to expand and shift in one direction. They then shrink at night and move in the opposite direction, which creates friction at the interfaces and stresses the materials in each layer.

The more temperature differential the layers are exposed to, the more they stress and shift.

Now imagine these films, packed tightly in the module, getting very hot during the day in the desert (measured inside module temperatures exceed 190°F in Arizona deserts), and freezing at below −20°F at night in winter. This process goes non-stop, 365 times a year.

This translates into ~3.650 min-max temperature cycles in 10 years, and close to 11,000 cycles in 30 years. Can the thin films withstand this constant push and pull, up and down, left and right? Would one of them give up and break down mechanically? Would that cause an untimely power drop, or complete failure?

The results from one, two, or even hundreds, of these cycles would go unnoticed, but the non-stop (30 years and over 10,000 cycles) effect of the never-ending push and pull of the layers will fatigue thin film structure, shifting it into a different performance mode. As the module gets older, the resistivity of the films and their interfaces increases proportionally, according to the internal heat build-up and dissipation within the module. Electrical output will drop by ~1.0% every year, partially due to the above effects, or combinations of them.

There is no getting away from the harmful effects of excess heat and moisture in field operations. They are variables in the PV generation equation, which cannot be ignored, but are hard to control.

Chemical Reactions and Thin Films Decomposition

All unprotected thin films—without exception—react with many chemicals. It is usually the interface (the boundary between the films) that is affected first and is where problems can be observed. Some films and interfaces will disintegrate instantly with a simple touch (human sweat contains salts), while others will withstand weak chemicals, and some will require strong acids or bases to dissolve or decompose them or their interface.

a. Two different thin film materials at rest

b. The same materials at 190° F

Figure 4-34. Thin film behavior under elevated temperature and humidity

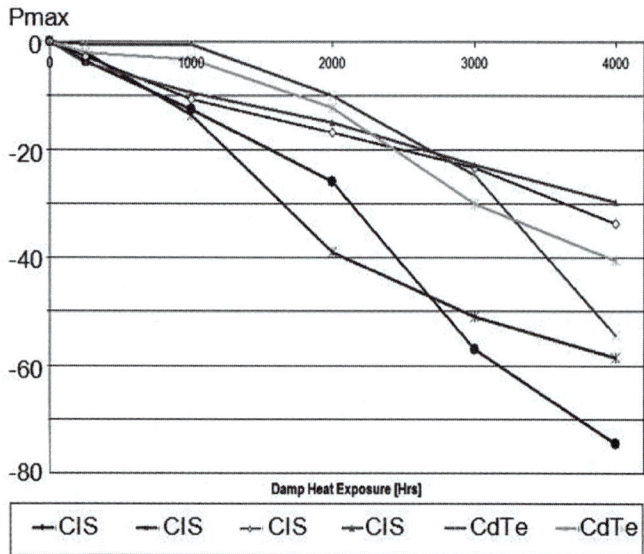

Figure 4-35. Damp heat degradation of CIS and CdTe modules (17) (post-light heat soaking)

Nevertheless, all thin films are subject to mechanical and chemical changes under certain conditions.

CdTe, CIGS, a-Si and other thin film structures, as well as interfaces between layers, are affected in a similar fashion. Some of them are more chemically resistive than others, but prolonged exposure to weak acids (brought on by moist air, or contained in rain water) penetrating the module lamination (or entering through cracked glass) will eventually cause the films to react, delaminate and decompose. The type and speed of the decomposition process, and the newly created chemical species, will be determined by the types of thin films, the active chemicals' species and the types of reactions these invoke.

Again, we count on the encapsulants and glass or metal frame to keep moisture, air and related chemicals out of the module for 30 years. How many modules will survive the test of time? What would be the total failure rate? These are questions to which we simply have no answers because there are no precedents.

Moisture ingress is the culprit of pronounced power output degradation of CIS and CdTe modules in Figure 4-36, reducing their output significantly within 6 months of exposure. This example also leads to the conclusion that good encapsulation is paramount, but since it is never perfect, harsh climate conditions will force moisture to penetrate thin film structure and change its composition and behavior, resulting in power loss and eventual failure.

Environmental effects initiate and accelerate the evolution of defects in TFPV modules. Damaged encapsulation allows moisture to penetrate modules and attack layers, resulting in their delamination or separation from the substrate, as shown in Figure 4-36.

Just as in tooth decay, once moisture or environmental acids and gasses find a gap in the encapsulation they start the decomposition process which cannot be stopped without outside intervention. A dentist has the option to mechanically separate (drill) decay out of the tooth surface, but drilling decomposition damage out of a TFPV module is impossible. This means that modules will start losing power at a rate proportional to the inflicted damage, usually much quicker than the standard 1.0% power loss per annum. Eventually—when the internal decay has affected large parts of the critical areas of the thin film structure—the affected modules will fail completely and must be replaced. The process is accelerated when affected modules are exposed to extreme heat and humidity (see Figure 4-37).

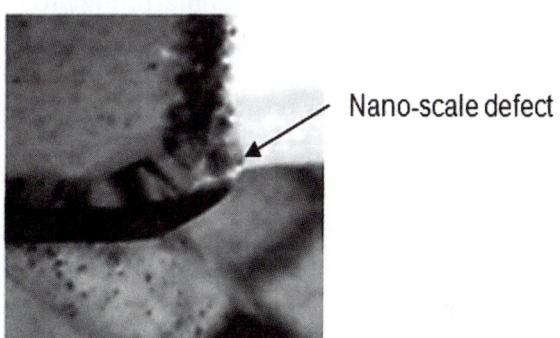

Figure 4-37. The invasion process has started (18)

The sum of effects depicted in Figure 4-38 play a significant role in compromising thin film structure integrity. Some of these are vicious and fast acting, while some are slow and cause less damage. The actions of each effect are hard to predict, because different operating conditions have their own peculiarities. It is even harder to predict the combined effect of these processes during non-stop, 30-year, on-sun operation.

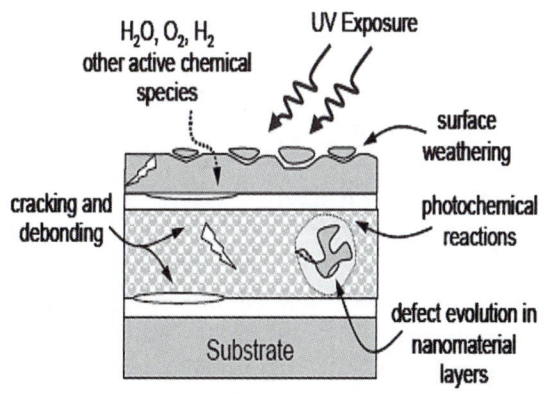

Figure 4-38. Thin films failure mechanisms (18)

The inevitable exposure to excess UV and IR radiation, thermal cycling, mechanical stress, moisture ingress, and chemically active environmental species

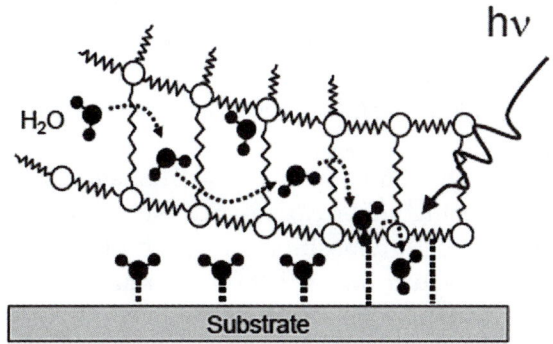

**Figure 4-36.
The chemical invasion process on molecularlevel (18)**

leads to unpredictable degradation, and unreliable kinetics and reliability models, because of the ever changing types and numbers of forces acting on the materials in inhospitable regions.

In summary, we don't know what to expect of fragile thin film layers in TFPV modules exposed to unending mechanical, chemical, electrical and thermal action and on-sun operation for 30 years or more.

Still, there is enough evidence to conclude that PV modules made with quality materials via proper processing would have a greater chance to survive over time than those made of low-quality materials, and/or using poor design and flawed manufacturing processes.

Below we review each of these technologies and their specific structure and function, focusing on their use in large-scale PV power generation and related issues.

The Major TFPV Technologies

We classify these PV technologies as "major" for the purposes of this text, because they are presently considered for large-scale PV power generation projects.

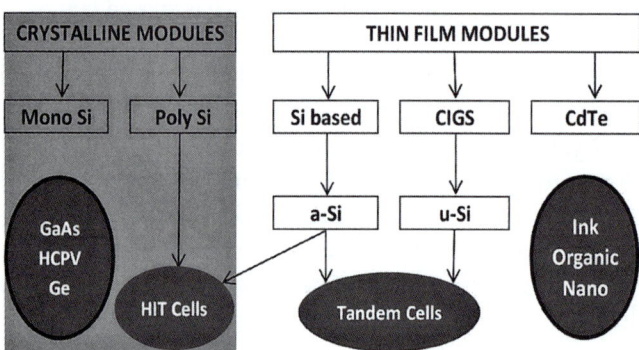

Figure 4-39. Key PV technologies 2010

These are the cadmium telluride, CIGS, and amorphous silicon thin films:

Cadmium Telluride (CdTe)

Cadmium telluride (CdTe) is a type of solar cell and module based on thin films of the heavy metal cadmium and its compounds, cadmium telluride (CdTe) and cadmium sulfide (CdS). CdTe is an efficient light-absorbing material, quite adaptable for the manufacture of thin-film solar cells and modules. Compared to other thin-film materials, CdTe is easier to deposit in mass production environments and more suitable for large-scale production.

CdTe bandgap is 1.48 eV, which makes it almost perfect for PV conversion purposes. At 16.5% demon-

strated efficiency in the lab, it is a candidate for a major role in the energy future. Mass production modules are sold with 8-9% efficiency. No significant increase is expected with the present production materials and methods, although manufacturing costs are down—well below $1.0/Wp. This price drop, however, is in response to pressure from low-cost c-Si manufacturers (mostly Chinese), so it might be a temporary situation. Prices in the $1.00-$1.50 range seem most reasonable for TFPV modules.

With a direct optical energy bandgap of 1.48 eV and high optical absorption coefficient for photons with energies greater than 1.5 eV, only a few microns of CdTe are needed to absorb most of the incident light. Because only very thin layers are needed, material costs are minimized, and because a short minority diffusion length (a few microns) is adequate, expensive materials processing time and costs can be avoided.

The structure of a CdTe TFPV module, as shown in Figure 4-40, consists of a front contact, usually a transparent conductive oxide (TCO), deposited onto a glass substrate. The TCO layer has a high optical transparency in the visible and near-infrared regions and high n-type conductivity. This is followed by the deposition of a CdS window layer, the CdTe absorber layer, and finally the back contact.

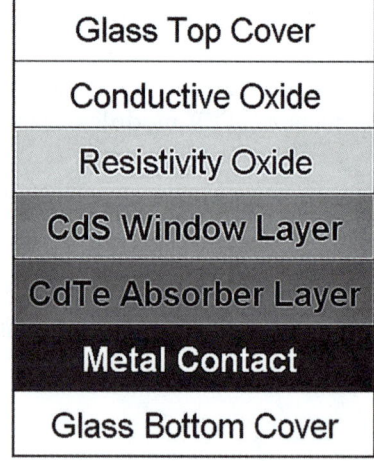

Figure 4-40. CdTe/CdS thin-film solar cell

For high-volume devices, the CdS layer is usually deposited using either closed-space sublimation (CSS) or chemical bath deposition, although other methods have been used to investigate the fundamental properties of devices in the research laboratory. In all cases, mass production and automation is possible, which is the greatest advantage of this technology.

The CdTe p-type absorber layer, 3-10 μm thick, can

be deposited using a variety of techniques including physical vapor deposition (PVD), CSS, electrodeposition, and spray pyrolysis. To produce the most efficient devices, an activation process is required in the presence of CdCl2 regardless of the deposition technique. This treatment is known to recrystallize the CdTe layer, passivating grain boundaries in the process, and promoting inter-diffusion of the CdS and CdTe at the interface.

Forming an ohmic contact to CdTe, however, is difficult because the work function of CdTe is higher than all metals. This can be overcome by creating a thin p+ layer by etching the surface in bromine methanol or $HNO_3/H3PO_4$ acid solution and depositing Cu-Au alloy or ZnTe:Cu. This creates a thin, highly doped region that carriers can tunnel through.

However, Cu is a strong diffuser in CdTe and causes performance to degrade with time. Another approach is to use a very low bandgap material, like Sb2Te3, followed by Mo or W. This technique does not require a surface etch and the device performance does not degrade with time.

CdTe PV modules manufacturing is a much more sophisticated process than that of the conventional c-Si modules which uses simple 1970s manufacturing equipment, materials and processes. CdTe TFPV modules are manufactured with the help of modern, complex and expensive semiconductor type equipment and processes. Because of that, the precision and accuracy of the resulting process steps, and ergo the quality of the final product, are limited only by the quality of the materials and supplies, and the capabilities of the engineers, technicians and operators on the production lines.

CdTe thin-film solar modules are now being mass produced very cheaply, and it is expected with economies of scale that they will achieve the cost reduction needed to compete directly with other forms of energy production in the near future. Since CdTe thin film PV devices still have a long way to go to achieve maximum efficiencies, it will be interesting to see which materials and methods are most successful.

The most efficient CdTe/CdS solar cells (efficiencies of up to 16.5%) have been produced using a Cd_2SnO4 TCO layer which is more transmissive and conductive than the classical SnO_2-based TCOs, and including a Zn_2SnO_4 buffer layer which improves the quality of the device interface.

CdTe PV research, done by manufacturers, universities and R&D labs focuses on some of these challenges:

a. Boosting efficiencies by exploring innovative transparent conducting oxides that allow more light into the cell to be absorbed and at the same time more efficiently collect the electrical current generated by the cell.

b. Studying mechanisms such as grain boundaries that can limit voltage.

c. Understanding the degradation some CdTe devices exhibit at the contacts and redesigning the devices to minimize this phenomenon.

d. Designing module packages that minimize any outdoor exposure to moisture.

e. Engaging aggressively in both indoor and outdoor cell and module stress testing.

These efforts are geared to address the main problems with CdTe PV modules: a) the relatively low efficiency which contributes to using more land and mounting hardware, b) temperature power degradation, c) annual power degradation, and other negative long-term effects.

Availability of the rare metals used in CdTe TFPV technology and their toxicity are other serious issues which manufacturers and regulators have put on the back burner. Let's hope that we won't have to wait for a serious accident before bringing these issues out in the open and discussing possible solutions.

CIGS Solar Cells

Early solar cells and modules of this type were based on the use of $CuInSe_2$ (CIS). However, it was rapidly realized that incorporating Ga to produce $Cu(In,Ga)Se_2$ (CIGS) structure results in widening the energy bandgap to 1.3 eV and an improvement in material quality, producing solar cells with enhanced efficiencies. CIGS have a direct energy bandgap and high optical absorption coefficient for photons with energies greater than the bandgap, such that only a few microns of material are needed to absorb most of the incident light, with consequent reductions in material and production costs.

The best performing CIGS solar cells are deposited on soda lime glass in the sequence—back contact, absorber layer, window layer, buffer layer, TCO, and then the top contact grid. The back contact is a thin film of Mo deposited by magnetron sputtering, typically 500-1000 nm thick.

The CIGS absorber layer is formed mainly by the co-evaporation of the elements either uniformly deposited, or using the so-called three-stage process, or

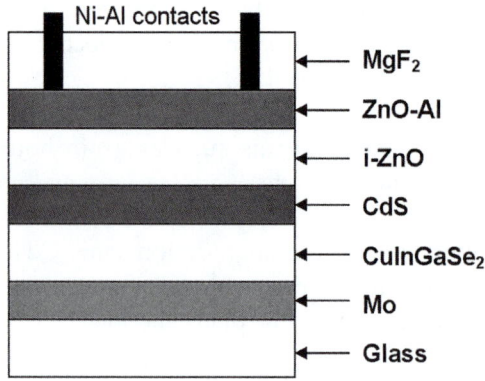

Figure 4-41. CIGS cell cross section

the deposition of the metallic precursor layers followed by selenization and/or sulfidization. Co-evaporation yields devices with the highest performance while the latter deposition process is preferred for large-scale production.

Both techniques require a processing temperature >500°C to enhance grain growth and recrystallization. Another requirement is the presence of Na, either directly from the glass substrate or introduced chemically by evaporation of a Na compound. The primary effects of Na introduction are grain growth, passivation of grain boundaries, and a decrease in absorber layer resistivity.

The junction is usually formed by the chemical bath deposition of a thin (50-80 nm) window layer. CdS has been found to be the best material, but alternatives such as ZnS, ZnSe, In_2S_3, (Zn,In)Se, Zn(O,S), and Mg-ZnO can also be used.

The buffer layer can be deposited by chemical bath deposition, sputtering, chemical vapor deposition, or evaporation, but the highest efficiencies have been achieved using a wet process as a result of the presence of $Cd2+$ ions. A 50 nm intrinsic ZnO buffer layer is then deposited and prevents any shunts. The TCO layer is usually ZnO:Al 0.5–1.5 μm. The cell is completed by depositing a metal grid contact Ni/Al for current collection, then encapsulated.

CIGS solar cells have been produced under lab conditions with efficiencies of 19.5%, and lately modules with efficiencies of 15.7% were verified as well. Commercial, mass produced, CIGS PV module efficiency, however, is still lower than CdTe PV modules—and this will have a major impact on their future unless ways to increase their efficiency and reduce their costs are found soon.

CIGS TFPV modules have similar problems as those plaguing CdTe TFPV technologies. They have low efficiency, require larger mounting infrastructure,

exhibit power loss under excess heat and have a significant annual degradation rate. Scarcity of materials and related toxicity issues are, as in the CdTe PV case, on the back burner for now. These issues must be evaluated from the point of view of large-scale installations, where thousands and millions of these modules will be installed. In such cases, minute amounts of toxic materials in each module are multiplied mega times and become a substantial threat to the environment. Also, special measures must be taken for proper disposal or recycling of these modules.

CIGS research is focused on several of today's challenges of this promising technology:

a. Pushing efficiencies even higher by exploring the chemistry and physics of the junction formation and by examining concepts to allow more of the high-energy part of the solar spectrum to reach the absorber layer.

b. Dropping costs and facilitating the transition to a commercial stage by increasing the yield of CIS modules—which means increasing the percentage of modules and cells that make it intact through the manufacturing process.

c. Decreasing manufacturing complexity and cost, and improving module packaging.

NOTE: At a meeting of PV specialists in February 2011, called PV Module Reliability Workshop (PVMRW), the degradation and longevity of PV technologies and products were discussed by representatives of several manufacturing companies. The susceptibility to moisture of SIGS modules was addressed as one of the major concerns, and packaging solutions were presented. Location-specific reliability tests and evaluations were also among the topics, which is a step in the right direction. We are glad that such open discussions are underway, since this is the fastest way to resolve the issues and put these promising technologies on the energy market.

Amorphous Silicon

Amorphous silicon (a-Si) is produced via thin film processes, based on depositing thin layers of silicon films on different substrates. Silicon thin-film cells are mainly deposited by chemical vapor deposition (CVD), typically plasma-enhanced (PE-CVD), using silane and hydrogen reactive and carrier gasses for the actual deposition. Depending on the deposition parameters and the stoichiometry of the process, this reaction can yield different types of thin film structures, such as amorphous silicon (a-Si, or a-Si:H), protocrystalline silicon or nano-crystalline silicon (nc-Si or nc-Si:H), also called micro-crystalline silicon.

These types of silicon feature dangling and twist-ed bonds, which result in deep defects (energy levels in the bandgap) as well as deformation of the valence and conduction bands (band tails), which lead to reduced efficiency. Proto-crystalline silicon mixed with nano-crystalline silicon is optimal for high, open-circuit voltage.

Solar cells and modules made from these materials tend to have lower energy conversion efficiency than those made from bulk silicon, but have some operating advantages (such as lower temperature degradation). They are also less expensive to produce, although the capital equipment expense is greater, due to equipment complexity.

a-Si has a somewhat higher bandgap (1.7 eV) than crystalline silicon (c-Si) (1.1 eV), which means that it absorbs the visible part of the solar spectrum more efficiently than the infrared portion. nc-Si has about the same bandgap as c-Si, so nc-Si and a-Si can advantageously be combined in thin layers, creating a layered cell called a "tandem cell," where the top a-Si cell absorbs the visible light and leaves the infrared part of the spectrum for the bottom cell in nc-Si.

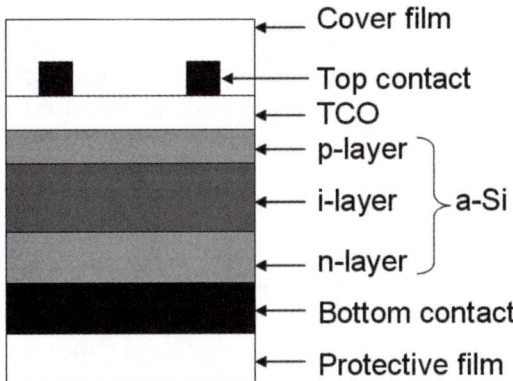

Figure 4-42. a-Si thin film structure

The biggest problem with a-Si TFPV technology and a barrier to its success, however, is its low efficiency. Today's best cell efficiencies are about 12% in the lab, which is almost 50% lower than other PV technologies. Mass produced a-Si cells and modules are in the 8% efficiency range today.

A second problem with a-Si is its manufacturing cost as related to initial capital investment, which is quite high as compared with the competing PV technologies. Two proposed solutions to this problem are high-

er manufacturing rates, and batch (simultaneous) processing of multiple modules. Good progress has been made in rates that are 3-10 times higher than those being used in production, but all this is still on a lab scale and yet to be proven in reality and on a large scale.

On the positive side, while some of the more efficient cells and modules lose about 20-30% of their output in the field, due to excess heat exposure, a-Si loses only about 5-10%, due to its lower temperature coefficient. Also, the active thin film structure is composed mainly of silicon films which have inert and homogeneous natures that show better chemical and mechanical stability than some of the competing thin films—in case of an encapsulation failure. a-Si modules are also more resistive to the negative effects of shading in the field. Of equal importance, a-Si modules do not contain any hazardous materials, which is paramount where large-scale PV installations are concerned. These qualities put a-Si on the top of the list of PV technologies suitable for large-scale power generation in deserts and other inhospitable areas.

Even with low efficiency (well under 10%), a-Si thin film technology is being successfully developed for building-integrated photovoltaics (BIPV) in the form of semi-transparent solar cells which can be applied as window glazing. These cells function as window tinting while generating electricity. It remains to be seen if the amount of generated electricity covers initial and operating expenses.

A triple-junction a-Si TFPV power system has been operating near Bakersfield, CA, for several years, and is providing proof of the excellent performance of this technology. The 500 kW grid-connects system has been performing well, meeting or exceeding its design goals. Performance data from this larger-scale installation confirm data obtained from smaller a-Si systems and prove that this thin film PV technology can be successfully used in large-scale power plants, if the low efficiency can be justified.

Great research effort is underway at universities and R&D labs around the world, geared towards solving efficiency and cost issues and obtaining a-Si that is truly competitive in the energy market. a-Si manufacturers need to work on understanding the key areas of this technology and the processes, and focus on their optimization by:

a.   Improving the light-stabilized electronic quality of a-Si and low-gap a-Si:H cells to achieve broader spectrum conversion, and increased and stable overall efficiency.

b.   Increasing the growth rates of a-Si, a-SiGe, etc. layers while maintaining high electronic quality, to obtain increased throughput and reduced capital cost.

c.   Developing high-growth-rate methods for nanocrystalline silicon while maintaining high electronic quality as needed for increased efficiency, stability and reduced cost.

d.   Understanding and controlling light-induced degradation in a-Si:H as needed for increased efficiency and understanding of the intrinsic limits of the efficiency.

e.   Developing *in-situ* in-line process monitoring for increased yield.

f.   Improving light management to obtain maximum efficiency.

g.   Improving stability and conversion efficiency of a-Si modules in actual use by addressing the Staebler-Wronski negative effects, where the conversion efficiency of the a-Si module decreases when it is first exposed to sunlight.

h.   Reducing capital equipment costs for manufacturing a-Si panels by improved manufacturing processes that include increasing the deposition rates.

i.   Improving module packaging designs to make them more resilient to outdoor environments and less susceptible to glass breakage or moisture ingress.

j.   Developing new module designs for building-integrated applications.

These and other similarly complex issues must be addressed, because the future of a-Si PV products depends on their resolution.

NOTE: The untimely exit of Applied Materials from the a-Si equipment manufacturing business in the summer of 2010 cast a shadow of doubt over the a-Si technology. Applied Materials is an example of a newcomer in the PV field with great potential and ambition, but inexperienced with the energy market's wants, needs, and overall peculiarities. Applied Materials had its own reasons to leave the field, but a-Si TFPV is here to stay. It is a promising technology that has already found niche markets, and will become even more popular with time, until it finds its place in the large-scale energy markets.

THE DEVELOPING THIN FILM TECHNOLOGIES

The thin film PV (TFPV) technologies we classify as "developing" for the purposes of this text are; silicon ribbon, epitaxial silicon, light absorbing dyes, organic thin films, ink thin films, nano-crystalline, and indium phosphide thin film.

Silicon Ribbon

Called EFG ("edge defined film fed growth"), this method is not exactly a "thin film" process as we know it, but the resulting material is thin enough, so it belongs in this category. Here, a graphite dye is immersed into molten silicon, making it rise into the dye by capillary action. It is then pulled as a self-supporting very thin sheet of silicon which hardens in the air above the dye. It can then be cut in different shapes and sizes for processing into solar cells and modules.

This method is more efficient than conventional c-Si ingot and wafer processes in terms of producing c-Si substrates of exact thickness and avoiding slicing it into wafers. Conventional processes waste 20-40% of the silicon material, use a lot of energy, and produce tons of hazardous waste materials.

Another similar process we need to mention is called "dendritic web growth process." It consists of two dendrites which are placed into molten silicon and withdrawn quickly, causing the silicon to exit and solidify as a thin sheet. A modification of this method now in use is called the "string ribbon method," where two graphite strings are used (instead of the dendrites) to draw the silicon sheet, which makes process control much easier. Again, the silicon sheet can be cut into different shapes and sizes.

In all cases the silicon produced by these methods is multi-crystalline with a quality approaching that of the directionally solidified material. Although lab tests show efficiencies in the 17-18% range, solar modules made using silicon ribbons and produced via these methods, generally have efficiencies in the 10-12% range.

After the initial hoopla that silicon ribbon technologies would dominate the market, their share is quite small—less than 1% of total sales today—and does not seem to be growing. This is mostly due to the fact that the process is not easy to control, and the wafers' surface is not uniform enough, thus resulting in breakage, processing defects, and performance inefficiencies. The silicon sheets-forming process is also complex and uses a lot of energy, which makes it comparably more expensive than some of the other mass produced TFPV technologies.

Epitaxial Thin Film Silicon

The high cost of silicon material accounts for about half of the production cost of current conventional, industrial-type silicon solar cells. To reduce the amount of consumed silicon, the photovoltaics (PV) industry is counting on a number of options presently being developed. The most obvious is to move to thinner silicon substrates by producing thinner Si wafers, or shaving the thicker wafers, but this is proving hard to do for a number of reasons. A more feasible approach is the so-called epitaxial deposition of a thin film of silicon on a cheap substrate, thus creating efficient but cheap solar cells.

More than one approach can be used to create such a thin film cell:

Epitaxial Single Crystal sc-Si

To create an epitaxial thin-film solar cell on a cheap substrate we start with highly doped sc-Si wafers (e.g., from low-grade silicon or scrap Si material), and deposit an epi layer of Si by chemical vapor deposition (CVD). The resulting mix of a high quality epi layer and a cheap substrate is a compromise between high cost and efficiency, and yet offers a solution to gradual transition from a wafer-based (heavy material dependence) to a thin-film technology (less material and more sophisticated processing). This process is easier to implement than most other thin-film technologies today, but it remains to be seen if its efficiency and cost will be able to compete in the energy market.

Epitaxial Polysilicon Thin Film

To produce thin-film polysilicon solar cells, a thin layer (only a few microns) of polysilicon Si is deposited on a cheap foreign substrate, such as ceramic or high-temperature glass. These seed layers are then epitaxially thickened into absorber layers several microns thick using high-temperature CVD with a deposition rate exceeding 1 m/min.

Polycrystalline silicon films with grain sizes between 1-100 m appear to be particularly good candidates. Good polycrystalline silicon solar cells can be obtained using aluminum-induced crystallization of amorphous silicon. This process leads to very thin layers with an average grain size around 5 m. This technology is still in R&D stages, but shows high cost-reduction potential and might become very important, especially in case of silicon shortage, or very high prices in the future.

Light-absorbing Dyes (DSSC)

These are special types of dye-sensitized solar cells, where a ruthenium metalorganic dye (Ru-centered) is used as a monolayer of light-absorbing material. The dye-sensitized solar cell depends on a mesoporous layer of nanoparticulate titanium dioxide to greatly amplify the surface area (200-300 m^2/g TiO_2, as compared to approximately 10 m^2/g of flat single crystal).

Photogenerated electrons from the light-absorbing dye are passed on to the n-type TiO_2, and the holes are passed to an electrolyte on the other side of the dye. The circuit is completed by a redox couple in the electrolyte, which can be liquid or solid. This type of cell allows a more flexible use of materials, and is typically manufactured by screen printing and/or use of ultrasonic nozzles, with the potential for lower processing costs than those used for bulk solar cells.

However, the dyes in these cells also suffer from degradation under heat and UV light, and the cell casing is difficult to seal due to the solvents used in assembly. In spite of these problems, this is a popular emerging technology with special applications and significant commercial impact forecast within this decade.

The first commercial shipment of DSSC solar modules was recorded in July 2009 from G24i Innovations.

Organic/Polymer Solar Cells

Organic and polymer solar cells are built from thin films (typically 100 nm) of organic semiconductors such as small-molecule compounds like poly-phenylene vinylene, copper phthalo-cyanine (a blue or green organic pigment), and carbon fullerenes and fullerene derivatives, such as PCBM. Energy conversion efficiencies achieved to date using conductive polymers are low compared to inorganic materials. However, they were improved in the last few years and the highest NREL certified efficiency has reached 6.77%. In addition, these cells could be beneficial for some applications where mechanical flexibility and disposability are important.

These devices differ from inorganic semiconductor solar cells in that they do not rely on the large built-in electric field of a p-n junction to separate the electrons and holes created when photons are absorbed. Instead, the active region of an organic device consists of two materials—one which acts as an electron donor and the other as an acceptor. When a photon is converted into an electron hole pair, typically in the donor material, the charges tend to remain bound in the form of an exciton, and are separated when the exciton diffuses to the donor-acceptor interface.

The short exciton diffusion lengths of most polymer systems tend to limit the efficiency of such devices. Nanostructured interfaces, sometimes in the form of bulk hetero-junctions, can improve performance. Instability of the films, especially under harsh environmental effects is a major problem, which needs to be resolved, before full-scale implementation. Even with its advantages, this technology still has far to go to full market acceptance and serious deployment.

Ink PV Cells

A fairly new development, this light-activated power generating product is based on a unique and patented solvent-based silicon nanomaterial platform that can be applied like ink on any substrate. Developers claim that this approach has cost savings over traditional silicon products by using less silicon and having a more efficient manufacturing process as well as unique optical advantages.

This new technology consists of processing the quantum dots in the silicon "ink" in a way that makes it possible to use the old "roll-to-roll" printing technology used for printing on paper or film. Applying ink directly on any substrate (including a flexible one) allows applications such as tagless printing for clothing labels and portable chargers for consumer and military customers.

By controlling the sizes of the dots from 2 to 10 nm, the absorption or emission spectra of the resulting film can be controlled. This allows capture of everything from infrared to ultraviolet and the visible spectrum in between which is not possible with conventional technology.

The technology is also used as an efficient light source. By controlling particle size, you can produce light of any color or a combination of particle sizes that will give off white light. This application might provide additional, and possibly larger markets for this technology in the near future—at least in some specialized areas.

Nano-crystalline Solar Cells

These structures make use of some of the usual thin-film light absorbing materials, but are deposited as a very thin absorber on a substrate (supporting matrix) of conductive polymer or mesoporous metal oxide having a very high surface area to increase internal reflections. Hence, the probability of light absorption increases.

Using nanocrystals allows one to design architectures on the length scale of nanometers, the typical exciton diffusion length. In particular, single-nanocrystal (channel) devices, an array of single p-n junctions between the electrodes and separated by a period of about a diffusion length, represent a new architecture for solar cells and potentially high efficiency.

We envision the development of this type of photo-conversion to be in the R&D labs for a while yet, but it opens new possibilities in areas where other technologies simply cannot compete, thus opening promising niche markets for these cells.

III-V Materials and Devices

These are PV technologies based on the deposition of thin films of the III-V materials. These devices are divided into single- and multi-junction devices as follow:

Single-junction III-V Devices

A number of compounds such as gallium arsenide (GaAs), indium phosphide (InP), and gallium antimonide (GaSb) have adequate energy band gaps, high optical absorption coefficients, and good values of minority carrier lifetimes and mobility, making them excellent materials for making high efficiency solar cells. These materials are usually produced by the Czockralski or Bridgmann methods, which provide high quality materials with increased efficiency and reliability, but at a higher price.

After silicon, GaAs and InP (III-V compounds) are the most widely used materials for single-junction (SJ) solar cells manufacturing. These materials have optimum band gap values (1.4 and 1.3 respectively) for SJ conversion of sunlight. The construction of solar cells made of these materials is similar to the regular single-junction c-Si solar cells discussed earlier.

The major disadvantage of using III-V compounds for PV devices is the high cost of producing the materials they are made of and the related manufacturing processes. Also, crystal imperfections, including bulk impurities, severely reduce their efficiencies, so that only very high quality materials could be considered. Too, they are heavier than silicon, which requires the use of thinner cells, but they are weaker mechanically, so their design requires a delicate balance of thickness vs. weight.

The combination of high efficiency, high price, crystal imperfections intolerance, and mechanical weakness makes these devices useful for limited applications, where efficiency and overall behavior is more important than price. Thus they are not widely used in the general PV market, but still can be found in some important niche markets.

Multi-junction Cells and Devices

Single-junction PV devices convert only a portion of the sunlight (with photons just above the band-gap level of the semiconductor material). The problem is that photons with lower or higher energy do not generate electron-hole pairs and are lost as heat, which is also detrimental to the cells, reducing their efficiency and deteriorating them over time.

One way to solve this problem and to increase the efficiency of the PV devices is to add more junctions, thus creating multi-junction (MJ) solar cells. By selecting materials, properties, number and types of junctions, and manufacturing processes designed to capture the majority of sunlight photons, we can reach very high efficiencies.

Thus far, multi-junction solar cells made primarily using the III-V compounds have clearly proven that by minimizing thermalization and transmission losses, large improvements in efficiency can be made over those of single-junction cells. These devices find use in generating power for space applications and in concentrator systems. They show great promise for high efficiency and reliability under harsh climate conditions, such as those in the deserts.

Future development of multi-junction devices using low-cost thin-film technologies is especially promising for producing more efficient and yet inexpensive devices. Cost reductions will also be significant when thin-film technologies are directly produced on building materials other than glass, because many materials such as tiles and bricks can be substantially cheaper than glass and have much lower energy contents.

The major devices in this group are gallium arsenide-based, germanium-based, and CPV solar cells.

Gallium Arsenide Based Multi-junction Cells

High-efficiency multi-junction cells were originally developed for special applications such as satellites and space exploration, but at present, their use in terrestrial concentrators might be the lowest cost alternative in terms of $/kWh and $/W. These multi-junction cells consist of multiple thin films produced via metalorganic vapor phase epitaxy. A triple-junction cell, for example, may consist of the semiconductors GaAs, Ge, and GaInP2.

Each type of semiconductor will have a characteristic band gap energy which, loosely speaking, causes it to absorb light most efficiently at a certain color, or more precisely, to absorb electromagnetic radiation over a portion of the spectrum. Semiconductors are carefully chosen to absorb nearly all of the solar spectrum, thus generating electricity from as much of the available solar energy as possible.

GaAs-based multi-junction devices are some of the most efficient solar cells to date, reaching a record high

of 40.7% efficiency under "500-sun" solar concentration and laboratory conditions.

This technology is currently being utilized mostly in powering spacecrafts. Demand for tandem solar cells based on monolithic, series-connected, gallium indium phosphide (GaInP), gallium arsenide GaAs, and germanium Ge p-n junctions is rapidly rising. Prices are rising dramatically as well.

Twin-junction cells with indium gallium phosphide and gallium arsenide can be made on gallium arsenide wafers. Alloys of In.5Ga.5P through In.53Ga.47P may be used as the high band gap alloy. This alloy range allows band gaps in the range of 1.92eV to 1.87eV. The lower GaAs junction has a band gap of 1.42eV.

In spacecraft applications, cells have a poor current match due to a greater flux of photons above 1.87eV vs. those between 1.87eV and 1.42eV. This results in too little current in the GaAs junction, and hampers the overall efficiency since the InGaP junction operates below MPP current and the GaAs junction operates above MPP current. To improve current match, the InGaP layer is intentionally thinned to allow additional photons to penetrate to the lower GaAs layer.

In terrestrial concentrating applications, the scatter of blue light by the atmosphere reduces photon flux above 1.87eV, better balancing junction currents. GaAs was the material of the highest-efficiency solar cell, until recently, when Germanium-based MJ cells capped the world record at 41.4% efficiency.

Indium Phosphide Based Cells

Indium phosphide is used as a substrate to fabricate cells with band gaps between 1.35eV and 0.74eV. Indium phosphide has a band gap of 1.35eV. Indium gallium arsenide (In0.53Ga0.47As) is lattice matched to indium phosphide with a band gap of 0.74eV. A quaternary alloy of indium gallium arsenide phosphide can be lattice matched for any band gap in between the two.

Indium phosphide-based cells are being researched as a possible companion to gallium arsenide cells. The two differing cells may be either optically connected in series (with the InP cell below the GaAs cell), or through the use of spectra splitting using a dichroic filter.

The presence of varying quantities of toxic materials in these devices must be considered when planning their use in large quantities.

Germanium-based Single- and Multi-junction Cells

Germanium (0.86eV band gap) is a semiconductor material, with properties far superior to other substrate materials used for PV cells and modules. It is ~40-50%

more efficient than silicon and has a much lower temperature coefficient. It is several times more expensive than silicon, too, but with new superior slicing techniques, it can be cut into very thin wafers, saving a lot of material. This, combined with its higher efficiency and less degradation than silicon, could put it on the competitors' list within the next few years.

Germanium-based solar cells have been used mostly for space applications, but a number of manufacturers have geared up for mass producing them for high concentration HCPV and other high efficiency applications (the record is currently 42.3% efficiency).

CPV Solar Cells

Concentrating photovoltaics (CPV) is a branch of the PV industry, using special cells, optics and tracking mechanisms, developed in the 1970s by several companies under contracts and financing from the U.S. Department of Energy.

Early CPV systems used silicon-based CPV cells, which had a problem with elevated temperatures. These were later replaced by GaAs-based multi-junction cells, which have much higher efficiency, but still suffer from the effects of high temperatures. At first GaAs CPV cells were made by using straight gallium arsenide in the middle junction. Later cells have utilized $In_{0.015}Ga_{0.985}As$, due to the better lattice match to Ge, resulting in a lower defect density.

As you can see in Figure 4-43, CPV cells are complex structures, consisting of many layers (some deposited, some diffused) in, or piled on top of, Germanium semiconductor material, which has more superior process and performance characteristics than silicon.

Current efficiencies for InGaP/GaAs cells are in the 40% range and constantly increasing. Research into methods to produce band gaps in the range between the Ge and GaAs is ongoing. Lab cells using additional junctions between the GaAs and Ge junction have demonstrated efficiencies above 41%. InGaP/GaAs CPV cells on GaAs substrate have demonstrated 42.3% efficiency.

CPV cells are mounted under lenses, which concentrate sunlight falling on the cells 100 to 1000 times. This allows high efficiency and reliability, better land utilization, and other benefits. Cell-lens assemblies are mounted on trackers, which track the sun precisely through the day, providing the most power possible. Efficiencies of 30-32%, measured in the grid are obtainable with these devices. We foresee CPV technologies as the primary choice for installation and use in large-scale power plants, especially those in desert regions.

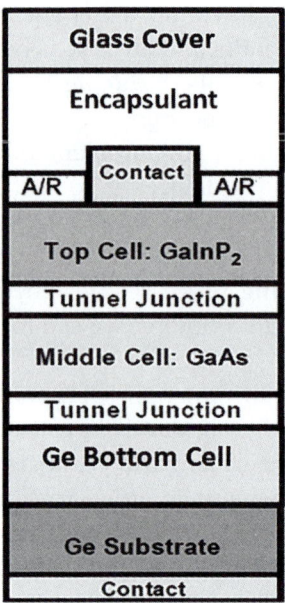

Figure 4-43. CPV cell

TEST RESULTS, ISSUES AND DEVELOPMENTS

To ensure the quality and proper function of TFPV modules, a number of tests must be conducted during the manufacturing process. Modules that pass these tests are then sent to EU and US labs for certification, to market these in the respective countries. Other sets of modules are sent for field testing to these or different facilities. While certification tests are standardized and mandatory (i.e., no modules can be sold without a UL label in the US), there are presently no official standardized field test requirements. So for now, the official certification tests are all we have to go by when evaluating TFPV modules.

Certification Test Results

We've been talking about potential problems with thin film PV modules and unintended consequences. Now we will take a close look at what official certification tests of all kinds of PV modules show. Keep in mind the above-mentioned issues as you review and evaluate the test results, and imagine what could happen if some of these modules were installed and operating in a power field.

PV Modules Tests 2007-2009

The results from a series of tests with several hundred PV modules from a dozen major PV module manufacturers, done by TUV Rheinland during 2007-2009 and published in *Photovoltaics International*, May 2010

(1), outline clearly the issues at hand with both, c-Si and thin film modules, as shown in Figure 4-44.

Thin Film PV Modules (extrapolated from Figure 4-44)

1% failed at the first wet resistance test (down from 20% in 2007)

12% failed after 200 thermal cycles* (down from 20% in 2007)

12% failed after 10 humidity freeze cycles† (down from 16 in 2007)

31% failed damp test (down from 70% in 2007). There is big problem here...

    5% failed outdoor exposure test.
    12% failed termination test.
    6% failed hail impact test.
    12% failed static load test.
    10% failed hotspot test.

In summary:
12% failed termination test
6% failed hail impact test

---

*200 thermal cycles represent 200 days on-sun operation, while 30 years of thermal cycling = ~10,000 cycles.
†10 humidity freeze cycles represent only part of an Arizona winter season worth of freeze cycles, while 30 years would consist of over 1,000 cycles, and many more in northern states.

12% failed static load test
10% failed hotspot test

Test Criteria

A module design shall be judged to have passed the qualification tests, and therefore to be certified, if each sample meets the following criteria:

a. Degradation of the maximum power output at standard test conditions (STC) does not exceed 5% after each test or 8% after each test sequence;

b. The requirements of tests 10.3 (and 10.20) are met;

c. There is no major visible damage (broken, cracked, torn, bent or misaligned external surfaces, cracks in a solar cell which could remove a portion larger than 10% of its area, bubbles or delamination, loss of mechanical integrity;

d. No sample has exhibited any open circuit or ground fault during the tests;

e. For IEC 61646 only: the measured maximum output power after final light-soaking shall not be less than 90% of the minimum value specified by the manufacturer (2).

Qualification test conditions are simple but stringent, and the quality of both c-Si and thin film modules

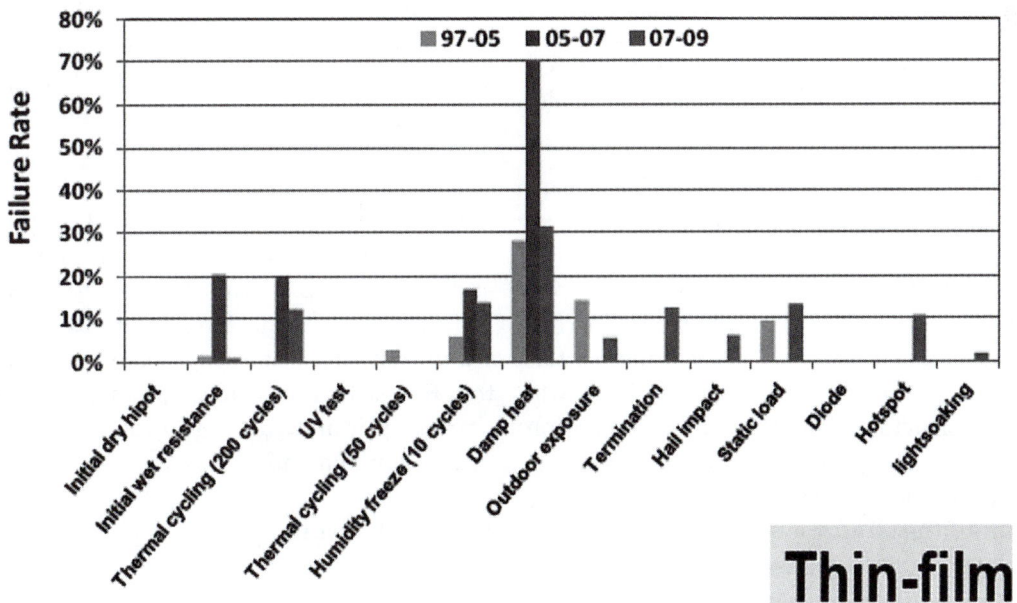

Figure 4-44. Thin film modules tests 1997-2009 (5)

tested until 2007 was absolutely unacceptable. Quality has improved in some areas during the last several years, according to the tests, but is still lower than practicable and profitable for use in large-scale PV power generating installations. Large failure rates would bankrupt any such installation.

An obvious conclusion from the above tests is that some modules perform better than others. Is this due to different quality materials, or because of different processes used? The answer is less than obvious, so this means that the issues at hand need to be resolved ASAP. The PV industry has a bright future, but is still learning how to walk, and we need to help it get on its feet sooner by maximizing product quality and reducing failures.

Damp Tests

This test seems to be the weakest point of TFPV technology, so a closer look is justified. Damp heat studies of CIGS and CdTe cells have been conducted by subjecting cells and min-modules to an environment of 60°C/90% RH.

Two key conclusions can be made:

1. Both CIGSS and CdTe cells degrade rapidly under 60°C/90% RH...

2. Damp heat stress will cause changes in junction transport properties and minority carrier transport characteristics of the cell absorber.

The damp tests in Figure 4-45 show fatal degradation for the un-encapsulated thin film's structure, which confirms that:

1. Thin film structures will be attacked, disintegrated and decomposed if and when exposed to the elements, and

2. Thin film structures depend exclusively on encapsulation for protection from the elements.

A series of tests performed by the author with different metal and non-metal TF structures exposed to hot and humid conditions ("sweat box" tests under different temperature and humidity regimes) show clearly that bare thin film structures (any type and combination thereof) will degrade if exposed to damp heat. See Figure 4-45. The destruction process usually starts slowly at the films' interfaces, and then accelerates quickly, causing delamination and/or destruction of the entire TF structure. TF structures enveloped in impermeable materials have a better chance to survive this test. An

important conclusion here is that the modules' encapsulation is the only thing separating them from destruction and total failure.

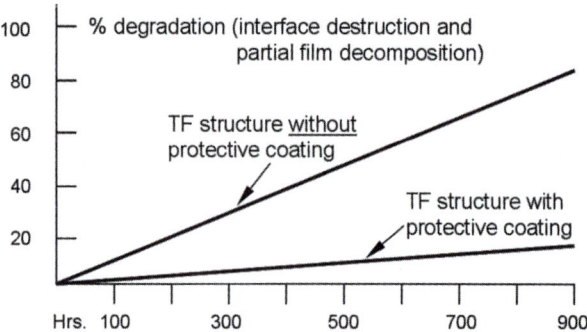

Figure 4-45. Damp test of thin film structure with and without protective coating

This raises a serious question, "What and how much protection is needed to ensure proper operation of TFPV modules, for 30 years in excessively hot and humid areas?" It is obvious that encapsulation determines performance and longevity of modules, because once moisture and other environmental chemicals and gasses reach the thin film structure, it undergoes unpredictable changes. These changes depend on the thin film composition and stability, and also on the nature of the attacking species, but most often the attacks will result in reduced power output and eventually lead to total failure.

NOTE: Thin-film PV modules are different from conventional c-Si modules, as follow:

1. The thin film structure is deposited directly on the front or rear glass cover, thus it is exposed to outside elements in case of delamination from the glass surface.

NOTE: *In c-Si modules, if the EVA delaminates from the glass, the cells are still enveloped in it, thus they are still protected from the outside elements.*

2. Most TFPV modules usually have no side frame, which leaves them fully dependent for protection on the edge sealers, which are fully exposed to the elements and could be easily damaged or destroyed.

These are important differences, because leakage via unframed module edges can easily reach the active thin film structure which is otherwise unprotected, thus damaging it and causing gradual power decrease and eventually total failure.

Field Test Results

There is a difference between the test results from tests done under lab conditions, and those performed under actual field conditions. The final results will depend on the type of modules used and weather conditions in the field, so keep in mind that results from tests under extreme heat in the Arizona desert sun or high humidity in southern Florida will be drastically different and probably much worst after 5-20 years of non-stop operation than what we see in the lab tests above.

Some partial, and far from complete, test data are shown below in support of our arguments of the efficiency and longevity of TFPV modules.

Field Test Data

Several modules were tested under field conditions (several years of outdoor operation), with the results below reflecting the degradation rate of different types of modules from different manufacturers.

The conclusions of the authors of these tests are:

"First, module degradation rate determinations should be made from performance data over periods of at least three years. Shorter time spans are likely to give inaccurate degradation rate (RD) values because of seasonal variations and initial module performance stabilization.

"Second, many (but not all) crystalline Si modules degrade at rates slower than the 1% per year rule of thumb. A more reasonable rule of thumb is probably 0.5% per year. Conversely, many (but not all) thin-film modules appear to have RD values somewhat higher than 1% per year.

"Third, RD appears to vary over a fairly wide range, from values as high as several percent per year, down to zero (no measurable degradation). It would therefore seem important for system designers to have accurate degradation rate information available."

The PV industry has accepted 1% annual degradation as "normal," but based on our and others' experience with PV modules, we question this acceptance as an unreasonable compromise of performance caused by mediocre materials quality and inadequate process design and execution. We would suggest that zero, or near-zero, annual degradation is possible (as we can see in the BP modules in these tests) and badly needed, if we are to rely on any PV modules to provide efficient and reliable power for 30 years, regardless of the location. Annual degradation rates close to zero would be a good indication of the excellence of materials and processes used in the modules which should be our goal for the near future.

Zero degradation rates have been achieved and maintained by the semiconductor industry for a long time. Can you imagine your Pentium processor which is made of similar materials and operates at comparably extreme temperatures and humidity conditions dropping 1% computing power every year? Since the ma-

terials, equipment and processes are similar, near-zero degradation rates should be expected from the TFPV industry too.

A major concern with quickly degrading PV modules, including TFPV, is that since we don't know why they are degrading, there is reason to suspect a serious, if not terminal problem within. It should be noted, however, that although degradation rates are sometimes related to failure rates, there is no proven direct correlation between these two, which emphasizes the complexity of the technology and the uncertainties we face.

Until materials and manufacturing processes are standardized to achieve zero annual degradation, we must keep in mind that if PV modules continue to operate even when the output power is gradually decreasing, the slow degradation is neither infant mortality nor normal life expectancy decrease. Instead, at least for now, it should be regarded as one of the factors contributing to the gradual "wear-out" mode, which should've been properly investigated and calculated during the design and test stages of any PV project. If many modules degrade at an unexpectedly fast rate, at some point they will shut down entire arrays which will no longer be able to meet the minimum input voltage window of the inverters, and eventually the entire system will shut down. This is a catastrophic failure that will render the power plant useless and out of commission, as we have witnessed on several occasions since the early 1980s.

CONCENTRATING PV TECHNOLOGY

Concentrating PV (CPV) technology has been around for 30 years. It was developed by several US companies in the 1970s and 1980s with the help of DOE and its satellite national labs. HCPV is the most efficient PV technology in the world, but its commercialization has been bogged down by a number of factors unrelated to its efficiency.

CPV equipment operation is somewhat different and more complex than other PV technologies. In contrast with 'flat-plate' PV modules, where a large area of photovoltaic material (usually crystalline silicon) is exposed to the maximum sunlight, CPV systems, as the name suggests, use lenses or mirrors to focus (or concentrate) sunlight onto a small amount of non-silicon photovoltaic material.

General Description

HCPV systems operate by concentrating sunlight through Fresnel lenses onto specially designed, and very efficient (over 40%) CPV solar cells. Additional components, such as secondary optics, insulators, heat sinks, and trackers are needed to keep the light focused precisely onto the solar cells, to dissipate the generated heat and conduct the generated electricity to the electric grid, or user's site.

CPV solar cells mounted into CPV assemblies are installed in modules, which are mounted on a steel frame—a frame that pivots on a pedestal, Figure 4-46. GPS controllers send a signal to the x-y drive motors which drive actuators to position the frame and modules exactly perpendicular to the sun all day long with a .01% degree margin of error.

Figure 4-46. HCPV tracker

Operation

HCPV systems (trackers) consist of several key components:

1. CPV solar cells
2. Heat sinks
3. Bypass diodes
4. Secondary optical elements
5. CPV assembly (containing the above components)
5. Fresnel lenses
6. CPV modules (housing the above components)
7. Steel frame
8. x-y drive gear-motors
9. GPS based controller

The CPV solar cells are made out of GaAs, Ge or other more efficient and more durable semiconductor materials with thin films deposited on them to create a multi-junction device of very high efficiency—over 42.3% presently. CPV cells are sophisticated semiconductor devices that have followed Moore's law to an

extent, as far as increase of efficiency per active area is concerned. At the very least, they are much closer to it than any competing PV technology to date.

The CPV cells are arranged into special assemblies, called CPV cell assemblies (see Figure 4-47) which ensures proper orientation, efficient collection of sunlight and cooling of cells during operation, as well as the proper conduction of electric power into the wiring harness. The cells are mounted into an aluminum heat sink block, which is designed to absorb most of the heat generated at the cell, thus keeping the cells cooler and more efficient during operation. The heat sink is attached to the bottom of the module, with the ribs protruding to the outside, where they are most efficiently cooled by occasional breeze.

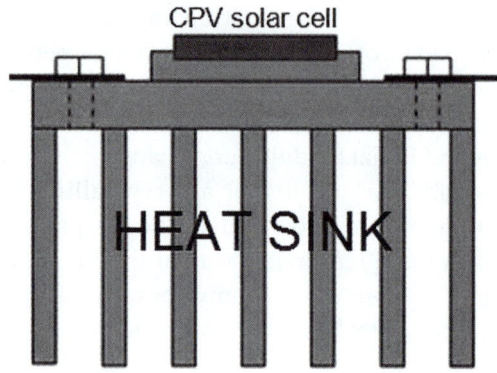

Figure 4-47. CPV cell assembly

Each cell is configured with a blocking diode which protects it from reverse bias currents and surges, and also isolates it from the circuit in case of total failure. The cell and diode are usually mounted on a heat sink which extracts heat from the cell during operation and dissipates it in the environment outside the module.

A Fresnel lens is used to capture a large area of sunlight and focus it onto the small CPV cell. The Fresnel lens is basically a flat (or slightly curved) plastic or glass lens that uses a miniature sawtooth design on its bottom to redirect and focus the incoming light onto the small area cell, several inches away from the lens. When the sawtooth teeth on the lens are arranged in concentric circles, light is focused at a central point, and CPV system. When the teeth run in straight rows, the lenses act as line-focusing concentrators, and the resulting equipment is called the linear-focus CPV system.

The concentration ratio of each CPV device can vary as well, depending on lens and cell design. For example, if sunlight falling onto 100-cm² Fresnel lens is focused onto 1-cm² CPV cell, the ratio is considered to be 100 suns, or 100 x. If the light from a 1000-cm² Fresnel lens is focused onto a 1-cm^2 CPV cell, then the ratio is 1000 suns, or 1000 x. If thus concentrated sunlight light falls onto a well designed CPV cell, it will produce 100, or 1000 times the electricity respectively that a normal c-Si PV cell of the same size would produce under the same operating conditions. Commercial concentration ratios are between 200 and 500 suns, and as much as 1000 suns, but there are theoretical and practical limits of min.-max. sun concentration levels, with the mid-range 400-600 considered the most efficient and practical for now, in the author's opinion.

Most CPV systems use only direct solar radiation, so these installations operate best under direct sunlight (such as in desert areas) and always involve trackers, forcing the modules to rotate and follow the sun all day, which keeps the lenses and CPV cells looking right at the sun at all times, thus generating maximum possible electric energy while the sun is shining.

The cells and cell assemblies are placed in modules, which are mounted on a large frame, which rotates around its two axes to follow sun movement all day. Tracking is achieved with one or two gear-motor assemblies, which get a signal from a photo-detector or GPS controller, which knows where the sun is at all times and runs the motors to move the frame accordingly.

Precise tracking is needed, to keep the sun constantly at exactly 90 degrees (±0.1 degree) with respect to the Fresnel lens and CPV cell, so that sunlight is focused onto the solar cell at all times. If the sunlight comes at an angle, or is diffused (as on a cloudy or foggy day), some, if not most, sunlight will get de-focused, reflected, or otherwise fall away from the cells, resulting in very low light-to-power conversion efficiency.

Tracking systems add cost in terms of motor and controller maintenance, but this cost is relatively small compared with other O&M cost savings that trackers provide. For example, the tracker's motor requires only annual lubrication and a single motor controls more than 50 kWp of PV. Also, tracker bearings require no lubrication and are designed for more than 25 years of use.

The operating and maintenance (O&M) cost of a utility-scale tracking system ends up being less than $0.01/kWh more than that of a fixed configuration. This calculation does not factor in the O&M savings from increased energy production and reduced land use, which is a different subject altogether.

Development Trends

Current research on high-performance multi-junction thin film devices, and the entire operation of CPV systems, focuses on several major challenges.

CPV Cells

1. Determining high-bandgap alloys based on I-III-VI and II-VI compounds and other novel materials for the top cell.

2. Considering low-bandgap CIS and its alloys, thin-film silicon, and other novel approaches for the bottom cell.

3. Studying the difficult task of integrating the thin-film tunnel junction (interconnect) with the top cell. This work includes understanding the role of defects, how they affect the transport properties of this junction, and the diffusion of impurities into the bulk material.

4. Fabricating a monolithic, two-terminal tandem cell based on polycrystalline thin-film materials that requires low-temperature deposition for several layers.

5. Avoiding deterioration of the top cell when fabricating the bottom cell if a low-bandgap cell is fabricated after a high-bandgap cell with a superstrate structure, such as CdZnTe.

6. Avoiding temperatures and processes that could damage the CIS bottom cell if a high-bandgap cell is fabricated on top.

CPV system

1. Developing efficient heat transfer materials for the components in the cell assembly.

2. Developing light and UV resistant plastic materials for the module cover lenses.

3. Developing more precise x-y controls, to maintain 0.01 degree accuracy.

4. Developing better gear drives for stable operation under wind conditions.

NOTE: The efficiency of CPV solar cells has been rising steadily since the 1990s. Starting with 15% efficiency in 1993 of CPV solar cells made by Spectrolab, the efficiency of CPV cells made by Sharp was 44.4% as of the summer of 2013.

At this rate, we expect to see efficiencies of 60% or higher within the next decade. This is possible because the efficiency of the materials involved in making CPV cells is not limited as is that of silicon, which theoretical maximum efficiency cannot exceed 28.5%.

NOTE: The "theoretical efficiency maximum" of solar cells is based on the fact that sunlight is made up of a bunch of photons with wavelengths. A lot of the total

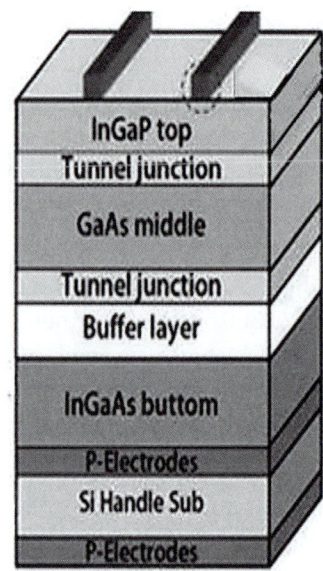

Figure 4-48. CPV cell configuration

energy is stored in the infrared band, but silicon is transparent to photons with near infrared wavelengths, so all the energy of these wavelengths goes right through the silicon solar cell unconverted.

A second problem with silicon is that it readily absorbs ultraviolet light. Its thirst for UV light is so strong that a thin layer of silicon can absorb all UV falling on it. The combination of these factors reduces the upper efficiency limit of silicon simply because many photons of different wavelengths cannot reach down to the p-n junction where the actual energy conversion takes place.

So, if we assume that all wavelengths in sunlight are 100% of the light hitting the solar cell, then silicon can trap and convert to electricity the absolute maximum of 28.5% of all these wavelengths, and we end up with about the maximum possible efficiency for silicon of 28.5%. This means that only 28.5% of all sunlight illuminating a silicon solar cell can be converted into electricity under the best of conditions.

CPV cells have the advantage of being made of a number of layers of different materials (Ge, Ga, In, As, etc.), which are superior in terms of efficiency. In addition, when sunlight goes through the array of different materials of the CPV cell, different wavelengths get absorbed by the different layers at each step of the process. This way we get to the 44.4% maximum efficiency today, which can easily go over 60% in the near future.

In conclusion, although there is still some work to do in the optimization of the CPV systems, we see this technology playing a major role in the more distant future, when it is developed to the level needed for reliable operation in large-scale desert installations.

This will allow these more complex and more efficient systems to compete with the cheaper and simpler fixed-mount c-Si and TFPV installations.

HYBRID PV TECHNOLOGIES

Hybrid PV technologies are those that combine the use of photovoltaics with other solar types, wind, or fossil fuels. This is done in special cases for the sake of practicality and/or efficiency. The combination between photovoltaic and thermal (PV-T) hybrid technologies is most useful in applications that require both electricity and hot water at the same time. Thus created hybrids can be divided into several types, according to their components and applications.

Present-day hybrid solar technologies involving photovoltaics and heat generation can be divided into:

1.   Photovoltaic-solar thermal hybrid, or PV/T, and
2.   Concentrating PV-solar thermal (PV-T) hybrid, and
3.   High-concentration PV-solar thermal hybrid, or HCPV-T.

A Word of Explanation and Clarification

PV-T is a combination of photovoltaic devices, which incorporate both photovoltaics and thermal heating. These can operate at 1x (1 sun) to generate electricity, while running water through the system for use somewhere else.

CPV-T, therefore, is a combination (hybrid) of PV concentrators which concentrate the sunlight 10-100 times onto a receiver tube covered with solar cells mounted on a receiver tube, through which water or cooling liquid flow. The trough and receiver track the elevation of the sun all day long (one-axis tracking); thus, the device generates more DC power per active area, and the water/coolant is at much higher temperatures than with the PV/T cousin.

HCPV-T is a combination of PV concentrators (mirrors or Fresnel lenses), which operate on higher magnification (100-1000 x) and track the sun in x-y direction (two-axis tracking) all through the day. These devices produce more power per area than their CPV-T cousin, while the water/liquid temperature is controlled to optimize the efficiency of the device.

We'll start with a close look at the mechanics and thermodynamics of the simplest PV-T system—that of a fixed-mounted flat panel equipped for generating both PV electricity and hot water capabilities, which makes it a PV-T hybrid.

These systems combine photovoltaic with thermal solar. The advantage is that the thermal solar part carries heat away and cools the photovoltaic cells. Keeping temperature down lowers the resistance and improves cell efficiency. Modified CPV systems have been tested where the CPV cells are cooled by active flow of liquid, thus generating both heat and electricity.

Below we take a close look at the PV/T device operation and their thermodynamics and static behavior, both of which could be used with some translation and extrapolation for use with CPV-T and HCPV-T devices. These calculations are absolutely necessary for the proper design of the devices and the power fields where these are supposed to operate.

The hybrid photovoltaic-thermal (PV/T) system basically consists of an array of PV cells positioned directly on top of the absorber plate of a conventional forced circulation type solar water heater—similar to those we see on roofs of houses.

PV-T Hybrid System

A PV/T solar collector is composed of:

1. Transparent cover allowing sunlight to pass towards the absorber and create a greenhouse effect. It is composed by one or more glass or plastic panes.

2. PV cells for the production of electricity.

3. Absorber plate for transferring heat to the water or in the tubes built into it.

4. Frame, for protection of the whole of these elements.

5. Insulator to limit losses from conduction through the walls back and side.

The schematics of the PV/T collector are shown in Figure 4-49. The top cover is represented by a glass sandwich that includes PV cells. The cell area can cover the entire active surface or can be distributed in a grid where the spacing between adjacent columns and rows can allow a direct gain of solar radiation to the absorber plate.

Different configurations of PV/T collector can be created by changing the cell area density, to balance electricity and thermal energy output of the system.

Dynamic Model of a PV/T System

Below, an explicit dynamic model suitable for PV/T system simulation is introduced. (7)

The effectiveness of PV/T system compared to a

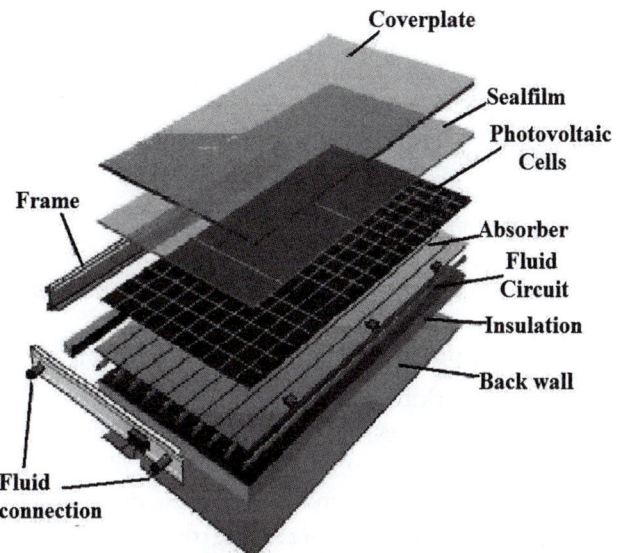

Figure 4-49. Hybrid PV/T

photovoltaic panel (PV) is underlined. The model provides the thermal state of various collector components and generates results for hourly and transient performance analysis (thermal/electrical gain).

The dynamic thermal model of the PVT collector is built upon the finite-difference control-volume technique. The PV/T collector is composed of four major components which represent the different nodes: a) glass cover, b) solar cell, c) absorber plate, and d) water in channels and in storage tank. See below detailed calculations.

The energy and fluid flow equations are developed on the basis of the four nodes. All subparts in each node are considered lumping together in proportion to give the average properties of the representing major component (Figure 4-50.)

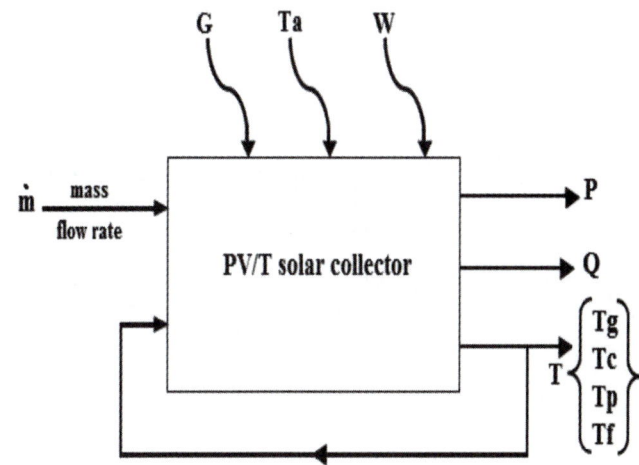

Figure 4-50. Modeling of PV/T system (7)

Where

Tg, Tc, Tp, Tf, Ta are respectively: the temperature of glazing, the solar cell, the absorber plate, the water circulation and the ambient temperature.

W is the wind speed,

G is the incident solar irradiation,

m is the mass flow rate of fluid,

P is the electric power output, and

Q is the thermal profit.

Since the PV/T system consists of several different elements working in unison, we need to consider the separate dynamics by analyzing separately, a) the glass cover, b) the solar cells, c) the absorber plate, d) the heated water, and e) the generated electric power.

Since these are elaborate thermodynamic and electromechanical operations, we will refer the reader to our book, *Solar Technologies for the 21st Century*, published in 2013 by The Fairmont Press, where we take a very close look at the different PV-T technologies—from silicon, to thin films, and their most advanced and futuristic cousins.

PV-T technology is quite simple, but very versatile, cheap, and efficient for use in certain locations, where both hot water and electricity are needed. It is particularly practical for use in remote locations, such as vacation cabins, field hospitals, etc.

CPV/T Technology

The concentrating photovoltaic hybrid (CPV/T) technology is a fairly new development, and although a number of companies are working on this concept, full commercialization and large-scale deployment are still far off.

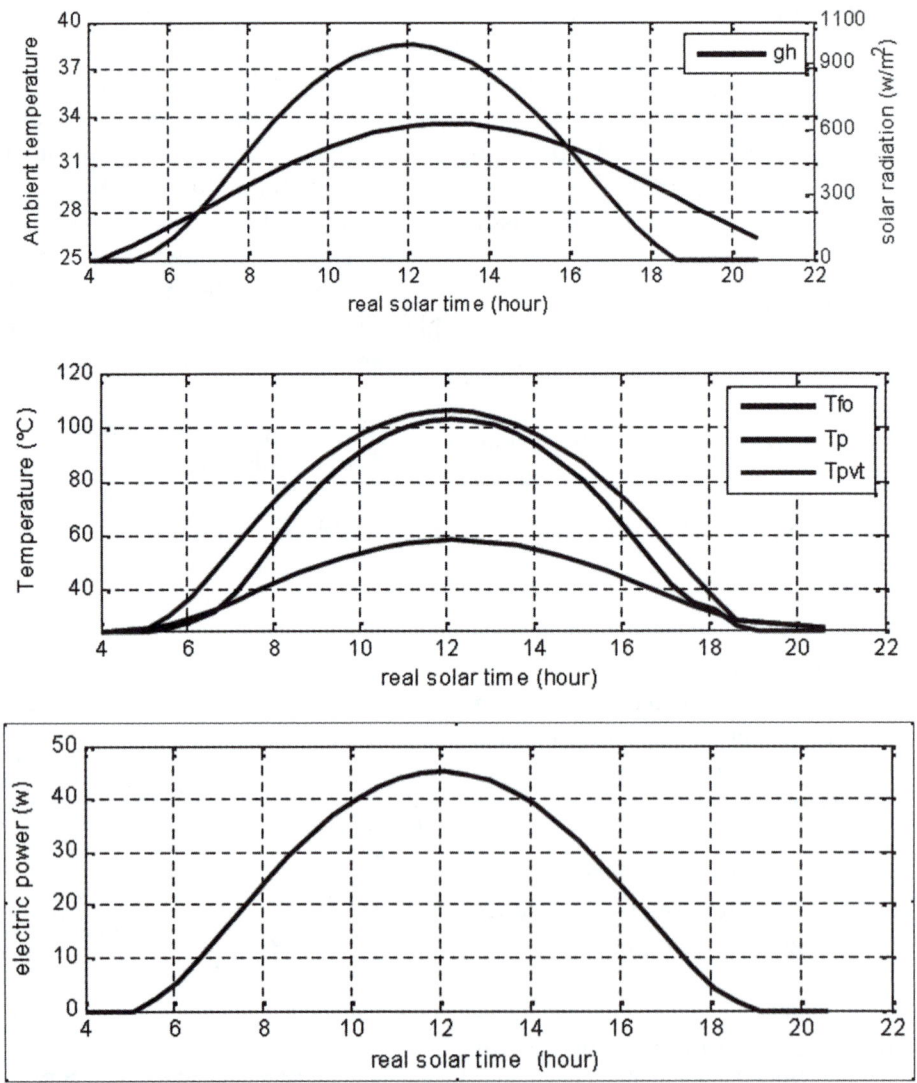

Figure 4-51. Simulation results of PV-T system operation

The CPV/T equipment usually consists of a parabolic trough lined with a mirror surface, focused on a bank of solar cells mounted on a heater tube through which flows water or some liquid. When the sun hits the trough, its mirror surface reflects the sunlight, directing it to the cells, which generate DP power at 15-20% efficiency. When the cells heat up under the sun's rays, they transmit the heat to the tube they are mounted on and heat the liquid running through the tube.

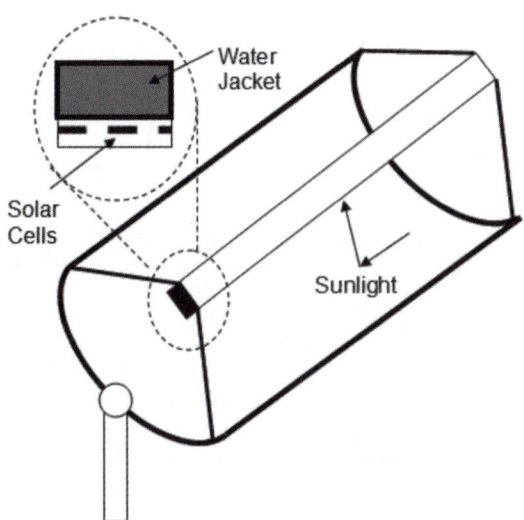

Figure 4-52. CPV/T one-axis tracker

The above dynamic and static calculations for the generic PV/T device could be used here too, with because the basic glass-absorber-cells-liquid configuration exists here in almost identical fashion. Their properties and behavior are similar, except for different results, due to much higher solar illumination, DC voltage and temperatures.

Several companies use this technology—by combining concentrated (low concentration) PV electricity production and heat collection to deliver simultaneously electricity and hot water for commercial, industrial and institutional applications.

Mirrors and single-axis trackers are used to focus light on a row of PV cells in a special CPV/T assembly. Heat, which is normally lost in a typical PV-only system is used to heat water that runs through the CPV/T assembly and cools the solar cells.

Cooler solar cells generate more electrical energy and thus generated hot water is used for heating or process water at the same time. Some of these are turnkey systems designed for easy assembly and rooftops or ground installations.

Although the electricity-hot water hybrid cogeneration equipment has a PV element, and thus competes with the conventional PV technologies, the dollar-per-watt metric is somewhat less applicable. The metric, in addition to the electricity generated within a certain time, includes gallons of hot water generated during the same time period.

The advantage here is that this type of technology does not compete head-to-head with solar panel makers but rather with natural gas. Since natural gas in the U.S. is cheap (roughly $0.02 to $0.03 per kilowatt-hour), this technology is most suited for locations with higher gas prices such as Japan and Europe.

Of course the climate must be suitable as well, because for this technology to function properly and efficiently, it needs direct unobstructed (desert-like) sunlight. Appropriate (niche market) customers are needed as well, those with demand for hot water. This includes the food and beverage industry, schools, hospitals, manufacturing facilities, military bases, etc.

Another advantage of the system is the capability to store hot water for later use. The ability to generate energy in off-grid applications is also advantageous, and creates another niche market.

In addition, thus generated heat can also be used for cooling applications, which opens the opportunity for supplying electricity and hot water to buildings with large "chilling loads," as well.

These CPV/T systems produce water at 70°C, and require no special permitting or roof modifications to support the additional load. They also come complete with integrated hydronics, controls, and inverters.

Another great advantage is that if the CPV/T system is SRCC- (Solar Rating and Certification Corporation) and IEC- (International Electrotechnical Commission) certified, it qualifies for both thermal and electric rebates. This includes the California Solar Initiative (CSI), which offers an incentive for solar hot water systems.

CSI thermal rebates, currently offered in the first-tier level of $12.82 per year for one displaced gas, complement the CSI photovoltaic rebates. This results in faster paybacks than traditional solar hot water or solar electric systems alone.

On top of that, the installations are also eligible for the 30 percent investment tax credit. With the CSI and federal rebates, CPV/T system customers can yield a return on investment in five years, while hedging against future utility price hikes and gas price volatility.

PV-T systems produce 3-5 times more energy (electricity and heat combined) and three times the greenhouse gas reductions of the competing solar technologies. When compared watt-per-watt usage, solar water heating is 3 to 5 times more efficient than PV, which ensures a much faster payback and essentially doubles the value of a CPV/T system.

Since this is an accepted way of doing things in China, Europe, and Austria, the technology will be widely accepted there.

The value of hot water production is, however, somewhat compromised by the plumbing aspect of hot water generation, placing this technology in limited-size niche energy markets.

HCPV-T Technology

High concentration photovoltaic/thermal (HCPV-T) hybrid technology is even newer and more undeveloped than its CPV-T cousin. As a matter of fact we know of only one company (SolarTech of Arizona) that is working on its optimization and commercialization.

The function of the HCPV-T system is similar to that of its older cousin, the CPV-T energy system. It also

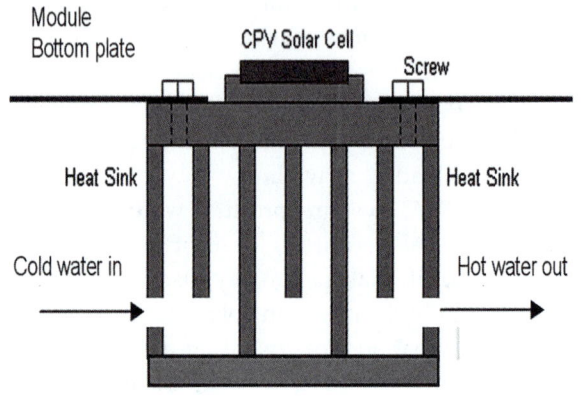

Figure 4-53. Solar cell heat sink and water heating assembly

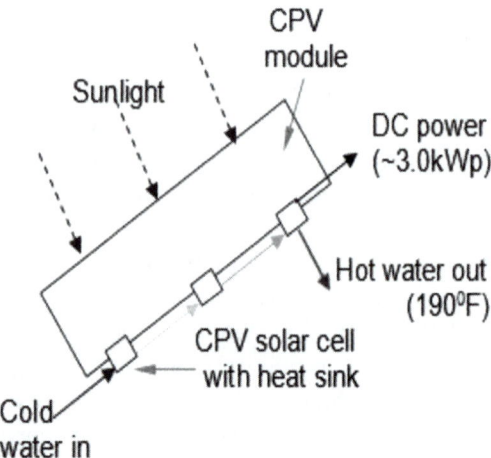

Figure 4-54. HCPV-T module cross section

requires tracking and operates at very high—over 60% overall—combined efficiency.

The dynamic and static calculations for the generic PV-T device could be used here too, because the basic glass-absorber-cells-liquid configuration exists here in almost identical fashion. Their properties and behavior are similar, except for different results, due to the high concentration of sunlight onto the modules, which results in much higher solar illumination, DC voltage and temperatures.

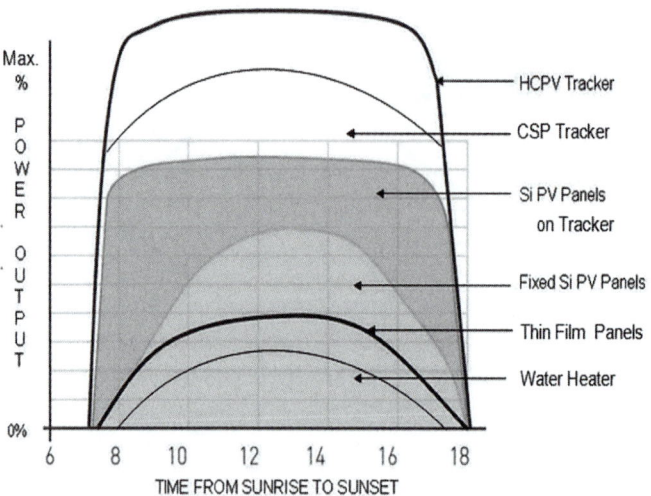

Figure 4-55. Efficiency of PV technologies

In summary:

- HCPV/T hybrid systems can be used also (with some modifications) without liquid cooling, using air cooling of the heat sinks only.

- The system can be built in different sizes, from 0.5kWp to 50kWp to fit different roofs and applications—including large-scale ground-mounted installations.

- As another option, six regular silicon solar cells are added to each HCPV cell assembly in a special arrangement, so that some of the sunlight that is reflected by the HCPV cell illuminates the six regular solar cells around it, thus producing additional DC power. In other words, this configuration increases the 3.0kWp power output of a standard seven modules HCPV/T system to 5.5kWp, without significantly reducing the temperature or amount of hot water produced by the thus modified reference system.

- Different combinations of these options allow unprecedented efficiency, product flexibility, and offer a number of application choices.

Total Energy Management (Via Hybrid Systems)

Figure 4-56 is a graphic representation of a functional, all-purpose combination power generator, consisting of a combo (hybrid) PV power/hot water/gas generator. This is a complete self-contained, self-controlled hybrid PV-T system for use in remote locations.

This system provides power on a 24/7 basis and covers the best of both worlds—DC/AC power and hot water for everyday needs. Such a system would be quite convenient for use in field hospitals, refugee camps and other such operations, where power and hot water are inaccessible.

This system would be exceptionally efficient in areas with lots of sunlight—desert areas are best, of course. It can be configured with or without batteries, and with or without a gas generator. In all cases, the solar collector(s) will provide much needed DC power and hot water during the day, where the only limiting factor is the amount of sunlight available to the collector(s).

By adjusting the controls and the different *modus operandi* of the system, we could obtain maximum efficiency under different climatic conditions. Such a system is what the future holds for a number of critical applications, so we foresee a bright future for these types of energy systems in the 21st century.

Hybrid CPV-T System Financial Analysis

CPV-T energy systems generate both DC electricity and hot water at the same time at a very high efficiency—40% and 20% efficiency respectively—totaling close to 60% overall utilization of solar power.

The amount of energy produced depends on the size of the system, its actual setup and operation, and—very importantly—the amount of sunlight available for its operation. We reviewed the design and function of CPV-T hybrid power generating systems in the previous chapters, so here we will present an example of the operation of a small- to medium-size concentrating PV (CPV) and thermal (T), or CPV-T hybrid system in the US deserts.

This system consists of a CPV tracker equipped with highly efficient solar cells (over 40% DC power at the cell), with cooling water lines, which feed a water heating loop with hot water as a final product.

Since CPV technology requires direct beam sun-

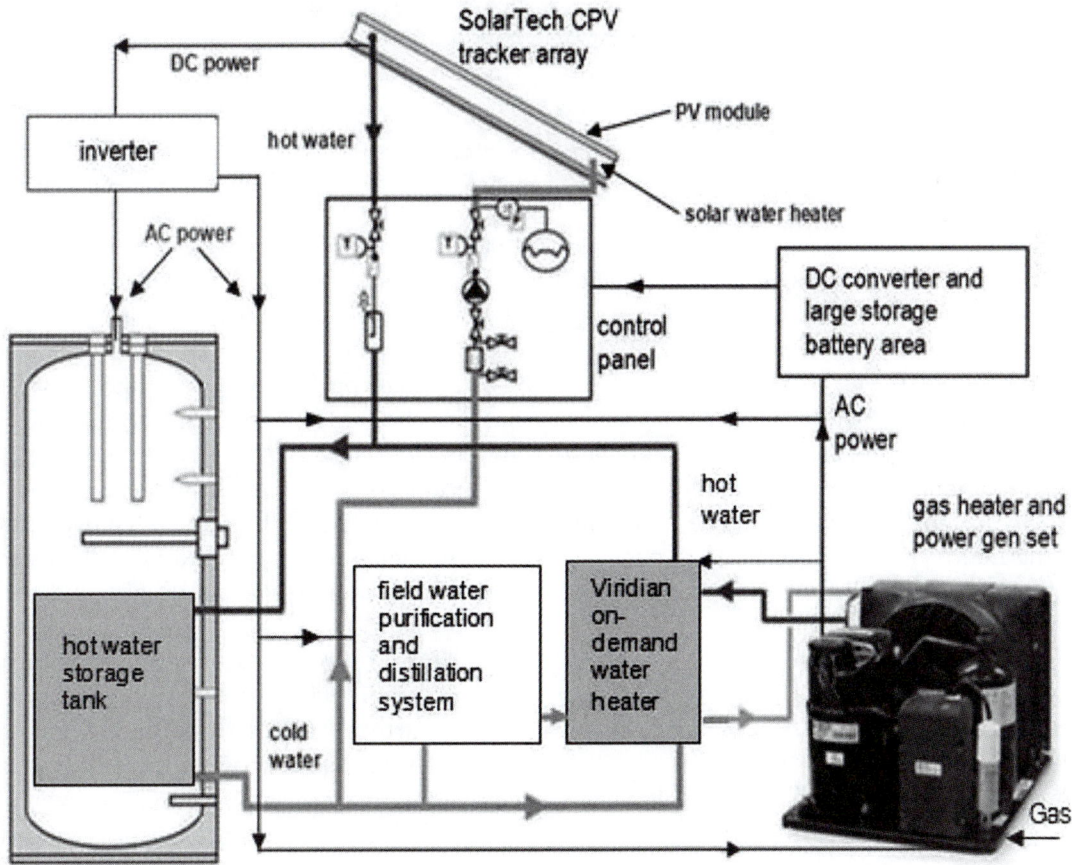

Figure 4-56. Total energy management system.

light, it is best suited for use in the southwest U.S. and other sunny locations around the globe.

For the present performance analysis we'll pick a location in the Arizona deserts with the following average performance criteria:

- 300-320 sunny days annually
- Average 900W/m² full solar insolation
- Average full solar insolation of 8 hrs. per day
  — Summer time full solar insolation for CPV use is ~10 hrs,
  — Winter time solar insolation for CPV use is ~6 hrs.

So, under ideal conditions 900 W/m² x 8 hrs = 7.2 kW/h energy is received daily per m². Each CPV-T unit is over 40% efficient and occupies ~6.0 m² area. Or, 7.2 kW/h x 6.0m² x 40% = ~17.3 kW/h daily generation (vs. 5.5 kW/h for PV panels*) 300 CPV-T units (1800 m²) would generate 1.0 MWp or ~8.0 MW/h daily averaged annually.

At $0.20 avg. PPA (including carbon credits, federal and local subsidies and incentives†) this represents $1,600/day, or $512,000 annual income from DC/AC power generation.

Also, each CPV/T unit generates hot water at ~20% efficiency (180W/m² = 614 Btu/m²). Thus, 614 Btu x 8hrs x 6.0m² x 320 days = 9.43 million Btus are generated annually. Or, our 1.0 MWp plant would generate an additional ~$180,000 annually from hot water generation.

Useful power generation (considering DC/AC and other conversion losses and O&M inefficiencies) would be ~20% less. Therefore, we can expect gross income during the first year of operation of our 1.0 MWp CPV/T plant to be ~$550,000‡.

Total capital expense for building the CPV-T power plant is estimated at $1.30/Wp for equipment and $2.50W/p for BOS, land and administrative expenses, or a total of $3.8 million is needed to install and start operation of the 1.0 MWp plant. Additional expenses of approximately 15% of gross income must be assumed

and allocated for annual O&M operations, which brings the total net operating income to ~468,000 annually.

Therefore, our 1.0 MWp CPV-T plant will be paid for in approximately 8 years, providing clean, green energy and reducing global CO_2 generation by over 1 million lbs. annually. The number of years will vary as other factors, such as government and local subsidies and incentives, carbon credits, taxes and initial investment repayment, are considered.

The drawback of this type of system, and where the uncertainty lies, is the maintenance of the complex key components—positioning controls, x-y gear assemblies, and the related motors, bearings, etc. In the best of cases, maintenance would be 2-5% higher than fixed-mount modules, but in reality we expect 5-10% higher maintenance costs. We must hope that technological advances will improve the system, to reduce the O&M costs.

SOLAR POWER FIELDS

So, we are planning to design an efficient and profitable PV power installation. A number of things must be considered in this process, the first of which is ascertaining how much solar energy is available and the most efficient ways to use it.

Before we go to our project, let's see how much energy we have to work with in general, and how it is used in our daily activities. The total solar energy reaching the Earth's atmosphere is estimated at 175PW (PW is 1,000,000,000MW). Thirty percent is reflected back into space and some is absorbed by the clouds. Whatever sunlight reaches the Earth's surface is absorbed by the oceans and land mass.

A major portion of the sunlight reaching the Earth falls on the world's deserts, because they are mostly void of cloud cover. Most large-scale solar power plants are located in desert areas, and that is also where most of the solar power will be generated in the future. This is why our emphasis in this text is on the operation of PV technologies in the world's deserts and the challenges they present.

Annual worldwide energy consumption is approximately 1/8000 of the total sunlight energy reaching the Earth' surface, so theoretically only a small part of the deserts could provide the entire world's energy demand. Putting this in practice, however, is quite complicated because capturing and converting sunlight into useful energy and delivering it to the point of use is not easy. So let's tackle the issues.

---

*CPV is several times more efficient than fixed-mounted PV panels. It also tracks the sun all day, thus getting maximum power possible from morning until evening.

†Federal, state and local subsidies might cover 30-40% of the initial cost.

‡Conventional PV panels lose 1% efficiency annually. CPV-T systems do not. Conventional PV panels lose 0.5% efficiency per degree C, CPV-T systems do not.

Sunlight for PV Generation

We mentioned above that sunlight coming from the sun must be captured and converted into its two forms that are most useful for human consumption, thermal and electric energy. To do this right, we need to know the properties of sunlight as well as the properties and behavior of everything related to the process of converting sunlight into useful energy.

We know that full unobstructed sunlight, like what we see in the deserts, is called "beam" or "direct" radiation, while when obstructed by clouds, dust and other particles in the atmosphere it is called "diffused" radiation. The direct and diffused radiations, as well as the albedo (light reflection from ground surfaces) are useful forms of energy. They have different properties under different atmospheric conditions and seasons, so we do need to know how they affect solar power generation in order to design a most efficient PV power plant.

Another factor to consider is the path that sunlight travels to reach the location of our PV plant. For this we need to take a close look at the Earth's path around the sun and around its axis, and understand the behavior of sunlight at the location we are considering. The Earth makes a full circle around the sun every 364.99 days, while at the same time the Earth makes one full revolution around its axis every 24 hours. The rotation of the Earth around the sun determines the seasons, while the rotation around its axis determines time of day. The combination of these two factors is very important for the proper design and operation of solar generating systems.

Calculating these two parameters, we can predict how much sunlight we can get at anytime of year and adjust the solar power collecting devices for maximum performance.

Figure 4-57 shows that on June 21 of every year the northern hemisphere is inclined slightly towards the sun. This "slight" inclination is enough to provide a shorter path for the sunlight, more intense direct radiation and generally warmer and sunnier summertime. On December 21 of every year, the Earth is inclined in the opposite direction, taking the northern hemisphere farther from the sun, where the sunlight travels a longer distance to reach us, which translates to less direct radiation and shorter, colder, darker days.

Figure 4-58 shows the amount of power produced by a solar power generating system at different seasons and dif-

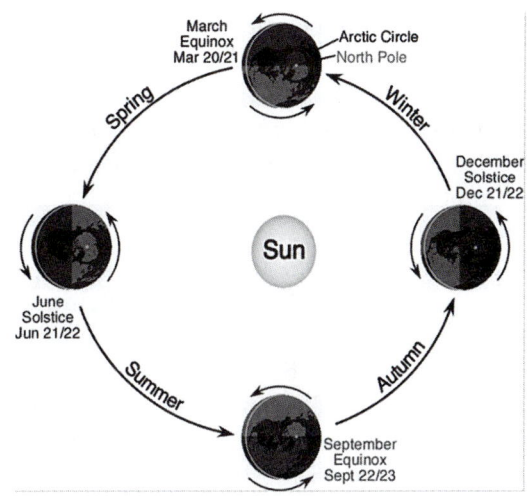

Figure 4-57. Earth path and cycles (seasons)

ferent hours of the day. Basically it tells us that we will get maximum power at noon on June 21st and much less at noon on December 20th of the same year, due to the Earth's position, as explained above. Anytime in between, we will get solar energy somewhere in between the above maximum and minimum levels. Again, it all depends on local weather conditions, because a cloudy and rainy day in December would produce almost the same amount of sunlight as such a day in June.

We also see from Figure 4-59 that PV modules will generate more energy if they are pointed directly at the sun all day (in effect tracking it), instead of just being anchored in a fixed position. The difference is exaggerated during the winter season, because of the sharper angle of the sunlight falling on fixed-tilt modules. We will expand on these details, including tracking vs.

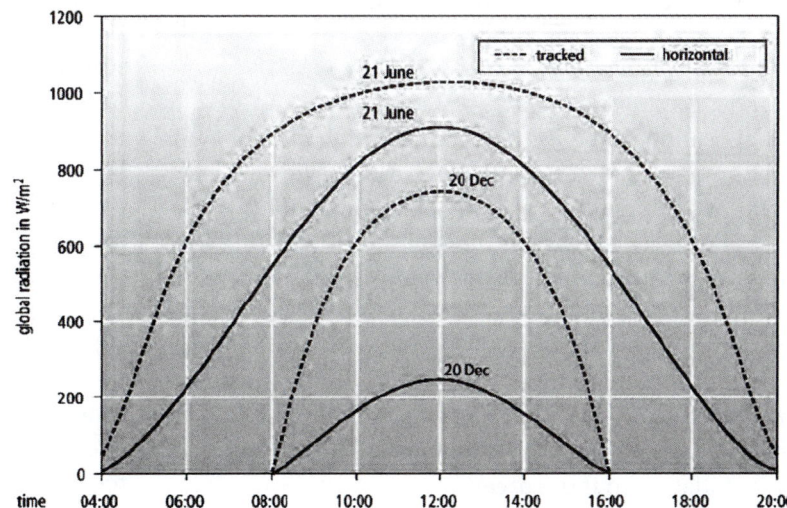

Figure 4-58. Seasonal global radiation

fixed solar power collection in this text, so for now we just need to understand that the most important parameters for efficient solar power generation are the geographic location, the seasons, local weather, time of day, the technology we use, and if we use tracking or fixed PV modules.

Insolation Levels and Variations

We can see now that the weather (cloud, fog and smog cover mostly) plays a great role in the performance of any PV installation. Inconsistent cloud cover caused variability issues (power fluctuations) which are undesirable and even harmful. There are some variability problems on mostly sunny days and fully cloudy days that will present some problems, mostly expressed in reduced output, but the variability is greatest during partially cloudy days, when the sun is randomly going in and out of the clouds. During this time the power output is going up and down uncontrollably, creating serious fluctuations of power being transmitted into the power grid.

Power output increases gradually from zero in early morning to full (peak) power at noon and then gradually back to zero by late afternoon. This is another, albeit more predictable and controllable, variable. On a clear sunny day that ascent and descent will be a smooth bell curve, but on a cloudy day it would be a mess of ups and downs of solar intensity and the related power fluctuations. Some fluctuations would be gradual, some fast, and some slow, but basically with no way to predict and compensate for them in advance.

There are a number of effects that influence the behavior of the PV system on partially cloudy days. These are related to special-temporary, incident angle, inverter, area affected, and temperature, all detailed further below.

Location, Location, Location

Location of the PV power generating system is the most important factor in the long-term performance expectations of the PV system or solar power field.

The darker areas on the U.S. map in Figure 4-59 show where the sunlight is more intense and where the power output of any type of solar generating device will be greatest. Obviously, the deserts of the southwest USA seem to be the most appropriate for this purpose, and that is why there are such a great number of solar (thermal and PV) power plants installed and planned for installation in those areas.°

The darker areas of the map are then most suitable for solar power generation. Of course any area will

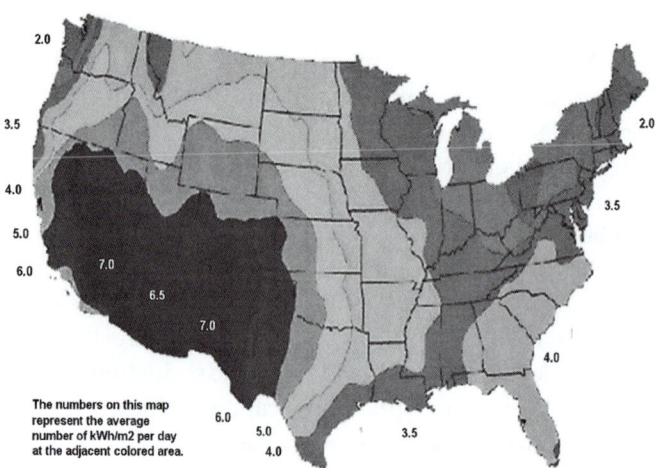

Figure 4-59. US solar radiation (in kWh/m²/day).

generate some power, but the darker areas will generate many times the power generated by the lighter areas. So again, location, location, location. A PV power field in Arizona, for example (with 7.0 kWh/m²/day solar insolation will generate several times the power of a similar setup in Maine or Washington state (with 2.0 kWh/m²/day).

These darker areas are the focal point of this text as well, because we believe that the energy future is related to the proper and efficient use of PV technologies in the US and world deserts in particular.

Unfortunately, the inhospitable climatic conditions in the deserts are problematic for most PV technologies, which is also something we are addressing, with the hope of shedding more light on the issues and bringing them out for discussion and solution.

Spatial-temporary Effects

These are short-time variations in cloud cover—the sun going in and out randomly. To summarize the effect of this variable on the power output of a solar plant, we need to take into consideration all other factors (see below) but basically, the larger the plant, the larger the output power fluctuations will be. Also, the shorter the duration of the sunlight intensity (insolation) fluctuations, the larger the power output effect.

In other words, if the sun comes in and out of the clouds every second or two, the PV system (collectors, transmission, inverters) will not have enough time to process the signal and convert it properly into useable energy. This is one of the major reasons we always recommend that large solar power plants should be installed in areas with high solar insolation and minimal weather fluctuations.

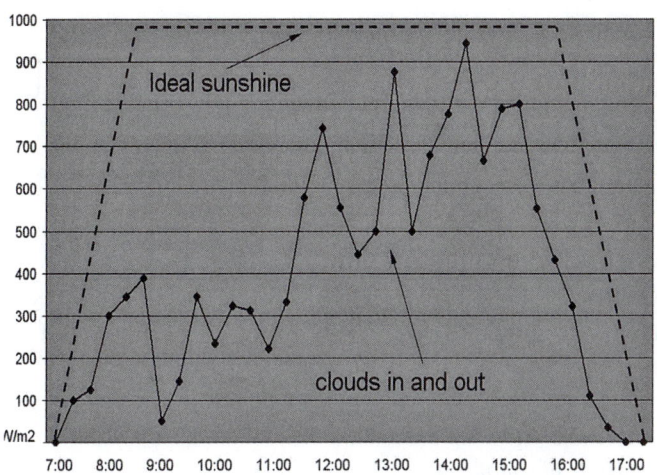

Figure 4-60. Partially cloudy day solar radiation readings

Incident Angle Effects

Incident angle effects are caused by improper positioning of the PV modules in relation to the sun. This anomaly could be caused by a number of factors, the most important of which is the awkward position of the fixed PV modules systems during early morning and late afternoon. During these times, fixed systems collect only a small percent of the overall PV power reaching their surface.

Inverter Effects

Inverter effects are caused by the inverters' inability to properly follow and adapt to the random ramp-up and ramp-down patterns of generated power during variable conditions. Because of that, inverters cannot convert 100% of the incoming DC power, which causes additional power losses. Basically, when a cloud covers the sky partially, the inverters sense the change and start regulating the power-down cycle, in a less than efficient manner usually. At varying points, the cloudy sky will reduce the power output from the modules to such a low level that the inverters cannot handle it and simply shut down. So even if the modules are generating some power, the inverters do not "see" it, and it is wasted. These abnormal conditions are caused by and/or identified as MTTP issues, IEEE 1547 dropouts, inverter "clipping" abnormalities etc.

Tracking Systems

Trackers are much better in collecting the maximum sun energy, due to the fact that their x-y drive controllers position the PV modules to face the sun properly at all times. Trackers, however, are affected by partial cloud cover even more than their fixed PV module cousins, because tracker controls might get confused by the sun hiding behind erratic cloud cover, thus not providing the best angle for sunlight collection.

Cloud Cover

The effects of cloud cover vary with the size of the power plant. Large plants cover large areas of land, where partially cloudy days might complicate things even further by throwing a shadow over one side of the field, while the other side is clear and gets full sun. This situation will make attempts to get a complete handle on the incoming vs. outgoing power almost impossible. This condition is especially critical in fields using trackers because the shaded side will act unpredictably, adding to the complexity of the variability factor.

Temperature Effects

Temperature effects are abnormalities caused by high temperature on solar cells and panels. Silicon and thin film PV modules drop 0.5% efficiency with each degree C temperature increase. Temperature increases are implicated in several failure or degradation modes of PV cells and modules, as elevated temperatures increase the stresses associated with thermal expansion and significantly increase degradation rates.

These factors are hard to keep track of, let alone control as needed for producing consistent maximum power output. Because of that, we need to take them into consideration during the design of the power field and then do whatever is necessary to control their effect during operation.

Derating Factors

Once we have captured solar energy via PV devices (solar cells or modules) we need to convert it into electricity. Some of the energy is lost during the conversion process; i.e., only 15% is converted by a PV module, and the losses continue down the line before the energy can be used. In a PV power plant, the loses are from PV equipment, wires, connectors, controllers, inverters, transformers etc.—equipment that is needed to capture and convert sunlight into AC power.

The losses from each piece of equipment determine its efficiency, and the corresponding power loss amount is the derating factor. The derating factors of all plant components must be used to calculate the PV system's ability to produce DC and AC power.

Some of the key factors are discussed below.

DC Rating (Nameplate)

The size of a PV system is its nameplate or DC power rating, which is the amount of DC power it is supposed to produce according to the manufacturer at STC (1,000 W/m² solar irradiance and 25°C module temperature). The DC rating of a PV system is determined by adding the total PV modules' power listed on each PV module in watts and then dividing the sum by 1,000 to convert it to kilowatts (kW); our 100 MWp PV system consists of 500,000 PV modules, each measuring 200 Watts at STC, and is expected to generate 100 MWp of power at STC.

This is a theoretical number, simply because PV modules seldom operate at STC in the field, and certainly not in the fields we are most interested in—harsh desert areas with the highest temperature extremes. Nevertheless, the DC rating is important for establishing a baseline of the generation power and is used in many consequent calculations and considerations.

DC Derating Factor

This is basically the difference between the DC rating (nameplate) as provided by the manufacturer and the actual power generated on location. We perform a series of field tests after installation to verify and baseline the performance at this particular location. The tests could be done with each string of modules independently, which will provide an average DC power produced for each string. The different strings could be added to obtain the actual total DC power produced by the entire installation. When compared with the nameplate, the difference will give us the actual DC derating factor of the entire power plant under full power. Field measurements are usually lower than the nameplate rating.

DC derating factor =
Actual generated DC power/Nameplate

A derate factor of 0.95, for example, indicates that post-install field testing power measurements at the location were 5% less than the manufacturer's nameplate rating measured at STC. Or, our power plant with 100 MWp nameplate produced only 95 MWp during a certain time period under actual operating conditions.

In this case:

DC derating factor =
95MWp/100MWp
or 0.95, or 95% of nameplate

During this test and after consecutive time-lapse tests, we can find

a number of variables and discrepancies which must be taken into consideration when estimating the initial overall plant efficiency, its performance levels, and the related DC derating.

DC to AC Derating Factor

Another critical variable of the overall performance estimate of a PV power-generating system is its DC to AC derating factor (or DC to AC conversion efficiency), which is simply the multiple of the derate factors of the different power plant components.

DC to AC Derating factor =
multiple of components' derate factors

In this case, DC to AC derating factor = 0.95 x 0.92 x 0.98 x 0.995 x 0.98 x 0.99 x 0.95 x 0.98 x 1.00 x 1.00 x 1.00 = 0.77. Or, 77% of the nameplate DC power will be converted into AC power at this particular location with this particular equipment. In other words, our 100 MWp power plant will generate 77 MWp of AC electricity and send it into the grid. In more detail:

PV Module Nameplate DC Rating

This accounts for the accuracy of the manufacturer's nameplate rating. Field measurements of PV modules may show that they are different from their nameplate rating or that they experience light-induced degradation upon exposure. A derate factor of 0.95 indicates that testing yielded power measurements at STC that were 5% less than the manufacturer's nameplate rating.

Component Derate Factors	PVWatts Default	Range
PV module nameplate DC rating	0.95	0.80–1.05
Inverter and transformer	0.92	0.88–0.98
Mismatch	0.98	0.97–0.995
Diodes and connections	0.995	0.99–0.997
DC wiring	0.98	0.97–0.99
AC wiring	0.99	0.98–0.993
Soiling	0.95	0.30–0.995
System availability	0.98	0.00–0.995
Shading	1.00	0.00–1.00
Sun-tracking	1.00	0.95–1.00
Age	1.00	0.70–1.00
Overall DC-to-AC derate factor	0.77	0.09999–0.96001

Table 4-6. Average derating factors as used in PVWATT (NREL)

Inverter and Transformer

This reflects the inverters and transformer's combined efficiency in converting DC power to AC power. A list of inverter efficiencies by manufacturer is available from the Consumer Energy Center. The inverter efficiencies include transformer-related losses when a transformer is used or required by the manufacturer.

Mismatch

The derate factor for PV module mismatch accounts for manufacturing tolerances that yield PV modules with slightly different current-voltage characteristics. Consequently, when connected electrically, they do not operate at their peak efficiencies. The default value of 0.98 represents a loss of 20/0 because of mismatch.

Diodes and Connections

This derate factor accounts for losses from voltage drops across diodes used to block the reverse flow of current and from resistive losses in electrical connections.

DC Wiring

The derate factor for DC wiring accounts for resistive losses in the wiring between modules and the wiring connecting the PV array to the inverter.

AC Wiring

The derate factor for AC wiring accounts for resistive losses in the wiring between the inverter and the connection to the local utility service.

Soiling

The derate factor for soiling accounts for dirt, snow, and other foreign matter on the surface of the PV module that prevent solar radiation from reaching the solar cells. Dirt accumulation is location- and weather-dependent. There are greater soiling losses (up to 25% for some California locations) in high-traffic, high-pollution areas with infrequent rain. For northern locations, snow reduces the energy produced, and the severity is a function of the amount of snow and how long it remains on the PV modules. Snow remains longest when sub-freezing temperatures prevail, small PV array tilt angles prevent snow from sliding off, the PV array is closely integrated into the roof, and the roof or another structure in the vicinity facilitates snow drift onto the modules. For a roof-mounted PV system in Minnesota with a tilt angle of 23°, snow reduced the energy production during winter by 70%; a nearby roof-mounted PV system with a tilt angle of 40° experienced a 40% reduction.

System Availability

The derate factor for system availability accounts for times when the system is off because of maintenance or inverter or utility outages. The default value of 0.98 represents the system being off 2% of the year.

Shading

The derate factor for shading accounts for situations in which PV modules are shaded by nearby buildings, objects, or other PV modules and arrays. For the default value of 1.00, the PVWatts calculator assumes the PV modules are not shaded. Tools such as Solar Pathfinder can determine a derate factor for shading by buildings and objects. For PV arrays that consist of multiple rows of PV modules and array structures, the shading derate factor should account for losses that occur when one row shades an adjacent row.

Sun Tracking

The derate factor for sun-tracking accounts for losses for one- and two-axis tracking systems when the tracking mechanisms do not keep the PV arrays at the optimum orientation. For the default value of 1.00, the PVWatts calculator assumes that the PV arrays of tracking systems are always positioned at their optimum orientation, and performance is not adversely affected.

Age

The derate factor for age accounts for performance losses over time because of weathering of the PV modules. The loss in performance is typically 1% per year. For the default value of 1.00, the PVWatts calculator assumes that the PV system is in its first year of operation. For the 11th year of operation, a derate factor of 0.90 is appropriate.

NOTE: Because the PVWatts overall DC-to-AC derate factor is determined for STC, a component derate factor for temperature is not part of its determination. Power corrections for PV module operating temperature are performed for each hour of the year as the PVWatts calculator reads the meteorological data for the location and computes performance. A power correction of –0.5% per degree Celsius for crystalline silicon PV modules is used.

PV Arrays

Typically, PV modules are not used alone, but in combination with a number of similar modules to create an "array." A PV array is simply a group of PV modules installed and wired together as a group. The PV arrays come in many forms, shapes and sizes, and each array can be fixed, sun-tracking with one axis of rotation, or sun-tracking with two axes of rotation. Fixed PV array is the cheapest and most common on the PV energy market. It is not as efficient as the tracking array, but it is the simplest, the cheapest, and the one requiring least maintenance.

The function, advantages and disadvantages of fixed vs. tracking arrays are quite important and must be considered in any PV project. The technical and financial aspects of different types of modules and arrays are discussed in more detail in following chapters.

A fixed array consists of a number of modules that are mounted permanently on a solid frame, usually steel or aluminum angles, which is cemented, or otherwise solidly fixed into the ground or on a structure. Tracking arrays are also mounted on a frame, but the frame is heavier and is mounted on a pivoting pedestal that allows it to rotate on top of it on one (x) or two (x-y) axis, thus following the sun all through the day. See Figure 4-61, b and c respectively.

The tracking frame moves with the help of a motor-gear assembly for a one-axis system, or via two motor-gear assemblies for a two-axis system. A sensor knows exactly where the sun is and sends a signal to the controller, which tells the motors to run when needed. This then activates the gears to move the frame into position.

As you can imagine, x-y trackers generally have higher comparative efficiency, because they are positioned most advantageously towards the sun (constantly at a 90-degree angle), thus receiving the maximum amount of sunlight and generating the largest possible amount of electric power from sunrise to sundown. Of course, multi-junction solar cells which have 2-3 times higher efficiency add to the advantage of tracking systems.

Module/Array Operating Parameters

Several key considerations must be kept in mind when designing and using PV modules and arrays. Some of these are:

Tilt Angle

For a fixed-mounted PV module, the tilt angle is the angle from horizontal of the inclination of the module top surface (0° = horizontal, 90° = vertical). Or, a PV module is at a 0° tilt angle when lying flat on the ground or mounted parallel to it. For a sun-tracking PV array with one axis of rotation, the tilt angle is the angle from horizontal of the inclination of the tracker axis. The tilt angle is not applicable for sun-tracking PV arrays with two axes of rotation, because they are always oriented at 0° towards the sun, or "looking" straight at it.

The default value of a fixed module is a tilt angle equal to the module's latitude. Installers might consider modifying the azimuth angle +/- several degrees according to the particular location or customer's needs. The overall intent is to maximize annual energy production without changing the tilt angle at any time.

Increasing the tilt angle favors energy production in winter, and decreasing the tilt angle favors energy production in summer. This is due to the low-in-the-sky position of the sun in winter, and high-in-the-sky position in summer. Of course, a compromise which would increase the generated power is the so-called "seasonal adjustment" of the tilt angle.

This consists of changing the angle of all modules in the power plant to match closely the seasonal changes of the sun angle. Ideally, this is done 4 times every year, at the beginning of each season at the particular location.

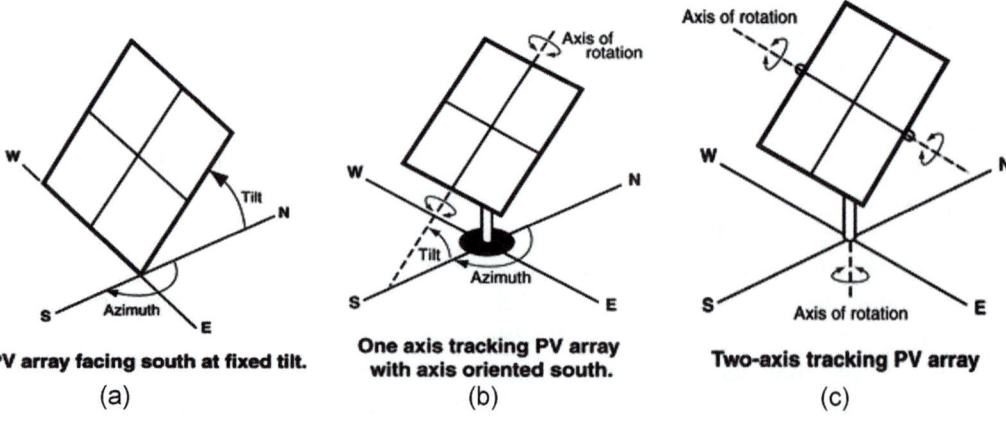

PV array facing south at fixed tilt.

(a)

One axis tracking PV array with axis oriented south.

(b)

Two-axis tracking PV array

(c)

Figure 4-61. PV array types

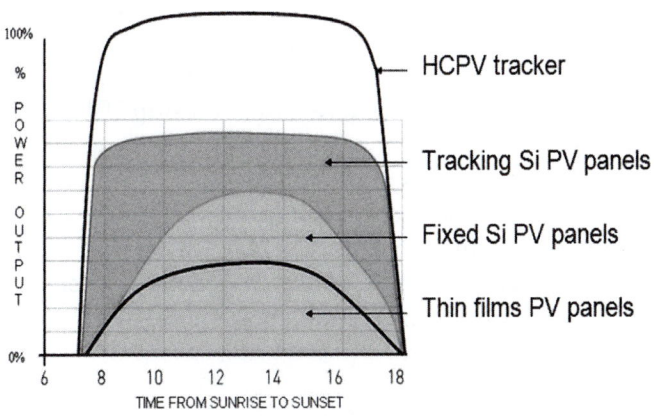

Figure 4-62. Performance of tracking vs. fixed PV arrays

Azimuth Angle

For a fixed-mounted PV array, the azimuth angle is the angle clockwise from true north (zero degree) to the south (180 degrees) that the PV array faces. For a sun-tracking PV array with one axis of rotation, the azimuth angle is the angle clockwise from true north of the axis of rotation. The azimuth angle is not applicable for sun-tracking PV arrays with two axes of rotation.

The default value for a fixed module is an azimuth angle of 180° (south-facing) for locations in the northern hemisphere and 0° (north-facing) for locations in the southern hemisphere. This normally maximizes energy production. For the northern hemisphere, increasing the azimuth angle favors afternoon energy production, and decreasing the azimuth angle favors morning energy production. The opposite is true for the southern hemisphere. Installers might consider modifying the azimuth angle +/− several degrees according to the particular location or customer's needs.

Seasonal changes of the azimuth angle are also possible, but not recommended, due to little benefit from a fairly major effort.

Power Rating

The size of a PV array is its DC power rating, or nameplate. This is determined by adding the PV module power listed on the PV modules in watts and then dividing the sum by 1,000 to convert it to kilowatts (kW). PV module power ratings are for standard test conditions (STC) of 1,000 W/m² solar irradiance and 25°C PV module temperature.

The maximum power generated by a single cell or module is determined by:

$$Pmax = Voc * Isc * FF$$

where:
Voc is the open-circuit voltage;
Isc is the short-circuit current; and
FF is the fill factor.

A small commercial type PV system consists of a number of modules, generating 5-500 kW total power. This corresponds to a PV array area (active area) of approximately 30m² to 3,000m², but it depends on the efficiency of the modules, and other factors which determine the overall PV system size; i.e., some thin film modules are only 6-8% efficient, so they will need at least 50% more area for installation plus additional mounting frames, wiring etc. Large-scale PV systems consist of thousands of PV modules, depending on the nameplate (maximum power generated at SCT, usually as claimed by the modules manufacturer).

DC-to-AC Derate Factor

The overall DC-to-AC derate factor accounts for estimated and calculated power rating), due to losses from the components in the power plant, while generating, transporting, converting and otherwise transferring the generated DC power into the AC grid. It is basically the mathematical sum of the losses (derate factors) triggered or caused by all components of the PV system. So, we need to multiply the nameplate DC power rating by an overall DC-to-AC derate factor of the system to determine its total AC power rating at STC.

Because STC is just a theoretical value provided by the manufacturer and derived basically under lab test conditions, we need to estimate the power rating during everyday operating conditions; i.e., a spring day in the Arizona desert might produce sunlight close to STC and the modules might even operate under STC conditions for a short while.

This, however, is not so during a hot day in July, when the PV modules, inverters and other components are extremely hot and when their efficiency drops significantly.

The overall DC-to-AC derate factor of the system is represented by the sum of all components' derate factors (as used by PVWatts), which is the baseline of the system. In the above case, we have a derate factor of 0.77. So 77% of the available power (generated by the modules) will be converted into DC and sent into the grid, if the module or arrays are operating under STC. This is a 23% loss due to the components' resistance operation and inefficiency.

As mentioned above, the derate factor would be quite different under extreme conditions—extreme desert heat in particular. This difference must be calculated as well, and important decisions must be made on the basis of the difference between STC and in-sun operation in extreme climates; i.e., the efficiency of a PV array or an inverter rating will drop 20-30% from the STC measurements when operated in the summer desert heat.

This drop of efficiency in the field must be taken into consideration when designing, installing and operating a PV system, because the negative effects under these conditions are usually quite significant. Ignoring these changes during the design or evaluation stage will result in serious unpleasant surprises in the field.

PV Cost Factors

The cost of installation of PV power plants during 2012-2013 can be broken down into the following segments:

Table 4-7. PV installation costs

Item	% of project
Hardware	20
Labor	20
Overhead	15
Management	13
Wiring	11
Profit (EPC)	9
Misc.	8
Land	6

Total installation costs vary with different technologies and locations, but the average PV installation in Arizona was $8.0/Wp in 2008, dropping to $6.0/Wp in 2010 and leveling at approximately $4.0/Wp in 2012 and beyond. The price of Chinese PV modules contributed significantly to overall PV installation price reductions, and it is expected to go up if Chinese panels become more expensive, due to the recent DOC restrictions, and/or due to natural price leveling as global PV markets stabilize.

Cost has been the main criteria used by U.S. installers and customers in choosing PV modules and BOS during the 2007-2012 solar boom-bust cycle. Quality has not been a major consideration, which shows ignorance and greed (bad combination) on the part of all involved; installers, investors, and customers.

Just because a brand new PV module looks clean and shiny, doesn't mean it would perform reliably during 30 years of non-stop operation. This is especially true in U.S. deserts, where 12-14 hours of blistering sun-

light every day, day after long, hot day, could destroy anything in its path. The PV modules, and especially their plastic components (encapsulation, edge seals, etc.) are no match for the powerful, non-stop UV and IR radiations.

We have learned from experience that even the best and most reputable manufacturers make low-quality PV modules from time to time. There are reports of many megawatts of failed PV modules, so today installers, investors, and customers alike are much more careful with the products they buy.

Performance and Reliability Factors

We've looked briefly at some of the key issues, and possible degeneration, of PV modules during long-term field operation, always remembering to extrapolate for use in the ever harsh desert environment. Now we will take a closer look at the practical expression of these phenomena, considering worst case scenarios and all possible outcomes.

Temperature Effect

A PV module exposed to sunlight generates heat as well as electricity. For a typical commercial PV module operating at its maximum power point, only 10 to 15% of the incident sunlight is converted into electricity, with much of the remainder being converted into heat.

The key factors which affect the efficiency and thermal behavior of PV modules are:

- The degree of reflection from the top surface of the module;

- The electrical operating point of the module components;

- Absorption of sunlight by the regions which are not covered by solar cells;

- Absorption of low energy (infrared) light in the module or solar cells;

- The packing density of the solar cells, and

- The overall quality of the solar cells and modules.

Each of these factors is seemingly independent in their origin and function, but is inter-related in their long-term effect on the module's efficiency and longevity. We will take a much closer look at the temperature effects below, so it suffices to say that any PV cell or module will lose ~0.5-0.6% of its total output per degree C increase of temperature. This is a significant number, which causes a lot of concern about the auditability of

PV modules for long-term operation in extreme heat conditions.

Mechanical and Thermal Effects

There are a number of materials in the PV module that act and interact differently with adjacent materials, depending on temperature, pressure and other factors. The major mechanical forces determining the interaction between the different layers in the module are:

a. Coefficient of friction is the force that resists the lateral motion of solid surfaces in contact with each other and moving in different directions. This includes the types of materials (substrates and layers of materials stacked on top of each other) of which PV modules are made.

b. Coefficient of thermal expansion (linear and volumetric) is the way different materials expand and shrink under different temperature gradients. In other words, all materials tend to change shape and size along the surface and across their volume, with changes in temperature, which ultimately results in mechanical friction if in contact with other materials.

These forces also determine a number of events and phenomena that occur in the modules over time. Hot and cold days, windy conditions, hail, storms, etc. have an effect on the modules, and all these events must be taken into consideration in the design and operation of PV power plants. The relations and interactions between the module's components could be described as intimate, ongoing, and relentless.

In the Arizona deserts, these materials must go through blistering 180°F temperatures during the day in summer and sub-freezing temperatures in winter, not to mention the effects of UV light. Also, moisture, air, environmental chemicals, and gasses penetrating the module will cause quick deterioration and even failure.

Since the coefficient of expansion of these materials is very different, they go through never-ending shifting, sliding and slipping, expanding and shrinking, constantly rubbing against each other in a never-ending dance—a soup of dissimilar molecules. This is where any poor design or deviation from the materials or manufacturing specs will be revealed, most likely as decreased performance or other failure.

Cracks, chips, pits, crumbling, voids, adhesion failures, delamination, chemical decomposition and reactions within the cells and the modules are expected during the 25-30 years of operation—due to natural elements. Some of these effects, such as yellowing of the EVA, or change of front surface color due to degrading of the AR coating, become visible to the naked eye. Most other internal and some external processes, however, start and continue visually undetected as time goes by.

Moisture and Chemical Ingress into the Module

This is another serious condition which could reduce the modules' efficiency and life. If it occurs soon after the modules are installed, it would very likely be traced to a manufacturing defect or handling problems during the transport or installation steps. At times, however, moisture in the modules is found months or years after they have been operating in the field. The reasons are usually defects in the laminate layers, caused by defective materials or improper handling or processing.

Desert sunlight is especially hard on the organic materials in the modules too, so it is usually only a matter of time before they start breaking down mechanically and chemically, at which point moisture and air could penetrate inside the modules.

Moisture ingress is a diffusion process (liquid diffusion that is). Its diffusivity depends on the module type, its frame construction and laminate materials composition and application. Moisture could penetrate into PV modules through the edge seals and from front or back cover defects (cracks, pores and such). Once in the module, moisture could easily penetrate through the encapsulants, causing them to delaminate, discolor, and mechanically disintegrate. In parallel with that, moisture could oxidize and otherwise attack the solar cells' metal contacts, causing them to degrade or fail completely.

The encapsulants and sealants have not changed much during the last 30 years, so the best defense we have in assuring the quality is to make sure that only quality materials are used, and that they are applied according to established manufacturing and QC specs.

Front Surface Reflection

Light reflected from the front surface of the module does not contribute to the electrical power generated. It is considered a loss which needs to be minimized. Reflected light does not contribute to heating the PV module. The maximum temperature rise of the module is therefore calculated as the incident power multiplied by the reflection. For typical PV modules with glass top cover, the reflected light contains about 4% of the incident energy.

Operating Point and Efficiency of the Module

The operating point and efficiency of the solar cell determine the fraction of light absorbed by the cell that is converted into electricity. If the solar cell is operating at short-circuit current or at open-circuit voltage, then it is generating no electricity and hence all the power absorbed by it is converted into heat.

Absorption of Light by the PV Module

The amount of light absorbed by the parts of the module other than the solar cells will also contribute to the heating of the module and does not contribute to generating power. How much light is absorbed and how much is reflected by the non-solar cell areas is determined by the color and materials of the rear backing layer of the module.

Absorption of Infra-red Light

Light which has an energy level below that of the band gap of the solar cells cannot contribute to generating free electrons and electrical power. On the other hand, if it is absorbed by the solar cells or by the module, this light will contribute to heating. The aluminum metallization at the rear of the solar cell tends to absorb this infrared light. In modules without rear aluminum cover, the IR light may pass through the solar cell and exit from the back of the module.

Packing Factor

Solar cells and modules are specifically designed to be efficient absorbers of solar radiation. The cells will generate significant amounts of heat, usually much higher than the module encapsulation and rear backing layer. Therefore, a higher packing factor of solar cells, in addition to increasing the generated power, will also increase the generated (parasitic) heat per unit area. This increase is harmful for long-term operation of modules, especially in areas of extreme heat, so the packing density must always be considered and adjusted accordingly to balance power output and module heating.

PV System Types

PV technologies manufacturers, supply chain companies, engineering teams, owners, investors and all participants are looking forward to the opportunities presented by solar power. The technical aspects of PV technologies complicate matters and make it hard to navigate in this relatively new field, so understanding the structure, function and issues of available PV technologies is the first step to successful design, installation and operation of a PV installation.

The major types of PV power generating systems for the purposes of this writing are residential, commercial, and utility installations, with emphasis on the latter.

Residential PV Systems

Let's start with residential systems and projects, which although not a subject of this book, are an important factor in today's solar energy scenario. Utilities love the residential PV market for a number of reasons; but, to be fair, residential projects are not the solution to our energy problems. And we expect that with the decrease and disappearance of government incentives and subsidies we'll see fewer residential installations.

On the other hand, residential installations are mini-power plants which help us understand the bigger issues facing us in large field installations. They also help in the "green" movement, so we hope that their numbers increase for these two reasons, if nothing else.

Figure 4-63 is a simple electrical wiring diagram of a residential solar power installation—our virtual PV system. It's about 5 kW—good enough for running the electric meter backwards several kWh a day, while Mom and Pop are at work and the kids are at school. Putting the roof to work? Not a bad idea. But it took some doing to get the system on the roof, get it connected, tested and blessed. And now, when it is all ready to produce power and help pay the monthly power bills, there are some problems as we will see below.

Again, residential installations are not the object of this book, but they parallel large-scale installations closely, albeit at a different level of size, complexity and difficulty, so we just can't resist the opportunity to point out the basic function and issues of this simple installation and then transfer these to our much larger projects.

Residential PV systems are usually classified as

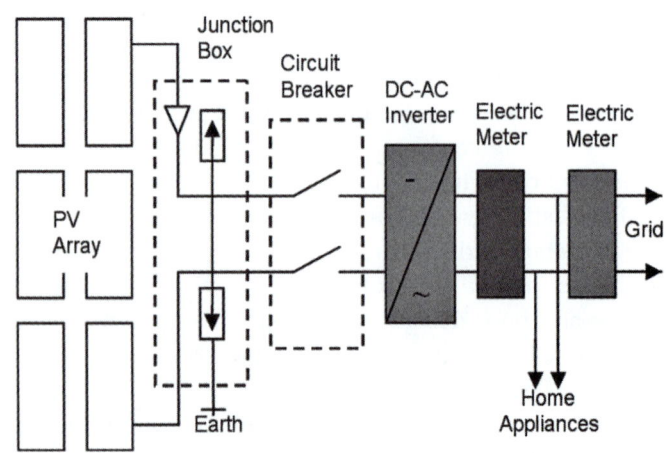

Figure 4-63. Residential PV installation

off-grid, or more often as grid-tied systems. We will not dedicate much time to off-grid systems, and will only point out that they usually consist of a small PV array, either portable, or built-in, intended to power part of a house, a remote cabin or a small piece of equipment, such as a water pump somewhere in the remote fields of Kansas or Texas. These PV systems are usually roof- or ground-mounted and power appliances and equipment, feeding DC power directly, or converting it to 120 V AC.

So, back to our residential installation. The PV array produces DC power and runs it through a PV disconnect for safety and maintenance purposes. The power then goes into a charge controller, which is a glorified battery charger. The DC power from the controller and/or the batteries goes to the house appliances that can run on DC power. Whatever is not used as DC in the house goes into the inverter, which converts it into AC power and sends it into the power grid. Simple, yes, but not trouble-free.

It can take months to agree on the design and file the forms to obtain the necessary permits and get the installation completed. Once that is done, our new PV array is ready to go. It "wakes up" in the morning by generating a small amount of power because the sunlight is still too weak to activate the electrons asleep in their holes and get them energized for another day of running up and down the wires. But soon the sun rises and more juice flows into the circuitry and into the grid. Yes, the system is running and the higher the sun gets, the more power it generates.

All of a sudden, however, there is an alarm. The PV array is disconnected. A wet wire from last night's rain has shorted, and the EGFP (equipment ground fault protection) device tripped, isolating the array from the DC loads and the inverter. After a couple of tries, the system is back on line and operational, but soon it is off again, this time because many such installations in the neighborhood have similar problems and the on-and-off mode of these has destabilized the grid. The inverter/controller is not capable of synchronizing, went into "islanding" mode, and our array is off the grid until the condition is remedied.

The next day the wind blows a bunch of leaves from the neighbors' trees onto the PV array and the power output is restricted by half. We are told that partially shaded cells in the modules are in danger of overheating and the module is threatened by a meltdown and even a fire, so somebody must climb on the roof and sweep the leaves. Our small PV power plant is up and running again, when, a day or two later, the output seems to be very low for some reason. A quick test points to a mod-

ule that has malfunctioned and is no longer producing full power. It could be a broken or shorted solar cell, but a sealed PV module cannot be repaired, so we call the maintenance crew to replace it. That effort is covered by contract or warranty. If not, the repair will cost us the last 6 months energy produced by the system.

Even with the best of efforts and impeccable professional maintenance, we notice that the array produces ~ 5-6% less than normal after 4-5 years of operation. The modules manufacturer's warranty says that even after 20 years of operation, the modules are guaranteed to produce 80% of the electricity they produced when they were new. So a 5-6% drop in output in 4-5 years is within the warranty claims. Sadly, there is not much we can do about that. It is a loss, which we should've estimated and allowed for at the very beginning.

Now, 20 years have gone by, the contract term is completed, and the array output is very low. The installation must be decommissioned and disposed of. Who is going to climb up on the roof to disconnect and disassemble it? What are we going to do with the modules and other hardware, which now are mostly junk and even considered hazardous waste (in the case of some types of thin film modules)? Can we throw them in the garbage? Nope. Many PV modules must be handled as hazardous waste, carefully disassembled, and packed and shipped as such to a corresponding recycling center. What if the PV modules manufacturer is out of business now and the insurance or recycling fund no longer covers the disassembly and shipping charges? Impossible? Yes, possible! Read the fine print very carefully before buying the modules and/or signing the contract. There are many manufacturers here today and gone tomorrow, so utmost caution is needed.

Our virtual and somewhat troublesome PV system above is a good reminder that an excellent design and planning for anything the future might bring are indispensible in assuring good results from any PV system, residential or large-scale. And large-scale systems are, of course, many times larger so that any design error, production quality issue, or maintenance negligence will cost us multiples in delays, poor performance, failures and financial losses.

Now for the larger, commercial type system.

Commercial PV Systems

A typical commercial PV system for a small business usually also consists of rooftop-mounted PV modules tilted at an angle of, or lower than, the latitude of the particular location. We won't spend much time on these, because the biggest difference between residential and commercial PV systems would be the number of modules and the size of the inverters used.

Trackers are seldom used in such installations, and when they are used on the roof they are usually small structures, though larger trackers could be used in ground-mounted commercial applications.

As you see, the array in Figure 4-64 is very similar to the residential one we discussed previously. Both arrays would have similar design, installation and operation considerations, except that the commercial arrays are much bigger and usually more complex and expensive. The problems of the residential PV system described above are encountered in these systems too, so we must make sure that they are well designed and installed, and that appropriate O&M procedures have been implemented.

Utilities Scale PV Projects

Here we must provide a definition and scope of utilities-type PV projects. A "utility" is a company that generates and/or distributes electrical power. The power can be generated by the utility itself, or purchased from elsewhere, but in both cases the utility is responsible for the proper and safe distribution and delivery of the power to the customers' interconnect points. Utilities-type PV installations usually deliver power exclusively to the utility's substation close to the solar field. The PV power fields could be as little as 1.0 MWp and up to a GWp or more.

For simplicity's sake we will refer to all commercial and utilities systems interchangeably as "large-scale" installations in this text, keeping in mind that these could be of different sizes and designations which we will point out as needed. We will take a closer look at large-scale PV systems in this and the following chapters.

Balance of System

Balance of system (BOS) is a generic term that describes all components needed to install, adjust and control a PV system, except the PV modules. This includes support racks, wiring, breaker boxes, switches, inverters, and batteries in off-grid systems. Land, labor and O&M expenses and components are usually not included in the BOS calculations.

BOS components are key elements of any PV power plant model. Their particular design, overall efficiency quality and actual field performance will determine the plant's success rate.

NOTE: We have not discussed "success rates" yet, because it is not a standard measurement unit, but in the framework of this writing success is determined by:

- Quality of location (sunshine availability and weather conditions)
- Quality of components; low- vs. high-quality manufacturers
- Quality of design, installation and O&M teams,
- Luck (lack of natural and man-made disasters)

So what does it take to design and install utilities' (large-scale) PV power plants?

PV Power Plant Planning

The objective of an efficient PV plant design is a) to generate power most efficiently at the lowest cost possible, and b) to obtain a high return on investment by generating maximum power output for the duration. First, this requires the use of PV modules, inverters and medium-voltage transformers with optimum efficiency, and limited wiring loss and losses due to shading and other obstructions, and with proper power generation

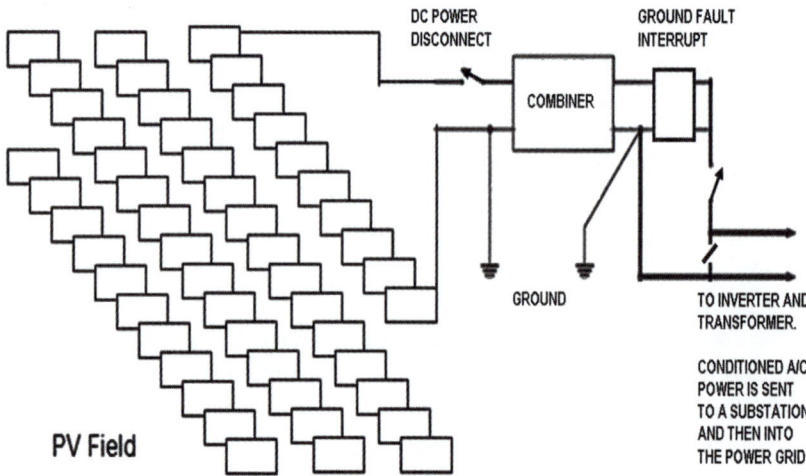

Figure 4-64. Commercial PV installation

and plant function monitoring and control.

Second, materials and installation costs should be reduced as much as possible, to minimize capital expenditures and maximize ROI. It follows that proper selection of PV modules, inverters and other BOS is essential at the planning and plant design stages. Cheap but inefficient or troublesome equipment will defeat the objectives of efficient and cost effective power production. Complete understanding of the efficiency, durability, cost variables, and making the proper equipment selection will determine the proper and efficient plant operation and return of investment (ROI).

There are a number of design parameters and options and related combinations that must be evaluated during the PV plant planning and design stages. Understanding the technology and its use under different conditions is paramount to ensuring successful plant design. Key parameters must be considered such as management, location and actual field design. Let's take a look at some of these.

Management Team

The starting point and foundation of a properly and efficiently designed, installed and operated PV plant is its management team. Different PV plants have different management structure, but in all cases there is a chief executive officer (CEO), or general manager (GM), who is basically responsible for the selection of the different managers and other officials and employees, and for the overall coordination of the activities at hand, for the duration.

VPs of technology, quality control, finance, and operations are part of the top management team, and report directly to the CEO. A number of different project managers, consultants, contractors and employees fill the ranks during planning, design, and installation, as well as during the operation and maintenance stages of the plant's lifetime.

The top management team is responsible for all aspects of the operation from cradle to grave, and its decisions have a major impact on the plant's proper and efficient implementation and operation. Thorough understanding of the respective disciplines and related hands-on experience, as well as following established industry methods and procedures are essential in guiding the team through the different stages and successfully completing the tasks at hand. Figure 4-66 outlines a strong management structure.

Implementation and operation of a properly de-

signed and efficiently operating PV plant requires highly capable and experienced team members functioning as efficiently and professionally as possible. The team is similar in structure and function to that of a hi-tech company working on a large project. Bringing the project to a successful end requires efficient daily coordination and communication among the managers, contractors, consultants and all other parties involved in the project during all stages.

With some variations, the team is usually led by a CEO who is in charge of all aspects of the operation from beginning to end. All VPs report directly to him and he reports to the owners and investors.

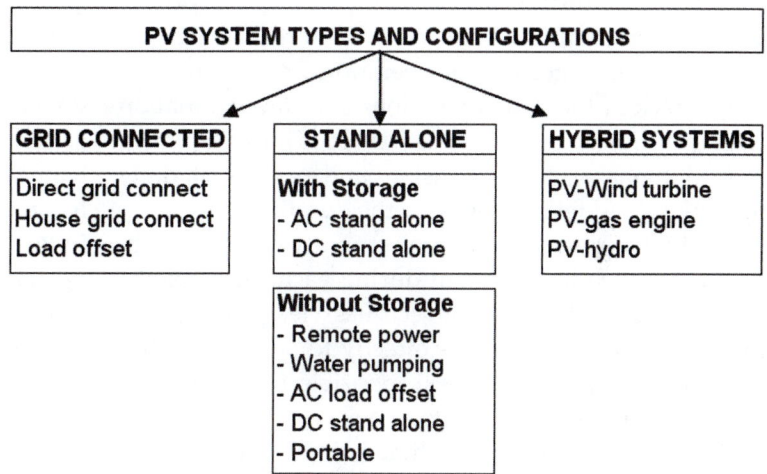

Figure 4-65. Types of PV systems

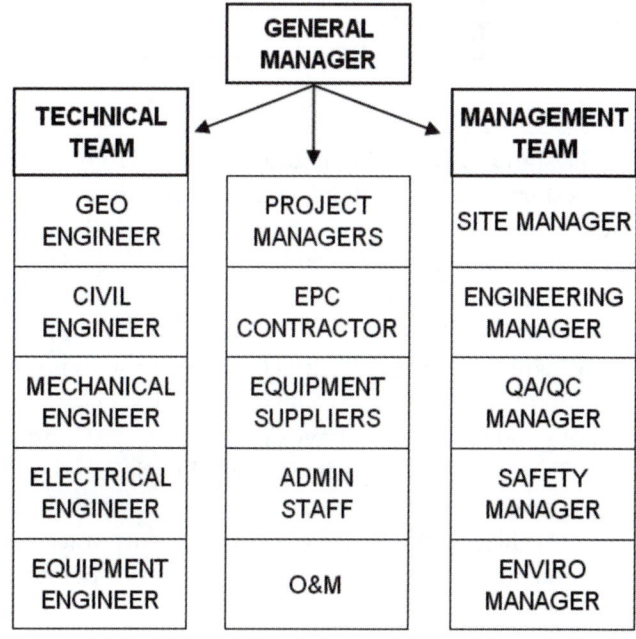

Figure 4-66. PV plant management structure

The day-to-day technical tasks during the design and implementation phases are managed and coordinated by a technical officer (VP of technology or CTO), who keeps track of the progress, meets with the different technical groups, consultants and contractors. In coordination with the CEO, the CTO makes the final decisions on all technical tasks and issues for the duration.

The day-to-day financial tasks during the design and implementation phases are managed and coordinated by a financial officer (VP of finance, or CFO), who keeps track of the daily expenses and other activities, and who in coordination with the CEO makes the final decisions on all financial tasks and issues for the duration.

The day-to-day operations (during the power plant's operation) are managed and coordinated by an operations manager (VP of operations, or COO), who keeps track of the daily operations and in coordination with the CEO (if CEO's mandate extends into the plant's operation phase), makes decisions and executes all daily operations and related tasks for the duration.

The PV power plant project is divided into sub-projects, which are different during each phase of the project. Each of these sub-projects has a lead, or a project manager (PM), who reports directly to one of the VPs, or to the CEO, and is fully responsible for the proper and efficient planning, design and execution of the sub-project and the tasks of which he is in charge. The PM, together with the CEO and the respective VPs and/or other responsible parties (consultants, contractors etc.), makes the decisions and then implements them accordingly on a day-by-day basis.

The planning and design process in detail:

Location Selection

Designing, deploying and operating a large utility type system is not a textbook event. There are no standards or set-in-concrete procedures to plan, design and execute the numerous tasks at hand. Each PV project is different from technical, administrative, regulatory and financial points of view.

Where do we start? Picking the right location is one of the first tasks on the list of responsibilities, because if it is not good enough, we have only ourselves to blame. If the PV plant is at a predetermined location, we will have to do our best to maximize the output by installing the most efficient PV system with highest output for the particular location, and ensure their proper operation for the duration.

In all cases, the planning, design and execution of the project is the responsibility of the designer/install-er/investor teams. The responsible team members must be fully aware of the conditions at the site and evaluate all possible combinations of location, weather, technology, materials and labor, as well as properly use all available management tools to provide the best design and implementation possible. Every detail should be taken into consideration, analyzed, calculated and entered into the overall formula, thus making proper decisions at every step.

What's in a location? There are a large number of conditions and variables to consider. Sunshine, or no sunshine? When, how long and how intense is the sunshine? Do clouds and fog visit the site frequently? Are there populated centers, commercial enterprises and roads nearby? Are there wild life in the area? Terrain issues? Environmental issues? Making sure that the proposed site has good sunlight during the day is a given. If it is located in a cloudy or foggy climate, such as in mountains or near the ocean, the management team must calculate the energy input and decide how to proceed under the circumstances. A PV power plant in Portland, Maine, will be different in construction and performance than one in Portland, Oregon, and even more so than one in the Arizona desert.

There are many parameters and issues that must be evaluated in a professional manner, and considered thoroughly to make sure that the proposed site is reasonably positioned for success, and that there will be no great obstacles in converting enough sunlight into AC power, to maximize the returns. Of course, all other land-related conditions (permitting, regulatory and socio-economic) must be included in the planning and design effort.

In addition to sunlight and other technical characteristics, see the list below of administrative considerations that must be evaluated during the very early stages of project development (mostly applicable for sites on public land in California) to make sure the location (land) meets the requirements for a PV power generation site:

a. The renewable energy project is proposed to be located on land identified by REAT that is suitable for renewable energy development.

b. The project will not use fresh ground water or surface water for power plant cooling.

c. The appropriate biological resource surveys have been completed using the proper protocols during the appropriate season.

d. A draft biological assessment (BA), if required for the project, has been tentatively approved by FWS, DFG and the appropriate lead agencies.

e. The appropriate cultural resource surveys, assessments, and project impact mitigation measures have been completed following the proper protocols and standards.

f. Ensure that all BLM (if project site is on BLM land) requirements and resource management plans (RMPs) have been addressed and incorporated in the project design, for projects located on BLM managed lands.

g. All the requirements of the local agency jurisdiction have been incorporated into the applications including but not limited to local zoning, general plan policies, land use, traffic, and height restrictions. The project will not be located on lands under a Williamson Act contract, require a zoning change, or general plan amendment.

h. All of the requirements of the Department of Defense (DOD) and nearby military installations have been addressed and incorporated into a project's design.

i. The project site does not negatively impact ongoing transmission corridor planning.

j. Phase I site assessment ASTM E1527 or other equivalent assessment method deemed acceptable by the appropriate regulatory oversight agency for the project site and linear appurtenances is conducted to determine if there are any environmental concerns.

k. The local fire protection district, or if necessary California Department of Forestry and Fire Protection (CALFIRE, Office of the State Fire Marshall), must be contacted to locate the proposed project site relative to fire hazard severity zones.

l. Soil surveys to identify soil types and the typical silt content of soils in many locations are conducted.

m. Flood and fire zoning is conducted to determine whether the site is located within flood or fire hazard zones and/or the development would result in flood or firefighting plain modifications.

This is not a straightforward process, and that is why an experienced project management team is essential to properly address and efficiently resolve all tasks and issues.

General Tasks

There is a long list of tasks to be completed, mountains of technical, regulatory and legal documents to go through, and many hours sitting in meetings in order to get a power installation up and running:

1. General site evaluation, map, orientation, scale, photos.
2. 1st assessment of land—size, technology and annual production.
3. Environmental impact study and assessment, regarding restrictions such as:
   a. Integral nature reserve
   b. Landscape conservation area
   c. Negative impact on natural scenery
   d. Priority area for agriculture, leisure, or flooding protection areas.
   NOTE: It is important to know the particulars of the regulation of application in the municipality and in the region.
4. Define and evaluate compensatory measures.
5. Site visit:
   a. Evaluation of data received—visual evaluation.
   b. Shading and site infrastructure evaluation.
6. Field design
7. Bidding procedure for EPC (contractor/installer)
8. Final solar yield study (by external expert
   a. Approach and boundary conditions
   b. Evaluation of the technical concept and the components used
   c. Yield forecast (annual yield, performance ratio, etc.)
   d. Description of methods and calculation programs used
9. Formation of the required legal entity (corporation, JV etc.)
10. Identifying the equity capital
11. Getting the required permits
12. The inscription to the special power generation registry (REPE)
13. Grid connection point evaluation and negotiations
14. Final inscription to the REPE
15. Financing aspects
    a. Pre-construction finance
       i. Land purchase
       ii. Land permitting

    iii. PPA negotiations
  b. Construction finance negotiations
  c. Long-term finance options
16. Signing contracts with stakeholders
  a. Land rent/lease contract
  b. Equipment purchase contract
  c. Installation contract
  d. Performance assurance contracts
  e. Contract for monitoring the plant
  f. Contract for operation and maintenance of the plant
  g. Contract for tax consultant (annual profit/loss declaration)
  h. Contract for project's technical and administration management
17. Construction phase
  a. Land leveling and preparation
  b. PV equipment installation
18. Finalizing the construction.
  a. Plant performance tests
  b. Plant acceptance procedures*
19. Inauguration of the plant
20. Power sale agreements take place
21. Plant O&M procedures take place

PV System Design Considerations

A number of technical factors and variables must be considered in the proper design of an efficient PV power generator. The performance and efficiency of the PV components, or of individual PV modules affecting the array performance must be well understood and used in the design effort. Some of these follow.

Reflection

Not all the photons which hit the cell and module can actually pass through to the p-n junction, because some of them are reflected by the cell AR coating and the module glass surface. Some of the sunlight hits the contact's metallic grid, and is also reflected. Reflection is different during different times depending on the location, technology used, time of day and the sun's intensity, angle and other climatic conditions.

---

*If the final inspection and acceptance tests are within spec, the power metering system is set to zero. From then on the produced electricity will be sold to the utility company as number of kW per day. This process is the same for small or large plants, but the length, magnitude and expense of the separate steps are proportional to the size.

Photons Energetic Levels

Not all incoming photons have enough energy to break the force holding the electrons into the electron-hole pair. Also, there are some photons which bring too much energy, which could actually generate electron-hole couples, with the exceeding energy being converted into heat, which further complicates electron generation.

Recombination

Not all the electron-hole couples are collected by the junction electric field and then sent to the external load. Instead, they recombine with opposite charges encountered along their path from the generation point toward the junction and beyond. There are a number of reasons for this phenomena and these must be investigated in light of the technology choice, location and sunlight quality.

Parasitic Resistances

Charges generated and collected into the depletion region must be sent into the outside load of the cell and module. The collection is performed by the metallic contacts, placed on both the front and rear sides of the cell. The manufacturing process creates an alloy between the silicon cell and the aluminum metal of the contacts and with it some interface resistance in the boundaries between the layers. This parasitic resistance causes heat dissipation, and further reduction of output, due to the resistance met by the electrons at the boundary. This condition is even more pronounced in amorphous silicon cells, because of the increased resistance, due to the random orientation of the crystals and atoms.

Temperature Coefficient

When the cell temperature gets higher than the standard test conditions (STC) of 25°C, its efficiency decreases around 0.5% per degree C temperature increase over STC. This phenomenon occurs because the conversion of the solar radiation into electrical energy by the PV cells is limited to only a part of the total radiation spectrum. The unused radiation is converted into heat which increases the cell temperature and reduces its output due to serial and shunt resistance effects.

Annual Degradation

A further problem of current PV technology is associated with the decrease of c-Si and thin film PV modules' performance over time. Basically, the output of a PV module is reduced by ~0.5% to 1.5% per year. This phenomenon is mainly due to thermic variations among the different points of the cell, which could cause micro fractures in different regions, reducing the mobility of free electrons. Such micro fractures generate a resistance for charges and reduce the electrons' capability to move freely in the bulk and reach the electrode for extraction into the external load.

Another reason for such persistent degradation is normal changes in the silicon material and the diffusion layer properties. Also, changes in the encapsulating materials (EVA yellowing) could be expected, decreasing optical transmission of the material and interfering with incoming photons.

Permanent Failures

A major reason for permanent failure of solar cells and modules is the creation of micro-fractures in the bulk material over time. The cracks are usually caused by torsions and flexions of the envelope materials (frame and encapsulants) due to mishandling, wind, and atmospheric agents. Wide temperature variations from extreme heat to below-zero freezing play a major role in the destructive processes as well.

The worst irreversible effect, however, is the penetration of the elements into the module interior via defects in the encapsulation. The cells undergo chemical attacks in such cases and only time separates them and the module from an untimely and complete failure. Intimate contact and strong bonds between cells and the support materials, as well as reliable protection from the elements, are highly recommended, so careful design, manufacturing, installation and operating procedures must be followed to optimize performance and limit permanent failure rates.

PV System Performance Considerations

There are a number of factors to consider, estimate, calculate and implement in the design, installation and operation of a sound PV power plant. Some of them follow.

Latitude and Longitude

This is a critical factor, because it determines not only the geographic location of the plant, but everything that is related to it, such as climate variations, obstructions, and air pollution; i.e., a solar power plant was installed some time ago in a seemingly good location, just to discover after a while that heavy dust from a nearby cement factory settled onto the solar equipment, reducing and even shutting down its energy production.

Tilt Angle

The tilt angle is usually set at the latitude +/–5 degrees, but variations of this rule should be considered for special effects, such as optimizing performance during certain parts of the day or season.

Seasonal angle adjustment makes sense under some conditions and for some types of modules but, after factoring labor into the equation, the difference might be negligible or even negative. One point in favor of seasonal adjustment is that it can be combined with the annual evaluation of field structure, PV equipment, inverters, wiring, etc., though this is seldom performed.

Tracking

To track or not to track? This is the question that many system design engineers must answer at some point during the design of any PV power plant. Trackers, like seasonally adjustable tilt, come at a price of both initial capital investment and O&M later on. Is it worth spending additional money and effort to gain several additional MWh? The calculations are not straightforward, due to the climate changes, so in many cases it is a gamble.

As a rule of thumb, c-Si modules should be tracker mounted in desert regions only, while tracking with thin film modules cannot be justified under most conditions, due to the already high BOS cost.

Solar Radiation Levels

Radiation levels are directly proportional to the amount of energy generated by the power plant. A number of factors must be considered to optimize power output, but it starts with bright sunshine falling on the PV modules. Without it, the power plant is like a car running on empty. This is why the desert areas are the preferred large-scale power plant locations. They are where radiation levels are the highest and where unobstructed direct beam radiation is most likely to be found.

Weather Conditions

Weather conditions at the particular location are the greatest unknown that faces power field designers. Climate variations can make the difference between a profitable and not-so-profitable PV power installation. Excess clouds, fog, smog, dust, strong winds, hail, heavy snow, etc. can bankrupt a PV plant, simply because the power output would be drastically reduced and, worse yet, the equipment itself might be damaged.

Historical weather data might help in the estimates, but no one can provide a precise long-term weather forecast, a science made even more difficult by the unpredictable world climate changes of late. Yet, there are regions that are more predictable than others, which brings us back to recommending desert areas as most suitable for large-scale power generation.

Temperature

Desert areas have their own problems. PV modules, installed in areas with normal temperature regimens will usually provide efficient and trouble-free operation for many years. This is not the case, however, for c-Si or thin film modules installed in desert areas. The extreme heat will add stress to the active structure and its laminating envelope, which will break first under the strong UV and IR radiation. This will allow water and gasses to enter the modules and disintegrate the active structure with time.

Strong sand storms and monsoon weather conditions are challenging to any type of PV design. These abnormalities must be taken into consideration when considering PV operation in open desert areas.

Humidity

Similarly so, c-Si and thin film modules installed in areas of high humidity (over 60%) of long duration, such as the several weeks of monsoon conditions in the Arizona desert, will suffer premature power degradation and failure, because the moisture could penetrate the laminate layer and attack the active PV structure, chemically disintegrating it with time.

Shading

The degree of shading is inversely proportional to the power output. Shade can come from trees, bushes, or improperly installed rows of PV modules. Shading could cause the creation of "hot spots," which will reduce the output and might even damage the affected cells and modules.

As a rule of thumb, PV systems must be clear of any surface obstructions. Short of that, a thorough analysis of the shading type and level, including any future changes, must be performed and taken into consideration in the final design. In some cases, the manufacturer's warranty might be void if shading or surface obstructions cause any malfunctions or failures.

Load Mismatch

A common problem in poor performance or failure of PV systems is load mismatch due to poor design and/or installation, or equipment defects or failures. Cells, modules, wiring, inverters, stringing, combiner boxes, etc. need to be precisely matched on paper and in the actual installation. Load mismatch can account for up to 20% power loss, and is often cited as a major cause for equipment failure.

Inverter Efficiency

Inverters have gotten very efficient and reliable lately—if properly installed and operated. Just like PV modules, however, they suffer from exposure to the elements (excess heat and moisture). Their efficiency will drop proportionally with temperature increases, and if not properly cooled most inverters will simply stop working with exposure to extreme temperature. Equipment failures have been documented under such extreme conditions, as well.

In-row Shadowing Losses

Shadowing of the panels in one row by those of the row in front occurs primarily in the early morning and late afternoon hours and is most obvious during winter months, due to the sharp angle of the sun's rays. Its occurrence and extent are functions of the latitude, time of year, time of day, panel tilt, panel slant height, row-to-row spacing and east/west orientation. Shadowing could be completely avoided by careful module placement in relation to surrounding rows and objects, and by increasing the row-to-row spacing. Row spacing, however, increases land use, wire costs and losses, and overall capital cost.

Wire Losses

In calculating wire losses, we need to consider the current in each wire resulting from the insolation, as reduced by the shadowing losses. Both power and energy losses are calculated. To calculate the energy loss, it is necessary to know the time (in hours) that a given level of current flows. These data can be calculated and verified after the power plant is in operation. The power level is sensed and sorbed into power density bands from 0 to 11mW/cm in unit steps, during every 30-minute power output measurement, and stored in a file. When a full year's calculation is completed, the data stored for each power density band are multiplied by half an hour and divided by the level of the power band. Having derived these data, calculating the total wire energy losses becomes routine.

Misc. Losses

Other losses that need to be calculated as lost time include periodic maintenance and emergency repairs, wind, lightning and hail damages, and other unforeseen events, which might force partial or complete plant shutdown.

Capacity Factor

A measure of performance of a power plant commonly used by utilities is its capacity factor. Another useful term is the annual kilowatt-hour produced per installed peak watt. These terms relate to each other as follows:

$$\text{Capacity Factor} = \frac{\text{Annual kWh/Wp}}{\text{\# of Hours/Year}}$$

The capacity factor for conventional systems is determined by utility system economic dispatch and unit availability on the following equation:

Generated Energy = (Insolation) x
(Conversion Efficiency) x (Time Interval)] – (Losses)

output usually occurs in the middle of the day and in the summer). The weather also plays a critical role in the final power output numbers. A persistently long cloudy period could cripple PV plant finances.

It is obvious, from Figure 4-67a that a bright sunny day will consistently produce the amount of energy we expect from the power field; i.e., the power field will be at its peak performance. The contrary is true during a partially cloudy day, during which the generated power will vary according to the amount of sunlight the power field receives at any given moment.

An important characteristic of solar energy systems is that their output may be complementary to the output of wind generators. Solar power is often produced during the peak load hours (mid-day) when wind energy production may not be available. Figure 4-68 illustrates this phenomenon and compares the average demand with the aggregate wind and solar plant output

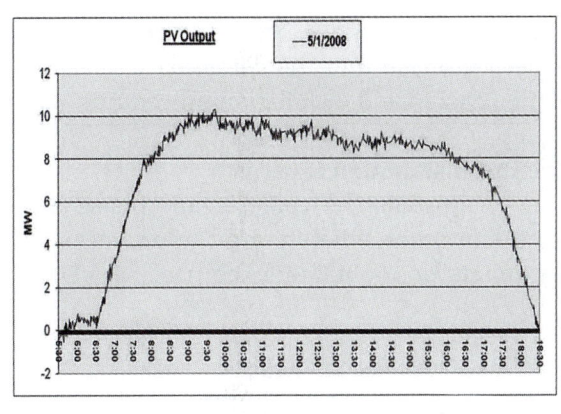

a. Sunny day

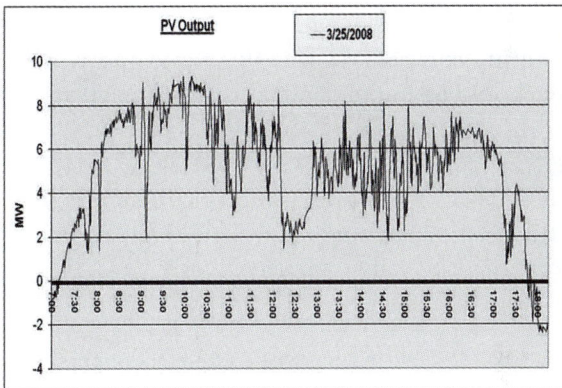

b. Partially cloudy day

Figure 4-67. PV plant output variability from day to day

where:

Insolation is the daily average kWh solar energy of the particular location, and # of hours/year are the total of hours the system has operated under full insolation, while losses are anything that prevents the system from generating its nameplate power output.

Power Output Variability

Considerable differences exist in the technical characteristics from one form of solar technology to another and from one location to another. One important characteristic shared by all types of solar power is their diurnal and seasonal pattern (i.e., peak

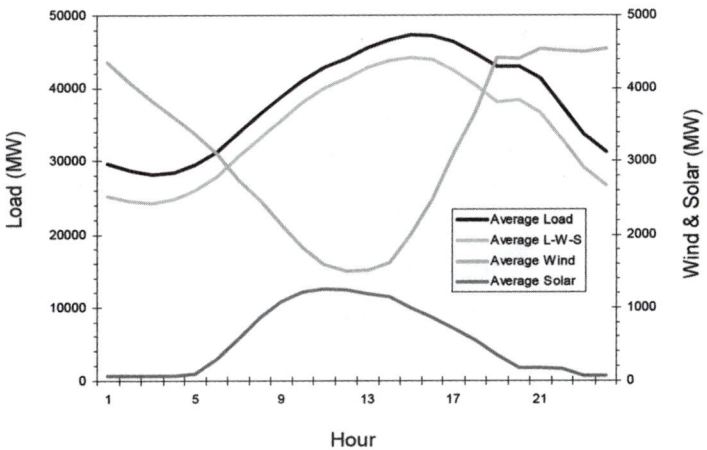

Figure 4-68. Variability and demand dependence

in California.

Variability around these average demand values for individual wind and solar resources can fluctuate significantly on a daily basis. However, as illustrated, solar and wind plant profiles when considered in aggregate can be a good match to the load profile and hence improve the resulting composite capacity value for variable generation. There are other factors to consider too—wind speed, air temperature, modules surface contamination etc., but with everything else kept constant, the sunlight intensity is the final determining factor of the variability and the amount of power generated.

Large photovoltaic (PV) plants proposed in the southwestern U.S. and Southern California, have the potential to place extremely fast ramping resources on the power distribution system. Under certain weather conditions, PV installations can change output by +/–70% within two to ten minutes, many times per day.

Therefore, since this variable load is hard to manage, these power plants should consider incorporating the ability to manage ramp rates and/or curtail power output as needed by the power network. This is something that utility companies are looking into and which eventually should be implemented on a national level.

Therefore:

• Variability of PV power output is not a simple linear function of variability in plane-of-array point irradiance, especially on partly cloudy days.

• Preliminary results suggest that >10 min variability of multi-MW PV plants can be approximated by the variability of point irradiance averaged over a similar time window.

• Short-term (<10 min) variability is influenced by the size of the plant, with variability decreasing with increasing size, as different weather patterns develop in the different zones of the plant(s).

THE INSTALLATION PHASE

Installation of components in the large-scale power PV field will start upon agreement by all parties on the technical, administrative and financial conditions, and after thorough evaluation of the design plans, specs, bids, proposals and contracts.

The actual work on the components and systems installation will follow established principals and methods, some of which are outlined below. In the absence of one accepted standard, the text below is only a guideline—a glimpse into the complexity of the PV power plants' design and installation procedures.

The Pre-installation Process

The installation (construction) phase of the power plant starts immediately after approval of the design documentation, obtaining the necessary permits, PPA

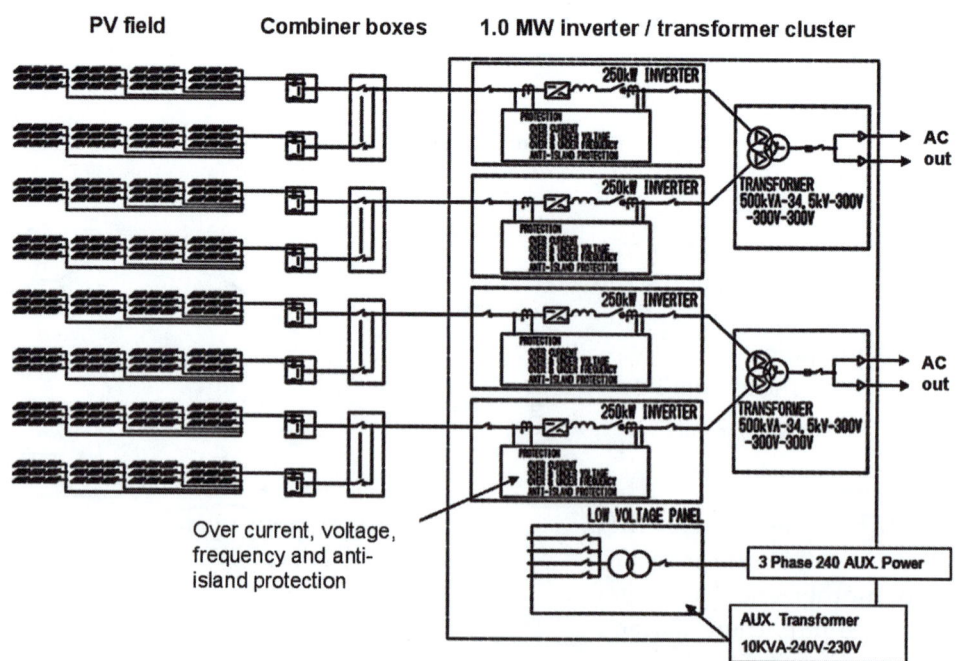

Figure 4-69. 1.0 MWp large-scale PV power generating plant

and financing. Before starting installation, however, the project manager and the coordinators of the respective areas of the installation process must make sure that all necessary steps of the planning and design processes have been completed successfully, and the relevant documentation has been properly executed.

The pre-installation process usually follows the steps outlined below:

1. Required permit documents and materials will be submitted to the authorities, and preliminary approvals will be issued prior to starting any construction activities.

2. Receiving schedules for plant equipment and materials, and the activities related to preparation for their installation will be finalized and followed through.

3. All equipment will go through a thorough initial inspection to verify quantity received, and to make sure that it has arrived without any modifications or shipping damage.

4. Actual field tests with some equipment (PV modules) should be performed to verify performance and compliance.

5. Installation instructions for each component will be finalized and reviewed, and the responsible personnel will be trained to become familiar with equipment and the installation procedures.

6. Length of wire runs from PV modules to combiner and inverter will be verified and documented. Trial runs must be performed to verify the process steps.

7. Ampacity of PV array circuits will be verified to determine the minimum wire size for current flow.

8. Wire runs must be verified based on maximum short circuit current for each circuit and the length of the wire run, and as follow:
   a. The minimum wire ampacity for the wire run from modules to combiner is based on module maximum series fuse rating printed on the label.
   b. The minimum wire ampacity for the wire run from combiner to inverter is based on the number of module series strings times the maximum series fuse rating.

9. The size of the PV array wiring must be such that the maximum voltage drop at full power from the PV modules to the inverter is 3% or less, for
   a. Wire run from modules to combiner
   b. Wire run from combiner to inverter

10. Length of wire run from inverter to main service panel must be established and verified. The goal is 1% voltage drop for AC-side of system (3% maximum).

11. Main service electric panels must be checked to determine if they are adequately sized to receive the PV breakers or whether the panels must be upgraded.

Once these procedures have been signed off by the responsible personnel—including the QC manager—the installation process can begin.

The Installation (Construction) Process

Installation of PV and BOS equipment should be done by a certified solar energy equipment installer/contractor. Several contractors, specialists in the different areas of the plant's construction could be employed as well.

The installation process usually follows the sample procedure below:

1. Review instruction manual and train technicians accordingly. The proper execution of this work effort will be supervised by the project manager and verified and documented by the QC manager and his crew.

2. The pre-installation check procedures include:
   a. Check all modules visually. Test the open circuit voltage and short circuit current of each module, before taking onto the field to verify proper operation. See checklist for detailed procedures.
   b. Check plug connectors and connector boxes.
   c. Check the attachment points and methods as indicated in the drawings.

3. The installation procedure includes:
   a. Mount modules on support structure and connect to conduit.
   b. Install PV combiner, inverter, and associated equipment to prepare for system wiring.
   c. Connect properly sized wire to each circuit of modules.
   d. Run properly sized wire (per drawings) for each circuit to the circuit combiners.
   e. Run properly sized wire (per drawings) from

circuit combiner to inverter over-current/disconnect switch.

   f. Run properly sized wire (per drawings) from inverter to utility disconnect switch.

   g. Run properly sized wire (per drawings) from utility disconnect switch to main service panel and connect circuit to the main utility service.

4. Use the checklist and drawings to ensure proper installation throughout the system by visual inspection. Sign off each step of the installation and verification procedures.

5. Verify that all PV circuits are operating properly and the system is performing as expected. Double check the checklist and drawings prior to executing the system acceptance test.

6. Final inspections will be conducted by the QC manager, the local authorities, and the utilities. Once approval is received, the system is ready for operation

7. The buy-down request form, with all necessary attachments, will be sent to the appropriate authorities to receive buy-down payments per agreed conditions.

8. The QC manager is fully responsible for the proper training of the technical personnel in charge of quality control procedures at each step of the design and installation stages. The QC manager also coordinates the proper documentation and records keeping, daily and periodic inspections of work sites, as well as the actual acceptance and performance evaluation of each step of the installation phase. The QC manager is ultimately responsible for following proper preparation, installation, inspection, verification and test procedures.

PV Power Plant Performance Evaluation

The performance evaluation phase will start immediately after the EPC contractor(s) signals completion of the installation and has performed start-up and initial performance and safety testing of each step of the process.

A step-by-step checklist of steps to be taken during the installation and performance evaluation procedures—all of which will be supervised and verified by QC manager and his QC inspectors—is to be developed ahead of time, to ensure a quality installation.

Upon completion of each step of the installation procedures, the QC manager and his inspectors will conduct performance evaluation of the components and systems. Tests designed to verify and confirm compliance with the design specs and requirements, as well as to test the performance characteristics of the components and systems at each step of the installation process will be executed accordingly. The results of these tests will be verified, approved and signed off by the QC manager.

When all construction stages have been completed, and the related components and systems have been signed off, the final test of the entire power plant complex will begin. With all modules and strings activated and connected in the circuit, a number of tests will be performed with each string, to begin with, and recorded as a baseline for each particular sting under the existing weather conditions.

The total power output—on the DC and AC sides—will be measured, and the appropriate calculations of the plant's efficiency, yield, etc. will be made and documented as well. The resulting data will be used as a baseline of the power plant performance under the existing weather conditions and for comparative purposes in the future.

System Certification and Documentation

Thorough documentation and record keeping is the best way to ensure efficient implementation of all phases of this project. A number of documents and record-keeping media will be developed for the different segments of the project implementation, such as:

1. General system documentation for installation and operation phases
2. Technical drawings for the same
3. Training documentation
4. QC manuals and inspection documentation
5. Non-conforming materials and procedures documents

These will be needed for inspection and verification during each step of the project by different specialists and responsible parties. The complete package of documentation will be submitted to the inspecting authorities for final inspection, verification and certification of the facility.

At the end of the construction phase, and after all quality checks have been performed and signed off by the QC manager, the appropriate authorities are notified to execute certification checks and tests. These vary from state to state and from project to project, but basically consist of review of all construction and QC documents and verification of the final performance test results.

Again, some operation and quality control policies and standards for the different stages of the PV products manufacturing, installation and operation do exist, but there is no single, all-encompassing and accepted by the worldwide PV industry standard for these. Until such a standard is implemented, we will improvise in some cases, and compromise in others. A number of serious gaps still exist in the operating and quality control procedures of the sand-to-modules manufacturing steps and the power plants' design-to-decommissioning processes.

Since we don't see any such standard emerging, especially in the US, we will use this text to bring some of the key issues out for discussion and eventual resolution.

OPERATION AND MAINTENANCE PHASE

Upon completion of the construction and installation stages, the responsibility for the operation of the new facility is transferred immediately to a team of specialists working for the plant owners, or to an independent contractor who is paid a fee to operate the plant for a certain amount of time. The engagement conditions are carefully discussed and officially agreed upon in advance and an operation and maintenance (O&M) contract is signed prior to starting the actual O&M work.

The O&M team has important responsibilities which range from simple janitorial work to solving the most complex issues and situations. The O&M management team is fully and irrevocably accountable to the project owners for all issues related to the proper and efficient operation of the plant.

Figure 4-70. Large-scale PV power plant

System Check and Yield Monitoring

As part of our QC/QA plan discussed above, we tested and verified the integrity and longevity of the PV products purchased for our 100 MWp power plant. Once all equipment is installed, the power plant will be switched on, tested, and certified. When all the inauguration champagne has been drunk, we will start the final step of the project—transfer of the plant's long-term operation and management to the O&M team.

Results from the final QC and certification tests will be accepted as a baseline of the plant's performance. Additional tests will be run under different weather conditions, which will tell us if the PV components conform to the manufacturers' specs, and if our planning, design and construction efforts were of the quality we claimed.

Initial O&M system tests consist of thoroughly checking all components, identifying defects and malfunctions, and documenting all events and procedures.

A final report of the initial O&M test must be issued by the engineering group conducting the tests. The report should include a thorough description of technical issues and the related financial impact—reflected in equipment malfunctions or yield loss.

System tests include visual examination of the PV modules and infrared check of each module at peak performance. These tests, done by qualified personnel, will spot damaged modules (cracked glass, discoloration, etc.) and will identify thermal malfunctions like hot spots, which could reduce the output power and/or damage the modules. These tests are especially important, and an absolute must, if no pre-installation tests were conducted

I-V curves for the different strings and sub-strings must be generated at peak power and in different weather conditions as well, to establish a baseline for each of them to use as a reference in the future. I-V curve tests could reveal inefficient or faulty module performance, wiring and other abnormalities. The tests must be performed by well trained and qualified personnel, to avoid erroneous results and conclusions.

Yield assessment must be performed at the same time and by the same team as well, which will ensure more reliable results. The yield assessment is an even more complex variable, so it suffices to say that unless it is done with utmost care by qualified personnel, the results would be erroneous or unrepeatable at best.

Operational Considerations, Tasks and Issues

Once the initial tests are done and the power plant is given a clean bill of health, normal operation starts. The O&M procedures of a PV power plant are a complex, sometimes expensive, but very important task. Daily observations must be documented and analyzed periodically, with appropriate action taken if abnormal conditions or behaviors are noticed. Yield monitoring and assessment is also a daily task—especially in the early days of the plant's operation. The O&M team is in charge of these tasks, and is ultimately responsible for everything going on at the plant, including the prevention of natural or man-made incidents.

Yield monitoring must be carried out properly and precisely too, since yield variations are expected on a minute-by-minute, and hour-by-hour basis. Things can change in an instant or overnight. They surely change monthly and yearly.

The dependencies are very complex, so their proper relation and documentation are very important. Even more important is their proper interpretation and the resulting corrective actions.

The PV power plant is a living entity that can be very dangerous if not treated properly, so only qualified personnel can run it efficiently, safely and profitably. These three factors are interrelated and require deep understanding of the behavior of each component and its function.

O&M team responsibilities include:

1. Materials and labor needed to operate efficiently
2. Solving mechanical and electrical problems
3. Voltage disturbances corrections
4. Frequency disturbances corrections
5. Islanding protection response
6. Power factor support
7. Reconnect after failure or P&M
8. DC injection into AC grid issues
9. Scheduled and unscheduled disconnects
10. Grounding and source circuit abnormalities
11. Ground fault protection failures
12. Overcurrent protection incidents
13. Containment of electromagnetic interferences of any sort
14. Personnel training and management of daily activities
15. Safety and accident prevention programs

PV plants are operated and maintained by an operator/contractor, who is trained and fully responsible for the system operation. Some of the duties of the operator/contractor are:

1. Wash PV array at scheduled time intervals, or when build-up of soiling deposits is noticed.

2. Periodically inspect the system to make sure all wiring and supports stay intact.

3. Review the output of the system daily to see if performance is close to the specs and previous year's reading.

4. Maintain a log of these readings to identify system problems.

5. Daily monitoring of the system is a key component of its proper operation, since it provides feedback to the operator as to total power and actual energy production metering. Without proper metering the operator will never know if the system is operating properly or not. A properly designed PV power plant will be equipped with the latest in remote monitoring equipment, which will register and record the power production of each string, as well as the total power pumped into the grid.

6. Weather watch in the form of a basic weather station is also needed to follow and record weather changes and alert the operators in case of drastic changes. Actual temperature and solar insolation at the site are also important and must be tracked constantly. The data will be analyzed periodically to calculate overall system efficiency, to prevent system problems, and to take corrective actions.

PV Plant Performance

The amount of power produced by a PV power plant depends on several factors, with sunlight availability and intensity being the major variables. Sunlight can ramp up and down rapidly, which is an important characteristic of large-scale PV power generation, but the utility system operators need to maintain a balance between the aggregate of all generators and loads.

General Principals

Several general principles must be maintained, to ensure the integrity of the grid, following the basic rules of conduct:

1. National electric system reliability must be maintained, regardless of the generation methods and their variability.

2. Generating sources must contribute to system reliability and should not cause unnecessary complications and interruptions.

3. Power industry standards and operating criteria apply to all generators. They are transparent and based on proper and efficient performance.

Understanding the characteristics of variable PV output over large areas of PV installations and correlation to the load are critical to understanding the potential impacts of large quantities of PV injected into the national energy system.

PV variability can drive localized concerns, which typically manifest themselves as voltage or power quality problems. These issues are distinct from grid system level issues of balancing, and should not be confused. Management and remediation options for local power quality problems are generally different from options for maintaining a balance between load and supply at the system level.

The complexity of injecting variable load into a steady power transmitting system is not to be overlooked, or taken lightly. There are a number of things that the utilities could do to control the variability of injected power, but the responsibility to ensure trouble-free operation falls squarely on the PV power plant owners and operators.

The local utility company can help in most cases, but it will not step in to solve problems at the PV plant. Good understanding of the variability issues and their consequences must be a priority for the owners and managers of the plant.

Large-scale Power Plants Output Variability and Issues

Basically, photovoltaics fall under the broader category of variable generation. The experience with appropriate, unified approaches for managing variable generation will ease integration issues. The most important lesson is that the dialogue regarding PV variability requires, above all else, additional time-synchronized data from multiple PV plants and insolation meters over spatial scales ranging from a square kilometer to greater than 10,000 square kilometers.

In all cases, the data will need to cover at least a year of measurements and should be synchronized with comparable load data to understand the net impact on the variability that must be managed by the system operators. Certain questions, particularly those concerning power quality and regulation reserves, will require data with a time resolution as high as multiple seconds.

Analysis of data from multiple time-synchronized PV plants will allow detailed evaluation of the degree to which rapid ramps observed in point measurements will be smoothed by large PV plants and the aggregation of multiple PV plants. Such studies will help remove unwarranted barriers to interconnection and provide the basis for setting appropriate interconnection standards that will allow solar energy from PV plants to

reach significant penetration levels.

The output variability observed by a single point of insolation measurement will not directly correspond to the total (daily or monthly) variability of a large PV plant, simply because one end of the plant might be sunny, while the other could be covered by clouds. A single point measurement ignores this and the sub-minute and sub-hour time scale smoothing that can occur within these multi-kW plants. This difference can be amplified when looking at sub-minute smoothing that can occur in very large-scale plants.

In summary, basically:

1. Extrapolation suggests that further smoothing is expected for short time-scale variability within PV plants that are hundreds of MW, but this needs to be confirmed with field data from large systems.

2. Diversity over longer time scales (10-min to hours) can occur over broad areas encompassed by a power system balancing area. Data from the Great Plains region of the U.S. indicate that the spatial separation between plants required for changes in output to be uncorrelated over time scales of 30-min is on the order of 50 km. The spatial separation required for output to be uncorrelated over time scales of 60-min is on the order of 150 km. The assumption that variability on a 15-min or shorter time scale is uncorrelated between plants separated by 20 km or more is supported by data from at least one region of the U.S. Additional data are required to examine this assumption in regions with different weather patterns.

3. Multiple methods will be used for forecasting solar resources at differing time scales. Weather variations such as clouds, rain, and snow are the primary influence in the solar forecast. It is important to recognize that clouds (and their rate and direction of movement) are visible to satellites and ground-based sensors, so some successful forecasting can be expected. Over longer time scales clouds can change shape and grow or dissipate, so numerical weather modeling methods may prove necessary. As with wind forecasting, solar forecasting will benefit from further development of weather models and datasets. Complete and error-free forecasting is needed and is a thing of the not-so-distant future.

It is obvious from the above, however, that no matter what we do, power output variability is here to stay, and that accurate and much needed error-free forecasting and power control are still not available. We do expect that, with all the work underway in these areas, we will have good results soon, which will allow us to predict and manage PV plants' power output variability efficiently enough to assure their reliability as grid-connected energy sources, thus bringing us closer to our energy independence.

PV TECHNOLOGIES FUTURE

PV technologies will no doubt provide some, if not most, of the electric power of future generations, but is what is their near- and mid-term future? In our opinion:

- *PV is an ideal energy source for our changing needs.* There are several reasons why PV solar power is such an attractive energy source. To begin with, it is clean for the most part of its operational cycle. Solar panels are typically guaranteed to perform for as long as 25 years, and produce electricity without pollution or emissions that can contribute to global warming. The process of creating the solar panels themselves is also clean, compared with the fossil fuels, but a lot of energy is used in it, which we discuss later in this text. PV panels have the lowest carbon footprint, utilizing the lowest amount of energy to do so for the most part.
- *There is a lot of solar energy available around the globe,* which helps make PV power generation a prime choice within the global mix of energy sources. Solar panels require nothing more than sunlight for the electricity generation process. This means that PV solar technology can provide energy security for virtually every nation in the world, helping to reduce the tension and uncertainty that carbon-based energy sources often create.
- *PV is location specific, but solar energy still can be generated virtually anywhere,* even in the heart of densely populated urban centers. It can help reduce the load on long-distance electricity transmission networks. Here PV solar is a significant improvement from both carbon and hydro power generation sources, which are often located far from where they are consumed.
- *PV modules generate electricity during peak summer energy demand hours* in most global markets This makes PV well-suited to replace carbon-based sources of peak energy demand, such as gas-fired turbines, which have a much larger impact on emissions.

- *PV is scheduled to provide over 10 percent of EU and U.S. energy demand by 2020.* Current developments in Europe and the U.S. underline both the strength and growth potential of PV solar energy. The European Union (EU) has already set a goal of meeting 20 percent of energy demand through the use of renewable sources by 2020. This might be too optimistic, so taking everything into consideration the European Photovoltaic Industry Association (EPIA) estimates PV power to meet as much as 10-12 percent of EU electricity demand by 2020.

Although solar energy makes up just 1 percent of total installed electricity generation capacity in the EU, it accounted for 10 percent of the newly installed capacity for 2008. At such growth rates, which are lower than the astronomic growth that the industry experienced over the past decade, the 10-12 percent goal of solar power in Europe by 2020 is a realistic one.

The situation is similar in the U.S. too. Several states have mandates to add 20-30% renewable energies to their energy mix by 2020, the share of PV installations is estimated to be in the 10 percent range by then.

- *PV has room to grow,* since the global solar industry has enough capacity to deliver enough PV solar products to make a difference in the energy mix in the short to medium term. To put this in perspective, in 2011 the global PV solar energy industry made enough solar modules to satisfy the entire electricity demand of California, which is one of the world's largest energy markets. With ample production capacity and an ideal clean energy product, the PV solar industry is more than capable of meeting even the most aggressive growth scenarios, both within Europe and globally.

Generally, the future looks very bright for PV solar.

RENEWABLE, GREEN, AND SAFE?

We all agree that the conventional energy generators (coal, oil, gas, and nuclear) are not renewable, green or safe. We have dedicated enough time and effort on explaining why this is so, and why we must be careful in the production and use of conventional energy sources.

But while speaking honestly on the subject, we must ask how renewable, green, and safe are the new alternative energy sources (solar, wind, hydro, bio- and geo-power)? Solar energy proponents and manufacturers claim their PV products are totally "renewable," "green" and "safe." Literally, they are claiming that:

1. Renewable: there are no supply chain problems, and none is expected. (As we will see below, this is not so for most of the "renewable" technologies.)
2. Green: there are no negative environmental effects during the cradle-to-grave lifespan of these technologies. Their components are nearly perfectly clean to manufacture, transport and use. (We will see below is not so for most of the "green" technologies.)
3. Safe: there are no serious safety issues related to the manufacture, transport, and use of these technologies and their products. (This is also far from the truth, as we will see below.)

Obviously, there are problems with the renewable, green, and safe technologies of the future, but how many?

Starting with solar technologies, we agree that its fuel, sunlight, is free, renewable, green and safe…to a point. Although solar energy conversion is a fairly simple and well understood process on theory, it requires complex materials and processes, all of which—including the finished devices—are far from perfect. Most of the materials are not efficient and reliable enough, and the manufacturing of these devices is a complex and expensive process. The overall result, therefore, combined with complex politics and regulations for the implementation of solar energy generators, is uncertainty at best.

Here we review how renewable, green, and safe are the different renewable technologies and their components, starting with the materials used in solar cells and modules manufacture and use.

MG Silicon Production

Basically, silicon is one of the most abundant materials on Earth—sand. There is more sand around us than anything else, so why even bother bringing it into this discussion? Because not all sand is suitable for solar cells manufacture, and a lot of pollution is generated during the mining, transport, and processing of silicon. In one estimate, over 7.0 tons of CO_2 are generated in producing just one ton of SG silicon. Then that much, or more, is produced during the subsequent steps of refining the silicon and converting it into PV cells and modules.

Most sand contains so much dirt and other impurities that using it for such a purpose would be like making a potato soup with one potato mixed with a bucket of dirt. Around 25% of the Earth's crust consists of sili-

con, which is not pure but is mostly in the form of "clay" and other alumino-silicate materials. Pure silicon dioxide (SiO_2), a.k.a. silica, from the Latin *silex* is a mineral best suited for making solar-grade (SG) silicon. Silica is also quite abundant, making up ~12% of the Earth's crust. So the best type of sand for our purpose is "silica sand," which contains a high percentage of silica. Silica sand is formed from the weathering of silicate minerals and rocks, as part of a natural cycle.

Naturally occurring silicate materials in contact with CO_2 and water are eroded over time into Silica and $CaCO_3$. All we must do then is find the place, dig out the silica sand, and extract it from the $CaCO_3$ and other ingredients with which it is mixed. The purer the sand, the less effort and energy it takes to convert it into useful SG silicon. There are a number of "pure" silica sand mines around the world, but the purity varies significantly from place to place.

Desert "sand" is often misunderstood to be the kind of Silica sand that one finds on beaches, and the kind we can use for solar cells. In fact it is not even close, for it is nothing more than dried earth (clay). One way to tell them apart is to spit into the palm of your hand, add a small quantity of the "sand" and then rub it. If it is clay, it will turn into brown mud, but if it is silica, it will just become damp and will clump together. Thus, as the Sahara Desert advances because of lack of rainfall, more sand appears, but really it is just earth turning into dust.

We've seen a number of plans to convert the Sahara's desert sand into solar cells, so we wonder what these engineers and scientists are thinking about, or if they know something we don't and will be having the last laugh. We will just have to wait and see. The few places on Earth where pure silica sand can be found are often isolated, meaning that unless the silicon foundries are built nearby, the sand must be transported—another great expense.

Silica and silica sands are also widely used for the manufacturing of many everyday products such as glass, optical fibers, diatomaceous earth, cement, and ceramics. They are also used as additives in foods, not to mention the use of silica sand in making millions of semiconductor-type silicon wafers. There is a lot of competition for it, and yet we don't foresee any major shortages anytime soon, although prices will certainly fluctuate with overall demand and energy costs going up and down.

So, the metallurgical grade (MG) silicon production starts with a dozen or so very large bulldozers digging a large hole in a sand pit. This special sand is loaded on trucks or train cars and transported to a melting facility for processing.

Here, a huge furnace, burning coal and oil is heated to thousands of degrees with the sand piled inside. After baking it for many hours, and adding tons of additives, the resulting MG silicon melt is taken out, cooled down and crushed into chunks. The MG silicon chunks are loaded onto trucks or train cars and transported to another production plant that will refine them to solar grade (SG) silicon.

Production of polysilicon material (the raw material needed for producing silicon solar cells) is on an extremely large scale. Mountains of sand are dug out and moved for conversion into solar grade silicon. As a matter of fact the quantity and quality of thus produced polysilicon raw material is a good indicator of the solar industry development.

China is again one of the largest producers and consumers of polysilicon.

The digging, transport and processing of large quantities of sand, and the bi-products of these processes, most of which generate, leak and release tons of dust, liquids and gasses into the soil, water table and the atmosphere are hard to assess, but the grand size of these undertakings is a good indication that they impact the environment, and the health of the workers and locals with a measurable negative component.

So how renewable, green, and safe is the MG polysilicon material?

Renewable? Maybe, if the mountains of sand dug out to be melted are replaced eventually, so that the surrounding environment and life forms are not damaged.

Green? Not so much, due to the extremely large quantity of processing materials and energy used to produce it, as well as excessive air, soil and water contamination during these processes.

Safe? Maybe, if properly manufactured and used. The concern here is with the mining and refining operations, where many people are exploited in the daily operations. Many are also exposed to unsafe working conditions, where accidents occur daily.

Silver, copper and other metals.

Huge quantities of silver, aluminum, copper and other metals, as well as plastics and many chemicals are needed to produce millions of PV modules. These metals are also dug out of mines on the earth's surface or deep into it. Here again, massive amounts of dirt are moved and

processed, to get the pure metals out.

Again, the dirt is dug out and processed via heat and chemicals—processes emitting great amounts of poisonous gasses and liquids—which then contaminate the air, soil and water table.

Large amounts of silver metal are used to provide good ohmic contact between the metal grid on top of the cell and the interconnecting wires. Silver is also used for reflective backing for mirrors in thermal solar plants. According to the VM Group in London, over 1,000 tons of silver have been projected for making PV modules in 2011. This is over the 1.0 million kilograms of silver used today, and the amount is projected to triple by 2016, to nearly 3,000 metric tons of silver used for making PV modules worldwide every year. If we add that much more silver metal for coating heliostat mirrors, we end up with some very large numbers. So the question here is, "How much silver will be left in the world in 10, 50 and 100 years if we use it at this pace?"

Silver is a precious metal, the price having gone from $4.00/ounce several years ago to over $40.00 today. Prices are expected to go higher. What will that do to PV module prices?

Similarly, prices of copper and aluminum metals have sky rocketed lately, and although there are large deposits of these left on Earth, the increased prices will play a significant role in PV manufacturing operations and cost.

Although there are significant amounts of these metals around the world, they cannot be considered "renewable." Because they are non-toxic they could be considered "green" to use, but the mining and refining operations, with their excessive air, soil and water con-

China Polysilicon Production

Year	2005	2006	2007	2008	2009	2010	2011	2012	2013
Production(Ton)	80	230	1000	2000	7000	13000	18000	23000	28000
Demand(Ton)	1151	3688	9194	16724	24143	28864	34465	25687	27265
Shortage(Ton)	1071	3458	8194	14724	17143	15864	16465	0	0

Global Polysilicon Production

Year	2005	2006	2007	2008	2009	2010	2011	2012	2013
Production(Ton)	30680	33390	37500	51000	73500	96500	115200	142000	168000
Demand(Ton)	33850	39520	46900	62940	81340	103440	121560	102150	122000
Shortage(Ton)	3170	6130	9400	11940	7840	6940	6360	0	0

Table 4-8. Polysilicon production in China and the world

tamination, are far from green. Safe? Yes, if we ignore mining labor exploitation, and safety violations.

Silicon Wafers and Solar Cells Production

MG Si produced at the mining and refining operations is delivered to poly silicon production plants to be purified and converted into solar grade silicon (SG Si). The SG Si refining plants are actually huge chemical factories where a number of solid, liquid, and gaseous chemicals (most of which are hazardous, toxic, and poisonous) require special handling, processing, transport, and disposal.

Here, all these materials, chemicals, and gasses are mixed, boiled, baked, sifted, crushed, liquefied, gasified, and solidified in a never-ending action. There a number of liquid chemicals that are quite expensive in this process, so they are recycled and otherwise reused via complex distillation, filtration, and other chemical process, all of which use huge amounts of electric power, cooling water, and additives.

Millions of cubic tons of CO_2 and other toxic liquids and gasses are the by-products of these processes. Some are difficult to recycle or capture, so they are just freely exhausted or disposed of into the environment without any treatment, as in many Asian polysilicon plants.

Organic chemicals such as silane, dichlorosilane (DCS), trichlorosilane (TCS), silicon tetrachloride (STC), and many others are mixed, heated, evaporated, condensed, and transported, along with many inorganic liquids and gasses such as HCL, HF, HNO_3, and H_2O_2. Some of these are also dumped in the soil or vented into the air, where they mix within the soup of other gasses. The resulting mixture of organic and inorganic compounds sometimes stagnates over population centers to accelerate global warming as it becomes part of the atmosphere.

Hazardous liquid by-products, some dangerously corrosive and even pyrophoric (self-igniting), are created, transported, and processed along the complex process sequence. All of these require special handling, placing chemical and fire safety on the top of management's list of priorities in most facilities.

The personnel are trained in the proper handling of these chemicals, including emergency procedures, for all eventualities. In addition, proper equipment and building designs/procedures are used throughout the facilities, which include ventilation, electrical system safety, static electricity control, control of all ignition sources, personal self-contained breathing apparatus use, and, of course, a no smoking ban (which is not fully enforced in most Asian facilities, so it is not unusual to see a worker smoking under a No Smoking sign.)

Figure 4-71. The No Smoking Asian culture

At the end of the SG Si purification process, the silicon material is crushed again for ease of transport and sent to different facilities for the manufacture of solar wafers, cells, and modules. At these facilities the SG Si chunks are melted in special, high-temperature furnaces in the presence of different gasses, where they are shaped into long cylindrical ingots (single crystal silicon) or square blocks (poly crystalline silicon). The rods and blocks are sliced into thin wafers on special saws, after which they are ready for processing into solar cells.

Thus produced wafers go through an elaborate manufacturing process to convert them into solar cells. After that they are tested and either shipped to another facility for processing into PV modules, or are assembled and encapsulated into PV modules at the spot.

Large amounts of electric power, chemical additives, slurries, liquids and gasses are used during the melting, shaping, cutting, slicing, cleaning, etching, baking, and assembly operations. The gasses, waste chemicals and slurries and cleaning liquids need to be processed and disposed of eventually—a hazardous undertaking as well. In many cases the gasses are released in the atmosphere, while the chemicals are dumped into a stinky lagoon nearby.

The sand-to-PV modules manufacturing process consists of a large number of thermal and chemical operations in which a lot of electric energy and thousands of gallons of different chemicals, liquids, and gases are used and disposed of. These amounts and expenses also need to be taken into consideration in the overall wafers-cells-modules manufacturing budget.

The work safety in these facilities, where hi-tech equipment and procedures are used and where strict processing and safety standards are enforced, is usually acceptable. The disposal of gases and chemicals in many cases, however, is problematic and in some cases the local environment is badly damaged.

The actual solar cell manufacturing and modules assembly process is executed in clean areas where, in most cases, safety and environmental standards are the norm. Nevertheless, a lot of energy and chemicals are used in this process, which must be considered in the energy balance estimates.

So, although over their lifetime crystalline silicon solar panels generate 10-20 times the energy required to produce them, the environmental damage during their production is sizable and in many cases irreparable. So how renewable, green and safe is the solar wafers and cells manufacturing process? Somewhat, when compared with conventional energy sources, but still a lot of work remains to be done to make their manufacturing processes truly environmentally neutral.

Thin-film PV Materials

Thin-film PV (TFPV) technologies leave their signature mark on the environment as well. The TFPV manufacturing process also starts in a dark, dusty, or muddy, mine somewhere in Asia or Africa. Low-paid men and women work in deplorable conditions, digging, dragging, loading, processing, and transporting the precious and often toxic metals. Health problems and even death are common occurrences among these workers, but the actual facts are not widely publicized.

The freshly mined raw materials are transported to refining facilities to be refined into useful form and shape. The raw materials are exposed to a number of complex mechanical, chemical, and electro-chemical operations to separate and purify the different metals. Dangerous gasses and chemicals are used in these processes too, and some of the resulting equally dangerous and toxic gases and chemicals are vented into the atmosphere or dumped close by. Some of the mining and refining operations look, feel, and smell like they have just jumped out from the pages of Dante's Inferno. Humans working there, in some of the worst cases, look like they belong on the same pages—not a pretty picture.

Thus refined metals are shipped to TFPV module manufacturing facilities for processing into modules. In sharp contrast with the above described "holes in the ground" mining and refining operations, the TFPV manufacturing facilities are sparkling clean, modern, semiconductor-type fabrication plants, with state-of-the-art equipment. Well-paid engineers and technicians follow well-defined processes executed in clean-room environments under the strictest of process controls. The safety, efficiency, and productivity of these facilities is the envy of the PV industry, and we have only praises for their setup, operation, and quality control.

Here, the refined and still toxic materials are placed in special chambers, where they are deposited in the form of very thin films onto glass substrates (panes) under near-ideal process conditions. The deposited films on the first glass pane are then covered with a second pane and encapsulated between them. The resulting TFPV modules are flash-tested and packed for shipping. This is a most efficient, cost effective, and high-volume production process that is leading the PV industry. These facilities are a glimpse of the future. It is how the PV industry of the 22nd century will be set up and operated.

Nevertheless, although the metals used in TFPV modules manufacturing are by-products of the mining and production of other metals, they are still scarce, in addition to being toxic. These are serious issues that the TFPV manufacturers are not willing to discuss openly, so we hope that we can bring the issues out for honest discussion.

Another issue of environmental concern worth mentioning here is the fact that most TFPV modules are frameless. That is, the active thin film structure (CdTe or CIGS) is deposited on a glass pane, covered by encapsulant and another glass pane. So, the thin film structure is protected from environmental attacks by a thin film of plastic, exposed to the elements at the open edges of the modules. Since no plastic material can last very long under harsh desert conditions, the thin edge seal would deteriorate under the relentless IR and UV bombardment and would allow moisture and harmful environmental gasses to attack and destroy the thin films. This will not only shorten the useful life of the TFPV modules, but might also result in environmental contamination.

While this might not be a serious problem in small installations, the millions of TFPV modules installed on thousands of acres of desert land in the newly proposed large-scale PV power plants pose a potential danger to the environment and life in the affected areas. More preliminary work must be done before a full proliferation of these unproven PV technologies in the US deserts occurs.

It was discussed in previous chapters that frameless modules are more prone to degradation due to ingress of moisture and environmental gases into the glass/glass modules (front and rear glass covers) which also retain excess heat more than modules with plastic or metal back covers. The excess heat could result in a number of unwanted effects (delamination, overheating, hot spots etc.).

Some TFPV modules are both frameless and of glass/glass construction; therefore, the active thin films inside are more prone to degradation and power loss. The frameless structure also facilitates the escape of toxic materials from the module in case of mechanical disintegration or chemical decomposition.

As discussed in the previous chapter, there are ways to improve the edge sealing of the TFPV modules. Some manufacturers actually wrap up the thin film structure in a sheet of protective material, similar to that used in c-Si PV modules. This completely seals the thin film structure and the module edges in one continuous envelope, thus preventing moisture from entering the module and attacking the thin film structure.

On top of that, some manufacturers add a metal frame around the module edges which is "glued" to the glass panes by edge sealer, thus providing a solid, several-layer barrier which protects thin films for a long time regardless of environmental attacks.

Most TFPV manufacturers, however, continue making frameless all-glass modules to keep costs down. Price vs. healthy environment? This doesn't sound very safe or green, does it?

Looking to the future, we see a number of issues that need to be resolved by the thin film PV industry. Making the cheapest product is one thing, but making it truly reliable and safe is another. Thin film PV modules manufacturers have not yet proven that their products are reliable and safe for 30 years operation—especially under desert conditions.

Following is a brief look at the materials used for making thin film PV modules.

Cadmium

Cadmium (Cd) is a toxic, carcinogenic heavy metal, generally recovered as a byproduct of zinc concentrates. Zinc-to-cadmium ratios in typical zinc ores range from 200:1 to 400:1. It is used for making NiCd batteries, electroplating, lasers, electronics, paints, and most recently in thin film PV modules.

In January 2010 USGS estimated ~600,000 tons of cadmium reserves worldwide (calculated as a percentage of available zinc reserves), of which the world mines and uses ~19,000 tons annually. If USGS is correct, in 32 years there will be no more cadmium.

Cadmium displaces zinc in many metallo-enzymes in the body, so cadmium toxicity can be traced to a cadmium-induced zinc deficiency. It concentrates in the kidneys, liver and other organs, and is 10 times more toxic than lead or mercury. Inhaling cadmium-laden dust leads to respiratory tract and kidney problems which can be fatal. Ingestion of significant amounts of cadmium causes immediate and irreversible damage to the liver and the kidneys. Japanese agricultural communities consuming Cd-contaminated rice developed itai-itai disease and renal abnormalities, including proteinuria and glucosuria.

Cadmium is one of several substances listed by the European Union's Restriction on Hazardous Substances (RoHS) directive, which bans certain hazardous substances in electrical and electronic equipment but allows certain exemptions and exclusions from the scope of the law. In February 2010 cadmium was found in an entire line of Wal-Mart jewelry, which was subsequently removed from the shelves. In June 2010 cadmium was detected in paint used on McDonald's tumblers, resulting in a recall of 12 million glasses.

Compared to other serious toxins, cadmium is more dangerous as it accumulates and is not dissipated. Even a negligible dose of cadmium in the air or water, inhaled or ingested daily, will accumulate to eventually reach toxic levels, causing cancer or organ failure.

USGS says, "Concern over cadmium's toxicity has spurred various recent legislative efforts, especially in the European Union, to restrict its use in most end-use applications. If recent legislation involving cadmium dramatically reduces long-term demand, a situation could arise, such as has been recently seen with mercury, where an accumulating oversupply of by-product cadmium will need to be permanently stockpiled."

So how renewable, green and safe are the cadmium-based PV technologies? From the above facts we see that cadmium is not a renewable commodity *per se*, but we don't foresee a shortage during the next 3 decades. It is, however, far from green and safe.

Tellurium

Tellurium (Te) metal is produced by refining blister copper from deposits that contain recoverable amounts of tellurium. Relatively large quantities of tellurium are also found in some gold, lead, coal, and lower-grade copper deposits, but the recovery cost from these deposits is too high to be worthwhile. Tellurium is used mostly in making steel and copper alloys to improve machinability, in the petroleum and rubber industries, and for making catalysts and some chemicals. One of the rarest elements in the Earth's crust, it is found in considerable quantities as a secondary metal in mining operations.

The world produces 100-200 tons of tellurium annually, and while its total availability is uncertain, we do not foresee a shortage anytime soon. Tellurium is used as cadmium telluride in manufacturing thin film PV modules. It is a mildly toxic material; nevertheless, utmost precaution must be taken when handling its pure form or its basic compounds as contained in the PV modules.

Tellurium and its compounds are known to cause sterility in men working with tellurium-containing materials, even under strict monitoring conditions such as in semiconductor fabs and hard disk manufacturing operations. Although there is significant amount of tellurium around the world and it cannot be considered "renewable," we do not foresee a shortage anytime soon. Due to its toxic properties it is not green, or safe.

Selenium

Selenium (Se) is a non-metal that is chemically related to sulfur and tellurium. It is obtained by mining sulfide ores, and is used in glassmaking, metallurgy, and pigments. While toxic in large amounts, trace amounts of selenium are needed for cellular function in most animals.

Selenium toxicity was noticed first by doctors who found increased sickness among people working with it. A dose as small as 5 mg per day can be lethal, causing selenosis. Symptoms include a garlic odor on the breath, gastrointestinal disorders, hair loss, sloughing of nails, fatigue, irritability, and neurological damage. A number of cases of selenium poisoning of water systems were attributed to agricultural runoff through normally dry lands.

Selenium quantity and price depend on mining operations of other metals and minerals, but we don't foresee a shortage anytime soon. Its use is estimated at 1,500-2,000 tons annually. Though there is a significant amount of selenium worldwide, it cannot be considered renewable, green, or safe.

Arsenic

There are over 1 million tons of arsenic (As) worldwide, of which 54,000 tons are extracted annually, mostly in the form of arsenic sulfur compounds. Another 11 million tons might be recovered from copper and gold ores. The main use of metallic arsenic is for strengthening alloys of copper and especially lead used in automotive batteries. Arsenic is toxic and poisonous. Although there is significant amount of it around the world, it cannot be considered renewable. Due to its toxic properties, it is not green, or safe.

Gallium and Indium

These and other hard-to-find-and-isolate mildly toxic metals are also used in significant amounts in thin-film PV modules manufacturing processes. These elements are rare, so they cannot be considered renewable. They are mildly toxic but could be qualified as green, or safe, if properly produced and used.

EVA and Other Plastics

A number of organic materials (plastics) are used throughout the entire PV module manufacturing process. They are too varied and complex to qualify or quantify in this text. Since their production is based mostly on fossils (extracts from crude oil, coal and such) they are not renewable, but we don't foresee shortage anytime soon. Because they are manufactured with the help of poisonous solvents and other toxic materials, we'd have a hard time classifying them as green or safe. They are, however, safe enough to work with, following basic precautions like wearing gloves and masks. Due to outgassing, their safety in long-term operations has been questioned and needs more research—especially in light of the large-scale PV installations in the deserts, where organics are most vulnerable and unpredictable.

Glass and Aluminum

The top surface of the silicon PV modules is covered with glass, while most thin film PV modules take two glass sheets—top and bottom. This is a lot of glass. Entire mountains of sand are melted and refined in the glass manufacturing process, where many other chemicals and a lot of energy is used as well. Many tons of toxic gasses, liquids, and solids are produced as well.

The back surface of the silicon PV modules is usually covered with a thin aluminum sheet. The production of aluminum metal also requires digging deep into the ground in aluminum ore mines, where thousands of tons of dirt are moved to get some of the aluminum ore contained in it. The ore is then purified chemically and the aluminum metal is separated electrochemically from the impurities. This process requires an enormous amount of electric energy. As a matter of fact, it is one of the most energy intensive metal working processes today. Again, tons of toxic gasses, liquids and solids are produced along each step of the aluminum mining, refining, and shaping process.

One can easily see that the complications here are endless, and so interwoven that we could write an entire book on the properties and effects of the different combinations of mining dangers, toxicity, adverse short- and long-term environmental and health effects, improper field use, etc. of the materials and components used in making and using PV cells and modules.

Many questions remain to be answered in these areas, so we must insist that these issues are openly discussed by all parties involved, including manufacturers and proponents of the PV technologies.

How do we justify the claim that PV technologies are renewable, green, and safe, if some of the materials used to manufacture them are not? Should we not qualify and use the different PV technologies according to the type and amount of non-renewable, not green and unsafe materials used during their manufacture and use?

NOTE: At the time of this writing, several manufacturers have applied for "non-toxic" certification of their PV modules. The trend will continue until it becomes an industry-wide standard, and we envision different types and levels of toxicity assigned to different types of PV modules in the near future.

This process will take awhile, but it is unavoidable, because the consumers must be fully aware of how renewable, green, and safe the products they use are and what to expect in the long run.

We will take even closer look at the issues related to the renewable technologies in the following chapters.

THE SOLAR INDUSTRY TODAY AND TOMORROW

The present-day brutal shakeout of the global solar manufacturing industry is not finished. Instead, it will continue and even increase in the near future. Industry insiders predict over 70% of the solar manufacturers worldwide will shrink, get bought, disappear all together, or otherwise exit the market by 2015-2017.

The world's total number of PV modules manufacturers is expected to go down to 125-150 companies, compared to 500 in 2012 and 650 in 2011. The 2010-2012 worldwide glut of PV modules slashed prices in recent years, driving many companies like Fremont's Solyndra into bankruptcy. The price plunge has been great for consumers, helping drive up the number of solar installations. But for photovoltaic manufacturers, the bloodletting continues.

Consolidation was rampant in the PV supply chain in 2012, the latest example of which is the consolidation (acquisition) of China's Hanergy Holding Group of MiaSole, the thin-film solar manufacturer headquartered in Santa Clara.

MiaSole, like many other solar companies was getting ready to make a big dent in the solar energy markets during the boom years, but was not able to take off. Its wings were clipped by the ongoing economic downturn and the plunging PV module prices.

Hanergy will keep MiaSole's Sunnyvale plant open (for awhile at least), retaining the 100-plus people employed there and maybe even hire more. Maybe! MiaSole's fledgling technology benefited from more than $550 million in venture capital over the years, but its sale price to Hanergy is just $30 million. 1:20 ROI ratio.

In 2012-2013 things got progressively worse for the major PV products suppliers too, with most upstream PV supply operations simply ceasing to exist, rather than being acquired by other companies. Many of the suppliers—most of them in Asia—actually have already stopped production, and will never restart.

Dozens of new solar factories in China created the PV modules glut, and have driven many U.S. solar companies out of business. But most of the newly established Chinese wanna-be solar-manufacturing companies won't survive the shakeout. The Chinese government will prop up some of the bigger companies, but most of the smaller ones will be left on their own. They will most likely shut their doors, or change the line of business and switch to manufacturing some other gadgets. Many of them switched to solar from some other business, so going back where they came from won't be too difficult.

A huge bumper crop of solar panels has already caused a sharp decline in the prices and bankrupted many manufacturers worldwide over the past two years. New reports say another 180 solar panel makers will likely go out of business or be bought by the end of 2014. Nearly half of them—or 88 companies—will shut down factories in countries where producing solar panels has become too expensive, namely the United States, Europe and Canada.

The prognosis is not only shocking, but it also answers a perennial question, at least for now, about whether solar manufacturing can thrive in some countries, including the United States. China, which has used state-owned banks and utilities to finance solar factory expansion and create domestic demand for solar panels, will continue to dominate solar manufacturing, though the government is reportedly working on rescuing only 12 large companies and forcing mergers in others. It is estimated that over 50 solar panel makers in China will not survive over the next three years.

Given where the industry is now and how committed China is for its solar manufacturing industry, it's very difficult for European and U.S. manufacturers to compete. In fact, by the end of 2014, most solar cells and panels manufacturing could disappear altogether in the United States.

China's rise as the world's epicenter for solar manufacturing has elicited resentment from rivals who believe Chinese companies haven't competed fairly. The U.S. Department of Commerce recently sided with petitioners of such a trade complaint, and imposed tariffs after finding that Chinese solar companies have indeed received illegal government subsidies and sold solar panels at below cost.

Signs of trouble began to show in early 2011, when changes in solar incentive policies in key European markets prompted solar panel makers' customers—distributors and project developers—to delay purchasing decisions. Prices for solar panels began to fall faster than manufacturers had expected. The prices dropped by about 50 percent last year and have continued to decline this year. At the same time, many manufacturers had built up massive factories and were counting on a huge surge in demand in the global market. In fact, they continued to churn out solar panels to keep their factories running and workers employed even though demand wasn't keeping pace.

First Solar saw flat revenues and lower earnings since the first quarter of 2011, and its stock plummeted to unprecedented and unforeseen lows. Young companies that were entering mass production of their technologies to compete effectively with larger rivals went bust, including Solyndra and Abound Solar. GE, which once embarked on an ambitious plan to build a 400-megawatt factory in Colorado, decided to shelve that project earlier this year. First Solar, long the king of low-cost manufacturing, decided to gradually shut down its big factory in Germany and put on hold its plans to build new factories in Vietnam and Arizona.

Other solar panel makers in the U.S., Europe and Asia have made similar decisions to shutter factories or file bankruptcy. SunPower is one of them. It suspended production at six of the 12 solar cell production lines and cut solar panel production by 20% in the Philippines, and laid off about 900 employees there.

Still, some solar manufacturers have proceeded with their plans to build new factories for a variety of reasons. Some thought the oversupply problem would be over soon; others needed to scale up their production to cut costs. As a result, the world will likely see 35 GW of excess solar panels for sale per year over the next three years.

The plummeting prices for solar panels are good news for installers, solar power plant developers, and ultimately consumers. Some developers have switched to solar panels instead using other types of solar technologies. An increasing number of manufacturers have entered the business of developing solar energy generation projects since they are not making money selling solar panels.

Solar Now and Later...

The U.S. solar industry has been the step child of energy sources, taken out of the closet when an energy crisis looms. The trend started with the Arab oil embargo in 1973, when U.S. politicians realized that oil is not the solution.

Solar was encouraged to show what it can do by billions of dollars thrown into R&D, production optimization, and new facilities construction. The industry giants at the time, Motorola, Shell, and a number of universities and national labs were the leaders and the beneficiaries of countless grants, tax breaks and subsidies. But try as it may, solar was not able to provide even a glimpse of hope for replacing fossil fuels or helping the desperate situation at the time.

When oil prices fell, solar was again abandoned.

A number of similar situations occurred later on, the latest during the last solar boom-bust. This time the entire world was on fire. Solar was the savior. Billions were thrown into worthless technologies and wasted on mismanaged companies.

Germany led the 2007-2011 solar boom-bust cycle with the most PV installations in the world. Ever! But relying on solar energy in Germany is like looking for water in the middle of the Sahara desert. Yes, some water is found in the Sahara desert too, but you cannot build a city around it...in most cases. In the same way, there is some sunshine in some places in Germany, but you cannot realistically build a sustainable national energy plan around it.

At 15% efficiency at full sunlight, PV modules drop to less than 5% under cloudy German skies. At that rate, you need an area 10 times the size of the entire German territory to provide even half of the country's energy needs on a constant and sustainable basis. But Germany has no extra land, or excess of money, so their solar went bust with a great bang, dragging the entire world solar industry down with it.

This woke up most PV cells and modules manufacturers, giving them a chance to stop relying on quantity, but to look into providing options to create successful technological propositions within the PV industry in order to keep the ball rolling.

Actually, the technology aspect of the PV industry *per se* was most often on the back burner. Instead, most manufacturers adapted the brute force approach, where technology is expected to meet only the very minimum industry requirements to satisfy module power ratings and price. Volume and lowering the base price were the drivers.

Within this approach, the key (and maybe the only) requirement at the time was credit availability with *market-share at any cost* as the prevailing line of operation in the U.S. and the developed countries, often inflating and pushing the limits of the global markets with strong corporate and financial back-up.

Other technology-agnostic methods included domestic market-share protectionism, which is achieved by pursuing trade barrier routes, or the reliance on government sponsorship and assisted marketing, to create perceived brand superiority.

A good example of this approach is the wide deployment of the cadmium telluride (CdTe) thin film PV technology, which is 5-6 years old and has no track record for long-term use in U.S. deserts. Regardless, the technology, not proved for large-scale desert use, was awarded billions of dollars of U.S. DOE loan guarantees, which allowed many millions of CdTe PV modules to be installed in U.S. deserts.

Now, thousands of acres of U.S. desert are covered with PV modules that offer no guarantees. If this were not enough, the CdTe PV modules contain significant amounts (8-9 grams each) of toxic, carcinogenic cadmium heavy metal in each module. That's not much, but there are millions of them on each acre. Eight or nine grams multiplied by several million modules is tons of toxic materials with potentially disastrous behavior.

The top and bottom glass-covers of the modules will survive the climate extremes in the desert during 30 years of non-stop operation. The vulnerable plastic edge seals and encapsulation in the frameless modules, however, will not even come close. They would be lucky to remain intact 5-10 years.

Once the edge seals and lamination are damaged, the fragile thin films inside will undergo major changes too. Moisture and the elements will finish the job of destroying the insides of the modules. So the question is not if, but when, the plastic encapsulation will be disintegrated by the merciless UV and IR radiation coming down non-stop day after day. How long would the disintegrating system be able to retain the toxic cadmium films from escaping in one or another form into the air, soil, and the water table.

Whether this was a wise move, or a one-time hasty judgment by ignorant politicians, remains to be seen, but one thing is sure: this is not the type of solid technological solution we need to pull us out of the energy and financial crunch.

In the long term, only the superior PV technologies—not the cheapest, or these backed by the German, Chinese or U.S. government subsidies—will pave the road to efficiency and safety enhancements and can be used to move the PV industry forward.

We have learned that technological progress cannot exist in an oversupply environment, and that setting up R&D labs and producing limited runs of high-performance solar wafers, cells, and PV modules, and publishing datasheets with amazing test results do not count as progress and create problems in the long run.

We learned also that lowering direct and indirect production costs does not denote technological progress. Cost reduction has nothing to do with squeezing the suppliers on price, and must be kept separate from technology innovation. Product quality, reflected in high efficiency and long-term reliability is the most important factor in assessing PV products.

Technology roadmaps set by academic or R&D labs, including U.S. DOE and its subjugate National Labs, were typically biased to their respective favorite technologies and the respective funding schemes, and were mostly harmful to normal private technology progress. Technology roadmaps were used by influential institutions to encourage funding schemes, and we have good examples of PV roadmaps that were created as investor relations sound-bites intended to convince the world that a credible technology path is under control. It suffices to mention Solyndra here.

Fortunately, the PV industry has largely ignored PV technology roadmaps, although the consequences have been a lot of wasted government funds. A number of heavily government subsidized thin film PV companies failed during the 2007-2011 solar boom-bust cycle. They were encouraged by interest groups, including National Labs, to believe that although their technology needs a lot of work, it can compete and survive. Many of them are now history, and many still struggle with the hope of a comeback.

The global PV industry was heavily subsidized during 2007-2011. The trend started with the overly generous European feed-in-tariffs (FITs), which propped up great, but unsustainable and temporary, demand. Many companies got in the solar business, attracted by the easy money it promised.

When the bust time came in 2010-2011, most of the newcomers were not able to adjust to the over-supply and extremely low prices, and are history now. That put an end to the prevailing strategy of just adding more and more production capacity in order to make more money, so now only a fraction of the former technologies and manufacturers will survive in the long run.

This time around we know better. We know that survival in the solar business is based solely on technological advantage, so we expect to see a new, more robust and more technologically aware PV industry, where technology advantage is the only measure of success.

We consider this time as transitional for the PV industry. It is a period when the survivors no longer rely on thinking that their own brand of technology is the only thing they should concentrate on. This is a new era of team work within the framework of the PV industry, where helping others mean increasing your own prospects for survival and success.

There are several dozen different next-generation PV technologies (mostly thin film based), which tried to make it but failed during the last boom cycle. Bad timing, or marketing hype...who knows? Regardless, this is not a good time for any of the next-generation to compete on the open market, so they may need to wait until they mature, or for the next boom cycle.

NOTE: The U.S. DOE supported a number of solar and wind projects during the last boom-bust cycle, through its loan guarantee program. The program offered DOE guarantees for loans from private lenders to energy projects in which the government promised to step in to cover the loan in the event of default.

The DOE loan guarantee program was actually created by a 2005 law, passed under former President George Bush. The program was expanded, changed and funded through the 2009 American Recovery and Reinvestment Act ("the stimulus"), a key piece of legislation for the Obama Administration.

During the last phase of the program, which basically ran out of money in 2010, 18 large wind and solar projects (representing 87% of the program) were financed to the tune of several billion dollars. Five large utility-scale solar photovoltaic (PV) and concentrating photovoltaic (CPV) plants supported by the US DOE's loan guarantee program went online in 2012. These were the Agua Caliente, Alamosa Solar, Antelope Valley Solar 1, Mesquite Solar and California Valley Solar Ranch plants which represent a total of 631 MW-DC of new capacity. As the largest of the five, the Agua Caliente PV reached 287 MW-DC, with more capacity scheduled to come online. Alamosa Solar is the largest CPV plant in the world at 30 MW-DC, nearly four times as large as the next-largest plant, and the only CPV plant among the five.

Many of the 18 projects are still under construction, including the 370 MW Ivanpah concentrating solar power (CSP) project, which will be the largest single-site CSP project in the world when completed. The bad news is that the era of large solar projects is over, because without government subsidies, private investments of billions of dollars for solar farms are just not available.

As much as we'd like to think that the solar industry is on its feet, and as much as PV equipment suppliers and manufacturers would like to think that their unique brand of technology will be a roadmap driver with global ramifications, we have another confirmation that they all—no exceptions—are at the mercy of supply/demand currents, and nobody (even governments with their large subsidies) can change that. Capitalism, what can you do...?

The customers will continue to decide the best technologies based on quality and price, and select the winners that the solar industry must develop and produce. End-users know enough about solar technologies, but they are not specialists so they usually buy not what is offered on the spec sheets, but what they need. Within the solar world, that means specific power in Watts that can be produced for many years, and real dollars spent for each unit.

So, the most important and maybe the only thing that matters for the long-term future of the PV industry is a substantial performance guarantee for its products:

a. Affordable initial price,
b. High efficiency per unit land,
c. Reliable long-term operation, and
d. Reasonable returns.

Solar Land Use

The US Bureau of Land Management (BLM) issued a new regulation in the summer of 2013 that is aimed at facilitating the development of solar and other renewable energy projects on public land. Previously, public land included in proposed solar or wind energy right-of-way applications remained open to mining claims.

The new rule is designed to avoid possible conflicting applications to use public land either for renewable energy projects or mining. But the new regulation means the BLM now has the authority to temporarily remove lands included in a renewable energy right-of-way application and lands offered for wind or solar energy lease from land appropriations such as mining claims.

Public land segregated under the new regulation will be reserved for solar or wind energy development for up to two years. The new regulation replaces an interim 'final rule' brought in by the BLM in November 2011 that first proposed segregation of public land.

Before the final rule came into effect, 216 new mining claims were located within solar energy right-of-way application areas. The segregation will simplify the administration of public lands by making such mining claims impossible, according BLM. What?

The U.S. solar energy zones are as follow:

Arizona

Brenda (Lake Havasu/La Paz) 3,348 acres/372 MW

Gillespie (Lower Sonoran/Maricopa) 2,618 acres/291 MW

Total 5,966 acres/663 megawatts

California

Imperial East (El Centro/Imperial) 5,717 acres/635 megawatts

Riverside East (Palm Springs–South Coast/Riverside) 147,910 acres/16,434 megawatts

Total 153,627 acres/17,070 megawatts

Colorado

Antonito Southeast (La Jara/Conejos) 9,712 acres/1,079 megawatts

De Tilla Gulch (Saguache/Saguache) 1,064 acres/118MW

Fourmile East (La Jara/Alamosa) 2,882 acres/320 MW

Los Mogotes East (La Jara/Conejos) 2,650 acres/294 megawatts

Total 16,308 acres/1,812 megawatts

Nevada

Amargosa Valley (Southern Nevada/Nye) 8,479 acres/942 megawatts

Dry Lake (Southern Nevada/Clark) 5,717 acres/635 megawatts

Dry Lake Valley North (Ely/Lincoln) 25,069 acres/2,785 megawatts

Gold Point (Battle Mountain/Esmeralda) 4,596 acres/511 megawatts

Millers (Battle Mountain/Esmeralda) 16,534 acres/1,837 megawatts

Total 60,395 acres/6,711 megawatts

New Mexico

Afton (Las Cruces/Dona Ana) 29,964 acres/3,329 megawatts

Total 29,964 acres/3,329 megawatts

Utah

Escalante Valley (Cedar City/Iron) 6,533 acres/726 megawatts

Milford Flats South (Cedar City/Beaver) 6,252 acres/695 megawatts

Wah Wah Valley (Cedar City/Beaver) 5,873 acres/653 megawatts

Total 18,658 acres/2,073 megawatts

GRAND TOTAL 284,918 acres/31,658 megawatts

The BLM move basically means that the U.S. is ready to add 31.66 GW of power, which is about the power generated by 15 nuclear power plants. Not bad as a start. But keep in mind that the above listed states could easily provide the entire U.S. energy load using a combination of solar and wind power plants. Adding hydrogen and other energy storage means for steady power generation could make the country totally energy independent.

This is the most plausible large-scale power generation scheme for U.S. for the next century and beyond.

NOTE: The new energy zones are logically located in the sunniest states.

WIND POWER

Wind power is a force that has been used through the centuries to provide mostly mechanical power to a number of agricultural and commercial operations. These include powering sailing ships and mill wheels. The sophistication of wind power equipment has increased, until today's amazing wind giants—the wind turbines—are powering cities. We see these overwhelming structures in many places, waving their giant arms.

There is a lot of wind available in many areas of the U.S. and the world, where wind energy is waiting to be harnessed efficiently, economically, and safely. Wind power is one of the cleanest technologies around. We'll see how clean it is below, but now we'll take a look at wind power in its present state.

Wind power is basically the conversion of wind energy into a useful form—mostly electric power—which is used locally, or sent into the national grid.

Large wind farms are of great interest to the power industry. This mostly due to the fact that these power plants produce a large amount of electricity, which

Figure 4-72. Wind power farm, or power plant.

translates into an equally large share of revenue. The large-scale power plants consist of hundreds of individual wind turbines which are connected to the electric power transmission network.

Offshore wind farms can harness more frequent and powerful winds than are available to land-based installations and have less visual impact on the landscape but construction costs are considerably higher. Offshore installations, however, are not readily accessible for maintenance, and the violence of the sea is a determining factor in the daily O&M. Waiting for calm weather can result in delays in installation and maintenance schedules. In these cases offshore turbines could be idling for long periods, thus reducing energy production and profits.

Large land-based wind farms don't have these problems, but face other obstacles, such as permitting, land availability, right-of-way (for accessing the power grid), and inconsistent wind velocity. Small land-based wind farms can provide electricity to remote locations and the local utility companies could buy surplus electricity produced by these as well.

Wind power is an alternative to fossil fuels, and unlike fossils it is renewable, widely distributed, and clean. It produces no greenhouse gas emissions during operation and uses little land. Although there are some environmental effects, these are much less problematic than those from other power sources.

Wind power made significant progress in the U.S. lately, but its growth has been slowed down for a number of reasons. Worldwide, Denmark is generating 25% of its electricity from wind, and another 83 countries are using wind power on a commercial basis. In 2010 wind energy production was over 2.5% of total worldwide electricity usage, and growing rapidly at more than 25% per annum.

Wind power levels are consistent on a year-to-year basis, but have significant variations on a hour-to-hour daily basis. This creates problems when wind power is a major contributor to a local electrical system. As the proportion of wind contribution increases, new approaches for using wind power need to be implemented.

Power management techniques such as having excess capacity energy storage, geographically distributed turbines, dispatchable backing sources, exporting and importing power to neighboring areas, or reducing demand when wind production is low, can greatly mitigate these problems. Mixing wind and solar generation is another feasible approach, for the peaks of wind and solar compliment each other. This could be used to level the energy production and provide power in peak peri-ods. Weather forecasting and management also permit the electricity network to be readied for the predictable variations in production that might occur.

One of the biggest problems wind power faces, despite its general acceptance by the public, is that the construction of new wind farms is not welcomed in most neighborhoods, due to aesthetics. The NIMBY (not in my back yard) sentiment is hindering the spread of the gentle giants around the U.S. and most of the developed world. This issue can be resolved only by locating large wind farms away from populated centers, which usually increases the final cost of wind power.

Wind Energy

Wind energy is the kinetic energy of air in motion. Total wind energy flowing through a specific area A during the time t is:

$$E = \frac{1}{2} mv^2 = \frac{1}{2} (Avtp)v^2 = \frac{1}{2} Avtpv^3$$

where

ρ is the density of air

v is the wind speed

Avt is the volume of air passing through A (which is considered perpendicular to the direction of the wind)

$Avt\rho$ is therefore the mass m passing per unit time.

Note that $\frac{1}{2} \rho v^2$ is the kinetic energy of the moving air per unit volume.

Power is energy per unit time, so the wind power incident on A (e.g. equal to the rotor area of a wind turbine) is:

$$P = \frac{E}{t} = \frac{1}{2} Apv^3$$

Wind is defined as movement of air across the surface of the Earth, affected by changes in temperature of the Earth's surface. It is usually directed from high to low pressure areas. The surface of the Earth is heated unevenly by the sun, depending on factors such as the angle of incidence of the sun's rays at the surface (which differs with latitude and time of day) and whether the land is open or covered with vegetation. Large bodies of water, such as the oceans, heat up and cool down slower than the land.

The heat energy absorbed at the Earth's surface is transferred to the air directly above it and, as warmer air is less dense than cooler air, it rises above the cool air to form areas of high pressure and thus pressure differentials. The rotation of the Earth drags the air around with it causing turbulence. All these effects combine to cause a constantly varying, and largely unpredictable, pattern of air movement (winds) across the surface of the Earth.

The total amount of economically extractable power available from the wind is considerably more than present human power use from all sources. Some estimates show that around 50 TW of useful power could be extracted from wind turbines. Other estimates show that 1,700 TW of wind power are available worldwide at an altitude of 100 meters over land and sea, from which over 100 TW could be extracted in a practical and cost-competitive manner.

Practical wind power generation, however, is usually from winds that are very close to the surface of the earth. This is because wind turbines are limited as to how high the blades can be located for safe operation. The maximum practical altitude is 200-300 feet. But winds are usually much stronger and more consistent higher up. This is forcing technological developments to generate electricity from high-altitude winds.

So, if the wind turbines cannot be higher than 300 feet, then we install them on high elevations. The only problem here is that these areas are usually far from population centers and grid connections, so new power lines must be installed, which becomes an economic barrier.

Wind Power Equipment

We saw some large equipment in use at coal and nuclear plants, so looking at a wind mill won't impress us much. Yet, they are very impressive mechanical units. Hundreds of feet tall, they are noticeable from a great distance. When these large giants are working side-by-side, they look like something out of this world. Looking at their large arms swinging in the air—200 feet high—whistling and whooshing nonstop, is an out-of-this-world sensation.

The Wind Turbine

A wind turbine is an electro-mechanical device that is designed to convert the kinetic energy of the wind first into mechanical energy, which can be used to drive machinery. Most often, however, it is used to generate electricity.

Today's wind turbines are manufactured in a wide range of vertical and horizontal axis types. Small wind turbines are used for water pumping, battery charging, auxiliary power on boats, and such. The large size wind

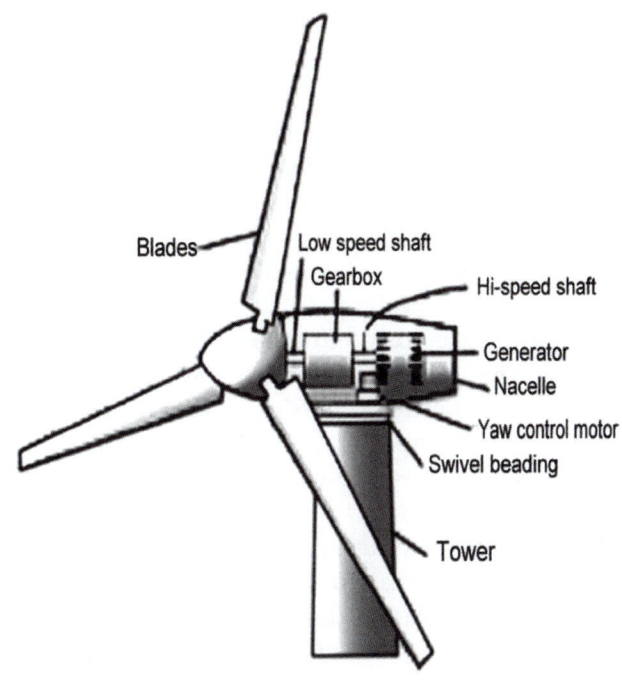

Figure 4-73. Wind turbine

turbines are usually used for grid-connected electric power generation, and their use is becoming increasingly important for commercial electricity generation.

Wind turbines have a number of key components:

- The structural support of the wind turbine includes the tower and rotor yaw mechanism.
- The rotor supports and controls the turbine blades for efficient and safe operation, to catch the maximum amount of wind and rotate the main axle.
- A gearbox or continuously variable transmission are attached to the main axle and convert its low-speed (but powerful) rotation to high-speed (low-resistance) rotation as needed for generating electricity.
- An electric generator and control electronics convert the rotational energy of the axle into electricity, which is sent into the grid.

The turbine blades are designed to rotate about either a horizontal or a vertical axis, with the horizontal type being much older and more common.

Wind Turbine Manufacturing

Prior to 2005, only one wind turbine original equipment manufacturer (OEM) assembled utility-scale turbines in the U.S. There were 28 wind turbine manufacturers in 2011. In 2012, 8 new facilities came online in 8 different states, so a total of 12 nacelle assembly facilities were online by the end of 2012.

Growth in U.S. wind-related manufacturing has occurred across the entire value chain, so there are currently 13 facilities producing blades and 12 tower manufacturing facilities, while the wind-related manufacturing facilities are spread across 44 states and employ more than 25,000 people across the country. At least 10 R&D facilities conduct advanced wind turbine research.

Growing domestic production has resulted in a significant trickle-down effect as OEMs establishing a manufacturing presence in the U.S. have attracted supply chain companies capable of supplying the thousands of components comprising a wind turbine. As a result, there are now at least 559 wind-related manufacturing facilities spread across 44 states supplying components to the wind energy industry.

The growing manufacturing capacity here is reflected in the increasing domestic content of turbines, with 67% of U.S.-deployed turbines' value being manufactured domestically in recent years, up from less than 25% prior to 2005.

Wind turbine assembly consists of about 8,000 components, some as strong and large as a skyscraper, and some as fragile and small as a semiconductor chip. The different components of the wind turbine system form sub-systems, as follow:

- Materials: turbines are primarily composed of large amounts of steel, but other materials, such as composites, ductile iron, concrete, aluminum, copper and adhesives, are also used.
- Equipment: a variety of components, such as fall protection, turbine lighting and other systems are needed. Turbines also require unique construction and on-site equipment.
- Structural: turbines use a huge number of fasteners, castings and other steel products.
- Power transmission: wind turbines have a sizable and complex power transmission system, requiring bearings, couplings, gears, hydraulic systems, brakes, machined and fabricated components and shafts, among other components.
- Electrical: the electrical system is a critical part of a wind turbine. Common components include power converters, controls, sensors and generator components.

There are several major wind turbine manufacturers worldwide: Gamesa, GE Energy, Goldwing, Siemens Power, Nordex, and Vestas, to mention a few. The wind turbine manufacturing, transport, assembly, and O&M process consists of the following steps (22).

Wind turbine manufacturing, transport, assembly, wind farm construction, and O&M procedures consist of the following steps.

- *Foundation*, or base, is the cement slab onto which the wind tower is mounted. The foundation consists of:
  — Rebar
  — Concrete
  — Casings
  — Bolts and nuts

- *Tower*, normally made of rolled steel tube sections that are bolted together to provide the support system for the blades and nacelle.
  The tower consists of:
  — Tower structure
  — Ladders
  — Lifts
  — Stairs

- *Nacelle* is the external shell or structure resting atop the tower, which houses most major components and sub-systems. The nacelle consists of:
  — Nacelle cover
  — Nacelle base
  — Heat exchanger
  — Controllers
  — Power electronics
  — Lubrication system
  — Filtration system
  — Insulation
  — Gearbox
  — Pumps
  — Drive train
  — Main shaft
  — Bearing assemblies,
  — Connecting shafts,
  — Electric generator, and
  — All electronic components that allow the turbine to monitor changes in wind speed and direction.

- *Rotor*, comprising several components which form part of a mechanism that captures the wind and converts its unidirectional motion into rotational energy. The rotor consists of:
  — Hub
  — Nose cone
  — Blades

— Bakes
— Rotary union
— Blade extender, and
— Pitch drive system.

- Beyond the major components, there are also many subcomponents and different materials used in a wind turbine. Some of these are:
— Transformers
— Bolts, nuts, and miscellaneous fasteners
— Wire and conduit
— Ceramics and plastic parts
— Paints and coatings
— Lighting protection system
— Communication devices
— Control, conditioning, and monitoring equipment
— Electrical interfaces and connections
— Circuit breakers and fuses
— Fiber optic cables
— Batteries
— Bearings

Most of these components are huge, heavy, and very expensive. The tower, for example, is over 26% of the total cost of a wind turbine, rotor blades 22%, the gearbox 13%, and the other components 5% or less.

The Manufacturing Process

Wind turbine components are manufactured by original equipment manufacturers (OEMs) who design and brand the different parts and assemble them in sub-assemblies. Some parts are shipped as single units, while some are put together in assemblies.

One supplier might roll large plates of steel into the towers that support the turbine. Another company makes the turbine blades from special carbon fiber materials, and a third might manufacture the electronic computerized control systems.

All parts and assemblies are shipped to final assembly at the manufacturing plant, or for final assembly in the field.

Wind turbine manufacturers operate similarly to automobile assemblers with parts that are partially made by the OEMs and partially in-house. They are system integrators, bringing together an estimated 8,000 precision-made parts and components to produce a wind turbine.

Each of these components might be produced and assembled domestically from imported inputs, or might be imported as an assembled product. In all cases,

wind turbine manufacturers put together as many sub-systems as possible in their production plants. The assemblies are then shipped to the field for final assembly.

The OEMs and specialty firms are part of a complex global supply chain.

- Tier 1 suppliers make large components such as towers, hubs, blades, or gearboxes. They include firms such as LM Wind (blades), SKF (bearings), and Winergy (gearboxes).

- Tier 2 suppliers produce subassemblies such as ladders, fiberglass, control systems, hydraulics, power electronics, fasteners, resin, machine parts, or motors. They include companies such as American Roller Bearings (power transmission bearings), Cardinal Fasteners (structural fasteners), and Timken (power transmission bearings).

A wind turbine is a significant investment. Price quotes range from $900/kW to $1,400/kW, so an average 2 MW turbine would cost between $1.8 million and $2.8 million, plus transportation, construction, installation, testing, insurance, and operation costs.

Each wind turbine assembler uses different sourcing strategies and levels of vertical integration. Some wind turbine manufacturers produce many major components internally or through subsidiaries, while others outsource most of their critical components.

For instance, some manufacturers produce blades, generators, or gearboxes in-house, while others opt for outside suppliers. Hundreds of smaller companies make specialized parts such as clutches, rotor bearings, fasteners, sensors, and gears for the wind industry.

Very high levels of expertise and specialization are required of wind turbine suppliers, with the level of precision similar to that of the aerospace industry. Turbine manufacturers often establish relationships with suppliers in the interest of quality, as failure in a turbine part can be very expensive to fix.

Wind turbines are expected to survive largely unattended in extreme climactic conditions for a design life of as much as 20-25 years of non-stop operation under any weather conditions. Product quality is also of concern to wind farm operators, as a malfunctioning turbine can reduce operating revenue and even cause a project to fail.

U.S. Wind Turbine Manufacturing Facilities

There are several major wind turbine manufacturers worldwide: Gamesa, GE Energy, Goldwing, Siemens

Power, Nordex, and Vestas, to mention a few.

At the end of 2011 there were more than 470 wind turbine manufacturing facilities in the United States, up substantially from the 30-40 wind-related manufacturing facilities nationwide 5-6 years earlier. Over that period, the number of tower plants increased from 6 to 18; blade facilities rose from 4 to 12; and nacelle assembly facilities grew from 3 to 14.

Total investment in wind industry manufacturing facilities in the United States has exceeded $1.5 billion. Greater demand for wind turbines, cost savings related to transportation, and concern about the risks associated with currency fluctuations are among the reasons wind turbine and component manufacturers have opened new production facilities in the US since 2005.

Even with increased domestic production capacity, wind turbine assemblers source parts and components on a worldwide basis, reflecting the industry's global supply chain. Many wind manufacturers with production facilities in the United States also produce elsewhere, typically in Europe and Asia.

Components Transport

Manufacturers use specialized means of transport to convey the wind turbines to their destination on the wind farm. These means of transport allow for access to any kind of terrain, including the most difficult, with a minimal impact on the environment.

The transport procedures could be classified as:

- *Road transport* uses ready access to rural and remote areas that are common locations for wind farms; however, limited carrier capacity, height, weight and length restrictions, in addition to rising fuel costs, state and local permitting issues, driver shortages and other issues, all pose challenges.

Figure 4-74. Wind turbine blades in transport

- *Rail transport* is cheaper than transport by road, particularly for long distances; however, height, weight, and length restrictions can be problematic, and rail lines don't run directly to wind farm sites, which necessitates road transport to the final destination.

- *Water transport* via barge is comparatively inexpensive; however, access to waterways for wind components is limited, and transport time can be slow. International transport is almost always done via ocean freight.

A number of major issues face the industry, such as varying state and local permit rules and restrictions, as well as varying engagement by state and local transportation officials.

There is also a limited supply of trailers and railcars capable of hauling wind turbine components, and a limited number of companies willing to make the investment to increase the supply. This is due to cost and the fact that the specialized equipment used to haul wind turbine components often cannot be used for other hauling, which limits its usefulness.

Wind Turbine Specs

Just to give the reader an idea of what we are talking about, here are some specs of these gentle giants—the largest among the renewable power generators:

Tower:

Purpose:	supports the entire assembly
Type:	3-section, bolted together steel tube
Material:	1.5 inch thick welded steel sheets.
Height:	230 ft
Bottom diameter:	14.0 ft
Top diameter:	6.0 ft
Weight:	100 tons.
Total height:	325 ft
Hub height:	240 ft

Rotor

Purpose:	rotates with the wind
Diameter:	175 ft
Type:	Upwind, stall regulated.

Hub

Purpose	holds and controls the blades
Type	spherical
Hub diameter:	6.0 ft
Weight:	4.0 tons

Blades

Purpose:	catches the wind and rotate
Type:	stall regulated
Blade length:	75 ft
Blade weight:	4.0 tons

Nacelle

Purpose:	houses main shaft, gearbox, and generator
Type:	fiberglass housing on a steel platform
Length:	20.0 ft
Height:	10.0 ft
Width:	7.0 ft
Weight:	25 tons

Main shaft

Purpose:	connects gear box and generator
Type:	almost solid, painted steel
Diameter:	3.0 ft
Length:	7.0 ft
Weight:	2.5 tons

Gearbox

Purpose:	connects the blades to the generator
Type:	helical-planetary
Ratio	1:81
Length:	6.0 ft
Width:	6.0 ft
Weight:	5.5 tons

Generator

Purpose:	power generation
Type:	asynchronous
Stator:	water-cooled stator
Windings:	air cooled
Power rating:	two 200 kW and 900 kW generators
Power produced:	2,500 MWh annually

Operation

Wind turbines are designed to capture the wind and convert its horizontal motion into rotational energy. Wind rotates the blades, which in turn rotate an electrical generator to produce electric current.

A computer connected to a number of sensors reads and analyzes the wind speed and other weather conditions around the wind turbine. It then makes decisions on the function of all active components and subsystems based on the gathered weather data and the wind speed and variability.

The computer constantly reads the blades' speed and selects which generator to use and when and how, based on its analysis of the weather and wind data.

At low wind-speeds, about <5 meters per second (m/s), the blades rotate at 15-16 rpm. This slow blade motion is converted to 1200 rpm by the gearbox and the motion is transferred to a 200 kW electric generator.

At high wind speeds, over 5 m/s, the blades rotate at over 20 rpm, which motion is converted to 1800 rpm by the gearbox and the motion is transferred to the 900 kW generator.

The computer decides which generator will operate at what blade speed and when it will make contact with the power grid to send the generated electricity.

The electricity generated by the chosen generator is conditioned by special on-site equipment to follow the grid sine-wave and is synchronized with the grid power via power controllers prior to sending it into the grid.

The computer shuts down the generator when the blade speed doesn't match its requirements or when it is disconnected from the grid.

Wind turbines operate at maximum 1000 rpm blade speed, which is controlled by air brakes. The brakes slow the blade rotation to prevent damage, and are designed to stop the rotation totally at high wind speeds to prevent an out-of-control condition.

Types of Wind Turbines

There are number of types of commercial wind turbines in use today.

Horizontal-axis

Horizontal-axis wind turbines (HAWT) are the most common types, and the one we review in more detail herein. These turbines are designed with the main rotor shaft and electrical generator at the top of a tower, and operate by pointing into the wind.

Smaller turbines are pointed by a simple wind vane, while large turbines generally use a wind sensor coupled with a servo motor. Larger turbines have a gearbox, which turns the slow rotation of the blades into a quicker rotation that is more suitable to drive an electrical generator.

Since a tower and the casing produce turbulence, the turbine blades are usually positioned upwind. Turbine blades are stiff, which prevents mechanical stress and fatigue of the material and also keep the blades from bending and smashing into the tower during high winds.

Downwind versions are used for small turbines, since they don't need an additional mechanism for keeping them in line with the wind, and because in high winds the blades can be allowed to bend which reduces their swept area and thus their wind resistance.

Large wind turbines used in wind farms for commercial production of electric power are usually three-bladed and pointed into the wind by computer-controlled motors. The high tip speeds of large turbines can reach over 320 km/h (200 mph), and are of high efficiency and low torque ripple, which contribute to reliable and safe operation.

The blades are usually colored white for increased visibility by aircraft and birds.

A gear box is used to step up the speed of the generator, but some designs use direct drive of an annular generator. Some models operate at constant speed, but more energy can be collected by variable-speed turbines which use a solid-state power converter to interface to the transmission system.

All turbines are equipped with protective features to avoid mechanical or electrical damage at high wind speeds. This is achieved by feathering the blades into the wind which ceases their rotation, which can be supplemented by brakes for even safer operation.

Vertical-axis

Vertical-axis wind turbines (or VAWTs) are different from the above discussed horizontal turbines in that the main rotor shaft is positioned vertically. The advantages here is that the turbine is fixed mounted and does not need to be reoriented into the wind to be effective. This is particularly advantageous on sites where wind direction is highly variable.

With a vertical axis, the generator and gearbox can be mounted on the ground, using a direct drive from the rotor assembly to the ground-based gearbox. This increases the mechanical stability of the system, and also reduces some expensive structural elements (like 300 feet of stairs in the horizontal axis type). It also makes maintenance and repairs much easier, faster, cheaper, and safer.

Key disadvantages include the low rotational speed with the consequential higher torque and hence higher cost of the drive train, and the inherently lower power coefficient.

The 360-degree rotation of the aerofoil within the wind flow during each cycle and hence the highly dynamic loading on the blade, the pulsating torque generated by some rotor designs on the drive train, and the difficulty of modeling the wind flow accurately present challenges to analyzing and designing the rotor prior to fabricating a prototype.

Vertical wind turbines require different operating conditions than their horizontal counterparts. For example, when a vertical turbine is mounted on a rooftop,

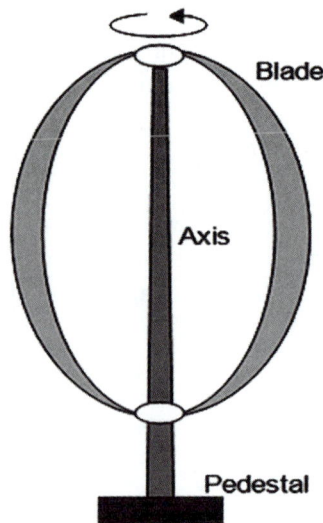

Figure 4-75. Vertical axis wind turbine

the building generally redirects wind over the roof, and this can double the wind speed at the turbine.

When the height of the rooftop mounted turbine tower is approximately 50% of the building height, it is near the optimum for maximum wind energy and minimum wind turbulence.

But wind speeds close to structures are generally much lower than at exposed rural sites, so a compromise must be found, because unpredictable turbulence and loud noise may occur in such cases.

Wind Farms

A wind farm is a group of wind turbines in the same location used for production of electricity. A large wind farm may consist of several hundred individual wind turbines, and cover an area of hundreds of square miles, but the land between the turbines may be used for agricultural or other purposes. A wind farm may also be located offshore.

Almost all large wind turbines have the same design—a horizontal axis wind turbine having an upwind rotor with three blades, attached to a nacelle on top of a tall tubular tower.

In a wind farm, individual turbines are interconnected with a medium-voltage (often 34.5 kV), power collection system and communications network. At a substation, this medium-voltage electric current is increased by a transformer to match the high voltage of the power grid.

Approximately 75% of the total cost of a wind farm is related to upfront costs such as the cost of the turbine, foundation, electrical equipment, and grid-connection.

A wind turbine is capital-intensive compared to

conventional fossil fuel fired technologies such as a natural gas power plant, where as much as 40-70% of costs are related to fuel and operations and maintenance procedures.

In turn, a wind farm does not need any fuel to operate. It is also one of the cleanest and greenest power generating technologies available.

World's Wind Farms

Many of the largest operational onshore wind farms are located in the US:

- Alta Wind Energy Center in Kern County, California, is the largest onshore wind farm in the world at 1020 MW, followed closely by the
- Shepherds Flat Wind Farm in Eastern Oregon at 845 MW, and the
- Roscoe Wind Farm in Texas at 781.5 MW.
- The Sheringham Shoal Offshore Wind Farm and the Thanet Wind Farm in the UK are the largest offshore wind farms in the world at 317 MW and 300 MW, followed by
- Horns Rev II in Denmark at 209 MW.

There are many large wind farms under construction around the world as well, including:

- The London Array offshore wind farm at 1000 MW,
- BARD Offshore 1 at 400 MW,
- Sheringham Shoal Offshore Wind Farm at 317 MW,
- Lincs Wind Farm, Clyde Wind Farm at 548 MW,
- Greater Gabbard wind farm at 500 MW,
- Macarthur Wind Farm at 420 MW,
- Lower Snake River Wind Project at 343 MW, and
- Walney Wind Farm at 367 MW.

Grid Operation

The power generated by wind turbines must be conditioned before plugging into the grid. Since induction generators are most often used for wind power, and they require reactive power for excitation, special substations are incorporated in wind-power generating systems, which include substantial capacitor banks for current conditioning and power factor correction.

Wind power is variable in nature, going up and down with the strength of the wind. The different types of wind turbine generators behave differently during transmission grid disturbances, so design engineers must pay special attention to the particulars of the site prior to installation. They use special *grid codes* that specify the requirements for interconnection to the transmission grid, which include the power factor, constancy of frequency, and dynamic behavior of the wind farm turbines during a system fault.

The grid operators also do extensive modeling of the dynamic and electromechanical characteristics of the wind power plant to ensure predictable and stable power during system operation. All in all, it takes a village to operate a large wind farm.

The future of wind energy depends on finding ways to level the power output. This can be done by combining wind with solar or gas power generation or by adding energy storage to the wind farm setup. Either of these is an expensive undertaking, so a new technology breakthrough is needed in this area.

Wind Power Plant Design and Construction

Like any power plant, new wind power plants go through a number of complex, lengthy, and expensive procedures. Some of the elements are very similar to those discussed in the other chapters, so we would limit this discussion to the wind-particular issues.

The cradle-to-grave process of a wind power plant consists of the following steps:

Environmental impact package
- Initial site evaluation
- Scope of work program
- Environmental impact report
- Environmental monitoring program
- Reclamation bonds

Plant development package
- Lease or buyout rights acquisition
- Mapping the area
- Site tests and analysis
- Site zoning

Land rights
- Land specifics and requirements
- Surface land and minerals ownership, etc.
- Operating and reclamation requirements.

Taxes and royalties
- Federal, state and local taxation,
- Royalties payments,

Process design and equipment set planning
- Concept wind power plant design
- Power plant process design
- Equipment selection and ordering
- Economic evaluation
- Safety and emergency procedures

NEPA procedures
- Lead EIS agency communications
- EIS draft and reviews
- EIS hearing and federal review
- CEQ filing and approvals

Permits
- Surface use and acquisition conditions
- Federal permits
- USFS land use
- State water use and mining
- State industrial siting
- Local permits

Site preparation and construction
- Site clearing and preparation
- Equipment delivery and assembly
- Site construction
- Equipment setup
- Support equipment setup
- Labor hiring and training
- Plant start-up and ramp-up procedures
- Full production specs and documentation

In more detail, the wind power plant goes through the following preliminary steps.

Site Assessment

Many factors related to the physical aspects of the proposed wind power plant—type of property, zoning regulations, transmission lines, environmental aspects, and the neighbors' perceptions about and acceptance of wind power—play a major role in designing a successful and profitable wind power plant.

All data related to environmental and weather conditions of the locale must be gathered, analyzed, and well understood to make an efficient, safe, and profitable wind farm design. These data include:

Land Considerations

Harnessing wind power has been done for many centuries, and can be a good investment today too. To get the most out of the investment, however, it is critical that turbines are located at the right place. A place with enough wind of the proper type is most suitable for commercial power generation.

As reviewed above, the turbines' placement depends on where and when the wind blows, the physical aspects of the property, zoning regulations, environmental concerns, and the neighbors' concerns about the physical aspects and noise of the turbines.

Proper site planning and adequate power plant design are absolutely critical for harnessing enough wind power, and efficient and profitable operation.

Connecting to the Grid

Wind power plants usually connect the turbines output to the existing power grid, so the design engineers must make sure that the turbines are near a grid-connection point. Otherwise, they need to design an expensive transmission line and sub-station to connect to the grid. The proximity to existing transmission lines is critical for minimizing infrastructure requirements and keeping costs down. High voltage lines cost about $1 million per mile, so sites with good wind and adequate access to the grid can be very valuable.

Utilities usually restrict how close a turbine can be to power lines, and there are restrictions about proximity to airports and other facilities which must be also considered in the preliminary design.

Zoning and Permitting

Wind turbines and wind turbine installation and operation is subject to local, state, and federal laws. Local zoning seems to be the most restricting simply because of the presence of tall towers. Neighbors constantly complain about the unsightly view of these giants, which has led to numerous lengthy and expensive court battles.

Special permits must always be obtained from the local planning commission, so knowledge of the local zoning laws early in the development of the wind project can help decrease or avoid unnecessary delays and expenses.

Most states also regulate the size of the electric generating facilities. For example, any power plant larger than 25 MW in some states must receive a permit from the Public Utilities Commissions. This requires an elaborate environmental impact statement (EIS), which takes a lot of time and money.

State permits usually supersede local zoning and other laws. Local, state, and federal permitting requirements for wind projects change often, but the federal laws are always a priority. There are also several governing bodies that may need to issue an approval prior to construction, depending on location and size.

For example, the Federal Aviation Authority (FAA) has authority as far as structures close to airports are concerned. In particular, the FAA must permit every structure over 200 feet tall near an airport or within flight paths. Since many commercial wind turbines are 200 feet or taller, the FAA has the say so in all cases.

Environmental Concerns

Wind energy is considered a non-polluting energy generator, but the construction and operation of any power plant brings the risk of disrupting ecosystems on the site and beyond. Wind and solar power plants are no different.

In most cases, they are not allowed in protected areas, such as wetlands or other sensitive areas. They also should not be located in migratory bird flyways because, like any large structure, they can kill birds. Wind turbines in scenic areas have caused numerous lawsuits, so these must be avoided.

The Land

Wind turbines are tall and heavy structures that require a solid foundation. The land mass should be able to support the weight of the turbine, as well as the weight of construction equipment during the field assembly and installation.

Turbines also require a lot of open space to harness the power of the wind, in addition to access roads and support facilities, so large land areas are required for large-scale power generation. The wind turbine platform itself, even the largest available, occupies only a few square yards, so in most cases the surrounding land can be used for farming and ranching.

The site planning must consider possible changes of neighboring properties or buildings, and the related changes required by local zoning laws.

The Neighbors

The neighbors are one of the biggest enemies of newly proposed wind turbine power plants. Not-in-my-back-yard (NYMBY) is a movement that is taking the world over. Wind turbines are very tall and make a lot of noise, which is especially bothersome at night. The planning process must include the neighbors and find out their concerns.

Turbines are best when installed where they will not be seen and heard by the neighbors. Active general public involvement at the early stages of the wind project process is a must and is one way to increase the likelihood of a timely permit decision and reduce the possibility of protracted litigation.

The general public includes residents and members of communities near the wind development and community officials and representatives of various interests, including economic development, conservation and environmental groups. All these individuals must be involved in the decision making process from the very beginning.

Of critical importance to the wind farm's long-term success is getting enough information on the weather and wind conditions of the area.

Wind Resource Assessment

Once the location has been (preliminarily) determined, a thorough assessment of wind availability, patterns and issues must be conducted. A wind map is generated, to provide a rough estimate of the wind class at the proposed site. The map basically denotes the seasonal and daily wind availability and average wind speeds during the different times.

A special, and very important, area of the preliminary search is obtaining reliable historical data on the weather patterns. Of special interest is the presence of violent activities in the area, such as storms, tornadoes, lightning strikes, earthquakes, wild fires, and other natural or man-made phenomena that might affect the performance of the plant equipment.

An area classified as Class 3 (good wind speeds and patterns) or higher, that is clear of trees and buildings, and preferably somewhat higher than surrounding obstructions, is best for efficient wind capture and power generation. Then we need to undertake some site-specific meteorological studies which would help determine the economic feasibility of the project.

Wind Speed

Speed is a most important factor to considered during the preliminary assessment, and precedes anything else. This is so very important because the power in the wind, which translates to electric power generated by the wind turbines, has a cubic relationship to wind speed. For example, a site with an average 20 mph wind speed contains nearly 60 percent more energy than a site with an average wind speed of 16 mph.

Wind speed varies from day to day, season to season, and year to year, and is different at different heights above the ground, so it is hard to obtain an accurate daily, monthly, or yearly average. Reviewing existing wind maps that show the history of wind activities in the area helps, but does not a guaranty that this is what will happen in the future. Also, wind maps, even the most sophisticated and up-to-date do not show everything we need to know about the local wind resource, since they are nothing more than computer models of the wind speed at any one spot.

Wind Speed Distribution

Wind has variable speed most of the time, and doesn't blow with the same force and from the same direction all the time. Ideal wind resource is one with relatively stable high speeds, without much change in the force or direction. Trees and vegetation in that are permanently deformed in one direction due to constant wind exposure indicate an area with a good wind resource, which would be suitable for wind power generation.

Wind Direction

The goal of the wind power plant designer is to locate the wind turbines so that they are exposed to the most energetic wind most of the time. Even though the wind pattern might indicate that the wind blows more frequently from the west, it is possible that more wind energy may come from a different direction if those winds, albeit of shorter duration, are stronger.

Wind directions, along with wind speed, determine the amount of power that the power plant can produce. The design engineers use a wind rose chart, generated from the wind resource patterns at the particular location and helpful in determining wind direction and distribution.

Wind Shear

Wind shear is the increase in wind speed at greater heights above ground. Usually power generation is increased by installing a turbine on a taller tower. This is why some of the wind towers are hundreds of feet in the air, or perched on hills.

Seasonal Wind Cycles

Electricity use also varies, with the seasons and at different locations. Most electricity used during the daytime and during the coldest or hottest months of the year. These factors must be considered in designing a new wind power plant, to make sure that the wind blows strongly when electricity is needed most. For example, wind turbines installed close to populated areas where the wind blows mostly at night are not a good match between the wind energy availability and the local power load.

Air Pressure and Temperature

Another critical factor in wind turbine performance is the local air pressure and temperature. Although these affect the amount of energy in the wind to a minor degree, a prolonged change in air pressure or temperature can have significant effect on the efficiency of the wind turbines. Regional data must be consulted to estimate the pressure and temperature variations and extrapolate their influences on the wind power plant performance.

Surface Obstacles

Even the best local weather and climate conditions would not help much if the wind coming to the power plant is obstructed by trees or structures. When wind blows around and over trees, buildings and other obstacles in the landscape, it slows down or becomes turbulent. If wind turbines are to be installed in such areas, they must be placed in a well calculated location where the influence of obstacles is minimized. In some cases the turbulence can be used to amplify the wind speed and boost the turbines' efficiency.

Surface Roughness

Surface roughness is a measure of the terrain and the type and density of vegetation in the landscape near the proposed wind power plant. The turbines will be affected by excess roughness, so as a rule of thumb, the smoother the terrain is within a 10-15 mile radius around the plant, the better the efficiency of the turbines would be. Because of that, a detailed determination of the land surface roughness is absolutely necessary.

Equipment Selection

All these factors impact the wind power generation which in turn determines the amount of electricity that can be generated by the proposed wind power plant on an annual basis.

The more accurate the information gathered by assessment teams about wind resource, the better the design and efficiency of the wind power plant will be. The turbines' type and size selection is decided after compiling and analyzing all available information.

The selection depends on the location, local wind resource, and a number of other factors, as well as on price and availability of the chosen systems. It varies based from project to project.

Owners of wind projects must consider all factors discussed above in addition to including consideration of long-term electricity production in the purchase of wind turbines.

Additional costs for condition monitoring systems (additional sensors in the turbine and analytical services), 24/7 operation monitoring services and climb assists or service lifts may be prudent (albeit expensive) additions, resulting in greater turbine availability and productivity.

The Business Model

When a suitable site is located, the next step is to determine how to proceed with the land acquisition, or lease. There are three basic ways to approach a wind power plant development.

There are three primary types of arrangements landowners and developers make regarding wind energy:

Leasing Land

A developer may lease or rent land for the life of the turbines, which is usually about 30 years. The land owner is compensated with a lump sum or with an annual royalty payment for the amount of electricity produced. Basing the lease on a share of revenues can help capture future increases in the value of wind power. Landowner payments are typically about $2,500 to $5,000 per wind turbine per year. In this arrangement, the land owners retain ownership of the land.

Wind Easements

A wind easement is a deed or will executed by the owner of a particular plot of land or air space to ensure a wind energy developer adequate exposure to the wind. Easements run in perpetuity unless the deed provides for termination. Developers usually compensate for easements with a payment upfront. Easements must be in writing and must be filed, recorded, and indexed by the local county recorder's office.

Land Buyout

Developers will sometimes purchase the land outright, and build and operate the wind power plant as they want and for as long they want. The land owner is paid a one-time price and no longer has access to the land or the wind resource.

Financing the Wind Power Plant

The business structure that has been chosen profoundly affects the costs and the financing of the project. There are several primary components in the cost of a wind project including the turbine itself, construction, interconnection fees, metering equipment, maintenance, and any consulting services you contract.

Various state and federal incentives may be used to reduce the wind project costs. There are also several grant programs available to wind developers. The economic rewards will depend on the business structure and financing mechanisms, which vary from case to case and from state to state.

Construction

A typical 1.5 MW wind turbine of a type frequently seen in the United States has a tower 240-260 ft high. The rotor assembly (blades and hub) weighs 48,000 pounds.

The nacelle, which contains the generator component, weighs 115,000 pounds.

These are huge, tall, and heavy components, which put together make some of the largest structures known to man today. Their installation requires special considerations and careful planning and execution. Some of the key procedures of the wind farm construction follow.

Wind Turbine Spacing

Wind turbines need a lot of space to avoid turbulence and other unwanted negative effects. Recent computer simulations, taking into account the interactions among wind turbines (wakes) as well as the entire turbulent atmospheric boundary layer, have determined that horizontal wind turbine farms require spacing between the wind turbines of about 6-10 times the rotor diameter. Large-scale wind farms, however, need about 12-15 rotor diameters for the most economically optimal setup, taking into account typical wind turbine and land costs.

Studies also suggest that vertical wind turbines may be placed much more closely together so long as an alternating pattern of rotation is created, allowing blades of neighboring turbines to move in the same direction as they approach one another. This in effect creates a wind current that might increase the efficiency of the affected turbines.

After the distance between the turbines, and the exact location of each turbine in the field has been decided, the actual field work commences.

Field Assembly

Once all components have been delivered on site, an experienced team of operators carries out the installation of the turbines. Field assembly phases of wind turbines and wind power plants follows.

Platform Construction

Before assembling the wind turbine in the field, the land is prepared. The surface around the base of the wind turbine is leveled, and a large hole is dug where the turbine is to be erected.

The hole surface is compacted and filled with concrete to form the platform which must be strong enough to support the entire structure even during extreme weather conditions.

Special large bolts are imbedded in the cement and are used to bolt the base of the tower to the concrete platform.

The concrete platform for an average wind turbine tower uses 58,000 pounds of reinforcing steel and contains 250 cubic yards of concrete. It can be 50 ft in diameter and 10 ft. thick near the center.

Tower Erection

The tower consists of several large steel pipe segments bolted together to form one long tube. The lower tower section is bolted onto the platform via hundreds of large bolts embedded in the concrete foundation. The other tower segments are placed one atop the other using lattice cranes, and bolted together.

NOTE: The cranes used for this operation are critical, and may be either of the caterpillar or hydraulic jack type. Caterpillar-type cranes are up to 30 feet wide and are able to change position easily. Jack type cranes are only 15 feet, but are suitable for working on difficult terrain, due to their narrow width.

Nacelle Installation

Once the tower segments are assembled, the next step is to install the nacelle, which is connected to the very top tower section. It is lifted piece by piece, and each component is bolted onto the framework and connected electrically as required.

Rotor Installation

The rotor assembly consists of three blades bolted onto a hub, which is a huge structure. The hub and blades can be assembled on the ground and then lifted up to be connected to the nacelle.

More often, however, due to the large size of the assembly, the hub is lifted and bolted first, after which the blades are lifted and bolted to it one by one. The latter method requires less space for maneuvering and makes the assembly process faster and safer.

Startup

When all sub-systems are installed, tested, and certified operational, the manufacturer representatives perform the startup operations. They follow special procedures to verify the proper function of each sub-system, and finally test and certify the proper operation of the entire unit. They take full responsibility for the proper execution of the assembly process and the startup procedures as needed for final certification of the turbine.

With all tests done, the manufacturer takes over the operation and maintenance of the wind turbine for a predetermined time, or throughout its working life.

Operation and Maintenance

Long-term productivity of wind turbines begins in the turbine's design phase and extends through the next 20 or 30 years.

Following is an expansion of the critical stages in a wind turbine cradle-to-grave life cycle, as detailed above.

Operation

Under normal operating conditions, wind turbine operation is fully automatic. Automated systems as well as on-site and remote operators determine the operational parameters and execute commands. Systems must be manually reset after line or grid outages.

Maintenance

A typical wind turbine requires routine service once or twice per year. Oil and filters need to be changed, operating components need to be inspected, and bolts need to be re-torqued.

Repair

Worn parts need to be routinely repaired or replaced every 5-15 years as part of the periodic maintenance program, depending on the component type and use. Some components may need to be replaced during unscheduled or emergency procedures due to environmental or electrical damage.

Warranty

An original equipment manufacturer (OEM) typically operates the wind project through the warranty period. Continued service from the OEM is typically optional.

The owner/operator should ensure that operational data are transferred to the owner on completion of the OEM service period. An additional warranty can be purchased to ensure uninterrupted operation of the turbine during its 24/7, 20-30 life span.

Offshore Wind in the US

Offshore wind power refers to the construction of wind farms in large bodies of water to generate electricity. These installations are a new development, intended to utilize the more frequent and powerful winds that are available in these locations and have less aesthetic impact on the landscape than land-based projects.

However, the overall design, construction, operation and maintenance of off-shore wind power plants is much more difficult and complex, so the costs are considerably higher.

As of 2011, offshore wind farms were at least 3 times more expensive than onshore wind farms of the same nominal power but these costs are expected to fall as the industry matures.

Siemens and Vestas are the leading turbine suppliers for offshore wind power. DONG Energy, Vattenfall and E.ON are the leading offshore operators.

In 2013, there were 105 GW of total wind power generated in Europe alone. Offshore wind power capacity was operational, mainly in Northern Europe at about 6 GW. More than 20 GW of additional capacity will be installed by 2015, when and the UK and Germany will become the two leading wind power markets.

Offshore wind power capacity is expected to reach a total of 75 GW worldwide by 2020, with significant contributions from China and the US.

There are 33 offshore wind projects in varying stages of development in the U.S., and while there are increasing numbers of offshore wind capacity in Europe and China, the U.S. has no operational offshore projects. There are, however, nine advanced-stage plans, representing nearly 4.0 GW of potential wind capacity here.

U.S. offshore wind power generation is scheduled for commercial operation by 2017, so the DOE awarded $28 million per year in advanced technology demonstration funding to seven projects. If that is enough and what else is needed, remains to be seen, but progress is made, nevertheless.

Onshore Wind Power Generation

Onshore wind power has been, is, and will remain a power source of significance and preference. The quantity of wind power generation is still relatively small, but the importance of generating power from wind in locations where other technologies are unavailable is increasing.

Since the 1980s the United States has led the world in installed capacity, but in the late 1990s Germany surpassed the U.S., and after leadership changes, Germany is now behind the U.S. with 30 GW vs. 60 GW of wind power installations.

China has been rapidly expanding its wind installations since the late 2000s and now has over 60 GW of installed wind capacity. Presently there are more than 200,000 wind turbines operating worldwide, with a total nameplate capacity of about 250 GW.

World wind power generation increased four-fold between 2000 and 2006, doubling about every three years, and continued to increase after that but at a slower pace of about 15-20% annually.

Wind power generates over 400 TWh annually, or about 2.5% of worldwide electricity, and the numbers are growing fast. Wind power generation is expected to reach over 10% of the total world's electricity by 2020. A number of countries are already close to that mark.

Denmark produces 28% of its grid electricity via wind farms. Portugal follows with 20%, Spain with 16%, Ireland with 15, and Germany with 9%. Eighty-three countries worldwide use a significant amount of wind power on a commercial basis.

Europe accounts for nearly half of the world's total wind power generation capacity. The financial crisis of 2008 changed the dynamics of the wind generation scenario, but progress is still evident in many countries, including the U.S.

All these factors impact wind power, which in turn determines the amount of electricity that can be generated annually by the proposed wind power plant. More, and more accurate, the information gathered by the assessment teams about the wind resource, the better the design and efficiency of the wind power plant would be.

Wind Power Cost

Commercial-scale wind power installations vary in type, size, location, and turbine manufacturer, all of which determines the overall cost. The number of turbines in the project, the cost of land and financing, the turbine purchase agreement specifics, and the construction contracts are the main parts of the financial equation.

Additionally, there are other unrelated components that play direct roles in determining the bottom line. Some of the most important are wind resource assessment, site analysis and design expenses, construction expenses, permitting and interconnection studies, utility system upgrades, transformers, protection and metering equipment, insurance, operational costs, warranty, maintenance and components replacements, legal and consultation fees, taxes and incentives.

Cost of Energy(COE)

COE is calculated using this equation:

$$COE = \frac{(FCR * ICC) + AOE}{AEPnet}$$

where

COE   is levelized cost of energy ($/kWh)(constant$)
FCR   is fixed charge rate (constant $) (1/yr)
ICC   is initial capital cost ($)
AEPnet is net annual energy production (kWh/yr)
AOE   is annual operating expenses, or

$$= \frac{LLC + (O\&M + LRC)}{AEPnet}$$

LLC ≡ land lease cost
O&M ≡ levelized O&M cost
LRC ≡ levelized replacement/overhaul cost

Neither cost includes construction financing or financing fees, because these are calculated and added separately through the fixed charge rate. The costs also do not include a debt service reserve fund, which is assumed to be zero for balance sheet financing.

Primary cost elements in each wind power plant's calculations include the cost of the following components and tasks:

Rotor
- Blades
- Hub
- Pitch mechanisms and bearings
- Spinner, nose cone

Drive Train, Nacelle
- Low-speed shaft
- Bearings
- Gearbox
- Mechanical brake, high-speed coupling, and associated components
- Generator
- Variable-speed electronics
- Yaw drive and bearing
- Main frame
- Electrical connections
- Hydraulic and cooling systems
- Nacelle cover

Control, Safety System, and Condition Monitoring

Tower

Balance of system
- Foundation/support structure
- Transportation
- Roads, civil work
- Assembly and installation
- Electrical interface/connections
- Engineering permits

When evaluating offshore turbines, the following additional components or elements are considered:
- Marinization (added cost to handle marine environments)
- Port and staging equipment
- Personal access equipment
- Scour protection

- Surety bond (to cover decommissioning)
- Offshore warranty premium

Wind turbines vary greatly in size and are getting larger as technology advances. They started at several kilowatts in the early 1980s to as large as 7 MW today. Most land-based wind turbines, however, are in the 1.5 MW to 3 MW range.

The major components also changed with time. European and U.S. wind turbine manufacturers have invested heavily over the decades in developing their respective turbine technologies, leading to improvements in the efficiency of wind blades and turbines and longer turbine life.

New wind turbine manufacturers, especially from China, are not yet globally competitive, because they lack state-of-the-art technology, focus mainly on producing smaller turbines, and experience significant quality control problems.

A typical wind turbine is made primarily of steel (about 90% by weight). Aluminum and other lightweight composites are also important, particularly for blade manufacturing. Other core materials include prestressed concrete, copper, and fiberglass.

The prices of the materials used in the manufacturing of wind turbines vary with the commodity markets, so a wind turbine made today might be less or more expensive tomorrow. Also, a wind turbine made in the U.S. would surely have a different price tag than one made in China. A major part of the varying prices is the cost of different materials and their percentage in the wind system makeup.

Table 4-9. Breakdown of materials in a wind system

Material	%
Steel	89.1
Fiberglass	5.8
Copper	1.6
Concrete	1.3
Adhesive	1.1
Aluminum	0.8
Core	0.4
Total	10.00

Turbines also utilize permanent magnets, cast iron, carbon fiber, rubber, epoxy, ferrite, brass, ceramics, and Teflon, albeit in much lesser quantities. Some of these materials, however, are rare, exotic, hard to obtain, and/or in limited quantities, which sometimes contributes to significant price increases or project delays. Raw materials availability and changing commodity prices of raw materials used in wind turbines are the major factor in determining production costs.

The cost breakdown of a U.S. manufactured wind turbine system (in percent of total cost) is shown in Table 4-10.

Table 4-10. Price breakdown of wind turbine components

Component	%
Tower	26.30
Blades	22.20
Gearbox	12.91
Inverter	5.01
Transformer	3.59
Generator	3.44
Main frame	2.80
Pitch system	2.66
Main shaft	1.91
Rotor hub	1.37
Nacelle housing	1.35
Brake system	1.32
Yaw system	1.25
Rotor bearings	1.22
Hardware	1.04
Cables	0.96
Total	**100.00**

Wind turbine prices range from as low as $900/kW to as high as $1,500/kW. This means that an average 2 MW turbine would cost between $1.8 million and $2.8 million, plus installation costs. Installation costs also depend on a number of factors, location and size of the power plant, type and make of the equipment, etc., and the installation could be as pricey as the wind turbines themselves.

Annual Operating Expenses

The expenses to consider when evaluating wind farm performance are expanded on below.

Land Lease Cost/Bottom Lease Cost

Annual operating expenses (AOE) include land or ocean bottom lease cost, levelized O&M cost, and levelized replacement/overhaul cost (LRC). Land lease costs (LLC) are the rental or lease fees charged for the turbine installation. LLC is expressed in units of $/kWh.

Levelized O&M Cost

A component of AOE that is larger than the LLC is O&M cost. O&M is expressed in units of $/kWh. The O&M cost normally includes:

• labor, parts, and supplies for scheduled turbine maintenance
• labor, parts, and supplies for unscheduled turbine maintenance
• parts and supplies for equipment and facilities maintenance
• labor for administration and support

Levelized Replacement/Overhaul Cost

LRC distributes the cost of major replacements and overhauls over the life of the wind turbine and is expressed in $/kW machine rating.

The economies of scale play an important role in the capital and operational expense calculations. Small-scale wind farms cost less initially, but are more expensive in the long run, since each kilowatt of energy produced costsw more.

The majority of commercial-scale wind turbines installed today are 2 MW in size, at a cost of $3-$4 million installed. Not bad—only $1.50-2.00 per Watt installed. The prices, however, vary with location and power field size, and could easily reach double the above-average estimate.

Wind power generation cost is estimated at $55.80/MWh, while coal is at $53.10/MWh, and natural gas at $52.50/MWh. Federal, state and local tax and other incentives can dramatically reduce the cost of a wind project.

Offshore wind turbines and power fields are more expensive to install, operate and maintain for obvious reasons. The estimated capital cost of an offshore wind power installation is in the range of $5 to $6 per Watt installed.

Once in operation, the power generated by a large-scale power farm cost about 5-6 cents per kW, everything included. Although this is a bit more than the cost of power produced by some fossil generators, but wind power is renewable energy, and we can count on it now and forever, without any environmental side effects.

Wind, Solar and the Grid

The major excuse for not adding more wind and solar into grid operations has been their variable nature. Their power output depends on, and varies with the ups and downs of wind and sun availability. Because of that, they could not be used for *on demand* (dispatched) power when additional power is needed by the grid operators.

Solar to the rescue. There are efforts today to demonstrate how the unique characteristics of wind and solar working together can, much like traditional generation, perform active power control (APC) to support the grid. The effort is focused on two areas of APC—the regulating reserves and the primary frequency control.

Grid operators would like to have more support (excess power) for transmission line overload, voltage drops, and frequency variations, but don't typically ask the renewables to provide it. On the other hand, the regulators have not awakened yet, and have not imposed the requirement to use renewables in that way.

So, wind turbine manufacturers can provide the capability to provide APC services, but see no demand for it from the customers and developers. The developers don't see any point in driving up costs by building in the capability to provide a service for which there is no demand from grid operators. The regulators see no point in requiring grid operators to buy a service from renewables they may get for free from traditional generators. And the utilities are hesitating for now, not knowing which path to take—renewables or no renewables is the question before them today— true catch-22 situation on a large scale.

So, if all parties work together, a complete solution would be found through APC, combined with other means, such as energy storage and combining wind and solar. While the future of large-scale energy storage is still uncertain, combining wind generated power at certain locations especially chosen for this purpose, with solar power generated nearby is one such solution that can be implemented immediately.

At such locations PV power is complementary to the output of wind generation, since it is usually produced during the peak load hours when wind energy production may not be available. Variability around the average demand values for the individual characteristic wind and solar resources can fluctuate significantly on a daily basis. However, as illustrated by Figure 4-76, solar and wind power plant profiles—when considered in aggregate—can be a good match to the load profile and improve the resulting composite capacity value for variable generation.

In this example, the average load (upper line) is closely followed during the day by the average output from the combined wind and solar generators (the second from top line) during the same time. This average is created regard-

less, and because of the fluctuations of the individual wind and solar power generators. This is a marriage made in heaven, and this combined power generating combination will work quite well if wind and solar power outputs can be matched as closely as the one represented here.

There are areas in the US and abroad where this scheme is hard to execute because the best places for wind and solar are at different locations (often miles apart). The lack of infrastructure at the most suitable locations is another factor to be considered. Because of that, it will require great effort and heavy financing to implement large-scale "wind-solar load matching" schemes anytime soon with existing technologies.

Nevertheless, to have matching wind and solar power outputs as a goal will force us to look seek the most suitable locations and appropriate technologies for this match. This will not happen overnight, but if we seek a solution seriously, we will have a large-scale power output—nationally—that matches the grid power loads.

A Game Changer

A brand new development is making energy specialists pause and wonder. The problems with wind projects lately, and falling solar panel prices, have prompted a number of wind companies to look into the competing technologies, and solar in particular.

The wind industry added more than 13 GW of capacity in 2012, but as a result of the fiscal cliff delays and hesitation, only 1/3 of that capacity is expected to be installed in 2013. At the same time solar is going on unhindered. Surging. It is expected that U.S. solar installations will surpass new wind additions in 2013 for the

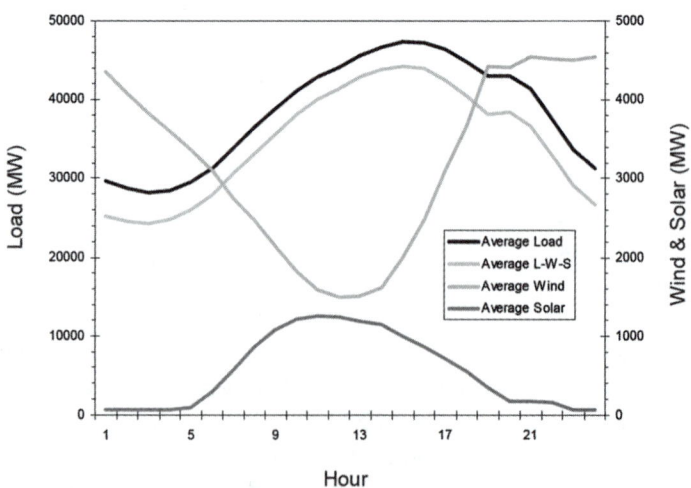

Figure 4-76. Simultaneous wind and solar generation (14)

first time ever.

So what is a wind investor to do? Sitting on idling turbines and feeling helpless does no good, so some of them are jumping head-first into solar technologies and projects, and some have hired solar specialists to help them evaluate and get into the solar business.

This is a new trend, extending throughout the supply chain, from consultants to construction and engineering firms. In extreme cases, wind companies are getting out of the wind business altogether.

Some of the more practical companies, like EDF Renewable Energy in San Diego, are developing solar-wind hybrid technologies and installing them in California's Mojave Desert. For example a 140 MW wind farm was constructed near a 143 MWp solar power plant, which is actually one of the best ways to level the energy output of combined power generation. Solar and wind work together very well, so why not? Wind companies already have many of the in-house expertise and field skills needed to develop energy projects. Many of the disciplines used in wind power installation are similar to those used in solar. GIS mapping, real estate contracts, transmission issues, and even the customers, are the same for both types of energy.

Because wind and solar go hand-in-hand so well, the future for the wind-solar hybrids is just emerging. Smaller-scale solar and storage projects are shaping as sources of future growth. Wind and solar generation can compliment each other on the grid, since the wind blows even when the sun isn't shining, and vice versa.

So, solar will become a substantial piece of the wind industry. It will compliment it and even help it grow more than it would on its own.

Environmental Effects

Most traditional energy sources have serious impacts on the environment in the form of solid, liquid or gas pollution. Compared with those, the impact of wind power is relatively minor. Wind power turbines consume no fuel and do not emit any kind of pollution. While a wind farm may cover a large area of land, many land uses such as agriculture are compatible, with only small areas of turbine foundations and infrastructure made unavailable for use.

There are concerns with bird and bat mortality from the large blades of wind turbines, but the extent of the ecological impact, if any, depends on specific circumstances. Until more data are generated or better ways to estimate the impacts are found, the prevention and mitigation of wildlife fatalities, and protection of natural resources is playing a significant role in the siting and operation of wind turbines.

Other negative effects that concern locals are the noise and the unsightly appearance of the giant wind turbines. These factors play a significant role in the siting and permitting processes.

Equipment Manufacturing Impact

It is generally accepted that the energy consumed to manufacture and transport the materials used to build a wind power plant is equal to the new energy produced by the wind plant within a few months. While this is true, we must take into account the pollution generated during the manufacture and transport of the large wind turbines and their support infrastructure and construction materials.

Imagine a 300-foot giant metal tube sticking up in the air. It is 10-15 ft. wide at the bottom and is cemented a dozen or more feet into the ground. Inside the tube, spiraling metal stairs lead to the top of the structure, where another giant is mounted. It is the electrical generator, complete with its own transmission and electrical components and controls. But the most spectacular pieces of the entire structure are the 3 or 4 blades, each 150 feet in length, swinging their long arms non-stop, as if challenging Don Quixote.

This massive structure contains many tons of steel, aluminum, copper, plastics and fiberglass. These materials were not blown in by renewable winds. Nope, they were dug out of the ground as metal ore, or pumped out as crude oil, from which the final components were molded and machined into their shapes.

A lot of solid, liquid and gas pollution was created during the mining, pumping, machining and transport operations. Making a 300-foot-long steel tube is no small task. Molding and machining 150-foot blades is another enormous task. All use a lot of energy and emit pollution. The manufacturing of the generator parts and the support infrastructure (spiral stairs, cement, rebar, etc.), together with the site construction work are also major polluting activities.

O&M Impact

Some pollution is also emitted during the operation and maintenance of wind turbines. It is not possible to operate any type of electromechanical equipment without having some sort of pollution. Operators, maintenance workers, and contractors drive to the site periodically for checks, testing, and maintenance. Replacement of key components is scheduled every few years, and parts are hoisted up and down the giant structure. These activities, including the manufacture of replacement parts, generate some pollution.

Still, wind turbines are considered pollution-neutral equipment, because the pollution generated during the equipment manufacturing operations is compensated by the pollution which is avoided by using wind power (instead of fossils) during long-term operation. It is estimated that a 2 MW wind turbine would compensate its pollution contribution within a year or two of normal operation.

Safety

Working with, or on, the monstrous wind giants is a dangerous business. Skilled and well trained technicians and experienced engineers are in charge of the different operations during the entire cradle-to-grave process of the wind turbine.

Safety is a priority in most wind power plant operations, but the dangers are constantly there. Because it is human to err, and equipment does malfunction from time to time, a number of accidents are reported during all stages of the operation. Falling from the high towers might be the most frequent cause of people human injury, and so we take a closer look at some of these events in the following chapters.

ENERGY STORAGE

We've seen that variability of PV power plants' output is unavoidable. PV power might be combined with other energy sources such as wind, to smooth the variations and even match the peak load, but even that is not a complete solution.

During cloudy or rainy days, output is limited and the only way to rectify that anomaly is to provide energy storage as a supplemental power generation. Stored energy can be used during periods of low energy generation or at night.

There are a number of potential energy storage solutions for use with solar power plants, some of which are applicable for PV power storage too. See below a complete list of presently available energy storage technologies, followed by a review of the most promising.

1. Thermal storage
    Steam accumulator
    Molten salt
    Cryogenic liquid air or nitrogen
    Seasonal thermal store
    Solar pond
    Hot bricks
        Fireless locomotive
        Eutectic system
        Ice Storage
2. Electrochemical storage
        Batteries
        Flow batteries
        Fuel cells
        Electrical
        Capacitor
        Supercapacitor
        Superconducting magnetic energy storage (SMES)
3. Mechanical storage
        Compressed air energy storage (CAES)
        Flywheel energy storage
        Hydraulic accumulator
        Hydroelectric energy storage
        Spring
        Gravitational potential energy (device)
4. Chemical storage
        Hydrogen
        Biofuels
        Liquid nitrogen
        Oxyhydrogen and Hydrogen peroxide
5. Biological storage
        Starch
        Glycogen
6. Electric grid storage

Thermal Energy Storage

This is the most widely used method of energy storage in thermal solar (CSP) plants. Heat is transferred to a thermal storage medium in an insulated reservoir during the day, and withdrawn for power generation at night. Thermal storage media include pressurized steam, concrete, a variety of phase change materials, and molten salts such as sodium and potassium nitrate. The most widely used heat transfer liquids are:

1. *Pressurized steam energy storage.* Some thermal solar power plants store heat generated during the day in high-pressure tanks as pressurized steam at 50 bar and 285°C. The steam condenses and flashes back to steam, when pressure is lowered. Storage time is short—maximum one hour. Longer storage time is theoretically possible, but has not yet been proven.

2. *Molten salt energy storage.* A variety of fluids can be used as energy storage vehicles, including water, air, oil, and sodium, but molten salt is considered the best, mostly because it is liquid at atmospheric

pressure, it provides an efficient, low-cost medium for thermal energy storage, and its operating temperatures are compatible with today's high-pressure and high-temperature steam turbines. It is also non-flammable and nontoxic, and because it is widely used in other industries, its behavior is well understood and the price is cheap.

Molten salt is a mixture of 60% sodium nitrate and 40% potassium nitrate. The mixture melts at 220°C, and is kept liquid at 290°C (550°F) in insulated storage tanks for several hours. It is used in periods of cloudy weather or at night using the stored thermal energy in the molten salt tank to generate steam and turn a turbine, which in turn generates electricity. These turbines are well established technology and are relatively cheap to install and operate.

3. 0. Pumped heat storage systems are used in CSP power plants and consist of two tanks (hot and cold) connected by transfer pipes with a heat pump in between performing the cold-to-heat conversion and transfer cycles. Electrical energy generated by the PV power plant is used to drive the heat pump with the working gas flowing from the cold to hot tanks. The gas is heated and pumped into the hot tank (+50°C) for storage and use at a later time. The hot tank is filled with solids (heat absorbing materials), where the contained heat energy can be kept at high temperature for long periods of time.

The heat stored in the hot tank can be converted back to electricity by pumping it through the heat pump and storing it back in the cold tank. The heat pump recovers the stored energy by reversing the process.

Some power (20-30%) is wasted for driving the heat pump and during the transfer and conversion cycles, but the technology can be optimized for use in large-scale PV plants.

In all cases, large heat energy losses accompany the energy storage processes. At least one third of the energy is lost during the conversion of stored heat energy into electricity. More is lost during the storage and following cooling cycles.

Battery Energy Storage

No doubt, this is the most efficient way to store a large amount of electricity generated by PV power plants. The generated DC electric energy is stored as DC power in batteries for later use. There are several types of batteries, and the most commonly used listed below.

Lead Acid Batteries

These are the most common type of rechargeable batteries in use today. Each battery consists of several electrolytic cells, where each cell contains electrodes of elemental lead (Pb) and lead oxide (PbO_2) in an electrolyte of approximately 33.5% sulfuric acid (H_2SO_4). In the discharged state, both electrodes turn into lead sulfate ($PbSO_4$), while the electrolyte loses its dissolved sulfuric acid and becomes primarily water. During the charging cycle, this process is reversed.

These batteries last a long time and can go through many charge-discharge cycles, if properly used and maintained. They are affected, however, by high temperatures, when the electrolyte can boil off and destroy the battery. Since there is water in the cells, the electrolyte can freeze during winter weather, which could destroy the battery as well.

Lithium Batteries

These are a mature technology, having been used widely for a long time in consumer electronics. They are actually a family of different batteries, containing many types of cathodes and electrolytes. The most common type of lithium cell used in consumer applications uses metallic lithium as anode and manganese dioxide as cathode, with a salt of lithium dissolved in an organic solvent. A large model of these can be used to store large amounts of electric power generated by a PV power plant, and due to their highest known power density they could be quite efficient—70-85%.

They are suitable for smaller PV installations, too, because scaling up to large PV plants would be a very expensive proposition.

Sodium Sulfur Batteries

These are high-temperature, molten metal, batteries constructed from sodium (Na) and sulfur (S). They have a high energy density, high efficiency of charge/discharge (89-92%) and long cycle life. They are usually made of inexpensive materials, and due to the high operating temperatures of 300-350°C they are quite suitable for large-scale, grid energy storage.

During the discharge phase, molten elemental sodium at the core serves as the anode, and donates electrons to the external circuit. The sulfur is absorbed in a carbon sponge around the sodium core and Na+ ions migrate to the sulfur container. These electrons drive an electric current through the molten sodium to the contact, through the electric load and back to the sulfur container.

During the charging phase, the reverse process

takes place. Once running, the heat produced by charging and discharging cycles is sufficient to maintain operating temperatures, and usually no external source is required.

There are, however, a number of safety and corrosion problems, due to the sodium reactivity, which need to be resolved before full implementation of this technology takes place.

Vanadium Redox Batteries

These are liquid energy sources, where different chemicals are stored in two tanks and pumped through electrochemical cells. Depending on the voltage supplied, the energy carriers are electrochemically charged or discharged. Charge controllers and inverters are used to control the process and to interface with the electrical source of energy.

Unlike conventional batteries, the redox-flow cell stores energy in the solutions, so that the capacity of the system is determined by the size of the electrolyte tanks, while the system power is determined by the size of the cell stacks. The redox-flow cell is therefore more like a rechargeable fuel cell than a battery. This makes it suitable as an efficient energy storage for PV installations.

A number of additional types of batteries are under development, and some show great potential for use in larger PV installations in the near future. Most batteries have problems with moisture, high temperature, memory effect, and use of scarce and toxic exotic materials, all of which cause longevity problems and abnormally high prices. If and when all these problems are resolved, the energy storage problems of PV power plants will be resolved as well.

Compressed Air Energy Storage

Compressing air into large high-pressure tanks is one of the most discussed and most promising energy storage methods for use with PV power plants today. It is a quite simple way of energy storage, using a compressor powered by the electricity produced by the PV plant compressing air into the storage tank. A lot of energy is lost by activating the compressor and, heat is wasted during the compression process, so there are several compressing methods that treat generated heat so as to optimize conversion efficiency. Some of these follow.

Adiabatic Storage

Adiabatic storage retains the heat produced by compression via special heat exchangers, and returns it to the compressed air when the air is expanded to gen-

erate power. Its overall efficiency is in the 70-80% range, with the heat stored in a fluid such as hot oil (300°C) or molten salt solutions (600°C).

Diabatic Storage

Here extra heat is dissipated into the atmosphere as waste, thus losing a significant portion of the generated energy. Upon removal from storage, the air must be re-heated prior to expansion in the turbines, which requires extra energy as well. The lost and added heat cycles lower the efficiency, but simplify the approach, so it is the only one implemented commercially these days. The overall efficiency of this method is in the 50-60% range.

Isothermal Compression and Expansion

This method attempts to maintain constant operating temperature by constant heat exchange to the environment. This is only practical for small power plants, which don't require very effective heat exchangers, and although this method is theoretically 100% efficient, this is impossible to achieve in practice, because losses are unavoidable.

There are a large number of other methods using compressed air, such as pumping air into large bags in the depths of lakes and oceans, where the water pressure is used instead of large pressure vessels. Pumping air into large underground caverns is another approach that is receiving a lot of attention lately.

Pumped Hydro Energy Storage

Pumped hydro energy is a variation of the old hydroelectric power generation method used worldwide, and is used quite successfully by some power plants. Energy is stored in the form of water, pumped from a lower elevation reservoir to one at a higher elevation. This way, low-cost off-peak electric power from the PV power plant can be used to run the pumps for elevating the water. Stored water is released through turbines, and the generated electric power is sold during periods of high electrical demand. This way the energy losses during the pumping process are recovered by selling more electricity during peak hours at a higher price.

This method provides the largest capacity of grid energy storage—limited only by the available land and size of the storage ponds.

Flywheel Energy Storage

Flywheel energy storage works by using the electricity produced by the PV power plant to power an electric motor, which in turn rotates a flywheel to a high speed, thus converting the electric energy to, and maintaining the energy balance of the system as, rotational energy. Over time, energy is extracted from the system and the flywheel's rotational speed is reduced. In reverse, adding energy to the system results in a corresponding increase in the speed of the flywheel. Most FES systems use electricity to accelerate and decelerate the flywheel, but devices that use mechanical energy directly are being developed as well.

Advanced FES systems have rotors made of high-strength carbon filaments, suspended by magnetic bearings, and spinning at speeds from 20,000 to over 50,000 rpm in a vacuum enclosure. Such flywheels can come up to speed in a matter of minutes—much quicker than some other forms of energy storage.

Flywheels are not affected by temperature changes, nor do they suffer from memory effect. By a simple measurement of the rotation speed it is possible to know the exact amount of energy stored. One of the problems with flywheels is the tensile strength of the material used for the rotor. When the tensile strength of a flywheel is exceeded, the flywheel will shatter, which is a big safety problem.

Energy storage time is another issue, since flywheels using mechanical bearings can lose 20-50% of their energy in 2 hours. Flywheels with magnetic bearings and high vacuum, however, can maintain 97% mechanical efficiency, but their price is correspondingly higher.

Electric Grid Storage

Grid energy storage is large-scale storage of electrical energy, using the resources of the national electric grid, which allows energy producers to send excess electricity over the electricity transmission grid to temporary electricity storage sites that become energy producers when electricity demand is greater. Grid energy storage is a very efficient storage method, playing an important role in leveling and matching electric power supply and demand over a 24-hour period.

There are several variations of this method, one of which is the proposed grid energy storage called vehicle-to-grid energy storage system, where modern electric vehicles that are plugged into the energy grid can release the stored electrical energy in their batteries back into the grid when needed. Far fetched, yes, but the future will demand many such ingenious approaches, if we are to be energy independent.

In conclusion, there are a number of other energy storage methods such as fuel cells, new types of batteries, superconducting devices, supercapacitors, hydrogen production, and many others under development, so the future looks bright in this area. In practice, however, there are a number of energy storage installations around the world, totaling over 2,100 MW, with the major technologies being:

1. Thermal energy storage is over 1,140 MW
2. Batteries energy storage is over 450 MW
3. Compressed air energy storage is over 440 MW
4. Flywheels energy storage is over 80 MW

Energy storage has many advantages, in addition to its unique potential to transform the electric utility industry by improving wind and solar power variability, availability and utilization. It can contribute to the overall energy independence and environmental cleanup by avoiding the building of new power plants and transmission and distribution networks.

Experts consider energy storage to be the solution to the electric power industry's issues of variability and availability, opening new opportunities for wind and solar power use.

Complexity, safety, price and other restraints, however, will need to be worked out well before any of the energy storage methods become accepted reality for large-scale PV installations.

Notes and References

1. "PVCDROM," C.B. Honsberg and S. Bowden, www.pveducation.org
2. Understanding PV Module Specifications, Justine Sanchez, Jan. 2009.
3. Mora Associates, Internal papers, http://www.moraassociates.com/
4. Optical Degradation Of C-Si Photovoltaic Modules, A. Parretta," G. Graditi
5. Testing the reliability and safety of photovoltaic modules: failure rates and temperature effects," Dr. Govindasamy TamizhMani 2010, "Photovoltaics International, Vol. 8, pp. 146-152.
6. Hot Spot Evaluation of Photovoltaic Modules, Govindasamy (Mani) TamizhMani and Samir Sharma, Photovoltaic Testing Laboratory (ASU-PTL), Arizona State University, Mesa, AZ, USA 85212
7. Five Reasons PV Modules Fail Product Certification Testing
8. Mora Associates, October 2009. http://www.moraassociates.com/publications/0903%20Concentrated%20Solar%20Power.pdf
9. Renewable Energy UK: http://www.reuk.co.uk/First-European-Solar-Power-Tower.htm
10. Environment News Service: http://www.ens-newswire.com/ens/mar2007/2007-03-30-02.asp
11. APS http://www.aps.com/main/green/Solana/About.html
12. Stirling Energy Systems company website: http://www.stirlingenergy.com/
13. National Renewable Energy Laboratory (NREL): dish/stirling report
14. Accommodating high levels of variable generation. NERC, April 2009.

15. Comparison of Degradation Rates of Individual Modules Held at Maximum Power, C.R. Osterwald, J. Adelstein, J.A. del Cueto, B. Kroposki, D. Trudell, and T. Moriarty

16. Adhesion and Thermomechanical Reliability of PV Devices and Modules, by Reinhold H. Dauskardt, Stanford University

17. Common Failure Modes for Thin-Film Modules and Considerations Toward Hardening CIGS Cells to Moisture A "Suggested" Topic Kent Whitfield, MiaSole.

18. Adhesion and Thermomechanical Reliability for PVD and Moddules, Reinhold H. Dauskardt

19. Nevada Solar One official website: http://www.nevadasolar-one.net/the-plant

20. CSP Today: http://social.csptoday.com/index.php

21. SolarPaces. http://www.solarpaces.org/News/Projects/projects.htm

22. Wind Turbine Manufacturing and Assembly. http://www.gamesacorp.com/en/products-and-services/wind-turbines/design-and-manufacture/manufacturing-and-assembly-process.html

23. 2009 global PV cell and module production analysis, Shyam Mehta I GTM research

24. IEEE Spectrum Online: http://www.spectrum.ieee.org/oct08/6851

25. National Renewable Energy Laboratory (NREL): http://www.nrel.gov/csp/troughnet/

26. Photovoltaics for Commercial and Utilities Power Generation, Anco S, Blazev. The Fairmont Press, 2011

27. Solar Technologies for the 21st Century, Anco S Blazev. The Fairmont Press, 2013

Appendix A

Brief History of Solar and PV Power Generation

Let's take some time now for a brief "walk" through history to see how our ancestors harnessed sunlight for their energy needs and what led to the more recent developments in the field. We must go very far back indeed to come to the first human use of sunlight as a "tool."

Solar energy is the foundation of life on Earth because every living being depends on the sun to provide the warmth and energy required to sustain life.

Since the beginning of time our ancestors have used sunlight to keep track of time, stay warm, dry clothes, and grow and dehydrate vegetables and animal products. They knew well the value of sunlight and appreciated its usefulness, since in many cases it meant the difference between a full or empty stomach, and even between life and death.

Early on, people began to realize that sunlight was beneficial to their health. In fact, vitamin D, which is produced in the body when exposed to direct sunlight (prevalent in the UV-B band of the sun spectrum), is a necessary component in maintaining good health. People who are deprived of exposure to sunlight are deficient in vitamin D and exhibit health problems, one of which is Ricketts (softening of the bones).

Without enough sunlight, some people experience a type of depression known as seasonal affective disorder (SAD). On the other hand, the ancients also knew well that excessive exposure to sunlight leads to unwanted effects, such as burned skin, skin discoloration and skin cancer.

The industrial revolution brought more opportunities for the use of the sun's energy because of an increase in knowledge and tools such as mirrors, lenses and optics. The use of these tools was limited to producing enough heat (thermal energy) for some practical purposes.

Early Solar Energy Developments

The scientific drive to capture and harvest the sun's energy dates back to the 18th century, when Sir Edmund Becquerel discovered, during his studies of the solar spectrum, that sunlight can be captured by different materials where it can be converted into useful energy. However, this ingenious observation faded into obscurity in the annals of history not very long after Becquerel's death.

Later in the same century, Mr. Auguste Mouchout, a French mathematics teacher, invented a steam engine which ran on solar energy. He got the attention of the French government and was awarded funds to continue his research. He built the first solar powered steam generator. The scheme worked quite well, and he was able to run a small 0.5 horse power steam engine using only sunlight as a power source. As an indicator of things to come, however, his invention was abandoned when his natural, renewable power source was replaced because coal became less expensive and was easily mined in England's deadly coal mines. The fact that coal is the dirtiest energy source did not stop people then, and it is not stopping them now, even though we are well aware of the consequences of using mass quantities of coal daily.

The first recorded PV conversion of sunlight into electric power is attributed to Sir Willoughby Smith, considered by some to be the father of photovoltaic solar energy. In 1873 he was experimenting with many materials, while looking for suitable candidates for making cables. He noticed that Selenium metal is very sensitive to sunlight, and was able to capture the electric power produced by the first known solar cell-like device.

By the end of the 18th century Sir William Grylls

Adams published a book called *Substitutes for Fuel in Tropical Regions*. Mr. Adams experimented with reflecting sunlight from mirrors to power a small steam engine. The 2.5 horse power engine (the most powerful renewable energy powered mechanical device to date) worked quite well and amazingly enough is in use today under the name of Power Tower. He also did work in which he discovered that illuminating a junction between selenium and platinum produces a photovoltaic effect.

Mr. Charles Tellier was a brilliant Frenchman who is famous for being the inventor of cold storage refrigeration and for outfitting the first steam ship with refrigeration so that meat could be transported by ship. In the 1880s he designed and built the first roof-mounted solar water heater. He simply installed pipes and plates on the roof of his house and was able to heat water for everyday use. However, he abandoned his invention in pursuit of more lucrative refrigeration ventures.

Enter the Americans. In the late 1800s one of the most brilliant mechanical engineers ever, Mr. John Erickson (Swedish immigrant to the States), was the first American renewable energy advocate. In 1877, he described using concave mirrors to gather sun radiation strong enough to run an engine. He also invented "sun engines," which collected solar heat for a hot-air engine. Apparently he was also something of a prophet because he is credited with words that we solar enthusiasts and specialists still often repeat. He essentially said, "In a couple of thousand years the coal fields of Europe will be exhausted, unless we use heat from the sun."

What a prophetic thought! However, he did not know that there is a lot of coal in America, and he did not anticipate the significant role of the other fossil fuels. Most importantly, he could not foresee how fast we will go through the coal and oil fields in a single century, so his 2,000-years prophesy must be revised to several decades before the coal and oil fields are exhausted.

The American solar revolution continued through the 18th and 19th centuries thanks to Mr. Aubrey Eneas, who established the commercial aspect of the solar industry by creating the first solar energy company in the world. The Solar Motor Co. sold their system for approximately $2,000 to Dr. A.J. Chandler of Mesa, Arizona. It was destroyed by a windstorm shortly after it was installed. When their second system was also destroyed by bad weather (a hailstorm) the company went out of business.

Large-scale commercial solar plants (to which this book pays special attention) were initiated by another American visionary, Mr. Henry Willsie, who built large solar thermal plants with nighttime storage in California in the early 1900s, a remarkable vision for those days.

The plants used flat plate collectors to heat water. The water was stored in insulated collectors, then tubes filled with sulfur dioxide ran through the tanks, and were transformed into high-pressure vapor. The vapor was then used to run an engine. This was the first large attempt to use stored heat at night. Unfortunately, the government and state incentives and subsidy programs of those days were not sufficient to support such a great endeavor, and the company went bankrupt.

Another large and most effective solar plant was built by Mr. Frank Shuman. His company, Sun Power Co., built a solar energy system—the largest generator to date. Shuman built the world's first solar thermal power station in Meadi, Egypt (1912-1913). The plant used parabolic troughs to power a 60-70 hp engine that pumped 6,000 gallons of water per minute from the Nile River to adjacent cotton fields. This system included a number of technological improvements, including absorption plates with dual panes separated by a one-inch air space.

Although the outbreak of World War I and the discovery of cheap oil in the 1930s discouraged the advancement of solar energy, Shuman's vision and basic design were resurrected in the 1970s with a new wave of interest in solar thermal energy, when the US Department of Energy (DOE) poured billions into R&D and testing of new solar thermal and PV technologies.

In 1954 Bell Laboratories engineers Calvin Fuller, Gerald Pearson, and Daryl Chaplin were working on something that had nothing to do with solar energy, when they accidentally discovered that silicon is a different material, the special properties of which can be used to make semi-conductor devices.

One thing led to another and soon enough they made the first recorded solar (PV) cell and then a solar panel. Its efficiency was only 6%, but that didn't discourage them and they continued working on the materials and processes, until other US and Japanese companies who were more focused on profit beat them to the solar gold rush of the 1970s.

In the late 1950s the first solar cells were deployed in space. We don't know the efficiency vs. cost of these first solar cells, but we dare guess that the ratio was astronomical. The Vanguard I satellite is credited with the deployment of the first solar powered space communications, using a 0.1 Wp, 100 cm^2 solar panel.

This venture ended with communication failure later (possibly due to deterioration of the silicon solar cells—a which problem still haunts the technology today). Vanguard I satellite, and its malfunctioning solar cells, are still part of the space debris that circles the Earth, and it serves as a daily reminder that our man-made solar technology still has a long way to go on the path to perfection. A number of US, Russian and other solar powered space craft followed, through the years, most of which functioned properly and completed their missions.

The PV Revolution (1963-2013)

PV devices were manufactured since the 1960s, as part of optical and semiconductor devices manufacturing, but the real PV revolution began with the manufacture of the first PV module. See the short list below of the development of the PV industry.

The infamous 1973 OPEC oil embargo shook the American public to the core. Those of us who were adults at the time remember that we suddenly became aware that our way of life was dependent on decisions made by people sitting thousands of miles away who did not have our interests in mind. We suddenly realized that something drastic needed to be done, if we were going to be energy independent.

The picture of long lines at the gas pumps is etched in the American psyche and has been a most powerful dose of reality and a constantly nagging reminder that in order to be free, we need energy independence. So in fact OPEC's embargo has been the engine behind the development of renewable energies in the US and the world. It sparked a great push in Congress and in the hi-tech community to take a close look at alternative fuels, such as wind and solar. A nationwide effort to develop and deploy such technologies was planned and implemented. However, when gas prices went down to pre oil-crisis levels the nation heaved a collective sigh of relief, and once again solar and wind technologies were put on the back burner, and many alternative energy companies went out of business.

On the positive side, during this short-lived 1970-1980 Alternative Energy Renaissance in the US, a large number of solar companies came into existence. Several large companies such as IBM, Motorola and Shell Oil, among others, were leaders in the solar energy R&D for cell and panel manufacturing. A large number of equipment manufacturers took off under the solar banner as well.

Silicon solar cells and panels were the predominant product in those days and the efficiency of the cells was increasing along with the optimism of the companies involved. The US government financed support through DOE and, with the technical assistance of its

national labs, was the driver of the effort to bring solar energy into the US energy market.

Let's look at the solar industry's history.

1963 Sharp Corporation manufactures the first silicon PV modules.

— Japan installs a 242 W PV array on a lighthouse, the world's largest at that time.

1964 NASA launches the first Nimbus spacecraft powered by a 470-watt PV array.

1965 Peter Glaser conceives the idea of the satellite solar power station.

1966 NASA launches the first Orbiting Astronomical Observatory, powered by a 1-kilowatt PV array, in order to provide astronomical data in the ultraviolet and X-ray wavelengths filtered out by the Earth's atmosphere.

1969 The Odeillo solar furnace, located in Odeillo, France, was constructed. This featured an 8-story parabolic mirror.

1970s Dr. Elliot Berman, with help from Exxon Corporation, designs a cost-effective solar cell at $20 a watt. Solar cells are used in navigation warning lights and horns on many offshore gas and oil rigs, lighthouses, railroad crossings and domestic applications.

1972 The French install a cadmium sulfide (CdS) PV system to operate an educational television at a village school in Niger.

— The Institute of Energy Conversion is established at the University of Delaware to perform research and development on thin-film PV and solar thermal systems, becoming the world's first laboratory dedicated to PV research and development.

1973 The University of Delaware builds "Solar One," one of the world's first PV powered residences.

1976 The NASA Lewis Research Center starts installing 83 PV power systems on every continent except Australia.

— David Carlson and Christopher Wronski, RCA Laboratories, fabricate the first amorphous silicon PV cells.

1977 The U.S. Department of Energy launches the Solar Energy Research Institute, a federal facility dedicated to harnessing power from the sun.

— Total PV manufacturing production exceeds 500 kilowatts.

1978 NASA's Lewis Research Center dedicates a 3.5-kilowatt PV system it installed on the Papago Indian Reservation in southern Arizona—the world's first village PV system.

1980 ARCO Solar becomes the first company to produce more than 1 megawatt of PV modules in one year.
— At the University of Delaware, the first thin-film solar cell exceeds 10% efficiency using copper sulfide/cadmium sulfide.

1981 Paul MacCready builds the first solar-powered aircraft (the *Solar Challenger*) and flies it from France to England across the English Channel.

1982 The first PV megawatt-scale power station goes on-line in Hisperia California. It has a 1-megawatt capacity system, developed by ARCO Solar
— Australian Hans Tholstrup drives the first solar-powered car (the Quiet Achiever) almost 2,800 miles between Sydney and Perth in 20 days—10 days faster than the first gasoline-powered car to do so.
— Volkswagen of Germany begins testing PV arrays mounted on the roofs of Dasher station wagons, generating 160 watts for the ignition system.
— The Florida Solar Energy Center's "Southeast Residential Experiment Station" begins supporting the DOE's PVs program in the application of systems engineering.
— Worldwide PV production exceeds 9.3 megawatts.

1983 ARCO Solar dedicates a 6-megawatt PV substation in central California. The 120-acre, unmanned facility supplies the Pacific Gas & Electric Company's utility grid with enough power for 2,000-2,500 homes.
— Solar Design Associates completes a stand-alone, 4-kilowatt powered home in the Hudson River Valley.
— Worldwide PV production exceeds 21.3 megawatts, with sales of more than $250 million.

1984 The Sacramento Municipal Utility District commissions its first 1-megawatt PV electricity generating facility.

1985 The University of South Wales breaks the 20% efficiency barrier for silicon solar cells under 1-sun conditions.

1986 ARCO Solar releases the G-4000—the world's first commercial thin-film power module.

1988 Dr. Alvin Marks receives patents for two solar power technologies he developed: Lepcon and Lumeloid. Lepcon consists of glass panels covered with a vast array of millions of aluminum or copper strips, each less than a micron or thousandth of a millimeter wide.

1989 The first high concentration PV (HCPV) tracker was designed and manufactured by Alpha Solarco, Inc. with the financial help of DOE and with the technical assistance of engineers and scientists of its National laboratories.
— The HCPV tracking system was installed in the Nevada desert, where it was operated successfully over 10 years.

1991 President George Bush redesignates the DOE's Solar Energy Research Institute as the National Renewable Energy Laboratory (NREL).

1992 University of South Florida develops a 15.9% efficient thin-film PV cell made of cadmium telluride, breaking the 15% barrier for the first time for this technology.
— A 7.5-kilowatt prototype dish system using an advanced stretched-membrane concentrator becomes operational.

1993 Pacific Gas & Electric completes installation of the first grid-supported PV system in Kerman, California. The 500-kilowatt system was the first "distributed power" effort.
— Alpha Solarco, with the assistance of DOE and NREL, redesigns the world's first full-scale HCPV tracking system with the latest state-of-the-art CPV cells and Fresnel lenses, which allowed it to achieve a world record of 18% efficiency at the time.

1994 NREL (formerly the Solar Energy Research Institute) completes construction of its "Solar Energy Research Facility," which was recognized as the most energy-efficient of all U.S. government buildings worldwide.
— The first solar dish generator using a free-piston Stirling engine is tied to a utility grid.
— The National Renewable Energy Laboratory develops a solar cell made from gallium indium phosphide and gallium arsenide that becomes the first one to exceed 30% conversion efficiency.

1996 The world's most advanced solar-powered airplane, the Icare, flew over Germany. The wings and tail surfaces of the Icare are covered by 3,000 super-efficient solar cells, with area of 21 m^2.

1998 The remote-controlled, solar-powered aircraft, "Pathfinder" sets an altitude record, 80,000 feet, on its 39th consecutive flight on August 6, in Monrovia, CA.
— Subhendu Guha, a noted scientist with his pioneering work in amorphous silicon, led the invention of flexible solar shingles, a roofing

material and state-of-the-art technology for converting sunlight to electricity.

1999 Construction was completed on 4 Times Square, the tallest skyscraper built in the 1990s in New York City. It incorporates more energy-efficient building techniques than any other commercial skyscraper and also includes building-integrated PV (BIPV) panels on the 37th through 43rd floors on the south- and west-facing facades that produce a portion of the building's power.

1999 Spectrolab, Inc. and NREL develop a PV solar cell that converts 32.3 percent of the sunlight that hits it into electricity. The high conversion efficiency was achieved by combining three layers of PV materials into a single solar cell. The cell performed most efficiently when it received sunlight concentrated to 50 times normal.

— NREL achieves a new efficiency record for thin-film PV solar cells. The measurement of 18.8 percent efficiency for the prototype solar cell topped the previous record by more than 1 percent.

— Cumulative worldwide installed PV capacity reaches 1000 megawatts.

2000 First Solar begins production in Perrysburg, Ohio, at the world's largest PV manufacturing plant with estimated annual capacity of 100MW.

— At the International Space Station astronauts begin installing solar panels on what will be the largest solar power array deployed in space. Each "wing" of the array consists of 32,800 solar cells.

— Sandia National Laboratories develops a new inverter for solar electric systems that will increase the safety of the systems during a power outage.

— Two new thin-film solar modules, developed by BP Solarex, break previous performance records. The company's 0.5-square-meter module achieves 10.8 % conversion efficiency, the highest in the world for thin-film modules of its kind. Its 0.9-square-meter module achieved 10.6% conversion efficiency and a power output of 91.5 watts, the highest power output for any thin-film module in the world.

— A family in Morrison, Colorado, installs a 12-kilowatt solar electric system on its home— the largest residential installation in the United States to be registered with the U.S. Department of Energy's "Million Solar Roofs" program. The system provides most of the electricity for the 6,000-square-foot home and family of eight.

2001 Home Depot begins selling residential solar power systems in three of its stores in San Diego, California. A year later it expands sales to include 61 stores nationwide.

— NASA's solar-powered aircraft Helios sets a new world record for non-rocket powered aircraft: 96,863 feet, more than 18 miles high.

— The National Space Development Agency of Japan, or NASDA, announces plans to develop a satellite-based solar power system that would beam energy back to Earth. A satellite carrying large solar panels would use a laser to transmit the power to an airship at an altitude of about 12 miles, which would then transmit the power to Earth.

— TerraSun LLC develops a unique method of using holographic films to concentrate sunlight onto a solar cell, instead of using Fresnel lenses or mirrors. This capability allows the modules to be integrated into buildings as skylights.

— PowerLight Corporation places online in Hawaii the world's largest hybrid system that combines the power from both wind and solar energy. The grid connected system is unusual in that its solar energy capacity—175 kilowatts—is actually larger than its wind energy capacity of 50 kilowatts.

— British Petroleum (BP) and BP Solar announce the opening of a service station in Indianapolis that features a solar-electric canopy. The Indianapolis station is the first U.S. "BP Connect" store, a model that BP intends to use for all new or significantly revamped BP service stations. The canopy is built using translucent PV modules made of thin films of silicon deposited onto glass.

2002 NASA successfully conducts two tests of a solar-powered, remote-controlled aircraft called Pathfinder Plus. In the first test in July, researchers demonstrated the aircraft's use as a high-altitude platform for telecommunications technologies. Then, in September, a test demonstrated its use as an aerial imaging system for coffee growers.

— Union Pacific Railroad installs 350 blue-signal rail yard lanterns, which incorporate energy saving light-emitting diode (LED) technology with solar cells, at its North Platt, Nebraska, rail yard—the largest rail yard in the United States.

— ATS Automation Tooling Systems Inc. in Canada starts to commercialize an innovative method of producing solar cells, called Spheral Solar technology, based on tiny silicon beads bonded between two sheets of aluminum foil—promises lower costs due to its greatly reduced use of silicon relative to conventional multicrystalline silicon solar cells.

— The largest solar power facility in the Northwest—the 38.7-kilowatt White Bluffs Solar Station—goes online in Richland, Washington.

Then the real PV revolution started around 2004-2006, with Asian manufacturers taking the lead in manufacturing enough PV modules to cover every house roof in the world. Europe and the U.S. bought and installed a lot of PV modules made by the newly formed Chinese companies. So began the latest solar boom-bust cycle of 2007-2012.

As many times before, government subsidies fell from the sky and those who had connections, or were able to come up with flashy proposals got millions of dollars. But this time, the subsidies and incentives did not dwindle within a year or so as it happened several times in the past. Instead they kept on coming, with Germany, Spain and France leading the solar pack—something that never happened before either. The Obama government followed, spending billions of dollars, much of which was simply wasted.

Then the whole solar thing crumbled in a dust cloud when the subsidies were reduced and hundreds of solar companies in Europe and the U.S. went bankrupt.

Nevertheless, a much stronger and resilient solar industry emerged from the dust, and this time it won't go back in the closet as it did so many times before.

Chapter 5

The Environment Today

*Having an energy conversation without talking about climate
is like talking about smoking and not talking about cancer.*
—*Chris Hayes*

OUR WONDERFULLY MADE (DELICATE) ENVIRONMENT

Just stop for a second to think how amazing everything around us is. It all seems so perfectly designed, so carefully put together, and functioning with utmost precision. And yet, it is so delicate and even fragile. It seems as if we changed one single variable even a little bit, the entire picture would collapse.

The Earth is positioned at the right place in the universe, with the perfect equilibrium between the sun's energy coming down to its surface and the amount of energy that is used and radiated back into space. This is an amazing phenomena that has kept life on Earth going for many millennia.

Think for a moment: if the Earth or its atmosphere were slightly out of place, or if the atmosphere were not composed of the exact amounts and types of gasses and particles as it is today, life on Earth would be quite different, or non-existent. This is a marvelous and yet somewhat unstable combination, which needs to remain this way in order to preserve human life and provide us with the comforts we enjoy daily.

There are many miracles around us, but the biggest one by far is the way the sun rises every day to provide light and warm the Earth—essential for every life form. The sun's rays revive the vegetation and provide abundant energy, most of which is simply wasted. We barely notice the sun on its way up in the sky, but imagine for a moment what would happen if it never shone again…surely, devastation of world proportions would soon follow.

The sun's radiation reflected back into space is regulated by the type and amount of gases and particles in the Earth's atmosphere. In the absence of atmosphere, the temperature on Earth would be about –16°C, and life would cease. Carbon dioxide (CO_2) in the atmosphere absorbs the reflected radiation and keeps some of its energy in it, thus warming the Earth enough to keep life at its present levels. This equilibrium maintains the Earth's temperature at ~15-16°C on the average.

CO_2 is absorbed mostly in the 13-19 μm wavelength band, while water vapor (also abundant in the atmosphere) is absorbed in the 4-7 μm wavelength band. Therefore, most outgoing radiation (70%) that escapes into space is in the "window" between 7-13 μm. If that window were filled with other gasses, then the escaping energy would trapped. And if that window were packed with these harmful gasses, temperatures would rise and life on Earth would change drastically, as we have heard time after time lately.

Since our "comfort zone" lies in a very narrow temperature window, and our maximum and minimum temperature tolerance is only slightly wider, we depend on the atmosphere's ability to balance the type and quantity gasses in it, to keep us alive and comfortable.

We certainly live in a borrowed place, on borrowed time—here today and gone tomorrow. Amazingly enough, after all this time of human life on Earth, we are still learning how to live in our "guest house" safely and yet productively. We are learning that many "natural" events (and others out of our control) could modify and even drastically change life as we know it. Just imagine a large meteor hitting Earth and pushing it

Figure 5-1. Sunrise on Earth…

slightly out of orbit. What would that do to gravity (if we survive the impact), the already narrow energy exchange window, the ocean tides, or the sunlight falling on Earth and its effect on living things?

Unthinkable, yes, and yet possible. We are not ready for such an occurrence. We consider it impossible—a one-in-a-billion chance. There are many such dooms-day scenarios—some much more tragic than others. We, however, must not ignore everything that can happen, and instead prioritize the problems and figure what we—as individuals or as a society—can do to alleviate or eliminate those that are under our control.

The list of energy interactions on Earth is long, they are overwhelmingly complex, and scientists are constantly finding new phenomena and revising their previous findings and conclusions. We will keep all these complexities in mind as we go along in this text, while focusing on (man-made) power generation (be it electric, heat, or what not). In parallel, we review the impact of the related technologies and processes on the Earth's overall energy balance, and our troubled natural environment.

The solution to any problem starts with recognizing that we have a problem, learning all we can of its nature and behavior, and then looking for ways to solve it. We all agree that we have a serious environmental problem, or rather many problems, some of which are created by power generation (burning coal, oil, and natural gas). We hear about the disaster caused by climate change every day, so now is the time to take a close look and learn all we can about them—including their origins and possible ways to reduce their negative impact on our environment and life on Earth.

This is what we are trying to do in this text by presenting a detailed account of current power generating sources and related environmental problems.

The Earth Phenomena

We have learned quite a bit about the marvels of our Earth through the centuries, and every new day we learn more and more. This is especially true today, when science and technology are advancing at such a fast pace. Most helpful in deciphering the mysteries around us are hundreds of satellites orbiting the Earth, looking from every possible angle at its oceans, ice caps, rivers, mountains, volcanoes, temperature changes, winds, etc.

The Satellites

Our knowledge and understanding of the events taking place on Earth has increased tremendously dur-

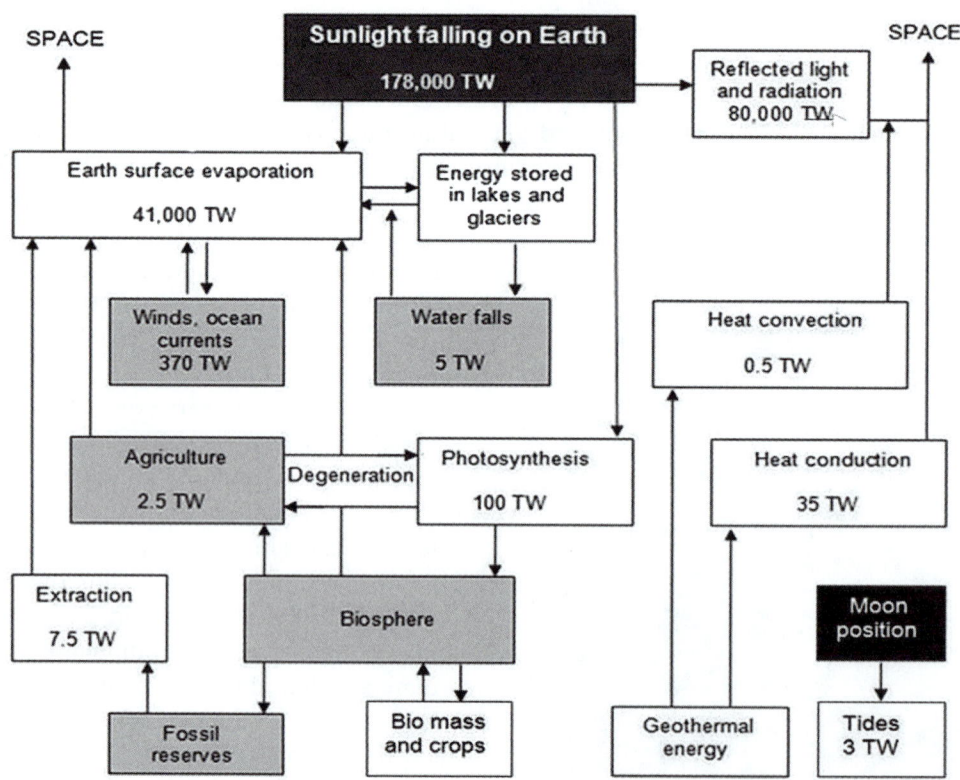

Figure 5-2. The Earth's energy balance and interactions

ing the last 50 years. The greatest contribution to this increase of information are man-made satellites. Hundreds of satellites circle the Earth, to observe the activities below for different purposes, such as environmental or weather monitoring, meteorological observations, map making etc. These are the Earth observation satellites. They operate at altitudes above 600 km, where the air-drag created by Earth's rotation is much less, and its effects are negligible.

The different satellites are designed for different types of detection—visual, thermal, UV, etc.—of different areas of the Earth and see things that we cannot even imagine. They can observe very large areas for extended periods of time, or focus on very small areas to see details that we can only guess.

Weather satellites are designed and equipped to monitor the weather and climate in different areas of the Earth. These meteorological satellites observe a lot of what's going on down here. They see city lights, fires, pollution damage, storms, snow and rain, ice formations, and the ocean currents. This, and many other types of environmental information is continuously collected by the satellites and sent to weather and other stations on Earth for analysis.

Weather satellites have helped in cases such as monitoring volcanic ash clouds, smoke from fires around the world, and other important events that might influence the weather and life on Earth in general.

Some key events, like El Niño, La Niña, and many others and their effects on the world's weather, are monitored daily from satellite images. Other satellites look at air quality, including the state of the ozone layer, and map the ozone hole above us. Hundreds of weather satellites owned by the U.S., Europe, India, China, Russia, and Japan provide continuous observations via visible light, infrared rays, lasers and other tools.

Another set of satellites are designed to assist with the environmental monitoring of the numerous events on Earth. These are set to detect changes in the Earth's vegetation, the atmospheric trace gas content, the overall state of the oceans, the ice cover, and many other variables. By monitoring vegetation changes over time, for example, droughts can be monitored by comparing the current vegetation state to previous averages.

These types of satellites are almost always in sun synchronous orbits. The sun synchronous orbits keep the satellites close to the poles, to get the desired global coverage by maintaining relatively constant geometry to the sun. Other satellites are in "frozen" orbits, which are the closest to a circular orbit that is possible in the gravitational field of the Earth. This way they can keep a constant eye on environmental variables of a defined area of interest.

This colorful field of different satellites at different orbits and altitudes provides a constant 24/7 watch over us and our environment. Observing, measuring, and keeping track of different variables of life on Earth, they provide us with invaluable information.

There is still a lot we don't know, but the body of knowledge is increasing by the day. We get a better and more complete picture of things that we could only guess about not long ago, which helps us in putting the entire puzzle together.

One overwhelming and undeniable conclusion we are reaching is that the Earth and its environment are going through major, unprecedented and unforeseen changes. Man-made activities are contributing to these changes via air and water pollution.

Electricity generated from fossils (coal and natural gas) as well as crude oil products used for transportation and other needs are being blamed for the greatest amounts of emitted pollution in the form of greenhouse gasses (GHG). These gasses are affecting us by creating a number of abnormalities, the final result of which is climate warming and other strange and dangerous effects. In this text we take a close look at all events related to electricity generation and the consequences.

ENVIRONMENTAL CONSIDERATIONS

"The environment is everything that isn't me," summarized our good friend Albert Einstein. While this is a good generalization, more precisely assessed, the environment is everything we see around us, and many things we don't see. Including the unimaginable depths of space and the oceans, and the great heights of the mountains. We also need to consider the tight relation between these, and how smoke from a factory in China would affect the marine life 5 miles under the ocean's surface, or the snow formation in the Himalayas.

Today's educated and responsible person has enough information and is fully aware of the environmental problems, and our responsibility to look at nature and the Earth's environment as an endangered species. Most of us agree that at this day and time, everything that is "not me," has to be treated the way we want to be treated.

There is no doubt that we humans have affected and even hurt the environment during the last 100 years. The damage is undeniable, and it only remains to be determined to what degree the we have harmed our environment and all life forms within it, including ourselves.

We also need to determine how much of this damage is man-made and what part of it is permanent and irreversible. Then, and only then, can we start remediation efforts.

Closing our eyes, or proclaiming helplessness and defeat, is not an option. We need to understand the problems, their sources, the related major issues, then plan and design solutions. There is nothing that can, or should, stop us from acting as responsible 21st century people. We have the understanding and the tools, so all we need is some time to agree on the most appropriate course of action, and implement it. Are we responsible enough to do all this unselfishly, efficiently, and quickly? That is a question that is still unanswered.

Figure 5-3. BP Deepwater Horizon, 2011

Are man-made disasters like the BP oil spill in the Gulf in 2010, or the Dust Bowl phenomena of 1934-1940 (yes, it was a man-made disaster on a large scale) going to happen again? Yes, very likely, but regardless of their nature, we are more prepared to protect life and property. We are more and more aware of the difference between man-made disasters and those which are purely Nature's whim. This gives us more control over the environment, our actions, and our own health and destiny. But how much control do we have?

NOTE: Environmental damage in a broad sense is a misnomer, because the environment only changes from one state to another, all we humans can do is watch and learn. It will surely survive in one form or another, just like it has during the millions of years in the past, where ice and heat cycles have ruled the planet. There have been many ups and downs through the years, and every time the environment has recovered splendidly and in most cases evolved even better. All of this, however, has been at the expense of the living things in it,

Figure 5-4. The Dust Bowl, 1936

since they (we) are much less tolerant to environmental changes.

We humans may not like the upcoming changes and may not even survive them this time around, if this pattern continues, but the environment will survive in one or another form, and it will find its balance with time. Even in the worst of cases, it will recover—even if humanity poisons itself to death and disappears altogether.

Since the serious environmental changes we are presently experiencing might have devastating effects on the human race, we need to consider the preservation of the environment (in its present form and shape) as a prerequisite for sustaining life on Earth, and as a vehicle to our own wellbeing.

Human activities have been blamed for recent negative environmental changes and, since there are no human activities that are absolutely pollution-free and totally environmentally friendly, there will always be some environmental effects and damages brought about by them. We just must be fully aware of consequences and take measures to balance the good and bad activities.

These are the major issues we will be tackling during the 21st century. Since most of the environmental changes and damages are being blamed on the power generation process, we will focus on its effects on the environment and human health in this text.

The goal of this text is to make a detailed analysis of the cradle-to-grave processes of power generation—and how they affect the environment during the different stages. We will allow ourselves to make some conclusions and provide recommendations, but it is you, the reader, who will make the final call. And all of us need to agree on a plan to take the necessary actions.

The Lessons of the Past

In London during the 1800s, at exactly 10:00 PM every night, bells would ring signaling the time when the chamber pots could be emptied directly on the streets. The bells were intended also to warn the unsuspecting pedestrians to watch for slippery stuff on the streets, or nasty, stinky, stuff falling down on their heads from the open windows above.

Imagine the noise of thousands of windows and doors opening at exactly 10:00 PM. And then try to imagine the stinky, gooey liquids flying in the air and running down the streets, pooling at the sidewalks. With no place to go, the goo would sit there and stink until wagon wheels, pedestrian's steps, or rain moved it.

According to the specialists of that day, "there was no other way." They could not even imagine central canalization and waste treatment as we know them today. It was too complex, and too expensive, so why bother? The old ways had worked for a long, long time.

So with the 10:00 PM noise and all-night stench they lived happily (not sure how happily) for many, many years with that man-made localized environmental disaster. Only God knows what the overall effect on human health this miserable lifestyle had at the time, but we are sure it was not small, or positive.

Amazingly, there are places in the world where people live in a similar—and even worse—stink and wretch even now, in the 21st century.

We can draw a parallel between our 1800s London case and what is happening today and imagine what the 22nd century -people will think of us. They will clearly see how disgusting, ignorant, selfish and negligent we have been; not unlike our assessment of the 1800s London crowd. Just like the Londoners of the past, we are "dumping" our sewer, garbage, and many pollutants so indiscriminately that large amounts of stinky, gooey poisons in the soil, air and the oceans are visible all around the world.

"There is no other way," say we, the intelligent 21st century people. Just like the ignorant Londoners of the 1800s we have accepted the unacceptable and have made it a way of life. As ridiculous, shameful and unsustainable as it might be, we still dump our stinky, gooey poisons whenever and in whatever way it suits us.

We are responsible for serious crude oil spills on land and in the oceans, large coal mine scars on the Earth's surface, and miners getting ill and killed underground, and thousands of tons of CO_2, SO_2 NO_2 and other poisons sent into the air daily. Would the 22nd century people add to that, "There are large areas of desert land covered with inferior solar technologies, rusting in the sun, some containing poisons like lead, arsenic, cadmium etc.?"

This is a dangerous and unhealthy affair from which we simply cannot find a way out. "There is no other way," say we, the intelligent, technologically advanced, 21st century people. Just like the ignorant and negligent Londoners in the 1800s, we have accepted the stinky abnormality, thinking that this is all we can do. And just like them we are choking and even dying in our waste, feeling helpless to change it. What a pitiful picture to behold...

Figure 5-5. The future is here...

China and India will account for 25% of the world's power use by year 2025, and doubling during the next decades. With that, pollution will increase proportionally. Things will get even worse after that. The waste will increase rapidly as the billions of inhabitants in developing countries are getting off their bicycles and getting into brand new shiny cars with diesel and gas engines. The need for power increases proportionally with the population growth, so we will pump more oil, and gas fracking will dominate environmental discussions.

The stink will only increase and with it disease and early death of millions. There is nothing we can do to change that. There is no other way...no doubt many Londoners are turning in their graves, overwhelmed by shame. Just like many of us (big business officials, regulators and politicians) will be turning in our graves ashamed by the guilt the future generations will ascribe to our pitiful actions and overwhelming inaction.

In 2012 over 990 micrograms per cubic meter of particles small enough to penetrate the lungs were measured in Beijing. This is almost 40 times the World Health Organization's safe limit. The air is thick with this and other pollutants. Sometimes it is even difficult to see 10 feet ahead, even during daylight hours. How far might they take this situation, and how long can they survive it?

The U.S. is not very far behind in this race. Just walk downtown Los Angeles or Salt Lake City in the summer months. Beijing revisited...

Evolution of Earth's Atmosphere

Life on Earth depends on the atmosphere, so we need to understand it and its changes, including its origins, to understand the rest and be able to control our destiny. The history of our environment—which is all that surrounds us—is long and complex. Gases released from Earth's molten interior created large amounts of gasses, which in turn created the first atmospheric conditions on the young planet.

Our primordial atmosphere consisted mainly of carbon dioxide (CO_2) and nitrogen (N_2), with trace amounts of methane (CH_4), ammonia (NH_3), sulfur dioxide (SO_2), and hydrochloric acid (HCl). Earth's gravity at the time was not sufficient to hold onto the much lighter hydrogen and helium gasses, so they were allowed to escape into space. Water vapor (H_2O) was also a significant atmospheric gas at the time, but eventually the water vapors condensed to form the oceans and other water bodies.

During the first 1-2 billion years, the levels of the prevailing gasses methane, ammonia, and carbon dioxide declined slowly, mostly due to geochemical and biological changes. CO_2 dissolved in the atmospheric water vapors, where it created droplets of carbonic acid (H_2CO_4)—the first acid rain condition—which reacted with the exposed rocks. At the same time, tiny photosynthetic organisms at the ocean surface also took CO_2 from the atmosphere and sequestered the carbon at their death in sedimentary rocks on the ocean's bottom. The air was cleaned from CO_2, with most of it sequestered in surface rocks and ocean sediments, thus poisonous CO_2 was removed from the atmosphere, allowing life forms to emerge.

Atmospheric nitrogen is a nonreactive gas, so it did not react or change much with time. It is still the prevailing gas in our atmosphere, with over 78% by volume of total content.

Not much oxygen (O_2) was present in our primordial atmosphere, but a number of chemical processes, including the photosynthetic ocean organisms, converted CO_2 into oxygen. So, the oxygen content in the atmosphere increased slowly at first, because oxygen is highly reactive, and combined with many minerals and substances.

Only when the planet's surface was fully oxidized did oxygen levels increase substantially, until finally reaching the current concentration of around 20%, which, combined with nitrogen, is enough to support all Earth's life forms, including humans. Our atmosphere, with its large free oxygen content is unique and quite different from all the celestial bodies in our solar system.

Free oxygen, however, is highly reactive and is depleted quickly in a number of reactions, unless replenished. Photosynthesis is the miracle that keeps oxygen at a constant level, which is what we owe our existence and well being to.

Atmospheric Regions

Earth's atmosphere has several distinct layers. At the bottom, extending from the surface to an altitude that varies between about 8 and 18 kilometers, is the troposphere. Some 80 percent of the atmospheric mass lies within the troposphere, and it's in the troposphere that most phenomena of weather occur. The temperature generally declines with increasing altitude, although particular meteorological conditions may alter this trend in the lower troposphere. A fairly sharp transition, the tropo-pause, marks the upper limit of the troposphere.

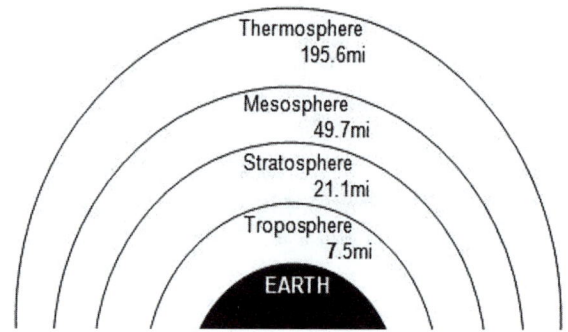

Figure 5-6. Earth's atmosphere

Above it is the stratosphere, which extends upward to some 50 kilometers. The stratosphere is calmer and more stable than the troposphere; only the tops of the largest thunderstorms penetrate into its lowest reaches. The stratosphere contains the well known ozone layer that protects us surface dwellers from harmful ultraviolet radiation.

The formation of ozone (O_3) requires life-produced oxygen, so here's another way in which life helped modify Earth's environment, in this case making the land surface a safe place to live. The absorption of solar ultraviolet radiation causes the stratospheric temperature to increase with altitude. Only the troposphere and stratosphere suffer significant impacts from human activity, and these two layers also play the dominant role in Earth's climate.

Above the stratosphere lie the mesosphere and thermosphere, where the atmosphere thins gradually into the near vacuum of space. There is no abrupt endpoint at which the atmosphere stops and space begins.

THE NATURAL EVENTS

There is a lot talk (and a lot of confusion) today as to the nature of the environmental problems we are experiencing. Man-made events no doubt have caused some changes in the environment, but we should always keep in mind that Nature is much more powerful than man. She can do, and undo, anything and everything man has done, or not done. The power ratio is overwhelmingly in her favor.

So, although we don't doubt that man has done some good and bad (mostly bad) things to the Earth's environment, we should not forget the force of the natural events, and their imminent impact on the environment and the humans living in it.

Here again, we have several groups of people, who look at the same picture, but see different things. Because of that, and/or ignorance, and/or protecting self-interests, in many cases they work against each other.

Let's look at some of the natural events and see how they compare, and relate, to the present-day man-made effects.

The Carbon Cycle

This is one of the most important elements of the subject at hand—power generation vs. environment. Carbon, and the carbon-controlled carbon cycle can be observed in every single thing around us—including our own bodies. Carbon is the source and the foundation of life. Without it, there would be no life on Earth. Period. But lately it has been also threatening our very existence. Partially due to our own fault, partially due to natural effects, the carbon cycle is changing, and our environment is deteriorating by the day. We are just now trying to understand why, and what can be done to reverse the negative trend.

Carbon

Carbon is one the most common elements on Earth, found all around us—including our own bodies. It has some very unusual properties, which make it one of the most versatile elements on Earth.

Its chemical symbol is C, with an atomic number of 6, and atomic weight of 12.0107. It belongs to group 14, period 2 and p-block in the periodic table. Its color varies from black in graphite to colorless in diamonds. It is found in countless combinations with different elements. But the most useful of them all, and one that is of greatest significance to energy production and the environment is its interactions with hydrogen and oxygen.

All fossils contain some combination of carbon and hydrogen (thus appropriately called hydrocarbons), and/or oxygen. The environmentally important substances also contain carbon in combination with hydrogen and/or oxygen (CO_2, CH_4, C_2H_6, etc.).

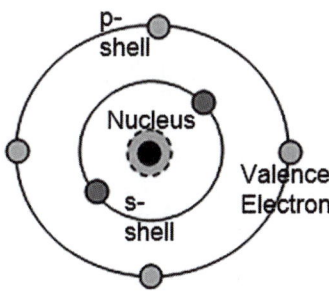

Figure 5-7. Conventional carbon atom representation

The carbon atom has 6 protons and 6 neutrons in its nucleus, and 6 electrons in the shells orbiting around it. The innermost shell "s" contains 2 electrons, which orbit non-stop around the nucleus and do not participate in any reactions. The outermost shell "p" contains the remaining 4 electrons, which also orbit non-stop around the nucleus, but are available to enter in chemical reactions under certain conditions.

The important thing here, and what distinguishes carbon from most other elements, is that all 4 outer electrons are capable of chemically reacting with a large number of elements. The reactions with hydrogen are the most abundant and spectacular. They are the foundation of all hydrocarbons, including fossil fuels (crude oil and natural gas).

On closer examination, things look a bit different and more complicated. Contrary to the conventional carbon atom representation in Figure 5-8, the four electrons' orbits are not planar, but are rather spread in the x-y-z planes.

Imagine a tripod-like structure, in the center of which there is the nucleus, surrounded by a circular shell with two electrons orbiting in it. The four legs around the nucleus are the outer electron orbits. These orbits are actually in a shape of the number 8, with one electron in each orbiting around the nucleus in a non-symmetrical number-8 shape pattern.

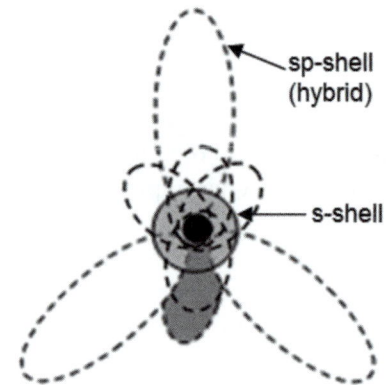

Figure 5-8. Electron distribution in a carbon atom

What we have is an electron configuration of the type:

$$\underset{1s}{\underline{2}} \quad \underset{2sp^3}{\underline{1}} \quad \underset{2sp^3}{\underline{1}} \quad \underset{2sp^3}{\underline{1}} \quad \underset{2sp^3}{\underline{1}} \quad \text{- \# of electrons}$$
$$\text{- shell order}$$

The inner shell "s-shell" still has 2 electrons, while the outer shell is actually a mixture (hybrid) between the inner and outer shells, so that the electrons orbit at an intermediate energy level "sp," located between the "s" and "p" shells. The hybrid "sp" shell is a 1 to 3 mix of the inner "s" shell and the outer "p" shell, so the electrons have approximately 75% of the "p" shell energy level.

Nevertheless, they are still considered valence electrons and are willing and able to enter into chemical reactions with a number of elements, as and when the conditions permit.

In all cases, and in all chemical reactions carbon enters in (voluntarily), all 4 electrons take an active part and play a key role. A special branch of the chemistry sciences—organic chemistry—deals with the amazing properties of carbon, and the countless reactions it can enter in, as well as the properties of the resulting thousands of different compounds created in the process.

For our purposes, we must point out herein that the many compounds made from carbon are good and beneficial to our health—products that we use in our daily lives as food, medications, cosmetics, etc. But an equal number of the carbon creations are toxic and otherwise harmful to the environment and human health. Some of these, including coal, oil and natural gas, are used in power generation, where they form another set of toxic and polluting gasses and substances that are harmful to the environment and all life on Earth.

Methane, carbon dioxide, and carbon oxide are some of the worst polluters, emitted in large quantities

during the production and use (burning) of fossils. They are blamed for all kinds of environmental problems, human suffering and illnesses. The controversial environmental contamination and life-threatening global warming, with their great and long-lasting negative effects, are in the news daily, and on the forefront of the environmental movement.

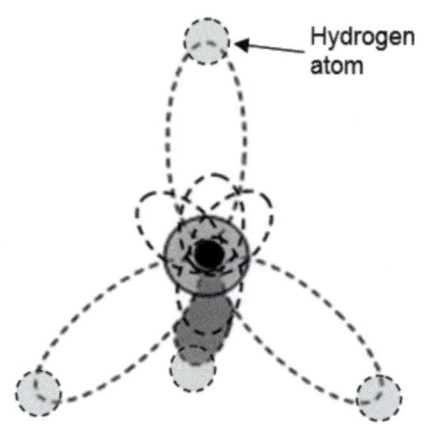

Figure 5-9. Methane formation

Methane is the simplest of all carbon-related elements, where four hydrogen atoms join with the four valence electrons of the carbon atom. This reaction forms the chemical compound methane, CH_4. This happens only under the right circumstances—temperature, pressure, and time—as is the case with the fossils' formation billions of years ago.

While on its own, methane is less harmful than carbon dioxide, it is unstable and readily decomposes to carbon dioxide:

$$CH_4 + 2O_2 \rightarrow CO_2 + 2H_2O$$
$$\text{1 part} \qquad \text{3 parts}$$

This is the biggest problem with methane gas, which is the main component of natural gas. It is easily converted into carbon dioxide, during which process 1 gram of methane becomes almost 3 parts of carbon dioxide, thus multiplying the negative effects of the GHG process by a factor of 3.

Raw methane gas is found escaping from natural gas wells, distribution pipelines, and point-of-use locations. This uncontrolled release is increasing, simply because the production and use of natural gas has been drastically increased during the last several years. It is also expected to increase further in the near future, thus increasing the air pollution and aggravating the related environmental, health, and global warming issues.

Carbon dioxide is officially considered the most dangerous gas for our environment today. It is blamed for the rapid increase of global climate warming, due to its role in disrupting the natural thermal exchange processes.

$$C + O_2 \rightarrow CO_2$$

It is also blamed for significant increase of damaging acidification due to the formation of carbonic acid:

$$CO_2 + H_2O \Leftrightarrow H_2CO_3$$

Thus created carbonic acid causes all kinds of damage to buildings and other structures in affected areas by dissolving some of the materials these are made of.

Carbon oxide is formed during incomplete burning (in oxygen-poor ambient) of carbon containing materials (usually coal, or wood). It is considered a serious poison, and is blamed for the death of many people and wild life.

$$2CO_2 \Leftrightarrow 2CO + O_2$$

NOTE: Some of the above descriptions and graphics of the carbon atomic structure and reactions are unconventional, but they are the most accurate and practical way to visualize the very important characteristics and behavior of the carbon atom and its products.

Carbon Use

Carbon the building block of life, and major part of our daily lives. It is all around us; in the air we breath, in the water we drink, in the foods we eat, in our houses, our furniture, cars, shoes, clothing, and basically in almost everything we breath, touch, eat, and use.

Just take a look at some of the chemical compounds it can create:

CO, CO_2, CO_3^{2-}, COS, CS_2, $CClN$, CCl_2O, CCl_2F_2, CCl_3F, CCl_4, CF_2O, CF_4, CN^-, CNS^-, $CHCl_3$, CHI_3, CHN, CHO_3^-, CH_5N, CH_6N^+, CH_2Cl_2, CH_2F_2, CH_2O, CHO_2, CH_2O_3, CH_3Cl, CH_3I, CH_4, CH_4N_2O, CH_4O, $C_2O_4^{2-}$, $C_2HBrClF_3$, $C_2HCl_3O_2$, $C_2HF_3O_2$, C_2H_2, $C_2H_2O_4$, C_2H_3Cl, $C_2H_3ClO_2$, C_2H_3N, $C_2H_3O_2^-$, C_2H_4, $C_2H_4Br_2$, $C_2H_4Cl_2$, C_2H_4O, $C_2H_4O_2$, $C_2H_4O_2$, C_2H_5Cl, C_2H_5NO, $C_2H_5NO_2$, C_2H_6, C_2H_6O, $C_2H_6O_2$, C_2H_6S, C_2H_7NO, $C_2H_8N_2$, $C_3H_3O_3^-$, C_3H_4, $C_3H_4O_3$, $C_3H_5N_3O_9^-$, $C_3H_5O_2^-$, C_3H_6, C_3H_6O, $C_3H_6O_2$, $C_3H_6O_3$, C_3H_7Cl, $C_3H_7NO_2$, $C_3H_7NO_2S$, $C_3H_7NO_3$, $C_3H_7O_2$, C_3H_8, C_3H_8O, $C_3H_8O_3$, C_3H_9N, $C_3H_{10}N^+$, $C_4H_2O_4^{2-}$, $C_4H_4N_2O_2$, $C_4H_4O_4$, $C_4H_4O_5^{2-}$, $C_4H_5N_3O$, C_4H_6, $C_4H_6NO_4^-$, $C_4H_6O_5$, C_4H_8, $C_4H_8N_2O_3$, $C_4H_8O_2$, $C_4H_9NO_3$, C_4H_{10}, $C_4H_{10}O$, $C_5H_5N_5$, $C_5H_5N_5O$, $C_5H_6N_2O_2$, $C_5H_8NO_4^-$, $C_5H_9NO_2$, $C_5H_{10}N_2O_3$, $C_5H_{11}NO_2$, $C_5H_{11}NO_2S$, C_5H_{12}, $C_6H_4Br_2$, $C_6H_4Br_2$, $C_6H_4Br_2$, $C_6H_5NO_2$, C_6H_6, C_6H_6O, C_6H_7N, $C6H_8N^+$, $C_6H_8O_6$, $C_6H_8O_7$, $C_6H_{10}N_3O_2^+$, $C_6H_{12}O_6$, $C_6H_{13}NO_2$, $C_6H_{13}NO_2$, C_6H_{14}, $C_6H_{15}N_2O_2^+$, $C_6H_{15}N_4O_2^+$, $C_7H_5NO_3S$, $C_7H_5N_3O_6$, $C_7H_5O_2^-$, $C_7H_6O_2$, $C_7H_6O_3$, C_7H_8, C_7H_{16}, $C_8H_6O_4$, C_8H_8, C_8H_{10}, $C_8H_{10}N_4O_2$, C_8H_{18}, $C_8H_{18}O$, $C_9H_8O_4$, $C_9H_{11}NO_2$, $C_9H_{11}NO_3$, C_9H_{20}, $C_{10}H_8$, $C_{10}H_{14}N_2$, $C_{10}H_{22}$, $C_{11}H_{11}N_2O_2$, $C_{12}H_{22}O_{11}$, $C_{16}H_{32}O_2$, $C_{18}H_{36}O_2$, $C_{27}H_{46}O$, C_{12}, C_{14}, C_{18}, C_{60}.

This is only a very, very small number of products of which carbon is a part. These and thousands of other carbon compounds comprise, or are found in, fuels, lubricants, plastics, textiles, paints, solvents, medical equipment, medicines, cosmetics, and on and on the list goes. As a matter of fact, it is even hard to imagine an area of our lives which is totally void of carbon related materials.

The Carbon Cycle

Carbon is also a major constituent in the carbon cycle of our Earth; a very important biological, geological, chemical, and physical phenomena which regulates the generation and consumption of carbon in all natural, and some man-made systems. It basically determines and controls the exchange of carbon among the biosphere, pedosphere, geosphere, hydrosphere, and atmosphere of the Earth.

In combination with the nitrogen and water cycles, the carbon cycle creates and controls a number of daily events that help the Earth support its life systems—flora and fauna—including humans. The carbon cycle basically consists of the movement of carbon and carbon-related species in and out of the different environmental systems, including its reuse and recycling throughout the biosphere.

Figure 5-10a and 5-10b represent the movement of carbon (and carbon species) between land, ocean and the atmosphere in billions of tons of carbon equivalent each year, where the global carbon cycle is divided into the major reservoirs of carbon interconnected by pathways of exchange in the atmosphere, the terrestrial biosphere, the oceans, (including dissolved inorganic carbon and living and non-living marine biota), the sediments (including fossil fuels, fresh water systems and non-living organic material, such as soil carbon), and the Earth's interior (including carbon from the Earth's mantle and crust.)

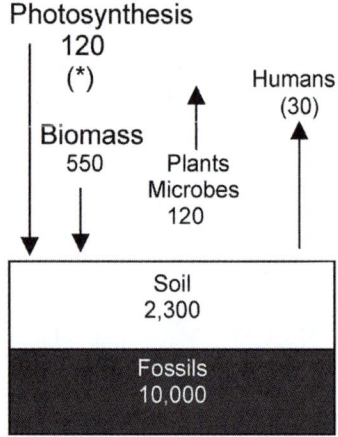

a. The land carbon cycle

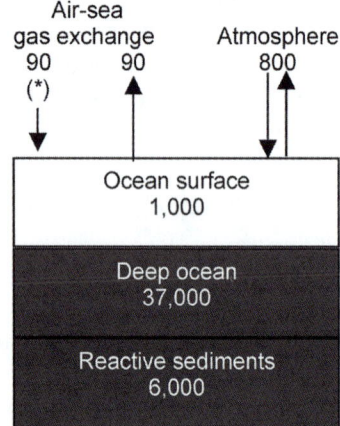

b. The sea carbon cycle

Figure 5-10. The carbon cycle on land and in the oceans (billions of tons)

*Human contribution to the overall environmental gasses exchange.

These carbon stores interact with the other components through geological processes, where the carbon exchanges between reservoirs occur as the result of various chemical, physical, geological, and biological processes. The ocean contains the largest active pool of carbon near the surface of the Earth. The natural flows of carbon between the atmosphere, ocean, and sediments is fairly balanced, so that carbon levels would be roughly stable without human influence.

Global Carbon Budget

The global carbon budget is the balance of the exchanges (incomes and losses) of carbon between the carbon reservoirs or between one specific loop (e.g., atmosphere ↔ biosphere) of the carbon cycle. An examination of the carbon budget of a pool or reservoir can provide information about whether the pool or reservoir is functioning as a source or sink for carbon dioxide.

Figure 5-10a shows the human contribution of 30 GT/year of carbon species in the atmosphere, which might seem small compared with the larger numbers of the natural carbon reservoirs. The man-made carbon emissions, however, represent the annual gas release, which when multiplied by 50 (for the last 50 years of rapid industrial development) produces an impressive 1,500 gigatons total of carbon related accumulation in the atmosphere. This large amount of carbon gases is overwhelming the natural gas exchange and overall environmental balance; thus, we see signs of drastic changes coming upon us…unless we reduce the amount of carbon released in the atmosphere.

But even if we stop all emissions today, it might already be too late, because some of the cumulative effects are long-lasting, and some of the damages are irreversible. Since we are certain that the human, carbon release-related, activities will not be reduced anytime soon, we are certain that the damage will continue, and get worse with time, as the developing countries increase fossils use for energy generation.

CO_2 Lifetime

We agree that there is a lot of CO_2 in the atmosphere. It is emitted by the coal and gas power plants, trucks, cars, etc. and most of it flows up in the air. Some of it remains in the area, while the rest is blown by the winds and taken to far-away places. Then what? How long does it stay suspended in the air?

There is a great deal of confusion on this subject. This is because there are multiple physical and biological processes involved in the removal of CO_2 from the air. The problem is that they behave differently, and at different rates in different situations, depending on local conditions.

Another confusion comes from the fact that the leading scientists—including the Intergovernmental Panel on Climate Change (IPCC)—have not made up their minds regarding the lifetime of CO_2. One report defined the lifetime of CO_2 as 50-200 years, while later it was reduced to 5 years. So which one is it—5 or 200 years? The difference is so great that we cannot help but wonder if there is any science to back these findings, or if these numbers were just plucked from someone's head.

And to make things even worse, the final report changed the language entirely, saying that carbon dioxide cycles between atmosphere, oceans, and land biosphere, so its removal from the atmosphere involves a range of processes with different time scales. As a result, 20% of it may stay in the atmosphere for many thousands of years. The lifetime range was increased from five to many thousands of years. This tells us that we know as much as these people do. Which is almost nothing.

The changes in the Summary for Policymakers have a lot to do with increasing the confusion on the issue, since many politicians and the media rely on it for reliable information. The exceptionally wide range of estimates unfortunately contributes to the confusion worldwide.

New studies attempt to clear the confusion over the lifetime of CO_2. The main CO_2 removal from the air processes are: a) vegetation growth, b) reactions with calcium carbonate in the oceans, c) reactions with igneous rocks like granite and basalt, and d) reactions with other gasses and substances in the atmosphere.

Vegetation absorbs CO_2 the fastest, but it's not well understood, since additional plant growth (and decomposition) also release CO_2, depending on local climate, so it is possible that the combination of all these natural processes produce as much CO_2 as is absorbed.

The oceans are credited with only a limited amount of CO_2 absorption, since sooner or later the ocean water reaches an equilibrium state with the atmosphere and can't absorb any more. Because the oceans have done this for a long time, it is likely that the saturation limit was reached long ago. At that point only the two longest duration effects can be attributed to CO_2 absorption; reactions with calcium carbonate in ocean sediments, and that in igneous rock. The calcium carbonate reactions take a very long time, so it is estimated that it will take tens of thousands of years to remove half of the dissolved CO_2 from the ocean waters. At the same time, igneous rocks' reaction takes even longer—up to hundreds of thousands of years.

Using the "half-life" model is not very practical in the case of carbon dioxide, because the physical system has too many variables and components, so a single atmospheric lifetime is not applicable. This is analogous to radioactive waste, where a variety of different radionuclides with a wide range of half-lives would not allow the determination of one single lifetime estimate. Similarly, the half-life (lifetime) of CO_2 in the atmosphere is too complex a variable to be expressed in exact terms or numbers.

There are published estimates that CO_2 would stay in the air for up to 200 years, but this isn't accurate or proven. We know that the natural geological processes that determine the return of CO_2 back into the Earth could take tens of thousands to hundreds of thousands of years. At the same time, the ocean and the biosphere are dependent on how much CO_2 is emitted into the at-

mosphere, which makes the CO_2 lifetime also a function of the amount of CO_2 gas emitted in the first place.

The conclusion we can make from all this is that a short-term (years) removal of CO_2 from the air by plants and the ocean is not a dominant factor in reducing CO_2 quantities. Instead, it seems that different chemical processes of long duration (up to hundreds of thousands of years) are most likely what control the process. It also seems probable that a certain percentage of emitted CO_2 will remain in the atmosphere forever.

Table 5-1. CO_2 emissions per kWh generated

Fuel	CO_2 emissions in kg per kWh
Coal	0.37
Gasoline	0.27
Light Oil	0.26
Diesel	0.24
LPG	0.24
Natural Gas	0.23
Crude Oil	0.26
Kerosene	0.26
Wood	0.39
Peat	0.38
Lignite	0.36
Bio energy	0

Obviously, there is a lot of CO_2 generated during the conversion of fossils (any and all fossils and their derivatives) into electricity. A simple calculation shows that a 1.0 GW coal-fired power plant will emit 370 tons of CO_2 per hour (1,000,000kWh x 0.37kg). This amounts to 8,880 tons per day and to 3.2 million tons per annum. This, multiplied by the thousands of such power plants around the world would bring the amount of CO_2 emitted in the atmosphere annually into many billions of tons. This is billions with a B. A very large number for our relatively small Earth and its fragile environment.

NOTE: Carbon dioxide emissions can be calculated as

$$Q_{CO2} = c_f/h_f \times C_{CO2}/C_m$$

where

Q_{CO2}	=	specific CO_2 emission (CO_2/kWh)
c_f	=	specific carbon content in the fuel (kgC/kg$_{fuel}$)
h_f	=	specific energy content (kWh/kg$_{fuel}$)
C_m	=	specific mass carbon (kg/mol carbon)
C_{CO2}	=	specific mass carbon dioxide (kg/mol CO_2)

NOTE: There is 55-75% heat lost during power generation which is not included, but must be considered in the final calculations.

As total worldwide emissions do not seem to be decreasing, we must understand and agree that as more CO_2 is emitted, more will remain behind in the atmosphere for a long, long time. Assuming that 20% of emitted CO_2 stays in the atmosphere forever, and that the ocean and biosphere are already saturated, then we are faced with ever increasing levels of CO_2 which quantity cannot be reduced by the natural cycle. If so, then the only option is to make sure that we take serious steps to de-carbonize our world ASAP.

We must realize that it might be too late to return to pre-industrial CO_2 concentrations even if we stopped emitting CO_2 today. The present state of the art also would not allow us to neutralize or absorb the great generated quantities of CO_2 on a daily basis, so short of developing some exceptional (extremely efficient and cost-effective) absorption technology, we will be witnessing rapid increase in CO_2 levels, and must be ready to accept the consequences.

Radically altering land use to absorb as much CO_2 from the atmosphere as possible is another, albeit unlikely, possibility to combat extreme CO_2 increase.

Last, the quoted above CO_2 lifetimes arbitrarily stop calculating the global warming potential (GWP) of CO_2 at around 100 years. But if the CO_2 lifetime were calculated over geologic time, it would increase by 50-100x, at the same time lowering the GWP of all other GHGs by equal amounts. This only confirms the importance of considering and implementing immediate CO_2 emissions reduction, if we are to avoid great climate calamity in the near future.

The Other Major Events
Water Vapor

There is a lot of water vapor in the atmosphere. It is most likely the highest concentration of any gas species in the lower altitudes of some regions of the world—and surely over the oceans. Since the oceans cover 2/3 of the Earth's surface, it is amazing that so few people are aware of the effects (including global warming) of such large quantities of gas around us.

The distribution of atmospheric water vapor, which is confirmed as significant greenhouse gas (GHG), varies across the globe. Equatorial and tropical latitudes are especially saturated by water vapor, especially during the respective summer months. This is especially evident in south Asia, where monsoon thunderstorms sweep the water vapor gas some 2 miles above the Earth's surface for extended periods of time.

Common sense tells us that water vapor is abundant, since in many cases, and unlike the other gasses, it is visible in the form of clouds. It also lets us know its presence in the sky by dumping buckets of rain or truck loads of snow on our heads. So how can we miss including water vapor in our GHG and global climate change calculations?

The excuse scientists give is that the measurement methods have not been precise enough until now, to provide reliable data, because ground- and the old space-based instruments, could not measure water vapor at all altitudes in Earth's troposphere (1-10 miles above ground.)

Now we finally have solid proof that increase in water vapor level is a major cause of climate change. NASA satellites have been giving some data about the heat-trapping effect of water vapor in the air, thus officially validating its role as a critical component of climate change. The scientists still don't know the exact extent of its contribution to global warming, so the debate will continue, but at least we will now include it in the discussions.

Water vapor has a heat-amplifying effect, which is powerful enough to double the global climate warming caused by increased levels of GHGs in the atmosphere. There are also scientific experiments that confirm the estimates of different climate models. Data from the Atmospheric Infrared Sounder (AIRS) on NASA's Aqua satellite continuously measure the humidity (water vapor concentration in the air) in the lowest 10 miles of the atmosphere.

AIRS is the first space instrument able to distinguish differences in the amount of water vapor at all altitudes within the troposphere. AIRS data are used to observe how atmospheric water vapor reacts to shifts in surface temperatures, from which changes the average global strength of the water vapor feedback can be calculated and modeled. When combined with surface-based measurements of humidity and temperature, the satellite data are used to build models of the interactions between water vapor, GHGs, and other gases in the atmosphere at different locations on Earth.

NASA's data are now filling the gaps in the global warming theories, by estimating the magnitude of water vapor feedback. It has been determined that increasing water vapor concentration leads to warmer temperatures, which in turn generate more water vapor into the air, thus creating a vicious cycle of water vapor and warming effects.

No doubt, the interactions are complex, but now we know that water vapor plays a significant role in climate change cycle. There is a big difference between the GHG effects in dry air vs. those in air that is saturated by water vapor. The water vapor amplifies the warming effect of other GHGs, the increase of which allows more water vapor to enter and remain longer in the atmosphere.

Specifically, the team found that if Earth warms by an additional 1.8 degrees Fahrenheit, the associated increase in water vapor will trap an extra 2 Watts of energy per square meter. Keeping in mind that the Earth's surface is approximately 510,072,000 square kilometers, or more than 510 trillion square meters, we see that the increase is equivalent to over 1.0 trillion kW of energy. This is an enormous amount of energy (heat mostly) that water vapor traps, thus increasing the global warming with time. NASA scientists now think the tropospheric water vapor feedback is an extraordinarily strong event, capable of doubling global warming, compared to carbon dioxide acting alone.

This is another confirmation of the previous model predictions that Earth's GHGs will contribute to a temperature rise of a few degrees by the end of the 21st century. The only new component in this estimate is the large presence, numerous effects, and great influence, of water vapor in the environmental processes.

So, it is now confirmed that water vapor is one of the biggest contributors to atmospheric phenomena that influence global warming. Its role has been underestimated and even ignored until now, but considering the vastness of the world's oceans and other water bodies, which evaporate huge amounts of water non-stop, we now must rethink and reconsider the role of water vapor in all this.

Including global water vapor in our climate change measurements and prognosis will give us a much better picture of what is going on in the atmosphere and what to expect in the future. One thing is for sure, the role of water vapor in global warming is much bigger than we previously thought.

The good news, in addition to the fact that now we can measure the water content in the troposphere precisely, is that the volume of global water evaporation in the atmosphere is fairly constant, which would make the estimates and predictions easier and more accurate. Or would it...?

Earth's Magnetosphere

One amazing thing that few people are aware of—although their lives literally depend on it—is the presence of a magnetosphere around our Earth. A magnetosphere is an area of space near our Earth that has magnetic properties in which charged particles (such as high velocity photons and energetic particles radiate from the sun) collide and are controlled by the force of the magnetic field.

The Earth's magnetosphere is the outer layer of the ionosphere, where in places the ionosphere and magnetosphere blend, and in places they are separate.

Near the surface of the Earth, the magnetic field lines are symmetrical and parallel and resemble those of an ideal magnetic dipole, while farther away, the field lines are significantly chaotic and distorted by external currents, such as collisions with charged particles hurling at Earth with the solar winds. Over the Earth's equator, the magnetic field lines become almost horizontal, then return to connect back again at high latitudes, while at high altitudes, the magnetic field is significantly distorted.

Looking at a 24-hour span:

a. On the dayside of the Earth, the magnetic field is significantly compressed by the solar wind to a distance of approximately 40,000 miles. The Earth's bow shock is about 11 miles thick and is located about 56,000 miles from the Earth.

The magnetopause exists at a distance of several hundred kilometers off the surface of the earth, and has been compared to a sieve, as it allows particles from the solar wind to enter our atmosphere. Kelvin–Helmholtz instabilities occur when large swirls of plasma travel along the edge of the magnetosphere at a different velocity from the magnetosphere, causing the plasma to slip past. This results in magnetic reconnection, and as the magnetic field lines break and reconnect, solar wind particles are able to enter the magnetosphere.

b. On the night side of the earth, the magnetic field is relaxed, since the sun's influence is reduced, and extends in the magneto-tail at over 3,900,000 miles in length, and is the primary source of the polar aurora; the amazingly colorful and pretty polar lights we see in the northern hemisphere.

So in practical terms, the magnetosphere with all its components, complex composition and strange behavior is a powerful shield that filters some of the most harmful energetic particles coming from the sun, space, and other celestial bodies in the universe. Only harmless, lower power particles can go through, thus we get relatively low power sunlight and mild weather patterns.

Without this shield, the amount and intensity of the solar winds and the matter from its great explosions—which emit particles that are thousands of degrees hot and travel at thousands of miles per hour—would damage the Earth and all life on it.

This is an amazing and quite spectacular phenomena, without which we would not even be here; yet, how many people are aware of its presence? We don't see many hands up in the air…

The Rain Forest

Oxygen is the engine of life. Without it there would be no life on Earth. Period. If there is not enough oxygen, or if it is contaminated with significant amount of impurities, life would be full of illness. Ninety percent of our nutritional energy comes from oxygen, and only 10 percent is derived from the food we ingest. Oxygen is the supreme element, the primary nutrient without which life couldn't exist. We can live without food for weeks and without water for between three to seven days, but without oxygen we have between 3 and 5 minutes. So, how important is it?

Yes, we all know this, but did you know that all the oxygen generated by the enormous Amazon rain forest—which is considered as the greatest oxygen generator in the world—is re-absorbed back into the vegetation and soil as soon as it is emitted. That's the end of our hope for clean air, you'd think. But not so fast, the amazing natural process doesn't stop there. Instead, it takes the forest's soil in the runoff waters and carries the oxygen locked in the oxygen rich substances to the oceans. Plankton in the nearby waters feeds on the substance and releases the oxygen in it.

Regardless of how the oxygen is regenerated, the rain forest is essential to its supply. Nevertheless, we are destroying it at a fast pace, and with that we are reducing its capability to provide us with oxygen. Yes, it is a long-term problem, but it is something that should not be ignored, because that is like cutting our own oxygen supply. Without enough oxygen we would not be able to even breath, let alone enjoy life to the fullest.

Volcanoes

Inside the earth, there are many volcanoes, which sometimes cause great damage upon eruption, which is the only thing we see and know about them. But the volcanoes also do a lot of good. Most of them emit gasses, which are blown into the sea, where they feed sea life, including large sea plankton colonies, which also gener-

ate large amounts of oxygen.

Would you believe that half of the oxygen we breath every day is generated by the different types of plankton in the world's oceans, mostly via the above described processes? Unfortunately, we cannot see these processes, but the satellites orbiting Earth do see and document these events…every day, day after day.

Lightning

Now think of lightning. Over 3 billion lightning strikes a day hit the Earth's surface. This is a lot of energy, created by the friction of water and ice particles in the clouds. The friction creates an electric charge, and when the charge grows large enough it is discharged, directing its enormous energy towards the nearest object in its path.

The temperature of a thunderbolt is 5 times hotter than the sun, and there is as much power in it, that if captured efficiently, it would power a city like Denver, CO, for 10 hrs. This enormous amount of energy, discharged into a small area, is why people are killed and trees put on fire when hit by lightning.

During the electrical discharge, the enormous electrical voltage and current splits the N_2 molecules in the air. The free N molecules get quickly oxidized into nitrates. The nitrates are then dissolved by the raindrops and fall onto Earth to feed the plants as a heavenly fertilizer. Thirteen thousand tons of nitrates are dissolved and fall with the rain on the rain forest alone. These are essential for the survival of life, for they feed the vegetation, which shelters and feeds the wild animals.

Wild Fires

Now let's look at wild fires from a different perspective. Fires basically destroy the old, but provide an opportunity for new life. The fires renew the forest by burning trees and animal remains, and deposit carbon-rich ashes on the ground, where new vegetation can feed on them.

Nine tenths of the forest's energy is stored in the leaves and tissues of the trees themselves. The forest floor is a porous mass that prevents minerals and nutrients from being washed away and lost. As soon as a tree falls, or a creature dies, decomposers begin to turn it into a food source and mulch. The vegetation to renew the cycle quickly absorbs the nutrients that are released. Forest fires help the renewal process by accelerating the normal aging processes, whereby a tree can be burned in minutes, instead of slowly decomposing for years. This way its nutrients are delivered to the soil quickly and efficiently.

This is the tightest, most efficient ecosystem in nature. Damaging one part of the system, however, like destroying too much of the rain forest, can bring a negative change to, and even destruction of, the entire system.

There are amazingly high numbers of wild fires around the world. We cannot see them all, but the satellites do. A satellite picture of the Earth during wild fire season makes it look like it is burning from end to end. About 19 million square miles are burned around the world annually according to their observations and calculations.

Wildfires occur on every continent except Antarctica. Wildfires are a common occurrence in Australia especially during the long hot summers usually experienced in the southern regions such as Victoria. Due to Australia's hot and dry climate, wildfires (commonly referred to as bushfires in Australia) pose a great risk to life and infrastructure during all times of the year, though mostly throughout the hotter months of summer and spring. In the United States, there are typically between 60,000 and 80,000 wildfires each year, burning 3 to 10 million acres of land depending on the year.

Over 200,000 acres are burned every day around the world, or over 150 acres every minute. Experts also estimate that 130 species of plants, animals, and insects are lost every day. Today, more than 20% of the Amazon rainforest has been destroyed and is gone forever. The land is being cleared for agricultural uses by fire, and some forests are being burned to make charcoal to power industrial plants.

There were an estimated ten million Indians living in the Amazonian Rainforest five centuries ago. Today there are less than 200,000. More than half of the world's rainforests have been destroyed by fire and logging in the last 50 years. At the current rate of destruction, the last remaining rainforests could be destroyed during the next 40-50 years.

Fossil records and human history contain accounts of wildfires, as wildfires can occur in periodic intervals. Wildfires can cause extensive damage, both to property and human life, but they also have various beneficial effects on wilderness areas. Some plant species depend on the effects of fire for growth and reproduction, although large wildfires may also have negative ecological effects.

The Oceans' Air-conditioning System

Now here is something that very few of us know. It involves special properties of water during freezing. The majority of this event happens at very cold weather at the ice-covered shores of Antarctica. Every winter, the ocean waters at the costline start freezing. Salty ocean water resists freezing, but at temperatures below –110 degrees F (40 degrees lower than the North Pole) the water finally gives in.

During the slow freezing process, the water does something unexpected. The freezing ice crystals release brine, which is squeezed from them like from a sponge. Brine runs out of the ice at a rate of 1 trillion gallons per hour.

The concentrated brine is heavier than the diluted water, so it slowly sinks to the bottom of the ocean. Trillions of tons of brine are released this way every winter and as the underwater pool grows larger, the brine sinks deeper and deeper into the 2-mile-deep abyss, where it will remain for centuries if undesturbed.

The ocean currents pick up some of the brine, and take it along for their never ending trips around the world. The cool brine lines up the currents paths around the globe and plays a major role in controlling the water and air temperatures.

At the equator, the ocean waters warm up and the cold brine rises, thus keeping the ocean temperature constant. This brine current regulates the ocean temp to +/– 1 degree, which affects the air above and with that the entire global climate. After each trip around the world, some of the brine eventually gets back home, where it is dissolved in the water, only to repeat the cycle next winter.

Imagine the absense of this little known event of global proportions. The surface temperature of the equatorial waters would rise every year, without the cooling effect of the cold brine, which eventually would damage the marine and land environment. So the Antarctica brine and its effect is another thing we must consider in the overall discussions about our environment.

Wind and Storms

Wind, rain, and snow are some of the most noticeable events in our weather pattern. Water vapor, megatons of it, rise up a mile or more over the oceans and other water bodies every day under the heat of the sun. High up, some of the water vapor cools and condenses in the cooler air. Some of the mass continues to move around, agitated by the changes. These activities create disturbances, which result in low and high pressure areas, which develop into wind currents. If the wind speed and intensity increase, they keep on building and swirling under the influence of the Earth's rotation, eventually evolving into storms.

The storms' power is expressed in very strong winds, hail, thunder and lightning, heavy precipitation, freezing rain, dust storms, blizzards, sandstorms, etc.

It is estimated that a large storm system carries enough mechanical and electrical energy to provide 200 times the world's electrical power.

Hurricanes are very strong storms that form in some tropical areas. Their power is also ominous and devastating if a population center is hit. Hurricane Katrina hit New Orleans in 2005 devastating parts of the city, killing more than 1800 people, and displacing 400,000. It broke the retaining walls around the city and flooded parts of it. It carried and dumped over 2 trillion tons of water.

We are defenseless against this scale of destructive power. All we can do is learn and understand what causes these events with the hope of predicting and avoiding them. Space weather satellite are quite useful in this respect. They can see the developing disturbances in the atmosphere and warn us of their approach.

The Sun's Role

The sun's energy reaching the Earth is the driver of all the activities around us. The sun's energy radiates equally around it, so the amount of energy reaching the Earth is only a very small portion of its total energy emitted in space. Yet, we still get over a billion terawatts of raw energy, which is many times that used daily around the world. The sunlight drives photosynthesis, creates winds, and helps humans with their daily tasks, providing light and warmth.

But sunlight can cause damage and hurt and destroy us too. A set of satellites, orbiting up to 22,000 miles above the Earth, collect data on the sun's activities daily. They record the spectacular Coronal mass ejections on the sun's surface, where billions of tons of matter, heated to thousands degrees Celsius are ejected in all directions in massive explosions.

Some of these explosions have been recorded to release the power of over 14 million Hiroshima atom bomb blasts. Hurling towards Earth at a speed of over a million mph, this large amount of energetic matter (solar winds) could strip our atmosphere and dry up the oceans within minutes. But another miracle is at play here, and watching over us all the time. It is the (mysterious in itself) magnetic field surrounding the Earth. It is our magnetosphere, which shields and protects us from this ominous destructive power.

The strong solar winds hitting the magnetosphere distort it 120,000 miles across in all directions, but it deflects or stops most of the sun's particles. During very strong solar winds, some of the most energetic particles penetrate the outer magnetic field, but the inner magnetic shield channels most of the particles to the pole regions. Here the sun's particles interact with particles in the atmosphere, the result of which is an event we see reflected in a magnificent aurora, or the polar lights. This amazingly beautiful light show is a reminder of the awesome power of the sun, and the incredibly important role it plays in our lives—although most of it goes unnoticed.

The satellites also detect and record the role humans play in changing the environment. Increased levels of CO_2, ice caps and melting glaciers, rising ocean levels and climate warming are some of the consequences of our daily activities.

THE NOT-SO-NATURAL EVENTS

While by definition it is easy to separate natural from man-made events, these are sometimes mixed over time, and get confused in the rhythm of Nature and man's daily activities. It is hard to tell where some of the events originate, which direction they come from, and what their overall effect is.

Since the environmental movement of the 1970s, the nature of environmental issues has changed. While the initial emphasis was on conventional air and water pollutants, which were the most obvious and easily measurable problems, newer issues are long-term problems that are not easily discernible and can be surrounded by controversy.

All energy sources and facilities emit some type and amount of harmful pollution in forms of gasses, liquids, or solids (particles and solid residue) during their lifecycle.

NOTE. The cradle-to-grave lifetime cycle begins from the initial idea, and runs through the production of raw materials (coal, oil, gas, metals for equipment manufacturing, silicon for solar cells, etc.), and through all stages of planning, design, permitting, installation, O&M, decommissioning and disposal of all materials and buildings. This also includes efforts to mitigate environmental and health damages, and the final effort of returning the area to its original condition.

The amount of GHG (carbon dioxide and other harmful gasses) emitted depends on the specific energy source, the method of power generation, and the equipment and facilities used in the process. In all cases and under all circumstances we can measure, or at least estimate the emissions from each location in grams of emission per kilowatt of generated power. These numbers can then be used to calculate the damages done by the particular energy source, and find ways to reduce or eliminate the harmful effects.

The following events are a mixture of natural and man-made conditions which we will review keeping in mind that the boundaries might be too fuzzy to distinguish one from the other. These are also major contributors to present-day environmental issues at different stages of human understanding and mitigation attempts.

Let's take a closer look at what man is (blamed for) doing wrong today:

CO_2 Emissions

Of all environmental culprits, CO_2 is the most notorious. It is the evil of all evils, and the reason for everything bad happening to the environment—or at least this is the present-day consensus. So let's take a look at CO_2 as the all-encompassing and most urgent concern as far as global warming goes. We need to examine it also because PV installations are measured in terms of tons of CO_2 emissions saved, as compared with those generated by fossil fuel plants of the same size during a certain period of time.

A gallon of gasoline, which weighs about 6.3 pounds, could produce 20 pounds of carbon dioxide (CO_2) when burned. Impossible? Yes, possible! The $C+O_2$ combination, expressed in CO_2 units, is a wicked one, with some very special properties. When gasoline or other carbon-containing fuels burn, the carbon and hydrogen separate. The hydrogen combines with oxygen to form water (H_2O), and carbon combines with oxygen from the surrounding air to form carbon dioxide (CO_2).

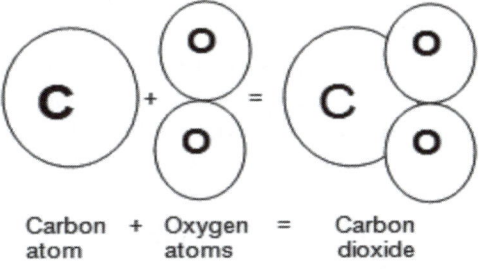

Carbon atom + Oxygen atoms = Carbon dioxide

Figure 5-11. CO_2 formation

At the present time, coal is responsible for 30-40% of world CO_2 emissions from fossil fuels. Carbon in coal and oil generate large amounts of CO_2 upon burning—four times more (in weight) than the original carbon content itself. This is because there is twice the amount of oxygen in the CO_2 molecule, and while O_2 is not harmful on its own, it is heavy and creates large amounts of CO_2. The resulting gas is the main constitu-

ent of the harmful GHG gasses that cause global warming.

$$C + O_2 = CO_2$$
$$1.0 \text{ gr.} \quad 3.67 \text{ gr.}$$

As can be seen, one unit of carbon (in coal or oil) produces almost four times the amount of CO_2. Who knew? And we now know for sure that CO_2, chlorofluorocarbons (CFCs), methane (CH_4), and nitrous oxide (NO_x) emissions cause greenhouse effect. Since global warming has been increasingly associated with the contribution of CO_2, we need to pay attention and understand the phenomena at play in this process.

The contribution to global warming of the different gasses in the form of GHG generation is believed to be as follows:

CO_2	55%	GHG effect
CFCs	24%	"
CH_4	15%	"
N_2Ox	6%	"

If and when the natural gas hydrates (NGH), or methane hydrates (see below for more details) become a primary energy source sometime in the future, this ratio will be changed in favor of methane, which is several times more capable of producing the GHG effect, because it produces large quantities of CO_2, as follows:

$$CH_4 + 2O_2 = CO_2 + 2H_2O$$
$$1 \text{ gr.} \quad \quad 2.75 \text{ gr.}$$

Either by raw gas escaping, or during burning, methane will create large amounts of CO_2, if and when large quantities of GHGs are extracted from the permafrosts and processed into useful fuels.

Other hydrocarbons, actually most of them, also produce large quantities of CO_2 simply because they react with oxygen to produce heavier molecules, as follows:

$$2C_4H_{10} + 13O_2 = 8CO_2 + 10H_2O$$
$$1.0 \text{ gr.} \quad \quad 3.03 \text{ gr.}$$

The reaction is $C + O_2 = CO_2$, where a carbon atom with an atomic weight of 12, and an oxygen atom with an atomic weight of 16 combine, producing a single molecule of CO_2 with an atomic weight of 44 (12 from one carbon atom and 32 from 2 oxygen atoms).

So, to calculate the amount of CO_2 produced from

a gallon of gasoline, the weight of the carbon in the gasoline is multiplied by 3.7 (44/12). Since gasoline is about 87% carbon and 13% hydrogen by weight, the carbon in a gallon of gasoline weighs 5.5 pounds (6.3 lbs. x .87). Then we multiply the weight of the carbon (5.5 pounds) by 3.7, which equals approximately 20 pounds of CO_2 produced by a gallon of gasoline.

Amazing! A gallon of gasoline we burn every 20 miles of driving creates 20 lbs. of poisonous CO_2. So this means that an average car leaves approximately 1 lb of poison with every traveled mile. This is doubled for SUVs, tripled and quadrupled for larger trucks and RVs, and multiplied many times over for jet planes, boats and other large vehicles. Who knew?

Thus, consider the case of family van that burns one gallon of gasoline every 10-15 miles (or every 5 miles if we drive a Hummer or an RV). Every 10-15 miles, we leave 20 lbs. of CO_2 behind us, which goes up in the atmosphere to accelerate the global warming process.

Every 100 miles driven in the family van generates 400 lbs. of CO_2—not a commendable footprint. A summer vacation trip of 1,000 miles will leave 4,000 lbs. (over 2 tons) of CO_2 footprint behind our happy family's van. And 100,000 families with similar summer trip plans will load the atmosphere with an additional 400,000,000 lbs. (200,000 tons) of CO_2 within weeks... 1 million families... you get the picture.

Imagine a 2 GW coal-burning power plant bellowing dense clouds of smoke all day long, or a cruise ship navigating aimlessly around the Gulf of Mexico burning thousands of gallons of diesel? Multiply that by thousands of such activities and you'll see that millions of pounds of harmful CO_2, and other gasses are emitted into the atmosphere every day. All these poisons travel up into the atmosphere, where they accumulate and do their damaging job non-stop.

Table 5-2 confirms the fact that coal is the worst GHG emitter. The rest of the fossils are not far behind, with nuclear, bio-, geo- and hydro-power showing the most respect for the environment. Of course, wind and solar are at the same level too, which means that they are our hope for energy independence and a clean environment.

Nitrogen Oxides

Nitrogen (N_2) is a predominant gas in the air we breath—over 78 percent in dry air, to be exact. It is a relatively inert element, which means that it doesn't participate readily in chemical reactions. At high temperatures, however, nitrogen combines with oxygen (at about 1,100°C) and forms a variety of nitrogen oxides

Table 5-2. GHG emissions from power generators
*Including all cradle-to-grave emissions
**CCS—carbon capture and sequestration

Technology	Grams CO_2 per kWh*
Coal, conventional	1100
Coal w / CCS**	950
Diesel, oil	770
Fuel Cell, H2 gas	650
Natural gas	440
Nuclear	60
Geothermal	40
Biomass	30
Biogas	15
Hydro, river run	15
Hydro, dammed	10
Wind, onshore	25
Wind, offshore	15
Solar, PV modules	20
Solar thermal, CSP	40

(NO_x).

The resulting gasses range from nitric oxide, or nitrogen monoxide (NO), nitrogen dioxide (NO_2); dinitrogen pentoxide (N_2O_5); and nitrous oxide, or "laughing gas" (N_2O).

The dominant component of NO_x gasses, NO, is not particularly harmful in itself, but NO_2 is toxic, and long-term exposure may result in lung damage and other illnesses. The reddish-brown color of NO_2 is why the polluted urban air has a distinct dirty brown appearance.

The worst part, however, is that NO_x gasses undergo further chemical reactions in the atmosphere with time and changing conditions. The most important reaction is that of NO which is readily converted into the more harmful NO_2.

Another important process results in photochemical reactions, driven by the energy of sunlight, the result of which is the decomposition of NO_2, during which reaction NO and an isolated oxygen atom are produced. This oxygen atom is very reactive and is responsible for the formation of ozone, which is another story, and which we review in more detail below in this text.

Fossil-fueled power plants, industrial use of fossils, and transportation are the major sources of NO_x emissions worldwide. The NO_x emissions do not come from the fossil fuels, but from the air in the combustion chambers, which is needed for the burning to proceed. So there's no way to prevent NO_x emissions by altering the fuels, or by removing nitrogen from the air supplied for combustion.

Nevertheless, there are a number of techniques available to help reduce nitrogen oxide production in power plants. Some of the practical methods consist of modifying the combustion chamber, controlling the flame geometry, using low-NO_x burners, air-fuel staging, catalytic combustion, adjusting the fuel-to-air ratios, and optimizing the fuel and air flow speed.

Recycling the exhaust gases through the combustion chamber is another efficient method of reducing NO_x emissions. The recycling reduces combustion temperature and with it the amount of NO_x produced. The problem here is that by reducing the combustion temperature, the thermodynamic efficiency is lowered, which also lowers the total useful energy generated by the power plant.

So any of the NO_x reduction methods either increases the cost of operation or reduces the efficiency and the total power output of the plant. The installation of additional scrubbers and their operation is an expensive undertaking which costs millions of dollars in initial construction and annual O&M procedures. Some countries have regulations and can afford such modifications, but the majority of the world is not concerned with NO_x emissions.

Similarly, NO_x gas emissions from transportation vehicles (diesel trucks especially) are controlled to a degree in the developed countries, but not so much in the developing world. Because of that, global NO_x emissions are presently rising uncontrollably.

Sulfur Emissions

Sulfur is present in coal and, to a lesser extent, in oil. Unless it's removed before combustion (a technologically feasible but very expensive process), when burned the sulfur produces sulfur dioxide (SO_2). However, the native sulfur content of fuels varies substantially, so sulfur reduction also can be accomplished by changing the fuel source. For example, coal from the western United States typically contains less than 1 percent sulfur, whereas coals from the Midwest may contain 4 to 5 percent sulfur.

Sulfur dioxide itself is detrimental to human health. As usual, the health burden falls most heavily on the very young, the very old, and those already suffering from respiratory diseases. Acute episodes of high SO_2 concentrations have resulted in outright mortality.

For example, in a 1952 air pollution incident in London, some 4,000 people perished when atmospheric SO_2 rose sevenfold.

Once in the atmosphere, SO_2 undergoes chemical reactions that produce additional harmful substances. Oxidation converts SO_2 to sulfur trioxide (SO_3), which then reacts with water vapor to make sulfuric acid (H_2SO_4):

$$SO_3 + H_2O = H_2SO_4$$

These reactions take place when the sulfur-containing gasses hit either water vapor or water droplets. In the liquid water, sulfuric acid dissolves into positive hydrogen ions and negative sulfate ions. Sulfate ions can join with other chemical species to make substances that, if the water evaporates, remain airborne as tiny particles known as sulfate aerosols.

These particles are typically well under 1/micron in size and are very efficient scatterers of light. As a result, they reflect sunlight and thus lower the overall energy reaching Earth. Consequently, sulfate aerosols have a cooling effect on climate.

Acid Rain

Acid rain and dry deposition (particles) of contaminated matter onto populated centers and other critical areas of human activities are primarily the result of SO_2 and NO_2 being emitted into the air. These gasses are generated in large quantities by fossil-burning power plants. They travel freely in whichever direction the wind blows, landing in different places. Upon contact with various surfaces, the chemicals in these gasses could change the acidity of the water or soil into which they fall.

High temperatures created by the combustion of petroleum cause nitrogen gas in the surrounding air to oxidize, creating nitrous oxides. Nitrous oxides, along with sulfur dioxide from the sulfur in the oil, combine with water in the atmosphere to create acid rain. Acid rain is a condition in which water droplets in the atmosphere meet SO_2 gasses and form sulfuric acid in the process. Thus formed dilute sulfuric acid falls to Earth during rain storms, resulting in acid rain. Raindrops today are significantly acidic—much more than a century ago.

Acid rain is formed via different mechanisms, as follow:

1. Carbon dioxide reacts with water to form carbonic acid.

$$CO_2 \text{ (gas)} + H_2O \text{ (liq)} = H_2CO_3 \text{(liq)}$$

Carbonic acid then dissociates to give a hydrogen (H^+) and a hydrogen carbonate ions (HCO_3^-) H_2CO_3 produces H^+ which makes it an acid, thus lowering the pH of the solutions and causing corrosion.

$$H_2CO_3(liq) = H^+ + HCO_3^-(dissociation)$$

2.   Nitric oxide (NO), which also contributes to the natural acidity of rainwater, is formed during lightning storms by the reaction of nitrogen and O_2, contained in the air.

$$N_2 (gas) + O_2 (gas) = 2NO(gas)$$

In air, NO is oxidized by the O_2 contain in it to nitrogen dioxide (NO_2)

$$2NO(gas) + O_2 (gas) = 2NO_2 (gas)$$

NO_2 in turn reacts with water to give nitric acid (HNO_3).

$$NO_2 (gas) + H_2O (liq) = 2HNO_3(liq) + NO(gas)$$

This acid dissociates in water to yield hydrogen ions and nitrate ions (NO_3^-), similar to the dissociation of carbonic acid shown above, which similarly lowers the pH of the solution, thus making it acidic and corrosive.

$$HNO_3(liq) = H+ + NO_3^- \text{ (dissociation)}$$

3. SO_2 in the emitted gasses combines with H_2O and O_2 in the air to produce sulfuric acid, which is one of the principal bad guys in acid rain damage that can affect any structure and formation exposed to it.

$$SO_2 (gas) + H_2 (liq) + O_2 (gas) = H_2SO_4(liq)$$

In all cases,

Emissions(gas) + Rain(liq) + Air(gas) = Acid Rain(liq)

The Acid Rain Effects

Falling rain with acidity of pH* 5 and below creates a number of unwanted effects where it:

---

*Technically speaking, pH is a measure of the concentration of the hydrogen ion p[H] in a water-based solution. Pure water has a pH of 7 +/- 0.1 at 25°C. Any solution with a pH less than 7.00 is acidic, while that with pH greater than 7.00 is basic or alkaline. Vinegar, for example, is strongly acidic (pH = 2 or 3), while bleach or ammonia are basic (pH = 10-12) depending on the concentration. The pH level of aqueous solutions is usually measured with a special pH meter, or by using paper or liquid indicators which change colors with change of pH.

- Affects the aquatic life causing reproduction in fish to falter. Death or deformity are widespread among young fish living in acidic waters.

- Amphibians and invertebrates suffer similarly, and because of that highly acidic water bodies and lakes do not support normal life. There are many such examples in the northeastern United States which has been particularly affected by acid rain created by the coal-burning power plants in the area. The same phenomena is observed in northern Europe and a number of other places around the world with high concentrations of coal-fired power plants.

- Many high-altitude lakes, even those in protected wilderness areas, have pH levels well below 5 and are considered "dead."

- Acid precipitation affects not only water quality; it also damages terrestrial vegetation, especially high-altitude trees.

- It also causes increased corrosion and weathering of buildings. Limestone and marble are particularly susceptible to damage from acid precipitation, as are some paints.

The effect of acid rain depends in part on geology; lakes or soils on limestone rock suffer less harm because the limestone can neutralize the excess acidity, but granite and quartz-based rocks lack this buffering effect.

Acid rain conditions in the northeastern United States from the burning of coal, and in the western United States from gasses generated by utilities and motor vehicles, have been causing problems since the beginning of the 20th century. The situation was partially exacerbated by the Clean Air Act, which forced coal power plants to use taller smoke stacks, thus resulting in transmission of acid rain gasses to much longer distances. This, of course, resulted in the contamination of larger land areas.

This is a good example of the complexity of the environmental issues, and how sometimes the best ideas geared to solve problems produce disastrous results.

During the Carter administration, a risk-averse policy was undertaken through the EPA and Council on Environmental Quality (CEQ), aimed to research and control the pollutants suspected to cause acid rain even in the face of scientific uncertainty and growing opposition by interested parties. The Reagan administration, however, was not that concerned and was much more environmental risk tolerant. It did believed that the scientific uncertainties surrounding environmentally caused exposure levels did not justify the necessary expenditures for their remediation. Therefore, any serious effort in that direction would unnecessarily curtail energy security and economic growth.

George H.W. Bush called for new Clean Air Act legislation to curtail SO_2 and NO_2 emissions. In 1990 he enacted amendments to the Clean Air Act where emissions were to be cut by over 12 million tons per year. A market-like system of emissions trading was implemented, and a cap on emissions was set during 2000, which was partially achieved by the installation of industrial scrubbers on the large emitters.

According to environmentalists, the initial costs in cutting emissions levels, to be paid by the utilities, was expected to be over $4.6 billion, resulting in a 40% rise in electricity costs. Instead, the total cost impact was only about $1 billion, which resulted in only 2-4% rise in electricity costs. The main reason for this "discrepancy" can be attributed to the fact that low-sulfur coal was used extensively in coal-fired plants, so no major facilities upgrades were needed to reduce the emission levels.

Other groups, however, insist that trillions of dollars have been spent since the 1970s on emission reductions and other environmental measures, which have resulted in little improvement of air quality and instead have created other, even bigger, problems.

NOTE: In 1990 the U.S. Congress decided that a 50% reduction in SO_2 emissions from power plants and a significant reduction in NO_x emissions from power plants were necessary first steps to address the acid rain problem.

This resulted in the 1990 Clean Air Act Amendments which created the U.S. Acid Rain Program. This started one of the most drastic changes in the way pollutants are handled in this country, and especially SO_2 emissions which were now strictly regulated. Rather than relying on command-and-control MO, Congress set a strict emissions cap for power plants and, in return, provided them with unprecedented flexibility in determining how to meet that cap.

The Acid Rain Program set the cap at 8.95 million tons of SO_2 per year, to be implemented in two phases. In Phase I, which began in January 1995, the largest, highest emitting electric utility generating units were required to reduce emissions. Phase II, which began in 2000, required all electric utilities to reduce their emissions to roughly one-half of 1980 levels or the 8.95 million ton cap.

Under the program, sources are required to hold allowances equal to each year's emissions. Participants are free to choose how they want to comply, but at the end of each year they have to surrender enough allowances to EPA to cover their actual emissions. Failure to comply with this provision results in automatic penalties, which are enforced by EPA.

Although the U.S. Acid Rain Program is not perfect and is not expected to resolve the issues at hand, it is one of the most robust, functional, and practical environmental programs ever, which should be used as a model of how to handle the threat of excess pollution. The biggest problem, again, is that while such a program can be implemented in the U.S. and Europe, the rest of the world—especially the developing countries—is far from it. Because of their rapid growth today, including increased pollutants, we cannot expect any great reductions in the global GHG emissions.

Scrubbing

Sulfur emissions are controlled in the U.S., but since sulfur pollution is in a form of gas, it cannot be removed by the standard particulate pollution controls. Because of that the most widely used sulfur-removal technique is flue gas desulfurization, or scrubbing.

The process is done in a wet scrubber, where the exhaust gases are forced through a water spray containing some base chemicals (usually $CaCO_3$ or $MgCO_3$. When the SO_2 gasses hit the water, they form sulfuric acid which immediately reacts with the bases in the scrubber water, thus neutralizing the acids.

$$2SO_2 + 2CaCO_3 = 2CaSO_4 + 2CO_2$$

In a dry scrubbing process the exhaust gas is run through a pulverized limestone, which neutralizes the acids. In each case, the chemical reactions yield solid calcium sulfate ($CaSO_4$), which can be separated from the gas stream and is removed along with other particulate matter via standard filtering or centrifuge action.

Wet scrubbers can remove the majority (over 98 percent) of all sulfur from the exhaust gases, with the price rising along with the removal rate. Scrubbing costs about 15 percent of the total cost of a coal-burning power plant. In addition there is a energy cost that could be close to 10 percent of the plant's total power output. On top of that, 3-4 percent of the power is used for particulate removal.

A great portion of this wasted energy is used to reheat the exhaust gases after the wet scrubbing so they can rise up the smokestack and be emitted into the atmosphere—such a waste of energy and money. But there is no way around it, at least in the U.S., although the utilities have found a way to avoid using gas scrubbers. Instead, they meet the sulfur emissions regulations with a number of strategies, such as switching to lower sulfur fuels, or trading so-called emissions credits.

By using these techniques, the coal-fired power plants are emitting less polluting gases when using more expensive low-sulfur coal and oil, and in some cases they can just pay emission credit penalties and keep on polluting as much as they want. How does this benefit the environment?

Gas scrubbers are widely used in Europe and Japan, but most other countries are much more flexible about using scrubbers, or any pollution reduction equipment which is one of the reasons for the increase in global air pollution.

Particulate Matter

The effects of small particles in the air have been of concern, and their effects are well known, but when it comes to predicting climate change (and their role in it) the picture is not that clear. The role of GHGs is quite clear, while the role of atmospheric aerosols and dust particles, as well as the effects of their interfacial chemistry on the climate, and their interactions with the GHGs and water vapor are not that clear. The reactions up in the troposphere, where a lot of these interactions occur, are quite complex and not easy to observe, measure and document.

We have known for awhile now that the ways in which atmospheric particles, such as mineral dust, affect climate are important, but now we know that they are poorly understood. There are numerous processes that particles play some role in, in the troposphere, such as heterogeneous chemical interactions with the atmospheric gases, cloud formations, optical interferences, and combinations of these. All contribute to the radiative balance (or forcing), which is the net difference between incoming and outgoing radiation.

The role of particulate matter in the atmosphere and its chemistry is oversimplified by the existing climate models. At the same time, field researchers find the real world's complexity overwhelming, so better understanding of particles and their impact on climate, the environment, and human health is needed.

Particulate matter is emitted in great quantities on a daily basis by coal and gas power plants, airplanes, diesel engines, and small volcanoes. Periodically, equally large amounts of particles are emitted by eruption of large volcanoes. The overall effect is complex, but we

think of it as basically negative, because it contributes to the formation of acid rain, which damages buildings and metal structures.

But how about positive effects? On September 11, 2001, all U.S.-based jet planes were grounded for three days. Ground climate tracking stations measured a significant increase of temperature at several points. We now attribute that anomaly to the fact that the jets' contrails were absent from the sky during that period of time. Without the particles in the contrails, the sun's rays were allowed to more easily penetrate the atmosphere and to heat the ground more than under normal flying conditions.

On the other hand, the eruption of Krakatoa in 1883 spewed ash and soot 50 miles high, and sent a cloud of particles around the world. It has been documented that the sun was hidden by the smoke, and that global temperatures dropped by several degrees.

No doubt, the particle content of our atmosphere is a major factor in the daily environmental events. How large a factor and how much this affects us is still debatable, but it must be included in future decisions which affect our environment and global warming in particular.

Figure 5-12. Many things to keep in mind…

Surely, the overall environmental picture has been complicated by man and Nature recently, and we are now having a hard time figuring it all out. Our atmosphere is packed with a mixture of different chemicals (CO_2, SO_2, NO_x, VOC), and substances (water vapor, particulate matter), and who knows what else has been emitted by man and Nature during the last century of intense industrial progress and humanity increase?

Nevertheless, modern science is putting the pieces

of the puzzle together…one by one…slowly but surely. There is no doubt that someday we will have the entire picture figured out, at which point decisive action will be taken to solve the major problems.

Photochemical Smog

Looking at the air above some densely populated centers (Los Angeles, Beijing, etc.) we see a brownish-yellow cloud that consists of a complex soup of chemicals. Most of these gasses come directly or indirectly from fossil fuel burning in stationary power plants and industrial enterprises, and also from transport vehicles.

Urban smog formation is due mostly to high concentrations of nitrogen oxides, as discussed above, hydrocarbons from incomplete combustion, production, handling, and storage of gasoline and diesel fuels. Significant amounts also comes from evaporation of organic solvents in paints, inks, dry-cleaning fluids, and similar chemicals in daily use around the world.

These pollutants are trapped under some weather conditions, the most important of which is air inversion. This is a complex phenomena, based on the fact that air temperature usually decreases with altitude, because the atmosphere is transparent and doesn't absorb much energy from sunlight.

Earth's surface, however, is not transparent and heats up during the day. It then transfers energy to the air above it at a rate at which the temperature declines with altitude (lapse rate), which is normally measured at 6.5°C per kilometer of altitude.

Air in contact with the hot Earth's surface, or mixed with hot gases from fossil fuel combustion, is hot and less dense than its surroundings, so it tends to rise. On its way up, the hot air expands and cools, using its internal energy as it goes, pushing against the surrounding air.

Most of the time, this cooling is not as great as the lapse rate so the hot air remains warmer and less dense than its surroundings as it continues to rise, carrying away any embedded pollutants. In an inversion condition, however, the air temperature either increases with height, or decreases more slowly than a rising mass of air would cool. Thus, the hot air cools and becomes denser than its surroundings, slowly sinking back down.

The air in this case is stable, and the layers closest to the Earth's surface are trapped in place. Trapped with the air are any pollutants it contains and many more are attracted and locked in place during the day. Nearby topographical conditions facilitate and accelerate the trapping mechanism. The Los Angeles basin is a good example of how nearby mountains trap polluted air and are assisted by the cool Pacific ocean to create and maintain inversion conditions.

While idling in the trapped air of the inversion, the polluting gas molecules are activated by sunlight which impacts enough energy upon them to start chemical reactions among them. A key reaction in this situation is the decomposition of nitrogen dioxide into nitric oxide, which also produces an isolated oxygen atom (ion):

$$NO_2 + \text{solar energy} = NO + O \text{ (free ion)}$$

The free oxygen ions are very reactive and react with molecular oxygen (O_2) to create another highly reactive chemical, ozone (O_3):

$$O + O_2 = O_3$$

On one hand, ozone in the higher stratosphere protects the Earth's surface from harmful UV radiation, but ozone in the lower atmosphere is harmful to human health. It is also a climate-changing greenhouse gas (GHG) blamed for climate warming and other environmental problems.

Ozone and O ions also are capable of initiating and supporting a number of additional reactions and effects. Additional harmful substances can be created in the process, because O_3 molecules and O ions facilitate reactions among hydrocarbons (HC) and nitrogen oxides that result in a host of substances, such as volatile organic compounds (VOCs) and so-called peroxyacyl nitrates (PAN).

This is photochemical smog. It causes not only eye irritation, but much more serious respiratory problems. It damages plants and many materials, such as paints, fabrics, and rubber.

In more detail its formation and behavior can be described as follow:

At night the levels of all air-suspended polluting substances are quite low, but the morning LA rush hour quickly increases the emissions of both nitrogen oxides and VOCs as people drive to work. Later in the morning, traffic dies down and the NO_x and VOCs begin to form NO_2, quickly increasing its concentration.

As the sunlight becomes more intense later in the day, NO_2 is broken down and its by-products form increasing concentrations of O_3. At the same time, some of the NO_2 reacts with the VOCs to produce toxic chemicals such as PAN.

As the sun goes down, the production of O_3 slows down and the ozone that remains in the atmosphere is then consumed by several different reactions.

A number of meteorological factors can influence the formation of photochemical smog: rain can reduce the photochemical smog as the pollutants are washed out of the atmosphere; winds can blow photochemical smog away replacing it with fresh air. The smog is then blown into distant areas, where it can cause similar problems.

There is no quick or easy way to reduce or eliminate photochemical smog, short of reducing or eliminating the emissions of NO_x, HC, and other polluters. NO_x emission standards for power plants and vehicles in the U.S. and other developed countries are playing a major role in keeping emissions low, but that is not the case in most developing countries, so here again, we don't see a reduction in photochemical smog in the near future.

Ozone Depletion

There has been talk about ozone depletion for decades, and we know that it means reduced concentration of ozone in the Earth's stratosphere (the ever-shrinking ozone layer). We also know that ozone is needed to block part of the sun's harmful UV radiation. But we still don't know the size of the problem and its actual effect on the Earth's environment. Nor do we know exactly what causes ozone layer problems.

Chlorofluorocarbons (CFCs), which have been used extensively in the 20th century, were blamed for much of the depletion of the ozone layer, so EPA and FDA banned CFCs in aerosol cans in the late 1970s. Did that solve the problem? Not sure...

In the 1980s we learned that the problem was much worse than before, and a massive (albeit controversial) hole in the ozone layer over Antarctica was identified. International agreements were made to reduce the ozone-damaging substances; i.e., the Vienna Convention, the 1987 Montreal Protocol, and a third agreement in 1990 in London. The 1990 Clean Air Act Amendments phased out production of CFCs in the US and required recycling of CFC products.

So, the phase-out of CFCs and similar policies are seen as a success, and a crisis seems to have been averted, yet, the ozone layer is still depleted. This, according to the proponents, is due to the longevity of CFC particles in the atmosphere, so the ozone layer will hopefully start showing signs of recovery by 2024-2025.

A lot of time, effort and money was spent on fixing the hole in the ozone layer. We don't doubt that most of these efforts are of some benefit, but we doubt that we have done everything just right and on time. Because of that, and other factors, it is unlikely that the ozone layer will become intact, or even close to what it was in the 19th century.

Heavy Metals

Not surprisingly, fossil fuels contain a number of different heavy metals, which are released in one or another form in exhaust gasses. There are many other ways for heavy metals to enter the environment. One of the most obvious is through wear on engines, turbines, and other machinery.

The heavier metals act as biological enzymes, which have a wide range of toxic effects on humans. Especially dangerous are the deleterious impacts on brain development in young children. For example, lead is a particularly serious contaminant with levels that remain high in urban air, soil and other surfaces.

Mercury is another key toxin particularly harmful to children and animals. It is found in coal and is emitted during coal burning at power plants or in home heating. Coal-burning power plants and the dominant source of mercury contamination. Mercury pollution in surface waters collects in the food chain and ends up at very high levels in larger fish. Many lakes of the central and eastern U.S. are so highly contaminated that fish there are unsuitable for human consumption.

A recent study shows that 1/5 of all Americans have mercury levels exceeding EPA recommendations, which are maximum 1 part per million (PPM). Mercury levels are presently in serious violation of federal standards, and although there are efforts to control it, its concentration is still rising in some areas of the U.S. and even more so in developing countries with high levels of coal-fired power generation.

Radiation

Radiation is usually not associated with fossil fuel combustion (at least in our minds), but coal contains small quantities of uranium and thorium and their radioactive decay products, such as radium. The uranium content is miniscule, about 1 ppm, but it varies widely to over 1,800 ppm of uranium in some U.S. coal mines.

Radioactivity ends up in the air during the burning of coal, and in fly ash in the particulate-removal devices. The direct radiation from fossil fuels is not a major concern, but there is a very large quantity of coal being burned every day around the globe, so the cumulative effects are unknown as yet.

NOTE: The radiation emitted during coal burning in some cases is higher than that emitted by a nuclear power plant during its normal operating cycle. Although it is not fair to compare coal with nuclear power, the fact is that there is 4-5 times more radiation emitted from some coal-burning power plants than emitted by nuclear plants.

Cement Production

Power plants are not the only polluters and energy guzzlers. There are other major culprits in the global energy and environmental pictures. The major ones are the cement and iron production industries.

The cement industry contributes about 5-8% to global anthropogenic CO_2 emissions, making it an important sector for CO_2-emission mitigation strategies. Large quantities of CO_2 are emitted during cement production, mainly from the calcination process of limestone, from combustion of fuels in the kiln, and from power generation.

Estimated total carbon emissions from global cement production are 350 million metric tons of carbon (MtC), 160 MtC from process carbon emissions, and 147 MtC from energy use. Overall, the top 10 cement-producing countries account for over 60% of global carbon emissions from cement production.

The amount of CO_2 emitted during cement production is nearly 900 kg of CO_2 for every 1000 kg of cement produced. Basically, there is nearly as much CO_2 produced as cement. Considering that there were 3.4 billion tons of cement produced worldwide in 2011, there were about 3.1 billion tons of CO_2 produced at the same time. Over 10 years, that is 31 billion tons. In 20 years, the cement industry will pump up 62 billion tons, and over 1,000 billion tons in 30 years…you get the (ugly) picture.

Globally, both cement production and steel production are indicators of national construction activity, with cement used mainly in building and road construction, and steel in the construction of railways, ships, machinery, and other infrastructure. CO_2 emissions are generated by carbonate oxidation in the cement clinker production process, the main constituent of cement and the largest of non-combustion sources of CO_2.

The world's cement production is heavily dominated by China, with an estimated share of 57% in global emissions from cement production, followed by India with a more than 5%. The United States, Turkey, Japan, Russia, Brazil, Iran and Vietnam produce between 1.5% and 2%.

With a continuing trend in China, global cement production increased by 6% in 2011. China increased cement production by 11% and was responsible for 57% of the world's cement produced, while production in Germany, Brazil and Russia increased by 10%, 6% and 3% respectively during the same time period, according to USGS estimates.

However, emissions are not directly proportional to cement production levels, since the fraction of clinker (in this industry the main source of CO_2 emissions) in cement tends to decrease over time. A recent study by the World Business Council on sustainable development has shown that the share of blended cement produced in recent years in most countries has considerably increased, relative to that of traditional Portland cement.

Consequently, average clinker fractions in global cement production have decreased to between 70% and 80%, compared to nearly 95% for Portland cement with proportional decrease in CO_2 emissions per ton of cement produced. Both non-combustion and combustion emissions from cement production occur during the clinker production process, not during the mixing of the cement clinker.

This has resulted in about a 20% decrease in CO_2 emissions per ton of cement produced, compared to the 1980s. At that time, it was not common practice to blend cement clinker with much other mixing material, such as fly ash from coal-fired power plants or blast furnace slag. According to EDGAR 4.2 data, this yielded an annual decrease of 250 million tons in CO_2 emissions, compared to the reference case of Portland cement production. A similar amount has been reduced in fuel combustion for cement production and related CO_2 emissions. So this leaves the cement industry with the task of figuring out how to stop emitting the other 29.6 billion tons every year. Fat chance, you say. We agree; this is not going to happen anytime soon, and especially now with the construction boom in China, India, Russia and many developing countries.

Emission mitigation options in the U.S. and other developed countries include energy efficiency improvement, new processes, a shift to low carbon fuels, application of waste fuels, increased use of additives in cement making, and, eventually, alternative cements and CO_2 removal from flue gases in clinker kilns. But even these improvements have a long way to go before making a major difference.

Iron and Steel Production

When looking at steel production, with related non-combustion CO_2 emissions from blast furnaces used to produce pig iron and from conversion losses in coke manufacturing, China accounted for 44% of crude steel production in 2011, followed by Japan (8%), the United States (6%), Russia and India (each 5%), South Korea (4%), Germany (3%) and the Ukraine, Brazil and Turkey (each 2%).

According to WSA (2012), global crude steel production rose 6.5% in 2011, compared to 10% in 2010. The

9% increase in China accounted for almost one-third of the global increase in production in 2011. Production plummeted in Australia (-12%) and South Africa (-22%). In 2011, it rose strongly in Turkey (+18%), South Korea (+17%) and Taiwan (+15%). Other significant increases were seen in Italy (+8%), India (+8%), the United States (+7%), Brazil (+7%) and Russia (3%).

As with cement production, the steel industry produces as much CO_2 as steel production. Actually more, for the production of 1.3 kg. of steel emits 2.0 kg. CO_2. Taking into consideration the total world production of more than 1.3 billion tons of steel, the steel industry produces over two billion tons of CO_2 annually. This is 20 billion tons in 10 years, 40 billion in 20 years. Still, this is 10 times less CO_2 emitted annually than that emitted by the cement industry.

In steel production, most CO_2 is generated in iron- and steel-making processes that use coke ovens, blast furnaces and basic oxygen steel furnaces. However, the share of electric arc furnaces and direct reduction in secondary and primary steel making, which generate much less CO_2 per ton of crude steel produced, is increasing over time. Lime and ammonia production, other industrial sources of CO_2 emissions, increased globally by an average of 5% lately.

There are efforts to account for and reduce CO_2 emissions from these industries, but again, most of the money and effort in this area are spent in the developed countries. Cement factories in the Third World usually make a mess of the local environment, with some extreme cases of entire towns covered in cement dust.

There are significant reductions in CO_2 emissions as a result of technological improvements and structural changes in steel production in industrialized countries during the past 40 years. Substantial further reductions in those emissions will not be possible using conventional technologies. Instead, a radical cutback may be achieved if, instead of carbon, hydrogen is used for direct iron ore reduction. This technology and the CO_2 generation emitted during the production of hydrogen as a reducing agent from various sources are the next goals for the steel industry.

Hazardous Wastes in the United States

With the advance of American industry and agriculture during the 20th century, hazardous wastes were becoming a serious problem. There was increased contamination of air, soil and water in all sectors of the American commerce. Finally, in the mid-1970s regulations were introduced, via the Resource Conservation and Recovery Act (RCRA), which were designed to govern hazardous waste from its initial generation to final disposition (cradle-to-grave regulation). At the same time, the Toxic Substances Control Act (TSCA) was designed to anticipate possible hazards from chemicals.

At the beginning of the century, someone had the idea of building a "dream community"—a three-block tract of land on the eastern edge of Niagara Falls, NY, where a short canal was proposed to connect the upper and lower Niagara Rivers. Cheap electric power generated by the rushing water would fuel industries and homes in this model city. It was the infamous Love Canal project.

The dream went through the now familiar "dream crusher" of bad economic and political circumstances, and by 1910 it was shattered. All that was left was a partially dug ditch where construction of the canal had begun.

For ten years, the canal was used as a municipal and industrial chemical dumpsite. Tons of unwanted and unidentified chemicals and other hazardous materials were dumped in it without any supervision or control. Love Canal will remain a perfect how-not-to example for dealing with hazardous materials.

The owner of the property, Hooker Chemical Company, covered the canal with earth and sold it to the city for $1. Like the ignorant Londoners, who dumped their chamber pots on the street every night, this chemical company dumped its hazardous waste in the lap of the city. City officials were happy to buy it so cheaply. Little did they know…

So, in the late 1950s, the city built about 100 homes and a school on top of covered hazardous acreage. Twenty-five years later someoney dug into the contaminated soil of the Love Canal and found a true-to-life industrial dump. There were 82 different chemical compounds identified, 11 of which were suspected carcinogens. These chemicals were not dormant under the cover; they were working their way upward through the soil, as their metal containers rotted and leached the contents into backyards and basements of unsuspecting home owners and the school.

Then the Love Canal issue exploded. Triggered by record rainfall, the heavy leaching of toxic chemicals was noticed. Corroding drums with their stinky contents could be seen breaking up through the grounds of backyards. Trees and gardens were turning black and dying. One swimming pool popped up from its foundation, afloat in a sea of chemicals. Puddles of noxious substances were in yards and basements, including school grounds.

There were faint, choking smells in the area. People coming in contact with the chemicals had burns on their hands and faces. Then birth defects and general ailments started to become obvious, and finally the citizens of Love Canal were evacuated from their homes.

Many children were born with defects and raised in illness in the Love Canal community. A baby girl was born deaf with a cleft palate, an extra row of teeth, and slight retardation. A boy was born with an eye defect. Benzene—a known toxin and human carcinogen—was prevalent.

President Carter approved emergency financial aid for the Love Canal area (the first emergency fund related to a environmental disaster), and the U.S. Senate approved a "sense of Congress" amendment authorizing federal aid to relieve the environmental disaster.

A plan was set in motion to detoxify the Love Canal area. A trench system was to be built to drain chemicals from the Canal.

After the events at Love Canal, the Comprehensive Environmental Response, Compensation, and Liability Act (CERCLA, or Superfund) was enacted in 1980 to assist in the cleanup of abandoned hazardous waste disposal sites. In the mid-1980s, the Hazardous and Solid Waste Amendments (1984) and the Superfund Amendments and Reauthorization Act (1986) were passed.

The aim of hazardous waste regulation is to prevent harm from occurring due to hazardous waste and to pass the burden of cleanup to the original producers of the waste. Some of the problems of hazardous waste regulation are that its negative can be difficult to detect and controversial and that, due mainly to the large amount of hazardous waste that is generated (214 million tons in 1995), regulation can be difficult and costly.

Implementation has been difficult, with years sometimes passing between legislation passage and initial regulations. Superfund was passed in December 1980, just before Reagan took office. The first administrator of Superfund was Rita Lavelle who had worked for a major hazardous waste generator. The result was that her implementation of Superfund was designed mainly to delay regulation, and the subsequent controversy resulted in the resignation of Lavelle, EPA administrator Anne Burford, and several other top EPA personnel. In 1986, Congress passed the Superfund Amendments and Reauthorization Act, increasing funding to $9 billion and providing for studies and new technologies.

By 1995, Superfund cleanup still took an average of 12 years per site, and costs for each site can range in the billions of dollars. Superfund, while showing improvements, has been probably the most criticized of environmental programs based on costs of remediation, implementation problems, and the questionable serious-

ness of the problems it addresses.

There are hundreds of "Love Canal-like" chemical dumpsites across this nation. Unlike the Love Canal, however, very few are situated so close to human settlements. Because of that, we might never hear about them, but without a doubt, many of these old dumpsites are time bombs with burning fuses—their contents slowly leaching out and the next victim could be a water supply, or a sensitive wetland.

The main problem is that ownership of these sites frequently shifts over the years, making liability difficult to determine in cases of an accident. No secure mechanisms are in effect for determining such liability.

It is within our power to exercise intelligent and effective controls designed to significantly cut such environmental risks. A tragedy, unfortunately, has now called upon us to decide on the overall level of commitment we desire for defusing future Love Canals.

Water Use

Water is a precious commodity, and is becoming even more so with the persisting draughts in our Southwest, and increasing water contamination in other parts of the country. There is also significant overuse and abuse of water by fuel production and power generation, which is a serious issue. With the increasing occurrence of long draughts in the U.S. and around the world, water use problems will only get worse.

Figure 5-13 shows how much water (in gallons per TJ of electric power generation). Obviously, natural gas wins this contest hands down, but please note that this applies only for natural gas reservoirs that do not need fracking. These deposits are basically caverns from

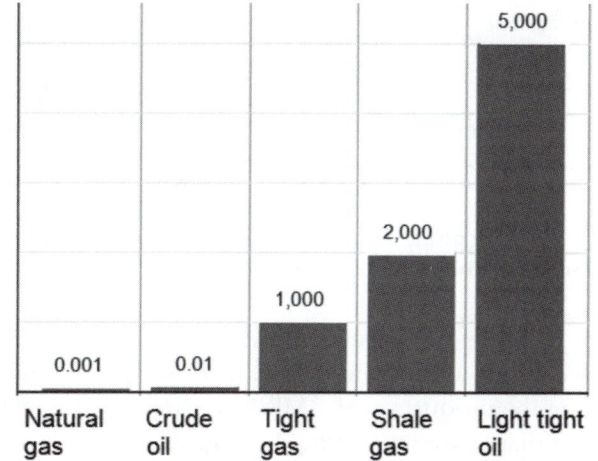

Figure 5-13. Water use during oil and gas production (in gallons per TJ*).
*1 terajoule (TJ) is the energy used to generate approximately 278 MWh of electricity, using the respective fuel source.

which the natural gas flows freely, or with a little the help.

Fracking, as reflected in the shale gas column in Figure 5-13, uses quite a bit water, and creates a big mess in the process, as we review in detail below. The difference is that fracking water pumped into the shale formations contains large amounts of different chemicals with different toxicities and poisonous properties.

This, multiplied by the thousands of sites using that much toxic water, produces a mind boggling quantity of water wasted for fracking and other purposes. Those millions of gallons then go into the ground and introduce toxins into our water tables, rivers and lakes.

Cooling Water

Cooling water is used in great quantities during fossil fuel electricity production. Steam generated during the burning of the fuel is sent to the turbine to turn it and generate electricity. On exiting the turbine, the steam must be cooled for ease of transport to the boiler, or in some cases of direct cooling, it is discharged back into the body of water from which it was pumped. During the cooling stage, a lot of fresh or recycled cool water is used to cool the steam and convert it back into water for reuse.

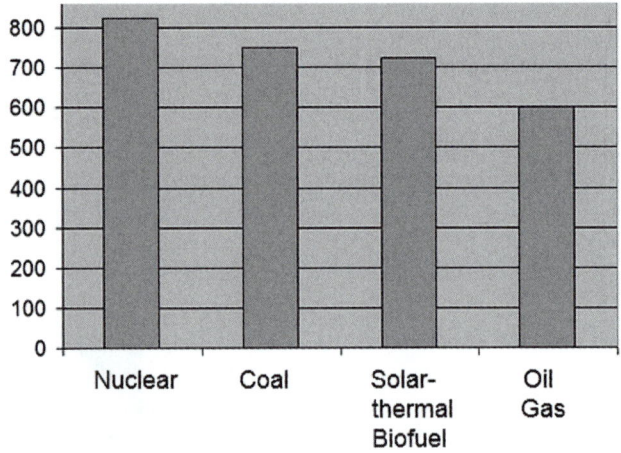

Figure 5-14. Cooling water use by different power plants (in gallons per MWh)

Looking at Figure 5-14, we see that over 825 gallons of fresh, cool, water are needed to cool the steam during the production of 1 MWh electricity at a nuclear power plant. Not much, you'd say. Maybe, but let's take a closer look.

A large nuclear plant generates 2.0 GW electricity 24 hours a day, at least 300 days a year for at least 30 years. In terms of cooling water use, our 2.0 GW nuclear

power plant looks like this:

2,000 MW x 24 hours = 48,000 MWh generated daily
48,000 MWh x 825 gallons = 39.6 million gallons per day
39.6 gallons x 300 days = 11.9 billion gallons per year
11.9 billion gallons x 30 years = 356.4 billion gallons

This is more than 350 billion gallons of waste water coming from one power plant during its 30-year lifetime—enough water to fill a 1,000-acre lake 1,000 feet deep. It also represents 356 billion gallons of hot water dumped into a nearby river or a lake, and a lot of hot water vapor being pumped into the atmosphere from the cooling towers.

This gets even worst when considering water used during mining, fracking, processing, and refining of coal, oil, and gas fuels. Enormous quantities of clean, fresh water are used in these processes, where it is converted into a dirty, toxic pollutant which is sometimes released into the environment, contaminating soil and water tables.

The waste water quantity from one source multiplied by the thousands of mines, oil and gas wells, and fossil-fired power plants, produces a number with too many zeros to count, and too many environmental effects to even describe, let alone solve.

Recirculation Cooling

Power plants' cooling towers may use river or lake water, seawater, or well water as a continuous source of fresh cooling water. The forced-draft cooling towers used in these plants continuously circulate cooling water through heat exchangers and other equipment where the water absorbs heat. The water is then exposed to the atmosphere where heat is transferred to the surrounding air, causing partial evaporation of the cooling water.

Water is a life-sustaining environment for many life forms, and indispensible for human life. Water cooling, with its large amount of byproducts—hot water and vapor—alters natural water environments and in many cases creates new environments. For example, recirculating cooling water systems support colonization by sessile organisms which use the circulating supply of food, oxygen and nutrients.

Large volumes of water lost during evaporative cooling may decrease natural habitat for aquatic organisms and increase the water temperature. The temperature increases modify aquatic habitat by increasing biochemical reaction rates and decreasing oxygen saturation capacity of the habitat.

The evaporated water is usually replaced by fresh

water from the nearby river, lake, or ocean. The evaporation process creates dissolved salts in the cooling water reservoir, so a portion of the circulating water is continuously discarded as blowdown water, to prevent the excessive build-up of salts. This increases the mineral content of the disposal site, which might alter the life forms in it.

Temperature increases might initially favor a population shift from species requiring high-oxygen concentrations of cold water to those thriving by increases of metabolic rates in warm water. In certain cases, the temperatures may become high enough to support thermophilic populations.

Direct Cooling

On very large rivers, and at coastal sites, the direct-cooled system method is often used, instead. Here, cooling towers are not needed, because a continuous freshwater supply is pumped in and out for cooling the steam. The waste heat is transferred to the river or the coastal water instead. These systems thus rely upon a good, continuous supply of fresh river, or seawater, for cooling. The warmed water is returned directly to the aquatic environment, often at temperatures high enough to negatively affect local aquatic life. Thermal pollution of rivers, estuaries and coastal waters is of significant consideration when analyzing the environmental impacts of power plants.

Some nuclear reactors use heavy water as cooling, because it is a weaker neutron absorber. This allows for the use of less enriched fuel. For the main cooling system, normal water is preferably employed through the use of a heat exchanger, as heavy water is much more expensive. Reactors that use other materials for moderation (graphite) may also use normal water for cooling.

In all cases, the environmental impact of this flood of hot water, and the significant water loss due to evaporation, cannot be easily assessed, but it is significant to be sure. This phenomena is even more important today, when we are experiencing a prolonged draught cycle in the southwestern US.

Cooling-water Chemistry

Depending on its location and use, all waters contain varying amounts of impurities. These are as a result from contact with the atmosphere, soil, and/or containers. Cooling water must meet certain requirements, so it is often treated by adding chemicals, in an attempt to maintain satisfactory heat exchange, prevent corrosion, and minimize the overall environmental impact.

The type and quantity of impurities and additives vary, but here is a list of the most common impurities, additives and related phenomena found in cooling waters:

- Total dissolved solids (TDS) is the total mass of solid residue in water, which remains when a measured volume of water is evaporated. The salinity of water is determined by the amount of salts in it, which also determine water density and conductivity changes, caused by different types and quantities of dissolved materials.

- Scale formation is an unwanted phenomena, which occurs in cooling systems, where due to the impurities in the water, deposits form on the walls of the pipes. The deposits increase with increase of total dissolved solids in the water going through the pipes. The most common solids associated with scale formation are calcium and magnesium carbonate and sulfate.

- Corrosion rates usually also increase with increase of salinity, due to increased electrical conductivity. The corrosion rate usually decreases after reaching a peak, because higher levels of salinity decrease dissolved oxygen levels, which in turn decreases the oxidation (corrosion) rate.

- The hydrogen content in cooling waters is expressed with water ionization into hydronium (H_3O) cations and hydroxyl (OH) anions. The concentration of ionized hydrogen (as protonated water) determines the water's pH (acidity or alkalinity). Low pH (acidic) values increase the rate of corrosion while high pH values encourage scale formation. Aluminum-based corrosion rates increase with pH values above 9. Galvanic corrosion may be severe in water systems with copper and aluminum components. Acid is often added to cooling water systems to prevent scale formation.

- Some concentration of polyphosphates, or phosphonates with zinc and chromates, and other similar compounds, are maintained in cooling systems to keep heat exchange surfaces clean. An artificially created film of gamma iron oxide and/or zinc phosphate inhibits pipe and container corrosion by passivating the active areas (the anodic and cathodic reaction points that initiate the corrosion mechanism). These additives increase the salinity and total dissolved solids in the waters.

Phosphorus compounds also contribute to biofouling of the cooling system, and/or to eutrophication of natural aquatic environments in which the blowdown waters are discharged.

- Chromates are also added for corrosion protection, and are effective in reducing biofouling. However, they contribute to residual toxicity. Their concentrations are reduced in favor of less effective corrosion inhibitors. Blowdown waters may also contain chromium leached from the surface of wood cooling towers, where chromated copper arsenate was used as a preservative.

- Oxygen content in groundwater pumped from wells is very low, but most natural water supplies include dissolved oxygen. In cooling towers it approaches saturation levels, which is desirable when blowdown waters are returned to the natural aquatic environments.

- Biocides in cooling waters are controlled by the addition of chlorine (in the form of hypochlorite) to decrease biofouling. Its concentration is kept at a level low enough to minimize the toxicity of blowdown waters when returned to the natural aquatic environment.

- Chlorinated phenols are sometimes used as biocides too, together with other additives, such as hypochlorite and pentachlorophenol. These, however, have reduced effectiveness at pH values greater than 8. Non-oxidizing biocides are basically more difficult to detoxify prior to release of blowdown water to natural aquatic environments, and might cause more damage in there too.

Residential and Commercial Water Use

A great amount of energy is used daily for domestic and commercial water and space heating and cooling.

Domestic Water Heating

A large amount of water in a house is heated for use in bathtubs, showers, dishwashers and washing machines. If we put all these together, we come up with over 50% use of electricity at the home. A bathtub is one of the greatest wasters of energy. U.S. bathtubs are the largest in the world. A standard American bathtub is 60" x 30" x 13." Depending on the depth of hot water drawn for a bath, this tub can hold between 40 and 60 gallons. Many specialized bath tubs exceed these dimensions.

Assuming 120°F temperature of the water in the tub, vs. 50°F of the incoming water, means that we need to elevate the temperature of 40-60 gallons of bath water by 70 degrees. One Btu of heat raises the temperature of one pound of water by one degree F. One gallon of water weighs 8.337 lbs, so .8.337 lbs of water x 70°F change requires 583.59 Btu.

Since 1 kWh = 3413 Btu, then 583.59 Btu/3413 Btu per kWh = 0.171 kWh electricity per gallon of water is needed to heat it from 50 deg. to 120 deg. 0.171 kWh x 40 = 6.8 kWh, or 0.171 kWh x 60 = 10.3 kWh.

So, taking a bath requires between 7 and 10 kWh of electric power for single dip. At an average cost of $0.20 per kWh, this pleasure would cost us $1.40 to $2.00, while at the same time the plant providing the electricity emitted several dozen kilograms of CO_2 in the air. Some people with the habit of refilling the tub a time or two, double and triple the electricity use and CO_2 emissions.

By comparison, taking a shower with today's efficient shower heads at 2.5 gallons per minute flow, uses 10-20 gallons of hot water, or between 1.7 kWh and 2.4 kWh—at least 4 times more efficient than taking a bath.

Cooking

The small ring on an electric cooker that is often used to heat water for tea, coffee, and meals has the same power as a toaster, 1 kW. The higher-power hot plates deliver 2.3 kW. If you use two rings of the cooker on full power for half an hour per day, that corresponds to 1.6 kWh per day.

A microwave oven of 900W actually consumes about 1.4 kW. If you use the microwave for 20 minutes per day, that's 0.5 kWh per day.

An electric oven guzzles about 3 kW when on full power. If you use the oven for one hour per day, and the oven is on full power for half of that time, that's another 1.5 kWh per day.

Washing machines, driers, and dishwashers use about 2.5 kWh each, while electric heaters and air conditioners guzzle 2-3 kWh electricity each.

Commercial Heating and Cooling

Commercial enterprises and small businesses also use a lot of electric power. Inside and outside lighting, space heating and cooling, appliances and electric equipment are the main users of electric power. A lot of electricity is also wasted by improperly functioning equipment and lighting fixtures.

Cooling Water Regulations

Millions of gallons of clean fresh water are used for cooling the steam of the power plants' turbines. The U.S.

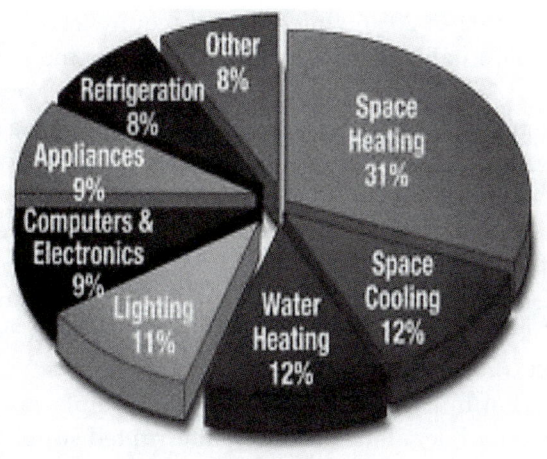

Figure 5-15. U.S. domestic electricity use

Clean Water Act requires the U.S. EPA to regulate the cooling water intake and release structures. EPA issued final regulations for new facilities in 2001, which was amended in 2003. Other EPA regulations for existing facilities were challenged in litigation, and EPA issued new proposed regulations in March 2011.

The EPA regulation, Water: Cooling Water Intakes (316b), states that EPA is developing regulations under §316(b) of the Clean Water Act. §316(b), which requires that the location, design, construction and capacity of cooling water intake structures reflect the best technology available for minimizing adverse environmental impact.

More than 1,500 industrial facilities use large volumes of cooling water from lakes, rivers, estuaries or oceans to cool their plants, including steam electric power plants, pulp and paper makers, chemical manufacturers, petroleum refiners, and manufacturers of primary metals like iron and steel and aluminum.

Cooling water intake structures cause adverse environmental impact by pulling large numbers of fish and shellfish or their eggs into a power plant's or factory's cooling system. There, the organisms may be killed or injured by heat, physical stress, or chemicals used to clean the cooling system. Larger organisms may be killed or injured when they are trapped against screens at the front of an intake structure.

There are three rulemaking phases addressing cooling water intakes:

Phase I rule, promulgated in 2001, covers new facilities.

Phase II rule, promulgated in 2004, covers large existing electric generating plants.

Phase III rule, promulgated in 2006, covers certain existing facilities and new offshore and coastal oil and gas extraction facilities.

Phase II mandates the management of cooling water at power plants. Only power plants with a total design intake flow of 50 million gallons of water per day are affected by this regulation. This is a very large amount of water, which allows many power plants to operate under the radar.

Case Study. Mohave Generating Station

This study is an example of incredible water waste, where it is most scarce and needed—in the desert. Mohave Generating Station, a 1.6 GW coal-fired power plant located in the SW USA desert near Laughlin, NV, at the border of California and Arizona, started operation in 1971. Southern California Edison was the majority owner and operator of the plant. Nothing unusual thus far—just thousands of tons of poisonous gasses pumped in the air and settling on the ground—40,000 tons of SO_2 poisons and that much CO_2 and other toxic gasses and particles every year, to be exact.

This is normal for coal-fired power plants, though, so the amazing, and thoroughly extraordinary twist here was the addition of a special and very unusual way to transport the coal from the mine to the plant. A water-slurry pipe transport system was engineered for this project!

The engineers designed it, and politicians and regulators allowed thousands of tons of coal for use in the power plant to be crushed, dissolved in water and transported from the mine in a 273-mile-long slurry pipeline. The pipeline ran from the Peabody Energy Black Mesa coal mine—located on lands belonging to the Navajo Nation and Hopi Tribe—to the coal-fired power plant located on the Arizona-Nevada border.

Please note: thousands of tons of coal were dug out of the ground, transported to the surface, crushed into powder, *dissolved in millions of gallons of pure desert water* and sent through the pipeline to the power plant.

Just imagine the amount of energy required to dig out and crush the fossils, make the slurry, and pump it hundreds of miles away. More than anything, imagine the millions of gallons of water pumped from the desert floor.

Isn't that one of the most amazing 20th century fairy tales? Doesn't it reflect great imagination and guts? So much waste—solid waste, liquid waste and gaseous waste.

It was amazing that anyone could think of such a thing, and that this project was sustainable in its original design. Sure enough, in 2005, the Mohave Generating Station ceased operations due to a Clean Air Act lawsuit and because Navajo and Hopi tribes passed resolutions ending Peabody's use of the Black Mesa aquifer.

"We had kind of hoped for a better outcome," a company official said.

According to the EPA, the coal plant was the dirtiest in the Western U.S., emitting up to 40,000 tons of sulfur dioxide and that much carbon dioxide and other gasses every year. This, in addition to wasting millions of gallons of precious desert water.

Now, another amazing thing is happening at the same place. Propped by political savvy, the owners of the failed plant are rewarded for this feat by receiving $20 million annually in the form of SO_2 credits—something for nothing.

Of course, not all water use abnormalities are so grotesque, but no matter how small, water misuse in sensitive areas is a serious issue, and we must look at it equally seriously and resolve it before it becomes unresolvable.

Recently, large-scale solar installations have been built in the world deserts, where they draw large amounts of water for equipment cooling purposes. The water table in deserts is a fleeting variable, putting it mildly. It means the difference between life and death for people who live in the deserts. Exhausting that life source might convert places like Las Vegas, NV, and Phoenix, AZ, into ghost towns, where only desert lizards can live. See below for details.

Case study: CSP

Now hear this: concentrating solar power (CSP) is the fastest developing large-scale solar power generating technology. The estimates call for over 24 GW of CPS power plants to be installed on 200,000 acres of BLM land by 2030. This is possible, and would be a great thing for the country—replacing 30-40 coal-fired plants and/or 12 nuclear stations.

The problem is that CSP requires water.

a. 30-40 gallons of water are used per generated MW to clean the mirrors, because dirty mirrors don't reflect well and will cause plant efficiency to drop.

b. 50-60 gallons are consumed per generated MW to make up for lost water (steam) in the turbines.

c. About 1,000 gallons of water are used for each MWh of generated electricity for steam cooling purposes.

Ignoring a. and b. above, we see that at 24 GW the U.S. CSP industry will produce about 24 GWh (24 GW every hour) in 2030, which would require 24 x 1,000 = 24 million gallons of water every hour for the cooling alone. Multiplying this by approximately 8 hours of daily power generation, we would need to empty a large lake of water every day just to provide cooling for the steam cycle.

This can be equated with emptying a 600-acre lake one foot deep every day. After a year, this amounts to a huge lake about 7,300 acres and 10 feet deep. No matter how you look at it, this is not a desert picture—certainly not in U.S. deserts.

That much water in the desert is simply not possible to find, let alone ensure uninterrupted supply of—especially during prolonged draughts, such as the one we are experiencing now. So we need to do something to change the requirements.

Air-cooled condensers come to the rescue (maybe) as a solution to using so much water for cooling, but they require a lot of energy, which would drop the efficiency of the plant significantly. Also, air cooling in 120-130 degree weather is not a very efficient proposition to begin with, so this method is still on the drawing board.

Abandoned Mines

There are many old, abandoned mines in the U.S. and around the world. Hundreds of abandoned mines in the Navajo Nation (the United States' largest Indian reservation) look like they might still be in use. You can see tailings, or waste products piled everywhere, and the land isn't fenced off. It looks like a picture from Mars, according to the locals.

The U.S. Environmental Protection Agency is assessing over 520 open abandoned mines over the vast Indian reservations, but there are at least 1,300 such mines in the territory. A number of bankruptcy settlements address the contamination issues, but are not enough to cover the vase expanse.

During the Cold War, private companies operated uranium mines under U.S. government contracts, which resulted in removing over 4 million tons of ore that went into making nuclear weapons and fuel. When demand dried up, companies simply abandoned the mines, and left them as they were.

Remediation work started 10 years ago, when the EPA mapped the mines by investigating company records and surveying the land with helicopters equipped with radiation detectors. EPA representatives are still visiting mines to determine their radiation levels and measure other toxic levels.

The mines expose the locals to uranium radiation through airborne dust and contaminated drinking water.

Many residents' homes were built using mud and rocks near mines, and some of that building material is radioactive. There are few published studies on the effects of uranium mines on nearby residents, but researchers at the Centers for Disease Control and Prevention and the University of New Mexico are working on health assessments, according to EPA officials. Researchers have known for decades that uranium exposure increases the risk of lung and bone cancers and kidney damage.

EPA started cleanup in some mines because they were worried about the effects on ranchers and their cattle, which drinks and grazes on the uranium-contaminated land. This is a difficult and expensive process, which will likely take decades. There are coal and uranium mines that are not even included in the EPA's list of abandoned mines.

Officials usually do not discuss or release their findings, but it is a well known fact that EPA contractors usually find radiation levels at the abandoned mines that were higher than the EPA's Geiger counters could measure.

Abandoned coal mines also contribute to continuous environmental damage. There are gas and liquid leaks from these mines, which contaminate local air, soil, and water supplies. Efforts to mitigate the damages and recover and restore the land to its original conditions are underway, but mostly on paper. The actual effort will take many years and millions of dollars to complete.

Abandoned Oil and Gas Fields

There are many abandoned oil and gas wells in the U.S., called orphans, which have created environmental and health problems in the past. Pennsylvania has more than 8,000 orphaned wells drilled over the last century and a half, and the Pennsylvania Department of EPA is unaware of the location or status of an additional 184,000 wells. Orphaned wells are not a problem of the past; newer wells can be orphaned by their operators, too, and left to someone else to clean up.

Nearly 12,000 coal-bed methane wells in Wyoming were idle as of 2011, neither producing nor properly plugged. Wyoming officials are concerned that several companies that operate coal-bed methane wells may file for bankruptcy if natural gas prices do not rebound or if the companies cannot sell off some assets to raise capital to comply with state environmental protection policy.

Industry specialists estimate that plugging a 3,000-foot-deep oil or gas well and reclaiming the drill site costs an average of $60,000, but some well reclamation costs have exceeded $100,000. Some operators claim that they spent nearly $250,000 per well to cap a shale gas well in Pennsylvania. A 2011 study estimated the cost of site reclamation, including reclamation of retention ponds and repairs to public roads to reach $500,000 to $800,000 per well site. Not a small change or small change…

Scattered across the oil and gas fields of Texas are nearly 8,000 abandoned oil and gas wells. The locals call them orphans. There are also nearlyl 5,500 additional wells that are inactive, but which are delinquent in meeting regulations.

Of course, there is a large number of unknown orphan wells, drilled decades ago, for which the records have been lost or never existed. Many of these were drilled when the environment was not part of the equation and no one knew to care.

Driving though Texas you'll see pump jacks bobbing up and down in a never-ending symphony of noise and smells, bringing up the oil. Some are only feet from homes, others are in forests surrounded by trees and vegetation. Today, however, most of the pumpjacks still in operation are low-flow, producing very little oil.

As an example, a Texas company failed to plug some of their old wells, so the authorities barred the company from doing oil and gas operations in Texas altogether in 2000. Five wells were not properly plugged, and the water table in the area is likely to be contaminated by migrations or discharges of saltwater and other oil and gas wastes. The company was fined over $200,000 plus court costs and fees for the damages, but there were no corporate assets available to pursue. The company just disappeared, and it is not the only one.

Thousands of wells have been abandoned over the years that have cost the state of Texas millions to clean up and plug. Since 1984, Texas has spent over $250 million from the Oil Field Cleanup Fund and other state and federal sources of funds for this purpose. Luckily, Texas taxpayers do not pay for the cleanup.

Now, oil and gas prices are higher, and drilling is booming again in the same regions of north and south Texas where the highest number of orphaned wells are located. Will things be different this time, or will history repeat itself? Are we looking at a new generation of orphan wells when the current boom subsides?

It seems like this time there is a much stronger awareness and oversight of these activities. The permitting process and state and federal regulations are in place and are enforceable. This time, insurance and bonds are required to start a well drilling and exploration. This includes insurance to cover the cost of cleanup and plugging the well. This will ensure that operators don't abandon wells as in the past.

THE LESSONS...

A number of major natural events must be taken into account and used lessons to be learned, when estimating climate changes. The enormous size and wide-reaching devastation from natural events like hurricanes and volcanos is so great that they make any man-made creation look like a toy.

These are the obvious events, which we can detect and observe without special instruments. Looking deeper underground and in the oceans, we see forces that are equal to none. Huge tectonic plates move slowly, creating earthquakes and tsunamis. Deep in the oceans magma is flowing and changing the ocean floor to cause effects that we cannot even account for. And these activities go on and on, non-stop, 24/7.

Human-activities go on 24/7 too, and no matter how small they can be as compared to some natural events, they are persistent and cumulative. Some of the effects from human activities grow with time too and are becoming more and more obvious.

In all cases, natural events and man-made activities play a significant role in our environment. It is very hard to separate the contribution of the natural and man-made events on the environment and the subsequent climate change, but they have had, and still are, affecting us and our environment one way or another.

Below we describe a few major events which might be connected to human activities, and which surely have affected the environment, and all life forms in it, including humans. These cases should be used as examples of what we should, or should not, do and what to expect in the future.

Easter Island

There is a small, totally isolated, island in the Pacific Ocean that can teach us what can happen to us and our Earth if we are not managing its resources carefully.

This micro-environmental lesson takes us to Easter Island, which long ago had a luscious sub-tropical forest, complete with palms and thick vegetation. It is the home of the tall Easter Island Palm trees, suitable for building homes, canoes, etc. The vegetation of the island provided fuel, wood, and other needs. With their sea-worthy canoes, Easter Islanders lived off a steady diet of porpoise. A complex social structure developed, complete with a centralized government and religious priests.

The Easter Island people built the famous statues and hauled them around the island. The construction of these statues became an obsession and peaked around 1200 to 1500 AD. At the same time, the tree population of the island rapidly declined as deforestation took its toll.

Around 1400, the Easter Island palm became extinct. Millions of rats took over the forest, eating the palm seeds and not allowing the trees to reproduce. With no palm trees to make canoes, the islanders could not go out to sea to fish. The islanders started hunting and eating the migratory birds and mollusks that populated the island at the time.

Soon all animal life on the island disappeared, and the forests lost their animal pollinators and seed dispersers with the disappearance of the birds. Today, only one of the original 22 species of seabirds still nests on Easter Island.

With the loss of their forest, the quality of life for islanders plummeted. The island became a barren piece of land in the middle of the inhospitable ocean. Drinking water supplies dried up, crop yields declined as wind, rain, and sunlight eroded the topsoil. Grass was used for occasional fires, and soon the islanders began to starve. Life worsened by the day, and the society order melted into chaos and disarray.

The survivors formed bands, and bitter fighting for survival erupted on the small island. By the arrival of Europeans in 1722, there were only couple of thousand people left (from 15,000 a century earlier), and there was almost no sign of the great civilization that once ruled the island other than a handful of the famous moai stone statues, which originally numbered over 900. Many fell victim to rival bands who toppled and destroyed them.

The island was further pillaged by slave ships that took many people to distant lands. By 1880 there were only 100 people left on the island and very little could be found of the great Rapanui civilization.

Easter Island is a prime example of what widespread deforestation can do to a society. As the forests are depleted, the quality of life falls, and order is lost. The example of Easter Island should be enough for us to reconsider our current practices.

Angry Mountains: the Power of Nature

At this very moment, at least 20 small and large volcanoes are erupting worldwide. In the past 10,000 years over 1,300 volcanoes have erupted, and the estimates suggest that there have been more than a million underwater explosions at the same time. These are five of the worst volcanic explosions that humankind has recorded.

Toba

74,000 years ago Toba volcano in Sumatra exploded. The blast was so strong that a mixture of ash and sulphur dioxide was thrown into the stratosphere, blocking out the sun's rays and causing the temperature to plummet. Some scientists believe that it almost led to the extinction of humanity, as only a few thousand people survived.

Vesuvius

In 79 AD Vesuvius erupted, and its pyroclastic flow destroyed the Roman cities of Pompeii and Herculaneum, burying them and thousands of their citizens beneath the lava and preserving their bodies.

Santorini Volcano

In 1600 BC Santorini erupted and buried the city of Akroteri and possibly gave rise to the legend of Atlantis. Three islands remained after the eruption—Thera, Therasia, and Aspronisi. Santorini caldera has a diameter 11 km by 7.5 km, with a depth of 390 m in the north area.

In 1650 BC a series of Plinian eruptions at Santorini volcano expelled 40-60 cubic km of lava, and created a regional tsunami. This eruption was possibly the main factor in the destruction of the Minoan civilization.

Tambora

In 1815 the Indonesian Tambora volcano erupted in the largest explosion ever recorded. About 150 cubic kilometers of ash (150 times more than was produced when Mount St. Helens erupted) was blown 44 km into the sky and spread for 1,300 km. Around 92,000 people were killed.

Mount Krakatoa

Krakatoa in the Dutch East Indies erupted in May 1883 and culminated with several destructive eruptions of the Krakatoa caldera in August of that year. During that time much of the island and its surrounding archipelago were destroyed. Continuous seismic activity was reported during the next 6 months.

As a consequence of the eruptions (dust and ash in the air), average global temperatures fell by as much as 2.2°F, the weather was affected for years, and temperatures did not return to normal until 1888.

Krakatoa's eruption injected a very large amount of sulfur dioxide (SO_2) gas high into the stratosphere, which was subsequently transported around the globe by high-level winds. This led to a global increase in sulfurous acid (H_2SO_3) concentration in high-level cirrus clouds. The resulting increase in cloud reflectivity (or albedo) would reflect more incoming light from the sun than usual, cooling the entire planet until the suspended sulfur fell to the ground as acid precipitation.

In addition, the pressure wave generated by the enormous final explosion radiated out from Krakatoa at 675 mph. It was so powerful that it ruptured the eardrums of sailors on ships in the area and caused a spike of more than 2-1/2 inches of mercury, as measured nearby. The pressure wave radiated across the globe and was recorded on barographs all over the world up to 5 days after the explosion. Barographic recordings show that the shock-wave from the final explosion reverberated around the globe 7 times. Ash was propelled to an estimated height of over 50 miles.

Five days later, the eruptions diminished rapidly, then Krakatoa was silent. Small eruptions, mostly of mud, continued for the next 2 months.

On 27 August, a rain of hot ash fell around Ketimbang, Sumatra. Approximately 1,000 people were killed by the flying hot ash from the massive explosion.

The eruption darkened the sky worldwide for years afterward, and produced spectacular sunsets throughout the world for many months. Weather watchers tracked and mapped the effects on the sky. They labeled the phenomenon the "equatorial smoke stream." This was the first identification of what is known today as the jet stream. This eruption also produced a Bishop's Ring around the sun by day, and a volcanic purple light at twilight.

The amount of gasses and ash emitted from the Krakatoa eruption equals that generated by many years of coal-burning worldwide. *One volcanic eruption* (natural event) can obliterate the results of years of efforts to reduce fossil-fuel generated air pollution (human event).

And Krakatoa is not the only major eruption in human history. Not all of them are as massive and as damaging, but the environmental damage and loss of human life is palpable, so we need to take all this into consideration.

Mount Pelée

In 1902, 150 miles south of Montserrat, Mount Pelée on the French Island of Martinique erupted, killing 28,000 people in a pyroclastic flow—a mixture of hot lava turned into a fluid by expanding volcanic gas and air. It is hot enough to melt glass and flows at speeds of around 100 mph. The volcano has been active since 1995 and may erupt at any point.

Mount St. Helen's

In the summer of 1980, Mount St Helen's in Washington State, erupted. The north face of the mountain collapsed, causing a massive rock avalanche. Almost

230 square miles of forest was blown down or buried beneath ash deposits. A column of ash rose hundreds of meters into the air and the eruption lasted for nine hours. Around 24,000 animals and 56 people died.

Earthquakes

Earthquakes have occurred on Earth's surface since the beginning of time. Thousands and thousands of earthquakes of different magnitudes occur every year, but most of them go unnoticed as they are either too weak on the Richter scale or happen far from populated centers. Large earthquakes, however, almost always result in loss of life, property, and environmental damage.

On May 22, 1960 the world witnessed Valdicvia, Chile's strongest earthquake ever, with a magnitude of 9.5 on Richter scale. It caused 20,000 fatalities. The second strongest earthquake on record occurred on December 26, 2004, with a magnitude of 9.3 on Richter scale. The ocean floor of west Sumatra and Indonesia were the epicenter of this earthquake that caused over 300,000 causalities and the disastrous tsunami in the Indian Ocean.

On March 27, 1964, Prince William Sound, Alaska, faced the third strongest recorded earthquake. It measured 9.2 on the Richter scale and caused a great deal of damage in Anchorage.

The quake in Kamchatka, 1952 having 9.0 magnitude, is the fourth strongest earthquake on record. After this comes the 2011 Japan earthquake, measuring 8.9 on the Richter scale.

On 26 December, 2004, the Sumatra-Andaman earthquake (9.2 on the Richter scale) with an epicenter off the west coast of Sumatra, Indonesia, caused a large tsunami (called 2004 Indian Ocean tsunami, South Asian tsunami, Indonesian tsunami, or the Boxing Day tsunami). The earthquake had the longest duration of faulting ever observed, close to 10 minutes. It caused the entire planet to vibrate as much as 0.4-05 inches and triggered other earthquakes as far away as Alaska. 200,000 people lost their lives in the tsunami, which was accompanied by massive infrastructure destruction and environmental damage.

Other large earthquakes are the Tangshan, China, earthquake of 1976, in which at least 255,000 were killed; the earthquake of 1927 in Xining, Qinghai, China, with 200,000 dead; the Great Kanto earthquake which struck Tokyo in 1923 with 143,000 victims); and the Gansu, China, earthquake of 1920 which killed 200,000 people. The deadliest known earthquake in history occurred in 1556 in Shaanxi, China, with an estimated death toll around 800,000.

Of course, we know about the 2012 earthquake off the coast of Japan that caused a large tsunami. The combined effect of these two natural disasters was total devastation of portion of Japan's coastline, and the destruction of the Fukushima nuclear power plant. The radiation emitted by the disabled nuclear reactors added a third and equally devastating component to the tragedy and completed its totality. Hundreds of square miles of coastland are uninhabitable and will remain so for decades to come.

The Fukushima, and the above listed disasters are a perfect picture of Nature at its worst, hitting man without warning and where we are most vulnerable. They are also a reminder of how small we are, as compared with Nature.

Ocean Flooding

New measurements have determined that Antarctica has warmed by about 4.40°F during the last century. This is causing fast melting of the global ice cap, which slowly elevates ocean levels. Some low-lying lands are already affected, and many more are expected to be flooded.

The Maldives

The Maldives are a group of 1,192 islands in the Indian Ocean, 250 miles from the south shores of India. It is not much different than many such island nations, except that the islands these people use for home are on average only 4 feet above sea level. In the middle of the Indian Ocean this is not much of a shelter, to be sure, and the Maldives people have their share of angry ocean stories to tell. But this is not the worst part. What is coming in the near future is what everyone is talking about and fears.

If and when the ocean level rises above a certain point (and we are talking about only one or two feet), then many parts of the island chain will disappear under water. The capital of the Maldives, Malé, is about 6 feet above sea level, but some of the reclaimed areas nearby are much lower and have been flooded by low-period waves in the past. Although the damage in those cases was minimal, the experience is a reminder of how vulnerable the Maldives can be to even a small rise in water levels.

These events and the ongoing talk about global warming, followed by the ocean level rising, have prompted those local officials to begin considering the implications of higher sea level. For that purpose they constructed a series of breakwaters on the outer coast of Malé, which will provide some protection for the capital from damaging storm waves. This barrier, however, would not prevent flooding from a sustained rise in water levels. Fortunately, even under the worst of conditions, it would take a long time for the ocean levels to rise more than one meter. This leaves Malé somewhat above the level of high tide for now.

There is, however, a more immediate concern—that of the dwindling of the freshwater table. With over 50,000 residents on one square kilometer of land, the annual refilling of the aquifer is much less than annual withdrawals for domestic and commercial use. As a result, fresh water is only available in the center of the island, and even there, it is decreasing. The locals use rooftop collections of rainwater for drinking, but cleaning and commercial uses still depend on groundwater.

The increased salinity of fresh water has reduced the vegetation on the islands. Malé has already lost its mango trees due to saltwater penetration. Although bananas and papayas have shorter roots, they could eventually be vulnerable, and less water would be available for irrigation. Fortunately, coconut trees tolerate saltwater, so there would be at least one supply channel left.

At this rate, the groundwater will be exhausted in a decade or two, so the ocean invasion is irrelevant in the eyes of the locals. While a political response might bring water from another island, or build a water desalination plant, sea level rise cannot be corrected by political action or controlled by technology.

During some of the previous storms, the reclaimed areas had to be evacuated, so a 2- or 3-foot water rise would completely inundate the reclaimed lands, and would leave the whole island under water. With that, the fresh drinking water supply would be unsuitable for human consumption. There would be no turning back. No amount of effort could save the islands and life on them.

Some islands are on a higher elevation—over 10 feet—so they can survive the rising ocean level much longer. But the fresh water usually is only a foot above sea level, so it is uncertain if it would move up with the rising ocean surface or get swallowed by it too.

So the Maldives have no choice but to adapt to sea level rise. There are several possible choices: abandoning the islands altogether, moving to islands of higher elevation, holding back the sea with dikes, and building the island upward. None of these choices is acceptable presently. People will not leave their homes, and moving to an adjacent island is a temporary solution because eventually the higher islands would also need to be abandoned.

Dikes have proven useful in many places. In the Netherlands, 50% of the country is below sea level and is protected by dikes and pumps. Although this can be a useful protection from waves, the conditions in the Maldives do not favor dikes, because the cost of building a permanent solid dike around an entire island is simply impractical. Also, there is the issue of the freshwater table. One would need to pump out the part of the water table where freshwater would normally reside. The cost of building and maintaining such a great undertaking could be greater than the value of the land being protected.

The loss of the waterfront view in Malé and the inconvenience in dealing with a wall around the entire island, would be unacceptable. So maybe the best way of protecting the islands would be to gradually elevate the islands. This would require a lot of sand and coral, but it would enable the islands to retain storage capacity for groundwater, and not substantially change their character.

The Maldives problem is a glimpse of what is coming our way on a grand scale, because only a 2- or 3-foot increase in the ocean level would sink Venice, parts of Florida, and many other low-lying areas of this world. Tuvalu—a tiny island country in the Pacific Ocean midway between Hawaii and Australia—is the first country where people are trying to evacuate because of rising seas. It certainly will not be the last.

The Tuvalu are relocating 11,000 people, but what about the 311,000 who may be forced to leave the Maldives by the end of the 21st century? Or the millions of others living in low-lying countries who may soon join the flow of climate refugees?

NOTE: Many natural events can have a similarly devastating effect, and we can do nothing to prevent any of those from happening. But we have the power to prevent man-made disasters. It is our responsibility to prevent any disasters over which we have control.

Bees Extinction

Albert Einstein said almost a century ago that if bees were to disappear, man would follow only a few years later. He has been wrong before, and we hope he is wrong this time too, because a mysterious condition has wiped half of the honey bee population the United States. The same thing is happening in Europe.

No one can explain it, but there are fears that a new disease, the effects of pollution, or the increased use of pesticides, could be to blame for "colony collapse disorder." The depopulation of bees could have a huge impact on the environment, and U.S. agriculture in particular.

Many key crops could die off without pollinating insects.

The suspects for this pending doom of a species are pesticides and other chemicals that are used in extremely high quantities. The levels of chemical pollution of the air and water table in the U.S. and abroad are increasing, so it would not be hard to imagine the negative health effects on bees and other animals these might have. It is hard to pinpoint one of the chemicals, or even a class of chemicals, that could be responsible for this disaster, but what is easy to see is that we have an excess of chemicals in the air and water supplies—the same air and water bees use.

Governments are on the watch, and in France in 2004, the government banned the pesticide Fipronil after beekeepers in the south-west blamed it for huge losses of hives. The manufacturers, of course, denied their products were harmful to bees. In Eastern Europe, beekeepers claimed that the losses in their country could be connected to cheap sugar substitutes used in mass honey production.

Initial studies of dying colonies in America revealed a large number of disease organisms present, with no one disease being identified as the culprit. If it turns out that the bees are dying from a disease, then a cure will be found sooner or later. If, however, the reason for the mass extinction on a global level is environmental pollution, then not much could be done. All that is known presently is that entire colonies are dying in large numbers, and we simply don't know why.

Bees are vital to bio diversity. There are over 130,000 plants for which bees are essential for pollination, from melons to pumpkins, raspberries and all kinds of fruit trees, as well as animal fodder like clover. Bees are more important than poultry in terms of human nutrition. Bees from one hive can visit a million flowers within a 300-square-mile area in a single day. Without them, most of the plants in the affected areas will not survive either.

Bees are not only helping us grow crops, but are also perfect indicators of the state of the environment. Judging from their state we could conclude that our environment is also dying of an unknown disease.

PRESENT-DAY GLOBAL ENVIRONMENTAL STATUS

During the last century, a number of natural events and increasing human activities have contributed significantly to changing the environment. The planet is faced with many environmental problems, some of which are local, but most of which are shared by all nations.

Key Environmental Issues

Following is a list of environmental problems considered to be the most significant issues facing our planet today:

- Energy sources depletion, due to excess fossils use for power generation is a leading source of environmental damage. Coal, oil and gas-fired power plants are the primary source of electricity across the planet and contribute to the majority of greenhouse gas released to the atmosphere. Alternate sources of energy are available, such as solar, wind and hydro among others; however they are only providing a small percentage of all energy needs in the country. Increasing the amount of energy generated by renewable sources is the most important step in minimizing environmental degradation caused by the production of electricity.

- Global climate warming as a consequence of excess fossils use is considered to be the most serious sign of climate change in recent times, the implications of which will become increasingly significant during the next decades. Governments around the world have begun addressing the effects of climate change, but without addressing the causes simultaneously, climate change will continue to be a major environmental problem.

- Water scarcity and pollution is just now coming on the radar of some U.S. states and many nations. Many large cities around the world have been faced with drinking water shortages, and are enforcing restrictions on water use.

- Agriculture is the leading cause of degradation and pollution in the waterways, where unsustainable irrigation practices and the release of fertilizers and pesticides within this industry are the predominant causes of water pollution. Lately, oil and natural gas fracking have been blamed for serious water table contamination of large areas as well.

- Biodiversity has been affected by unsustainable land use, which has led to the degradation of many valuable ecosystems, resulting in the loss of biodiversity. There are thousands of land-based species on the threatened species lists, and the list is growing. We humans depend on the diverse ecosystems for oxygen production, water filtration, nutrient flow and pollination. Loss of this biodiversity is jeopardizing many of the services we take for granted. We must not ignore it.

- Toxic chemicals, heavy metals, and other poisons exist in small amounts in nature, but during the last 200 years man-made pollutants have been dumped in extremely large quantities in the world's air, soil, and water. The sources are many, and most of them have caused severe environmental problems. The most affected areas are agricultural and heavy industrial developments. Contamination of any area of our lives is long-lasting and in some cases permanent. Reducing the use of fossils, fertilizers, and other toxic chemicals used in large-scale applications, is one step that needs to be taken to reduce the toxic pollutants.

- Air pollution, and especially the release of greenhouse gases is blamed for most of the climate change problems. There are a lot different gasses released during the burning of fossil fuels.

- In addition to the main culprit, carbon dioxide, sulfur and nitrogen oxides are also emitted in the atmosphere, where they cause considerable environmental problems. Acid rain, caused by these compounds damages living and man-made environments.

- Air pollution is also caused by the release of dust and other particulate substances into the air which also affect the health of animals and humans.

- Ozone layer depletion has been attributed to the release of chlorofluorocarbons (CFCs) into the atmosphere. Once CFCs reach the upper atmosphere, they cause ozone molecules to break apart causing a hole to form, the largest of which is over the Antarctic. The atmosphere is very important as it blocks many of the harmful UV rays from the sun that can damage living tissue. In an effort to reduce this process, CFCs have been banned in many manufacturing processes and products.

- Oceans and fisheries are also suffering from pollution and overfishing. A great number of previously valuable fish species have experienced catastrophic population declines during the last several decades. The collapse of the Atlantic Cod Fishery is one such example. It shows clearly how human activities have exploited the planet's natural resources to the brink of extinction. There are many other species of fish and marine organisms that are threatened by unsustainable fishing practices. Better control of these important resources is needed, without which many of the marine species will become extinct, or unviable as a food source.

- Deforestation of the world's forests occurred at extreme speed during the 20th century. Much of the Australian continent has now been cleared for agricultural and pastoral land use, as well as for our ever-expanding towns and cities. Deforestation basically destroys vital plant and animal habitat, which leads to a loss in biodiversity and the increasing degradation of important ecosystems.

- Waste management improprieties have resulted in many global environmental problems. The amount of waste has been increasing as a result of increased population and the related manufacturing and packaging processes. Governments, businesses, and individuals have been trying to recycle some of these products, minimizing the volume of waste as well as the use of natural resources, but these efforts are not enough. A global approach to waste management and recycling is needed.

Air Quality

An increase of "anthropogenic" gases in the atmosphere is one of the greatest dangers for the environment because they absorb in the 7-13 µm wavelength range. They are the particularly harmful gasses—carbon dioxide, methane, ozone, nitrous oxides, and chlorofluorocarbons (CFCs). These gases disturb and even prevent the normal exchange and escape of energy and eventually lead to an increase in the temperature of the Earth, thus changing the climate. There is scientific evidence that CO_2 levels will double by 2030, which will most likely cause global warming, increasing temperatures 1~4°C on average. This increase might accelerate with time, taking the global warming to unpredictable and unimaginable levels.

This accelerated warming trend will change wind patterns and rainfalls, and as a result may cause the interior of continents to dry out, while the Earth's oceans rise. These harmful effects will only increase with time unless the trend of releasing anthropogenic gases is interrupted.

Clearly, human activities have now reached a scale where they are impacting the planet's environment and its attractiveness to humans. Technologies with low environmental impact and no greenhouse gas emissions are becoming increasingly important. Since the energy sector is the major producer of greenhouse gases via the combustion of fossil fuels, technologies such as wind and solar that can substitute for fossil fuels must be considered seriously and used broadly.

Humans' Role

It is becoming very clear that we cannot control cosmic and natural actions and their effects on our lives. We can only understand them better, and try to predict how best to stay safe. We can, however, control our own actions precisely. The satellites help us understand the situation better, and with the help of their information, we can modify our behavior for our sake, and that of future generations.

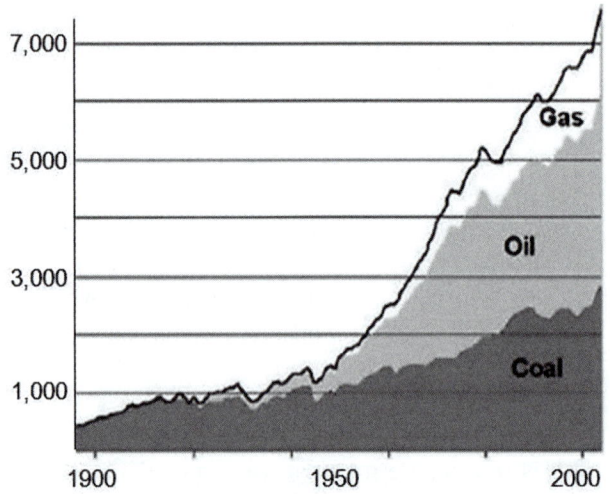

Figure 5-16.a Global CO_2 emissions from fossil fuels in the 20th century (in million tons of carbon)

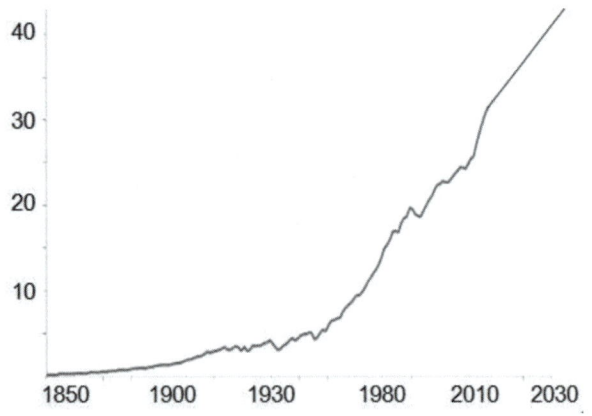

Figure 5-16.b Total global CO_2 emissions (in Gt CO_2)

Just during the last 50 years, worldwide GHG emissions have increased several fold. It is clear that they are out of control, and it seems that they will continue rising, because many new coal and natural gas power plants are being built in many countries, and thousands of cars are added to the world fleet every year.

With the increase in fossil power generation, and gasoline and diesel emissions, we are headed into an uncharted territory. The Earth's atmosphere has not been loaded with such large quantities of toxic gasses since its creation, so it is hard to foresee the effects on our environment and our lives.

A picture is worth a thousands words, as they say. Looking at Figure 5-17, it is not too difficult to figure out who the culprits are. The U.S. leads the world in fossils use and CO_2 emissions, and the gap is increasing as we speak. The amount of poisons in the air, and their negative effects on the environment are increasing too.

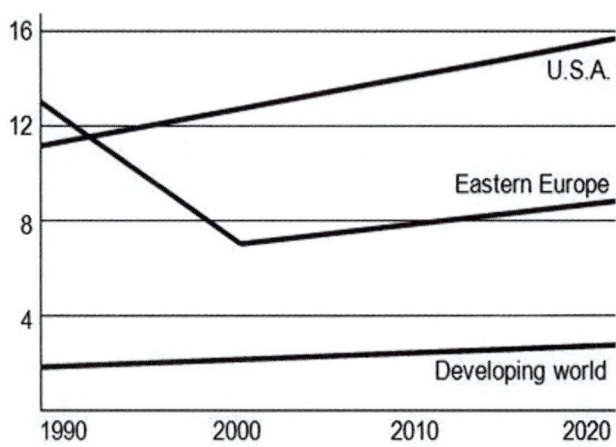

Figure 5-17. CO_2 emissions per capita (tons/year/person).

All power-generating facilities have some adverse effect. For example:

- Coal, oil, and natural gas mining, pumping, fracking, transport, storage, and burning create toxic and other harmful gases, liquids and solids. These byproducts damage the environment and human health.

- Nuclear facilities are ticking bombs that can take many people's lives. Their byproducts are piling ever higher and there is still no solution as to what to do with them.

- Hydroplants are built on dams, which cover large land areas by flooding them permanently, disrupting millions of people's lives. Damaged dams break and the ensuing floods are devasting. Even looking at the better side of hydroplants, water shortages have severely limited their placement areas.

- Solar PV facilities can cause a number of problems, including potential glare and glint hazards to aircraft, trains, and highway traffic, and can impact agricultural lands and open space/habitat lands.

The desert locations are more affected, because they are usually very large—thousands of acres containing millions of PV modules and BOS equipment, working day and night under excruciatingly adverse conditions.

- Depending on their location, technology, and site design, wind farms have the potential for killing migrating or foraging raptors and bats, adversely affecting the visual landscape, creating aviation hazards, and causing noise problems if located near urban areas.

- Geothermal facilities can affect rare and endangered plant and animal species, cultural resources, the quantity and quality of local water supplies, and visual landscapes. Geothermal projects can also cause or contribute to local and regional air quality problems through emission of moderate amounts of regulated air pollutants, although they are required to use best available emissions control technology and provide emission offsets to comply with local air district regulations.

- Biomass plants can cause regional increases in criteria pollutants and particulate matter, post ash disposal and local land use concerns, and increased water use (if a facility uses water cooling towers or employs "wet scrubbers" to reduce hydrochloric acid emissions).

- All renewable energy facilities (in deserts and not) face environmental issues, depending on the technology, location, and size. For renewable facilities in the desert, the primary environmental concerns are biological and cultural resources, water supply, visual impacts, transportation-related visual hazards, and land use, as discussed in the following sections. Depending on the project, there may also be air quality, hazardous materials, noise, public safety, and local community concerns.

The Anti Man-made Movement

There are, however, numerous arguments against the man-made global warming theory, some of which make sense and deserve a second look. The environmental phenomena are too complex to put in a box and label as this or that. They can go either way, depending on human activities and Nature's plans. While we can see, understand, and even predict human activities, we cannot foresee what Nature has planned for tomorrow, next year and next century. This might be the greatest variable of all and something we should be fully aware

of and prepared for.

There is a natural balance that man has not been able to figure out completely—or control. Environmental issues are serious matters, with many people involved on both sides of the debate who have plausible pros and cons. They all deserve equal time and respect.

There is evidence that some of the events we see today are transitional and a part of the natural evolution of the Earth. Just like there was an Ice Age or two, there might be a time "Boiling Age." During such a time, temperatures could get so high that life on Earth might cease to exist altogether. Like our predecessors froze to death (and we don't know why exactly), future generations might over heat and die (never knowing exactly why).

Then new deposits of vegetation could be laid into the Earth's crust to be used by the new generations millions of years from today. It's one point of view.

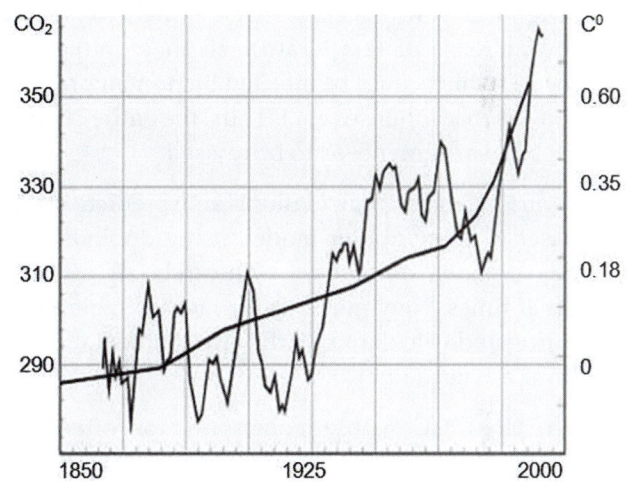

Figure 5-18. Increase of global CO_2 (in ppm), left, and Temperature increase (in degree C), right

The CO_2 levels measured in the summer of 2013 exceeded the 400 ppm mark, which is considered as maximum safe limits of CO_2 concentration in air, but the numbers are rising.

No one can argue that we are living in a period of increased air, water and soil pollution. Some of it is of natural, some of man-made origin. While the majority opinion is that the effects of man-made pollution exceed those of natural events, there are those who disagree.

The views and facts supporting environmental decay are overwhelming, while the counterviews are not as well advertised and are sometimes even laughed at. These counterviews are supported by 17,000 respected scientists who have signed a petition circulated by the

Oregon Institute of Science and Medicine, claiming that there is no convincing scientific evidence that human release of carbon dioxide, methane, or other greenhouse gases is causing catastrophic heating of the Earth's atmosphere.

For fairness' sake, below is a partial list of the global warming counter-claims as expressed by a number of environmental scientists, organizations and specialists on the matter.

Disclaimer: The author is not involved with environmental, anti-environmental, or any related organizations or movements. The ideas and opinions expressed herein represent solely the author's own understanding of the environmental issues of the day.

The major counter claims are:

1. Satellite readings in the troposphere (the most affected area) show slight warming during the last quarter century. Land-based temperature measurement stations have been known to reflect the increase of temperature in their immediate locale, which could be affected by human presence (paved roads, houses etc.). Thus, the entire claim of global warming needs to be revised.

2. Global warming calculations and predictions are based on a computer model, using dubious "flux adjustments" methods, which can be significantly off at times. New methods for more reliable monitoring and calculating of the environmental conditions are needed.

3. The UN IPCC, whose reports are most often used in defense of global warming, says, "The Earth's atmosphere-ocean dynamics is chaotic: its evolution is sensitive to small perturbations in initial conditions. This sensitivity limits our ability to predict the detailed evolution of weather; inevitable errors and uncertainties in the starting conditions of a weather forecast amplify through the forecast. As well as uncertainty in initial conditions, such predictions are also degraded by errors and uncertainties in our ability to represent accurately the significant climate processes."

   This makes it clear that the situation is not as clear as presented by the environmental movement. New, bias-free methods for measuring and evaluating the earth-ocean-atmosphere dynamics are needed.

4. There was a period in human evolution (~ 5000-3000 BC) known as the "climatic optimum," when temperatures were much higher than today's. Civi-

lization (in whatever form it was in those days) survived and progressed, mostly because people wore less clothing in those days. But seriously, rising temperatures might teach us a new way of life—more humble and practical.

Just like the Earth experienced a number of cold-hot cycles, the new one is driven, at least in part, by natural phenomena galore, which in some cases are much more powerful than those caused by human activities. The cumulative effect of these is obvious, but which effect is caused by which phenomena and how much is yet unclear, so the work has to be extended in the area of distinguishing the natural from man-made events.

5. Hasty, grand-scale efforts to quickly reduce the greenhouse effect without having a solid understanding of the situation might have side effects that we cannot even imagine, let alone foresee, right now. The different governments are approaching and handling these efforts in their different and, at times, clumsy, partial, and fragmented ways.

   The final cumulative effect of such efforts is even more complex to understand and might be complicating further the present situation, thus contributing to further, more serious, and undesirable environmental changes.

6. Lately, new scientific data (2010 tests and observations) show that the ozone hole is shrinking, even though human activities and related damage are on the increase, so we cannot draw an exact parallel and don't know why exactly this is happening and/or if this process will continue in this direction.

So who is right and who is wrong? Or could it be that they are all right...or maybe all are wrong? We'd like to leave it at this, but emphasize the importance of continuing the work in the above areas.

No matter what, we all agree that the climate is changing somewhat; we only don't agree on the reasons and speed of change. We also agree that this is a serious problem and that, if it continues, uncontrollably serious consequences will follow.

We also seek to learn exactly what's going on and offer solutions to the problems. We have not reached an agreement on the methods; thus, the debate continues. This is the first step towards making progress, so with the skeleton out of the closet, we can agree that we have problems, bring them out in the open, and look for solutions.

Talk is cheap, so as responsible citizens of Earth we must do our personal best to contribute to the well-being of the environment, on which our long-term survival as a species depends. The short-term solution is to live healthy, natural lives by considering the environment in everything we do. Crushing gas guzzlers, installing efficient light bulbs, and turning off the AC and heaters when not at home (sorry Spot and Kitty), might be a good first step in the right direction.

Stopping coal and oil burning are the next steps, but this is not easy, so a long battle awaits us. Energy generation and the resulting environmental issues will be with us for a long time, because we need both—the energy and the environment. Of course, using solar and wind energy efficiently and safely is the best way to provide energy while reducing pollution. This is also going to be a long and difficult road—which, as a matter of fact, is getting more difficult by the day.

Energy generation is big business, so environment problems or not, it will continue as is for a long time to come. We just need to better understand and control it and its problems. As we can see from Table 5-3, all energy sources produce some pollution (solar and wind too) simply because a lot of energy and special raw materials are used during their manufacturing, transport, installation, and operation.

Table 5-3. CO_2 emissions from different energy sources

Plant type	CO_2 Emissions in grams / kWh
Lignite, power	1153
Bituminous coal	949
Lignite, heat	729
Hard coal, heat & power	622
Natural gas, power only	428
Natural gas, heat only	148
Biogas, heat and power	409
Hydro power	40
Nuclear power	32
Solar power, PV	30
Solar power, CSP	25
Wind energy, on-shore	24
Wind energy, off-shore	23

Of course, the pollution from a coal-burning plant is much more than that from a wind or solar plant, but the coal plant can produce a lot of power on demand—anytime we need it. Solar and wind are dependent on sunshine and wind...

Let's agree that none of the energy sources is a winner. None of them can carry us through to energy independence and a clean environment. Let's agree that we will use all of them as rationally and efficiently as possible, to obtain a plausible compromise that we all can live with, and which would also please future generations.

The Battle for Sustainability

Environmental sustainability deals with survival of the Earth's ecosystems in our world's ever-increasing levels of technological and economic activities. The planetary ecosystem consists of a complex, dynamic, but fragile network of sub-systems and interactions, which are constantly in motion, trying to maintain a balance, which can be disrupted, or even irreversibly damaged, by human activities. Sustainable development reflects these concerns, with emphasis on materials and resources, and the related pollution.

A number of human factors influence the interaction between humanity and the environment.

1. The human representatives of the environmental struggle are:
   — The producers, or those companies and individuals who use technology and tools to produce things, or provide services. In our case, mining operations, power generating, and power use entities.
   — The people who make money and control the process of production and consumption. In our case those are the investors and shareowners of mining operations, power plants, and utilities.
   — Governments and other large bodies, who to some extent control the activities of the other human groups.
   — The environmentalists who officially, or unofficially, counteract some of the actions of the above parties.
   — The consumers, or those who use the products and services. This is all of us who pay the power bills every month.

2. On the other hand, there are also the environmental factors in play here, which humans interact with in their daily effort to produce goods and provide services. These are mainly the resources from which producers make goods and provide services.

Resources + People = Products + Services

The major problem in this equation is that while humans can adjust their behavior to fit the needs of any situation, the natural environment is passive (fixed) and usually has no way of responding one way or another to human actions. So, people have an advantage in that they can dictate the level of exploitation of the resources without the environment being able to respond and defend itself from over-exploitation and the related damage.

Also, there is a conflict of interest among the human groups. Producers and investors make money by exploiting resources and ignoring the environmental damage these activities cause. Governments and environmentalists, on the other hand, try their best to protect the environment. The different environmental protection groups use different methods with varying results. Sometimes the conflict results can be measured in dollars, but more often they are expressed in non-monetary terms, such as clean environment and improved human health.

Producers + Investors = Environmental Damage

Governments + Environmentalists
= Environmental Protection

NOTE: For fairness' sake, we must clarify here that the producer and investor groups are not the bad guys. They are capitalists who work within the existing laws to provide services which we all need and cannot live without. In that respect they are the good guys. In all cases, we must respect their efforts, and find ways to protect the environment without treating the producer and investor groups as an evil we need to eliminate.

The sustainability model is now complete: we see the conflicting human groups—producers and investors locked into economic conflict with each other on one hand, and with government bodies and environmentalists on the other. All these groups are working separately, usually in an uncoordinated fashion with or against the natural environment.

The environment is the ultimate recipient (of good or bad things) resulting from the efforts of the different groups. The customers are the innocent bystanders, who have little say in the battles, but who pay a major part of the cost of the battle—both with their dollars and health.

Since in the capitalist society everything is measured in dollars, we see:

$Profits = $Gross – $Environmental cost

NOTE: The environmental cost can be measured in dollars, but only partially. There is a large part of the "cost" variable that cannot be expressed in monetary terms, and some of it is, intentionally or unintentionally, simply hidden from our view.

For protection, the environment depends on the efforts of people and governments, which always come at a cost. Sometimes that cost is significant and results in great financial and environmental damage. At times the environment is also able to defend itself, and even constrain human activities directly or indirectly, often adding to the cost, which further complicates the situation.

The issues before those of us who are involved in the environmental battle, and are trying to understand this complex situation and diffuse the conflicts, are many and varied in nature. By focusing mostly on the economic side of the equation, our interests only partly reflect the political, cultural and ideological complexity of our society. The other costs, some of which are hidden or ignored, must also be taken into consideration.

One of our goals in this text is to bring ALL issues (including the hidden and forgotten ones) out in the open. This way we can have a better and more detailed view of them and look for better ways to solve them.

Global Warming Issues

Pollution from energy generation accounts for over 50% of all air, soil, and water pollution today. Electric power production from coal and oil, the largest contributor to global warming, is blamed for environmental damages. EPA estimates that fossil fuel-based power generation has an environmental health cost of 10.5 cents per kilowatt hour—almost as much as it's actual market cost.

This means that its actual cost is double its present market value, half of which is adverse health effects. And we, the consumers, are the ones who end up paying for it with our taxes and our health.

Environmental buzzwords are all around us: anoxic waters, ocean deoxygenation, climate change, global warming, global dimming, fossil fuels, rise in sea level, greenhouse gas, ocean acidification, shutdown of thermohaline circulation, conservation, species extinction, pollinator decline, coral bleaching, coral reefs extinction, holocene extinction, invasive species, poaching, endangered species, dam impacts, environmental degradation, eutrophication, habitat destruction, environmental health dependency, air quality, asthma, electromagnetic fields, electromagnetic radiation, indoor air quality, lead poisoning, asbestos poisoning, sick building syndrome, genetic engineering, genetic pollution, genetically-modified food controversies, intensive farming, overgrazing, irrigation, water depletion, irrigation-water pollution, water pollution, eonoculture, environmental effects of meat production, slash and burn, pesticide drift, plasticulture, land degradation, land pollution, desertification, soil conservation, soil erosion, soil contamination, soil salination, land misuse, urban sprawl, habitat fragmentation, habitat destruction, ozone depletion, CFC, light pollution, noise pollution, visual pollution, nonpoint source pollution, point source pollution, rain water pollution, acid rain, marine pollution, ocean pollution, ocean dumping, oil spills, thermal pollution, urban runoff, water crisis, marine debris, ocean acidification, ship pollution, wastewater contamination, fish kill, algal bloom, mercury in fish, air pollution, smog, tropospheric ozone, volatile organic compound, particulate matter, sulphur oxide, nanotechnology, nanotoxicology, nanopollution, nuclear issues, nuclear fallout, nuclear meltdown, nuclear power, radioactive waste, overpopulation, burial, water crisis, overpopulation in companion animals, tragedy of the commons, consumerism, consumer capitalism, planned obsolescence, over-consumption, overfishing, blast fishing, bottom trawling, cyanide fishing, ghost nets, Illegal fishing, unreported and unregulated fishing, shark finning, whaling, logging, clearcutting, deforestation, Illegal logging, mining, acid mine drainage, mountaintop removal mining, slurry impoundments, toxins, chlorofluorocarbons, DDT, endocrine disruptors, dioxin, toxic heavy metals, herbicides, pesticides, toxic waste, PCB, bioaccumulation, biomagnification, waste, e-waste, litter, waste disposal incidents, marine debris, medical waste, landfill, leach rate, recycling, incineration, Great Pacific Garbage Patch, resource depletion, exploitation of natural resources, overdrafting, energy conservation, renewable energy, efficient energy use, renewable energy commercialization.

NOTE: See Appendix B for alphabetized, and more detailed list of environmental buzzwords.

The above list is quite an array of words, conditions, and situations, isn't it? So how do we know what is good and what is bad behind each of these terms? Where do we start, once we have determined that there is an environmental problem? What are the most important issues, and how are these interconnected? What should we do to help the environment, ourselves, our way of life, and that of future generations? Do we know what to do, and do we care enough to do the right thing ASAP, or should we procrastinate some more, hoping that the issues will just go away, or that someone can do a better job…sometime in the future?

"You can always count on Americans to do the right thing—after they've tried everything else," Winston Churchill reportedly said a long time ago. We believe that Americans will not fail this time—and one can even see the signs of their trying to do the right thing today—but everything else has not been tried as yet. So, it might take a generation or two before things are done right, but the Americans will do the right thing…some day! Let's just hope that it is not too late by then.

Environmental Damage Examples

On December 5, 1952, the residents of London, England, awoke to the dawn of a five-day reign of death. A temperature inversion had trapped the coal smoke from the city's furnaces, fireplaces, and industrial smokestacks, creating a "killer fog" that hovered near the ground. People began to die from respiratory and cardiopulmonary failure. Not until the weather system that had trapped London's pollution finally loosened its grip, and the soot-filled air cleared out, did death rates return to normal. The end of the episode saw more than 3,000 dead, and many more people suffered the coal smoke aftermath. It is not hard to imagine such a scenario developing again, and over more highly populated centers—something we are just not prepared for.

Driving north from Hong Kong into mainland China, you'll notice dozens, if not hundreds, of large factories belching black smoke into the air and discharging fizzling, green-brownish liquids into the ground. Walking down the streets of major Asian cities, you'll notice most people wearing masks over their mouths and noses. This unprecedented environmental pollution on such a large scale started some 20-30 years ago, and it is getting worse as we speak. It coincides with the tremendous growth of the Asian industrial complex at the expense of local and world environments and the health of the people working and living close to the polluters.

But you don't have to go to Asia to see examples of man-made hazmat dumps and generators of poison gasses. Drive by any large paper, cement, or chemical factory, or any coal-burning power plant, in the US or Europe and you'll see the signs of pollution: heavy smoke in the air, dead trees, dusty fields, green and brown bubbling lagoons, and other signs of man's intervention and recklessness. Yes, this is the mark of the fast-growing capitalist society, which we all must agree must change before it is too late.

Just mentioning the word Chernobyl sends chills through the spine of every Russian or European who lived through that nightmare. Of course, many did not survive the disaster, while many more are still suffering, and many generations will go on bearing the tell-tale signs of this larger-than-life nuclear disaster. With hundreds of nuclear plants operating well past their life expectancy, we won't be surprised if we witness more such accidents in the near future.

Let's not forget the Exxon Valdez, Deepwater Horizon and Fukushima Daiichi nuclear plant nightmares, different forms of man-made pollution related to energy production which had detrimental effects to the environment and life forms in it, including people.

The 2010 collapse of the coal mine in Chile, where 30 miners made the world news surviving for many days buried underground, and the Japanese nuclear disaster where many people were not that lucky, are yet other serious reminders of the dangers in the conventional energy field. The people involved in these events will never forget the day and hour when the Earth shook and took its victims. We shouldn't forget either and should consider replacing these dangerous technologies with safer and friendly wind and solar power generation.

In the grand scheme of things, each of these events might be a small thing in itself, but connected they have a profound and most negative effect on the environment and human life. Making this connection, however, is a very complex undertaking, with many variables and unknowns, thus the split among scientists.

Solar cells and modules manufacturing, transport, and recycling processes also emit large amounts of CO_2 and other gasses into the atmosphere. They also fill the county dumps with rusting and harmful materials, so we will take a closer look at these phenomena.

There are failed solar power plants in the US, that were supposed to bring us a bright energy future back in the 1980s and 1990s but instead created a new phenomenon, which we call "solar junkyards." Why did these high-visibility installations fail? Was it the technology, the installation, or the operation that failed? Did the failed equipment cause any damage to the surrounding environment beyond the visual pollution and the rusting metal parts? Several other solar projects failed within 10 years of installation in the 80s and 90s, either because the technology was not efficient and reliable enough, or because of poor planning and management. Readily available and cheaper conventional energy sources did not help the matter much either.

There is no question that all industries and energy-generating technologies use natural resources and generate waste byproducts. Renewable energies (wind, solar, etc.) are no exception. The only question is how

to estimate, control, and reduce the negative effects. We don't have the answers to most of these questions, but hopefully this text will address some of the issues and bring them out for discussion.

Not much has changed, even after all the evidences and continuous talk about the environmental disasters around us. How long can this continue before we run out of fossils and suffocate ourselves to death?

NOTE: The impact of environmental deterioration is all around us and increasing daily. All you have to do to confirm this is to drive through parts of Texas, Pennsylvania, Ohio, Colorado and many other states. Thousands of new holes for gas and oil fracking and geothermal power are drilled daily basis all around the nation. In Texas alone, 1.4 million geo-thermal drill holes have been recorded. The Earth is beginning to look like a Swiss Cheese, and the scars go deep.

Leaking chemicals and gasses can be found in many backyards, rivers and lakes in the Midwest and other parts of the country. The impacts from these are compounded daily as well. When one hole is drilled, its negative effects are combined with those of the adjacent holes, so we cover large land mass with a multitude of ongoing dangers and unknowns (from chemical and geo-mechanical points of view), the long-term effect of which we can't even guess.

A most noticeable result of the environmental wars is the mass exodus of American enterprises, and export of American technology and jobs, overseas. This movement, which started in the early 1980s, was caused by the inability or unwillingness of American businesses to comply with the new complex and expensive environmental regulations. Many were forced to move their manufacturing operations to places that have no environmental regulations and offer cheap labor. China, Mexico and other South American and Asian countries were, and still are, the "beneficiaries" of this new phenomena.

These actions have resulted in enriching US companies at the expense of contaminating the air, land and water in the host countries. The trend continues, although at a slower pace and at somewhat reduced contamination levels.

Climate Agreements

At the Copenhagen climate conference in 2009, 167 countries responsible for almost 90% of global greenhouse gas emissions agreed that the power platforms of their economies are raising the average temperature around the world. To avoid catastrophic climate change, they determined, the increase must not be greater than 2 degrees Celsius. To stay below that limit, their aggregate economies must not put more than another 565 gigatons of carbon dioxide (or its equivalent in other greenhouse gases) into the air before 2050.

Ultimately, the nations agreed, they must move to power platforms that do not generate more greenhouse gases than oceans and plants can absorb without causing catastrophic instability in the climate system. Sounds good on paper…and some effort is underway, but it is too insignificant as compared to conditions and requirements set by the Copenhagen agreement.

The facts are overwhelming. The global economy put into the atmosphere a record level of emissions in 2011, producing 31.6 gigatons of greenhouse gases. At this pace, the world will pump over 1,250 gigatons of GHG in the atmosphere by 2050, which is twice the amount agreed upon in Copenhagen.

Chinese emissions alone rose 9.3 percent; American emissions fell 1.7 percent; but both are expected to increase further, with China outstripping the U.S. 10 to 1. Third World populations are imitating industrial history, and a number of developed nations are burning mostly coal to produce electricity, consuming energy most inefficiently.

The rise of so many from poverty has the tragic paradoxical effect of threatening to destroy the climate for them and everyone else, thus relegating billions to more hardships in the future than they experienced in the past. Global emissions are increasing at roughly 3% a year, approximating the global economic growth rate. At this rate, in 16 years, total emissions will have exceeded the 565-gigaton limit, and doubled by 2050.

The United States consumed 4,326 TWh of electricity in 2011, roughly as much as China did. Excluding hydropower and nuclear power, renewable energy in the United States constituted only 3% of electric consumption, but in China, it was merely 1.3%. Gas, coal and oil provided 70% and 80% of the two countries' consumption, respectively. In a word, these two economies are roughly the same in terms of the energy solutions they use and the problems they face.

At the same time, China consumed 17% hydropower, while the United States consumed 20% nuclear power; but neither is likely to be able to add enough capacity in those segments to address economic needs or climate change's requirements. They need plans for moving to similar power platforms, with neither country having an advantage over the other in terms of the energy price to business and residential consumers.

A healthy rivalry with the United States in adding more clean energy might motivate China to move quickly to the new power platform. In the U.S., however, we have our own energy problems and have decided to resolve them by increasing natural gas and shale oil production. Back to square one…

Per capita, Americans consume about 250 kWh of electricity each day in the form of heating, lighting, air conditioning, transportation, and consumption of products made with electricity. Europeans and the Japanese consume about half as much, and the Chinese even less. This indicates that investment in energy efficiency and infrastructure can readily reduce the amount of energy that the U.S. economy uses, which in turn would reduce emissions.

This won't happen soon, however, because regulatory, legal, and financial obstacles block hundreds of billions of private sector investment in efficiency measures.

The United States could adopt an official plan for converting to electric, and other non-fossil types of commercial and public transportation. China already has a plan to put 5 million electric vehicles on the streets by 2020, and 500,000 by 2015. If China succeeds in achieving this goal, it will have 43% of the expected global electric vehicle market, and 0.4 percent of the global passenger fleet will be electric. China also will have created about 20,000 direct jobs in this electric car market.

NOTE: In December 2011, more than 190 countries met for two weeks in Durban, South Africa, for the United Nations sponsored climate change discussions and negotiations. The goal of the UN Framework Convention on Climate Change (UNFCCC) is to stop global warming by all means possible—but focusing on limiting global carbon emissions.

Two weeks and two days of talks, this was the longest UNFCCC meeting ever. At the end, the world decided on the "Durban Platform for Enhanced Action." A two-page document that commits (on paper) all countries to cut carbon emissions. This is the first time a unanimous decision on the subject has been made. This is the first time the world's three biggest emitters, the US, China and India, have signed a legal treaty to cut carbon. This is the first time when a glimpse of real progress was seen…on paper.

The proposed "road map" will guide countries toward a legal deal to cut carbon in 2015, but it will only come into affect after 2020. The road map is still on paper, but the talks are on track.

Still, 2020 is years away, and there is no guarantee that the map will be fully agreed upon and in force by then. Even if it is, it might be too late for some. The expectations of certain countries, like the small island states and some charities, are for much stronger and immediate resolution. They are afraid that nothing obligates the large countries to act, and there are no dates assigned for actions leading to stopping global warming.

The point is that, as things stand now, carbon emissions will be allowed to peak by 2020, and only then start to come down. Maybe. This makes no sense, and the delay is perceived as unjustified hesitation, and even a ploy to buy more time, which will not allow the world to limit temperature rise by 2050 to 20°C as planned.

THE U.S. ENVIRONMENTAL HISTORY

The environmental awareness in the US grew in the 1960s, until finally in 1970 President Nixon signed the National Environmental Policy Act (NEPA). This initiated the "environmental decade" in the US, when lots of good and not-so-good things happened. NEPA created the Council on Environmental Quality to oversee the environmental impact of events caused by federal actions, the Feds checking on the Feds. And then, the Environmental Protection Agency (EPA) was created, thus consolidating the efforts of all other hastily put together agencies into a single authoritative entity.

During the 1970s, the effort was focused on estimating and controlling the generation of pollutants in the air, surface water, groundwater, and solid waste disposal. Pollutants such as particulates, sulfur dioxide, nitrogen dioxide, carbon monoxide, ozone, as well as the issues of acid rain, visibility, and global warming were put on the agenda. Some preliminary measures were taken and some pollution limits were set.

Dissolved oxygen, bacteria, suspended and dissolved solids, nutrients, and toxic substances such as metals in surface water, as well biological contaminants, inorganic and organic substances, and radionuclides in ground water were regulated. And solid waste contaminants from agriculture, industry, mining, municipalities, and others were put on the agenda as well.

Several amendments of the Federal Water Pollution Control Act and the Clean Air Act emphasized the environmental concerns and moved the field into an uncharted territory. The limits and standards prescribed by these, to be enforced by the individual states, were without merit, and some were unattainable. The know-how and the state of the art were simply unavailable to achieve these goals at the time.

And then the confusion was augmented by the fact that each state was responsible for the preparation and implementation of the environmental plans, which still had to be approved by EPA. This included the provision of obtaining permits from the EPA to emit pollution into any and all surface waters.

The U.S. Congress enacted a massive public works program, designed to assist in the construction of water and waste treatment plants for municipalities. There were also deadlines and penalties for automobile emission standards in new cars, which eventually resulted in the development and adoption of catalytic converters, thus greatly reducing automobile pollution.

When Reagan took power, he was not sure what to think of these new developments, and soon developed new and different view of the situation and set different priorities. And so eventually through the appointment of different heads of departments, the design and operations of environmental protection measures was changed from very stiff regulation to almost voluntary, cooperative regulation.

For the duration, environmental laws were written and interpreted more favorably for industry interests. The Office of Management and Budget (OMB) was given power to require a favorable cost-benefit analysis of any environmental regulation before it could be implemented.

New regulations were delayed, and often key requirements were waived, and, when OMB was given even more power, all regulatory agencies were required to submit yearly proposals to account for all major environmental regulation. This allowed the OBM, whenever it chose, to reduce regulatory efforts before any proposed regulations became public.

As a confirmation of his distaste of environmental regulations, and the related renewable energy efforts, Reagan quickly removed the solar panels that his predecessor Carter had installed on the roof of the White House's West Wing.

Free market, without any boundaries and or conditions, is what Reagan believed in.

And so, the White House was solar-free for 30 years, until October 2010, when president Obama decided to install solar panels on the White House roofs again. This, at least symbolically showed his belief in renewables. In 2012, however, he gave up on renewables and jumped on the old and tested, "Drill, baby, drill" bandwagon. From then on, oil and especially natural gas became kings of the country's energy policy.

How about the environmental issues? Oh, yea, we'll look into that—later.

The first Bush administration introduced a mixture of innovation and restriction in the environmental regulations. William Reilly, was the first environmentalist to head the EPA, so considerable regulation was initially passed. Then a total freeze was put on new regulations.

Industry-favorable rulings, such as the redefinition of wetlands and the allowance of untreated toxic chemicals in local landfills, were enacted. Then In 1992, Bush opposed international efforts at the Earth Summit in Rio de Janeiro, Brazil by refusing to sign the biodiversity treaty and lobbying to remove all binding targets from the proposal on limiting global carbon dioxide emissions.

President Clinton promised a change in the direction of the national environmental policy. With the help of Al Gore, Carol Browner, and Bruce Babbitt, he supported environmental protection. He eliminated the Council on Competitiveness, and returned regulatory authority to the respective agencies. Clinton and Gore strongly believed, and still do, that environmental protection and economic growth are not incompatible. We have seen signs of the opposite, but the jury is still out.

Clinton, however, was an astute politician who was willing to compromise when needed. He failed on enacting grazing fees in the West and cleanup of the Everglades for this reason, and his support of the NAFTA and GATT took the country in a different direction.

To his credit, Clinton created the President's Council on Sustainable Development, signed the Kyoto Protocol, although he did not submit the treaty to the Senate, and stood firm against attempts to roll back environmental laws and regulations. He increased the EPA's budget, and much of the country's natural resources were put under greater protection, such as the restoration of the Everglades, and more notably the increase in size of the Everglades National Park.

President George W. Bush entered into the environmental debacle with a bang. He introduced the legislative initiative Clear Skies, the goal of which was to reduce three major pollutants: sulfur dioxide, nitrogen dioxide, and mercury. For the achievement of this goal, the trade of pollution credits, a market based system, was introduced.

But the Clean Air Act already had provisions to control air pollution on a national level, in which a program called New Source Review (NSR) required power plants to add anti-pollution technologies before they can expand. The new Clear Skies initiative basically removed NSR provisions and deregulated some of the standards. This prompted nine northeastern states to file suit in federal court to prevent it from becoming law, since they saw it as an assault on the Clean Air Act. The Clear Skies initiative was eventually defeated.

Bush also refused to sign the Kyoto Protocol, fearing negative consequences for the U. S. economy. He also did not agree that India and China were exempt from Kyoto's requirements and saw that as a barrier for any further negotiations. The scientific community was convinced that Bush made a covert attempt to silence the science and block data showing acceleration in global warming. But looking at Bush's background, we see big oil written all over it, so no wonder!

Then Bush reversed a campaign promise to regulate carbon dioxide emissions from coal-burning power plants. He promised to enact policies to make power plants meet clean-air standards, but that was then; now they would not be required.

He also approved a rule that large farms can claim that they do not discharge animal waste to avoid oversight from the Clean Air Act. Unregulated big oil and big farms are good for the economy, but detrimental to the environment, but Bush forgot about the latter part during the latter part of his governance, despite the fact that Bush W's administration issued more regulations than any other administration in U.S. history. Basically lots of work for naught!

Enter Obama. His 2008 presidential election was filled of environmental criticism and promises, which eventually helped him win over his rival, John McCain. Without any doubt, Obama won the backing of all mainstream environmental groups and all tree-huggers. Upon election, appointments such as that of Steven Chu, the Nobel prize-winning physicist was seen as a confirmation that his presidency was serious about environmental issues.

And sure enough, Obama pushed the renewable agenda hard, and followed through on its promises. Alas, the political and economic tides turned against the renewables and the rest is history.

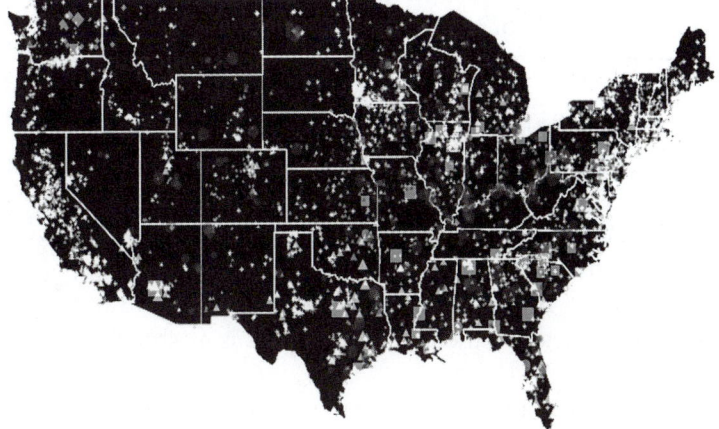

Figure 5-19. U.S. power plants and CO$_2$ distribution (light areas)

The renewables are partially on hold, and on the government's back burner now, and the environmental issues are still here with us awaiting resolution. All indications point to the fact that they will only get worse, since the emphasis is now on "drill, baby, drill." Fracking for oil and gas, and mining for coal is on the increase and quickly becoming the solution to all our energy problems, with the related environmental problems kept in the background. We will let the esteemed readers make their own conclusions and try to figure what will happen next.

The Environmental Regulations

We are so used to having regulations for everything we do, that in most cases we don't even blink an eye when we hear about a new regulation, or that an old regulation has been changed. Plus, there are so many regulations that it is nearly impossible to keep track of them, so we live in a regulation haziness, for lack of better word. Only when we are directly affected either negatively or positively, we see clearly what is being regulated and take some action.

Environmental regulations have been, and are, a huge part of business life in the great U.S. Starting in the late 1960s, the U.S. government started establishing rules and regulations, which were later translated into laws enforced by different government and non-government entities.

By 1998, following a number of environmental disasters, the Environmental Law became one of the governing factors in business life in the U.S. While it might have contributed to cleaner environment, it also was the driving factor behind the mass exodus of many U.S. companies and the general deterioration of manufacturing capabilities in the U.S.

Over 10 million factory jobs went overseas between 1995 and 2010. And many just went away, never to return. This changed our society so much so that today business activities consist of mostly consumer services.

Nevertheless, the Environmental Law is the rule of the land now, so everything we do must be within its framework, and business needs to be conducted within its boundaries, regardless of the other consequences.

A number of agencies are in charge of different aspects of the Environmental Law. A list of the most important entities and their responsibilities is as shown in Table 5-4.

The sheer number of agencies and the wide diversity of their responsibilities suggest inefficiency and fragmentation. Stepping on toes and finger pointing is

Table 5-4. List of government agencies involved in environmental work, and their responsibilities.

Federal Agency	Environmental Responsibilities
White House Office	Overall policy, Agency coordination
Office of Management and Budget	Budget, Agency coordination and management
Council on Environmental Quality	Environmental policy, Agency coordination, Environmental impact statements
Department of Health and Human Services	Health
Environmental Protection Agency	Air and water pollution, Solid waste, Radiation, Pesticides, Noise, Toxic substances
Department of Justice	Environmental litigation
Department of the Interior	Public lands, Energy, Minerals, National parks
Department of Agriculture	Forestry, Soil, Conservation
Department of Defense	Civil works construction, Dredge and fill permits, Pollution control from defense facilities
Nuclear Regulatory Commission	License and regulate nuclear power
Department of State	International environment
Department of Commerce	Oceanic and atmospheric monitoring and research
Department of Labor	Occupational health
Department of Housing and Urban Development	Housing, Urban parks, Urban planning
Department of Transportation	Mass transit, Roads, Aircraft noise, Oil pollution
Department of Energy	Energy policy coordination, Petroleum allocation research and development
Tennessee Valley Authority	Electric power generation
Department of Homeland Security / United States Coast Guard	Maritime and environmental stewardship, National Pollution Funds Center (NPFC)

an every day occurrence. Nevertheless, this is a good and needed step towards protecting the environment, and we are sure that much more unity and efficiency will be built into it with time.

These agencies have introduced a number of environmental legislations since the beginning of the 20th century, as shown in Table 5-5.

Conclusion: The problem in the U.S. is not energy deficiency, but energy use inefficiency. Enough energy is available at all times and will be available for a long time. The problem is that energy is badly abused, overused, and even wasted. Educating the public and implementing some energy use rules and restrictions might go long way in ensuring our energy independence. This seems to be more urgent, and would have a greater positive impact on our energy and environment future, than finding new energy sources.

Table 5-5. The US Environmental Laws

Year	Law	Year	Law
1899	Refuse Act	1974	Safe Drinking Water Act
1918	Migratory Bird Treaty Act of 1918	1975	Hazardous Materials Transportation Act
1948	Federal Water Pollution Control Act	1976	Resource Conservation and Recovery Act
1955	Air Pollution Control Act	1976	Solid Waste Disposal Act
1963	Clean Air Act (1963)	1976	Toxic Substances Control Act
1965	Solid Waste Disposal Act	1977	Clean Air Act Amendments
1965	Water Quality Act	1977	Clean Water Act Amendments
1967	Air Quality Act	1980	CERCLA (Superfund)
1969	National Environmental Policy Act	1984	Resource Conservation and Recovery Act Amendments
1970	Clean Air Act (1970)	1986	Safe Drinking Water Act Amendments
1970	Occupational Safety and Health Act	1986	Superfund Reauthorization
1972	Consumer Product Safety Act	1986	Emergency Wetlands Resources Act
1972	Federal Insecticide, Fungicide, and Rodenticide Act	1987	Clean Water Act Reauthorization
1972	Clean Water Act	1990	Oil Pollution Act
1972	Noise Control Act	1990	Clean Air Act (1990)
1973	Endangered Species Act	1993	North American Free Trade Agreement
2003	Healthy Forests Initiative		Forest services

Air Quality Standards

The contents of different gasses and particles in the air we breathe determine its quality, or suitability to support healthy lives. To put some order and provide some control of the polluting components in the ambient air, the U.S. government has established standards. These standards determine the maximum amount of pollutants in the air in our homes and work places.

The EPA has set national ambient air quality standards for six principal pollutants, which are called "criteria" pollutants, as listed in Table 5-6. Units of measure for the standards are parts per million (ppm) by volume, parts per billion (ppb) by volume, and micrograms per cubic meter of air ($\mu g/m^3$).

The Clean Air Act identifies two types of national ambient air quality standards. Primary standards provide public health protection, including protecting the health of "sensitive" populations such as asthmatics, children, and the elderly. Secondary standards provide public welfare protection, including protection against decreased visibility and damage to animals, crops, vegetation, and buildings.

There are also standards for the amount of air pollutants emitted by power plants and industrial enterprises. Most air toxics originate from human-made sources, such as power plants, cars, and trucks, factories, refineries, as well as indoor sources such as cooking and cleaning.

"Major" pollution sources are these that emit 10 or more tons per year of any of the listed toxic air pollutants, or 25 or more tons per year of a mixture of air toxics. These sources may release air toxics from equipment leaks, when materials are transferred from one location to another, or during discharge through emission stacks or vents.

"Area" pollution sources are smaller-size facilities that release lesser quantities of toxic pollutants into the air: less than 10 tons per year of a single air toxic, or less than 25 tons per year of a combination of air toxics. Emissions from individual area sources are often relatively small, but when viewed collectively, their emissions are of great concern, especially when large numbers of these small sources are located in heavily populated areas.

Table 5-6. National Ambient Air Quality Standards

Pollutant [final rule cite]		Primary/ Secondary	Averaging Time	Level	Form
Carbon Monoxide [76 FR 54294, Aug 31, 2011]		primary	8-hour	9 ppm	Not to be exceeded more than once per year
			1-hour	35 ppm	
Lead [73 FR 66964, Nov 12, 2008]		primary and secondary	Rolling 3 month average	0.15 µg/m³ [1]	Not to be exceeded
Nitrogen Dioxide [75 FR 6474, Feb 9, 2010] [61 FR 52852, Oct 8, 1996]		primary	1-hour	100 ppb	98th percentile, averaged over 3 years
		primary and secondary	Annual	53 ppb [2]	Annual Mean
Ozone [73 FR 16436, Mar 27, 2008]		primary and secondary	8-hour	0.075 ppm [3]	Annual fourth-highest daily maximum 8-hr concentration, averaged over 3 years
Particle Pollution Dec 14, 2012	PM$_{2.5}$	primary	Annual	12 µg/m³	annual mean, averaged over 3 years
		secondary	Annual	15 µg/m³	annual mean, averaged over 3 years
		primary and secondary	24-hour	35 µg/m³	98th percentile, averaged over 3 years
	PM$_{10}$	primary and secondary	24-hour	150 µg/m³	Not to be exceeded more than once per year on average over 3 years
Sulfur Dioxide [75 FR 35520, Jun 22, 2010] [38 FR 25678, Sept 14, 1973]		primary	1-hour	75 ppb [4]	99th percentile of 1-hour daily maximum concentrations, averaged over 3 years
		secondary	3-hour	0.5 ppm	Not to be exceeded more than once per year

The U.S. EPA publishes periodically a list of "source categories," indicating whether the sources are considered to be "major" sources or "area" sources and sets air pollution standards for all major sources of air toxics. Some area sources that are of particular concern are included as well.

We will take much closer look at these sources and the related standards in the following chapters.

ENERGY-RELATED ENVIRONMENTAL FACTS

Different fuels, and materials used as fuels, produce varying amounts of energy and accordingly emit different amounts of pollutants. Some examples follow:

1. One MT (metric ton) of coal burned in a coal-fired power plant emits 745 kg of carbon as CO_2 and similar gases One ton is 1,000 kg, so the coal to pollutant ration is 1.0 to 0.75. Only about one-fourth of the coal's actual substance is converted into energy, while the rest goes up in the atmosphere as CO_2 and other gasses and solids.

    — While the emitted gasses float up into the atmosphere and are then taken for a ride around the world, the resulting solids are hauled away as hazardous waste in form of ash and soot to a distant dumpsite, where they will stay forever.

    — In the U.S., 131 million tons of coal are used annually as combustion products. About 40% of the total mass is used and converted into heat and smoke, while nearly 75 million tons are disposed of as solid waste.

2. A typical coal-burning plant, 1GW nameplate, burns over 6,600 tons of coal daily, or the equivalent of 66 railroad cars, 100 tons each, every day. In the process, in addition to electricity, it generates:

    — 3,500,000 tons of CO_2 per annum, which, combined with the waste from thousands of similar plants around the world, goes up into the atmosphere and contributes to the greenhouse effect, feeding global warming trends

    — 10,000 tons of sulfur dioxide (SO_2), causing acid rain that damages forests, lakes, and buildings, and forms small airborne particles that can penetrate deep into the lungs

    — 500 tons of small airborne particles, which can cause chronic bronchitis, aggravated asthma, and premature death, as well as haze-obstructed visibility

    — 10,000 tons of nitrogen oxide (NO_x), as much as would be emitted by half a million late-model cars. NO_x leads to formation of ozone (smog), which inflames the lungs, burning through lung tissue and making people more susceptible to respiratory illness

— 700 tons of carbon monoxide (CO), which causes headaches and places additional stress on people with heart disease

— 200 tons of hydrocarbons, volatile organic compounds (VOC) which form ozone

— 200 pounds of arsenic, which will cause cancer in one out of 100 people who drink water containing 50 parts per billion

— 110 pounds of lead, 4 pounds of cadmium, other toxic heavy metals, and trace amounts of uranium. These are extremely toxic and deadly in very small quantities.

— Over a million tons of ash and soot, which need over 10,000 railroad cars to transport to the dumpsites

3. One MT (310 gal) of crude oil emits 584.5 kg of carbon as CO_2 along with similar gases. Oil burning power plants—tens of thousands around the world—have similar problems to those described for coal plants. The emitted gas types and quantities are different, but the end effects are the same—heavy environmental pollution and serious threat to human health.

4. One gallon of gasoline emits ~ 2.77 kg of carbon as CO_2 and similar gases that are harmful to human life and the environment.

5. One cubic meter of natural gas emits 0.5 kg of carbon as CO_2, as well as similar gases.

6. One seventieth of a teaspoon of mercury (several drops) deposited in a 25-acre lake can make the fish unsafe to eat.

7. Biofuels, trees and bushes, emit 50% of their weight in carbon-based gases during burning.
   — A major part of the world's air pollution is caused by burning firewood and other biofuels.
   — The majority of the African population still uses large amounts of firewood and other biofuels for their daily needs, so we need to find a way to replace them with renewables. Solar is the fastest, cheapest, and cleanest way to do this.

8. One ton of natural gas, methane, floating free in the atmosphere traps as much global warming-causing radiation as 20 tons of CO_2 in the same place.

9. Fine-particle pollution from US power plants cuts short the lives of over 30,000 people each year. In more polluted areas, fine-particle pollution can shave several years off many of its victims' lives. Hundreds of thousands of Americans suffer from asthma attacks, cardiac problems, and upper and lower respiratory problems associated with fine particles from power plants.

   The elderly, children, and those with respiratory disease are most severely impacted by fine-particle pollution from power plants. Metropolitan areas with large populations near coal-fired power plants feel their impacts most acutely; their death rates attributable to pollution are much higher than in areas with few or no coal-fired power plants.

10. Power plants outstrip all other polluters as the largest source of sulfates, the major component of fine-particle pollution in the U.S. Approximately two-thirds, more than 18,000, of the deaths due to fine-particle pollution from power plants could be avoided by implementing policies that cut power plant pollution containing sulfur dioxide and nitrogen oxide.

Some progress in this area has been made already, and more activities and regulations are planned for the near future in the U.S., but the rest of the world is not even close to this. The grand scale pollution will continue for the foreseeable future, especially in the developing countries.

The only good news here is that the environmental awareness in the U.S. and abroad is increasing across the board, so that events and accidents get more publicity, and average folks are more involved in the debate. Thus creating attention allows quick resolution of some cases, for instance the BP oil spill, and the Katrina disaster.

Figures 5-20a and 5-20b graphically show the major pollution sources of today. How big each of these is, what types of pollutants it is made out of, and how damaging it is to us all depends on the location and type of source. Even when we know the details of each source, putting the whole local (let alone global) picture together is almost impossible, due to the number of factors involved.

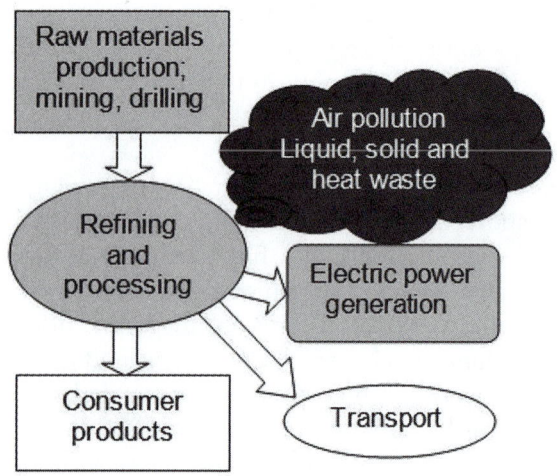

Figure 5-20a. The commercial pollution process.

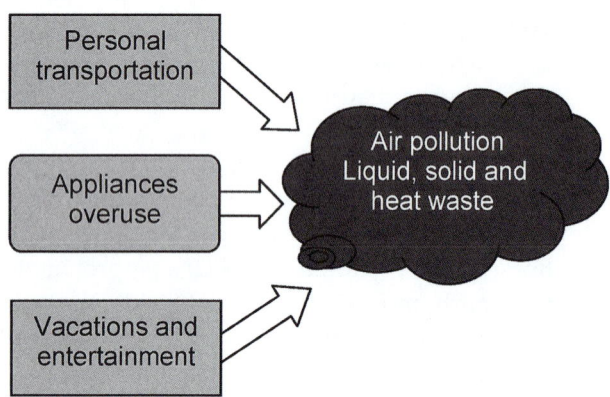

Figure 5-20b. The residential pollution process

What we know for sure is that:

1. The air and water pollution levels are increasing.

2. Most of the GHGs are emitted by fossil power plants.

3. GHGs are having a growing negative effect on our environment.

4. The environmental changes are greatly affecting all life forms, including humans.

5. Long lasting, dramatic negative changes are expected soon, if we don't take drastic measures.

With this in mind, where do we start? And since we are on the subject, let's take a closer look at the different energy sources and power generating technologies, and their contribution to the environmental issues of today.

COAL

Coal is a major electric power generator—producing about half of the electric power in the U.S. and the world. It is also a major green house gasses (GHG) emitter, emitting about half of the U.S. and global GHGs. So, while we cannot live without coal, it has been blamed for a number of serious environmental problems and human maladies.

It is only fair to emphasize that we ALL use coal—voluntarily and without complaint when we need its products: light, heat, etc. Without coal, our lives would be quite different. The American dream would be covered with darkness, enveloped in silence, and we all would be forced to endure extreme temperatures and other difficulties daily.

We respectfully bow before the tireless and brave miners, who go down into the mines every day, risking their health and lives for our comfort's sake. We need to thank them every time we flip the light switch, or turn the air conditioner or heater on.

The same thanks go to the thousands of railroad workers, drivers, processing and power plant operators and engineers, and the utilities employees, all of whom are working under difficult conditions 24/7 towards providing energy to power our lives.

With all that said, we must be also acutely aware of the damages coal has inflicted, and continues to inflict, to the U.S. and global environment such as serious global warming, ice melting, etc. Problems of profound long-term impact are related to GHGs emitted by coal-fired power plants.

And yet, coal is here to stay, so we need to learn as much as we can about it and its effects, to make better decisions in the future.

The Environmental Impact of Coal Mining

Mining is a complex, expensive, dirty, and very dangerous undertaking. Generations of miners have been digging coal and dirt for centuries, to provide fuel to power stations where the coal is converted into electricity as needed to power our lives.

Most of us have no idea what mining is, and what miners go through every single day, Most of us think that coal mining is the root of the problem, and yet we use its main byproduct (electricity) without remorse and without looking back. We are so used to flipping the switch and instantaneously getting light or heat, that the rest is totally irrelevant. Just like after flushing the toilet, we turn our backs at it and do not think of the rest of the process. We pay for these services, thus they are for somebody else to take care of.

Fair enough, this is capitalism after all, but if we are to blame coal and those involved in the process for the bad things around us, we need to take a close look at the entire picture and see where and how we fit in. We need to at the very least, and for fairness sake, learn about coal production and its use, and then figure out a way to reduce its negative effects.

We do hope that this text would serve, at least partially, the purpose of bringing us closer to the coal miners and coal use to position our selves in the picture, and work together on solving the issues of today.

Externalized Cost of Mining

Safety is of utmost importance in the coal mining and processing industry. Coal mining deep underground involves a higher safety risk than coal mined in opencast pits. However, modern coalmines, especially these in the developed countries, have rigorous safety procedures, health and safety standards. This, combined with extensive worker education and training have led to significant improvements in safety; both in underground and surface mining.

Regardless, the job is still extremely dangerous, and even with all added precautions, there are still serious problems within the industry. Mining accidents do not happen often, but when they happen they take many lives and cause worldwide excitement.

The majority of coal mine accidents and fatalities occur in China in other developing countries. Most accidents there are in small mines, often illegally operated. In these mines, mining techniques are labor intensive, use very basic equipment, and safety is not a priority. The Chinese government is taking steps to improve safety levels, including the forced closure of small-scale mines and those that fail to meet safety standards.

But mining accidents do still occur at times even in the US. Besides the large accidents that we hear about from time to time, there are smaller accidents daily, and many more unseen ones where people get hurt or sick as a result of mining effects.

In addition to the actual in-mine accidents, miners and local people are sickened by pollution from coalmines and coal fired power plants, shortening their lives and burdening the health care system with costly care. Fish are poisoned when coalmines dump waste into streams, starving their predators, depriving subsistence fishermen, and straining stocks that support commercial fisheries. The taxpayers also pay to subsidize coal use and clean up its aftermath.

As a result of all this, which is what we call "externalities," the future generations will be heavily impacted directly by the added cost, and indirectly by the effects of global warming from the carbon dioxide that burning coal, oil and natural gas spew into the air.

NOTE: Externalities are unintentional side effects of an activity that affects people unrelated to the activity in question. A negative externality is one that creates side effects that could be harmful to either the general public or the environment.

A power plant that pollutes the air, soil and water of the particular local might be a good example of this process. The resulting pollution creates health issues among the locals, and/or degrades the quality of their local air, soil, or water supply. The pollution can then spread in a wider area and eventually around the globe as well.

The factory owner does not pay directly the additional cost to address any health issues or to help maintain the cleanliness of the air, soil, or water. Only through special legislation, or legal measures the harmed third parties can get justice and receive compensation for damages. Insurance coverage carried by most mine owners, and other financial instruments are designed to take care of some of the externalities, but not all.

A positive externality, on the other hand, is another unpaid benefit that is unrelated to the activity in question. A neighborhood garden, created by volunteers might offer its aesthetic beauty to benefits all people in the community.
Anyone that gains additional benefits from these activities without contributing to their creation or maintenance is a "free rider."

Both negative and positive externalities are forms of market failure, since the free market does not account for the activities in question, does not allocate sufficient resources, and does not (one way or another) take care of the activities and all parties involved.

There are today attempts to introduce taxes to:

• Discourage negative activities that create harmful effects, by charging parties involved in these activities, and

• Provide subsidies for activities creating positive benefits, thus compensating these activities and further encouraging their development. These are now known as Pigovian taxes and subsidies.

NOTE: Pigovian taxes on pollution is looked at as a much more efficient way of dealing with pollution as an externality than government imposed regulatory standards. Taxes leave the decision of how to deal with pollution to individual sources by assessing a fee or "tax" on the type and amount of pollution that is generated. Therefore, in theory, a source that is looking to maximize its profit will reduce, or control, their pollution emissions whenever it is cheaper to do so.

An efficient solution to negative externalities is to include them in the cost for those engaged in the activity. Thus, the externality is "internalized." Many externalities (pollution) can be internalized through the creation of well-defined property rights. Taxes and subsidies are typically not necessary as long as the parties involved could reach an agreement. In such case it matters not who is the owner, so long as property rights exist and free trade is possible.

No matter what approach is used, when all externalities are accounted for they are no longer market failures, and the different activities do not need government intervention. We, however, are still far from this idealized scenario.

The monetizable impacts of coal are damages due to mining accidents, coal processing and transport accidents, global climate change, public health damages from NO_x, SO_2, PM2.5, mercury emissions, government subsidies, and lost value of abandoned mine lands.

> *Globally, the externalized costs of coal are presently estimated to exceed $500 billion. This is almost trice the estimated total economic value of coal, which is around $280 billion; estimated at $40 per ton and about 7 billion tons of annual global coal production.*

A 2011 study estimated the true cost of coal's life cycle and its waste streams at $345 billion annually in the United States alone. It further calculated that if all the externalized costs of coal were accounted for, it would increase the retail coal electric power prices by 18-28 cents/kWh.

And another study of the benefits of increased electricity generation versus the much larger detrimental effects of coal consumption, estimated the true cost of coal to be 170% of the retail price.

But regardless if the real cost of using coal is 1 billion or 1 trillion, money cannot ensure a clean environment for the future generations. Only real action can. And of course, there are ways to reduce the pollution and its effects. More efficient equipment and processes are the first step. A recent studies on the effects of downwind air pollution from coal-powered plants estimate that, if properly done, each dollar spent on airborne pollution controls could save $50-100 in annual costs

downwind.

We will take a much close look at these statistics and the reasons for these discrepancies in this text, but would like to emphasize here the fact that the complex, expensive and dangerous coal mining, processing and burning processes have much more complex and more difficult to understand and estimate components. These are expressed in direct, indirect, and hidden, costs; the meaning of which we need to understand well, to optimize the cradle-to-grave coal processes and reduce their negative effects.

In all cases, we must be aware of the problems, while keeping in mind that coal is a necessary evil. We also need to treat coal and the people who work in the coal industry with respect and admiration, because their efforts and sacrifices make our lives comfortable and prosperous.

Coal Mining Environmental Effects

Starting with the planning, location, evaluation, and exploration activities at a potential mine site, there are a number of environmental effects.

Some of the negative effects during the initial, pre-mining, activities are:

a. *Acoustics*, or noise level, is associated with the site evaluation as related to activities that would typically generate low levels of temporary and intermittent noise. For any blasting activities, for example, the impacts would be similar to those typical for the construction and mining phase.

b. *Air quality*, including global climate change and carbon footprint impacts to air quality during pre-mining exploratory activities, would include temporary and local generation of vehicle emissions and fugitive dust from vehicle traffic and ground disturbances. These impacts are unlikely to exceed air quality standards, or impact climate change in any way, but need to be added to the list for completeness sake.

c. *Cultural resources* refer to any cultural, historical, tribal, etc., material present on the surface that could be disturbed by vehicular traffic, ground disturbances, and pedestrian activity, including the collection of artifacts. Drilling, seismic surveys, and other sampling methods could also affect cultural resources buried below the surface. Depending on their physical placement and/or level of visual intrusion, site exploration activities could affect areas of interest to Native Americans. Surveys conducted during this phase to evaluate the presence and/or significance of cultural resources in the area would assist developers in designing the project to avoid or minimize impacts to these resources.

d. *Ecological resources* refer to disruptions to wildlife and impacts to wildlife and aquatic habitats that could result from vehicular traffic, ground disturbances, and pedestrian activity during the site evaluation and exploration phase. The introduction and spread of invasive vegetation could occur as a result of vehicular traffic. For any blasting activities, the impacts would be similar to those experienced and justified during the construction and mining phase. Surveys conducted during this phase to evaluate the presence and/or significance of ecological resources in the area would assist developers in designing the project to avoid or minimize impacts to these resources.

e. *Environmental justice* of site evaluation and exploration activities are primarily limited to sampling activities and would not result in significant high and adverse impacts in any resource area; therefore, environmental justice impacts are not expected at this phase.

f. *Hazardous materials and waste management* refers to the impacts from use, storage, and disposal of hazardous materials and waste in the area. These should be kept to the minimal to none if appropriate management practices are followed.

g. *Human health and safety* concerns are the occupational and public health and safety risks normally associated with generic construction and outdoor activities, such as working in potential weather extremes and possible contact with natural hazards, such as uneven terrain and dangerous plants, animals, or insects. These are limited during the site evaluation phase because of the limited range of activities.

h. *Land use* impacts would likely be temporary and localized during site evaluation and exploration activities. These activities could create a temporary disturbance to wildlife and cattle in the immediate vicinity of the project site while workers are present. Access to the area for continued recreational use could also be affected, especially if blasting is conducted. There may be visual impacts from the presence of equipment and access roads, potentially impacting the recreational experience.

i. *Paleontological resources* refer to any fossil material present on the surface that could be affected by vehicular traffic, ground disturbance, and pedestrian activity, including the collection of fossils. Drilling, seismic surveys, and other sampling could also affect paleontological resources buried below the surface. Surveys conducted during this phase to evaluate the presence and/or significance of paleontological resources in the area would assist developers in designing the project to avoid or minimize impacts to these resources.

j. *Socioeconomics* during site evaluation and exploration activities are temporary and limited and would not result in socioeconomic impacts on employment, local services, or property values.

k. *Soils and geologic resources*, including seismicity/ geo hazards, consist of borings for soil testing and geotechnical surveys as needed to provide useful site-specific data on soils and geologic resources. Surface effects from pedestrian and vehicular traffic could occur in areas that contain special soils such as crypto biotic soils. Most site evaluation and exploration activities would be unlikely to activate geological hazards or increase soil erosion. For any blasting activities, the impacts would be similar to those described for the construction and mining phase.

l. *Transportation* impacts are not anticipated during the site evaluation phase. Transportation activities would be temporary and intermittent, and limited to low volumes of heavy- and medium-duty pickup trucks and personal vehicles.

m. *Visual resources* activities during site evaluation and exploration would have temporary and minor visual effects caused by the presence of vehicles and equipment.

n. *Water resources*, both surface water and groundwater, would likely receive minimal impact to water resources, local water quality, water flows, and surface water/groundwater interactions during site evaluation and exploration. For any major drilling and blasting activities, the impacts would be similar to those encountered during the construction and mining phases. Limited amounts of water needed for drilling samples could be trucked in from off-site.

Environmental Effects of Mining Operations

There are numerous damaging environmental impacts that occur during mining, preparation, combustion, waste storage, and transport of coal.

Some of the major environmental and human health impacts are as follow:

- Acid mine drainage (AMD) refers to the outflow of acidic water from coal mines or metal mines, often abandoned mines where ore- or coal mining activities have exposed rocks containing the sulphur-bearing mineral pyrite. Pyrite reacts with air and water to form sulfuric acid and dissolved iron, and, as water washes through mines, this compound forms a dilute acid, which can wash into nearby rivers and streams.

- Air pollution from coalmines is mainly due to emissions of particulate matter and gases including methane (CH_4), sulfur dioxide (SO_2), and nitrogen oxides (NO_x), as well as carbon monoxide (CO).

- Coal dust stirred up during the mining process, as well as released during coal transport, can cause severe and potentially deadly respiratory problems.

- Coal fires occur in both abandoned coalmines and coal waste piles. Internationally, thousands of underground coal fires are burning now. Global coal fire emissions are estimated to include 40 tons of mercury going into the atmosphere annually, and are three percent of the world's annual carbon dioxide emissions.

- Coal sludge, also known as slurry, is the liquid coal waste generated by washing coal. It is typically disposed of at impoundments located near coalmines, but in some cases it is directly injected into abandoned underground mines. Since coal sludge contains toxins, leaks or spills can endanger underground and surface waters.

- Floods such as the Buffalo Creek Flood caused by mountaintop removal mining and failures of coal mine impoundments

- Forest destruction caused by mountaintop removal mining—According to a 2010 study, mountaintop removal mining has destroyed 6.8% of Appalachia's forests.

- Greenhouse gas emissions caused by mountaintop removal mining releases large amounts of carbon through clear cutting and burning of trees and through releases of carbon in soil brought to the surface by mining operations. These greenhouse gas emissions amount to at least 7% of conventional power plant emissions.

- Loss or degradation of groundwater are frequent

events, since coal seams are often serve as underground aquifers. Removal of coal beds may result in drastic changes in hydrology after mining has been completed.

- Mountaintop removal mining has caused radical disturbance of 8.4 million acres of farmland, rangeland, and forests, most of which has not been reclaimed.

- Heavy metals and coal are created through compressed organic matter containing virtually every element in the periodic table—mainly carbon, but also heavy metals. The heavy metal content of coal varies by coal seam and geographic region. Small amounts of heavy metals can be necessary for health, but too much may cause acute or chronic toxicity, or poisoning. Many of the heavy metals released in the mining and burning of coal are environmentally and biologically toxic elements, such as lead, mercury, nickel, tin, cadmium, antimony, and arsenic, as well as radioisotopes of thorium and strontium.

- Methane released by coal mining accounts for about 10 percent of U.S. releases of methane, which is a potent global warming gas.

- Mountaintop removal mining and other forms of surface mining can lead to the drastic alteration of landscapes, destruction of habitat, damages to water supplies, and air pollution. Not all of these effects can be adequately addressed through coalmine reclamation.

- Coal dust is usually stirred up during the mining operations, and during coal transport. Coal dust is a serious health problem, which is responsible for severe and potentially deadly respiratory problems. "Black lung" is one of the deadly diseases attributed to extended coal dust breathing.

- Land subsidence may occur after any type of underground mining, but it is particularly common in the case of long wall mining. Large-scale land subsidence can have disastrous consequences

- Waste coal, also known as "culm," "gob," or "boney," is made up of unused coal mixed with soil and rock from previous mining operations. Runoff from waste coal sites can pollute local water supplies.

- Water pollution from coal includes the negative health and environmental effects from the mining, processing, burning, and waste storage of coal.

In addition to the above, transportation factors into environmental effects, as coal is often transported via trucks, railroads, and large cargo ships, which release air pollution such as soot and can lead to disasters that ruin the environment, such as the Shen Neng 1 coal carrier collision with the Great Barrier Reef, Australia that occurred in April 2010.

Equipment Manufacturing Carbon Footprint

A number of large and small pieces of equipment are used during mining. Starting with the mine design and construction, we see the pollution taking place in a shape of deep tracks in the ground and heavy plumes of smoke in the air from large trucks and bulldozers crawling all over the place. And there are also trains and trucks used for transporting the equipment to the mine.

All this machinery was made somewhere on the planet some time in the past, and their manufacturing processes and transport created a significant pollution footprint. Since most of these pieces of equipment are used only temporarily, we cannot assign the entire footprint to them, so we would assign a percentage of it to the manufacturing and transport of mining equipment. (A)

And then, the main dirt diggers and transport pieces of equipment arrive in wooden boxes or on back of enormous trailers or railroad cars. These are assembled with the help of other equipment and put to work after creating another set of pollution problems. (B)

In addition, there are many other items and small pieces of equipment, tools and consumables—some for personal use, and some for specialized operations. These are shovels, helmets, computers, power drills, boots, shoes, overalls, first aid kits, dynamite sticks, goggles, and the list goes on. All these were also made sometime in the past somewhere around the world and transported to the mine. During their manufacturing processes and transport, they also left a significant pollution footprint. (C).

Then, to complete the pollution footprint picture, we must add to that the footprint of the people involved in the entire process—engineers and technicians involved in the equipment manufacturing, transport, installation, setup, and operation. These people drive cars and ride on planes, all of which leaves another significant set of pollution footprints (D)

And so, the total pollution footprint of the mine's equipment cradle-to-grave process is expressed by:

$$P_f = A + B + C + D$$

Where:
- P_f is the total pollution footprint
- A is the mining equipment manufacturing and transport to the mine
- B is mining equipment assembly, test and installation at the mine
- C is the manufacturing and transport to the mine of tools and consumables
- D is the pollution footprint of the equipment personnel during the design and setup phases.

Combining the pollution footprint of A (the mining equipment manufacturing and transport) with B (mining equipment assembly, test and installation), adding C (the manufacturing and transport of the tools and consumables), plus D (the pollution footprint of the equipment personnel) gives us the environmental footprint of the mining equipment before even starting the mining operations.

And the pollution footprint is significant, to be sure! It goes deep and wide, stretching from one part of the world to the other.

To put a value on it we must take inventory of all items delivered to the mine, and needed for its design, construction and operation. We must take a close look at the manufacturing of a dragline, a bulldozer, a dump truck and a number of other pieces of equipment used at the mine.

Keep in mind that some of these are some of the largest pieces of equipment in the world, and that it takes thousands of tons of metals to make them. Each of these started as an iron ore dug out from another mine somewhere in the world, which was transported to a smelter. The molten metal was shaped in different forms and shipped to the different parts manufacturers, who drilled, welded and otherwise constructed parts for these vehicles.

And again, remember that we are talking about huge pieces of metal—some as big as an entire building. One single bolt from the dragline might be over a foot long, and its bucket as big as a railroad car. These parts are then packed and loaded on railroad cars or trucks to be shipped to the assembly facility. The parts of a large dump truck or a dragline might require a dozen railroad cars for transport.

NOTE: For example, draglines are massive structures, some weighing over 13,000 tons and as tall as a 20-story building. An average dragline weighs 8,000 tons and is only 10-12 stories high. It would have a 55 cubic yards bucket that can reach over 250 feet and scoop 200-400 tons of material at a single stroke.

8,000 tons of metal are used to manufacture one

single dragline in which the metal started as iron ore dug out from another mine somewhere around the world. The ore was then loaded on railroad cars or boats and shipped to the smelter. Since the iron content in iron ore is about 50-60%, half of the transport is waste, which has to be removed somehow and shipped somewhere to be disposed in a landfill or other such formation.

At the smelter, the iron ore is unloaded and sorted, and based on the furnace type and melting method, different amounts of iron ore, coal, limestone and recycled steel are mixed and loaded in the furnace to be melted. The furnace is heated to 1,700°C and the mix is melted in the presence of pure oxygen, injected in the furnace.

In the first step of the process, two tons of iron ore, a ton of coal, 0.25 tons of limestone, and 0.15 tons of recycled steel are mixed to produce one ton of crude steel. The iron produced is useless for all practical purposes, so it has to be refined further to improve its physical and chemical qualities.

In the second step of the steelmaking process, the crude steel is transferred into a different furnace, where it is heated at 1,700°C again to remove impurities such as sulfur, phosphorus, and most importantly, excess carbon. Different quantities of alloying elements, such as manganese, nickel, chromium, and vanadium are added at that time, as needed, to produce the exact final steel quality required.

Recycled steel is made in an electric arc furnace, where one ton of recycled steel, 150 kg of coal and 45 kg of limestone are mixed to produce one ton of crude steel in another furnace operating at the same hellish 1,700°C temperature.

NOTE: Global steel production is heavily dependent on coal. About 70% of the steel produced today uses coal, because in addition to adding coal to the mix, coal often is burned to maintain the furnace temperatures.

But getting back to our dragline, for the manufacturing of the 8,000-ton structure, we've used approximately 16,000 tons of iron ore, 2,000 tons of limestone, 1,200 tons of scrap steel, and 40,000 tons of coal that we burned during the melting and forming processes. A catch 22 situation—we need a lot of coal to mine a lot of coal. The more coal we mine, the more coal we use in the process.

This is a lot of pollution, in addition to that created by 4 unit trains, pulling 100 railroad cars with 100 tons of coal in each car. An additional 50 railroad cars of limestone and scrap metal were pulled from several hundred miles to the smelter too.

And this is just the raw steel material, which then

had to be treated, forged, drilled, welded, machined, and otherwise shaped into thousands of parts for the dragline.

Molded parts were then loaded on another train, or on a bunch of trucks, and transported to a machine shop for final welding, drilling, and polishing operations, and so forth, as needed to convert the raw material into useful machine parts. The finished parts are loaded, again, on trucks or trains for transport to the equipment manufacturer for final machining and assembly. Here we also see several additional long trails of dust, burning fossils and air pollution.

After one more loading and unloading operation, the parts finally arrive at the mine for final assembly and testing of the dragline before being put to work. This is a long, winding process, with many stop-and- go, loading and unloading, and shipping steps.

And this is not all. In addition to the dragline, there are many other large and small pieces of equipment in the surface and underground mines. For example: hydraulic shovels, 50-70 tons; wheel loaders, 40-50 tons; rear-dump trucks, 10 tons; rotary drill, 15 tons; dozers, 20 tons; road grader, 25 tons; water and other trucks, 10 tons each, etc.

And let's not forget that the coal is transported to the power plants via train cars, each of which weighs another 30-40 tons—mostly steel. Several unit train compositions of about 100 cars each are needed to transport the mined coal to the power plants, so here we have to add another 100-150,000 tons of steel to be produced to serve one mine.

Putting a weight and dollar value to all this would be too long and complex of a procedure for our purposes, so it suffices to say that the pollution effects during and after all these steps are significant.

Mining Equipment Pollution

And now, we have started the mine operation and see another set of pollution footprints. And again, they are significant. As an example, at the surface mine, our 8,000-ton dragline is powered by electric power provided by several diesel generators. During an average work day and under a full load, these will burn 2,000 gallons of diesel every hour to make the large bucket move up and down as needed to scoop coal and dirt.

Some draglines are plugged into the grid, using 20-50 MW of electric power, which was generated in a nearby coal-fired power plant—a coal monster drinking its own blood and adding more pollution to the environment.

Several bulldozers and dump trucks are helping

the dragline dig and transport the coal. They also burn a lot of fuel in their never-ending run-about, so the entire area is fogged with dust and soaked in diesel fumes and lubricating oils, leaving their pollution imprint hour after hour, day after day,.

This goes on non-stop for the 20-30-year duration of the mining operation! And this does not even include the damage done to the land, which is a different, but not less serious, type of environmental damage.

Spare parts for these monsters are periodically arriving from the parts manufacturers, after leaving their pollution footprint all over the place too. We will attempt to assign a number to the quantity of air and land pollution, and related dollar numbers to these activities and their environmental effects in the following chapters.

And after 20-30 years of non-stop operation, the mine, whether it is surface or underground, is finally declared exhausted, at which point it has to be shut down and decommissioned. The decommissioning and land reclamation are major, expensive, and polluting undertakings. The equipment and materials used during the decommissioning and waste disposal process create additional air and ground pollution, which is not to be ignored.

Additional, specialized equipment and personnel, such as environmental specialists and inspectors, are usually brought in to assist and/or coordinate the effort. With that, more pollution footprints are left at the already exhausted mine.

When the final tally is made, a significant part of the emissions and overall pollution is attributed to the mining equipment and support personnel, adding to a significant number.

Coal Mining Risks and Dangers

Mining, processing and transporting coal is very dangerous work. Underground mining is classified as full of uncontrollable risks and the most dangerous workplace. Policemen, firemen, and other people in risky positions also put their lives on the line every day, but they at least have the equipment, tools, and weapons to defend themselves.

In comparison, at the moment a miner walks to his workplace, he is absolutely unprotected and is fully aware that at any moment one of the hundred pickaxes could bring a disaster. A spark could ignite collected gasses. No technology can foresee and protect him from occasional, unplanned, and unexpected breaks into a water vein, which could cause roof collapse and fill the room with water.

In all cases, even in minor accidents in these tight places, miners could be hurt or even killed. And there are many examples of this happening even today, when we have such sharp awareness of the dangers, have amazing technologies at our disposal, and are taking serious precaution to avoid accidents.

The wooden or metal props that support the roof may break or the pillars of coal may not be strong or large enough, and the roof may fall in, crush, and bury the miners. The technology helps, but it cannot see well through the thousands of tons of coal and earth above, and so accidents happen even in the safest mines, if there is such a thing.

And then there are always poisonous and explosive gases in the mines, because the coal was made under water, and the gas which was formed at the same time could not escape in its entirety, often remains under tremendous pressure, and is continuously bubbling out from the coal. And nobody can predict what kind of gas will leak today, or tomorrow. Even if and when detected, it might be too late.

Build-up of hazardous gases is known as damps, possibly from the German word dampf, which means steam or vapor. Some of the most dangerous damps are:

Black damp is a mixture of carbon dioxide and nitrogen that can cause suffocation in these enclosed spaces. It is formed as a result of carbon reactions (oxidation) with oxygen from the atmosphere.

White damp is air containing carbon monoxide, which is toxic even at very low concentrations. Certain death follows at higher concentrations.

Stink damp is named for the rotten egg smell of the hydrogen sulphide gas. It can explode at some concentrations and is also very toxic.

After damp is a gas similar to black damp gas, and consists of carbon monoxide, carbon dioxide, and nitrogen, gasses that form in enclosed areas after a mine explosion. They are toxic and are very dangerous to humans in higher concentration

Firedamp consists of methane, which is a highly flammable gas that explodes in 5%-15% concentration. In higher concentrations, above 25%, it causes asphyxiation. It is one of the most dangerous gasses in the mines.

Most of these gasses could cause an explosion if exposed to an open flame in the presence of air. Fine coal dust in some concentrations is also known to explode.

Miners used to work by candlelight in the past, which was extremely dangerous for the above reasons. Candles were replaced by the present day safety lamps, where miners wear a small bulb on their helmets, powered by a battery that is mounted between their shoulders. Even with safety lamps, however, the danger of explosions is still present. Pushing large amounts of fresh air through the shafts is the only way to make a mine safe from dangerous and explosive gases.

Modern mining in the U.S. results in approximately 20-40 deaths per year due to mine accidents. In the developing countries, many miners die either through direct accident in coalmines or through health consequences from working under poor mine conditions.

China has the highest number of coal mining related deaths in the world, with official statistics claiming that 6,027 deaths occurred in 2004, while only 28 mine related deaths were reported in the U.S. in the same year. Today China mines still kill 2,000-3,000 miners annually.

Coal production in China, however, is twice that in the U.S., while the number of coal miners is around 50 times that of the U.S., making deaths in coal mines in China four times as common per worker (108 times as common per unit output) as in the U.S.

In 2006, fatal work injuries among miners in the U.S. doubled from the previous year, totaling 47. These figures can in part be attributed to the Sago Mine disaster of January 2006. The 2007 mine accident in Utah's Crandall Canyon Mine, where nine miners were killed and six entombed, speaks to the increase in occupational risks faced by U.S. miners. In 2010, the Upper Big Branch Mine disaster in West Virginia killed 29 miners.

Mining efficiency and safety have improved significantly in the last several decades by the introduction of new and improved methods such as long wall mining, hazardous gas monitoring, the use of safety-lamps, and a number of modern electronic gas monitors, gas drainage, electrical equipment, and ventilation. All these improvements have reduced many of the risks of rock falls, explosions, and unhealthy air quality encountered in mining operations.

Statistical analyses show that 1990-2004, the industry cut the rate of injuries by more than 50%, and the fatalities were cut down by 75%.

New materials for mine support braces, called Atlas Cribs, contain a mix of hardwoods and a main lateral element that make them stronger than those used in the past. The new cribbing systems take up 40% less useful area than existing ones and may be up to 50% more efficient in terms of airflow.

As an example of the present day developments, the improved safety features in Australian mining have dramatically increased the forecasted average life expectancy of the working male. It is envisioned that by 2025, life expectancy of mine workers will be similar to that of the average Australian male worker.

But even when great developments and safety precautions, the mining related dangers are not completely eliminated, and according to the Bureau of Labor Statistics, mining remains the second most dangerous occupation in the U.S.

Mining has been and always would be one of the most dangerous occupations on Earth. Contemporary mines collapsing or exploding and burying many people under the rubble have demonstrated this time after time.

And on top of all that, outside the mines, but a consequence of mining operations, many miners get lung diseases and other illnesses that make their lives even harder. Chronic lung diseases, such as pneumoconiosis (black lung) were once common in miners, leading to reduced life expectancy. In some mining countries black lung is still common, with 4,000 new cases of black lung every year in the U.S.—4% of workers annually—and 10,000 new cases every year in China (0.2% of workers).

External Cost of Coal

To the electricity customer, coal is relatively cheap. But missing from the sticker price are coal's major impacts on ecosystems, human health, and the overall economy. In addition to mining accidents that claim the lives of many, people are also hurt and killed during coal transport and processing.

Many more are sickened by pollution from coal-fired power plants, shortening their lives and burdening the health care system with costly care. Fish are poisoned when coalmines dump waste into streams, starving their predators, depriving subsistence fishermen, and straining stocks that support commercial fisheries.

Global warming from the carbon dioxide that burning coal spews into the air will heavily impact future generations. As taxpayers we pay to subsidize coal use, and then to clean up its aftermath.

Externalized cost refers to the additional, sometimes hidden, costs of coal production and use. The owners, who are directly and indirectly responsible for everything happening at or around their facilities and others who are directly involved in the process, usually do not pay for those costs.

The coal mining companies, the coal-using power plants, and the electrical utilities normally set the coal market price, and so some of the costs, including externalities, are not included in the price. But coal has many externalized costs, which must be reflected in the final price to obtain its true cost. This addition would reveal that, although coal appears to be cheap, it is much more

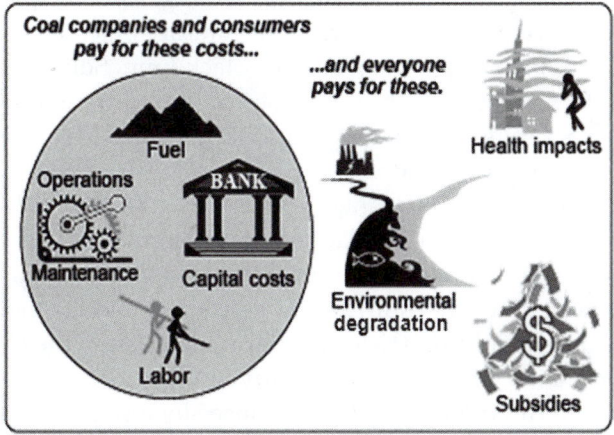

Figure 5-21. Coal cradle-to-grave process

expensive to our society as a whole.

NOTE: Generally speaking, true cost is the difference between the market price of a commodity and its comprehensive cost to society as a whole, including its production and use effects. *True cost* is used to draw attention to missing or hidden costs that are not found in the market price. The positive and negative factors that are not reflected in the market price, but are part of the true cost, are called externalities.

In the case of coal production and use, one of the negative externalities is air pollution. The mining and combustion of coal generates large amounts of pollution, which are not reflected in the final market price. Damage to the environment and to human health is also not included, but is instead paid for mostly by the taxpayers. Damage to locals' livelihood, such as tourism or fishing, are paid indirectly by the affected companies and individuals.

Most coal mining in the U.S. is surface mining, which destroys the original ecosystems at the mine site completely and irreversibly. Coal companies are required to reclaim the site after mining by restoring the original ecosystem, but this is difficult in most places, and impossible in others, such as wetlands areas. In the process, mining operations destroy fish and wildlife habitats, which has rippling effects not only on their specific populations, but also on the local human residents that rely on them.

Beyond that, when the footprint of the mine itself is destroyed, the surrounding areas and lands are affected too. Discharging mine runoff into nearby waterways, and sending coal dust across the landscape changes the nature of the local flora and fauna. It reduces life expectancy of fish, damages their immune systems, and suffocates fish eggs. The toxins in the soil, water, and air also affect the birds.

And so, it is obvious that the hidden cost is paid by a third parties who are not involved in the process, simply because the price is determined by the coal producers and large users, the utilities. If we take a close look at true cost of coal including all externalities, we end up with billions of dollars every year.

The estimated total economic value of coal is over $200 billion annually, while the externalized costs are estimated to be twice that amount. The total hidden costs of coal combustion in the United States alone have been estimated to be over $60 billion annually. Respectively, an estimate of the effects of air pollution controls show that each dollar spent on airborne pollution controls saved over $50 in annual costs to the environment and population downwind.

Another study estimated the true cost of coal at up to $500 billion annually in the United States alone. And, according to the same study, if all the externalized costs of coal were accounted for, it would add almost 18 cents/kWh to the price of coal power generation. And if this is so, then coal will jump from the cheapest power generator today, at 2-3 cents per kW, to the most expensive at almost 10 times that amount.

The true cost of coal alone is estimated at almost twice the retail price. Or if coal sells for $40 per ton now, if the true cost is used, the price would be nearly $80 per ton.

Solid Waste

Coal mining operations release a number of solid toxic pollutants, some of which remain behind as solid waste, and some of which are released into the water and the atmosphere. Many of these pollutants are responsible for a large number of illnesses and premature deaths, not only of animals, but also of people living nearby, as well as people directly involved in the industry. And of course, people worldwide are affected one way or another, sooner or later, too.

Coal-fired power plants generate toxic solid wastes, which include ash, sludge, and boiler slag left over from burning coal to make electricity. Over 100 million tons of these wastes are produced every year in the U.S. alone. They contain carbon particles, and also chemical toxins, such as arsenic, mercury, chromium, cadmium, uranium and thorium.

Liquid Waste

Coal mining and processing operations use water in some steps of the process. Some of the water is recycled, but a significant amount is dumped in whatever local formation possible. In the past the liquid waste was dumped into nearby streams and lakes, making them hazmat dumpsites. This practice is still used in a number of third-world countries. Imagine the misery the locals must endure, living in this toxic chemical nightmare.

In addition to the daily soil, water and air pollution, the solid and liquid wastes also create a large and expensive storage problem, which remains on the property forever. Large piles of ash, and pools of bubbling liquids can be seen by most coal processing and burning plants. Their effect is great and long lasting. Even when the site is decommissioned, their effect remains and continues to harm the local environment and the people who live nearby.

Air Emissions

Coal-fired power plant emissions released into the atmosphere contain nitrous oxides which are responsible for industrial and urban smog, sulfur dioxide which is the primary reactive agent behind acid rain, mercury which accumulates in the food chain, and large amounts of carbon dioxide which is the most important greenhouse gas contributing to climate change.

There is also the toxic aspect of some of the gasses emitted during burning of coal and other fossil fuels.

Table 5-7. Exposure limits for CO gas in ppm

Exposure (hours)	Causing sickness	Causing death
0.5	1000	2000
1	600	1600
2	300	1000
4	150	400
6	120	200
8	100	150

It is obvious from Table 5-7 that 30 minutes of exposure to 1,000 ppm of carbon oxide (CO) in the air we breath will put us in the hospital with a lung damage and who knows what other organ failures. Double this amount to 2,000 ppm and we might get permanent damage to our health, ending with death in some cases.

There are presently locations in China where the CO concentration is approaching these limits, and where people are suffering and dying as a consequence.

Coal mining itself also releases significant amounts of methane, another extremely potent greenhouse gas. Coal mining is responsible for over 25% of the energy-related methane emissions in the U.S. as well.

Coal dust in mines and near storage and transport facilities contributes to serious respiratory illnesses such as asthma and pneumoconiosis, black lung. Solid combustion wastes, such as fly ash, pollute groundwater near storage facilities, contaminating individual and community water supplies.

Airborne pollutants have a larger footprint. Despite air pollution regulations, toxic emissions such as soot, sulfur dioxide, and nitrous oxides from coal-fired power plants are estimated to be responsible for thousands of deaths due to lung disease each year in the U.S. and Canada. A government study in Ontario found that the coal-fired plants in that province alone were responsible for an average annual total of about 660 premature deaths, 920 hospital admissions, 1,090 emergency room visits, and 331,000 minor illnesses. The number of unreported, or underreported health issues is several times larger. See Figure 5-22.

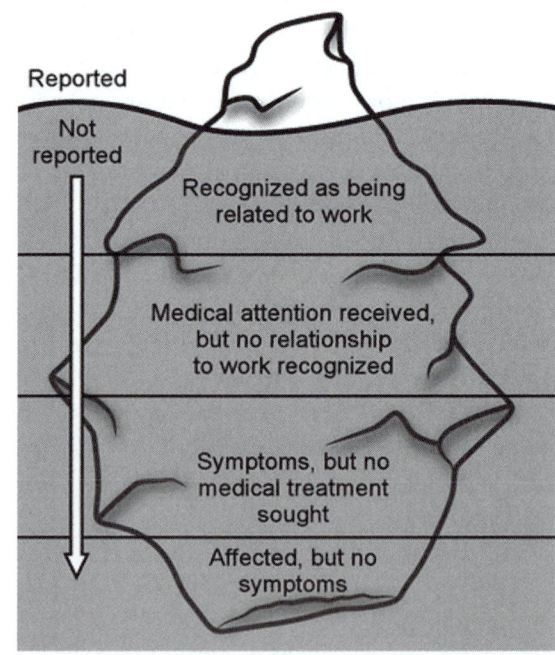

Figure 5-22. Coal related health problems

Coal-fired power plants are a major source of atmospheric mercury, which accumulates in the food chain and can damage the developing nervous systems of human fetuses, as well as leading to reduced immune function, weight loss, reduced reproduction rate, mental defects, and other neurological problems. The health problems go on and on, leaving us believing that coal mining is one of the most dangerous occupations in the world.

Mitigation

Many of the environmental impacts resulting from coal mining and use activities may be avoided during the process. Some could be mitigated after the fact, and some are physically impossible or way too expensive to mitigate.

Resource-specific mitigation measures can be applied to avoid or minimize impacts from coal mining. A thorough assessment is needed to identify and implement appropriate mitigation measures, as well as the potential impacts on a specific resource. Site-specific variables and factors must be evaluated in detail, to determine whether the impact can be avoided or mitigated. A decision must be made then as of what action can be taken, and how effective the mitigation measure and its overall cost-effectiveness would be.

Usually there is some overlap and redundancy built into mitigation measures, but to be fully effective, they should be designed over and above the minimum requirements of applicable laws and regulations. Guidance on conducting impact assessments and identifying appropriate mitigation measures for specific projects is needed, and so specialized body of specialists must be consulted for best results.

Coal Train Derailments

As if the solid, liquid, and air damage from coal mining and transport is not enough, we must add here the number of train accidents, where entire trainloads of coal have been derailed and spilled their cargo onto the nearby land. The recovery efforts, in most cases, have been even more devastating to the local environment than the actual accident.

Table 5-8 gives a list of train accidents and derailments in the U.S., 2010 to 2012.

Imagine the mess, railroad cars laying on their sides, coal spilled all over the place, and the entire area covered with thick coal dust. Not a pretty, or safe, picture. The frequency with which these accidents happen tells us that there is a problem somewhere. Is it the extraordinary weight of the train compositions, the speed with which these move, or the rail structure? Whatever it is, it is a serious environmental issue and since these accidents will continue, we need to be aware of their consequences and enter the damages in the overall cal-

Table 5-8. U.S. train accidents and derailments

Grantville, KS	November 2012
Painstville, KY	November 2012
Ashby, NE	October 2012
Oktaha, OK	September 2012
Ellicott City, MD	August 2012
Grants, NM	August 2012
Raleigh, WV	August 2012
Saline County, KS	July 2012
Havelock, NC	July 2012
Jefferson County, KS	July 2012
Princeton, IN	July 2012
Pendleton, TX	July 2012
Northbrook/Glenview, IL	July 2012
Mesa, WA	July 2012
Portageville, MO	June 2012
Junction City, KS	June 2012
Collins, MS	May 2012
Salmon Arm, BC	April 2012
Houston, BC	February 2012
Hinton, Alberta	January 2012
Vanderhoof, BC	January 2012
Montrose, IA	December 2011
Vanderhoof, BC	December 2011
Galland, BC	December 2011
Topeka, KS	November 2011
Peetz, NE	October 2011
Charleston, WV	October 2011
Emmett, KS	September 2011
Denison, IA	July 2011
Omaha, NE	July 2011
Bloomington, IN	July 2011
Ashdown, AK	July 2011
Pueblo, CO	November 2010
Surveyor, WV	April 2011
Kearney, NE	September 2010
Quantico, VA	August 2010
Drummond, MT	August 2010
Ferry Farm, VA	July 2010

culations of the coal's contribution to the environmental damage.

Environmental Impact

The environmental impacts of coal transportation, even without the accidents, include air pollution, water pollution, solid wastes, noise levels, safety and traffic hazards. Direct environmental impacts can occur at the mine, where the coal is being transferred, transported or loaded. Indirect environmental impacts from coal transportation largely result from release of methane gas and the combustion of fuel for the transportation itself.

Coal transportation is not required to follow unique environmental controls, since it is usually integrated with extraction and utilization operations. The greatest problem from coal transportation is coal dust entrainment. It is estimated that coal transported in open cars emits 0.1-0.2% of its weight in dust particles along the way. So, a 10,000-ton unit train would spew about 100-200 tons of dust along its route every day.

Using covered hopper cars is one of the solutions to this problem, but it is impractical for coal transport because of loading and unloading difficulties. Instead, water and/or chemical and petrochemical additives are sometimes used to reduce dust creation. Water usually reduces the heating value of coal by 1-2%, while the additives usually increase it, but may also create undesirable pollutants.

Dust control at loading and unloading facilities generally involves cyclones in series with filters or scrubbers for the exhaust air. The cyclones are standard single-stage units, especially designed to handle small coal dust particles.

Different quantities of methane gas are released during coal transport and storage as well. A study in Europe concluded that 0.27 kg of methane gas is emitted per ton of coal during the transport and storage procedures. Large amounts of diesel fuel are used during the coal transport, whether by train, truck, or barge. The same study estimated that over 10 grams of CO_2 and small amounts of methane and NO_x gasses are released for each ton-mile travelled during coal transport. Trucks emit approximately 10-20 times the polluting gasses per ton-mile than trains. With the billions of tons of coal used around the world annually, this is a significant amount of pollution that needs to be addressed in conjunction with the other emission sources.

Mining Accidents in the U.S.

Train accidents, however bad, are not the worst problem in the mining industry. Mining accidents are by far more devastating to the mines and the people who work in them.

Mining, the job of digging coal and other useful materials out of the earth, is by far one of the world's most dangerous occupations. Public concern about the toll of deaths, injuries and destruction in mine accidents has prompted passage of much-needed safety legislation and intensified the search for safer methods and improved training practices and technology.

There is also a trend of growing cooperation among industry, labor and government, which has contributed to safer and more healthful mining in recent years. As a result, mining deaths and injuries have declined significantly, although even very low injury and death numbers are still unacceptable in our society.

In the early 1900s, mine explosions and other accidents claimed thousands of victims. For example, in 1907 alone there were 3,242 deadly mining accidents. A mine explosion killed 358 people near Monongah, VA. Fires, explosions and cave-ins caused many deaths and injuries in the past. Although the numbers of serious accidents have been reduced, they still happen. With each passing decade, the annual number of mining deaths and the even more significant rates of injuries have declined measuring numbers of injuries against hours worked.

Generally speaking most non-coal mining has proven to be less deadly than coal mining. Annual coal mining deaths had numbered more than 1,000 a year in the early part of the 20th century, but have decreased to an average of about 451 annual fatalities in the 1950s, and to 141 in the 1970s. The yearly average in coal mining decreased to 30 fatalities from 2001-2005.

The rate of coal mining deaths decreased from about 0.20 fatalities per 200,000 hours worked by miners (or one death per million production hours) in 1970 to about 0.07 fatalities in 1977 and an average of 0.03 fatalities for the 2001-2005 periods. During a period in 1992, from May 27 to July 14, the coal mining industry did not experience any fatal accidents while producing many million tons of coal—a period of rare length in mining history.

The Monongah Mining Disaster was the worst mining accident of American history, when 362 miners

Table 5-9. Mining fatalities, USA

Mining fatalities and injuries		
Year	Annual Deaths	Annual Injuries
1936-1940	1,546	81,342
1941-1945	1,592	82,825
1946-1950	1,054	63,367
1951-1955	690	38,510
1956-1960	550	28,805
1961-1965	449	23,204
1966-1970	426	22,435
1971-1975	322	33,963
1976-1980	254	41,220
1981-1985	174	24,290
1986-1990	122	27,524
1991-1995	99	24,201
1996-2000	86	17,500
2001-2005	62	12,952
2006-2007	69	11,800
2008-2009	48	N/A
2010-2011	69	N/A

were killed in an underground explosion on December 6, 1907 in Monongah, West Virginia.

The U.S. Bureau of Mines was created in 1910 to investigate accidents, advise industry, conduct production and safety research, and teach courses in accident prevention, first aid, and mine rescue.

A number of factors have contributed to the dramatic safety improvements in the U.S. mining industry since the turn of the century, in addition to the creation in 1910 of the U.S. Bureau of Mines. Some of these are:

- Federal and state laws were introduced to better advise and regulate the mining industry.

- The creation of the Federal Coal Mine Health and Safety Act of 1969 and the Federal Mine Safety and Health Act of 1977.

- The creation in 1973 of the Mining Enforcement and Safety Administration in the Interior Department, which assumed safety and health enforcement responsibilities from the Bureau of Mines.
  — The creation of the present Mine Safety and Health Administration (MSHA), which was moved to the Labor Department.

- Safer and more productive mining machines and methods were introduced lately, which increased the awareness of the importance of effective accident prevention programs. And a more cooperative attitude toward safety issues by the mining industry, labor, and government plays important role as well in improving the safety record.

There were over 448,500 miners in the US in 1900, whose numbers steadily dropped down to 260,000 in 1955, 108,000 in 2000, and up again to 143,500 in 2011. The fatalities also dropped significantly, as can be seen in Table 5-9 down from hundreds per year in the early 1900s to 21 in 2011. Which, of course, is 21 too many, and yet signifies an undeniable progress in the safety of U.S. mining operations.

A large proportion of the total number of miners are working in the coalmines, and although there have been immense improvements in technology, the dangers are the same and the risks are still too great. We do owe a lot to our brave miners, although most of us have no idea of the hardship they endure on daily basis for our comfort's sake.

Amazingly enough, there is very little information on the subject. It seems as though there is some sort of an official gag order, or unofficial code of silence surrounding mining life and even denser one around mining ac-cidents. As a civilized society, we should be given much more information on the lives and well being of those who risk their lives on daily basis. Going deep under the ground every day, and working 8-10 hours under millions of tons of earth over your head is not a small thing, and not many of us would volunteer for it.

NOTE: As a matter of fact, many of us would not even volunteer to visit a mine, if they knew how dirty and dangerous it is in there. And honestly speaking, the author is one of these people, having lived through the horrifying experience of visiting a deep underground mine in Ukraine. After a quick descend In that half-mile deep coalmine shaft, which is typical for a coal mine in that part of the world, there were dozens of half-naked men crawling on their stomachs, digging coal in a 3 foot high coal vein. There was no protective equipment, nor ceiling supports at this area.

The temperature at that depth was above well above 100°F, so the coal dust, mixed with sweat, was covering the miners' bodies from head to toe. A picture from Dante's Inferno…with shiny black bodies wiggling in the coal dust and mud in a 3 feet claustrophobic overhead space. And that picture doesn't show the horror of millions of tons of earth above…with supports (even if there were any) that may, or may not, keep it from collapsing.

It is impossible to ignore the bravery and endurance of these people, and all miners around the world. Going to a war battle is a piece of cake, compared to going down in the mine. Down there, planning and training go only that far. Nature is in full control every inch of the way, and it does not obey our rules and regulations. Crawling 8-10 hours every day on your stomach in a dusty hole deep in the ground is not only tiring, but also desperately brave. You never know what will happen the next moment, such as an instant flood or devastating explosion.

Of course, the conditions in the U.S. coalmines are much better and safer, but what kind of contraption can keep a million tons of ceiling from collapsing? What guarantee is there that a machine won't malfunction and run unexpectedly into a group of miners? At those depths, and under those conditions, any malfunction could be fatal.

Mine Accidents Around the World

Mine work conditions in other parts of the world are much worse than these in the U.S. Some examples of mine accidents in China, which has one of the worst safety records in the industry follow:

In November, 2009 a mining accident in Heilongjiang killed at least 104 people. A methane explosion followed by a coal dust explosion is thought to have caused it. Three top officials involved with the mining company were promptly dismissed.

A coal mining accident in Sichuan in November, 2010 left 28 people trapped underground. There were 41 workers in the mine doing safety work to expand the mine's capacity from 50,000 to 60,0000 tons, when unexpectedly an estimated 4,000 cubic meters of water broke through a side wall and flooded the mine shaft where the workers were working. Officials are unsure what exactly caused the flooding, but the safety procedures were immediately implemented. Pumps were brought to the mine to pump the water and assist with the rescue efforts, but it was too late.

On August 30, 2012 an explosion killed 45 people at the Xiaojiawan coal mine in Sichuan province. A few days later on September 3, 2012, 14 miners were killed at Gaokeng Coal Mine in Jiangxi province.

China, which uses coal to produce 70% of its energy consumption, is the world's deadliest country for mine accidents—some 2,600 people died in 2009 alone.

In August, 2012 a similar mine explosion in Sichuan province killed 26 miners, marking it as one of the biggest coalmine disasters of the year. China suspended eight officials and arrested two others over the coal mine accident The eight suspended officials include Fuyuan county's coal industry bureau chief and the bureau's deputy director, the official Xinhua news agency said, quoting Fuyuan's publicity office, as if arresting the mining chief will improve the working conditions, but this is how China deals with bad news.

In December, 2012 another 17 miners were killed when an explosive device was set off as part of the work routine, triggering a blast in the gas-filled mine shaft located in the Huangnihe township in Fuyuan. The families of the 17 dead miners will receive compensation of $150,000 each. Not bad for the poor families, but the women are now widows, and the children will grow up fatherless. Is this a good deal?

China's mines are the deadliest in the world by far, because of lax enforcement of safety standards and a rush to feed demand from a robust economy. China is also a place where the governing communist party looks upon human life differently. Many qualified miners refuse to work in China's coalmines because coal mining is a high-risk occupation in China. That creates a vicious circle, where accidents caused by unqualified miners leads to a higher probability of qualified people to refuse working in the coalmines, so the circle goes round and round.

Lax safety culture in China is also to blame for the accidents, so lately China has been relying on high-tech production equipment and revised techniques to change the trend. Intrinsic safety processes and facilities have been designed to reduce the dependence of work safety on human behaviors to a minimum.

More money is being invested for safety training, and in the implementation of a system of rewards and punishments for safe behavior. This way, more qualified employees are expected to enter the coal mining, which in turn would lead to much improved mine safety, thus closing the vicious safety circle.

Abandoned Mines

Abandoned mines are an issue that is hidden, intentionally and unintentionally, from the public eye. Abandoned mines cause problems to the surrounding lands, surface and underground waters, and watersheds, all of which could be contaminated or scarred by the extraction, beneficiation, or processing of coal, ores and minerals. Abandoned mine lands usually affect areas where mining or processing activity is officially determined to have ceased.

Abandoned mines are found all around the world. They are in private, mixed, and federal lands adding to the complexity of the issue, since there are different rules and regulations that govern the different locations. For example, a number of federal statutes address environmental contamination issues associated with abandoned mines, but they do not apply to private lands. And then, since the Federal statutory authority is spread among several agencies with no one agency having overall statutory responsibility, the effort is fragmented at best, if present at all.

There are many types of mines, each with their own unique characteristics, making cleanup efforts varied, both in terms of cost and approach. The three main types are coal, hard rock, and uranium.

Most abandoned coalmines in the U.S. are found in the East and tend to be small to medium-sized. Sixty percent of these mines can be found in just three states: West Virginia, Pennsylvania, and Kentucky. Larger sites are found in the West, albeit in much smaller numbers.

Most abandoned coalmines are located on state-owned land. These sites also tend to be in closer proximity to populated areas. Many times, homes and other buildings have been constructed on top of underground mine workings and subsidence can become a problem.

The Office of Surface Mining Reclamation and Enforcement (OSM), within the Department of the Interior, is the primary Federal agency responsible for abandoned coalmine reclamation. A national program, established by a 1977 law, is in place that includes an inventory of high priority sites, a reclamation fee paid by the coal mining industry, and a funding mechanism comprised largely of grants to states and Indian tribes with approved programs. The priority is on sites posing health and safety hazards.

There is an inventory of high priority abandoned coalmines maintained jointly by OSM and program states and Tribes. There are a number of other types of mines such as iron and phosphate, in addition to thousands of sand, gravel, and clay pits and quarries that are not addressed by Federal abandoned mine lands programs at all.

No single national AML program exists; rather, several authorities and multiple departments and agencies address abandoned mines sites occasionally, and usually as part of other, broader programs. Funding for remediation projects is spread among separate appropriations for participating departments and agencies. Federal and state agencies are doing more than ever before to display their spatial data and exchange information, but this is where the effort dwindles in the bureaucratic mix of issues.

There is a "polluter pays" principle in force in the U.S. that requires the Federal government, where possible, to compel responsible parties to clean up their sites or help cover the costs. Priorities focus on water quality and sites involving release of potentially hazardous substances. The enforcement of this policy is partial and little information exists on its compliance by the coal industry, as evidenced by the large number of abandoned mines that are just that, abandoned. No one is held responsible for the environmental damage, human health issues, and other consequences resulting from abandoned mines.

So, the coal mining industry leaves its mark, even after operations have ceased. Abandoned underground and surface mines account for the longest lasting damage to the environment. Although there are signs of revival of the movement to secure abandoned mines, we do not see it being resolved any time soon. So it will be up to the future generations to clean up our mess, including the mess of abandoned coalmines.

Environmental Impact of Coal-fired Power Generation

When the power plants start operation we see the real pollution footprint. And this one is huge, the largest legal emission of pollutants in the world. Coal mining and burning for electric power generation is a necessary evil. We cannot imagine our lives without electricity.

It is part of the American dream. It is something we need and want, and something without which our lives would be quite hard.

On the other hand, there are a number of serious environmental effects from coal mining, transport and burning. These occur throughout the entire life span of the coal processes, starting with exploration, mining, preparation, transport, combustion, down to the toxic gas releases and waste solid storage.

Power Plant Equipment Carbon Footprint

A number of large and small pieces of equipment are used in the power plant design, construction, testing and operation. Starting with the plant design and construction, the carbon footprint starts at site location, where deep tracks in the ground and heavy plumes of smoke in the air from large trucks and bulldozers crawling all over the place can be seen day after day. And there are also trains and trucks used for transporting the equipment to the mine.

All this machinery was made somewhere on the planet some time in the past, where and when their manufacturing processes and transport created a significant pollution footprint. Since most of the construction equipment is used only temporarily we can assign only a small part of the carbon footprint to the manufacturing and transport of the power plant equipment. (A)

Even before construction is complete, the main power equipment pieces arrive in wooden boxes or on back of large trailers, or railroad cars. These are assembled with the help of other equipment and put to work after creating another set of pollution problems. (B)

In addition, there are many other items and small pieces of equipment, tools and consumables—some for personal use, and some for specialized operations. These are computers, helmets, boots, goggles, shoes, first aid kits, etc., etc. the list goes. All these were also made somewhere around the world, sometime in the past, and transported to the power plant. During their manufacturing processes and transport they also left a significant pollution footprint. (C).

Then, to complete the pollution footprint picture, we must add to that the footprint of the people involved in the entire process—engineers and technicians involved in the equipment manufacturing, transport, installation, setup, and operation. These people drive cars, ride on planes, all of which leaves another significant set of pollution footprints (D)

And so, the total pollution footprint of the power plant equipment cradle-to-grave process is expressed by:

$$P_f = A + B + C + D$$

where

P$_f$ is the total pollution footprint from equipment manufacturing, transport, and maintenance

A   is the equipment manufacturing and transport to the power plant

B   is equipment assembly, test and installation at the plant

C   is the manufacturing and transport to small tools and consumables, and

D   is the pollution footprint of the equipment personnel during the design and setup phases.

Combining the pollution footprint of A (power plant equipment manufacturing and transport) with B (equipment assembly, test and installation), adding C (the manufacturing and transport of the tools and consumables), plus D (the pollution footprint of the equipment personnel) gives us the environmental footprint of the plant equipment before even starting the power plant operations.

And the pollution footprint is significant, to be sure! It goes deep and wide; stretching from one part of the world to the other. To put a value on it we must take inventory of all items delivered to the plant, and needed for its design, construction and operation. We must take a close look at the manufacturing of a dragline, a bulldozer, a dump truck and a number of other pieces of equipment used at the mine.

Keep in mind that some of these are some of the largest pieces of equipment in the world, and that it takes thousands of tons of metals to make them. Each of these started as an iron ore dug out from another mine somewhere in the world, which was transported to a smelter. The molten metal was shaped in different forms and shipped to the different parts manufacturers, who drilled, welded and otherwise constructed parts for these vehicles.

And again, remember that we are talking about huge pieces of metal—some as big as an entire building. One single bolt from a boiler furnace might be over a foot long, the entire unit as big as a railroad car. After manufacturing, these parts are packed and loaded on railroad cars or trucks to be shipped to the assembly facility. The major parts of a turbine or a furnace might require a dozen of railroad cars for transport.

The parts are assembled into major components, or entire units and after one more loading and unloading operation, they finally arrive at the power plant floor for final assembly and testing, before being put to work.

This is a long a windy process, with many stop and go, loading and unloading and shipping steps.

Again, putting a dollar value, or a number in tons of hydrocarbons, would be too long and complex procedure for our purposes, so it suffices to say that the pollution effects during and after all these steps are significant. We will take a second, closer look at these steps and their environmental effects in the following chapters.

Power Plant Equipment Pollution

And now, after starting the power plant operations, we see a significant pollution footprint for the duration of the operation and maintenance procedures too. As an example, plant equipment uses electric power to run pumps, fans, and for all control equipment. During an average workday and under a full load, these pieces of equipment will use several megawatts of power.

Using the generated power increases the overall environmental effect and carbon footprint.

And then, all equipment needs repairs and eventually replacement. Spare parts for the pieces of equipment in need of repair periodically arrive from different parts manufacturers, after leaving their pollution footprint on the way too. We will attempt to assign an accurate number—quantity of air and land pollution—and a related dollar numbers to these activities and their environmental effects in the following chapters.

And after 20-30 years of non-stop operation, the power plant is finally declared finished and is scheduled for a shut down and decommissioning. The plant decommissioning and land reclamation are major, expensive, and polluting undertakings. The equipment has to be disassembled and removed from the buildings, loaded on trucks or trans and transported to a recycling facility or a waste disposal site. In all cases, equipment and materials used during the decommissioning and waste disposal process create additional air and ground pollution, which is not to be ignored.

Additional, specialized equipment and personnel (environmental specialists and inspectors), are usually brought in to assist with the effort. And with that more pollution footprints are left at the plant site.

In most cases additional equipment is brought in to mitigate and reconstruct the plant site to its original state. Another set of carbon and other pollution footprint is left behind when this process is completed.

When the final tally is made, a significant part of the emissions and overall pollution are to be attributed to the power plant equipment and support personnel. This number is significant and we will go through the calculations in the next chapters as well.

Power Plant Emissions

During the operation of a coal-fired power plant we can identify a number of the worst polluters known to man. And it is the enormous quantity of those pollutants that makes it intolerable. And yet, we don't see anyone striking at power plants. Why? Because we need their product. We need the jobs they provide, and we need the electricity they produce. Catch 22; can't live with them, can't live without them.

No, we don't need to strike at power plants. And yet, we need to know what we are dealing with. We need to see and understand that without any significant action, by the end of this century we will have burned all fossils and kill the environment and many people within.

The major polluters emitted by coal-fired power plants are:

Gas Pollutants

- Toxins from electricity generation in the U.S. release nearly 400 million lbs. of toxic air pollution annually, or over 50% of the total national emissions. Coal burning power plants are the leading sources of toxic air pollution in all but four of the top 20 states by electric sector emissions.

- Air pollution from coal-fired power plants includes sulfur dioxide, nitrogen oxides, methane, carbon monoxide, particulate matter (PM), heavy metals, and toxic materials. The heavy smoke from the smoke stacks lead to smog, acid rain, increased toxins in the environment, and numerous respiratory, cardiovascular, and cerebro-vascular ills.

- The major negative effects from these air pollution sources can be attributed to emissions of particulate matter, combined with the effects of sulfur dioxide, nitrogen oxides, and carbon monoxide on human health.

- Mercury emissions from coal-fired power plants are the largest source of mercury in the United States, accounting for about 41% of industrial releases. Mercury is a poison, which causes a number of illnesses in humans._

- _Sulfur dioxide released by coal burning power plants is the largest human-caused source of sulfur dioxide; a pollutant gas that contributes to the production of acid rain and causes significant health problems. Coal naturally contains sulfur, and when it is burned, the sulfur combines with oxygen to form sulfur oxides, which when mixed with air moisture produce sulfuric acid, which causes acid rain.

- Radioactivity in coal is limited to small amounts of the radioactive elements, uranium and thorium. When coal is burned, however, the fly ash contains uranium and thorium at up to 10 times their original levels. Large amounts of fly ash can cause significant health damages in populated centers.

Liquid Pollutants

- *Coal combustion waste* is the nation's second largest waste stream after municipal solid waste. It is disposed of in landfills or "surface impoundments," which are lined with compacted clay soil, a plastic sheet, or both. As rain filters through the toxic ash pits year after year, the toxic metals are leached out into the local environment.

- *Acid mine drainage* is a by-product of mining operations and consists of unintentional release of acidic water from both; operating and abandoned coal mines. Coal mining activities expose the sulfur-bearing mineral pyrite to the moist air, and the reaction produces sulfuric acid, which can leak into the water table, and/or wash into local lakes, rivers and streams with unpredictable consequences.

- *Coal sludge, or slurry*, is a liquid generated during washing coal in the coal preparation plants. These are very large quantities of coal particles containing wastewater, which is disposed of at waste sites and impoundments near coalmines. In many cases the slurry is pumped into abandoned underground mines and other cavities. The toxins contained in the slurry enter in, and contaminate, the underground and surface waters._

- *Heavy metals* abound in coal mines, and vary from location to location in type and quantity. Small amounts of heavy metals are usually harmless to humans, but extended exposure, or higher quantity of any heavy metal, could cause acute or chronic poisoning of humans and all life forms. A number of heavy metals and other toxic materials are encountered in the mining and use of coal. Some of these are lead, mercury, nickel, tin, cadmium, antimony, and arsenic. Some radioisotopes of thorium and strontium are found in some locations as well.

Particulate Pollutants

- Particulate matter is also included in the tiny particles of fly ash and dust that are expelled from coal-burning power plants. Exposure to this particulate matter is related to an increase of respiratory and cardiac diseases and mortality.

- Significant quantities of black carbon residue are released during incomplete combustion of coal in the coal burning power plants, which contributes to additional climate change.

- Particulate matter contained in coal includes the tiny particles of fly ash and dust that are expelled from coal-burning power plants. Studies have shown that exposure to particulate matter is related to an increase of respiratory and cardiac mortality.

- Transportation of coal from the mines to the power plants is done via trucks, railroads, and large cargo ships, Since the coal is usually loaded in open containers, there is a significant release of coal air pollution such as soot along the way. The soot can lead to disasters that ruin the environment in the affected areas. Collisions of transport vehicles, resulting in spilling of large amounts of coal, have also contributed to large environmental damages in the past.

Solid Pollutants
- Solid waste from coal burning is one of the largest waste stream in the US, second only after municipal solid waste streams. The solids in form of ash and soot are disposed of in landfills, also called surface impoundments. These are usually lined with compacted clay soil, and/or plastic sheets, and as rainwater filters through the toxic pits, with time, the toxic materials, including heavy metals and other toxic chemicals, leach out into the local environment, contaminating the soil and water table.

- Radioactive materials are found in coal. Some amounts of uranium and thorium are most frequently found at some locations. Although these are usually in fairly small amounts, when coal burns, the fly ash contains traces of uranium and thorium at up to 10 times their original levels. Burning such coal and blasting even very small amounts of radioactive materials day after day, all day long. would harm the environment in the area.

Land Effects
- Mountaintop removal mining and other forms of surface mining lead to drastic alteration of the local landscapes. The overall mining operations destroy the habitat, damage the water supplies, and cause

air pollution. Many of these effects cannot be remediated by coalmine reclamation, thus they cause a permanent damage to the local environment and life forms in it.

- Floods resulting from deforestation and/or failed ine impoundments could further damage the landscape and contribute to long term or permanent damage of the environment.

- There are estimates that forest destruction caused by mountaintop removal mining operations has destroyed nearly 7% of Appalachia's forests.

- Mountaintop removal has also caused radical disturbance of over 8 million acres of farmland, rangeland, and forests in the US. Most of which has not been, and most likely will never be, reclaimed

- Long wall mining also causes land subsidence, which can occur after any type of underground mining, and which causes serious land changes and damage.

Thermal Effects
- Coal fires can occur in both abandoned coalmines and in coal waste piles. There are thousands of underground coal fires burning non-stop in the US and abroad. The emissions from all these fires are estimated to generate about 3% of the global carbon dioxide emissions, including about 40 tons of mercury annually.

- Thermal pollution from the coal fires, but in much larger extent from coal burning power plants (cooling water dumped in lakes and rivers) is responsible for the degradation of water quality in many water bodies. The increased temperature impacts fish and other life forms by decreasing oxygen supply and affecting the local ecosystem balance.

Water Effects
- Groundwater degradation is expected after mining. Coal beds often serve as underground aquifers, and their removal impacts the land, thus causing drastic changes in hydrology.

- Waste coal, known as "culm," "gob," or "boney," is basically unused coal mixed with soil and rock during the mining operations. It has no commercial value, so it is dumped nearby as waste. Runoff from these waste coal sites will leach into the soil, polluting it and the water table.

- There is enormous quantity of water used during power generation. Water is used mostly for cooling the outgoing steam, and is the second only to agriculture, the largest user of water.

- There is significant water table pollution during and after coal mining operations, as well as during and after burning the coal. This includes the negative health and environmental effects caused by the entire mining, processing, transport, burning, and waste storage of coal.

Climate Change

- The impact of coal plants on the climate is undeniable. About 30% of America's carbon dioxide emissions are generated by coal burning power plants. This makes coal undeniably a huge contributor to global warming. A significant quantity of black carbon residue, resulting from incomplete combustion of coal in the coal burning power plants, is an additional and significant contributor to climate change.

- Greenhouse gas emissions are also caused by mountaintop removal mining. During the initial stages, large amounts of carbon containing gasses are released through clear cutting and burning of trees and bushes. Additional releases of carbon are released from the soil, which is brought up to the surface during mining operations. It has been estimated that these gas emissions contribute to 6-7% of the power plant emissions.

- Methane gas released by coal mining operations is responsible for over 10% of all air releases. Methane is a potent global warming gas, thus it is a major contributor to climate change as well.

Health Effects

Gasses emitted during coal combustion affect the respiratory system and cause a variety of adverse health effects. Air pollutants—among them nitrous oxide (NO_2) and very small particles, known as PM2.5—adversely affect lung development, reducing forced expiratory volume (FeV) among children.

This reduction of FeV, an indication of lung function, often precedes the subsequent development of other pulmonary diseases. Air pollution triggers attacks of asthma, a respiratory disease affecting more than 9% of all children in the U.S. Children are particularly susceptible to the development of pollution-related asthma attacks. This may be due to their distinct breathing patterns, as well as how much time they spend outside. It

may also be due to the immaturity of their enzyme and immune systems, which assist in detoxifying pollutants, combined with incomplete pulmonary development.

These factors appear to act in concert to make children highly susceptible to airborne pollutants such as those emitted by coal-fired power plants. Asthma exacerbations have been linked specifically to exposure to ozone, a gas produced when NO_2 reacts with volatile organic compounds in the presence of sunlight and heat.

The risk to children of experiencing ozone-related asthma exacerbations is greatest among those with severe asthma. That risk exists even when ambient ozone levels fall within the limits set by the EPA to protect public health.

Coal pollutants trigger asthma attacks in combination with individual genetic characteristics. This gene-environment interaction means that some individuals are more susceptible to the respiratory health effects of coal pollution. The genetic polymorphisms that appear to make people more susceptible include those that control inflammation and those that deal with oxidative stress, or the presence in cells of highly reactive molecules, known as free radicals.

Coal pollutants play a role in the development of chronic obstructive pulmonary disease (COPD), a lung disease characterized by permanent narrowing of airways. Coal pollutants may also cause COPD exacerbations, in part through inflammation, an immunologic response. PM exposure disposes the development of inflammation on the cellular level, which in turn can lead to exacerbations of COPD, the fourth leading cause of mortality in the U.S.

Pollutants produced by coal combustion can also damage the human cardiovascular system. Coronary heart disease (CHD) is a leading cause of death in the U.S. Air pollution is known to negatively impact cardiovascular health.

The mechanisms by which air pollution causes cardiovascular disease have not been definitively identified but are thought to be the same as those for respiratory disease: pulmonary inflammation and oxidative stress. Studies in both animals and humans support this theory, showing that pollutants produced by coal combustion lead to cardiovascular disease, such as arterial occlusion (artery blockages, leading to heart attacks) and infarct formation (tissue death due to oxygen deprivation, leading to permanent heart damage).

Recent research suggests that nitrogen oxides and PM2.5, along with other pollutants, are associated with hospital admissions for potentially fatal cardiac rhythm disturbances.

In addition to the respiratory and cardiovascular systems, the nervous system is also a target for coal pollution's health effects. The same mechanisms that are thought to mediate the effect of air pollutants on coronary arteries also apply to the arteries that nourish the brain. These include stimulation of the inflammatory response and oxidative stress, which in turn can lead to stroke and other cerebral vascular disease. Several studies have shown a correlation between coal-related air pollutants and stroke.

In some patients, ambient levels of PM2.5 have been correlated with hospital admission rates for cerebro-vascular disease; PM10 has been correlated with hospital admission for ischemic stroke. Keep in mind that 87% of all strokes are ischemic. PM2.5 increase has also been associated with an increase in the risk of, and death from, a cerebro-vascular event among post-menopausal women.

Coal pollutants also act on the nervous system to cause loss of intellectual capacity, primarily through mercury. Coal contains trace amounts of mercury that, when burned, enter the environment. Mercury accumulates and increases in concentration as it travels up the food chain, reaching high levels in large predatory fish. Humans, in turn, are exposed to coal-related mercury primarily through fish consumption. Coal-fired power plants are responsible for approximately one-third of all mercury emissions attributable to human activity.

A nationwide study of blood samples in 1999–2000 showed that 15.7% of women of childbearing age have blood mercury levels that would cause them to give birth to children with levels exceeding the EPA's maximum acceptable dose for mercury.

This dose was established to limit the number of children with mercury-related neurological and developmental impairments. Researchers have estimated that between 317,000 and 631,000 children are born in the U.S. each year with blood mercury levels high enough to impair performance on neuro-developmental tests and cause lifelong loss of intelligence.

NOTE: Oxygen free radicals are a normal cellular constituent and play critical roles in the control of many cellular functions in our bodies. The concentration of oxygen free radicals is normally increased during exposure to air pollution, tobacco smoke, pesticides, and organic solvents. (Free radicals are atoms or molecules that contain at least one unpaired electron in an atomic or molecular orbit and are therefore unstable and highly reactive.)

At high concentration of any of these air components their highly reactive molecules damage lipids, proteins, DNA, cell membranes, and other cellular components in the affected human organisms. This is the cause for oxidative stress, which is an important contributing factor in a variety of diseases, including atherosclerosis, hypertension, rheumatoid arthritis, and diabetes mellitus. Oxidative stress can also cause some neuro–degenerative disorders such as Alzheimer's disease and Parkinson's disease, as well as affect negatively the normal aging process.

This is one of several key mechanisms implicated in the pathogenesis of diseases caused or aggravated by coal pollutants, such as cardiovascular and pulmonary disease.

Conclusions

So, since we cannot and will not stop using coal, regardless of how bad it might be, we at least need to know all about them, and do our best to make sure that it will be around for a long time without killing us.

And so, looking at the entire cradle-to-grave process of coal production and use, we see the following steps:

1. Coal mine
   — Planning and design
   — Permitting
   — Land preparation
   — Facilities construction
   — Equipment purchase, delivery and installation
2. Daily operations
   — Coal digging
   — Onsite transport
   — Coal preparation (on-site)
3. Coal transport
   — Loading
   — Unit train transport
   — Unloading
4. Coal preparation (off-site)
   — Sorting
   — Washing
   — Treating
5. Coal burning power plants
   — Unloading
   — Pulverizing
   — Steam generation
   — Power generation
   — Gasses, ash and cooling water disposal
6. End of life decommissioning and waste disposal
   — Mine or plant shut down and disabling
   — Equipment disassembly and demolition'
   — Facilities demolition

— Waste disposal
— Land decontamination and reconstruction

This is just an overview of the major steps and their effects on the environment. These are explored in greater depth in the other chapters of this text, but you can imagine the tremendous environmental effects of most of these steps. Starting from the pollution of the land clearing and facilities construction, to the final waste disposal, thousands of acres of land could be affected, and millions of tons of toxins released in the air, soil, and water of the mine location. And of course, many people would be affected too. Some will be stressed, some made ill, and some will even die, all for the sake of coal production and use.

The Coal Facts

Here are a number of facts that deserve our attention, and some of which also need our help:

Fact: coal is here to stay and its use will increase with time.

Fact: we have a 100-year coal supply and most nations are relying on it for their future development and progress.

Fact: coal is absolutely needed now for the quick, efficient, and profitable development of our current capitalist societies.

Fact: coal is killing the environment and the people in it, and is creating a dangerously accelerating climate warming condition.

Fact: people who work in the coal and other energy industries are not villains! They are only doing their job, and deserve our respect, because we need their services and final product—electricity.

Fact: environmentalism is just a fancy talk today that has produced minimal results.

Fact: driving electric cars saves the immediate environment, but pollutes a different place, where the electric power was produced.

Fact: most people do not care where electricity comes from, and what can be done to change things, especially if it means a personal sacrifice

Fact: coal will last about 100 years, after which there will be no more coal.

Fact: we clearly do not care what the future generations will think about that, and/or what will they do without coal.

Fact: we will no doubt continue using coal no matter what, until it is totally gone.

Fact: the day when the last piece of coal on Earth is burned, will mark the start of a new era in human development, not a happy one, and we are glad we will not be there to witness it.

Fact: the future generations will think of us as selfish people, who so quickly and stupidly burned one of the most precious gifts Earth had to offer—the fossils.

We would like to emphasize here that as far as evaluating the pros and cons of coal mining and use are concerned, the glass is half full. We do recognize that man's activities, coal mining and burning included, have an impact on the environment in general. There is no question about that; and the impact is significant. We, however, must also admit that we cannot live without coal right now—whatever the consequences.

So, the only reasonable thing we can do is understand and clarify the effects of this impact—negative and positive. We need to understand how the processes work and what the actual and calculable final results of these are. With this information in hand, we could then make a better assessment and decide how much coal we need, and how to proceed.

What can we do to retain our energy independence, without burning all fossils and destroying the environment, while living in the comfort zone we are so used to? This is the question before us and those coming after us in the 21st century.

CRUDE OIL

Crude oil is the fuel that has been powering several key sectors of the world economies for over a century now. It is still a key fuel used in transportation, home heating, power generation (peaking power plants), and many commercial and industrial operations. In many cases, switching to other fuels is very hard, and sometimes impossible.

Because of these difficulties and inconveniences, crude oil will remain a key fuel for several decades, especially for powering cars and trucks. It will remain so until the last drop is pumped out of the ground. And so, like it or not, crude oil is here to stay for a long while. But its quantity in the ground is limited, so after we have pumped it all out—some suggest at least 50 more years—we will be forced to do without. How exactly will depend on our actions during the next 50 years.

No matter what, crude oil, and the impact of its production, transportation and use, deserves a very close look. We are using this commodity in its different forms every day, so we need to understand very well what it is, and what it is not. This way we would be prepared to discuss the issues at hand and even do something about the problems it is presenting us with.

General Description

Crude oil comes in several types, shapes and colors. At first sight, is a dark yellow, brown, and even black. It is an oily liquid that is found in natural underground reservoirs in many places in the U.S. and around the world. Crude was formed millions and billions of years ago, when layers of dirt, rock and sand covered the remains of animals and plants. With time, heat and pressure underground turned the fossil remains into organic liquid; crude oil, which is often mixed with impurities and accompanied by natural gas.

This is why crude oil, natural gas, and coal are called fossil fuels. In its natural state, crude oil is not very practical for use. Because of that, after the oil and gas are extracted, they are processed into fuels that are more practical to use as fuels and other petroleum products, such as cosmetics, plastics, and medications.

Crude oil is a mixture of a wide variety of constituents, mostly hydrocarbons, which are chemicals composed of hydrogen and carbon and other chemical compositions. Crude oil also contains hundreds of substances that include benzene, chromium, iron, mercury, nickel, nitrogen, oxygen, sulfur, toluene, and xylene, to mention a few.

Total petroleum hydrocarbons is a term used to describe the several hundred chemical compounds that originally come from crude oil.

There are four types of crude oil:

Class A are the light, highly volatile oils. They are highly fluid and toxic to humans, and include jet fuel and gasoline.

Class B are the non-sticky oils. They are waxy and less toxic to humans, and include diesel fuel and light crude oil.

Class C are the heavy, sticky oils. They are sticky or tarry, brown or black in color, and not overly toxic. This category includes most crude oils.

Class D are the non-fluid oils. They are non-toxic and include heavy crude oils. This type of oils is most difficult to clean up, and if spilled, their impacts on waterfowl and wildlife can be severe.

Crude oil is refined to produce gasoline, diesel fuel, jet fuel, residential fuel oil, kerosene, liquefied petroleum gases such as propane and other fuels, used to produce heat or electric power. Other products made from crude are lubricants, waxes, ink, crayons, eyeglasses, tires, CDs and DVDs, ammonia, dishwashing liquid, and some health and personal care products. The United

States is the third top crude oil-producing country, after Russia and Saudi Arabia.

When crude oil is burned, it emits chemicals that are harmful to human health. These chemicals include carbon dioxide, carbon monoxide, lead, nitrogen oxides, particulate matter, polycyclic aromatic hydrocarbons, sulfur dioxide, and volatile organic compounds.

Exposure to burning crude oil means exposure to all these chemicals and high levels of particulate matter, which affect different people differently. Exposure to burning crude oil may harm the passages of the nose, airways, and lungs. It may cause shortness of breath, difficulty breathing, coughing, itching, red or watery eyes, and black mucous. Tar balls, found on beaches look harmless, but handling them may cause an allergic skin reaction and skin rashes.

Oil spills, that happen often in the U.S. and abroad, are very dangerous to the environment and all life in it, including humans by direct exposure to crude oil, by touching contaminated objects, or eating contaminated seafood. The effects of such contact are irritated eyes, skin, and respiratory system. This also may cause dizziness, rapid heart rate, headaches, confusion, and anemia. Prolonged skin contact with crude oil may cause skin reddening, edema, and burning of the skin.

Chemicals that are found in crude oil, are associated with its production and use, or are made from it (all of which are toxic in some way and to some extent), are: Acetone, Arsenic, Benzene, Bisphenol A (BPA), Cadmium, Carbon Dioxide, Carbon Monoxide, Chlorine, Chlorofluorocarbons (CFCs), Chromium, Diesel, Dioxins, Ethylene Glycol, Ethylene Oxide, Formaldehyde, Gasoline, Lead, Mercury, Methane, Methanol, Nanoparticles, Natural Gas, Particulate Matter, Perchlorate, Perchloroethylene (PCE, PERC), Persistent Organic Pollutants (POPs), pesticides, Phthalates, Polybrominated Diphenyl Ethers (PBDEs), Polychlorinated Biphenyls (PCBs), Polycyclic Aromatic Hydrocarbons (PAHs), Polyvinyl Chloride (PVC), Propane, Radon, a number of organic solvents, such as paint thinners, cleaners, and so forth, Styrene, Sulfur Dioxide, Toluene, Uranium, Volatile Organic Compounds (VOCs), etc.

This is not the complete list. Obviously, it's not a small task to even list all the different chemicals, let alone review the ramifications of their effects on the environment and human health. Because of this complexity, and the difficulty it presents, we will take only a cursory look at the environmental effects of crude oil production, storage, transportation and use.

We hope that this brief narration, providing the essentials of the problems at hand, will give the esteemed reader a good idea of what we are dealing with, and why we need to look for ways to reduce and eliminate the harms caused by crude oil, its derivatives, their by-products, and waste products.

Production

Most countries in this world depend on the production of oil to support and fuel their economies. The global trend is to increase crude oil production, since it brings badly needed income. In some third world countries that also brings unrest, internal intrigues, armed conflicts, and even wars.

While the local social and political problems are usually temporary and on a small scale, we all well know that the overall global effect of crude oil production and use is causing severe, permanent, large scale damage to the environment and the people's health. Oil production can disrupt the lives of humans, animals, and fish life of the region, as we have seen on number of occasions. Oil waste dumping, production pollution, and spills wreak havoc on the surrounding wildlife and habitats and have already harmed land, air, and sea animals, and plant species in a number of areas around the world.

The effects on marine life especially are caused by either the physical nature of the oil, such as physical contamination and smothering, or by its chemical components, such as toxic effects and accumulation leading to tainting. Marine life is also seriously affected by cleanup operations after oil spills, or indirectly through physical damage to the habitats in which plants and animals live.

The animals and plants most at risk are those that come in direct contact with oil slicks on the sea surface. We have seen pictures of marine animals such as reptiles, birds, and other wild life on shorelines, as well as mariculture plants covered by black, unsightly oil layers of oil. Manual cleanup is an awkward, and imperfect process that sometimes does additional damage.

Runoffs from petroleum processing and petrochemical plants are known to have dumped tons of toxic wastes into local rivers and lakes, thus contaminating the life giving water source of animals and people. Entire bays and lagoons along many a coastal line have been covered by ugly oil blotches from the spills and runoff of toxic chemicals.

The environmental damage of oil production is also known to directly affect human health and life in the region. Just ask the fishermen in the Gulf of Mexico, or Alaska. Damage can include pollution of water resources and the soil for many years to come. Environ-mental devastation affects humans directly, because it damages the vegetation, wild life, and livestock, and interferes with the normal daily lives. Not to mention that living near contaminated areas also affects the health of people living in or nearby the contaminated sections.

Oil spills can also interfere with the normal working of power stations and desalination plants that require a continuous supply of clean water. The safe operation of coastal industries and ports is often affected as well. In some cases, inner conflicts over oil-producing regions in some parts of the world have been known to create additional hardship to the locals. We have witnessed environmental damage related to oil resources created as a side effect of the conflict, or, associated with military aggression that is intended to take over, or damage, the natural resources of the region.

In summary, crude oil is not evil. It is a needed commodity, without which life would be quite difficult. Some of the consequences of its production and use, however, have brought forward a great number of serious issues that we need to understand, discuss, and eventually reduce and eliminate. For the good of the environment, and mankind in general, we should not continue using such large quantities of oil as if there is no tomorrow, until the last drop is pumped out of the ground, until more of us die in the toxic pollution, or until the world becomes a boiling pot.

Case Study. Horizon Deep Water

9:45 p.m., April 20, 2010. A geyser of seawater erupted from the marine riser onto the large oilrig, shooting 240 ft into the air during the final phases of the drilling operation. An eruption of mud, gas, and water followed. The gas ignited, which created a series of explosions, turning into a firestorm onto the platform, killing several people and hurting others.

The blowout preventer failed and the stream of the wicked mixture coming from the depths of the ocean continued to flow uncontrollably for days to come. The Gulf was a mess and the local marine life paid the ultimate price.

At the initial stages of the disaster there were 126 crewmembers on board. Eleven of them were killed instantly during the initial explosion. Several were thrown, or jumped, in the water below, but were recovered with some injuries. The rig was evacuated soon after, and the injured workers were airlifted to nearby medical facilities.

The oilrig continued to burn and emit copious amounts of smoke for the next days and a half, and finally sank two days later, resting on the seafloor close by. And then the reality hit, and the nightmare began.

The oil well continued to spew large amount of crude oil in the Gulf of Mexico for three months. After several attempts it was finally capped and then sealed permanently. The well was declared dead two months later.

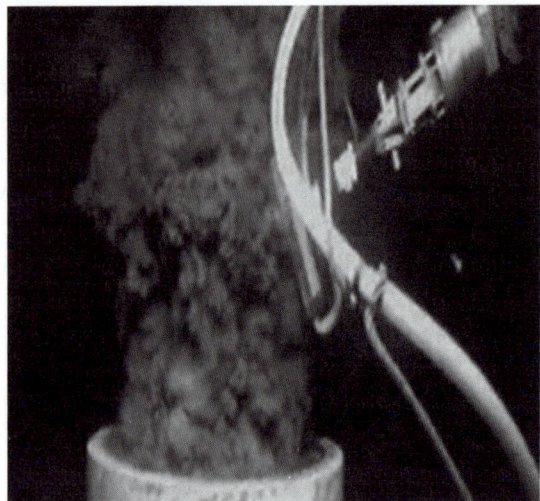

Figure 5-23. BP oil pipe spewing raw oil.

The world watched in disbelief at the drama developing before their eyes. The locals, and the local economy, went into a limbo at first, and then switched to damage control. What followed was highly dramatic: birds covered with oil, workers cleaning the beaches at night, oil floating in the water and on the cost line. One bit of bad news followed the other, day after day, week after week.

And then the U.S. EPA, under BP advice, used millions of gallons of Corexit EC9500A and EC9527A as dispersants to mitigate the oil damages. These chemicals are toxic, and not the most effective on EPA's list of approved dispersants. Although other products have better toxicity and effectiveness ratings, BP decided to use Corexit.

The decision was based on the fact that it was available immediately. And EPA allowed it for use on such large and environmentally sensitive area. Millions of gallons were injected in and sprayed over thousands of acres ocean area.

The EPA denied requests for information about the composition and safety of the Corexit products. Only later, after a lawsuit, was it disclosed that the dispersants contain propylene glycol, 2-butoxyethanol, and dioctyl sodium sulfosuccinate. Why did BP and EPA have to hide these very important facts? What else are they hiding from the public, who pay for their services and ultimately for their decisions and mistakes?

Test results showed that the dispersants contain cancer-causing agents, hazardous toxins, and endocrine-disrupting chemicals. Several of these chemicals are severely toxic, as follows; five are associated with cancer, 33 with skin irritation ranging from rashes to serious burns, 33 are linked to eye irritation, 11 are suspected of being potential respiratory toxins or irritants, 10 are suspected kidney toxins, eight are suspected or known to be toxic to aquatic organisms, and five are suspected to have a moderate acute toxicity to fish. A large menu, where anyone affected can pick and chose what to suffer or die from.

Thousands of gallons of this mixture were sprayed into the ocean. But wait, Corexit was banned from use on oil spills in the United Kingdom a decade ago for obvious reasons. And more importantly, no toxicity studies have been ever conducted on this product at all, although 2-butoxyethanol in Corexit EC9527A was identified as a causal agent in the health problems experienced by cleanup workers after the 1989 Exxon Valdez oil spill.

According to the environmental scientists, the dispersants can cause genetic mutations and cancer, and expose marine life like sea turtles and Bluefin tuna to an even greater risk than the crude oil alone. The dispersants poured into the Gulf were picked up by the current and the winds, and were washed on shore through the entire Gulf coast. Only the locals know the extent of the damages to their local environment and livelihood.

In May, 2010, a letter was sent to BP outlining the concerns related to potential dispersant impact on Louisiana's wildlife and fisheries, environment, aquatic life, and public health. Officials requested that BP release information on their dispersant effects. After three underwater tests, the EPA approved the injection of dispersants directly at the leak site to break up the oil before it reached the surface. Later on that month, independent scientists suggested that underwater injection of Corexit into the leak might have been responsible for the oil plumes discovered below the surface.

EPA then gave BP 24 hours to choose less toxic alternatives to Corexit from the list of dispersants on the National Contingency Plan Product Schedule, or alternatively to provide a detailed reasoning why the approved products did not meet the required standards.

By end of May, BP was using about 26,000 U.S. gallons a day of Corexit. After the EPA directive, the daily average of dispersant use dropped to about 23,000 gallons a day. In the end, it was estimated that over 2 million gallons of this chemical mixture were dumped into the gulf. USCGs attempts to verify if BP was exceeding approved volumes failed, and it was widely speculated that BP was lying to Congress and to the Coast Guard about how much dispersant they were shooting into the ocean.

Only one thing is for sure, the total damage to the gulf waters and the coastline will not be known for decades to come. BP was forced to pay billions of dollars for environmental mitigation work and to the locals, but no matter how much money they pay, the gulf won't be the same for a long, long time.

And now BP has TV commercials that describe the Gulf coast as heaven on Earth, even better than before. As if the millions of gallons of poisonous oil and dispersant chemicals dumped in the ocean somehow fixed something that was wrong in there, and improved the water quality and the entire coast line—capitalism at its best.

Case Study, Kuwait

One of the most spectacular events in recent world's oil history was the sight of the flames and dense smoke bellowing from many burning oil wells in Kuwait during and after the 1990-1991 war. Iraqi armed forces set fire to 789 individual Kuwaiti oil wells, which were left burning for days and weeks, resulting in catastrophic consequences. The local ecology in the entire Persian Gulf was damaged, some permanently. The damage caused of the burning oil wells will take generations to restore to even close to pre-war condition. Some of it will never be the same.

Amazingly enough, little attention was paid to the potential impact of a sustained damage to the regional environment, but by the end of 1990 the experts finally realized that burning millions of barrels of oil per day is something to be concerned about. In early 1991, the estimates were made that more than six million barrels of oil were burning daily in Kuwait, and the initial assessment of the environmental impact was staggering.

A variety of environmental disasters were feared, with the amount of soot generated every day being one of the major problems. We know that one gram of soot can block out two thirds of the light falling over an area of 10 square meters, so the soot generated by burning 4-5 million barrels of oil per day would generate a plume of smoke able to cover the entire United States and part of Canada—not a small thing, but what to do?

Uncontrolled weather patterns carried the smoke plumes great distances and hampered agricultural production in several distant areas of the world. In addition, about 250 million gallons of oil flowed in the gulf, which exceeded over 20 times the amount spilled in the Exxon Valdez Alaska. This caused irreparable harm

to the biological diversity and physical integrity of the gulf. There was oil covering 440 miles of Saudi Arabia's coastline, which will take years before the oil can be cleaned by men, or swept away by the natural forces of the water.

By the end of 1991, the burning oil wells were capped, but the damage to the Kuwaiti economy and the Persian Gulf environment were already done. The assessment revealed that hundreds of miles of the Kuwaiti desert were left uninhabitable, due to the newly created oil lakes and soot from the burning wells. The oil spillage changed the ecology, putting it in serious risk. Nearly two million migratory birds visit the gulf shores each year on their way north, and during the war thousands of cormorants died as a result of exposure to oil and smoke from the leaking and burning oil wells.

The fishing industry in the gulf was brought to a halt. From 120,000 tons of fish a year prior to the war, now the numbers were several times lower. The gulf coast people depend on fishing as a subsistence activity, and the oil spillage and smoke disrupted their normal activities, not only during the war, but permanently, since the spawning of shrimp and fish patterns changed.

Many species, like green and hawksbill turtles are classified as endangered species, but the oil well leakage and smoke did not give them much of a chance. As a result, their populations, together with those of leatherback and loggerhead turtles, dugongs, whales, dolphins, cormorants, flamingoes, and sea snakes were decimated.

This was an unjustifiable, man-made environmental disaster, which made no sense whatsoever. Nevertheless, the local environment and the people living in it are the innocent victims, who will be paying for it with their livelihood, health, and lives for some time to come.

Case Study. Ecuador

Over 50% of Ecuador's national budget is funded by oil exports, so continued and expanding oil production is of utmost importance. It is the lifeblood of the country, and is absolutely needed to ensure the country's well being. The plans are to increase production and foreign investment. This is the good part.

The bad part is that this dependence on oil revenue is hindering Ecuador's full development as industrialized nation. It has also created environmental enforcement blindness with damaging consequences to the Amazon region and the eastern part of the country. For the last 20 years, the locals have been resisting the expanding oil exploration to protect their rights to the ancestral lands.

The oldest Indian tribes in the Amazon region, which not very long ago numbered in the thousands, have been reduced to the hundreds. This human devastation is mostly attributed to the pollution brought upon the region by oil production. Careless and cheap production methods have caused a serious water contamination, which in turn has led to increased cases of cancer, abortion, dermatitis, and many other maladies. Drinking, bathing, and fishing water contains a level of different toxins that is much higher than any safety limits.

The oil companies are also responsible for deforestation of thousands of acres of trees in the rain forest. Their actions, including dynamiting the earth, spilling vast amounts of oil, destroying habitats, and fouling rivers are responsible for exterminating the fish population in the local streams and rivers. The wild game is also gone, which has forced many tribes to retreat deeper into the jungle.

It was documented that our good old friend, Texaco, has already spilled nearly 20 million gallons of crude oil in the jungle, and has abandoned hundreds of hastily installed toxic waste ponds. A dangerous practice of using oil for roads cover to reduce dust, allows oil to flow into rivers in uncontrolled manner. The newly constructed roads for the oil production activities have devastated more than 2.5 million acres, and the deforestation process continues at a rate of over 350,000 hectares a year.

The oil production is responsible for a number of environmental problems in the Amazon region. The Sierra highlands have been almost completely deforested, and in the Orient numerous mammals are in danger of extinction.

Oil waste in the past that placed in holes in the ground contaminated the forests and the rivers, while ruptures in the major pipeline have discharged over 18 million gallons of oil into the Amazon in the past two decades. This, compared with the 10 million-gallon Exxon Valdez spill, is a major disaster in progress with no end in sight.

Any such activities in the U.S. would certainly put the guilty in jail, but out there in the jungle, anything goes for as long as needed, and nobody is held responsible for one of the greatest environmental damages on Earth. Nor will anyone be ever held responsible for it, but the locals continue paying for it all with their livelihood, health, and lives.

Crude Oil Transport

Crude oil is usually produced in remote locations, or foreign countries. This requires expensive transport vehicles and elaborate methods to bring these products to refineries, or for use in populated centers. This is a massive undertaking, requiring the use of different type and size oil tankers, pipelines, trucks, and barges.

Oil Tankers

Oil tankers are large ships, designed and build with only mission in mind: to efficiently and safely transport large quantities of crude oil and other petroleum products over large distances. Today the tankers can be separated into two basic categories, crude oil tankers and petroleum product tankers.

Crude oil transport tankers move raw, unrefined oil from the places where it's pumped out of the Earth, to the refineries where it's processed into fuel and other products. These are very large ocean ships that are equipped with all support needed for quickly traversing large distances.

Oil tankers for transport of petroleum products (gasoline, diesel, etc. fuels) are smaller than crude tankers, and designed to move already-processed petroleum products to markets where those products can be sold and used. In many cases these tankers carry a most dangerous and highly flammable cargo, so their design and use is somewhat different.

Oil tankers can also be classified by their size as well as their occupation. The size classes range from inland or coastal tankers of a few thousand metric tons of deadweight (DWT) to the mammoth ultra large crude carriers of 550,000 DWT. Tankers move approximately 2,000,000,000 metric tons of oil every year. Second only to pipelines in terms of efficiency, the average cost of oil transport by tanker amounts to only two or three U.S. cents per one U.S. gallon.

Some specialized types of oil tankers have evolved. One of these is the naval replenishment oiler, a tanker that can fuel a moving vessel. Combination ore-bulk-oil carriers and permanently moored floating storage units are two other variations on the standard oil tanker design.

The main oil loading ports in 2005 were located in western Asia, western Africa, north Africa, and the Caribbean, with 196.3, 196.3, 130.2 and 246.6 million metric tons of cargo respectively loaded in these regions.

The main oil discharge ports were located in North America, Europe, and Japan with 537.7, 438.4, and 215.0 million metric tons of cargo respectively discharged in these regions.

Due to their immense size, oil tankers provide an easy and inexpensive way to transport oil over long distances. In fact, it only costs around two to four cents per gallon to transport oil using a typical large, ocean going tanker. Oil tankers must be credited with providing the much-needed commodity when and where we need it most.

They, however, have presented us with immense problems as well, since some of the worst man-made environmental disasters have been the result of oil tanker accidents that badly contaminated oceans, waterways, and beaches. The Exxon Valdez spill in Alaska is one such example, which, 20 years after the fact, is still causing major problems in the affected areas. As a result, they are subject to stringent design and operational regulations.

U.S. tankers are constructed and operated under strict regulations. Companies use a communication network of telephone, telex, and satellite systems to locate and control their tankers. On board the ships, crews follow strict safety measures, minimizing loss of personnel and product damage. A number of safety measures are used for added safety, including automatic collision avoidance systems track approaching ships, alerting a tanker to an obstruction on its course.

There have been many developments in improving the tanker operations to reduce the frequency and amount of oil spilled. At one time, tankers discharged dirty ballast water, oil mixed with sea water, which was needed for the return trip into the ocean. This is no longer allowed, so improvements have been made in tanker design, and now new tankers have segregated ballast tanks. These tanks are used only for ballast, so water and oil are kept apart.

New tanker designs also require double-hull construction in accordance to the Oil Pollution Act of 1990, so double-hull construction is found on all new ships built after 1993. However, these new vessels represent only 14% of the world's tanker fleet of over 4,000 vessels. So over 3.500 aging, single-hull, oil tankers are still crisscrossing the world's oceans. Not a comforting thought, but a reality we have to live with, keeping our fingers crossed and hoping that none of these old giants will decide to break in two in our waters any time soon.

One, maybe even more threatening reality we live with today, is the risk of terrorism on the high seas. The ocean oil transport has always been the weak link of the oil industry, but it has become even more so in recent times with the emergence of global terrorism.

Nearly half of America's oil is imported and transported via ocean oil tankers, so terrorists and unfriendly governments aim to disrupt the free flow of crude oil into the U.S. by cutting oil transportation routes. Attack-

ing oil tankers sometimes does this, as it happened in 2002 when a French supertanker was attacked and damaged off the coast of Yemen.

There is no doubt that the terrorists intent on hurting the U.S. and the West economically by interrupting the flow of oil to American, European, and Asian markets. There have been a number of planned attacks against oil tankers in the Arabian Gulf and Horn of Africa, most of which have been thwarted. Many terror experts have expressed concern that Al-Qaeda, or other terrorists, might seize a tanker and crash it into another vessel, or into a refinery or port.

Cutting the "economic lifelines" of the world's industrialized societies is an attractive target, and a goal, that won't diminish in importance to the terrorists any time soon. Such attacks, if successful, would disrupt life in the West and also affect the gulf oil countries, which are heavily dependent on oil revenues for their survival. This threat won't go away, and will only grow bigger with time, thus increasing the ocean oil transport risks. This, in turn, might contribute to an increase in oil prices, and negatively affect world economies.

Pipelines

The major quantity of crude oil moved around the U.S. flows through several major and some regional pipelines. The network of crude oil pipelines in the U.S. is extensive, with over 55,000 miles of crude oil trunk lines (usually 8-24 inches in diameter) delivering oil to the regional markets.

There are also close to 40,000 miles of small gathering oil transport lines (usually 2 to 6 inches in diameter) located primarily in Texas, Oklahoma, Louisiana, and Wyoming, and smaller systems in a number of other oil producing states. The small lines gather the oil from many individual wells, both onshore and offshore, and connect to larger trunk lines.

The largest, and most familiar to all of us pipeline is the Trans Alaska Pipeline System (TAPS). It, unlike most pipelines, has significant portions of the pipes installed on pedestals above ground.

Crude oil produced in Alaska flows south to the coastline, where it is loaded on tankers and shipped to the U.S. west coast. From the tank ships, the crude is pumped into another pipeline and is then finally delivered to refineries along the U.S. west coast for processing into gasoline, diesel, and other commodities.

The other major U.S. pipeline is the Keystone pipeline, designed to transport synthetic crude oil and diluted bitumen from the Athabasca oil sands region in NE Alberta, Canada to the United States. The oil other

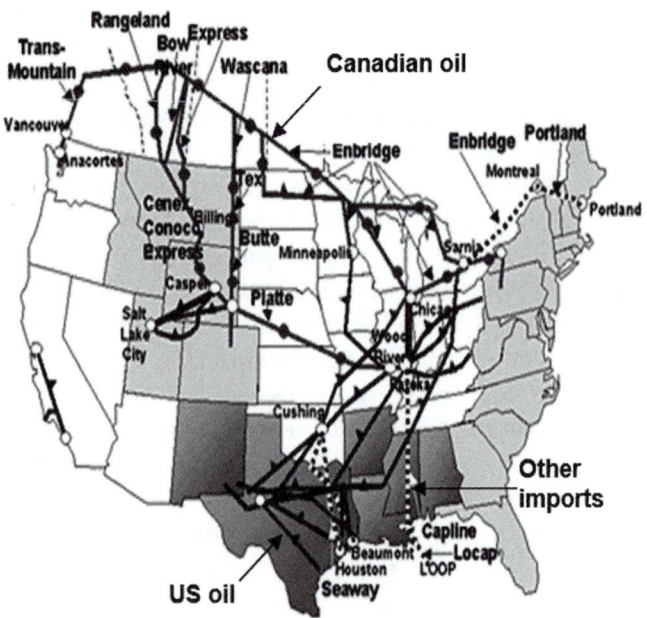

Figure 5-24. The U.S. major oil pipelines

products are delivered to refineries in Illinois, the Cushing oil distribution hub in Oklahoma, and proposed connections to refineries along the Gulf Coast of Texas. Presently the Keystone Pipeline and Keystone-Cushing Extension are operational, while two proposed pipeline expansion segments, the Keystone XL Pipeline and the Gulf Coast Project, are in developmental stages. When these segments are completed, American crude oil would enter the XL pipelines at Baker, Montana and Cushing, Oklahoma for nationwide distribution.

The Keystone XL has been shrouded in serious controversy and lawsuits from oil refineries and criticism from environmentalists, but in March 2012, President Obama endorsed the building of the southern half of the pipeline and work is now underway, still amidst vigorous criticism and under protest by different groups.

Amazingly enough, there is little known environmental damage related to oil pipelines. A recent big oil spill was recorded in Alberta, Canada, when in the summer of 2012 a local pipeline broke and spilled over 150,000 gallons of sulfur-rich crude oil into southern Alberta's Red Deer River. Some of the oil washed into the Gleniffer reservoir, the source of drinking water for thousands of area residents, forcing the provincial government to implement intense monitoring of water and air quality.

As a result of the spill, people detected oil in the drinking water, and local fields and waterways are suspected to be contaminated. The cleanup took a major

effort, which lasted until the end of the summer, and the long-term effects are still unknown.

All ten worst oil leaks from the Alaska pipeline took place before 1990, and an estimated 300,000 gallons of crude oil have been spilled. Nevertheless, no new accidents have been reported for over two decades, due to line controls improvements and updates. The alarm system was upgraded to detect and report any leaks quickly. Another improvement is the line volume balance system. It measures the total oil that goes into the pipe, versus the total oil coming out of the pipe, and the difference determines if there are small, slow leaks in the pipe. Also, a new transient volume balance system was added in 1998, which uses complex computer models to determine (theoretically) the pressure at different places in the pipe and compare that to the actual readings. This way, the line flow and pressure are monitored 24/7, thus reducing the risk of large spills, and eliminating slow leaks.

Newer pipelines are equipped with all necessary equipment for spill detection and other abnormalities. The stability of some parts of the national oil pipeline network, however, is a looming issue. It is, for most part, an old structure and many parts are in need of repairs. For example, the U.S. government has plans to refurbish some areas of the Alaska pipeline, but there is no guarantee that this will happen any time soon, and the future of the pipeline is uncertain.

There are also other issues related to oil pipelines that need to be taken into consideration, such as risks of potential terrorist attacks that need to be addressed and resolved in the near future.

Everything considered, the oil pipelines are still the most economically efficient and environmentally friendly method to transport oil that exists today.

Pipeline Accidents

The oil transport has always been the weak point of the oil industry. The situation has grown even more dangerous recently with the increase of global terrorism.

About 40% of the world's oil flows through pipelines, which are quite vulnerable to terrorist attacks. The pipelines are thousands of miles long, and in most cases run across some of the most volatile areas in the world. A homemade explosive device could rupture the steel pipe and shut the flow of oil through it for a long time.

Protecting the long pipelines, some running through desolate areas, is not possible, which makes them potential and easy targets for terrorists. Such an attack in the summer of 2001 on an oil pipeline that feeds Saudi Arabia's Ras Tanura terminal was averted at the nick of time. This is the biggest oil-loading point in Saudi Arabia, and damaging it could have caused an enormous financial harm to the country, while at the same time reducing the oil shipments.

Oil pipelines are the cleanest and safest way to transport oil and its products over long distances. Nevertheless, accidents happen. There are numerous examples of this since 2012, as follow:

A Sunoco pipeline ruptured and spilled about 117,000 gallons of gasoline in Wellington, Ohio, late on January 12. Some residents were evacuated for a week.

On January 31, a fuel pipeline to the Milwaukee, Wisconsin Mitchell International Airport was found leaking. Jet fuel had been smelled for about two weeks in the area, and was found in runoff water in the area.

On February 15, 2012, in Arenac County, Michigan, oil was discovered in the soil around a 30-inch Enbridge crude oil pipeline.

Two cars that were drag racing went off the road they were on, and crashed through a fence and into a crude oil pipeline in New Lenox, Illinois on March 3. The pipeline was ruptured, and the crude oil ignited. Two men from the vehicles were killed, and three others seriously burned.

A crude oil pipeline leaked near Grand Isle, Louisiana on March 17, spilling as much as 8,400 gallons of crude oil. There were no injuries reported.

A petroleum products pipeline burst near Jackson, Wisconsin on July 17, releasing about 54,000 gallons of gasoline. At least one family self evacuated due to the leak. At least seven water wells nearby were contaminated from benzene in the gasoline.

An Enbridge crude oil pipeline ruptured in Grand Marsh, Wisconsin, releasing an estimated 1,200 barrels of crude oil. The pipeline had been installed in 1998. Flaws in the longitudinal welds had been seen during X-ray checks of girth welds.

A jet fuel pipeline near Chicago, Illinois, began leaking on August 27. The burst pipeline spilled an estimated 42,000 gallons of jet fuel into a ditch that empties into the Calumet Sag Channel in Palos Heights, Illinois.

On November 20, about 38,000 gallons of crude oil spilled from an Enbridge pipeline at a tank farm in Mokena, Illinois.

On March 18, 2013 a Chevron eight-inch petroleum products pipeline ruptured along a seam, spilling diesel fuel into Willard Bay State Park near Ogden, Utah. Wildlife was coated with diesel, but, the fuel was prevented from entering into water supply intakes. About 25,000 gallons of diesel were spilled.

The ExxonMobil 20 inch Pegasus crude oil pipeline spills near Mayflower, Arkansas, on March 29, causing crude to flow through yards and gutters, and toward Lake Conway. Wildlife was coated in some places. Twenty-two homes were evacuated due to the fumes and fire hazard. Workers collected approximately 12,000 barrels of heavy crude and water.

In March 2013, a Canadian Pacific Railway Ltd, train derailed 14 of its 94-car, mile-long train. Estimates are that 20,000 to 30,000 gallons, or 475 to 715 barrels, have leaked.

The Keystone oil pipeline has already seen twelve oil spills in North Dakota. The largest of these included about 400 barrels of oil. Is this a bad omen for the newly proposed, massive, Keystone pipeline extension?

Trucks and Trains Transport

Large quantities of crude oil are transported across great distances on water and land. On water, the most practical transport vessels are barges for transport on rivers and lakes, and oil tankers for ocean transport, which we discussed above. On land, crude oil and petroleum products are moved via trucks and trains, in addition to pipelines, which we also discussed above.

Tank truck oil transport is a needed method for short distance oil transport, and delivery of petroleum products to remote destinations, gas stations, refineries, and such. Tank trucks are trucks with a large tank on back. The tank may be insulated or non-insulated; pressurized or non-pressurized; and designed for single or multiple loads, often by means of internal divisions in their tank. Some of these are semi-trailer trucks, all of which are difficult and dangerous to drive on the highways due to their high center of gravity.

The pipeline industry is facing opposition to new projects, but oil transport via railroad is surging. Within several short months, people who had never considered moving oil by train are reconsidering and embracing the idea. The oil railroad shipments are still small, at least for now, but the estimates are that presently 75,000 barrels are transported by rail from Canada. The amount is expected to increase to 100,000 barrels in 2013 and further thereafter.

Rail transport, however, is still quite expensive. It costs twice as much to ship oil by train., which might add $5 to $10 more a barrel. But one advantage might change the equation. Heavy oil requires an expensive thinner called diluent to move by pipe. In contrast, by rail, it moves undiluted, which might even the playing field on transportation costs. In addition, with rail, companies can rapidly switch destinations and markets, since rail networks reach most points of the U.S.—including areas, such as the Gulf Coast and California, which are areas that pipes from Canada do not reach.

Another problem with road and railroad transport is collisions with local and migrating animals. Trains kill over 200 moose per year, and over 700 per year are killed by road traffic. Along with the negative impacts on the surrounding fauna, roads and railroads present a clear and present danger to the stability of the local and migratory animals.

Nevertheless, grand plans are in the making for transporting large quantities of crude oil from the Canadian oil sands by rail. This is a new area of competition for the railroads with the pipelines, which have dominated the oil transport business for the last century.

These plans may have to be revised, however, in light of the Quebec's oil-train disaster in the summer of 2013, when a run-away train derailed and blew up. Several thousand gallons of crude oil and oil products went up in smoke, while that many more spilled on the ground. A number of people were killed and the entire town of Lac Megantic on the southern border of Quebec was devastated.

The deadly oil-train derailment is set to bring intense scrutiny to the dramatic growth of shipping crude oil by rail. This century-old practice has been unexpectedly revived and expanded by the surge in shale oil production, but now has to be revised together with the planned Keystone pipeline.

Crude Oil Storage

The U.S. has enormous crude oil storage capacity. Millions of gallons are delivered and stored in different U.S. storage facilities daily. The different facilities range in size and designation as follow:

National Strategic Petroleum Reserve

The largest U.S. storage is the so-called strategic petroleum reserves. It is a large emergency storage of oil maintained by the United States Department of Energy. It was started in 1975 after oil supplies were cut off during the 1973-74 oil embargo. Its intention is to mitigate future unscheduled oil supply disruptions, to avoid damage to the U.S. economy and its military.

This is by far the largest storage of crude oil in the world, with capacity to hold up to 727 million barrels of crude oil at any given time. The actual inventory varies, but is usually maintained at levels high enough to ensure at several months of oil supplies in the U.S. in case of natural disaster or emergency.

The oil is stored at four sites on the Gulf of Mexico, near major centers of petrochemical refining and pro-

cessing. Each site contains a number of artificial caverns created in salt domes below the surface. The caverns were created by drilling down and then dissolving the salt with water, at a cost of $4 billion in 1975 dollars. Each cavern is up to 3,000 feet below the surface, and the size is about 180 x 1,800 feet deep. The capacity of each cavern is up to 37 million barrels.

The advantage to store oil in salt caverns is in reduced costs, since it is roughly 10 times cheaper to store oil below surface. In addition, there are no leaks from the salt caverns, and there is a constant natural churn of the oil due to a temperature gradient in the caverns.

Despite the undisputable advantages, this type of storage has its problems, as evidenced by the failure of a similar large capacity oil storage facility at Weeks Island, Louisiana. The facility had a capacity of 72 million barrels, stored in a conventional room and pillar near surface salt mine. The facility, built in the 1970s, functioned well until 1993, when a sinkhole was formed, which allowed fresh water to flow uncontrollably into the mine. The salt deposits are easily dissolved by fresh water, and there was a danger of eroding the walls and the ceiling, causing the structure to fail.

The storage facility was emptied and decommissioned in 1999, and the mine was backfilled with salt-saturated brine. 98% of the petroleum stored in the facility was recovered, thus preventing the oil from leaking into the aquifer that is located over the salt dome.

China is in the midst of building emergency crude reserves equivalent to 100 days of net imports before 2020. The project is proceeding in three phases, according to a plan approved by the state council. The national oil storage will be consist of about 600 million barrels, which is near the U.S. 727 million barrel capacity.

China finished building the first phase of its storage in 2009, and spent an average $58 a barrel buying crude for filling it in 2008. Construction of the second phase was completed in 2012, and the third one is to be finished in 2020.

In the fall of 2012, however, China stopped filling up its strategic petroleum reserve facilities, which reduced the demand on the global crude oil market. The reason for this interruption is unclear, but it may be related to the increasing economic uncertainty in the country. The third phase of the oil storage buildup is still on schedule.

Commercial Oil Storage

Crude oil is also stored at large storage facilities at port terminals and refineries around the U.S. It is usually stored in large above ground steel tanks at these facilities, where oil is pumped in and out as needed. Smaller facilities, such as gas stations, also store petroleum products such as gasoline and diesel, but in smaller, underground storage tanks. These tanks are used daily so they have to be replenished periodically.

Commercial oil storage tank are large containers, which usually operate under no pressure. In some exceptional cases, they are under some, usually little, pressure. They can be installed above, or buried under ground. Above ground storage tanks are most often cylindrical in shape, and installed perpendicular to the ground. They have flat bottoms and a fixed or floating roof. A number of environmental and OSHA regulations apply to the design and operation of any storage tanks, depending on the nature of the petroleum products contained within.

Aboveground storage tanks differ from underground storage tanks in the kind of regulations that are applied in each case.

Storage tanks are also available in many shapes: vertical and horizontal cylindrical; open top and closed top; flat bottom, cone bottom, slope bottom and dish bottom. Large tanks tend to be vertical cylindrical, or to have rounded corners transition from vertical side wall to bottom profile, to easier withstand hydraulic hydrostatically induced pressure of contained liquid.

Container tanks for oil transportation are designed to handle varying degrees of pressure. When a storage tank is mounted on a truck or a trailer, the rig is then called a tanker.

Petroleum products can and seep through any opening, so special consideration must be made for their safe and secure storage. A bunding, or containment dike, built around above ground storage tanks is often the solution required to contain any leakage.

Some storage tanks also need a floating roof instead of a fixed roof. The advantage of a floating roof is that it literally floats on top of the oil, and rises and falls with the oil level inside the tank. This way the vapor space above the oil level is decreased, which virtually eliminates evaporation. Floating roofs are recommended as a safety and pollution prevention measures in the petroleum refining industry.

Metal oil storage tanks that are in contact with the ground must be protected from corrosion, to prevent escape of the oil through the corroded area and into the ground. Cathodic protection is the most effective and common corrosion control techniques for steel tanks. It consists of applying small electrical charge to the tank, which effectively prevents the corrosion from taking place.

Tanks for petroleum products storage are chosen according to the flash point of the substance. Liquid fuels in refineries are usually stored in fixed roof tanks, and floating roof tanks.

1. Fixed roof tanks are meant for liquids with very high flash points, (e.g. fuel oil, water, bitumen etc.) Cone roofs, dome roofs and umbrella roofs are usual. These are insulated to prevent the clogging of certain materials, wherein steam coils within the tanks provide the heat. Dome roof tanks are meant for tanks having slightly higher storage pressure than that of atmosphere (e.g. slop oil).

2. Floating roof tanks are broadly divided into external floating roof tanks, usually called floating roof tanks, and internal floating roof types. these tanks are used for liquids with low flashpoints (e.g. ATF, MS. gasoline, ethanol). These tanks are a type of a cone roof tanks with a floating roof inside which travels up and down along with the liquid level. This floating roof traps the vapor from low flash-point fuels. Floating roofs are supported with legs or cables on which they rest.

Another common type found in some areas is the open roof type tank, which is used to store waste products and water. These are, of course, the easiest and cheapest storage tanks to build and maintain.

Other classifications for petroleum products storage tanks depending on the product type and the location in a refinery, are:

*   COT, or crude oil tankages
*   PIT, or product and intermediate storage tankages
*   DISPATCH, or dispatch area tankages
*   UTILITIES, or tanks made in the power plant area, for storage water etc.
*   OSBL tanks are the first three types under outside battery limit tankages
*   ISBL tanks are usually mini tanks that are found in the production units of a refinery (as neutralization tanks, water tanks etc.)

For low flash-points fuels, and most gasses, the tanks are usually spherical, also called spheres, for storing and transport of LPG, hydrogen, hexane, nitrogen, oxygen etc.

The obvious dangers related to any petroleum storage tanks are: explosions, fires, leakage, spillage, evaporation, etc. All these risks are addressed in EPA and OSHA regulations, and the industry has a fairly good safety record as far as storage tanks and facilities are concerned.

Environmental Impact of Oil and Petroleum Products

The production and use of petroleum products creates a large number of environmental problems. Starting with the oil drilling and pumping stages, we see many examples of crude oil spills on land or in water, where it poisons plants and animals, and can contaminate the water table.

The next stage, burning of petroleum-based fuels, is a process that releases toxic gases that pollute the air and the land. It is also suspected to contribute to global climate change.

Oil Rig Environmental Impact

Oil drilling processes have caused accidents and damage the health of people working on the rigs, or living nearby. Land and offshore rigs do cause, directly or indirectly, environmental damage during their entire cradle-to-grave lifespan: from the moment of locating the oil, to drilling and pumping it to the surface, and to the infrastructure required to drill and transport it.

Land oil drilling is known to contaminate the soil, water table and the air. Accidents caused by using improper techniques, or negligence, have created large oil spills that are hard to clean and usually result in permanent damage to the affected areas.

In all cases, offshore drilling and oil well exploitation are much more dangerous to the people involved, as well as to the surrounding environment. The actual environmental impacts vary in intensity, depending on many factors, so we will present just a quick picture of the situation:

Figure 5-25. Ground oil contamination by leakage

Locating the Oil

There are a number of methods and many tools used during the search for oil. Seismic surveys are one of the most efficient, and most used, but they have been proven to negatively impact fish and marine life. Whales in particular are extremely sensitive to the seismic waves generated when searching for oil and gas deposits in the seabed. The noise causes them to become disoriented, which can lead to disruption to migratory patterns and even mass beachings. Seismic waves also do impair the health and hearing of fish.

Alternatives to the standard seismic surveys are under investigation today, that are safer for marine life, thus reducing the environmental impact.

Effects on the Ocean Floor

Offshore drilling inevitably disrupts the seafloor habitat and the local benthic communities. The actual footprint of the drill rig, undersea pipelines, dredging ship channels, the cuttings and other drilling debris, etc. cause great disturbance in the area, which in most cases leave a lasting and unrepairable impact on the ocean floor.

The problem here is that many of the world's most sensitive ocean floor habitats are also good sources of oil and gas. The Gulf of Mexico, the arctic and the Great Barrier Reef are all good examples of extremely diverse ecosystems, while having significant oil and gas deposits.

On the positive side of things, offshore oilrigs are good habitat for fish, and as a matter of fact there is a program, called "rigs to reefs," where old abandoned oilrigs are not disassembled, but instead are tipped over and left on the ocean floor to become artificial reefs.

Ocean Water Pollution

Offshore drilling causes both drilling fluid and crude oil spills and leaks.

Drilling fluids are used to lubricate, cool and regulate drill pressure. They, however, contain petroleum products and heavy metals, which are toxic to marine life. The impacts of drilling fluids differ significantly, because they are made up of different types and concentrations of chemicals, and are applied in many different ways. Documented impacts from drilling fluids include effects on the health and reproduction of marine life, reducing the populations of bottom-dwelling creatures and biomagnifying toxic substances in the food chain. Using drilling fluids that have low aquatic toxicity and high biodegradability is one solution.

Crude oil spills, leaks and catastrophes are another

major consideration. Specialists claim that there is much more oil spilled into the global oceans by marine transportation vessels, commercial operations, and natural seeps than all offshore oil and gas drilling. This, according to them, has made marine life pre-adapt to oil in the water.

On the positive side of things, since there is so much oil drilling in the oceans, the pressure in the oil deposits is reduced, which in turn reduces the amount of oil leaking into the ocean from the natural seeps. All of this creates a mixed opinion about the amount of water pollution caused by offshore oil drilling—in the absence of catastrophic oil spills like the Exxon Valdez and Deep Water Horizon.

State, local and federal regulations of late also help to control intentional discharges into the ocean from offshore drilling, especially in the U.S. waters. This, however is not well documented, so offshore oil drilling still has a significant negative impact on fragile marine and coastal ecosystems. The risks of devastating spills are another key factor that has to be taken into account. So the question remains, "Is it worth taking such risks, and what can be done to reduce or eliminate them?"

Air Pollution

Air pollution is generated from the operation of machinery on offshore oilrigs as well as the burn-off of gases. Without factoring in the air pollution from its end product or the refinement process, the oil platforms themselves have an impact on local air quality and on global climate change. It is estimated that, over its lifetime, which is ten to twenty years, "a single rig can pollute as much as 7,000 cars driving 50 miles per day" (USPIRG). The NRDC States that "an average oil and gas exploration well spews roughly 50 tons of nitrogen oxides, 13 tons of carbon monoxide, six tons of sulfur oxides, and five tons of volatile organic chemicals."

Short of stopping oil drilling, however, there are few ways to prevent some of the negative environmental impacts of offshore oil drilling. Some of the measures that should be considered are a thorough environmental assessment and remediation process prior to oil exploration, which is especially important for offshore rigs close to land and in ecologically sensitive areas. New, much more sophisticated analyses and regulations would be required to minimize the accident and to provide quick, efficient, response in case of fire or leakage.

Developing comprehensive and efficient environmental health and safety standards would ensure sufficient and enforceable methods to prevent oil spills.

A set of management plans and standards are also needed to ensure the quick and efficient response to accidental oil spills. The deployment of appropriate technologies and methods to remediate accidental spills would prevent the devastating water and coastal contamination, such as these experienced during and after Exxon Valdez and the Deep-water Horizon accidents.

Oil Spills

An oil spill is the release of a liquid petroleum hydrocarbon into the environment, especially marine areas, due to human activity, and is a form of pollution. The term is usually applied to marine oil spills, where oil is released into the ocean or coastal waters, but spills may also occur on land. Oil spills may be due to releases of crude oil from tankers, offshore platforms, drilling rigs and wells, as well as spills of refined petroleum products (such as gasoline, diesel) and their by-products, heavier fuels used by large ships such as bunker fuel, or the spill of any oily refuse or waste oil.

Major oil spills include the Kuwaiti oil fires, Kuwaiti oil lakes, Lakeview Gusher, Gulf War oil spill, and the Deep-water Horizon oil spill. Spilt oil penetrates into the structure of the plumage of birds and the fur of mammals, reducing its insulating ability, and making them more vulnerable to temperature fluctuations and much less buoyant in the water. Cleanup and recovery from an oil spill is difficult and depends upon many factors, including the type of oil spilled, the temperature of the water (affecting evaporation and biodegradation), and the types of shorelines and beaches involved. Spills may take weeks, months or even years to clean up.

Crude oil spills can occur during many stages of its production, transportation, and use. It can leak from wells drilled on land or in the sea. Pipelines can break and leak, causing oil to spill during transportation. Oil tankers may collide and/or sink, slowly releasing huge loads of crude oil into the water. Other accidents or disasters at oilrigs or storage terminals can cause toxic oil products to spill from power plants, refineries, and even gasoline stations. There are also natural phenomena, where some oil seeps from openings in the sea floor.

Unintentional spills and leaks release about 15 million barrels of crude oil into the environment each year. Petroleum companies spill about 30% of the total oil spills during production and transportation. The remaining 60% is released in spills during industrial and private consumption, and 10% is accounted for in natural ground seeps.

This is a fairly small amount, compared with the total amount of oil products used, this is still a major environmental concern. Most of the chemicals in petroleum products are toxic to living things, so they can poison plants, animals, and even people.

The clean up is a messy, difficult, and expensive procedure, so oil spills caused by accidents involving giant oil tankers or rigs, provoke public anger at oil companies. This is what happened in 1989, when the tanker Exxon Valdez struck a reef off southeastern Alaska, spilling nearly 11 million gallons of crude oil in the pristine Alaska waterways.

A similar case is the huge oil spill in the Gulf of Mexico in 2010, when a BP deep water oil rig exploded, killing 17 workers. The explosion also ruptured the oil pipe at the bottom of the ocean spilling millions of still unaccounted for gallons of crude oil into the waters of the Alabama coast of the Gulf of Mexico.

The cleanup efforts are in some respect even more damaging, because there are no good, let alone proven, ways to successfully separate the spilled oil from the water, and clean the affected surfaces. In both cases mentioned above, major damage was done to the local environment by the cleaning procedures, and even more so by the large amounts of different untested chemicals used in the efforts.

Oil Spills Cleanup

Large offshore oil spills like the Deep-water Horizon are catastrophic and are worth taking a closer look. There is the effect of the oil spill itself, but then—and as importantly—there are the effects of the cleanup efforts.Large oil spills in the ocean usually drift to, and spread onto, the shores, where they either remain cohesive or break up due to wave action. The oil changes and degrades naturally with time mostly by natural effects of sunlight and microorganisms. This process, however, is very slow and might take many years to complete. The oil spilled during the Exxon Valdez accident is still lingering on the Alaskan shoreline, almost 25 years after the fact.

Oil spill on the shoreline contaminates the entire water and terrestrial environments, and, since oil is toxic, it is detrimental to wildlife in coastal and marine environments that get close to it. The entire balance of the eco-systems is affected and in many cases it is even completely destroyed. Efforts to reconstruct the affected areas have not been very successful, because we simply lack the technology needed to fight and remediate the effects of large oil spills.

Oil spill cleanups are another serious problem that can introduce additional complexities and risks into the local ecosystem. Mechanical devices, such as floating

Figure 5-26. 2010 Deep-water Horizon oil spill.

traps, are often used to contain the oil, while a number of other physical, biological and chemical methods are used to remove it.

Physical methods of oil removal consist of using shovels and mechanized equipment to separate and remove the oil from the water. This way large amounts of oil can be removed, but at the same time marine and coastal environments can be damaged beyond repair.

Biological methods and bioremediation include the addition of specialized bacteria and other microorganisms to speed up the oil degradation.

Chemical methods include the addition of chemical dispersants, which break the oil down into smaller particles. This is also a dangerous approach, because most marine life and vegetation are sensitive to the chemicals and might be harmed by its unintended action.

NOTE: Large quantity of Corexit chemical dispersant were used in 2011, following the Deep-water Horizon oil leak, as part of the emergency cleanup effort. This was a large-scale assault on the marine environment in the gulf. Millions of gallons of Corexit were dispersed over the ocean in a short period of time. The concentration of this potentially toxic chemical in parts of the gulf was extreme, and has lasting effects on the area. The long-term effects of such large quantity of unproven for this use of chemicals is unknown, and the tests continue as we speak.

A major problem caused by the millions of gallons of dispersants (mixtures of different organic and inorganic chemicals) sprayed over the ocean, was that they formed plumes of small oil particles. Some of these settled on the ocean floor, some floated away, but a significant portion were able to sneak under the oil barriers (since they were floating under the surface) and settled on the shoreline. Some considered the use of such large quantity dispersants a mistake, and the effects of which eventually damaged the shoreline environment and life in it, and complicated the cleanup effort.

Oil Leakage

Oil platforms, oil tankers, storage tanks and pipelines can leak. Petroleum distillates contaminate water and surface runoff and kill almost all life. Crude oil is a mixture of many different kinds of organic compounds, many of which are highly toxic and cancer causing (carcinogenic). Oil is "acutely lethal" to fish, killing it at a concentration of about 4000 parts per million (ppm), or 0.4% oil content in the water. Crude oil and petroleum distillates are also known to cause birth defects in animals and people.

Benzene in crude oil and gasoline causes leukemia in humans, and also lowers the white blood cell count in humans, which would leave people exposed to it more susceptible to infections. At long term exposure to even very small amounts, in the parts per billion (ppb) range, benzene is known to cause terminal leukemia, Hodgkin's lymphoma, and other blood and immune system diseases.

Waste Oil

Waste oil is basically oil that has been used in engines or for other purposes. It usually contains breakdown products and impurities from the use. Some examples of waste oil are used oils such as hydraulic oil, transmission oil, brake fluids, motor oil, crankcase oil, gearbox oil and synthetic oil. Many of the same problems associated with natural petroleum exist with waste oil. When waste oil from vehicles drips out of engines onto streets and roads, the oil travels into the water table bringing with it such toxins as benzene. This poisons both soil and drinking water. Runoff from storms carries waste oil into rivers and oceans, poisoning them as well.

Air Pollution

The majority of petroleum products are used as fuel, which is burned at power plants and cars. Large quantities of exhaust gases and particles are generated during the different burning processes, which pollute the air in large areas. Petroleum fuels burned to power vehicles, heat homes and businesses, and generate electric power are a leading cause of air pollution in many countries.

The exhaust gases contain toxic carbon monoxide, sulfur dioxide, and nitrogen oxides, which are poisonous to plants, animals, and people. Sulfur dioxide and nitrogen oxides can combine with water in the atmosphere, raising the water's acidity. This water can then fall back to the surface as the so-called "acid rain," where it can damage property and pollute the environment.

There have been a number of steps taken during the last 40 years to reduce the emissions of these gases, but this type of pollution remains a problem in many areas. Although burning petroleum fuels causes less pollution than burning an equivalent amount of coal, the amount of gasses released in the atmosphere and the damage done to the environment is almost the same.

Exhaust

When oil or petroleum distillates are burned (see combustion), usually the combustion is not complete. This means that incompletely burned compounds are created in addition to just water and carbon dioxide. The other compounds are often toxic to life. Examples are carbon monoxide and methanol. Also, fine particulates of soot blacken humans' and other animals' lungs and cause heart problems or death. Soot is cancer causing (carcinogenic).

Acid Rain

High temperatures created by the combustion of petroleum cause nitrogen gas in the surrounding air to oxidize, creating nitrous oxides. Nitrous oxides, along with sulfur dioxide from the sulfur in the oil, combine with water in the atmosphere to create acid rain. Acid rain causes many problems such as dead trees and acidified lakes with dead fish. Coral reefs in the world's oceans are killed by acidic water caused by acid rain.

Acid rain leads to increased corrosion of machinery and structures (large amounts of capital), and to the slow destruction of important archaeological structures like the marble ruins in Rome and Greece.

Volatile Organic Compounds

Volatile organic compounds (VOCs) are gases or vapors emitted by various solids and liquids, many of which have short- and long-term adverse effects on human health and the environment. VOCs from petroleum are toxic and foul the air, and some like benzene are extremely toxic, carcinogenic and cause DNA damage. Benzene often makes up about one percent of crude oil and gasoline. Benzene is present in automobile exhaust.

More important for vapors from spills of diesel and crude oil are aliphatic, volatile compounds. Although "less toxic" than compounds like benzene, their overwhelming abundance can still cause health concerns even when benzene levels in the air are relatively low. The compounds are sometimes collectively measured as "Total Petroleum Hydrocarbons" or "TPH."

Climate Change

Humans burning large amounts of petroleum create large amounts of CO_2 (carbon dioxide) gas that traps heat in the earth's atmosphere. Also some organic compounds, such as methane released from petroleum drilling or from the petroleum itself, trap heat several times more efficiently than CO_2. Soot blocks the sun from reaching the earth and could cause cooling of the earth's atmosphere.

Mitigation

Conservation and phasing out is the best way to avoid increased problems in the future, such as creating laws to completely phase out the use of petroleum (Sweden's 15 year phase-out plan). Making use of petroleum more efficiently via better technologies is on the agendas of many companies and governments, but the expectations are low. This has been tried in the past, and it so happens that every time we find a more economical way to use fossils, we immediately justify ways to waste more of them, thus nullifying the overall positive effect.

Substitution of other energy sources with "cleaner" energy sources such as natural gas and biodiesel, especially in critical areas like cities, would go long way to improving life conditions and the environment. Using biomass instead of petroleum is a possibility, because anything that can be made from oil can be made from cellulose, and cellulose is one of the most abundant renewable materials on Earth. Plastics can be created from cellulose instead of from oil too. Motor oil and grease can be made from some plants and from animal fat.

Implementing safety measures will decrease the risk of spills. Double hull oil tankers, and false floors at gasoline stations to catch gasoline and oil drips from making it into the water table is a good start.

Global Warming

Presently, burning petroleum fuels is considered to be a major factor in global climate change. It has been agreed that the average temperature of Earth's surface has risen about 1.0°F during the last two centuries. The ever-increasing concentrations of greenhouse gases, generated by fossil fuels including crude oil derivatives, are responsible for most of the warming phenomena.

Methane and carbon dioxide, named greenhouse gases, trap heat from the sun and hold it near Earth's surface, and since carbon dioxide is the largest portion of waste gases produced by burning petroleum fuels, the danger is increasing daily.

It has been also agreed that the concentration of carbon dioxide in the atmosphere has risen significantly during the same time, which corresponds to the warming trend. These are complex issues, and we will take a much closer look at them, and the related environmental phenomena, in the following chapters.

Externalized Cost of Oil Drilling, Refining, and Use.

Oil drilling is a hazardous operation both from environmental and human health points of view. Although safety is paramount in oil drilling and production operations in the U.S., there are still problems, which result in accidents and injuries. Besides the large accidents that we hear from time to time, there are smaller accidents daily, and many more unseen ones, where people get hurt or sick as a result of the effects of oil drilling and the related operations.

Oilrig and refinery workers, as well as local people, are sickened by pollution from the gas emissions and liquids escaping from the work sites. Hydrofracking is the ultimate example of contamination of soil and water table, where harsh chemicals dumped intentionally or unintentionally in their habitat poison fish and wild life.

Resource exploration, extraction, processing and distribution cause various health risks to people, including drilling, processing and distribution accident injuries, and pollution-related illnesses. In 2006 petroleum production workers had 20.8 fatalities per 100,000 workers, which is much higher than typical service industry jobs but lower than other heavy industries such as truck drivers (27.5 deaths), coal mining (49.5 deaths), and loggers (87.4 deaths).

Compensation costs are often much smaller than society's willingness to pay to prevent damages, since generous compensation may encourage some people to take additional risks. This suggests that total petroleum production, processing, and distribution environmental costs are many times larger than cleanup and compensation costs, perhaps $10 to $30 billion annually in the U.S., which averages $1.60 to $4.80 per barrel, or 3.8¢ to 11.4¢ per gallon of petroleum products consumed, or 0.2¢ to 0.6¢ per vehicle-mile.

The externalized costs of oil production and use are estimated to be in the billions. Over $250 billion, according to some estimates, when all oil related damages are concerned—including human health. And another study of the benefits of increased electricity generation versus the much larger detrimental effects of oil consumption, estimated the true cost of oil to be over 250% of the retail price.

As a result of all this, which is what we call "externalities," global warming from the exhaust gases will heavily impact the future generations and liquid wastes that oil production and use spew into the air and spill into the soil.

On the economic side, the U.S. trade deficit can be attributed largely to petroleum imports. For example in 2009 the U.S. had a $381 billion trade deficit, of which $253 billion was from oil imports. A major Federal study estimated that oil dependence cost the U.S. economy $150-$250 billion in 2005 when petroleum prices were $35-$45 per barrel, which suggests that these costs currently total $300 to $500 billion annually, equivalent to $85 to $140 per barrel, $2.00 to $3.00 per gallon, or 10¢ to 15¢ per vehicle-mile.

Dependency on imported resources imposes military, political and economic costs associated with protecting access to foreign petroleum supplies. For example, Persian Gulf military expenditures currently average about $500 billion annually, plus indirect and long-term costs, such as lost productivity and future disability costs from military casualties. These costs average at least $140 per imported barrel, about $3.33 per gallon, or about 16¢ per vehicle-mile.

It is estimated that the externalities and hidden costs of crude oil's life cycle amount to over $800 billion annually in the U.S. alone, which is twice as much as the official estimates (somebody hiding something?) This additional cost is equivalent to adding about $8.25 to the price of gasoline at the pump.

The 2010 Deep Water Horizon oil spill cleanup and compensation costs amount to a total of $20-40 billion. Assuming one such catastrophic spill occurs each decade, this averages $2-4 billion a year, or approximately 5% of total annual crude oil expenditures. However, this only includes direct, legally recognized damages from major spills; it excludes "normal" damages caused by petroleum production and processing (oil wells, refineries and transport facilities) and by smaller spills, and uncompensated ecological costs such as existence and aesthetic losses from destruction of wildlife and landscapes.

We will take a much close look at these statistics and the reasons for these discrepancies in the following chapters. We would like to emphasize here the fact that the complex, expensive and dangerous oil drilling, exploitation and use (burning by power generators or cars) have some components that are very complex and more difficult to understand, let alone provide accurate estimate of.

In all cases, we must be aware of the problems, while keeping in mind that coal is a necessary evil. We also need to treat coal and the people who work in the coal industry with respect and admiration, because their efforts and sacrifices make out lives comfortable and prosperous.

Oil Equipment Manufacturing Impact

A number of large and small pieces of equipment are used during mining. Starting with the oil rig design and construction, we see the pollution taking place in a shape of heavy plumes of smoke in the air from large trucks and bulldozers crawling all over the oil site. And there are also trains and trucks used for transporting the production equipment to the mine, the exhausts of which are significant.

And don't forget that all this machinery was made somewhere on the planet, some time in the past, where and when their manufacturing processes and transport created a significant pollution footprint as well. Since most of these pieces of equipment are used only temporarily, we cannot assign the entire footprint to them, so we would consider a percentage of it to the manufacturing and transport of oil rigging equipment. (A)

And then, the production equipment arrives in wooden boxes or on back of enormous trailers or railroad cars. These are assembled with the help of other equipment and put to work after creating another set of pollution problems. (B)

In addition, there are many other items and small pieces of equipment, tools and consumables—some for personal use, and some for specialized operations. These are shovels, helmets, computers, power drills, boots, shoes, overalls, goggles, first aid kits, chemicals, etc., etc. the list goes. All these were also made somewhere around the world, sometime in the past, and transported to the oil site. During their manufacturing processes and transport they also left a significant pollution footprint. (C).

Then, to complete the pollution footprint picture, we must add to that the footprint of the people involved in the entire process—engineers and technicians involved in the equipment manufacturing, transport, installation, setup, and operation. These people drive cars, ride on planes, all of which leaves another significant set of pollution footprints (D)

And so, the total pollution footprint of the mine's equipment cradle-to-grave process is expressed by:

$$Pf = A + B + C + D$$

where

P_f is the total pollution footprint

A is the oil rigging equipment manufacturing and transport to the drill site

B is oil production equipment assembly, test and installation at the drill site

C is the manufacturing and transport of tools and consumables to the new well, and

D is the pollution footprint of the equipment personnel during the design, setup, drilling, and production phases of the operation.

Combining the pollution footprint of A (the oil equipment manufacturing and transport) with B (oil production equipment assembly, test, and installation), adding C (the manufacturing and transport of the tools and consumables), plus D (the pollution footprint of the equipment personnel) gives us the environmental footprint of the oil rigging and production equipment before even starting the oil drilling operations.

And the pollution footprint is significant, to be sure! It goes deep and wide, stretching from one part of the world to the other.

To put a value on it we must take inventory of all items delivered to the site, as needed for its design, construction and operation. We must take a close look at the manufacturing of an oilrig, a bulldozer, a dump truck and a number of other pieces of equipment used at the oil well site.

Keep in mind that some of these pieces are quite large, and that it takes many tons of metals to make them. Each of these pieces started as an iron or aluminum ore dug out from a mine somewhere in the world, and which was transported to a smelter. The molten metal was then shaped in different forms and shipped to the different parts manufacturers, who drilled, welded and otherwise constructed parts for the equipment.

Remember that we are talking about huge pieces of metal—the oil well pipes are 20-30 feet or more long, and the oil rigs are hundreds of feet high—mostly made out of different metals. A drill bore might need 5,000 feet of large and small diameter tubing for casing.

After manufacturing of these parts and pieces of equipment, which usually is an energy intensive process, they are then packed and loaded on railroad cars or trucks to be shipped to the assembly plant, where they are assembled into major components, or entire pieces of equipment. After one more loading and unloading operation, they finally arrive at the oil well site for final assembly and testing before being put to work.

This is a long, winding process, with many stop and go steps, loading and unloading and shipping operations—all of which require a lot of energy and generate a lot of toxic gasses in the process.

Putting a dollar value to all this would be too long and complex procedure for our purposes, so it suffices to say that the energy use and pollution effects during and after all these steps are significant. We will take a second, closer look at these steps and their environmental effects in the following chapters.

Oil Equipment Production Impact

And now, after starting the power plant operations, we see a significant pollution footprint for the duration of the operation and maintenance procedures too. As an example, at the remote oilrig, a number of large diesel generators provide power for the drilling operations and personnel accommodations. During an average workday and under a full load, these will burn 1,000 gallons of diesel.

Several bulldozers and dump trucks are serving the oilrig during the drilling of the oil well. They also burn a lot of fuel in their never-ending run-about, and so the entire area is fogged with dust and soaked in diesel fumes and lubricating oils, which leave their pollution imprint day after day, hour after hour, non-stop for the duration! And this does not even include the damage done to the land, which is a different, but not a less serious, type of environmental damage.

Spare parts for these monsters are periodically arriving from the parts manufacturers, after leaving their pollution footprint all over the place too.

And there are a number of activities that require the use of different equipment during the 20-30 years of non-stop operation of the oil well, until it is finally declared exhausted. At this point the well has to be shut down and decommissioned. The decommissioning and land reclamation are major, expensive, and polluting undertakings. The equipment and materials used during the decommissioning and waste disposal process create additional air and ground pollution, which is not to be ignored.

Additional, specialized equipment and personnel (environmental specialists and inspectors), are usually brought in to assist and/or coordinate the effort. Some of the equipment has to be disassembled and disposed of as hazardous waste, so it is loaded on trucks and transported to a landfill. And with that more pollution footprints are left at the already exhausted well site.

When the final tally is made, a significant part of the emissions and overall pollution are to be attributed to the oil drilling and production equipment and that of the support personnel. This number is significant and we will go through the calculations in the next chapters as well.

Summary

Crude oil is an essential part of our society. It is part of our daily lives; both in keeping us comfortable at home, filling our gas tanks, and driving our economic progress. Yes, it is also an air polluter, we cannot with it, yet we cannot without it. Where do we draw the line?

The first step in answering that question is to learn all that we can about what crude oil is, where we get from, and how we process and use it. This is what the following text is all about, and we will expand on the subjects at hand in the next chapters.

NATURAL GAS

Natural gas is the dominant energy source in the U.S. presently. Mostly due to the optimization of the old hydrofracking process, natural gas production has increased several fold during the last several years. The production and use of natural gas is considered a blessing, and a savior, of our energy problems.

Properties

Natural gas is a hydrocarbon mixture consisting primarily of saturated light paraffin-type compounds such as methane and ethane. These substances are gaseous under atmospheric conditions, and the mixture usually contains impurities and other hydrocarbons, such as propane, butane, pentane, and hexane.

Natural gas is found in porous sedimentary rocks beneath the earth's surface. Production companies explore, drill, and bring the natural gas to the surface. Transmission companies operate large pipelines that bring the gas from the production sites ("wellheads") to "gate stations" where distribution companies, like Enbridge St. Lawrence Gas, bring the natural gas to homes and businesses through a network of underground pipelines.

In natural gas reservoirs even the heavier hydrocarbons occur for the most part in gaseous form because of the higher pressures. They usually liquefy at the surface (at atmospheric pressure) and are produced separately as natural gas liquids (NGLs), either in field separators or in gas processing plants.

Natural gas we know and use is a combustible gas, a fossil fuel that contains primarily methane. Contrary to common belief, it contains no carbon monoxide, and its by-products (produced during burning natural gas) are primarily carbon dioxide and water vapor.

Natural gas is a colorless, tasteless, odorless, and non-toxic gas. Because it is odorless, the commercial gas we use in the U.S. contains a powerful chemical called mercaptan, which is added to the gas in very small amounts, to give it smell of rotten eggs. This strong smell is helpful in detecting the source of any gas leak, and is an advance notice to take preventative measures.

Natural gas is about 40% lighter than air, so when it leaks it dissipates into the air, unless constrained by a closure or a container. It also has a fairly high ignition temperature and a narrow flammability range. This means that natural gas needs very high temperatures, above 1,100°F, to ignite. It burns best in a mix of 4-15% gas in air, and such mixtures should be protected, because they can easily be ignited by an open flame source.

Gas Production

Natural gas is most often found in, or near, oil fields or coal beds. It is sometimes also isolated in natural gas fields. Increasing quantity of gas is being extracted today from previously thought impossible resource types, such as sour gas, tight gas, shale gas, and coal bed methane. The world's largest gas reserves (in billion cubic meters) are in Russia 47,570, Iran 26,370, Qatar 25,790, Saudi Arabia 6,568, and United Arab Emirates 5,823.

There is an estimate that the 175,400 billion cubic feet are available globally. In addition, about 900 trillion cubic meters of "unconventional" gas such as shale gas, of which 180 trillion may be recoverable, is also available. This abundance is confirming natural gas as the fuel of our immediate future, and a good way to an efficient energy transition.

Natural gas usually contains significant amounts of ethane, propane, butane, and pentane, which are heavier hydrocarbons that must be removed prior to the methane being sold for fuel or as a chemical plant feedstock. Other non-hydrocarbon impurities, such as carbon dioxide, nitrogen, and hydrogen sulfide also need to be removed before the natural gas can be transported and used.

Fracking is the most widely used process for natural gas extraction. Its development during the last decade is responsible for the extreme popularity of natural gas and its expanding use in the U.S. With that fame and glory, however, come a number of serious problems, which deserve our undivided attention, awaiting resolution.

There are over 750 different chemicals and other components used in hydraulic fracturing products, which offer many complex and potentially dangerous ways to contaminate the land and the water supply. Some of the key components used in the fracturing process are common and harmless, such as salt and citric acid, coffee, and walnut hulls, which are basically harmless. Others, however, are extremely toxic, such as benzene and lead.

Methanol was the most widely used chemical in hydraulic fracturing used until recently. It was used in 342 hydraulic fracturing products, regardless of the fact that it is a known air pollutant, on the list of potential regulation under the Safe Drinking Water Act. Other most widely used dangerous chemicals were isopropyl alcohol (used in 274 products), 2-butoxyethanol (used in 126 products), and ethylene glycol (used in 119 products).

In April 2011, the House Energy and Commerce Committee released a new report on the hydraulic fracturing (fracking, or hydrofracking) products used by oil and gas service companies. The report found that from 2005 through 2009, hundreds of millions of gallons of hazardous or carcinogenic chemicals were injected into wells in more than 13 states. The complaints from people and businesses in the affected areas are increasing by the day. The intensity and size of the damages is also on the rise, and a number of law suites have been filed in several states.

The Committee asked 14 leading oil and gas service companies to disclose the types, volumes, and chemical contents of the hydrofracking products used from 2005 through 2009. This report is the first to contain a comprehensive national inventory of chemicals used by hydrofracking companies during the drilling process. "Hydraulic fracturing has helped to expand natural gas production in the United States, but we must ensure that these new resources don't come at the expense of public health. This report shows that these companies are injecting millions of gallons of products that contain potentially hazardous chemicals, including known carcinogens. I urge EPA and DOE to make certain that we have strong protections in place to prevent these chemicals from entering drinking water supplies," said Henry Waxman, ranking member of the House Energy and Commerce Committee.

The key findings of the report were:

- The 14 leading oil and gas service companies used more than 780 million gallons of hydraulic fracturing products, not including water added at the well site. Overall, the companies used more than 2,500 hydraulic fracturing products containing 750 different chemicals and other components.
- The components used in the hydraulic fracturing products ranged from generally harmless and

common substances, such as salt and citric acid, to extremely toxic substances, such as benzene and lead. Some companies even used instant coffee and walnut hulls in their fracturing fluids.

- Between 2005 and 2009, the oil and gas service companies used hydraulic fracturing products containing 29 chemicals that are known or possible human carcinogens, regulated under the Safe Drinking Water Act (SDWA) for their risks to human health, or listed as hazardous air pollutants under the Clean Air Act.

- The BTEX compounds—benzene, toluene, xylene, and ethylbenzene—are SDWA contaminants and hazardous air pollutants. Benzene also is a known human carcinogen. The hydraulic fracturing companies injected 11.4 million gallons of products containing at least one BTEX chemical over the five-year period.

- Methanol, which was used in 342 hydraulic fracturing products, was the most widely used chemical between 2005 and 2009. The substance is a hazardous air pollutant and is on the candidate list for potential regulation under SDWA. Isopropyl alcohol, 2-butoxyethanol, and ethylene glycol were the other most widely used chemicals.

- Many of the hydraulic fracturing fluids contain chemical components that are listed as "proprietary" or "trade secret." The companies used 94 million gallons of 279 products that contained at least one chemical or component that the manufacturers deemed proprietary or a trade secret. In many instances, the oil and gas service companies were unable to identify these "proprietary" chemicals, suggesting that the companies are injecting fluids containing chemicals that they themselves cannot identify.

Water Use

The hydrofracking process uses enormous amounts of water, as needed to dilute the chemicals and to pump them under high pressure in the rocks containing the gas deposits. The water is sometimes pumped up from the water table, but very often it is delivered to the site via trucks. In all cases, the depletion of the local water table and the mess created by the water trucks are other concerns that have enormous impact on the local environment and human health.

The major concerns can be separated into a) incoming fresh water use, and b) recycled and wastewater procedures.

Fresh Water Use

For example, hydraulic fracturing in the Pennsylvania's Marcellus shale requires close to a million gallons of water every day. A million gallons is a lot of water, and even though a mixture of recycled water from previous fracturing operations is usually used for part of the process, lots of fresh surface water from lakes and rivers is used as well.

In defense of this large use of fresh water, we must admit that power plants use much more for cooling and other needs. Scrubbers on coal burning thermoelectric power plants consume 4 to 5 million gallons of water per day. It was estimated that in the recent past, the Great Lake States power plants used over 50 billion gallons per day.

And then, there are public water supply withdrawals, which are the next largest amount of water resources in use in the U.S. The estimate at the same time and states was over 10 billion gallons of fresh water withdrawn by public water systems daily.

In this context, water withdrawals for hydraulic fracturing appear to be small relative to power plant cooling withdrawals, and similar to (small to medium) public water supply withdrawals. Nevertheless, the concern over where and when of these withdrawals are made, and how they will be regulated, remains.

Ensuring adequate downstream water quantity and quality for both human and ecological needs must be a priority. Seasonally fluctuating water flows mean that more water is available during certain parts of the year relative to others. On top of that, the U.S. is in the midst of one of the longest lasting draughts in our history. This, combined, with unpredictable weather patterns of late, and the threat of global warming, pose serious concerns over the future of our fresh water supply.

Given the potential density of gas wells needed to exploit gas reserves in some states, the likelihood that many of the wells will be located near small streams, and the need for large quantities of water in a relatively short period of time, there is legitimate concern regarding the over exploitation of water, even if the negative impact is temporary. Therefore, rules and regulations are needed to ensure that water withdrawals are performed in a way that is considerate of natural conditions, existing withdrawals for other purposes, and ecological health.

Waste Water

Large amount of fluids are created at the fracking site by mixing proppants (sand and other abrasives), and a number of chemical additives into water. The proppants keep the newly created fractures in the shale from resealing once the pressure is reduced.

Chemical additives are added to serve a number of purposes including: friction reducers that are added to reduce the friction pressure during pumping operations. Surfactant are used to increase the recovery of injected water, and biocides are used to inhibit the growth of organisms that could produce gases (particularly hydrogen sulfide) that could be dangerous as well as contaminate the methane gas. Scale inhibitors are used to control the precipitation of carbonates and sulfates.

Some common components, such as guar gum, polysaccharides, and certain alcohols and acids found in the fracking liquids, are relatively safe, but others, such as hydrocarbon distillates and biocides can cause significant damage when spilled or leaked into environmental or drinking water

The type and number of chemical additives varies, since fracturing fluids are tailored to local geology, so it is impossible to determine the exact chemical composition of a "typical" fracturing fluid. As a matter of fact this is a subject of a growing controversy, as the exact formulas are not open for discussion.

After hydraulic fracturing is complete, some of the injected fluid is pumped back to the surface. Usually, about 10% of the injected fluid returns to the surface within a month. Thus returning high volume liquids are referred to as flowback, and they contain all the chemical additives used during hydraulic fracturing plus whatever else they picked up on the way up.

In addition to the input chemicals, the flowback water also contains chemical constituents associated with the shale, since the rocks it flows through naturally contains high levels of salt, metals, and organic compounds. Some of these dissolve in the fracking fluid and will eventually be brought to the surface with the flowback water. In fact, many most troublesome wastewater components are of geological origin, including arsenic, strontium, radium, and other metals and compounds.

The flowback is classified as an industrial wastewater and needs to undergo proper treatment and/or disposal. As such, large amounts of this waste are usually contained on-site in closed-loop tanks. This is much better than the old practice of storing flowback in open pits, where it inevitably leaked into the soil and the water table.

Thus stored flowback must be treated or disposed via only a few approved ways, as follows:

- Industrial treatment followed by reuse in subsequent hydraulic fracturing operations; however, there are currently no industrial waste treatment facilities capable of handling flowback waters, simply because they do not have sufficient capacity to accommodate such large quantities of new waste.

- Industrial treatment followed by discharge to publicly owned treatment works (POTWs) for further treatment is a possibility, but most POTWs are not designed to properly treat the types of contaminants typical in most flowback waste waters.

- Treatment at POTWs that have an approved pretreatment program for industrial waste is the best way, but getting program approval is difficult and not many facilities are capable of obtaining it.

- Underground injection in federally permitted disposal wells requires a special federal permit and specific geologic conditions that are not common in most areas. Disposal by injection in abandoned wells is possible, but it usually requires trucking wastes to distant disposal wells, which increases significantly the production cost.

- On-site treatment followed by reuse (recycling) is the best choice, but treatment technologies are not developed as yet, and so this method has not yet been adopted widely in practice.

Each of these options is imperfect, and has a number of advantages and disadvantages. And so, presently, the flowback is handled in whichever way is most convenient for the production site.

Produced Water

Certain amount of the remaining water in the well (including naturally occurring waters in the formation) are continuously withdrawn and stored at the surface. It is called produced water. The volume of that water varies during the well life cycle, depending on the time frame and the formation type and behavior. Produced water volumes tend to be quite small relative to flowback water, but with time the total amount of produced water can be quite large. Produced water also contains toxic chemicals, since it spends most of the time in contact with the shale. During that time it picks up greater amounts of geology-associated constituents such as salts, total dissolved solids (TDS), and a number of metals and organic materials, and naturally occurring radioactive materials (NORM.)

Reuse of produced water is not practical since it requires higher levels of treatment, so industrial treatment is the only option for disposing of produced water. Underground injection in disposal wells is another op-

tion, while treating at POTWs is an unlikely option at the present.

Basically speaking, waste management of fracking liquids is a complex issue, which varies from state to state and from site to site. There are risks associated with each step of the process, and although there are a variety of strategies in theory, new approaches and regulations are needed to protect environmental and public health.

The use and disposal of toxic liquid chemical additives during hydraulic fracturing requires stringer regulations, to establish and standardize the best practice in the industry. The management of solid wastes, using current rules and management strategies, seems adequate enough, but continuous monitoring and better compliance enforcement are needed.

Gas Leaks

Natural gas is a major factor in the U.S. economy. It is the energy of our near-to-mid-range energy future, since it is abundant, clean, and cheap. The number of production wells is increasing by the day, and with that, the concern about the environmental and safety issues related to its production and use is growing too.

Natural gas is no doubt helping us solve our energy problems, and, by emitting substantially less CO_2 than coal and oil, it is reducing the global warming, but by how much? How about the big problems caused by fracking that people are talking about, and the claims of uncontrolled methane gas leaks during the production, transport, and use of natural gas. Natural gas emits roughly half the CO_2 of coal, but it also releases substantial amounts of methane into the atmosphere and groundwater during its cradle-to-grave life span. Scientists have projected that, if left unchecked, these emissions could in fact contribute to the warming effect and make it even worse than it is now. This is so because methane is many times more potent greenhouse gas (GHG) than CO_2.

The different GHGs are assigned individual Global Warming Potentials (GWPs) labels, which compare the gases' warming effect with that of CO_2. CO_2 is assigned a GWP of one and is used as a baseline to compare GHG emissions from different sources. By multiplying a mass of a particular gas by its GWP, you find the equivalent of the mass of CO_2 emissions it would take to produce the same warming effect in a 100-year period.

Methane, or CH_4, is a greenhouse gas that has a multitude of sources. It is produced in many domestic and commercial operations, including fossil fuel production, livestock, bio mass burning, and waste management. Methane is many times more efficient at trapping radiation than CO_2. As a matter of fact, it has a GWP of 25, which means that it is at least 25 times more dangerous to the climate than CO_2. Methane emissions account for over ten percent of all anthropogenic greenhouse gas emissions on Earth, the second highest next to CO_2.

About 60% of all CH_4 emissions into the atmosphere are somehow related to human activities. About 20% of these anthropogenic emissions come from natural gas and petroleum production, refining, and use. About 60% of the total global methane emissions are in the U.S. and are expected rising by eight percent by 2020, due mostly to the projected growth of the natural gas production and use.

Methane leakages are detected during production, due to failing well casings, escaping gas from pores in the earth, and venting. It also escapes during refining, usually through venting and leakages in storage tanks. Leakage occurs during normal transport and storage, where emissions occur both through intentionally made vents and non-intentional leakages. Venting is a necessary procedure involving the "continuous bleed" of gas from devices that control gas flows, levels, temperatures, and pressures. Unintentional leakages occur during all stages of the infrastructure, from connections between pipes and vessels, to valves, storage tanks, compressors, and other equipment.

The claims that the natural gas industry is rife with methane leakages are on the rise.

Lately the trend is to replace coal burning with natural gas burning, since it emits about half the amount of CO_2.

But if these leaks are left as is in the present, they seriously reduce natural gas' capacity to decrease our GHG emissions. On the contrary, there is evidence that natural gas is not a suitable replacement for coal in its "as is" state of use. Estimates are that methane leakage rates must be kept below two to three percent, to get to a level comparable in GHG emission levels as coal.

However, this is not what is happening today. A new study, published in February 2012, by the National Oceanic and Atmospheric Administration (NOAA) and the University of Colorado, based on observations at a natural gas field in Denver, show that up to four percent of the accidental methane leakage was escaping into the atmosphere. There are documented cases where a staggering eight to nine percent of methane produced at some facilities is leaking into the surrounding air.

In addition to damaging the atmosphere and possibly increasing the climate warming, during its production methane gas also leaks into our water supplies. Many other chemicals used during hydrofracking are also responsible for unusual events and water contamination. High levels of leaked methane in water from natural gas production wells in shale-gas drilling and hydrofracking sites are reported daily. Water samples from many private groundwater sites confirm the presence of methane and other chemicals related to fracking. In many cases, the water contamination is spread a long ways away from the wells.

Methane is flammable, so there is always a risk of fires and explosions. It also presents a high risk of asphyxiation. These additional problems, together with the methane leakage and water contamination issues, must be kept under control and minimized by the natural gas owners and users, as we move into our new energy future. This is the only way to ensure an efficient and safe transition away from coal and petroleum energy sources.

Gas Explosions

Another real danger of producing and using natural gas for domestic and commercial heating is the risk of explosion. This disaster can occur naturally, or can be man-made. It usually occurs when a large pool of natural gas collects in one area and is then intentionally or unintentionally ignited. In either case, the damage of property and human life could be significant.

A natural gas well in a wooded area of Indiana Township, northeast of Pittsburgh exploded in July 2012, killing two people and sparking a fire that spewed black smoke for hours. Welders working on the site of the explosion caused the well to catch on fire and explode.

Another well in north-central Pennsylvania lacking proper pressure-control systems exploded earlier in 2012 as a crew was preparing to hook it up to a pipeline. No one was injured in this case.

Additional seven people were injured in a rig explosion in West Virginia's Northern Panhandle around the same time, when the drilling crew unintentionally struck a pocket of methane gas while sinking a natural gas well through an abandoned coal mine.

And in northeastern Pennsylvania construction flaws in several gas wells were responsible for allowing gas to seep into the area's groundwater.

The safety accidents and water table contamination incidents related to natural gas production are increasing in number and seriousness of their consequences. This will not stop the enormous progress of the natural gas development in the U.S., but should serve as a reminder that this is a dangerous business—from several points of view—and because of that we need to take a close look at the entire situation. We need to have a good understanding of the risks involved in the gas production, to be able to avoid serious accidents.

Gas Accidents

A massive gas explosion in November 2012, destroyed a downtown Springfield, MA bar, damaged 42 buildings with 115 residential units, including a daycare center, and sent debris flying across the area. The event injured 18, including nine firefighters and two police officers, who were sent to a local hospital. Amazingly, there were no fatalities.

Gas workers venting a gas leak at the site got indications of a gas leak, and knowing that that the building was about to explode, ducked for cover behind a utility truck. Several firefighters and police officers joined them just before the blast. Most of the injured were in that group, and the truck that saved their lives was demolished. A large hole in the ground, where a multistory brick building stood before the blast, is left as a reminder of the disaster. Dozens of people have been forced from their homes due to the blast, and police prevented any non-emergency personnel from getting near the blast area. The explosion blew out windows in a three-block radius, leaving at least three buildings irreparably damaged and causing emergency workers to evacuate a six-story apartment building that was buckling. Three buildings were immediately condemned, and 24 others require additional inspections by structural engineers to determine whether they are safe.

Another, similarly tragic natural gas explosion took place in the summer of 2010 in a San Bruno neighborhood, near San Francisco airport. A massive fireball started by a failure in a Pacific Gas & Electric Co pipeline initiated the explosion, which ignited fires that engulfed more than 50 buildings and killed at least one person. The loud boom of the explosion was followed by the total destruction of 53 homes, and 120 others were damaged to a degree. A number of people were injured by the blast and fires and were taken to local hospitals and burn treatment centers.

As a matter of fact, there are gas leaks and explosions very often in the U.S. and the abroad. Some are considered major, so they find a place in the media, but most are considered minor and do not get reported. How minor destroying a person's home is remains to be decided, but in any case, the production and use of natu-

ral gas remains on the list of dangerous things to do.

All this damage was because of a gas leak. Could it happen again somewhere else? You bet! But this is the price we pay for using cheap energy, and there would be no changes, except some minor safety improvements.

Here is a list of natural gas accidents that have occurred in 2012 alone:

A gas pipeline exploded & burned in Estill County, Kentucky on the evening of January 2. Flames were reported reaching over 1,000 feet high. Residents up to a mile away from the failure were evacuated.

A forest fire caused a gas pipeline to explode and burn in Floyd County, Kentucky, on January 7.

On January 9, a man was killed, and another person injured, in a fiery house explosion from a leaking 4-inch cast iron gas main installed in 1950 in Austin, Texas. Gas had been smelled in the area for several weeks prior to this. Gas company crews had looked along the affected property for a leak, but were unable to find it.

On January 13, an 8-inch gas pipeline exploded and burned in a vacant agricultural field in Rio Vista, California.

A Tennessee Gas Pipeline gas compressor had a major leak "that sounded like a rocket" in Powell County, Kentucky, forcing evacuations of nearby residents on January 14.

A contractor excavating for a communications company caused a massive gas explosion and fire at a condominium complex on January 16 in West Haverstraw, New York, injuring two firefighters and two utility workers.

Workers in Topeka, Kansas who were installing a yard sprinkler system on January 30 hit a gas line. Gas from the leak later on exploded in a nearby home, burning a 73-year-old woman, who died several weeks later.

A 30-inch gas transmission pipeline burst near Baton Rouge, Louisiana on February 13. Residents in the area were evacuated for a time, but there was no fire.

On March 5, a leak at an Enid, Oklahoma pipeline storage spread propane fumes in the area, forcing evacuations.

On March 29, an employee accidentally left a valve open during maintenance work on a Williams Companies gas compressor station near Springville, Pennsylvania. Later, gas leaked through the valve, causing alarms to evacuate workers in the compressor building. Later, the gas exploded and burned.

A 12-inch gas pipeline exploded and burned for five hours near Gary, Texas on April 4. There were no injuries, but the rupture site was only 200 feet from that pipeline's compressor station.

On April 6, two gas company workers were mildly burned when attempting to fix a leak on a four-inch gas pipeline leak in DeSoto County, Tennessee. The pipeline exploded & burned during the repairs.

A gas pipeline exploded and burned in Terrebonne Parish, Louisiana, on April 9. The accident was reported first by a satellite monitoring the area to the NRC.

Two men escaped with only minor burns after a bulldozer they were using hit a 24-inch gas pipeline near Hinton, Iowa on April 25.

A 26-inch gas transmission pipeline ruptured on June 6 in a compressor station near Laketon, Texas. Gas escaped from the 50-ft-long rupture, igniting, leaving a crater 30 feet in diameter, and burning two acres of agricultural area and telephone poles.

On June 8, near Canadian, Texas, a track hoe operator suffered burns, after a fire from a leaking four-inch gas gathering pipeline that was undergoing maintenance. Fumes entered the engine of the track hoe and ignited.

A contractor was killed and two others injured after an explosion at a BP gas compressor station in Durango, Colorado on June 25. BP, Halliburton, and the other contractors were fined $7,000 each for safety violations in that work.

Four contract workers were injured during a flash fire at a Wyoming gas processing plant.

A 14-inch gas gathering pipeline exploded and burned on July 18 near Intracoastal City, Louisiana. There were no injuries or major property damage reported.

On July 23, a compressor station operated by Williams Companies in Windsor, New York was venting gas in a "routine procedure"—during a lightning storm—when the vent was ignited by lightning, causing a fireball hundreds of feet into the air.

On August 28, an Atmos Energy repair crew struck an eight-inch gas main in McKinney, Texas, causing a fire. Four Atmos workers were treated for injuries and 1,000 Atmos gas customers lost gas service for a time.

On September 6, a ten-inch gas gathering pipeline exploded and burned near Alice, Texas. Flames reached 100 feet high, and caused a ten acre brush fire. There were no injuries.

An explosion & fire hit a Crestwood Midstream Partners gas compressor station in Hood County, Texas on September 6. Heavy damage to a sheet metal building resulted, but, there were no injuries reported to crew there.

A Colorado interstate gas compressor in Rio Blanco County, Colorado, caught fire on September 11. There were no reported injuries.

Two men were injured in an explosion and fire at a natural gas production facility east of Price, Utah on November 20.

On November 23, a gas company worker looking for the source of a reported gas leak in a Springfield, Massachusetts strip club pierce a gas line. The gas later exploded, injuring 21, devastating the strip club, and damaging numerous nearby buildings.

A malfunction in a gas compressor caused a fire on December 4, north of Fort Worth, Texas. There were no injuries.

On December 5, a 16-inch gas pipeline at 500 psi of pressure exploded and burned near a natural gas plant in Goldsmith, Texas. A fireball 250 feet high was created after the explosion, destroying 12 to 15 utility poles, and caliche and rocks the size of bowling balls damaging a road. There were no injuries reported.

On December 11, a 20-inch gas pipeline owned by NiSource Inc., parent of Columbia Gas, exploded along I-77 between Sissonville and Pocatalico, West Virginia. Several people had minor injuries, 4 homes were destroyed, and other buildings damaged. Early reports announced the NTSB was investigating as to why alarms in the Control Room for this pipeline did not sound for this failure.

An independent contractor installing fiber-optic cable for a cable company in Kansas City, Missouri inadvertently struck an underground gas line on February 19, 2013. Gas later caught fire, and created an explosion that destroyed a popular local restaurant, killing one of the workers there, and injuring about 15 others near the scene.

Electricity Generation

About 20% of the U.S. electricity today is generated by natural gas, and that number will grow to 25-30% by 2020. Natural gas from the wells is sent to the power plants usually via pipelines, since it is the cheapest way to move this commodity. In some cases the transportation is done via compressed (high pressure) containers loaded on trucks, ships, or trains.

Natural gas burns cleaner than oil and coal, since it produces less CO_2 per unit of energy released. Burning natural gas produces about 30% less CO_2 than burning petroleum, and about 45% per cent less than burning coal.

For example, coal-fired electric power generation emits around 2,000 pounds of CO_2 for every mWh generated. This is almost double the CO_2 released by a natural gas-fired electric plant for the same amount of power generated. Because of this higher carbon efficiency of natural gas generation, natural gas is the fuel of choice today. This has led to reduction in CO_2, which have been unexpectedly low recently. For example, the first quarter of 2012 the CO_2 emissions were the lowest since 1992.

Natural gas is taking a major role in the national electricity generation, where it is used via cogeneration, gas turbines and steam turbines to replace coal fired power generation. Natural gas is also in co-generation with renewable energy sources such as wind or solar. It is also a good choice for powering peak-load power stations, operating in tandem with hydroelectric plants.

We have witnessed the conversion of a number of grid peaking power plants and some off-grid engine-generators to natural gas. Natural gas provides particularly high efficiencies through combining gas and steam turbines in the so-called combined cycle mode power generation.

Combined cycle power generation using natural gas is currently the cleanest available source of power, and is widely and increasingly used, since natural gas can be obtained at increasingly high quantities and reasonable costs.

In combined cycle power plant (CCPP) steam produced in a heater/boiler unit by burning gas, oil or coal, drives a turbine generator, which in turn generates electricity. The waste heat from the gas turbine is sent back in the system to assist in the steam production process. This recycling of live steam saves energy and ultimately generates additional electricity.

In more detail; the heat output of the turbine flue gas is reused and utilized to generate more steam by passing it through a heat recovery steam generator (HRSG). Here the energy of the recycled steam is used (again) as input heat to the steam turbine power plant. This represents a combination of two power generation cycles, which increases the efficiency of the plant.

Comparing the electrical efficiency of a typical one-cycle power plant (without the use of waste heat utilization), which is typically between 25% and 40%, a CCPP can achieve electrical efficiencies of 60 to 70% and more. Adding supplementary firing further enhances the overall efficiency, which brings a high fuel utilization factor to the plant, thus ultimately contributing to a low lifecycle cost.

Electricity and heat generation by natural gas powered Combined Heat and Power (CHP) plant is another variation, where both heat and power are generated and distributed for use by the population. This type of co-generation is considered the most energy efficient, and quickest way to optimizing energy efficiency and to further cut carbon emissions. Because of that, a number of U./S. coal-fired plants are converted to gas-fired, CCPP, and CHP plants.

Other technologies, i.e. fuel cell, solar, wind, etc., may eventually provide cheaper and cleaner options for converting natural gas into electricity, but as yet all these are too expensive.

Domestic Use

Natural gas is widely used for domestic and commercial heating. It is fed into stovetops to generate heat and for cooking, In the U.S. it is supplied to delivered to homes and businesses via pipes for use in natural gas-powered ranges and ovens, natural gas-heated clothes dryers, heating/cooling, and central heating.

Home and commercial building heating includes boilers, furnaces, and water heaters. Compressed natural gas (CNG) is used in rural homes, where it is stored in large containers in the back yard. Independent natural gas suppliers throughout the United States supply natural gas. Since CNG is less economical than LPG, LPG (propane) is the dominant source of use in remote and rural areas.

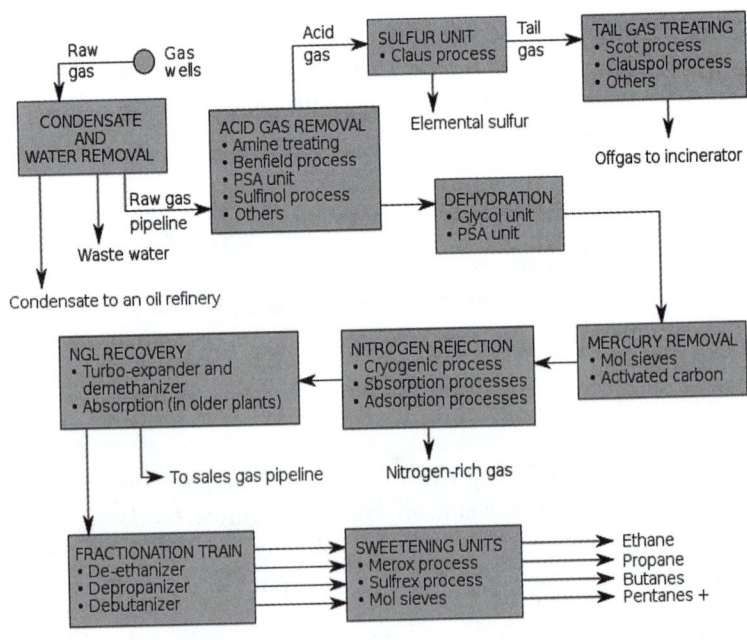

Figure 5-27. Natural gas processing and products

Gas Processing

It is obvious from Figure 5-27 that natural gas can be processed into a number of useful products and processes. It is, for example, a major feedstock in the production of ammonia, via the Haber process. Large quantities of natural gas are also used in the production of fertilizers.

Some aircraft manufacturers are developing liquid natural gas (LNG) and hydrogen-powered aircraft engines. The goal of the programs is to develop LNG and hydrogen variants of the conventional jet engines used in passenger and cargo aircraft. The advantages are that at current market prices, an LNG-powered aircraft would cost $200 less to operate per each ton of the aircraft, which is roughly equivalent to 60% lower cost. In addition, there are considerable reductions of CO_2, hydrocarbons, and NO_x emissions expected when large fleet of LNG powered aircraft engines are deployed.

The main advantage of LNG as a jet engine fuel is that it has more specific energy than the standard kerosene mixes. LNG also has lower burning temperature which helps cool the air, which the engine compresses for greater volumetric efficiency. This could in effect replace using intercoolers and can also lower the temperature of the exhaust.

Natural gas can be used to produce hydrogen, via the hydrogen reformer process. Thus produced hydrogen can be used in many applications, such as: fuel in modified hydrogen vehicles, a feedstock for the chemical industry, a hydrogenating agent, in oil refineries.

Natural gas is also used in the manufacture of a number of commodities, such as fabrics, glass, steel, plastics, paint, and other products.

On the bad side of things, there are some methane emissions during all steps of the production-transport and use of natural gas and its products. These emissions are presently unaccounted for, and usually uncontrolled. Due to the GHG character of the methane gas, however, firm controls must be established and enforced across the entire industry, to account for, and reduce, the GHG emissions.

Use in Transportation

Natural gas accounts for only a very small percentage of transportation energy in the U.S., approximately 2.5% percent, compared with a 95% use of petroleum fuels. But there are grandiose plans to change the ratios in favor of natural gas used for vehicle transport. For example, recently T. Boone Pickens introduced what he calls the Pickens Plan, under which the U.S. would undertake a massive effort to convert vehicle fleets over to natural gas. This would not be so hard to do, according to him, as the technology is all available "off-the-shelf" right now.

According to him, "Natural gas already has a tremendous advantage, particularly when used for trucks and fleet vehicles. Most trucking today is round-trip, one-tank routes. There are approximately 1.5 million miles of gas pipe and distribution lines crisscrossing the country, making natural gas available on nearly every street and community in America today."

And according to the Natural Gas Supply Association: "Natural gas is the cleanest of all the fossil fuels... combustion of natural gas ... releases very small amounts of sulfur dioxide and nitrogen oxides, virtually no ash or particulate matter, and lower levels of carbon dioxide, carbon monoxide, and other reactive hydrocarbons."

Both of these statements need clarification, for they ignore some major issues:

- Yes, there are natural gas lines on every street, but you cannot pull to any line and fill you gas tank. Much more equipment and expense is needed for that to happen.

- Yes, natural gas is much cleaner as far as far as sulfur, nitrogen and carbon oxides emissions are concerned when burning. But taking a close look at the production, transport, and storage issues we reviewed above (methane and chemicals leaks in the air and soil), the picture changes drastically and needs some modifications.

So, let's get down on our knees and elbows and take a close look at the exhaust pipes of the different fuels and engines in use today. A 2010 report by the National Academy of Sciences (NAS) examined environmental externalities of the major energy sources, allowing for a side-by-side comparison. Natural gas powered engines show lower CO_2, CO, VOCs, and NO_x than gasoline and diesel engines. Natural gas engines, however, emit unburned methane gas, which is a serious GHG.

The damages calculated by NAS are based on health and other environmental effects of these kinds of emissions.

Table 5-10 shows that compressed natural gas (CNG) vehicles are somewhat less damaging than gasoline. Approximately 91% as damaging in health and other environmental effects per VMT, and about 78% per gasoline gallon equivalent. Overall, natural gas has 89% the carbon footprint of gasoline in transportation, which results in 11% reduction. Other studies show even greater reduction of over 20%. So far, so good. Natural gas is a cleaner substitute for gasoline for autos and trucks, as far as gasses coming from the exhaust pipes are concerned.

A report from the U.S. Department of Energy (DOE) cites other studies comparing the emissions of natural gas vehicles to those of gasoline and diesel vehicles produced the following results:

Table 5-11 shows that compressed natural gas (CNG) vehicles offer environmental benefits over gasoline in all aspects of GHG emissions, except in terms of methane emissions. The methane emissions from CNG are much greater than those from gasoline vehicles, so the net decrease of GHGs pollution is marginal, even if the CO_2 emissions are much lower. Methane is a serious GHG gas contributor, so this situation deserves a much closer look.

The environmental impact of natural gas is especially significantly lower than diesel fuels, mostly due to reduction in particulate matter (PM), with 80-90% less PM for CNG engines. The nitrogen oxide and VOC figures for heavy-duty vehicles suggest that CNG is better in these areas also.

Other studies of the emissions of different vehicles show that the CO emissions are somewhat ambiguous. Here, natural gas produces much lower CO emissions in cars, delivery trucks, and buses, but far more CO emissions in semis and garbage trucks. This mystery is still to be resolved.

In any case, no doubt that CNG has some advantages that need to be explored. But don't forget that the emissions from the exhaust pipe are only part of the story. We need to also assess the environmental and health damage done by the different fuels during their production, transport, processing, and storage.

The fuel supply pathway also makes a big difference in the fuel's GHG emissions. For example, if a non-North American natural gas is imported as LNG via ocean tanker and then regasified and compressed to produce CNG, thus produced CNG would reduce lifecycle GHG emissions by only 5 percent compared with gasoline.

In turn, if domestic natural gas is used, life-cycle GHG emissions are reduced by 15 percent. If gas that otherwise would be flared or landfill gas is used as the

feedstock, then the overall net GHG emissions can be negative.

We must not forget that methane gas (a serious GHG) escapes during the production of natural gas too, while there is much less GHGs generated during petroleum products production. If we then compare the entire well-to-tailpipe life cycle of the different fuels we might find out that CNG is more dangerous to the environment after all.

The jury is still out on this one, so we encourage the esteemed reader to get more familiar with the issues at hand to be better educated on the subject, thus being able to make the right decisions.

Environmental Impact of Natural Gas

All fossils—including natural gas—generate large amount of hydrocarbons and other harmful and toxic gasses. Some more than others, as seen in Figure 5-28 and 29.

As seen in Figure 2-29, natural gas contributes the least to air pollution, as compared to oil and coal, but it is still injecting millions of tons of GHG gasses in the atmosphere. So, instead of 5 billion tons generated by

Table 5-10. Damages based on health and other environmental effects

Vehicles	Mean health and other non-GHG damages in dollars per vehicle mile traveled (VMT)	Mean health and non-GHG damages per gasoline gallon equivalent (gge)	Carbon footprint in CO_2 equivalents in grams/VMT
Gasoline vehicle	$.0132	$.2983	552
Compressed natural gas vehicle	$.0120	$.2335	492

Table 5-11. CNG vs. gasoline vehicles

Pollutant	GHGs reduction
Volatile Organic Compounds (VOCs)	-10%
Carbon Monoxide (CO)	-20% – 40%
Nitrogen Oxides (NOx)	0%
Particulate Matter (PM)	-80%
Methane	+400% (increase)

Fossil Fuel Emission Levels - Pounds per Billion Btu of Energy Input

Pollutant	Natural Gas	Oil	Coal
Carbon Dioxide	117,000	164,000	208,000
Carbon Monoxide	40	33	208
Nitrogen Oxides	92	448	457
Sulfur Dioxide	1	1,122	2,591
Particulates	7	84	2,744
Mercury	0.000	0.007	0.016

Figure 5-28. Comparing fossil fuels pollution levels

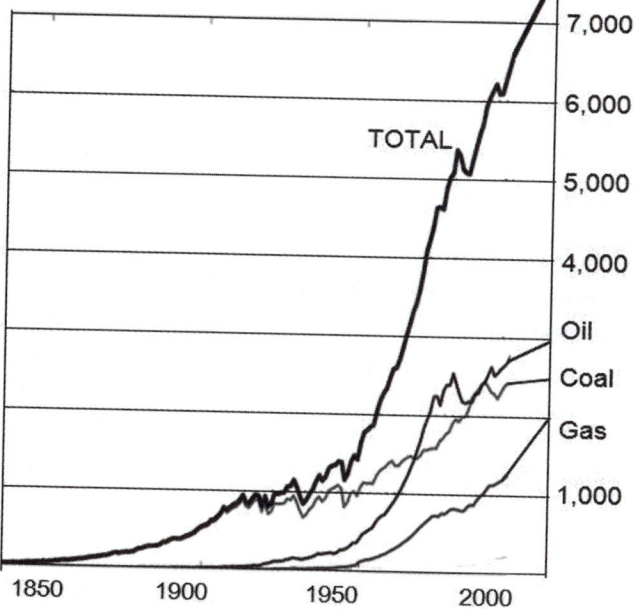

Figure 5-29. Annual global fossils emissions, in million tons of carbon.

oil and coal, natural gas will produce 1.5 billion tons of damaging, toxic gasses annually. Smaller, but not a small enough number, which raises a number of good questions, for which we just have no answers for now.

Adding to this cesspool of toxins another 5-6 billion tons of carbons generated by cars worldwide, and we can then see why we should be concerned with human activities contributing to global warming and other environmental and human maladies.

The Concerns

New discoveries and developments in the natural gas industry lately have brought up a new hope for energy independence and environmental cleanup. With that, however, a number of issues, related to the gas production and use have surfaced as well. None of these are new, but the extreme expansions of drilling and exploration in several parts of the U.S. and the world have forced a new look at the situation.

The major environmental and health issues, arising from the drilling, extraction, and use of natural gas are as follow:

Drinking Water

People have expressed various concerns about hydraulic fracturing, most frequently a fear that it might cause contamination of underground sources of drinking water. Supporters of fracturing argue that it will not cause contamination because the formations being fractured typically are located thousands of feet below drinking water aquifers, and the fractures created by the fracturing process will not travel anywhere near that far. Indeed, even many critics of fracturing agree that the fracturing process itself is unlikely to cause contamination.

If contamination occurred, it most likely would be the result of a well construction failure—such as improper casing or cementing—that allowed fluids to travel up the side of the well from a deeper formation that contains oil or gas to a shallower formation that contains a source of drinking water. A hydraulically fractured well is no different than oil or gas wells, which pass through a shallow water aquifer on the way to deeper formations. Millions of such wells have been drilled, and contamination problems rarely occur.

Nevertheless, fears still exist. The main regulations that protect against such contamination are state regulations. Each state with oil and gas activity requires a company to obtain a permit for drilling a well, and each state has regulations that impose standards for the construction, casing and cementing of wells.

The main federal law that protects underground sources of drinking water, the Safe Drinking Water Act (SDWA), does not apply to the hydraulic fracturing process itself, so long as diesel is not used in the fracturing fluid.

Chromium-6 in the Water

Hexavalent chromium, otherwise known as chromium-6, or Cr(VI), is frequently used in fracking operations. It is an extremely toxic substance, which has been causing contamination of drinking water around drilling sites, and there are a number of court actions pending.

Cr(VI) and its compounds are genotoxic carcinogens, which cause increased risk of lung cancer if inhaled. Ingestion of Cr(VI) can also cause irritation or ul-cers in the stomach and intestines. Capillaries in kidneys and intestine are also affected.

The U.S. Occupational Safety and Health Administration OSHA permissible exposure limit (PEL) for airborne exposures to Cr(VI) is 5 $\mu g/m^3$, while the National Institute for Occupational Safety and Health proposed a recommended exposure limit (REL) of 0.2 $\mu g/m^3$ for airborne exposures to Cr(VI).

There is no U.S. EPA Maximum Contaminant Level (MCL) for drinking water, though the current MCL for total chromium is based on the assumption that all of it is Cr(VI). California has finalized a Public Health Goal of 0.02 parts per billion (ppb or micrograms per liter) and is now in the process of establishing an enforceable MCL.

Oil and gas companies like EnCana, Imperial Oil, Suncor, ConocoPhillips, ExxonMobil, etc., generally don't do the hydraulic fracturing themselves, but instead hire specialty services to do it. Each of the big players in the multi-billion-dollar fracking industry—Halliburton, Calfrac Well Services, Schlumberger, BJ Services (all of which operate in Western Canada) has its own recipe for fracking fluids, of which they are fiercely protective. The precise nature and concentrations of the chemicals in these "proprietary fluids" are not even fully known to government regulatory agencies.

Because of that, the public has no way of knowing what's in the fracking fluids. By 2007, there were 449,000 natural gas wells in 32 American states, an increase of more than 30 percent since 2000, with serious episodes of groundwater contamination near drilling sites documented in at least seven states.

A case of excess Cr(VI) found in the drinking water in Hinkley, California led to a major class action lawsuit against Pacific Gas & Electric, which finally paid the plaintiffs more than $200 million in 2006. A major movie, titled Erin Brockovich, was also made, depicting the pains of the locals on one hand, and the maneuvers of the companies and regulators involved in the case.

In the same year EnCana was fined $266,000 by the state of Colorado for "failure to protect water bearing formations," a company spokesman complained to the press that environmentalists had been spreading "misinformation" about fracking and creating a climate of fear about hydraulic fracturing fluids.

It is more than apparent that fracking is creating a serious conflict, where the increase of cheap energy production is causing serious health issues. And just like in the Erin Brockovich case, the drilling companies and their supporters vehemently deny that their rigs are causing any problems.

So it seems that, just like in the case of lead, asbestos, and nicotine debacles, many people have to get sick and die first before the companies involved admit their role and do something about the problems they are causing. And just like in those cases, a lot of time will pass by before any significant actions are taken.

Temporary Inconveniences

Temporary inconveniences arise during the drilling process, where the area around a well site and the local populated centers could see increased traffic, noise, dust, and bright lighting as needed for around-the-clock drilling. These are necessary evils that are under evaluation, and there are already government regulations addressing these issues. Although some improvement can be expected, there is no way to completely eliminate the traffic, noise, lighting etc., so the battle continues.

Air Quality

Hydraulic fracturing is basically a polluting activity, which has a negative effect on the local environment. Its indirect effect on air quality is positive, because it is used to produce natural gas, which is by far the cleanest burning fossil fuel. But people and researchers are concerned that when fracturing is complete, the high pressure of the formation being fractured is allowed to push the necking water back to the surface, where such "flowback" water is recovered. As it flows up the well, the flowback water is accompanied by significant quantities of natural gas. If that gas is vented, as it sometimes has been, the venting of the natural gas could have an adverse impact on air quality, and natural gas (methane) is many times worst greenhouse gas (GHG) than CO_2, which is considered the evil of all evils as far as global warming is concerned.

Several states have implemented regulations to prevent the venting of natural gas that accompanies flowback, and require that the gas be recovered in most cases and flared in others. On federal level, the U.S. EPA recently proposed regulations to prohibit venting of natural gas all together.

Water Consumption

This is another serious concern, because hydraulic fracturing (hydraulic means water assisted) of a horizontal well typically uses millions gallons of water. This is not such a large amount compared to many industrial and agricultural uses, but in areas of limited water supplies, finding water for use in fracturing creates serious long-term problems. Some states have implemented, or are considering implementing, water use regulations.

Fracking Fluids

Fracking fluids may be based on acid, gel, water, or oil. Most fracturing work is conducted using water-based fluid. In addition to water, fracture fluids can contain a wide array of additives, each designed to serve a particular function.   For example, in hydraulic fracturing of deep shale gas zones, water commonly is mixed with a friction reducer to lessen the resistance of the fluid moving through the casing; biocides to prevent bacterial growth; scale inhibitors to prevent buildup of scale; and proppants, such as sand or ceramic beads to hold the fractures open. This type of fracturing process often is referred to as a slick water fracture. It is the use of additives, such as those listed above, that has raised one of the concerns about hydraulic fracturing.

A small number of potential fracture fluid additives, such as benzene, ethylene glycol and naphthalene have been linked to negative health effects at certain exposure levels. However, most additives contained in fracture fluids, including sodium chloride, potassium chloride and diluted acids, present low to very low risks to human health and the environment.

Disclosure

The disclosure, or rather lack of disclosure, of the actual chemicals used in fracturing fluids is another hot issue that is not going to go away until fully resolved. Most hydraulic fracturing companies keep the composition of their fluids confidential to protect any competitive advantage they gain through experience and research. This sounds suspicious to the affected people, and makes fighting spills and their negative health effects difficult, so some companies have begun making voluntary disclosures. Several states have also enacted regulations requiring such disclosure, with some limited protection for additives that a company can demonstrate constitute a trade secret.

In addition, some companies have responded to public concerns by developing fracturing additives that are composed entirely or mostly of substances that qualify as food additives. This, in our opinion is the best, if not the only, way to solving this critical issue. That will not make the public concerns with fracking go away, but will take one of the biggest problems off of the agenda.

Flowback Water Disposal

One of the biggest concerns lately has been the recovery and disposal of flowbackwater. This is liquid that loosely resembles water, but in actuality it is a muddy concoction of fracturing additives, chemicals, and substances that dissolve into the water from the formation being fractured. The mixture usually includes metals and even dangerous radioactive materials.

Underground injection wells provide a safe means for the disposal of flowback in some cases, but there are not many such underground injection control wells. The controversy regarding whether some existing wastewater treatment plants can adequately treat the flowback continues with no answers in sight. Some states do not allow flowback mixtures to be sent to certain treatment plants.

Recycling of flowback is becoming increasingly the solution, but there are limits to the quality and quantity of recycled flowbackwaters. If and when an efficient recycling method is found, it will have several benefits, for it will a) reduce the supply of new water needed, and b) reduce disposal volumes.

The disposal of flowback, whether it is by underground injection or by treatment and discharge, is regulated by the federal Clean Water Act, which, however, cannot control the unintentional spills of fracturing fluids.

Although fracturing accidents are not much different than other potentially hazardous substances, such as those coming from refineries and chemical plants, the large scale deployment of this technology makes them more visible and with greater impact. For that purpose, the states have regulations addressing the prevention, containment and control of spills of hazardous or potentially hazardous substances.

Flowback Pathways

Some hydraulic fracturing reports show the exposure effects of additives that can be contained in hydraulic fracturing fluids without considering their relative availability via exposure pathways. For example, one study found that depending upon the design of the fracture job and the specific formation dynamics involved, anywhere from 30-70% of fracturing fluids are returned to the surface through the well.

Unrecovered treatment fluids are typically trapped in the fractured formation via various mechanisms such as pore storage and stranding behind healed fractures, thus isolating them from ground water. There are cases, however, where this is not the case, and the fluids find alternative pathways, which lead into people's back yards, basements, and even drinking water supply.

Isolation

Ground water contamination resulting from the flowback of fracture fluids returned to the surface through casing would require simultaneous failures of multiple barriers of protection. These could be caused by simultaneous failure of casing strings and cement sheaths, so the risk profile for such an event is low. The greatest risk of contamination of ground water by fracture fluids, therefore, remains the potential for fluids to migrate upward within the casing/formation annulus during the fracturing process.

So, the most effective means of protecting ground water from upward migration in the annulus is the proper cementation of well casing across vertically impermeable zones and ground water zones. Proper cementation creates the hydraulic barriers that prevent fluid incursion into ground water. The amount and placement of cement needed for this purpose will vary depending upon several factors, all of which could be controlled to provide a solid barrier capable of preventing harmful flowback.

The Anti-fracking Movement

Even in best of cases, the anti-fracking movement is here to stay and is growing by the day. It is a powerful movement that is capable of making some changes in the fracking industry as we know it. Its agenda varies according to local priorities and group composition. Public consultation is the preferred method in some countries like France. In Australia rural conservation issues dominate the battles.

Generally speaking, the movement is divided into four broad camps of people who:

1. Desire a better deal from the gas industry
2. Advocate further study into the environmental and economic impacts of unconventional gas development
3. Demand a complete ban on hydraulic fracturing
4. The majority demand tighter regulation of gas development

Some factions of the anti-fracking movement are not opposed to hydraulic fracturing per se, but simply want to get a better economic opportunity, taxation, compensation deals, and raise rebellion against the existing system. In the U.S., among other things, there is an opposition to energy companies from Texas and Oklahoma dominating the industry in Pennsylvania and New York.

The anti-fracking movement in Pennsylvania, for example, is questioning the state's low taxes on unconventional gas development, calling for both a severance tax (i.e. based on volumes extracted) and royalty rates in line with those in other parts of the country.

The internationalization of the anti-shale and anti-coal seam gas activist movements in defense of "the world's underground water supplies" was an important development in 2012. On a declared World Day Against Fracking/CSG in July, for example, a key activist group opposing Australian coal gas development spoke at a major national anti-fracking rally in Washington, DC, situating itself explicitly within the international anti-fracking movement.

And on top of that, there are a number of lawsuits against fracking companies, all of which will determine the way the industry develops in the future.

Summary

No matter what happens now or in the future, fossils are here to stay one way or another. And they will stay with us until completely exhausted. There is no question about it. There is no other way in this capitalist reality we live in. The fossils provide cheap energy, which we need for our personal comfort and to keep the businesses running.

Here in the U.S., we will be driving large cars, and will heat and cool our houses with fossil fuels until the last drop of coal, oil, and gas deposits are used. The transaction will be slow, marked by gradually increasing fuel prices, but no matter how high the prices go, the fuel supplies will end sooner of later. Crude oil will go first, followed by natural gas, and then coal. By the middle of next century there will be no fossils. Period. And the way we are using them, it might be sooner.

OK, so big deal, no fossils. So what? Well, this is the big question, what? But we don't have the questions, and don't care about much about it, so it will be the next generations who will have to answer that question and take care of the related issues.

And there will be a lot of issues, because at the present level of fossils exploitation and use, we are creating a real environmental problem. As the Earth's population increases, fossil fuel use increases, increasing the generation of green house gasses and other toxins. The extreme emissions are overwhelming the environment already, so we cannot even imagine what would happen if the emissions are increased by a factor of two or three, as predicted to happen by the next century.

Soon we won't have any clean air to breath, and the oceans will swallow the land. But none of that is going to stop us—until it actually happens. At that time it might be too late to do much about it anyway, so the world will continue digging, pumping, and burning fossils until they are gone. At that time things will change— some for the good, some for the bad.

And we will take a look at these extremes in the next chapters as well.

METHANE HYDRATES

Natural gas hydrates, a relatively unknown to the public energy source, are also called methane hydrates, or clathrates. They are a variation of natural gas, where combining water and gas molecules under certain conditions forms non-stoichiomelric, ice-like compounds. These molecules have crystalline (ice-like) structure, which is formed when temperature, pressure, gas saturation, water salinity, pH, etc. were favorable millions of years ago. They are also referred to as flammable ice or combustible ice because the ice-crystal formations burn when defrosted and ignited.

We take a much closer look at this very promising fuel of the future in the next chapters.

Very large quantities of this unusual material were formed millions of years ago and are usually found in the depths of the oceans, or in the permafrost of the North Pole. Their chemical composition is such that the water molecules in the hydrate combine into polyhedral cages through hydrogen bonds. The gas molecules are, therefore, trapped in and enclosed within the prison walls of the die cages forever…or until released by some form of energy.

There are three types of methane hydrate structure. They all include pentagonal dodecahedra of water molecules enclosing methane. This geometry arises from the happy accident that the bond angle in water is fairly close to the 108° angle of a pentagon. Generally, the dodecahedra are slightly distorted so that three dodecahedra can share an edge. This requires a dihedral (inter-face) angle of 120 degrees, whereas the dihedral angle of a true dodecahedron is 116.5 degrees. Between the dodecahedra are other cages of water molecules with different shapes. In practice, not all cages are occupied by hydrocarbons, but occupancy rates of over 90% occur.

Significant energy is needed to release the gas from its icy prison, and since the conditions deep down below on the ocean bottom, and the permafrost wilderness, don't change much with time, the gas will stay in there until the end of time, or until a natural disaster rescues it. But most likely, it will be man, who some day will figure a way to break the prison walls and release large quantities of gas for use on Earth.

This type of fuel is made of colorless hydrocarbon and water molecules, so it so usually white or colorless.

Some gas hydrates in the Gulf of Mexico, however, have yellow, orange, or even red tint. Other samples from the Atlantic deposits are gray or blue. The colors are most likely due to impurities mixed in the crystals and have no other meaning.

In nature, methane is the most common "guest" molecule to form natural gas hydrate. If 99% or more of the guest molecules are methane, then the natural gas hydrate is called methane hydrate. It, and most other hydrocarbon gases, always burns when ignited. Methane hydrate is regarded as an ideal clean fuel energy for the future.

Methane hydrates are common in sediments deposited in high latitude continental shelves and at the slope and rise of continental margins with high biopresence. Biological products provided the organic matter that was buried in the sediment many millions of years ago, which under the pressure and temperature and after exhausting the oxygen supply, sulfate, and other electron acceptors, eventually generated methane through fermentative decomposition and/or microbial carbonate reduction. The resulting gas was then frozen in the depths of the Earth, crystallized, and perfectly preserved until now as methane hydrate.

The properties of sediment-hosted gas hydrates are strongly determined by texture, structure, and permeability of the sediment and the mode of supply of methane. The water molecules from a well-defined crystal lattice (the host lattice) containing cavities into which small gas molecules (guests) may be adsorbed; under appropriate conditions the adsorption energy may then reduce the free energy of the hydrate sufficiently to make the hydrate phase stable than either pure water or ice. In the crystal lattice of hydrate guest–guest interactions are negligible. The host lattice is considered merely to give rise to an environment in which the guest molecules evolve, and the thermodynamic properties of the hydrate result from the classical behavior of individual guest molecules within the cavity potential.

The hydrate formation process can be described as gas absorption, primary and secondary nucleation, growth, agglomeration, and breakage. The interaction between hydrate and the host sediment at the grain level has been highlighted in recent years as laboratory and analytical investigations have shown that hydrate is not restricted to forming in a unique way in the pore space.

Parameters affecting gas hydrate formation and dissociation include temperature, pore pressure, gas chemistry and pore water salinity. Any change in the equilibrium of these parameters may result in dissociation and/or dissolution of the gas hydrate.

At 30 atmospheres pressure, methane hydrate begins to stabilize at temperatures above 0°C, and is stable at 100 atmospheres and 15°C. This has two important practical implications. First, it's a nuisance to the gas company, because they have to dehydrate the natural gas pipes thoroughly to prevent methane hydrates from forming in their high-pressure gas lines.

Environmental Concerns

Methane hydrates are stable on the sea floor at depths below a few hundred meters and will be solid within sea floor sediments. Chunks occasionally break loose and float to the surface, where they are unstable and effervesce as they decompose.

The stability of methane hydrates on the sea floor has a whole raft of implications, the most important of which is that they may constitute a huge energy resource in the future. Also, natural, or man-made disturbances might suddenly destabilize sea floor methane hydrates, triggering submarine landslides and huge releases of methane. This would spell a catastrophic disaster, because methane is a very effective greenhouse gas, and large methane releases might spell large disaster for Earth and it inhabitants.

Such large releases may explain sudden episodes of climatic warming in the geologic past. The methane would oxidize fairly quickly in the atmosphere, but could cause enough warming to affect other mechanisms, such as release of carbon dioxide from carbonate rocks and decaying biomass, which could keep the temperatures elevated.

On the bright side, many scientists believe that methane hydrates are one of the major (if not the only) long-term energy sources of our future. The estimates are that at least 200 years of energy reserves are stored in that form, awaiting exploitation and use by man.

Their global abundance and distribution suggest that they may become energy resources of the future. With increasing energy demand and depleting energy resources, gas hydrates may serve as a potentially important resource of future energy requirements for several centuries.

We will take a much closer look at the methane hydrates in the following chapters.

NUCLEAR POWER

Nuclear power is the most amazing of all energy sources. Its might, efficiency, and ease of use are overwhelmingly attractive and are the main reason for its quick proliferation. In less than half a century, the amount of electricity generated by nuclear power tops the list of major energy providers.

The controversies surrounding nuclear power safety and waste disposal have also topped the charts of concerns. And deservingly so, because the damages caused by nuclear plants rival these of all other energy generators combined. There are no mining, oil drilling, or any other accidents and incidents that come even close to the terror caused by nuclear disasters like Chernobyl and Fukushima. And there are no other industries that are shut down overnight from fear of the unknown, as happened in Germany in 2012, when all nuclear plants were ordered to shut down by 2020.

So, we can think of nuclear power as the Genie in the bottle that has the power to save the world, or destroy it, depending on how it is managed. But is proper management the only key to success in using nuclear power safely and efficiently? We'll review the different issues and possibilities of nuclear power, in light of the related environmental and safety issues at hand.

NOTE: The modern commercial nuclear power generating reactors use fission reaction to burn mostly uranium based nuclear fuels. Nuclear fission is a nuclear reaction, or a rapid radioactive decay process, where the nucleus of an atom splits into several lighter nuclei. This process also produces free neutrons and photons in the form of gamma rays, and releases huge amount of energy.

This monstrous energy release is the goal of the fission reaction, but it is also what makes nuclear power so dangerous. Maintaining the rate and safety of the reaction is easily achieved with today's sophisticated process control equipment…most of the time. The problem is that occasionally, exceptional circumstances, such as an operator mistake at Chernobyl and natural disaster at Fukushima, create abnormal conditions. Under such conditions, the operators lose control of the process and the reactors overheat and self-destruct, taking the entire plant with them.

In such cases, many people are hurt and killed, which ultimately hurts the entire nuclear power industry.

Nuclear Fuels

Nuclear fuels contain immense amount of power. Just think; one kilogram of nuclear grade uranium contains the energy of 3,850 kilograms of coal. This makes it nearly four million times more powerful than the most common power source today. A handful of uranium can replace 40 railroad cars full of coal. It also avoids the generation of thousands of tons of harmful gasses, liquids and solid waste materials generated during coal burning. Amazing!

The commercial nuclear fuels are typically based on uranium oxides, which are used instead of the pure metal, because the oxide melting point is much higher, and because they cannot burn, since they are already in the final, oxidized state of the metal.

Radioactivity

All fuels used for generating electricity in nuclear plants are radioactive materials. The most used are uranium and thorium, which are found in nature, as Naturally Occurring Radioactive Materials (NORM), which is used more specifically for all naturally occurring radioactive materials where human activities have increased the potential for exposure compared with the unaltered situation.

Concentrations of actual radionuclides may or may not have been increased; if they have, then these materials are somewhat different, and are classified as Technologically-Enhanced (TENORM).

Long-lived radioactive elements such as uranium, thorium, and potassium and any of their decay products, such as radium and radon are examples of NORM. These elements have always been present in the Earth's crust and atmosphere. The term NORM exists also to distinguish "natural radioactive material" from anthropogenic sources of radioactive material, such as those produced by nuclear power and used in nuclear medicine, where incidentally the radioactive properties of a material is what makes it useful.

Radioactivity is a part of nature, which can be explained as an unusual (and maybe unnatural) state of matter. While everything is made of atoms, which are pretty stable under normal conditions, the atoms of radioactive materials are unstable, which is usually due to the fact that they have too much energy, and are usually referred to as isotopes.

When radioactive atoms spontaneously release their extra energy, as they do continuously, they are said to decay. All radioactive atoms decay eventually, though they do not all decay at the same rate. After releasing all their excess energy, the atoms become stable and are no longer radioactive. The time required for decay depends upon the type of atom.

Radioactive Decay Rate

Radioactive decay rates are normally stated in terms of their half-lives, and the half-life of a given nuclear species is related to its radiation risk. The dif-

ferent types of radioactivity lead to different decay paths, which transmute the nuclei into other chemical elements. Examining the amounts of the decay products makes possible radioactive dating.

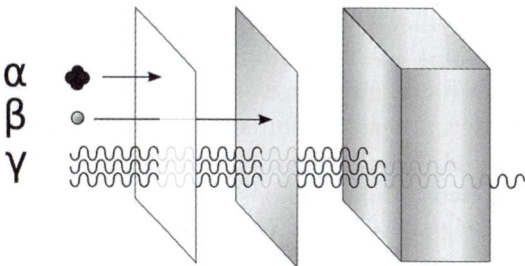

Figure 5-30. The radiation particles

Radiation from nuclear sources can be defined as Alpha, Beta, and Gamma, since it is the most convenient way to analyze them as three distinct species by their effects on/by magnetic and electric fields.

Alpha Radiation

Alpha (α) particles are helium-4 nuclei, containing two protons and two neutrons and their nuclei. They interact with matter very heavily, and at their usual velocities only penetrate a few centimeters of air, or a few millimeters of low-density material (such as the thin mica material which is specially placed in some Geiger counter tubes to allow alpha particles in). This means that alpha particles from ordinary alpha decay do not penetrate skin and cause no damage to tissues below.

Some very high-energy alpha particles compose about ten percent of cosmic rays, and they are capable of penetrating the body and even thin metal plates. However, they are of danger only to astronauts, since they are deflected by the Earth's magnetic field and then stopped by its atmosphere.

Alpha radiation is dangerous when alpha-emitting radioisotopes are ingested (breathed or swallowed). This brings the radioisotope close enough to tissue for the alpha radiation to damage cells. Per unit of energy, alpha particles are at least 20 times more effective at cell-damage as gamma rays and X-rays. See relative biological effectiveness for a discussion of this. Examples of highly poisonous alpha-emitters are radium, radon, and polonium.

Beta Radiation

Beta-minus ($\beta-$) radiation consists of an energetic electron. It is more ionizing than alpha radiation, but less so than gamma. Beta radiation from radioactive decay can be stopped with a few centimeters of plastic or a few millimeters of metal. It occurs when a neutron decays into a proton in a nucleus, releasing the beta particle and an antineutrino. Beta radiation from linac accelerators is far more energetic and penetrating than natural beta radiation. It is sometimes used therapeutically in radiotherapy to treat superficial tumors.

Beta-plus (®+) radiation is the emission of positrons, which are antimatter electrons. When a positron slows down to speeds similar to those of electrons in the material, the positron will annihilate an electron, releasing two gamma photons in the process. Those two gamma photons will be traveling in approximately opposite directions.

Gamma Radiation

Gamma (©) radiation consists of photons with a frequency of greater than 1019 Hz. [1] Gamma radiation occurs to rid the decaying nucleus of excess energy after it has emitted either alpha or beta radiation. Both alpha and beta particles have an electric charge and mass, and thus are quite likely to interact with other atoms in their path. Gamma radiation is composed of photons, which have neither mass nor electric charge. Gamma radiation penetrates much further through matter than either alpha or beta radiation.

Gamma rays, which are highly energetic photons, penetrate deeply and are difficult to stop. They can be stopped by a sufficiently thick layer of material, where stopping power of the material per given area depends mostly (but not entirely) on its total mass, whether the material is of high or low density. However, as is the case with X-rays, materials with high atomic number such as lead or depleted uranium add a modest (typically 20% to 30%) amount of stopping power over an equal mass of less-dense and lower atomic weight materials (such as water or concrete).

Isotopes Decay

Radioactive isotopes undergo half-life disintegrations, where half of the original sample will disintegrate in a certain amount of time. This is essentially independent of temperature and other usual rate-determining factors and is called the half-life ($t1/2$). During the elapse of another half-life period of the same duration, half of the sample left from the first disintegration will also disintegrate.

The process continues until one atom remains, and the decay of the last atom completes the transmutation of one element into another. Half-lives vary widely to where some uranium isotopes have half-lives on the order of 109 years, while other isotopes, particularly those

Table 5-12. Half-life (decay) of nuclear waste materials

Compound	Years
Americium-241	460
Americium-242	150
Cesium-135	2 million
Cesium-137	30
Curium-242	45
Curium-243	32
Iodine-129	160 million
Neptunium-237	2.1 million
Plutonium-239	24,000
Plutonium-241	13
Radon-226	1,600
Strontium-90	28
Technetium-99	200,000
Thorium-230	76,000
Tritium	13

which are man-made, may have half-lives of microseconds.

The decay follows a logarithmic pattern, as follow:

$$\ln = \frac{No}{N} = kt$$

where:
No   is   the starting sample (or the reference count taken after 60 seconds),

N   is   the amount of sample remaining at time t (or the number of counts in succeeding minutes).

k   is   the rate constant for the decay, which is a measure of the tendency of the atoms to decay spontaneously, and which is different for each isotope. So the solution of k allows identification.

Rearranging the above equation results in:

$$y = mx + b$$

which is the equation of a straight line in slope/intercept form.

A plot of the natural log of the counts per minute vs. time will thus give a line whose slope is -k. The intercept is a number we cannot measure since we have no way to obtain an instantaneous count at t=0.

The rate constant is related to the half-life, t1/2, by a simple expression:

$$t_{1/2} = \frac{0.6931}{k}$$

Radioactive Materials and Waste

The issue with transport and storage of used nuclear fuel (nuclear wastes) is second only to the risk of nuclear accidents. A lot of rules and regulations have been designed and implemented through the years to limit the risk of exposure to harmful nuclear radiation.

There are several systems of nomenclature in use, but the following is generally accepted:

Exempt waste is excluded from regulatory control because its radiological hazards are negligible.

Low-level waste (LLW) contains enough radioactive material to require action for the protection of people, but not so much that it requires shielding in handling or storage.

Intermediate-level waste (ILW) poses serious threat and requires appropriate shielding. If it has more than 4000 Bq/g of long-lived (over 30 year half-life) alpha emitters it is categorized as "long-lived" and requires more sophisticated handling and disposal.

High-level waste (HLW) is sufficiently radioactive to require both shielding and cooling, if it generates >2 kW/m^3 of heat and has a high level of long-lived alpha-emitting isotopes.

Environmental Impact of Nuclear Power

When the nuclear power plants start operation, we see the real pollution footprint. And this one is huge: the largest legal emission of pollutants in the world. Nuclear power used for electric power generation is a necessary evil. We cannot imagine our lives without electricity. It is part of the American dream. It is something we need and want, and something without which our lives would be quite hard.

On the other hand, there are a number of serious environmental effects ascribed to nuclear power. These occur throughout the entire life span of the power generation process, starting with the design and construction phases, and end with the plant decommissioning and waste disposal.

Nuclear Power Plant Construction, Carbon Footprint

A number of large and small pieces of equipment are used in the nuclear power plant design, construction, testing, operation, and decommissioning. Starting with the plant design and construction, the carbon footprint starts at a site location, where deep tracks in the ground and heavy plumes of smoke in the air from large trucks and bulldozers crawling all over the place can be seen day after day. And there are also trains and trucks used for transporting the equipment to the mine.

The list of equipment used during the construction, start-up and testing of a nuclear power station is long, so we will provide only the major pieces of equipment:

- VHL crane with 1200 ton capacity at a 130 foot radius and a height of 200 feet

- Pipe bending machines would be utilized by module and pipe spool fabricators and for support of plant construction activities.

- Different types of automatic welding machines would be utilized for welding large bore piping, containment liners, condenser tube sheets, and condenser shells.

- Automatic rebar assembly machines ABWR used to improve rebar fabrication productivity and reduce labor man-hours associated with fabricating rebar mats and wall panels. One automatic rebar assembly machine could be used at each construction site.

- Two or three 6.9kV switchgear panels

- Nine 480V motor control centers

- Four 125VDC uninterruptible power supply systems

- Three 120VAC uninterruptible power supply systems

- Three 5 MW emergency diesel generators, not required for passive safety designs

And, of course, there are a lot of materials used in the construction of a single nuclear reactor, with an estimate as follow:

• Concrete*	460,000	cu. yards
• Reinforcing steel and embedded parts	46,000	tons
• Structural steel, other steel and decking, 25,000 tons.		
• Large bore pipe, over 2½ inch	260,000	feet
• Small bore pipe, less than 2½"	430,000	feet
• Cable tray	220,000	feet
• Conduit	1,200,000	feet
• Power cable	1,400,000	feet
• Control wire	5,400,000	feet
• Process and instrumentation tubing	740,000	feet

*Note: This does not include concrete used for general site preparation.

And much more equipment and materials are needed for the construction of the other, more conventional, parts of the power plant—boilers, condensers, turbines, generators, water coolers, stacks, etc.

A lot of metals, plastics, wood, and other materials were used for manufacturing of this machinery, which was made somewhere on the planet some time in the past, where and when their manufacturing processes and transport created a significant pollution footprint. Since most of the construction equipment is used only temporarily, we can assign only a small part of the carbon footprint to the manufacturing and transport of the power equipment to the plant. (A)

Even before site preparation is complete, the main power equipment pieces arrive in wooden boxes, on back of large trailers, or railroad cars. These are assembled with the help of other pieces of large equipment (cranes etc.) and are put to work after creating another set of pollution problems. (B)

In addition, there are many other items and small pieces of equipment, tools and consumables—some for personal use, and some for specialized operations—that are needed for the construction and operation stages. These are computers, helmets, boots, goggles, shoes, first aid kits, and many other consumables. All these were also made somewhere around the world, sometime in the past, and transported to the power plant. During their manufacturing processes and transport they also left a significant pollution footprint. (C).

Then, to complete the pollution footprint picture, we must add to that the footprint of the people involved in the entire process—engineers and technicians involved in the equipment manufacturing, transport, installation, setup, and operation. These people drive cars, and ride on busses, trains and planes, all of which leave another significant set of pollution footprints, which otherwise would no be emitted. (D)

And so, the total pollution footprint of the power plant equipment cradle-to-grave process is expressed by:

$$Pf = A + B + C + D$$

where

Pf   is   the total pollution footprint from equipment manufacturing, transport, and maintenance

A   is   the equipment manufacturing and transport to the power plant

B   is   equipment assembly, test and installation at the plant

C   is   the manufacturing and transport to small tools and consumables

D   is   the pollution footprint of the equipment personnel during the design and setup phases

Combining the pollution footprint of A (plant equipment manufacturing and transport) with B (equipment assembly, test and installation), adding C (the manufacturing and transport of the tools and consumables), plus D (the pollution footprint of the equipment personnel) gives us the environmental footprint of the mining equipment before even starting the power plant operations.

And the pollution footprint is significant, to be sure! It goes deep and wide, stretching from one part of the world to the other. To put a value on it, we need to take inventory of all items delivered to the nuclear plant and needed for its design, construction, and operation. We need to take a close look at the manufacturing of the reactors, turbines, cooling systems, etc. that are components of a nuclear power plant.

These are some of the largest pieces of equipment in the world, and that it takes thousands of tons of metals to make them. Each of these started as an iron ore dug out from another mine somewhere in the world, which was transported to a smelter. The molten metal was shaped in different forms and shipped to the different parts manufacturers, who drilled, welded and otherwise constructed parts for these vehicles.

Remember that we are talking about huge pieces of metal—some as big as an entire building. A nuclear reactor is several stories high. After manufacturing, the different parts are packed and loaded on railroad cars or trucks to be shipped to the assembly facility. The major parts of a turbine or a furnace might require a dozen of railroad cars for transport.

The parts are assembled into major components, or entire units and after one more loading and unloading, they finally arrive at the power plant floor for final assembly and testing, before being put to work.

This is a long, windy process, with many stop and go, loading and unloading, and shipping steps.

Putting a dollar value, or a number in tons of hydrocarbons, would be too long and complex procedure for our purposes, so it suffices to say that the pollution effects during and after all these steps are significant.

Nuclear Power Plant Equipment Pollution

And now, we have started the power plant operations and see another set of pollution footprints. And again, they are significant. As an example, plant equipment uses a lot of electric power to run pumps, fans, and all control equipment. During an average workday and under a full load, these pieces of equipment will use several megawatts of power.

Using the generated power increases the overall environmental effect and carbon footprint.

And then, all equipment needs repairs and eventually replacement. Spare parts for the pieces of equipment in need of repair periodically arrive from different parts manufacturers, after leaving their pollution footprint on the way too. We will attempt to assign an accurate number—quantity of air and land pollution—and a related dollar numbers to these activities and their environmental effects in the following chapters.

And after 30-40 years of non-stop operation, the nuclear power plant is finally declared finished and is scheduled for a shut down and decommissioning. The plant decommissioning and land reclamation are major, expensive, and polluting undertakings. The equipment has to be disassembled and removed from the buildings, loaded on trucks or trains and transported to a recycling facility or a waste disposal site. In all cases, equipment and materials used during the decommissioning and waste disposal process create additional air and ground pollution, which is not to be ignored.

Additional, specialized equipment and personnel (environmental specialists and inspectors) are usually brought in to assist and/or coordinate the effort. And with that more pollution footprints are left at the plant site.

In most cases, additional pieces of equipment are brought in to mitigate and reconstruct the plant site to its original state. Another set of carbon and other pollution footprints are left behind when this process is completed.

When the final tally is made, a significant part of the emissions and overall pollution are to be attributed to the power plant equipment and support personnel. This number is significant and we will go through the calculations in the next chapters as well.

Nuclear Plant Operations

The average nuclear power plant operates 24/7, 365 days a year, except when shut down for periodic or preventative maintenance. Even when the plant is shut down for these procedures, it is fully staffed. Under normal load, an average nuclear power plant generates approximately 12.0 billion kWh of electricity annually.

The average non-fuel O&M cost for a nuclear power plant is estimated at one and a half cents/kWh, which means that over $140 million (or close to one fifth of the gross income) is spent on operations and maintenance by each plant every year. This is a major and expensive effort that has to be done right to ensure the efficiency and safety of the plant operations.

Maintenance

Proper periodic and preventive maintenance and surveillance programs, implemented periodically and/or daily, are critical to ensuring the efficient and safe operation of a nuclear power plant. What this means is, that in addition to the usual maintenance and safety steps taken at the other power plants, here a set of strict procedures is implemented to ensure the safety of key equipment, making sure that it will function when it is supposed to and how it is supposed to—including in emergency situations.

All moving parts and critical components, such as emergency generators, pumps, and manual and automatic valves are tested periodically, usually every couple of months. Experience counts in doing this job properly in this environment, so all plant personnel are trained and officially licensed to work with nuclear equipment.

The maintenance personnel go through craft-specific training as needed to qualify for performing the plant equipment maintenance. The training programs are certified and controlled by the accrediting board of the National Nuclear Training Academy.

Engineers at the power plant are responsible for the different systems at the plant, and are in charge of the operations and maintenance work, including the preventive maintenance, repairs, and modifications of the systems under their control. Engineers also undergo training programs that are certified and controlled by the accrediting board of the National Nuclear Training Academy.

Just like every experienced pilot pays close attention to every single noise and vibration coming from the engines or the frame of the plane, so are nuclear plant operators, technicians and engineers alert. They are well familiar with all the sounds and vibration of the equipment, and use a number of gauges and test equipment to pinpoint any abnormal sound or vibration that might indicate a problem or degradation. In any such case, immediate action is taken to correct the problem, or deficiency causing the problem.

If there is any hesitation or failure, during start-up or normal operations, even more immediate actions are taken, and in some cases the reactor, and/or the entire plant, are shut down. Even in case of not so serious problem, strict technical specifications require the plant to be shut down if the problem is not corrected within a certain period of time, depending on the safety level of the equipment.

At least every two years the power plant must be shut down 30-60 days for periodic maintenance. The work during this important time includes: removal of reactor head and the upper internals and refueling the reactor, if needed.

Preventive maintenance on equipment that runs continuously is done every 5 years. At that time, pumps, valves, transformers, turbine-generator set, and other key components are inspected and tested for proper operation. The equipment components that do not look, or operate, as required by the technical specifications are replaced. At that time modifications or replacement of the major equipment, such as a steam generator, is done as well.

Nuclear Fuels Transport

The International Atomic Energy Agency (IAEA) has established advisory regulations for the safe transport of radioactive material. These regulations are recognized throughout the world as the uniform basis for both national and international transport safety requirements in this area.

Requirements based on the IAEA regulations, and procedures for their execution, have been adopted in about 60 countries and a number of key international organizations and businesses.

Packaging

Most radioactive materials—including fresh uranium nuclear fuels—have low radioactive emission levels, so they require only simple protection during transport and storage. The nuclear waste materials, however, are hot, so the principal assurance of safety in their transport is the design of the packaging, which must allow for foreseeable accidents. In all cases, the consignor bears primary responsibility for this.

Many different nuclear materials are transported and the degree of potential hazard from these materials varies considerably. Different packaging standards have been developed according to the potential hazard posed by the material.

"Type A" packages are designed to withstand minor accidents and are used for medium-activity materials such as medical or industrial radioisotopes. Ordinary industrial containers are used for low-activity material such as U_3O_8.

Containers for high-level waste (HLW) and used fuel are robust and very secure and are known as "Type B" packages. They maintain shielding from gamma and neutron radiation, even under extreme conditions.

There are over 150 kinds of Type B packages, and the larger ones cost over $1.5 million each

In France alone, there are some 750 shipments each year of Type B packages. This is in relation to 15 million shipments classified as "dangerous goods", 300,000 of which are radioactive materials of some kind. Smaller amounts of high-activity materials (including plutonium) transported by aircraft will be in "Type C" packages, which give even greater protection in all respects than Type B packages in accident scenarios.

Radiation Protection

Transporting radioactive materials, including nuclear fuels, requires eliminating radiation exposure to those involved in the transport and the general public along transport routes. Packaging for radioactive materials includes, where appropriate, shielding to reduce potential radiation exposures. In the case of some materials, such as fresh uranium fuel assemblies, the radiation levels are negligible and no shielding is required.

Other materials, such as used fuel and high-level waste, are highly radioactive and purpose-designed containers with integral shielding are used. To limit the risk in handling of highly radioactive materials, dual-purpose containers (casks), which are appropriate for both storage and transport of used nuclear fuel, are often used.

As with other hazardous materials being transported, packages of radioactive materials are labeled in accordance with the requirements of national and international regulations. These labels not only indicate that the material is radioactive, by including a radiation symbol, but also give an indication of the radiation field in the vicinity of the package. Personnel directly involved in the transport of radioactive materials are trained to take appropriate precautions and to respond in case of an emergency.

Environmental Protection

Packages used for the transport of radioactive materials are designed to retain their integrity during the various conditions that may be encountered while they are being transported thus ensuring that an accident will not have any major consequences. Conditions which packages are tested to withstand include: fire, impact, wetting, pressure, heat, and cold. Packages of radioactive material are checked prior to shipping and, when it is found to be necessary, cleaned to remove contamination.

Although not required by transport regulations, the nuclear industry chooses to undertake some shipments of nuclear material using dedicated, purpose-built transport vehicles or vessels.

Transport and Storage Accidents

There are a lot of complex technologies, equipment sets, chemicals, and procedures involved in nuclear fuel and waste transport and storage. In every step of the way, there is a chance—albeit small—for something to go wrong. And when it does, very bad things happen.

A few incidents have occurred during transport and storage of nuclear materials. Some of the occurrences involve improper disposal of radioactive material, defective shielding during transport, or when materials were simply abandoned or even stolen from a waste storage site.

As with all hazardous materials, any impropriety has negative results, such as causing environmental contamination or hurting people. With nuclear materials, the dangers are multiplied many times. Radiation is a silent killer, which cannot be detected by exposed humans, that makes them vulnerable to its deadly action.

There are a number of examples of radiation gone astray.

In one such example in the Soviet Union, nuclear waste stored in Lake Karachay was blown over the area of the dried lake during a dust storm. At Maxey Flat, a low-level radioactive waste facility located in Kentucky, containment trenches covered with dirt, instead of steel or cement, collapsed under heavy rainfall into the trenches and filled with water. The water that invaded the trenches became radioactive and had to be disposed of.

In Italy, several radioactive waste deposits were allowed to flow into river water, thus contaminating water for domestic use. In France, in the summer of 2008, numerous incidents happened. At the Areva plant in Tricastin, liquid containing untreated uranium overflowed out of a faulty tank and about 75 kg of the radioactive material seeped into the ground during a routine draining operation. The radioactive waste then flowed into two rivers nearby, contaminating their waters.

In another case, over 100 people were contaminated with low doses of radiation during a similar routine operation. In other cases of radioactive waste accidents, lakes or ponds with radioactive waste accidentally overflowed into the rivers during heavy storms.

In December 2011 top government official of the Japanese government admitted that nuclear substances were found in the waste of Japanese nuclear facilities. Although Japan did commit itself in 1977 to these inspections in the safeguard agreement with the IAEA, the reports were kept secret from the inspectors of the International Atomic Energy Agency. Japan did start discussions with the IAEA about the large quantities of enriched uranium and plutonium that were discovered in nuclear waste cleared away by Japanese nuclear operators. And although most nuclear substances have been properly managed as waste, and from that perspective, there is no problem in managing safety, the violation is nevertheless still being investigated.

To this we can only add that if such things could happen in Japan (where such bad things are not tolerated usually), then they can happen anywhere.

The practice of scavenging of abandoned radioactive material, which is common in some parts of the world, has caused several cases of radiation exposure. This problem is most frequently found in developing nations, which have less regulation of dangerous substances, and where black markets for scavenged goods and scrap metal are flourishing.

The scavengers and those who buy the material are almost always unaware that the material is radioactive, and are only interested in its aesthetics or scrap value. This is also due to lack of responsibility and accountability on part of the radioactive material's owners, and the absence of regulation concerning radioactive waste. Lack of enforcement of such regulations has been significant factors in radiation exposures as well.

One incident of significant proportions happened in September 1987 at Goiânia, in the Brazilian state of Goiás. An old radiotherapy source, containing live nuclear materials, was stolen from a hospital disposal site. It was then put on the black market and handled by many people, four of which died soon thereafter. Over 110,000 people were tested for radioactive contamination, and 250 were found with significant levels of radioactivity.

An intensive cleanup operation forced removal of topsoil from several sites, and several houses were demolished in the process, and all objects from within those houses were removed and tested too. The International Atomic Energy Agency called this case "one of the world's worst radiological incidents."

Transportation accidents involving spent nuclear fuel from power plants are unlikely to have serious consequences due to the strength of the spent nuclear fuel shipping casks.

Case Study: The Hanford Nuclear Site

The Hanford Site is the best example of large-scale radioactive materials leakage. It is an old, mostly decommissioned, government nuclear production complex on the Columbia River in Washington state. It was established in 1943 as part of the Manhattan Project, and is where the first full-scale plutonium production reactor in the world was built. Plutonium manufactured at the site was used in the first nuclear bomb, tested at the Trinity site, and in Fat Man, the bomb detonated over Nagasaki, Japan.

There were nine nuclear reactors and five large plutonium-processing complexes at the site, which produced plutonium for most of the 60,000 weapons in the U.S. nuclear arsenal. The biggest problem is that the scientists, who are credited with a number of achievements, simply did not pay much attention to the safety procedures and waste disposal practices. It is now a known fact that the Hanford's operations released significant amounts of radioactive materials into the air and into the waters of Columbia River, which threatened the health of residents and damaged ecosystems.

A huge volume of water from the Columbia River was used to cool the nuclear reactors. The water was treated chemically for use by the reactors and was then returned back into the river. The used water was stored in large tanks for up to six hours for cooling and as an anti-radiation measure. Long-lived isotopes, however, were not affected by this retention, and several terabecquerels of radiation and numerous chemicals from the pre-cooling treatment were injected into the river every day. The unsuspecting locals were kept in the dark by the federal government. Only much later there was data released of high radiation levels measured downstream as far west as the Washington and Oregon coasts.

Today the Hanford still holds 53 million gallons of high-level radioactive waste. It is stored in 177 underground tanks, spread around the site. Some of these tanks are leaking radioactive and chemically polluted water waste into the soil and groundwater. Most of the liquid waste has been transferred to more secure double-shelled tanks, but nearly 3 million gallons of that waste, in addition to 27 million gallons of salt cake and sludge, remain in the old, single-shell water tanks. There are also additional 25 million cubic feet of solid radioactive waste on site. All this waste was scheduled to be removed and disposed of (or properly stored in long term repositories) by 2018, but the date was changed to 2040.

There are estimated 270 billion gallons of contaminated groundwater in the area as a result of the leaks, and one million gallons of highly radioactive waste is traveling through the groundwater table toward the Columbia River. It is expected to enter the river during the next 20-30 years, if not stopped before that.

There have been 685,000 curies of radioactive iodine-131 released into the nearby river waters and air from the Hanford site between 1944 and 1947. Clean up costs are estimated at $2 billion a year.

In summary, the great potential and convenience of using nuclear power cannot be ignored, and the genie should not be put back in the bottle. It, however, should be given the due respect, which requires deeper understanding. We also cannot and should not ignore the environmental effects of nuclear power, when calculating the risks in using it. The risks can be reduced with improving the nuclear materials and technologies and enforcing stricter process controls.

Nuclear Waste Storage

During fission, neutron absorbers, called neutron poisons, build up slowly to a level where they absorb so many neutrons that the chain reaction stops, even with the control rods completely removed. This process is similar to taking a very long shower until all hot water is used. Even when the shower handle is turned to the maximum hot water lever, the water comes out cold and gets colder with time.

This is the point when the fuel has to be replaced with fresh fuel, even though there is still a substantial quantity of uranium-235 and plutonium present in the rods.

The spent fuel can be reprocessed, but that involves handling highly radioactive materials, since the fission products removed from the fuel are a concentrated form of high-level waste, as are the chemicals used in the process.

Most of the spent nuclear fuel today is stored in on-site fuel storage areas, which has become a monumental task involving extensive data collection and processing activities, accompanied by protests by environmentalists and the constant threat of terrorism and undercapacity.

On-site Storage

Radioactive waste is hazardous to most forms of life and the harmful to the environment, Because of that, it is strictly regulated by government agencies. Radioactivity diminishes over time, so waste is typically isolated and stored for a period of time until it no longer poses a hazard.

The period of time depends on the type of waste. Low-level waste that with low levels of radioactivity per mass or volume, such as some of the common medical or industrial radioactive wastes, may need to be stored only a few hours or days. High-level wastes, such as spent nuclear fuel or by-products of nuclear reprocessing, however, must be stored for years at a time.

Upon removal from the reactor, the nuclear fuel is stored either, a) in water pools, or b) is loaded in special containers and stored in dry storage at the power plant, or is transported to a remote location.

Spent fuel pools (SFP) are most frequently used for short-term storage of used nuclear fuel. These are actually pools of water, typically 40 or more feet deep, with the bottom 14 feet equipped with storage racks designed to hold fuel assemblies after removal from the reactor. Each pool is specially designed for the type of reactor and fuel rods to be stored in it. The water both cools the fuel rods and provides shielding from radiation emitted from them.

In many countries, the fuel assemblies stay in the reactor for 3 to 6 years, after which they are stored underwater in the on-site SFP for 10 to 20 years before being sent for reprocessing or to dry cask storage. While only about 8 feet of water is needed to keep radiation levels below acceptable levels, the extra depth provides a safety margin and allows fuel assemblies to be manipulated without special shielding to protect the operators.

The Nuclear Regulatory Commission estimates that many of the nuclear power plants in the United States will be out of room in their spent fuel pools by 2015, most likely requiring the use of additional temporary storage of some kind.

Case Study

Most of the world's used nuclear fuel is stored in on-site water pools. While there are few accidents involving water storage, an incident causing a prolonged interruption of cooling due to emergency situations, the water in the spent fuel pools may boil off, resulting in large amounts of radioactive elements being released into the atmosphere.

During the Fukushima nuclear plant disaster in March 2011, one of the spent fuel pools lost its roof and was reported to be emitting steam. Spent fuel pools at Fukushima were not equipped with backup water-circulation systems or backup generators for ensuring water circulation during emergencies. It was later on assumed that the pool had boiled over and dried up.

If the pool dried up and the rods were exposed, they would reach criticality, setting off a nuclear chain reaction and not an explosion. The chances of criticality in a spent fuel pool are very small, and usually avoided by the dispersal of the fuel assemblies. Other methods, such as inclusion of a neutron absorber in the storage racks can help to control the reaction, which is not difficult, because spent fuel has a low enrichment level and cannot self-sustain a fission reaction.

Spent fuel pools lack the "four-ft.-thick concrete cocoons" typical for operating reactors in nuclear plants, but are instead housed in conventional buildings that are susceptible to aircraft strikes, explosives, and natural disasters, as was the case with Fukushima.

Successful terrorist attacks on spent fuel pools are possible, and if it leads to a propagating zirconium cladding fire, it could result in the release of large amounts of radioactive material.

In 1997, the Brookhaven National Laboratory estimated that a massive calamity at one spent-fuel pool could ultimately lead to 138,000 deaths and contaminate 2,000 square miles of land.

Dry spent fuel storage, or *dry cask storage*, is used to store high-level radioactive waste, such as spent nuclear fuel that has already been cooled in the spent fuel pool for at least one year. The casks are steel cylinders that are either welded or bolted closed.

The cask is usually filled with inert gas to protect the fuel rods from corrosion. The steel cylinder provides leak-tight containment of the gas and the fuel inside. Additional steel, concrete, or other material to provide additional radiation shielding to workers and the public envelops each cylinder.

Some cask designs can be used for both storage and transportation, and various other dry storage cask system designs exist. Some are designed for vertical and others horizontal placement in the storage bins. The concrete vaults provide the best and most permanent radiation shielding.

Some casks are designed for vertical placement on a concrete pad at a dry cask storage site. These use both metal and concrete outer cylinders for radiation shielding.

Currently there is no long term permanent storage facility anywhere in the world, so dry cask storage is designed as an interim safer solution for freeing the spent fuel water pool storage, and until a better solution is found for permanent storage.

Basically speaking, the short-lived wastes with low-to-medium radiation levels are stored in near-surface disposal areas, while high-level wastes are preferably deposited in deep burial or transmutation sites.

In the United States, the used fuel is usually stored (on-site or in permanent storage), while in Russia, the United Kingdom, France, Japan and India, the fuel is most often reprocessed to remove the fission products, and the fuel can then be re-used. Most countries reprocess the fuel carrying out single plutonium cycles, while India is planning multiple recycling schemes.

Long-term Storage

Long-term and permanent storage are a key problem for the nuclear industry. "Gorleben" is a German built national deep geological repository for radioactive waste and interim storage. The waste from Germany's nuclear power plants is reprocessed in France, and the unusable remains are sent back to Germany in spent nuclear fuel shipping casks for final storage at Gorleben.

In the woods around two kilometers to the southwest of Gorleben there are now four different large units: an interim storage unit for dry cask storage, a storage unit for hot radioactive waste, a conditioning plant, and a pilot plant in a salt dome.

The surrounding air in dry casks, standing in a hall above ground, cools the nuclear waste and vitrified waste block containers. Permission has been granted to store 420 dry casks on the site. At approximately 20 tons of nuclear waste per cask, this represents about 8,400 tons of waste fuel to be stored at the site.

In the Gorleben waste dump (Abfalllager Gorleben), hot nuclear waste, mostly from German power plants, is stored in the short term too.

Originally, more such projects were planned by the nuclear energy industry, for example a reprocessing plant for nuclear fuel at Dragahn, to the west of Dannenberg, and a nuclear power station at Langendorf by the Elbe. However, both plans were rejected as impractical to carry out and abandoned forever.

In the U.S., we have our own Gorleben permanent storage plant, which was abandoned, when the Yucca mountain depository was canned due to a number of reasons. After spending a decade of intense work, and over $6 billion tax payers money, digging a large hole in the mountain, in 2012 the entrance was locked up and the key was thrown away for good. The U.S. has no long term nuclear waste storage plans at the present.

Nuclear Fuel Reprocessing

After nuclear fuel is loaded in the reactors and is used for 12-18 months, it loses its efficiency and has to be replaced. The old fuel rods are removed, and a new batch is installed in the reactors. The used fuel is usually sunk in the water storage pools for cooling for long while, after which it is packed in storage casks and placed in long-term dry storage.

Lately, however, several nations have started to reprocess the spent fuel in an attempt to reuse it, instead of dumping it in the storage sites. Nuclear reprocessing technology has been sufficiently developed to chemically separate and recover fissionable plutonium from spent nuclear fuel.

The current standard reprocessing method, is PUREX (Plutonium and Uranium Recovery by EXtraction.) The PUREX process is a liquid-liquid extraction method used to reprocess spent nuclear fuel. It is the most developed and widely used process in the industry presently. The goal here is to extract uranium and plutonium, independent of each other, from the fission products.

The PUREX process is a straightforward chemical reaction, where the spent irradiated fuel is dissolved in nitric acid, and the insoluble solids are filtered out. An organic solvent, such as tributyl phosphate (TBP) in a kerosene solution is added to extract the uranium as $UO_2 (NO3)2 \cdot 2TBP$ complex. The uranium is stripped from the kerosene solution by back-extraction into nitric acid, from where it can be easily recovered.

The plutonium and the transuranium elements americium and curium remain in the aqueous phase. Treating the kerosene solution with aqueous ferrous sulphamate, which selectively reduces the plutonium to its +3 oxidation state, separates plutonium. The plutonium passes into the aqueous phase.

Note: The PUREX process produces large volumes of liquid wastes, which if not handled properly result in radioactive contamination of groundwater, such as the case at the Hanford site, discussed below. There have been 685,000 curies (25.3 PBq) of radioactive iodine-131 released into the nearby river waters and air from the Hanford site between 1944 and 1947. Clean up costs are estimated at $2 billion a year.

Plutonium extracted from commercial power reactors typically contains a lot of weapons grade Pu-240, so it is useful in making nuclear weapons. The chemicals used in the PUREX process, however, are strictly monitored, so this is not easily done, which reduced the threat of terrorism and other unwanted incidents.

There are also a number of modified PUREX processes, such as UREX (URanium EXtraction) process, which is used to save space inside high-level nuclear waste disposal sites. Here, the uranium which makes up the vast majority of the mass and volume of used fuel is removed and recycled as reprocessed uranium.

Reprocessing can be used to extract plutonium from the spent fuel, to produce nuclear weapons. A better use of reprocessed plutonium is to recycle it back into MOX nuclear fuel for thermal reactors.

Reprocessed uranium is the bulk of the spent fuel

material, which can be reused as fuel, but at a high cost, so this option is economically feasible only when uranium prices are high.

In addition to recycled plutonium and uranium from spent fuel, a breeder reactor can use all the actinides, thus closing the nuclear fuel cycle. This can eventually lead to multiplying the energy extracted from a natural uranium fuel source by over 60 times.

Reprocessing of spent nuclear fuels also, and very importantly so, reduces the volume of high-level waste. This, however, does not by itself reduce the final radioactivity or heat generation, so a geological waste repository is still needed. So, the challenges of waste repository site location and cost apply here too.

Reprocessing is also politically controversial, because of the potential to contribute to nuclear proliferation, and increased vulnerability to nuclear terrorism. The high cost of reprocessing, as compared to the once-through fuel cycle forced the Obama administration to step back from President Bush's plans for commercial-scale reprocessing. Instead, we now have a program focused on scientific research, instead of commercial reprocessing. At this time, commercial nuclear fuel reprocessing is performed routinely in France, Russia, Japan, and India.

The Global Nuclear Energy Partnership is a U.S. plan to form an international partnership to see spent nuclear fuel reprocessed in a way that renders the plutonium in it usable for nuclear fuel but not for nuclear weapons. Reprocessing of spent commercial-reactor nuclear fuel has not been permitted in the United States due to nonproliferation considerations. All of the other reprocessing nations have long had nuclear weapons from military-focused research-reactor fuels except for Japan.

The potentially useful components dealt with in nuclear reprocessing comprise specific actinides (plutonium, uranium, and some minor actinides). The lighter elements components include fission products, activation products, and cladding.

Nuclear Plants Decommissioning

There are 104 nuclear power plants in the U.S., which were designed for 30-40 years operation. The oldest US plant is 42 years old, with the average age of the U.S. fleet at 31 years. In the 1990s 12 plants were closed down for economic reasons. Most of the remaining plants are now close to, or past the age limit, so there are plans to extend the lives of 71 nuclear reactors by an extra 20 years with the option of further future extensions.

73 plants marked dark grey have received license

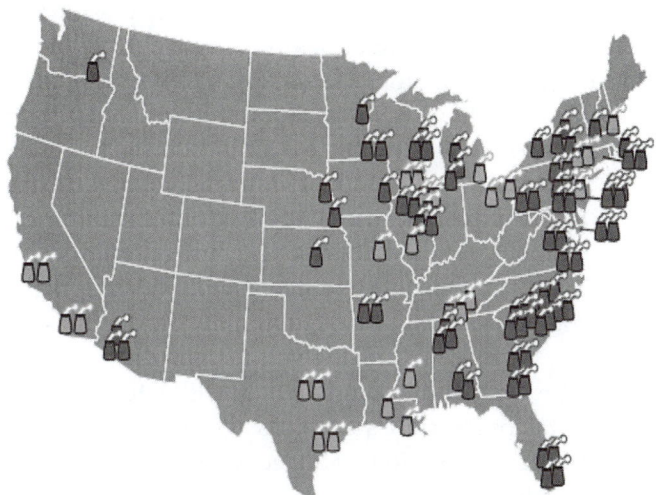

Figure 5-31. The U.S. nuclear power plants

extensions for additional 20 years.

31 plants marked with light grey are operating under the original 40-year licenses, and will apply for, or are in the process of applying, for extension.

In all cases, nuclear plants past the age limit will have to invest in extended operation modifications and refurbishment work, at a costs of about \$750/kW. In many cases this boils down to spending up to \$1 billion per plant to meet the 20 year license extension requirements. The refurbishment of some plants will cost much more than that, with some estimates going up to \$3.5 billion per plant for just extending its life by 20 years.

It seems that building a new plant might be easier and cheaper… Nevertheless, this is only one of the complexities of the nuclear power generation. The most urgent problems are these related to a number of environmental and safety concerns.

Abandoned Mines Cleanup

Abandoned uranium mines are causing a lot of problems in some areas of the world, including the U.S. Despite efforts made in cleaning up uranium sites, mines in the Navajo nation and in the states of Utah, Colorado, New Mexico, and Arizona are still contaminated. Hundreds of these abandoned mines have not been cleaned up, and present environmental and health risks in many, mostly already disadvantaged, communities.

In 1978, Congress passed the Uranium Mill Tailings Radiation Control Act, which was designed to assist in the cleanup of 22 inactive ore-processing sites throughout the southwest. This also included constructing 19 disposal sites for the tailings, which contain a total of 40 million cubic yards of low-level radioactive material. The Environmental Protection Agency estimates that there are 4000 mines with documented uranium production, and another 15,000 locations with uranium occurrences in 14 western states, most found in the Four Corners area, NM, and Wyoming.

The Uranium Mill Tailings Radiation Control Act amended the Atomic Energy Act of 1954 and gave the Environmental Protection Agency the authority to establish health and environmental standards for the stabilization, restoration, and disposal of uranium mill waste.

Title 1 of the Act required the EPA to set environmental protection standards consistent with the Resource Conservation and Recovery Act, including groundwater protection limits; the Department of Energy to implement EPA standards and provide perpetual care for some sites, and the Nuclear Regulatory Commission to review cleanups and license sites to states or the DOE for perpetual care.

Title 1 established a uranium mill remedial action program jointly funded by the federal government and the state. Title 1 of the Act also designated 22 inactive uranium mill sites for remediation, resulting in the containment of 40 million cubic yards of low-level radioactive material in UMTRCA Title 1 holding cells.

In 2007, the U.S. House Committee on Oversight and Government Reform in consultation with the Navajo nation, the Environmental Protection Agency (EPA), and other governing bodies developed a coordinated Five-Year Plan to address uranium contamination. Such interagency coordination efforts are beginning in the state of New Mexico as well.

Author's note: Geological surveys and studies of uranium mines decommissioning and restoration in Texas, for example, found that not even one single site has been completely restored to pre-mining levels. It was also officially documented that the majority of the closed mining sites had elevated uranium, even after the restoration was "completed."

NRC reviews concluded that each of the 11 sites at three abandoned mines certified by the agency as "restored" had at least one important pollutant above baseline levels, as recorded before mining began. The conclusion was that restoring water to baseline levels was not attainable for many of the most important contaminants, including uranium.

Some regulators and mining industry executives call attempts to fully restore aquifers at uranium sites idealistic. The usual excuse is that the water was contaminated with uranium before mining began, even though the records tell a different story. Yes, we believe that the best, if not only way to resolve this is for the responsible EPA officials and proponents of uranium mining and their families, to move into residences near the contaminated areas. This is the only way, to find out if the ground water is safe to use for human consumption. Fair is fair.

Nuclear Power Plant Environmental and Safety Concerns

Starting with giving proper credit, the contribution of nuclear power plants in supplying efficiently and cheaply huge amounts of electric power is undeniable. It is also undeniable that the nuclear power industry prevents over two billion metric tons of CO_2 per year to be generated by fossil fuels. This is in addition to preventing millions of tons of ash and suds, generated by fossil-fired power plants, from being deposited in the landfills.

Amazingly, according to the specialists, a properly designed and efficient nuclear power plant releases less radioactivity into the atmosphere than a coal-fired power plant. The land contamination on the nuclear power plants' sites and beyond is significantly reduced, as compared with the fossil fueled operations, as well.

But the negative aspects of nuclear power generation cannot be ignored either:

- Starting with mining and purifying of uranium ore, we see the dirtiest and most dangerous processes on Earth. Here thousands of people are sickened and die from mining activities and radiation.

- Transporting uranium ores and nuclear fuel to and from the mines and power plants poses a serious contamination risk to humans as well.

- Waste nuclear fuel can't be thrown in the city dump, since it is still radioactive and potentially deadly, and stays that way for centuries. An average nuclear power plant generates over 20 metric tons of used nuclear fuel annually, most of which is classified as high-level radioactive waste. Globally, this is roughly 2,000 metric tons a year of solid waste that emits high dozes of radiation and heat. This active material corrodes the containers it is enclosed in and in all its forms it is lethal to life forms that happen to be nearby.

- Nuclear power plants also produce large amounts of low-level radioactive waste in the form of radiated parts, equipment, and water. Even this low-level radioactive waste is dangerous and requires special containers, storage and disposal.

- Currently, the nuclear industry lets nuclear waste cool for years before mixing it with glass and storing it in massive cooled, concrete structures. This waste has to be maintained, monitored and guarded to prevent the materials from falling into the wrong hands. All of these services and added materials cost money, on top of the high costs required to build a plant and the associated risks of accidents.

Nuclear Plants Safety

But the worst of all, when talking about nuclear power, is the constant treat of nuclear accidents. Just mentioning Chernobyl or Fukushima evokes memories of massive destruction, death and suffering. Nuclear reactions are very delicate from engineering and process points of view, and require extremely high level of accuracy and precision. Large scale nuclear reactions, like these in large nuclear power plants, are some of the most complex, delicate, and at the same time most dangerous operations on Earth.

Running a nuclear plant is like walking a tightrope. One is in full control when able to keep balance on the tightrope high up in the air. As soon as balance is lost, however, the event is totally out of control and all of a sudden—at a blink of an eye—it becomes a complete and irreversible disaster.

And while the tightrope walker can end up with a broken limb, a nuclear plant disaster can devastate an entire area, or a nation, and brings fear to the entire world. How big is the risk? Is it worth it? Are there better ways? These are the questions before the global nuclear industry and us presently. Walking the nuclear tightrope might be exciting, fun and profitable, but what if and when…?

And unfortunately the uncertain condition will be with us for the foreseeable future, which in turn is putting the nuclear industry in an awkward position. It is the giant that can protect our society from collapse due to lack of energy when the fossils are gone, but at the same time this giant can kill many of us (if not all of us) if we are not diligent and careful enough. So we just need to find the balance, and that is the intent of this book. Getting familiar with the issues is the first step toward an intelligent and efficient approach in solving the issues at hand.

The Environmental Issues

Nuclear power, like all power generating options, has an impact on the environment, some of which is quite negative. It all starts at the uranium mine.

The environmental issues with both leaching methods are much more serious than any of the other types, because of the imminent danger of ground contamination due to leaks, or breaks. Because of that, the location has to be self-contained in such a way that it does not contaminate the soil and the water table. The ore body also needs to be permeable enough so that the acids can penetrate and dissolve the uranium.

The environmental laws today also require strict monitoring of the surrounding ground water for possible contamination. The monitoring usually continues for many months and even years after the mine has been shut down too.

In the recent past, mining companies used to abandon mines, due to bankruptcy or other reasons, thus leaving the responsibility of mine reclamation to the government. Today, however, the mining laws require that companies set aside money for reclamation during the planning stages of, and well before starting, the uranium mine. The money is held as insurance towards enforcing the environmental requirements, should the company abandon the mine and/or go bankrupt.

Health Risks of Uranium Mining

Like all surface or underground mining, mining ores of any type is a complex, dirty, and dangerous operation. Mining uranium ore is exceptionally dangerous because of the added danger of high-level radiation, which is extremely harmful to all living matter.

Biological Damage

Different types of radiation cause different damages to living cell. For low levels of radiation exposure, the biological effects are so small they may not be detected. And as a matter of fact, we are exposed daily to these extremely low dozes that come from different sources.

Fortunately, our body has repair mechanisms against damage induced by radiation as well as by chemical carcinogens. Nevertheless, as the dosage increases, damage would imminently occur. At that point the biological effects of radiation on living cells may result in three outcomes:

1. Injured or damaged cells that repair themselves, resulting in no residual damage

2. Cells die, much like millions of body cells do every day, but are then being replaced through normal biological processes

3. Cells do not (or incorrectly) repair themselves, thus resulting in some sort of a biophysical change

The radiation exposure in the U.S. comes primarily from medical products and procedures. It represents almost 50% of all radiation exposure cases in the country. The rest of the exposure rates are attributed to a number of natural causes, such as radiation from space, from the soil, and consumer products. Only one-tenth of one percent of the documented radiation problems are related to industrial and occupational incidents.

Radiation exposure and the development of cancer are related to populations exposed to relatively high levels of ionizing radiation (e.g., Japanese atomic bomb survivors, the Chernobyl accident victims, and recipients of selected diagnostic or therapeutic medical procedures).

Cancers caused by high-dose exposure to radiation (greater than 50,000 memo) include leukemia, breast, bladder, colon, liver, lung, esophagus, ovarian, multiple myeloma, and stomach cancers. There is also a possible association between ionizing radiation exposure and prostate, nasal cavity/sinuses, pharyngeal and laryngeal, and pancreatic cancer.

The timely detection of radiation caused cancers depends mostly on the type and level of radiation. It has a latent period, which can vary from several months to many years. Radiation exposure caused cancers cannot be distinguished from any natural cancers, or these resulting from of exposure to other carcinogens.

Exposure to radiation surely causes cancers, but there are no data to verify the threshold of occurrence of cancer following exposure to low doses, especially these below 10,000 mrem (100 mSv). Nevertheless, any amount of radiation may pose some risk for causing cancer to different people, and the risk is higher with higher radiation exposures.

The essential difference here is that high radiation doses destroy living cells, while low doses tend to only damage or alter the genetic code (DNA) of irradiated cells. When many cells are killed the tissues and organs are damaged immediately and permanently. The effect is similar to that of flesh burnt by fire, or chemical attack. If the radiation level is high enough, the body response is Acute Radiation Syndrome, which has a high probability of death.

This syndrome was observed in many atomic bomb survivors in 1945 and emergency workers responding to the 1986 Chernobyl nuclear power plant accident. Approximately 134 plant workers and firefighters battling the fire at the Chernobyl power plant received high radiation doses, between 80,000 and 1,600,000 mrem (800 to 16,000 mSv) and suffered from acute radiation sickness. Of the seriously affected 28 died within the first three

months from their radiation injuries. Two people died during the first days as a result of combined injuries from the fire and radiation.

It is estimated that 50% of a population would die within thirty days after receiving a high dose of between 350,000 to 500,000 mrem (3500 to 5000 mSv) to the whole body, over a period ranging from a few minutes to a few hours, depending on the health of the individuals before the exposure and the medical care received after the exposure. Similar exposure of only parts of the body will likely lead to more localized effects, such as skin burns.

Low radiation doses of less than 10,000 mrem (100 mSv) but spread out over long periods of time (months and years) don't cause an immediate problem to any body organ. Eventually, however, low doses of radiation would occur at the cell level, but the changes may not be observed for up to 20 years after exposure.

The chance of getting cancer after low-to-medium level radiation exposure is about five times greater than a natural genetic effect.

The amount of radiation that can be emitted by an U.S. nuclear power plant is strictly regulated, although there is no relation between populations living near nuclear facilities and increased risk of death from cancer. Nevertheless, the risk of a nuclear accident cannot, and should not, be ignored or belittled. We know well now, after seeing the devastation caused by nuclear incidents, that nuclear plants are sleeping giants that willingly supply us with bountiful amount of energy…BUT watch out if and when the giant is awaken from his slumber and decides to play havoc on its neighbors.

When that happens, there is no going back. At that point the nuclear plant becomes a weapon of mass destruction that does not obey rhyme or reason. The sleeping giant will not pick and chose, but will kill everybody and everything hundreds and thousands of miles around it. It is an unstoppable, ominous, deadly menace, which we must understand well, and respect profoundly, while trying to figure out a better way to control it. We must do this if we are to live and survive a long-term cohabitation, which (the survival and cohabitation) is essential to our future wellbeing.

Human Exposure

Humans get exposed to uranium (or its radioactive isotopes) by inhaling dust in the air or by ingesting contaminated water and food. The amount of uranium in the air is usually very small; however, people who work in factories that process different chemicals, such as phosphate fertilizers, or live near facilities that deal with nuclear power or weapons, could be affected. Living near, or working in, a coal-fired power plant, facilities that mine or process uranium ore, or enrich uranium for reactor fuel, could also present increased exposure to uranium radiation. People living or working in buildings constructed over natural or man-made uranium deposits may have an increased incidence of exposure to radon gas.

Most ingested uranium is excreted after digestion. Only one-half of one percent is absorbed when insoluble forms of uranium, such as its oxide, are ingested, whereas absorption of the more soluble uranyl ion can be up to five percent. However, soluble uranium compounds tend to quickly pass through the body whereas insoluble uranium compounds, especially when inhaled by way of dust into the lungs, pose a more serious exposure hazard.

After entering the bloodstream, the absorbed uranium tends to bio accumulate and stay for many years in bone tissue because of uranium's affinity for phosphates. Uranium is not absorbed through the skin, and alpha particles released by uranium cannot penetrate the skin.

Incorporated uranium becomes uranyl ions, which accumulate in bone, liver, kidney, and reproductive tissues. Uranium can be decontaminated from steel surfaces and aquifers.

Lung Cancer

Uranium ore emits radon gas, high exposure to which is a major problem in the uranium mines. Significant increase in lung cancer deaths has been identified in epidemiological studies of uranium miners. Many of these have been attributed to exposure to radon.

Radon is a product of the radioactive decay of uranium so underground uranium mines usually have very high concentrations of radon. Uranium miners exposed to 50 to 150 picocuries of radon per liter of air (2000–6000 Bq/m^3) for about 10 years have shown an increased frequency of lung cancer.

Statistically significant excesses in lung cancer deaths were present after cumulative exposures of less than 50 WLM. Many uranium miners in the Four Corners region contracted lung cancer and other pathologies as a result of high levels of exposure to radon in the mid-1950s.

The increased incidence of lung cancer was particularly pronounced in Native American and Mormon miners, because those groups normally have low rates of lung cancer. Safety standards requiring expensive ventilation were not widely implemented or policed during this period.

Recently, ventilation and other safety measures have been implemented in an attempt to reduce radon levels in affected uranium mines in operation. The measures have been effective enough so that the average annual exposure of uranium miners has fallen to levels similar to the concentrations inhaled in average homes.

This has reduced the risk of occupationally induced cancer from radon, although it still remains an issue both for those who are currently employed in affected mines and for those who have been employed in the past. In any case, the risk of exposure of miners nowadays is much smaller than in the early years of mining.

Toxicity

Normal functioning of the kidney, brain, liver, heart, and other human organs can be affected by uranium exposure, because, besides being radioactive, uranium is a toxic metal. It can also cause damages to the human reproductive systems. Radiological effects are generally local because alpha radiation, the primary form of 238U decay, has a very short range, and does not penetrate skin.

Uranyl (UO+2) ions, such as from uranium trioxide or uranyl nitrate, as well as other hexavalent uranium compounds, have been shown to cause birth defects and immune system damage in laboratory animals. Although there are published studies claiming that no human cancer has been seen as a result of exposure to natural or depleted uranium, exposure to uranium and its decay products, especially radon, are widely known and are considered significant health threats to all people and living forms involved.

Exposure to strontium-90, iodine-131, and other fission products is unrelated to uranium exposure, but may result from medical procedures or exposure to spent reactor fuel or fallout from nuclear weapons. Although accidental inhalation exposure to a high concentration of uranium hexafluoride has resulted in human fatalities, those deaths were associated with generation of highly toxic hydrofluoric acid and uranyl fluoride rather than with uranium itself.

Fine uranium metal grains (powder) are also a fire hazard because uranium is pyrophoric. Uranium powder will ignite spontaneously in air at room temperature. Uranium metal is commonly handled with gloves as a sufficient precaution, and is usually contained in closed vessels so it does not present any danger, if the safety measures are followed, and people do not inhale or ingest it.

Uranium Mining Contamination

Uranium mining has changed with time. Today it is very likely to see thousands of small black boxes spread over large areas. Each box is an injection site, where a mixture of chemicals is pumped into the ground to dissolve the uranium ore, separate out the uranium, and then suck it back out to be refined for nuclear fuel.

"Caution. Radioactive Materials" signs can be seen at the entrance gates.

Instead of digging large holes in the ground, as the conventional mining process requires, operators inject a mixture of sodium bicarbonate, hydrogen peroxide and oxygen into the rock deep below ground to separate out the minerals and bond to the uranium. Then, they vacuum out the uranium-laden fluids to make a fine powder called yellowcake. The process leaves a toxic mix of heavy metals and radioactive ions floating in the groundwater and generates millions of gallons of waste that need to be dumped deeper underground.

The federal Safe Drinking Water Act, implemented in the early 1980s, prohibited disposal of waste in aquifers, but the law allowed regulators to exempt aquifers if they determined that water was too dirty to use, or buried too deep to be worth pumping to the surface, or unlikely to be needed.

Twenty-five years ago, the EPA, state officials, and the energy industry agreed that polluting the water beneath some of the uranium mining sites was an acceptable price for producing cheap nuclear energy. The Safe Drinking Water Act forbids injecting industrial waste into or above drinking water aquifers, but the EPA issued what are called aquifer exemptions that gave mine operators at the ranch permission to ignore the law.

Since then EPA has issued more than 1,500 such exemptions nationwide, allowing energy and mining companies to pollute portions of nearly 100 drinking water aquifers. At the time when EPA granted these exemptions, the scientists believed that the underlying reservoirs were too deep to be used for drinking water, and that even if they did, no one was likely to use it. There was also an assumption that the mine operators would be responsible enough to contain the pollution in the shallower rock layers and remediate the damages when the mine closes down.

Fast forward three decades, and now science progress, changing climate, and deteriorating financial situation are also changing the assumptions. A severe drought across the U.S. West has made water more precious, and in addition, new technologies have made it economically viable to retrieve from great depths, where they find serious water contamination, radioactive

chemicals, no less.

So, there is a serious contamination issue that not only is not going away, but also is growing larger as this type of mining is expanding. Wyoming is one of the locations of such uranium mines, where a few people are affected, at least for now. The mines and the locals are stuck in the middle of a conflict between state and federal regulators whether to allow more uranium mining—and accept the damage that comes with it—or not.

The EPA is stuck between a rock and a hard place. If they allow mining, it could damage the water table, but rejecting it means jobs losses and economic damage, not to mention the potential political and legal repercussions from the state and the energy industry. So the EPA is vacillating over what to do.

This is bringing into the open the dilemma to choose between cheap domestic energy now vs. the need to protect water resources for the future. The outcome could set a precedent for similar battles sparked by the resurgence of uranium mining in Texas, South Dakota, Arizona, New Mexico and many other states.

With time, Federal regulators have also become less certain that it is possible to clean up contamination from uranium mining. At many locations removing radioactive pollutants from drinking water aquifers have failed and so on a number of occasions uranium and its byproducts have migrated beyond the containment zones.

And there are other consequences with this type of mining. While the process water is supposed to be filtered and re-injected, millions of gallons are usually removed and disposed of permanently. Million after million makes many millions of gallons, and as a consequence, sooner or later, the ground water table would drop—100 feet and more, in some cases.

In some cases wells that had routinely produced ten gallons a minute, or more, are presently struggling to produce a quart, in some places by 100 feet.

So the locals are also stuck between a choice of high water table with polluted water, and low levels of ground water that are also polluted. What a choice!

With uranium mining booming, the EPA receives a large number of requests for aquifer exemptions. So far, EPA records show, the agency has issued at least 40 exemptions for uranium mines across the country and is considering several more.

In Texas, proposals for new uranium mines have triggered bitter fights between state officials and the EPA. In 2010, Texas regulators gave a mining company preliminary permission to pollute a shallow aquifer, in an area from which 50 homes draw water from wells near the contamination zone. EPA scientists were concerned by the mining area's proximity to homes and believed that the natural flow of water would send contaminants toward their water wells.

At first, the agency notified Texas officials that it would deny an exemption for the mine unless the state did further monitoring and analysis. Texas regulators refused, stating that, "It appears the EPA may be swayed by the unsubstantiated allegations and fears of uranium mining opponents," according to the Texas Commission on Environmental Quality.

The scary part here is that the Commission on Environmental Quality is supposed to defend the environment and the affected people. Instead, as it appears to be the case here, such commissions are tools in the hands of the energy industry. So with friends like these, who needs enemies?

As the case dragged on without a final determination, many people worried that the EPA would go back on its initial decision and capitulate to appease Texas authorities, with whom it has clashed repeatedly. "This aquifer exemption issue might become a sacrificial lamb that the federal government puts on the altar to try to repair some relations with the state," according to a government insider. And sure enough, the EPA approved the exemption soon after that. Now the locals are the actual sacrificial lambs.

One way to solve this dilemma is to make a rule, where the responsible EPA officials and their families are to move into the 50 local homes within the pollution zone, to see if they can use the ground water. If they use it for 2 years without any problems, then the locals can safely return to their homes.

Many disputes over aquifer exemptions focus on water people might need years in the future, but in many cases the risk is immediate. Some of the affected locals already use the ground water near the polluted areas for drinking and cooking.

And the problem is aggravated by the expansion of oil and gas fracking wells, which are operating near the already contaminated areas. Pumping large quantities of hazardous chemicals deep underground opens the possibility of cross-contamination, where the huge amounts of chemicals from nearby uranium and gas fracking wells start getting mixed. Hazardous chemicals from the gas fracking well mixed with radioactive chemicals from the uranium wells penetrating into the water table are another potential, and even more dangerous, threat to deal with.

This is a serious health and a water supply issue that is propagating on extremely large scale. The U.S.

is a large country, but when you dig millions of deep holes in it, and fill them with toxic and radioactive chemicals, it might just become a large hazardous, radioactive dumpsite with time. Politicians and regulators are aware of all this, so we count on them to take serious measures in preventing the large destruction of our lands.

Nuclear Plant Accidents

Nuclear power is the most powerful, elegant, and cheap power available to man. When the nuclear reactor is under control, it works cleanly, tirelessly, and efficiently day and night without rest or any complaints. When it gets out of control, however, it is a monster, the equal of which we have never seen. The nuclear disasters at Chernobyl and Fukushima Daiichi are witnesses to its uncontrolled fury.

Chernobyl

The city of Pripyat in Russia was built in 1970 to house scientists and workers of the nearby Chernobyl Nuclear Power Plant. Pripyat had over 50,000 residents and was brimming with life. It served well the locals during the 15 years of its existence, and during Chernobyl's construction and operation—until that infamous day in 1986, when the nuclear reactor melted down and took the plant with it.

More than 28 years after the accident, the buildings still stand tall as if waiting for their old inhabitants to return. The city is, however, nothing but a blood-chilling image of a ghost town, devastated by a nuclear power gone seriously wrong. The bad went to worse at that critical time after the explosion, when the authorities (purposely) failed to warn the residents of the nuclear accident on time, but instead issued an evacu-

Figure 5-32. A ghost town.

ation notice on the third day after the explosion—too little, too late.

This was three days more than most of the people exposed to the cloud of radiation could tolerate. Thousands got sick and many died shortly thereafter. Less than two miles away from the reactor, the ghost town is still littered with the remnants of the people who once lived there; the signs of their hasty abandonment, albeit too late, are frozen in time.

The officials downplayed the magnitude of the catastrophe, and the Soviet-era type politics of misinformation continue to this day. The official estimates of 4,000 people expected eventually to die from cancer-related illnesses as the result of the accident are an underestimate, to say the least. Major environmental organizations have accused the report of whitewashing Chernobyl's impact and state that more than 100,000 people have already died as a consequence of the disaster, and many more are still dying and expected to die.

The environmental damages of the area around the plant are total and permanent. The damages also extend all through Russia and parts of Europe and Asia; however, most of them are temporary and remediation measures have erased the effects in most cases.

NOTE: The author was born in that part of the world and had a chance to visit the region in 1988. The devastation two years from the accident even hundreds and thousands of miles from Chernobyl was palpable, but what was most shocking was the fear in people's eyes every time Chernobyl was mentioned.

Even people who knew nothing about nuclear power, nor about exactly what happened at Chernobyl in 1986 had acquired an animal-like fear from the vicious, invisible killer that spread all over the place and that might be close enough to hurt them. The fear was real. Fear from the unknown fueled by the uncertainty imposed by the then-communist system, where people were not even allowed to ask questions about Chernobyl. That fear alone had very likely made many people sick and even shortened the lives of many others.

Today, the Chernobyl nuclear power plant sits inside a fenced area, the famous exclusion zone. Radioactive remnants of the failed reactor still linger inside the 24-story concrete and steel encasement, which was hastily erected after the accident in an attempt to bury and forget the problems. As a symbol of one of the final deeds, and a lasting reminder, of the inefficient, corrupted, totalitarian, communist system it still sits there; full of cracks, leaky, and structurally unsound. It is about to collapse, just like the communist system did in 1990. Still emitting enough radiation to cause a second disas-

ter of similar magnitude, it is reminding us day after day that nuclear power is a force that is be reckoned with, and that we must be very careful how we handle it.

New encasement is planned to slide over the existing cracked sarcophagus to seal in the remaining nuclear fuel. At an estimated cost of two billion dollars, it is another reminder of the way things were, and that it pays to do things right the first time around.

Within the Exclusion Zone there are also dozens of abandoned villages, where collapsed houses and huts are disappearing under vegetation overgrowth. Hundreds of old people have returned to their village homes, and live in the radiation, ignoring the dangers. How many of them will survive is unclear, but nobody cares anyway, so those who die from it will just join the ranks of the undercounted and unaccounted for victims of this huge, unprovoked disaster.

Chernobyl is undeniably a lasting symbol of the mighty power of nuclear energy. It is awesome in its viciously dark glory, and a symbol of unstoppable devastation. Nuclear power can be a good friend that works for us day and night, but in a split moment it can also turn into an ugly monster that would not hesitate to destroy everything and kill anybody in its wake.

Fukushima Daiichi

A wicked earthquake and tsunami combination surprised Japan in March 2011. The Fukushima Daiichi nuclear power plant on Japan's eastern coast was also surprised and its major support systems failed. Their failure resulted in nuclear reactors running out of control, and used fuel storage tanks evaporating, triggering three meltdown incidents in a short time period. Assisted by hydrogen explosions at the site, the meltdowns caused massive escape of radioactive material in the environment.

Initially several workers were severely injured or killed by the disaster conditions. Some drowned, and some were hurt by falling equipment, mostly as a result from the earthquake. There were no immediate deaths due to direct radiation exposures, but at least six workers have exceeded lifetime legal limits for radiation and more than 300 have received significant radiation doses.

Mass evacuations, tests and checks followed, but the damage was already done and now we could only watch, sympathize, and expect to see more disasters and negative consequences. The plant was totally destroyed within a short time period and the radiation was reduced to minimum.

Two years afterwards, predicted future cancer deaths due to accumulated radiation exposures in the population living near Fukushima are inconclusive. But it is certain that it would take decades to decontaminate the surrounding areas, to decommission the plant, and to get life in the area somewhat near normal.

The locals were affected the most, but the radiation spread quickly to distant areas too. Over 3,000 individuals from a town over 15 miles away from the disabled nuclear plant also bore detectable levels of radioactive cesium in their bodies. Their total dose of less than one milliSievert is considered safe, and no radiation sickness was observed. Nevertheless, the exposed men, women and children need to be watched for the long-term effects of the radiation for the rest of their lives.

The damages are noticeable in the local wildlife as well. One example of the continuing damage is the pale grass blue butterfly, a delicate local insect, famous for the way it changes the colors and patterns of its wings in response to environmental changes. Butterflies caught in the Fukushima region six months after the meltdowns (a generation in butterfly lifetime terms) had different colors and patterns than before. Some of the butterflies also had badly deformed legs, antennae, wings and even eyes. The deformities persisted and got even worse in the second generation of offspring as well. The same deformities were found in butterflies collected from the wild away from the failed plant. Such results are found in research labs, where normal butterflies are exposed to radiation from cesium particles like those escaping from Fukushima Daiichi. This leads to only one answer; the damage is due to radiation.

How many more changes to wildlife and the human population will be encountered in the future remains to be seen. The affected, however, will live in fear of developing cancer, or some other radiation-related illness, for the rest of their lives, asking, "Is it worth it?"

NOTE: These are the largest and most damaging nuclear power accidents since the inception of the commercial nuclear technology. But here is where the similarities end. The Chernobyl accident happened during the reign of communist awkwardness, and was caused by inferior Russian made technology, clumsily operated by poorly trained technicians.

The Fukushima nuclear accident was caused by natural events, triggering an earthquake, followed by a large tsunami. Faced with that awesome force, even the superior made in the U.S. technology, and U.S. trained technicians and engineers could not prevent, nor contain, the nuclear meltdown. The nuclear plant was dead in the water—literally. What followed was a disaster that no one had ever even thought possible.

So, here we have two different accidents; one man-made and the other nature-made (with some help from imperfect humans). But the results are the same: complete, thorough and merciless devastation of environment and human life. We were not able to prevent neither disaster, even though we were aware of the dangers and took measures (albeit inefficient) to prevent them.

These two accidents open a large hole in the safety track of nuclear power use, a hole so large that the entire world fears that a third accident could easily slip through the same hole—even if we were advised ahead of time of the possibility. The fear was/is so great that some governments decided to shut down all their nuclear facilities as the only way to prevent another Chernobyl, or Fukushima.

There is a nuclear power plant close to many large population centers in the Western world, so the burning question—fueled by the memories from the two greatest and totally different nuclear disasters we discussed above—is, who is next? And when?

But even more importantly, it is time for the different governments—and the world community as a whole—to take much closer looks at the pros and cons of using nuclear power and come up with a long-term plan that minimizes the environmental and health risks and yet provides enough power for normal life. Not an easy task, but it is one that is urgent in nature and that we cannot/should not ignore.

HYDROPOWER

Hydropower is the potential energy of water locked in one or another type of water body, usually created by a man-made structure. The hydropower source could be a stream, river, lake, waterfall, ocean, etc. Hydropower is used primarily to generate electricity, and here the conventional dammed-type hydro facility (hydroelectric dam) is the most common type of hydroelectric power generation.

The different types of hydropower are:

- Conventional, large hydroelectric dams, which usually are huge projects in the GW size

- Medium size hydro projects of ten MW or more, equipped with artificial water storage reservoirs

- Small hydro projects of ten MW or less, with small, or no artificial water storage reservoirs

- Run-of-the-river hydroelectricity, which captures the kinetic energy in rivers or streams, without the use of dams

• Micro hydro projects providing up to a few hundred kW, which could be of either type

• Pumped-storage hydroelectricity stores water pumped during periods of low demand to be released for generation when demand is high.

• Ocean tide and wave installations, as the name suggests, use the power of the ocean water. We will review these below in this text.

Hydros dammed facilities, or dam generated electricity, represent the major part of water used in the total power generation scheme today. Although the water in these is used in a different way, and is not wasted or contaminated, the environmental effects (evaporation, land damage, etc.) are serious and we take a close look at them below as well.

We reviewed the different types of hydropower generators, their function and use in the previous chapters, so we will now focus on the effects of these on the environment and human life in it.

Environmental Impacts of Hydro Power

Producing electricity using hydroelectric power has some advantages over other power-producing methods. It, however, also has some disadvantages—mostly related to financial and environmental factors.

At a glance:

Advantages of hydroelectric power:

• Fuel is not burned so there is minimal pollution

• Water to run the power plant is provided free by nature

• Hydropower plays a major role in reducing greenhouse gas emissions

• Relatively low operations and maintenance costs

• The technology is reliable and proven over time

• It's renewable—rainfall renews the water in the reservoir, so the fuel is almost always there

Good thing, no doubt. But world hydropower capacity can be expanded only by a factor of two at best, since a limited number of good sites remain available for development, mainly in Africa, Asia, and Latin America. In the United States, it is estimated that more than half of the hydropower generating capacity is already tapped, and most of the remaining potential dam sites would adversely affect sensitive environments, so their implementation is questionable at best.

Hydropower generation also has a bad side. A number of great environmental and health effects have been attributed to it, as follow:

Disadvantages of hydroelectric power

• Huge projects with high investment costs

• Hydrology dependent (precipitation)

• Inundation of land and wildlife habitat

• Loss or modification of fish habitat

• Fish entrainment or passage restriction

• Changes in reservoir and stream water quality

• Frequent droughts affect the power generation regimes

• Displacement of local populations

• Loss of natural and ethnic landmarks, and entire cultures

Construction Carbon Footprint

A number of large and small pieces of equipment are used in the dam, the water reservoir and hydropower plant design, construction, testing, operation and maintenance, and decommissioning. Starting with the reservoir and dam construction, the carbon footprint starts at a site location, where deep tracks in the ground and heavy plumes of smoke in the air from large trucks and bulldozers crawling all over the place can be seen day after day. And there are also trains and trucks used for transporting the equipment to the site.

The list of equipment used during the construction, start-up and testing of a large hydropower dams and the associated power plants is too long and complex for us to deal with in this text.

Figure 5-33. Concrete bucket used at Hoover dam.

It suffices to take a look at the concrete buckets used in building Hoover dam, however, to get some understanding of the large size and quantity of different equipment used during the construction. Just imagine what size cranes and motors were used to lift these huge, seven by seven foot, 18-ton steel monsters all day long, day after long day, nonstop for five-six years.

And then imagine the size and number of dump trucks, railroad cars, etc. equipment needed to transport dirt and rocks away from the site, and deliver cement and gravel back to it. There were also huge air compressors, power generators, power drills, etc. equipment used during the construction of dam and the peripheral and support structures.

And even more sophisticated equipment and materials were needed for the construction of the power plant, including its huge power generators, transformers, etc.,

A lot of metals, plastics, wood and other materials were used for manufacturing of this machinery, which was made somewhere on the planet some time in the past, where and when their manufacturing processes and transport created a significant pollution footprint. Since most of the construction equipment is used only temporarily, we can assign only a small part of the carbon footprint to the manufacturing and transport of the power equipment to the plant. (A)

Even before site preparation is complete, the main power equipment pieces arrive in wooden boxes, on back of large trailers, or railroad cars. These are assembled with the help of other pieces of large equipment (cranes etc.) and are put to work after creating another set of pollution problems. (B)

In addition, there are many other items and small pieces of equipment, tools and consumables—some for personal use, and some for specialized operations that are needed for the construction and operation stages. These are computers, helmets, boots, goggles, shoes, first aid kits, and many other consumables. All these were also made somewhere around the world, sometime in the past, and transported to the power plant. During their manufacturing processes and transport they also left a significant pollution footprint. (C).

Then, to complete the pollution footprint picture, we must add to that the footprint of the people involved in the entire process—engineers and technicians involved in the equipment manufacturing, transport, installation, setup, and operation. These people drive cars, and ride on busses, trains and planes, all of which leaves another significant set of pollution footprints, and which otherwise would no be emitted. (D)

And so, the total pollution footprint of the power plant equipment cradle-to-grave process is expressed by:

$$P_f = A + B + C + D$$

Where:

P_f is the total pollution footprint from equipment manufacturing, transport, and maintenance

A   is the equipment manufacturing and transport to the power plant

B   is equipment assembly, test and installation at the plant

C   is the manufacturing and transport to small tools and consumables

D   is the pollution footprint of the equipment personnel during the design and construction phases.

Combining the pollution footprint of A (plant equipment manufacturing and transport) with B (equipment assembly, test and installation), adding C (the manufacturing and transport of the tools and consumables), plus D (the pollution footprint of the equipment personnel) gives us the environmental footprint of the mining equipment before even starting the power plant operations.

And the pollution footprint is significant, to be sure! It goes deep and wide; stretching from one part of the world to the other. To put a value on it, we must take inventory of all items delivered to the nuclear plant, and needed for its design, construction and operation. We must take a close look at the manufacturing of all kinds of equipment and materials used in dam and hydro-power plant building.

Keep in mind that some of these are some of the largest pieces of equipment in the world, and that it takes thousands of tons of metals to make them. Each of these started as an iron ore dug out from another mine somewhere in the world, which was transported to a smelter. The molten metal was shaped in different forms and shipped to the different parts manufacturers, who drilled, welded, and otherwise constructed parts for these vehicles.

And again, remember that we are talking about huge structures; some are the biggest in the world. After manufacturing, these parts are packed and loaded on railroad cars or trucks to be shipped to the assembly facility. The major parts of a hydro-turbine might require a dozen of railroad cars for transport. The parts are assembled into major components, or entire units and after one more loading and unloading, they finally arrive at the power plant floor for final assembly and testing, before being put to work.

Also, millions of tons of concrete are used for the construction of large hydropower plants. This process also requires mining the raw materials, processing, and transporting them, at a great expense. These processes also generate huge amounts of pollution all through their cradle-to-grave life. This is a long, windy process, with many stop and go, loading and unloading, and transport steps—all of which also generate a lot of pollution.

Putting a dollar value, or a number in tons of hydrocarbons, would be too long and complex procedure for our purposes, so it suffices to say that the pollution effects during and after all these steps are significant. We will take a second, closer look at these steps and their environmental effects in the following chapters.

Equipment Maintenance Carbon Footprint

And now, after starting the power plant operations, we see a significant pollution footprint for the duration of the operation and maintenance procedures too. The power plant equipment needs repairs and eventually replacement. Spare parts for the pieces of equipment in need of repair or replacement are made all over the world, and periodically arrive from different parts manufacturers, after surely leaving their pollution footprint on the way.

It is hard to assign an accurate number to the quantity of air and land pollution as a result of the pollution created by the plant equipment replacements, but we will address their environmental effects in more details in the following chapters.

Thus created pollution is similar in type and quantity to that generated by the replacement equipment in the conventional power plants. The final tally shows that a significant part of the emissions and overall pollution are to be attributed to the power plant equipment maintenance and replacements, and the support personnel. This number is significant and we will go through the calculations in the next chapters as well.

Environmental and Safety Concerns

Starting with giving proper credit, the power produced by the world's hydropower plants would prevent nearly one billion metric tons of CO_2 per year to be generated by fossil fuels. A properly designed and efficiently functioning nuclear power plant will release a very small amount of harmful gases into the atmosphere that is thousands of times less than a coal-fired power plant.

Hydropower plants also prevent millions of tons of ash and suds, generated by fossil-fired power plants, from being deposited in the landfills, and land contamination on the sites and beyond is significantly reduced as well.

Overall, hydropower is a clean and cheap type of power generation. It does not pollute water, soil, or air.

Environmental Impact

Nevertheless, hydropower facilities have large, and some cases extraordinary, environmental impacts on the environment. Large flooded areas can change drastically, and otherwise negatively affect, local land, homes, and natural habitats in the dammed area.

Since most hydroelectric power plants utilize a large dam to create a large lake on a previously running river, the new structure obstructs fish migration and affects their populations. The hydroelectric power plant also changes the water temperature and reduces the river's flow.

These changes may harm native plants and animals in the river and on land. Reservoirs may cover people's homes, important natural areas, agricultural land, and archeological sites. In many cases, building dams requires relocating local people.

In recent years scientists have studied the hydropower's negative environmental impacts. The results point to the fact that large dams can harm ecosystems in a number of ways, such as:

- Killing plants and displacing animals, including endangered species, when reservoirs are flooded

- Alter river flow rates, the quantity and character of sediments moving through the channel, and materials that make up streambeds and riverbanks

- Modif water parameters such as temperature and levels of nutrients and dissolved oxygen

- Degrading downstream channels, floodplains, and deltas by reducing the transport of nutrients and sediments below dams

- Blocking migration of fish and other aquatic species up and downstream

- Methane, a strong greenhouse gas, has been detected in some reservoirs and is emitted to the atmosphere.

- The man-made reservoirs emit excess CO_2 and/or methane from rotting submerged vegetation and carbon inflows from the catchment area.

The effects of dams are hard to estimate. For example, their contributes to climate change depends on many factors, including whether the flooded land was previously a carbon source or sink and what land use changes result from building the dam and displacing people from the flooded area. It has been estimated that warm, shallow tropical dams emit more GHGs than deep, cold dams at higher latitudes.

Hydropower Plants Safety

The safety at hydropower plants can be divided in several stages: site location and evaluation, construction, and O&M. While the usual types of accidents and incidents associated with site development and construction are expected, the operation of hydropower generating plants is the safest of all energy sources available today.

Once the dam, the power plant and the reservoir have been created, the plant operation is very safe. Usual maintenance procedures are needed for the duration, but except in these cases, when the plant has to be partially or completely shut down, it provides clean and cheap electricity for a long time.

Ecosystem Effects

Ecosystem impacts caused by a hydroelectric project vary, and largely depend on:

1. Size and flow rate of the river or tributary at the project location
2. Local climatic and habitat conditions, past and present
3. Type, size, design, and operation of the project
4. Cumulative impacts upstream or downstream of affected lands and other projects

NOTE: The first two variables largely depend on a complex set of geologic, geographic, and weather conditions, and hydro project designs are typically based on these natural dynamics.

Dammed storage reservoirs hold water as needed to adjust a river's natural flow pattern, and release water when needed to correct the flow, and/or when the demand for electricity is highest. Since much more energy can be produced from water falling 100 feet above a turbine than from ten feet (the height is called head), it is logical to expect that hydroelectric projects producing the most electricity are on tallest dams with largest storage reservoirs.

Run-of-the-river projects are less intrusive, and simply allow water to pass through the turbines at about the same rate that the river is flowing. Generally, the river level upstream of the project is fairly constant, with small daily and somewhat larger seasonal, fluctuations.

Keeping in mind that no two storage or run-of-the-river projects are the same, thus no generalization can be made, and we will take a look at some of the possible ecosystem changes due to their presence:

Sedimentation

Sediments, consisting of fine organic and inorganic materials are typically carried by the river and are suspended in the lake water. With time, however, these fine particles stagnate and start collecting behind the dam walls. During the building of the dam, man-made and natural erosion of lands adjacent to a reservoir can also lead to sediment build-up behind a dam. The build-up varies according to lake-river-dam relation, and the ability of the river (or dam operation) to "flush" the sediments past the dam. It also varies based on the natural conditions of the river and its upstream tributaries.

When sediments collect to a certain level, the ecosystem is affected in several ways. Downstream habitat conditions can decline because the sediments that provided important organic and inorganic nutrients are no longer available. And also, sediment build-up behind a dam causes "nutrient loading," because more nutrients are now available, thus more organisms populate the area to consume the nutrients, which can further deplete the oxygen levels in the lake. Similarly, gravel carried by the upstream river can be trapped behind a dam, which deprives the downstream river from the movement of gravel as part of establishing spawning areas for fish, thus important habitat conditions can be affected as well.

Erosion

Higher upstream, in the lake, and lower downstream water levels change the shoreline vegetation and overall environmental balance, which can also lead to increased erosion. For example, the lack of vegetation along the shoreline allows the river or reservoir waters to cut deeply into the banks. This can result in further changes to a riparian zone and the species that live in it. Increased upstream erosion also increases the amount of sedimentation behind a dam.

Stratification

Dam reservoirs are basically man-made lakes, created by damming the river when the project was built. The upstream river is affected somewhat, but it continues its run up to the lake, when it dumps its waters into it. The downstream river, and its environment along its shores, however, is seriously impacted. The water level is much lower, and the flow is significantly slower than previously. Surface temperatures tend to become warmer as the slower moving or "slack" water absorbs heat from the sun.

Since the water in the lake is stationary, with no intermixing of the layers, the colder water sinks toward the bottom because of its higher density. This causes a temperature layering effect called stratification. The bottom layer is the coldest, with the temperature gradually increasing upward, with the top layer being warmest.

Stratification causes other ecosystem effects, due to the fact that as colder water sinks toward the bottom of the lake, it slowly loses oxygen and remains low on oxygen. When dam outlets are opened, a syphoning effect occurs, where water from the bottom is sucked up into the turbines and released downstream. The colder, oxygen-depleted waters are now integral part of the river waters, and the downstream habitat conditions change because of the reduced temperature and oxygen level in the water. These changes vary, depending on the region and the local flora and fauna.

Air Emissions

Hydropower installations do not emit any gasses during operation, simply because no fuels are burned. However, the dammed areas contain large amounts of vegetation, which is left over from the old riverbed when the dam was built, in addition to new vegetation grown after the dam was completed. These types of vegetation decay with time in the newly created lake, causing the buildup and release of methane, which is a potent greenhouse gas.

Some lakes are very big, which increases the potential of large gas releases.

Super-saturation

Super-saturation (the opposite of stratification) occurs in the downstream waters, when air becomes trapped in water spilled over a dam as it hits the pool below, creating turbulence. Since air is comprised of 78% nitrogen, the level of nitrogen dissolved in the water can increase dramatically. The super-saturated water retains the excess nitrogen for a long time, and can get into the tissues of fish and other species in these waters. If fish swim from a supersaturated with nitrogen waters to a lower pressure area, a condition similar to "the bends" in scuba diving can occur. Stratification and super-saturation could occur in the same waters, which could

cause lower oxygen and high nitrogen content. Any of these effects could cause injury and death to downstream fish.

Inundation

A dammed river creates a lake, which raises the water level behind the dam from a few feet to several hundred feet. When stream banks and riparian areas become covered by the reservoir's higher water level, the result is called inundation. The habitat conditions change and a new equilibrium emerges. A different set of dynamics begin impacting species that traditionally grow, nest, feed, or spawn in these areas.

When in operation, the level of water in a reservoir varies on a daily basis as needed to produce electricity, thus creating a "power peaking" situation. This occurs usually when more water is released in certain peak hours, when the electricity demand increases. In a riparian zone, (the area where moist soils and plants exist next to a body of water) this may result in shoreline vegetation not being effectively reestablished and eventually damaged or eliminated.

Damage to Fish Population

Following currents downstream, fish are sometimes sucked into the turbines and injured or killed by quickly rotating blades. Attempts to help fish, like when they are captured, trucked, or barged around the dams, they experience increased stress and disease, which result in decreased homing instincts and survival rates.

The changes of the affected ecosystems vary greatly from project to project, and so do changes in affected habitat. Each project has different habitat conditions, and so the extent of ongoing impacts requires a good deal of understanding and investigation.

When affected ecosystem undergoes changes, a new pattern of biological activity and equilibrium emerges and a new dynamic equilibrium takes hold. This changes the way plants, fish, and wildlife that populate these areas live. Only time can tell which species could adapt well, and which exhibit a gradual, sharp, or complete decline.

The possible habitat changes are endless, but since this is an important element in the environmental effects of energy generation, we must take a close look, beginning with fish that can be affected by the new dam construction:

• Salmon seem to be most affected by new dam constructions, for they depend on periodic migration up and down streams and rivers. Depending on the species, the migration patterns vary dramatically, but in all cases when salmon is faced with a new dam, it loses the battle and entire species can change behavior or disappear all together.

Salmon, and fish in general, can face a number of different and changing ecosystems, related to hydroelectric projects. Based on their life cycle and migration and spawning patterns, fish are affected by a number of factors.

- Stagnant waters in a reservoir can strongly affect salmon, because they become disoriented in motionless waters, and also the length of time downstream it takes smolts to reach the ocean may increase. Both of these conditions increase exposure to predators and result in decrease of fish population.

- Fish passing through or around a dam become stressed, injured, disoriented, or die in contact with turbines, the walls of the dam, or deflection screens. They then exit into a relatively small area of the downstream river where their exposure to predators is increased. Fish passage rates are estimated at over 90%, and yet fish that passes through a dam face a great risk to be hurt or killed.

- Super-saturation is a danger for fish, for if too much nitrogen is absorbed in the bloodstream, air bubbles form and create the equivalent of "the bends" in deep water divers. At higher nitrogen levels, fish and some other aquatic species suffer and even die.

- When adult fish migrate upstream, the dam is a physical barrier, and if there is no "fishway," then passage to spawning grounds is lost. In many cases there are fish ladders, fish locks, fish elevators, and transportation of fish upstream via truck. In all cases fish are exposed to real dangers at dam crossings, and salmon, which do not feed during migration journey, lose energy fast and time lost at the dam crossing becomes a critical survival issue.

- Dams create changes in downstream habitat conditions for plant life as well. Macroscopic plants in some estuaries are an important food source for fish, but some of these plants are disappearing, due to adverse conditions caused by dams in the rivers.

- Fish are also affected by loss of riparian vegetation, sedimentation, erosion, and temperature changes, caused by non-dam activities, such as farming, logging, and land development. At the same time,

some fish thrives in the new conditions, where Squawfish, for example, usually found below the dams where they can easily feed on smolts flowing down to the sea.

- Also, slower moving waters and temperature changes in the dammed rivers provide improved environments for warm water fish such as smallmouth bass and walleye, who prey on salmon smolts moving downstream. Predators above and below the dam endanger the salmon smolts, but the journey is not finished until they survive the sea lions as they finally enter the sea.

- The introduction of non-native fish to northwest rivers further complicates the situation. Warm water fish such as smallmouth bass and walleye are examples of non-native species introduced to northwest rivers by humans. Examples of non-native trout include brook and rainbow trout. While many anglers enjoy catching these fish, it is important to note that their improved conditions are at the cost of poorer conditions for native stocks of salmon and trout.

Wildlife

River shores, and riparian vegetation provide critical habitat for birds, waterfowl, and many mammals. A new hydroelectric dam usually inundates a free-flowing river, and so the nesting, forage, and cover provided previously by these areas are temporarily or permanently lost.

Having lost their usual habitat, most animals move to other areas, where they may not do as well for a number of reasons. Many ground birds like pheasant and grouse, for example, require cover and cannot successfully move to higher, more open ground.

As the water levels stabilize at a new height, vegetation in riparian zones often re-emerges and/or new species can re-populate an area. In all cases, when the riparian zone re-emerges it is different. It adapts to the new stagnant or slow moving water conditions, rather than those of a free-flowing river. In such cases, certain species decline, others become more abundant, while some will populate these areas for the first time.

Ducks and geese are examples of waterfowl that thrive in stagnant dam reservoirs. For some of these species, reservoirs are providing an important alternative to the wetland areas that they formerly occupied. Canada geese, for example, have adapted to the new conditions, and are now including reservoirs as part of their migration pattern.

In Summary

Hydroelectric dams, just like nuclear plants, are important if not critical part of our energy balance. They are also here to stay, evolve, and even increase with time. They, however (just like nuclear plants) are huge projects that can affect the local environment and all life in it—including human. If not properly done and managed, they can even kill animals and people.

A poorly designed, built, or maintained dam, for example, can collapse and annihilate the entire area and its population. Dams affect the ecosystems of rivers and their surrounding areas, to different degrees, mostly depending on whether a dam is part of a storage or run-of-the-river hydroelectric project. Other variables include the size and flow rate of the river or tributary where the project is located, the existing habitat and climatic conditions, the type, size, and design of a project, and whether a project is located upstream or downstream of affected lands and other projects.

As time goes on, some species fair well, others sharply or completely decline, and some are minimally affected.

There are also natural conditions that can dramatically affect the health of a river's ecosystem and habitat. Drought years impact most critically important stream flows, and the entire eco-system changes as a result.

Beyond these natural conditions, a host of man-made (non-dam related) activities are contributing to serious environmental changes in river basins. Some of these are:

- Reduced stream flows from irrigation withdrawals

- Altered vegetation from land development, housing, parking lots, roads, etc.

- Loss of riparian areas, changes in water temperature and quality, loss of large woody debris, erosion, and sedimentation can come from various types of logging practices, agricultural activities and other land uses, for example the grazing of cattle, mining, and the building of roads

- Changes in estuary conditions caused by wetland drainage, diking, and navigational improvements

- Introduction of hatchery fish (which now comprises over 75% of the salmon population) is affecting the gene pool, viability, health, and abundance of "wild" salmon runs.

- Catching large quantities of fish by both commercial and sport fishermen

Land Use

One of the worst environmental impacts of hydropower plants involving humans is the fact that thousands of acres of land are needed to create an efficient hydro dam and power generation system. For that purpose, large areas of land are prepared for flooding by forceful resettlement of the local population, flooding the areas forever, and erasing socio-ethnic land marks and entire population centers.

One of the most remarkable and darkest examples of this destruction of local environment and damage to human activities is the China's Three Gorges Dam. It is the largest hydroelectric project in the world, one that provides 18 GW of electricity, a critical asset for China that relies heavily on coal to meet its fast-growing energy needs.

And while the project avoids the production of many millions of tons of CO_2 by replacing the fossil power generators, to achieve this grandeur, the 400-mile long reservoir flooded thousands of acres of land around the riverbed. Many rural valleys, cultural sites, and villages were flooded and erased from the face of the Earth. More than 1.3 million people, from 13 cities, 140 towns, and 1,350 villages on the banks of the Yangtze River, were forcefully evacuated and resettled in unfamiliar locales and left in difficult living conditions. They were promised plots of land and small stipends, about seven-eight dollars a month as compensation.

The Chinese government has decided, under significant public outcry and negative publicity pressure, to curb environmental deterioration in the Three Gorges Dam region by 2020. It will properly handle the negative

Figure 5-34. The Three Gorges Dam, China

effects brought by the project to the middle and lower reaches of the Yangtze River, and improve the long-term mechanisms for geological disaster prevention. The government pledged to stick to the principle of putting people first and promoting sustainable development in post-construction work. Maybe this is a bit late, but better late than never.

The need to "curb water pollution in the middle and lower reaches of the Yangtze River," which affects eight provinces with an area of 633,000 square kilometers has been set as a priority for the local governments. The area is also China's most densely populated, which means significant environmental pressure might just finish the job.

Nevertheless, some extensive and un-repairable damage has been done already. There's been a lot less rain, a lot more drought, and the potential for increased disease to a large population, according to social and medical specialists. The Three Gorges dam and reservoir is considered as the great granddaddy of all man-made environmental changes ever.

In spite of these negative aspects, hydropower is an attractive alternative to fossil fuels for many countries with available water resources. In addition to their low pollutant emissions, hydropower plants provide dispatchable power: their output can be raised or lowered quickly to meet fluctuating levels of demand.

This is quite advantageous, when compared with the other renewable sources such as wind and solar energy generators, which produce energy intermittently—only when the wind blows or the sun shines—so they are not as responsive to daily market conditions.

One way or another, hydropower is here to stay. The fact that it cannot be expanded in any significant way is not of consolation to the affected people, but the good news is that there will be not many more affected by hydropower expansion.

Water vs. Energy Dilemma

Water and energy production are closely and inextricably linked, but while the amount of energy needed is increasing, the amount of water needed to produce it is decreasing.

The role of water in energy production is often referred to as the water-energy nexus, as the relation is getting more clearly important. It is getting more attention than ever before, but only recently the water issues related to energy production have been put officially on the table.

NOTE: Unfortunately, hydropower generation—which uses the largest amount of water of all power generators—is not considered (officially) a renewable power source, so lately the issue was brought up before the U.S. Congress for a vote. If water is a renewable source is debatable, for there are many ways to look at the water generation, storage, preservation, and use.

Electric power generation uses over 15% of the world's total water withdrawal, which is estimated to increase to about 20% by 2050. Some of the water use increase is driven by power plants and expanding biofuels production. The vulnerability of the energy sector to constraints in water availability can be expected to increase, as can issues around how the quality of water is affected by the energy operations.

Companies that provide energy infrastructure, and governments regulators are taking an increasingly holistic approach in recognizing that water and energy are two equal parts, but on the opposite sides of the same equation. This means that looking at every aspect of water use in energy generation is the starting point.

Sometimes, energy efficiency requires higher energy use, such as with some high efficiency power plant technologies, but in all cases lots of water is used and even more is wasted due to evaporation, spillage, spoilage, etc. in the huge dam reservoirs.

Lately, the emphasis has been on technologies that can reduce carbon emissions and water use at the same time. For example, a new coal plant in South Africa, the Kusile project, uses five percent of the volume of water compared to a conventional new coal-fired power plant. This is achieved by the introduction of dry cooling, which is more expensive, but reduces water use significantly.

In the U.S., water continues to be the second biggest concern of utilities, which are in some cases competing with farmers for water rights because of the significant requirements for hydraulic fracturing of shale gas wells.

Water producers are also concerned with the relation between water and energy. In the U.S., drinking and wastewater operations account for up to four percent of the total energy use in the country. That figure is expected to grow here and worldwide as populations grow and the demand for both water and energy increases proportionally too. Many catch 22 factors must be considered. For example, more water-efficient irrigation often involves using much more energy for pumps.

And finally, wastewater is a term that has to be eliminated from the water industry vernacular all together, because there is simply not enough water to waste any more. Instead, we need to look at it as an opportunity to recover valuable resource, instead.

Case Study: Three Gorges Dam

The Three Gorges Dam that went into operation in 2003 has a combined total generating capacity of 22.5 GW, which is the equivalent of ten-fifteen nuclear reactors. The construction of the $22.5 billion dam forced the relocation of 1.4 million people, which has been subject to heavy criticism by the locals and experts worldwide.

Beijing has long held up the dam as a symbol of its engineering prowess, a solution to the frequent floods of China's longest river and a source of badly needed electricity.

The project began in 1993 despite warnings the weight of the reservoir would dangerously alter central China's geology, uproot millions of people, poison water supplies by trapping pollution and disrupt the Yangtze watershed.
The dam has created a reservoir stretching up to 370 miles through the scenic Three Gorges region, which is crisscrossed by geological fault lines.

The dam is 7,661 ft long 594 ft high, for which 27.2 million cubic meters of concrete, and 463,000 tons of steel (as much as needed to build 63 Eiffel Towers) was used, and 102.6 million cubic meter of earth were moved, for the dam wall alone.

With the lake water level at its maximum of 574 ft above sea level, it is 361 ft higher than the river level downstream. At that point the dammed lake is about 410 miles long and 3,700 ft wide. It contains 32 million-acre feet of water with a total surface area of 403 square miles. The lake flooded a total area of 244 square miles of land, compared to the 520 square miles of lake created by its largest competitor, the Itaipu Dam.

The criticism about potential environmental damage that would result from such an extensive construction project still persists. Some say that hydroelectric power should not be considered as a renewable energy source because of the irreversible environmental damage that results from these projects.

Needless to say, hundreds of miles of one of the world's most majestic rivers in the world, Yangtze River in the Hubei Province, and its habitat are changed forever. Most of the existing wild life and vegetation were destroyed, and some rare species (like the Yangtze dolphin) are now extinct, together with the local villages and cultural sites. The local population was relocated to urban centers, thus changing their centuries- long way of life totally and permanently.

Regardless of the damages, the Chinese government won't stop here. Huge hydropower cascades have been proposed and are being constructed in some of China's most pristine, and biologically and culturally

diverse river basins, such as the Lancang (Upper Mekong) River, Nu (Salween) River, and upstream of Three Gorges Dam on the Yangtze River and tributaries. China is changing, and so is its environment.

So, what environmental results can we expect to see from such a large hydro project?

Greenhouse Gases

The main environmental benefit of the Three Gorges Dam is the reduction of carbon emissions. However, it has been found that the dam does cause greenhouse gases to be released into the atmosphere, just not in the form of industrial pollution. In reservoirs, the breakdown of vegetation and organic material that accumulates actually releases carbon dioxide into the atmosphere! Therefore, while proponents claim that hydroelectric energy is a "clean" energy source, this is not entirely the case.

Water Pollution

Vegetation is not the only thing that will accumulate behind the dam. The dam has blocked approximately ten million tons of plastic bags, bottles, animal corpses, trees, and other detritus that would otherwise have flowed out to sea. The Yangtze River is already one of the most polluted rivers in the world. Because of its proximity to several city centers, dumping industrial waste and sewage has always been a serious problem.

More than 265 billion gallons of raw sewage are dumped into the Yangtze annually. In addition, the reservoir itself flooded 1,600 abandoned factories, mines, dumps, and potential toxic waste sites. Because the dam prevents any of this material from being washed out to sea, water quality in the Yangtze has become much worse since construction of the dam began.

This project claims to yield social benefits: less air pollution will result in better health and a higher standard of living. But in reality, millions of residents of the Three Gorges Dam area rely on the Yangtze River as their only water source. In Fengdu County alone, which lies on a tributary of the Yangtze River, contaminated water affects the lives of 50,000 people.

Siltation

Because of reduced water speed behind the dam, an estimated 530 million tons of silt will accumulate behind the dam. Critics claim that the spillway built into the dam, with a discharge capacity of 116,000 cubic meters, is still not of sufficient size to prevent siltation from occurring behind the dam. Rising silt levels could eventually cause sections of the Yangtze to be impassible for shipping, impacting Chongqing, which relies on Yantze River trade. Silt accumulation could even block the sluice gates that are essential to controlling water levels behind the dam. In the event of heavy rainfall, rather than working to control the waters, the dam could actually cause more flooding to occur upstream. In addition, the reduced water speed will hinder the power generating capacity of the hydroelectric dam and contribute to accumulation of pollutants and toxins in water, reducing fresh water availability.

Ecosystem Disruption

The giant hydroelectric dam serves as a physical barrier that disrupts the river ecosystem. In addition to water pollution, habitat fragmentation will have a detrimental affect on all species within the Three Gorges Dam area. In an environmental impact assessment, it was determined that there are 47 endangered species in the Three Gorges Dam area that are supposed to be protected by law. Two of the most popular marine animals in China, the Chinese River Dolphin and the Chinese Sturgeon are included in the list of species at risk. Ecosystem disruption poses not only environmental problems, but economic problems as well. The physical barrier interferes with fish spawning, and, in combination with pollution the dam will have a serious impact on the fishing economy of the Yangtze River.

Deforestation

Deforestation is another factor that refutes China's claim that the Three Gorges Dam is a "clean" energy source. Forests are a major carbon sink and work to negate greenhouse gas accumulation in the atmosphere. However, deforestation (burning trees) actually emits carbon dioxide into the atmosphere, and is responsible for 20% of the world's greenhouse gas emissions.

An immense amount of deforestation occurred for the construction of this project, mainly to provide farmland in the surrounding areas for those whose homes and farms were flooded by the reservoir. Much of this land is located on the steep slopes of the gorges, and has been determined as unsuitable land for farming. In addition, the three gorges dam area is geographically unstable, and deforestation has increased the risk of landslides. Because of this, residents are being forced to relocate for a second time.

Landslides

The most current environmental concern with the Three Gorges Dam is the prevalence of landslides. So far there have been 91 places where the shore has collapsed,

with a total of 36 kilometers of land caved in. Some of these landslides have triggered 50 meter-high waves on the reservoir behind the dam. In Fengjie County alone, officials have designated more than 800 disaster-prone areas. The potential for geological disaster is threatening the lives of millions of residents in the area. Large dams increase the possibility for earthquakes because of increasing geological pressure from rising water. Over 360 million people live within the watershed of the Yangtze River. In the chance of earthquake or dam collapse, millions of people who live downstream will be endangered.

Landslides have resulted from a culmination of factors. The Three Gorges area has been always been geologically unstable before construction on the dam began. When relocation began, many people were moved to higher land in the valley just above the flood line. Farmers cleared land to plant crops or orange trees, but deforestation contributed to soil erosion and destabilized many hillsides. Construction crews are now reinforcing the hillsides with concrete to prevent more landslides. Some residents have received aid from the government, but most are camping out in tents nearby for lack of money and transportation to be relocated. Most residents are farmers and fishermen who were forced to leave their villages for higher land and put their life savings into these new homes that were not built on reliable land.

In summary, the good things about a hydro power project are that they:

- Generate reliable, clean and cheap power most of the time,

- Do not generate significant amount of pollution during operation. The Three Gorges hydro project, for example reduces coal burning by 31 million tons per year, while at the same time it avoids the emission of 100 million tons of greenhouse gas emissions, millions of tons of dust, one million tons of sulfur dioxide, 370,000 tons of nitric oxide, 10,000 tons of carbon monoxide, and a significant amount of mercury.

- Operate with very little maintenance and last a long time

- Provide long-term jobs and economic opportunities to the locals

On the other hand, hydro power projects:

- Erase entire areas and their inhabitants from the face of the Earth

- Seriously change the local environment

- Downstream riverbanks are expected to become more vulnerable to flooding

- Downstream silt flow reduction makes some structures vulnerable to inundation

- Benthic sediment buildup causes biological damage and reduces aquatic biodiversity

- Landslide incidents in the new lake can create serious problems

- River navigation is restricted or totally blocked by the dams

- A real danger of dam collapse by natural forces or terrorist attacks

OCEAN POWER

The ocean's waves and tidal currents are considerable energy sources, so it makes a lot of sense to harness all that formidable and free- for-the-taking power. At first glance it seems that it is power similar to that of the rivers that drive hydropower dams or the wind that drives wind turbines, but is it? Is ocean power generation and feasible option to take us into the 22nd century?

The ocean power concept is quite simple: the moon's gravitational pull lifts billions of tons of sea water up into the world's rivers, coastal waterways, and lagoons. When the water flows back out to sea at low tide, its energy dissipates and, if we don't use it, it is wasted.

Instead, we can harness the sea energy in several ways: a) using wave power, b) using tidal power, and c) using ocean water temperature variations in a process called "ocean thermal energy conversion."

The different ocean power generating methods are as follow:

Ocean wave power consists of harnessing the power of the never-ending in-and-out motion of the waves. The waves go back-and-forth and up-and-down ceaselessly, and, with each motion there is a lot of power generated and used. All we need to do is capture it.

One way to do that is to force air in and out of a chamber with a diaphragm attached to a piston, or a spinning wheel. In either case, the newly created motion by the waves can power a turbine and a generator, which can produce electricity. There are actually such systems in operation today that power lighthouses and warning buoys.

Ocean Tidal Power involves using the difference

between the high and low tide, and capturing the energy as the water rushes in and out through a special channel. This method is similar to the power generation in hydroelectric dams, where the running water does the work by turning turbine blades to generate electric power. Some large installations in Canada and France are already generating enough electricity this way to power thousands of homes.

Ocean Thermal Energy Conversion (OTEC) systems use the temperature differences between deep and surface waters to extract energy. Since there is a heat differential, heat can be extracted from the heat interchange between two stations positioned at different depths. There is an experimental station in Hawaii working on the development of this technology, hoping to produce large amounts of electricity someday that could compete with the conventional power generating technologies.

Ocean energy has a number of advantages over off-shore wind power, because, a) tides are constant and predictable, thus there are no interruptions due to variability (as is the case of wind power generation), and b) ocean water's natural density is much greater, thus it requires fewer turbines to produce the same amount as that of wind power.

But the technological difficulties and great cost of building tidal power generating arrays at sea, and then getting the power back to land, however, is proving more difficult than anticipated. Ocean technologies are still in their infancy, and so most of them are still in the experimental stages. The industry is maturing, however, and costs are dropping, so there is a good chance that the ocean could power nearly two percent of U.S. energy needs by 2020.

There are a number of companies worldwide working on the development and implementation of ocean power technology. Ocean Power Delivery Ltd., in Scotland, for example, has a wave system called Pelamis that, when installed off California's coast, will capture the wave-battered central coast with wave power generated electricity.

Seattle, Washington based Aqua Energy has installations off the coasts of Oregon, Washington and British Columbia, and is planning to provide hundreds of megawatts of ocean energy to the local utilities in the near future.

New Hampshire based Tidal Energy Company is developing tidal power in the Piscataqua River between New Hampshire and Maine. Another company, Verdant Power, is already providing Long Island City, New York, with electricity through tidal river turbines, and is also installing tidal power systems in East River, NY.

Environmental Issues

There are a number of advantages to using ocean power, some of which are: it is a plentiful, predictable, renewable, clean, and environmentally friendly energy source, needs no external fuel, and is always available and ready to serve.

There are some disadvantages too, and some of them are overwhelming.

- There are some safety risks with ocean power generation.

- Harnessing the power is difficult.

- It can cost a lot of money and requires further research.

- If the whole tidal/wave energy scheme does get popular, real estate will be losing money for beach-front houses since they will be using the beaches for the tidal/wind farms.

- It is not much good financially, depending upon where you put it.

- May interfere with mooring and anchorage lines, commercial and sport fishing.

- Waves can be big or small, so you may not always be able to generate electricity.

- Ways of transporting the electricity from the sea onto the land have to be found

- Not many people have tried to generate electricity this way yet so the equipment is expensive

- It is believed that harnessing wave or tidal power will eventually slow the rotation speed of the planet. It is currently believed that we could cause as much as a full day of loss to our calendars every two thousand years by collecting enough energy from waves and tides.

In addition, there are a number of additional variables and issues:
- *Lack of good depth data.* One of the major obstacles with any wave resource study is lack of long-term ocean wave measurements inside the 100-meter-depth contour, where refraction effects result in spatially inhomogeneous wave parameters. Lack of data makes it difficult or impossible to mark the optimum locations for WECs

- *Research and Cost.* Another critical obstacle to developing WEC technology in California is the lack of research support to motivate coordinated

efforts in advancing the technology. In contrast, the European Commission has increased its support for WEC projects since the beginning of the Joule Program 2,3. The last decade of research and development represented more than 20 large projects backed by hundreds of millions of dollars. The "Atlas of Wave Energy Resource in Europe" and the "Exploitation of Tidal and Marine Currents" are two prime contributions of the last decade.

- *Regulatory Issues.* Several federal, state and local authorities have overlapping jurisdiction over a project. An exhaustive list of the maritime boundaries recognized by local, state, federal and international law is beyond the scope of this report.

- *Environmental Issues.* To date, there are a limited data available on the environmental impact of wave farms that are in continuous operation. In one study, however, T. W. Thorpe examined the potential environmental impacts of various technologies. Relative to other forms of electric generation, including other renewable sources such as sunlight or wind, wave energy conversion is expected to cause little adverse environmental impact.

- *Operational activities.* Once the wave farm is installed, the main impacts will come from increased operational activity to maintain the devices. Some of the potential effects include wave hydrodynamics (the transport of sediments along the shorelines), creation of artificial habitats (attachment surfaces for a variety of algae and invertebrates), change of migration route for marine mammals, noise, navigational hazards, visual effects and impacts on some forms of recreation, such as scuba diving and jet skiing

Conclusions

There are serious technical and bureaucratic challenges to harnessing wave energy in California and other parts of the United States. The regulatory process is complex and expensive. One simple measure that could advance this clean technology is establishing a point of contact, one office that will be in charge of permits on behalf of all legal and formal stakeholders. Such an office could combine the state and federal interests and implement all existing laws and requirements on behalf of the governing and overseeing regulatory bodies. The combined administrative process and complexity of jurisdictional modus operandi unduly burdens the progress of the technology.

Hydropower Future

All hydroelectric plants (dammed or ocean power) use water to generate electricity, so it is considered a renewable fuel. This status, however, in the face of increasing global warming and extended draughts have been questioned lately. Environmental awareness has supported the use of renewable fuels, including hydro-electricity, wind and solar power, and during the past decade, the federal government has provided tax incentives to renewable energy sources, such as the Production Tax Credit, which provides tax credit to the power industry operators.

There are also tax credits to competitors like solar and wind power plant builders and operators, while hydropower facilities receive only half the credit solar and wind get. Keep in mind that the US Army Corps of Engineers, a federal agency, generates about 24% of the hydro industry revenue, operates 75 power plants and produces 25% of the nation's hydroelectric power. So lower government investment into industry operations is a discrepancy and a significant problem, given that the federal government owns a significant number of hydropower facilities and government contracts constitute a substantial part of industry revenue.

The hydroelectric power plant construction has stalled lately. Declining demand for hydroelectric power, rising awareness of the environmental impact of hydroelectric power plants and drought conditions, have contributed to steadily declining revenues lately. Competition from fossil fuels, wind and solar power has hindered the hydropower growth.

Industry revenue has declined approximately two and a half percent, or $894.9 million annually. Demand for hydroelectric power and improving precipitation levels might result in turnaround of annual revenue grow to about six-tenths of a percent at a profit of over 30.0%, which is actually down from previous estimates of nearly 35.0% in the late 2000s.

The top four hydro industry construction firms have less than half of market share, while the US Army Corps of Engineers has by far the largest share of industry revenue. In general, the federal government and state governments have built and operated the major hydroelectric facilities, and the US Army Corps of Engineers continues to be a major player in the industry.

In the past several years, competition and other forces have forced many companies out of the industry, and the number of firms in the Hydroelectric Power Plant Construction business is estimated to fall to about 20, and going further down as competition remains strong. High operating costs stemming from environ-mental compliance will force a number of small players out, and/or force them into consolidation.

Nevertheless, the hydro industry revenue is forecast to increase every year until 2020. The increased demand for electricity, accompanied by a large-scale shift away from fossil fuel-based and nuclear power promises to renew growth in the next number of years. Demand for hydroelectric power is rising, which increasingly supports a steady demand for new hydroelectric power plants.

SOLAR POWER

The solar power industry went through another revival during 2007-2012, which is settling down into a more reasonable pace, accompanied by the slow but inevitable acceptance of the technology as a competitor of the conventional energy sources (coal, oil, and gas). Still in its infancy, it shows a great promise. Solar is flexible, easy to manufacture and install, and requires minimal O&M effort and expense.

But most importantly, it generates no pollution whatsoever during its long-term operation. We clearly saw the environmental effects—mostly negative—of using coal, oil, and natural gas. Now we will take a look at the cleaner technologies; solar, wind, biomass, etc. and their impact on the environment, starting with solar.

Solar Materials and Equipment Manufacturing

The lifetime analysis of renewable technologies shows significant amounts of energy used during all steps of their life cycle; from the initial manufacturing of the equipment and facilities setup, and all through the transport, installation and operations steps of the solar power plants, ending with the decommissioning, recycling and waste disposal of the equipment and land remediation.

In addition to using a lot of electricity, the manufacturing of solar components emits a number of polluting substances, be it in gaseous, liquid, or solid form.

Amazingly enough, the pollution emitted during manufacturing of "green" solar cells and modules is as much or more than that emitted during the manufacturing of uranium fuel. Digging out and melting sand and silicon for solar wafers, processing them into solar cells and encapsulating these into PV modules requires a lot of energy, which is mostly fossil generated. There are also large quantities of polluting gases, liquids, and solids generated during the entire process.

Only a very detailed analysis of the entire cradle-to-grave manufacturing process of solar materials, wafers, cells, and modules could provide a complete picture of the energy use and the degree of environmental pollution caused by the renewable technologies.

It is generally assumed that solar technologies are very clean on the back end of their life cycle (once installed and operational), and this has been the focus of the entire industry, since it is what the average person would ever see—the clean shiny solar modules on the house roofs that need no fuel and emit no pollution for the duration.

The front end of the operation, however, is a different story. This is the manufacturing process, done in a remote and obscure commercial complex somewhere in the China provinces, where enormous amounts of energy are used and unlimited amount of gasses, liquids, and solids are blown up into the air, or dumped in a surface lake nearby at each step of the process.

Only taking a close—very close—look of the activities would give us a complete and fair picture, and would allow comparative analysis of all energy generating technologies. We have taken such close look at the entire process in our previous books (see references 27 and 28).

So, what we see when taking a close look at the renewable energy sources is:

1. Energy used during:
    *   All manufacturing processes
    *   Transport, installation, and field tests
    *   Long-term operation and maintenance
    *   Recycling and waste disposal operations

2. Pollution generation during:
    *   Manufacturing of solar materials, cells, and modules
    *   Transport and installation in the field
    *   Long-term operation and maintenance
    *   Recycling and waste disposal operations

3. Other environmental impacts
    *   Large land areas are cleared and otherwise modified during solar power plants' construction
    *   There is a lot of traffic, dust, and noise during the construction with negative impacts on the locals
    *   The land and wildlife in it are negatively impacted for the duration (25-30 years, or more)
    *   Some solar modules contain toxic materials,

which could cause large-scale air, soil, and water contamination

Solar Cells and Modules

Although solar cells and modules do not emit much pollution on the field, they are responsible for a large amount of energy use, as well as pollution in form of gas emissions, and liquid and solid waste during their manufacturing, transport, installation, O&M, and decommissioning stages.

Let's take a look at the energy and pollution caused by solar cells and modules:

Lifetime Energy Balance

Lifetime energy balance (LEB) is the energy used during the PV products manufacturing, transport, installation, and operation, compared with the power they generate during their useful lifetime. This is also related to the environmental benefits from using solar energy, as related to the total amount of CO_2 that is not emitted in the cradle-to-grave process, as compared to the conventional energy sources.

LEB is an important factor, which needs to be kept in mind when analyzing and calculating the energy benefits from a PV power plant. LEB basically tell us how much energy we save by using PV energy-generating sources.

The solar cells and modules manufacturing process starts with melting and purifying sand in huge, energy-guzzling furnaces. The produced metallurgical grade (MG) silicon is crushed in huge mills and further purified in a complex network of chemical and electric equipment, again using enormous amounts of natural resources and energy. A lot of toxic gasses and liquids are generated during this process as well.

The product at this point is solar grade (SG) silicon of varying purity, the quality of which depends on the raw materials and process quality. The SG silicon is crushed again and melted again in large furnaces at high temperatures for a very long time.

Thus produced ingots of mono or poly silicon are sliced into thin wafers onto which the solar cells will be built. The wafers are cleaned, baked, fired several times, and coated several more times until finally a solar cell emerges at the end of the line. They are then sorted, lined up, and vacuum-bake sealed into the module frames, then transported to the location. The next time these PV modules are transported will be at the end of their life cycle, going to the crusher.

This requires energy, materials, and resources, and a lot of harmful gases, liquids and solids are emitted during manufacturing. Fortunately, today's production equipment and processes are very efficient, but even so, making a solar cell and module is an energy-consuming and environmentally harmful undertaking.

So we hope that the 30 years operation of our solar modules will justify the expense and the pollution. It all depends on how efficient and durable the PV modules are. Consider this equation for lifetime energy balance (LEB):

$$\text{LEB} \quad \frac{E_{mfg} + E_{prod} + E_{trams} - E_{inst} - E_{O\&M} - E_{decom}}{E_{gen}}$$

Where:

E_{mfg} = energy used during manufacturing of the production equipment and facilities setup

E_{prod} = energy used during production of materials, wafers, cells, and modules

E_{trans} = energy used to transport materials, modules, and BoS to PV site

E_{inst} = energy used to assemble and install the PV power plant

$E_{O\&M}$ = energy used to operate the PV power plant (support services)

E_{decom} = energy used to decommission, transport, and recycle the PV field

E_{gen} = energy generated during the life of the PV power plant

In all cases, Egen must be much higher than the sum of the other sources of energy used in order for the system to be an effective energy source.

The term "energy payback" describes this "energy in-energy out" ratio and is what we will have to consider when designing, pricing, and justifying a PV system. In other words, how long do we need to operate a PV system before we recover the energy used, and pollution generated, during its manufacture, transport, and operation before it is decommissioned?

There are energy payback estimates ranging from 1 to 4 years for different technologies; more specifically:

• 3-4 years for systems using current multi-crystalline silicon PV modules

• 2-3 years for current thin-film PV modules

These estimates, however, vary from product to product and from manufacturer to manufacturer. The cost of energy (crude oil in particular) also has a great effect on the estimates, so these numbers must be adjusted periodically.

The ever-changing socio-economic situation in different countries is another great factor and we expect that the present-day economic slow-down and worldwide financial difficulties to drastically reshape these and most other estimates as well.

Lifetime Carbon-emissions Balance

Similarly, a system's lifetime carbon emissions balance (LCB) is a factor that takes into consideration the CO_2 and other carbon-based waste compounds emitted during the manufacturing and use of PV components vs. the amount of CO_2 and other carbons saved by using the PV components instead of coal-, oil-, or gas-fired power generation.

The solar wafers, cells, and modules manufacturing processes generate significant amounts of CO_2 and other harmful gasses. Even more gasses and other wastes are generated during the 30 years of operation and maintenance cycle, all of which must be taken into consideration when comparing different renewable sources and when talking about the advantages of PV technologies over the conventional energy sources.

Consider this equation for lifetime carbon balance (LCB) for a PV power plant:

$$\text{LCB} \quad \frac{C_{mfg} + C_{prod} + C_{trams} - C_{inst} - C_{O\&M} - C_{decom}}{C_{gen}}$$

Where the carbon pollution was emitted during:

C_{mfg} = manufacturing of the production equipment, and for initial production plant setup

C_{prod} = manufacturing of initial materials, wafers, cells, and modules

C_{trans} = transport of materials, modules, and BoS to the PV power plant

C_{inst} = land preparation, construction and installation of the PV power plant

$C_{O\&M}$ = long-term operation and maintenance

C_{decom} = equipment recycling at EOL, and for remediation of the PV field

C_{gen} = is the carbon-based pollution saved by the PV power generation, as compared to that of a coal-, oil-, or gas-fired power plant.

For example, a natural gas-fired power plant emits about two pounds of CO_2 per kWh of electricity generation. Including the rest of the hydrocarbons generated during its cradle-to-grave setup, operation and decommissioning, we could get up to 2.5 lbs. per kWh. Or 2.5 million pounds per each MW of electricity produced. Coal- and oil-fired power plants emit even more.

At the present, PV power plants do not emit anything close to this huge number, so the carbon and other emissions from PV power plants can be compared only with those from other renewable sources. This is one of the greatest, and absolutely undisputable, advantages of the solar technologies.

In all cases, Csave in PV power plants is always much higher than the sum of all emissions, so usually PV plants receive carbon credits for the CO_2-free power generated during their lifetime.

The total quantity of CO_2 generated during the cradle-to-grave cycle of PV components and plants is usually compensated within 3-4 years by much smaller carbon footprint as compared to conventional power generators.

Environmental Impact

We have looked at the environmental impact of the materials used in the manufacturing of different "renewable" energy-generating technologies. We saw that some of them are not renewable, while others are not green and safe—at least from the point of view of the materials, and their use in the manufacturing process.

Now we will take a close look at the impact of the related technologies during their installation and long-term use. Just like any other place where people and equipment operate, the PV installations have some impact on the local environment—quite negative in some cases. As the land area used for these plants increases, so do potential negative effects, some of which are as follow:

Environmental impact studies and analyses show that large amounts of CO_2 and other environmentally unfriendly gasses and toxic liquid by-products are generated during the manufacturing, transport, and recycling stages of PV modules and other components. Usually this is much less than the amounts generated by fossil-fuel power production of similar size during the 20-30 years operation of such components. Even if we assume the least advantageous 1:6 ratio used by some experts for energy payback comparing, PV systems will still prevent many tons of pollution from entering the atmosphere by using solar energy instead of the conventional fossil fuels. The larger the PV plant is, the more harmful gasses that will be kept unreleased vs. conventional energy generation.

Various sources use different calculation methods and come up with different estimates, so we are taking a middle road, assuming that each kilowatt hour (kWh generated by burning coal produces ~1.5 lbs. CO_2 and other harmful gasses (CO, SO_2, NO_2 etc.). This

means that a small, commercial PV system of ten kWp operating in Arizona will produce 20,000 kWh electric power annually, or total of 500,000 kWh (considering the losses) during its 30-year lifetime. This, then, means that our small ten kW commercial PV system will save the environment from absorbing 750,000 lbs of harmful gasses during its lifetime.

Wait—not that fast! While the above is true, we must consider how much CO_2 was generated during the production of the PV modules and other components in this example. PV systems are estimated to have created (during their manufacturing, transport, installation, operation, and recycling cycles) the average of a quarter pound of CO_2 per kWh produced, or, to put it another way, another 125,000 lbs of CO_2 just went up into the air. So in the end, our small ten kWp system will still save 625,000 lbs (750,000-125,000) of poisonous gasses from entering the atmosphere during 30 years of operation. Still, that's not bad for our humble PV system.

Now, let's look at our larger 100 kWp system. Using the same logic, we see that it will prevent 6,250,000 lbs of harmful gases from entering the environment every year. How about a one MWp system? Now we are talking... 62,500,000 lbs of poisonous gasses kept back from reaching us. A very large-scale 100 MWp system will keep a total of 6,250,000,000 lbs from changing the climate and causing global warming during its 30 years of operation. A 500 MWp plant will reduce the CO_2 emissions by five times this amount, and on it goes.

Of course these are only estimates, with a significant margin of error and enough variables to move the decimal point in either direction. Nevertheless, the numbers are significant and leave no shadow of a doubt that we are talking about major forces at play—forces that must be well understood and controlled if humans are to live a normal life on Earth for another millennia, or more.

NOTE: No large quantity of CO_2 gas is produced during the actual on-sun operation of PV modules, but there is some measurable outgassing of other gasses and substances from them and the peripheral components during long-term field operation.

Also, as new technologies (thin-film modules containing poisonous elements as Cd, Te, As, etc.) are being installed in ever-increasing numbers on thousands of acres of desert lands, we need to consider and reconsider where we install and how to use them.

And although the emitted gas amounts are very small, the power fields get larger and larger in size, so we need to pay more attention to the outgassing and its negative effects. Since some of the new PV technologies have no history, no precedent, and no proof or any other data to show their safety for the duration, we must be careful how we apply them.

So let's take a look at the different solar technologies from environmental and safety point of view.

CSP Power Generation

Concentrated solar power (CSP) or solar thermal technology is considered to be environmentally friendly, except for the environmental impact during the manufacturing of the components (mirrors, support structures, steam turbine, cooling towers etc.). A lot of energy is used during that process. Tons of metals and other materials are consumed too, the production of which requires a lot of energy, and generates large amounts of harmful liquids and gasses.

Production of mirrors, when compared to the overall PV cells and modules manufacturing process, is less energy-intensive and more environmentally friendly, yet uses lots and lots of energy and toxic materials. The types and quantities of these activities and their by-products must be entered into the equation, if we are to get a good idea of the overall energy balance.

Like all power plants, CSP power generation has some impact on the local area:

- CSP equipment uses a lot of water, which is not abundant in desert areas where most CSP plants are located, creating another set of problems for the locals.

- Since the technology is based on use of mirrors, the terrain before installation needs to be equalized (leveled and developed), which requires seriously disturbing thousands of acres of virgin desert land. The impact of this intrusion is significant, but the future will tell how good or bad this activity is.

- Mirrors do not require much maintenance. Once installed, however, they must be cleaned at a small cost (water and workforce) and a lot of mess—muddy terrain and run-off that causes concerns with water table contamination in US deserts.

- The plants are almost neutral for landscape except for the solar power towers, which stick very high above the ground and are at times considered a nuisance or visual pollution.

- The noisiest parts of the CSP systems are the steam turbines and the Stirling engines (in dish Stirling case), but the plants as a whole are quiet. To our knowledge, there are no documented reports of noise complaints from locals.

- CSP equipment may have occasional spilling of oil or coolant, but this is negligible and preventable.

Water usage in CSP energy generation process—steam generation and cooling—is one of the major issues plaguing this technology. Water is the most precious commodity in the desert. Every drop of it is needed for the survival of the species living in it. And there is not much water in the desert at all, and is getting less and less too.

Table 5-13. Cooling and process water use per MW/hour generated by the different energy sources.

Technology Used	Water consumption Gal/MWh generated
Hydroelectric	4500*
Geothermal	1400
Solar Trough	850
Solar Tower	850
Nuclear	600
Fossil Thermal	450
Biomass	450
Coal, IGCC	350
Natural Gas	180
PV	5
Wind	0

* Due to river/lake evaporation

Surprise, surprise, hydro-electric wastes more water than any of the other energy generators combined. Who knew? There is a good reason for that, and it becomes obvious when looking at the map of a hydro dam. The lake behind it could be as large, or larger, than a large city.

So let's compare the water use (or waste) from 100 MW power plants powered by the different energy generators:

100 MW hydroelectric plant operating 24 hrs a day, 365 days a year, wastes nearly 3.9 billion gallons of water every year

100 MW geothermal power plant operating 24 hrs a day, 365 days a year, wastes nearly 1.2 billion gallons of water every year

100 MW solar trough, or solar tower plant operating 24 hrs a day, 365 days a year, wastes nearly 370 million gallons every year (turbine steam cooling)

100 MWp photovoltaic plant operating 24 hr. a day, 365 days a year, wastes about 0.5-1.0 million gallons of water every year, mostly used for washing the modules.

Or a ratio of 3900:1200:370:1=Hydro:Geo:CSP:PV. And the winner is….

In all cases, this is a large waste of a precious resource, especially in the deserts, which is where some of these technologies (solar) function most efficiently. And of course, the striking fact is that the major CSP technologies, solar trough and solar tower, are usually—no, always!—installed and operated in high deserts, simply because they operate most efficiently there.

Billions of gallons of fresh water wasted every year in each of these installations is something that the deserts are not capable of providing. We have seen a drop in the water reservoirs and water tables in a number of locations in Arizona and California deserts, so we see this power generation method as unsustainable, impractical, and even harmful to the environment because it is robbing the deserts of their most precious resource—water.

NOTE: When speaking about water waste in the desert, the most incredible example, and an expression of total disregard of the desert environment and human life is/was the Mohave Generating Station. This monstrous project used millions of gallons of desert water to transport coal powder from a mine 200 miles away from the power plant. These are desert locations, mind you, where water is as precious as gold—and even more so, because people in the desert can live without gold, but cannot live without water.

This case has nothing to do with water use by renewable energy sources, but it clearly shows how some seemingly well-intentioned decisions can turn into a waste of precious resources, leading to an imminent environmental disaster. Using water for CSP power plants in the deserts, however, gets very close to unreasonable and unsustainable as is emphasized by the Mohave Generating Station case. There are several CSP power plants in the Arizona and California deserts which will fall victims to depleted water tables during the next 20-30 years. Some will not survive, since the fight for desert water is just now beginning and with the ongoing climate change, it promises to be brutal.

PV Power Generation

PV power plants are basically environmentally friendly, but the general environmental conditions apply here too. As PV technology was developing, it was not until the 1980s that researchers began to consider its environmental implications. As its use expands daily, pressure is applied by the scientific community and administrations that all costs of the creation and use of energy systems are taken into account.

The oil crisis had demonstrated the need to reduce the world's dependence on imported oil, while the Chernobyl and Japan nuclear accidents alerted the world to the hazards of nuclear power. Larger environmental problems such as global warming and acid rain also reiterated the need to decrease our dependence on fossil fuels.

The first German-American workshop was organized in Ladenburg, Germany, in October 1990, to discuss the "External Environmental Costs of Electric Power: Analysis and Internalization." Papers at this workshop considered environmental damage and ways in which environmental costs may be internalized. PV was not discussed specifically at this workshop; however, the impacts of external costs on wind energy were covered and can be easily related to those of the PV industry.

Ottinger's group at Pace University, Centre for Environmental and Legal Studies, published an extensive review of environmental costs/risks and covered all electricity generation technologies, including photovoltaic installations. Various environmental costing models were also discussed, and this has formed the basis of many of the studies on external/environmental costs that have been published.

Knut Sorensen, Statistics Norway, published an extensive report on life cycle analysis with regard to energy systems. This report outlines the principles of life cycle assessment and how they may be applied to energy systems, particularly renewable energy technologies.

The summary of a 1997 report, "Environmental Aspects of PV Power Systems" indicates that the immediate risks to human health and the environment from production and operation of PV modules seem to be relatively small and manageable.

The methodology developed was applied to multi-crystalline and amorphous silicon cells and gives a comprehensive breakdown of the technologies involved and how the life cycle analysis is structured. The results are divided into environmental, social, economic, and other impacts, showing a significant impact on its respective area of influence. Impact type and size vary from case to case, but the overall conclusion is that the environmental impact of all PV technologies must be analyzed.

The PV industry has progressed since 1997 and many things have changed. They must be taken into account when discussing environmental aspects of PV power generation.

Table 5-14. Immediate and long-term environmental and health issues considered.

TASK	IMMEDIATE CONCERNS	LONG TERM CONCERNS
SUPPLY CHAIN OPTIMIZATION	~Investigate the availability and short term constant supply of rare and exotic materials such as Cd, Te, In, Ga, As, Ge and Ag now and in the future ~Optimize the methods and improve the efficiency and safety of rare, scarce and exotic materials mining, manufacturing operations and field use.	~Investigate solutions for supply chain shortages ~Develop thinner active film layers in TFPV modules ~Optimize efficiency of rare and toxic materials use ~Optimize EOL module decommissioning procedures ~Design new materials and products for complete recycling and safe waste disposal systems
EFFICIENT ENERGY USE	~Develop methods to reduce energy use during silicon material, cells and modules production ~Optimize energy use for module frames and BOS	~Optimize energy consumption of Si processes ~Optimize energy consumption of recycling processes ~Optimize energy-efficient frame and BOS designs
IMPROVEMENT OF CLIMATE CHANGE CONDITIONS	~Optimize CO2 mitigation potential of PV technologies ~Investigate release of fluorinated (FFCs) and other toxic and unsafe compounds during manufacturing ~Investigate air and land contamination from PV modules operating in extreme climates ~Design & suggest hybrid energy generation options	~Investigate the CO2 mitigation potential of autonomous PV systems ~Develop FFC alternatives for use in PV production ~Optimize gas and liquid release methods ~Investigate the role and impact of dynamic assessment methods
HEALTH AND SAFETY CONCERNS	~Optimize safe use of compressed and explosive gases in the manufacturing processes ~Investigate and develop procedures for safe use of "black list" materials such as Cd, Te and As in manufacturing and long term field operations	~Develop safer materials and safer alternatives ~Investigate using thinner active cell layers ~Develop more efficient material utilization methods ~Investigate the long-term risks from (low-level) releases of "black list" materials in large scale fields
RECYCLING AND WASTE CONCERNS	~Investigate leaching of heavy metals from modules in long term landfills ~Optimize module & BOS waste management options	~Investigate the environmental aspects of relevant recycling and waste management methods ~ ~Investigate and optimize long term landfill safety

a. PV power fields are growing in size. From the MWp maximum size in the 1990s, we are now witnessing 500 MWp PV power plants under development. This represents millions of PV modules installed on thousands of acres, so the expansion in size means larger quantities of harmful effects which need to be accounted for and taken care of before it is too late.

b. The largest PV power plants are to be installed in the U.S. deserts, where failure rates are many times higher than in moderate climates. This is also a new phenomenon, the negative consequences of which could be too great with time, and should not be ignored.

And worst of all, the largest fields in the world have been installed in the U.S. deserts, where many technologies (thin film PV included) have not been previously used, so we have no data to confirm their reliability and safety during 30 years of non-stop operation under the blistering desert sun and heat. And some of them contain significant amount of toxic and even carcinogenic chemicals (cadmium, tellurium, arsenic, indium etc.)

Environmental Impact of Solar Power Plants

Regardless of the manufacturers' claims on the numerous benefits of solar, and the media buzz on the subject, all solar power plants do have some effect—at times negative—on the environment. Disturbing the land, expelling native animals and even people from the plant's territory is how every project starts. Traffic around the site, clouds of dust, digging holes in the ground, bringing millions of tons of cement and metals, with the accompanying noise, exhaust fumes etc., do leave a scar on the local environment.

And then things happen during 30 years of no stop sizzling under extreme sunlight, and bathing in rainstorms. PV modules are not everlasting. Instead, they are actually quite fragile. With fragile organic materials used for encapsulating and sealing the equally fragile active layers, susceptible to corrosion and deterioration, only time separates each and every PV modules from a failure and even total destruction.

The worst part of the field operations is the fact that some solar cells and modules contain toxic and hazardous materials, such as lead, indium, arsenic, cadmium, etc. While these are in small quantities in each call and module, the number of modules is extremely large—

there are millions of thin film PV modules in each solar power plant.

In this case, the small amount of poison in each module multiplied millions of times produces a significant amount of potential toxicity, which presently has been basically ignored and the potential danger is classified as "insignificant."

And even worse is the fact that most of the thin film technologies are new, and have no proven track record of being reliable or safe for long-term desert operation. Left under the blistering desert sun, the poisons inside the fragile modules will bake and boil until eventually finding a way out.

One accident with these modules will reveal that the danger is not insignificant, but it might be too late because large-scale contamination with any of the poisons would be catastrophic for the location and its immediate inhabitants.

c-Si PV Power Plants

Silicon based PV modules are considered the most durable and least damaging to the environment than all other types of solar generators.

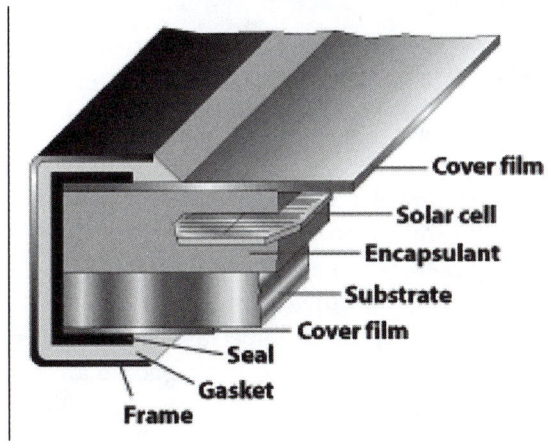

Figure 5-35. Silicon PV module

Looking at Figure 5-35, one can see that the solar cells are well protected by encapsulation and sealers, so it would take the desert elements some time before penetrating inside the module and damaging the solar cells.

Silicon-based cells pose minimal risks to human health or the environment according to reviews conducted by a number of national labs and other entities. This is due mostly to the fact that the solar cells are encased in heavy-duty glass and plastic materials, so there is little risk that any of the contents can be released into the environment in form of gaseous, liquid or particle contamination.

In the event of a fire, it is theoretically possible for hazardous fumes to be released and inhalation of these fumes could pose a risk to human health, but these risks are not substantial given the short-duration of fires and the relatively high melting point of the materials present in the solar modules.

Also, the risk of fire at ground-mounted solar installations is remote because of the precautions taken during site preparation and the removal of flammable and burnable materials.

A much greater risk in PV power fields is the potential for shock or electrocution during normal operation, or in an emergency situation.

On the overall, the strength of electromagnetic fields produced by photovoltaic systems does not approach levels considered harmful to human health established by the International Commission on Non-Ionizing Radiation Protection. Also, the occasional small electromagnetic fields produced by photovoltaic systems rapidly diminish with distance and would be indistinguishable from normal background levels within several yards.

Thin Film PV Power Plants

Thin-film PV cells and modules are the "new kid on the block," and have not been thoroughly tested and proven safe, especially for use in large-scale power fields in the deserts. We will briefly address a number of issues herein, but we would like to encourage the reader to take a closer look at the available literature and make an independent decision on the subject.

CdTe and CIGS thin-film PV modules have seen a quick rise and have been deployed successfully in large numbers around the world lately. The low efficiency and other issues are obviously not hindering the TFPV technology deployment (most likely due to favorable incentives and subsidies), so they are growing faster than the other PV technologies currently available. And amazingly enough, they are the first PV technologies planned to be deployed in gigantic 250 MW and 550 MW power fields in the U.S. deserts.

This is quite unusual, even abnormal, because CdTe and CIGS thin-film PV modules are a fairly new development and have neither been thoroughly tested nor proven reliable or safe for some applications—especially for use in the harsh U.S. deserts, which is exactly the location planned for these gigantic power fields.

The key issues here are:

1. Some thin film PV modules contain compounds of cadmium (Cd), tellurium (Te), selenium (Se),

arsenic (As), and other metals and chemical compounds.

2. The active thin film layers in the TFPV modules are mechanically fragile structures, which could easily be disintegrated by heat-freeze action, and/or mechanical friction, bending or impact upon the modules.

3. The thin films are also, under the right conditions, chemically active compounds. They can easily be decomposed, or reacted by moisture, rainwater (via weak acids and other chemicals containing in it), as well as by almost anything else that enters the modules.

4. Presently most thin film modules consist of two glass panes within which the thin films are encapsulated and sealed within a plastic layer. This is not enough protection, so damage to the active structure during the more than 30 years, long-term, non-stop operation is expected.

5. The active thin films in some TFPV modules are encapsulated by layers of organic polymers, which could easily break down, disintegrate and decompose under intense IR and UV radiation in the deserts with time. Once that happens, the thin film structures are vulnerable to the elements, which will eventually penetrate the module and destroy them.

6. Millions upon millions of thin film PV modules have been planned for installation onto thousands upon thousands acres in the U.S. deserts, the immense scale of which undertaking is where the real danger lies.

7. Toxic materials based thin film PV modules used in the desert, where temperatures within the modules could reach 180°F, and where summer storms, rain and hail, would aggravate the above mentioned mechanical and chemical degradation to the point where major changes in the modules and the thin film structures are to be expected with time:

   — The never-ending heat-freeze action of the desert environment will stress and eventually damage and stress the thin film structure

   — The encapsulating layers will eventually break down with time, thus allowing the elements to penetrate the module, react with the toxic thin films and decompose them.

   — The resulting from the above actions particulate, liquid, and gaseous contamination might

damage air, soil, and water table in the local area, and might even pose threat to human health and threaten all life forms in the area.

Note in Figure 5-36 that the oxide and the active materials of the thin film PV modules are deposited directly onto the front glass. There is no encapsulation at that level, so the environmental moisture and gasses have only a thin layer of sealer at the edge of the module, stopping them from penetrating inside and disintegrating the active layers. How long would it take the blistering desert sun and blinding UV radiation to do that, do you think?

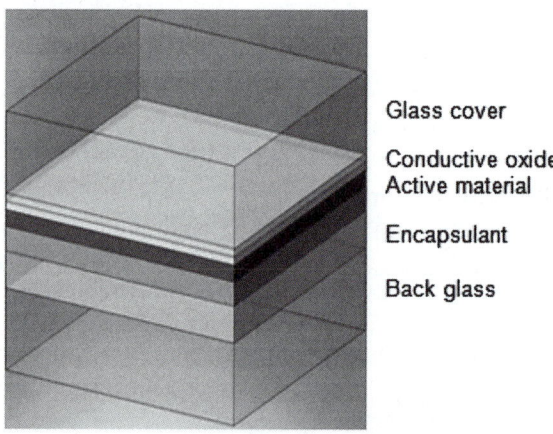

Glass cover

Conductive oxide
Active material

Encapsulant

Back glass

Figure 5-36. Thin film PV module

And on top of that, most thin film PV modules have no side frame. So what will happen if the toxic layer is attacked when moisture penetrates the sides of the frame-less modules is anyone's guess. Mixing toxicity with solar power—especially in the desert—is an uncomfortable subject, and most people are staying away from it. But we cannot wait until the unthinkable happens before addressing the issues at hand.

Actually, a number of scientists and scientific organizations have looked at the toxicity issues of PV modules and have published papers on the subject, as follow:

1. Scientists at Brookhaven National Laboratory (BNL) in the USA, have been publishing health and environmental information of interest to the PV industry since the 1970s, mostly funded by the United States Department of Energy. The work was started by Moskowitz and then continued until the present day by Fthenakis. It was the early studies by Moskowitz that first alerted the PV industry and environmental scientists to the possible

hazards associated with the manufacture, use and disposal of PV modules containing toxic materials.

2. In 1995, BNL and other scientists published a comprehensive study on the health and environmental issues of the manufacturing, use, and disposal of thin film modules. They examined the hazards associated with producing and using thin film modules, focusing on the potential of workers in manufacturing facilities to be exposed to chronic, low levels of Cd. They also review regulations and control options that may minimize the risks to workers and discuss recycling and disposal options for spent modules.

3. Hynes, Baumann and co-workers in the U.K. have published several papers on environmental aspects of many thin film deposition processes. These include environmental risk assessment and hazard assessment of the manufacture of CIGS based thin film PV cells, the chemical bath deposition of CdS and the deposition of alternative window materials to CdS for use in thin film modules. Steinberger from the Fraunhofer Institute in Munich has investigated such risks of Cd containing thin film modules in the operation phase, considering hazards that may occur due to fire, weather influences, or damage of the module due to mishandling.

4. Steinberger first identifies the amount of material in the modules and then investigates the concentrations of selenium, cadmium, and tellurium in the air due to a fire lasting about one hour. His results show that there is no acute danger posed by such fires, and that the releases of cadmium or selenium from a burning PV module are less than those given out by a coal-fired power station in normal operation.

5. Dr. Fthenakis has considered the cadmium emissions from cadmium telluride thin film cells also. He has taken a cradle to grave approach and comes to some interesting conclusions. The Cd present in a NiCd battery is elemental Cd and not CdTe, a much more stable and insoluble form. Coal and oil burning power plants routinely produce Cd emissions, whilst a PV cell does not produce any Cd emissions during its operation. Cd can either be used or discharged into the environment, where it is normally "cemented", and buried or land-filled as hazardous waste.

In summary, the above works have several things in common:

1. They all recognize the serious implications of using cadmium and other potentially toxic metals in PV products but offer no concrete solutions to avoid or minimize the obvious dangers.

2. They are all old, outdated, and incomplete. Nevertheless, due to the seriousness of toxic exposure (and to avoid liability and further responsibility), they always recommend more studies and further investigations of the related harmful phenomena and effects.

3. They usually refer to tests done under "standard," or "normal" conditions, which usually means dry air and 25°C operating temperature. These conditions, however, are very far from the extreme heat and humidity in the world's deserts and other areas where the majority of these products are planned for installation.

4. The actual lab tests, although properly executed for lab test, offer no real solutions. Their conclusions and recommendations lack scientific proof of the point at hand, and fail in the attempt to somehow extrapolate the results of a small lab bench test to the behavior of the millions of modules in a mega PV power field in the desert.

5. They offer neither actual test data, nor any kind of scientific proof for 10, 20, or 30 years' exposure of potentially toxic metals containing PV modules to a harsh desert environment. And we have not seen any long-term tests to date, done under actual extreme-desert or excessively humid climatic conditions, which is our main and only concern.

So, what will happen to these untested and unproven-for-this-application PV modules, containing heavily toxic and carcinogenic materials and operating non-stop during 30 years under the desert blistering heat? How would we explain large-scale air, soil, or water table contamination in these fields, which is likely to happen during the 30 years of non-stop, bake-freeze daily cycles? Who will be responsible for the damages to the environment and peoples' health? Who is going to pay for the cleanup, medical treatment, and resulting lawsuits?

Some of these issues have been quite superficially (if not irresponsibly) addressed presently by the manufacturers, but they are far from being fully addressed, let alone resolved. Instead, regardless of the potential dangers, mega-fields consisting of millions upon millions of Cd-toxic compounds containing PV modules are planned for installation on thousands of acres in extreme climates. There is a lot of money to be made before the window of opportunity closes, so the race is on.

The manufacturers and the responsible parties are, due to ignorance or negligence, simply closing their eyes to the dangers, hoping that it will be OK somehow. We hope so too, for their sake and for that of future generations because if something goes wrong in those mega-fields, we all might end up with the greatest environmental disaster even known to man. God forbid!

Failures

In our second book on solar energy, *Solar Power for the 21st Century*, published in 2013 by The Fairmont Press, we reviewed the most promising technologies for use in the future, and also presented a long list of failed solar products and manufacturing companies. Many of them failed simply because they tried to jump even before learning how to walk.

Dozens of thin film PV modules manufacturing and R&D companies folded during the 2007-2012 time period. The solar tsunami continues, and most companies and many of the thin film PV technologies will never come back, at least not anytime soon.

As a confirmation of the infancy status of the PV industry, hundreds of thousands PV modules, made by one of the most respected manufacturers in the world, the German-based Scheuten Solar Holding, have been declared a fire risk by the Dutch authorities.

Over 650,000 Scheuten 'Multisol' PV modules, manufactured between September 2009 and October 2010 have been documented to have a design flaw in the junction boxes that would lead to fretting corrosion of the tin plated contacts, which could produce unexpected performance and even fire. The junction box is labeled "Solexus" and made by Dutch firm, Alrack.

The concern is that the fault could lead to the melting of the junction box, which could result in PV string/system overload, overheating, and failure, which could result in disconnection from the inverter and/or monitoring system. Roof, or BIPV, system installations with fire sensitive materials are of major concern, because the overheating and melting junction box could potentially cause a serious fire as well.

There had been already 15 fires across Europe directly attributed to Scheuten modules. The modules with the faulty junction boxes were shipped across Europe, the U.S., Australia and China. Another complication comes from the fact that in March 2012, a new

company, Scheutuen Solar Solutions, took over all commercial activities of the defunct Scheuten Solar Holding. Since Scheuten Solar Solutions is a completely separate company, it has no legal liability for the faulty junction boxes, therefore there is no immediate remedy.

In October 2012, insurers acting for Scheuten Solar Holding decided to engage Suncycle, a third party company, which specializes in test and repair services for the solar industry. Suncycle's job was to identify the faulty modules, and apply TÜV certified solutions to them and the installations, if at all possible.

Luckily, the insurance company has paid out for repairs on all the "high risk" systems, such as BIPV systems and such in public buildings and schools. These plausible measures, however, account for only approximately 10% of the total number of potentially affected PV modules.

Suncycle carried out a route-cause analysis of the faulty installations by using approved corrective procedure of re-soldering of the contacts and filling the junction boxes with potting agent. However, Dutch authorities are not very happy with that effort, and are undertaking lifetime tests to test and verify that this repair will last the service lifetime of the modules.

To complicate things, the manufacturer of the junction boxes, Alrack, is refuting the findings, feeling that it had been singled out by the authorities in a witch hunt, since similar problems are found in junction boxes from different vendors. The claim is that the fault is caused by Scheuten Solar design and manufacturing errors, instead. As a matter of fact, this particular junction box was a Scheuten patented design, made exclusively by Alrack for Scheuten, thus negating any liability claims.

These issues aside, the biggest question is what will happen to the remaining 90% of the modules? The bankruptcy of Scheuten Solar means that they are no longer responsible for the problems, and the insiders fear that the installers might be found liable for the cost of the repairs.

The first failures of the faulty modules resulting in fires were in France, where there are a large number of BIPV roof installations, as a result of the previously (but now largely gone) generous feed-in tariff for 'in-roof' installations. In July 2012, the French trade associations TPAMPS and GPPEP warned their members of the potential fire risk due to defective junction boxes on the Scheuten modules. At the same time, several French authorities undertook an investigation into the fires, and documented the defective junction boxes produced by Altrak as the cause, thus clearing the modules from any responsibility.

This is not a good start for the infant solar industry. A major international failure like this puts a shadow of a doubt on the quality of the solar products, and opens a number of questions about their long-term performance.

Luckily, most of the defective Scheuten PV modules are installed in cloudy areas, where the temperatures are moderate to cold. The situation might be much more serious had the defective modules been installed in desert areas where the temperatures are much higher, aggravating any problem.

Desert Power

The world produces and uses ~15 terawatts of electricity annually, which would require ~75 million acres of land to produce, assuming five acres per each MW generated at 15% efficiency, and provided that the PV modules will last long enough to make a difference. This means ~120,000 square miles of desert land are needed to power the world with this type of equipment.

The world's land surface area is ~55 million square miles. The Sahara Desert covers over five million square miles (almost ten percent of the world's land area), so we would need only a small sliver of its (otherwise useless) land to power the entire world. This isn't possible at this time, for a number of technological, logistical, and financial reasons, so we need to find ways to use the deserts close to the point of use (populated centers, enterprises etc.) where we could provide enough power to significantly reduce the use of conventional fuels consumed at these areas.

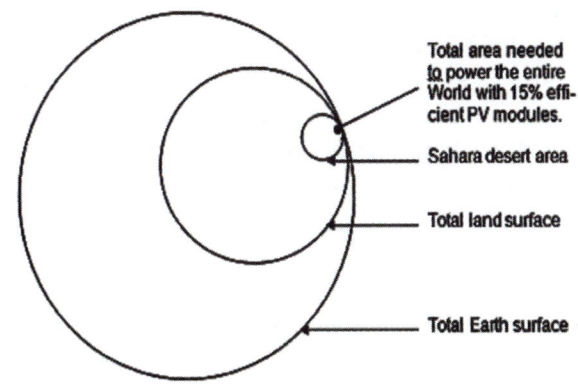

Figure 5-37. Land area needed to power the entire world

Per some estimates, the world's deserts take an area of nearly 18 million square miles (or close to 30% of the world's land area). And since this is where the best solar irradiation is found, we have no shortage of good energy sources to provide all the power we need. We only have to find a way to capture this abundant and constant source, and transport its energy to where we can use it.

The U.S. generates ~1.1 terawatts of electricity, which would require ~8,000 square miles of 15% efficient PV modules installed in the desert to generate. This is an area of 80 miles by 100 miles in the Arizona or Nevada deserts. Imagine driving from Phoenix, AZ, to Las Vegas, NV, among a forest of solar equipment and installations feeding the national power grid.

Far fetched, yes, but this is all the future generations will have left, after we've leached all the crude from the ground and polluted the atmosphere with coal to the point of no return, providing electric power as we know it today. Such a huge project, however, is not practical to undertake in its entirety today. Practical use of PV power today would be to locate smaller solar power generating plants near populated and industrial centers instead. This could provide enough electricity to reduce our dependence on foreign oil and partially eliminate the problems associated with its production, transportation, use, and the resulting pollution.

Now imagine large-scale PV fields where 40 or 50% efficient PV equipment is operating in the Arizona desert wastelands. This automatically reduces the land use by a factor of 3 or 4. Imagine that. Suddenly, things look more doable. Instead of 120,000 square miles, we are now talking about 30,000-40,000 square miles to power the entire world, and only 2,000-3,000 square miles to power the entire U.S. This is a huge difference, but still far removed from today's reality, although some advances in the technology, design, manufacturing, and use might bring us close to the target soon.

One ray of hope is the high concentration PV (HCPV) technology that is 42% efficient today. When all the bugs are worked out, HCPV just might take the lead in desert power generation.

The U.S. Deserts

U.S. deserts, especially those in southern Arizona and southeast California, are unique in that elaborate, extensive, and well-maintained water irrigation systems were developed there during the last 50-60 years, converting some parts into productive and very busy man-made agricultural and commercial areas. Many small and large populated centers are thriving there as well, with an excellent infrastructure (railroads, highways, electrical transmission lines, substations, etc.), which is well established and functioning very efficiently.

This makes adding solar power plants in these areas an ideal solution to solar energy generation. All this should make adding solar capacity to the conventional energy mix an easy thing to do, or at least much easier than doing the same thing in the Sahara desert. The fact that the energy costs are increasing, while energy supplies are decreasing and the world is choking of pollution should add to the ease and desire of implementing solar energy in the U.S. deserts.

We have been talking about this exact situation since the 1970s without significant practical results, so not much has changed during the last 40 years in the large-scale PV power generation area. Now, when energy independence and environmental cleanup are on the priority list and there's lots of talk about them, we still don't see many large-scale PV plants operating in the deserts.

But the deserts are still there, reminding us about the abundant energy under our noses and that all we have to do is get it. Getting is not going to be easy, or quick, so we just have to persist in our goal of converting the U.S. deserts into the energy source we so desperately need.

Here is a detailed list of U.S. deserts suitable for large-scale PV installations:

- Red Desert is in Wyoming

- Alvord Desert is in eastern Oregon

- Owyhee Desert is in northern Nevada, SW Idaho and SE Oregon (Yp Desert is a portion of the Owyhee Desert in Idaho)

- Black Rock Desert is a dry lakebed in northwestern Nevada (Smoke Creek Desert is an extension of the Black Rock Desert)

- Great Salt Lake Desert is in Utah

- The Great Basin Desert is in Nevada

- Tule Desert is in Nevada

- Amargosa Desert is in western Nevada

- Painted Desert is in Arizona

- Mojave Desert is in California (Death Valley is in California—also considered part of the Mojave Desert and part of the Great Basin.)

- Chihuahuan Desert is in Arizona, Texas, New Mexico, and Mexico

- Trans-Pecos Desert is in west Texas

- White Sands is in New Mexico

- Sonoran Desert is in U.S. and Mexico

- Lower Colorado Desert is in California and Arizona

- Low Desert of Southern California is in California

- Yuha Desert is in Imperial Valley, California

- Lechuguilla Desert is in southwest Arizona

- Tule Desert is in Arizona and Mexico

- Yuma Desert is in southwest Arizona

The most suitable for large-scale PV power generation deserts are located mostly in the southwest U.S., and occupy a significant portion of the territory of the states of Arizona, California, New Mexico, Nevada and Texas. There are also some areas in Utah and Colorado with desert, or desert-like climate as well, which are suitable for solar installations.

The U.S. deserts vary in climate, flora and fauna, and are mostly poor in natural resources, but are all blessed with one efficient, constant and unending energy resource—a lot of hot, bright sunshine—almost every day of the year, nearly all day long—precious sunlight, waiting to be harvested.

On the flip side of the coin, the deserts have a basically hostile, dangerous and even deadly climate with extreme temperatures (extreme heat during the day and extreme cold during the night), high humidity during monsoon seasons, lack of water and vegetation, and mostly poor infrastructure. The harsh climate is hard on the PV equipment intended for long-term operation forcing power degradation and failures.

These problems are being worked on as we speak. It is only logical and practical to point out, therefore, that even small portions of the U.S. deserts are capable of providing a major portion of the electric power to the U.S. and neighboring countries in the future. The climate and behavior of the deserts have been studied for a long time, and are well understood, so with the necessary precautions and proper solar technology selection, design, installation and operation, deserts might—and should—become the hub of solar energy generation for the U.S., Mexico, and Canada in the not-so-distant future.

Safety and Environmental Issues in the Desert

And speaking of the desert, this is a good time and place to emphasize the fact that the desert areas is where the maximum amount of sun energy is concentrated, where we see the maximum MW of PV modules installed recently. It is also where we expect most of the efficient and profitable future large-scale power generating plans to be located. This brings a number of issues into play, some of which are very serious and critical to the future of the PV and energy industries.

To start with, please remember that the deserts are the harshest and most unforgiving areas in the world. The deserts have no friends. The deserts are merciless killers, and they attack ferociously anything and everything that dares challenge their power.

Anything left on the desert floor such as metals, glass, ceramics, plastics, and every other element and substance known to man, will be attacked and eventually changed, or destroyed by the desert sun with its IR and UV radiation, sand and rain storms, as well as its never ending dry and humid, heat and freeze cycles.

Work and operation in remote desert areas is difficult, and sometimes impossible. Even in civilized countries and developed areas, paved roads and other infrastructure are few and far between, which makes regular maintenance also quite difficult. PV modules and people alike must endure the climate extremes—heat and freezing, dust, storms, etc. The IR and UV radiation in the desert extremes attacks the PV modules, they suffer, and with time undergo serious changes, deterioration, and failures.

Desert-based PV installations are exposed to the whims of Mother Nature, which is quite cruel in these areas, so some foreseen and unforeseen damage has to be expected—and in more exaggerated form than in any location around the world.

In most cases PV modules contain plastic materials (EVA etc.), which are used as laminators and edge sealers, but the desert IR and UV radiation eats plastics for breakfast and spits them out as useless, shapeless masses within several short years. What will happen to the modules when the protection is destroyed is anyone's guess. We, however, don't see anything good coming out of it.

The most likely outcome in such cases is that the desert elements will penetrate inside the modules and will start a direct offensive action, comprised of a mixture of mechanical, thermodynamic and chemical aggression. At this point the active films inside the modules (Si solar cells or thin films) are on their own, but from long previous experience we know that they have no chance. Performance degradation and total failure will follow soon enough.

Another serious and unavoidable danger, in addition to unrelenting extreme heat, is that of sand storms and lightning strikes, which can damage the structures mechanically or electrically. They can also cause additional damage by sandblasting the PV modules' optical elements, thus reducing their efficiency or eventually rendering them useless. Of course, frequent and serious surface soiling is an unavoidable damage and another expense we must face in the desert.

There is no known method of preventing wind and sand damage, but some precautions could and should be taken during the design and installation stages, as follows:

1. Gravel-type deserts are best suited for large-scale PV installations, because they contain less free sand and are less likely to cause damage by sandblasting critical components.

2. Build protective wind barriers around the edges of the power plants to reduce the wind speed and minimize the sandblasting effect.

3. Incorporate in the overall system design an efficient way to stow trackers, or to turn them in the direction of the wind, thus protecting their optical side from sandblasting damage.

We need to remember that work in the desert is always difficult for a number of reasons, some of which we discussed above. Large-scale PV installations are a new phenomenon and we don't have enough experience to be able to take all precautions needed for safe and efficient operation. So no doubt that the first large-scale installations will be the "guinea pigs" of the utility scale PV power generation in the US.

Let's hope these guinea pigs survive the test of time, and even more importantly; that they behave well, and don't make us victims of our haste, negligence and ignorance.

Case Study. Thin Film PV in the Deserts

Large-scale solar power plants in the deserts are becoming the norm, a standard of efficient power generation. How about the environmental side of things? What do we expect, or not expect from these during 30 long years of on-sun operation in world's most ferocious deserts?

First Solar, manufacturer and developer of CdTe PV modules and power fields is installing millions of their CdTe PV modules on thousands of acres desert land in California and Arizona. But wait…CdTe PV modules are a new product that has never been proven efficient and safe for desert operation. Never.

And remember that each of the millions CdTe PV modules installed in the US deserts contains 8-9 grams compounds of the toxic, *carcinogenic heavy metal cadmium*. So what do we expect to happen?

To get a better idea of the issues related to the

toxicity of CdTe modules see below excerpts from an Environmental Report (C.9 Hazards and Hazardous Materials) issued by the San Luis Obispo County Planning Commission) on a large scale project, proposed to contain over 9.0 million CdTe modules spread over 4,000 acres desert land in California—on top of San Andreas fault line, no less.

Hazardous Materials Related to Cadmium Telluride PV Module Technology

The PV modules panels proposed for use at the Proposed Project site contain cadmium telluride (CdTe), which is formed when elemental cadmium (Cd) is reacted with tellurium (Te), and also contain a smaller amount of cadmium sulfide (CdS).

The total onsite quantity of cadmium telluride in the modules would be approximately 123.0 tons and cadmium sulfide would be 2.45 tons. Therefore, the total amount of cadmium and tellurium that is fully encapsulated within the modules at the site would be approximately 59.5 tons and 65.4 tons, respectively.

The solar modules, based on various testing data (NGI, 2010b; SAL, 2010; Steinberger, 1997), exceed both the State's Total Threshold Limit Concentration (TTLC) of 100 ppm for cadmium and the Soluble Threshold Limit Concentration (STLC) of 1.0 ppm for cadmium (SAL, 2010).

The TTLC is a total composition analysis that does not factor in the potential for release.

The U.S. EPA has classified cadmium as a probable human carcinogen ("Group B1"; EPA, 2000).

Cadmium telluride and cadmium sulfide, the two compounds of cadmium used in the solar modules, are currently regulated within the group of cadmium and cadmium compounds. CdTe appears to be less toxic than elemental cadmium in terms of acute exposure, but the highly reactive oxidizing surface of CdTe when in quantum dot form can damage cell membranes, mitochondria, and cell nuclei.

Tellurium compounds are highly toxic and teratogenic (causative of birth defects); exposure can also cause intensely bad breath and body odors, and in higher doses can cause chronic effects to the liver and acute effects to the digestive tract, such as nausea and constipation.

The solar panels, based on various testing data, exceed both the State's Total Threshold Limit Concentration (TTLC) of 100 ppm for cadmium and the Soluble. Threshold Limit Concentration (STLC) of 1.0 ppm for cadmium.

The module cost includes the recycling costs, so

that the end user has already pre-paid for modules to be recycled and it would cost them more to do anything other than recycling the modules through First Solar.

Some of the studies performed to determine the environmental impacts of CdTe module technology question the economic and technical viability of CdTe module recycling and whether cadmium should be used in a "green" technology.

Hazardous Materials During Construction

There is a small chance that panels broken severely during installation could release CdTe particles or flakes into the environment during panel removal and off-site transport. Removal and off-site transport of broken panels would therefore pose a significant risk to on-site personnel and members of the public at the Visitor Center and in residences surrounded by the project.

Mitigation Measure HZ-1.7 would require that broken panels be collected by personnel wearing protective respiratory gear and placed in airtight containers for offsite shipment in order to reduce the potential for broken panels to pose a health risk to project personnel and members of the public.

Hazardous Materials During Operation

Out of the approximately 9 million modules to be installed onsite, it is expected that approximately 36,000 modules would break during the three year construction period and an average of 2,880 100 modules would break on average each year during operations; and 72,000 2,500 modules (0.80 0.03 percent) would break during project operation over the 25-year module life.

In the event of a broken module, the amount of cadmium and tellurium that would be available for release would be much less than the 6 and 6.6 grams, respectively, that are contained in each module; where only the CdTe located along the fracture lines would have the potential to be released from the solid CdTe and CdS film matrices of the modules.

It is possible that very small amounts of cadmium could leach out of a broken module if the cadmium were exposed to natural precipitation that has a low pH. Testing results of CdTe module leaching potential (NGI 2010b; SAL, 2010) indicate that CdTe has a greater potential for leaching if exposed to low pH liquids, which could occur if CdTe is exposed to low pH rainwater (acid rain). These studies and tests have shown that leaching from the module material, particularly Cd is strongly dependent on pH conditions. While Cd leaching at the material's intrinsic pH is low due to sorption/precipitation, a lower pH may cause substantial leaching. Thus,

CdTe film that is exposed to natural precipitation in the environment that has a low pH (pH<6) could exhibit substantial leaching of Cd and Te.

Other site specific and PV module design factors that have been considered are as follows:

- Each module contains approximately 6 grams of cadmium, modules are normally completely encapsulated so exposure of Cd to the environment could only occur from broken/fractured modules; and only 108,000 2,500 modules are expected to break over the life of the project. This represents a total project life release potential of 33 lbs of cadmium, if the panels were finely ground and exposed to low pH liquids.

- The applicant has proposed a module collection and recycling program, as part of the project description that will be subject to County inspection and enforcement, which will limit the potential exposure time of any broken modules to the elements.

- The breakage pattern for the modules, due to their design including a strong laminate material, is similar to safety glass, which will crack but not shatter. This would keep the very thin CdTe and CdS containing surfaces encapsulated under the expected module breakage scenarios and would significantly reduce the potential for environmental exposure of the very thin CdTe and CdS containing surfaces.

- The Applicant completed an ambient air sampling analysis of broken module handling in 2010 and found that all of the airborne cadmium concentrations, including those from a personal air sampler for the worker handling the modules, were at least ten times below First Solar's internal action level of 1.0 g/m^3 and at least 30 times lower than OSHA's action level of 2.5 g/m^3. This sampling analysis is conservative in comparison with potential outdoor exposures since it was conducted in an enclosed warehouse.

- The active footprint of the project would be approximately 4,100 acres, so under worst case conditions, where 33 lbs of cadmium (the maximum amount of Cd expected to be able to be released over the life of the project) were mixed evenly with the top foot of soil under the project area that would increase the cadmium concentration in the soils by approximately 0.22 parts per billion (ppb), or if a single panel (4 feet by 1.97 feet) were to release its entire 6 grams of cadmium the surface soil at a depth of one foot, assuming all the cadmium is mixed evenly in the first foot of soil, would have its average cadmium concentration increased by 17 ppm.

- Acid rain is not considered a concern in the area of the Carrizo Plain (BLM, 2009), due to the remoteness and low level of development in the area. However, normal rain, due to the absorption of CO$_2$ forming carbonic acid, has a pH of approximately 5.6. Additionally, if future development, with emissions of nitrogen and sulfur compounds (NO$_x$ and SO$_x$), in the area increases then the concern regarding acid rain, or acid fog, could increase.

- Rainfall in the area averages approximately 7 to 9 inches per year, and is sporadic, infrequent and undependable, which would limit the initial leaching potential of Cd from broken modules, if inspected properly and removed quickly after being severely damaged, and would also limit the movement of Cd through the soil column into underground aquifers.

- As described in the groundwater study, groundwater levels in area wells are between 10 and 40 feet below ground surface.

NOTE: In our expert opinion, this report brings more questions from scientific and socio-economic nature, than it answers. And while it addresses (albeit very superficially) some of the key issues, most of them remain unanswered, such as:

1. A number of assumptions were made in the report that simply lacks scientific proof and merit.
   a. Assumptions without scientific proof are just that; assumptions, and cannot/should not be used to justify poisoning thousands of acres—even if the chance is small.
   b. This is especially true when the report is issued by government authority and backed by taxpayers' money and loan guarantees.

2. Large quantity of toxic materials containing product, spread over very large land areas is not some-

thing that we can justify as a scientific experiment, especially when human health and life are concerned and might be affected on the long run,

3. Even if small percentage of modules are broken (1% of 9.0 million modules is still a great number; over 90,000 modules), or catch on fire, or if in any way release their toxic contents in the air, soil and water table, the impact to the local environment and life forms in it would be tremendous. Nearby population centers, shallow water table, heavy winds, mixed with large amount of toxic materials contained between the fragile glass panes on top of the ready to blow any day San Andreas fault, is a hazmat nightmare and something that must be thoroughly evaluated and not just superficially estimated and dismissed as "negligible."

Good planning, no doubt of people who probably never had a chance to learn about, let alone work with, cadmium to be aware and beware of its vicious nature. The planners (or the investigators writing the report) also seem to know very little about thin film solar modules, let alone their behavior under 30 years of blistering desert sun.

It is also quite easy to see the bias (mixed with ignorance on the subject) in the report writing; the major issues are addressed, but very superficially discussed, and usually dismissing the dangers of any toxic cadmium contamination as "remote."…although there is absolutely no scientific evidence to support the conclusions or hide the bias:

It is more than obvious that this report was done in haste and issued under duress. It was done to meet a deadline and accelerate the permitting process, without enough effort to evaluate the risks properly and justify using toxic cadmium materials in such a very large project…in the desert…on top of San Andrea active seismic fault, no less.

Why are we exposing ourselves and the environment to real danger using unproven and untested products in such large quantities? Using 120 tons of carcinogenic, heavy metal, cadmium, spread evenly over 4,000 acres is something that should make us pause and take a very, very close look at what we are doing. Do we need to use cadmium at all? Isn't there any other way of doing this?

The question of cadmium toxicity is actually quite simple and one doesn't need to be a Nobel laureate to answer it properly. It goes like this:

Table 5-15. Cadmium safety questions

	Question	Answer
1.	Do CdTe PV modules contain cadmium compounds?	Yes
2.	Is cadmium toxic and carcinogenic element?	Yes
3.	Could cadmium escape from the modules in field operations?	Yes
4.	Would the escape be facilitated by high desert temperatures?	Yes
5.	Are we installing millions of CdTe PV modules in the U.S. deserts?	Yes
6.	Are CdTe PV modules proven reliable and safe for desert use?	No
7.	Who will be responsible in case of a large-scale air-soil contamination?	?

For the interested reader, we have expanded each of these answers in our previous books on solar energy (see ref. 27 and 28.)

These questions are similar to those asked during the large-scale use of lead, asbestos, and nicotine and the following respective debacles. Are we headed into another one with cadmium?

Well, it is too late now. The work at the Topaz Solar Farm is well under way and it is hailed as an example of large-scale success. Although we do agree that it is success in terms of the conventional way of thinking, we fear that will become a major disaster in the not very distant future. What an inheritance we are leaving to the future generations, who will be forced to clean up this and many other messes we made lately.

And as if this was not enough, there are other issues to consider as far as CdTe PV modules discrepancies are concerned:

Case Study. UL Certification Bypass
In the summer of 2012 First Solar was able to "beat the system" once again by introducing a modification to the meaning of "UL certification" of PV modules as we know it. A lowly LA County safety inspector discovered that 4 million of the First Solar CdTe PV modules at the Antelope Valley Solar PV plant lack proper UL certification and dared to report the discrepancy to his superiors.

But with time First Solar and their partners were able to lean hard on the LA County officials and as a result, "…the parties have agreed on a modification to the problematic connectors that will not impose undue burden on First Solar but will satisfy the County's safety concerns."

Obviously, the County officials are more worried about inconveniencing First Solar than any possible damages and other consequences from large quantity of uncertified product.

To the best of our knowledge, no one has ever been able to do such a daring, and so well publicized, large scale bypass of UL certification procedures in violation of US electrical code with such a long lasting effect; 30 years on-sun operation in the world's most ferocious deserts.

But the worst part in this case is that the millions of CdTe PV modules, lacking UL certification have not been proven efficient or safe for long-term desert operation to begin with. And on top of that, each of these modules contains significant quantity of compounds of the *toxic, carcinogenic heavy metal cadmium*.

With a long history of defects, recalls and rejects in the past involving this type of modules, we know that they are not perfect. Lacking UL certification makes them even more, and more dangerously, so. Looking at the recall of thousands of Schluten PV modules for defective junction boxes, we discussed above, we wonder if we won't see a similar situation in the US deserts in the near future too.

So what if the field bursts into flames some day? What if the mighty San Andreas Fault opens up and swallows millions of the cadmium-ridden modules and the cadmium contamination spreads over large land areas and reaches the underground water table? What would the esteemed LA County and First Solar officials say and do then?

Oh, yes, not possible, of course! But we've heard that on several occasions already; the latest one from BP, Exxon, the nicotine, asbestos and many other large corporations in our past that brought us huge disasters with untold environmental damage, human suffering and death.

The officials involved in these cases should not worry though, because corporate officials seldom get held personally responsible, so full blast ahead we go; neither hell or high water…nor authorities or cadmium can stop us!!!

PV Modules Recycling

While the solar cell is the heart of a photovoltaic system, on a mass basis it accounts for only a small fraction of the total materials required for a solar panel. The outer glass cover constitutes the largest share of the total mass of a finished crystalline photovoltaic module (approximately 65%), followed by the aluminum frame (~20%), the ethylene vinyl acetate encapsulant (~7.5%), the polyvinyl fluoride substrate (~2.5%) and the junction box (1%). The solar cells themselves only represent about four percent (4%) of the mass of a finished PV module.

Proper decommissioning and recycling of solar panels both ensures that potentially harmful materials are not released into the environment and reduces the need for virgin raw materials. In recognition of these facts, the photovoltaic industry is acting voluntarily to implement product take-back and recycling programs at the manufacturing level.

Collectively, the industry recently launched PV Cycle, a trade association to develop an industry-wide take back program in Europe. In the United States and Europe, product take-back and recycling programs vary by manufacturer and project. The earlier projects did not consider this option, so they will be the first Guinea Pigs in the near future.

While recycling methods and take-back policies vary by manufacturer, the most frequently recycled components are the cover glass, aluminum frame, and solar cells. Small quantities of valuable metals including copper and steel are also recoverable. The ethylene vinyl acetate encapsulant and polyvinyl fluoride substrate are typically not recoverable and are removed through a thermal process with strict emission controls and the by-product ash land-filled. Following this process, the glass and aluminum frame are separated and typically sold to industrial recyclers.

The solar cells are then reprocessed into silicon wafers with valuable metals recovered, reused or sold. Depending on the condition, the wafer can then either be remade into a functioning cell or granulated to serve as feedstock for new polysilicon.

If not properly decommissioned, the greatest EOL health risk from crystalline solar modules arises from lead containing soldering compounds. Under the right conditions it is possible for the lead to leach into landfill soils and eventually into water bodies.

There is a much greater risk in recycling of thin film based PV modules, due to the high toxic content in some of them. Proper, much more complex and expensive procedures must be followed as needed to ensure the safety of the decommissioned land, the labor during decommissioning, the transport and the actual recycling and disposal processes.

PV companies worldwide are actively moving towards the recycling of their products, both for manufacturing waste and end-of-life modules. EU companies have proposed a voluntary take back system capable of meeting the future waste recycling demands. The new recycling process lines must be capable of processing crystalline silicon and thin-film modules alike. The silicon recycling is now at the pilot stage, and reuse of silicon material will be timely for the industry.

US companies have been reclaiming solar cells and semiconductor process wafers for many years, so the expertise and equipment are available. Scaling up to accommodate the large demand of the future is a key to success here.

Recycling and reclaiming reduce the energy payback time by a factor of 4 in the best-case scenario, but this depends on the available insolation at the PV power site and the particular PV technology used.

The forecast is that 40,000 MT of PV components will be ready for decommissioning and recycling by 2020, and this number will double or triple in the following decade. This includes silicon and thin-film based PV components recycling. The thin-film component will be ~ 20% by then. CdTe thin-film PV modules, or 8,000 MT, will be the majority of the recycled products in this category. 8,000 MT CdTe PV modules is a lot of modules which, with an average of 8-9 grams of cadmium* in each module, could create a serious hazmat debacle if not handled and processed properly.

NOTE: Cadmium is one of the six most toxic carcinogenic heavy metals on Earth, which together with tellurium, selenium, arsenic and other toxic metals and their compounds must be handled with utmost caution during the uninstall, transport, crushing, and disposal. Disposal of some components as hazardous waste is another major issue to be addressed and fully resolved in the years to come, because special handling, transport, processing, and containment would be required.

The EU already has directives for voluntary and extended manufacturer responsibility, where the decommissioning, transport, storage, processing, and disposal of the modules are the ultimate responsibility of the original manufacturer. The directives have been integrated into the legal system of several member states. Different paragraphs outline the registration, packaging, transport, waste disposal, documentation, legal responsibilities, etc. These components of the overall effort to protect the environment and life during all stages of the manufacture, use, and recycling of PV products clearly place the responsibility on the manufacturers' shoulders. Customers and users are required to be aware of the issues at hand and to observe and complete their obligations as well.

This means that whoever made the PV products is legally responsible for them and obligated to dispose of them at end of their useful life. The manufacturer is obliged to assure the proper execution of this process in all cases—even if no longer in business. Special arrangements, such as insurance or delegation of responsibility must be provided at the time of installation and be well documented prior to starting the actual work on each

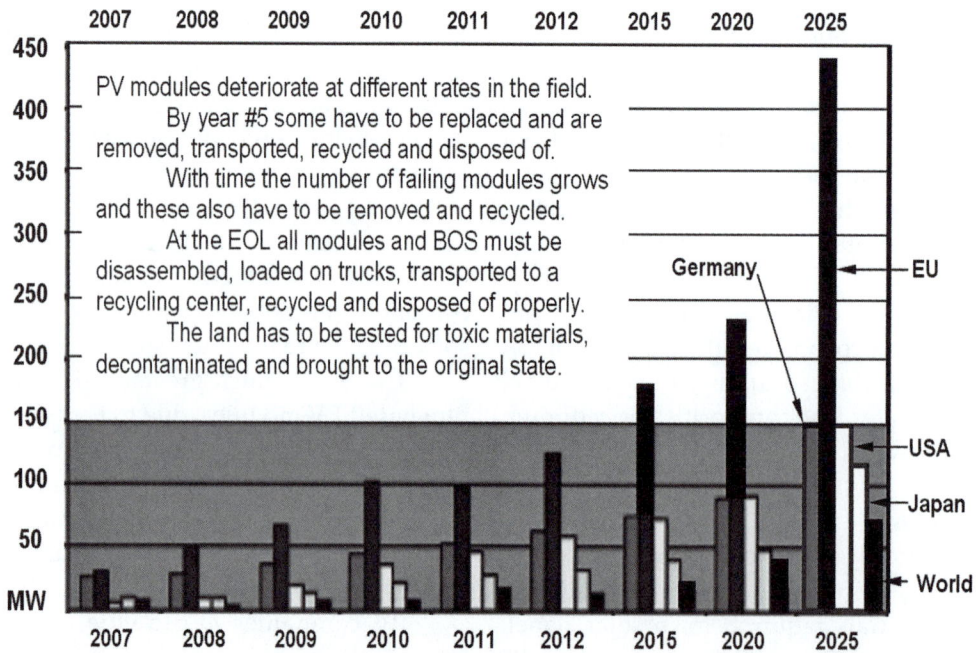

Figure 5-38. Forecast of PV waste recycling in the decades to come

project. The cost of the decommissioning process is to be agreed upon and reflected in the installed cost of the power plant.

Every year around the world, a large quantity of PV modules will reach their end-of-life state, become obsolete, or fail. From all these old modules, structural steel, aluminum, inverters, wiring, and other hardware will need to be disassembled, sorted, loaded on trucks, and transported long distances for recycling and/or disposal. This is a great effort, which in many cases is neither planned nor taken into consideration during the PV plants' design and financing stages. If this is not done properly, or if it is hidden from view, then we need to assume irresponsible behavior, something that we need to watch out for.

PV modules recycling consists of a number of steps that need to be considered, planned, and properly executed during recycling and disposal procedures. Some of these operations are accompanied by toxic gas and liquids generation, so special caution must be exercised during their execution as well.

Also, the proper final disposal of waste materials and related chemicals and gases is absolutely necessary. That too is the responsibility of the project owners and products manufacturers.

Recognizing and embracing cradle-to-grave responsibility for products and land safety, as well as proper handling and disposal, must be one of the conditions to participate in any PV project in the US. We have no reason to ignore this critical aspect of PV industry development, regardless of what other countries do or do not do. The future generations' wellbeing depends on our decisions.

Solar Plant Decommissioning

The solar plants designers, installers, investors, and operators, in addition to the responsibility to ensure the safe plant operation, are also fully responsible for the proper decommissioning and disposal of the plant's components, as well as for final cleaning and bringing the land to its original state.

As can be clearly seen in Table 5-17, the manufacturer is legally responsible for the safety and proper execution of all steps from the beginning to the end of the useful life of their products. The retailers, installers, and plant operators are also responsible in some stages of the product life. Overall, all entities who have been involved in the power plant's planning, design, instal-

Table 5-16. PV modules recycling steps and methods

RECYCLING OF PV MODULES AT EOL

c-Si MODULES			TFPV MODULES		
RECYCLABLE	kg/m²	%	RECYCLABLE	kg/m²	%
Glass	10.0	90	Glass	15.0	90
Aluminum	1.4	100	Aluminum	0	0
Solar cells	0.5	90	Solar cells	0.1	90
EVA, Tedlar	1.4	0	EVA, Tedlar	0	0
Ribbons	0.1	95	Ribbons	0	0
Adhesives	0.2	0	Adhesives	0.2	0

RECYCLING AND DISPOSAL METHODS

Mechanical	Crushing, attrition, density separation, flotation, adsorption, radiation, laser beam, metal separation, and other methods.
Chemical	Acid / base treatment, extraction with solvents, dissolving, precipitation, slagging, and other methods.
Thermal	Incineration, burn-out, pyrolysis, melting, slagging, and other similar methods.
EOL disposal	Recycling into the same product, recycling into another product, recovery of energy from thermal treatment of organic layers, utilization of mineral fractions (e.g., concrete, road material, etc.), and landfill disposal.

Table 5-17. End-of-life outline of the participants' responsibilities

EOL TREATMENT OF TFPV MODULES	DECISION AND EOL* NOTICE ⇨	REMOVAL ⇨	TRANSPORT ⇨	RECOVERY & DISPOSAL
GENERAL REQUIREMENTS	Notify proper authorities of EOL	Proper and safe procedures use	Authorized Hazmat carrier use	Authorized facilities use
ORGANIZATIONAL RESPONSIBILITY	Plant operator	Manufacturer and operator	Manufacturer	Manufacturer
TECHNICAL RESPONSIBILITY	Plant operator	Manufacturer and operator	Manufacturer	Manufacturer
FINANCIAL RESPONSIBILITY	Plant operator	Manufacturer and operator	Manufacturer	Manufacturer
LEGAL RESPONSIBILITY	Plant operator	Manufacturer and operator	Manufacturer	Manufacturer

lation, and operation are responsible to one degree or another for the proper execution of the respective steps, including the final decommissioning, recycling, and disposal of the plant components and land cleanup.

Cost of Environmental Issues

The environmental costs of PV plants' setup and operation is defined by monetary quantification of the socio-economic and environmental effects and damage they do (and will) as they inflict a local area, a nation, and the world as a whole during their cradle-to-grave life cycle. These effects and the related damages could be expressed in $ per kWh generated, for lack of better way, and should account for all materials, procedures, and events from cradle to grave.

Included in these calculations are: environmental effects; human health; materials production; effects of use and disposal (materials, gasses, chemicals) on agriculture; noise; audio and visual pollution; ecosystem effects (acidification, CO_2 damage); and all other effects. Thusly obtained numbers could be used to provide a scientific basis for legislative and regulatory policies, energy taxes and incentives, global warming policy adjustments, etc.

Costs are defined as the monetary quantification of the socio-environmental damage, expressed in euro-cents/kWh, with the possibility of providing a scientific basis for policy decisions and legislative proposals such as subsidizing cleaner technologies and energy taxes to internalize the external costs. It looks at all energy-production technologies using a methodology developed for this project that allows the various fuel cycles to be compared. An outline of the initial results for the PV fuel cycle, starting with a very small sample of PV systems,

shows that the results are not consistent and require more work.

There has been pressure from the PV industry for the PV fuel cycle to be re-done using a larger sample of more representative systems, but this is still in the making. So, one of the earliest publications from this project by Baumann et al. is still valid. In this paper the author outlines the basic assumptions and requirements of the methodological framework for the quantification of external costs and compares the environmental effects of different energy technologies, including renewables and the conventional technologies of coal, oil, nuclear, and natural gas.

Basically speaking, PV systems must be designed and manufactured with long-term environmental concerns and considerations in mind, which must include:

1. Manufacturing materials and procedures, including the production and use of MG and SG Si, thin-film metals and chemicals, glass panes, metals frames, gasses, chemicals, etc. process supplies

2. Solar wafers and cells manufacturing equipment and processes

3. Module encapsulation and framing processes

4. Evaluation of direct and indirect processing energy (including transport, storage, etc.)

5. Gross energy requirements of input materials (supply chain and internally generated products and byproducts)

6. Allocation schemes used in the calculations

7. Separate thermal energy, electrical energy, and "material energy" calculations

8.	End-of-life recycling and disposal calculations (including transport and storage)

There are a number of dislocated efforts in the above areas, but no uniform, standardized method presently exists that is capable of capturing all environmental factors into one, all-encompassing methodology. Such a methodology is needed to account for the effects of the above concerns on the PV manufacturing processes and long-term use of the related PV products.

Conclusions

In conclusion, solar energy is still abundant and readily available, waiting to be harnessed for the good of mankind. We have seen the solar industry's ups and downs of the past decades and have learned much from the lessons of the past. Starting now we should make solar energy a priority for our energy future, until we achieve the goals of energy independence and a clean environment.

Technological and market conditions were not ripe for the full implementation of solar energy in energy markets until recently, and there were other barriers, too. Nowadays, however, the environmental and energy situations in the U.S. and the world have changed so that there is no going back—solar is here to stay! Existing and future solar energy companies will be on the forefront of alternative energy development, thus bringing bright, efficient and safe solar energy and clean environment to future generations.

A major focus presently is (and will be for the foreseeable future) on access to the coveted desert lands with their abundant sunlight. This opens a huge market, where millions and billions of PV modules could be installed, so the battle is just now starting. The goal of this book is to provide an unbiased review of the technological aspects of the competing solar technologies and bring their advantages and disadvantages out into the open.

These are exciting times, and we all should participate in the energy revolution using our God-given gifts and abilities to move it ahead quickly, thus ensuring its progress and ultimate success. Future generations will definitely appreciate our efforts and the results thereof.

WIND POWER

Wind energy is basically the movement of air from an area of high pressure to an area of low pressure, caused by the uneven heating of the surface of the Earth. This causes hot air to rise, and as a result, cooler air moves in to replace it.

Wind power is one of the oldest forms of energy use, but large-scale wind farms are a new phenomenon. Starting in the early 2000, new wind farms have been popping up all around the world increasing at an astonishing 25% a year. And even then, wind provides only a very small fraction of the U.S. and world's energy.

Modern wind turbines are impressive giants, as tall as a 20-story building with two or three 200-foot-long blades, swinging like the arms of a giant. The wind spins the blades, which turn a shaft connected to a generator that produces electricity. These are turbines on horizontal axis, while the blades of wind turbines on vertical axes are different, and look like a giant egg-beater suspended high in the air.

In all cases, these gentle giants generate a lot of power—if there is wind to turn the blades. The biggest wind turbines, rated at 2-2.5 MW, each generate enough electricity to supply about 600 U.S. homes. Smaller turbines erected in a backyard can produce enough electricity for a single home or small business. Large-scale wind farms have hundreds of turbines lined up together in a particular way in especially windy spots, like a windy valley or along a mountain ridge.

Wind is a clean source of renewable energy that produces no air or water pollution. And since the wind is free, operational costs are nearly zero once a turbine is erected. Mass production and technology advances are making turbines cheaper, and many governments offer tax incentives to spur wind-energy development.

Although large wind farms cover large land areas, the land is still available for many uses, such as agriculture and other activities that can deal with the small ar-

Figure 5-39. Large wind turbine

eas of turbine foundations and other infrastructure that occupies some part of the land.

Global wind generation quadrupled between 2000 and 2006, and went through another boom cycle during 2007-2012, which has now leveled. At the end of 2012, global capacity was more than 70 GW.

Germany leads the world with the most installed wind energy capacity, followed by Spain, the United States, India, and Denmark. France and China are making good progress in wind generation too. It is possible, if this pace continues, that by 2050 one third of the world's electricity needs will be met by wind power.

The major disadvantages of wind power generation are that:

- Wind turbines are large, intrusive, and some think ugly.

- Turbines are noisy, and the neighbors complain about the constant noise they make.

- Wind turbine blades kill birds and bats.

- The major problem is that wind is variable; if there is no wind, there's no electricity.

- The variability requires additional fuel to be used by peaker (on-demand) power plants as needed to stabilize the load and meet demand. This creates additional pollution and adds significant expense to the O&M operations.

Environmental Impact of Wind Power

Although compared to the traditional energy sources (coal, oil, and gas), the environmental impact of wind power is relatively minor, since wind power uses no fuel and emits no air pollution in operation.

Nevertheless, like the other energy sources, it uses a lot of energy during its cradle-to-grave life cycle. Wind turbine materials must be mined, transported, processed, manufactured, and disposed of, as is the case with all other power plants. The energy consumed during these processes is significant and can be equated to the energy produced by the wind plant during several months, and some time even years.

CO_2 emissions of wind power are estimated to range from 15- to 35-tons per GWh of energy produced, which is equivalent to the CO_2 emission from producing the concrete and metals for making the wind-turbine foundation and its structure.

Another significant issue that recently has been in the spotlight is the production of permanent magnets used in some wind turbines. The magnets are made out of the rare earth metal neodymium, which is mined and exported by China.

Serious pollution concerns associated with the extraction of this rare-earth element have prompted government action in recent years. A number of international research efforts have sprung out in response, in an attempt to refine the extraction process. Other efforts are underway on turbine and generator designs geared to reducing and even eliminating the use neodymium. Several wind turbine manufacturers are no longer using permanent magnets for direct drive turbines, thus avoiding the bad publicity and responsibility for the bad environmental imprint of rare earth mining.

Because wind is inherently in flux and unreliable, wind-powered energy grids require additional fossil-fuel-based energy to balance and stabilize them. Wind is obviously a pure, clean energy source, but to convert the energy it produces to electricity requires fossil-fuel-based energy.

Wind turbines additionally require the area around them to be clear of trees to maximize efficiency requiring an average of 50 acres per megawatt of capacity. The GE 1.5-MW turbine model needs at least 32 acres and the Vestas V90 model needs 78 acres for each tower on a mountain ridge.

Most wind turbines are constructed at high altitudes to gather in more wind. Because of this, many wind turbines have experienced damage due to icing. To combat this problem, de-icing fluid is place on the wings of wind turbines. The de-icing fluid is typically made up of two toxic chemicals known as propylene glycol and ethylene glycol. The de-icing fluid used on offshore wind farms as well as wind farms located on farm land is hazardous to the local fish and cattle population and contaminates the local food, soil, and groundwater near wind turbines.

In the mid-Atlantic Highlands, wind turbines will kill an estimated 33,000 to 111,000 bats by 2020. Bats are particularly vital to an ecosystem because of the hundreds of billions of insects they consume every year. A study done in 2008 shows that a wind farm in at Altamont Pass, California, kills an average of 80 golden eagles per year, while Exxon Mobil kills 100 times that with its industrial tanks.

Wind farms may affect weather in their immediate vicinity. Spinning wind turbine rotors generate a lot of turbulence in their wakes, like the wake of a boat. This turbulence increases vertical mixing of heat and water vapor that affects the meteorological conditions downwind. Overall, wind farms lead to a warming at night and cooling during the daytime. Using more efficient rotors or placing wind farms in regions with high natural turbulence can reduce this effect. However, warming at night could "benefit agriculture by decreasing frost damage and extending the growing season. Many farmers already do this with air circulators."[64][65][66]

A number of studies have used climate models to study the effect of extremely large wind farms. One study reports simulations that show detectable changes in global climate for very high wind farm usage, on the order of 10% of the world's land area. Wind power has a negligible effect on global mean surface temperature, and it would deliver enormous global benefits by reducing emissions of CO_2 and air pollutants.

Another study suggested that using wind turbines to meet 10% of global energy demand in 2100 could actually have a warming effect, causing temperatures to rise by nearly 2°F in the regions on land where the wind farms are installed. Smaller increases are expected in areas beyond those regions. This is due to the effect of wind turbines on both horizontal and vertical atmospheric circulation. While turbines installed in water would have a cooling effect, the net impact on global surface temperatures would be an increase of 0.3°F.

NOTE: We must mention here that neither this author, nor the authors of the studies mentioned above, has anything against wind power. On the contrary, we feel obligated to bring the issues at hand into the open, to encourage an open dialog among all parties involved. We are actually very optimistic about the potential of wind power as a worldwide energy source, and hope that the mentioned studies and the controversies that they might create would serve as a foundation for future research.

Safety

Operation of any utility-scale energy conversion system presents safety hazards. Wind turbines do not consume fuel or produce pollution during normal operation, but still have hazards associated with their construction, operation and maintenance.

With the installation of thousands of industrial-sized wind turbines, there have been work-related accidents, and many worker fatalities during their construction, operation, and maintenance. There are over 1,000 reported cases of accidents, malfunction and other serious issues related to wind turbine installation and operation (23). Working on a wind turbine is indeed a dangerous occupation.

The incidents and accident reports are sad and eerie. Just to mention a few as examples:

1975—Worker fell from tower while removing small turbine and the body found near tower.

1981—Worker atop nacelle, run-away rotor, no lanyard, fell from tower and died.

1984—Worker, driving tractor as tow vehicle, tractor flipped over crushing him.

1989—Worker atop nacelle, servicing nacelle, with no brake, lanyard caught on main shaft protrusion, death attributed to "multiple amputations" as he was dragged into the machinery.

1991—A 16-year-old boy died of asphyxiation in a windmill accident on his family's farm. Climbed the windmill to retrieve a broken coupling, and was caught by the rotating shaft, and his clothing strangled him.

1994—Worker inside base tower section during winter when a large chunk of ice fell, cutting him in half.

1997—Worker killed inside prototype turbine at test field when blade parts and turbine housing flew up to 500m.

2002—Two men fell 10m within the turbine tower. The one above fell on his fellow worker and was killed on the spot.

2004—34-year-old service technician fell from the turbine to his death.

2008—Worker in the tower of one of the turbines fell to his death when his safety belt broke.

2011—Iowa man dies after falling 60 feet from a wind tower.

Living near wind farms also seems to be hazardous, too:

A 54-year-old pilot died in a plane crash in 2009. Flying near a wind farm with several 400-foot turbines, he attempted to maneuver around the turbines but then crashed in a field.

During the 2013 hurricane season, a huge wind turbine blade flew off and landed on a high school building. Luckily there were no injuries.

There are numerous accounts of fires, lightening strikes, excess-wind torn blades, towers collapsing, and a number of other problems encountered on wind farm fields and the surrounding areas. There is an estimate that the mortality rate from wind power accidents during 1980–1994 was approximately 0.4 deaths per TW/h

Figure 5-40. Collapsed wind turbine.

power generation. A further decline in the death rate down to 0.15 deaths per GWh was reported in 2000, which is attributed mostly to better safety procedures and controls, as well as to a much greater total cumulative wind generation.

Other types of injuries and causes for death accidents attributed to the entire wind power life cycle have been reported as well. Most worker deaths involve falling from great heights, or becoming caught in machinery while performing maintenance inside tight-spaced turbine housings.

For example, if a turbine's controls and/or brakes fail, the turbine can spin freely, accelerating up to the current wind speed until it finally disintegrates or catches fire. This is rare occurrence and the odds of a major turbine fire or disintegration is on the order of 0.001% over the 20-25-year lifespan of a modern wind turbine. Nevertheless, accidents happen, and the percentage matters not to those who are around the failed giant.

There are incidents involving turbine gondola fires, which cannot be extinguished because of their height, so, fueled by gear oil and lubricants, they are sometimes left to burn themselves out. In such cases, in addition to hurting or killing humans, the fires also generate significant amount of toxic fumes, and sometimes cause secondary fires on the ground below.

There are reports of several turbine-ignited fires that have burned dozens of acres of shrub each. However, newer wind turbines are built with automatic fire extinguishing systems similar to those fitted on some jet aircraft engines. The autonomous FIREX systems, for example, which can be retrofitted to older wind turbines automatically, detect a fire, order the shut down of the turbine unit, and immediately completely extinguish the fires. This, of course, increases the initial cost and the O&M expenses of the wind power installation, so it is an option that is used only in some cases.

Ice formation on turbine blades is another hazard to be considered during the initial design, because chunks of ice can be thrown off the blades during operation. The flying chunks are potential safety hazards that have led to shut downs of turbines in some locations.

Modern turbines can detect ice formation, which usually causes excess vibration during operations, and shut down automatically. Automatic electronic controllers and safety sub-systems monitor these and many other aspects of the turbine's operation to determine if the turbine is operating within specs and within the safety limits: the generator, tower structure, and the local environment. These systems can temporarily shut down the turbine in case of high winds, ice accumulation, electrical load imbalance, excess vibration, and other such problems.

Recurring or significant problems cause a system lockout and notify the maintenance team that inspection and repair are needed. Most systems also include multiple passive safety systems that stop operation in case of failure of any part of the electronic control system.

Aesthetics

Aesthetic issues, although quite important in our daily lives, are subjective in character. Some people find wind farms pleasant and optimistic, seeing them as symbols of energy independence and local prosperity. This positive depends on the person's relation to the industry, their personal interests, and other factors, some of which are variable and might change with time and developments.

Although in general wind turbines have a smaller footprint than other forms of energy generation such as coal and gas plants, they usually use a lot of land. Modern wind installations use much more land than the older types, so the turbines are widely spaced, and the field has a less cluttered appearance. Because of that, there are more people affected by life at the periphery of, or close to, a large wind farm.

Wind farms are often built on land that has already been cleared, and they coexist easily with other agricultural land uses such as grazing and crops.

Some wind farms are close to scenic or otherwise undeveloped areas, so aesthetic issues are important for onshore and near-shore locations. There have been predictions that wind farms will damage tourism in some areas, but lately a new phenomenon is taking place where some wind farms have themselves become tourist attractions. A number of wind installations have visitor centers and offer tours. They have ground level observation facilities and some even offer observation decks atop turbine towers.

Residents near turbines complain of the aesthetics, the noise and "shadow flicker" on nearby residences caused by rotating turbine blades, when the sun passes behind the turbine. This can easily be avoided by locating the wind farm so that to reduce or eliminate unacceptable shadow flicker. This can be achieved also by turning the turbine off for the worst time of the day, when the sun is at the angle that causes most offensive flicker.

Large wind towers also require aircraft warning lights, which may create light pollution at nighttime. Complaints about these lights have caused the FAA to consider allowing fewer lights per turbine in certain areas. Nevertheless, wind turbines present real danger to low flying aircraft during the day and night.

Noise

Medical professionals claim that noise from wind turbines is an important disadvantage of wind turbines, especially when they are located very close to populated centers. The controversy centers on the ultra-low frequency sounds emitted by wind turbines—especially the large ones—that can affect people, and even affect human health in some case. The claims are that the thumping noise from wind turbines could affect the mood of people, and may even cause physiological problems such as insomnia, headaches, tinnitus, vertigo, and nausea.

Studies have been published that show that some people could experience stress or irritation caused by the swishing sounds wind turbines produce. A small minority of those exposed report annoyance and stress associated with noise perception. These are actually irritations that are similar to local and highway vehicles traffic from some industrial operations and from low-flying aircraft.

Since annoyance and irritation are not diseases, they most likely won't be taken seriously by the health community, but must be considered in future research projects.

In any case, we must not ignore the fact that wind turbines are a problem for some people living or working nearby. Turbine "blade thump" noise causes a health problem known as wind turbine syndrome, which includes the following symptoms: sleep disturbance, headache, ringing or buzzing in the ears, dizziness, vertigo, nausea, visual blurring, rapid heart rate, irritability, problems with concentration and memory, panic episodes associated with sensations of internal pulsation or quivering, which arise while awake or asleep.

Wind power also could cause economic problems, such as: homes located near wind turbines lose significant value; some homes become impossible to sell and are abandoned by their owners; wilderness areas lose economic value as recreational and vacation locations; tourism supported businesses suffer.

Large wind power installations are of real concern to some of the locals, whether real or perceived, and this must be taken into consideration as we proceed with our plans to double and triple the wind generation during the next several years. We need to determine if the turbine is operating within specs and safety limits; the comfort of some people cannot and should not be based on the discomforts of others.

BIOMASS

Most of us think of renewable energy as that delivered by the wind and the sun but there are other renewable sources of equal importance. Biomass, plant material and animal waste, is one of these. It is actually the oldest source of renewable energy, since it was widely used by our ancestors and by millions of other people around the world.

Even now, biomass supplies more renewable energy, including bio-power electricity, than wind or solar power. Sustainable biomass is a critical renewable resource, which if developed properly, can be an efficient and cheap power generator.

Biomass is a renewable energy source not only because the energy it comes from the sun, but also because biomass can re-grow over a relatively short period of time. Through the process of photosynthesis, chlorophyll in plants captures the sun's energy by converting carbon dioxide from the air and water from the ground into carbohydrates—complex compounds composed of carbon, hydrogen, and oxygen.

When these carbohydrates are burned, they turn back into carbon dioxide and water and release the energy they captured from the sun. In this way, biomass functions as a sort of natural battery for storing solar energy. As long as biomass is produced sustainably—meeting current needs without diminishing resources or the land's capacity to re-grow biomass and recapture carbon—this rechargeable battery will last indefinitely and provide sources of low-carbon energy.

Table 5-18. U.S. bio-power generation estimate

Renewable Resource	Capacity Potential (in GW)	Electric Generation (billion kWh)
Energy Crops	83	584
Agricultural Residues	114	801
Forest Residues	33	231
Urban Residues	15	104
Landfill Gas	2.6	19
Total	**248**	**1,739**

A wide range of biomass resources are considered beneficial, because they provide energy at reduced overall carbon emissions and provide other benefits at the same time.

Some of the beneficial resources are:

- Energy crops that don't compete with food crops for land

- Crop residues such as wheat straw or corn stover

- Sustainably harvested wood and forest residues

- Clean municipal and industrial wastes

Beneficial biomass use can be considered part of the terrestrial carbon cycle, which is the balanced cycling of carbon from the atmosphere into plants during their growth cycle, and then into soils and back into the atmosphere during the plant decay cycle. Carbon in the form of carbon dioxide is taken up, or recycled, by plant growth within a relatively short time, which compensates for the carbon dioxide emissions during burning, resulting in a low net carbon emissions.

If used instead of coal, oil or natural gas, biomass sources displace carbon emissions from fossil fuels generally maintain and even increase the stocks of carbon stored in soil or plants. The most effective and sustainable biomass resources vary from region to region, depending on the efficiency of the process of its conversion into its final application as bio-power, bio-fuels, bio-products, or heat.

The different biomass energy sources are:

- Energy crops are grown on farms in large quantities, so that they don't displace or even reduce the normal food production by growing them on marginal lands, or pastures, or as double crops by rotations with food crops.

- Native trees and grasses can be used also, since they require fewer synthetic inputs and do not pose risk the to agro-ecosystems.

- Crop residues are parts of a plant left after harvesting of most crops. In many cases, depending on soils and slope, a certain fraction of crop residues is left in the field to maintain erosion protection and nutrients recycling. Some fraction of the crop residues, however, can be collected for renewable energy in a sustainable manner.

- Manure from livestock and poultry contains valuable nutrients and is usually used as a fertilizer. Some types of manure can be converted to renewable energy through anaerobic digesters, combustion, or gasification. The digesters produce biogas that can be burned to generate electricity.

- Woody biomass in form of bark, sawdust, shavings, and other byproducts of milling timber and papermaking are the largest source of biomass-based heat and renewable electricity. Lumber, pulp, and paper mills use these energy sources for both heat and power.

- Urban wastes are generated everywhere people live. The biomass wastes comes in many forms, including tree trimmings, shipping pallets, leftover construction wood, and municipal garbage such as paper that wouldn't be recycled, food, yard waste, and so forth. These can be burned to generate heat and electricity. Some dumps are retrofitted to capture methane gas that can also be burned for heat and electricity generation.

Environmental Impact

Biomass is different from the other energy sources in many ways, and in many ways it is less polluting than the fossils. Nevertheless, it also has environmental impacts and risks, some of which are the sustainability of the resource use, air quality, and carbon emissions.

Sustainability

Biomass (crop) harvesting involves removal of crops, residues, trees, or other resources from the fields, with the subsequent transport and processing of the gathered materials. The removal process has the potential to deplete the land's ability to support future crops, or it can degrade other indicators of sustainability.

Biomass markets demand additional removals of residues, crops, or trees, thus increasing the impacts from these activities. Additional harvests of crop residues or the growth of energy crops require additional research and additional policies to minimize impacts.

There are no established procedures and standards for sustainable biomass productions. Since the development of new and larger biomass markets means larger biomass removal from fields and forests, especially forestry residues and small diameter trees, the risk of environmental damage grows proportionally.

Since woody biomass is a low-value product, sustainability standards should be relatively easy and inexpensive to implement and verify. These standards should ensure that all nutrients removed during a biomass harvest are replenished, and that the removal does not damage long-term productivity of the land.

Air Quality

The emissions from biomass burning systems can impact the local air quality. The emissions vary depending on the biomass type, the type of power plant, and its pollution controls.

Generally speaking, biomass resources emit less sulfur and mercury than coal during burning, so the emissions from these are much lower. Since sulfur emissions cause smog and acid rain and mercury is a known neurotoxin, burning biomass is much safer for the local environment.

Biomass-burning power plants also have less nitrogen oxide emissions than conventional coal plants. Bio power systems that use either fluidized bed or gasification emit NO_x at levels that are comparable to new natural gas plants. NO_x emissions create harmful particulate matter, smog, and acid rain, which results in poor air quality and billions of dollars of public health costs each year, so here again, biomass is the preferred energy source.

Stoker boilers, however, do emit significant quantities of particulates and carbon monoxide, which can be significantly reduced with fluidized bed and gasification systems. Generally speaking, advanced biomass power plants produce significantly lower air emissions than conventional coal plants using similar equipment.

Carbon Emissions

Nevertheless, it is undeniable that burning or gasifying biomass does emit carbon into the atmosphere.

After all, all this carbon dioxide that the plants absorbed during their growth has to go somewhere. And it usually goes back to where it came from—the atmosphere.

Climate change concerns have put biomass' carbon emissions under additional scrutiny. This is a fairly new development and the efforts to understand and optimize this energy source continue, so for now we can group biomass resources into two general categories based on their net carbon impacts. The important distinctions are made between a) biomass resources that are beneficial in reducing net carbon emissions, and b) biomass resources that would increase net emissions.

The *beneficial biomass* is clearly distinguished by its potential to reduce net carbon emissions. These beneficial resources exist in substantial supplies and can form the basis of increasing production of bio-power and biofuels. Sustainable, low-carbon biomass can provide a significant fraction of the new renewable energy we need to reduce our emissions of heat-trapping gases like carbon dioxide to levels that scientists say will avoid the worst impacts of global warming. Without sustainable, low-carbon bio-power, transforming to a clean energy economy will likely be more expensive and take longer.

Harmful biomass approaches include clearing forests, savannas, or grasslands as needed to grow energy crops. Like all our energy sources, bio-power has environmental risks that need to be mitigated. If not managed carefully, biomass for energy can be harvested at unsustainable rates so that it damages ecosystems, produces harmful air pollution, consumes large amounts of water, and produces net greenhouse emissions. Displacing food production for bioenergy production was proven as a wrong approach. Harmful biomass has several negative effects, and can add net carbon to the atmosphere by either directly or indirectly decreasing the overall amount of carbon stored in plants and soils.

Firewood

Firewood is a big business in many countries. Including the U.S. and other developed countries. The firewood business is, however, perfected and expanded in the developing countries. Large forests and wooded areas are cut to replenish supplies for the firewood markets in the cities. Large quantities of wood are also used to make charcoal, which is a hot commodity in the populated centers.

Although most countries have anti-deforestation laws, many people are involved in the wood gathering, preparation, and selling of firewood and charcoal. Some are not aware of the laws, and others don't care simply because they have no other choice. And so, the large-scale deforestation of the poorest countries in the world continues unhindered, thus creating a major issue that is affecting the global environment and contributing to the climate changes.

In any case, providing a lot of oil and oil products to the poor is not possible, nor is there a chance to provide them with energy via any of the conventional energy sources such as coal, gas, or nuclear. So it becomes obvious that only renewables could alleviate the worsening worldwide firewood situation.

For now, however, firewood is a major energy driver in the poor developing countries. Many people and entire families are dedicated to the business of gathering, sorting, transporting, and selling firewood to their neighbors in the suburban areas, where there is no more wood left for burning.

Firewood use in the world's poorest regions has been recognized as a contributor to local air pollution, public health concerns, and more recently global climate change. But in many places of the world the locals are struggling to overcome the effects of black carbon, generated by thousands of firewood fires in houses and businesses.

About a third of the world's population still burns wood and other biomass for cooking, heating, and lighting. This accounts for whopping 13% of global energy consumption. The problem is that the burning process does not completely break down the wood, which results in the release of particulate matter and harmful gasses into the environment.

The wood soot contains carbon monoxide, heavy metals, and carcinogenic dioxins such as benzene and formaldehyde. These poisons are at times concentrated in closed spaces and land formations, with detrimental health effects for those affected. There are numerous well- documented cases that include asthma, respiratory infections, decreased lung function, malnutrition, cardiovascular disease, and cataracts. These effects are particularly harmful to the elderly, young children, and the poor—who are actually the majority of the people forced to live under these conditions.

The indoor firewood stove is basically a miniature toxic waste plant, according to global environmental professionals. Health organizations are warning that poor air quality conditions may increase the risk of swine flu and other health challenges, with the situation potentially exacerbated in small towns and villages.

Studies by climate scientists conclude that burning firewood may affect the global climate as well. For example, when wood or coal generated soot settles on light-colored surfaces, snow, or ice, it reduces the capac-

ity of these surfaces to reflect sunlight and contributes to atmospheric warming. Whether the soot is from fossil fuels or a biomass, the result is the same.

It was also determined lately that the firewood-generated black carbon's warming effect is much greater than initially estimated. The particulates contained in it are possibly the second most significant greenhouse gas after carbon dioxide, and three times more potent in its climate-altering effects.

Burning firewood as a primary fuel source or for business purposes contributes to increased levels of deforestation and adds to the climate change concerns.

For example, the city of Coyhaique in Chile recently ranked as one of the worst in particulate air pollution. Most of that city's residents, 97%, burn firewood as a primary fuel for cooking, heating, and various business purposes. Firewood in Chile is four to five times cheaper than natural gas, and seven times cheaper than electricity and most homes are not even equipped for use anything else but firewood.

In most developing countries, firewood is not recognized as a fuel by the government although clearly it is the second largest source of energy in the country. There are no policies to take into account the firewood use and it is as if the issue doesn't exist.

Forest Fires

Another great environmental problem of renewable nature is the occurrence of large-area forest fires. These usually occur naturally, but sometimes are man-made by careless drivers, campers, or hikers.

Forest fires are one of the largest sources of particulate-matter pollution in the U.S. and other parts of the world. They can have significant impacts on local air quality, visibility, and human health. Emissions from forest fires can travel great distances, affecting air quality and human health far from the originating fires. These emissions include: particulate matter, carbon monoxide, atmospheric mercury, ozone-forming chemicals, and volatile organic compounds.

The industry specialists estimate that an acre of primarily coniferous forest that burns completely will emit approximately 4.81 metric tons of carbon into the atmosphere. Most of the released gasses, 80-90%, are in the form of carbon dioxide (CO_2). The rest is carbon monoxide (CO) and methane (CH_4).

For example, a record-setting 96,385 wildfires in 1996 destroyed about 9.87 million acres of forest in the United States. These forest fires accounted for 47.47 million metric tons of carbon emissions in the affected areas. This is compared to the total nation's annual carbon dioxide emissions that are estimated at around 6.049 billion metric tons.

In 1997, several fires burned relatively thin-trunked tropical trees in Indonesia. At the end of the cycle, the devastated forests were covered in carbon-rich peat, measuring up to 20 meters thick in places. As a result, the Indonesian fires were estimated to have released approximately 2.0 giga-tons (one giga-ton equals 1,000 billion tons) of carbon, which was almost one third of the world's annual emissions at the time and over 300 times the total amount of CO_2 released in the U.S. during that entire year.

Planned and controlled burning is practiced often to manage large forest fires. Although it could hurt people involved in the process, it is still far more desirable than uncontrolled wildfires that can greatly impact air quality for longer periods of time and elevate the risk to human health and safety.

There are also other types of wood burning used in many places around the world, such as: industrial burning, slash and wood-residue burning, land clearing, agricultural burning, backyard burning, outdoor wood-fired boilers, campfires and beach fires, burning garbage, and construction debris burning. The combined negative effects from air pollutants emitted by these sources cannot be calculated easily, but they are significant and should not be overlooked.

Other types of carbon releases to be noted are those from vegetation that decays once the fires have been extinguished. Another, a long-term effect, is losing the forests that absorbed carbon dioxide from the atmosphere and thus can helped slow global warming.

And so, the overwhelming deduction from all this is that Nature has its ways that we humans cannot even understand, let alone help in any way. As a matter of fact, looking at the above activities and the related issues, we must deduct that our intentional or unintentional intervention in Nature's business of keeping the environmental balance in check are feeble at best.

But we need to agree also that the overall effect on the environment arising from our daily activities is negative. And increasingly so…

NOTE: Flying over some areas of Asia or Africa at night, one can easily notice hundreds and thousands of fires on the ground below. Even large cities, like Taipei, Beijing and others have a multitude of brush fires daily, with plumes of smoke coming from their suburbs that is most visible at night.

Large areas of bare land, where forests and woodlands once were, can be seen for miles in certain areas too. These bare areas create additional problems, such as soil erosion, and are becoming increasingly troublesome in a number of countries.

Human health is adversely affected in all areas where there is indiscriminant wood burning. In addition to the dangers associated with wood gathering and transport, the toxic gases emitted during wood burning are a major health issue in many countries. Lung and other problems are common and many people get sick and die as a consequence.

Wood burning cannot be eliminated completely, for it has some useful purposes, but providing alternative energy sources for people in places such as India and Sub-Saharan Africa, who are forced to burn wood daily, would help their development and contribute significantly to cleaning the environment from harmful gasses and the related health effects.

In conclusion, biomass, including forests, crops, and grasslands, is a major energy source which is also responsible for a number of serious environmental problems. Some of these are socio-economic issues, which cannot be resolved any time soon by implementing technological improvements, or any clever maneuvers. Here governments must take steps to control the wood burning, and/or implement policies and strategies for its replacement, and implement efficient pollution control measures.

NOTE: Using solar and wind energy in parts of the world where wood cutting and burning is predominant is one way for these technologies to make the greatest and most immediate positive impact on the natural environment and peoples' health. This can be done very quickly and efficiently, if and when governments decide to act. Money, of course, is the major obstacle to the success of such an enterprise, so a worldwide movement in the 21st century, focused on solving the firewood problem, is needed to find a way to help the people and reduce the deforestation and biomass-burning related problems.

Now, here is a subject that not many people are aware of, and many would like to keep locked in the closet. Are renewables pollutants? Keep on reading…

POWER PLANT SPECIFICS

Different power plants have different fuels and O&M characteristics, which combined with a number of complex equipment and process issues, make it very hard to compare the final results from their activities. The following is an attempt to bring some clarity to the different issues related to power plants O&M.

Internal Energy Use

Table 5-19 is a list of how much energy (usually fossil fuels) is used by the different technologies (in MJ per kWh of generated power) just to keep the power plant running.

Table 5-19. Outside energy used to run a power plant (in MJ* per kWh) *MJ is a measure of energy equal to about 0.278 kWh.

Plant type	MJ	
Coal	9.00	
Hydro	0.10	
Wind*	0.12	(2.50 MJ/kWh with compensation)
PV*	1.50	(6.00 MJ/kWh with compensation)
Geo	0.54	
Bio	0.05	

At a first glance, Table 5-19 tells us that the amount of fossils used by solar and wind is quite low, but this is only part of the total picture, because these power generators are variable, and if there is no sun or wind, there is no power. Because of that, they require substantial fossil fuels to be burned, which otherwise would not be burned, to substitute for the loss of power caused by their variability during idling in poor weather conditions, such as cloudiness or no wind. Thus, the increased MJ of energy used per total (expected) kWh power generation, as needed in order to compensate for the energy losses somewhere in the national power grid.

What this means is that, for every kWh of electricity generated by a coal-fired power plants, 9.0 MJ of fossil fuels have been burned in the process just to keep the plant running and generating that 1.0 kWh of electric power. Since 1 kWh is equal to 3.6 MJ of energy, we see that it takes 9.0 MJ of coal to generate 3.6 MJ of electric energy. This is because of a combination of things, but mostly because of the inefficiency of the process, as we will see in the discussion about plant efficiency below.

For base-load power plant operation, units that run continuously, start-up energy, wasted energy to keep the plant equipment running, may be a negligible fraction of total energy in the order of 0.5-1.0%. However, power plants operating in volatile or competitive markets or as marginal providers of power, such as peaking power plants, shut down and startup frequently and as needed by the load demand. This leads to waste of fuel and eventually to equipment deterioration, which affects plant efficiency. For the peaking power plants, the wast-ed energy could represent 5-10% of total energy used just to keep the plant running at variable power levels, and to vary the speed of power generation according to the load fluctuations.

Geo- and bio-power sources are different in that they could be more consistent and very efficient as far as not using much fossil energy, but unfortunately their share is very small presently, and their future is not clear. Because of that, we don't expect them to be a significant contributor to the U.S. power generation any time soon.

Power Plant Efficiency

The energy used to run a fossil-fired power plant is a variable that takes into account the fact that a lot of energy is wasted in the process, as follows:

Table 5-20. Energy losses in a coal-fired power plant

Losses	%
Condenser	52.5
Boiler losses	5.5
Turbine-generator	1.5
Works auxiliaries	1.0
Steam range and feed radiation	0.5
Power plant efficiency	*39.0%*

Amazingly enough, almost two thirds of the energy of the incoming coal is wasted during the condensation of the steam, according to Table 5-20. In other words, the process is self-defeating; it uses a lot of coal to heat the water and convert it into steam, but then cold water is brought from an outside source to cool the steam and convert it into warm water.

Here is where the process losses half of its efficiency, which results in waste of half of the coal energy in one single step. So next time we think of a coal-fired power plant we need to consider the fact that slightly one-third of the thousands of tons of coal burned every day are converted into useful energy. The rest of the coal's energy is converted into and emitted as waste heat, and gas, liquid, and solid pollution.

This sounds so 19th century: two-thirds of the energy input is lost in outdated and inefficient equipment and process steps. A better and more efficient way to use the precious and dwindling fossils must be found—and soon!

The basic efficiency formulas of the different power plant cycles are as follows:

$$\text{heat generation efficiency} = \frac{\text{output heat energy}}{\text{total energy input}}$$

$$\text{power generation efficiency} = \frac{\text{output power energy}}{\text{total energy input}}$$

$$\text{plant efficiency} = \frac{\begin{array}{c}(\text{output power energy} + \\ \text{output heat energy})\end{array}}{\text{total energy input}}$$

In the example in Table 5-20, our coal-fired power plant has 39% electric energy output efficiency, derived from theoretically calculated 100% coal energy input. The sum of the total power output (heat and electricity) divided by the total energy output gives us the plant efficiency of 39% in this case.

NOTE. The heat energy output could be significant if some or all of the waste heat generated during the condenser cooling, where half of the energy is lost, is captured and used.

Power Plant Pollution

Different power plants emit a variety of gasses, liquids, and solids. Most of these are released into the environment in one form or another.

The major pollutants from power plants are:

CO_2 Emissions

Table 5-21 is a list of grams of CO_2 (equivalent) emitted by the different technologies that contribute to global warming.

Table 5-21. CO_2 emissions (per kWh power generation)

Plant type	CO_2 gr.
Coal	566.00
Hydro	10.00
Wind*	11.00
PV*	104.00
Geo	41.00
Bio	250.00

Table 5-21 shows that for each kWh electricity generated by a coal-fired power plants, 556 grams of CO_2 have been generated during the cradle-to-grave coal mining-transport-burning process sequence.

As an example, a 500 MW coal-fired base-load power plant, operating continuously would generate approximately 3.9 billion kWh electricity annually, or:

500 MW x 24 hrs/day x 325 days/annum = 3.9 B kWh/annum

Converting this into grams and tons of CO_2:

3.9 B kWh x 566 grams = 2,207 trillion grams/annum
2,207 T grams = 2,207,000 tons of CO_2/annum
2,207,000 tons x 30 years = 66.21 million tons of CO_2 is generated during life cycle

So, in the end, 66.1 million tons of CO_2 (a big WOW) are emitted into the atmosphere during the operation of our coal-fired power plant that generates 500 MW of electricity. CO_2 is directly responsible for the increase in global warming, and 66 million tons is amazingly large number when generated by one single power plant. When multiplied by the thousands of such plants around the world (over 50,000 with 8,000 in the U.S. alone), we get billions of tons of CO_2 emitted annually that contribute to the global environmental deterioration.

In addition, a typical uncontrolled coal plant emits 14,100 tons of SO_2 per year. A coal plant with emissions controls, including flue gas desulfurization, smokestack scrubbers, emits 7,000 tons of SO_2 per year.

NO_x Emissions

An uncontrolled coal plant also emits about 10,300 tons of NO_x per year, but with emissions controls added, including selective catalytic reduction technology, it emits 3,300 tons of NO_x per year.

An average uncontrolled coal power plant also emits: 500 tons of particulate matter, 720 tons of carbon monoxide, 220 tons of hydrocarbons and volatile organic compounds (VOC), 225 pounds of arsenic, 170 lbs.

Table 5-22.
NO_x emissions in grams per kilogram of burned fuel

Fuel	NOx emission in g / kg fuel
Oil	3.0
Kerosene	3.0
Coal	4.5
Propane	2.3
Gasoline	27
Hydrogen	0
Natural Gas	1.0
Butane	2.3
Wood, dry	0.7

of mercury, 114 pounds of lead, 4 pounds of cadmium, and trace amounts of uranium.

For example, the U.S. electric energy-generating sector emits about 2.8 billion tons of CO_2 annually—roughly 25% of global CO_2 emissions, and half of the total U.S. energy-related CO_2 emissions annually.

Coal-fired power plants emit most of it; about 80% of the total, while natural gas and oil are responsible for about 20% of the total.

SO_2 Emissions

Sulfur dioxide (SO_2) emissions are characteristic for coal-fired plants, and it is where the cleanup efforts are concentrated. SO_2 is one the highly reactive gasses found in the atmosphere. The largest sources of SO_2 emissions, over 73%, are from fossil fuel combustion at power plants. Other industrial facilities such those extracting metal from ore, as well as the burning of high sulfur containing fuels by locomotives, large ships, and non-road equipment, emit about 20% of the total.

Coal plants are the United States' leading source of SO_2 pollution, taking a major toll on public health by contributing to the formation of small acidic particulates that can penetrate into human lungs and be absorbed by the bloodstream. SO_2 also causes acid rain that damages crops, forests, and soils, and acidifies lakes and streams.

A typical uncontrolled coal plant emits 14,100 tons of SO_2 per year. A typical coal plant with emissions controls, including flue gas desulfurization, smokestack scrubbers, emits 7,000 tons of SO_2 per year, or about half of its uncontrolled counterparts.

Since SO_2 is linked to acid rain and a number of adverse effects on the human respiratory system, EPA first set standards for SO_2 concentration limits in 1971. The EPA standard calls for a 140 ppb in any 24-hour period, and an annual average standard at 30 ppb as needed to protect human health. There is also a 3-hour average secondary standard at 500 ppb, intended to protect the public welfare in emergency situations.

In addition, EPA revised the primary SO_2 standard in 2010 and established a new one-hour standard at a level of 75 parts per billion (ppb). Two existing primary standards were revoked because they would not provide additional public health protection as given by the one-hour standard at 75 ppb.

See Appendix E for some historical data on SO_2 emissions in the U.S.

Phosphates Emissions

Below is a list of grams of phosphates (equivalent) emitted by the different technologies (per kWh of gener-ated power) that contribute to global acidification.

Table 5-23 tells us that, for each kWh of electricity generated by coal-fired power plants, 1.1 grams of phosphates have been generated during the cradle-to-grave coal mining-transport-burning process sequence.

Table 5-23. Phosphates emissions (per kWh power generation)

Fuel	POx gr.
Coal	1.10*
PV	0.45
Geo	0.20
Bio	0.10
Hydro	0.04
Wind	0.06

As an example, a 500 MW coal-fired base load power plant, operating continuously, would generate approximately 3.9 billion kWh electricity annually, or:

$$500 \text{ MW} \times 24 \text{ hrs/day} \times 325 \text{ days/annum} =$$
$$3.9 \text{ B kWh/annum}$$

Converting this into grams and tons of phosphates:

3.9 B kWh x 1.1 grams = 4.29 B grams/annum
4.29 B grams = 4,290 tons of phosphates/annum
4,290 tons x 30 years = 128,700 tons of phosphates
  during life cycle

So, in the end, 128,700 tons of phosphates were generated during the operation of our coal-fired power plant, as needed to produce 500 MW electricity. Phosphates are directly responsible for increase of global acidification and eutrophication (increase of algae, and oxygen depletion in water bodies).

128,700 tons generated by one single power plant, when multiplied by the thousands of such sources, means that there are millions of tons of phosphates generated annually around the world that contribute to the global environmental deterioration.

Particulate Matter Emissions

Particulate matter, soot or fly ash, is also specific to coal-fired power plants. These are very small—micron size—particles that float in the air and can cause chronic bronchitis, aggravated asthma, and premature death, as well as haze obstructing visibility.

A typical uncontrolled plant emits 500 tons of small airborne particles each year. The small particles concentrate in the immediate vicinity, but winds can blow them away at great distances.

Bag-houses, consisting of centrifuges and filters, installed inside coal plant smokestacks, can capture as much as 99 percent of the particulates by filtering and separating them from the smoke before exiting the smokestack.

Steel Use

Following is a list of grams of iron ore and other raw materials, used to manufacture production equipment for the different technologies (per kWh of generated power.)

Table 5-24. Steel use in power plant construction and operation

Plant type	Steel gr.
Coal	2.60*
Hydro	1.80
Wind*	3.50
PV*	4.25
Geo	3.20
Bio	0.50

*This means that for each kWh electricity generated by coal-fired power plants, 2.6 grams of iron ore have been used previously, or are used presently, somewhere in the cradle-to-grave coal process sequence.

As an example, a 500 MW coal-fired base load power plant, operating continuously would generate approximately 3.9 billion kWh electricity annually, or:

500 MW x 24 hrs/day x 325 days/annum = 3.9 B kWh

Converting this into grams and tons of iron ore:

3.9 B kWh x 2.6 grams = 10.14 B grams iron ore

10.14 B grams = 10,140 tons iron one/annually

10,140 tons x 30 years = 30,140 tons iron ore

So, in the end, 30,140 tons of iron ore have been dug out, processed into metal and machined into parts to be assembled into mining, transportation, and power plant equipment, as needed to support the 500 MW coal-fired power plant operations during its 30-year-long life cycle. This does not include the amount of iron ore and energy used for the manufacturing of the equipment used in the iron ore mining, transport, and processing.

The GHG Emitters

The different energy sources have different levels of GHG emissions and safety, as can be seen Figures 5-41 and 5-42. These are complex variables that need more attention and better understanding, to ensure efficient and safe operation and use in the future.

Figure 5-41 shows the different levels of GHG emissions for similar amount of energy produced during various stages of production and use of the major power generating sources. Coal, for example, generates the most GHG while burning during power generation. Solar, on the other hand, uses a lot of energy and emits most GHG during its manufacturing process as the silicon ingots, wafers and cells manufacturing process is extremely energy hungry.

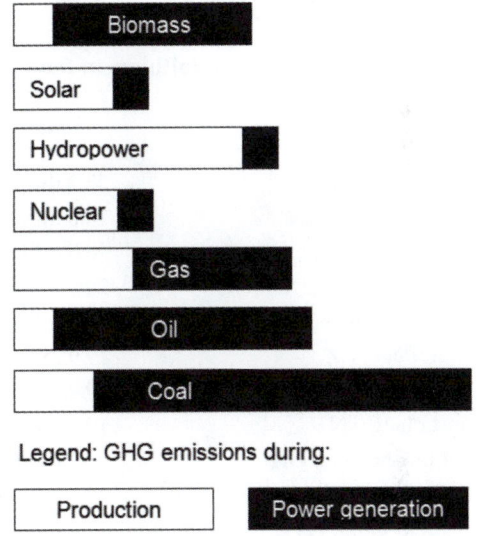

Figure 5-41. GHG emissions during production and power generation

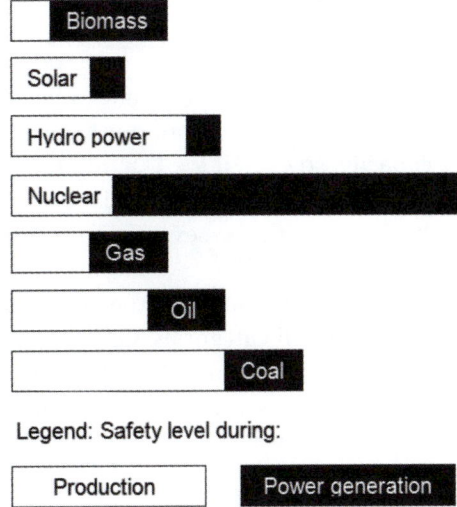

Figure 5-42. Safety during production and power generation

Figure 5-42 shows the safety levels for similar amount of energy produced during the different stages of production and the use of the major power generating sources. Coal, for example, causes injuries and fatalities during mining, the production operation. Nuclear, on the other hand, is dangerous during use, where it could cause major damage, including environmental damage, illness, and death.

NOTE: The above data are not to scale. They only show the relative proportions of GHG emissions and safety levels of the different energy sources and power generating technologies.

The U.S. Polluters

An example of the biggest coal-fired power plant polluters in the U.S. follows.

Table 5-25. The largest air polluters in the U.S.

U.S. coal-fired plants	Annual CO_2
Scherer plant, Juliet, GA	25.3 million tons
Miller plant, Quinton, AL	20.6 million tons
Bowen plant, Cartersville, GA	20.5 million tons
Gibson plant, Owensville, IN	20.4 million tons
W.A. Parish, Thompsons, TX	20.0 million tons
Navajo plant, Page, AZ	19.9 million tons
Martin Lake plant, Tatum, TX	19.8 million tons
Cumberland plant, TN	19.6 million tons
Gavin plant in Cheshire, OH	18.7 million tons
Sherburne County, Becker, MN	17.9 million tons
Bruce Mansfield plant, PA	17.4 million tons
Rockport plant, Rockport, IN	16.6 million tons

Extrapolating CO_2 emissions for the next 30 years, we get an astounding 66 billion tons of CO_2 being pumped into the atmosphere by the U.S. power generating industry alone. China, India and other countries rely on coal power, and are planning to increase their electricity capacity, so even if the U.S. reduces its fossils use, regardless of all the talk and negotiations, the global emissions by 2020 would be several times higher than today.

In conclusion, we clearly see the effects of coal as the worst polluter in all categories. Oil and gas are also polluting, but to a lesser degree. What remains as not so clear is the role of the renewables in this picture.

We know that they are clean in the back end, since they do not produce significant amounts of harmful gasses, but looking at the front end of their cradle-to-grave life cycle, we see a lot of energy used to produce the raw materials needed for making their equipment and infrastructure, its transport and processing, etc.

We also see that, due to imperfections caused by variability, the proper use of some renewables requires additional fossils to maintain the electrical grid consistency and integrity. With this information in hand, we can get a better idea of the overall effect different energy generators have on the total national and global energy generation now and in the future, and can also judge more accurately their contribution to pollution and global warming.

Life Cycle Balance

The recently increased concerns about the environmental effects of power generation by different energy sources calls for a detailed review and greater focus on the upstream and downstream impacts of the respective energy conversion systems.

Life Time Energy Use

There is a lot of energy used during the lifetime of an oil or gas well and a fossil-fired power plant. Starting with the exploration of land areas for productive wells, and during the construction and operation of the wells and power plants, different types and quantity of energy are used at each step of the process, as follow:

$$En(f)=D+C+E+P+T+OM+G+S+R$$

En(f) is energy use in a fossil-burning process
D is well and power plant location and discovery
C is well and power plant construction
E is production equipment manufacturing and transport
P is fuel production
T is fuel transport
OM is fuel use (well and power plant O&M)
G is emissions treatment
S is well and power plant decommissioning
R is recycling of equipment

This is a mathematical representation of the energy life cycle of a fossil-fired power plant. The total energy used is the sum of all energy uses during the life cycle of the plant—including the energy used during fuel production and all other variables during the power plants lifetime.

Of course, solar and wind power plants use free fuel, so some of the energy use is eliminated. And so, the equation for the energy use of a solar or wind power is somewhat shorter, as follow:

$$En(r)=C+E+OM+S+R$$

Where
Ev(r) is environmental effects of a renewables process
C is power plant construction
E is production equipment manufacturing and transport
OM is power plant operation and maintenance (O&M)
S is power plant decommissioning (land restoration)
R is recycling and disposal of production equipment

Lifetime Environmental Effects

There is a lot of gaseous, liquid and solids pollution created during the lifetime of an oil or gas well and fossil-fired power plant. Starting with the exploration of land areas for productive wells, and during the construction and operation of the wells and power plants, different types and quantity of pollution are emitted during each step of the process, as follow:

$$Ev(f) = D + C + E + P + T + OM + S + R + P$$

Where:
Ev(f) is environmental effects of a fossil-burning process
D is well and power plant location and discovery
C is well and power plant construction
E is production equipment manufacturing and transport
P is fuel production
T is fuel transport
OM is O&M including fuel use
G is emissions treatment
S is well and power plant decommissioning
R is recycling of equipment
P is penalties and legal settlements

This is a mathematical representation of the environmental effects during the lifetime of a fossil-fired power plant. The total environmental impact is the sum of all environmental effects during the life cycle of the plant—including the pollution generated during fuel discovery, production and all other variables during the power plants lifetime.

Of course, solar and wind power plants do not emit much, if any, pollutants, so the environmental impact equation for a solar or wind power plant is somewhat shorter, as follow:

$$Ev(r) = C + E + OM + S + R + P$$

Where:
Ev(r) is environmental effects of a renewables process
C is power plant construction
E is production equipment manufacturing and transport
OM is power plant operation and maintenance (O&M)

S is power plant decommissioning (land restoration)
R is recycling and disposal of production equipment
P is penalties and legal settlements

Generally speaking, life cycle energy and environmental assessment considers the energy use and the environmental impacts (and the interrelations) of the different systems and products all through their cradle-to-grave life cycle, which starts with the exploration and production of raw materials and fuels, including the production and operation of the production equipment, and up to their disposal or recycling.

Our energy and environmental assessment evaluates and calculates several energy consumption and environmental impacts, including the use of fossil energy during the life cycle of the energy systems, and the related GHG emissions, contributing to global warming, as well as these contributing to global acidification and eutrophication.

NOTE: Acidification is a decrease in pH and increase in formation of acid in seawater, while eutrophication is the excessive algae growth in water caused by nitrates and phosphates, and other changes.

RENEWABLES' CHALLENGES

We have spent enough time discussing the environmental damages resulting from fossils production and use, so here is a short list of the negative impacts most frequently associated with renewable materials and power plants:

Biological Resource Impacts

Utility scale solar and wind energy projects are often installed on lands that provide habitat for sensitive species like raptors, bats, desert tortoises, kit foxes, various reptiles and amphibians, Mohave ground squirrels, and sensitive plants. Solar PV and solar thermal parabolic trough projects generally cause greater habitat loss than wind farms and solar thermal heliostat and power tower projects because sites often need to be leveled to accommodate a linear design, which typically cannot be altered to avoid sensitive areas.

Heliostat and power tower projects do not necessarily require that a site be leveled, impacts on habitats can be less. The site topography can be maintained and some vegetation left intact, since that technology has far greater flexibility regarding where the mirrors are located and they do not always need to be in a line.

Wind energy projects, if located in key migration

routes or foraging areas, can affect bird and bat species through collisions with turbine blades and through barotraumas, such as tissue damage and lung failure, caused by rapid air-pressure reduction when bats and some birds get too close to moving turbine blades.

Wind farms generally cause less absolute habitat loss within a project footprint than utility scale solar facilities because habitat for plant and wildlife species remains between turbines. Indirect impacts to wildlife outside the turbine footprint can result from roads, vehicles, and noise that may render a site generally unusable by wildlife depending on the usage on the site and density of turbines. It may be easier to protect rare plant populations on a wind energy site. In addition to habitat loss, most large renewable generation projects, both solar and wind, can potentially affect wildlife movement patterns, particularly if they are proposed in or near migration corridors or impede the connections between sensitive species populations, which can be critical to the species' local and regional health and survival.

Water Supply Impacts

Water is limited in the desert, and groundwater basins are often already in an overdraft condition. Fresh water is an increasingly critical resource, not only in the desert regions, but also throughout California. Increasingly, power plants may be competing with other local users for diminishing water supplies. As California's population and water demand continue to grow, the Department of Water Resources anticipates that the state will experience water supply shortfalls of more than several million acre-feet within the next 10 years.

In the desert region, the majority of proposed utility scale renewable energy facilities use either wind or solar technologies. The solar technologies are further categorized as either solar thermal or PV. Wind and solar facilities require large areas of open desert land to take advantage of higher wind speeds or to maximize the collection of solar radiation, but their water use can vary significantly.

Solar thermal facilities, which use steam turbine generators, must dissipate waste heat. The preferred technology for heat dissipation is evaporative cooling. Use of this technology requires a sizable volume of water during operation.

Wind technologies and PV do not require thermal cooling equipment, resulting in significantly less water use. Activities such as grading and dust control for construction of both PV and solar thermal projects may require significant water use.

Mirror washing throughout the life of a project may also contribute to significant water use. Water needs for PV panel washing are estimated as one-tenth of the requirements for solar thermal power mirror washing values.

Renewable energy facilities can take advantage of different strategies to reduce their water consumption. Solar thermal facilities can also use alternative approaches, such as dry cooling (air cooled condensers) and hybrid cooling, which are available and commercially viable. This can reduce a project's water demand by up to 90%, and simplify the analysis involved in the permitting process. Rather than using fresh water, renewable projects can use degraded water, also known as non-potable water, which can be treated and reused for power plant process water.

Surface Water Impacts

Federal and state regulations protect many of the ephemeral and intermittent streams in the desert region because they are important sources of sediment, water, nutrients, seeds, and organic matter for downstream ecosystems and provide habitat for many species. Unlike other streams, in the desert streams typically have relatively long periods where no flow occurs, punctuated by episodic flows of relatively short duration and high intensity.

Site design must also be modified where important biological resources are identified and site drainage would have an impact. Diversion of high velocity flows through and around a site can be difficult where there is a need to mimic natural conditions and potential impacts up and downstream of a project site must be decreased. Temporary erosion and sediment protection measures should be installed to control soils disturbed by construction.

Visual Impacts

Utility scale solar thermal power plants or wind farms can cover many square miles, including the power block facilities, access roads and transmission lines, and cause major visual changes in non-industrialized desert or mountainous landscapes with scenic values. The steam plumes produced by the wet cooling towers of solar thermal power plants may also change the view of the landscape.

Geothermal power plants, including well pads, steam pipelines, power generation facilities, access roads and transmission lines, may occupy as much as 350 acres, and power plant wet cooling towers can produce steam plumes, all potentially causing similar visual impacts on undeveloped desert or mountainous terrain.

Cultural Resources Impacts

State laws define cultural resources as buildings, sites, structures, objects, and historic districts. There are three kinds of cultural resources: prehistoric—related to prehistoric human occupation and use of an area; historical—associated with Euro-American exploration and settlement of an area; and ethnographic—materials important to the heritage of a particular ethnic or cultural group, such as Native Americans.

A major challenge to the development of lands, especially in the southern desert, is the lack of comprehensive information regarding the locations and significance of cultural resources. While some archaeological sites are small and well defined, historic and prehistoric landscapes can stretch for miles.

Many of the elements within these and other areas of historical significance have not been identified or evaluated. Information on both historical and archaeological sites is scattered among city, county, state, and private archives, multiple information centers, and state and federal agencies, such as the California Office of Historic Preservation, the National Register of Historic Places, and the California Register of Historic Resources.

Scarce and fragmented information, along with confidentiality requirements limiting access to cultural resource information, can make it difficult for developers to select sites that will avoid significant cultural resources. This can cause delays or inaccuracies in the resource analysis during the licensing process and create the need for more extensive site surveys, especially in remote desert areas.

Much of the land under consideration for solar and wind development includes Native American ancestral lands that are centuries old and contain artifacts, burials, historical villages, trails, plants, animals, landscapes, and vistas with cultural and spiritual significance. The spiritual value of these areas and artifacts is separate from the archaeological and historical value of these or other cultural resources and, from the perspective of Native Americans, the loss of the use of these lands or their spiritual context within the landscape cannot be mitigated. Often, only tribal elders or tribal historic preservation officers have information about landmarks and other areas of significance to Native Americans.

Another significant challenge to avoiding or mitigating cultural resource impacts, especially under the California Environmental Quality Act (CEQA), is the lack of flexibility in site location and design once a project reaches the application phase. Developers frequently fail to adequately consider the potential cultural sensitivity of a site through appropriate resource studies and discussions with knowledgeable technical specialists and Native American tribal representatives before settling on a final location. To avoid cultural resources, staff and tribal representatives must have the opportunity to identify resources before site finalization.

Land Use Impacts

Most desert lands are owned by the federal government and managed for multiple uses by the BLM and National Park Service. The Department of Defense also owns and manages large tracts of desert land for military purposes. Siting renewable energy facilities on BLM and National Park Service lands can affect existing and future multiple uses such as recreation, wildlife habitat, livestock grazing, and open space.

For example, solar thermal facilities within the BLM's California Desert Conservation Area Plan have significantly impacted or restricted other uses of the land. Similarly, siting renewable energy facilities on or near Department of Defense lands may affect military operations and related programs.

If located in productive agricultural areas, solar thermal or PV projects that require grading of many acres may result in the permanent loss of crop and grazing lands. In contrast, wind energy projects are generally compatible with agricultural land uses and may even help farmers preserve their farms with supplemental income received from leasing land to wind developers.

The average wind farm requires 5.5 acres of land to produce one MW of electricity, allowing land outside the turbine footprint to remain available for planting and grazing. However, wind projects can affect agricultural resources through soil disturbance during construction and the loss of agricultural land from installing access roads, wind turbine towers, and transmission lines.

Geothermal facilities are usually land intensive and can result in permanent loss of productive agricultural land due to geothermal steam well field development, steam pipeline installation, construction of the power plant facilities and transmission lines, and permanent access roads to develop and maintain all of the steam field and power plant facilities.

Transportation-related Visual Hazards

Solar thermal, PV, wind, and geothermal technologies present significant hazards to general aviation and military flight activities, as well as to motorists on the nation's roads and highways, and railroad crews on their normal runs.

Solar thermal and PV plants, with their huge number of mirrors and collectors, can emit glint and glare that can pose a nuisance to pilots. They can even cause flash blindness, which is especially dangerous during takeoff and landing, so solar plants located near airports could be considered especially dangerous.

Wind turbines cause turbulence, which can affect low flying aircraft such as light planes and helicopters, due to upward airflow disruption. Wind turbines are also being blamed for interrupting bird flight paths and even killing them due to collision with the turning blades, and/or disorienting them by means of the heavy airflow disruption in the field.

The evaporative and dry cooling towers of some solar thermal plants and cooling towers of geothermal plants may emit high velocity, hot air plumes, disrupting airflow and potentially causing severe turbulence to low flying aircraft as well.

The Department of Defense has also raised concerns about thermal plumes from power plants located near military flight areas and their effect on radar operations. All very tall structures, including wind turbines and solar power towers, have the potential to interfere with low flying aircraft and with military flight zones that have structure height restrictions.

The Future...

A number of efforts are either completed or underway to help promote the development of utility-scale renewable electricity generating facilities, and especially these in the state of California.

Some of these efforts and initiatives are:

Renewable Energy Transmission Initiative

In 2007, the Renewable Energy Transmission Initiative (RETI) was initiated as a joint statewide effort combining land use and transmission planning factors among the CPUC, the Energy Commission, the California ISO, and investor-owned and publicly owned utilities. The primary goals of RETI were to:

1. Help identify the transmission projects needed to accommodate California's renewable energy goals

2. Ease the designation of corridors for future transmission line development

3. Facilitate transmission line and renewable generation siting and permitting

The stakeholder-driven process identified competitive renewable energy zones throughout the state with the greatest potential for cost-effective and environmentally responsible renewable energy development.

Renewable Energy Action Team

To address challenges with permitting renewable projects in sensitive California desert regions, the Renewable Energy Action Team (REAT) was formed in 2008 to streamline and expedite the permitting processes for renewable energy projects, while conserving endangered species and natural communities at the ecosystem scale. Based in part on recommendations from the RETI process, the REAT is developing a Desert Renewable Energy Conservation Plan (DRECP) for the Mojave and Colorado Desert regions.

In December 2010, the REAT also published the multidisciplinary Best Management Practices and Guidance Manual: Desert Renewable Energy Projects to help project developers design projects that minimize environmental impacts for desert renewable projects. The manual provides guidance on initiating permitting processes, conducting land-use assessments and surveys, decisions on water use and quality, roadway planning, avoiding conflicts with aviation, and grid interconnection issues.

Desert Renewable Energy Conservation Plan

In conjunction with other federal, state, and local agencies and stakeholder groups, the REAT is developing the DRECP to identify areas in the Mojave and Colorado Desert regions suitable for renewable energy project development and areas that will contribute to the conservation of sensitive species and natural communities. The DRECP encompasses about 22 million acres in Kern, Inyo, Los Angeles, San Bernardino, Riverside, San Diego, and Imperial counties. It will promote development of solar thermal, utility-scale solar PV, wind, and other forms of renewable energy along with associated infrastructure like transmission lines.

The DRECP will be a Natural Community Conservation Plan (NCCP) and will serve as the basis for one or more Habitat Conservation Plans (HCP).145. As required by state and federal law, the environmental impact of the DRECP will be analyzed in a joint environmental impact report and statement, along with the NCCP.

Solar Energy Development Programmatic Environmental Impact Statement

At the federal level, the U.S. Department of Energy, Energy Efficiency and Renewable Energy Program, and the U.S. Department of the Interior, Bureau of Land

Management, are preparing a Solar Energy Development Programmatic Environmental Impact Statement (PEIS) to assess environmental impacts from programs intended to promote environmentally responsible utility-scale solar energy in six Western states.

The draft PEIS was issued December 16, 2010, and in May 2011 the Energy Commission and the California Department of Fish and Game (DFG) submitted joint comments on the draft with the following recommendations:

a.   Abandon further consideration of the Iron Mountain Solar Energy Zone (SEZ).

b.   Consider designating and studying additional SEZs on previously disturbed lands in the western Mojave Desert.

c.   Delay final PEIS-triggered amendments to the affected Land Use Management Plans until the DRECP process is complete in 2012.

d.   Fully consider and address all Energy Commission and DFG comments made previous to and in response to the publication of the draft PEIS. A supplement to the draft PEIS was released in the fall of 2011.

Cross-agency Coordination

State and federal agencies are working to streamline the permitting of renewable energy projects in California by increasing cross-agency cooperation and coordination, with several multi-agency agreements already in place.

In 2007, the Energy Commission, the U.S. Department of the Interior, and the BLM signed a memorandum of understanding (MOU) on agency roles, responsibilities, and procedures for joint environmental review of solar thermal projects proposed on federal land.

In 2009, the Energy Commission entered into an MOU with the California State Lands Commission to ensure timely and effective coordination during the Energy Commission's thermal power plant review process.

In 2010, the State of California and FERC signed an MOU to coordinate and share information for reviewing offshore wave and tidal energy projects.

In 2010, the Energy Commission and the Departments of General Services, Corrections and Rehabilitation, Transportation, Water Resources, and Fish and Game signed an MOU to promote the development of renewable energy projects on state buildings, properties, and rights-of-way. The State Lands Commission and University of California subsequently joined the MOU.

Transmission Infrastructure Issues

In addition to the environmental, planning, and permitting issues identified in this writing, California also faces challenges to planning and permitting power lines and other transmission infrastructure needed to bring electricity generated by large-scale renewable facilities to consumers. Governor Brown's Clean Energy Jobs Plan states that the Energy Commission "should 'fast-track' projects based on their anticipated ability to deliver clean energy to market. The permitting time for these projects, which now can take six to eight years, should be dramatically reduced, and in no case be longer than three years." Furthermore, the plan states, "As Governor, I will ensure that all agencies involved work together with a sense of urgency to permit the new transmission lines without delay."

We are still waiting. Although we have seen some progress, lately the Governor seems busy with other projects.

Smart Meters Health Problems

Smart meters are considered as one of the solutions to efficient grid operation, but they are also causing the latest environmental and health risk phenomena, a direct result of the hasty energy revolution of late. What happened was an unexpected blow below the belt for the new and budding smart grid technology. It is something that we need to take a close look at, because it defines the moment and its problems.

As a result of a number of federal, state and utilities programs, many thousands, and maybe millions, of smart meters were installed in some states lately, where they replaced the old, analog meters. It appears now, however, that radio frequency (RF) radiation emitted by some smart meters is actually hurting some people. Some people are affected by the RF radiation, causing them sleep loss, heart palpitations, dizziness and other problems.

For example, Maine's highest court ruled in July 2012 that state regulators have failed to properly address the safety concerns about the new smart meters that are installed in many homes. The ruling, however, had no immediate impact on more than 600,000 smart meters already installed in homes and businesses across the state.

The Supreme Judicial Court ordered the Maine Public Utilities Commission to reconsider a complaint that raised health concerns, and the plaintiff urged the panel to use the opportunity "to hold full evidentiary hearings on this and look at it under the bright lights."

The Maine PUC issued a brief statement saying

the panel is considering how best to comply with the Supreme Court's unanimous ruling.

The Public Utility Commissions (PUC) usually has a duty to look into any and all health concerns before installing the new devices. After the findings, the PUCs are providing an option to opt out of the new meters, but the opt-out provision doesn't assure safety of those who already have smart meters, and is also meaningless for people who live in congested neighborhoods where they're surrounded by smart meters. What's next?

Another mistake, driven by hasty implementation of smart grid components, is that a lot of easy money has been already thrown in and much more is expected. Health issues are a show-stopper in many cases, and those who don't consider them when implementing new technologies and products do pay the price.

There are a number of cases we see having similar faith in the near future too. Human health and energy generation go hand in hand and one must be aware of the risks of doing, or not doing something, that affects human health. What good is it to do something supposedly good that will hurt people?

In any case, the questionable smart meters are an example of bad start for the smart grid technologies' development and implementation. One thing we don't want to do is turn the customers against us, and the smart grid technology as a whole. If that happens, then the work in that important area will become many times more difficult and expensive.

NOTE: The author has been involved in developing processes using RF radiation (RF plasma deposition and etch in the semiconductor and solar industries), and is well aware of the damages excess RF radiation can cause some people. Large doses, or continuous low power, RF radiation causes different maladies; some of which are quite painful and at times long lasting.

For some reason, however, the RF radiation effects on human health are not well known and poorly understood. Companies who use RF also tend to sweep them under the rug for a number of reasons, so in light of the extremely large scale of deployment of these RF radiation sources, we'd like to bring the issue in the open for discussion by the scientific community and the public. This might prevent another large- scale health debacle, such as the one with hasty smart meter implementation.

Lifecycle Costs

In a free market, the price of any product must reflect accurately the total value of the product. Instead, the cost of energy is veiled in foggy rules and uncertainties. The energy market is placing an artificially low value on fossil fuels in spite of the fact that they are getting depleted and becoming increasingly more valuable.

This is because many of the true lifecycle costs of the fossils are hidden and/or are simply being passed onto consumers, via different commercial channels, and/or taxes, which hide the value and consumers are unaware of what exactly they are paying. And they are even less aware that they are paying these other tangible costs, thus the purchase decisions are not based on the true cost of the commodities.

Some costs, such as the cost of revitalization of land after the mountains are removed, is only partially paid for by the coal companies, while the customers foot the largest part of the bill. Many companies shut down once the mining equipment shows up, and these people go on unemployment that we pay for, while the communities lose their tourism income.

Water treatment plants downstream from coal mines need to upgrade their equipment to prevent the additional sludge in the rivers and streams, and the federal and state taxes pay for that.

Homes in mining communities lose much of their value due to coal dust, some go into foreclosure, and the mining companies do not compensate for this loss.

Thousands of people get sick and some die every year due to coal operations and the cost is taken up by the insurance companies or Medicare/Medicaid, and that becomes an additional cost to us. Roads and highways in many areas take a serious beating from heavy coal mining and gas and oil fracking equipment, and need costly repairs paid for mostly by the taxpayers.

Politicians talk about ending subsidies for fossil fuels, but this is small potatoes compared with the size of the industry, and won't make much, if any, difference. The status quo won't be changed as long as fossil fuel companies continue to be allowed to pass their large, hidden costs on to the consumers through different media or taxes.

Adding a carbon tax on top of the already subsidized and artificially manipulated commercialization model of energy generation makes sense to a point. It further complicates the already complicated business model and adds another layer of misunderstanding and abuse to the cost of energy.

Instead, or maybe in addition to, a carbon tax, the true cost of energy needs to be reflected in the price that we pay for energy. That would indeed drive up the cost for some types of energy, which is unacceptable to some people, but that's the only way the free market can work properly. The free market *should* drive our energy decisions, but it is not doing so today.

Industry lobbyists and some politicians are driving energy decisions today in return for favors from large campaign contributors, such as coal, gas, and oil companies. Congress needs to get involved and pass fair legislation to normalize the lifecycle cost for all fuel resources. A level playing field for all resources is needed, with a true accounting of the lifecycle costs, so the free market can decide the winners and losers.

NOTE: All the hoopla around the carbon taxation reminds us of the bully that is willing to pay a quarter to anyone s/he hurts. I'll punch you in the eye, although I know it is wrong, and to make it all go away I will pay you a quarter. But a quarter won't make the pain go away, nor will it ensure against another punch in the eye by the bully. No matter how much the coal burning plants pay, that won't reduce the pollution that they emit or the damage and pain that causes.

And so at the end, the coal burners will just pass the increased cost to the customers. This way the customers who live in the affected areas get hurt twice; first by breathing polluted air, and then again by paying for the carbon tax to somebody else who does not live in the affected area. Fair? You be the judge.

In all fairness, we must agree here that coal is a necessary evil, and that we must not fight against the people in the industry, such as those who go down in the mines, or those who burn the coal in power plants. These are honest, hard-working folks, stuck in a controversial situation, which we all need to address and solve without punishing those who are doing their job properly for the larger good.

ENVIRONMENTAL UPDATE

What happened in Rio de Janeiro during Earth Summit, 2012? "Spinning wheels and a waste of time," is the direct answer of some of the attendees.

A more complete answer would be to say that 30 years ago, on June 20, 1992, during the first-ever earth summit at Rio de Janeiro, 155 nations and the EU signed the Convention on Biological Diversity (CBD). The expectations were high, the work ahead enormous, but the only results we've seen since then is more result-less meetings and more empty talk, devoid of actual positive results.

1992 promised a great beginning, and was a milestone in human development. It confirmed a worldwide commitment to form a global alliance to protect habitats, species and genes. The goal was to shift to the sustainable use of resources. That includes making important policy, economic, and managerial changes to guarantee the equitable distribution of resources across local, regional, and global communities.

Sounds good, no?

Fast forward 30 years and note that all local, regional, and global level benchmarks for sustainable development remain unmet, so the more than 20 participants gather in Rio again to discuss the same agenda. Specialists observe that a "charade for green capitalism" has grown like a cancer during the past 30 years.

Rising world population and environmental degradation are inflicting unprecedented changes, such as shrinking resources due to unsustainable development and ongoing global conflicts mostly in the poorer parts of the world.

Sustainable water management, particularly in Asia, could ignite serious conflicts or "water wars" involving all nations of the subcontinent, according to specialists. This is compounded by climate change, which has irreversible consequences for every sector of economies of these and many other countries.

Glacier melting, decreasing crop yields, and variability in monsoon and sea-level rise are estimated to have a strong regional presence as well. These impacts increase the risk of food insecurity and incidences of malnutrition. Increased frequency of violent and catastrophic natural events such as floods, droughts, cyclones, and tsunamis is a danger to human populations.

There is a prediction of a 30% decrease in the agricultural yields by the mid-21st century, due to the changing environmental and social conditions. Unless timely action is taken, this might lead to increased food insecurity and even doom for the subcontinent population.

The world policy makers are talking and talking, but they are not taking any decisive measures. Meanwhile, the critical environmental degradation now upon us might become a major reason for more natural and social disasters and even armed conflicts in many areas of the developing world. There will be lots of suffering around the world—and even death—if we do not pay heed to nature's warnings and agree to do something drastic in the near future.

Thirty wasted years in meetings and talks without any results, as evidenced by the Rio's Earth Summit in 2012, is not a good foundation to build our hope for resolving the environmental and social issues. One, however, has to hope that, as things get worse and more obvious, a future Earth Summit will produce more decisive results. We see no conditions for this to happen any time soon, but let's hope and pray...

EPA or no EPA? This is the question of the 21st century.

EPA's role in the environmental cleanup is still stuck somewhere between fully responsible and looking-the-other-way. There are some things coming from the EPA, but many ideas are either half-baked, or baked on the wrong side. There are a number of examples to justify such a statement, but it will take too much space here, so we'll give EPA due credit in trying to do the right thing as efficiently as possible.

One good thing that is still in the works is EPA-452/R-12-001 rule, stating:

> *The proposed EGU GHG NSPS will limit greenhouse gas emissions (GHG) from new fossil fuel fired electric generating units (EGU) constructed in the United States in the future.... This proposal requires that all new fossil-fuel fired units that exceed 25 MW in capacity be able to meet an emission rate standard of 1,000 pounds of CO_2 per megawatt hour (lbs CO_2/MWh) calculated over a rolling 12-month period. It also proposes an alternative compliance option that would allow units to meet the 1,000 lbs CO_2/MWh standard using a 30-year averaging period. These standards could be met either by natural gas combined cycle (NGCC) generation with no additional GHG control or coal-fired generation using CCS.*

Great, right? Maybe so, if the rule were not so generous and so open-ended that the end result is:

1. Presently coal-fired power plants emit approximately 1,500 lbs CO_2/MWh, so dropping this to 1,000 lbs CO_2/MWh is significant, but still far from enough. And so, a 500 MW coal power plant is actually emitting 500,000 lbs of CO_2 in the atmosphere every hour and 12,000,000 lbs of CO_2 every day.

2. Presently a 500 MW coal-fired power plant will emit 6.6 billion lbs CO_2 per annum. With the new rule, this amount will be reduced to 4.4 billion lbs of CO_2 per annum, but only in the very distant future, because only newly built plants are affected. Not bad as far as progress is concerned, but it is still 4.4 billion CO_2 toxic gasses pumped in the atmosphere every year by just one plant.

3. There are 594 coal-fired power plants in the US as of the 2009 count, with approximately 330,000 MW of combined power generation. Several dozens of new coal-fired power plants are in the making, so the number will grow significantly with time. This is 2,890,800,000,000 lbs (2.9 trillion lbs, right?), or 1.3 billion tons (yes, billion with a capital B) tons of CO_2 being pumped into the atmosphere every year by the US power plants alone. Multiplying this ever increasing number by the pounds of CO_2 per MW generated worldwide (by thousands of dirty coal-fired plants) produces a number with too many zeroes to even count.

4. The 30 years "averaging period" opens a large loophole where many, if not most, plant operators will squeeze through, delaying the CO_2 sequestration for as long as possible.

In all cases, the half-baked EPA rule won't provide much environmental protection from large CO_2 emissions in the US for a long time—if ever! And this is only the tip of the iceberg, because most of the several thousand coal-fired powered plants around the world are totally unregulated and spew as many poisons into the air as they wish whenever they wish.

China alone generates 2 billion MWh per annum by its 2,000 coal-fired power plants, almost 10 times the US numbers discussed above, and also burns that much coal for other domestic and industrial purposes. How many zeroes of pounds of CO_2 and other toxic gasses does this represent? As a matter of fact, China is expected to emit as many poisonous gasses by 2025-2030 as the entire world together. And so, the immense cloud of stinky, poisonous gasses containing many stinky, poisonous chemicals—some of which are many times more dangerous to the environment and human health than CO_2—go into the atmosphere every day where they produce the negative effects that we all know and fear.

With this large-scale, ongoing debacle, the big question remains, "How long is nature going to be able to keep its balance with this large cloud of toxic gasses thrown at her?" Won't she choke and cough out of existence one of these days? It's more likely that we'll all choke to death first.

Comparing conventional energy sources with the solar technologies of today is not a straightforward process; however, although there is no clear line that can be drawn between them, there are definite differences that can be identified and quantified as pluses and minuses. Although our objective is not to compare the different technologies from an environmental point of view, we will discuss the characteristics and draw some conclusions to open the subject to an honest discussion. For obvious reasons, this may not happen any time soon, but make no mistake about it, it will happen eventually!

The Environmental Activities

There is no lack of environmental concern and activities today. The problem, however, is that the movement is sporadic, at best, and comes and goes in waves as the events develop or demand. Nevertheless, the battle rages on with several types of people on both sides of the front lines.

Looking at Figure 5-43 we see the two groups on either side of the environmental battlefield.

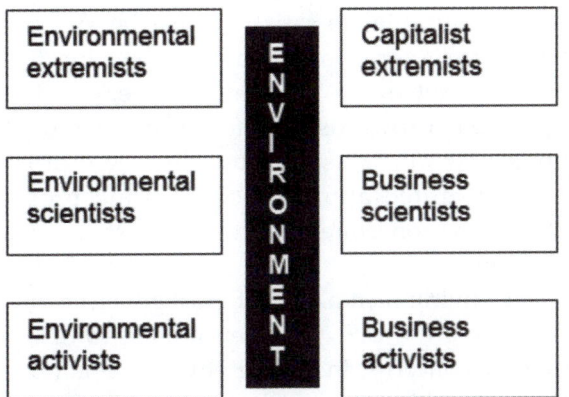

Figure 5-43. The environmental battlefield

On the left side are the environmentalists, led by the most vocal of all sub-groups, the environmental extremists. The *environmental extremists* are people who see only the evil side of the situation, which might be triggered by personal convictions or self-protecting interests. They usually do not even consider the civil exchange of ideas, and peaceful resolution of the matter at hand is not an option. Their principle is, "My way, or the highway." The glass is always empty, so they excel in building any small issue into a world-shaking monster. Reacting, and over-reacting, they voice their convictions as loudly as possible, and cannot be bothered by reason. Negotiations are one-sided, and violence is the final measure in some cases. Sometimes the police squads become forcefully involved, make arrests, and aggravate the conflict—which may be the goal.

The *environmental scientists* are the brains of the movement. They clearly see the situation, understand the issues, and know what can be done. In many cases, however, they either do not present their findings and ideas clearly enough, or are misunderstood, which only adds fuel to the conflict.

NOTE: Although the author officially does not belong to any of these groups and sub-groups, he identifies with this group, only because it is the one that is most efficient and truthful in finding, analyzing, and disclosing the real facts. It is also the group that is most disinterested in the actual outcome of the battle as long as correct information and sound decisions are used in analyzing and resolving the issues at hand.

The *environmental activists*, which sometimes include both groups mentioned above, the environmental extremists and the scientists, are the face and muscle of the movement. They are driven by the principle that evil prospers when good men do nothing. This group publishes magazines and articles, gets engaged in debates and public demonstrations, and organizes protests against projects and companies they consider damaging to the environment and the people's health.

On the other side of the environmental issues we have the interested groups, led by the sub-group of capitalist extremists and opportunists.

The *capitalist extremists* group usually includes the people who have the most to gain or lose from the matter at hand. Actually, most often it is their representatives that we see on the front lines, since the beneficiaries are fat cat rich people and companies that don't like to get their hands dirty. Tobacco, lead, asbestos, and oil companies come to mind here. This sub-group has done the most damage to the environment by pushing products and services that are extremely harmful. Just think of the asbestos debacle with thousands of people hurt and millions of dollars wasted, just because the manufacturers and their supporters wanted to make a lot of money by pushing a product that they knew was harmful.

The *business scientists* are the brains of this group. They are well funded when they go to work every day serving their overlords. Their findings are very often manipulated to suit the owner's whims and needs. Scientists employed by tobacco companies ultimately were found guilty of such crimes, and one has to wonder how they lived with themselves for so many years. Human scruples are endless and unexplainable, so we should not be surprised much by those events.

The *business activists* are the lobbyists and spokesmen for large companies who are paid to say and do everything possible to protect the interests of the bosses. This group sometimes also includes people from the above two groups, the capitalist extremists and business scientists. Some of these people have also done more harm than good in the past to the society in large, including serious damage to the environment and human health, by defending the un-defendable.

And the battle goes on—who is going to win?

Today

Today 70% of greenhouse gas emissions (GHG) emissions are blamed on fossil fuel production and combustion for electrical generation. These emissions are projected to increase, as the global population will grow to 9 billion by 2050, mostly in developing countries. If this trend continues, delivering new energy services for the developed world and sustaining economic growth in the developing countries will result in a tripling of annual GHG emissions.

Such drastic increase of pollution will have a dramatic effect on our environment, so there are efforts under way in developed and developing countries to arrest and reverse the growth in GHG emissions and lower the carbon footprint of development.

Since the energy sector is a primary target of these efforts, capacity is being built to integrate lower carbon development objectives into long-term, 20- to 30-year, energy planning processes. New technologies and measures to lessen carbon footprints are being exchanged. There is significant focus on scaling up renewable energy sources, efficiency measures for the supply and demand sides, loss reduction, and cleaner fossil fuel combustion technologies. Simultaneously, the climate is also changing as a result of anthropogenic GHG emissions that are now estimated to surpass the worst-case emission trajectory drawn under the Intergovernmental Panel on Climate Change (IPCC) in its third assessment report (IPCC, 2001a).

The urgency of the above actions to control emissions is undeniable. The need to adapt to unavoidable climate consequences from the damage already induced in the biosphere can be no longer ignored. If nothing is done, future generations will have to deal with much higher temperatures, rising sea levels, severe changes in sea surface conditions and coastal water quality, increased weather variability, and more frequent and extreme weather events. Stabilizing the global GHG emissions below 2°C above pre-industrial levels at that point would be like using an umbrella after the rain has stopped.

Some of the events that are taking place are irreversible, and some can only get worse. The end result of all this would be loss of land from rising sea levels, increase of sickness worldwide, and serious changes in flora and fauna around the world.

The energy supply chain is also vulnerable to climate variability, and extreme events can affect deeply the energy resources and supplies by 2050. On the supply side, the amount of energy generated by solar, wind, hydro, and biomass would be affected by weather changes in mostly negative ways. On the demand side we will see an increase in the seasonal demand, due to increased need for heating and cooling. This discrepancy will not be workable, because oil and natural gas supplies will diminish and prices will go disproportionally high by 2050.

Thus far, governments have been maximizing the energy supplies to satisfy industrial and societal demands for energy by all means possible to keep things moving. In the U.S. this was reflected in the Obama's push towards oil and natural gas fracking, opening new oil fields, and building new pipelines. This shortsighted approach could bring prosperity today, but the consequences would be grave for future generations.

The environmental MO of most governments thus far, including the U.S., has been limited to discussing immediate concerns, including environmental damage and climate mitigation as related to power generation. Some knee jerk actions have been taken, like shutting off the German nuclear plants in the wake of the Fukushima nuclear disaster, but in most cases the energy sector is not included in the decision making process and the environment is not of major consideration.

As we enter into the last phase of fossil energy use and as we are now finally considering the damages already done, we must keep in mind that:

- Climate change is upon us, and will be increasingly affected by the energy decisions we make now and in the near future. Changing trends, increasing variability, greater extremes, and large year-to-year variations in climate parameters in some regions will dominate the generation of power and determine its effect on the environment.

- Climate changes impact the entire energy supply chain, with direct effects on energy resource endowment, infrastructure, and transportation, and indirect effects that include other economic sectors such as water quality and quantity, agricultural production, etc. These effects are like a double-edged sword: the energy generators affect the climate change and the climate change affects them. Who is who and what the outcome would be is unclear as yet, but in all cases we must be proactive rather than just reactive.

- We must understand this double-edged sword and the related intricate and delicate energy/climate interactions so that we can simultaneously control: a) the power generation, b) its effect on the environment, and c) the effects of the climate change on the power generation industry.

- The energy industry presently is focused mainly on the responsibility for greenhouse gas mitigation rather than on the management of the energy products and services. Changing the focus would bring immediate and significant positive results in both energy use and environmental protection.

- Adaptation to the upcoming changes is a must, since they are equal to, or greater than, other business risks. The existing and new energy infrastructure as well as any future planning must consider emerging climate conditions and their impact on new designs, and construction, operation, and maintenance operations.

- Risk-based planning is critical to properly address the impacts and harmonize the actions within and across sectors. Some of today's unsustainable practices will have to be eliminated through new investments in long-lived infrastructures and associated consumption patterns.

Energy and Environment Timeline

Figure 5-44 shows the incremental increase of energy use with corresponding increase of the environmental issues, while at the same time the fossil resources are slowly, but permanently, dwindling down to zero. This paints a scary picture of future—that of life without reliable energy resources.

2013 Update: The level of carbon dioxide in the atmosphere reached a record 400-ppm in mid-May, 2013. The official reading taken by the National Oceanic and Atmospheric Administration at the top of Mauna Loa volcano in Hawaii was 400.06 and is considered an important bellwether for the status of Earth's atmosphere. Readings in some other areas far exceed that milestone, but areas far from pollution sources have not reached such high levels.

The last time Earth's atmosphere contained 400-ppm of carbon dioxide was 2.5 million years ago, during the Pleistocene epoch. The average temperatures during that time rose as much as 180°F. Sea levels rose over 100 ft. higher than current levels and a number of great and disastrous changes followed.

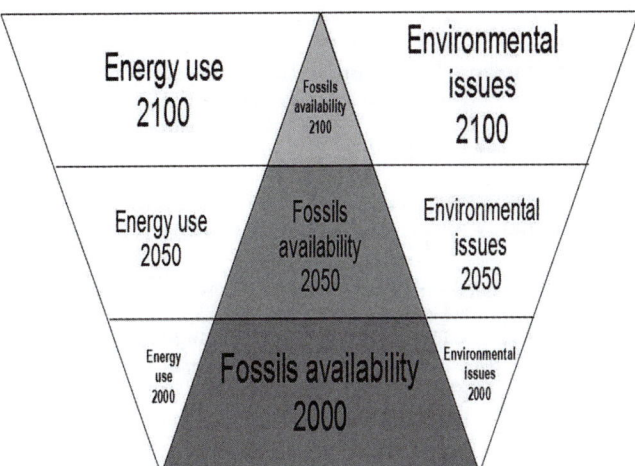

Figure 5-44. Energy availability and use vs. environmental issues

CO_2 levels have been stable at about 300-ppm during the previous 800,000 years, and there is no known geologic period in which the rate of increase of CO_2 levels has been so sharp. The level was about 280-ppm at the advent of the Industrial Revolution in the 18th century, when the burning of fossil fuels began to soar, reaching 316-ppm in 1958 and up to 400-ppm today.

In the last 55 years, CO_2 levels went up by over 100-ppm, a 25% increase. At that rate, the world can expect the CO_2 levels to exceed 600-ppm levels sometime next century. Any increase above that level would seriously affect all types of life on Earth, in addition to bringing a number of unspeakable environmental changes. The combined effect would devastate the land and life in large areas of the Earth.

Time to wake up, people…

Notes and References

1. *Global Warming.* http://www.aproundtable.org/tps30info/globalwarmup.html.
2. *What is the Energy Payback for PV?* US DOE.
3. *RE-Powering America's Land: Renewable Energy on Potentially Contaminated Land and Mine Sites,* EPA, 2008.
4. *Energy Payback Time (EPBT) and CO_2 mitigation potential,* Evert Nieuwlaar, Erik Alsema.
5. *RoHS web page.* http://www.rohs.gov.uk/
6. *The World's Worst Environmental Disasters Caused by Companies.* http://www.businesspundit.com/the-worlds-worst-environmental-disasters-caused-by-companies/
7. *Environmental Aspects of PV Power Systems,* http://www.energycrisis.org/apollO$_2$/pvenv1997.pdf
8. Externe E. *Impact Pathways of Health and Environmental Effects,* http://www.externe.info/
9. USGS: http://minerals.usgs.gov/minerals/pubs/commodity/cadmium/mcs-2010-cadmi.pdf
10. http://www.fas.org/ota/reports/9344.pdf
11. http://www.iiasa.ac.at/Admin/PUB/Documents/IR-02-073
12. Topaz Solar Farm Project, *Draft Environmental Impact Report,* 2011

13. Kan A. *General Characteristics of Waste Management: A Review.* Energy EducSci Technol Part A 2009; 23: 55–69.

14. Demirbas AH. *Inexpensive Oil and Fats Feedstock for Production of Biodiesel.* Energy Educ Sci Technol Part A 2009; 23: 1–13.

15. Kirtay E. *The Role of Renewable Energy Sources in Meeting Turkey's Electrical Energy Demand.* Energy Educ Sci Technol Part A 2009; 23: 15–30.

16. Hazar H, Oner C, Nursoy M. *Effects of CrN Coating of Cylinders on Engine Performance.* Energy Educ Sci Technol Part A 2009; 23: 71–85.

17. Kvenvolden K. *Gas Hydrates – Geological Perspective and Global Change.* Rev Geophys 1993; 31: 173–87.

18. Mahajan D, Taylor CE, Mansoori GA. *An Introduction to Natural Gas Hydrate/Clathrate: The Major Organic Carbon Reserve of the Earth.* J Petrol Sci Eng 2007; 56: 1–8.

19. Hendriks EM, Edmonds B, Moorwood RAS, Szczepanski R. *Hydrate Structure Stability in Simple and Mixed Hydrates.* Fluid Phase Equilibr 1996; 117: 193–200.

20. Kvenvolden A. *Gas Hydrates as a Potential Energy Resource – A review of their methane content.* In: Howell DG, editor. *The Future of Energy Gases –* US geological survey professional paper 1570. Washington: United States Government Printing Office; 1993. p. 555–61.

21. Farkhondeh M, Gheisi AR. *An Introduction to Natural Gas Hydrate.*

22. Transportation. Methane gas hydrate report. Iran: Tehran University; 2002.

23. Tucholke BE, Bryan GM, Ewing JI. *Gas-hydrate Horizons Detected in Seismicprofiler Data From the Western North Atlantic.* AAPG Bull 1977; 61: 698–707.

24. *Wind Turbine Accidents and Failures,* http://docs.wind-watch.org/fullaccidents.pdf

25. JC Winnie environmental blog: http://www.innovationsreport.com/html/reports/energy engineering/report-82659.Html

26. Global Greenhouse Warming.com: http://www.globalgreenhousewarming.com/solar-parabolictrough.html

27. *Photovoltaics for Commercial and Utilities Power Generation,* Anco S Blazev. The Fairmont Press, 2011

28. *Solar Technologies for the 21st Century,* Anco S Blazev. The Fairmont Press, 2013

Appendix A

A. Clean Air Act and Amendments

1955   Pollution Control Act

1959   Reauthorization

1960   Motor vehicle exhaust study

1963   Clean Air Act Amendments

1965   Motor Vehicle Air Pollution Control Act

1966   Clean Air Act Amendments of 1966

1967   Air Quality Act of 1967 National Air Emission Standards Act

1970   Clean Air Act Amendments of 1970

1973   Reauthorization

1974   Energy Supply and Environmental Coordination Act of 1974

1977   Clean Air Act Amendments of 1977

1980   Acid Precipitation Act of 1980

1981   Steel Industry Compliance Extension Act of 1981

1987   Clean Air Act 8-month Extension

1990   Clean Air Act Amendments of 1990

1991   Technical correction to list of hazardous air pollutants

1995-96 Relatively minor laws amending the Act

1998   Amended Section 604 re methyl bromide Border Smog Reduction Act of 1998

1999   Chemical Safety Information, Site Security and Fuels Regulatory Relief Act

2004   Amendments to §209 re small engines

2005   Energy Policy Act of 2005 (amended §211 re fuels) 2007 Energy Independence and Security Act of 2007 (amended §211, re. fuels)

      P.L. 84-159

      P.L. 86-353

      P.L. 86-493

      P.L. 88-206

      P.L. 89-272, Title I

      P.L. 89-675

      P.L. 90-148

      P.L. 91-604

      P.L. 93-15

      P.L. 93-319

      P.L. 95-95

      P.L. 96-294, Title VII

      P.L. 97-23

      P.L. 100-202

      P.L. 101-549

      P.L. 102-187

      P.L. 104-6,

      P.L. 104-59,

      P.L. 104-70,

      P.L. 104-260

      P.L. 105-277, Section 764

      P.L. 105-286

      P.L. 106-40

      P.L. 108-199, Division G, Title IV, Section 428

      P.L. 109-58 P.L. 110-140

B. Clean Water Act and Amendments

1948   Federal Water Pollution Control Act

1956   Water Pollution Control Act of 1956

1961   Federal Water Pollution Control Act Amendments

1965   Water Quality Act of 1965

1966   Clean Water Restoration Act

1970   Water Quality Improvement Act of 1970

1972   Federal Water Pollution Control Act Amendments

1977   Clean Water Act of 1977
1981   Municipal Wastewater Treatment Construction Grants Amendments
1987   Water Quality Act of 1987
       P.L. 80-845 (Act of June 30, 1948)
       P.L. 84-660 (Act of July 9, 1956)
       P.L. 87-88
       P.L. 89-234
       P.L. 89-753
       P.L. 91-224, Part I P.L. 92-500
       P.L. 95-217

C. Ocean Dumping Act and Amendments

1972   Marine Protection, Research, and Sanctuaries Act
1974   London Dumping Convention Implementation
1977   Authorization of Appropriations
1980   Authorization of Appropriations
1980   Authorization of Appropriations
1982   Surface Transportation Assistance Act
1986   Budget Reconciliation 1986 Water Resources Development Act
1987   Water Quality Act of 1987
1988   Ocean dumping research amendments
1988   Ocean Dumping Ban Act
1988   U.S. Public Vessel Medical Waste Anti-Dumping Act of 1988
1990   Regional marine research centers
1992   National Coastal Monitoring Act
1992   Water Resources Development Act
       P.L. 92-532
       P.L. 93-254
       P.L. 95-153
       P.L. 96-381
       P.L. 96-572
       P.L. 97-424
       P.L. 99-272, §§6061-6065
       P.L. 99-662, §§211, 728, 1172
       P.L. 100-4, §508
       P.L. 100-627, Title I
       P.L. 100-688, Title I
       P.L. 100-688, Title III
       P.L. 101-593, Title III
       P.L. 102-567, Title V P.L. 102-580, §§504-510

D. Safe Drinking Act and Amendments

1974   Safe Drinking Water Act of 1974 P.L. 93-523
1977   Safe Drinking Water Act Amendments of 1977 P.L. 95-190
1979   Safe Drinking Water Act Amendments P.L. 96-63
1980   Safe Drinking Water Act Amendments P.L. 96-502

1986   Safe Drinking Water Act Amendments of 1986 P.L. 99-339
1988   Lead Contamination Control Act of 1988 P.L. 100-572
1996   Safe Drinking Water Act Amendments of 1996 P.L. 104-182
2002   Public Health Security and Bioterrorism Preparedness P.L. 107-188 and Response Act of 2002

E. Solid Waste Disposal Act, Resource Conservation and Recover Act (RCRA)

1976   Law to Control Hazardous Wastes, End Open Dumping, and Promote Conservation of Resources
1980   Hazardous Waste Regulations
1981   First Storage Permit Under RCRA
1984   Hazardous and Solid Waste Amendments of 1984,
1988   Standards For Underground Storage Tanks
1990   Land Disposal Restrictions for Hazardous Wastes
1999   Revision of Standards for Air Emissions from Hazardous Waste Combustors

F. Insecticide, Fungicide, and Rodenticide Act and Amendments

1938   Federal Food, Drug, and Cosmetic Act
1947   Federal Insecticide, Fungicide, and Rodenticide Act P.L. 80-104
1954   Federal Food, Drug, and Cosmetic Act Amendments
1958   Food Additive Amendments of 1958 (including the Delaney Clause)
1964   Federal Insecticide, Fungicide, and Rodenticide Act Amendments P.L. 88-305
1970   Transfer of pesticide residue responsibility to EPA
1972   Federal Environmental Pesticide Control Act P.L. 92-516
1975   Federal Insecticide, Fungicide, and Rodenticide Act Extension P.L. 94-140
1978   Federal Pesticide Act of 1978 P.L. 95-396
1980   Federal Insecticide, Fungicide and Rodenticide Act Amendments P.L. 96-539
1988   Federal Insecticide, Fungicide, and Rodenticide Amendments of
1990   P.L. 100-532 1990 Food, Agriculture, Conservation, and Trade Act of 1990 P.L. 101-624
1991   Food, Agriculture, Conservation and Trade Amendments of 1991 P.L. 102-237
1996   Food Quality Protection Act (FQPA) of 1996 P.L. 104-170

1996   Food Quality Protection Act of 1996

2004   Pesticide Registration Improvement Act of 2003
P.L. 108-199, Division G, Title V

2007   Pesticide Registration Improvement Renewal
Act P.L. 110-94

Appendix C

The recklessness of the present generations is quite obvious in a number of failed projects and disastrous events since the 1970s.

Below is a list of some of the environmental events and disasters of the past half-century to keep in mind:

1969   Blow-out at the Union Oil Platform A at the Santa Barbara, CA, coast line spews an estimated 80,000-100,000 barrels of crude oil into the channel and onto the beaches, fouling the coastline from Goleta to Ventura, as well as the northern shores of the four northern channel islands. (Oil and tar deposits still linger on the local beaches.)

1970   National Environmental Policy Act was signed, creating the Council on Environmental Quality to advise the President on environmental issues.

— General Motors president Edward Cole promises "pollution free" cars by 1980 and urges the elimination of lead additives from gasoline in order to allow the use of catalytic converters. (Catalytic converters are in, but pollution free cars are still in the queue and remain a long way from reality.)

— Earth Day celebration in San Francisco organized by John McConnell

— First nationwide Earth Day organized by Sen. Gaylord Nelson and Dennis Hayes

— Clean Air Act passed

— Natural Resources Defense Council created

— Friends of the Everglades founded by Marjory Stoneman Douglas

— Lake Michigan Federation founded

— Environmental Protection Agency signed into law

Appendix B

Periodic Table of the Elements

— Occupational Health and Safety Administration (OSHA) bill signed into law

1971 Chamber of Commerce warns of dangers arising from enforcing pollution regulations

— Passage of Animal Welfare Act and Wild and Free Ranging Horse and Burro Protection Act

— President's CEQ acknowledges racial discrimination negatively affects urban environment

— Greenpeace founded in Victoria, B.C., to oppose atomic testing in Alaska

1972 W. Eugene Smith completes his essay on the crippling effects of mercury pollution

— First regional treaty to regulate dumping of radioactive wastes in Europe

— EPA announces all gasoline stations are required to carry nonleaded gasoline

— Buffalo Creek disaster occurs in West Virginia, where strip mining kills 125 people

— Congress passes: Federal Water Pollution Control Act, Coastal Zone Management Act, Ocean Dumping Act, and the Marine Mammal Protection Act

— Toxic Substances Control Act (TSCA) law passed

— First bottle recycling bill passed in Oregon

— Supreme Court supports Sierra Club over Disney Inc. in battle about development

— United Nations Conference on the Human Environment convenes in Stockholm, Sweden

— UN Environment Program (UNEP) acts on the recommendations of Stockholm meeting

1973 Eighty nations sign the Convention on International Trade in Endangered Species (CITES)

— Arab oil embargo panics US and European consumers; prices quadruple

— Congress approves Alaska Oil pipeline

— A group of Himalayan villagers stops loggers from cutting down a stand of hormbeam trees

— Endangered Species Act passed by Congress

— Tellico Dam controversy: Endangered Species Act blamed for stopping project

1974 F.S. Rowland and M.J. Molina blame CFCs for breaking up ozone in a catalytic cycle

— Congress passes Safe Drinking Water Act to be administered by EPA

— K. Silkwood dies in a suspicious accident, involving Kerr-McGee nuclear weapons facility

— Worldwatch Institute founded

1975 Atlantic salmon return to Connecticut River after 100-year absence

— Congress passes Hazardous Waste Transportation Act

— Greenpeace leads the Great Whale Conspiracy battle

— Standoff over logging in Brazil's Amazon region by local rubber tappers

— Federal court says EPA has authority to regulate leaded gasoline

— Catastrophic failure of Grand Teton Dam in Idaho causes 14 deaths and lots of damage

— Chemical explosion in a Milan, Italy, spreads dioxin, causing chloracne in 300 school children

— National Academy of Science report on CFCs gasses warns of damage to ozone layer.

— Congress passes: Resource Conservation and Recovery Act (RCRA), Federal Land Policy Management Act, and the Whale Conservation and Protective Study Act

— Urquiola oil spill, La Coruna, Spain

— Liberian tanker Argo Merchant crashes by Nantucket Island, leaks 9 million gallons of oil

— The Land Institute founded in Salinas, Kansas

— The International Primate Protection League formed in Thailand

— American Museum of Natural History forced to halt cat experiments

1977 U.S. Department of Energy created by President Jimmy Carter

— Congress passes Soil and Water Conservation Act; and the Surface Mining Control and Land Reclamation Act

— Ecofisk oil well blowout occurs in the North Sea

— U.S. Supreme Court upholds the 1973 Endangered Species Act and stops construction of Tellico Dam

— Allied Chemical Company and state of Virginia settle lawsuit over extensive contamination of James River

— Federal Clean Air Act amendments require review of all National Ambient Air Quality Standards by 1980

— Congress adds additional protection for Class I National Park and Wilderness air quality

1978 Propylene gas explosion occurs in Tarragona, Spain

— The Amoco Cadiz wrecks off the coast of France and loses 68 million gallons crude oil

— Energy Tax Act creates federal ethanol tax incentive of 5 cents per gallon
— Lois Gibbs and her neighbors form the Love Canal Homeowners Association
— Robert Bullard begins investigating Triana, AL, where DDT had contaminated a stream. Environmental justice movement is born as a result
— US Congress passes: National Energy Act, Endangered American Wilderness Act, and the Antarctic Conservation Act

1979 Three Mile Island nuclear power plant loses coolant and partially melts down
— IXTOC I oil well blowout occurs in Bay of Campeche, Mexico; large area contaminated
— Earth First! organized by Dave Foreman, Howie Wolke, and Mike Roselle
— Bean v. SWM lawsuit filed, challenging the siting of a waste facility
— EPA suspends and later bans domestic use of 2,4,5-T, Agent Orange component
— Appropriate Community Technology demonstration, one of the first alternative energy exhibitions on the national and international level, held on Washington, DC, mall
— Greenpeace vessel rams the Portuguese pirate whaler Sierra on the high seas
— J.J. LaFalce and D.P. Moynihan propose "superfund" legislation

1986 The Chernobyl nuclear plant reactor number four shows unusual and, as it turns out, unsafe systems test at low power. A sudden, rapid growth in power output takes place, and when an attempt is made for an emergency shutdown, an unexpected and more extreme spike in power output occurs, leading to a reactor vessel rupture and a series of explosions. The environment in the local and adjacent areas is ruined and inhabitable for the next century or more. Thousands died, many more thousands got ill, and the disaster is still unfolding.

1989 The Exxon Valdez ran aground, resulting in the second largest oil spill in US history, estimated at 500,000-750,000 barrels and listed as the 54th largest spill in history.

2003 Summer heat wave in Europe takes 35,000 lives
— Earthquake in Iran kills 40,000

2004 Hurricane Jeannine kills 3,037 people
— Asian tsunami kills 250,000 people

2005 Hurricane Katrina devastates New Orleans and kills 1,836 people
— Earthquake in Pakistan kills 75,000 people

2008 Myanmar cyclone kills 146,000 people
— China earthquake kills 70,000 people

2009 Global swine flu creates worldwide chaos and kills 11,800 people

2010 BP oil spill from Deepwater Horizon oilrig disaster spills millions of gallons of crude oil into the Gulf of Mexico. (The disaster is still unfolding, and the oil will be damaging the environment and threatening life forms and humans in the Gulf for many years to come.)
— Haiti earthquake devastates several cities and kills over 300,000 people
— Iceland volcanic eruption paralyzes European air traffic for several days
— Mining accident in Chile buried 30 miners and riveted the world's attention to the sage of their survival and eventual rescue

2011 Japan earthquake and tsunami in March 2011 devastate several hundred miles of populated coastal area. Thousands of people were killed and many are still missing. Four nuclear reactors were damaged and still leak radiation. Japan is confronted with long-term uncertainty and large recovery expense
— Record floods occurred in Thailand, Cambodia, Myanmar, Vietnam, and Laos, affecting over 3 million people. Over 2,828 lost their lives to a series of flooding events of varying origins in Southeast Asia since August 2011 in the above-mentioned nations. Worldwide supply-chain disruptions occurred in technology sector, and billion-dollar losses and severe parts shortages rippled to corporations of developed nations. The assumption of safety from floodwaters is now being questioned in many nations thought or assumed to be prepared.

2012 Extreme heat and drought conditions in the several US regions caused heavy damage to crops and livestock, the like of which has not been seen for decades.
— Strong earthquake in Iran kills several hundred, and thousands are injured and hospitalized
— Floods in North Korea and the Philippines leave thousands homeless.

Appendix D

Historical U.S. Government Legislation/Regulation in SO_2 Control

The Air Pollution Control Act of 1955: Public Law 84-159

In 1955, the first Federal legislation related to air quality was signed into law by President Eisenhower. The Air Pollution Control Act of 1955 by no means established any control or regulatory measures. It simply acknowledged the existence of air pollution problems and authorized the Secretary of Health, Education and Welfare to conduct research to better understand the causes and effects of air pollution and provide technical assistance to State and local government agencies. This Federal legislation granted $5 million annually for five years to fund Federal research. During the legislative process, great concerns over the involvement of Federal government into the then believed local issues were expressed. Consequently, the 1955 act specifically stated that air pollution control was primarily a responsibility of State and local government agencies. The 1955 act was amended in 1961 to continue Federal research funding for four more years.

In 1962, under President Kennedy, another amendment to the 1955 act was passed. In addition to all principles contained in the 1955 act, the 1962 amendment called for research to be performed by the U.S. Surgeon General on health effects from motor vehicle exhaust. This was the first time that health effects related to air quality were investigated by a Federal agency.

The Clean Air Act of 1963: (Public Law 88-206)

As requested by President Kennedy, Congress passed the Clean Air Act in 1963. This was the first time that the term "clean air" was used in Federal air legislation. Under the 1963 act, a grant in the amount of $96 million over a three-year period was established for State and local government agencies to conduct research and local control programs. To have non-federal agencies participating in research marked a major shift from the 1955 act, which only authorized Federal agencies to be the recipient of research funds. In addition to broadening the recipients of research funds, the 1963 act also granted Federal authority to address interstate air pollution issues, which was mainly due to the combustion of high sulfur content coal and oil at the time. The next piece of major air legislation was in the form of an amendment to the Clean Air Act of 1963.

In 1965, for the first time, emission standards were established for new motor vehicles by the enactment of the Motor Vehicle Pollution Control Act. In addition to the establishment of vehicle emission standards, the 1965 act for the first time also acknowledged the air pollution issues and health threats at our borders with both Mexico and Canada.

The 1967 Air Quality Act Amendment provided a fundamental change in the role of Federal government in air quality control. By now lawmakers realized that research by Federal agencies was not a substitute for regulation. The Federal government had a duty and right to establish and enforce air quality rules. The 1967 amendment required the Secretary of the Department of Health, Education, and Welfare to divide part of the nation into Air Quality Control Regions in order to facilitate planning, monitoring, and controlling. The 1967 amendment also established emission standards for stationary sources and expanded research activities. The era of Federal air regulation and enforcement began with the enactment of the 1967 amendment.

The Clean Air Act of 1970: Public Law 91-604)

By the late 1960s, the environmental movement in the country was in high gear. Under President Nixon, Congress in 1969 passed the National Environmental Policy Act (NEPA). Less than one year after the NEPA passage, the U.S. Environmental Protection Agency (EPA) was established by Presidential Executive Order in 1970. The newly established EPA consolidated all environmental regulatory functions located in various executive departments and agencies. On the air quality side, since the enactment of the 1967 Clean Air Act, progress was slow. In response to public outcry, Congress passed the Clean Air Act Amendments in 1970. The 1970 amendments were a complete rewrite of the 1967 act.

The 1970 amendments required the newly created EPA to set the National Ambient Air Quality Standards (NAAQS) to protect public health and welfare, New Source Performance Standards (NSPS), and National Emission Standards for Hazardous Air Pollutants. The 1970 amendments required various States to submit State Implementation Plans (SIP) for attaining and maintaining the NAAQS. The amendments also authorized private citizens to sue polluters or government agencies for failure to carry out provisions of the Act. The 1970 act was enacted in the midst of the environmental enthusiasm throughout the nation. It required that by 1975 all areas would attain clean air status. Carbon monoxide and hydrocarbon emission from automobiles would be reduced 90% from the 1970 level by 1975; and nitrogen oxide emissions from automobiles would achieve a 90% reduction from 1971 levels by 1976.

The same year Congress passed the 1970 Clean Air Act, the 1970 Federal-Aid Highway Act (FHA) was enacted as well. The 1970 FHA incorporated certain requirements relating to environmental quality. Full consideration of economic, social, and

(Continued)

Historical U.S. government legislation/regulation in SO₂ control. (*Concluded*)

environmental impacts of highway projects would be assessed according to the 1970 FHA. With air quality, the 1970 FHA added section 109(j) to Title 23 of the U.S. Code. Section 109(j) stated that "The Secretary, after consultation with the Administrator of the Environmental Protection Agency, shall develop and promulgate guidelines to assure that highways constructed pursuant to this title are consistent with any approved plan for - (1) the implementation of a national ambient air quality standard for each pollutant for which an area is designated as a nonattainment area under section 107(d) of the Clean Air Act; or (2) the maintenance of a national ambient air quality standard in an area that was designated as a nonattainment area but that was later redesignated by the Administrator as an attainment area for the standard and that is required to develop a maintenance plan under section 175A of the Clean Air Act." For the first time in history, the need for highway projects to be consistent with SIPs developed under the 1970 Clean Air Act was legally required.

In 1974, in response to the Arab oil embargo and a desire to achieve energy independence, Congress passed the Energy Supply and Environmental Coordination Act (ESEC). The 1974 ESEC loosened some of the 1970 act requirements due to their effects on energy efficiency. The ESEC also pushed back the deadline for compliance with new vehicle emission standards specified in the 1970 act due to technology availability. As required in the 1970 FHA, regulations related to consistency development between transportation plans/programs/projects and SIPs were issued by U.S. DOT in 1975.

The Clean Air Act Amendments of 1977 was a significant piece of legislation regarding air quality. The 1977 amendments required EPA to review and update the NAAQS at five-year intervals. Under the Prevention of Significant Deterioration (PSD) subpart, the ambient air pollutant concentration in Class I area was virtually allowed no increase at all. For non-attainment areas, the 1977 acts authorized several provisions with respect to the NAAQS. One of the key concepts was the emission offset for stationary sources. By using the emission offset concept, new sources could be established by simultaneous reduction of the existing sources. The 1977 acts stated that no Federal agency could engage in, support in any way or provide financial assistance for, license, or permit, or approve an activity that did not conform to a SIP that had been approved or promulgated, but did not further define "conformity." Although the "conformity" concept was developed in the CAA, more progress was needed with regard to the implementation goal of the conformity regulation.

The Clean Air Act Amendments of 1990: (Public Law 101-549)

The next air quality legislation after the 1977 amendments was the passage of the Acid Precipitation Act of 1980 under President Carter. For the next ten years, no significant Federal air quality legislation was enacted until the modern air quality bill "The Clean Air Act Amendments of 1990" was passed under President Bush.

The 1990 CAA Amendments were a substantial rewrite of the 1970 Act. The 1990 CAAA granted significantly more authority to the Federal government than any other air quality legislation. With nine titles, subjects ranging from smog, motor vehicle emissions, and toxic air pollution to acid rain were considered. To address the smog issue, deadlines were established in areas according to five severity classifications ranging from marginal and moderate to serious, severe, and extreme. New regulatory programs and permitting were granted in order to control acid rain. New and stricter emission standards for motor vehicles were also established beginning with the 1995 model year. The National Emission Standards for Hazardous Air Pollutants program was also authorized to expand to much broader industries and activities.

To attain the NAAQS, as in the past, the State was still primarily responsible for developing the SIP that outlined methodologies and programs, and demonstrated attainment through air quality modeling. On issues related to air quality and transportation projects, the 1990 CAAA Title I, Part D, Subpart 1, Section 176 (c) "Limitations on Certain Federal Assistances" expanded an earlier provision in 1977 CAA Amendments known as the "conformity requirement". Section 176(c) stated that "No department, agency, or instrumentality of the Federal Government shall engage in, support in any way or provide financial assistance for, license or permit, or approve, any activity which does not conform to an implementation plan after it has been approved or promulgated under Section 110. No metropolitan planning organization designated under Section 134 of Title 23, United States Code, shall give its approval to any project, program, or plan which does not conform to an implementation plan approved or promulgated under Section 110."

Further, it went on defining that "conformity to an implementation plan means-(a) conformity to an implementation plan's purpose of eliminating or reducing the severity and number of violations of the national ambient air quality standards and achieving expeditious attainment of such standards; and (b) that such activities will not - (i) cause or contribute to any new violation of any standard in any area;(ii) increase the frequency or severity of any existing violations of any standards in any area; (iii) delay timely attainment of any standard or any required interim emission reductions or other milestones in any area." The statutory breadth of "Federal involvement in any activity" language is the same as the one adopted in the 1969 National Environmental Policy Act. It has reflected our nation's commitments and desires to improve air quality.

Chapter 6

Political and Regulatory Aspects of Energy and Environment

So one day millions of Americans marched. Politicians had no choice but to take notice.
Twelve Congressmen were dubbed the Dirty Dozen, and seven were kicked out of office.
The floodgates were opened. We got the Clean Air Act, the Clean Water Act,
and the Safe Drinking Water Act. We created the EPA.
The quality of life improved because concerned citizens made their issues matter in elections.

—Senator John Kerry

The U.S. political system and some politicians play a decisive role in the ups and downs of the energy-environment debate and activities. Sometimes they are the solution, and sometimes they are the problem. We, the people, have not been effective enough in influencing the political decisions, but we are getting more aware of our powers.

Starting with the example given by Senator John Kerry, and following similar actions through the last several decades, we have been making progress towards having control over our destiny, and that of the future generations. But the battle has just started and will continue for a long time.

A good understanding of the overall situation, the enemy's tactics, and the battlefield terrain, prefaces all successful field battles. This is followed by a thorough planning and efficient implementation of the agreed upon strategy.

Our intent here is to present a detailed and unbiased account of the energy-environmental battlefield, including the tools and tactics employed by the parties on both sides of the debate.

If you don't think that there is a battle in the energy and environmental fields, then you need to look around you and pay attention to what's going on more carefully. It's not hard to see the signs. Better yet, keep on reading.

It seems as though the energy and environmental problems come and go according to some unwritten law of Nature. In the 1970s we got panicky about gas prices, and then we forgot about it. This cycle repeated several times after that, and is back today, where we are exceedingly worried about our present energy security, the fu-

ture environment, and our personal safety and comforts.

But crisis like these were plaguing the world even much earlier. Just take a look...

The 1800s Environmental Crisis

Going way back in history, we see similar panics coming and going across the entire nation from time to time. We saw in the previous chapter the mess Londoners were living in the 1700-1800s, when at 10 o'clock every night, people would dump their chamber pots on the streets. Imagine the noise, stink, and goo covering the streets and sidewalks. And many thinkers of the time warned, that if this environmental abuse goes on for too long, it might be the end of London.

These people could not even think of ways to stop the misery they were living in, just like we cannot think of a good way to eliminate the environmental misery we are living in. But all the chamber pot problems in London went away when somebody proposed and built a central sewer system. The canals under the streets would take care of the centuries-long misery. Imagination, clear thinking, and technology solved the problem, and Londoners have never looked back.

Similarly so, in the late 1800s and the early 1900s the world was getting increasingly overwhelmed by another misery and creating another environmental disaster. The modern era was taking over by leaps and bounds, and the growth was most visible in urban centers like London, Paris, New York, Chicago and others. The population of the U.S. increased by over 30 million during the final two decades during the 19th century alone.

This growth required transportation. Moving people and goods was essential for sustained and profitable progress. And here is where a big problem emerged, and grew fast into a world wide epidemic.

Horses created the problem when different sizes and shapes of horse drawn carts were used exclusively for all transportation needs. This brought in a great number of problems, such as gridlock in the cities, increased traffic accidents and fatalities, and high insurance costs.

Huge amounts of corn and wheat were fed to horses, while there were people dying from hunger. This, in turn, drove food prices up and caused shortages of some commodities, but the worse problem was yet to come.

As the number of horses on city streets increased, so did the solid waste, air pollutants and toxic emissions, all of which endangered the environment and the individuals' health. The problem grew bigger with time, and it got so big and important that it reminds us of today's worries about climate change, melting ice cap, rising ocean level, and other disasters, brought up in part by similar transportation problems.

So let's go back to the early 1900s and see if we can see the parallel. The horse was a versatile and powerful helper since the beginning of humanity. It could do many types of work in the countryside, but was used in even larger numbers in the cities, pulling streetcars and private coaches, hauling construction materials, unloading freight from ships and trains, even powering industrial machines that produced furniture, rope, beer and clothing.

Figure 6-1. Horses, horses, horses everywhere in 1900

Passenger cars, ambulances, and fire trucks were all pulled by horses. There were over 200,000 horses working in New York City alone, which was about one horse for every 17 people. And as their numbers grew, so did the problems with feeding and cleaning them, and cleaning up after them. Horse-drawn wagons were clumsy and clogged the streets even in best of circumstance.

And then horses would misbehave, would leave a mess on the streets, get hurt and even die on the streets, which increased the traffic chaos and caused delays and accidents. There are some gruesome pictures from these days of dead horses laying on the streets, and in many cases being sawed off for removal.

And of course, there was the unmistakable noise from clacking iron wagon wheels and horseshoes onto the pavement. That was the beginning of the noise pollution in the big cities, and it had such bad effects that horse traffic on some city streets around hospitals and other sensitive areas was restricted to certain hours or totally banned.

Accidents increased too, since horses and wagons are not easily controlled in tight quarters and even less so on crowded city streets, which get slippery after rain and snowfall. Three of every 17,000 locals were involved in a horse-related accident and one of those died.

But the worst was still to come. An average horse produced about 20-30 pounds of horse dung a day. With over 200,000 horses, that's about five million pounds of horse manure on the streets of New York alone. Streets were covered with stinky, gooey horse manure. It had to be scooped and hauled away, so with time there would be horse manure piled as high as 50-60 feet in some "storage" areas. It was pretty bad in the winter, but in the summertime it was impossible to live with. The stink was extreme. Flies feasting on the storage area bounty would invade the houses and attack people, bringing misery, illness, and death.

The rains would reduce the stink, but a soupy, gooey, stream of horse manure would flood the streets and seep into people's basements. And, of course, all this is pollution, air, soil, and water pollution that affected human life. The manure was breeding flies and rats that spread deadly diseases. And, of course, the horse was the one to blame. But wait, who brought the horse into the city? Who used it for ensuring comfort and piling up profits? Isn't this similar to how we blame coal and oil for the environmental problems today? Isn't there a lesson that we need to learn from this parallel?

Just like today, environmentalists of the day were concerned with all this, so they gathered in New York by the end of the 19th century to attend the first international "urban planning" conference. It could be viewed as the father of the modern environmental movement, but horse manure was on the top of the agenda instead.

Horse-created pollution was the evil of the day, with a number of doomsday scenarios floating around. People were insisting on finding quick solutions, since it was spreading fast and getting worse all over the world. And just like today, the specialists discussed the issue, but did not find a solution. Instead they gave up and went home after three days instead of the scheduled ten, not unlike the attendees of the 2012 environmental conference in Rio, which was similarly mostly talk, not much do, and lots of frustrated attendees leaving early too.

The politicians of the 19th century couldn't come up with any useful answers, try as they may, nor could agree on any decisive action. Just like today, they were confused by the complexity of the situation and uncertain which path to take.

And so, the end of the world was near in 1900, according to the extreme environmentalists. And in reality, the quality of life in the large cities was deteriorating quickly. There were estimates at the time that if things went unchanged, in 50 years or less every street in London would be buried under nine feet of horse manure and corpses of dead horses.

And yet, the locals could not survive without the horse, although it was becoming quite obvious that it is causing a major problem. That is similar to today: we need coal and oil, but they are killing us.

Something had to be done in 19th century London, but nobody had the answers. But all of a sudden, the horse and its problems disappeared almost overnight, without organized revolutions or government intervention, things changed for the better. Technology and Henry Ford came to the rescue.

The self-propelled streetcars and automobiles replaced the horse, and the problem vanished and was forgotten quickly. It is similar to the way we forget the problems today, the temporary high energy prices and increased frequency of natural disasters, as soon as they go away.

The 1900 city dwellers' environment and health problems were solved by technology. Technological innovation stepped in to replace the old, tired, and stinky horse. It was not replaced by another living and less stinky animal, but by a brand new, lifeless, clean and shiny machine. Little they knew at the time that this new improvement would prove to be as stinky and even more polluting and dangerous than the horse it replaced.

The streetcars and the automobile were much cleaner, more efficient and much more convenient. They were the "environmental saviors" of the 1900s. Cities around the world no longer stunk of horse dung and the grateful citizens embraced the new invention passionately. This is where our story, and our real environmental problems started.

The 20th Century

The solution to the energy and environmental problems of the 19th century turned out to be the biggest problem of the 20th century and beyond. The transition from horsepower to mechanical horsepower was quick and decisive. The horse replacement technologies, motorized vehicles of all sorts, shapes, and sizes, have grown proportionally fast and furiously. Their numbers have increased from thousands to billions during the last 100 years. And so now the carbon emissions from more than a billion cars and trucks, thousands of coal-burning power plants, and other such technologies replaced the inefficient and stinky "*horse power*" with more efficient, but equally stinky and polluting "*horsepower*" of the modern society.

The technological advancements in transportation and power generation are causing the Earth's atmosphere to saturate with toxic gases and the global climate to gradually warm up. And the stink this is causing is not limited to London, or New York, but is affecting the entire Earth and its population. And we, just like the 19th century Londoners, see no immediate solution to the problems, which is not very surprising, because if the solution is not right in front of us, we are inclined to assume that there is no solution. This, of course, has been proven wrong time after time.

With some time and effort humankind has found solutions to most of its problems one way or another. Some of them, however, are more difficult and take longer to resolve than others.

Our ingenuity and survival drive are very powerful weapons, however sometimes the solutions are not there where we are looking, expecting and hoping them to be. At other times, we must be fully convinced first before taking decisive action. With time we will, no doubt, find the solutions to all our problems when the conditions are right and ripe.

Technological advances have been long considered to fix all problems, but we now think that technology is only part of the final solution of today's problems. There are a number of political and socio-economic measures that will serve us much better in finding solutions to our energy and environmental problems.

The problems are growing bigger by the day, and we are still hesitating, but it is only time before we find a way to deal with them. Or, as Winston Churchill put it, "We can always count on the Americans to do the right thing—after they have exhausted all the other possibilities."

Sure enough, we are close to exhausting the possibilities of the fossils and are killing ourselves in the process, so it is time to do the right thing—and soon!

The Political Precedent

The U.S. political machine has been faltering for a while now, sometimes more than others. During the first decade of the 21st century, the democratically controlled House developed and passed the American climate and energy security act (ACESA) of 2009. It created the U.S. carbon cap-and-trade program, and would have established an initial carbon emission target of reducing 2005 levels by 17% in 2020.

Despite the apparent strong support by the Democratic Party and the President, the democratically controlled Senate failed to consider any form of ACESA 2009. This started an uphill battle on all issues that reached the U.S. Congress during the first Obama administration, and continued in a similar fashion during his second Presidency.

Prior to the recent Copenhagen summit negotiations the President announced his climate policy plans to commit the U.S. to carbon reductions identical to ACESA 2009 under certain conditions. Once again the democratically controlled Senate did not support the Copenhagen summit due to issues concerning the economy, raising political tensions on this and other issues.

The next round of developing a climate policy was to incorporate different elements into a combined energy-climate policy proposal, which includes many of the above energy strategies, but focused on diversifying energy sources including renewable power, clean coal and nuclear.

Clean coal and nuclear power development is now on the back burner for a number of reasons (clean coal was sidelined by the EPA's new standards that prevent the construction of new coal power plants, while the Fukushima nuclear disaster put an end to the U.S. nuclear power plans at least for now.)

Today

On June 27, 2013 President Obama presented his climate policy proposal, based on the U.S. becoming more involved internationally, and controlling carbon emissions from power plants as a new and highest priority.

U.S. carbon emissions from fossil fuel use peaked in 2007 at over 6.0 billion metric tons per year (BMT/yr.) but total emissions have since declined by about 12% in 2012, which is due mostly to reduced coal and petroleum consumption during the economic slow down.

In turn, natural gas consumption increased during the same time by almost 10%, due mostly to recent increases in domestic production and decline in natural gas prices, which resulted in substantial 'fuels switching' from more expensive and dirty coal to cheaper and cleaner natural gas. This trend is encouraged by the administration and will accelerate with time. Natural gas is the new king of the energy hill.

NOTE: It seems that the administration is focused on making natural gas a priority in the battle for energy independence and a cleaner environment. This might be a step in the right direction as short-term solution. Long-term use of natural gas as a primary fuel for power generation is unreasonable, however, because it is a) in limited quantities, and b) is a serious pollutant.

Another reason for reduced emissions is the increased light vehicle fuel efficiency standards (CAFE) put in place by past administrations, and the combination of general energy efficiency upgrades and the 2007-09 economic recession. All these factors accounted for about 83% of reduced U.S. carbon emissions during the 2007-2012-time period.

At the same time wind and solar power generation capacities have increased by 600% and 300% respectively over the past five years. Expansion of these renewables have accounted for about 13% of total reduced U.S. carbon emissions from 2007-12.

Projected U.S. Carbon Emissions

Projections now include the impacts of all significant regulations and market factors that can affect energy production and consumption. With everything considered, it is now projected that the total U.S. carbon emissions will increase by 2020 due to projected economic growth, growth in natural gas and coal consumption, and increased vehicle use.

Those are somewhat surprising projections, but reasonable, nevertheless, and pointing firmly to the fact that our energy and environmental problems are not going away and that they might grow proportionally in the near future.

A few of the big environmental problems are:
- Global warming
- Air, soil, and water pollution

- Deforestation
- Greenhouse gases increase
- Population increase and displacement
- Nuclear weapons proliferation
- Increasing world tensions
- Increasing world hunger and sickness
- Growing list of endangered species
- Diminishing fish stocks in the oceans

Let's take a closer look at the political side of the power generation and the related environmental issues of today:

U.S. ENERGY POLITICS

NOTE: The U.S. political machine seems broken. The space between the two isles in Congress is wide, and a long time will pass until we see functional political and regulatory systems in place. Because of that, the energy sector—and especially the renewable energy technologies and companies—will be driven by the inertia of the political and financial moments. Many small companies are lost in the political fog, hoping that the politicians won't mess up even more the already messed up energy picture in the U.S.

The U.S. Energy Sector

The major energy technologies and fuels, powering the U.S. economy, are shown in Table 6-1.

Energy Security, Independence, and Survival

There is a lot of talk now in Washington, DC, and other high places about our energy present and future. This then is a good time and place to clarify the meaning of, a) energy security and safety, b) energy independence, and c) energy survival.

NOTE: The latter was added by the author since it is quite important, but somewhat ignored.

In brief:

a) Energy security and safety is ensuring an uninterrupted energy supply today and tomorrow, by employing efficient accident and crime prevention measures

b) Energy independence is simply the idea of producing our own energy so that we don't depend on anyone else by importing any fuels or energy products

c) Energy survival, however, is ensuring that we have enough energy now and in the future, so that we

- Crude oil   37%
- Natural gas   26%
- Coal   21%
- Nuclear   8%
- Renewables   8%

The major sectors of the U.S. economy are:
- Transportation, $535 billion business, where:
  94% is powered by crude oil products
  6% is powered by natural gas and other fuels

- Electricity generation, $357 billion business, where:
  48% is powered by coal
  21% is powered by nuclear power
  19% is powered by natural gas
  12% is powered by renewables
  NOTE: This ratio is changing dramatically now.

- Industrial uses, $217 billion business, where:
  52% is powered by crude oil products
  34% is powered by natural gas
  14% is powered by renewables

- Heating and cooling, $125 billion business, where:
  58% is powered by natural gas
  21% is powered by electricity
  11% is powered by renewables
  10% is powered by oil products

Table 6-1. U.S. energy use by key sectors (in 2012)

and/or the future generations, don't end up in an energy blackout of some sort. This is where we are failing most, so it is a subject that is buried deep in our consciousness and we prefer to keep it there for now!

The problem is that these terms are very important, yet they are confused in the minds of many people, including the politicians, regulators, and other decision makers. And so, for example, while focusing on our energy security, we might be overlooking ways to achieve our energy independence. Or, an even more probable, scenario is that while focusing on our energy independence by making sure we have enough energy today, we might be ignoring taking care of our long-term energy survival.

It seems that that is exactly what is happening now: we are doing everything possible to achieve energy independence that we are willing to burn every last piece of coal and drop of oil in the process—regardless of the consequences. This reckless drive would leave the next generations without any fossils, which will not only jeopardize their energy independence, but will also compromise their energy security and their way of life. Just imagine living without oil: no lubricants, no plastics, no fertilizers, and no medicines.

The above three terms—energy security, independence, and survival—while meaning different things are interwoven in an integral way and must be addressed as equal in importance and weight. One cannot exist without the other, especially in the long run. If we ignore one, our present and/or future energy balance would be at risk.

Energy Security

There are a number of reasons that energy security is vital for normal life in our society. Without energy, or in the case of serious interruptions of the energy supply system, we would be vulnerable to a number of internal and external threats. Energy security is one of the pillars of national security for modern nations. Without energy the industrial machine stands still and does not produce anything. Products that are produced cannot be moved to the markets. Armies also stand still and cannot even get to the battlefield. Each nation must have enough energy to function properly. Interruption of the energy sector increases the risks of internal and external turmoil.

Internal Risks

There are a number of internal risks to our energy security. Unforeseen natural events and man-made accidents in mines, transport routes, refineries, and power plants threaten to disrupt the energy supply chain. Mine accidents are still happening in the U.S. and around the world. They take lives and shut down mining operations temporarily or permanently. Railroad and transport ship accidents and spillage can close a transport route indefinitely and do significant damage to the environment. Hurricane damages can and do shut down refineries almost every year, but the worst and most dangerous of them all are nuclear power plant accidents.

As the state-of-the-art and the related energy technologies mature, and we learn how to handle the natural and man-made accidents, the internal risks are getting more manageable. With that, the number of mine, railroad, and transport ship accidents is significantly reduced. Refineries, because of their complex outdoor infrastructure, on the other hand, are vulnerable to the force of the hurricanes and other natural events and not much can be done to improve that situation. Nuclear accidents are also a rare occurrence, but when they happen the local devastation is total and its effects are felt over broad areas. This is a critical component in considering our energy security and safety. One single nuclear plant accident can disrupt the energy supply, destroy the entire area, and kill and sicken thousands. This is a serious issue that needs to be taken into consideration as we consider our energy options for the 21st century.

Now computers run everything, including our energy infrastructure. Every step of our energy supply chain, from mining operations to transporting, processing, refining, and using energy sources is monitored and/or controlled by computers. Internal terrorism is one way to gain control and damage a refinery or a power plant. There are a number of reported incidents, and an even greater number of unreported incidents.

Just recently, in January 2013, critical control systems in two U.S. power plants were found intentionally infected with computer malware brought in via USB drives. The infected computers controlled critical systems for the power generation equipment. Intentionally planted malware poses a real threat by allowing the attackers to disable key equipment, thus disrupting its operation or destroying it all together.

In 2012, a backdoor in a piece of industrial software, used to control power plants, allowed hackers to illegally access a New Jersey company's internal heating and air-conditioning system. One of the infections was accidentally discovered after an employee called in IT technician to troubleshoot the USB drive. A simple virus check discovered sophisticated malware, capable of doing a lot of damage to the plant equipment.

Since this technology is so new, the defense mechanisms have not been fully developed and/or deployed, as was in this case. The workstations lacked backup systems, so they were lucky to discover the malware before it was activated.

Another intentional malware attack, also spread by a USB drive, affected ten computers in a steam turbine control system of the power plant. The incident resulted in downtime for repair of the impacted systems, which delayed the plant restart by three weeks.

The stuxnet worm and the flame malware were developed by the U.S. and Israel to spy on, and even control, critical systems in power plants. In the summer of 2012, these programs successfully disabled an entire enrichment facility in Iran. These programs relied on USB drives to store the commands, propagate attack codes, and carry intercepted communications over computer networks. Microsoft has patched these vulnerabilities on Windows computers, but there are additional steps to be taken by power plant and other energy sector operators.

These examples are lessons in safety precautions

and a call to action by owners and operators of critical infrastructure, who must develop and implement serious security policies to maintain up-to-date antivirus mechanisms and manage system patching and the use of removable media.

External Risks

The U.S. has many enemies. Traveling around the world, one can see the signs of animosity towards the U.S. in almost every country. Each of these has their own reasons for hating and ways to inflict damage and pain to the U.S.

Figure 6-2.
Terrorist attack on French oil tanker Limburg in 2002

Terrorist attacks targeting oil facilities, pipelines, tankers, refineries, and oil fields are referred to as "industry risks," because they are part of daily life in the energy sector. The energy infrastructure is extremely vulnerable to external sabotage, and oil transportation, with its exposure at the five ocean chokepoints, is on the top of the risks list. The Iranian controlled Strait of Hormuz is a prime example of a chokehold, where one attack on a Saudi oil field or on tankers in the Strait of Hormuz could disturb the oil supply. A prolonged conflict in the area would surely throw the entire world energy market into chaos.

International terrorism affecting the world's energy reserves is of great concern lately as well, as evidenced by NATO leaders meeting in Bucharest in 2008, where international terrorism against energy resources was one of the key subjects. The group discussed the possibility of using military force to ensure the energy security of the region. One of the possibilities discussed include strategic placement of NATO troops in the Caucasus energy fields to police and protect oil and gas pipelines from terrorist attacks.

The U.S. energy supply and energy infrastructure are in the terrorists eyesight too, and attacks are, no doubt, planned daily in the terrorists' dens around the world. But how would they do that? We are too far away, and too powerful, to invade by sea or air. Instead, they do it by terrorism, which could be a physical attack on people or structures, but that doesn't work very well either, so recently they have been choosing different weapons and changing the battlefield tactics.

And again, nuclear power represents one of the worst and most dangerous risks to our energy security and safety. Computer warfare is the name of the game now, so a terrorist could gain access to a computer terminal at a power plant or refinery and simply put it of commission, or worse.

Nuclear reactors are potential terrorist targets, since they are not designed to withstand attacks by large aircraft, rockets, and other air-born weapons. A well-coordinated attack, using powerful weapons, could damage the reactors in a nuclear plant, which will in turn have severe consequences for human health and the environment.

A recent study concluded that such an attack on the Indian Point Reactor in Westchester County, New York, could result in high radiation within 50 miles of the reactor, and cause 44,000 deaths from acute radiation sickness. Additional 500,000 long-term deaths from cancer and other radiation-caused illnesses would be expected as well.

Terrorists could also target a spent fuel storage facility by using high explosives delivered by ground or air vehicles. This would also result in radiation contamination of the immediate area. A terrorist group may infiltrate the personnel of a nuclear plant and sabotage it from inside. They could, for example, disable the cooling system of the reactor core, or drain water from the cooling storage pond. An internal attack is perhaps the most likely, and most dangerous, terrorist attack on a nuclear-power reactor.

There is also an inextricable link between nuclear energy and nuclear weapons, which pose the greatest danger related to nuclear power. The problem is that the same process used to manufacture low-enriched uranium for nuclear fuel, also can be used for the production of highly enriched uranium for nuclear weapons.

Expansion of nuclear power generation could, therefore, lead to an increase in the number of rogue states with nuclear weapons, produced at their 'civil' nuclear programs. This is exactly what we are seeing being played out in Iran and possibly North Korea. The use of nuclear power would, at the same time, increases the risk that commercial nuclear technology will be used to construct clandestine weapons facilities, as was done by Pakistan in the recent past.

Energy Independence

Depending for energy (oil in particular) on the whims of the dictators of politically unstable countries is the major energy security risk at the moment. Our economy is still exposed to manipulation of energy supplies, such as the OPEC-orchestrated oil crisis of 1973, and the extraordinary jump of oil prices in 2008.

In 1973, the American government realized that we have a big problem and started a feverish race towards developing new energy sources to obtain energy independence. Soon after the crisis was averted, the energy independence urgency gave way to making a quick buck by importing cheap Arab oil. The efforts to implement new, renewable energy sources fizzled away, and were shelved until the next energy crisis.

Oil imports are vulnerable to intentional or unintentional disruptions, due to in-state conflicts, exporters' interests, and/or non-state players targeting the supply and transportation of oil resources.

The 1973 oil embargo is a good example of how oil supplies can be used against the U.S. The Arab nations decided to punish the U.S. for its support of Israel during the Yom Kippur War and turned the spigot off. This was also the case during the economic negotiations during the Russia-Belarus energy dispute in 2007-2008. As a result, Putin shut down the Druzhba pipeline, which supplies oil to Germany, Poland, Ukraine, Slovakia, the Czech Republic, and Hungary, which caused several days of extreme anguish and led to power failures and misery in those countries.

Wars, political conflicts and many other factors, such as strikes, can also prevent the proper flow of energy supplies. Venezuela is a prime example of everything that can go wrong with the oil supply chain. First it was the nationalization of the oil industry, followed by strikes and protests. Several years after the fact, Venezuela's oil production has yet to recover fully.

Since the nationalization of oil, Hugo Chávez threatened to cut off supplies to the U.S. time after time. He was holding American oil exports hostage and used them extensively to further his ideas and political agendas. His death in the spring of 2013 marks a new era in the relations between our two countries, but long-term relationships are predicted to continue to fluctuate. Exporters like Venezuela are driven by economic and political incentives, which at times forces them to limit their exports. In other cases, export revenues are used to finance terrorist groups like Hamas and Hezbollah.

And amazingly enough, the U.S. is paying the expenses on both sides of the conflicts. Saudi Arabia gets $150 billion annually from the U.S. oil exports, about $4 billion of which goes to the Wahhabis to train their children to hate and fight us. Then we pay to fight these children when they grow up.

Now there is also increased competition for energy resources around the world, due to the increased population and improving standards of living in India, China, and other developing countries. This creates energy price increases such as the unprecedented jump in oil prices to $180/bbl in 2008.

Increased competition over energy resources may eventually lead to the formation of security pacts between the major powers to enable an equitable distribution of oil and gas. If and when this happens, however, it will affect positively the developed economies, while the developing countries will continue the daily struggle to supply fuels to power their homes and fledgling economies.

The concerns with the pending *oil peak* are lurking on the horizon too. This means reduced amounts of oil and higher prices, which will create another wave of competition among the major importers.

One big problem with the energy independence movement is that it had become a mantra of environmentalists and others interested in pushing their agendas of renewable energy, climate change, etc. Interest groups justify subsidizing expensive and unreliable energy sources that are unable to compete on the market with oil and gas.

A close look at the energy independence situation reveals that different interest groups think that their way is the only way of achieving energy independence. The fossils are indispensible for providing reliable and cheap power, so they need to be supported. Wind and solar are the solutions for the future, so they need to be supported too. The problem is that the support structure is limited and crumbling, so different energy sources must find a way to self-support while taking the country closer towards energy independence. This, however, requires a thorough understanding of the issues on both sides of the debate and coordinated effort, both of which are missing now.

The Energy Independence And Security Act of 2007

For the purpose of ensuring our energy security and independence, the U.S. Congress passed the energy independence and security act of 2007. It is an act of

Congress addressing concerns with U.S. energy policies. It was originally named the clean energy act of 2007.

In brief, the act consists of:

- *Title I-energy security through improved vehicle fuel economy*, which requires increases in fuel economy standards for passenger cars and establishes the first efficiency standard for medium-duty and heavy-duty commercial vehicles

    Estimated savings for Americans are $22 billion by the year 2020 and significant reductions in emissions will be equivalent to removing 28 million cars from the road. Title I is responsible for 60% of the estimated energy savings of the bill.

- *Title II: energy security through increased production of biofuels*, which contains the first legislation that specifically requires the addition of renewable biofuels to diesel fuel.

    Biomass-based diesel fuel must be able to reduce emissions by 5o% when compared to petroleum diesel. Biodiesel is the only commercial fuel that meets this requirement thus far.

- *Title III: energy savings though improved standards for appliance and lighting* contains standards for ten appliances and equipment.

    When fully implemented, the Title III modifications will avoid the burning of millions of barrels of oil, which will save millions of dollars and contribute to cleaner environment.

- *Title IV: energy savings in buildings and industry* establishes new initiatives for promoting energy conservation in buildings and industry.

    When fully implemented, Title IV modifications will reduce the energy used in federal buildings by 30% by the year 2015.

- The act also provides: awards for developing a hydrogen economy; funding of R&D of renewable technologies; expanding research of carbon sequestration technologies; new training programs for "Energy efficiency and renewable energy workers;" new initiatives for highway, sea, and railroad infrastructure; small business loans toward energy efficiency improvements; modernization of the electricity grid to improve reliability and efficiency via smart grid technologies; new federal standards for drain covers and pool barriers; and exclusions for people who have UV sensitivity that can be triggered by the higher UV radiation of the CFs.

This act is a solid step forward, and there are already some good results to be reported from the above measures.

Energy Survival

This is the hardest component of the energy dilemma. It is the skeleton in the closet, which no one wants to talk about, let alone do something about. Energy survival refers to the continuance of the energy supplies in the future, so that the coming generations do not experience a sudden and irreversible lack of fossil fuels. Such plunge into the darkness is unacceptable, so it is our responsibility to do everything possible to avoid it.

In addition, current excessive use and abuse of fossil fuels is bringing increased emissions, which are causing adverse environmental effects. Continuing at this rate of use of fossils will put the world's population in increasing danger of land loss, air pollution, global warming, and many other negative effects. The combination of these effects puts human wellbeing and health in danger, so we cannot continue to do nothing to solve the problems. These are serious issues that deserve our full attention.

Here is why:

1. We know and agree that *energy security and safety* are a must, for they affect us directly. Because of that, all parties are working together and doing everything possible toward those goals.

2. We also know that *energy independence* is important for maintaining our way of life, so we are doing everything possible to ensure it too.

3. *Energy survival*, however, is not on the list of our priorities. It does not affect us directly today, because it is a long-term problem. It does not generate profits, and since we don't have to deal with its consequence directly it is kept hidden in the closet of our guilty collective subconscious. This makes the subject quite uncomfortable for discussion.

Most of our actions to ensuring energy independence, such as the increased exploitation and use of fossils, including the increased use of coal in China, and fracked oil and gas in the U.S., are severely damaging to the integrity of the long-term energy survival of the affected countries and the entire world. These increased activities and fossil use deplete the limited resources, and pollute the environment.

We are only postponing the inevitable transition to non-fossil economies, doing it simply because we are too comfortable with the way things are now, and are not willing to sacrifice for the sake of future generations. So as things are going now, we will be out of oil, gas, and coal by mid-end of this century. What are the people living then going to do in a fossil-less society? What will they think of us?

There is a chance that by then all energy sources will be replaced by new and renewable sources. Using solar, wind, biomass, and nuclear energy might be enough to substitute for all the fossils are providing us today. These replacements, combined with more efficient use of residential and commercial energy, might be just enough to provide everything that society needs.

It is more likely, however, that there would be problems during the delayed transition that will result in energy- and fossil-based consumer goods shortages. It is difficult to predict when, and what exactly can be expected at that time, but looking around us today and seeing fossils in everything around us, we doubt that the life style of those who follow in our steps will be similar to ours.

One could argue that it might take longer than a century, but whatever it takes, the fossil supplies are limited, so they will be gone eventually. If not this century, for sure during some time in the next century to come they will be no more. Sooner or later one of the next generations is going to wake up in a fossil-less world. Not a drop of oil, or piece of coal left on Earth. Just imagine what a very cold, dark and sad day that would be.

There will surely be many days before that, when people will gather together to figure out what's happening with their energy sources and reserves. And they better have a solution in hand by the time the last piece of coal and the last drop of oil go up in smoke. If they have not found substitutes by then, their lives will be quite miserable,.

We, the present generation, are obviously not concerned very much with the approaching end times of fossil energy. The U.S. energy economy, until 2020 and beyond, is based totally on fossils. The world is mining more coal than ever, pumping more oil than ever, and increasing gas and oil fracking to the highest levels imaginable. The use of all these precious fuels is increasing dramatically, especially in the developing countries, and the trend is growing.

Whatever fossils Nature was able to prepare for us during the billions of years in the past, we have dug and pumped out at least half of the total already, and are getting ready to dig and pump out the rest within this century. That will leave the next generations with next to nothing in ready-to-use fossil reserves.

This makes our energy survival short-lived enterprise of ensuring enough energy now, but with no provisions for the future. Is there any way to change that? If there is, we don't see it. Capitalism dictates living well today and letting tomorrow take care of itself.

A closer look at the different energy technologies, and deeper understanding of their function is needed to properly evaluate their usefulness and the related environmental effects. We will start with the fossils, since they are the most important and most polluting part of our energy and environment cycles.

Obama's 2013 Energy Policy

President Obama has had to make decisions about energy, perhaps based on bad technical advice, which he had no way to evaluate properly. Taking Solyndra's case as an example, Mr. Obama could not have been able to distinguish a cylindrical thin film PV module from a brick in the wall, and yet he had to make a half-billion dollar decision to finance that Solyndra patented technology.

His technical advisers, some of whom have a vested interest in thin film technologies, backed Solyndra, so Mr. Obama authorized the huge loan. Solyndra's technology had no chance: it was too complex, fragile, inefficient, and expensive. Solyndra failed and the U.S. taxpayer ate the huge bill.

Figure 6-3. Our energy past

Obama at first embraced the "renewables at all costs" idea and followed through during his first term, until Solyndra—and a number of other multi-million dollar failures.

All this has forced the Obama administration to take the only direction available: hydrofracking for gas and oil and reducing CO_2 emission. That can be done by quickly ramping up natural gas and slowly ramping down coal.

It seems as though nothing else matters, as fracking is the solution, and increases in vehicle efficiency and CAFÉ standards are just welcome bonuses. Now, natural gas and perhaps nuclear energy are the only games in town that guarantee energy independence and a clean environment.

The newfound abundance of gas and the ease of constructing gas power plants are overwhelmingly powerful arguments for extreme gas use in the short-term. New EPA standards for power plants favor gas over coal too, and so new coal plants cannot even be build in the U.S. As a result, the U.S. leads the world in CO_2 emission-reductions, in part due to those conversions. Over the last five years, coal's share of electricity production in the U.S. has dropped from about half to a third. At the same time, natural gas use has increased from a fifth to over a third, with nuclear power steady at about a fifth, and hydro at over a fifteenth in the energy mix. The rest of the energy generators are too small to count for now.

Human health is another factor that needs to be considered here, since coal was killing about 25,000 Americans annually, while gas only kills about 3,000. Equally importantly, the gas-for-coal approach has bi-partisan support, but replacing coal with gas only gets us so far in addressing the climate change concerns. Total replacement of coal by gas can be done in the U.S. and a few other countries, but in best of cases this would merely slow the rate of CO_2 increases in the atmosphere, not reverse or stop it. Atmospheric CO_2 recently exceeded 400 ppm.

Recognizing that replacing coal with gas does not resolve the climate change concerns, the President is still pushing heavy subsidies for solar, wind, and other renewables. The U.S. will also proceed with nuclear energy use, but very carefully, and watching several new nuclear plants being built to make sure they operate safely before expanding the nuclear industry share. This is a long process, which brings us to 2030 and possibly beyond for significant nuclear power developments.

China, India, and other developing countries are still increasing fossil fuel use and GHG emissions much faster than the U.S. and the other developed countries can reduce it. And recently, Germany and some other European countries have joined the race in building new coal-fired power plants, and switching from gas back to coal power. There are many reasons for this move, but the overall effect is minimizing and even nullifying the CO_2 reduction successes in the U.S.

So natural gas is the game changer, at least in the U.S., and is our hope for cheap energy and cleaner environment right now. However, the overemphasis on natural gas has several negative effects:

- It disregards the environmental damage done by fracking sites
- Puts the future of the renewables, especially solar and wind industries, in question since their large costs and large physical footprint do not bring many or quick benefits

The economics also show that natural gas, combined with other energy generators such as nuclear, would be much more reliable and less environmentally damaging than any other combination. And so, we have a temporary short-term energy and climate plans, which implement gas and oil fracking as an alternative to coal and other energy sources.

But fracking has many issues that are also on Obama's agenda. Recently the U.S. bureau of land management (BLM) issued rules governing fracking operations on public lands that would bring some integrity to the now uncontrolled procedures. For the first time ever, the fracking operators will be forced to disclose the chemical composition of the fracking fluids and manage wastewater procedures.

America is on the only path available at this time to become energy independent and reduce CO_2 emissions through extracting gas via fracking and burning it as an alternative to coal. Gas reigns for now, but the problems follow closely behind so there may be some serious developments in the U.S. energy sector in the near future.

Obama's Energy Legacy

President Obama has an agenda but is stuck with uncooperative Congress, so to get anything done he needs to offer lots of compromises.

Thus, a straight path to be taken in the energy-environment debacle may be easy to outline, but much more difficult to follow. Nevertheless, what is needed to succeed in the energy-environment battle is as follows:

1. Urgent tasks and projects:
   a. Emphasis on safety and environmental protection of natural gas exploitation is a national urgency that needs to be resolved before we experience another large-scale asbestos-like disaster
   b. Increased basic research and technical support of renewable technologies is absolutely needed to prop up and support the different technologies during hard times. This would require re-

directing the efforts of the major national labs on renewable energy generation and environmental protection optimization

c. Standardization of the manufacturing and operation procedures of all energy source is worthwhile endeavor, which, when fully implemented, would bring a level of clarity and fairness in the energy-environmental arena

2. Intermediate concerns:
   a. Increased loan guarantees for mature renewable technologies and projects
   b. Increased emissions tax at the expense of reduced corporate gains
   c. New utility regulations at the expense of corporate earnings

3. Long-term solutions
   a. Establish a new U.S. bank, or financial organization, that deals exclusively with energy and environmental projects
   b. Encourage U.S. private investment by compromising the repatriation of offshore profits and other means

THE FOSSIL ENERGY SOURCES

The fossil energy sources are our old, proven, and reliable friends: coal, oil, and natural gas. They have provided us with plentiful energy for a century now. Yes, they have also created a number of problems, but we need them and are not willing to stop using them, or even slow down their use. However, we also realize that their supplies are limited and that they will come to an end. At the very least we need to start talking about the transition to non-fossil use, and introducing new technologies and methods to replace the fossils. The change (transition) starts with admitting that there is a problem that we need to address.

Then we need to understand all technological, environmental, political, financial, and social issues related to fossil energy production and use. With that knowledge in hand we can then prioritize our actions and design a path to the gradual transition to reduced fossil use.

Politics are integral part of the solution, because the transition is unthinkable without the active participation and leadership of our political leaders and regulatory bodies. So where do we start? Let's look at the some of the political activities and issues related to the

major energy sources and the related technologies, starting with our oldest and most reliable friend, coal:

COAL

Coal has been a major part of the 20th century economic development, providing reliable and cheap electric power and many consumer products for over a century now. We have to be thankful for all the benefits that it has provided for us.

We simply would not be where we are today without coal. Coal led the industrial revolution, and is still powering industry and providing products for the world's economies. Its use is actually increasing, with many developing countries demanding more power and goods for their comfort and economic prosperity.

In 1970, the U.S. Congress amended and considerably strengthened the clean air act of 1963, and created the environmental protection agency (EPA). A set of new source performance standards (NSPS) was established and further strengthened in 1978, setting strict limits on the amounts of sulfur dioxide, nitrogen oxide, and particulate emissions (per ton of coal) emitted by new coal-fired power plants.

Clean air act amendments of 1977 also created three geographical classes (class I, II, and III) to classify existing air quality in the U.S. In class I regions the air quality is relatively pristine, and new emissions sources are very strictly regulated. To maintain the air quality, the regulations required the installation of pollution controls for new coal-fired plants. It was estimated that by 1980, the utility industry was spending $1.8 billion each year on pollution controls alone.

The high cost of meeting the emission requirements contributed to a steep decline in new coal-fired power plant projects during the 1980s, and, by the late 80s, there were almost no new coal-fired power plants. At the same time, the lax regulations on natural gas emissions led to a boom in power plants fired by natural gas.

The electricity generated by natural gas-fired power plants production increased from 2-9% per year in the 2000s. Coal-fired power generation, on the other hand, went down 2% annually from the previous average of 7% annual growth rate in the 1980s. This trend continues now, and might even grow fast, due to the increase in the number of conversions of coal- to gas-fired power plants.

President George W. Bush resurrected coal-fired power generation in the U.S., which was in a steady decline since the late 1970s. The nation was faced with steadily rising oil and volatile natural gas prices, so coal was seen as a reliable, low-cost energy alternative.

That, however, also increased public concern about air pollution and global warming, which was especially emphasized in the aftermath of Hurricane Katrina. The global warming issues were put on the center stage by Al Gore's receipt of the 2007 Nobel Peace Prize for his work on climate change. These events caused an increase in public opposition to new coal-fired power plants and gave a rise to the anti-coal movement in the U.S. and abroad, which were especially strong in the U.K. and Australia. The movement made coal-fired power projects politically costly, and spurred further shifts in public opinion against coal-fired power.

The Bush administration dismissed the 2002 EPA report on the subject of global climate change. The administration continued to oppose mandatory limits on carbon emissions, and obstructed the adoption of global climate change plans at the U.N.'s climate change conference in Bali in 2007.

Figure 6-4. Coal-fired plant pollution

In addition, the administration started to pressure the EPA to relax the pollution regulations for coal plants, thus allowing increased emissions. New rules were established to refer to hourly emissions rate, and extend the lifespan of older power plants operating without expensive pollution controls. The new rules considered a power plant to be running cleanly if its hourly emissions were at least equal to its historical maximum. This was all that was needed, even if the power plant's total yearly emissions were above the limits.

To top it off, the EPA also considered another rule that would've permitted more power plants to be built close to national parks and wilderness areas.

Enter President Obama, one of the most energy-aware of all Presidents. During his first term he pushed the renewables as the solution to our energy and environmental problems and put coal on the back burner for a while. Then he tried to prop up solar and wind power generation, pumping billions of taxpayer dollars in their development and deployment during the latest solar boom-bust cycle of 2007-2012.

That approach didn't work well, because these energy sources are too complex, immature and fail in several key market requirements. Solyndra's put an end to the unwavering support the administration had promised to the renewables.

Over $150 million worth of ads paid for by the fossil fuel industry were run to oust President Obama during his second-term campaign, but green ads in support of Obama outnumbered the fossil fuels ads two to one. During the same time of his failed Presidential campaign, Mitt Romney stood in front of a coal-fired power plant and announced that it kills people, but soon he promised to revive the coal industry.

Obama is being blamed for the problems in the coal industry, but the reality is that it is price driven. Natural gas is now taking the lead, because it is easy and cheap to produce, more convenient, and cleaner to burn. Crude oil is also on the political agenda, focused on the huge Canadian oil sands and other oil sources.

The energy markets have strict requirements with price, availability, reliability, safety, and ease of operation, and clean operation as the prime measures and requirements. Coal, unfortunately, fails on several of these measures and does not meet some of the basic requirements, so its future in the U.S. is uncertain.

In 2012 the EPA put the last nail in the coal industry's coffin. It issued a rule limiting the amount of carbon dioxide that a *new* power plant can emit per generated MW of electricity. While solar, wind, nuclear, and even natural gas-fired power plants can operate under the new limit, coal-fired power plants cannot, and it might mean the end of coal power. The only question is what would the new coal industry look like if it survives the onslaught.

But note that the *new* ruling simply means that no *new* coal-fired plants will be build any time soon in the U.S., because they simply cannot meet the emission limits. At the same time, however, the old coal-fired plants still can emit as much, or nearly as much, as they want to.

Coal-fired plants are still the largest single source of carbon emissions in the U.S., and even if Obama follows up on his promise to respond to the threat of climate change, it will not affect the emissions from existing coal-fired power plants much, if any.

The President announced his plans to tackle the emissions of existing power plants in his 2013 State of the Union address, but it is still not clear about how this will be done. He then followed his agenda with the climate policy in the summer of 2013, by insisting that the U.S. should lead the world in reducing GHGs. Would that become another big blow to coal?

Not so fast! China, India, and even some European countries are presently increasing the use of coal, so those and their GHG emissions are here to stay on the global level. And the U.S. is an active participant, because, while proudly cutting down the use of coal in the country, we are equally proudly exporting the excess to the world, thus encouraging its use and its increased GHG emissions.

The War On Coal

Anti-coal words and policies are serious problems facing the coal power industry. The EPAs new rule, to be implemented in 2013-2014, expands the oversight of air emissions, bottom ash management, and disposal at U.S. power plants. It also sets standards for how utilities deal with coal ash, a toxic byproduct of burning coal that is often stored in giant, uncovered and unlined ponds.

This rule has been in the making since 2008 in response to an environmental disaster involving the failure of a restraining wall at a 40-acre coal ash-slurry pond in eastern Tennessee. A billion gallons of toxic slurry inundated two rivers and a nearby town, causing serious environmental and financial damage.

Since many coal-fired plants use water to move the bottom ash, the resulting slurry cannot be discharged and is usually stored. The new EPA standards would classify the ash-slurry as hazardous waste, the disposal of which would be difficult and very expensive. Since there are huge amounts of slurry involved (approximately 20% of bottom ash is stored as slurry), the estimated cost of compliance with the new rule across the power industry (but mostly affecting coal-fired plants) could exceed $20 billion.

Some call these new regulations a "war on coal," but the simple truth is that the U.S. government and the people have awakened to the environmental realities of today and that burning coal is a big problem. U.S. coal makes sense to a point, and although we need it and cannot stop using it, we need also to control it, so we will.

The fossil energy industry has a long history of being the good guy some of the time, and the bad guy at other times. Nevertheless, we must remember that we all benefit tremendously from the cheap electric power coal has been providing for a century now, so we must be careful when chastising it and hastily shutting down coal mines and power plants.

At the same time, we need to remember also that since its very beginning, the coal industry has been misleading the American public with false advertisement, denials, and misinformation. The misnomer *clean coal* was invented by coal executives, who have been using the phrase in advertising ads since the 1920s. A commercial ad of that era promises that: "*clean coal* will develop more heat and make for mutual satisfaction." And no, they were not ignorant on the matter; they were just intentionally misleading the public.

Not much has changed since then. To buy some more time, the coal industry has been making claims and promising things they cannot deliver. Just like asbestos, lead, nicotine, oil, gas and many others, coal executives used, misused, and abused their influence to spread misleading and even dangerous misinformation at times.

The coal industry misinformation machine got in top gear in the 1970s, after the clean air act was passed. The favorite theme of the time was that any attempts to reduce the deadly smoke emitted from power plants stacks are unreliable and too expensive. Reducing the smoke meant reducing the quality of life and killing the American dream.

The coal industry referred to the proposed by EPA gas scrubber additions as "monstrous contraptions," producing toxic, "oozy gook," which is worse pollution than anything else. According to them, the result from the new additions would be major blackouts if utilities were forced to meet the requirements of the clean air act.

Figure 6-5. But seriously, coal is very big business

Another coal misinformation campaign was reflected in the 1970s and 1980s ads, claiming that the oil and gas supplies will be gone in 10-15 years, but that there is 500 years worth of coal available. The ad owners knew very well that this was not true, and that none of it could be proven, yet they pushed the false information.

And even now, there are many TV commercials telling us about the wonders of coal, gas, and oil. These are so convincing that if people from Mars were to come to Earth today, they would think that coal, oil, and gas were just recently discovered, and that they are the only hope for saving our way of life.

Global warming was another target of the coal commercial ads. Even in the late 1990s, coal executives and supporters unabashedly proclaimed that there is no hard evidence that global warming is occurring. And if it was, there was no proof that carbon dioxide is the primary cause for it. And even if that was proven, there was no way to show evidence that coal is a major problem in that respect.

What makes these misinformation campaigns so damning is not only that all claims turned out to be wrong, but also that they proved that the coal is willing to do and say anything to keep America hooked on coal, no matter what. One thing the coal executives did not consider is the fact that the American public can be mislead for a while, but not forever, and the bad facts can be hidden for a while, but not forever.

We now see that the U.S. public is aware, albeit superficially, of the key issues of the day.

Most of us believe that:

- Energy source depletion is increasing and the end is near

- Climate change issues are here to stay and will only grow worse with time

- The greatest amount of GHGs are emitted by coal-fired power plants

- The amount of pollution can no longer be ignored, so something has to be done soon

While we appreciate coal's contribution to our wellbeing and understand their fight for survival, coal must face the facts and look for ways to minimize the damages. Instead, coal is increasing its political presence and wants to have a voice in the White House, as reflected in their increasing lobbying efforts.

The amount of money spent on lobbying has increased from three million dollars in 2000 to $17 million in 2012.

There are over 11,000 lobbyists in Washington, or 25 per congressperson. There were over 35,000 lobbying reports filed by the U.S. Congress in 2010. Upon termination of their terms, about half of U.S. congressional staffers switch to lobbying activities, which more than doubles their salaries.

The political developments of late are promising from energy generation and environmental points of view. The energy field was tilted in favor of coal until recently. Coal benefited from cheap prices and subsidies at the front end, while ignoring the bad effects of air and soil pollution on the back end. Restrictions on coal burning would level the field some, thus allowing fairer competition.

We are not going to get rid of coal. We don't want to get rid of coal, because we need it, and it will be with us for a long while. Coal, however, has to have relevant control, and be lined up with the other energy sources for fair and more productive competition, not to mention that this is the only way to contribute to cleaning the environment.

U.S. Coal Politics

In the summer of 2013 President Obama came up with calls for increased regulations on carbon emissions in his new climate policy. The coal industry, as the largest power generator, which emits the largest amount of GHG pollution, would be hit the hardest. Most U.S. power companies and many politicians supporting the coal industry's interests expressed their dissatisfaction with the terms in Obama's proposal. The coal industry is, no doubt, in for some tough years ahead. More than 280 coal-fired generating units will be shut down in part due to stricter EPA regulations. The American coalition for clean coal electricity (ACCCE), a partnership of industry groups, claims that the number of coal plants slated for shutdown is five times greater than the EPA predicted would be forced to shut down due to its regulations.

The EPA's new emissions limits (which has been now delayed) rule for power plants essentially bans the construction of new coal-fired power plants. The rule would limit newly built power plant carbon dioxide emissions to 1,000-pounds-per-megawatt-hour, which only combined-cycle power plants that are powered by natural gas are able to comply with.

Coal-fired electric generating plants will be shut down across 32 states, with the hardest hit states being Ohio, Pennsylvania, Georgia, West Virginia, Virginia, North Carolina, Kentucky and Indiana. And the number of coal units being forced to close continues to grow, while it is not certain what damage these regulations might cause the U.S. economy and to the many states that depend on coal for jobs and affordable electricity.

The list of coal plants slated for shutdown has been expanding rapidly since the summer of 2012 when the energy information administration estimated that 175 coal-fired generators, or eight and a half% of the U.S.'s coal-fired capacity would be retired in the coming years due to declining demand for electricity, higher prices, and stricter environmental regulations.

A major factor in this discrepancy is that the shale boom has caused cheap natural gas to quickly and steadily replace coal consumption for power generation, while new environmental regulations have continually made it less economical to build coal plants. Now the ACCCE estimates that more than 200 coal-fired power plants, or over 30 GW of power generation, would be shut down across 25 states due to the above-mentioned considerations.

The coal industry defenders are usually different organizations from coal states, which are defending their interests, including politicians in high places who have benefited most from coal industry's consistent donations. Most coal companies lobby on legislation relating to coal and greenhouse gas emissions, and they donate to candidates who will back their interests. In both of these areas, coal companies often butt heads with those supporting climate change initiatives.

In 2012, the mining industry gave roughly $7.5 million to Republicans, compared to only $806,500 to Democratic candidates, and the split on energy and environmental issues along party lines is increasing.

Some utilities claim that any regulations on carbon emissions would harm American consumers, and the coal industry won't just stand by and suffer the blow of emissions restrictions. The American coalition for clean coal energy, for example, plans to conduct polling and advertising expenditures to resist the Obama administration's efforts. According to them, coal-fired power plants cannot meet the proposed measures, and so the war with words and the lobbying continues.

The coal industry has come together on the lobbying front, demonstrated by over 90 organizations that came together to lobby on the stop the war on coal act of 2012, which passed in the House soon thereafter. The bill was lobbied by the top coal and energy companies, but never received a vote in the Senate, and was threatened with a Presidential veto. It would have protected the coal industry from the new environmental changes.

The battle is raging on many fronts and levels. There are no winners as yet, but we already see some

great changes in the U.S. coal and energy industries, and are expecting many more in the near future.

Coal Mining Regulations

Starting in the 1930s, some states instituted land management and reclamation laws. Later on in the 1970s, when there was significant energy development activity in the West, Congress enacted the surface mining control and reclamation act (SMCRA), which mandated strict regulation of surface mining. It was the first comprehensive national surface mining law, and was a tough one.

The most extensive regulations affecting surface mining are a consequence of SMCRA. Under the law, individual states that establish federally approved enforcement programs have the primary responsibility for enforcing mining regulations in their jurisdictions. Where no such programs exist, the federal law is implemented by the office of surface mining reclamation and enforcement in the Department of Interior.

Other federal laws with significant impact are the clean air act, the clean water act, and the national environmental policy act. In addition, each state where surface mining occurs has its own set of laws and regulations. Beyond the specific requirements of the major federal laws, there are many other legislative acts that affect some or all mining in this country.

Some of the key legislative acts are as follows:
1906 Antiquities act of 1906
1918 Migratory bird treaty act of 1918
1934 Fish and wildlife coordination act of 1934
1960 Multiple use—sustained yield act of 1960
        Archeological salvage act 1960
1963 Endangered species act of 1963
1964 Wilderness act of 1964
1966 Historic preservation act of 1966
1968 Wild and scenic rivers act 1968
        National trails system act 1968
1969 Bald eagle protection act of 1969
        Surface mining control and reclamation act of 1970
1970 Mining and minerals policy act of 1970
1974 Safe drinking water act of 1974
        Forest and rangeland resources planning act of 1974
        Archeological and historical preservation act of 1974
1976 National forests management act of 1976
        Noise control act of 1976
        Resource conservation and recovery act 1976
1977 Soil and water resources conservation act of 1977

1978 American Indian religious freedom act of 1978

Coal Power Regulations

The majority of coal that is mined around the world is used for electric power generation, which we all know is a dirty business. The coal power industry has been under scrutiny and is blamed for major environmental damage, so in 2012 the U.S. EPA proposed new source performance standards (NSPS) under section 111(b) of the clean air act (CAA). The intention of the new rule is to control even more carbon dioxide (CO_2) emissions from new fossil fuel-fired (coal and natural gas) power plants. The lower limits are now set so low that no new coal power plants can be built. The existing coal-fired power plants are not directly affected, but they still have to comply with the existing regulations and emission standards.

The EPA proposed standard requires new coal power plant units to meet a CO_2 emissions standard of 1,000 pounds of CO_2 per megawatt-hour of generated power. This is impossible, because coal-fired power plants emit at least twice this amount. So this new standard effectively bans the construction of new coal units.

Actually, a new coal-fired power plant could meet the new requirements, but achieving the standard would require the use of carbon capture and storage equipment, which is untested, unreliable, and very expensive technology.

EPA analysis shows that the new standard would not have much, if any, impact on the existing U.S. electric power sector. However, the construction of new coal plants is now nearly impossible, so this means that all new power plants will be gas-fired. This could eventually increase electricity costs, if and when natural gas prices get higher than EPA's projections, and if new coal plants cannot be built.

CRUDE OIL

In recent decades, Republicans and Democrats have camped in the two opposing corners of the energy debate and the related ideologies, theories, and developments. The Republicans support high oil and gas production and consumption, while the Democrats favor lower oil and gas production and consumption, And no wonder; both Bush presidents were oilmen, while Jimmy Carter advised us to put on an extra sweater to save energy.

Until recently, America has been stuck in the worst of both ideologies. We had low fuels (fossils and renew-ables) production levels and consumed a lot of energy. That has changed somewhat lately. Energy (natural gas, wind, and solar) generation is up now and the consumption is down. Oil and gas production have risen to the highest levels in a long time, and energy consumption is significantly down (albeit temporarily) as compared with the years past.

The boom in oil and gas drilling is an unplanned and even unexpected economic lift, and although President Obama is not one of the biggest oil and gas supporters, he is supporting it to promote job growth, ensure our energy independence, and clean the environment.

The skeleton in the closet now, and a big shadow on the political horizon, is the undeniable fact that oil and gas fracking pollutes the local soil and groundwater. Nevertheless, the EPA and all other political and regulating authorities seemed to turn their heads the other way, at least until now. The issues grew so big that they could no longer be ignored, so there are moves toward federal regulation of some parts of the fracking process.

Obama is not planning to resurrect the carbon cap-and-trade program until the results from the California's cap-and-trade experiment have been carefully analyzed. A carbon tax would be feasible, since it is far less susceptible to fraud than a cap-and-trade scheme, and it would not be a job killer that some suspect it would be. It is also needed to keep the environmentalists happy, while we are still involved in the debate about the benefits of cheap, plentiful natural gas, which is replacing coal in electric power generation.

Obama established the Gulf of Mexico drilling moratorium in response to the public's outcry about the irresponsible BP actions, which killed 11 people and spilled millions of barrels of oil into the gulf. The temporary moratorium is a necessary measure, similar to the way Ronald Reagan paused the space program in the wake of the Challenger disaster in 1985. Just as that measure did not affect the space program much, so the Gulf moratorium will not affect the oil industry much. And recently things seem to be going back to normal.

The Obama administration has agreed to guarantee tens of billions of dollars in loans to power utilities for building new nuclear power plants. Although this program was started by the second Bush administration, Obama is happy to continue it for the sake of energy independence and clean air.

The keystone XL pipeline was not that fortunate. It was rejected by Nebraska Republicans, who were concerned with environmental damage to the sensitive Sand Hills region. The second Obama administration, however, is rethinking the project, and might approve a re-routed keystone XL. One way or another, the XL line will be built eventually by Obama or the next U.S. President.

The U.S. petroleum usage has declined drastically since 2005 (when it was at its peak), and now we produce more oil than even imagined. As a result, the oil imports have fallen from 60% in 2005 to 40% in 2012. So how could it be that the price of oil is still going up, if we're producing more and using less?

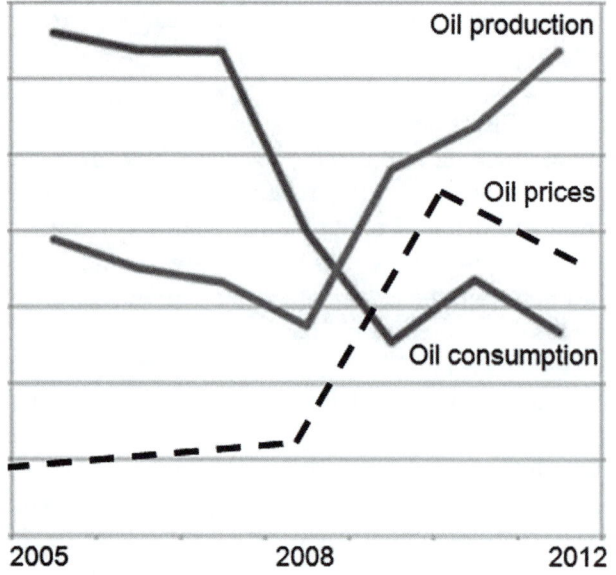

Figure 6-6. U.S. Oil production, consumption, and price

It seems that the rest of the world, especially the developing nations, are getting thirstier for oil, and this is what is driving the demand and dragging the oil prices higher too. For example, China used 4.5 million barrels of oil per day in 2008, while the demand for 2015 is estimated at over 14 million barrels every day. India is following close, and so are other countries, with Russia and ex-Soviet block countries in third place.

Faced with this situation, oil companies are changing their strategies, and our government is revising its policies. Nevertheless, while there is room for reducing oil prices in the U.S., the world oil prices are going up, which drags the overall U.S. prices up too.

Peak Oil

Peak oil is a term with a special, significant meaning. It was coined in 1956 by a Shell oil geophysicist Hubert who predicted with some accuracy that U.S. oil production would peak by 1970. This estimate has to be revised now in light of the discoveries of new oil sources, but Mr. Hubert didn't have a way to predict the new technologi-

cal achievements that allowed this development.

According to the specialists, the oil production in Saudi Arabia is also close to its peak, which simply means that it will not be able to supply the world's growing energy needs. Oil production in 33 out of 48 oil-producing countries, including Kuwait, Russia and Mexico also already peaked. Global oil production is now also approaching an all-time peak too and no one can predict what will happen next.

It took Nature over 300 million years to make the crude oil and natural gas we have now, but we managed to burn close to half of the two and a half trillion barrels of global oil reserves in a single century. The world now consumes 85 million barrels of oil per day, or 40,000 gallons per second, and demand is growing exponentially. How long before we drain the remaining 1.25 trillion barrels?

As a clarification, peak oil means that there is still oil, but that we have reached the highest production point and now our ability to produce high-quality, cheap, and economically extractable oil on demand is diminishing. We are at a point where the oil producers are reaching their limits. There is less oil, it is deeper down in the ground, and it requires more effort and expenditure to get it out. The quality of the oil deep down the reservoirs is also inferior and harder to pump out.

We now know how much is available around the world, and have estimated 20-30 more years of use at this level of production, but beyond that, oil production will begin a permanent and irreversible decline. And there is nothing we can do about it, short of to stop using so much oil. The major issue is the lack of further growth, followed by gradual, then steep decline.

Actually, the global oil discovery peaked in the mid 1960s and has followed a steady decline ever since. According to industry specialists 90% of all known reserves are now in production, so very few major discoveries remain to be made. The picture has changed some by the use of new hydrofracking technology, which extracts oil from shale formations, but that quantity is limited. The Canadian sands are also a new development that will buy us several more years of unlimited oil use.

Nevertheless, oil is now being consumed 4-5 times faster than it is being discovered, and the situation is becoming critical. The consumption of limited resources is a temporary venture that has an end. The faster we use them, the faster the end will come unless we change our behavior.

The only uncertainty about peak oil is its timing which is difficult to predict accurately. Over the years, accurate prediction of oil production was confronted by fluctuating ecological, economical, and political factors, which imposed many restrictions on its exploration, transportation, and supply and demand.

In 2009, Kuwait University and the Kuwait oil company collaborated in a study to predict the peak date using multi-cyclic models, depending on the historical oil production trend and known oil reserves of 47 major oil production countries (to overcome the limitations and restrictions associated with other previous models.) Based on this model, world production is estimated to peak in 2014. Other experts, oil companies, and analyst firms estimate the peak date between now and around 2020.

Who's right and who's wrong matters not. What's certain is that the global production will go into a permanent decline within our generation. This, in turn, will increase the global competition to unprecedented levels.

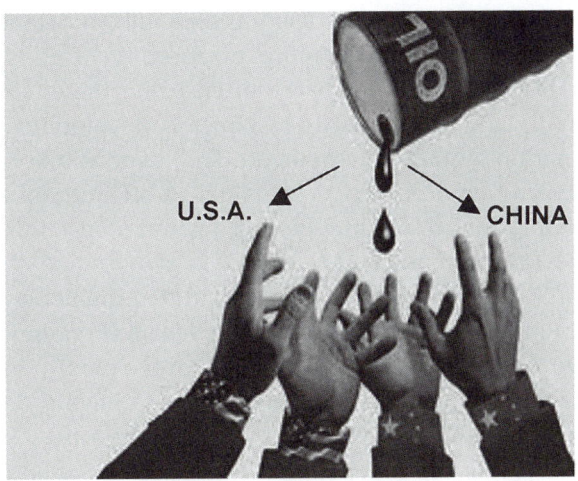

Figure 6-7. Me too, me too...

At a current average global population and consumption growth rate of 2.5% annually, by 2030 the world will need 50% more oil, and oil producers will have to double their production to achieve this, which is not feasible in even the most optimistic scenario.

Keep in mind that almost 80% of the world that lives in developing countries is only now starting to use oil and gas. Over 900% of all projected incremental oil demand comes from non-OECD countries, which will keep oil prices rising.

If and when a sudden and sharp oil production decline in the global supply occurs, Saudi Arabia will be able to maintain current rates of production for several years, but will not be able to increase production enough to meet the expected increase in world demand. There is no likely scenario that some new frontier, or future developments, can replace Middle East oil declines.

Senior Saudi energy officials have already warned

the U.S. and Europe that OPEC would have an "extremely difficult time" meeting demand and that the Saudi reserves have been overstated by as much as 40%.

Some oil companies have been quietly publishing the news about declining discovery trends, based on their research. They are basically preparing us for the doomsday scenario, when crude oil will be listed as an endangered species. "The era of easy oil is over," is the writing on the wall, which we prefer to ignore or deny for now! Sooner or later, however, the reality will hit, and then what? How do we live without crude oil?

The Alternatives

Most of us think that oil depletion is either one big lie, or that we can solve it with our advanced technologies. While technology helps, as in the case of hydrofracking, it cannot change the laws of physics, and once an oil well is empty no more oil can be pumped out of it, even with the most sophisticated technology.

With the major fossil fuel dwindling, there is simply not enough time to replace it with a similarly efficient and cheap fluid. Solar, wind, waves, and other renewables are all marginal energy providers and also need a lot of energy to fabricate, transport, and construct, all of which require fossil fuels.

Renewables are simply incompatible in this context and the new fuels and technologies required would take a lot more time to develop and require access to abundant supplies of cheap fossil fuels, putting the industrial adventure out of business. It is estimated that a global solar, wind, or other renewable energy system would take a century to build and would consume great amounts of silicon, iron, and other materials and a lot of energy from fossils.

Obtaining usable oil from tar sands requires huge amounts of energy, as it has to be mined and washed with super hot water. From an energy balance, it takes the equivalence of two barrels of oil to produce three, which is still positive but poor in terms of energy economics.

Nuclear power plants operating today are simply too complex and expensive and take ten years to build, relying on a fossil fuel platforms for all stages of construction, maintenance, and extracting & processing nuclear fuels. Additionally, uranium is also a rare and finite source with its own production peak and the related dangers and safety issues. Since 2006, the uranium price has already more than doubled.

Nuclear fusion is the kind of energy that the world needs. However, mastering it has been several years away for the past 50 years, and following the NIF and other experiments, it still is.

Alternative energy sources cannot replace fossil fuels at the scale, rate, and manner at which the world currently consumes them. Human ingenuity simply cannot override the upper limits of geology, chemistry, and physics. The world's energy crisis cannot be solved by the alternative energy sources alone. They are too immature and unreliable, and as such are not the silver bullet that will solve all our problems.

Other energy sources, like methane hydrates, billions of tons of which are buried under the ocean floor, will require a lot of time to develop efficient and safe technologies for their extraction. Energy demand, however, cannot wait and is surging as we speak, while many of the world's conventional oilfields are going into quick decline.

The world is blinding itself to the reality of its energy problems, ignoring the scale of growth in demand from developing countries and placing too much faith in the alternative sources of power, instead of reducing the use of fossils. A combination of measures is needed to avoid the fossil-less trap we are building now.

U.S. Oil Well Regulations

In response to a number of events in the last half of 2010, the U.S. bureau of ocean energy management, regulation and enforcement (BOEMRE) issued the final rule for standardized emergency management system (SEMS) requires all contractors to have "operating procedures" and a "mechanical integrity plan" that accompanies all critical equipment in addition to a "hazard analysis."

Contractors may adopt sections from an operator's SEMS program, but the operator and contractor must have document-agreed policies. These requirements affect practically all offshore operations from drilling activities to lifting point certification, and the contractors must provide documentation and evidence for satisfying key areas of the SEMS such as safety and environmental performance with written and documented safe work practices.

This was followed by the issuance of:

a. The 'idle iron' notice to lessees (NTL), which became effective in October 2010, which addressed the increased hurricane activity during the last decade, mandating the decommissioning of idle wells and oil platforms

b. The work place safety rule was issued by BOEMRE in response to the BP Deepwater Horizon oil spill,

while at the same time, ordering all GOM operators to have a fully-implemented SEMS according to the guidance of "development of a safety and environmental management program for offshore operations and facilities."

As a mandated requirement, this is a significant change, as operators must now implement a SEMS to ensure that policies and procedures are in place, thus ensuring the overall safety of the projects.

These regulations have turned a new page for the Gulf of Mexico (GOM) oil and gas industry operators. They have firmly reiterated or imposed more new stringent requirements associated with offshore operation.

In October 2011, BOEMRE, (formerly the minerals management service, MMS), was split into two entities: the bureau of ocean energy management (BOEM) and the bureau of safety and environmental enforcement (BSEE) as part of a major reorganization.

BOEM is now in charge of ensuring the environmentally and economically responsible development of the nation's offshore resources. The responsibility for safety and environmental oversight of offshore oil and gas operations, including permitting and inspections, is now BSEEs responsibility.

The tightened regulations and requirements are having the intended impact on the decommissioning of platforms, and increasing the safety of the environment and personnel. The new regulations also have a direct impact on the execution of well salvage projects.

Overall, the independent oversight of the oil and gas industry is now much more stringent and allegations of misconduct are pursued, with sizeable penalties levied against operators for violations of the safety and environmental regulations of BOEM and BSEE. The new situation has forced a greater dialogue between the operators and the authorities over managing well drilling, use, and abandonment. This will ensure that appropriate and realistic legislation is put in place, e.g. decommissioning in deep-water environments.

Structural Integrity Management

In addition to the already mentioned regulations, the new BOEM and BSEE agencies are implementing reforms that increase oversight of offshore operations, particularly during critical phases of drilling, as part of the effort to ensure the mechanical and structural integrity of oil wells and the related activities. Part of this effort includes annual scheduled inspections of facilities and periodic unannounced inspections of and gas operations.

For the first time in a U.S. regulatory framework, performance standards have been introduced that are similar to those in the North Sea, for the development of systems and identifying personnel requirements to address safety and environmental risks. An oversight program is being used for reviewing and evaluating operators' compliance with SEMSs new safety performance standards.

A fully implemented SIM system will greatly assist operators with satisfying the mandated regulatory changes by:

- Managing risk and identifying platforms and wells that present the highest risk in addition to those that are required to be decommissioned as stipulated in the 'idle iron' NTL

- Development of inspection strategies to fulfill the mandated requirements for the periodic inspection of offshore facilities while assisting with targeted mitigation

- Help satisfy the requirements of an SEMS with a view to improving safety performance and lessening risk to the environment

- Inclusion of a decommissioning strategy to assist in risk management and development of a salvage program

These regulations and measures will help in promoting and controlling safety practices in the oil drilling and exploitation industry. The only question here is: why did it take that long to do this? Did we have to wait so long as to blow up an oilrig, kill a dozen innocent workers, and contaminate the entire Gulf of Mexico before doing the right thing?

Decommissioning

The Gulf of Mexico is a major oil producer, where a major challenge for the oil and gas industry has recently been developing. It is the obligatory decommissioning (or rather proper decommissioning) of fixed-jacket-type structures in water depths greater than 500 ft. Four fixed-type platforms have been decommissioned to date, and all of them have utilized special artificial reef site (SARS) or Louisiana artificial reef program (LARP) in a designated large area reef site (large area reef site (LARS)). These methods simply consist of letting the entire structure sink to the ocean bottom where it becomes a reef.

For the deeper water fixed platforms reefing in place as part of a SARS and/or LARS presents the most cost-effective and safe method of decommissioning.

This can significantly reduce safety concerns by using diver-less technologies.

Figure 6-8. Oil rig—a truly big business

There are another 31 fixed-jacket-type platforms located in depths between 500 Ft and 1,750 Ft in the Gulf alone. The trend to date has been to donate part of or the entire platform to an artificial reef site and this certainly provides the most cost effective and safest method for these deeper water platforms. There is no indication LARP or the Texas artificial reef program (TARP) will not consider any one of these 31 platforms as a donation to a reef site or designated as a reef site.

One of the significant benefits of reefing or partial reefing in place is the ability to choose not to remove well conductors to 15 ft below mud line. When the lower half of the jacket is designated as a reef site and will remain standing, the well conductors need only be removed down to the top of this lower section. This brings a significant cost and time saving to a decommissioning project and should prove attractive to operators.

Rigs and platforms at shallower locations must be removed properly, and safely disposed in their entirety. These activities are getting more attention by the day, so we expect that they will be carried out properly and safety.

International Activities

Many countries, like Norway, Australia, Nigeria, and the U.K. have legislation governing the abandonment or decommissioning of offshore oil and gas rigs. Since many of the offshore installations are outside the national territorial waters, which are covered by international law, there are a number of international agreements and regulations that apply to the manner in which abandoned structures may be removed and disposed of.

The international regulations on the decommissioning of abandoned offshore oil and gas installations have progressed through a number of stages.

The most distinct phases are the pre-Brent Spar era and the post-Brent Spar, the latter of which was initiated in response the Brent Spar incident, when international organizations such as the international maritime organization, Oslo and other regional organizations had to revisit their guidelines, rules, and regulations on the subject.

Note: Brent Spar was a large oil storage and tanker-loading buoy in the Brent oilfield in the North Sea. In 1991 the owner, Shell Oil, decided to decommission the facility and filed an application for disposal of the huge and badly rusted and contaminated structure by dumping it in the ocean about 150 miles from the west coast of Scotland.

Following the approval of the application by the British government, Greenpeace organized a worldwide high profile media campaign against this plan and activists occupied the Brent Spar for several weeks. Following a wide spread public and political opposition in northern Europe, including a boycott of Shell service stations, as well as arson attack on a service station in Germany, Shell abandoned its plans to dump the rig in the ocean.

Brent Spar was temporary moored in a Norwegian fjord and in 1998 Shell decided to re-use much of the main structure in the construction of new harbor facilities in Norway.

All parties were left licking their wounds and planning new strategies based on the lessons learned from the Brent Spar incident.

Now, offshore installations that are placed within a country's internal waters and the territorial sea are subject to the laws of the country, rather than to international law. In the marine areas falling under the jurisdiction of international law, the coastal states have a right to erect structures in the area and to exploit the resources in it, according to Article 60 of the United Nations law of the sea convention of 1982. The state is obligated to create safety perimeter zones of 1,500 feet, properly equipped as needed for the safety of navigation in the area of the installation itself.

The U.S. Refineries

In 2010, there were 150 operating U.S. refineries, but around that time the U.S. oil refinery industry quietly started closing a number of oil refineries. Instead, unknown to the public, oil companies are increasingly shipping our oil overseas for refining because there are not enough refineries to process the vast amounts here.

At the same time we are shutting down refineries, we are barred from building any more.

Sunoco closed its two Pennsylvania refineries, ConocoPhillips shut down its refineries in Pennsylvania and New Jersey, and the Hess Corporation closed the U.S.'s third-largest refinery in the Virgin Islands, just to mention a few.

In retrospect, 10 years ago no Chinese oil company was even in the top 100, while today two Chinese oil companies are in the top five, and soon might even surpass Exxon Mobil as No. 1. In the past decade alone China built 25 new oil refineries, while no new refineries have been built in the continental U.S. since 1975.

Figure 6-9. U.S. refinery scheduled for shut down

Why are the U.S. refineries shutting down? Is this part of the new world order, where, although we have enough oil in the U.S., we are forced to ship it overseas for refining? The oil business in the U.S. is becoming mainly distribution, and prices are going up. While the world's demand for oil continues to rise, so will oil prices because the oil companies are profit driven and they will sell their oil at world prices, even in the U.S.

Under these conditions, no matter what we do here in the U.S., oil and gasoline prices will go up. The population of our global village will continue to increase, which will cause increased demand of oil, thus keeping prices high.

Oil For Transportation

Someone said once that burning oil for energy or to power our cars is like burning Picassos for heat. How true! This is for sure what the next generations will think of what we are doing now. Oil is a valuable and scarce commodity used to make so many products that we use every day that the thought of simply burning it may be unthinkable in the near future.

Crude oil molecules are so flexible that they can be transformed into substances that serve as clothing, medicines, building materials, carpet, skin care products, sporting goods, agricultural chemicals, perfumes, and myriad other products.

And yet, because oil is still the most convenient, cost-effective, and widely available source of liquid fuels, we are using it for most of our transportation needs. Millions of cars, trucks, boats, trains, and planes run on crude products, with little prospect of fuel substitutes on the grand scale that would be required.

Other energy sources are available, but try running a 100-car-long train, or a 777 airplane with coal, gas, nuclear, solar, wind, or any other power source available today, and you'll see that diesel and jet fuel are irreplaceable for these and many other applications. While there are electric cars for short-distance transport, long distance transport is far from getting electrified any time soon—ever heard of an electric eighteen-wheeler or electric airplane?

In 2007 the total world consumption of oil was 27.3 billion barrels, of which 16.8 billion barrels, 61%, were used for powering personal and commercial transportation vehicles. Of this, 8.1 billion barrels were used as diesel/gasoline, 6.9 billion barrels as motor gasoline, and 1.8 billion barrels were used as aviation fuels.

U.S. Vehicle Emission Standards and Regulations

Vehicle emissions standards in the U.S. are dictated and enforced by the EPA. The state of California has special regulations dictating more stringent vehicle emissions standards, and the other states follow either the national or California standards.

The California air resources board (CARB) sets California's emissions standards. California's automotive market is one of the largest in the world, so CARB has a great influence over the emissions requirements major automakers must meet to sell to the California auto market.

Several other U.S. states follow California's emissions standards, so CARB rules have broader implications on the entire U.S. auto market. CARB's policies have also influenced Europe's emissions standards, which increase their influence to a global level.

Federal "tier 1" regulations went into effect starting in 1994, in an attempt to regulate harmful emissions, "tier 2" standards were phased in from 2004-2009 so that cars and light trucks (SUVs, pickup trucks, and mini-

vans) are treated differently.

California's attempt to regulate greenhouse gas emissions from automobiles faced court challenges from the federal government, but in 2009 EPA decided to partially adopt California's standards on greenhouse gas emissions from vehicles.

In an effort to decrease emissions from heavy-duty diesel engines faster, the CARBs Carl Moyer program funds upgrades that are in advance of regulations. The EPA has separate regulations for small engines, such as grounds-keeping equipment.

The different U.S. states must also promulgate miscellaneous emissions regulations to comply with the national ambient air quality standards.

European Emission Standards

The European Union has its own set of emissions standards that all new vehicles must meet. Currently, standards are set for all road vehicles, trains, barges, and off-road mobile machinery such as tractors. No standards apply to seagoing ships or airplanes.

European emission standards define the acceptable limits for exhaust emissions of new vehicles sold in EU member states. The emission standards are defined in a series of EU directives staging the progressive introduction of increasingly stringent standards.

Currently, Euro IV standards regulate emissions of nitrogen oxides (NO_x), total hydrocarbon (THC), non-methane hydrocarbons (NMHC), carbon monoxide (CO) and particulate matter (PM) emitted from most vehicle types, including cars, trucks, trains, tractors and similar machinery, and barges, but excluding seagoing ships and airplanes. For each vehicle type, different standards apply.

Compliance is determined by running the engine at a standardized test cycle at special locations. In all cases, non-compliant vehicles cannot be sold in the EU, but new standards do not apply to vehicles already on the roads. No use of specific technologies is mandated to meet the standards, though available technology is considered when setting the standards. New models introduced must meet current or planned standards, but minor lifecycle model revisions may continue to be offered with pre-compliant engines.

According to the German federal automotive office, 37.3%, or 15.4 million cars in Germany out of total car population of 41.3 million vehicles, conform to the 2009 Euro 4 standard. What that means is that two thirds of the cars in one of the most technologically advanced nations in the world are running around without any emission controls. Combined with the crazy, unlimited top speed on the interstate auto bans, the vehicle pollution controls in Germany cannot be held as a good example. Compare that with the much tighter U.S. emission controls system, where 100% of all vehicles manufactured in 1996 and beyond must pass annual or bi-annual "smog" test.

China Emission Standards

Due to rapidly expanding wealth and prosperity, the number of cars and trucks on China's roads has been growing quickly. The millions of vehicles, in addition to the coal-fired power plants, increased the ongoing pollution problem to the point where air in some large cities is unsuitable for human life. Because of that, China was forced to enact emissions controls on automobiles in 2000, which were equivalent to Euro I emission standards.

China's state environmental protection administration (SEPA) upgraded the emission control standards again in 2004 to the Euro II standard. A more stringent emission standard, national standard III, equivalent to Euro III standards, went into effect in 2007, and then a Euro IV-like standard took effect in 2010.

Beijing introduced the Euro IV standard in advance in 2008, and became the first city in main land China to adopt this standard.

Even after that, the air, land, and water pollution in China shows no signs of going away. It is increasing, supported by the government plans to introduce new coal-fired power plants and millions of new vehicles on the roads.

Oil Politics

Crude oil is primarily used for fueling transportation vehicles: cars, trucks, boats, trains, and planes. Large amounts of crude oil are also used for manufacturing consumer goods: plastics, medications, chemicals, fertilizers, etc. Another major use of oil has been as a tool in the hands of politicians on the national and international political arena.

The beginning of oil politics is somewhat hazy, but one remarkable expression of it was the U.S. Supreme Court's breaking up the Rockefeller's Standard Oil trust monopoly in 1911. The trust controlled a large part of the U.S. oil production, transport, refining, and processing of petroleum products. The trust grew fast as the use of oil expanded from home lighting to the automobile. Gasoline, which was a worthless byproduct until then, all of a sudden became a gold mine and brought untold wealth to the Rockefellers.

But in 1911 the U.S. Supreme Court made a decision to break up the trust, which was split in several sep-

arate entities, which became even more valuable than the initial Trust was, and things have been different on the U.S. oil scene ever since.

Then came the OPEC oil embargo in 1973, and crude oil has been an increasingly important aspect of national and international politics. Now, competition for this scarce but vital resource is increasing, and oil is a vital part of the strategies of all countries.

U.S. Oil Politics

Oil is a major commodity in the U.S., where about most of the energy we use comes from crude oil. In 2011, for example, total U.S. petroleum consumption was 18.8 million barrels per day, or 36% of all the energy we consumed. So we still consume more energy from petroleum products than from any other energy source—including coal, gas, nuclear and all the rest.

The U.S. has about 5% of the world's population, but is responsible for 25% of the world's oil consumption. Unfortunately, we have only a small part of the world's proven oil reserves. The estimates until recently were that we have only 25 billion barrels of proven conventional oil reserves, but new technological developments are changing the picture. Recent estimates show over 2 trillion barrels of oil can be extracted from the U.S. shale deposits. Oil extraction from shale deposits is game changer and we have to consider this as a new and promising future of energy independence.

Nevertheless, we consume about 20 million barrels of crude oil per day, half of which is processed and used as gasoline. Simple math tells us that we use over 7 billion barrels annually, which added to the total world use, comes to over 30 billion barrels annual use, which is increasing. Obviously, at this rate it won't take too long to pump out every last drop of the world's oil reserves, which is the reason for the worldwide competition and the increased role of national and international politics and diplomacy in the oil business.

The US oil industry is divided into three sectors: upstream (exploration and production); midstream (processing, storage, and transportation) and downstream (refining, distribution, and marketing). Companies in the oil industry may engage in one specific sector, such as Kinder Morgan or El Paso—which engage in only the midstream sector. Companies may also engage in all three sectors through integrated affiliates, such as ExxonMobil and ConocoPhillips.

Some historical developments in the U.S. include:

- 1859—The first oil well was drilled in Pennsylvania by George Bissell and Edwin L. Drake. This was in fact the first successful use of a drilling rig on a well drilled especially to produce oil.

- 1865—The first commercial oil well in the U.S. was drilled in New York, when it was discovered that New York's crude oil is very high in paraffin.

- 1911—The breakup of the Rockefeller's Standard Oil trust, in addition to producing dozens of new enterprises, also introduced a measure of fairness in the U.S. petroleum industry which still dictates the nation's oil politics.

- 1920—The mineral leasing act was amended to include crude exploration and production activities. Submerged lands located within specified distances of state coastlines are subject to state regulation. Oil activities on submerged lands on the outer continental shelf (OCS) beyond state jurisdiction are governed by the outer continental shelf lands act (OCSLA).

- 1930—The discovery of the East Texas oil field in the 1930s led to a boom in oil production that caused prices to fall fast. This forced the intervention of the railroad commission of Texas, which took control of the production and pricing mechanisms. The Commission retained de facto control of the market until the rise of OPEC in the 1970s.

- 1982—The federal oil and gas royalty management act of 1982 authorizes the U.S. department of the interior to establish a comprehensive system to accurately determine and collect oil royalties and other payments. Rates and terms of service of interstate transportation of oil by pipeline are regulated pursuant to the interstate commerce act of 1887 and the energy policy act of 1992 (EPAct92), as applied by the federal energy regulatory commission (FERC).

- 1994—Federal "tier 1" emission standards and regulations went into effect in 1994, and are designed to regulate the type and amount of GHG gasses cars and trucks can emit to reduce harmful emissions in the environment.

- 2004—"Tier 2" standards were phased in from 2004-2009. "Tier 1" was modified so that cars and light trucks (SUVs, pickup trucks, and minivans) were treated differently under certain standards.

- 2006—President Bush signed into law the Gulf of Mexico energy security act of 2006. The act significantly enhances OCS oil and gas leasing activities and revenue sharing in the Gulf of Mexico (GOM). The act:
  a. Shares leasing revenues with Gulf producing states and the land and water conservation fund for coastal restoration projects
  b. Bans oil and gas leasing within 125 miles off the Florida coastline in the eastern planning area, and a portion of the central planning area, until 2022
  c. Allows companies to exchange certain existing leases in moratorium areas for bonus and royalty credits to be used on other GOM leases

- 2008—President Bush lifted the executive withdrawal (except as to national marine sanctuaries) and the U.S. Congress did not renew its annual moratorium that prohibited new oil and gas leasing along the OCS, allowing future lease sales to proceed in those areas. Currently, the only remaining portions of the OCS closed to potential leasing are that portion of the eastern Gulf of Mexico protected through the Gulf of Mexico energy security act of 2006 and the national marine sanctuaries covered by the executive withdrawal.

- 2010—In the wake of the Deepwater Horizon spill of 2010, a proliferation of regulations on drilling in the Gulf of Mexico hit the oil industry. These policies have caused production in the gulf to slow down dramatically.

- 2012—Two new discoveries of massive oil deposits have been found in just the last year: the Coronado find, 180 miles off of Louisiana and an enormous 6 miles deep; and the Shenandoah, 200 miles south of the Louisiana coast. The recent Interior department auction for Gulf of Mexico leases proved that the Gulf is becoming very active again, with average annual leases per acre increasing from $450 to more than $700.

Case Study: Keystone XL Pipeline

The Keystone XL pipeline extension is one of the most interesting cases in the history of the U.S. energy and the related politics and regulation machinery. A seesaw of measures and on-and-off decisions offered us a glance into the inner workings of the administration and its support organizations and institutions.

Granted this is a complex, huge, and expensive project with many and serious consequences whichever way it goes. Obama's administration and its watchdogs are analyzing all aspects of the project and are considering all possible scenarios. Here we present impartial analysis of the political aspects of this great undertaking.

The original Keystone pipeline was completed in two segments: The Keystone mainline and the Cushing extension.

In more detail:

1.   The Keystone mainline is 1,353 miles of 30-inch pipeline from Hardisty, Alberta, to the U.S. refineries in Wood River and Patoka, Illinois. The U.S. portion of the pipeline runs 1,086 miles from the border in Cavalier County, ND, and has been in service since June 2010. It has the capacity to deliver up to 590,000 bpd of Canadian crude oil to U.S. refineries and export terminals.

2.   The Cushing extension is 298 miles of 36-inch pipeline from Steele City, NE, to crude oil terminals in Cushing, OK. The Cushing extension has been in service since February 2011.

The Keystone XL pipeline is a new project, originally proposed in 2008, also in two segments, as follows:

•   The Gulf Coast pipeline project is 485 miles of 36-inch pipeline linking the Cushing, OK, tank farms to refineries in Houston and Port Arthur, TX. This includes the Cushing marketlink project that would provide oil-receiving facilities to transport U.S. crude oil to the Gulf Coast.

•   The Keystone XL pipeline project, 875 miles of 36-inch pipeline would run from Hardisty, Alberta to Steele City, NE, Baker, MT, and then to Gulf Coast refineries. About 100,000 bpd of the new line's carrying capacity would be set aside to transport oil from Baker's facilities.

The 2008 Presidential permit application of the Keystone XL project included both pipeline segments, but one was dropped, so the 2012 Presidential permit application, Keystone XL Project, refers to only the northern segment, starting at Alberta, with a carrying capacity of 830,000 barrels per day (bpd) of sands crude oil.

Upon completion of the new extension, the entire Keystone pipeline system would ultimately have the capacity to deliver up to one and a third million bpd of crude oil.

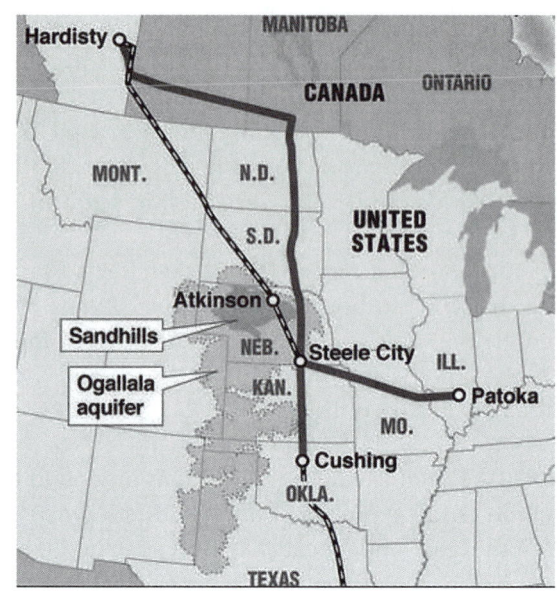

Figure 6-10. The Keystone XL line

The new pipeline extension would consist of 875 miles of 36-inch pipe, running mostly underground across half a dozen U.S. states. The pipeline would cross the Canadian-U.S. border, so it requires a Presidential permit from the U.S. State Department.

A decision to issue such a permit is based on the project's ability to:

a.   Serve the national interest
b.   Avoid potential impacts on the environment
c.   Have a positive economic impact
d.   Assist in ensuring our energy security
e.   Not affect negatively affect our foreign policy
f.   A number of other factors

Environmental impacts became a major issue very early and are evaluated and documented in an environmental impact statement (EIS) under the national environmental policy act (NEPA). TransCanada originally proposed the pipeline extension and applied for a Presidential permit in 2008. After a final EIS for the original project was released in August 2011, the State Department began a 90-day public review period to make its national interest determination.

The first major issue during this review was a concern over environmental impacts in the Sand Hills region of Nebraska. In response, the Nebraska legislature enacted new state pipeline siting requirements in an attempt to reroute the pipeline route through Nebraska. The State Department concluded that it would not have sufficient information to evaluate an altered pipeline route as needed to meet the deadline imposed by Congress and denied the permit.

The southern segment of the original Keystone XL proposal, now called the Gulf Coast project, does not require a Presidential permit, has been approved by the relevant administrative bodies, and is currently under construction.

In May 2012, TransCanada reapplied to the State Department for a Presidential permit to build the northern, cross-border segment of the pipeline, which initiated a new NEPA process after Nebraska approved a new route through the state, avoiding the Sand Hills.

In March, 2013, the State Department started drafting EIS for the newly reconfigured Keystone XL pipeline which was made available for public comment until April 22, 2013, after which, the 90-day public review period for the national interest determination begins.

The Controversies

The Keystone XL Pipeline has been a most controversial project, where several groups have expressed their con- or pro- sentiments in no uncertain ways. Proponents support the pipeline project because it would increase the diversity of the U.S. petroleum supply and economic benefits, especially jobs. The opposition is concerned with the greenhouse gas emissions from the Canadian oil sands. They also fear continued dependency on fossil fuels, and the risk of a potential ground and water table contamination from oil leaks. A possibility of selling thus transported oil instead of using it domestically, after assuming all the risks, is also on their agenda.

The U.S. Congress is also split on the pipeline issues, and so its destiny is uncertain for now. A number of con- and pro-Keystone XL pipeline bills were introduced too. In the 113th Congress, several legislative proposals from the prior Congress have been reintroduced:

- The energy production and project delivery act of 2013 (S. 17) would eliminate the Presidential permit requirement for the reconfigured Keystone XL Project.

- The Keystone for a secure tomorrow act (H.R. 334) and a Senate bill to approve the Keystone XL project (S. 582) would directly approve the Keystone XL project under the authority of Congress to regulate foreign commerce.

- The northern route approval act (H.R. 3) would eliminate the Presidential permit requirement for Keystone XL and require issuance of permits for water crossings by the Army corps of engineers within 90 days of an application, among other provisions.

- In March 2013, the Senate passed an amendment to the Fiscal 2014 Senate budget resolution (S.Con. Res. 8) that would provide for the approval and construction of the Keystone XL project (S.Amdt. 494).

The battle in Congress and in the different states continues.

International Oil Politics

Crude oil has a more complicated and violent history than all other energy sources. There have been a number of serious international incidents and even wars instigated by oil. They are too many to even list here, so we will mention only the most important.

Some historical developments worldwide were:

- 1928—The Achnacarry agreement or "as-is agreement" was signed in Achnacarry, Scotland by the then global oil producers. It was an early attempt to restrict petroleum production, but it was not fully agreed upon.

- 1944—The Anglo-American petroleum agreement was another attempt (in continuation with the as-is agreement) to extend the oil restrictions internationally, but was openly opposed by the U.S. oil industry and so President Roosevelt withdrew from the deal all together.

- 1949—Venezuela approached Iran, Gabon, Libya, Kuwait, and Saudi Arabia in an attempt to create an oil cartel. Additional meetings and discussions were held here and there, but nothing happened for the next 10 years.

- 1960—It took a while, but in 1960 officials from Iraq, Venezuela, and three gulf countries gathered for a secret meeting in Baghdad. This time the Arab representatives were wearing suits instead of their usual white garb. They were also sitting at a table in a hotel lobby, instead of on the ground of their tents. The meeting was called in response to the attempts of the U.S. to force import quotas on Venezuelan and Persian Gulf oil to support the Canadian and Mexican oil industries.

  After five-day negotiations, the representatives founded the organization of petroleum exporting countries (OPEC), which was led by Iraq during the next three decades. The oil cartel quickly grew in membership, output, and influence as time went on. Its objective was to control oil production and even world politics.

- 1973—The OPEC agenda was/is to protect the interests of the founding members, but it exceeded its rights with the 1973 oil embargo against the U.S. and Western Europe. That did not work out as planned, and the embargo was lifted in a hurry, hurting the pride and the pockets of OPEC members.

- 1990—OPECs pride and influence was even more badly damaged in 1990, when Iraq invaded Kuwait, another OPEC member. The action fell under the United Nations sanctions, and with the intervention of the U.S. Armed Forces, Iraq and OPEC oil infrastructure was badly damaged.

Iraq has the third-largest reserves of oil, but after the 1990 war, they dropped to 13th place in the international oil production table. Oil wells were destroyed and unattended, pipelines rusted, and oil engineers and specialists emigrated. The devastation of the oil fields and the country itself was completed during the 1993 U.S. invasion of Iraq. A large percentage of the oil wells were put on fire and shut down, and for the last 20 years there has been only a trickle of oil coming from Iraq.

Now Iraq is trying to recover its oil production and its glory, planning to triple and quadruple oil production   to start with. This has the potential of transforming the global oil industry by injecting large amount of oil on the world market. On the other hand, this development threatens the other founding members of OPEC.

Saudi Arabia would be especially hurt by Iraq's resurrection as a world oil power, for it has to share its leadership of OPEC. Iran faces an even greater and more serious setback, because it exports the major part of its oil production to China, thus avoiding the world's consternations over its nuclear program. Chinese oil companies, however, are now turning their attention to Iraq, and this effort, backed by the U.S., might further isolate Iran and bring more misery to its population.

- 2005—The 1,100 miles long Baku–Tbilisi–Ceyhan pipeline was built to transport crude oil, while the Baku-Tbilisi-Erzurum pipeline was built to transport natural gas from the western side (Azerbaijani sector) of the Caspian Sea to the Mediterranean Sea—bypassing Russian pipelines and Russian control.

- 2007—Russia signed agreements with Turkmenistan and Kazakhstan to connect their oil and gas fields to the Russian pipeline system, effectively killing the Baku–Tbilisi–Ceyhan and Baku-Tbilisi-Erzurum undersea pipelines.

- 2009—China completed the Kazakhstan–China oil pipeline from the Kazakhstan oil fields to the Chinese Alashankou-Dushanzi crude oil pipeline in China. Currently the pipeline's oil-carrying capacity is at 14 million tons per year. It is expected to reach a nominal capacity of 20 million tons per year in 2014.

- 2009—China also completed the Kazakhstan-China gas pipeline from the Kazakhstan gas fields to the Chinese West-East Gas Pipeline in China. In 2010 China and Kazakhstan signed an agreement on a new pipeline branch from western Kazakhstan to China. The second stage of development would eventually boost the annual gas exports to China by 25 bcm, or a total of 65 bcm per year.

Saudi Arabia Oil

Most oil-producing countries have been in steady decline for a while, so the oil-richest Middle East was our only hope until recently. While the U.S. is finding ways around its dependence of imported oil, most of the world is not that lucky. The Middle East has met the world's needs thus far by increasing production on demand, but with its own oil peak on the horizon continuing to respond in this manner for very long is questionable.

Saudi Arabia meets about 70% of global oil demand, but 90% of this demand-meeting production comes from, and is limited to, only 5 mega fields, which are old and at risk of unplanned and sudden oil production reduction and even collapse.

There have been signs of production falling into depletion, and expensive secondary recovery techniques are used to recover oil by injecting enormous amounts of seawater. For example the Ghawar oil field (the largest ever) requires about 7 million barrels of seawater daily to be pumped in the oil reservoirs to boost production. How long can they pump 7 million gallons of sea water in there?

The big problem is that once Saudi Arabia's oil production reaches a peak, probably in the next decade, its production will decline and that is when a catastrophic global oil shortage will begin. The entire Saudi oil system is old and tired, and its reserves are deliberately and wrongly overestimated, so we cannot, and should not, rely on it to save us when the global peak oil hits.

The Saudi Politics

Saudi Arabia has been, and is still, using oil and its enormous wealth as a carrot or a stick as needed to reward or punish companies and nations. Starting with the 1973 oil embargo, when Saudi Arabia decided to punish the U.S. and the West for doing something they did not like, the Saudi elite continued leveraging their oil and wealth on the world stage.

Just recently, during the 2013 events in Egypt, Saudi Arabia pushed against the West's efforts to pressure Egypt's new government to end its crackdown on the Muslim brotherhood. Saudi Arabia's oil money, and their whole-hearted backing of the military, took place openly and decisively.

The calls for peace in Cairo from the west are countered by the Saudis supporting Gen. Abdel Fattah el-Sissi, who led the coup d'état and threw in prison the legally elected Egyptian President Mohammed Morsi. The kingdom has pledged its unwavering support to the general's cause, and has promised to make up for any loss in foreign aid resulting from the military's brutal crackdown on the Muslim brotherhood.

NATURAL GAS

Natural gas has been, and still is, a major and very important energy source in the U.S.'s and the world's economies. Half of the households in the U.S. use natural gas for heating and cooking, and gas is widely used in commercial and industrial operations as well. Presently, a significant part of the U.S. energy generation is fueled by natural gas and we rely on it to provide heat and electricity on daily basis.

This is the good part. The bad part is that there are negative components in the natural gas production and use. The increased use of hydrofracking in very large areas, for example, is a major detriment to environmental and human health. Also, burning natural gas emits a significant amount of GHGs, which has to be taken into consideration every time we discuss the environmental aspects of power generation.

Hydrofracking is viewed as the solution to our economic and energy problems, and we are encouraging the quick development of new hydrofracking sites and expanding the existing ones.

In 2005, Bush-Cheney pushed a massive energy bill that exempted natural gas drilling from federal clean water laws. This action was followed by additional exemptions that were incorporated into other major laws and government regulations.

There are at least seven major federal regulations exempting fracking, or components of it, from the federal environmental protection and conservation laws.

- Fracking is exempted in the clean water act and safe drinking water act, via the "Halliburton loophole," exempting energy companies from revealing the chemicals used in fracking fluid (see note below)

- The superfund law, exempting polluters from remediating carcinogens (benzene, diesel, etc.) released into the environment

- Department of the interior's new fracking regulations require drillers to publicly reveal the contents of fracking fluids *only after* drilling operations have taken place, not before

- The resource conservation and recovery act, exempting fracking from federal hazardous waste regulations

- The toxic release inventory under the emergency planning and community right-to-know act

- The comprehensive environmental response, compensation, and liability act

- The resource conservation and recovery act

- The national environmental policy act

Note: In 2002 the EPA briefed congressional staff about the dangers of hydraulic fracturing, especially concerning benzene contamination in drinking water. Shortly thereafter, however, the EPA inexplicably revised their position, saying that fracturing would not contaminate drinking water with levels of benzene above federal standards. Was this change as a result of a nudge from above?

EPA officials explained the reversal by "new information obtained from an unidentified industry source." And, of course, the "industry source" is still unidentified. Did EPA officials, under pressure by the White house, bluntly lie to the U.S. taxpayers?

In any case, as a result of the EPA reversal, Cheney's energy task force removed any mention of contamination concerns from the national energy plan, and pushed their pro-fossils agenda forward unhindered. The deregulation of oil and gas exploration led by the Bush/

Figure 6-11. Fracking fluid spill

Cheney administration has been blamed for the careless and hasty handling of drilling permits, which is believed to be partially responsible for the BP oil disaster in the Gulf of Mexico.

There are new regulations on the way (see the following), which will force gas drilling operators and contractors to disclose their methods and especially the chemical composition of the fracking fluids they use. It may take a while for this to happen, and it will most likely be partial solution full of holes, but we hope that this move will help to open the doors to an honest discussion on the issues at hand by all parties involved.

As of 2012, only four of the 31 states with intensive hydrofracking have implemented any significant drilling safety rules. Only five of the 31 states have adopted disclosure rules, which still allow for "proprietary trade secrets" to remain undisclosed. This annuls the effectiveness of the disclosures, so that we still do not get enough information on the key chemicals used by the operators and contractors.

Currently, the EPA is not allowed to set conditions for hydraulic fracturing or even require states to have regulations of their own. The extreme number of hydrofracking developments in the 31 states, and the immense quantities of chemicals pumped into the ground day and night without any control or oversight, is mind-boggling.

Now the key word in political and energy circles is *hydrofracking*. It is the ticket to economic prosperity and energy independence, but at what cost? Besides

the fact that overproduction of natural gas (and falling prices) might stifle new drilling and hiring, there is the big problem of pollution created in the areas around the drill sites.

The process requires huge volumes of pressurized, chemical-laden water to break apart the gas-containing rock formations deep underground. The process consumes scarce water resources, which is a particular concern in the West, and also poses a danger of contamination when the chemicals are spilled into local aquifers.

In rural Pennsylvania, and many other states, the gas industry is the primary employer. With almost 3,000 wells, there is a lot of money flowing into the region. It is supposed to revitalizing commerce and farming. The truth, however, is much different.

Some local farmers have become millionaires, have run away to Bermuda with the money and shut down their farms. Others who refused to sell land for shale gas development and have stayed put are now plagued by ever increasing shale-related problems like groundwater contamination from methane leaks.

Although there are a number of examples of such contamination, the industry insists that the risks are small to nearly nonexistent. Actively supported by the government, the natural gas industry continues intensive and uncontrolled drilling in the 31 states, and we doubt that any changes will take place by 2016.

Gas Use Regulations

By far, the largest consumer use of natural gas in the U.S. is for heating, cooling, and cooking in homes and commercial, and industrial enterprises. More than half of the 120 million U.S. households and approximately five million U.S. businesses consume natural gas for these and other purposes.

Recently, a dramatic increase in available gas supply, by the surge in shale gas production and significant recent infrastructure investments in interstate pipelines and new storage capacity, has reduced the price of gas and made it even more reliable and a cheaper energy source for use at homes and businesses.

Natural gas also, and most importantly, fuels over 20% of the U.S. electrical power generation, second only to coal, and that percentage is growing very fast lately. The U.S. DOE reports that more than 85% of new electrical generation capacity built in the U.S. over the last decade uses natural gas.

Natural gas-fired power plants are the least expensive source of new power supply: almost 40% less costly than coal, 45% less than wind and 50% less than nuclear power. In addition, natural gas-fired power plants pro-

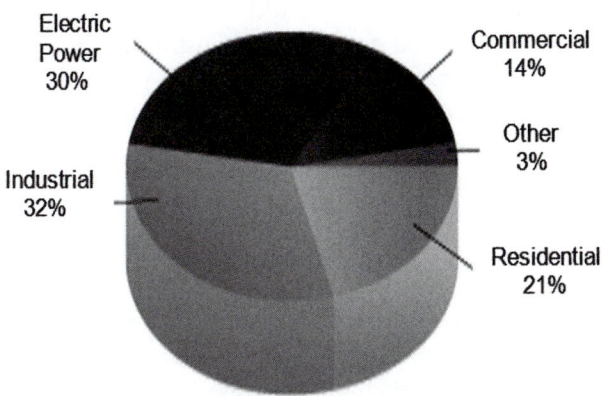

Figure 6-12. Natural gas use

duce low emissions and use less water and land than most alternatives.

And so, natural gas is in, but its quick expansion on the energy markets brought new issues to be resolved by the political institutions and regulatory agencies. As the natural gas industry developed, so did the complexity of maintaining regulation.

Natural gas history:

• 1800s—Natural gas was predominantly manufactured from coal, to be delivered locally, generally within the same municipality in which it was produced. Local governments, seeing the natural monopoly characteristics of the natural gas market at the time, deemed natural gas distribution a business that affected the public interest to a sufficient extent to merit regulation, but not much was done at the time.

• 1900s—Natural gas began to be shipped between municipalities, and so the gas markets were no longer segmented by municipal boundaries. This meant that the local governments could no longer oversee the entire natural gas distribution chain, and a regulatory gap developed between municipalities.

• 1907—State level governments were forced to intervene and regulate the new 'intrastate' natural gas market, and determine prices by creating public utility commissions and public service commissions to oversee the regulation of natural gas distribution. The first states to do so were New York and Wisconsin.

• 1928—Several states attempted to assert regulatory oversight of the interstate pipelines between 1911 and 1928, but finally the U.S. Supreme Court held that such state oversight of interstate pipelines violated the interstate commerce clause of the U.S. Constitution. So, interstate pipeline companies were beyond the regulatory power of state-level government. Without any federal legislation dealing with interstate pipelines, these decisions essentially left interstate pipelines completely unregulated, creating another regulatory gap.

• 1938—Ten years went by without any gas regulations, but then the federal government passed the natural gas act (NGA) of 1938, which marks the first real involvement of the federal government in setting prices for interstate gas transmission companies.

The NGA gave the federal power commission (FPC) jurisdiction over regulation of interstate natural gas sales, as well as limited certification powers. NGA quickly regulated that no new interstate pipeline could be built into a market already served by another pipeline company.

• 1942—The NGA certification powers were extended to cover all new interstate pipelines and transactions. To build a new interstate pipeline, or expand an existing one, companies must first receive approval from the FPC.

• 1944—The Supreme Court determined that wellhead prices were subject to federal oversight if the selling producer and the purchasing pipeline were affiliated companies. However, the FPC contended that if the natural gas producer and pipeline were unaffiliated, natural market forces existed that would keep wellhead prices competitive. No further decision was made for 10 years.

• 1954—Ten years go by and the Supreme Court finally ruled that natural gas producers selling natural gas into interstate pipelines fell under the classification of natural gas companies in the NGA, and were subject to regulatory oversight by the FPC. This way the rate at which producers sold natural gas into the interstate market would be regulated much the same as natural gas that was sold by interstate pipelines to local distribution utilities.

• 1960—FPC decided to set rates based on geographic areas, and since the U.S. was divided into five separate producing regions, the FPC set rates for all wells based in a particular region. The interim ceiling prices were based on the average natural gas contract prices paid in a particular area.

The process for determining area wide rates took much longer than anticipated, so by 1970 rates had been set for only two of the five producing areas. The problem was that that there were many wells in each area with vastly different production costs.

- 1974—The FPC finally determined that area wide pricing was not feasible, so it adopted national price ceilings for the sale of natural gas into interstate pipelines. Realizing that the prior price ceilings, based on the cost-of-service approach, were much lower than the market value of interstate natural gas, the FPC set a national price ceiling of $0.42 per million cubic feet (mcf) of natural gas. Although this price ceiling doubled the prices that had been set during the 60s, it was still significantly less than the market value of the natural gas being sold. This system of price controls was in place until the passage of the natural gas policy act (NGPA) in 1978.

- 1978—At the peak of natural gas supply shortages of the time, the U.S. Congress enacted legislation known as the natural gas policy act (NGPA) as part of a broader legislation known as the national energy act (NEA). The idea was to revise the federal regulation of the sale of natural gas, so the act had three main goals:
  1. Creating a single national natural gas market
  2. Equalizing supply with demand
  3. Allowing market forces to establish the wellhead price of natural gas

  The act attempted to accomplish these goals by setting maximum lawful prices for the wellhead sale of natural gas, as well as by breaking down barriers between intrastate and interstate natural gas markets. The FPC was therefore abolished and replaced with another body, the federal energy regulatory commission (FERC), under the Department of Energy organization act of 1977. Under the NGPA, FERC was given jurisdiction over the same areas as the FPC, with the exception of the importing and exporting of natural gas, which was the jurisdiction of the new U.S. Department of Energy.

- 1985—FERC issued Order No. 436, changing the way interstate pipelines were regulated. The order established a voluntary framework under which interstate pipelines could act solely as transporters of natural gas, rather than filling the role of a natural gas merchant. This order provided for all customers the same possibilities that industrial fuel-switching customers had, thus avoiding the earlier discrimination problems.

Basically, FERC allowed pipelines to offer transportation services to customers who requested them on a first come, first served basis. The interstate pipelines were barred from discriminating against transportation requests based on protecting their own merchant services. Although the framework established by order 436 was voluntary, all of the major pipeline systems eventually took part.

- 1989—Congress passed the natural gas wellhead decontrol act (NGWDA) that allowed a complete deregulation of wellhead prices. Under the NGWDA, the NGPA was amended and all remaining regulated prices on wellhead sales were repealed. The NGWDA also stated that first sales of natural gas were to be free of any federal price regulations.

- 1993—All remaining NGPA price regulations were eliminated, allowing the market to completely determine the price of natural gas at the wellhead.

- 1993—The natural gas and EPA launched the natural gas STAR program to reduce methane emissions, and the program has shown dramatic reductions of methane emissions since its inception. More than 904-billion cubic feet (Bcf) of methane emissions were eliminated through the STAR program, with 86 Bcf eliminated during 2009 alone.

- 2010—Finding itself under intense congressional and public pressure, the U.S. EPA announced that it would lead a $1.9 million comprehensive, peer-reviewed study on the impacts of hydro fracking on water quality and public health.

- 2012—Almost two years later EPA issued the first progress report on the matter, which boiled down to providing technical specifics on the fracking process, and reporting on what EPA plans to do to complete the study. The final report is due sometime in 2014—four years after inception—and will provide conclusions and recommendations. The recommendations will then be reviewed and discussed by congressmen and regulators, and eventually—most likely sometime in 2016—new laws would be drawn to protect the environment from damages done by uncontrolled and unsupervised hydrofracking.

The problem is that by 2016 the fracking sites will double, the ground and air contamination, and other serious damage could reach proportions that might not allow easy or cheap remediation.

New regulations by EPA and other agencies are in the making, which will make the natural gas production process more transparent, and recommend standards for GHG emissions during natural gas hydrofracking and use.

Gas Industry Misinformation

One of the most annoying and misleading TV commercials in 2013 was one paid for by the gas industry. A sharply dressed and eloquent woman showing clean graphics of gas well and fracking deep under ground, explained the benefits of gas drilling.

The commercial's graphics are basic, at about 3rd grade level, but the speaker explains in a convincing that the entire gas drilling and use business is clean and invisible. While it might be so in some respects, it is very far from clean and safe in many other aspects of the operations. She, however, would not touch any of these issues for obvious reasons.

Getting down from cloud nine of natural gas heaven, we reach into the local environmental considerations that warrant caution. Issues like road wear and tear, excess noise, air and water pollution, and surface management of fuel and waste, although not unique to fracking, are nevertheless present in large quantities during well drilling and fracking operations. It is a dirty business, no matter how you look at it and no matter how clean the TV ads are. The issues, however, are misrepresented, downplayed, and/or bluntly denied by the industry and its supporters.

A review in the duke environmental law & policy forum reached the conclusion that: "...hydraulic fracturing is a safe and effective way to recover oil and gas from shale formations." Safe to whom? Where did the Duke writers get the information to base their conclusions on? We also wonder how many times they got their hands dirty at a gas well, to reach such a simple solution of such a complex issue?

But the ace in the stack of magic cards was delivered by exiting EPA head Lisa Jackson, who told the U.S. Congress that there are no "proven cases where the fracking process itself has affected water." Despite all the cases to the contrary floating around, she says that

there is no need to worry without any consideration for the people whose lives are affected and even ruined by the gas industry.

But this is not the first time we've heard such misinformation from high places, for it is exactly what the nicotine, lead, and asbestos industry officials said to Congress in the past, too. And they were quite convincing, which led to the disastrous debacles dragging on much longer than they should have and cost many people their health and even their lives.

We need gas, and are willing to put up with its problems as much as we can, but we need to bring the issues into the open and discuss honestly both sides of the problems, instead of hiding them behind flashy TV commercials of gas companies and misleading statements of people with agendas.

We know that there are problems, so it only makes sense to clear them up before they become too large to handle. The problems are getting increasingly serious, and the longer we postpone discussing and resolving them, the larger they will get and the more difficult their final resolution will be.

NOTE: Natural gas is a blessing and a curse. It is a blessing because it provides abundant and cheap energy that will help us on the road to energy independence.

It is a curse, because some of the millions of drilling sites and gas wells are contaminating the local soil and water tables, causing a lot of pain, discomfort, and even illness and death to the locals.

We need to resolve this dilemma before it gets too big to handle, instead of hiding behind the thin veil of misinformation. The truth always comes out sooner or later. Hopefully it won't be too late in this case.

The Anti-fracking Movement

The fracking-or-no-fracking fight boils down to tighter regulations. Nobody is arguing about the benefits of natural gas—they are many. But while the industry denies vehemently that there are no bad effects, many people and organizations have formed an unofficial anti-fracking environmental movement.

The no-fracking-way movement requests tighter regulations, enforcement, and accountability, and many participants are ready to drop their objection to hydraulic fracturing, if an agreement on these is achieved.

The key issues that need to be discussed and agreed upon, according to the movement, are:

- Mandatory disclosure of fracturing chemicals and volumes used,

Figure 6-13. No fracking way!

- Restrictions on well placement
- Compliance with well and pipeline permitting and construction criteria
- Responsible water use
- Control of wastewater storage, transport, and disposal procedures
- Reduction of methane and CO_2 emissions during drilling and production

Although the anti-fracking movement needs to see compliance on each of these fronts, the most important is the disclosure of fracturing chemicals. Since 2010 legislation has been introduced at both state and federal levels to compel disclosure, and the Obama administration has mandated disclosure for drilling on federal lands. And yet, there are trade secret exemptions embedded in the laws, along with a comprehensive federal disclosure requirement, such as that contained in the FRAC act, a disclosure bill introduced in the U.S. Congress.

NOTE: The fracturing responsibility and awareness of chemicals act (H.R. 1084, S. 587, or the FRAC act) was introduced in the U.S. Congress in 2008, as an addendum to the safe drinking water act, for the purpose of defining hydrofracking as a federally regulated activity. Its primary requirement is for disclosure of the chemical additives used in the hydraulic fracturing fluid, which is vehemently opposed by the gas industry.

Regardless of the outcome of the FRAC act, the battle is considered won by the environmentalists, mostly due to the high visibility of the issue, and the level of public outcry demanding full disclosure. So, the focus of the movement has shifted to other areas of environmental regulation. Water usage and wastewater, or produced

water, management is one of the most potent environmental concerns of the anti-fracking movement worldwide.

The proponents argue that millions of gallons of water used for hydraulic fracturing place a stress on scarce local water supplies. In the western U.S., for example, a record drought is raising tensions between gas companies and farmers over water pricing and access.

Well placement issues reflect an array of environmental, health and safety, and cultural concerns. The risk of surface contamination from toxic wastewater is a serious issue that they insist on bringing out for open discussions. The anti-fracking movement insists on excluding sensitive ecologies, critical watersheds, historic locations, and densely populated areas. There are reported and documented controversies over drilling beneath cemeteries, in state parks, historic preservation sites, near schools, hospitals, and other sensitive structures.

Local regulation is an anti-fracking strategy partly as a reaction to the indifference of local and national policymakers about the negative impacts of fracking. In the U.S. the local authorities are the focus of anti-fracking movements. Communities throughout the U.S. Marcellus shale region, for example, have implemented local ordinances regulating some aspects of drilling activity, such as traffic and noise levels. In New York, state courts upheld local bans against industry lawsuits, setting a precedent that may be enshrined in the state's energy policy. In Pennsylvania, a 2009 state Supreme Court decision gave preference to local ordinances of energy regulation, which has resulted in a complex local micromanagement of regulations and fees.

Internationally, the battle on the local front is on the forefront in many countries around the world, such as France, Bulgaria, the Czech Republic, and South Africa. Green party politicians in Australia have tried to replicate the successful local result obtained in the U.S. by introducing legislation in mid-2011 that would override arbitrated consent and allow farmers to block gas exploration outright.

In Poland, communities have banded together to use private property rights, consent requirements and formal petitions to deflect exploratory drilling. In one case, they have sued a geophysical services company for allegedly forging consent documentation. The police have taken unprecedented action, arresting and imprisoning the activists in a number of cases, because they are labeled and treated as national traitors.

What is next for the movement? Who will win the battle? These are questions that will not be fully resolved, at least in the U.S., until the final EPA report is issued in 2014 on the subject of hydro fracking. At that time, the battle will most likely move into the courts until a final decision is taken and appropriate laws for control of hydrofracking are implemented by the U.S. Congress.

THE RENEWABLE ENERGY SOURCES

Renewable energy sources are going through revolutionary changes. Some will progress and prosper more than others, depending on the political winds and the overall socio-economic situation during the next several years. It is hard to predict what will happen exactly, but we venture guess that there will be some surprises ahead.

For a first time in the four decades since the 1973 OPEC sabotage of the oil imports, America is finally poised to break free of its energy crisis. We hear stories of huge domestic energy reserves, especially huge supplies of natural gas that new technologies allow to be extracted from shale rock.

We already economic windfalls from these activities too. Consumers save more than $100 billion annually as a result of the natural gas boom, and nearly $1 billion per day is contributed to the economy. This is 2.2% of GDP, or the same as the economy's growth rate in recent years.

The environmental benefits are also calculable. Cleaner-burning natural gas is replacing dirty coal as our primary source of electricity, which leads directly to immediate reductions in GHG emissions. Gas power plants are cheaper to install and operate, resulting in cheaper power.

Another critical advantage of gas-fired power plants is that they are also easily integrated with renewable energy sources, such as wind or solar. They are easy to turn on and off, and the power level can be easily adjusted up and down as dictated by demand.

This means that gas can work well in concert with wind or solar power by supplementing them when winds are calm, or the sun isn't shining. This way, natural gas turbines can ensure that electricity generation remains constant at all times.

For example, in 2010, Florida Power and Light brought online a new hybrid power plant connecting one of the country's largest solar thermal power plants with an existing natural gas power generating complex. This way, cheaper power can be produced 24/7 regardless of the weather changes.

This is a critical and much needed development,

for it will make these variable energy sources more reliable. Because of that alone we expect that the cooperation between gas and the renewables will continue to grow in the future.

SOLAR POWER

Solar and politics go hand in hand, not necessarily for the benefit of solar most of the time, but the relation is clear: they need each other. On many occasions since the 1973 oil embargo, solar has been brought out of the closet and paraded as a best friend and a helper by politicians.

Those actions were needed to show that the politicians are doing something to help the people during the periodic global energy emergencies and high fuel prices. In every case, however, shortly after the urgency was gone, the friendship was forgotten, and the normal drilling energy policies took precedent, and solar was then shoved back in the closet.

As President Obama put it, the relation has been that of shock to trance:

> We go from shock to trance. You know, oil prices go up, gas prices at the pump go up, everybody goes into a flurry of activity. And then the prices go back down and suddenly we act like it's not important, and we start, you know, filling up our SUVs again. And, as a consequence, we never make any progress. It's part of the addiction, all right. That has to be broken. Now is the time to break it.

During the shock times, solar and wind are hailed as the new promising energy sources and lots of money is thrown at them—until the emergency is gone, at which time they are no longer needed. Lately, however, the trend has been changing.

There is no doubt that wind and solar will become more a part of our energy future, but the road has been long and slow, and as things are going now we can expect anything—good or bad—to befall the renewables.

Solar Politics Background

After the latest solar boom-bust cycle of 2007-2012, solar was actually promoted again to the best friend status. It was even encouraged by generous government subsidies to spread its wings and soar high. And it went high, until the government clipped its wings again, and it is now spiraling down, trying to stay afloat, and to avoid a hard crash landing.

There were staggering numbers of solar companies

Figure 6-14. Solar (PV) power plant

going bankrupt between 2010 and 2012. Hundreds of silicon and thin film solar cells and module manufacturers are no more. Companies involved in thin film PV technologies were most affected, primarily due to the fact that the technology is too new, less efficient, and still needs a lot of work to be able to compete with the more mature power generators.

The U.S., German, French, U.K., Italian, and Spanish governments were the big spenders, spending billions of dollars on grants, subsidies, tax credits, and other incentives during this period. Much more was spent than was economically reasonable and justifiable. The government bureaucrats decided which company will get how much and for what. Lobbyists pitched tents on the White House lawn, and did not spare a penny to wow the lawmakers and decision makers. The energy and excitement of the moment were palpable, and the money river flowed freely down 1600 Pennsylvania Avenue.

And then, when the frenzy was over and most of the money was gone, the veil from the entire affair was lifted. What we saw varied from fairly good to mediocre and in some cases even catastrophic. Solyndra is only one example of money (half a billion of it) given to the wrong company and spent so badly that the case will be in the "how-not-to" section of business textbooks for a long time. And this is only one of the failures, many more of which dotted the solar and wind horizons at the time.

We have an entire chapter of these failures in our book, *Solar Technologies for the 21st Century,* published by The Fairmont Press in 2013.

So What Went Wrong?

It all started in 2009, when the Obama Administration decided to take an unprecedented step to pump billions into funding the solar industry. There were a lot of reasons given for this action: jobs creation, energy independence and efficiency, fossils reduction, price uniformity, etc. The money came from various parts of the stimulus act, and other initiatives, and was spent as soon as it hit the beneficiaries' bank accounts. The problem was that in many cases it was spent irrationally, unprofessionally, and at times even fraudulently.

There were exciting success stories in the U.S. during at the beginning of the frenzy. Manufacturing costs were going down and the consumer prices were lowered significantly. Solar projects and products sales rose to unprecedented levels, and solar panels were flying off the shelves because they were more affordable than ever.

Similar developments were observed in other countries. Germany, with its cloudy skies, led the race in a decisive way at first, but then the Chinese government ramped up subsidies and propped up their solar products manufacturing machine with $30 billion in basically free money, which made it very hard to compete.

The other puzzle is that it is even harder to imagine how this came to pass, since most of Germany and the U.K. have an average of 100 W/m^2 incident solar radiation, which is many times less than what we consider normal for solar operations.

This means that in Frankfurt, Germany, a 15% efficient solar panel would generate an average of 15 W/m^2 at the very best. This is 10 times less than what a similar solar panel generates in the Arizona deserts under 1,000 W/m^2 incident solar radiation. And yet, Germany went all the way and installed the most megawatts of rooftop and large scale power generators than any other country at that time. There is a lesson somewhere in all this, but it is hard to see at a first glance. Getting deep into it, however, we see that it was government money that drove the solar installations at the time, and that without it nothing like this could've happened.

China is now at the top as the solar market leader. Chinese solar panels captured nearly 70% of the global market, including that in the U.S. It is a price-driven business. This forced most U.S. companies to abandon the comfortable easy-money pace they were adapting, and instead to scramble and compete with the cheap China-made solar products.

The battle was getting overheated in the summer of 2012. The U.S. government doubled its efforts to help the struggling solar sector as much as possible. The U.S.

DOI initiated an anti-dumping action against Chinese PV module manufacturers, slapping them with high taxes.

We could blame the Chinese for all the bad things that happened, but we failed to see the numerous signs and indications at the time that Solyndra and many others like it had too many problems, which made them risky investments. In the worsening economic situation, trying to prop-up the solar companies with unstable products in an unstable economy, with many other priorities to consider, was a bad business decision. It put the government in a position to run business that it does not understand, and since money alone cannot fix technological problems, Solyndra and many like it, went bankrupt. The government got a black eye, and he taxpayers lost billions of dollars, in addition to losing their confidence in solar companies and products. Now natural gas is the *new solar;* drilling for shale oil and gas is what we are into now and for many days to come.

But What Caused the Anomaly?

Hopefully, we have learned the lesson that the federal government should stay out of the private business section—especially when complex technologies are involved. And equally importantly, the feds should not play bankers, but let the loan business and the investing to the private sector.

NOTE: DOE was/is the specialist, and White House advisor, on all technological issues and projects.. At the time, DOE engineers knew very well that CIGS thin films inside a glass tube with 50% direct solar exposure (Solyndra's aborted method) is not the way to generate effective, reliable, and cheap solar power. They knew very well also that thin films are too fragile to be relied on, and that Solyndra's products did not work well, let alone having a successful track record.

At the same time DOE business and financial specialists knew very well that Solyndra is not a solid business enterprise, and that building a new building before having a proven product is like putting the cart in front of the horse. And yet, they advised Obama to invest billions of dollars in these unproven technologies and a shaky company.

Federal Solar Legislation

The role of the federal government during the 2007-2012 solar boom is undeniable. Good or bad, it was a determining factor in all solar developments during the period and beyond. At the very least, we learned a lot of lessons at the time, and many more are left to be discussed and analyzed.

Some of the major legislations and regulations that played a role at the time, and some of which still govern the industry are as follow:

Federal Investment Tax Credit

In October 2008 the U.S. Congress passed a historic legislation that extended the 30% federal investment tax credit (ITC) for both residential and commercial solar installations until December 31, 2016. Part of the H.R. 1424, the Emergency Economic Stabilization Act of 2008, the 30% tax solar energy credit was designed to:

- Address the U.S. financial crisis
- Create a large domestic solar energy industry
- Create hundreds of thousands of new jobs
- Create a bright future for solar energy in the U.S.
- Ensure our energy independence

The 30% ITC, no doubt, is the most significant federal policy ever enacted for the benefit of the U.S. solar industry. In addition to extending the tax credit until 2016, the new legislation also:

- Eliminated the $2,000 cap for residential solar electric installations, creating a true 30% tax credit as of December 31, 2008

- Eliminated the prohibition on utilities from benefiting from the FTIC credit

- Allowed eligible projects to take a "grant in lieu of tax credit" under Section 1603 of the American recovery and reinvestment tax act

- Authorized $800 million for clean energy bonds for renewable energy generating facilities, including solar

Some additional benefits from the ITC implementation were:
- The ITC for both residential and commercial consumers is available for both photo voltaics and solar water heating systems

- The ITC is a one-time credit, but may be carried forward, if not completely useable in the tax year

- ITC allowed alternative minimum tax (AMT) filers, both businesses and individuals, to take advantage of the credit

- Business owned systems are also be eligible for MACRS 5-year Accelerated Depreciation*

- Municipal and non-profit entities do not have to worry about these tax issues, as they are generally tax-exempt

- The solar system owner can take advantage of the solar tax credit directly

- Bonus depreciation† was expanded to 100% for solar projects placed in service in 2011, and 50% for projects placed in service in 2012

According to industry specialists, more than 28 GW of electricity will be generated from solar energy by 2016, which is equivalent to a dozen nuclear plants and is enough to power more than 7 million homes. It seems that this is possible, but it is still uncertain if the goal will be reached, or maybe exceeded

The 2009 federal stimulus bill started the solar ball rolling. The key provisions were placed in categories to reflect how solar energy companies, their clients, or the industry in general will benefit from and gain access to specific funding for solar projects:

- Tax code provision: Effective upon enactment unless noted otherwise, the solar tax manual to be updated

- Enhanced funding for existing state programs: Federal funds will be directed to states for distribution. State agencies will provide access to funds.

- Agency-specific appropriations: Funds directed to specific agencies for programs or projects that are most likely already in the pipeline

Another major nation-wide policy that helped establishing the role and direction of solar energy in the U.S. was the implemented during the 2007-2012 period: the renewable portfolio standard.

---

*MACRS Accelerated Depreciation mandates that investment in solar power generating equipment and its installation are subject to 5-year accelerated depreciation under the IRS' modified accelerated cost recovery system. Somewhat confusing is the fact that solar power equipment is considered a 5-year asset, while full depreciation takes six years. Could this be a mistake made in the haste to pass all these rules and regulations?

†Bonus Depreciation is the acceleration of the otherwise applicable depreciation, thus creating a "sooner" depreciation option. A 100% bonus depreciation means that the whole project's applicable tax depreciation is accelerated to 2011.

The Renewable Portfolio Standard

The majority of states in the U.S. have established a renewable portfolio standard (RPS) that requires utilities to supply a specified percentage of electricity used from renewable resources, including solar. RPS is an important tool to expand state solar markets if designed with differential support for solar technologies.

The problem is that the RPS is applicable to all renewable resources that compete, and favors the least-cost projects such as wind and landfill gas. Large-scale solar projects also might benefit from it, but it is unlikely that smaller-scale solar distributed energy projects would benefit due to high cost and solicitation barriers.

The states have increasingly provided differential support for solar with an RPS in several ways:

- Establishing a *solar share or set-aside*, which is a requirement for some portion of the RPS to come from solar resources specifically, including distributed solar power generation

- Using a *solar multiplier*, which gives more credit to solar electricity than other forms of generation toward meeting RPS targets

The goal of these mechanisms is to strengthen solar markets by allowing solar technologies to compete against the less costly renewable technologies. Both of these have been instrumental in driving solar development in a number of states. However, many states have moved toward set-asides and away from multipliers, due to the greater success with the former approach. Industry analysis shows that the impact of state RPS *set-asides* on solar PV show 67% of PV additions from 2000 through 2006 came from states with active RPS solar targets. Further, the future impact of existing state RPS solar set-asides could be sizable, with 2-3 GW possible by 2015, assuming full compliance by participating states.

Renewable Energy Certificates

Renewable energy certificates (REC) are created when renewable generators produce electricity. One REC represents 1000 kilowatt-hours (,or 1 megawatt-hour, of electricity sent into the grid.

RECs represent the property rights to the environmental, social, and other non-power qualities of renewable electricity generation. A REC, and its associated attributes and benefits, can be sold separately from the underlying physical electricity associated with a renewable-based generation source.

RECs provide buyers with some flexibility, when:

- Procuring green power across a diverse geographical area

- Applying the renewable attributes to the electricity use at a facility of choice

This flexibility allows organizations to support renewable energy development and protect the environment when green power products are not locally available.

RECs usually include the following primary attributes and information:

- The type of renewable resource producing the electricity

- The vintage of the REC (the date when it was created)

- The vintage of the renewable generator, or the date when the generator was built

- The renewable generator's location

- The RECs eligibility for certification or renewable portfolio compliance

- The renewable generation's associated greenhouse gas emissions (if any)

RECs are used as the "currency" of renewable electricity and green power markets. They can be bought and sold among multiple parties, and they allow their owners to claim that renewable electricity was produced to meet the electricity demand they create.

Another reason that individuals and organizations are buying RECs is to satisfy a number of other environmental and non-environmental goals, such as to:

- Avoid the carbon dioxide (CO_2) emissions associated with conventional electricity use

- Reduce some types of air pollution

- Hedge against future electricity price increases for onsite and some utility products

- Serve as a brand differentiator

- Generate customer, investor, or stakeholder loyalty and employee pride

- Create positive publicity and enhance public image

- Demonstrate civic leadership

At the point of generation, the solar or wind energy generating farm, both product components can be sold together or separately, as a bundled or unbundled product. In either case, the renewable generator feeds the physical electricity into the electricity grid, where it mixes with electricity from other generation sources. Since electrons from all generation sources are indistinguishable, it is impossible to track the physical electrons from a specific point of generation to a specific point of use. Thus the limitation that it is the REC *product* that conveys the attributes and benefits of the renewable electricity not the electricity itself. So, if the physical electricity and the associated RECs, are sold to separate buyers, the electricity is no longer considered "renewable" or "green."

Then how do we know what is what? There are two approaches to verifying REC ownership and the right to make environmental claims:

- Via REC contracts and an audit of the chain of custody, and/or
- Via REC issuance and retirement within tracking systems

Both of these approaches help buyers avoid double counting and double claims and ensure against fraud. Of the two, REC tracking systems (REC issuance and retirement within the specific tracking system or systems) provide greater transparency when tracking RECs, since it follows them from the point of creation to the point of final use.

Note: *green-e energy certified* RECs are a version of the RECs system that verify and certify that genuine renewable energy sources such as wind, solar or biogas, or truly clean, renewable, energy has been delivered to the power grid, which helps reduce carbon emissions from fossil fuel-based electricity.

Many individuals and businesses interested in energy conservation aim also to support a clean energy future. Through the purchase of green-e energy certified RECs, they are guaranteed a direct support of the development of renewable energy projects. These certificates also ensure that the electricity these RECS represent, and which is used in business operations, manufacturing, events, company headquarters, etc., comes only from clean, renewable energy sources.

RECs were responsible for the installation of a number of solar installations, even in places with limited sunlight, such as Pennsylvania, New Jersey, New

York, etc.—especially in the beginning of the latest solar boom-bust cycle of 2007-2012.

Federal Regulations Applicable to Solar Energy Development

Federal legal and regulatory requirements apply to specific activities associated with solar energy development. The extent to which these apply to specific solar projects depends upon the nature of the project, its location, and size. Federal regulations and requirements affecting solar energy development are as follow:

Acoustics (Noise)
- Noise control act

Air Quality
- Clean air act

Cultural Resources
- American Indian religious freedom act
- Antiquities act
- Archaeological and historic preservation act
- Archaeological resources protection act
- Executive order 11593: protection and enhancement of the cultural environment
- Executive order 13007: Indian sacred sites
- Executive order 13175: consultation and coordination with Indian tribal governments
- Executive order 13287: preserve America
- Historic sites, buildings, and antiquities act (historic sites act)
- Illegal trafficking in Native American human remains and cultural items
- National historic preservation act
- Native American graves protection and repatriation act
- Theft and destruction of government property

Ecological Resources
- Bald and golden eagle protection act
- Clean water act
- Endangered species act
- Executive order 11988: floodplain management
- Executive order 11990: protection of wetlands
- Executive order 12996: management and general public use of the national wildlife refuge system
- Executive order 13112: invasive species
- Executive order 13186: responsibilities of federal agencies to protect migratory birds
- Federal insecticide, fungicide, and rodenticide act
- Fish and wildlife coordination act
- Migratory bird treaty act
- National wildlife refuge system administration act
- Noxious weed act
- Rivers and harbors act
- Wild free-roaming horses and burros act

Energy Resource Development
- Tribal energy resource agreements

Environmental Justice
- Executive Order 12898: Federal Actions to Address Environmental Justice in Minority Populations and Low-
  Income Populations

Hazardous Materials & Waste Management
- Comprehensive environmental response, compensation, and liability act
- Emergency planning and community right-to-know act
- Executive order 12856: federal compliance with right-to-know laws and pollution prevention requirements
- Federal insecticide, fungicide, and rodenticide act
- Hazardous materials transportation act
- Pollution prevention act
- Resource conservation and recovery act
- Toxic substances control act

Health and Safety
- Emergency planning and community right-to-know act
- Executive order 13045: protection of children from environmental health risks and safety risks
- Occupational safety and health act

Land Use
- Air commerce and safety act
- Coastal zone management act
- Farmland protection and policy act
- Federal land policy and management act
- National trails system act
- Rivers and harbors act
- Soil and water resources conservation act
- Wild and scenic rivers act
- Wilderness A\act

National Environmental Policy Act
- National environmental policy act

Paleontological Resources
- Antiquities act
- Paleontological resources preservation
- Theft and destruction of government property

Soils and Geological Resources
- Farmland protection and policy act
- Soil and water resources conservation act

Water Quality
- Clean water act
- Safe drinking water act

Figure 6-15. The U.S. renewables

From this list we clearly see that solar and wind have limitations in terms of location and technology use. This means that we cannot place a solar or wind farm anywhere we want. The list is long and the law is very clear: Thou shall not—unless absolutely certain! A thorough understanding of solar energy and solar projects development specifics, as well as the local area and the related rules and regulations, is absolutely needed to get a clear picture of the situation, when evaluating a location for a solar project.

NOTE: We take a much closer look at the solar power plant design, permitting, construction, and operation in our book, *Photovoltaics for Commercial and Utilities Power Generation*, published by the Fairmont Press in 2011. The overall conclusion is that a successful solar project of any type or size requires a lot of time, money, and expertise. Connections at the right places helped a lot of companies in the past, but that approach is much harder to implement now.

The Present-day Renewable Industry Turmoil

The solar industry came out of the recent solar boom-bust cycle wide-eyed and bushy-tailed. They recognize the problems, but are not sure exactly what can be done to solve them without revealing too many of the problems.

Recently, the two major U.S. based renewable energy industry groups (AWEA, representing the wind industry and SEIA, representing the solar industry) have dropped out of the American legislative exchange council (ALEC) because of its effort to wipe out all state-level clean energy programs.

ALEC connects businesses and about 2,000 state lawmakers to push free-market legislation. State lawmakers who are members of ALEC often introduce mod-

el bills in their home legislatures, which is an increasingly controversial practice that has been widely criticized by liberal and environmental groups and some government watchdogs. Companies like Koch Industries, Exxon Mobil Corp., Duke Energy and Peabody, are part of ALEC's energy, environmental and agriculture task force, and are influential in crafting energy legislation.

The American wind energy association (AWEA) and the solar energy industries association (SEIA) joined the ALEC coalition several years back because they wanted a seat at the energy decisions table. They wanted to influence the revision of state renewable energy mandates in 29 states and the District of Columbia. But then both groups decided to drop out after ALEC adopted a bill supporting the *electricity freedom act* model. This bill would end requirements for utilities to generate certain amounts of electricity from wind and solar, so both SEIA and AWEA dropped out early in 2013. ALEC also refused to take up SEIA's proposal to ease permitting costs for distributed generation.

AWEA warned state lawmakers to beware of ALEC's decisions that seem to be dictated by fossil fuel companies. They wanted to also warn ALEC's members about the misinformation that is geared to affect their future decisions. They also warned them about ALEC's targeting each one of the 29 states with renewable energy portfolio standards (RPS).

ALEC insists that it is just a platform of lawmakers interested in repealing the state programs, and not the conservative coalition as a whole. Lawmakers, according to ALEC, repeatedly raise the concern that consumers should not be forced to pay for politically-backed energy sources like solar and wind through government mandates.

Several states are expected to introduce bills to repeal their RPS programs in 2013-2014, and the state legislators seem to have taken the initiative on these issues. In North Carolina, ALEC reps introduced a bill to repeal the state's RPS program, which currently requires utilities to procure 12% of their energy from renewable sources by 2021.

Similar efforts are under way in Virginia, Ohio, Kansas, Arizona, Missouri and Wisconsin, states with Republican majorities in the legislature. Missouri has a democratic governor.

The state Senate in Virginia is split, although a republican lieutenant governor can weigh in and change the results. The legislation, however, is a actually a repeal of the state's RPS program under ALEC influence. And although there is no direct connection to ALEC, it is involved through supporters. The bill is a very smart, backhanded way to get rid of the RPS in the state. Other states will follow this example soon…if ALEC has anything to say about it.

Arizona

Arizona is the solar energy capital of the world. At least this is what the local politicians call it. In that they are right. In one single day—any time of the year—Arizona receives as much energy as the entire countries of Germany and UK combined receive during several weeks of the year.

There is only one problem in Arizona—politics. In 2012, at the last minute, partisan politics killed tax credit legislation. Bill SB1380 appeared to be heading for a final read on the floor of the Senate, but at the last minute, the governor's office decided to modify state building language, and implement a $8,000,000/year cap and a reservation system. So they basically agreed to drop the cap and reservation requirement for a portion of the existing tax credit, primarily residential hot water.

Then during a closed-door meeting, the leadership in the House and Senate decided in a closed door meeting to drop the per year cap on the three new credits from $2,000,000 to $200,000 and not make the new credits effective for 18 months from that date.

In 2013 Arizona politicians were moving aggressively in the same direction. The Arizona Corporation Commission (ACC), which is Arizona's version of a public service commission, has taken a number of distinct steps, which can be interpreted as anti-solar. This is part of a broader trend to attack state based policies supporting clean energy. The latest of these is the ACC proposal of a model bill for repealing the state renewable portfolio standards (RPS) programs.

The ACC measures that seem designed to undercut support for solar are puzzling, since three of its members have been running on a platform in support of the state's solar agenda. They call themselves the "Solar Team."

Recently, the ACC also introduced a measure that would remove sales to the largest customers from the basis on which renewable portfolio targets are calculated. Since the RPS is based on a ratio, reducing the baseline for calculating the target will reduce the absolute amount of renewable power needed to meet the targets and the associated support.

This action comes just after another widely criticized decision by the ACC to eliminate state incentives for solar installations on, or attached to, commercial buildings. The elimination of support for commercial solar, in particular, will have a measurable slow-down effect on the fast growing solar market for distributed commercial solar projects. It was the first and arguably most innocuous of these three steps, however, that provides some insight into why the ACC has acted as aggressively against the solar industry as it has.

In March, 2013, the local utility Arizona public service (APS) began charging what is effectively a reliability fee that was approved by the ACC last May. In announcing this lost fixed cost recovery fee (LFCRF) to customers, APS specifically references renewable and energy efficiency adoption by ratepayers as the cause for the utility selling less power, and therefore the reason for the need to recover an additional fee from all power customers to cover the utility's fixed costs. The fee is small, no more than a dollar or two per month for residential customers, but it is important in the general scope of things and on the long run will amount to millions and billions of dollars.

This seems similar to other such rate adjustments used as part of the process to ensure adequate revenue for utilities. But at a closer look, it is more similar to other attempts to remove lost revenue concerns from utilities for energy efficiency and distributed generation penetration by ensuring adequate revenue collection—regardless of the actual number of kilowatt hours sold by the utility.

Alone, the LFCRF would mean only a clear effort to associate higher bills with solar power and energy efficiency, but in context with the RPS reduction, and the elimination of support for commercial solar, it can be seen as both a key element of the coordinated action against solar development in the state.

The other large Arizona power company, Salt River project (SRP) is using solar energy with a twist. They

have to be in the solar game, and they are, but in a different way. Without the hassle and expense of building solar power plants, they offer a solar program to their customers, called community solar, which is nothing more than a clever use of somebody else's solar generating capabilities, taking the credit,
and charging your customers for it.

Instead of spending money on new solar plants, they offer solar power generated at solar plants mostly in other states or on the roofs of those who can afford solar and sell it to their customers who cannot afford solar or don't have a roof for solar, as part of their portfolio of energy goods. This way the utility is the good guy, while at the same meeting the state mandate, and making some money in the process. Clever, but buying electricity from other states is hardly the best way to promote solar electricity in the solar capital of the world.

At the same time, we must look at all this from the utility company's point of view. This is dog-eat-dog business, and the shift in competitive balance will become even more severe as the installed price of solar continues to decline, and the number of solar installations increases. Many utilities report losing money from solar installations, which are variable and even disruptive and use their infrastructure for free.

Since most of the utility's electricity delivery costs are fixed infrastructure costs, they stand to incur additional expenses and losses, which have to be recovered somehow.

Clever schemes, price increases, and other maneuvers are to be expected in the future. That way the fascinating battle for and against solar in the solar capital of the world continues, with politics, regulators, and utilities in the driver's seat.

Energy Subsidies

The solar industry got a huge boost during 2009-2012, when Obama's stimulus package threw billions of dollars in subsidies at solar power companies in hopes of dramatically increasing production quality and quantity. The bonanza is now over, and federal, state, and local subsidies and incentives are being slashed, leading some to conclude the future of solar power in the U.S. is dimming.

We should not forget that the now infamous solar subsidies and loan guarantee programs brought us Solyndra and a number of other failures during the recent solar boom-bust fiasco. The problem is that the solar industry needs subsidies to survive, but building an industry on subsidies and incentives is not economically sustainable. It can be done for a while—as it was done during 2008-2012-time period—but the money eventually runs out, which is happening right now. Federal stimulus incentives have run out and are not being renewed. States are also slashing their solar power subsidies. Oregon recently cut its solar business tax credit by 99%. Arizona and many other states may follow in their steps. And utilities all over the country are complaining about lost revenue due to the increase in solar power generation.

Depending on whom you ask, you'll get different answers and suggestions. But taking a closer look, we see that all energy generators benefit from or another type of subsidy. Coal, for example has been subsidized for the longest time. There are many, many ways in which coal is subsidized. Public land giveaways, tax credits, subsidized railroads, and many such are the ways our government subsidizes coal.

At 10-14 cents per kWh for a new power plant, coal is having a difficult time competing with cheaper wind, solar, and natural gas power plants. If 10-14 cents per kWh were added onto its price, and no subsidies were used, no one would even consider building a new coal plant.

And then, there are also the pollution externalities, which include the cost of pollution, injuries, and other maladies caused by coal mining and power generation, which alone are enough to price coal out of the market if they are included in the pricing equation.

Germany has been held up as a solar leader, and some days, during short periods of peak solar power production bursts, solar power has nearly met the country's energy needs by itself. This is how many solar power plants were installed under the cloudy German skies during the last 5-6 years.

Yet, even with a million solar systems in the country, costing many billions of dollars to install and operate, solar still accounts for less than 5% of the total German electric power generation. The price of electricity is high in Germany, and the country recently slashed drastically the subsidies paid to solar power generators. This was a major blow to the solar industry, which, in addition to the constantly cloudy skies over most of the country and the ongoing solar trade wars with China, puts a dark shadow of uncertainty over the German solar industry.

So, are subsidies good? It depends on whom you ask.

The China Invasion

And speaking of China, the Chinese government spent a lot of money during the last decade subsidizing a fast-growing solar industry, with grossly excessive manufacturing capability. Millions of PV modules and BOS (inverters, wiring, controls, batteries, structural elements, etc.) were produced—mostly for export.

The strategy was simple and efficient, but unsustainable. The aim was to manufacture as many solar products as possible, drop the prices, and flood the global energy markets.

The strategy worked for a while, and now there are millions of Chinese made PV modules and other components on the roofs and solar fields in Europe and the U.S. Many more, however, are sitting in warehouses somewhere in the Chinese manufacturers' stores, or at shipping terminals.

Things changed drastically lately, when the entire solar market hit a bump in the road, followed by sanctions by the U.S. and German governments against the cheap Chinese solar imports. Now there is a real trade war going between these countries, the end of which cannot be predicted.

Figure 6-16. Mass production line a la China

The low-cost PV modules and peripherals made in China were the preferred components in many, if not most, solar installations in the U.S. and Europe, all through the 2007-2012 solar boom-bust-cycle. Many companies and individuals benefited from the abundant supply of cheap goods. Things got quite complicated, though, due to availability, quantity, quality, and price issues and so the debate is still ongoing.

On one side of the debate are solar installation companies and project developers for whom Chinese made, low solar panel prices mean lower project development

costs overall. These groups want the Chinese imports to continue, regardless of the immediate results and long-term consequences.

On the other side are U.S.-based solar manufacturers who compete directly with Chinese imports. They claim that artificially suppressed Chinese manufacturing prices are making it impossible for other solar panel manufacturing companies to survive. The U.S. politicians support this group and want the Chinese imports to stop.

A third group of companies, equally concerned about this case, but generally less vocal, is a group of companies that sell solar manufacturing equipment and other upstream products, such as poly silicon and chemicals, to China. Those companies generally side with the installers in opposing tariffs, not because they do not believe there is wrongdoing on the Chinese side, but simply because they are afraid that the new tariffs might trigger retaliatory action from China that would most likely target and hurt them.

These different groups on the various sides of this debate have their own interests at stake, and their opinions on the case reflect their desires to protect their bottom lines. Regardless of their position on the issue, however, they all have to live with the new reality of reduced imports and higher prices of Chinese solar products, at least for now and until the Chinese find a way around the trade barriers.

Table 6-2. Major PV plants (over 10MW)

Country	# of plants	MWp installed
China	132	3,137
Germany	106	2,896
U.S.	87	3,136
India	66	1,190
Spain	72	1,151
Italy	26	622
Canada	27	550
France	15	519
Ukraine	8	433
U.K.	6	87

China now leads the world, hitting over 3.0 GWp PV installations as Table 6-2 shows. The cumulative worldwide installations of large scale PV plants (over 10 MWp) presently stands at about 14.5 GW, with about 3.75 GW installed in the first part of 2013 alone. So solar is alive, no doubt. The only question is how does this compare with what could've been if everything were going as smoothly as it was 2-3 years ago, and what can we expect in the future.

China is a major player, like it or not, and what it does next will determine how the solar game is played. And there is a lot going on in the solar field in China. On the international front, there are anti-dumping disputes with the U.S. and the European Union, while domestically some solar companies are failing and need to be propped up financially. A number of solar projects are planned, but where is the money coming from? The uncertainty increases daily, so we have to wait to see what will happen during the next few years with the solar industry in China.

The Retaliation

The trade wars among the giants continue with the Chinese government imposing anti-dumping import tariffs on U.S. and South Korean poly silicon manufacturers of up to 57% as of July 2013. The Norwegian group Renewable Energy Corp.'s U.S. units (REC USA) and AE poly silicon are among the hardest-hit producers: REC solar grade silicon and REC advanced silicon materials will receive the highest rates of 57%, as will AE. Hemlock Semiconductor Corp. and MEMC (now SunEdison) face 53.3% and 53.7% rates, respectively.

This latest action by the Chinese government is in direct response to the U.S. DOC decision in the summer of 2012 to impose duties of as much as 250% on Chinese PV modules to retaliate for the bankruptcies of a number of U.S. manufacturers, which are thought to be caused mainly by the extremely cheap, government subsidized Chinese products.

The Chinese government objects to the U.S. tax-exemption program for the advanced-energy manufacturing industries, supported by the federal government and some states. This was their main objection and focal point of this investigation.

Beijing launched an investigation into alleged anti-dumping of the raw material by South Korean poly silicon producers in 2012 as well. The result of that action is that South Korea's KCC Corp. and Korean Advanced Materials will also face a high rate at 48.7%, and OCI will see the lowest at 2.4%.

China's commerce ministry launched an investigation into European imports of solar grade poly silicon too late in 2012 just weeks after the European commission began its inquiry into alleged anti-dumping practices by Chinese manufacturers. Chinese and EU negotiators have been working intensively in Brussels in an effort to reach a settlement on the ongoing trade dispute involving provisional European import duties on Chinese-manufactured photovoltaic products. In the end

China spared European poly silicon producers, especially Germany, after the parties reached an agreement on the matter in the summer of 2013. As a result, most European poly silicon producers, like Wacker and others, have been spared the increased import duties.

China appears to be specifically targeting solar-grade poly silicon, which is used primarily in the manufacturing of solar cells and modules. Electronic-grade poly silicon, which is used in the semiconductor industry as well as other electronic market segments such as optics and micro-electromechanical systems (MEMS) is exempted from the new increased tariffs.

For the short term, this action will serve the purpose of boosting Chinese poly silicon productions, but in the long run it will very likely lead to higher prices of poly silicon in China.

The Bigger Picture

As we saw, there are some problems in the solar energy industry and the solar markets, but new problems seem to arise often now, some of the more serious related to the increased use of solar energy in the U.S. The problems are many and quite complicated, so we will focus on the most relevant for this moment, as follow:

Upper Mid-class Beneficiaries

Most of the people who can afford a solar installation have been, and still are, upper middle-class individuals and rich corporations. They get the tax and energy overproduction of their solar panels, which results in reduced monthly power bills. The rest of the customers, mostly the lower middle to lower class and poor people end up paying the increased energy fees (see the following).

Power Grid Use

Going back to the solar country of California, industry insiders claim that California will get into a situation where the power transmission and distribution system are used for free by all. The problem is that the thousands of small solar customers with solar panels on their roofs typically sell power to the grid during the day to offset the cost of using electricity at night.

This way, the solar rooftop generators are just using the grid as a storage device for free. They are not only not paying for the service, but are actually getting paid for using it, which is unfair to the utilities, who spend a lot of money to install and maintain the grid. And since somebody has to take care of and pay for it, as the number of solar rooftop installations increases, the utility bills continue to rise for all.

The unfair part of this equation, however, is that non-solar customers, the poorer of us, who may be already in financial difficulties, end up paying a major part of the bill. We get the bill for something we have not done, nor are we even part of. We basically pay for rich people to install solar on their roofs and for utility companies to take care of it.

The California solar initiative that encouraged the rooftop energy systems, added 245 MW of solar panels in 2011 and nearly twice as much in 2012. In 2013 the Golden State boasted 120,000 net metering customers, producing almost 1.5 GW of electricity. That's nearly half of the solar power generated across the entire country, with New Jersey as a distant second.

This means that the free grid usage problem is increasing with each new system that goes on a roof, and the utilities grid maintenance expenses are paid by a quickly shrinking number of consumers who cannot afford solar panels on their roofs. So the millions of non-solar users in the middle and low-income population will pay for the solar installations and reduced bills of the 120,000 rich people and companies. The non-solar customers will be expected to absorb about $1.5 billion annually in increased fees.

The flaws in California's complicated energy policy are becoming increasingly clear. It appears now that California's push to generate a third of its power from renewable sources by 2020 would lead to soaring infrastructure costs and even, according to some, a significant damage to the environment. The power grid is overused and underpaid, which increases the costs to the utilities.

The massive amount of money coming in from the federal government in support of the solar and wind projects is the enabler for California's rush into renewable energy. California companies received over $4 billion in Department of Energy loans as part of the American recovery and reinvestment act.

But that money is gone, and now as the solar installations get older and in need of repairs and replacements, another problem is brewing—who is going to take care of the dilapidating distributed solar installations when in need, if and when the installers are out of business as some already are? Who is going to repair the leaky roofs on which the solar panels are installed? Lots of issues are left to resolve, and most of them promise to grow with time.

The Future of Solar

Amazingly enough, and contrary to our initial predictions, the latest solar boom-bust came and went and solar is still here. This has never happened before, so it is a good thing and an indicator of promising changes coming to the solar industry. Every previous such event was followed by solar retreating behind the front lines and getting shoved back into oblivion for a long while. Not this time! Solar is here to stay, with California leading the way.

The Solar Country of California

Yes, California is the size of a large country—one of the largest in the world—as far as solar energy is concerned. The number and size of solar initiatives and projects in California during the latest solar boom-bust cycle of 2007-2012 is mind-boggling.

Figure 6-17. California's sunny (solar) future

A number of legislations enacted in California during that period of time fed and accelerated the solar developments in the state and the country.

Some of the key legislations at the time were:

California solar initiative (CSI) was created in 2006 with a budget of $2.4 billion with the goal of installing nearly 2.0 GW of solar energy generators by 2016. The goal includes 1,750 MW of capacity from the general market program, as well as 190 MW of capacity from the low- income programs. The *CSI-thermal program* provides incentives for solar water heating and other solar thermal technologies to residential and commercial customers of PG&E, SCE, SoCal Gas, and SDG&E utilities.

Million solar roofs was created in 2007 and mandated: a) Increasing the cap on net metering, a program that allows solar customers to get a credit on their electric bill for excess power generated by their solar system. SB 1 increases the cap from 0.5% of a utility's total load to 2.5%, enabling approximately 500,000 new solar system owners to get into the net metering program b) that solar panels become a standard option for all new homebuyers, enabling new home buyers to choose to add solar panels to their new home while it is being constructed. The bill also directs the California energy commission to determine if and when solar power should be mandated on new construction as a standard, non-optional feature. c) Requiring that the state's municipal utilities create their own solar rebate program, totaling $800 million in rebate funds to drive municipal utility ratepayers toward solar power. d) Directing the California state licensing

AB 380 expands the small renewable generation feed-in-tariffs (FIT) to: a.) FIT will be offered to any eligible renewable generating facility with a capacity of not more than 1.5 MW, and b. FIT will be made available upon request, on a first come first served basis, until the combined statewide cumulative rated generating capacity of those electric generation facilities equals 500 megawatts.

AB532 requires that solar energy equipment is installed on all new state constructions and existing state buildings, parking lots and swimming pools that are heated with fossil fuels or electricity.

AB 920 requires electric distribution utilities and cooperatives to compensate eligible customer-generators, who are generating electricity with solar and wind energy systems, for any excess electricity they supply to the grid. The utilities and cooperatives will either provide a direct payment or credit to the customers.

AB 1399 exempts trees and shrubs planted prior to the installation of the solar energy system that might be shaded.

AB1470 created a 10-year statewide incentive program to encourage the installation of approximately 200,000 solar water heating systems that offset natural gas usage for water heating homes and businesses throughout the state.

AB 1714 removed the requirement for solar customers to switch to time-of-use (TOU) rates until after 2009, and allows customers that install a solar system before then to stay on their existing rate. This was not a complete elimination of the requirement, but it was the best immediate solution that was agreeable to all parties.

Solar Water Heating Programs

It is quite obvious, from the above federal and state legislations, and these are only short lists, that the politicians have given solar the needed political and financial support to ensure its survival. And sure enough, solar power generation is doing well in California, even now, when most other states and countries are pulling the rug

from under solar energy. The situation, however, is quite different in many other states, where either the climate (not enough sun), or politicians (not enough interest) are hindering the full development of solar energy.

While PV may not be best suited for some of the Northern climates, due to low sunlight levels, solar water heating still makes sense. Because of this and other reasons, there is a revival in the sector lately. And again, the politicians are trying to help. There were a number of new regulations and policies established in California and other states with that purpose in mind.

Some of the state Solar Water Heating support programs are:

California Solar Initiative

The California Solar Initiative (CSI) Thermal Program offers cash rebates of up to $2,719 for solar water heating systems on single-family homes. Multifamily and commercial properties qualify for rebates of up to $500,000. This helps save money on gas or electricity bills by harnessing the heat of the sun.

Rebates vary depending on the type of solar water heating system, location, shading, and other design factors. A typical homeowner with a solar water heating system displacing natural gas can expect a rebate of about $2,200 at the initial incentive level. Rebates for electric-displacing systems are around $1,400 for the average system. Eligible low-income natural gas customers may qualify for higher incentives under the low income program. Incentives will decline over time as the program meets certain benchmarks, so customers are encouraged to apply for their rebate early.

Funding for the CSI-Thermal program comes from ratepayers of PG&E, SCE, SoCalGas, and SDG&E. The California public utilities commission oversees he rebate program as part of the California solar initiative.

Income-eligible single-family residential customers who are participating in a CPUC-approved gas corporation energy savings assistance program, ESAP, or who have income-eligible renters that meet the requirements can receive rebates of up to $3,750.

The maximum rebate that can be awarded to multifamily dwelling and commercial customers is $500,000. Multi-family dwellings that qualify for the income-eligible program can currently receive a higher rebate level up to a maximum of $500,000 per site.

SMUD Solar Water Heater Rebate Program

The Sacramento municipal utility district's (SMUD) solar domestic hot water program provides rebates and/or loan financing to customers who install solar water heating systems. The amount of the rebate depends on how much electricity the system will offset annually:

    800 to 1,399 kWh: $500
    1,400 to 2,199 kWh: $1,000
    2,200 kWh or greater: $1,500

All solar water-heating units must meet standards set by the solar rating and certification corporation (SRCC), be installed by a SMUD-approved solar contractor, and pass inspection by SMUD representatives.

Oregon Solar Water Heater Program

To develop the solar water heating market across all sectors and gain long-term solar water heating savings to benefit the customers of PGE, Pacific Power, NW Natural and Cascade Natural Gas in Oregon, Energy Trust has structured the program to address the primary market barriers of cost, quality and awareness.

The program provides *cash incentives* to eligible program participants to reduce the upfront costs associated with installing solar water heating and pool heating systems. The incentive amount varies with type, size, and location of the installation.

The program ensures minimum installation standards for systems applying for program incentives to help promote system performance and longevity through a network of design firms and trade ally installers who are familiar with the program requirements. The program also provides industry support in the form of training and cooperative marketing assistance for active trade allies, as well as consumer outreach and education to help inform Oregonians about their solar options.

Kentucky Solar Water Heater Loan Program

The Kentucky solar partnership (KSP) and the mountain association for community economic development (MACED) partner to offer low interest loans for the installation of solar water heaters. Loans cover the full equipment and installation cost. Flexible rate loans and terms are available, and they may cover 100% of the equipment and labor costs for solar hot water systems. Approved loans require a 5% down payment. Solar collectors must be rated by the solar rating and certification corporation (SRCC) or the equivalent.

Residents and businesses must be located in a participating eastern Kentucky county to apply for the loan. A copy of the application can be downloaded from the program web site listed above. The application process includes a solar site assessment, which is to be completed by a solar water-heater installer to determine if the site is acceptable. If the loan application is accepted, the cost of the assessment will be included in the loan; if it is not accepted, the Kentucky solar partnership will reimburse the cost of the assessment up to $50.

Nevada Solar Water Heater Loan Program

The valley electric association (VEA), a nonprofit member-owned cooperative, developed the domestic solar water heating program to encourage energy efficiency at the request of the membership. VEA partnered with Great Basin College to train and certify installers, creating jobs in the community, and also with Rheem Manufacturing and a local licensed contractor to install the units. A site visit is performed to determine the best installation and system design for each member.

Members have the option of paying cash or making an initial down payment of $50 on the unit and financing the remainder of the purchase price/installation with an interest-free installment loan for a period of nine to fourteen years. This program is currently only offered to those members in VEA's service territory.

International Solar Water Heaters Programs

Solar water heaters (SWH) are simple, cost-effective, and sustainable means of heating water for domestic and commercial uses. In addition to being simple to manufacture and operate, SWHs reduce GHG emissions and save electricity use. They also offer a lot of other benefits to individuals and governments, especially in countries where energy demands are exceeding capacity or in remote locations—SWH can reduce pressure on the national power system and diminish pollution produced by conventional energy sources. Economic benefits include enhanced employment opportunities and the creation of small- and medium-sized SWH businesses. The development of such businesses could, in turn, lead to job creation, improved product quality, and reduced SWH prices.

A number of projects funded by governments and international organizations are geared to accelerate the global commercialization and sustainable market transformation of SWHs, thus reducing the use of electricity and fossil fuels for hot water uses. These projects encourage market development, have shown success in the affected countries, and are expanded in other countries with good SWH potential.

The international organizations contribute financing, global knowledge, and management components. The programs implement the global knowledge and management component of the participating organizations, some of which are; observatoire méditerranéen de l'energie (OME), latin American energy organization

(OLADE), European solar thermal industry federation (ESTIF), and the international institute for energy conservation (IIEC).

Presently one example of these programs is implemented under the UNDP's national execution modality (NEX), and consists of national programs for five countries: Albania, Chile, India, Lebanon, and Mexico. Work in the country programs evolves around addressing the most common barriers to SWH development: the national and local policies and regulations, finance, business skills, information, and technology.

UNEP, in cooperation with its partners, is reaching out to other countries for the initiation of the second phase of the project. The short-term goal is to engage 10 more countries in national programs, while in the long-run the programs could be applied over the entire African and South American continents.

The California Utilities

California's investor owned utilities (IOU) utilities are not happy with the way things are going. Solar installers and the IOUs have different ideas on the issues at hand and confrontations, such as the one at the clean-tech forum in San Francisco in the spring of 2013, are becoming the norm.

edison electric institute (EEI), the association of U.S. shareholder-owned electric power utilities, recently published a startling report calling distributed energy resources (DER) "disruptive technologies" that threaten the very existence of today's U.S. electric utility industry. The authors of the EEI report and the commentary that followed view solar primarily as a threat to their business model.

At the same time, most solar industry insiders blame the utilities for being the biggest obstacle to the growth of solar in the country. The consensus is that the left hand does one thing, while the right hand does the opposite. The independent utilities (IOUs) say all the right things in public, while in real life and regulatory proceedings they are doing everything possible to stop solar. The excuse the utilities give most often is that they're not anti-solar, but that they're just looking out for the rights of their customers and that solar is interrupting their usual MO, thus forcing them to spend a lot of time and money on the problems brought upon the grid and the utilities normal operations by the newly introduced solar DER of roof-top solar installations.

But there is another battle between the utilities and the customers with solar installations on their roofs. SDG&E, for example, has a top tier rate of around $0.30 per kWh (as in hot summer afternoons when the A/Cs come on), which all customers try to avoid in their monthly energy bills. At the same time SDG&E is using the lower $0.07-0.10 per kWh cost of producing energy from DERs and other renewables. This is creating a gap, with the end result being that the utility charges their other customers that difference of about $0.20. This, of course, is an unfair and unsustainable situation that needs to be resolved.

Since the utilities are stuck between the solar installers and the customers, they are trying to figure out a way to subsidize the solar power in a way that doesn't help the other, non-solar, customers.

The California utilities have seen, no doubt, an increase in rooftop solar with growth rates at over 40% a year. There were over 400 new solar installations in San Diego in the month of July 2012 alone, and over 700 installations in February 2013. Nevertheless, over 90% of the electricity customers do not have solar on their roofs, and many can barely pay the existing bills, and yet get charged the difference for solar which they don't need and can't afford.

The California public utilities commission is playing an arbitration role in the solar price wars, and in 2012 rejected a rate raise proposal from SDG&E, for a network use charge, which would have made PV customers pay for using the electric distribution grid.

The utilities have other tricks up their sleeves and will continue trying. A new cost-benefit analysis from the CPUC on net energy metering is now triggering the next stage of the battle. Who will win is unclear, but the utilities are stuck between a rock and a hard place—the regulators and the customers. The customers are also split in two distinct categories: the minority DERs on one hand, and the majority poor customers on the other. Judging from previous lessons, we think that the customers will lose the battle in a big way and the biggest losers will be the poorest among us.

Cap and Trade, a la California

As always, California leads the pack making things even sweeter for solar companies doing business in the sunshine state. A new environmental law went into effect in the summer of 2013, which is expected to raise the cost of doing business for companies with carbon emissions. So coal and gas, here come the new competitors: solar and wind.

California implemented the new cap and trade system, which requires over 350 companies—utilities, power generators and others—to begin paying for the carbon dioxide they emit according to the type and amount of emission. Other companies—solar, wind, biomass, and other such power generators—will benefit by receiving emission credits according to the quantity of energy they produce that eliminates emissions of GHG gasses.

Polluting companies receive allowances for the quantity of emissions they emit. These allowances are set at a certain level, which decreases substantially over the next several years. This measures is geared towards pushing the affected companies to reduce their emissions and to reduce buying emission credits. It also benefits enormously the renewable energy sources.

This new law is one of the many measures California is using in its effort to reduce the greenhouse emissions down to acceptable levels.

The first cap and trade program we know of was initiated and implemented in New England some time ago. It was, however, incomplete, since it only covered the local electric utilities. Instead, the California cap and trade program covers companies and industries across the entire state-wide economy. Hundreds of companies are now involved in this program, with millions of workers and participants. All these people are involved in the newly created mechanism, which is the beginning of a new era: the creation of a new and more fair energy market while at the same time cleaning the environment.

There is only one problem. The benefits and penalties will not be shared equally by the manufacturers of renewable energy equipment (the solar panels and wind mills producers.) The solar cells, panels, inverters, and support structures need to be manufactured, transported, and installed, all of which require using coal and natural gas. The same is true for windmill manufacturers, where the windmill blades, generators, and support towers also use a lot of electric power during manufacturing. If the amount of fossil energy used during these operations is taken into consideration by the new cap and trade program, it might affect the bottom line of the renewable technologies manufacturers negatively.

Nevertheless, even with this handicap, and the reduced subsidies for wind and solar power, which are expected to fall further, the renewables will be able to stand on their own feet—eventually. The situation now is totally different from the one following boom-bust cycles of the past, which gives us a reason to be optimistic.

First we must overcome the other big problem for the solar equipment manufacturers: the collapse of solar prices, brought on largely by cheap Chinese imports. The harsh tariff battle in 2012, and the resulting substantial tariffs for Chinese-built products, did little to help American manufacturers. All Chinese solar makers have

to do to avoid the tariffs is move some of their manufacturing operations offshore. And so the battle for a strong solar industry in the U.S. is just now starting.

We the People...

U.S. politicians listen to us, the people, especially in election seasons, the important issues are brought down to the grassroots level and discussed openly and honestly—sometimes. People in different states have different problems, ideas, and opinions, but lately the responses of the American public to the issues at hand have boiled down to as seen in Figure 6-18.

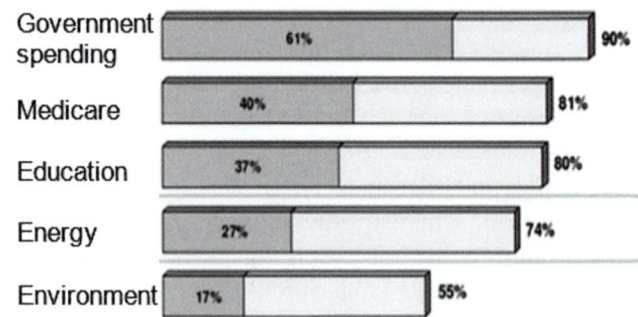

Figure 6-18. The important issues to be addressed.

Figure 6-18 shows a list of priorities according to California's voters. The priority in 2013 was getting hold of and controlling government spending, as seen in the top row of the graph. Although energy and environment are listed last in Figure 6-18, they are on the politicians and many other people's and companies' agendas.

Weather we care or not, we all pay gas and electricity bills monthly, so we are, willingly or unwillingly, quite involved in the continuum of energy efficiency, environment, and all their ramifications.

Figure 6-19 shows the California voters' preference for power generation and use. Solar is the winner by far!

Nevertheless, there is a serious split into groups in the U.S., with the politicians on top of the list. The greatest and most significant division along ideological lines ever rules the U.S. Congress now. People on both sides of the isle do not even consider compromise as an alternative. As a result, we have seen some amazing developments, most of which are negatively affecting the entire U.S. economy.

It is hard to do any meaningful business with Congress so divided. Partially because of that, the energy sector is in turmoil as well. We saw the results from failing government policies reflected in the bankruptcies of dozens of solar companies and the cancellation of numerous projects lately.

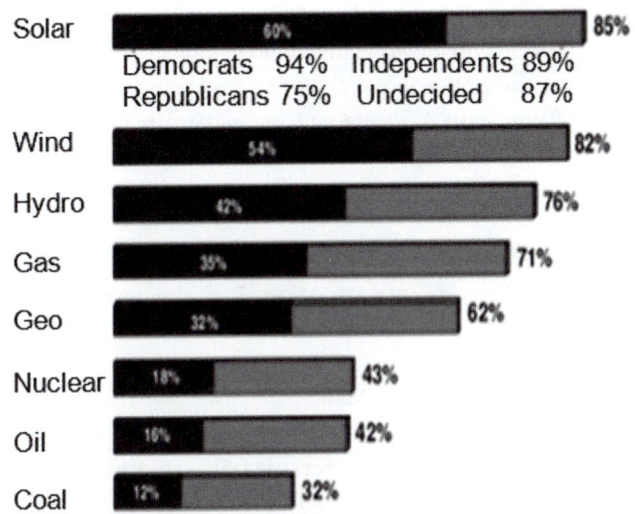

Figure 6-19. We all agree that solar is our best choice

Figure 6-20. The U.S. Congress in (divided) session

We saw the shifts from solar to wind, then to nuclear, and now to natural gas...what's next?

Master-limited Partnership

The Republican Party took full advantage of the Solyndra debacle in 2011 and 2012 to show the inadequacy of the Obama administration and the U.S. DOE. There were claims of billions of dollar wasted on renewable energy companies and projects and a number of investigations were started to figure out what happened, and to point fingers.

Washington's high profile fighting over Solyndra painted the GOP as unsupportive of renewable energy, but things have changed lately. In the post-Solyndra era, some conservative Republicans are coming out to back renewable energy. Conservative groups, such as americans for prosperity, and conservative Republicans like

Rep. Mike Pompeo of Kansas are beginning to come out in support of the idea of expanding a business structure known as a *master-limited partnership*, or MLP, which thus far has been available only to coal, oil, and natural-gas companies and projects. They insist that it is time for MLP to be made available to all renewable-energy companies and projects too.

MLPs are businesses set up as partnerships that are taxed only once, via their shareholders, instead of at both the shareholder and corporate levels, as publicly traded corporations are taxed. This would level the playing field some more, and make the process more fair by providing similar tax and business structures to all energy companies and projects. Since MLPs are one major area, the renewables, has been disadvantaged, this new development would benefit them immensely. It would bring them closer to LCOE and make it easier to compete with the fossils. Legislation to do just that was introduced in April 2013, by Sens. Christopher Coons, D-Del., and Lisa Murkowski, R-Alaska. A bipartisan group of House members is expected to follow suit soon with a similar proposal.

The potential deal-breaker is that some congress members think that if Congress is to expand MLPs to include renewable energy, the other tax subsidies, such as the controversial wind-production tax credit, must be repealed as well. Since this is a nonstarter for other congressmen, who view the MLP as a complement to those tax credits and certainly not as a replacement, the future of MLPs is questionable this time around.

The Solar Wars

Arizona, the solar capital of the world, is in the midst of a war. It is a war for and against solar. The lineup is impressive; the state legislature, the Arizona corporate commission, and the local utilities against the U.S. solar industry. It is hot in Phoenix in the summer of 2013, close to 120°F at times, and the non-stop battle for Arizona's rooftops is close to the boiling point.

While the Arizona summer cools into fall, the solar war will only get hotter. The latest controversy is who started a local cable TV ad that portraying third party ownership specialist companies Sunrun and SunCity as "the new Solyndras;" as corporate carpetbaggers from California coming to raid Arizonans and steal their hard earned tax dollars. So the battle heats up.

It is not so much the substance of the message that is critical in Arizona, as who is behind it. Anyone can put out a message and misinformation in the U.S. What is critical here is that it is the Arizona public services (APS), the state's largest utility company, has a finger in

Figure 6-21. Arizona's near-term solar future

this misinformation campaign.

To an extent, APS has a right to worry about solar, and in fact lately has vociferously resisted the spread of solar through net energy metering. Solar is becoming a serious competitor and the local residential rooftop PV systems cost APS and its non-solar customers about $20 million a year, simply because solar empowered customers dodge paying about $1,000 a year for grid services that are essential to solar operations. APS ends up paying for the grid operation and maintenance, but the solar customers use it for free and even get paid for it.

PV installations in Arizona have mushroomed from 900 rooftop systems in 2009 to 18,000 by June 2013, averaging 550 new installations each month. This is affecting APS profit margins in a number of ways, and so, in the summer of 2013, APS filed proposals to the Arizona corporate commission (the state's regulator, among other things) that could almost double charges for residential users.

Thus far APS has denied any involvement in the ads, but many Arizonans smell a rat and believe that there is already a strong connection between these TV ads and APS. Barry Goldwater, a former Republican House Representative in Washington and chairman of the group "tell utilities solar won't be killed" (TUSK), also got involved in the war, blaming APS for covert actions.

There is much at stake in Arizona, where 38% of the electricity generated is from coal, 28% from nuclear and 27% from natural gas. That action by APS is the beginning of a real war with solar, simply because APS doesn't want to lose its monopoly over power generation and distribution.

During the initial years of solar growth (2007-2010) APS made a mistake and ignored the solar rooftop market and allowed (and even helped) private companies to do a terrific job on the solar roofs, which now they feel is threatening their bottom line.

But the anti-solar war is not in Arizona only—it is nationwide, with Arizona as the test ground. The initial salvo was launched via the TV ads. The second phase of fighting over Arizona's rooftops is in the planning stages.

There is one more aspect of the renewable power sources that needs our attention. It is the newly developed problem with crime and bribes.

The Czech' Unfair Legislation

Foreign investments in the solar energy projects in the Czech Republic have been hit with unfair treatment, so an arbitration lawsuit was filed in May 2013 against the Czech state. Ipvic, an association of mostly German closely-held companies that invested in the Czech business, claims unfair play by the state and is seeking compensation for considerable financial loss suffered by investors as a result of the sudden retroactive discriminatory change introduced by the Czech legislation.

In an effort to curb a sudden surge in solar plant installations that threatened to raise electricity prices, Czech lawmakers passed a law in 2010 imposing a retroactive tax of 26% on solar plants hooked to the grid during 2009 and 2010. The law also raised fees for plants built on agricultural land and slapped an additional 32% levy on carbon credits awarded to the companies, which reward environment-friendly technologies. These changes significantly reduce, and in some cases obliterate, the profits that the investors were hoping to make on their investment.

This move by the Czech state surely does seem unfair, because they are not taking into account the considerable sums of money the German and other investors poured into the solar infrastructure of the country in good faith and in accordance with Czech laws at the time. Changing the laws now without a notice or consultation with the investors is a wrong and illegal practice that needs arbitration, according to the association.

As a matter of fact several other EU countries—Bulgaria, Romania and others—took similar measures in 2012 and 2013, which were forced by the worsening economic climate in the region.

Crime and Bribes

This is one of the subjects that everyone wants to stay clear of. Especially people involved in the so called clean tech: solar, wind, biofuels, geo- and ocean-energy. *Clean*, after all, implies virgin purity on all levels, so even just talk about unclean things and actions could violate the *clean* principle.

The achievements of late in the sector have been exciting, and both the financial and the green communities are optimistic about the possibilities. Yet we are faced with an ugly and very ordinary risk of getting involved in the oldest business challenge of all: corruption.

Remember Solyndra? That was a supreme example of how bad things can get when corruption on high levels, mixed with ignorance and negligence, gets out of control. There are other such examples of extreme lobbying, misinformation, clumsy technical decisions, etc. abnormalities resulting in the loss of millions of taxpayers' dollars.

The U.S. foreign corrupt practices act (FCPA) prohibits companies and individuals from corruptly paying, offering, or promising to pay anything of value, directly or indirectly, to any officials to obtain or retain business or gain an improper advantage. To comply with the FCPA, clean tech companies must overcome the challenges typical of two of the most bribery-prone sectors—infrastructure and energy. Surprised? And this is in addition to a number of new challenges.

For a glimpse in the costs associated with FCPA violations, we should take a look at the $1.6 billion in fines levied by U.S. and foreign governments against German conglomerate Siemens AG. This huge company is involved in energy and infrastructure projects all over the world. And Siemens is not shy or afraid of going into some countries with questionable socio-political systems, and does not hesitate to pay bribes to foreign officials to win contracts.

Siemens typically pays bribes using special accounting procedures, including off-book accounts and slush funds. They seem to have developed a special system to disguise illegal, immoral, or at best improper, bribe payments. Of the $1.4 billion in bribes paid by Siemens during 2001-07, over half were channeled through third parties.

Siemens had a system, where consulting agreements were designed so that a number of consultants' only duty was to convey bribes. This includes payments to a partially state-owned company in Italy in connection with two power plant projects, as well as payments to a former director of the Israel Electric Company for four contracts to build and service power plants.

And not to be left behind, government officials in China were paid bribes for the installation of high-voltage transmission lines. How many millions of dollars were paid for these projects is uncertain, but we dare say the number was several million times greater than $1.

A number of "eco-corruption" reports exposed the link between massive state subsidies for wind and solar development in Italy and a totally corrupted energy market in the country.

Enter the world solar energy industry; the clean and green branch of the old, corrupted, fossil industry. In spite of the challenges, many clean tech companies, which are often fledgling, startup companies, fail to make compliance a priority and fail to implement measures that could protect them from both legal and reputational fallout.

Why are so many clean tech companies taking a serious regulatory gamble? One theory is that their tepid response is bolstered by the mistaken belief that because they work toward a socially conscious goal (clean and useful energy) that they are somehow exempt from scrutiny by the U.S. government. It's a risky assumption, but it had worked in many cases in the past and even more obviously so during the recent solar boom-bust cycle of 2007-2012.

The enforcement agencies have long focused on the infrastructure and energy industries, levying increasingly heavy fines on these sectors. Given the overlap among these industries, the hybrid clean tech sector may not be far behind in attracting the government's attention, but for now it enjoys a preferential treatment.

The clean tech industry was awash with funding, which exacerbated FCPA compliance concerns. Because spending is largely on research and development level, internal controls should've been more rigorous. In challenging compliance environments like China, funding is routinely allocated at a local level, making meaningful formal controls impossible.

For example, one solar industry expert described a situation in which a foreign minister promoted the possibility of a solar project in his developing country. However, after doing some due diligence, the company discovered that the minister actually owned an interest in the project himself through a shell company.

Clean tech companies should implement measures, such as centralizing accounting systems to ease corporate headquarter review, to ensure that money is both coming from and going to legitimate sources. Companies should also have FCPA controls addressing the use of petty cash; third-party contracts and payments, including sales and marketing agents; contracts for the lease of facilities and equipment; gifts, entertainment, and hospitality payments; and employee status, including current or previous government employment for employees and their immediate family members.

Emerging industry regulations and "energy audits" are often ill-defined and subject to abusive practices. Similarly, government funding and subsidies surrounding projects, particularly in developing countries, can lack regulatory transparency.

In challenging markets, clean tech companies can face such risks as confusion over which ministry controls allocation of a project or whether demands from a foreign official are legitimate. Clean tech companies need to have clear FCPA compliance policies in place to deal with opaque regulations and overreaching foreign officials. Anti-bribery training can also be used to teach employees how to respond to bribe demands. The direction from the top is crucial. Senior management must foster a culture of compliance and let their employees know that bribery will not be tolerated, even if it means walking away from business.

Many clean tech projects involve extensive dealings with foreign governments, from contract bidding to permitting to environmental review and enforcement. Many of these dealings, some of which involve the discretion of a foreign official, are handled through third parties (middle men). Business agents can pose a particular risk, as they might have formerly served in the government or be related to a senior government official.

The FCPA specifically bans committing a prohibited action through a third party when knowing that the third party will perform that action. Clean tech companies may be pressured to work with business agents. Companies must balance this pressure to be well connected with the prospect of an agent making an improper payment to secure that connection. Under the FCPA, companies may be vicariously liable for the conduct of their consultants, distributors, sales agents, and other third parties, even if the company lacks knowledge of their wrongdoing.

WIND POWER

On October 3, 2008, the U.S. emergency economic stabilization act of 2008, H.R. 1424, was enacted into law and includes a new federal-level investment tax credit to help consumers purchase small wind turbines for home, farm, or business use. Owners of small wind systems with 100 kilowatts (kW) of capacity and less can receive a credit for 30% of the total installed cost of the system.

The credit will be available for equipment installed through December 31, 2016. This legislation marks the first federal incentive for small wind systems since 1985. The incentive was further expanded through the Ameri-

can recovery and reinvestment tax act of 2009, which removed the financial cap that had been present in the 2008 legislation.

This is good for the country's energy security and the environment. But like with any good thing, there are problems. With the economic uncertainty looming over the country and the world, we wonder if wind is the best alternative to energy generation. The wind industry is pressing Congress hard for a last-minute extension of the Section 1603 subsidy. Political pressure has worked pretty well thus far, with a contingent of members anxious to bask in the 'green' status of the technology.

The American wind energy association (AWEA), the trade group that represents mostly wind turbine manufacturers, leads the effort. But there are several problems, not the least of which is the fact that most of the companies it represents are headquartered in Europe and Asia. So, is this a case of American money going to foreign companies?

Costs

Looking at the 1603 grant for wind power reveals some facts that could make people scratch their heads. During less than two years, 2009-2011, the U.S. treasury distributed nearly $10.0 billion in cash grants to "green" companies. Of this, over 80% (nearly $8.0 billion) was handed to wind developers representing 12.3 GWp of installed wind capacity. Projecting this into final costs of projects under development, we come up with several times this amount to be spent on wind installations by 2015.

And then, wind is an intermittent and unpredictable energy source, so most wind power plants operate at 20-25% capacity factor, meaning that only 1/4 of the 12.0 GWp are utilized on 24/7 basis. The wind power intermittency also creates unwanted instability in the national power grid as well, which presents additional technical difficulties and expenses to the grid operators.

In addition, maintenance and component replacement costs (which could be astronomical, due to the complexity of the hardware), or accidents and incidents, are not included in these calculations, so in worst-case scenario we might end up with another large bill for little energy generation.

Comparative analysis shows that the same amount of money spent on nuclear power plants, for example, would generate 3-4 times more, and much more reliable, electricity than the wind farms. Eight billion dollars is a lot of money to spend on any technology, not to mention that 40 cents of each dollar spent on this program are borrowed.

Another major issue that did not get much publicity is the fact that a lot of the U.S. taxpayer's money went to support foreign turbine manufacturers. American money going to foreign companies was a trend during the boom-bust cycle of 2007-2012 that was accepted as normal, so billions were paid to Chinese and EU companies for bringing their products—solar panels and wind turbines—for use in the U.S. According to AWEA's quarterly reports for 2011, 63% of the 3.4 GWp of wind turbines installed in the first three-quarters of the year in the U.S. were purchased from European and Asian turbines manufacturers. Some of that money was yours and mine.

Figure 6-22. Large scale wind power generating plant.

The developers get upfront cash for the turbine and other components purchases, which provides them with minimal incentive to negotiate lower prices with the manufacturers. They also know that the higher a project's capital costs, the more 1603 money will flow in their pockets. Turbine costs represent over 55% of the project's cost, so turbine manufacturers are able and willing to keep their prices high too. The result is inflated prices, and more taxpayers' money down the drain.

These problems are spread over the entire energy industry, because intermittent resources such as wind and solar, call for much higher construction and operational costs, which push up energy prices due to fewer hours of efficient operation to spread the inflated costs over.

So the question is, is the taxpayers' money well spent? The money from wind does not transfer to project owners until a wind facility is in service, so the public has no idea of the total cost of 1603. When we get the final tally, we might be quite unpleasantly surprised.

Now we have an entire industry partially reliant on 1603 grants, which are used to spend a lot and produce little. The outgoing Interior Secretary Ken Salazar stated that wind has become not only the nation's top source of new electricity in 2012, but that the "sweet spots" in the Massachusetts coastal waters could power 1.7 million homes. "We control the ocean floor," Salazar said. "We get to decide what it is that happens."

Not so fast, sir. Control of the ocean floor, even if true, does not mean quick development of off-shore wind farms on it, or controlling the winds for better efficiency. And the Republicans also have something different to say on the matter. And they do, via vehement opposition to any renewable energy production tax credits—including these for wind. The credits were extended for one more year in the end-of-the-year fiscal cliff negotiations in 2012, but thousands of jobs were lost because of the delays and the uncertainty of an extension.

Salazar also advised all states to follow the California example of obtaining 33% of its energy from renewable sources by 2020. Another example to follow is the California cap-and-trade program that currently covers electric power plants and large industrial plants, but will be phased for heating and transportation fuels by 2015.

But here is the rub—California is significantly ahead of Congress because the state has a renewable energy standard, implemented on state level by then Republican governor, Arnold Schwarzenegger, and carried on by his successor, the Democrat Jerry Brown.

Since such cooperation now is only possible on state level, it is unlikely to be found in the U.S. Congress, so it is unlikely that such programs will be implemented on federal level. If a miracle happens, however, a national policy would need to include a cap-and-trade program a la California.

Cap-and-trade forces polluters to pay for emissions, theoretically prodding companies to adopt cleaner and more energy efficient technologies. This alone would promote the use of wind power, and will help it to compete with the fossil sources more than any subsidies.

President Obama tried pushing a national cap-and-trade initiative, but it failed to win congressional approval.

On state level only 30 states have adopted renewable energy standards thus far, mostly in Republican strongholds. Many states, however, are rolling up their "welcome solar" mats and putting them away until the next crisis.

Europe had a record year in offshore wind development, installing 369 turbines. During the same time, Denmark announced it now gets 30% of its energy from wind farms. The U.S. is trying to catch up, but has a long way to go.

Amazingly enough, there are private investors still willing to put billions of dollars into wind farms, but are instead sitting on the sidelines, while America's wind power is hoping for a national policy. The state-by-state model is clearly working for California, but not for the rest of the states. If the U.S. Congress does not introduce a national model for developing wind power generation, the U.S. will remain on the sidelines in the area of wind power generation, at least until a feasible national wind power policy is introduced some time in the future.

Tax Credit…Again

Production tax credits (PTC) were a part of the Energy policy act of 1992 ((EPACT92) and are intended for wind and bio-energy resources. The purpose of the PTC is to support renewable energy based upon the environmental, economic, and energy security benefits that renewable energy resources can provide. Besides wind energy, the PTC also covers closed loop biomass, geothermal power, and half the rate for open loop biomass, hydropower, landfill gas, and municipal solid waste. The PTC provides a 2.2 cent per kilowatt-hour benefit for the first ten years of a renewable energy facility's operation. It is only available for wind energy equipment located within the U.S. and only if electricity produced is sold to an unrelated party. Any unused credits may be carried forward for up to 20 years following generation.

There are several incentives that go along with a wind production tax credit. The PTC provides a 2.1 cent per kilowatt-hour benefit for the first ten years of a renewable energy facility's operation. A second incentive of PTC is that wind developers can receive a 30% investment tax credit (ITC) in place of the PCT. This only applies if the projects are placed in service between 2009 and 2013. Lastly, a third incentive of the PCT is providing grants that cover up to 30% of the renewable energy projects. This program is under the Department of Treasury and is effective for wind projects that are placed in service in 2009-2010 or construction that is begun by 2010 and plans to be in service before 2013.

A recent analysis shows that projects that cost $1,500/kW or less are likely to receive more value from the PTC, while projects that cost more than $2,500/kW are likely to be better off with the ITC.

A one-year extension of a key tax credit for the wind industry was included in the fiscal cliff deal that Congress passed in March 2013. The 2.2 cents tax credit for each kWh of energy produced by new wind installations for their first 10 years of operation, has been a major driver for wind development across the country during the past two decades. This will allow all new wind projects that go online in 2013 and 2014 to claim the credit.

This credit is immensely important to the industry, because it represents over 30% of the wind projects' value, according to wind power insiders. Without it, most wind projects just won't happen.

This was confirmed recently, when the "fiscal cliff" was looming over the industry, threatening to reduce or cut the tax credit. Without this life line the industry was doomed. The threat of expiration of the credit wrecked havoc on wind development across the country. The industry came to a screeching halt, and no new projects, repowers, or retrofits moved forward. The entire sector froze, waiting to see if the credit was going to be extended.

As a result, turbine-parts manufacturing and assembly plants laid off thousands of workers, developers put new projects on hold, utilities postponed maintenance of aging turbines, and investors held their breath for the duration. Over 35,000 additional jobs were in jeopardy, and the entire industry was paralyzed.

This represented a loss of momentum, which slowed down many new projects even after the credit was extended. And so, it became quite obvious that, although the wind industry has been around for centuries, in commercial wind energy terms and/or as a profit making institution, it is still in its infancy. It obviously cannot walk on its own. It still needs support to survive, but governments and investors are getting increasingly reluctant to continue providing financing.

So, what would happen if the politicians decide to cut support in the near future? Would that mean an end to the wind industry in the U.S.? This is anyone's guess now, of course, but judging by the fiscal cliff experience of 2012, we dare guess that without the 2.2 cents lifeline, the wind industry might survive but in a much different, weaker form. There are more cliffs coming our way, so we will have a chance see what would happen.

NOTE: California's wind industry has an advantage. Although ultimately it also cannot survive on the production tax credit alone, it is benefiting from the generous 33% state renewable energy standards—California's goal for 2020—in which effort wind and solar are integral part of. And so, politicians, regulators, utilities investors, manufacturers, and installers need to work together to find ways to grow the U.S. wind industry, at least in California. Then California will again lead the way for the rest to follow.

Federal Support for the U.S. Wind Power Industry

Worldwide the wind power industry is driven by various types of government support, which range from tax credits to incentive policies like feed-in tariffs. These incentives have been much larger in several foreign countries than in the U.S., which has helped to spur the manufacturing of wind turbines in Europe and Asia. More recently, however, many countries—especially in Europe—have begun to reduce subsidies for renewables, including wind.

In Europe, feed-in tariffs are among the policy tools that have been used to promote wind power, and have been credited by industry advocates like the European wind energy association with driving renewable energy growth, particularly in Denmark, Spain, and Germany. However, faced with difficult fiscal and economic situations, some European countries have reduced their wind power feed-in tariffs and are taking a more critical look at their renewable energy policies. For instance, in 2010, Spain announced that it would reduce its wind subsidies by 35% from January 1, 2011, to January 1, 2013.

Some of the leading global wind turbine manufacturers, including Vestas and Gamesa, have downsized their operations to remain competitive, while others may place even more emphasis on exporting. China's renewable energy law, which took effect in 2006, is one measure that has driven growth in the domestic market. China introduced a feed-in tariff for wind power generation in 2009.

The Chinese government also implemented various policies to encourage the development of local manufacturing and technology development.

In the U.S., various federal policies also have been instrumental in the development of a domestically based wind power sector, including:

- The production tax credit (PTC)/investment tax credit (ITC), which was renewed in 2012

- Advanced energy manufacturing tax credit (MTC), which reached its funding cap in 2010 (no additional funds were allocated to continue with the MTC)

- Section 1603 treasury cash grant program, which required that wind projects begin construction by December 31, 2011, and be placed in service by December 31, 2012

- Section 1705 loan guarantee program for commercial projects, which includes manufacturing facilities that employ "new or significantly improved" technologies

The wind industry asserts that a national renewable electricity standard is needed to create long-term stability and to attract investment in new turbine production facilities. Without such a standard, the political and economic winds will continue blowing the wind industry around the choppy energy market waters.

Production Tax Credit (PTC);
Investment Tax Credit (ITC)

The production tax credit (PTC) was the main policy tool in the deployment of U.S. wind power, first adopted during the Administration of President George H. W. Bush as part of the energy policy act of 1992 (P.L. 102-486). It has been a significant driver of the recent growth of the U.S. wind industry, but it is not a permanent part of the tax code and has lapsed on a number of occasions.

In each of the years during which the PTC lapsed (2000, 2002, and 2004), meaning that it expired prior to being renewed, the level of additional deployed wind capacity slowed or collapsed when compared to the previous year's total: 93% in 2000, 73% in 2002, and 77% in 2004.

Yet, when the PTC incentive was extended in 2004, 2007, and 2009, the industry responded positively, increasing wind power capacity compared to the previous year. An exception to this trend in 2010 was a drop in wind capacity of nearly 50% from 2009, even with the PTC in place. In 2011, at 6,816 MW, annual installed wind capacity increased by 30% over the previous year. The annual cost of the PTC is estimated at about $1 billion a year.

Congress provided a three-year extension of the PTC through December 31, 2012, as part of the American recovery and reinvestment act. The PTC provides an inflation-adjusted per kWh income tax benefit over the first 10 years of a wind project's operations, which in 2010 was 2.2 cents per kWh, and is a critical factor in financing new wind farms. To qualify, a wind farm must be completed and start generating power while the credit is in place, which would be by the end of 2012. Wind project developers may elect to receive a 30% investment tax credit (ITC) in place of the PTC if the projects are placed in service prior to the end of 2012.

The ITC was extended in 2012, and now AWEA advocates for a phase out of the ITC over six years, which it argues would encourage continued investment in the industry and would allow for extended growth of domestic turbine manufacturing. The Governors' wind energy coalition has called for a multi-year extension of the PTC of at least four years.

Given the uncertainty about the continuation of the ITC, along with the possible loss of other tax benefits, some in the industry have begun to refer to 2013-2014 as "the valley of death" in which wind industry support programs will end without any replacement policies. And it is very possible that they are right.

Advanced Energy Manufacturing Tax Credit (MTC)

The advanced energy manufacturing tax credit (MTC), also referred to as Section 48C of the Internal Revenue code, was authorized in Section 1302 of the American recovery and reinvestment act. The MTC provided a 30% credit for companies for investments in new, expanded, or re-equipped clean energy domestic manufacturing facilities built in the U.S.. Wind, solar panels, and electric vehicle batteries were among the 183 projects funded through the MTC before reaching its cap of $2.3 billion in 2010.

The Obama administration has requested another $5 billion for the 48C tax program. An extension of the MTC was passed through the security in energy and manufacturing act of 2011 (SEAM). It includes one significant change from the original MTC; higher priority would be given to facilities that manufacture—rather than assemble—goods and components in the U.S.

Fifty-two wind manufacturing projects were awarded $364 million in tax credits under the MTC program. Beneficiaries included many manufacturers that were already active, or that had announced that they intend to open new facilities in the U.S.

Other Wind-related Programs

Tax benefits for wind projects include accelerated tax depreciation and bonus depreciation; the latter allowed wind farm owners to write off more than 50% of the capital costs of building a wind farm in 2008, 2009, and 2010. The 2010 tax act increased the first-year bonus depreciation to 100% for new qualified property acquired and placed in service between September 8, 2010, and December 31, 2011, rather than 50% for the qualifying property. Bonus depreciation dropped to the lower 50% rate in 2012.

Another ARRA incentive is a grant system administered by the U.S. Treasury Department. In lieu of tax credits, wind projects can receive a cash payment of up to 30% of the qualified capital costs. The Section 1603 treasury cash grant program allows developers to opt

for a cash payment instead of a tax break. To qualify, construction had to begin by December 31, 2011. Wind projects under construction by year-end 2011 were to be placed in service by December 31, 2012. Many in the wind industry credited the grants for keeping the sector healthy during the 2008 and 2009 recession.

Section 1705 loan program, a temporary ARRA program administered by the Department of Energy, authorized loan guarantees for certain renewable energy projects, including wind projects. The program, which funded 26 projects, including four wind generation projects, expired on September 30, 2011. The combined wind commitments totaled $1.7 billion, or 9% of the $18.8 billion in 1705 program funding. The Caithness Shepherds Flat wind generation project, said to be one of the largest onshore wind farms in the world, received a $1.3 billion loan. GE manufactured the wind turbines. Loan guarantees were also extended to three other wind generation projects: Kahuku Wind Power, Granite Reliable, and Record Hill Wind. No wind turbine manufacturers were funded under the 1705 program.

State Renewable Portfolio Standards

State renewable portfolio standards have encouraged the growth of the U.S. wind energy industry by requiring companies that sell electricity to retail customers to obtain a specified share of their electricity from renewable generation. By the end of 2012, mandatory RPS programs existed in 29 states and the District of Columbia.

The U.S. wind industry has long called for a national standard to increase investor confidence in the sector's long-term prospects. No such measure has passed Congress, although bills to establish national renewable standards have been passed by the Senate on three occasions and by the House of Representatives once.

In conclusion, the expansion of the U.S. wind power manufacturing base of late is impressive, mostly thanks to government subsidies, loans, tax breaks, and other incentives. Its future also depends, at least in part, on government policy decisions. The production costs of U.S. plants that make turbine components appear to be competitive with those in other countries, and the difficulty and expense of transporting very bulky products over long distances serves as an obstacle to import competition.

Nonetheless, there are several obstacles that may impede the expansion of wind energy manufacturing in the U.S., as follow:

1.   The history of government policy-induced boom-and-bust cycles in wind and solar energy devel-

opment and investment may lead wind turbine manufacturers, component suppliers and investors to conclude that future U.S. demand for their products is too uncertain.

2. Wind is a variable power source and the utilities are becoming increasingly concerned with the additional effort and expense this is causing. Energy storage, or combined operation with other energy sources, are the only solutions, but none of these is easily solved.

3. The availability of adequate transmission for power generated by wind farms is limited and expensive. Most wind farms are located at a distance from the urban areas where most electricity is consumed, and a shortage of transmission capacity could hamper wind farm creation or expansion.

Congress will have to evaluate the seriousness of transmission issues in the context of other federal efforts to support wind generation, if wind is to expand on a national scale. And there are other problems.

Environmental Politics

No doubt, wind is feasible, renewable, clean, and a green power source. We in the U.S. need a lot of power, and wind is one of the sources we rely now, and will do even more so in the future. Wind power plants are popping up all over the country and are bringing economic revival to some areas.

Farmers in Texas, for example, are making $10,000-15,000 annually from the land lease of each wind turbine on their property. And as an added benefit, they can also work the land if they want, although few do so for a number of reasons.

On the other hand, there have been numerous claims of wind turbines causing all kinds of illnesses, which experts attribute to a form of motion sickness caused by the low frequencies of the turbine blades, and the visual effects of their non-stop rotation. Shadowing visual effects have been pointed as permanent nuisance, and low-frequency vibrations from the turbines have been blamed for nausea and other symptoms by putting pressure on the ear canal. Any of these effects, however, have been difficult to prove or disprove.

Wisconsin has become a battleground on this issue recently, with noise level studies done on a large wind farm. Several houses, abandoned by their occupants, who blame the turbines for causing a variety of health issues, were converted into test labs for the purposes of

Figure 6-23. Large and nosy wind power plant

determining the noise levels and the effects thereof.

Microphones and other pieces of test equipment were installed in the houses and in nearby locations, and the tests were conducted over the course of several days. The microphones picked up all kinds of noise, including barely-audible, inaudible, and very low-frequency noise generated by the turbines. The noise was most audible in the houses closest to the turbines—about 1000-1500 feet from the site. The low-frequency infrasound noise detected at that distance was directly matched to noise generated by the nearby turbines.

A report on the findings was issued, and the findings prompted the state republicans to act. They called for an emergency moratorium on wind permits in the state, stating the findings of the report as a proof that wind farm turbines generate "dangerous" infrasound levels.

The health experts, however, are undecided if turbine noise could to blamed for the health issues, including nausea, headaches and other symptoms. Such determination was well beyond the scope of the field study, which labeled the issue as "serious," but called for further research into the matter. Such findings would possibly affect the future of the industry, so much more thorough tests and research must be done before drawing final conclusions and making decisions.

Politicians have been involved in wind power heavily too, but their contribution thus far has been one-way only—that of supporting the manufacturers and installers of wind power equipment. Some more regulation is needed to protect the interests of the minority of people who have been hurt by wind power equipment.

The Political-social Issues

Wind is good for some and bad for others, which obviously creates friction in the communities and a lot of problems arise where there were no problems before wind power showed up.

Some of the key political and social issues of wind power, especially that installed close to population centers, are:

- Wind power siting is not regulated by federal or state laws, so the critically important initial assessment and decision of where to put a wind turbine plant, and what can be expected from it, is left to the local communities.

- The locals, especially these living in small villages, are usually not technology-savvy and lack the necessary technical skills and scientific knowledge to assess the pros and cons of having a wind power plant next door. This can lead to misunderstandings, misconceptions and eventually to bad decisions and friction among the locals.

- The U.S. DOE, EPA, other government agencies, and national labs are emphasizing and over-emphasizing the benefits of wind power, but are not interested in looking at the negative side of the issues. Nor are they interested in providing the locals with unbiased technical information and advice to help them make the right choices.

- Wind power companies are making a lot of money on each turbine they put up, so they do everything possible to sell the locals on the benefits of wind power, often forgetting to point out the downsides, or downplaying them.

- Wind companies have specially designed techniques and contracts with confidentiality clauses that forbid people to discuss the contract points and issues openly.

- In some cases, the wind company salespeople use misinformation and other unorthodox and even illegal methods to sell their product, which has resulted in dividing entire towns and turning neighbors against each other. They are now getting the reputation of *carpetbaggers*, which is not a good thing to be in a supposedly clean and green business.

- The fact that each wind turbine uses many tons of fossils that emit many tons of GHGs during its huge parts manufacturing, transport, installation, and operation is usually ignored or downplayed, which is also not a good thing to associate with a clean and green business.

- The health and social issues caused by large wind turbines—obstruction, flickering, low-frequency noise, bird killing, ice damage, property values reduction, etc.—are ignored and even ridiculed by wind power officials, which is a slap in the face to the locals.

- After 20-30 years of use, the wind turbines inevitably will be abandoned, creating a junk yard on many American hills. At that time, the original installer would be long gone and another set of issues will be left for the locals to resolve.

NOTE: It is hard to imagine that a person, or persons, could make a conscious decision to put a 400 feet tall wind turbine 600 feet away from a rural home with children playing in the back yard. To do this, one must be either totally oblivious to the potential problems at hand (in which case s/he should not be at a position to make any such decisions), or totally careless as of the long-term negative consequences such a monstrosity so close to a home would have on the lives of these children for the next 20-30 years, and even for the rest of their lives.

The tragic part in this case is that the homeowner who allowed the wind turbine to be installed so close to her home most likely has not been properly informed.

The even more tragic part in this case is that once the wind turbine is installed, it is not going away for 20-25 years, and the problems it brought upon the household will also be around and haunt the inhabitants for that period of time as well.

This is actually only a partial list of issues, which could be expanded into several pages of detailed information on the entire spectrum of political, social, technical, financial, and logistics issues surrounding wind power projects, especially these located near populated centers.

With time, we believe, there would be stricter federal and state laws that would resolve the major complaints, so we only hope that the wind industry won't use and abuse the existing laxness in the system to its benefit, and hurt the locals more than it has already done.

HYDROPOWER

Water is required for all life and is used in many productive ways. Water was used for navigation, irrigation, and its power was converted to mechanical energy to perform work in flour mills and other crafts.

Later on it was used to build drainage for wastewater and sewage.

From the very beginning, the U.S. government appreciated the importance of water for supporting human life and daily activities, and established policy on water use in all areas of life, including interstate navigation, flood control, irrigation, etc.

Soon enough scientific methods and policies were developed about water conservation that view water as natural resources. The public health aspects of water and its pollution were addressed since the very beginning as well.

Federal planning was intensified with the development of the country's hydropower potential. Since WWII, federal hydropower policy has become entwined and affected by these and other broader policy concerns. Changes in hydropower policy have also attempted to address severe new challenges caused by the level of national energy consumption and questions of energy.

Hydropower today can easily be divided into large-scale hydro projects, and small- to medium-size projects. The large projects are always government sponsored, paid, and owned, while the other types could be either government or privately owned. In all cases, hydro power is an important energy source of national importance, so the U.S. has had a functional hydropower policy since the beginning of time. It includes a number of laws, rules, regulations, and programs that govern the national water resources, including the hydroelectric power generation industry. The policy has changed with time, as water uses and the related technologies change and develop. Socio-economic and commercial development considerations spurred its growth and are reflected in the changes of late.

The general survey act of 1824 authorizes the President to order surveys of water transport paths and canals of national importance, from a commercial or military point of view, or as necessary to ensure the transportation of public goods and mail. This responsibility was assigned to the U.S. corps of engineers.

The U.S. army corps of engineers (USACE) has been the main authority in the management of the U.S. water resources, their maintenance and use. Initially water management was limited to development of water-based navigation and its safety. This includes the management of all hydro projects in the U.S., regardless of ownership.

The general survey act empowered the military to chart transportation improvements vital to the nation's military protection or commercial growth. Army engineers helped design state and privately sponsored roads, canals, and railroads, and soldiers cleared forests and put in roadbeds. This work was conducted under the direction of the executive branch.

Much of this activity supported river and harbor projects, which the corps planned and undertook, as well as the surveys of roads and canals, and later railroads. Over the years, an elaborate system of roads and canals was developed in many areas of the country. The U.S. Corps of Engineers took the lead in managing the water resources, including flood control and developing the related sciences. Irrigation in the western states and increasing demand for electric power soon were on the top of the list of priorities.

Increased water use and demand for electric power forced new water conservation and better utilization concerns to be added to the list of national priorities recently, with the different disciplines handled by various agencies and organizations. The Federal Energy Regulatory Commission (FERC) has been the main regulatory body for the industry since the late 1970s. And now, FERC is responsible for all efforts related to licensing of new construction, re-licensing, and oversight of existing projects.

FERC officials are responsible for dam safety inspections and environmental monitoring of the affected areas. federal and state natural resource agencies, Indian tribes, and state water quality agencies are involved in the environmental review and decision-making.

The regulatory bodies are: the U.S. environmental protection agency, the Department of Agriculture's forest service, the Department of Commerce's national marine fisheries service, and the Department of the Interior. On the other hand, the national hydropower association supports and lobbies for policies in favor of the hydropower industry.

The Politics

Hydropower politics and policies in the U.S. include a number of laws, rules, regulations, programs, authorities, and agencies that govern the national hydroelectric industry. Federal policy concerning waterpower is one of the oldest in the energy sector, and has been developed over considerable time—even before electricity was in wide use.

The different laws and regulations have changed from time to time, according to different water uses, available technologies, and other considerations. The priority was often switched according to different and competing uses of water, flowing water, and its energy, etc. Increased population and commercial demands also affected the regulatory changes and the growth of the industry.

Federal policies regarding the national water resources were already established long before modern electricity came to being, so previous uses and decisions, as well as government policies and agencies were changed to include the new use of water as energy source.

A major federal agency that has to be credited with the initiation and expansion of hydropower is the U.S. Army corps of engineers (USACE). There was a federal policy regulating interstate waters, dated 1824, as the commerce clause, which implementation was limited to development of navigation and its safety. Shortly thereafter, with the general survey act the USACE took the lead in managing water resources.

By the 1850s, flood control was added to its list of tasks and a need to better understand the water related science and technology became urgent. Most of the work on the early improvements was legislated by rivers and harbors legislation and was executed USACE.

By the end of the 19th century, new technical demands were being made for water management, including large scale irrigation in the western U.S. states, and soon thereafter demand for the recently developed electric power in all states became a priority.

The government regulations and the interests of the various government agencies and private organizations drive the hydroelectric industry. Since 1977 the federal energy regulatory commission (FERC) has been the main regulatory body for the industry, and is still responsible for licensing new hydro projects construction. FERC also oversees the re-licensing, and operations oversight of existing projects, including dam safety inspections and environmental monitoring.

The environmental concerns, issues, and implications are managed by federal and state natural resource agencies, Indian tribes, and state water quality agencies. The U.S. environmental protection agency (EPA), the U.S. Department of Agriculture's forest service, the U.S. Department of Commerce's national marine fisheries service, and the U.S. Department of the Interior are responsible for different areas of the hydropower projects development in the country. The national hydropower association is a private trade organization, an industry advocate, which lobbies for policies in of the hydropower industry.

The U.S. Department of Energy's hydropower program is responsible for research and development of new or more efficient technologies and processes. The hydroelectric industry is assisted by a number of government programs, such as the renewable portfolio standards and various other financial incentives, including the production tax credits (PTC/ITC), loan guarantees, clean renewable energy bonds (CREB), qualified energy conservation bonds (QECB), and other instruments.

One of the first attempts to control and regulate the hydropower projects in the U.S. was through the federal power act enacted in 1920. The act is still in force, with additional legislation tacked to it to reflect the changing times. The federal power act created the federal energy regulatory commission (FERC) as the sole licensing authority for hydroelectric power generation. FERC's responsibilities grew with time, and now include conservation and protection of natural waterways and the wildlife within them.

The act also outlined FERC's jurisdiction over federal streams and other bodies of water under U.S. Congress' jurisdiction to regulate commerce among the U.S. states and foreign countries. In other words, FERC is the ultimate authority with unlimited power to oversee any and all activities on any U.S. waters.

A number of amendments to the act included wildlife protection and the responsibility for studies into the feasibility of increasing hydropower capacity of the existing dams.

Lately, environmental protection and safety of energy projects, including hydropower generation, have been high on the politicians' agendas. Because of that, the U.S. Congress has passed a number of additional laws and regulations on the subjects, affecting the hydropower generation in the country.

The Legislation

Some of the legislation, regulations, and activities affecting hydropower of the past and present are:

The Northwest Ordinance

Early Americans used the rivers and lakes for navigation and transport. Over time these waterways became the trading routes, which carried the new world's goods and soon became the object of rivalry between competing colonial powers.

With this heritage and its independence, the fledgling government established control over its borders, with trade in mind. With the country's vast unsettled western frontier, early policy and precedent was set in 1787 by the Northwest Ordinance, which established free usage of its interior waterways and connecting portages. These conditions would be included in the lands of the Louisiana Purchase in 1803, which doubled the country's size, and later in all territorial acquisitions.

The many rivers also provided the basis for advantageous commerce not only for transport, but also because waterpower would run water wheels and mills, generally in rapids or waterfalls and where water flow was sufficient.

The General Survey Act

The general survey act was passed in the early 1800s ruled all subsequent rivers and harbors acts that were passed throughout the 19th century except during financial crises and the Civil War. After the war, internal improvement spending rose considerably, particularly in the eastern states with abundant water resources.

During this time, new demands for flood control improvements began appearing, along with a new source of power from steam. By the 1830s, commercial success of steamboat navigation and transport became widespread and pushed demand for more river and canal improvements. With much the same technical expertise as needed for earlier roads and canals, the U.S. corps of engineers was assigned to conduct scientific studies of rivers and other water bodies to improve the country's water system.

The Endangered Species Act

The Endangered Species Act (ESA) was passed in 1973 to protect endangered species from the negative effects of anthropogenic actions. ESA distinguishes between endangered and threatened species, and protects them both. The federal agencies are responsible for ensuring that no activity is allowed to affect the listed species or modify their critical habitat—whatever the cost.

ESA protects aquatic types with migration patterns and feeding habits that might be affected by the construction of a dam. An example of affected species is the depletion of salmon population in the Columbia River due to the construction of 75 dams.

ESA had become the main hindrance in licensing new hydropower projects, because it has priority over any and all other government and state activity. It is, therefore, the first barrier in the permitting process that supersedes any construction project. And since there is always a protected species or two in any one area, new projects are delayed or cancelled. This makes it very hard to initiate a hydropower project, since private investors are hesitant to get involved in the complex and expensive permitting process with uncertain outcomes.

Electric Consumers Protection Act

The electric consumers' protection act (ECPA) was an amendment to the federal power act that was voted into law in 1986. It contained mainly provisions for wildlife protection, that requires FERC to give equal consideration to non-power generating values such as the environment, recreation, fish, and wildlife, as are given to power and development objectives when making hydroelectric project licensing decisions. All major studies are now to be performed even before the project is authorized.

Please note that permitting and authorization are two different things. A project must be authorized, before it can go into permitting stages. So, the thought of applying for such a project is like entering a life-size labyrinth with your eyes closed. You have no idea of the place or size of the obstacles or which direction to follow. In addition to complicating the already complicated picture, ECPA also caused a major increase in licensing fees.

And to top it off, a provision in ECPA requires FERC to work with fish and wildlife agencies to investigate and enforce mitigation of environmental impacts caused by existing and operating dams and hydropower plants. This, of course, is another long and expensive process, and the development of, and compliance with, we have no information on.

The Hydropower Improvement Act of 2011

The hydropower improvement act (HIA), voted in 2011 is actually a resurrection of a 2010 proposal that was never voted on, because the congressional session terminated before the bill even reached the floor. HIA seeks to substantially increase the capacity and generation of renewable hydropower resources in the U.S.

The bill was introduced shortly after the Fukushima disaster and its timing was considered questionable, or rather politically motivated. Nevertheless, HIA sets a dynamic hydropower agenda for the nation, some of the key highlights of which are:

- Establishing of a competitive grants program, and directing the Energy Department to produce and implement a plan for the research, development, and demonstration of increased hydropower capacity

- Providing the federal energy regulatory commission with the authority to extend preliminary permit terms, to work with federal resource agencies to make the review process more efficient for conduit and small hydropower projects, and to explore a possible two-year licensing process for hydropower development at non-powered dams and closed loop pumped storage projects

- Calling for studies on the resource development at bureau of reclamation facilities and in conduit projects, as well as on suitable pumped storage locations. Importantly, by utilizing existing authorizations, the bill does not represent new funding.

It seems now, as demonstrated by the rare bi-partisan approval, that hydropower has more multi-region and bipartisan political support than any other clean energy technology. Hydropower provides about 7% of the total US electricity generation, and over two-thirds of the entire renewable electricity. It cheap and uninterrupted, so it is a major contributor to our energy independence and security.

The Hydropower Regulatory Efficiency Act of 2013

The hydropower regulatory efficiency act of 2013 (H.R. 267) is a bill that was introduced into the U.S. House of Representatives of the 113th U.S. Congress on January 15, 2013. It passed the House on February 13, 2013 by a vote of 422-0. It is now awaiting Senate's attention and disposition.

The act is intended to change some of the regulations in the U.S. surrounding hydropower by making it easier for smaller hydropower stations to be created. According to the bill's proponents, current regulations are unwieldy and represent a significant hurdle to creating more hydropower plants.

The legislation would also require the federal energy regulatory commission (FERC) to find ways to further improve the regulatory process. H.R. 267 would also amend the public utility regulatory policies act of 1978 (PURPA) and the federal power act. Currently, hydropower projects that produce 5,000 kilowatts or less of power can avoid having to get certain licenses, and H.R. 267 would raise that amount to 10,000 kilowatts, facilitating the speed at which smaller hydropower projects could be built.

H.R. 267 would basically alter some existing regulations to make it easier for smaller plants to get approval quickly, because presently it takes about five years for small to medium size hydropower projects to get approval.

The Hydropower Improvement Act of 2013

The hydropower improvement act of 2013 (S.545) passed out of the U.S. Senate committee on energy and natural resources (ENR) in May 2013, by a voice vote and moved to the full Senate for consideration. The bill would encourage expanded hydropower production by removing some licensing barriers for small hydropower

development. It would also require a study on the feasibility of a streamlined two-year permitting process at existing dams and pumped storage projects, a move that could help boost hydropower investment across the nation.

The bill does not provide authorization to build new large dams, but will help to streamline the permitting process for the construction of many small size dams and hydropower generating plants. This is especially important for the state of Washington, which is blessed with lots of water, and where hydropower is a major power source.

The U.S. DOE Hydropower Program

The U.S. DOE's hydropower program is a part of the DOE office of wind and hydropower technologies, which mission is to conduct research and development that will improve the technical, societal, and environmental benefits of hydropower and provide cost-competitive technologies that enable the development of new and incremental hydropower capacity.

The research is performed in conjunction with other federal agencies and groups involved with the industry. Progress and results are evaluated through the actions of a technical committee of experts. The three national laboratories involved with the program include: Idaho national laboratory, Oak Ridge national laboratory, and Pacific Northwest national laboratory.

A number of private research and development programs at universities and other organizations and financial incentives are also used to assist, improve, and promote hydropower. There are also a number of financial incentives helping the industry, such as: the renewable portfolio standards, renewable energy production tax credits (PTC/ITC), loan guarantees, clean renewable energy bonds (CREB), and qualified energy conservation bonds (QECB).

The National Hydropower Association

The national hydropower association (NHA) has several policy priorities on their agenda, such as the implementation of a new and more efficient regulatory process. According to NHA, expediting a two-year licensing process for minimal impact projects would allow hydro to be competitive with other renewable technologies. A tax credit parity is also on the agenda, because hydropower currently receives only half of the rate per kWh under the PTC/ITC, and it should be increased to be equal with other renewable technologies.

Incentivizing renewable electricity production, extending the MTC, CREBS, and ITC, as well as establishing a federal clean and renewable energy standard that promotes hydropower development, are also on the list of NHA priorities. Continued investment in research and development for both conventional and non-conventional hydropower projects is on the bottom of the list, but has a great importance for the further development of hydropower in the U.S.

Hydropower Status Change

Hydropower is not officially recognized as renewable energy and some U.S. legislators want to amend the state constitution to say that hydropower is a renewable energy source. A piece of legislation called house joint resolution 4200 introduced in Washington state senate intends to change the state constitution to recognize hydropower as a renewable energy resource.

A voter-approved initiative 937 passed in 2006 by vote of 52%. It requires utilities with 25,000 customers and more to buy at least 3% of their power from renewable sources, such as wind and solar. This amount is to be gradually increased to 9% by 2016, and then to 15% in 2020. But amazingly enough, hydropower is not considered renewable.

Proponents claim that hydropower owners and operators are unjustifiably punished by the exclusion and as a result they, and the economic development of the state, are suffering.

The opponents, in the legislature argue that this would force the utilities to buy power they don't need from wind or solar, and to sell hydropower to California and other states. This in turn would drive up the cost of electricity, and make the state less attractive to businesses that are considering moving there.

A dedicated group, citizens for protecting our Washington energy rates (POWER) was launched with the backing of state legislators, chambers of commerce, ports, business organizations, cities and public-utility districts, and others with the intention to amend the initiative.

Environmentalists, however, argue that the initiative is working well and doesn't need to be amended. The purpose of the initiative is to encourage development of other types of renewable energy and to build on the hydropower tradition, thus ensuring that tomorrow's energy sources are cleaner than today. Diversifying the renewable energy sources is the point, they claim. They are worried that, while two-thirds of the state's power comes from hydro, there are no new power sources to fill the gap.

Upgrades to existing hydropower plants count toward the renewable requirement and made up about 22% of renewable energy sources used to meet the requirement in 2012. Wind brought the most power for the utilities to meet the renewable standard, with hydropower close second.

The initiative has prompted development of new energy sources, bringing jobs and money to the state's economy, but the proponents hope that the proposed resolution will encourage more debate about renewable standards and whether the standards written into the initiative are in the best interests of the state. Open discussions would bring out more fairness as far as the power generation and rates go.

To amend the constitution, however, the new resolution has to go through a public hearing and votes in House and Senate committees, votes by the full House and Senate with two-thirds of the members voting in favor, and be signed by the governor. If all of that happens, the question would go to the voters, where a majority vote is needed for passage.

At the very least, this action will open the doors for a debate: is hydropower a renewable energy source, or not? The people will have the last word in this case.

The Debate…Large vs. Small

Measures favoring emerging renewable technology and "green" energy often exclude "large" hydropower, due to significant and permanent environmental damage done by large dam and storage reservoir construction. Small projects are perceived as having lower impacts, so some of them are included in the list of "green" technologies and projects.

Research has been done on this subject by a number of organizations, and a paper was recently presented that points out that valid comparisons must compare impacts per unit of output. The impacts of a single large hydro project must be compared with the cumulative impacts of several small projects yielding the same power and level of service.

For example, small projects generally require a greater total reservoir area than a single large project, to provide the same stored water volume. Nevertheless, small hydropower induces lesser damage to the immediate land area, and is a necessary and useful complement to the electricity generation mix, particularly in rural areas.

However, it is also true that the most fundamental determinant of the nature and magnitude of impacts of hydropower projects are the specific site conditions rather than the scale of the project. It is also important to optimize development with respect to the complete river system in the project design and development.

As a confirmation, in February 2013, the U.S. House of Representatives voted overwhelmingly, 422-0, in favor of a bi-partisan piece of legislation, the hydropower regulatory efficiency act of 2013, H.R. 267 (see previous paragraphs for details) to streamline the process for approving the construction of new, smaller hydropower and conduit power projects. The U.S. Department of Energy is charged with conducting a study on pumped storage opportunities, and potential hydropower generation from existing conduits.

A national hydropower association's study estimates that there will be nearly 1.0 million hydropower related jobs created by 2025. These are well paying jobs in manufacturing, construction, engineering, and operation. This is also a good step towards increasing our hydropower capacity, which could double over the next few years.

The U.S. is blessed with abundant energy resources, and during the last several years we have more clearly understood the importance of utilizing them all in harmony, as needed to increase our energy output and create new jobs. We finally have some hope for energy independence and low energy costs. H.R. 267 is a path towards converting this opportunity into reality. It is a good and logical step towards making better use of this renewable source of energy.

There are a number of government programs that support the development and operation of hydropower generation in the U.S. Some of these are the: renewable portfolio standards(RPS), the renewable energy production tax credits (PTC), loan guarantees, clean renewable energy bonds (CREB), and qualified energy conservation bonds (QECB).

At the same time, the U.S. Department of Energy's water power program researches, tests, evaluates, and develops innovative technologies capable of generating renewable, environmentally responsible, and cost-effective electricity from water resources. This includes hydropower as well as marine and hydro kinetic energy technologies and projects.

All these programs help in the effort to develop a stable hydropower industry in the U.S. by providing financial, political, technical, and administrative support.

Dam Failures

Dams are basically a cement barrier flung across flowing river water. They slow down the river flow, which usually creates a large lake on the upstream side of the barrier. A section of the dam, called a spillway, allows water to flow in a controlled way. The water flows either intermittently or continuously, and in many cases hydroelectric power generation plants are installed on the downstream side of the spillway.

Dam structures are under immense pressure by the water in the lake above. They, like time bombs, are loaded and ready to explode at the right time. This can happen when a dam is broken, resulting in serious destruction of the downstream environment and the population. Dam failures are rare, but the immensity of damage and loss of life when they occur makes them comparable to that of atomic bombs.

For example, the failure of the Banqiao Reservoir Dam (see Case Study following) in Henan Province, China in 1975 caused the largest number of casualties in the history of large dam building. 171,000 people were killed, and 11 million people lost their homes. A number of other dam failures have been recorded, and more dams are feared to fail in the future, as many world dams are quite old and some have outlived their life expectations.

Case Study: Banqiao Reservoir Dam

Banqiao reservoir dam was a large dam on the Ru River in China, the construction of which started in 1951 and was finished at a record time in 1952. The rush job—under the supervision of Soviet engineers and consultants—as well as the lack of hydrology data in the region, produced a dam structure that was below even the laxest Chinese standards. The dam was made of clay and was about 80 feet high with maximum discharge rate of 1742 m³/s.

Following the 1954 Huai River great flood, the upstream reservoir of Banqiao was extended and the Banqiao Dam was increased in height by additional 10 feet. The total capacity of the reservoir at that point was nearly 400,000-acre-feet, with additional 300,000 acre feet reserved for flood storage.

The rush job, accompanied by engineering errors, resulted in cracks in the dam walls and the sluice gates soon after the completion. A fix, resulting in another rush job, was designed and executed by the Soviet engineers, who proudly called the structure the iron dam, which, according to the Soviet advisors, was unbreakable.

For 20 years the dam did its job, but another great flood in August 1975, following Super Typhoon Nina that dumped a year's worth of rain in 24 hours, caused a lot of damage in its structure. Following a series of miscommunications and operating errors and sedimentation blockage of the sluice the operators at Banqiao Dam sent the first dam failure warning via telegraph. Soon after, a smaller Shimantan Dam broke upstream.

A half hour later, the water level at the Banqiao dam crested three feet higher than the wave protection wall on the dam, and it too collapsed.

Figure 6-24. The unbreakable Banqiao Dam

As if in a domino effect, this precipitated the failure of 62 dams in total. Over 15 billion m³ of water were released in total downstream as result of the multi-dam failure. This created a wave six-miles-wide and over 20-feet high, which rushed unobstructed onto the plains downstream at a speed of over 30-miles-per-hour. The water flooded an area of 35 miles long and nine miles wide, creating large temporary lakes where fields and villages stood before. Seven counties, thousands of square miles of countryside, and countless communities were inundated.

Evacuation orders had not been fully delivered due to weather conditions and poor communications. Telegraphs failed, signal flares fired by the military were misunderstood, and the flood caught messengers. When the flood hit the unprepared populace, tens of thousands were carried downstream and many others fled their homes.

The Chinese officials blamed the abnormal rain for the dam failure, calling it a natural, as opposed to man-made, disaster. The poor engineering and shoddy construction were not considered as part of the failure. In an attempt to protect other downstream dams, a number of flood diversion zones were created, where the population was evacuated and entire areas inundated. In addition, the army deliberately destroyed several dams to release water in desired directions.

Nevertheless, several of the flood diversion areas downstream of the dams soon overflowed and failed, forcing the creation of additional flood diversion zones and evacuations. Additional dams were bombed and destroyed in an attempt to control the flood and protect the large dams downstream.

Major roads and railroads in the affected areas were out for days, as were other crucial communications lines. Over 40 thousand soldiers were deployed for disaster relief, but they could not prevent most of the failures and communication disruptions. Two weeks later, over a million people were still trapped by the waters, and relied on airdrops of food and disaster relief. Epidemics and famine erupted among the trapped survivors.

The final results were about 230,000 people killed during and after the dam's failure, six million buildings collapsed, and 11 million residents were affected one way or another. There are many such examples in the recent history of that part of the world, and a lot of lessons were learned, so we can only hope that such disasters will not happen again.

Case Study; The Rampart Dam

The Rampart Dam, 31 miles southwest of the village of Rampart, Alaska and about 105 miles west-northwest of Fairbanks, Alaska was supposed to be one of the most remarkable hydro projects in the world at the time. The U.S. Army corps of engineers proposed to dam the Yukon River in Alaska and construct a hydroelectric power plant on it.

The dam would have created a water reservoir roughly the size of Lake Erie, which would have made it the largest man-made water reservoir in the world. The dam was to be a large concrete structure 530 feet high and 4,700 feet long. The hydro power plant would have generated between four to five GW of electricity, depending on the seasonal river flow changes.

The project was supported by many politicians and businesses in Alaska, but was, nevertheless, canceled in response to numerous objections. The local Native Alaskans protested the planned inundation of nine villages, and conservation groups would not allow flooding of the large Yukon Flats wetlands, since it is a breeding ground for wildlife and waterfowl. The high cost of the dam and the limited benefit to mainland America was another critical objection.

Finally, when the U.S. Secretary of the Interior at the time, Stewart Udall, weighed in formally and opposed construction of the dam in 1967, the project was shelved for good.

And then in 1980, U.S. President Jimmy Carter created the Yukon Flats national wildlife sanctuary, which put the final nail in the dam's coffin by formally protecting the area from development and permanently disallowing any similar projects in the future.

There is a lot of unused water in the U.S., but this case is an example of how using this natural energy source is not as easy as it sounds. This case also reflects the immense power of the U.S. politicians, who with one stroke of a pen can stop a major development.

NUCLEAR POWER

Our relation with nuclear energy started with a great bang—literally. It all started that ominous day of August 1945, when the U.S. dropped the world's first A-bombs on Hiroshima and Nagasaki. On one hand, this precisely-executed military act put an end to the Japanese aggression and ended WWII, thus saving many lives and re-establishing the U.S. position as a world leader. On the other hand, however, in one instant of infamy that will always be with us, this barbaric action of world proportions completely destroyed the two cities, killed thousands, and brought enormous suffering to many other thousands.

Looking at both sides of the Hiroshima and Nagasaki bombing makes it hard to summarize the action as good or bad, which is the case with most political decisions as well. They are usually partially good and partially bad—according to those who are affected. This is the case now, with politicians trying to decide how to handle nuclear power generation.

On one hand, it is the best, most powerful, most efficient, cheapest, and cleanest fuel available to man, but on the other hand it is also the most dangerous ever. Politicians are stuck in a catch 22-scenario, so we see a lot of hesitation and doubts on the nuclear issue around the globe now.

In any case, our relations with nuclear power have been growing lukewarm for these and a number of other reasons. Things got even more complicated after the Chernobyl accident, and even more so after the Fukushima nuclear plant accident. While we could blame inferior Soviet nuclear technology and poorly trained operators for the Chernobyl accident, Fukushima was constructed with superior and up to date U.S. made technology, which was thought to be indestructible, and optimally trained operators. Nevertheless, it was destroyed. The malfunction caused the reactors to explode and spread nuclear radiation over a large area.

What followed was sad for Japan and around the world at the same time. Politicians took action—which appeared ridiculously extreme in some cases—to avoid similar disaster in their countries. Germany went so far as deciding to shut down all nuclear plants in the country, while France kept going on as if nothing happened. The reaction in the U.S. was mixed, with lots of talk about nuclear safety, but very little was done on the matter.

The Hiroshima and Nagasaki bombings will remain as a reminder of the two awesome powers of our age: political decisions and nuclear energy, so that now nobody ever questions their potential. We should always keep in mind that the politicians make things happen. These things, however, can be good or bad. Hiroshima and Nagasaki are reminders that a political decision made by a dozen old men can destroy entire cities and kill thousands.

Figure 6-25. U.S. nuclear power plant

Nuclear power has ominous powers. A small package of nuclear materials deployed in nuclear power plant can provide electricity for an entire city, while a similar package deployed in a nuclear bomb can devastate a city. Although few in number, the nuclear power plant accidents of late are a constant reminder of the awesome powers of nuclear energy, and how it does not choose its victims. We now know that it can kill not only enemies, but also anyone who happens to be in its path.

In the beginning...

The Manhattan Project is the granddaddy of nuclear power. It is what started the nuclear power development in the U.S., resulting in the first atomic bomb ever. In August 1939, prominent physicists drafted a letter, warning of the potential development of extremely powerful bombs of a new type by the Germans. It urged the U.S. to take steps to accelerate the research into nuclear chain reactions and build uranium ore inventory.

Albert Einstein was one of the co-signers of the letter, which was delivered to President Franklin D. Roosevelt. The advisory committee on uranium was formed to investigate the issues raised by the letter. The committee reported back to Roosevelt in November 1939, that uranium would in fact provide a possible source of bombs with destructiveness vastly greater than anything now known to date.

Building the nuclear materials inventory was task number one, which was to be brought to fruition by the Oak Ridge facility in Tennessee. It was to produce enriched uranium for the first atomic bombs. The Oak Ridge site was selected because of ample supplies of water, good source of labor, and a lot of available electricity. It was spread over 56,200-acre site in a tightly controlled security area, spanning three Appalachian valleys.

Work on the plant construction began in 1942, with a preliminary goal of using two methods of uranium enrichment: gaseous diffusion and electromagnetic separation. Since it was uncertain which method was more likely to succeed, both had to be tried, so two different uranium processing plants were build. The Y-12 plant utilized calutrons for the electromagnetic separation method, while the K-25 plant used gaseous diffusion.

A third facility known as X-10 housed a graphite plutonium production reactor and the facilities needed to extract plutonium from the irradiated fuel to prove the feasibility of scaling up the lab experiments. Work with the reactor started in November 1943, and four months later the world's first few grams of plutonium were produced.

The Y-12 plant was designed to use the electromagnetic separation method, and started production in November of 1943. The Y-12 plant consisted of nine main processing buildings and over two hundred support buildings, constructed especially for developing of this process.

The primary process used calutrons—large arrangements of electro-magnets that separated weapons grade U-235 out of naturally more abundant U-238. Y-12 employed 22,000 workers in the peak war years, but the gaseous diffusion process at the K-25 Plant proved to be more effective for uranium enrichment and Y-12 was mothballed at the end of the war. Later the massive Y-12 facility became a nuclear weapons production facility and large-scale lithium separation plant, a material critical to the hydrogen bomb.

The K-25 Site occupied a 1,700-acre, and was the last of the big Oak Ridge sites to become operational. It was the world's first gaseous diffusion plant, the method of uranium enrichment with the best theoretical basis, championed by the British, but which had never been tried in practice until then.

K-25 consisted of 50 four-story buildings totaling 2,000,000 square feet. It contained a series of over 1,000 huge cells linked in a cascade through which uranium hexafluoride gas traveled, with small fractions of the U-235 isotope separated by a barrier material with microscopic pores. After a number of trials, it was decided that K-25 would produce partially enriched feeder material for the Y-12 process.

By the spring of 1944 neither plant was producing any usable nuclear materials. A lot of risks and effort, and even greater amount of money was poured into the Oak Ridge project. A third technique, thermal diffusion, was developed and 2,142 columns, each over 40 feet tall, were built within 90 days.

By the beginning of 1945 none of the processes worked as designed, until Oppenheimer introduced a desperate solution running all three enrichment processes serially. The thermal diffusion process achieved less than 2% enrichment, but this slightly enriched material greatly increased the efficiency of the gaseous diffusion process. When this product, enriched to about 23%, U-235, was fed into the calutrons of the electromagnetic separation process, the result was 84-89% enrichment, good enough for weapons. Eureka! The nuclear age had started.

By the spring of 1945, Oak Ridge had shipped approximately 132 pounds of enriched uranium to Los Alamos to be assembled in the bombs. The Oak Ridge uranium was used in "Little Boy," the bomb dropped on Hiroshima on August 6, 1945.

Nuclear Military Tests

In 1957 about 16,000 U.S. solders, used as guinea pigs, were forced to stand by and witness nuclear tests up close and with minimal, or no protection. The operation, called plumbbob nuclear tests, consisted of 29 consecutive explosions, of which only two did not produce any nuclear yield. Twenty-one laboratories and government agencies were involved in the preparation and execution of the tests, with the full awareness of live human participation.

Operation plumbbob tests contributed to the development of warheads for intercontinental and intermediate range missiles and they also tested air defense and anti-submarine warheads with smaller yields. They included 43 military effects tests on civil and military structures, radiation and bio-medical studies, and aircraft structural tests. Operation plumbbob had the tallest tower tests to date in the U.S. nuclear testing program as well as high-altitude balloon tests. One nuclear test involved the largest troop maneuver ever associated with U.S. nuclear testing.

In addition, 1,200 pigs were subjected to bio-medical experiments and blast-effects studies during operation plumbbob. There were 719 pigs used in various experiments on Frenchman Flat. Some pigs were placed in elevated cages and provided with suits made of different materials, to test which materials provided best protection from the thermal pulse. Most pigs survived, but with third-degree burns to 80% of their bodies. Other pigs were placed in pens behind large sheets of glass at measured distances from the hypocenter to test the effects of flying debris on living targets.

U.S. Air Force, Army, Navy and Marines participated in exercises Desert Rock VII and VIII during operation plumbbob. They were interested in knowing how the average soldier would stand up, physically and psychologically, to the rigors of the tactical nuclear battlefield. Studies were conducted of radiation contamination and fallout from a simulated accidental detonation of a weapon; and projects concerning earth motion, blast loading, and neutron output were carried out.

Nuclear weapons safety experiments were conducted to study the possibility of a nuclear weapon detonation during an accident. On July 26, 1957, a safety experiment, "Pascal-a," was detonated in an un-stemmed hole at NTS, becoming the first underground shaft nuclear test. The knowledge gained here would provide data to prevent nuclear yields in case of accidental detonations—for example, a plane crash. The Rainier explosion, conducted September 19, 1957, was the first fully contained underground nuclear test, meaning that no fission products were vented into the atmosphere. This test of 1.7 KT could be detected around the world by seismologists using ordinary seismic instruments. The Rainier test became the prototype for larger and more powerful underground tests.

Plumbbob released 58,300 kilocuries of radioiodine (I-131) into the atmosphere. This produced total civilian radiation exposures amounting to 120 million person-rads of thyroid tissue exposure, or about 32% of all exposure due to continental nuclear tests.

These tests were the biggest and the most controversial nuclear test series to ever take place in the continental U.S., as part of a study of the effects that nuclear explosions had on structures, people and animals. About 16,000 American troops were exposed, as well as some 1,200 pigs. The final tab still is not known, but a 1997 National Cancer Institute Study estimate found

Figure 6-26. Nuclear explosion during operation plumbbob

that the plumbbob tests could be responsible for causing approximately 38,000 cases of thyroid cancer and some 1900 deaths.

In addition to civilian exposure, troop exercises conducted near the ground near shot "smoky" exposed over three thousand servicemen to relatively high levels of radiation. A survey of these servicemen in 1980 found significantly elevated rates of leukemia, or ten cases, instead of the baseline expected four.

These tests will go into history as the most infamous acts of disregard for human life by the U.S. Armed Forces ever. The results of the tests were not published until much later, so the public was not aware of the real danger the troops were intentionally exposed to. When the truth came out, it reflected badly on the budding civilian nuclear power industry.

Commercial Nuclear Power

President Truman saw the benefits of using nuclear energy for peaceful needs and issued a request two months after the end of World War II. The original legislation went through an 11-month debate in Congress, with the major stumbling block being the issue of whether the new technology should be controlled by the military or civilian agencies.

The military argued that the threat of nuclear energy was too great, so that information about nuclear technology should not be released to private companies. But the new technology needed a lot of work and research to be properly and efficiently used for electricity generation, so scientists were involved in convincing the majority.

The bill passed and transferred control of nuclear energy to a civilian authority. The newly created atomic energy commission (AEC) was tasked to create a policy for domestic control of nuclear power. It was to be developed within a general mandate that all nuclear materials, facilities, and programs were to be controlled entirely by the U.S. government.   The act also prohibited the exchange of information about nuclear energy with other nations. The joint committee on atomic energy (JCAE) was also created and was given a broad authority over virtually every aspect of the nation's nuclear energy policy for military and peacetime applications.

AEA of 1946 received objections from many private corporations that wanted greater access to nuclear information, and opportunity to develop private nuclear facilities. The industry continued to lobby the U.S. Congress for a greater role in the peacetime development of nuclear power. Finally in 1954, President Dwight D. Eisenhower asked Congress to pass new legislation on nuclear energy, which would give the industry a much larger role in nuclear power development.

The atomic energy act of 1954 was created, ordering the AEC to provide private companies with the information they needed to build nuclear power plants. It also authorized companies to build, own, and operate nuclear plants, thus establishing the ground rules under which nuclear power operates in the U.S. today.

One thing that was unclear at the time was of technical nature. Which nuclear power design is the best choice for a nuclear power generation. Boiling water, pressurized water, or some other system were the choices for production of nuclear power, in response to which hesitation, the AEC established the power demonstration reactor program (PDRP) in 1955, which was designed to last about seven years.

The goal of the AEC was to assist private companies by conducting basic research on nuclear power production in its national laboratories, and to subsidize research by private industry. One of the first tasks was to provide adequate fissionable fuels needed to operate nuclear power plants at no charge to companies. All the private companies had to do is provide the financing, construct, and operate the demonstration facilities.

PDRP started by a contract the AEC and the yankee atomic electric company, signed in 1956. It resulted in the construction of the yankee nuclear power plant at Rowe, MA. Seven prototype plants followed under the PDRP until it was shutdown in 1962.

By 1960, most of the roadblocks to the development of nuclear power facilities had been removed, and at that time two nuclear power plants were already in operation. The first one was the Shippingport nuclear power station, on the Ohio River about 25 miles from Pittsburgh. The second plant was the Dresden nuclear power station, in Morris, Illinois.

There was a genuine growth in nuclear plant construction during the next two decades in the U.S. From two in 1960, the number of nuclear power plants grew to 12 in 1965, 17 in 1970, with additional 94 plants in operation by 1990. In the early 1970s, about 5% of the nation's electrical energy was generated by nuclear power plants, increasing to about 11% in 1980, 15% in 1985, and 20% in 1990.

Other countries followed. While almost non-existent in the generation of electrical power throughout the world in 1960, nuclear power grew to account for over 50% of the electrical energy generated in four nations—Belgium, France, Lithuania, and the Slovak Republic—and more than 40% in five other nations—Armenia, Bulgaria, Slovenia, Sweden, and the Ukraine.

The quick growth of nuclear power in the U.S. during the 1970s brought out a number of issues related to the use and regulation of nuclear energy. The major one, however, and one that was impeding the development of nuclear power was the issue of possible accidents and the resulting liability.

Everyone was aware that an accident at a nuclear power plant was possible, and that it might have catastrophic results. The memories of the detonation of "little boy" and "fat man" over Japan were still fresh. At the same time the Brookhaven national laboratory came out with the WASH-740 report, which stated that a nuclear power plant accident, depending on the location and gravity of the event, could result in about 3,000 deaths, 43,000 injuries, and property damage of about $7 billion.

This, of course, stirred the old wounds and raised serious concerns about the overall safety of nuclear power plants. In an attempt to resolve the standstill on the issue, the U.S. Congress passed the Price-Anderson act in 1957, which limited the accident liability to $500 million in government funds. Additional $60 million was available from private insurance companies, thus providing the grand total of $560 million of liability funds per accident.

This ceiling was raised in 1988 to $7.0 billion to be paid out of a fund maintained by fees paid by companies who own and operate nuclear facilities. This in fact relieved the U.S. government of any liability in the case of an accident.

The control over all aspects of nuclear power was still a responsibility of the atomic energy commission, created 25 years earlier. The problem was that it was expected both to promote the use of nuclear energy and to regulate its use, so in 1974 the energy reorganization act (ERA) was passed. It introduced many changes in the way energy issues were managed within the government. The act created two new agencies: the energy research and development administration (ERDA) and the nuclear regulatory commission (NRC).

A key ERDA assignment was to promote the peaceful development of nuclear energy applications, while the primary responsibility of NRC was to monitor the planning, construction, and operation of nuclear power facilities, ensuring their safety and security. Only three years later, ERDA was abolished when the 1977 Department of Energy organization act created a new cabinet-level department by that name. Tasks originally assigned to ERDA were reassigned to the new Department of Energy (DOE). Today, most of ERDA's original mission has been assumed by the DOE's office of nuclear energy, science and technology.

In 1953, President Eisenhower announced before the U.N. gathering that the U.S. was prepared to share information on the peaceful development of nuclear power with other nations. This forced revision of the U.S. policy on nuclear energy, although not much happened for a while. Succeeding U.S. administrations have been more successful in their cooperation with other nations in developing peaceful applications of nuclear energy around the world.

The Nuclear Power Cycle

The cradle-to-grave cycle of nuclear fuel is a long and complex chain of events. It is unlike anything else we use as fuels or otherwise. Its power is immense and can be used to do great things when under control; once out of control, however, it is a vicious killer that has no mercy on anything and anybody that happens to be in its way.

There are many steps and sub-steps, facilities, pieces of equipment and techniques in the nuclear power generation cycle. It all starts with mining the primary uranium ore, U-235 which is similar, but more dangerous than those of coal and other minerals. The ore usually contains about 0.71% uranium at this point, so it is sent to a number of facilities for processing. First, yellowcake, or uranium oxide (U_3O_8) is produced and sent to the conversion plant for conversion into uranium fluoride (UF_6), which is then enriched to 4.5% U-235.

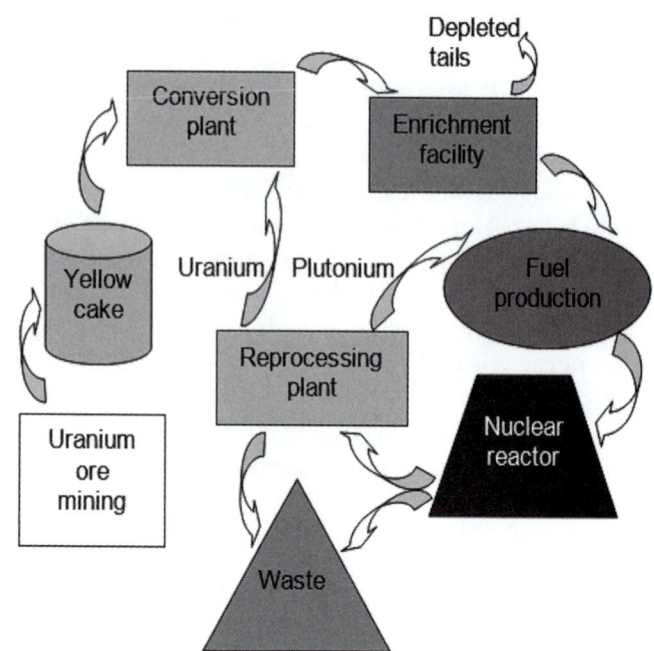

Figure 6-27. Nuclear power lifecycle

Thus enriched uranium is ready for use, and is sent to a fuel fabrication plant to be mixed with other materials and shaped into convenient form for use in nuclear reactor rods. The rods are shipped to the nuclear power plant, and are fitted in a nuclear reactor where they generate electricity for several months.

After a while, the uranium in the rods loses its power, at which point it is taken out of the reactor and is shipped in shipped to a reprocessing facility or to be disposed of. The reprocessing plant processes the spent uranium fuel into lower grade uranium and plutonium, which are used again in the process cycle.

Shipping among all steps of the process is done in specially designed containers that vary in type and size according to materials and location.

The shipping and all other steps of the cradle-to-grave cycle are governed by a number of regulations, and are controlled and supervised by a number of government bodies.

Nuclear Power Regulation

Nuclear power generation—each and every step of the process—is the most regulated power generation industry. There are a number of rules, regulations, laws and so forth that govern each step, each move, and each change. We cannot possibly review all of them in detail, so we will limit this writing to the key regulations.

The nuclear power industry regulations can be divided into several major groups, as follows:

Civilian Uses
- Atomic energy act of 1954, and amendments
- Energy reorganization act of 1974
- Reorganization plans

Nuclear Waste
- Nuclear waste policy act of 1982
- Low-level radioactive waste policy amendments act of 1985
- Uranium mill tailings radiation control act of 1978

Non-Proliferation
- Nuclear non-proliferation act of 1978

Fundamental Laws Governing the Processes of Regulatory Agencies
- Administrative procedure act (5 U.S.C. Chapters 5 through 8)
- National environmental policy act

In more detail:

Atomic Energy Act of 1954

This is the fundamental U.S. law on both the civilian and the military uses of nuclear materials. The civilian use allows for the development and the regulation of nuclear materials and facilities in the U.S. It states: "the development, use, and control of atomic energy shall be directed so as to promote world peace, improve the general welfare, increase the standard of living, and strengthen free competition in private enterprise."

Under the atomic energy act of 1954, a single agency, the atomic energy commission, had responsibility for the development and production of nuclear weapons and for both the development and the safety regulation of the civilian uses of nuclear materials.

Reorganization Plans

Several reorganization plans followed. Plan number three of 1970 established the U.S. environmental protection agency (EPA) and gave it a role in establishing "generally applicable environmental standards for the protection of the general environment from radioactive material."

Reorganization Plan number one of 1980 strengthened the executive and administrative roles of the NRC in emergencies, transferring to it "all the functions vested in the Commission pertaining to an emergency concerning a particular facility or materials … regulated by the commission."

This reorganization also provided that all policy formulation, rulemaking, orders, and adjudications would remain at the sole discretion of NRC.

Energy Reorganization Act of 1974

This act established the nuclear regulatory commission (NRC). The act of 1974 split these functions, assigning to one agency, now the Department of Energy, the responsibility for the development and production of nuclear weapons, promotion of nuclear power, and other energy-related work, and assigning to the NRC the regulatory work, which does not include regulation of defense nuclear facilities.

The act of 1974 gave NRC its authoritative structure and offices. The later amendment to the act also provided protections for employees who raise nuclear safety concerns.

The civilian use of nuclear materials and facilities is licensed and enforced by the NRC as "the commission may deem necessary or desirable to protect health and safety and minimize danger to life or property."

NRC must conform to the act's procedural requirements, including allowing the opportunity for hearings and federal judicial review as and when needed. In some cases, NRC can agree to discontinue its regulatory authority over some materials licensees if the state's regulatory program is compatible with the NRC's as needed to protect public health and safety. The NRC retains authority over all nuclear power plants within a State and any and all exports of nuclear materials from / to the state.

An amendment to the act established compensation and limits on liability for injury to off-site persons or damage to property caused by nuclear accidents.

Nuclear Waste Policy Act of 1982, Amended

This act appointed the federal government's responsible for the permanent disposal of high-level radioactive waste and spent nuclear fuel. At the same time it dictated that it is the generators' responsibility to bear the costs of permanent disposal.

Amendments to the act have transferred the waste disposal efforts to the Department of Energy, which was charged to study Yucca Mountain, Nevada as a potential long-term waste disposal and storage site.

In case that a permanent repository is to be built there, a congressional review of the recommendation would be needed, and NRC will then issue an authorization to construct the facility.

The act also provides for extensive state, tribal, and public participation in the planning and development of permanent repositories.

Low-Level Radioactive Waste Policy
Amendments Act of 1985

This act makes the states responsible for the disposal of low-level radioactive waste generated within their borders, or to use facilities serving a group of states. The facilities will be regulated by the NRC or by states that have such agreements with the NRC. NRC is to establish standards for determining when waste streams are of sufficiently low concentrations or quantities as to be classified as "below regulatory concern."

Uranium Mill Tailings Radiation Control Act of 1978

This act established programs for the handling and control of mill tailings at uranium or thorium mill sites, to prevent or minimize environmental contamination. NRC now has the regulatory authority over mill tailing at sites under NRC license after 1978.

Nuclear Non-Proliferation Act of 1978

This act seeks to limit the spread of nuclear weapons by establishing criteria governing U.S. nuclear exports licensed by the NRC. It also specified steps to strengthen the international nuclear safeguards system.

Administrative Procedure Act

This act governs the procedures of federal administrative agencies and their rulemaking and adjudication. It provides affected persons adequate notice of proposed rules, a chance to comment at a hearing "on the record." Interested parties now have the right to petition an agency for the issuance, amendment, or repeal of a rule. The act also provides standards for judicial review of agency actions.

Subsequent amendments incorporated several other acts that cover a great range of processes, including the access to information. Agencies are required to make their rules, adjudicatory decisions, statements of policy, and so forth, public. The NRC is now also required to hold meetings in public, with exception to matters of national security, and release of information about individuals is no longer allowed.

The act also provides mechanisms for resolving differences by negotiations among a limited number of parties, as needed to reach a consensus and avoid litigation over the disputed rulings. Agencies are now required to use negotiation, mediation, arbitration, and related techniques in place of adjudication, enforcement, rulemaking, or court litigation.

Agencies must also consider the special needs and concerns of minorities, and every rule is to be submitted to Congress for 60 days before being made effective.

National Environmental Policy Act

The national environmental policy act (NEPA) established a national policy aimed to promote, save, and clean the environment. It also established the President's council on environmental quality (CEQ).

NEPA set up procedures for all federal government agencies to prepare and issue environmental assessments (EAs) and environmental impact statements (EISs), which contain statements of the environmental effects of proposed federal agency actions.

Every proposal for a major federal action affecting the human environment now requires a detailed statement on the environmental impact of the proposed action, as well as alternatives. The statement is to accompany the proposal through the agency review process.

The act also established a council on environmental quality in the executive office of the President, which has issued regulations on the preparation of environmental impact statements and on public participation in the preparation of the statements.

NEPA's procedural requirements apply to all federal agencies in the executive branch, except the office of the President, the U.S. Congress, and the federal courts.

Early Nuclear Safety Issues Concerns

The U.S. was first to recognize, and use, the awesome power of nuclear energy for electric power generation, but there were problems from the very beginning, starting with uranium supply uncertainties. To ensure adequate supplies of uranium for national defense, the U.S. Congress passed the U.S. atomic energy act of 1946, creating the atomic energy commission. AEC had the undisputed powers to control uranium mining, including setting the price of uranium as needed to meet national needs.

The high price for uranium ore created the uranium "boom" in the early 1950s, which attracted many prospectors to the Four Corners region of the country. Moab, Utah became the Uranium-capital of the world, when uranium ore was discovered in 1952. Although the U.S. uranium ore sources were considerably less potent than those in some African countries, they were preferred and actively exploited.

Initially, the U.S. government and its military were the largest consumers of uranium, but the orders declined in the 1960s, and finally the uranium procurement program was terminated in the late 1970s. At the same time a new market emerged, and the era of commercial nuclear power plants was born.

Nuclear power brought out a number of other difficult issues. The technology was virtually the same as

Figure 6-28. Nuclear safety procedures

that used for weapons development, so it was classified information. Handing out that information to builders of nuclear power plants meant giving it to private companies, which the military seldom does. The private industry was also reluctant, because the new technology meant spending lots of money on something that had uncertain future, which could result in huge financial losses.

The safety of nuclear reactors was also a matter of concern to scientists and government officials almost from the moment that such facilities were first being seriously considered. Less than a year after it was formed, the atomic energy commission established a group called the reactor safeguard committee (RSC), whose function was to advise the AEC on issues of reactor safety.

Although the prevailing view among the experts was that reactor accidents were highly unlikely, the RSC committee took a different and far-reaching view by taking into consideration the possible consequences for human life and the surrounding environment. It suggested:

1. Nuclear power plants should be built as far from heavily populated areas as reasonably possible.

2. Research should be initiated to provide sound scientific data about the probability of an accident's occurring and the effects that might be expected from a reactor accident.

The creation of the NRTS in Idaho in 1949 was a result of the committee's recommendations. The RSC was reconstituted in 1953 and renamed the advisory committee on reactor safeguards (ACRS). Since that time, the ACRS has functioned as a watchdog on nuclear safety issues, first for the ACE, and later for its successor, the nuclear regulatory commission.

The concerns about the safety of nuclear power plants were now official, and supported by the two WASH-740 reports, which for 15 years seemed to be a matter of theoretical concern of little relevance to the day-to-day issues of nuclear power plant construction and operation.

All fears and precautions expressed by RSC and the WASH-740 were suddenly and dramatically confirmed in practice on March 28, 1979, when news of a serious accident at the Three Mile Island nuclear power plant was made public.

The Three Mile Island (TMI) accident in 1979, as is the case with many industrial accidents, resulted from the right combination of electro-mechanical failures, and human errors. During a routine maintenance operation, a safety device controlling the flow of cooling water through the reactor core failed, shutting down the circulation of water. Temperatures in the reactor core rose quickly, creating the possibility of a meltdown.

To some people, a meltdown seems comparable to the uncontrolled fission reactions that take place in a nuclear weapon. They imagined that a nuclear power plant that experiences a meltdown would explode like little boy or fat man. But such is not the case. The reactor core in a nuclear power plant never contains enough uranium or plutonium to permit the kind of explosion that occurs with a nuclear weapon. A meltdown is dangerous enough in its own way, however. For example, large amounts of radioactive gases are released from the reactor core. And, in theory, enough heat is generated to blow the core and the surrounding building apart, releasing those gases to the atmosphere. To prevent such an event, the core and its related components are housed within a containment dome, a steel-reinforced concrete structure designed to withstand almost any explosion that might occur within the core.

Chernobyl

By far the most serious nuclear accident in history, and the one that confirmed the deadly nature of nuclear power, was the failure of unit 4 of the Chernobyl nuclear power plant, near Kiev, Ukraine. During routine safety tests on the reactor core of Unit 4 on April 25, 1986, two different maintenance crews made a series of mistakes that caused the reactor core to overheat and, eventually, to explode. It is worth noting here that the explosion was of chemical and not nuclear character. But the explosion, nevertheless, was one of the largest ever recorded.

A quarter of the core, with a mass of about 500 metric tons, was expelled into the atmosphere. Temperature reached during the explosion was estimated at over 2,225°C. Fire quickly spread throughout the plant and was extinguished only through the heroic efforts of 186 firefighters from 37 different stations. Many of them lost their life in the process and as a consequence of radiation sickness.

Soon after the accident, Soviet air force bombers were directed to dump large amounts of sand, clay, and dolomite on the burning plant, which contributed to extinguishing the fires. One of the many tragic, and almost immediate, consequences of the Chernobyl disaster were the fatalities among firefighters and rescue workers who were exposed to very high levels of radiation in the days following the fire. In less than a week following the explosion, 29 firefighters lost their lives to radiation sickness.

Control of the fire did not, however, end the threat posed by the explosion. Radioactive gases released from the reactor core were blown to the northwest by prevailing winds, carrying them as far away as the U.K. Officials later estimated that the total amount of radiation released in the explosion was 200 times that produced by the two bomb explosions over Hiroshima and Nagasaki in 1945.

The number of deaths attributable to radioactive poisoning is virtually impossible to know, although the Ukrainian government has estimated that number at 4,229 for the period between 1986 and 1996.

Some authorities suggest that the actual number of deaths from radiation poisoning was much greater.

Figure 6-29. Chernobyl nuclear power plant control center

The number of individuals killed as a result of the Chernobyl accident, however large it may be, hardly begins to estimate the overall damage caused by the accident. By some estimates, as many as a million people in Europe have been sickened or directly affected by the radiation, and 10 million people may have experienced at least some level of health problems as a result of it. In the regions closest to Kiev, such health problems have been studied in considerable detail and found to include an increased rate of thyroid cancer among children and an elevated number of birth defects among newborn children in the Ukraine and the neighboring country of Belarus. Fallout from the explosion has also seriously contaminated large areas of the ground in the Ukraine, Belarus, and Russia.

According to some estimates, 21% of the ground in Belarus is contaminated with one of the most dangerous radioactive isotopes, cesium-137, and Belarusian officials estimate that 16% of their land will still be contaminated in 2016 and beyond. The Ukrainian government's solution to the Chernobyl accident was to construct an enormous concrete sarcophagus that would completely cover the Unit four plant. The sarcophagus was designed to last for hundreds of years, trapping 26 million cubic feet of radioactive material, including 97% of the plant's original fuel rods.

This led to another failure—within five years, high temperatures inside the sarcophagus caused the concrete shell and its supporting pillars to weaken and break apart. By 2004, dozens of holes and cracks, covering more than 10,000 square feet had opened up in the face of the sarcophagus. Concern began to grow in the international community about what some experts called one of the most dangerous nuclear facilities in the world.

In April 1996, a conference was held in Vienna, Austria, at which nuclear experts from around the world initiated a discussion as to the steps that could be taken to make the Chernobyl site safer. As a result a plan was made for French and German governments to work with officials of the Ukraine to construct a new, larger, and stronger shelter for the unit four reactor.

That shelter was to consist of a 20,000-ton steel box, 100 meters by 120 meters by 260 meters (about 300 feet by 350 feet by 800 feet) in size, about as tall as a 37-story office building. The box is to be built on open-land adjacent to the sarcophagus and then slowly slid into place around the deteriorating concrete structure. Plans called for completion of the project in 2008.

The sarcophagus construction lasted 206 days, starting with the construction of a cooling slab under the reactor to prevent the hot nuclear fuel from burning a hole in the base. It took four hundred coal miners to dig the 551-ft-long tunnel. Robots did some of the work because the building became overly radioactive. The difficulties resulted in poor work quality, resulting in faulty seams of the structure.

More than 400,000 cubic meters of concrete and 7,300 tons of metal frame- work were used during the erection of the sarcophagus, which included 740,000 cubic meters of heavily contaminated debris and soil buried inside. Over 60 boreholes were drilled in the structure to allow observation of the interior of the core, and some ventilation shafts were made to allow some convection inside. Filtration systems placed in the holes restrict radioactive material from escaping into the environment.

More work on stabilizing the structure continued, but all that the sarcophagus is expected to last only 20–30 years before requiring restorative maintenance work. But the nightmare is not over yet. Rain-induced corrosion of supporting beams threatens the sarcophagus' integrity. The rainwater leaking through the sarcophagus' roof cracks and holes is becoming radioactively contaminated then seeping through the reactor's floor into the soil.

A new and more sophisticated work is planned to start in 2015, when a new safe confinement is to replace the existing sarcophagus, which will be dismantled and the radioactive material removed. If that would solve all the problems remains to be seen, but one thing is for sure—this is too much to ask from the locals. Many innocent people were killed and many more sickened for the sake of cheap energy production.

One could ask what could be worse than this, and the only answer would be two Chernobyl accidents. Then imagine three…or four Chernobyl-size disasters around the world. Our Earth and the people on it could handle only that much, and such a picture approaches the limits.

The Game Changer…

In the beginning the nuclear industry and some politicians painted a wonderfully rosy picture of the potential of nuclear power as the cure of all energy evils forever. The rosy picture, however, soon proved to be an illusion.

On March 28, 1979, an accident occurred at the Unit Two reactor of the Three Mile Island nuclear power plant in the middle of the Susquehanna River near Harrisburg, Pennsylvania. Although no lives were lost and no injuries attributable to the event that occurred, the accident was to become the most serious setback to the development of nuclear power in the U.S..

At 4 a.m., failure in the non-nuclear, secondary cooling system was followed by a stuck-open pilot-operated relief valve in the cooling primary system. The problem was not corrected on time, so large amounts of nuclear reactor coolant were allowed to escape.

The plant operators did not recognize the loss-of-coolant accident and did not react in time, which was considered to be due to inadequate training. Other reasons were cited later on, such as computer problems, ambiguous control room indicators, etc. An indicator light misled an operator into thinking that there was too much coolant water present in the reactor, forcing him to manually override the automatic emergency cooling system of the reactor.

The reactor core overheated and, although it did not undergo a complete meltdown, enough heat was generated to cause radioactive gases to be released from the reactor core. The gases escaped from the containment dome through the plant's normal ventilation system and into the atmosphere above and around the plant. It took the operators 12 hours to realize what is happening and to contain the gases.

They thought the accident had been brought under control with that. Alas, the nightmare was just now beginning. The operators discovered a huge bubble of hydrogen gas with a volume of about 1,000- cubic-feet that had collected inside the containment building above the reactor core. Hydrogen is volatile and explosive gas, the ignition of which would have resulted in a huge explosion, most likely causing serious damage and destruction.

Confusing communications and the NRC's decision to release 40,000 gallons of radioactive wastewater directly in the Susquehanna River led to even more confusion, and a total loss of credibility with the press and community.

At that time, an emergency evacuation of an area of 10 miles around the plant was recommended. Pennsylvania governor Richard Thornburgh decided to ignore the recommendation, instead ordering the evacuation of pregnant women and preschool children only, and only from the immediate area of about one-mile radius of the plant. What was to stop the radiation going way beyond his imaginary safety zone? Had the hydrogen bubble exploded, the plant and a large area around it might've looked just like Fukushima did in the spring of 2011. The governor, the state and the entire nuclear industry would've been up to their necks in legal troubles.

But the governor lucked out, and the state and

the nuclear industry breathed a breath of relief. The hydrogen bubble gradually disappeared over the following few days and no major damage of the reactor was reported. Five days of nuclear hell, during which time many workers, engineers, and members of the U.S. nuclear regulatory commission worked non-stop to understand and correct the problem were over.

This case set a precedent, which persists even today. It also caused a reversal in public attitudes about nuclear power, with support for nuclear power dropping from 60 to 30% almost overnight. At the same time opposition to nuclear power generation grew from 30 to 60%, and was accompanied by demonstrations and manifestations.

Although the Three Mile Island accident was the worst nuclear power plant accident in U.S. history, it was neither the first nor the last of such events in the country. In November 1955, for example, an experimental reactor at the national reactor testing station (NRTS) in Idaho Falls, Idaho, experienced a partial meltdown. Six years later, a similar accident occurred in a second reactor at NRTS, releasing radiation into the surrounding area. Similar accidents occurred at: the Enrico Fermi plant in Detroit in 1966; in Decatur, Alabama, in 1975, and at the Rancho Secco plant near Sacramento, California, in 1978.

Around the world, in October 1957, a reactor at the Windscale plant north of Liverpool, England, caught fire, resulting in the release of radiation to the surrounding environment. Similar events occurred at the Chalk River nuclear power station in Ontario, Canada, in 1958; in Saint-Laurent, France in 1969; and in Shevchenko in the then-Soviet Union in 1973.

The TMI accident opened the eyes of the public to the dangers of nuclear power. It was now confirming that nuclear power plants are not as safe as promoted by the industry and the politicians. This started a nation-wide opposition against the proliferation of nuclear power for electricity generation in the U.S. It later on grew into a global movement, when many nations started joining the nuclear club.

NOTE: *Nuclear power is a blessing and a curse. When it is under control, it is a blessing; it is the most powerful, efficient, and cost effective way to generate electric power known to man.*

When, however, it is out of our control, it is a vicious killer, second to none that devastates anything and kills everyone in its path.

We have been quite successful controlling it, but from time to time the curse comes out and we then end up paying the highest price possible—losing many human lives.

2013 Status

After the Fukushima nuclear disaster, the U.S. and world nuclear energy entered a period of confusion and hesitation, with only 1.2 GW of nuclear generation capacity installed in 2012 globally, compared to 32 GW of solar power.

In 2011 over $300 billion was invested globally in renewable technologies and projects, vs. a few billion on new nuclear projects. And on top of that, the global nuclear power generation decreased by 7% in 2012 for a number of reasons. Is this what the end of the "nuclear renaissance" looks like?

Obviously, nuclear power is declining as a power source, and is being replaced by natural gas and the renewables, which are beginning to rival it and the other conventional fuels. It won't be too long before these and other alternative energy sources would be able to compete with major power and utilities sectors without subsidies or any other support. The largest investment in solar energy was in utility-scale power plants, followed by rooftop PV installations.

The major problem with nuclear power (besides the safety issues) is that nuclear plants require ever-increasing amounts of time and money to build. This, combined with political and regulatory issues plaguing the industry, means that there is much less construction and growth of nuclear plants. In addition, existing nuclear power plants are running fewer hours, thus producing less energy, which increases the operating expenses while at the same time the electricity prices have to be lowered to compete with other energy sources.

And so, the nuclear industry can now blame the lack in nuclear investment and deployment on its renewable energy cousins, who are now have grown up and are willing and able to fight. The old and tired nuclear power industry is recognizing that the renewables are the new kid on the energy block and, like it or not, have to put up with.

The half-a-century long nuclear power monopoly is now seriously challenged by the renewables, which are also threatening the utilities' business model with their new and unorthodox ways. They are complicating and undercutting the current power-generating capacity and transmission, and are making them less profitable. This is best expressed in Europe (and Germany in particular), where the recent rapid increase in wind and solar energy generation with very low operating costs is squeezing out the utilities and their investors.

The nuclear vs. renewables power generation debate and the battles around it continue. While we may be on one or other side of the battle, we all must realize that we need them all—nuclear, the fossils, and the renewables. We just have to agree on how to proceed for the benefit of humanity. There is no way to make everyone happy, but the goal is clear: finding the right path to energy independence and clean environment. This will surely make everyone happy.

The Opposition

The opposition to the use of nuclear energy for both military and peacetime applications started shortly after the conclusion of World War II. At that time it was directed against nuclear weapons testing and development. During the late 1940s, the memories of the horrible attacks on Hiroshima and Nagasaki were still fresh in the minds of people around the world. The terrible risks of atmospheric testing of weapons that was part of the arms race between the Soviet Union and the U.S. soon became all too apparent.

Nevertheless, the potential benefits of nuclear energy for providing cheap and clean electricity were also quite obvious at the onset. The environmentalists recognized that nuclear power plants are the best available technology for replacing the smoke-belching, pollution-generating, health-endangering fossil-fueled power plants that they so strongly opposed.

Because of that, most environmental groups endorsed, with reservations, the construction of nuclear power plants during the 1950 and 1960s. The sierra club, for example, worked with Pacific Gas and Electric (PG&E) during the early 1960s in an effort to find a suitable location for a nuclear power plant that the utility intended to build. They eventually signed off on PG&E's selection of Diablo Canyon for its plant, although the site was known to contain a major earthquake fault.

The Methodist Church of England went so far as encouraging the development of nuclear by claiming that nuclear energy is an integral part of nature, just as much God's creation as sunshine and rain. Americans also favored the construction of nuclear power plants by a majority of about two to one until the mid-1980s

Organized opposition to the development of nuclear power in the period leading up to that time was largely local and sporadic. Small groups organized to oppose the construction of specific nuclear power plants because of their potential aesthetic, environmental, and/or health effects. People were not sure of what to expect from the new nuclear power. Some were concerned about possible releases of radiation, while others worried about the contamination of local water tables by wastes from the plants. Still others objected to disruption of the national beauty of the local area by the plant and

its operation. The protest tools used at the time included public meetings, forums at local colleges, speeches by outside experts, newsletters and other publications on general and specific nuclear-related issues, and sales of T-shirts and buttons.

A large and vigorous movement opposing the development and use of nuclear weapons grew up in nations around the world. That movement had only modest impact on the arms race, however, with political factors playing a more important role in the continued development of nuclear arsenals in the U.S., the Soviet Union, Great Britain, France and other nations.

Many of the antinuclear weapons groups, however, later evolved into or developed subsidiary programs in opposition to nuclear power plants. For example, the Greater St. Louis Committee for Nuclear Information was created in 1958 to provide information about the use of nuclear energy in weapons development and use. Eventually, however, the organization also embraced questions of nuclear power plant safety and operation.

Early proposals for the development of peacetime applications of nuclear energy met with mixed responses. It was virtually impossible, to some extent, to separate the concept of "nuclear energy" as used for power plants with the kind of nuclear bombs dropped on Japan in 1945. The fears of a nuclear holocaust engendered by the events of Hiroshima and Nagasaki transferred naturally in many peoples' minds to the risks posed by a nuclear power plant.

Perhaps the best-known and most widely studied nuclear power plant protest of the late 1970s was over the proposed construction of a reactor in the town of Seabrook, NH. At first, the plans were met with modest objections from a local environmental group, which later on grew to much more vigorous, especially when groundbreaking actually began for the facility. Protestors created an organization that they called the clamshell alliance, a name that was to go down in the history of antinuclear protests in the U.S. and throughout the world.

The clamshell alliance mounted its first protest meeting on the site of the proposed Seabrook plant on May 1, 1977. More than 2,500 men, women, and children attended that protest, designed to be a nonviolent act of civil disobedience against construction of the plant. When protestors refused to leave the site, police arrested 1,414 of the demonstrators, all of whom were jailed for periods of up to 12 days awaiting trial.

This apparent defeat for the clams (as they came to be called) only strengthened their resolve to fight PSNH's plans for the Seabrook nuclear facility. They continued to conduct protest meetings at the site of the plant over the next decade. In some cases, those protests became violent. In 1979, for example, police used tear gas, attack dogs, and riot equipment to remove more than 2,000 protestors from the construction site. The largest rally mounted by the clams was held at Seabrook on June 8, 1978, when more than 10,000 people showed up to demonstrate against the proposed facility.

Actions of the clams delayed, but did not stop, completion of the Seabrook plant. Even when construction had ended, however, the PSNH's problems were not over. Governor Michael Dukakis, of neighboring Massachusetts, refused to cooperate in a program of emergency planning exercises required before the NRC would license the plant.

Finally, in 1990, the NRC decided to issue an operating license without the cooperation of Massachusetts officials, arguing that the state would certainly cooperate in case a real emergency were ever to occur. Seabrook continues to operate today under the management of FPL Energy.

In spite of opposition from antinuclear groups and its own internal problems, the nuclear industry experienced its greatest success in history in the decade from 1965 to 1975. During that period, 224 nuclear power plants were ordered by industry. In the period of 1972 to 1974 alone, 108 new orders were placed, more than have been ordered in all of history before and since. Nuclear energy seemed on its way to a growing and significant role in the U.S. energy equation as the 1970s grew to a close. Then came the Three Mile Island accident of March 28, 1979, and the antinuclear movement was suddenly and spectacularly revitalized.

On May 7, 1979—two months after the TMI nuclear plant accident—about 65,000 people from a wide variety of groups marched in Washington, D.C., opposing nuclear power development in the country. This was followed by a rally at Battery Park in New York City that drew an estimated 300,000 people.

In 1980 a group of General Electric stockholders formed the GE stockholders alliance against nuclear power, a group working to convince the giant company to withdraw from its huge nuclear power and nuclear weapons programs. At about the same time, a consortium of 30 municipal utilities in western Massachusetts withdrew more than half of its financial commitment to the Seabrook nuclear project. Some regulators also added to nuclear industry woes by shifting financial responsibility for accidents from customers to shareholders.

In response to the public pressure, the NRC and other regulatory agencies added a number of licensing rules and construction provisions to new plants, and new and stricter operation regulations to the existing nuclear power plants. This caused the cost of building and running nuclear power plants to increase 3-4 times or more. Nuclear power was no longer cheap or profitable, so the power companies began to abandon plans for the construction of new nuclear plants.

Instead, the more traditional and less-expensive fossil-fueled power plants became popular. For example, one of the last nuclear power plants to be licensed, the Midland nuclear reactor in Michigan was converted to natural gas operation in 1990 when its was decided that rising costs and public opposition to nuclear power were too great.

And so, the U.S. went back to depend on fossil fuel and nuclear-generated electrical power in the U.S. was put on the back burner. Nuclear power generation rose to nearly 20% by 1988, but then it leveled off and remained nearly constant over the next 15 years. The number of nuclear power plants (about 100) in operation in the U.S. has remained constant ever since.

The last nuclear power plant in the U.S. was ordered in 1978, and no new plants have been ordered in the U.S. (without later being canceled) since 1973.

In Europe a mixed situation exists. Considerable nuclear power capacities have been developed, notably in Belgium, France, Germany, Spain, Sweden, Switzerland and the UK. In many countries development of nuclear power has been stopped and phased out by legal actions. In Italy the use of nuclear power was barred by a referendum in 1987; however, this is now under revision. Ireland also has no plans to change its non-nuclear stance to pursue nuclear power in the future.

Today, the story of nuclear power plants in this country and around the world can be divided clearly into two areas: a) nuclear waste disposal issues, and b) fear of nuclear accidents.

The waste disposal issues are serious, but are not immediate and work is under way to solve them, as we will see later on in this text.

The effects of nuclear accidents are immediate and can be divided into:

1. Post-WWII nuclear weapons proliferation and pre-nuclear electric power generation, when immediately after WWI, the world was faced with a nuclear annihilation and the U.S. was, willingly or unwillingly, forced to launch heavy research into nuclear energy for both military and civil uses. When the clouds of the nuclear wall receded, what was left was a functional nuclear power generating network that provides a lot of cheap power.

2. Pre-Three Mile Island and post-Three Mile Island events, which started the official anti-nuclear movement in the U.S. led by the environmentalists, was kept low level, and looked at as a nonsense and a nuisance by the industry and the politicians.

3. Pre-Chernobyl and post-Chernobyl events forced many governments to pay attention and even get involved in the international efforts to control nuclear power. Nuclear power lost its attractiveness, and was associated with evil and the nuclear industry went into defense mode.

4. Pre-Fukushima and post-Fukushima nuclear power plant failure put the last nail in the nuclear power's coffin. (Or did it?) At the very least, it elevated the nuclear plants safety issues to the highest level possible, making the politicians feel the increased pressure and even forcing them to order the closure of power plants in several countries.

Fukushima Daiichi Accident

Fukushima nuclear plant was another product of the years of post-WWII nuclear power development. Its six reactors were built between 1970 and 1979, using U.S. technology and technical supervision. It employed the latest in safety equipment and procedures. It, however, confirmed that nothing can match the power of Nature. Even superb American-made technology is powerless when faced with its unlimited powers.

It has been two years since the great east Japan earthquake and tsunami hit northeastern Japan and caused the meltdown of the Fukushima nuclear power plant—the world's worst nuclear disaster since Chernobyl. As the people begin to rebuild, signs of a cancer outbreak from the radiation of the troubled nuclear power station are beginning to show.

At 2:46 p.m. on March 11, 2011, the 9.0 M_W Tōhoku earthquake hit the island of Honshu, Japan, which affected the six-reactor Fukushima Daiichi nuclear plant on the east cost. The earthquake resulted in maximum ground accelerations of 5.07-5.50 m/s2 at Units two, three and five, which is 10-15% above their designed tolerances. The ground acceleration values were, however, within the design tolerances at Units one, four and six.

The Fukushima facility was designed with earthquakes in mind, and would've been able to withstand this one, given a chance. But it was not given a chance. The earthquake was followed by a large tsunami, which took advantage of some design discrepancies and overwhelmed the safety measures built into the plant.

At the time of the accident, all reactors in units one, two, and three were operating and underwent an automatic shutdown when the earthquake struck. The reactors in units four, five, and six had been luckily shut down for periodic inspection. When the reactors in units one, two, and three shut down, and units four, five, and six already had already shut down, the entire plant stopped generating electricity, which in turn discontinued the electric power supply needed to operate the plant properly.

At the same time, one of the two connections delivering off-site power for reactors one to three also failed. In response, all 13 on-site emergency diesel generators (two for each of the units one to five, and three for unit six) fired-up automatically, and provided power to the cooling and control systems. All was well, and plant was once again under control.

50 minutes after that, however, all hell broke loose when a 50-Foot high tsunami ran over the 19 ft seawall around the plant, and flooded the basement of the turbine buildings. The water flooded the emergency diesel generators in the basement, as well as all the electrical switching systems in it.

Approximately an hour after the earthquake hit, the generators shut down the power to the cooling pumps of the running reactors. The plant was disabled and the reactors were without cooling and out of control. TEPCO, the plant owner, notified the authorities that a major nuclear accident was underway.

The Fukushima II plant was also struck by the earthquake and the tsunami, but it had design changes which prevented flooding, so it sustained much less damage. A major difference was also that the emergency generators and the electrical control equipment were located in the watertight reactor building, thus allowing power to the plant even after the earthquake and the tsunami. There were also three additional backup generators in buildings higher on the hillside. These generators kept on running, and that would have been enough to save the reactors, but unfortunately, but the switching stations for the reactors' cooling systems for Units one through five were located in the now-flooded turbine buildings. If the switching stations had been on a higher ground, the power would not have been cut.

But as it was, the diesel generators and the switching stations in the flooded turbine buildings failed, so now the emergency power for the control systems was supplied by batteries that were designed to last about eight hours. More batteries and mobile generators were sent, but were delayed by poor road conditions, arriving six hours after the tsunami struck.

Attempts to use portable generators to power the cooling pumps failed, because the switching stations were flooded. The effort then was focused on installing new lines from the grid directly to the cooling systems, which resulted in restoring power to Units five and six, allowing the cooling equipment to be restarted.

The reactor in Unit four was in shut-down mode when the earthquake hit, and all fuel rods had been safely removed, but four days into the incident, an explosion damaged the fourth floor rooftop area of the Unit four reactor, opening two large holes in the outer building wall. The water in the spent fuel pool was feared to be boiling and in danger of evaporation, which would expose the fuel rods and create another explosion.

Reactors five and six were also not operating when the earthquake struck, although, unlike reactor four, they were still fueled. The reactors have been closely monitored, as cooling processes were not functioning well.

In October 2012, Japanese authorities reported that the ground under Fukushima Unit four was sinking and that the structure may collapse.

At the end, after all the heroic efforts of the plant personnel and the numerous "what could've and should've been" discussions, the entire campus of Fukushima nuclear plants I and II, and all six reactors, were shut down and put out of commission. Air and water radiation escaped from the damaged reactors, and 160,000 people living near by were evacuated. Their future, as well as that of the Fukushima nuclear plant, and the Japanese and global nuclear industry are uncertain.

Fast forward. Two years later, the world is slowly recovering from the shock and is moving on, albeit somewhat unsteadily. Not so in Japan. Although the

quick and brave action of the workers at the plant may have averted a nuclear catastrophe, and mass evacuation of the areas affected by the Fukushima radiation saved many lives, the concern now is that the full effect of the disaster is unknown and is yet to be seen.

Since day one, the authorities have insisted that no one has died as a result of radiation from Fukushima, and that the overall effects on human health are small. Nevertheless, results of tests carried out on more than 130,000 children who lived around Fukushima reveal a frightening picture. 40% of the children are showing early signs of thyroid cancer. And on top of that, based on other such cases, the experts say that other radiation-related diseases will not become apparent until 2020, or later.

What's going on? The locals were evacuated within the first few days, and even then only time can tell if any damage may already have been done to their health. People living up to 25 miles away from the plant were not evacuated until six weeks after the accident, and might have been affected even more than the rest.

It also seems now that the food chain in the area is contaminated too. Radioactive materials are showing in all farm produce, such as spinach, tea, milk and beef, some as far as 200 miles away from the plant. And there is water contamination to worry about now too. Fish caught near the plant recently showed radiation levels 5,000 times over the acceptable limits.

The radiation from the damaged reactors has not been fully contained as well. The reactor is being constantly cooled with huge amounts of water, but there is no more storage for the wastewater. There is a daily risk of radiation in form of contaminated air or water escaping the containment areas. And as to make things even more questionable, the owner of the plant is considering dumping thousands of tons of wastewater that is contaminated with tritium and chemicals into the ocean. This would spread the radiation contamination even farther and make things much worse.

And as if this was not enough, the government is pressuring the thousands of people who fled Fukushima in 2011 to return to the area. They have been told that it is completely safe to go home, and that they will not be eligible for any compensation if they stay away.

Experts add to the confusion with conflicting analysis, saying that the radiation released was about 10% of the Chernobyl disaster, while other experts claim that it is closer to 40%. The politicians base their position on radiation risks on the fact that very few Fukushima residents received doses over 100 millisieverts per year, which is unconfirmed threshold for increased cancer

Figure 6-30. Fukushima nuclear power plant blow up

risk. We now know, however, that radiation affects different people differently, and that cancer can occur in much lower doses in many cases.

The Fukushima nuclear disaster showed us, once again, that nuclear reactors are very dangerous. They can cause significant damage to the local environment and the health of populations. They also damage entire national economies, where the financial cost of a meltdown is borne by the public, while the companies that designed, built, and operated the plants sit idly by, unaffected for the most part. There are presently 436 nuclear reactors around the world, and none of them is immune to human errors, mechanical failures, natural disasters, or any of the many other serious incidents that could cause a disaster, which could affect millions of people.

Two yeas after the fact, the Fukushima nuclear disaster is still in the daily news, not only in Japan, but all around the world. It is still affecting profoundly the 160,000 who fled their homes because of radioactive contamination, and continue to live in limbo. These people live with false hope of returning to a normal life—similar to that of the unfortunate Hiroshima and Nagasaki victims.

Amazingly enough, the Japanese politicians are eagerly pushing to move the people back into the contaminated areas and restart the reactors. Driven by political and economic purposes the politicians are acting against the will of the Japanese people and global community. And unfortunately, it seems like the case will be going on for a long time. After a long period of hesitation, the issue of contaminated water from the damaged reactors surfaced in August 2013, when Japan's prime minister ordered finding a quick solution to stop the spread of radioactive groundwater around the nuclear power plant. Amazingly enough, one of the proposed methods includes freezing the surrounding ground.

The proposal came from TEPCO, the plant operator, and consists of setting up a subterranean barrier around the plant by freezing the ground around it. This might prevent groundwater from leaking into the damaged plant and carrying radioactive particles with it as it seeps out into the surrounding soil and ocean waters.

Presently, a forest of storage tanks surrounds the plant, as TEPCO tries to manage the hundreds of tons of water used every day. A suggestion by specialists to bring a flotilla of empty oil tankers, fill them up with the contaminated water and dispose of it somewhere else was rejected for obvious reasons, but where is "somewhere else?"

An underground barrier was already built around the plant to prevent contaminated groundwater from reaching the sea. It is not working very well, however, and contaminated water is seeping out into the bay without any possibility of controlling, let alone stopping, the flow.

This is uncharted territory and TEPCO, with the help of the Japanese government is trying to find a long-term solution. Freezing the water in the subterranean barrier is the next step. But is this a long-term solution? How much would it cost to install and maintain the cooling installation? What if it losses power?

There is no feasible solution in sight, just guesswork, which only complicates the already complicated question of the destiny of nuclear plants around the world. The constant reminder of Fukushima will be around for a long time, and with it the question, "what if" will live in our memory forever.

If history is to be used as a guide, Fukushima will fade away from the minds of politicians soon enough, and nuclear energy will undergo another boom cycle—until the next Fukushima nuclear accident.

NUCLEAR WASTE ISSUES

Plant safety is the major issue facing the nuclear power industry. Another, although not as urgent, issue is that of nuclear wastes. It became gradually as troubling as those surrounding the construction and operation of a nuclear reactor. The use of nuclear materials for power production, scientific research, medical tests and treatments, and other applications generates waste materials that must be disposed of, or recycled.

The disposal is of primary concern, because it has to be done in an environmentally sensitive way. Mining uranium creates very large amounts of rock, dirt, and other waste materials, called tailings, which are in most cases contaminated. In the past these waste materials were used for landfills, roads, and concrete block, brick, and mortar for construction uses.

Soon the dangers posed by these materials became obvious, so the tendency to use them in any settings where humans might come into contact with them discontinued. As of 1999, the U.S. agency for toxic substances and disease registry estimated that there were about 140 million tons of uranium tailings in the U.S. In the vast majority of cases, these wastes are simply left in large storage ponds near the site from which they are extracted. The primary risk posed to human health by these tailings is lung cancer that results from the inhalation of radioactive gases by people living nearby.

The nuclear wastes can be divided into several

groups, the most prominent of which are:
- High-level wastes
- Low-level waste
- Transuranic waste

High-level Nuclear Waste

Spent fuel from nuclear reactors is uranium and/or plutonium removed from a reactor after being used at a point that it can no longer sustain a nuclear chain reaction. About one-fourth to one-third of the fuel assemblies in a reactor core are replaced each year. Spent fuel is "hot" physically and highly radioactive. It is stored at the reactor site in one of two kinds of locations: first in spent fuel (water) pools, and then in special casks in dry storage sites.

High-level radioactive wastes removed from nuclear reactors come in two forms:

- Spent (used) reactor fuel, removed from the reactor, and accepted for disposal
- Waste materials remaining after spent fuel is reprocessed

Spent nuclear fuel is used fuel from a reactor that is no longer efficient in creating electricity because its fission process has slowed. This material, however, it is still thermally hot, highly radioactive, and potentially harmful. Until a permanent disposal repository for spent nuclear fuel is built, licensees must safely store this fuel at their reactors.

Reprocessing extracts isotopes from spent fuel that can be used again as reactor fuel. Commercial reprocessing is currently not practiced in the U.S., although it has been allowed in the past. Significant quantities of high-level radioactive waste are produced by the defense reprocessing programs at Department of Energy (DOE) facilities, such as Hanford, Washington, and Savannah River, South Carolina, and by commercial reprocessing operations at West Valley, New York. These wastes, which are generally managed by DOE, are not regulated by NRC; however, they must be included in any high-level radioactive waste disposal plans, along with all high-level waste from spent reactor fuel.

Because of their highly radioactive fission products, high-level waste and spent fuel must be handled and stored with care. Since the only way radioactive waste finally becomes harmless is through decay, which for high-level wastes can take hundreds of thousands of years, the wastes must be stored and finally disposed of in a way that provides adequate protection of the public for a very long time.

The different types of nuclear wastes can be also divided into:

Commercial High-level Nuclear Waste

Spent fuel pools are large, swimming pool-like, storage areas on site, in which spent fuel assemblies are lowered in and kept submerged under more than 20 feet of water. After several months of "cooling," the nuclear materials can be transferred into a dry storage.

The dry storage method consists of enclosing the fuel in air-tight and leak-proof steel drums filled with an inert gas. Dry-cask storage has been used both for wastes removed directly from a reactor core and for wastes that have had a chance to cool off in a spent fuel pool. The problem with these cylinders is that, as with any other metal containers, they have a tendency to crack and break open, releasing radioactive materials into the surrounding environment.

About 98% of waste fuel is being stored at the power plant from which it had been removed, and the remaining 2% has been removed to other storage locations.

Spent fuel is dangerous, and, with high-level nuclear waste in particular, is very radioactive now, and will continue to be very radioactive for thousands or tens of thousands of years.

Military high-level waste

A second kind of high-level nuclear waste is defense high-level nuclear waste, resulting from programs for the production of nuclear weapons. High-level nuclear waste consists of two kinds of isotopes:
- Isotopes with short half lives that emit high levels of radiation but tend to become less dangerous within a relatively short period of time (a few hundred years), and
- Isotopes with long half-lives that emit somewhat lower levels of radiation but tend to pose a risk for a much longer period of time, usually many tens of thousands of years.

NOTE: The half-life of a radioactive isotope is the time it takes for half of the isotope to decay, that is to give off radiation and change into a different isotope. The two isotopes of uranium present in high-level nuclear wastes, uranium-235 and uranium-238, have half-lives of 713 million years and 4.5 billion years, respectively. Both pose a threat to human health for a long time after they have been removed from a reactor core.

Low-level Waste

The largest volume of nuclear waste is low-level waste. It is any type of nuclear waste that is not classified as high-level or transuranic waste. Low-level wastes emit significantly less intense radiation over shorter periods of time than is the case with high-level wastes.

Low-level wastes are generated at nuclear power plants, fuel fabrication facilities, uranium reprocessing plants, hospitals, medical schools, universities, chemical and pharmaceutical manufacturers, and research laboratories. They consist of the everyday waste materials used at these facilities, materials such as piping, scrap paper, rags, plastic bags, masks, gloves, medical equipment parts, protective clothing, cardboard, packaging material, organic fluids, and materials used in water treatment systems

There is confusion on the issue of low-level radiation, because the nuclear industry and government define "low-level" waste in terms of volume. The confusion comes from the fact that there can be a very large concentration of radioactivity (high-level radiation) in a small package, vs. small concentration in a big package.

The medical waste from diagnosis and treatment shipped in one year from most states usually gives off a fraction of one curie of radiation. In contrast, each nuclear reactor generates hundreds and thousands of curies in "low-level" waste every year.

Nuclear reactor waste is usually very concentrated: solidified liquid emits about 2 curies per cubic meter; filter/demineralizer sludges emit about 10 curies per cubic meter; cartridge filters emit about 20 curies per cubic meter; demineralizer resins emit about 160 curies per cubic meter. Primary components average 1000 to 5000 curies per cubic meter—and yet, all this material is legally considered low-level.

NOTE: The amount of radioactivity, measured in curies, indicates how much radioactive energy the waste emits. One curie = 37 billion disintegrations or radioactive emissions per second from a radioactive material.

About 90% of the nuclear wastes in the U.S. are low-level byproducts of nuclear materials. About two-thirds are produced during weapons research and production, and about one-third from commercial operations. Spent fuel contributes a small amount to the overall volume of nuclear wastes produced, only about 0.2%. Spent fuels, however, tend to be highly radioactive, accounting for about 96% of the radioactivity produced by nuclear wastes in this country.

In the 1940s and 1950s, low-level wastes were usually disposed of by placing them inside a concrete-filled barrel, which was then buried underground. In some cases, such wastes were dumped into the ocean. Both of these solutions are unacceptable, for they release radioactive materials into the ground or into ocean water

with time.

In the 1970s most low-level wastes were being shipped to one of three central burial sites, at Beatty, Nevada; Richland, Washington; and Barnwell, South Carolina. Later on Nevada and Washington decided to restrict the dumping on their territory, so the U.S. Congress passed the low-level radioactive waste policy act in 1980. It requires each state to be fully responsible for all the low-level nuclear wastes generated within its borders. The states were also encouraged to join together in finding solutions. In such cases, a single disposal site would be selected for each of the compacts, a site to which all nuclear wastes in the member states could be shipped.

It soon became obvious, however, that this wouldn't be easy to do, so the U.S. Congress passed the low-level radioactive waste policy amendments act of 1985, providing for sanctions against states that did not make progress toward the development of waste disposal site, or were not involved in a joint compact with other states to do so.

By 2004, 10 interstate compacts were created by all 50 states except for Massachusetts, Michigan, New Hampshire, New York, North Carolina, and Rhode Island. Some unusual geographic associations have resulted from those shifts, with the Texas Compact, for example, consisting of Texas, Maine and Vermont.

Transuranic Waste

The third major category of nuclear wastes is called transuranic wastes. These are similar to low-level wastes, except that they include a significant amount of radioactive isotopes with very long half-lives (a few thousand years or more). The transuranic wastes are produced almost exclusively as a result of nuclear weapons research and development, and pose a somewhat different disposal problem due to the very long duration of their radioactivity.

Initially, transuranic wastes were stored in together with other low-level wastes; in concrete-filled steel drums and buried in shallow ditches. Although everyone was aware that this is unsatisfactory because of the long-term threat such wastes posed to human health and the environment, it took an act of Congress to change things. The defense authorization act of 1979 (now public law 96-164) authorized the construction of a permanent underground storage area for transuranic wastes to be called the waste isolation pilot plant (WIPP).

The site was located in the Chihuahuan Desert of Southeastern New Mexico, where a giant cave was constructed to hold the wastes. It was about 2,150 feet underground inside a 2,000-foot thick salt formation, which has been geologically stable for more than 200 million years. This provides the time frame needed for long-term storage of transuranic wastes.

There were objections of New Mexico residents and environmental groups, who were not convinced that the storage area was as safe as claimed, but the project was completed and WIPP started receiving shipments of transuranic wastes in 1999. They are expected to remain safely in there for thousands of years to come.

Transportation of Spent Nuclear Fuel

Once the spent fuel is removed from the reactor, the fission process stops, but the spent fuel assemblies still generate significant amounts of radiation and heat. Because of the related residual hazard to human health, spent fuel must be shipped in containers or casks that shield and contain the radioactivity and dissipate the heat.

Over the last 40 years, thousands of shipments of commercially- generated spent nuclear fuel have been made throughout the U.S., most of which have been between different reactors owned by the same utility to share storage space for spent fuel. Some of the shipments go to a research or recycling facilities for further tests or processing.

In the near future, because of the planned use of a central high-level waste repository, the number of these shipments by road and rail is expected to increase. The NRC regulates spent fuel transportation through a combination of safety and security requirements, certification of transportation casks, inspections, and a system of monitoring to ensure that requirements are being met. There have been no major radiation-related accidents during shipment of nuclear materials since the beginning of the nuclear industry.

Yucca Mountain Saga

The nuclear power industry has gone through some changes and has resolved a number of problems, but several remain. These are the basic fear of nuclear accidents, and the disposal of high-level wastes produced by nuclear power plants and weapons research and development. U.S. Department of Energy (DOE) has estimated that, as of 2004, nuclear power plants in the U.S. had generated about 49,000 metric tons (54,000 short tons) of high-level radioactive wastes. These wastes are currently being stored in on-site temporary facilities in 68 locations around the country.

The total amount of radioactivity contained within these wastes has been estimated at about 30 billion cu-

ries, with perhaps 300 times that amount coming from high-level defense wastes. DOE also estimates that the amount of nuclear waste will rise to a total of about 105,000 metric tons by the year 2035.

Something has to be done to store this mountain of nuclear waste, so as early as 1957 the national academy of sciences (NAS) issued a report that recommended burying nuclear wastes deep within geological formations. Salt domes were the preferred formation, because of their advantage of being largely impermeable to water and resistant to heat. This reduces the likelihood that radioactive materials would be seeping out into the groundwater.

After trying and testing a number of potential sites, and taking a lot of time doing it, the U.S. Congress stepped in and Yucca Mountain (90 miles NW of Las Vegas) was chosen and designated by law as the America's nuclear waste landfill in 1987. Congress passed an amendment to the NWPA requiring the DOE to focus exclusively on the Yucca Mountain site. That decision was based in part on a desire to reduce additional costs of developing a nuclear waste facility and, to some extent, a concern about the ongoing delay in making a decision on this issue.

Figure 6-31. Yucca mountain repository access tunnel

The design of the Yucca Mountain repository site has changed in some respects over the two decades during which it has been considered. In general, the plan was to bore at least 50 tunnels into the mountain at levels of between 660 and 1,600 feet beneath the surface, and about 1,000 feet above the water table, the level below which the soil remains saturated with water. The total length of all the tunnels is estimated to be about 100 miles.

Radioactive wastes transported to the site from around the country will be delivered first to one of the buildings at the site, where they would be encased in specially designed canisters made of very strong, highly resistant nickel alloy. The canisters will then be delivered by remote-control equipment from the surface buildings to the tunnels, where they will be placed under drip shields made of a titanium alloy designed to protect them from water seeping into the tunnel and dripping from the ceiling. As each tunnel fills, it will be sealed off with specially designed barriers that allow the release of heat generated by the wastes but protect against the escape of radiation into the surrounding area.

Initial estimate for the project was set at somewhat less than $1 billion, but the costs as of 1996 had already reached more than $4 billion.

For most of the 1990s, proponents and opponents of the Yucca Mountain project carried out a host of research projects attempting to design a safe facility and to demonstrate that it would, in fact, be safe, or unsafe, depending on who was making the presentation. Bureaucratic hurdles delaying completion of the project were being overcome one by one, and in 1997 the DOE completed construction of an exploratory studies facility at the Yucca Mountain site. This facility was designed to test the technology that was ultimately to be employed at the site.

In 1998, DOE issued a Yucca Mountain viability assessment, detailing what is needed to construct the facility. It described its operation, outlined the procedures needed to obtain licensing of the repository, and estimated its final cost. A year later, the EPA issued its environmental impact statement for the site, outlining the necessary radiation protection steps needed to ensure the safety of humans in the area and the environment.

It looked like the U.S. would soon be able to bury all its nuclear waste in Yucca Mountain. This, however, did not happen. New problems continued to arise that fed concerns about the safety of storing high-level wastes deep within the mountain. In 2003 DOE studies showed that groundwater leaking into the repository site might cause deterioration of the canisters in which nuclear wastes were to be buried, causing them to leak and release radioactive materials into the ground water. In 2004, the federal appeals court for the District of Columbia ruled that the DOE's plans for ensuring the safety of stored wastes for a period of 10,000 years was inadequate. The department needed to amend its plan to provide for an even longer period during which the general public would be protected from radiation.

And the wheels moving Yucca Mountain project ahead started turning again, but this time the pressure from environmentalists and the locals was increased to the max. Politicians were at the forefront of the movement, and finally in 2010, the U.S. Department of Energy bent under the pressure and announced it would withdraw its application for a license to store nuclear waste there. Yucca Mountain was dead. The U.S. once again is without any hopes for a central nuclear waste depository.

Decommissioning

Last, but not least, on the list of problems of the U.S. nuclear power industry is another difficult, but not urgent, problem. It is the decommissioning of old nuclear power plants. Nuclear power plants grow old, like anything else, and must eventually be shut down and dismantled. Nuclear power plants are designed to last about 30 years, after which time it must be decommissioned.

A 30-year limit on the operation of nuclear power plants is included in all licenses issued by the nuclear regulatory commission (NRC). There are presently three forms of decommissioning: DECON, SAFSTOR, and ENTOMB.

DECON allows the company to close the power plant, remove equipment, tear down the structure, and transfer wastes and contaminated materials to a safe storage site.

SAFSTOR allows the plant to stop power production, but permits it to maintain the plant until some future date, at which time DECON can begin.

ENTOMB is used when unusually high levels of radiation are present at a site, in which case the entire plant is encased in a structurally sound material (like cement) to prevent the release of radiation. The site is closely monitored and maintained until it is safe to begin a DECON procedure.

The cost of decommissioning a nuclear power plant depends on the type chosen, and on a number of other factors. The type of reactor used and the geographic location of the plant are major decision points. The average cost of decommissioning a plant is over $325 million. This cost is paid for by the nuclear industry, which collects a tax from ratepayers of $0.01-0.02 per kWh of electricity used. These funds are deposited in a trust fund managed by the NRC for use in paying off future costs of decommissioning power plants.

Decommissioning of nuclear power plants is a real concern for many individuals, who point out the risks associated with the dismantling, transport, treatment, and storage of wastes, equipment, fuel, and other materials taken from a plant that has been shut down. It is impossible to prevent some radioactive materials from remaining at a plant site or escaping into the surrounding environment, thereby increasing the risk of illness and death to humans, other animals, and plants in the region.

The process of decommissioning a nuclear power plant is controlled by the NRC, which issues permission to proceed with decommissioning work, and monitors the efforts.

Nuclear Terrorism

As a consequence of 9/11 and other events during the last decade, there is renewed concern among politicians, scientists, bureaucrats, and ordinary citizens about the dangers of nuclear terrorism. Two of the hijacked planes had flown less than 30 miles from the Indian Point nuclear power facility in Buchanan, New York. The Three Mile Island nuclear power facility near Harrisburg, Pennsylvania, was not far from the crash site of the fourth aircraft and might have even been the target of the hijackers.

Direct attacks on nuclear facilities by terrorists are a frightful form of nuclear terrorism. In addition to planes, terrorists could use a truck full of explosives driven into a nuclear power plant. There is also the threat of armed attacks by a group of terrorists on a nuclear facility.

What, if any damage, could have been done by such attacks is uncertain, and yet, the potential of something like this happening is causing a significant concern.

Nuclear terrorism actually refers to the use of nuclear materials—-enriched uranium or plutonium in fuel rods, spent fuel, nuclear wastes, and other materials—in a terrorist attack. These materials could also be used to make nuclear weapons, and "dirty bombs." The technology is quite sophisticated and beyond the ability of most terrorist groups, but the potential and the fear of the unknown, are there, and that is the scary part.

Dirty bomb, also known as a radiation dispersal device (RDD), is a conventional bomb to which have been added radioactive materials. Upon explosion, in addition to the blast effect, these bombs release high levels of radiation over wide areas. Dirty bombs can be made by any terrorists with fifth-grade educations, provided they gain access to nuclear materials.

In the beginning stages of nuclear power, such attacks were not considered as credible threats to nuclear facilities. As a matter of fact, licensing regulations specifically excused plants from preparing themselves against outside attacks. Instructions from 1967 read, "An applicant for a license to construct and operate a production or utilization facility is not required to provide for design features or other measures for the specific purpose of protection against the effects of (a) attacks and destructive acts, including sabotage, directed against the facility by an enemy of the U.S., whether a foreign government or other person."

How times change. This position was changed in 1977 by the adoption of regulations requiring nuclear facilities to have a security plan to protect against "radiological sabotage," described as "any act that could directly or indirectly endanger public health and safety by exposure to radiation."

These provisions seem inadequate, in that nuclear power plants should be required to have plans to protect themselves against attacks by larger groups of individuals far better equipped to inflict damage on the plant.

A task group in 1986 warned that "the probability of nuclear terrorism is increasing." It pointed out that NRC's design basis threat model had "several problems." "The models were designed a decade ago when the threat of nuclear terrorism was thought to be mostly from anti-nuclear protesters. Today's wide range of threats is not covered by the models."

The NRC ignored those suggestions until a truck bomb was exploded in the basement of the world trade center (WTC) in 1993. Then the agency made its first changes in its DBT plans in 16 years. Those changes called for increases in plant safety requirements to include attacks by truck bombs, like the one that had occurred at the WTC. Except for that change, however, the 1977 DBT requirements remained largely in place.

Meanwhile, there is evidence that the integrity of nuclear power plant security may be somewhat less robust than what the industry claims. Experts continue to dispute the security of nuclear power plants. On the one hand, the industry argues that "No other private industrial facilities have the combination of robust physical protection, well-trained and armed security forces, and emergency response capability that is found at every nuclear power plant in the U.S."   On the other hand, the critics believe that "despite September 11, both the industry and the agency that regulates it continue to resist making any significant improvement to dismally inadequate and outmoded security regulations." They claim that the NRC is "behind the curve, and fighting the last war, rather than protecting against threats that can materialize without warning."

Nuclear Renaissance

President George W. Bush brought new hopes for nuclear power in the U.S. Starting in 2000, the long decline in nuclear power plant development in the U.S. appeared to be over. At that time, the prospects for the construction of new reactors seemed so good that a number of enthusiasts began to talk about a "nuclear renaissance."

A new era was supposed to revive the U.S. and global nuclear industries. Nuclear renaissance was the talk of the town. At a meeting in Washington, D.C., on September 10-12, 2002, industry representatives and U.S. government officials presented an overly optimistic outlook for nuclear power in the coming generation.

In the spring of 2003, a nuclear renaissance forum was held in Chicago under the sponsorship of Framatone and Westinghouse, both large nuclear plant manufacturers. The nuclear renaissance had already begun. The efficiency and output gains of existing nuclear plants were equivalent to building 23 new 1,000 megawatt plants. U.S. nuclear power production represented 20% of total power generation on the country, and public opinion about nuclear power plants seemed to have taken a more positive direction.

In 2004 about 65% of those interviewed supported the use of nuclear energy as one of the way to provide electricity in the U.S. This, versus only 46% of those interviewed responded positively to this question in 1983.

A nuclear renaissance was likely to be even more dramatic on an international scale, with the international atomic energy agency predicting demand for electricity to increase fivefold by 2050. This demand requires quadrupling of the number of nuclear power plants operating at the time. But nuclear power in the developing nations, especially those in the Far East, was thought to be the most affected. China announced that it would quadruple its nuclear capacity by adding 32 new reactors to its existing 11 plants by 2020, while India expected to increase its capacity from 14 to more than 50 plants by 2020.

What led to this short-lived nuclear renaissance? Increased safety at nuclear power plants in the U.S. is one of the reasons, since no major accident has occurred in this country since the Three Mile Island event in 1979. The U.S. public appeared more relaxed about the safety of nuclear power production. A more favorable regulatory atmosphere in the federal government was another reason for optimism.

President Bush's national energy policy of 2001 strongly recommended increased use of nuclear power as a source of energy, and made a number of recommendations designed to achieve this objective. These included encouraging the NRC to facilitate industry efforts to expand the number of nuclear power plants in opera-

tion in the U.S., and urging the commission to extend licenses on existing plants. It also suggested the need for legislation that would transfer some of the financial risk of nuclear power plant construction and operation from industry to the federal government.

Members of the U.S. Congress began to introduce bills designed to promote the development of nuclear power. This led to the adoption of a strategic plan for light water reactors research and development that provided federal support for industrial research on new reactor designs.

This new enthusiasm was also expressed, although in a relatively short period of time, by the regulatory agencies. As a result, the regulatory process got much more predictable, thereby reducing investor uncertainty. And another factor for the nuclear renaissance was the evolution of the environmental concerns. The effects of waste gases produced by fossil fuel plants took center stage at the time, which highlighted the pollution-free advantages of nuclear power generation.

After the signing of the Kyoto protocol on climate change in 1992 (although it did not include the U.S.), the power industries went into a frenzy in the search for new methods for the production of energy with reduced emissions of greenhouse gases. The issue was getting most of the attention, and nuclear plants were winning on all sides of the environmental debate.

The development of nuclear power plants also benefited from the economic advantages of nuclear power production. Electricity generated by nuclear power plants was about 10-15% cheaper than electricity from coal-powered plants. This clear advantage of nuclear plants gave great emphasis on their role in solving the nation's energy dependency.

But, as in any other case, there were many individuals and organizations that consider the use of nuclear power as "nuclear fantasy," "nuclear nightmare," or "nuclear resurgence." In other words, this was nothing but a revival of the same problems with nuclear reactors that have been debated for half a century.

George W. Bush was called "the nuclear President," and blamed for pushing a nuclear agenda to benefit his own friends and supporters in the energy industry. Nuclear terrorism was one aspect of a nuclear renaissance that troubled some people. As more nuclear power plants come on line in the U.S. and around the world, more targets become available to terrorists, and with that, security issues became more numerous and difficult. Providing security for nuclear reactors is not easy, and the uncertainty surrounding terrorist actions was/is alarming to the public.

According to insiders, the nuclear renaissance came at a really bad time. Bands of terrorists trying to get their hands on nuclear materials, or damage the nuclear infrastructure was not something the average person could accept. The risks were too great and outweigh the benefits by a large margin.

So, on one hand, nuclear enthusiasts promise safe nuclear power growing in some parts of the nation and many parts of the world, and the general public once again was treated to a rosy view of the future in which nuclear fission will benefit people throughout the world.

At the same time, the critics continue to raise issues about safety, cost, environmental effects, and other aspects of nuclear power that might prevent it from ever reaching the potential promised by supporters. Fundamental questions about the role of nuclear energy in the life of everyday individuals, which were first raised in the late 1940s, are still not completely answered. They seem likely to remain as a challenge for the world nuclear industry for the foreseeable future.

GEOTHERMAL

Geothermal energy technologies can be broken into four major categories:

1. Conventional hydrothermal
2. Low-temperature hydrothermal
3. Enhanced geothermal systems (EGS)
4. Direct use (including geothermal heat pumps, GHPs)

While the first three categories generate electricity, the fourth is used primarily for heating and cooling and hot water production. There are also differences in technology maturity and market characteristics, which also vary with time and location.

According to the U.S. Department of Energy (DOE) the geothermal technologies can be divided in more detail into the following categories:

Hydrothermal
- Conventional technology—Steam, dual flash, flash, binary
- Shallow (1-3 km), hot (150°C or more), naturally occurring, localized

Enhanced Geothermal Systems (EGS)
- Near-hydrothermal field EGS
  — "Almost" hydrothermal fields, which lack per-

meability and/or in-situ fluids
  — Near-term, lowest cost EGS, which are likely to be developed first
- Deep EGS
- Deployable "anywhere," or drill until high temperatures found
- 3+ km deep, no natural permeability and/or in-situ fluid, fracture and flow
- Long-term, higher costs are most likely to follow successful near-field tests

Oil and Gas Co-Produced Fluids
Direct Use
Geo-pressure Fluid
Ground Source Heat Pumps

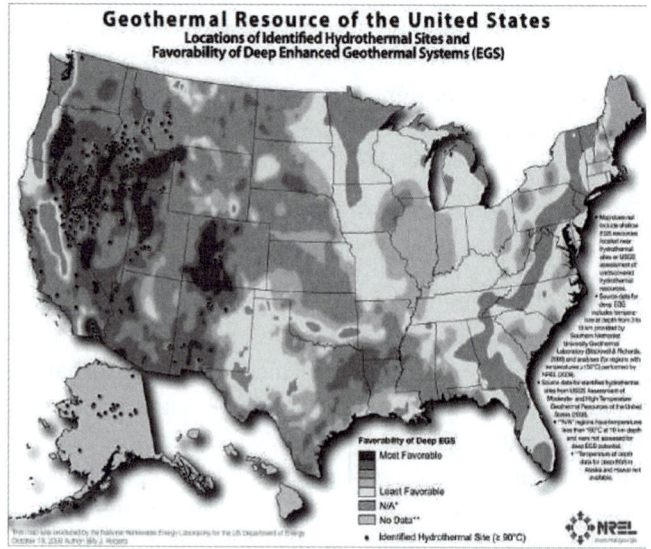

Figure 6-32. Geothermal energy sources in the U.S.

Presently, there are over 9.0 GW of identified geothermal sources in the U.S., predominantly in the southwest states. The total available (but yet to be discovered) geothermal capacity that can be exploited with existing technology in the U.S. is slightly over 30.0 GW. With some additional R&D and using superior technologies (possibly by 2050), the potential of geothermal power in the U.S. is over 100.0 GW.

Deeper drilling, in the range of 3-6 kilometers depth, excluding drilling in federally protected lands, could bring the total geothermal energy reserves in the U.S. to over 500.0 GW.

Slightly over 2.0 GW of geothermal power has been developed in the U.S. thus far. It appears now that the pace of geothermal resource development has been largely related to the electric capacity, and the political attitudes at each given period of time. Changes to

PURPA and inconsistent funding levels for research and development, for example, have contributed to slow growth in geothermal electricity development, despite highly volatile electricity prices, an abundant resource, and public interest surrounding local and diverse resources.

One of the biggest barriers to geothermal energy production is the risky and inefficient process of searching for energy sources capable of producing recoverable energy. To solve that problem a bipartisan group of U.S. Senators introduced legislation to facilitate the lease of federal land for geothermal energy production.

Government policies have the potential to drive the development of renewable energy resources through technology development, risk and barrier reduction, and price equalization.

Development of the geothermal resource markets require the following of public policy:

- Long-term (multi-year) upfront cost defrayment to reduce risk and provide support until power production begins

- Targeted policies in accordance with resource availability

- Appropriately sized incentives to meet the needs of the full range or some portion of the range between 250 kilowatts (kW) to multi-megawatt facilities

- Appropriate recognition of the environmental and load benefits of base-load renewable energy generation

Policy affects the energy markets, with the new renewable energy sources being most dependent on proper and efficient policy.

The major factors, affecting the renewable energy markets are:
- Technology availability, efficiency and cost
- Institutional structures
- Resource availability
- Social acceptance
- Economic context
- Political currents
- Environmental concerns

The major issues in developing new renewable sources are:
- Land use
- Financing
- Site permitting
- Power transmission

The Regulations

The geothermal production expansion act of 2011 addresses some of these issues by allowing for non-competitive leasing of a very limited amount of federal land at fair market value. This would aid the expansion of already identified geothermal resources without the delay of competitive leasing and without the risk of opening up the property to speculative bidders who have no actual interest developing the property.

After a number of delays and glitches, the bill was finally introduced in Senate in February 2013 as the geothermal production expansion act of 2013. It amends competitive lease provisions of the geothermal steam act of 1970 to allow an area of qualified federal land (land that is otherwise available for leasing under that act) that adjoins other land for which a qualified lessee holds a legal right to develop geothermal resources to be available for a noncompetitive lease to such lessee at fair market value per acre if:

1. The area of qualified federal land consists of not less than one acre and not more than 640 acres and is not already leased or nominated to be leased

2. The qualified lessee has not previously received a noncompetitive lease in connection with the valid discovery for which data has been submitted

3. Sufficient technical data prepared by a qualified geothermal professional has been submitted by the qualified lessee to the applicable federal land management agency that would lead individuals who are experienced in the subject matter to believe that there is a valid discovery of geothermal resources on the land and that such thermal feature extends into the adjoining areas.

The Act also defines "fair market value per acre" as a dollar amount per acre that shall be:

1. Equal to the market value per acre as determined by the Secretary of the Interior within 180 days after the secretary receives an application for a lease

2. No less than the greater of four times the median amount paid per acre for all land leased under such act during the preceding year or $50

The bill directs the secretary to:
1. Publish a notice of any request for such a lease

2. Determine fair market value in accordance with procedures established by the secretary

3. Provide to a qualified lessee and publish, with an

opportunity for public comment for a period of 30 days any proposed determination of the fair market value of the area the qualified lessee seeks to lease

4. Provide the lessee and any adversely affected party an opportunity to appeal the final determination of fair market value in an administrative proceeding before the applicable federal land management agency

It also prohibits the secretary from accepting any nomination of land for leasing after publication of a notice of request to lease such land unless the request has been denied or withdrawn.

Geothermal energy exploration can be a costly and inefficient process and it is that financial uncertainty that has been a barrier to increased use of geothermal energy as a replacement for fossil fuels. The geothermal production expansion act makes it easier for the federal government to lease to legitimate geothermal energy producers on lands adjacent to those already proven to be "hot spots." This makes it more likely to increase geothermal energy production with less up-front cost. Lessees are limited to no more than 640 acres per lease and must pay fair market value for the lease as determined by the Department of Interior. The bill also increases the annual rental payments for the newly acquired land to ensure that the taxpayers get a fair return for leasing the land this way.

Passing this bill would help to reduce one of the biggest barriers to geothermal energy production by greatly increasing the chances that the costs of exploration into geothermal energy are met with actual production. This way we can get more geothermal energy from those projects and help lower the cost of getting that energy out of the ground.

But for now, let's take a look at the present geothermal policy and procedures.

A recent resurgence in geothermal project development results from increased interest in domestic resources, high and volatile energy prices, and an interest in lower environmental impact energy choices. Today 103 hydrothermal plants are under development in 13 states, which will produce nearly 3.0 GW of power. As always, policy drivers impact geothermal development heavily.

Some of the key polices include:

1. The availability of the federal production tax credit (PTC), opened to geothermal energy in 2004 for a portion of the wind credit and to the full credit in 2005

2. The existence of state renewable portfolio standards (RPS) to augment the risk-reduction effects created by PURPA. In addition to the power-purchase risk reduction offered by PURPA and state-level RPSs, the revised federal geothermal leasing regulations (BLM 2008) are expected to expedite project timelines and drive the current market

3. State and utility financial incentives (e.g., state permitting expedition, tax abatement policies) are being implemented to draw developers into states. Due to the piecemeal process of policy development and the different reasons policies are put in place, there is no unified strategy for federal and state incentives promoting geothermal resource development.

The most recent additions to the policy landscape for geothermal production are the changes and updates to financial incentives for geothermal electricity generation in ARRA. The long-term impact of this policy development is not currently known due to the recent nature of the law.

The Policies

There are a number of policies that contribute to the further development of the technology and expansion of the geothermal markets in the U.S. Some of these are:

The Energy Policy Act (EPAct) of 2005 and 2008

This act had two primary provisions affecting geothermal energy production:

1. It authorizes an update to a 1978 U.S. geological survey (USGS) resource assessment, which identified geothermal resources for hydrothermal power generation on federal lands in the western U.S.

2. It also outlines the process for unitization of geothermal resources by federal geothermal leaseholders.

NOTE: A new assessment of moderate- and high-temperature geothermal resources in 13 states identified 241 geothermal sites on private or accessible public lands in the western U.S. Because leasing public land has historically presented a challenge for developers, it is necessary for the government to facilitate their leasing and access to areas with known geothermal resources.

An estimated 90% of the nation's hydrothermal resources are located on federal lands.

EPA 2005 amended the leasing regulations for geothermal resources located on federal lands. The legislation requires that the bidding process be competitive (as opposed to sealed), which has opened up the resource nomination process to the market. The BLM is required to hold lease sales at least every two years to ensure that leasing applications are processed. Furthermore, the legislation required that a backlog of leasing applications prior to 2005 be processed.

The EPA also changed the royalty shares between federal, state, and county governments to 25%, 50%, and 25%, respectively. BLM-held geothermal auctions yielded the highest per-acre bid in all of the previous BLM auctions. The BLM also released leasing decisions on BLM land, which allocates federal land available for drilling. It also identifies a reasonable development scenario for the land, and adopts best management practices for the land.

The second provision, outlined in EPA 2005 for the holders of federal geothermal leases, is to ensure efficient use of the geothermal pools. Multiple landowners or federal leaseholders are allowed to combine the geothermal resources as needed to spread around the initial investment and optimize the use of the resources.

The regulations of 2007 define two types of agreements that can be made between federal leaseholders:

1. Unit agreement is a plan of development and operation for the production and utilization of separately owned interests in the geothermal resources as a single consolidated unit without regard to separate ownerships.

    b. Cooperative agreement is a plan of development and operations for the production and utilization of geothermal resources, in which separate ownership units are independently operated without allocation of production.

Leaseholders must negotiate among themselves to identify the specific distribution of costs and benefits for each leaseholder. Unitizing leaseholders must present a unit plan to the BLM for review and approval, then BLM officially establishes the geothermal production unit.

PURPA Offer Contracts

The public utility regulatory act (PURPA) was implemented in 1978 and is still in control of some parts of geothermal development. PURPA has helped to reduce the avoided costs to utilities, making geothermal less attractive for developers, except in some cases where avoided costs are high enough to attract geothermal developers.

In Idaho, for example, PURPA rules led to the development of the Raft River project in 2008, primarily because avoided cost rates are higher than in other states due to higher natural gas prices. With the changing gas situation and reduced prices, however, this scenario is no longer viable.

Leasing Rights

Access to federal lands for geothermal projects is limited due to a number of issues, including environmental concerns. Different requirements exist for BLM, USFS, and tribal lands too, so the lease and acquisition regulations vary depending on the type and location of the land in question. In response, BLM completed an analysis on environmental impact to facilitate leasing processes, and issued the programmatic environmental impact statement (PEIS), which defines appropriate resource-available areas, streamlines the leasing process, and spells the best practices for project and land management for hydrothermal projects in the western U.S.

This PEIS serves to promulgate interagency coordination and public-private partnership in project development. Eventually BLM would be able to assign geothermal rights to oil and gas leaseholders, which would allow them to sell geothermal electricity to the utilities.

Pump Property

A geothermal heat pump property is equipment that uses ground water as a thermal energy source to heat or cool a residence or business, if the unit meets the requirements of the Energy Star program, when the heat pump is purchased.

As part of the emergency economic stabilization act of 2008, a 30% incentive was added for geothermal heat pump property, valid through December 31, 2016. It is capped at $2,000 For installations prior to January 1, 2009.

Qualifying geothermal heat pump property installed after December 31, 2008 is eligible for 30% of the installed cost without a cap, as provided under the American recovery and reinvestment tax act of 2009 (ARRA). This incentive is available for taxpayers installing qualifying equipment at their primary residence or a second home, but not for a rental property.

Two options exist for the commercial incentive:

1. An investment tax credit of 10% of the installed cost is available through 2016

2. An option of taking a grant in lieu of the credit, worth 10% of the installed costs for equipment placed in service during 2009-2010-time period

In addition to the federal programs, a number of states have enacted their own policies and procedures for development of geothermal power. Some of these are:

State R&D Programs

Because the scale of research and development is typically large and requires extensive investment, states are generally not well- positioned to implement R&D programs without federal support. California is the only state with a state-funded R&D program for geothermal. Using funds from leasing royalties, California makes R&D funds available to qualifying applicants under the geothermal resources development account (GRDA) (CEC 2008). From its inception in 1980, the program has funded at least four geothermal projects, as well as a number of direct-use projects (CEC 2008).

State Renewable Portfolio Standards

Developers have cited state renewable portfolio standards (RPS) policies have been cited by developers as a significant driver for geothermal development, as they encourage utilities to sign power purchase agreements for geothermal power and serve to reduce the uncertainty that power available will be purchased.

Eight of the 13 states with planned geothermal plants have passed renewable portfolio standards. Only New Mexico's RPS has a set-aside for geothermal (together with biomass for a 10% total starting in 2011), in an effort made by the legislature to ensure a diversified energy portfolio resulting from the RPS. To encourage and to attribute higher value to geothermal development, New Mexico's RPS has a two-fold multiplier for geothermal energy. This multiplier strategy within the RPS mechanism is most commonly used for solar technologies that are rarely the least-cost option.

Despite developers citing RPS as market drivers for geothermal, there is currently no correlation between states with RPS and increased geothermal development. Since geothermal projects require multiple years from planning to implementation, RPS policies must be in place for multiple years to have an effect, possibly explaining the lack of correlation between policy and capacity growth.

States with ambitious RPS targets (like California and Nevada) seem to have more geothermal power plants in development, although this analysis did not examine the relationship between a higher level of geothermal resources and the existence of an RPS that strongly encourages geothermal development.

Ownership, Unitization, and Permitting

State policy relating to geothermal resources for electricity production varies by state and is not well defined. Two particular challenges to geothermal development include:

1. Ownership of the resources

2. Potential or requirements for unitization of state and private land

The impact of these policy variations across state lines may be a barrier to geothermal development, so further research and better understanding of the laws and structures (such as through the ARRA data system described previously) could be of high value to developing geothermal resources.

Ownership of the geothermal resources can be ownership of the surface rights, and is needed because lack of resource ownership clarity can create barriers to development.

Geothermal resources are abundant in the U.S., but the lack of understanding of their nature, potential, as well as the unitization rules and regulations may be a barrier to efficient development.

Figure 6-33. The Beehive Geyser

NOTE: Unitization of geothermal resources allows multiple landowners or leaseholders to pool the geothermal resource to optimize their expenses.

Many states clarify the ownership and unitization rights of leaseholders on state lands, while unitization of private resources is less clearly outlined and state rules vary on the subject.

Regulatory permitting, too, can be a hindrance to geothermal development, since multiple state regulatory bodies are responsible for permitting geothermal wells. This makes the process cumbersome, and the lack of clarity causes delays in permitting and project development, which in turn increases the capital expenses.

Ownership, unitization, and regulatory permitting are only three major issues affecting the geothermal industry, where increased clarity of the rules and interests of states are needed. This will help developers to gain a better understanding of the process in the different states. A broad review of the legislative and regulatory barriers is also needed to identify areas where regulatory and legislative clarity is needed to reduce the barriers to geothermal resource development.

Internationally

Geothermal-power is theoretically available in any place on Earth, but it is much more convenient to use at some special locations. Iceland is one of these lucky places where abundant heat and steam can be obtained by digging a few meters into the ground.

Iceland

Iceland is the geothermal capital of the world. It is benefiting from an especially favorable geological location, where there are many active volcanoes providing pockets of hot underground rocks. These areas are hot enough to allow the generation of geothermal energy for residential heating and electricity generation. During the winter months, pavements in some cities, like Reykjavík and Akureyr are heated to melt the snow and allow traffic to move safely.

Five major geothermal power plants exist in Iceland, which produced approximately 26.0% of the nation's energy in 2011. In addition, geothermal heating meets the heating and hot water requirements of approximately 87% of all buildings in Iceland. Apart from geothermal energy, 73.8% of the nation's electricity is generated by hydropower, and 0.1% from fossil fuels.

Consumption of primary geothermal energy in 2004 was 79.7 petajoules (PJ), approximately 53.4% of the total national consumption of primary energy, 149.1 PJ. The corresponding share for hydropower was 17.2%, petroleum was 26.3%, and coal was 3%. Plans are underway to turn Iceland into a 100% fossil-fuel-free nation in the near future. For example, Iceland's abundant geothermal energy has enabled renewable energy initiatives, such as carbon recycling international's carbon dioxide to methanol fuel process. The following are the five largest power stations in Iceland.

Japan

Japan is on a new course of energy independence, looking for anything and everything that can replace or at least supplement nuclear. The Japanese government introduced a feed-in tariff that forces the ten electric generation monopolies to buy renewable energy at, or above-market rates, while the environment ministry abolished guidelines that restrict geothermal development in some national parks.

Many companies are jumping on the geothermal bandwagon and planning to build geothermal plants in the mountains of Fukushima prefecture, which is famous for its hot springs. The problem is that at best it will take ten years before they can start generating electricity, which reflects some of the difficulties of developing new energy business in Japan.

The major problem with geothermal power development is the cultural climate in Japan, where hot springs and spas are sacred. There are strict rules about bathing in these water bodies, where human bodies must be absolutely clean beforehand and clothing and tattoos are not allowed. The geothermal industry is having a hard time persuading the hot springs owners and the local communities that its projects would not spoil the local springs and spas.

To speed things up, Japan is looking for help from Iceland, which generates the same amount of geothermal energy as Japan, though Japan has a more than 400 times larger population. Iceland's experience suggests that Japan does not need subsidies to develop geothermal energy. Instead, it needs better legislation, careful management of underground reservoirs, and an entrepreneurial vision.

Summary

The historical and current policy picture in the U.S. reflects a piecemeal approach to geothermal resource development, and often reflects geothermal development as a part of collective renewables policies, without geothermal-electric specific policies in place.

Unrelated technologies are sometimes defined as geothermal in the policy language, despite the obvious differences. This discrepancy results in difficulties in evaluating policy impacts on electricity from geothermal resources, because electricity production technology is then in competition with other renewable technologies that may be further along in development or better understood by the public, and are therefore chosen.

Findings are inconclusive as to the direct impact of specific policies on electricity production from geothermal development, although there appears to be a connection between federal policies and historical geothermal development.

Finally, there is empirical and qualitative evidence that the impact of state-level policies are funding-limited instead, resulting in a lack of private sector investment related to the uncertainty of actually receiving the incentive before the state funding is exhausted. That is, incentives for central generation geothermal need to be sized appropriately to the amount of investment needed on a larger scale, and often state policies are too limited in their ability to fund incentives to have a large impact on project costs.

This results in lack of a focus on geothermal-electric development specifically, and lack of adequate resources to support the specific technology. New options are needed for filling the gaps in policy development through additional measures and innovative mechanisms, for instance, feed-in tariffs, land leasing are needed, and if properly implemented, might have a larger impact than the current suite of policies.

BIOMASS AND BIOFUELS

Biomass is a serious issue on the agenda of politicians and proponents. The biomass power generating industry in the U.S. consists of approximately 11.0 GW of summer-operating capacity. Biomass energy sources actively supply power to the grid, producing about 1.4% of the total U.S. electricity supply.

The new hope power partnership in Florida is the largest biomass power plant in North America. The 140 MW facility uses sugar cane fiber (bagasse) and recycled urban wood as fuel to generate enough power for its large milling and refining operations as well as to supply renewable electricity for nearly 60,000 homes in the area. The facility reduces oil use by more than one million barrels per year. It also recycles sugar cane and wood waste, which preserves landfill space in the community.

President Bush was one of the first to call for biomass use as energy source. He said that the U.S. needs "to move beyond a petroleum-based economy," and de-

velop energy (biofuels) from biomass. This issue is quite popular with the U.S. public now, and is supported by the majority in Congress. The congressional biomass subsidies, as well intended as they might be, are still driven by farm-state politics rather than by the urgency for technology development.

The Logistics

The importance of biomass for fuel production is not unnoticed by the major oil and chemical companies. Most of them are working on evaluating biomass, and many investors are looking for ways to make money on biomass investment opportunities, which will be good for the country's energy security and the environment. But here again, we see that not everything about biomass and biofuels is rosy. So what is the problem?

Corn Ethanol

The major practical use of biomass now is in the form of corn crops—growing and processing corn to produce ethanol-based biofuels. The bioethanol is mostly used for automobile fuel in a mixture we know as "gasohol." It consists of 10% ethanol and 90% gasoline, where gasohol has higher octane, or antiknock, properties than gasoline and burns more slowly, coolly, and completely, resulting in reduced emissions of some pollutants. However, it also vaporizes more readily, potentially aggravating ozone pollution in warm weather.

Ethanol-based gasohol in which the ethanol is made from corn is expensive and energy intensive to produce. It is also incompatible with some types of rubber seals, diaphragms, and paint finishes and can cause damage when in higher concentration.

Since 1998, many American automobiles have been equipped to run on E85, a mixture of 85% ethanol and

Figure 6-34. Corn gasohol

15% gasoline. Methanol-based gasohol is also expensive to produce and is toxic and corrosive, and its emissions produce cancer-causing formaldehydes.

Since using alcohol is the law of the land in most states, it gets generous federal and state subsidies. These range from subsidies to exemptions from gasoline taxes for gasohol production. The influx of money from government and other sources caused an exceptional increase in growing and processing bio-ethanol during the last decade. In 2005, for example, over four billion gallons of ethanol were mixed in the total gasoline pool of 120 billion gallons. Politicians from corn-states and other proponents of renewable energy are ecstatic about the prospects of growing a lot of corn under these subsidies, and support the trend.

But there are glitches. One is the belief of many energy experts that using corn to make ethanol is not effective in the long run because the net amount of crude oil saved by gasohol use is minimal. Also, the cultivation of corn is highly energy-intensive. and requires a significant amount of oil and natural gas to be used in growing, fertilizing, harvesting, and transporting it. Additional, and very substantial fossil supplied by diesel or natural gas sources, is used during the processing (the fermentation and distillation processes) of corn into ethanol.

When these fossil energy inputs are subtracted in the overall energy calculation of the conversion process, the net amount of oil that is displaced by the use of ethanol in gasohol is quite small. It takes two-thirds of a gallon of oil to make a gallon equivalent of ethanol from corn. So, basically, every gallon of ethanol used in gasohol displaces about one-third of a gallon of crude oil. Still a gain of energy, but at what cost?

A federal tax credit of 10 cents per gallon on gasohol, costs the taxpayer a hefty $120 per barrel of oil-displaced cost. Is this sustainable alternative for the U.S.?

The situation is much different in other countries and with other biomass types. Brazil is the best-known example of efficient and cheap energy crops production and their conversion into bio-ethanol for use in gasohol. But Brazilians use sugarcane, grown in a tropical climate, followed by a conventional fermentation and distillation, which produces a high yield of ethanol.

Brazil has been producing bio-ethanol since the early 1970s, and now 40% of automobile fuel in the country is bio-ethanol based. It competes with gasoline…and amazingly enough without any government subsidy. It is speculated that with the world price of sugar falling and the lessening of trade restrictions on both sugar and sugar-derived ethanol, Brazil might become a net exporter of this biofuel.

Cellulosic Biomass

The interest in using cellulosic biomass (crop remains, switch grass, domestic waste, etc.) as a new, renewable, energy source is growing quickly. There is an estimate of about 150 billion tons of annual cellulosic biomass production worldwide. Cellulosic biomass is different, because it is usually in form of wild-growing vegetation, or a byproduct, so in all cases, much less fossil energy and products is used in its cultivation.

There are several ways to convert cellulosic biomass into liquid fuel for practical use in cars or power generation.

The *chemical approach* calls for the cellulosic material to be exposed to gasification in the presence of oxygen. This process produces synthesis gas (syngas), which is a mixture of hydrogen and carbon monoxide. The syngas can be converted into liquid fuels by conventional chemical techniques. The cost varies with location, but can be estimated to be in the range of $50 to $70 per barrel of oil. As crude oil prices continue to go up, syngas fuel production will become more widely spread.

The other major process of converting cellulosic biomass into fuels, consists of the production of new enzymes as needed to break down the difficult-to-digest cellulosic feedstock into simple sugars. Once separated, the sugars can be fermented into ethanol or other liquid biofuels products. This approach is more energy efficient, and less polluting, so it is preferred, but is also much harder to conduct properly and efficiently.

The difficulty comes from engineering an organism to produce enzymes that: a) break down the cellulosic material, and b) more efficiently ferment the sugars into ethanol. Realizing this exciting prospect will not be easy.

There are several additional hurdles in the path to cheap bio-fuels from cellulosic materials. A process has to be developed that reduces the harsh pretreatment required to dissolve the solid cellulosic feedstock at the beginning of the production sequence. Then, the concentration of ethanol has to be increased to a point to be tolerated by the enzymes, and finally, an efficient process must be developed to separate the ethanol from the process liquor.

Critics of biomass argue that the conversion of sunlight into plant material is "inefficient," and that impractically large amounts of land would be required to produce significant amounts of biofuels. At present, artificial photosynthesis is not an option, but it is an important basic research goal.

Researchers spent many years assembling the

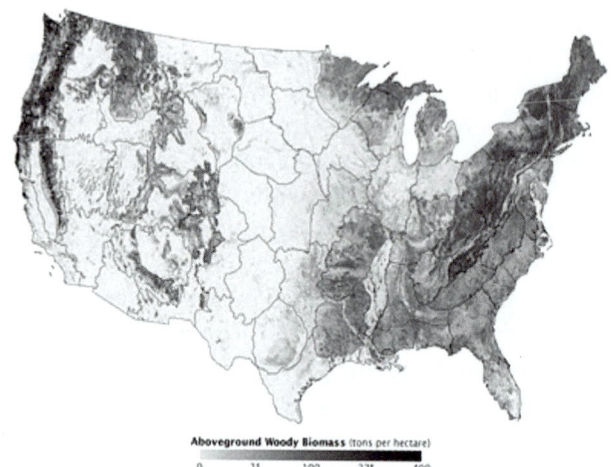

Figure 6-35. U.S. forests and biomass cover

national forest map, using space-based radar, satellite sensors, computer models, and enormous quantities of ground-based data. The end result, according to NASA, is the most detailed view of forest structure and carbon storage assembled for any country in history.

NOTE: Forests cover about 30% of the Earth's surface, and represent the largest terrestrial source of carbon that we have available for immediate use. Evaluating all carbon sources, scientists now believe that nearly 50%% of all carbon on the planet is stored in our forests. The interactions between the long-term carbon storage (forests, fossils, etc.) the man-made, short-term carbon stores (croplands and pastures), is still one of the greatest unresolved puzzles. Due to its enormous size and importance, it remains an important area of scientific investigation.

Expanding knowledge of our forests will eventually lead to better understanding of the carbon distribution around the world. It is well known now that the amount of carbon stored in a tree equals about 40-50% of its dry biomass. By estimating the quantity of biomass contained in all the trees in all the world's forests, we can estimate how much total carbon is being stored on land. Over time, we would get a full grasp on the mechanism of carbon creation and use, and its movement around the planet.

With that said, we have to conclude that we have an awesome quantity of clean, renewable energy source at our disposal—if and when we are able to control the conversion process as needed to produce energy and biofuels. At this time, the short-term goal is to figure out a process that produces biofuels at the $40-50/barrel oil equivalent. All this requires funding, and so President Obama issued a directive in 2009 requesting the USDA

to make available additional funding for advanced biofuels development and commercialization. In response to this 30-day biofuels directive, USDA issued funding notices for a number of biofuels-related provisions and programs established in the food, conservation, and energy act of 2008.

As an example, one such program is the biomass crop assistance program (BCAP, Section 9011 of the 2008 farm bill). BCAP provides financial assistance for farmers seeking to establish new energy crops, as well as payments to cover the cost of collecting, harvesting, storing, and transporting renewable biomass. Qualified entities are eligible to receive a matching dollar payment for each dollar they receive from a qualified biomass conversion facility, up to a maximum of $45. Environmental review of the portion of the program dealing with the establishment of new crops is still pending.

The USDA also released in 2009 a notice of funding opportunity (NOFA) for the repowering assistance program (Section 9004). It provides financial assistance to re-tool existing bio-refineries to use renewable cellulosic biomass (agricultural residues, byproducts, wood, etc.) as the primary source of process energy in the facility.

By reducing fossil energy use in bio-refineries, the overall carbon footprint and climate impacts of biofuels can be greatly reduced. The number of awards and size of payments under this NOFA will vary depending on applicant response, but individual grants will not exceed 50% of project costs or $5 million, whichever is less.

Biofuels

Biofuels have become a very important, albeit controversial, issue in the U.S. and international politics. It is commonly believed that biofuels are good for a number of reasons, as follows:

Economic impacts
- Agricultural development
- Fuel diversity
- Income taxes increase
- International competitiveness
- Jobs creation
- Petroleum imports reduction
- Plant investments increase
- Sustainability

Environmental impacts
- Air pollution reduction
- Biodegradability
- Carbon sequestration_
- Greenhouse gas reductions

- Higher combustion efficiency
- Land and water use improvements

Energy Security
- Domestic distribution
- Domestic targets
- Fossil fuels use reduction
- Ready availability
- Renewability
- Supply reliability

These are complex and interwoven subjects and problems. And as with any good thing, there are problems, as we shall see below.

International Politics

Twenty-seven countries, the EU, Brazil and the U.S. have biofuel mandates. If these mandates are met as outlined, the global biofuel production will grow to about 250 billion liters by 2020. This is a significant increase from the present production of 170 billion liters by OECD countries.

The mandates were a mostly political response to a mixture of problems: high oil prices, cash from foreign investors, and failed crops (such as jatropha.) But whatever the reasons for the promotion of biofuels in the recent past, they have diminished even further and so for many governments and many U.S. states, the policies to encourage domestic consumption of biofuels remain only on paper. And if everything goes as it is at the present, things will not get any better anytime soon.

Some Asian countries are planning to abandon biofuels in exchange for help in stabilization of the energy supplies and prices. This means that if the oil-rich countries help them financially, there would be less biofuel and oil prices could go high again, a win-win situation for all involved.

Some of the second-tier biofuel producers, like Argentina, Indonesia, and Malaysia, produce for both domestic and export markets, but their capacity for biofuel exports (as opposed to exports of biofuel crops), will remain limited for a long time. This is due to the policies of the big markets (the EU, US, and Brazil), which favor domestic production and control over both domestic and imported supply by multi-nationals.

The growing biofuels markets of China and India are limited mostly by food security concerns, and China has banned the construction of new ethanol production plants that use grains. Instead, it is exploring production of non-grain crops on marginal lands, with little success so far. India is also staying away from using its grain supply for biofuels. There are hungry people to feed first, and before filling the gas tanks of the rich people.

Domestic ethanol production is focused on sugar cane, while biodiesel uses mostly jatropha. Both of these crops have problems and have failed dramatically to produce a steady and cheap supply. So, Chinese and Indian companies are looking overseas at opportunities for biofuel production, and some are working on setting up ethanol projects in various African and South American countries.

The Real Problems

There are no miracles in this world. Everything obeys the established scientific principals. Replacing gas with ethanol is not the solution to all of our problems. As a matter of fact, it creates some problems that were not foreseen by politicians and regulators. Some of these are:

The Politics

The biofuels story is one of good political decisions turning into bad policies, accompanied by good intentions generating bad consequences. The biofuels industry became big political issues in the last decade, which grew into a big business, and then fell into the abyss of increasingly controversial global-near-disaster.

The biofuels drive in the U.S. was intended to support farmers, provide energy security, and reduce our dependence on foreign oil. At the same time, biofuels were hastily promoted as the solution to the environmental problems, and a major contributor to increasing our economic independence. Biofuels would reduce the foreign oil, and environmentalists challenge the assertion that biofuels, particularly corn ethanol, offer a meaningful reduction in greenhouse gas emissions.

Current U.S. biofuels mandates do not represent the most efficient or precise instrument to meet any of the policy's stated goals. Although current biofuel mandates are not a good policy, they certainly represent an issue that has achieved political success. In the U.S., both Republicans and Democrats support biofuels, especially in farm states, so biofuel consensus is viewed as a great success.

The politicians see the strength of the pro-biofuels cause, because their usefulness can be justified in so many ways. This fact, in the involvement of masterful politicians is very useful in building support for biofuels. The industry support has been overwhelming, because production and use of biofuels impacts the major policy areas of energy policy, environmental policy, and agricultural development policy.

So why is it a bad policy? Simply because it lacks what good policymaking requires: precision and clarity of purpose. In this case, the hasty biofuels hoopla created unrealistic political realities of forming coalitions, which benefited from ambiguity, hiding costs, accepting second-best justifications, and packaging policies together to further broaden support for the sake of support. Biofuels are an instrument, not a policy or a political end.

The drawbacks to increased biofuels production, according to the specialists, were missed by the policymakers. The abnormalities occurred because: the rapid growth of the biofuels industry caught people (including farmers) by surprise, land-use change was ignored in energy accounting calculations, the magnitude of soil and biomass carbon loss upon land conversion was under-appreciated, and the selective use of a life-cycle assessment (LCA) methodology was not suited to good policy making.

These are factors that need to be used as warning signals while energy prices push politicians and policy makers to look for quick-fire alternatives.

Increase in Emissions

The EPA has warned for a while about the increase in total emissions during the production and use of biofuels. Dry corn-based ethanol, for example, that is converted into usable fuel using natural gas and coal-generated electricity, emits 20 pounds of GHGs per gallon during its production, as compared to 25 pounds per gallon for gasoline emitted mostly at the tailpipe. In addition, building the new biofuels production and use infrastructure (new crop fields, increased fertilizer use, new refineries, etc.) would eliminate the difference all together.

As a matter of fact, ADM, one of the largest biofuels producers is also one of the world's largest polluters. Just one of ADM's ethanol production plants is expected to have annual air emissions of 540 tons of volatile organic compounds (VOCs), 1.5 billion tons of sulfur oxides, 1.2 billion tons of carbon monoxide, 840 tons of nitrogen oxides, and 150 tons of other hazardous air pollutants.

Since ethanol was established as a fuel additive some time ago (replacing MTBE, which is a known carcinogen), there is a measurable increase in ozone and smog content in California's air. This is one of the most apparent, measurable, large-scale side effects of ethanol use to date. And as ethanol use increases, as planned, the ozone and smog will increase as well. And no one can predict what the final long-term effect of the increased smog pollution on human life would be in such a densely populated area.

The difference is not that great, so the biofuels policy, as it stands today, is not justifiable on the grounds of its climate friendliness alone. The policy targets only consider green house gas reductions and disregards detrimental impacts on ecosystems and human health, such as particulate matter from inferior air quality. This, therefore, according to industry specialists makes the mandates misguided and misinformed.

Increased Food Scarcity

Globally, U.S. biofuel policies have been heavily criticized, because diversion of food to energy crops has pushed up the prices of staple crops like corn in some developing countries. But the cost to people's lives from rising food prices cannot be measured properly when there is no consensus on the extent to which biofuels contribute to the price rises? There is no clear answer for this complex question.

Food vs. fuel is the debate, which was provoked by the biofuel's popularity and global growth. It addresses the risk of diverting food for biofuels crops production. Biofuels replacing food crops is considered a detriment to the global food supply, but the problem is that farmers are increasing the production of these crops, often through government subsidy incentives, so their land is shifted away from the traditional non-biofuel crops, which in turn drives up their prices due to the decrease in production.

Although there is no substantial increase in demand for the food staples, like corn and cassava, which sustain a large part of the world's poor, the anomaly contributed to the increase in the price of the other crops used by these individuals.

A recent study shows that market-driven expansion of ethanol in the U.S. increased maize prices by 21%

Figure 6-36. "Food, Not Fuel" movement

in 2009, as compared with 2004 levels. In 2011 biofuels production, and the related subsidies were considered leading causes of agricultural price shocks.

The *food vs. fuel* argument was even renamed to *food or fuel,* and so the debate continues internationally. It is controversial, with varying significance, and a number of variables, such as: what are the causes, and what is the ultimate impact? What is also unclear is what our (the people's and politicians') roles are in resolving the issues at hand and making biofuels equal participants in the fight for energy independence, clean environment, and social equality.

Land Grabbing

The politics of energy generation and use affect all of us, but the developed countries are the most affected, simply because they use most of the energy generated now. On the other hand, the politics of food deeply affect the developing countries. Especially lately, the widely spread drive for growing biofuel crops has created new markets and even new economies in some parts of the world. Africa seems to be most affected. In the past decade, an area of land eight times the size of the U.K. has been sold off globally as land sales rapidly accelerate. This land could feed a billion people, equivalent to the number of people who go to bed hungry each night. Instead the land is now, or will be later on, used to produce energy crops.

In poor countries, foreign investors have been buying an area of land the size of London every six days. This new phenomenon has been labeled land grabbing. Land grabbing is land acquisition that violates the human rights of the locals, flouts the principles of free and informed consent, is not based on a thorough assessment of social-economic and environmental impacts, avoids transparent contracts with clear and binding commitments on employment and benefit-sharing, and eschews democratic planning and meaningful participation in the projects at hand.

Large-scale land grabbing is the worst expression of the phenomenon. It is a large-scale land acquisition that can be defined as the acquisition of any tract of land larger than 200 hectares, or twice the median landholding, according to the national context. It is also larger than the average land holding in most developing countries.

There are two main areas of interest in land grabbing for investors.

The first is for production of biofuels and there is a huge demand for biofuels globally. The land has been used mainly for planting soy, palm oil, and sugar cane to produce ethanol for exports to Europe and North America. The second reason for land grabbing is producing food, also for export to the Middle East and Asia.

This bounty is happening on a continent where most of the countries have food insecurity, and where one in four people goes hungry every day. All this inequality is created mainly for the sake of providing biofuels for the rich people to drive their SUVs where and when they wish.

There are estimates that more than 60% of investments in agricultural land by foreign investors between 2000 and 2010 were in countries where food security was a major challenge. Africa's land is the most targeted, with known deals equaling nearly five percent of the continent's total agricultural area. While foreign investment is normally thought of as good for a country, some of the large land deals potentially threaten the livelihoods of 80 million small landholders, farmers, and pastoralists on the continent.

There is a difference between land deals and land grabs. Land grab essentially means that the communities, many of which are poor communities, lose their land and livelihood as a result of transactions that take place sometimes between governments and investors, and sometimes between elites and foreign investors. These processes leave families basically without any alternative livelihood. And in many cases the transactions are accompanied by violence and conflict. The countries most affected by land grab deals include, Ethiopia, Tanzania, Sudan, the Democratic Republic of Congo, and Madagascar. There have been over 700 deals since 2000 in these and other African countries, which are equivalent to the land area of the entire countries of Kenya or Cameroon.

Case Study: Ethiopia

Thousands of people in western Ethiopia are being driven off their lands so the government can sell large tracts for commercial agriculture to national and foreign companies. Since the 2008 global food crisis a number of countries like Saudi Arabia, the United Arab Emirates, India, and China have been buying vast areas of arable land across Africa to grow food to feed their growing populations and lately for biofuel production. This has caused global food prices to rise an average of 70-80% over the last decade alone.

In Ethiopia the government is forcibly moving tens of thousands of people out of the remote Gambella region in western Ethiopia. The displaced people receive little to no compensation and are forced to live in places without adequate water supply, food, or health and edu-

Figure 6-37. Land grabbing benefits all—except the local poor

cational facilities.

The government has already resettled over 1.5 million people from Gambella and the regions of Afar, Somali and Benishangul-Gumuz. Gambella is the size of Belgium with population of 607,000 and has rich and fertile soil, which is why the foreign and domestic investors have leased large tracts of land. Over 9.5 million acres of land have been already leased at very favorable prices.

This is land grabbing at its worst: done by rich multi-nationals at the expense of the poor and defenseless local populations who are left to suffer and go hungry. Up to 123.5 million acres of African land, double the size of Britain, have been leased by governments, multinational companies, or wealthy investors. The Ethiopian government has approved and signed agreements for 815 foreign-financed and owned agricultural projects since 2007.

Asian and Middle East companies have bought 560 million acres of farmland in the developing countries on the African continent, often at bargain prices, some at less than a dollar per hectare. Ethiopia now supports the export of fruit and vegetables worth $60 million annually, as well as flowers worth $160 million per year, while per capita income is around $1,000 per year, which qualifies Ethiopia as the world's poorest country.

Until now the land grabbing was mostly for food production, but now the crime is intensifying, with investment banks, hedge funds, commodity traders, corporations and business tycoons grabbing some of the world's cheapest land. Not for food, but for profit. Biofuel crops could be grown on these lands, exported for processing into biofuels and for use by the rich coun-

tries. The Ethiopians get nothing, and the displaced are not even properly informed, let alone consulted. The land grabbing crime is expanding, and is only going to cause further deterioration of the country and the entire African continent.

Soil Erosion and Deforestation

Huge demand for biofuel has led to clearing land for energy crops. For example, in Indonesia alone, over 9,400,000 acres of forest have been converted to plantations since 1996. Trees are most efficient in removing CO_2 through photosynthesis, many times better than sugar cane, corn, or most other biofuel feedstock crops. Large-scale deforestation of mature trees contributes to un-sustainable global warming atmospheric greenhouse gas levels, loss of habitat, and a reduction of valuable biodiversity both on land as in oceans.

Farming for biofuel production eliminates permanently great forested areas, which causes unacceptable loss of biodiversity for the sake of marginal decrease in fossil fuel consumption. The loss of biodiversity also makes heavy dependence on biofuels very risky by reducing our ability to deal with some diseases, such as blights, that affect some of the important biofuel crops that are grown in these areas. Food crops can recover from blights by mixing old stock with blight resistant wild strains, but as biodiversity is lost to excessive agriculture, the possibilities for recovering from blights are reduced and even lost.

Under normal operating conditions, a significant portion of the biomass is left on the fields to support the soil resource and boost the growth of the new crops. If all the biomass is removed, the soil will suffer and with time will become less productive and more prone to erosion during periodic rain seasons.

Increased Water Use

Growing large land areas of energy crops uses a lot of water as well. Assuming significant amounts of water recycling (which takes a lot of energy), it takes about five gallons of new water to produce the fermentation mix needed to make one gallon of ethanol. So, our 1000 million gallons bio-ethanol plant needs 500 million gallons of new water annually to operate properly and efficiently.

An ethanol plant that produces 100 million gallons a year uses about the same amount of water needed by a town of five thousand people. The fear of excess water withdrawal from the aquifer has caused significant opposition to plants in some communities.

In addition, there are approximately 5-13 gallons of

wastewater to dispose of for each gallon of ethanol produced. So, our 100 million gallons bioethanol production plant will also produce 500 to 1,300 million gallons of wastewater. The wastewater can do substantial damage if discharged directly into waterways so it needs to be treated to reduce the pollutant content, which requires more water and more energy, and emits more pollutants.

Even though some energy crops may produce less greenhouse gas than gasoline, they have greater aggregate environmental costs than gasoline, if and when air and water pollution, soil degradation, and a number of social effects are considered. Biofuels also use a lot of land, which in many cases could be better used to supply food for a malnourished population.

The Brazilian use of sugarcane as the feedstock for ethanol production makes a lot more sense than using corn grain as the feedstock. There is actually a net energy gain when starting with cane sugar.

Nevertheless, in all cases the water problems and air pollution associated with ethanol production and from automobile exhaust fumes, as well as pollution from ethanol plants means that there are significant environmental drawbacks that need to be considered in the overall estimates.

Accidents and Fatalities

One thing about corn production that is not well known is the fact that there are more accidents and deaths in corn production than there are in coal mining. In addition to countless worker accidents during corn field preparation, harvesting, and transport, there are also a significant number of fatalities. In most cases we don't hear about these cases, because they happen on smaller farms that are exempt from most federal health and safety rules.

There are hundreds of thousands of corn silos on small and medium-size farms and at local grain terminals, where corn is stored before being transported for processing. Most of these operations employ fewer than 10 workers, so they are exempt from most federal health and safety rules and are in many cases ill equipped.

Minors often work at these silos for their parents, or close relatives, or just to earn few bucks. They are exempt from all labor regulations, which is a feature of federal law since 1938, based on the supposition that parents will take extra care of their own children. But the system is not working, because there have been over 80 deaths in silos since 2007, and most of the victims were minors.

Federal labor standards apply only to the 13,000 largest grain handling facilities, and there are very few accidents at these facilities. According to the Department of Labor's communication to the small-size silo operators, "As an employer of workers facing these hazards, you have the legal obligation to protect and train your workers. Criminal prosecution would be recommended in future egregious cases."

But the silo deaths and injuries continue. One example is the case of a 14-year-old, working in a commercial grain-elevator complex, who was sent into a 500,000-bushel storage tower to loosen corn kernels that were sticking to the side. Shortly after he and other teenage workers entered the bin in July, 2010, a manager at the base opened two floor holes to speed the flow of the grain. The sudden action dragged the boy, who was walking atop the corn to help it flow, toward the floor of the bin. The wall of corn fell on him, engulfing him under the corn as he screamed for help. Another teenager walking nearby rushed over to aid him and also was quickly entrapped. Both teenagers died in seconds. A third young worker was injured when he became trapped trying to save his friend who was trapped moments earlier. Pinned against the lifeless body of his friend for nearly 12 hours, as 300 rescuers worked to drain the bin and free him, he managed to keep his head above the corn and survived.

In another case, 17-year-old high school seniors were working inside a commercial grain bin in Kremlin, Oklahoma operating a 10-inch sweep auger on the floor. The leg of one of the boys got caught in the auger, and when the other one tried to help him, he also became ensnared in the machinery. Each teenager lost a leg. These boys were ill-equipped to do a job that even adults should not do, thus sacrificing the boys to save a buck and get more corn out, were the complaints of the grieving parents.

Experts have documented more than 800 serious entrapment cases in silos during the last two decades, a count that is likely shy by hundreds because many accidents go unreported.

The federal government proposed new child labor rules for agriculture in 2011, the first major revision in nearly half a century. The proposed regulations would have barred young workers from entering silos and other enclosed spaces, and set new limits on the height of ladders that they could climb, and other safety precautions. But they went much further in other areas, prohibiting teenagers from doing a broad array of farm tasks including herding livestock and driving large farm vehicles.

The reaction of the farm community, however, was

intense, with thousands of farmers writing in protest. Even some parents of children killed in farm accidents opposed the measures.

Both parties in Congress demanded that the rules be killed in their entirety, thus squandering an opportunity to improve working conditions on small farms. The White House stood silent on the matter and finally ordered the Department of Labor to kill the proposal.

The Department of Labor has increased enforcement in recent years, from 663 citations for grain handling violations issued in 2008, the number jumped to 1,532 in 2011, but federal regulators had no jurisdiction over small farms. Instead, worker safety officials fine the violators some arbitrary dollar amount for general safety violations—an amount that is some times cut in half once the malfunctioning equipment is fixed and new warning signs are posted.

In the end, the status quo remains and with corn production increasing to produce bioethanol, even more young workers will be maimed and killed in the nation's silos.

The Failures

In the summer of 2012 the federal government tried to recoup at least $5.0 million out of the $6.5 million Thompson River Power LLC biomass power plant received in American recovery and reinvestment funds. The funds were received only several short months before the company filed for bankruptcy. The U.S. Treasury awarded the grant in 2010, ostensibly to reimburse developers of renewable energy with cash payments equivalent to 30% of their project's costs. The grant to Thompson River, majority-owned by a Minnesota private-equity firm, was to convert a coal-fired plant to burn wood, which is considered a renewable power source.

After receiving the funds, and seeing the mounting troubles, Thompson River was sold to Wayzata investment partners, which filed for bankruptcy in the bankruptcy court for the district of Delaware just one week after the settlement with the state was signed. As they say in the old country, "It is not crazy who eats two cakes, but rather who gives them to him."

Thompson River Power, LLC owned and operated a 14 MW power plant that provided low cost steam and power. The company was incorporated in 2007 and is based in Wayzata, Minnesota. It was an old coal-fired power plant on which a new ownership group, led by Wayzata, spent more than $20 million to bring into compliance with emissions rules and burn "clean coal" only. After finishing the work Wayzata announced that the

plant would burn only wood and biomass, which made it eligible for grants and subsidies from the recovery act money—as long it was technologically capable of producing power. Soon thereafter, however, the plant owners found out that what they had promised is just hot air and they simply couldn't operate the plant profitably by just burning wood and sure enough, Thompson River Power, LLC is no more.

Politicians and regulators could have been much more diligent, and saved taxpayers a lot of money if they have looked more carefully in the operation to see that from the very start it has been plagued by poor design, shifting goals, hundreds of environmental violations, and investigations of criminal activities. But it gets even worse. Insiders report that the plant never operated either as a coal- or wood-burning plant after receiving the money. It produced neither power nor new jobs, both of which were requirements for the $6.5 million subsidy. Did they lie to the government, or did the government officials just close their eyes and hand the money over?

Present Day

The U.S. government has issued new standards to raise biofuel production estimates. The EPA now requires the production of 14 million gallons of so-called cellulosic biofuels, those made from grasses and woody materials. That is almost twice the previous 8.7 million-gallon requirements in 2012. But according to EPA's own records, no cellulosic fuel was produced in 2010 or 2011 at all, and only about 25,000 gallons was produced in 2012. All this was in the wake of a U.S. Court of Appeals for the District of Columbia decision to throw out the 2012 mandate for cellulosic biofuels all together. The court said that the mandate is based on *wishful thinking* rather than on accurate estimates.   The administration insisted that increased use of biofuels will lower GHG emissions that contribute to global warming, and well as lower U.S. dependence on foreign fuel. The EPA also believes that the proposed standards are a reasonable representation of expected production of biofuels in the future.

The biofuels mandate is part of a 2007 renewable fuels law that requires a certain amount of ethanol and other renewable fuels to be mixed in with gasoline each year. Despite annual EPA projections for millions of gallon of biofuels made from switch grass, corn husks or wood pulp, little production has materialized.

On the good side of things, and despite that track record, the renewable fuel industry considers the new EPA mandate realistic, citing recent breakthroughs in which several long-delayed biofuel projects have come online. Two companies, in Mississippi and Florida, have recently begun production of cellulosic biofuel, and dozens more are moving forward, including plants under construction in Iowa, Kansas and Michigan.

The promised production of biofuels has failed to materialize thus far, yes, but after years of setbacks caused by the financial downturn and other issues, the industry is poised for a major breakthrough in the post-2013 era of EPA biofuels mandate. A major, $550 million, biofuels production plants by Abengoa Bioengergy to convert crop residues into ethanol in southwest Kansas is expected to generate 75 megawatts of electricity and 15 million gallons of ethanol per year.

OCEAN POWER

The world's oceans contain the largest amount of renewable (albeit potential) energy known to man. Its vast shores are blasted day and night by powerful waves, and even more powerful currents flow back and forth around the world. That is a lot of energy waiting to be harnessed, but this is not an easy task. The inhospitable ocean environment with its storms, corrosion, and other unpredictable phenomena is hard to work with and very few materials and structures can withstand its uncontrollable and capricious powers. Nevertheless, we are trying. There are several technologies that have already shown good progress, but most of them are still far from large-scale commercial applications.

Tidal Power Technology

Wave-power devices have been around for a long time, the first being in the 18th century. For hundreds of years the effort was idle, until the mid-1970s, when the Arab oil crisis prompted governments to release money, inspiring scientists to develop wave generators. One such generator, known as the salter's duck, was planned for installation in Scotland. The contraption consisted of curved, floating canisters the size of a house. These were strung together and tethered to the ocean floor, and when tossed about by the waves, each one would rock back and forth. Hydraulics attached to the floaters would convert the rocking motion to rotational motion, which in turn drove a generator and generated electricity.

A single duck was capable of generating six MW of electricity, or enough to power around 4,000 homes. Several ducks would power an entire city. Initial estimates put the cost of generating electricity by the ducks at nearly $1 per kilowatt-hour (kWh), which was far more than nuclear power at the time.

As with all other renewable technologies, as soon as the oil crisis subsided, the program was shut down, this one by the British government in 1982.

Figure 6-38. Ocean wave energy generator

Tidal-power technology, for a number of reasons, is in its infancy, but a there are a handful of speculative ventures under way in the U.S. and around the world. The ocean renewable power company (OrpC) has a $2.5 million tidal grid-compatible power system, the first in the U.S. A stationary barge contains the power generator, which is turned by two spinning turbines below the surface to generate electricity. The turbines, or foils, look like a whirling double helix and are moved by the ocean waves and currents and generate enough power to run the control room and charge the batteries of a coastguard vessel.

Although a small model can be made to work easily, a large commercial plant is a different animal. Way back in the 1930s Franklin Roosevelt unveiled a federal project to harness tidal power with dams, but the project failed a year later. Other initiatives also have come and gone through the years. Although the state-of-the-art has improved tremendously since Roosevelt, the tremendous destructive powers of violent ocean waves and currents as well as the corrosive action of salty water create some formidable challenges that are still to be resolved. The competition from the other energy sources does not help the cause of tidal power either, and, although it has a tremendous potential, as federal money goes away, tidal power in the U.S. might have to wait for another renewable energy boom cycle.

The 1980s were boom years for a number of energy technologies. The U.S. government, through its technological offices, administered a number of wind, solar, and other alternative energy development programs, which unfortunately, were dropped in the 1990s.

OTEC

the ocean thermal energy conversion (OTEC) permit office was an example of one of the early high hopes for renewable energy that turned into a bust. Its goal was to develop energy generation technology for using the thermal difference of the ocean waters. It opened its doors in 1981 and closed them in 1994. There was not one single successful OTEC development, nor permit issued during the 13 years of its existence.

The OTEC office was part of America's national oceanic and atmospheric administration (NOAA)—the marine counterpart of the country's space agency, NASA. OTEC's goal was to exploit the difference in temperature between the top of the ocean and the bottom, to develop technologies capable of driving turbines powered by the ocean temperature differentials and generate electricity for general use.

The reason for this effort, and the incentive behind it, was the oil-price spike of the 1970s. But once the incentive went away after the oil prices went down and stabilized, the interest in alternative sources of power, and the money supporting the respective efforts, evaporated. With that, the advances in wind and solar were frozen in time, and so were any hopes of developing power from the oceans. OTEC was canned together with all other ideas for renewable power development.

Fast forward 30 years, and alternative power sources are back in fashion. And OTEC is one of them—again.

This time, just like the last one, it all started with government grants and incentives, but through the involvement of private companies we might actually see results this time. The idea of power generation using free fuel is quite attractive, so long as the capital cost is not too high. Most of the equipment bits and pieces needed to make the ocean power equipment already exist in other areas of engineering, such as deep water oil drilling.

A range of companies, including some of the world's largest concerns, is working on the ocean power generating technologies now. The most common OTEC design uses a fluid with a low boiling point—typically ammonia, which circulates through a network of pipes. The ammonia liquid is first vaporized in a heat exchanger that is warmed by surface water with a temperature of around 25°C, or higher. Thus vaporized gas creates enough pressure to spin a turbine and generate electricity. The gas is then sent to a condenser, where it is cooled by cold seawater pumped from the deep where the tem-

perature is about 5°C. Thus condensed ammonia liquid is sent back in the first heat exchanger and the process is repeated ad infinitum. This means that OTEC plants can be built anywhere in deep ocean waters with surface temperature above 25°C.

The U.S. Department of Defense is interested in this technology for providing power for its bases in the Pacific and Indian Oceans, but the Pentagon's budget limitations would delay the efforts. Lockheed is working with a smaller firm in Hawaii to build a 10 MW pilot plant, which planned to be in operation by 2015. A 100 MW power plant will follow by 2020, if the first project is successful.

The larger plants, however, bring extraordinary challenges, which are not even addressed by the smaller, experimental power plants. The 100 MW OTEC power plant, for example, will require building and maintaining a very large inlet pipe. This enormous pipe is 3/4 mile long and 30 feet in diameter, and the pumps that are needed to power this immense water flow would use almost all the energy the system can produce. This would decrease the efficiency and increase the cost of large OTEC power plants above the acceptable, so new technology will have to be developed to address the technological and financial constrains.

A more practical, hybrid type of OTEC project is planned in the Bahamas. Cold water will be pumped from the ocean depths to provide cooling for a resort hotel at a cost of $100 million. Then, the same water can be used to generate about 10 MW electric power.

NOTE: The first OTEC plant was built in 1930 at Matanzas Bay, Cuba. It was successful in consistently producing over 20 kW of electricity for a while, but was eventually destroyed by the ocean wind and waves. Eight decades later, with not much progress to report, the OTEC technology could use the overall technological advancements of late and finally find its place in the energy mix.

Federal Regulation

Non-federal hydroelectric power projects, including tidal and wave energy projects that are interconnected with the interstate electric transmission grid, are subject to licensing by the federal energy regulatory commission (FERC). Traditionally, FERC has only issued 30-50 year licenses for commercial-scale projects. However, in light of the need for developers to be able to deploy projects on a short-term basis to evaluate the economic and technical feasibility and the environmental effects of various technologies, FERC has created a stream-lined pilot project licensing process to allow the licensing of demonstration hydrokinetic projects for testing purposes.

Pilot projects must be small, short-term, avoid sensitive locations, subject to modification or shut-down if unforeseen impacts occur, subject to plans for monitoring and safeguarding public safety and environmental resources, and removed, with the site restored, at the end of the license term unless a commercial license is issued.

All tidal and wave energy projects, whether interconnected with the electric grid or not, are subject to permitting by the U.S. Army corps of engineers (COE) under Section 404 of the clean water act (regulating the discharge of dredged or fill materials into waters of the U.S.) and/or Section 10 of the rivers and harbors act (regulating construction and other work in navigable waters).

State Regulation

Tidal and wave energy projects are subject to permitting by the department of environmental protection (DEP) under the Maine waterway development and conservation act (MWDCA), the state's one-stop hydropower permitting law. The MWDCA requires an evaluation of the full range of potential economic and environmental impacts of a project, including impacts on public safety, wetlands, water quality, fish and wildlife resources, historic and archaeological sites, public access, and energy generation. DEP has permitting jurisdiction over all tidal and wave energy projects located in state waters (those waters within three miles of the mainland and any island that is part of Maine).

Tidal and wave energy projects are also subject to review under Section 401 of the clean water act, which requires that any applicant for a federal license or permit for an activity that may result in a discharge to navigable waters obtain a certification from the state that the activity will not violate applicable state water quality standards. These standards consist of designated uses and numeric and narrative criteria designed to ensure that Maine 's waters satisfy the swimmable-fishable goals of the clean water act. These standards also include an anti-degradation policy requiring that existing in-stream uses be maintained and protected. DEP has certification authority over all tidal and wave energy projects located in state waters.

The U.S. Tidal Power Progress

According to a 2008 DOE report, when combined with hydropower and other water-based resources, tidal and wave power generation could help to raise the U.S. electricity supply to 15% by 2030. When combined with growing solar and wind sectors, tidal and wave have the potential to add to a strong and expanding renewable energy portfolio.

The final outcome, however, depends on the ability of these technologies to attract enough private capital to get off the ground. Until now they have depended largely on federal financial support, which is not a guaranteed thing and is actually going away.

Still, the DOE report is another indication of the potential of the U.S. to develop clean, homegrown energy that generates not only power, but also creates jobs that come along with such development; 15% by 2030 might seem like a long way to go, but the technology is there, and our decisions today are the only barrier to legitimate energy tomorrow.

In 2012 FERC issued the first ever commercial license to a tidal power project in the U.S. to the Verdant Power, whose turbine design and East River project site have been under development for years. The first turbines were installed at this site in 2002. The first turbines got mangled by the fierce tides, so it took a while for the company to redesign and improve the initial design.

And now, the 1.0 MW project is expected to sell enough energy to Con Edison to power almost 1,000 nearby homes. The first 5 turbines are expected to be installed and operational in 2014. This is a big moment for the tidal power industry and the entire renewable energy industry. The results from this project will certainly affect the U.S. energy policy and the regulation of tidal energy generation.

Case Study: Maine

Tidal power in Maine is attracting a lot of attention and might be used as an example for other states working with tidal power projects.

Federal-State Coordination

In 2009, Maine became the first state on the east coast and only the third state in the country to sign a memorandum of understanding (MOU) with the federal energy regulatory commission (FERC) to coordinate procedures and schedules for review of tidal energy projects in state waters or in federal waters (beyond the three-mile state territorial limit) where the projects affect resources or uses in Maine's coastal zone.

Ocean Energy Legislation

Also in 2009, the Maine legislature passed and the governor signed into law an act to facilitate testing and demonstration of renewable ocean energy technology.

This law was enacted to streamline and coordinate state permitting and submerged lands leasing requirements for renewable ocean energy demonstration projects so that the state of Maine can become an international proving ground for testing new technologies in specific locations along the coast in an environmentally responsible manner.

The 2009 law provides that a municipality may not enact or enforce any requirement for a tidal energy demonstration project located within the municipality that is stricter than the requirements of the general permit process, and the municipality has the burden of proving that the project is located within its municipal boundaries.

The law amended the Maine waterway development and conservation act (MWDCA) to establish a new general permit process for tidal energy demonstration projects. To qualify for a general permit as a tidal energy demonstration project, a project must use tidal action as a source of electrical power; must have a total installed generating capacity of five megawatts or less; and must be proposed for the primary purpose of testing tidal energy generation technology, including mooring or anchoring systems and transmission lines, and collecting and assessing information on the environmental and other effects of the technology.

The general permit process for tidal energy demonstration projects is designed to dovetail with the FERC pilot project licensing procedures for hydrokinetic technologies. In applying for a general permit, an applicant must submit:

1. A copy of a pilot project license application, as filed with FERC, along with all information required by FERC

2. A proof of general liability insurance for the project

3. Demonstration of financial and technical capacity to construct and operate the project

4. A copy of an environmental assessment for the project issued by FERC under the national environmental policy act (NEPA) that includes a finding of no significant environmental impact (FONSI)

5. An acknowledgement that the DEP may require the applicant to take remedial action under the law, including the cessation of operations and removal of project facilities, to protect natural resources and/or public safety

Once all the required information has been filed, the DEP must act within 60 days on an application for a general permit and water quality certification for a tidal energy demonstration project.

Usually a general permit for a tidal energy demonstration project is valid for the term of the pilot project license issued by FERC. The DEP may grant one or more extensions of the general permit term to coincide with any approved extension(s) of the pilot project license or any related annual license issued by FERC.

The 2009 law also amended the natural resources protection act (NRPA) to establish a new general permit process for offshore wind energy demonstration projects, including wave energy test projects. To qualify for this general permit, a wave energy test project must use ocean wave energy to produce electricity; be proposed as part of an offshore wind energy demonstration project; be designed and sited to test production of electricity from wave energy in conjunction with and in a manner that complements electricity produced by an offshore wind energy turbine; employ up to two wave energy converters, each of which may use different technology that is not already in use in the Gulf of Maine for commercial energy production, for the primary purpose of testing and validating the overall design of the converter and related systems; and may include a mooring or anchoring system and an ocean sensor package.

In 2010, the Maine legislature passed and the governor signed into law an act to implement the recommendations of the governor's ocean energy task force. This law was enacted to overcome economic, technical and regulatory obstacles and to provide economic incentives for vigorous and efficient development of promising indigenous, renewable ocean energy resources in ways that recognize the concurrent need to sustain the ongoing biological integrity of the State's waters, the vitality and productivity of ocean harvests and the differing needs and uses of the seas and other natural resources and to ensure the provision of these benefits to the people of the state by the careful use of such public resources for renewable ocean energy production.

The 2010 law provides that a municipality may not enact or enforce any ordinance that prohibits the siting of a tidal or wave energy project, including associated facilities, within that municipality and may only regulate a project or part of a project located within its boundaries.

The 2010 law amended the MWDCA to provide that it is the policy of the state to encourage the attraction of appropriately sited development related to tidal and wave energy, including any additional transmission and other energy infrastructure needed to transport such energy to market, consistent with all state environmental standards; the permitting and siting of tidal and wave energy projects; and the siting, permitting, financing and construction of tidal and wave energy research and manufacturing facilities. Thus, all applications for tidal and wave energy projects must be processed in keeping with this policy.

The 2010 law also sought to encourage tidal and wave energy development by:

• Requiring that the public utilities commission take into account the state's renewable energy generation goals in determining the public need for proposed transmission lines

• Directing the public utilities commission to solicit proposals for long-term contracts to supply installed capacity and associated renewable energy and renewable energy credits from one or more tidal energy demonstration projects

• Directing the governor's office of energy independence and security to make recommendations to the legislature regarding terms and conditions for long-term contracts to supply installed capacity and associated renewable energy and renewable energy credits from renewable ocean energy projects

• Directing the Maine port authority to assess existing port facilities and make recommendations to the legislature regarding acquisition of real estate needed to facilitate renewable ocean energy development opportunities.

• Directing the bureau of revenue services to report to the legislature regarding whether and under what circumstances ocean energy-generating equipment in transit within the state on April 1 is exempt from personal property tax.

• Establishing a renewable ocean energy trust fund to protect and enhance the integrity of public trust-related resources and related human uses of the state's submerged lands.

The 2010 law also made several procedural changes in existing law to streamline the review process for tidal and wave energy projects. Under these changes:

• The DEP has original jurisdiction over any tidal or wave energy general permit application, while the board of environmental protection only has authority to hear any administrative appeal of the commissioner's decision;

• Any judicial appeal of a DEP or BEP decision on a tidal or wave energy general permit must be made directly to the Maine Supreme court, instead of going first to superior court

• The DEP may enter into an agreement for outside review of an application for a tidal or wave energy project without requiring that the applicant consent to the outside review and agree to pay all costs associated with the review

• Tidal and wave energy projects are not required to be consistent with land use regulation commission zoning, even if located in an unorganized territory.

Internationally
The Severn barrage

The Severn barrage project is one of the most grandiose plans for using ocean power ever. It is a plan for building a barrage from the English coast to the Welsh coast over the Severn tidal estuary. Damming (barraging) the Severn estuary (and Bristol Channel) has been a topic of discussion since the 19th century. This would be a huge engineering feat, on the level of the world's biggest and most daring construction projects.

It is actually a multi-purpose project, to be used for: transport links, flood protection, harbor creation, and tidal power generation. Recently the tidal power generation has taken a priority. Although the Severn tidal power feasibility study of 2010 claims that the project can generate about 5% of the Britain's electricity, the government concluded that there was no strategic case for building the barrage. Instead, it will continue to investigate emerging technologies for future use.

With the financial crisis of late, the Severn barrage, together with the U.S. tidal power development projects is going to be delayed for what might be a long while.

REGULATORY ASPECTS OF POWER GENERATION

The U.S. energy sector is driven by political decisions. A decisive factor in its development is the regulatory body, consisting of a number of federal and state agencies. These are entities like BLM, DOE, DOL, DOD, EPA, the core of engineers, and other organizations, paid for by U.S. taxpayers dollars to inspect, control, and regulate the development and use of energy in the U.S.

Regulatory Bodies

There are many, many organizations, regulations, programs, and issues related to the energy-environment developments. We cannot possibly review all of them, because an entire book would be needed for that. Instead, we will provide a number of aspects and issues that we feel are most important to understand and work on their future optimization.

The Energy Regulators

The federal and state governments, with the help of a number of agencies, put their two pence in the energy regulations, thus establishing the direction of the country in its battle for energy independence and clean environment.

The major players in the energy business in the U.S. are:

The Federal Energy Regulatory Commission

The federal energy regulatory commission (FERC) is an independent regulatory agency within the Department of Energy that rules over many energy related projects and issues. FERC is also the leading regulatory body in determining the impact of energy and energy generation on the consumers. It has jurisdiction over electricity generation, pricing, licensing for hydroelectric plants liquid natural gas (LNG) terminals, and oil pipeline transport rates.

FERC is a rate administrator, and licensing body, and is most infamously remembered for allowing gross oversight of energy prices by Enron. Nevertheless, FERC is still around (Enron is not) and will continue to be a major player in determining important issues like utility deregulation, and the oversight of major natural gas, hydropower, and LNG projects.

Hydropower Regulation

The federal power act of 1920 gives the federal energy regulatory commission the exclusive authority to issue licenses to nonfederal hydroelectric power projects on navigable waterways and federal lands. FERC may issue licenses to corporations, states or municipalities for the purpose of "constructing, operating, and maintaining dams, water conduits, reservoirs, powerhouses, transmission lines, or other project works necessary or convenient for the development and improvement of navigation and for the development, transmission, and utilization of power..." The FPA specifies that such licenses shall only be issued upon any part of the public lands and reservations of the U.S. if it will not interfere or be inconsistent with the purpose of the reservation.

The commission's office of energy projects is responsible for administering the hydropower program. All licensing matters and environmental compliance ac-

tivities are managed from Washington, DC. Dam safety and public safety inspections are also coordinated from Washington, DC. Engineers located in New York, Atlanta, Chicago, San Francisco, and Portland, Oregon inspect all projects periodically to ensure dam safety and public safety.

The commission employs many specialists to evaluate all phases of constructing, operating and maintaining all regulated hydropower projects, including: mechanical, civil, and electrical engineers; geologists, soil scientists, historians and economists; fishery biologists, aquatic ecologists, wildlife biologists, botanists and ecologists; and outdoor recreation planners and land-use planners.

When issuing a new license, FERC considers the power and development purposes of the project, but also gives equal consideration to the purposes of energy conservation, the protection, mitigation of damage to, and enhancement of fish and wildlife (including related spawning grounds and habitat), the protection of recreational opportunities, and the preservation of other aspects of environmental quality.

FERC issues hydropower licenses for 30-50 years. When a license expires, the applicant may apply to FERC for a new long-term operating license. Because many public laws and regulations (particularly with regard to the environment) were enacted after the original licenses for these projects, the relicensing process can be very complex and expensive, involving a many stakeholders.

The expense and complexity of relicensing (in addition to the potential contentiousness and the possibility of legal disputes delaying license) has prompted FERC to reform the relicensing process several times. In 1997, FERC approved the alternative licensing process that was designed to encourage settlement agreements. In 2003, FERC approved the current "default" licensing process— the integrated licensing process—that is intended to make the process more predictable, efficient, and streamlined by encouraging early identifications of issues and better integrating other agency permitting processes.

See Appendix A.7 below for a detailed list of laws and regulations affecting hydropower relicensing.

The Nuclear Regulatory Commission

The nuclear regulatory commission (NRC) is an independent agency of the U.S. government, established by the energy reorganization act of 1974. It is a successor agency to the U.S. atomic energy commission and is in charge of overseeing nuclear reactor safety and security, reactor licensing and renewal, radioactive material safety, and spent fuel storage, security, recycling, and disposal.

The NRC's major mission now is to regulate the use of nuclear materials, byproducts, and special nuclear materials as needed to ensure adequate protection of public health and safety. It is also in charge of promoting the security of nuclear materials and their use, and protecting the environment.

The NRC's regulatory authority consists of: commercial nuclear reactors for generating electric power and research and test reactors used for research, testing, and training; nuclear materials, including uses of nuclear materials in medical, industrial, academic settings, and facilities that produce nuclear fuel; and waste nuclear materials and their transportation, storage, and disposal of nuclear materials and waste, and decommissioning of nuclear facilities from service.

The NRC is headed by five commissioners, each appointed by the U.S. President for five-year terms. One of the commissioners is the chairman and official spokesperson of the commission.

California Energy Commission

The California energy commission (CEC) is the state's primary energy policy and planning agency. It was created by the legislature in 1974 with headquarters in Sacramento, California. Its basic responsibilities in setting the state's energy policy are as follows:

- Licensing thermal power plants 50 megawatts or larger

- Forecasting future energy needs

- Promoting energy efficiency and conservation by setting the state's appliance and building efficiency standards

- Supporting public interest energy research that advances energy science and technology through research, development and demonstration programs

- Developing renewable energy resources and alternative renewable energy technologies for buildings, industry, and transportation

- Planning for and directing state response to energy emergencies

The governor of California appoints commissioners to staggered five-year terms and selects a chair and vice chair every two years. One member is selected from the public at large, while the rest represent the different fields of engineering, physical science, economics, environmental protection, and law.

Energy Efficiency Legislation

Energy efficiency seems to be an important part of the national energy policy now. It is also a political phenomenon. When other legislation was stalled in Congress, President Obama signed the American energy manufacturing technical corrections act (H.R. 6582) in 2012, which received bipartisan support. The law is a modification of the enabling energy savings innovations act (H.R. 4850) and includes elements of the Shaheen-Portman Senate bill. It is geared toward ensuring energy efficiency and was praised by environmentalists, who also cautioned that there is far more work to be done.

The bill contains only minor changes to the current modus operandi, which include coordination of research and development of efficiency technologies for industry and a study of barriers to industrial electrical efficiency.

Also included in the bill are best practices for advanced metering in the federal government, and disclosure of energy and water usage by federal facilities. There are also technical corrections and specific fixes to recently enacted standards, uniform treatment of conventional and tankless water heaters, and clarification of periodic review of commercial equipment standards and of DOE's response to petitions regarding standards.

The bill also relaxes some standards, including rules for walk-in coolers, over-the-counter refrigerators and water heaters. The major function of this bill, however, is that it lays the groundwork for more significant bills which call for stronger national model building codes, more loan guarantees for efficiency upgrades and increased research and development on energy efficiency.

It is widely accepted on the local and federal levels that energy efficiency is a money-saver and a job creator. It is on that level that we will see some work done in pushing through legislation amongst politicians, since they love to claim increased jobs numbers.

U.S. ENVIRONMENTAL REGULATIONS

The U.S. is adhering to strict regulation of air, water, and soil, which were established some time ago. At the same time new regulations are also being developed as we speak. The key regulations controlling the affected areas, companies, and industries follow.

The Environmental Regulators

The Environmental Protection Agency

The environmental protection agency (EPA) is a federal agency, created in 1970 for the purpose of protecting human health and the environment by writing and enforcing regulations based on laws passed by Congress. The agency is led by an administrator, who is appointed by the President and approved by Congress. Although EPA is not a cabinet department, the administrator is normally given a cabinet rank.

The EPA has its headquarters in Washington, D.C., regional offices for each of the agency's ten regions, and 27 laboratories. The agency has approximately 17,000 full-time employees and engages many more people on a contractual basis. More than half of EPA human resources are engineers, scientists, and environmental protection specialists; other groups include legal, public affairs, financial, and information technologists.

The EPA's main mission is to protect human health and the environment, and to ensure that:

- All Americans are protected from significant risks to human health and the environment where they live, learn and work
- The national efforts to reduce environmental risk are based on the best available scientific information
- Federal laws protecting human health and the environment are enforced fairly and effectively
- Environmental protection is an integral consideration in U.S. policies concerning natural resources, human health, economic growth, energy, transportation, agriculture, industry, and international trade, and these factors are similarly considered in establishing environmental policy
- All parts of society—communities, individuals, businesses, and state, local and tribal governments—have access to accurate information sufficient to effectively participate in managing human health and environmental risks
- Environmental protection contributes to making our communities and ecosystems diverse, sustainable, and economically productive
- The U.S. plays a leadership role in working with other nations to protect the global environment

Summaries of environmental laws and regulations that EPA has issued, or has been somehow involved in their formulation and/or enforcement of are listed following. We review some of the ones listed previously, so the following is only the complete list.

The following regulations are intended to protect human health and the environment, where EPA is charged with administering all or a part of each.
- Atomic energy act (AEA)
- Chemical safety information, site security and fu-

els regulatory relief act
- Clean air act (CAA)
- Clean water act (CWA) (original title: federal water pollution control amendments of 1972)
- Comprehensive environmental response, compensation and liability act (CERCLA, or Superfund)
- Emergency planning and community right-to-know act (EPCRA)
- Endangered species act (ESA)
- Energy independence and security act (EISA)
- Energy policy act
- EO 12898: Federal actions to address environmental justice in minority populations and low-income populations
- EO 13045: protection of children from environmental health risks and safety risks
- EO 13211: actions concerning regulations that significantly affect energy supply, distribution, or use
- Federal food, drug, and cosmetic act (FFDCA)
- Federal insecticide, fungicide, and rodenticide act (FIFRA)
- Federal water pollution control amendments (part of the clean water act)
- Food quality protection act (FQPA (part of FFDCA and FIFRA)
- Marine protection, research, and sanctuaries act (MPRSA), or the ocean dumping act)
- National environmental policy act (NEPA)
- National technology transfer and advancement act (NTTAA)
- Noise control act
- Nuclear waste policy act (NWPA)
- Occupational safety and health (OSHA)
- Ocean dumping act (part of the marine protection, research, and sanctuaries act)
- Oil pollution act (OPA)
- Pesticide registration improvement act (PRIA) (part of FIFRA)
- Pollution prevention act (PPA)
- Resource conservation and recovery act (RCRA)
- Safe drinking water act (SDWA)
- Shore protection act (SPA)
- Superfund (part of the comprehensive environmental response, compensation, and liability act)
- Superfund amendments and reauthorization act (SARA) (part of the comprehensive environmental response, compensation, and liability act)
- Toxic substances control act (TSCA)

The EPA also has the responsibility of maintaining and enforcing national standards under a variety of environmental laws, in consultation with state, tribal, and local governments, and its enforcement powers include fines, sanctions, and other measures.

To accomplish its mission with all its tasks, the U.S. EPA develops and enforces regulations, gives grants for environmental projects, studies environmental issues, sponsors partnerships with universities and private businesses, teaches people about the environment, and publishes information related to the environment.

The Bureau of Land Management

The bureau of land management (BLM) is the regulatory authority responsible for the reclamation on federal lands. The BLM manages energy development, including leasing, permitting, inspection, and enforcement for 256 million surface acres and 700 million subsurface acres of mineral estate in the U.S.

On the state level, oil and gas conservation commissions, boards and divisions regulate reclamation on private and state lands. For example, in Wyoming, extensive oil and gas activities and regulatory overlaps led to the creation of a coordinating office, the Jonah interagency mitigation and reclamation office (JIO).

State oil and gas conservation commissions, divisions, and boards are an important regulatory authority for reclamation activities on state and private lands, and, in some cases, on federal lands. These include: the Colorado oil and gas conservation commission; the Montana board of oil and gas conservation; the New Mexico energy, minerals, and natural resources department oil conservation division; the Utah division of oil, gas, and mining; and the Wyoming oil and gas conservation commission. State lands offices, boards, and commissions may also set reclamation bonding requirements and oversee reclamation activities for oil and gas disturbances on state lands.

It appears, however, that the control of activities and the regulation enforcement on federal lands is much more consolidated, structured, transparent, and in most case, more efficient, while the regulation on the state levels is more fractured and lax.

In any case, BLM is an important regulating body, because it has the final word in permitting and authorizing use of natural resources and any type of development on federal lands.

The U.S. Forest Service

Established in 1905, the Forest Service (USFS) is an agency of the U.S. Department of Agriculture. The USFS manages public lands in national forests and grasslands. The USFS is the largest forestry research organization

in the world, and provides technical and financial assistance to state and private forestry agencies.

The job of USFS managers is to help people share and enjoy the forest, while conserving the environment for generations to come. Some activities are compatible, and some are not.

The main activities of the USFS are as follows:

- Protection and management of natural resources on national forest system lands

- Research on all aspects of forestry, rangeland management, and forest resource utilization

- Community assistance and cooperation with state and local governments, forest industries, and private landowners to help protect and manage nonfederal forest and associated range and watershed lands to improve conditions in rural areas

- Achieving and supporting an effective workforce that reflects the full range of diversity of the American people

- International assistance in formulating policy and coordinating U.S. support for the protection and sound management of the world's forest resources

National forests and grasslands encompass 193 million acres of land, which is an area equivalent to the size of Texas, and USFS has the last word in permitting well drilling, power plant development, and other activities affecting fuels and power generation, so it is an important member of the regulatory team.

State Regulation

The most obvious trend at the state level is the dramatic rise in the number of bills that directly or indirectly regulate GHG emissions. In particular, the number of introduced bills that would have directly or indirectly regulated greenhouse gases more than quintupled from 2006 to 2007 and the number that were enacted more than sextupled.

2007 marked the beginning of the energy race, which climaxed in 2008 before things started to quiet down. There are still activities in the federal and state legislations, but they are not as well defined and numerous as these of the 2007-2009 time period. Actually it all started with the new Bush administration of 2006.

Vice President Dick Cheney played a largely hidden and little-understood role in crafting policies on national security, the economy, and the environment.

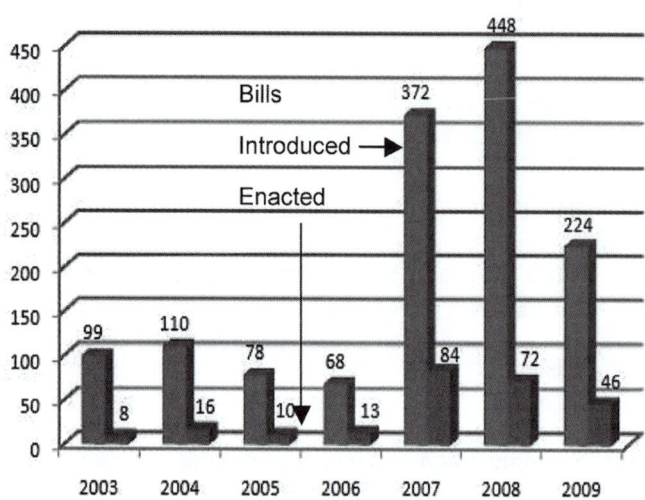

Figure 6-39. GHG regulating bills in the U.S.

Bush's major contribution to the environmental protection legislation was in 2005, when politicians tried to exempt fracking from the safe drinking water act (the 1974 law that regulates the injection of waste and chemicals underground) using EPA's 2004 study to justify that effort. With the help of then-Vice President Dick Cheney (the former head of Halliburton) President Bush's landmark energy legislation, the 2005 energy policy act, included a provision that *prohibited* the EPA from regulating fracking under the safe drinking water act. Instead, regulation would be left to the states, many of which had underfunded agencies, looser standards, and less manpower than the federal government.

NOTE: Halliburton pioneered the hydrofracking technology and owns many patents. As a large oil and gas field services provider it is heavily involved in the fracking activities.

After nearly a decade, EPA is just now looking into changing the fracking-related regulations.

As a result of the discrepancies, there was general dissatisfaction at the time, and many state and national legislators decided to implement more aggressive government regulations, especially the emission of GHGs by fossil power generators and other such sources of pollution (as reflected by the huge jump of bills from 2006 to 2007 seen in Figure 6-39).

This, however, was done quietly, and there were no open campaigns or demonstrations to regulate greenhouse gases because any such effort would make energy more expensive. Politicians do not want to be associated with that part of the problem, so they used other means and methods to promote anti-pollution legislation.

And then there was Al Gore's movie, *An Inconve-*

nient Truth, released in 2006 and becoming the third highest grossing documentary at the time. It also brought an unprecedented and unexpected attention from all areas of the socio-political life in the country, thus affecting the national and international political currents.

The movie won two Academy Awards and was very effective in convincing many people, including politicians, that serious government action was needed to control GHG emissions. Al Gore was then awarded the 2007 Nobel Peace Prize.

NOTE: Mr. Gore was instrumental in the 1997, when, as vice president, he helped negotiate the Kyoto protocol, which created binding commitments for Turkey, Russia, the U.S., Canada, Australia, New Zealand, and Japan to reduce their greenhouse gas emissions to 5% below 1990 levels by 2012. The mission on the American side, however, was a failure because then President Clinton, supported by the U.S. Congress, refused to ratify the protocol.

Command and Control Regulation

Environmental regulation in the U.S. relies on *command-and-control* policies in which the regulators, typically government bodies, investigate cases and set standards or limits in response to what they find. They also apply these uniformly to a broad category of sources using different approaches.

There are three types of command-and-control mechanisms that regulators can choose to implement:

• Ambient
• Emissions
• Technology standards

An ambient standard sets the amount of a pollutant that can be present within a specific environment. An example of this would be when a regulator sets a limit on ground-level ozone [parts per million or "ppm"] allowable within a city's limits. This is also an example of an indirect regulation because, although emissions from individual sources are being restricted, the ambient level is what the standard is attempting to control.

Emissions standards are much more common as they seek to limit the amount of emissions released by a firm, industry, or area. It differs from an ambient standard because its use does not determine the ambient level of a pollutant in the environment; rather, it attempts to reduce the overall amount of a pollutant released on a firm-by-firm basis.

Technology-based standards force polluters to use a

particular pollution control technology that they deem reasonably cost-effective, such as installing scrubbers on smokestacks.

The primary advantage of command-and-control mechanisms is that they provide quick and clear results, using simple-to-monitor compliance that requires the regulators to only make sure that the standards are met. This is especially useful in urgent cases, where a quick solution must be found. In all cases, the emissions reduction goal must be reached or the violators are penalized.

Simple enough, but command-and-control mechanisms have several drawbacks too. Information uncertainty is a major issue, since it is very costly for regulators to gather necessary information, and often the only information available is from reporting source, which is like letting the wolf guard the sheep. Polluters, on the other hand, don't have many choices as of how to meet the standards, which are strictly dictated by the regulators. So there is a lack of incentives for the polluters to research new and creative ways to reduce their emissions.

Command-and-control mechanisms are uniformly applied across broad categories of sources, so this cannot be the most cost-effective way to decrease emissions. Also, marginal costs for limiting emissions vary among the sources, which guarantees that equity will not be achieved. And so the polluters are not charged for the marginal cost of pollution that they continue to emit, but only for the pollution that they abate, which is economically inefficient MO.

Economic incentives have begun to play a larger role in both national and international environmental policy recently. Regulators have begun to look at incentives as a more flexible and lower cost alternative, and it is expected that the regulatory system will be made more effective by promoting environmentally efficient choices with less government interference. Incentive-based policies aim to encourage polluters to find innovative, low-cost ways to reduce their environmental emissions by offering rewards or by doling out punishments in the form of taxes, fees, marketable permits, or liability.

Taxes or fees are charged per unit of pollution, the value of which is determined by the regulator. Marketable permits allow companies to pollute at a level that is marginally cost-effective, which allows them to buy additional permits if they fail to meet the set targets. They can also sell excess permits if they exceed their internal pollution reduction targets.

Liability involves establishing a precautionary level that allows for the greatest benefit to society, and holding firms to that standard if a problem arises. Liability puts the burden on the firm to take certain levels of precaution with respect to environmental issues, or to be held accountable for any negative results.

Incentives have several advantages, including allowing the source to play a role in determining the most cost-effective way to reduce their emissions and, thereby, in meeting their marginal costs. All types of incentives adhere to the semi-marginal approach, which creates an efficient or "least cost" overall solution. When compared to command and control mechanisms, the regulators require less information under an incentive program since there is greater motivation for polluters to devise their own innovative solutions. In this case the regulator does not need to know how cost-effective various control options will be, or what the cost is at any particular installation, because the source will be held accountable for all of their actions and will pay both pollution control costs and damage costs.

One problem is that the affected sources are often in opposition and begin to perceive economic policy instruments as imposing higher costs than command-and-control regulations. Taxes also present political obstacles since no industry likes to see increased taxes, and politicians do not want to lose support by passing legislation that includes more taxes.

When looking at environmental issues, politicians are primarily concerned that something must be done and less interested in the specific choice or design of the policies. Usually the economic incentives are approved by a political system where the bargaining processes become important and more technical and legal in nature, and are sorted out between officials, experts, and the affected parties. Command-and-control regulation is still common in the U.S., but more and more, legislation is using market mechanisms, or a combination of command-and-control along with market mechanisms. This seems to best meet the demands for environmental solutions of the day.

Global Warming Solutions Act

The global warming solutions act was originally introduced in 2004, but it took several years to mature and generate sufficient political momentum to pass. With the support of leading environmental groups, the California legislature passed the act in 2006, and Governor Arnold Schwarzenegger signed it. The global warming solutions act, although short on solutions, points in the right direction. It requires California to reduce its GHG emissions to 1990 levels by 2020 (approximately a 25% reduction from 2006 levels). Despite the title, the act does not lay out the regulations to actually reduce carbon dioxide and greenhouse gas emissions. Instead, it gives the California air resources board the authority to develop the necessary rules to achieve the goals.

Several states, like New Jersey, Hawaii, Massachusetts, and Connecticut decided to follow California. In 2007 New Jersey passed the global warming response act, which is even a stricter version of the California's act. It committed New Jersey to reducing emissions to 1990 levels by 2020 and then to 80% reduction of 2006 emissions by 2050.

Hawaii followed in 2007 by passing the global warming solutions act, which requires GHG emissions to be reduced to 1990 levels by 2020. In 2008, Massachusetts followed too by passing its own global warming solutions act, which requires greenhouse gas emission reductions of between 10 and 25% below 1990 levels by 2020 and 80% reduction below 1990 levels by 2050.

Connecticut passed a global warming solutions bill in 2008, too, which requires GHG emissions reduction of 10% below 1990 levels by 2020, and 80% reduction below 2001 levels by 2050.

Washington State passed their own climate action and green jobs bill, which limits state GHG emissions to 25% below 1990 levels by in 2035 and 50% reduction below 1990 levels in 2050. It, however, does not empower a regulatory agency to develop any regulations for that purpose. Instead, the state's department of ecology is charged with creating recommendations for the bill's implementation.

The states of Oregon and Florida have taken a slightly different route in this area. In 2007, Oregon passed the global warming actions bill with the goal of reducing GHG emissions to 10% below 1990 levels by 2020 and to 75% reduction below 1990 levels by 2050. Again, the bill did not specify the regulations necessary to achieve these goals. Instead, it established a global warming commission responsible for recommending ways to meet the goals. Similarly, the Florida legislature passed the Florida climate protection act of 2008, which did not set GHG emissions reduction targets. Instead, it charged the Florida department of environmental protection to develop a cap-and-trade program for electric utilities and to bring that program to the legislature for approval.

In 2008, Maryland was headed to pass its own global warming solutions act, but the bill was defeated. Similar to the binding greenhouse gas emissions limits in other states, the bill would have required Maryland to reduce GHG emissions by 25% by 2020. In 2009, Maryland's legislators crafted a new bill that sought to deal with the concerns raised in 2008. This new bill requires Maryland to reduce GHG emissions 25% below 2006 levels by 2020. It did not specify how Maryland would achieve this goal, but instead required the Maryland's department of the environment to create a plan and for the state legislature to consider the plan. The plan required ensuring no loss of existing jobs in the state's manufacturing sector, a net increase in state jobs, a net economic benefit to the state's economy, and no adverse impact on the reliability and affordability of electricity. This is simply not possible, since all studies on cap-and-trade agree that it increases costs, so the plan was voted down again in 2013.

Air Quality Regulation

Air pollution is the greatest single environmental impact of the world's indiscriminant use of fossil fuels. Despite of several decades of fossil fuel consumption growth in the U.S., air quality now is generally better than it was in the 1970s. This is mostly due to the implementation of the clean air act of 1967, and its amendments of 1970, 1977 and 1990.

These amendments are responsible for strengthened the 1967 air quality act, which succeeded the 1963 clean air act and the 1965 motor vehicle pollution act, and even before that, the 1955 air pollution control act set the first nationwide air quality policy.

The clean air act basically identifies six substances that it calls criteria pollutants, and establishes national standards for their maximum concentrations in ambient air. These substances are: carbon dioxide, lead, nitrogen dioxide, ozone, particles, and sulfur dioxide. It does not include some of the other pollutants, which are becoming more prominent now.

The national ambient air-quality standards (NAAQS) also includes limits that are designed to protect human health. Secondary standards in NAAQS are associated with the general public welfare, including environmental quality and protection of property.

The NAAQS, however, does not directly address quantity of total emission of pollutants by the polluting sources. Instead, it specifies their concentrations in a given volume of ambient air. This means that a coal-fired power plant can billow thousands of tons of carbon soot high up into the air, as long as the air that people breath down below is within the set limits. This also allows individual states and local municipalities to set limits and policies that ensure that their air meets the national standards.

On national level, the U.S. EPA is in charge of establishing emissions standards for a number of pollutants and their sources.

Emissions standards are not set in stone, but evolve over time. The evolution of vehicular emission standards for nitrogen oxides progress through several levels is called tiers. The new tier 2 vehicle emissions standards, phasing in through the first decade of the twenty-first century, are complex and allow vehicle manufacturers some flexibility in emissions among their different vehicles.

So have these complex regulations and standards improved our air quality? The emissions of the criteria pollutants have declined substantially since the 1970s, despite rising energy use, vehicle miles traveled, and GDP. However, most of this reduction occurred before 1995; wringing further emissions reductions from technological advances in the face of rising energy consumption and vehicle use is proving more difficult.

Air Quality Standards

The content of different gasses and particles in the air we breathe determine its quality, or suitability to support healthy lives. To put some order and provide some control of the polluting components in the ambient air, the U.S. government has established standards. These standards determine the maximum amount of pollutants in the air in our homes and work places.

The units of measure for the standards are parts per million (ppm) by volume, parts per billion (ppb) by volume, and micrograms per cubic meter of air ($\mu g/m^3$).

The EPA has set national ambient air quality standards for six principal pollutants, which are called "criteria" pollutants, as listed in Table 6-3: carbon monoxide, lead, nitrogen dioxide, ozone, particles, and sulfur dioxide. The clean air act identifies two types of national ambient air quality standards. Primary standards provide public health protection, including protecting the health of sensitive populations such as asthmatics, children, and the elderly. Secondary standards provide public welfare protection, including protection against decreased visibility and damage to animals, crops, vegetation, and buildings.

There are also standards for the amount of air pollutants emitted by power plants and industrial enterprises. Most air toxics originate from human-made sources, such as power plants, cars, and trucks, factories, refineries, as well as indoor sources such as cooking and cleaning.

Table 6-3. National Ambient Air Quality Standards

Pollutant [final rule cite]		Primary/ Secondary	Averaging Time	Level	Form
Carbon Monoxide [76 FR 54294, Aug 31, 2011]		primary	8-hour	9 ppm	Not to be exceeded more than once per year
			1-hour	35 ppm	
Lead [73 FR 66964, Nov 12, 2008]		primary and secondary	Rolling 3 month average	0.15 $\mu g/m^3$ [1]	Not to be exceeded
Nitrogen Dioxide [75 FR 6474, Feb 9, 2010] [61 FR 52852, Oct 8, 1996]		primary	1-hour	100 ppb	98th percentile, averaged over 3 years
		primary and secondary	Annual	53 ppb [2]	Annual Mean
Ozone [73 FR 16436, Mar 27, 2008]		primary and secondary	8-hour	0.075 ppm [3]	Annual fourth-highest daily maximum 8-hr concentration, averaged over 3 years
Particle Pollution [71 FR 61144, Oct 17, 2006]	PM2.5	primary and secondary	Annual	15 $\mu g/m^3$	annual mean, averaged over 3 years
			24-hour	35 $\mu g/m^3$	98th percentile, averaged over 3 years
	PM10	primary and secondary	24-hour	150 $\mu g/m^3$	Not to be exceeded more than once per year on average over 3 years
Sulfur Dioxide [75 FR 35520, Jun 22, 2010] [38 FR 25678, Sept 14, 1973]		primary	1-hour	75 ppb [4]	99th percentile of 1-hour daily maximum concentrations, averaged over 3 years
		secondary	3-hour	0.5 ppm	Not to be exceeded more than once per year

Major pollution sources are these that emit 10 or more tons per year of any of the listed toxic air pollutants, or 25 or more tons per year of a mixture of air toxics. These sources may release air toxics from equipment leaks, when materials are transferred from one location to another, or during discharge through emission stacks or vents.

Area pollution sources are smaller-size facilities that release lesser quantities of toxic pollutants into the air: less than 10 tons per year of a single air toxic, or less than 25 tons per year of a combination of air toxics. Emissions from individual area sources are often relatively small, but when viewed collectively, their emissions are of great concern, especially when large numbers of these small sources are located in heavily populated areas.

The U.S. EPA publishes periodically a list of source categories, indicating whether the sources are considered to be major sources or area sources, and sets air pollution standards for all major sources of air toxics. Some area sources that are of particular concern are included as well.

The clean air act (CAA) is the ultimate federal law that regulates air emissions from stationary and mobile sources. This law authorizes the U.S. EPA to establish national ambient air quality standards (NAAQS) to protect public health and public welfare by setting standards and regulating emissions of hazardous air pollutants.

The setting of these pollutant standards was coupled with directing the states to develop state implementation plans (SIPs), applicable to appropriate industrial sources in the state, to achieve these standards. The act was amended in 1977 and 1990 primarily to set new goals (and new dates) for achieving attainment of NAAQS since many areas of the country had failed to meet the deadlines.

Section 112 of the clean air act addresses emissions of hazardous air pollutants, which was revised in 1990 to first require issuance of technology-based standards for major sources and certain area sources. Major sources are defined as a stationary source or group of stationary sources that emit or have the potential to emit 10 tons per year or more of a hazardous air pollutant or 25 tons per year or more of a combination of hazardous air pollutants. An area source is any stationary source that is not a major source.

For major emitting sources, the CAA Section 112 requires that EPA establish emission standards that require the maximum degree of reduction in emissions of hazardous air pollutants. These emission standards are commonly referred to as maximum achievable control technology (MACT) standards. Eight years after the technology-based MACT standards are issued for a source category, EPA is required to review those standards to determine whether any residual risk exists for that source category and, if necessary, revise the standards to address such risk.

Reducing air pollution from the largest source of emissions is one of EPA's national enforcement initiatives. EPA is taking action to eliminate or minimize emissions from coal-fired power, acid, glass, and cement plants, and petroleum refineries.

Air Toxins

The national emission standard for hazardous air pollutants *(NESHAP)* addresses leaks, flares, and excess emissions from refineries, chemical plants and other industries can contain hazardous air pollutants (HAPs) that are known or suspected to cause cancer, birth defects, and seriously impact the environment. Leaking equipment is the largest source of HAP emissions from petroleum refineries and chemical manufacturing facilities, in particular:

Coal-fired power plants—There are approximately 1,100 coal-fired electric utility units in the U.S. with an overall capacity of 340,000 megawatts. This sector emits approximately two-thirds of the nation's emissions inventory of sulfur dioxide (SO_2) and approximately one-third of the nitrogen oxides (NO_x). Investigations of this sector have identified a high rate of noncompliance with NSR/PSD when old plants are renovated or upgraded.

Petroleum refineries—Since 2000, the EPA has engaged in an enforcement initiative specifically focused on addressing air emissions from petroleum refineries and has reached innovative, multi-issue, multi-facility settlement negotiations with major petroleum refining companies. These settlements have resulted in significant emission reductions of NO_x, SO_2, benzene, volatile organic compounds and PM.

Air quality is constantly monitored during the construction, installation, operation, and decommissioning of mining, gas, and oil drilling, and all energy generating sources and facilities. The air quality has to be always within the standards and limits set by EPA. Special measures are taken in cases that violate the applicable standards and limits.

National Ambient Air Quality Standards

In Section 109, the clean air act requires the EPA to establish national ambient air quality standards (NAAQS) for air pollutants that endanger public health or welfare, in the administrator's judgment, and in which the presence in ambient air results from numer-

Figure 6-40. Coal-fired power plant

ous or diverse sources. The standard is designed to protect the air quality as far as public health and welfare is concerned, providing an adequate margin of safety.

Originally, the act required that the NAAQS be attained by 1977 at the latest, but due to widespread difficulty in complying, the deadlines have been extended several times. Under the 1990 amendments, most areas not in attainment with NAAQS must meet special compliance schedules, staggered according to the severity of an area's air pollution problem. The amendments also established specific requirements for each nonattainment category.

The EPA has promulgated NAAQS for six air pollutants: sulfur dioxide (SO_2), particulate matter (PM2.5 and PM10), nitrogen dioxide (NO_2), carbon monoxide (CO), ozone, and lead. The EPA is also required to review the scientific data upon which the standards are based, and revise the standards every five years, or as otherwise deemed necessary. Thus far, the EPA has taken more than five years to revise the standards.

Transported Air Pollution

The clean air standards and their implementation and enforcement are complicated by the fact that air pollution is not confined to one place and respects no political or geographic boundaries. This creates a problem of *transported* air pollutants that has become very important as the EPA attempts to develop effective compliance strategies to achieve both the ozone and the PM2.5 NAAQS.

The 1990 clean air act amendments provided EPA and the states with new tools to address the transport

problem through this provision. One of those tools is section 176A, a provision that permits the EPA, either on its own or by petition from any state, to establish a transport region to address regional pollution problems contributing to violations of a primary NAAQS.

A special commission of the EPA and state officials is in charge of making recommendations to the EPA on appropriate mitigation strategies. The EPA is then required under Section 110(k)(5) to notify affected states of inadequacies in their current state implementation plans and to establish deadlines for submitting necessary revisions.

The 1990 amendments statutorily also created an ozone transport region (OTR) in the Northeast. This provision (Section 184 of the act) required specific additional controls for all areas in that region, and established the ozone transport commission for the purpose of recommending to the EPA region-wide controls affecting all areas in the region.

Nonattainment Areas

A number of special requirements were established for the different nonattainment areas, making them subject to specified control requirements, with more stringent requirements. Nonattainment areas are classified on the basis of a "design value," which is derived from the pollutant concentration (in parts per million or micrograms per cubic meter) recorded by air quality monitoring devices. Using these design values, the act created five classes of ozone nonattainment, which are:

• Ozone nonattainment areas
• Carbon monoxide nonattainment areas
• Particulate nonattainment areas
• Transported air pollution

While the first areas are clearly identified per location and quantity, the last one, the transported air pollution, is different, for it is not contained in one place but is rather spread all over the country and the world. This complicates the clean air standards and their implementation and enforcement, because air pollution in most cases is not confined to one place and respects no political or geographic boundaries. This creates the problem of *transported* air pollutants that has become very important as EPA attempts to develop effective compliance strategies to achieve both the ozone and the PM2.5 NAAQS.

The 1990 clean air act amendments provided EPA and the states with new tools to address the transport problem through this provision. One of those tools is

Section 176A, a provision that permits the EPA, either on its own or by petition from any state, to establish a transport region to address regional pollution problems contributing to violations of a primary NAAQS.

A special commission of EPA and state officials is in charge of making recommendations to EPA on appropriate mitigation strategies. EPA is then required under Section 110(k)(5) to notify affected states of inadequacies in their current state implementation plans and to establish deadlines for submitting necessary revisions.

The 1990 amendments statutorily also created an Ozone Transport Region (OTR) in the Northeast. This provision (Section 184 of the act) required specific additional controls for all areas in that region, and established the Ozone Transport Commission for the purpose of recommending to EPA region-wide controls affecting all areas in the region.

The Emission Standards for Mobile Sources Title II of the Clean Air Act is an extension of the Transported Air Pollution and has required emission standards for automobiles since model year 1968. The 1990 amendments significantly tightened these standards. For cars, the hydrocarbon standard was reduced by 40% and the nitrogen oxides (NO_x) standard by 50%. These standards— referred to as tier one standards—were phased in over the 1994-1996 model years.

Tier two standards, requiring emission reductions of 77% to 95% from cars and light trucks were promulgated in February 2000, and were phased in over the 2004-2009 model years. To facilitate the use of more effective emission controls, the standards also require a more than 90% reduction in the sulfur content of gasoline, beginning in 2004.

California's zero emission vehicle (ZEV) program is also intended to promote the development of alternative fuels and vehicles. Section 209(b) of the clean air act allows the EPA administrator to grant California the authority to develop its own vehicle emissions standards, provided that they are at least as stringent as the federal standards.

In addition to setting more stringent standards for all vehicles, California also established a program requiring auto manufacturers to sell ZEVs (electric or hydrogen fuel cell vehicles) in the state beginning with model year 2003. This program has been substantially modified since then, and now allows credit for hybrid and partial ZEV vehicles in addition to true ZEVs. It has served as an incubator for new and lower emission vehicles and technologies during the last decade.

The hazardous air pollutants law was revised by the clean air act amendments of 1990. It establishes programs for protecting public health and the environment from exposure to toxic air pollutants, and contains four major provisions: maximum achievable control technology (MACT) requirements; health-based standards; standards for stationary "area sources" (small, but numerous sources, such as gas stations or dry cleaners); and requirements for the prevention of catastrophic releases.

EPA is required to set standards for sources of the major pollutants that achieve "the maximum degree of reduction in emissions" taking into account cost and other non-air-quality factors, and to set health-based standards to address the risk of adverse health effects or a threat of adverse environmental effects after installation and use of MACT.

EPA is also required to establish standards for stationary "area sources" that are known threats of adverse effects to human health or the environment, and to address prevention of sudden, catastrophic releases of air toxins to be headed by an independent chemical safety and hazard investigation board.

The acid rain control requirement was added by the clean air act amendments of 1990 (Title IV). It set goals of reducing annual SO_2 emissions in two steps. In phase one the owners/operators of electric generating facilities larger than 100 MW have to meet tonnage emission limitations. Phase two included facilities larger than 75 megawatts, with a deadline of January 1, 2000. Compliance has been 100% thus far.

The stratospheric ozone protection Title VI of the 1990 Clean air act amendments outlined the U.S. international responsibilities under the Montreal protocol on substances that deplete the ozone layer. Section 606(a)(3) provides that the EPA is required to adjust phase-out schedules for ozone-depleting substances in accordance with any future changes in Montreal protocol schedules. As a result, the phase-out schedules contained in Title VI for various ozone-depleting compounds have now been superseded by subsequent amendments to the Montreal protocol.

Environmental Impact Analysis

To understand the relation between power generation (including resource production, transport, use and their effects) and the environment (as far as the damage from the energy sector is concerned) we need to understand and take a close look at the different factors that play at each stage of the process. There are many and very complex factors in this equation, which require deep understanding and complex solutions.

One such solution is the *environmental impact analy-*

sis (EIA) that is required in most cases where new energy or environmentally sensitive projects are to be constructed. It is conducted to assess that the potential impact of a proposed development or a project would have on the natural and social environment. This may include an assessment of both the short- and long-term effects on the physical environment, such as air, water and/or noise pollution, as well as effects on local services, living and health standards, and aesthetics.

In enacting the national environmental policy act (NEPA) of 1969, Congress required all agencies of the federal government to give equal consideration to environmental consequences as well as to economic motivations and technological feasibility when making a decision that could affect the quality of the human and natural environment. NEPA also established the council on environmental quality within the executive office of the President to ensure that federal agencies would meet their obligations under the act.

One provision of the law requires that an environmental impact statement (EIS) be written for major federal actions and made available to all, including to the general public. An EIS must include: the environmental impacts of a proposed action; unavoidable adverse environmental impacts; alternatives—including no action; the relationship between short-term uses of the environment and maintenance of long-term ecological productivity; irreversible and irretrievable commitments of resources; and secondary/cumulative effects of implementing the proposed action. Now, most state and local governments also require that environmental impact analyses be conducted prior to any major development projects.

Environmental impact analyses are often challenging because they call for making projections with incomplete information. Methods of assessing the impacts typically include both objective and subjective information making it difficult to quantify. Therefore, the methods are frequently seen as complex and, oftentimes, controversial. Despite being a requirement for many development projects, the function of an environmental impact statement is merely procedural.

There is no specific legal force of action if information stemming from an environmental impact analysis confirms that a particular project may harm the environment. As a result, it is often left up to the courts to rule on whether risks to the environment are overstated or not.

Although environmental impact analysis often raises more questions than it answers as it examines the various links between social, economic, technological, and ecological factors involved in a potential development project, it also provides a practical and interesting approach to the understanding and appreciation of the many complexities and uncertainties involved with these interrelationships.

One of the major issues lately, as related to energy production, is the air, water and soil contamination by mining and gas and oil drilling operations. These activities are regulated by a number of U.S. regulating bodies, but the system is full of gaps, is not fully developed and/or is simply dysfunctional in several critical areas.

Water Quality Regulations

Water is a precious commodity all over the world. We need it for sustaining our daily lives and for commerce. Water availability and quality have been, and still are, major issues in the U.S. We go from draughts to floods at different places and times, and the quality of our drinking water is questionable in many cases.

Water use and quality in the U.S. is regulated by the clean water act (33 U.S.C. § 1251 et seq.), or the federal water pollution control act, which goal is to restore and maintain the chemical, physical, and biological integrity of the nation's surface waters. The EPA is the federal agency responsible for creating and enforcing national water quality regulations under the clean water act, but each state and Native American tribe develops their own program for implementing and enforcing clean water act requirements.

The clean water act includes the national pollutant discharge elimination system (NPDES) permitting process, which establishes pollutant limits on the discharge of produced water that generally include a volume (quantity) and concentration (quality).

Pollutants under the NPDES program fall into one of three categories:

1. Conventional
2. Non-conventional
3. Toxic

There are two types of permits under the NPDES program that allow for the discharge of pollutants from point sources. These are: a) individual permits, which are specific to an individual facility; and b) general permits, which cover multiple facilities within a specific permit category. These permits are applicable to those facilities engaged in the production, field exploration, drilling, well completion and well treatment in the oil and gas extraction industries.

In 2006, the EPA published a final rule that effectively exempted storm water discharges of sediment from construction activities associated with oil and gas facilities unless the facility had a discharge of storm water resulting in a discharge of a reportable quantity of oil or other hazardous substances.

This rule was challenged in court and subsequently vacated in natural resources defense council v. the U.S. environmental protection agency. After that, the effective storm water requirements are those regulations in place prior to the 2006 rule plus additional clarification of activities included in the CWA 402(l)(S) exemption, which specified that EPA and states shall not require NPDES permits for uncontaminated storm water discharges from oil and gas facilities.

Provisions of the CWA particularly relevant to oil and gas development are:

- 33 U.S.C. § 1321 (2006) oil and hazardous substance liability—A Congressional declaration of policy against discharges of oil or hazardous substances into or upon the navigable waters of the U.S. The policy calls for the development of enforcement mechanisms to ensure compliance.

- Safe water drinking act (42 U.S.C. § 300f et seq.) (2006)—The safe drinking water act (SDWA) was established to protect public health by regulating public drinking water supplies and to protect sources of drinking water. It creates a joint federal and state system to ensure compliance with standards. The EPA and authorized states enforce primary drinking water standards, which are contaminant-specific concentration limits that apply to certain public drinking water supplies. The underground injection control (UIC) program was established by the SDWA to protect underground sources of drinking water from potential contamination from injection wells. Over 90% of the produced water from the onshore oil and gas industry is injected (U.S. EPA, 2000).

- 33 U.S.C. § 1342 (2008) National pollutant discharge elimination system—Establishes the NPDES program for discharges into navigable waters and provides for state primacy. But section (l)(2) provides that the administrator shall not require a permit for discharges of storm water runoff from oil and gas exploration, production, processing, or treatment operations or transmission facilities, composed entirely of flows which are from conveyances or systems of conveyances used for collection and conveying precipitation runoff and which are not contaminated by contact with, or do

not come into contact with, any overburden, raw material, intermediate products, finished product, byproduct, or waste products located on the site of such operations.

- 33 U.S.C. § 1362 (24) (2008)—Defines the term "oil and exploration, production, processing, or treatment operations or transmission facilities" as "all field activities or operations associated with exploration, production, processing, or treatment operations, or transmission facilities, including activities necessary to prepare a site for drilling and for the movement and placement of drilling equipment, whether or not such field activities or operations may be considered to be construction activities."

Provisions of the SDWA particularly relevant to oil and gas development are:

- *§ 300h et seq., protection of underground sources of drinking water*— Established the UIC program to prevent contamination of underground drinking water resources

- *§ 300h (d)(1)(B)(ii) protection of underground sources of drinking water*—Excludes the underground injection of fluids related to hydraulic fracturing operations for oil, gas, or geothermal activities from the term "underground injection." EPA Regulations, promulgated from the CWA and the SWDA that affect oil and gas, are found in Title 40 of the code of federal regulations. Rules of particular interest include:

- *40 C.F.R. pt.112 oil pollution prevention*—Establishes procedures, methods, equipment, and other requirements to prevent the discharge of oil from non-transportation-related oil and gas facilities into navigable waters of the U.S. or adjoining and contiguous areas. The rule applies if the facility, due to its location, could reasonably be expected to discharge oil into the navigable waters of the U.S. and it meets criteria based on certain onsite storage capacities.

- *40 CFR pts. 435.30-435.32 onshore oil and gas extraction point source*—Prohibits the discharge of water pollutants from any source associated with production, field exploration, drilling, well completion, or well treatment.

- *40 C.F.R. pt. 122, EPA administered permit programs;* the national pollutant discharge elimination system (NPDES)—The NPDES program requires permits for the discharge of pollutants from any point source into waters of the U.S., however storm water from oil and gas operations is exempted from the NPDES requirement in § 122.26.

- *40 C.F.R. pt. 122.26(a)(2), storm water discharge exemption*—The director may not require a permit for discharges of storm water runoff from mining operations or oil and gas exploration, production, processing or treatment operations or transmission facilities, composed entirely of flows which are from conveyances or systems of conveyances (including but not limited to pipes, conduits, ditches, and channels) used for collecting and conveying precipitation runoff and which are not contaminated by contact with, any overburden, raw material, intermediate products, finished product, byproduct or waste products located on the site of such operations.

- *40 C.F.R.* pt. 122.26(c)(1)(iii), situations when storm water permits are needed—Requires storm water discharge permits when a facility has a discharge of reportable quantity for which notification is required or contributes to a violation of a water quality standard.

- *40 C.F.R.* pt. 122.26 (e)(8), permit authorization for small construction activities—Requires permit authorization for any storm water discharges associated with construction activities at oil and gas sites between one and five acres in size by 12 June 2006.

- 40 C.F.R. pts. 144-48, underground injection control program—Establishes the minimum requirements that each state must meet to obtain primary enforcement authority of the UIC program in that state.

- *The ocean dumping act,* Title I of the marine protection, research, and sanctuaries act of 1972 (MPRSA, P.L. 92-532)—Aims to regulate intentional ocean disposal of materials, and the related research, which is often referred to just as the ocean dumping act, contains permit and enforcement provisions for ocean dumping. Research provisions are contained in Title II, concerning general and ocean disposal research. This act controls the activities of all dredging and other ocean dumping operations, including those of oil tankers, which have been blamed for large-scale ocean contamination.

- *The solid waste disposal act/resource conservation and recovery act*—Defines solid and hazardous waste,

and authorizes the EPA to set standards for facilities that generate or manage hazardous waste. This includes establishing a permit program for hazardous waste treatment, storage, and disposal facilities, including disposal facilities for municipal solid waste. The RCRA was last reauthorized by the hazardous and solid waste amendments of 1984.

The U.S. EPA is the regulating body on the federal level and is responsible for setting national standards, goals, and limits. States and tribal governments can acquire primacy for the SDWA's underground injection control (UIC) program and the CWA's national pollutant discharge elimination system (NPDES) program by meeting the EPA's primacy requirements.

States that have primacy programs must have requirements as stringent as the federal requirements, but are allowed to set more stringent state-specific requirements for these programs. Since individual states can acquire primacy over their respective programs, it is not uncommon to have varying requirements for these programs from state to state.

Different states have adopted the existing, or are working on new, regulations for oil and gas field development, production, use, and decommissioning.

Billions of barrels of wastewater are produced during oil and gas drilling and fracking operations every year in dozens of states, which amounts to nearly eight barrels of water used in one form or another for every barrel of oil produced.

Water produced or used during oil and natural gas production comprises 80% of the oil and gas industry's residual waste requiring management and disposal. Management of produced water from the oil and gas industry is regulated under rules enacted federally by the clean water act (CWA) and the safe drinking water act (SDWA).

The concerns about the quantity and quality of water used in the affected by oil and gas drilling locations are increasing and new regulation is expected in the near future.

Land Reclamation

Land reclamation after drilling or mining operations have ceased is an obligatory measure that requires companies to return the land; its surface, vegetation and even wild life to pre-drilling or pre-mining state. Most companies oblige and do their best, but this is a very difficult task, especially in semiarid lands of the Rocky Mountain Region, and many other areas of the U.S. Constant rains cause soil organic matter and biomass levels to remain low, so the successful reclamation of disturbed lands is challenging and very expensive.

Reclamation specialists have been working under the guidance of the surface mining control and reclamation act to restore lands disturbed from mining activities since the 1970s. That has lead to some successful, and some not-that-successful stories, but the picture of what can be done and what cannot is quite clear.

The reclamation of disturbed oil and gas lands from abandoned oil and gas wells and sites is not strictly regulated through a uniform federal act. Because of that, the resulting regulatory structure is complex and can be confusing, resulting in inefficiencies and damage to the environment and people's health.

Also, the total surface disturbance from oil and gas development is much greater than the area of land disturbed from mining activities, and that ratio is increasing daily. These factors, along with questions of invasive species and drought, deepen the challenge of achieving reclamation success.

Herein we present the basic goals of reclamation, and the reclamation process needed for a successful reclamation of lands disturbed by gas and oil drilling and exploration:

Reclamation Goals

The primary goal of reclamation on oil and gas lands is to restore site stability and ecosystem functions, returning disturbed lands to their original use or use prior to disturbance, such as crop production or wildlife habitat. The benchmark for successful reclamation typically is the establishment of a native plant community that is self-sustaining and meets standards for density

Figure 6-41. Land reclamation work

and forage production, and the re-contouring of all disturbed surface areas to match or blend with the original landform.

Reclamation Process

In modern, environmentally friendly field developments, an operator's permit to drill usually includes a limit on the total surface area that can be disturbed at one time. Because of this restriction, interim reclamation is conducted during the construction, drilling, and well production phases of oil and gas development to ensure that surface disturbance is within the limits established in the drilling permit. During interim reclamation, land on a well site that is not being used for production but has been disturbed should be undergoing the reclamation process through re-contouring, topsoil replacement, and re-vegetation.

Final reclamation is also required after a well is depleted or if it proves to be dry. The well must be plugged, and the well site and other areas disturbed by road or pipeline construction must be reclaimed and plant communities must be restored. The timeline for reclamation after a well is plugged varies by state.

Operators on federal lands must include a reclamation plan in their surface use plan of operation to be approved by the bureau of land management (BLM) or by the U.S. forest service (USFS). BLM and USFS expectations for a reclamation plan can be found in the Chapter 6 of the agencies' *Gold Book: Surface Operating Standards And Guidelines For Oil And Gas Exploration And Development*.

The BLM finalizes an operator's abandonment notice, with final approval being contingent upon reclamation meeting the standards of the surface managing agency. Throughout the reclamation process, the operator holds responsibility for monitoring reclamation progress and ensuring its success.

Topsoil and Soil Amendments

Preserving and salvaging sufficient topsoil is an integral part of reclamation and is necessary for reclamation success. Until topsoil is used during interim or final reclamation, the *Gold Book* stipulates that it should be kept separate from subsurface materials and that erosion controls should be implemented to protect the topsoil stockpile from wind and water erosion as well as impacts of heavy machinery.

Reserve Pit Reclamation

Reserve pits are a holding area for the dumping and dilution of drilling fluids, drilling cuttings, and operation fluids produced by exploration and production in the natural gas industry. Because of the hazardous nature of pit storage materials and the potential for contamination, the *Gold Book* recommends that operators use a closed-loop pit system or line open pits with an impermeable liner.

Regulatory standards for reserve pit structure (closed-loop or open-loop, lined or unlined) and reserve pit reclamation practices and timelines vary widely by state (see reclamation comparison table). Generally, pit materials must be dried or solidified prior to backfilling. Although oil and gas wastes are exempt from hazardous materials regulation by RCRA, some nonexempt materials do exist and must not exceed standards set forth in CERCLA prior to backfilling and reclamation.

Contouring and Erosion Control

Good reclamation of roads starts with good design and construction. Re-contouring is required during both interim and final reclamation. All disturbed surface areas, including the well pad, road areas, and pipeline flows, must be re-worked to sit at the original contour or to blend with the original landform. Adequate erosion control will provide for site stability and generally comes with successful re-vegetation.

Re-vegetation

The establishment of a self-sustaining plant community is vital in marking reclamation success. Standards for re-vegetation on oil and gas lands vary by state but typically include: a specified level of cover, density, vigor, resiliency, diversity; control of highly competitive non-native species; and freedom from noxious weeds.

Re-vegetation can be done using many approved methods for re-seeding and culturing, including drilling, broadcast seeding, hydro-seeding, dozer track walking, mulching, irrigating, and fertilizing. If seeding fails due to drought or other extreme conditions, the surface management agency may grant the operator a delayed timeline for re-seeding until the adverse conditions have passed. They may also require additional culturing such as mulching or irrigating.

Soil type, market availability, wildlife needs, and agency or landowner requirements should all be considered when choosing a seed mix for a site. While the surface management agency or a private landowner may approve select non-native species for reseeding, mixes composed primarily of species indigenous to the area being seeded typically are preferred or required. In some cases, the appropriate agency field office will prescribe an already determined seed mix.

The natural resources conservation service's plant materials program runs in partnership with local agencies to identify plants that will meet specific conservation needs in the specific affected areas. Species performance levels are tested, and those plants that are high performing are released, along with cultivation techniques, to the private sector to be developed commercially. Standards for successful reclamation include limits on noxious weeds and practices for successful weed control.

Superfund

The comprehensive environmental response, compensation and liability act of 1980, as amended (CERCLA statute, CERCLA overview), or commonly known as the "superfund," is an environmental program established to address abandoned hazardous waste sites. This law was enacted in response to the surprise discovery of toxic waste dumps such as Love Canal and Times Beach in the 1970s. This way, the EPA can force the clean up of such sites as well as to compel responsible parties to perform cleanups and/or reimburse the government for any cleanups done as a result of their negligence or inability to complete the job.

The superfund basically established a liability boundary for past and current operators of contaminated facilities to be financially responsible for the costs of cleanup. In case the responsible parties cannot pay for the cleanup, CERCLA authorizes the federal government to finance the cleanup to ensure the protection of human health and the environment, using what is referred to as "orphan shares."

The superfund authorizes the EPA to locate and hold responsible all parties that may have been involved in contamination of the environment to minimize the damages and the resulting costs of cleanup on the "polluter pays principle."

The superfund cleanup process is complex, lengthy, and expensive in most cases. It consists of a number of steps that need to be taken to assess the potential problematic sites, place them on the national priorities list, and establish and implement appropriate cleanup plans and programs. The EPA also has the authority to: conduct removal actions where immediate action needs to be taken, enforce against potentially responsible parties, ensure community involvement, involve states, and ensure long-term protectiveness.

All this work is done according to the national oil and hazardous substances pollution contingency plan (NCP), which is a regulation applicable to all federal agencies involved in responding to hazardous substance releases and the related contamination issues.

Tens of thousands of hazardous waste sites have been located, analyzed, and cleaned as needed to protect people and the environment from contamination.

The EPA's office of solid waste and emergency response (OSWER) in Washington, D.C. oversees the superfund program. The office of emergency management within OSWER is responsible for short-term responses conducted under the authority of superfund. The office of superfund remediation and technology innovation and the federal facilities response and reuse office, also within OSWER, have the lead for managing the long-term superfund response program, the latter for responses involving federal facilities. In addition, OSWER manages the federal brownfields program.

The EPA has established 10 Regional offices around the U.S. that are responsible for implementing many of EPA's programs, including the superfund program. For the superfund, EPA regions are the front line in responding to releases of hazardous substances and other environmental emergencies.

The superfund related regions are:

- Region 1—ME NH VT MA RI CT
- Region 2—NY NJ PR VI
- Region 3—PA DE DC MD VA WV
- Region 4—KY TN NC SC MS AL GA FL
- Region 5—MN WI IL MI IN OH
- Region 6—NM TX OK AR LA
- Region 7—NE KS IA MO
- Region 8—MT ND WY SD UT CO
- Region 9—CA NV AZ HI
- Region 10—WA OR ID AK

Carbon Tax or Cap-and-trade?

Clearly, it's in our best interest to wean ourselves gradually from fossil fuels. This conclusion follows obviously from the bad news we hear daily, about global climate warming, pollution, etc. But how are we to reduce fossil fuel consumption in a world where energy use is so closely tied to our daily lives, where the population is increasing by the day, and where developing countries are set on emulating the developed world's material wellbeing?

Carbon Tax

Carbon tax is a type of carbon pricing of fuels. The more carbon a fuel contains, the higher the tax. It is believed by some to be one of the ways to equalize the markets by taxing all fuels based on the amount of carbon that they contain and ultimately put into the air. The carbon tax is thought as a way of reducing the im-

pact of fossil fuel combustion on the environment, and is expected to encourage shifts from coal and oil to renewable energies.

A carbon tax imposes a tax on each unit of greenhouse gas emissions and gives firms (and households, depending on the scope) an incentive to reduce pollution whenever doing so would cost less than paying the tax. As such, the quantity of pollution that is reduced depends on the chosen level of the tax. The tax is set by assessing the cost or damage associated with each unit of pollution and the costs associated with controlling that pollution. Getting the tax level right is key: if it is too low, firms and households are likely to opt for paying the tax and continuing to pollute, over and above what is optimal for society; if it is too high, the costs will rise higher than necessary to reduce emissions, impacting on profits, jobs, and end consumers.

A carbon tax could be quite regressive, if not properly designed and executed; in such cases it often has a greater impact on low-income consumers than on the well to do. Proponents of a carbon tax have suggested redistributing some of the tax revenue based on income, but that action may conflict with others, such as using carbon-tax revenues to fund research into non-fossil energy sources.

Although carbon-based taxation is a new and relatively untried idea, taxes on fuel itself have long been with us. European countries, in particular, use the gasoline tax as an instrument of environmental policy, explicitly encouraging lower fuel consumption, minimizing environmental impacts, and guiding consumers to fuel-efficient vehicles.

The gasoline tax is one big reason why, as noted earlier, half of the new cars that are sold in Europe are fuel-efficient diesels. European gas taxes are considerable, amounting to some 60%-80% of the total fuel cost. For the U.S., that number is only about 30%. An increase in the low U.S. gasoline taxes, as sensible as it would seem, has been politically unachievable for many years. The last increase, in 1993, amounted to a mere 4.3 cents—less than the typical variations in gasoline prices from week to week.

The idea of an official carbon tax in the U.S. is still in discussion mode. In March 2013, a bicameral Congressional task force introduced a discussion draft on carbon taxes. It marks a trend (or a wish) toward simpler and more transparent ways to price carbon pollution.

The draft proposes taxing CO_2 pollution, especially six non-CO_2 greenhouse gases (GHGs), which account for about 20% of the climate damage from U.S. GHG emissions. These are: methane, nitrous oxide, sulfur hexafluoride, hydrofluorocarbon-23, perfluorinated chemicals and nitrogen triflouride, which are to be calculated at CO_2-equivalent rates.

These emissions total about 263.3 million tons of CO_2-equivalent, or roughly 4% of the 6.7 billion tons CO_2-equivalent of U.S. GHG emissions reported in 2011. The draft proposal covers about 90% of total emissions, or 5% more than the 85% coverage of the previous proposals that apply only to CO_2 emissions.

The draft proposes applying emission fees to facilities whose emissions of those gases exceed the 25,000-ton CO_2-equivalent per year threshold of the EPA's GHG reporting rule.

There are, however, still a number of questions to be answered and agreed upon. How high should the tax and the escalation rate be? What should the revenue be used for? The Congressional task force offered a menu of options and asked the public to weigh in on their favorites. But these are very technical and complex issues, to which the public will have a hard time providing any reasonable suggestions. Because of that, and due to a number of conflicting points in the proposal, we see the issue of carbon tax in the U.S. hanging around different committees for a long time to come.

Cap-and-trade

As an alternative to the carbon tax, the cap-and-trade scheme allows a governing body to set limits on carbon emissions, and issue allowances to individual emitters that permit a certain amount of carbon emissions. These allowances can either be granted free at the outset or auctioned to raise money to be used, for example, for research into energy alternatives. If a company produces less carbon than it's allowed, it can sell its allowances on an open market. This way, the cap-and-trade scheme provides a market-based incentive to reduce emissions.

A cap-and-trade system sets a maximum level of pollution, a cap, and distributes emissions permits among firms that produce emissions. Companies must have a permit to cover each unit of pollution they produce, and they can obtain these permits either through an initial allocation or auction, or through trading with other firms.

Since some firms inevitably find it easier or cheaper to reduce pollution than others, trading takes place. While the maximum pollution quantity is set in advance, the trading price of permits fluctuates, becoming more expensive when demand is high relative to supply (for example when the economy is growing) and cheaper when demand is lower (for example in a recession). A price on pollution is therefore created as a result of

setting a ceiling on the overall quantity of emissions. In more detail:

A cap sets a maximum allowable level of pollution and penalizes companies that exceed their emission allowance. This, according to some, is the best way to guarantee lower emissions. The cap is a limit on the amount of pollution that can be released, measured in billions of tons of carbon dioxide (or equivalent) per year. It is set based on science methods and covers all major sources of pollution. The cap limits emissions economy-wide, covering electric power generation, natural gas, transportation and large manufacturers.

Emitters can release only limited pollution and permits or allowances are distributed or auctioned to polluting entities. There is one allowance per ton of carbon dioxide, or CO_2-equivalent heat-trapping gases. The total amount of allowances will be equal to the cap. A company or utility may only emit as much carbon as it has allowances for. This way companies can plan ahead, while each year, the cap is ratcheted down on a gradual and predictable schedule. Companies can plan well in advance to be allowed fewer and fewer permits, which in turn results in less global warming pollution.

Trading gives companies options to buy and sell allowances, which leads to more cost-effective pollution cuts, and incentivizes the investment in cleaner technologies. Some companies may find it easy to reduce their pollution to match their number of permits; others may find it more difficult. Carbon-fired power plants would be most affected.

In all cases, companies can turn pollution cuts into revenue. If a company is able to cut its pollution easily and cheaply, it can end up with extra allowances, which can be sold to other companies. This provides a powerful incentive for creativity, energy conservation, and investment since companies can turn pollution cuts into dollars—a win-win situation for all involved.

The European union has adopted cap-and-trade to help meet its goals under the Kyoto protocol, and today you can track the European carbon index (or the price of carbon allowances as traded on the open market) just like any other commodity or stock.

The European climate exchange represents about 90% of all exchange-traded carbon transactions under the European union's emission trading system. In Europe, power trading is always accompanied by carbon trading.

The U.S. entered the cap-and-trade through the Chicago climate exchange (CCX), which was launched in 2003 for the purpose of starting the American environmental revolution. It was supposed to introduce

American business into the 21st century as smokestack industries bought and sold greenhouse gas emission allowances. Carbon futures and options would turn financial speculators into tree-huggers.

From 2003 through 2010 CCX operated as a comprehensive cap and trade program with an offsets component. In 2010, the CCX shareholders cashed out of this big idea for about $600 million. The intercontinental exchange (ICE), an electronic futures and derivatives platform based in Atlanta and London, purchased the three exchanges, the Chicago climate exchange, Chicago climate futures exchange and European climate exchange.

The combination brings the still-small U.S. carbon market closer to the profitable world of global over-the-counter (OTC) energy trading, which ICE specializes in. It also consolidates carbon emissions trading under the tents of two major commodity exchanges, ICE and CME group, which operates the New York mercantile exchange's nascent platform for carbon trading, the green exchange.

In 2011 CCX launched the Chicago climate exchange offsets registry program to register verified emission reductions based on a comprehensive set of established protocols. Participants interested in acquiring registered offsets may apply to become a CCX registry account holder by filling out the participant agreement.

The Differences

Carbon tax and cap-and-trade have exactly the same outcomes in some cases, since they are both ways to price carbon. However, in reality they differ in many ways. One difference is the way the two policies distribute the cost of reducing pollution. With cap-and-trade, it has often been the case that permits are given out for free initially (known as grandfathering). This meant cheaper compliance for industry in the early stages of the scheme, because they only paid for any extra permits bought from other firms, and not for the initial tranche of permits given to them to cover most of their emissions under business as usual.

This approach is obviously popular with industry and explains why grandfathering has been used, since it helps get firms to accept controls on emissions in the first place. By contrast, with a tax there is an immediate cost for businesses to pay on every unit of greenhouse gas produced, so there is a bigger initial hit to the balance sheet. While grandfathering is better for near-term business profitability, it is not necessarily the best outcome for society. It, for example, deprives the government of valuable revenues, which it could raise in auctioning the permits initially, and which could be used to reduce other taxes.

The two mechanisms also differ in how they perform under uncertainty about the costs and benefits of reducing emissions. Under a tax, the price of emitting a unit of pollution is set, but the total quantity of emissions is not. Therefore a tax ensures everyone knows the price being paid (at least for the immediate future) for each unit of carbon dioxide emitted, but uncertainty remains about the actual quantity of emissions.

Conversely, cap-and-trade provides certainty about the quantity of emissions (it cannot exceed the cap), but uncertainty about the cost of achieving these reductions. Which is preferred depends on how sensitive the level of environmental damage is to changes in emissions, compared with how sensitive the cost of reducing pollution is to the same changes. If the level of environmental damage is more sensitive, then it is important to be sure what the quantity of emissions is, which points to cap-and-trade.

Also, if the cost of reducing pollution is more highly sensitive to changes in emissions, it is better to be sure about the cost of cutting emissions, which points to a tax. What this means for climate change policy is debated. In the short term, most economists agree that uncertainty alone argues for a tax.

Climate change depends on the stock of greenhouse gases in the atmosphere, and in each year the increase in that stock due to new emissions is small, so the environment probably is not that sensitive to the uncertainty about the level of emissions brought about by choosing a tax, at least over a year or two.

On the other hand, the cost of reducing pollution is highly sensitive to changes in emissions, since it can be expensive for businesses to change their production methods abruptly. In the long-term, however, it is less clear whether a tax is preferable, because big changes in the stock of greenhouse gases in the atmosphere may cause substantial environmental damage.

Some economists recommend that a hybrid model that may offer the best of both worlds. In such case, a cap on emissions (to regulate the quantity of pollution) can be used, but with added adjustment mechanisms such as a carbon price floor or ceiling. This modification would keep the price of a permit within acceptable bounds. Hybrid schemes, however, are more complex and require more intervention by the regulators.

In any case, while which method is best suited is debatable, one thing is certain; we are running out of time. An efficient method of accounting for, and controlling carbon pollution is needed for global implementation to cut GHG emissions as soon as possible.

Case Study: California

California is an exceptional state. As far as energy generation is concerned, it is one of the largest producers and consumers in the country and even the world. It generates more electricity than many countries in this world and has always led the country and the world in innovation and the practical implementation of life-changing initiatives, including energy.

California has a high per capita gross state product and high energy prices. California's climate attracts people from throughout the country, and the entertainment industry and Silicon Valley have created great economic wealth in California.

Lately, however, California's regulations have driven up energy prices even higher, and will continue to push up energy prices. For example, California motorists are required to use a special motor gasoline blend called California clean burning gasoline, making California have the highest gasoline price in the lower 48 states.

California has also enacted regulations to increase the price of energy in an effort to reduce carbon dioxide emissions. These regulations are geared to facilitate renewable energy use and enhance protection of the environment in the state.

Nevertheless, California imports more electricity than any other state, and recent state laws prohibit utilities in California from entering into long-term contracts with coal-fired power plants for electricity imports.

In 2012, the electric power in the state was produced by natural gas, 55.7%; nuclear power generation, 15.5%; hydroelectric 13.5%; and geothermal 6.4%. The rest of the energy sources (wind 2.8%, biomass 3.0%, coal 1.0%, and solar 0.3%) amounted to less than 9%.

California has large oil deposits that account for more than a tenth of the nation's oil production, and more than a tenth of the nation's oil refining capacity. California also provides about 2% of the annual natural gas production in the U.S. There are also large deposits of offshore oil and natural gas, but, although the federal moratorium expired in 2008, the Obama administration, and the state and local governments will not allow these resources to be further developed. So, to meet rising state demand, there are proposals to build liquefied natural gas (LNG) import terminals in the state.

California also has substantial geothermal potential and is home to the world's largest complex of geothermal power plants, providing over 6% of the state's power. It also has wind power potential, but wind currently provides less than 3% of the state's electricity. Though California's deserts provide significant solar power potential, today only a minimal portion of the state's electricity is generated from this source (0.3%), even though the world's largest solar power facilities are located in California's Mojave Desert.

California is considered a leader and an example of environmental awareness to the other U.S. states and the world, which is reflected in the rapid implementation of renewable projects in the state recently.

Regulatory Impediments to Affordable Energy

In some cases regulations imposed in the name of reducing carbon dioxide and greenhouse gas emissions are especially costly. Carbon dioxide is a byproduct of the combustion of all carbon-containing fuels, such as natural gas, petroleum, coal, wood, and other organic materials. There is no cost-effective way to capture the carbon dioxide output of the combustion of these fuels thus far, so any regulations that limit carbon dioxide emissions will either limit the use of natural gas, petroleum, and coal, or will dramatically increase their prices, or both. The final result is ever increasing fuel and energy prices to be paid by the people.

And sure enough, California has some of the nation's highest prices for gas, diesel and electricity use. With the increase of renewables in the state, the utilities are finding themselves in a dead-end street. They must play the green game, which is costing them too much money and effort, so the customer ends up with higher monthly bills.

California's regulatory environment that affects the cost of energy or its use is as follows:

Greenhouse gas (GHG) emissions cap was introduced in September 2006 when the California State Legislature enacted the global warming solutions act, A.B. 32. This act caps greenhouse gas emissions at 1990 levels by 2020. It is the first state program to impose a cap on greenhouse gas emissions and include enforceable penalties to violators. Under this program, utilities with coal-fired power plants are violators, and they pay significant penalties for excess emissions.

Ban on new coal-fired power plants is part of an interim greenhouse performance standard that requires that all new base-load generation plants produce no more GHGs than a combined-cycle gas turbine power plant.

Coal-fired power plants produce excess GHG emissions, so to eliminate the penalties and reduce other expense, the utilities are replacing the coal with gas-fired power, since gas is cheaper and cleaner. They also introduce renewable (wind and solar) power plants, but all these replacements and additions cost billions of dollars on top of all other expenses. So, by reducing one expense, the utilities acquire another one, which—you guessed it—the customers end up paying.

California utilities are allowed to "decouple" revenue from the sale of electricity and natural gas. This way, California has enabled utilities to increase their revenue by selling less electricity and natural gas whenever they want. That allows the utilities to increase their revenue by manipulating the market as they see fit. Since the primary goal of any capitalist enterprise is to maximize profits, guess who will end up with the bill? Yep, you guessed right again.

A feed-in tariff (FIT) for renewable energy requires investor-owned utilities to purchase renewable energy at an increased price. Utilities must buy all renewable generation under three megawatts within their service territories, until they hit a statewide total cap of 750 megawatts. Large public utilities must also set up programs to buy all renewable generation under three megawatts. By increasing the cost of renewable energy, this law increases electricity prices for consumers and businesses.

The FIT seems reasonable, until a closer look reveals that 90% of Californians do not use renewable energy. They have no solar panels on their roofs or wind turbines in their back yards. Yet, while those who can afford solar and wind installations (the 10%) get paid for the power these produce, the average and unsuspecting tax payer (who doesn't even know what solar is and is busy making ends meet) ends up paying a major part of the price increase brought upon by the expanding use of renewables.

Cap and trade agreement is part of the western climate initiative (WCI), which is a regional agreement between American and Canadian government officials to target greenhouse gas reductions. It consists of enactment of a cap-and-trade scheme to reduce greenhouse gas emissions 15% below 2005 levels by 2020.

Here the utilities buy and sell points according to how much GHGs they generate. Of course, the goal is to generate as little as possible, but this is the most expensive alternative, so the utilities are caught in a dilemma—continue as is and pay some penalties, or spend a lot of money on upgrades and renewables to reduce the penalties (and the GHG emissions).

Renewables portfolio standard (RPS) is a mandate that requires the utilities to generate and/or sell a cer-

tain percentage of electricity from renewable sources. The state's RPS requires utilities to provide 33% by 2020, by either producing the required electricity in state or importing it from out-of-state. In addition, most renewable facilities had to have been constructed after September 26, 1996 to be counted towards the RPS.

Here constructing renewable power plants (solar, wind, bio-, geo-power, etc.), or buying renewable energy from other sources is mandated, so the utilities must comply. No matter which way they chose, the monthly power bills in California will increase incrementally as time goes on. There is no way around it.

A special blend of gasoline called California clean burning gasoline is required by use in the state. In Imperial County, and the Los Angeles metropolitan area, motorists are required to use a special blend of california oxygenated clean burning gasoline. Also, California imposes a low carbon fuel standard (LCFS). Governor Arnold Schwarzenegger issued Executive Order S-01-07, requiring a 10% reduction in the carbon intensity of all transportation fuels.

Automobile fuel economy standards, an attempt to regulate greenhouse gas emissions from new vehicles, was introduced by assembly bill 1493, passed in 2002. It allowed the California air resources board to develop regulations to reduce greenhouse gas emissions from passenger vehicles if the state received a waiver from EPA.

New residential and commercial buildings are required to meet energy efficiency standards. The state's specific code, from Title 24, Part 6, exceeds the requirements of the 2006 international energy conservation code (IECC). The IECC, developed by the international code council, is a model code that mandates certain energy efficiency standards. Assembly bill 1103, passed in 2007, also requires all non-residential buildings to report their annual energy use. New and renovated state buildings must also meet the silver LEED standard, which is one level of the U.S. green building council's leadership in energy and environmental design (LEED) rating system. A wide variety of independent state agencies must also seek new energy efficiency standards.

Appliance efficiency standards are imposed by the state's appliance efficiency regulations, which include mandates for consumer audio and video products, metal halide lamp fixtures, pool pumps, general service incandescent lamps, water dispensers, walk-in refrigerators and freezers, hot tubs, commercial hot food holding cabinets, under cabinet fluorescent lamps, and vending machines. Additionally, assembly bill 1109, passed in 2007, requires the California energy commission to impose minimum efficiency standards for all general-purpose lights.

The comprehensive environmental response, compensation, and liability act (CERCLA), or the superfund, established a liability boundary for past and current operators of contaminated facilities to be financially responsible for the costs of cleanup. In case the responsible parties cannot pay for the cleanup, CERCLA authorizes the federal government to finance the cleanup to ensure the protection of human health and the environment, using what is referred to as "orphan shares."

CERCLA is intended to locate and hold responsible all parties that may have been involved in contamination of the environment, to minimize the costs of cleanup on the "polluter pays principle."

Some of these regulations are overly ambitious and restricting, which affects economic growth, while others are (albeit unintentionally) not intended to protect the customers' interests. Because of this combination of unfortunate factors, it is not clear how these regulations will play in the present energy and financial climate and in the long run.

We know from the past that Californians are quite patient—to a point. When that point is reached, however, then things happen and laws are forcibly changed. As things are going now, we estimate the point of no return to be reached by 2015-2016, at which time the state government and the utilities will have to provide answers to satisfy the majority.

THE POLITICS OF ENERGY AND ENVIRONMENT

Energy generation and the environmental protection have been, and still are, dependent on national and international politics. They are holding hands together, dancing the never-ending dance of needs and wants, successes and failures. As a matter of fact, there are very few aspects of politics, which do not include energy and the related environmental issues, that are directly or indirectly part of it. And, yes, there is no way of separating energy from its effects on the environment. Pick any subject that the politicians in the U.S., the EU, Asia, Africa, or Australia are working on today, and you will see that sooner or later, a number of issues on energy or environment popping up. They are integral part of our life now.

Let's try naming some issues discussed by the politicians of today. From A to Z; agriculture, Bald Eagle, biodiversity, cloning, drainage, elephants, endangered species, forests, gas, hardwood, hurricanes, Indian, jails, kids, landfill, medical, noise, ocean, overpopulation, packaging, pouching, quality product, rain, shipping, trees, urban, vegetables, world hunger, work place, x-rays, young adults, zebras. Yes, they all have one thing in common; they are all somehow related to energy, or the environment, or both.

The actual debate on the issues related to energy in the U.S. started in 1973, with the Arab oil embargo, which awoke us from the previous 20 years of dreaming the American Dream. Around the same time, the environmental issues became obvious and were seriously addressed in the U.S.

So we have had more than 40 years of experience and non-stop debate on these issues. There were many successes and many failures during that time. We have achieved and learned a lot, but even more is left to do before we reach the ultimate balance between energy independence and clean environment.

The last chance to make a difference is in front of us. If we miss it, future generations will have to deal with some serious negative consequences, caused by our ignorance or selfishness in dealing with the major energy and environmental issues.

Energy and Politics

The key energy-related concepts used by politicians, regulators, and utilities now are: petroleum, natural gas, coal, nuclear, renewables, electricity, energy efficiency, and energy independence. Yes, electricity, energy efficiency, and energy independence are not energy sources, but they are equally important in discussing the U.S. energy policies.

And the environment, and especially the way energy production affects the environment in the U.S. and the world, is another major issue. Actually, it is hard to separate these two, since they are so closely related.

Or as President Obama put it in his speech on earth day, 2009:

The choice we face is not between saving our environment and saving our economy—the choice we face is between prosperity and decline. We can remain the world's leading importer of oil, or we can become the world's leading exporter of clean energy. We can allow climate change to wreak unnatural havoc across the landscape, or we can create jobs working to prevent its worst effects... The nation that leads the world in creat-

ing new energy sources will be the nation that leads the 21st century global economy.

He obviously sees the relation, but seems unconvinced that we can have both clean environment (reduced GHG emissions) and prosperous economy (abundant energy). Instead, he seems to think that we must sacrifice one to have the other, and that we cannot find the right balance to enjoy both energy independence and acceptably clean environment. In the summer of 2013, he called for expansion of our solar and wind efforts as part of his newest climate policy.

During one of his best events in 2008, President Obama described America's dependence on oil as resembling a "shock and trance" cycle. Our growing demand for foreign oil, he said, creates skyrocketing energy prices, leading to dramatic calls for energy independence and sudden cutbacks in our consumption that quickly dissipate once the price of oil drops—beginning the cycle all over again.

Regardless, the U.S. is now almost fully energy independent. It happened almost overnight, due to new gas and oil discoveries and new, much more efficient, exploration technologies. We do not import any natural gas, coal, or nuclear fuels, which have in fact already made 99% our electricity generation oil-free. Nuclear power, coal, wind and solar power plants are mostly used to produce electricity, which contributes to our energy independence. Oil is used exclusively for transportation and for manufacturing consumer goods, and we have learned how to limit its use in power generation, thus reducing the imports.

This has changed the political arena. Hydro and nuclear power are not on the political agenda, at least not in a negative way. Wind and solar are on the back burners, with their futures hanging on future taxes and other regulations. Coal and fracking for oil and gas, however, are heavily on the energy-related political forefront now.

The future of coal and gas is somewhat predetermined, with reduced coal, and increased gas, production, mostly due to pricing (gas is much cheaper) and environmental (gas is much cleaner) concerns. There is a well-defined trend to replace coal-fired power generation with gas-fired generation, the main reason for which is the abundance of gas, and its lower costs and reduced GHG emissions.

We still import significant quantities of crude oil for our transportation needs, and that creates problems for the politicians, but through keeping high prices at the gas pump, discovering new oil reservoirs in the U.S., and mixing bioethanol with gas, the oil imports are un-

der control and even diminishing slowly.

So, looking at the above discussion, we see that the energy politics now boil down to the issues of:

a.   Coal vs. gas use for power generation
b.   Crude oil supply and prices for transportation
c.   Tax deductions to keep the renewables alive and going

It is easy for us to say that the issues are simple, but the politicians are split. Some want to drill many oil and gas wells, and import more oil from Canada (instead of buying it from the Arabs) and eliminate tax deductions for wind power and solar power, because those sources are not mature enough. Other politicians want to restore tax deductions for wind and solar power, so that they can grow and catch up with their older cousins, the fossils, which are undeservingly receiving billions in tax and other benefits. There is also a battle to strip away intangible drilling costs, oil depletion allowances, and other energy-related deductions.

A significant part of the U.S. energy generation capacity depends on the margins provided by tax breaks. Increasing taxes on energy producers usually reduces production and raises prices, while tax deductions keep wind and solar projects going and help oil and gas wells to stay profitable. Smaller wells and wind and solar power projects would not have been even started if the tax breaks were not present.

One critical point is the now famous 30% investment tax credit (ITC) which benefits the renewable energy generators, and which is due to expire in 2016. Billions of dollars in direct grants, subsidies, and loan guarantees went into propping up wind and solar manufacturers and installations during 2007-2011, as part of a number of federal and state programs.

NOTE: Most of these programs are history now, so the wind and solar industries are at a critical point. The ITC is keeping them going for now, so we will have to wait and see what will happen when it is gone too. In our opinion, without that credit and other government subsidies and incentives, most of the wind and solar installations would not have been even started during 2007-2012, and most of them would not be profitable even if they had found a way to start.

Political and Special Interests

Any mention of energy, energy supply in the context of conservation and environment eventually boils down to the fact that it is impossible to separate the different aspects of the subject from the politics that surround it. There is a connection between these, most likely because our energy supply is the life-blood of the economy, which politicians are extremely interested in.

The problem is that politicians' turnover is high, so they like quick and short-term solutions, but most importantly they would not touch measures that would cost them their jobs. Not to mention that the political parties depend on donations from the different industries, so they are vary careful not to cut the branch they are sitting on.

Government officials often refuse to do the right thing because in so doing they might do something that would hurt them or their "associates." Sometimes they claim that they do the things they do in defense of the national interests, which makes it hard to argue. Any environmental control measures, for example, are going to hurt the economy, so that is not something politicians would do willingly unless they are protected in some way from the voters' revenge.

And this is even more so in the developing countries of the world, because they know well that the rich, developed countries telling them to reduce GHG emissions is hypocritical. After all, the advanced nations of North America and Europe only became rich through intensive manufacturing. Since the eighteenth century, the rich, developed countries became that way after using large amounts of energy, and have produced high levels of pollution for almost a century now. So how could their politicians even bring the question of sacrificing their fragile economies for the sake of a clean environment?

The developed world, and the U.S. in particular, is determined to do the right thing and lead the world by example in reducing GHG emissions at all costs and even if it hurts some. Is the world going to follow voluntarily? Not likely, so we keep on trying and hope for the best.

The Beginning...

Let's go back in the not-so-distant history now. The organization of the petroleum exporting countries (OPEC), which included a dozen or so countries (mostly Arab) rich on oil and gas, was formed in 1960 to give them more leverage in their negotiations with oil companies and governments.

A dozen years later, in 1973, OPEC turned the oil spigot off and the U.S. woke up one day with long lines and high prices at the pump. Not a pretty sight, and one that threatened to kill the American dream, but the entire episode went down in history as a temporary inconvenience that was not to be repeated.

Over the years, OPEC's power has grown considerably, to the point that it could, and does, drive up the world price of oil whenever its members agree to limit production. Thus, OPEC is a classic example of a cartel, a group of entities that act together to affect market prices by controlling the production and marketing of an important global product.

OPEC-type cartels have been illegal in the U.S. since 1890, when Congress passed the Sherman antitrust act (Title 15, Section 1 and following of the U.S. Code), which states, "Every contract, combination in the form of trust or otherwise, or conspiracy, in restraint of trade or commerce among the several states, or with foreign nations, is declared to be illegal." Antitrust law violators can face criminal charges as well as civil lawsuits brought by victims of their illegal actions. A victim who wins a civil suit is awarded three times the amount of his or her damages.

The Sherman act was directed at American companies such as John D. Rockefeller's Standard Oil Company. Its language does not rule out suits against foreign countries, but those suits are restricted by "act of state" doctrine, under which a country's actions within its own borders cannot be questioned in another country's courts. The act of state doctrine is not part of international law, but federal courts in this country apply it to avoid interfering with the President's constitutional authority to conduct relations with foreign countries.

In the international association of machinists and aerospace workers v. OPEC, 649 F.2d 1354 (9th Cir. 1981), a labor union attempted to sue OPEC. A federal appeals court held that the act of state doctrine prevented it from hearing the merits of that lawsuit. Some legal experts and members of Congress believed that the appeals court came to the wrong conclusion. They argued that the act of state doctrine does not apply to countries engaged in purely economic activity.

In 2007, as the price of oil rose, the House of Representatives overwhelmingly passed the "No oil producing and exporting cartels act of 2007"or"NOPEC" Act (H.R. 2264). Section 2 of NOPEC would extend the Sherman act to foreign countries acting as a cartel to limit the production or distribution of, fix the price of, or otherwise restrain trade in the American market for petroleum products. NOPEC also "overrules" the decision in the international association of machinists' case by specifically making the act of state doctrine inapplicable to lawsuits against oil cartels. The attorney general can file a lawsuit against OPEC, but private citizens cannot sue on their own. The NOPEC Act died in the Senate and no further action was ever taken, nor expected any time soon.

OPEC's 1973 oil embargo did one good thing: it changed the world and us, and we all have not been the same ever since. We learned that trusting and relying on oil-rich nations for our energy needs is not a workable solution for both efficient oil use and keeping the world at peace.

President Carter

Shortly after taking office in 1977, while the U.S. was still shaken by the OPEC embargo, President Jimmy Carter addressed the nation to rally support for the national energy plan that he was about to propose to Congress. The plan was based on 10 fundamental principles that included economic growth, protecting the environment, fairness to all, developing new energy sources, and, most importantly, conservation.

The President set out a number of goals to be reached by 1985, the most important of which were: cutting America's oil imports in half, establishing a strategic petroleum reserve, increasing the nation's coal production by two-thirds, and using solar energy in more than 2.5 million homes.

Here are some excerpts from the president's historical remarks, which are even more pertinent today:

Tonight I want to have an unpleasant talk with you about a problem unprecedented in our history. With the exception of preventing war, this is the greatest challenge our country will face during our lifetimes. The energy crisis has not yet overwhelmed us, but it will, if we do not act quickly.

We simply must balance our demand for energy with our rapidly shrinking resources. By acting now, we can control our future instead of letting the future control us...

Our decision about energy will test the character of the American people and the ability of the president and the Congress to govern. This difficult effort will be the "moral equivalent of war"—except that we will be uniting our efforts to build and not destroy.

I know that some of you may doubt that we face real energy shortages. The 1973 gasoline lines are gone, and our homes are warm again. But our energy problem is worse tonight than it was in 1973 or a few weeks ago in the dead of winter. It is worse because more waste has occurred, and more time has passed by without our planning for the future. And it will get worse every day until we act.

The world now uses about 60 million barrels of oil a day and demand increases each year about 5%. This means that just to stay even we need the production of

a new Texas every year, an Alaskan North Slope every nine months, or a new Saudi Arabia every three years.

Obviously, this cannot continue.

The world has not prepared for the future. During the 1950s, people used twice the oil as during the 1940s. During the 1960s, we used twice as much as during the 1950s. And in each of those decades, more oil was consumed than in all of mankind's previous history.

Ours is the most wasteful nation on earth. We waste more energy than we import. With about the same standard of living, we use twice the energy per person as do other countries like Germany, Japan and Sweden.

We can't substantially increase our domestic production, so we would need to import twice the oil as we do now. Supplies will be uncertain. The cost will keep going up.

I am sure each of you will find something you don't like about the specifics of our proposal. It will demand that we make sacrifices and changes in our lives. To some degree, the sacrifices will be painful—but so is any meaningful sacrifice. It will lead to some higher costs, and to some greater inconveniences for everyone.

But the sacrifices will be gradual, realistic, and necessary. Above all, they will be fair. No one will gain an unfair advantage through this plan. No one will be asked to bear an unfair burden...

Other generations of Americans have faced and mastered great challenges. I have faith that meeting this challenge will make our own lives even richer. If you will join me so that we can work together with patriotism and courage, we will again prove that our great nation can lead the world into an age of peace, independence and freedom.

NOTE: Carter's energy policy received mixed reviews at the time, and commentators are still divided over it. Some praise him for anticipating that the energy depletion would eventually cause a crisis and for understanding the economic and political importance of energy independence. Others, however, believe that he not only overstated the problem, but also tried to address it with a heavy-handed regulatory approach that offered few incentives to find new sources of energy. He continued:

If we fail to act soon, we will face an economic, social and political crisis that will threaten our free institutions.

But we still have another choice. We can begin to prepare right now. We can decide to act while there is time. That is the concept of the energy policy we will present on Wednesday. Our national energy plan is based on ten fundamental principles.

The first principle is that we can have an effective and comprehensive energy policy only if the government takes responsibility for it and if the people understand the seriousness of the challenge and are willing to make sacrifices.

The second principle is that healthy economic growth must continue. Only by saving energy can we maintain our standard of living and keep our people at work. An effective conservation program will create hundreds of thousands of new jobs.

The third principle is that we must protect the environment. Our energy problems have the same cause as our environmental problems — wasteful use of resources. Conservation helps us solve both at once.

The fourth principle is that we must reduce our vulnerability to potentially devastating embargoes. We can protect ourselves from uncertain supplies by reducing our demand for oil, making the most of our abundant resources such as coal, and developing a strategic petroleum reserve.

The fifth principle is that we must be fair. Our solutions must ask equal sacrifices from every region, every class of people, and every interest group. Industry will have to do its part to conserve, just as the consumers will. The energy producers deserve fair treatment, but we will not let the oil companies profiteer.

The sixth principle, and the cornerstone of our policy, is to reduce the demand through conservation. Our emphasis on conservation is a clear difference between this plan and others that merely encouraged crash production efforts. Conservation is the quickest, cheapest, most practical source of energy. Conservation is the only way we can buy a barrel of oil for a few dollars. It costs about $13 to waste it.

The seventh principle is that prices should generally reflect the true replacement costs of energy. We are only cheating ourselves if we make energy artificially cheap and use more than we can really afford.

The eighth principle is that government policies must be predictable and certain. Both consumers and producers need policies they can count on so they can plan ahead. This is one reason I am working with the Congress to create a new Department of Energy, to replace more than 50 different agencies that now have some control over energy.

The ninth principle is that we must conserve the fuels that are scarcest and make the most of those that are more plentiful. We can't continue to use oil and gas for 75% of our consumption when they make up 7% of our domestic reserves. We need to shift to plentiful coal

while taking care to protect the environment, and to apply stricter safety standards to nuclear energy.

The tenth principle is that we must start now to develop the new, unconventional sources of energy we will rely on in the next century.

These exact words we hear today—35 years later. And although, no doubt, progress has been made, as compared with other technologies, the power generation has not moved one iota forward. (16)

The U.S. Energy vs. Environment Dilemma

What is more pressing in the short term, and most dangerous in the long-term, the economic or the climate crisis? This is a loaded question that very few people could give a convincing answer to. It is like choosing between cancer and jumping from an airplane without a parachute. Which scenario gives you better chance to survive?

The best answer is to pinch oneself and wake up to something different—anything would be better than these two choices. And so is the present energy and environmental situation. We need a lot of energy, so we burn a lot of fossils and at the same time emit a lot of toxic gasses in the air we breathe.

Only money—a lot of money—can make a real change in this dilemma. Obama's government threw a lot of money—billions of dollars—at different energy and environmental companies and projects during 2008-2012, but the results were dismal. As a matter of fact, the embarrassments outnumbered the successes by a great margin.

This was a good lesson that government's role is limited to supporting basic research and assisting with finances and efficient regulations whenever needed; not dictating the business direction and speed, which is the role of private sector investment.

Only large and well-placed private investments and a lot of effort can solve the present energy and environmental crisis. The U.S. is capable of doing this, and even can show the rest of the world how to do it. If the world follows, as we think that it will if the U.S. comes up the magic formula, then things will change quickly and we could hope for good news on the global energy and environmental fronts.

In 2009, the world gathered in Copenhagen for a climate conference. Representatives of 167 countries, responsible for nearly 90% of global GHG emissions, discussed energy and environmental platforms of their economies and agreed that they are partially responsible for global climate warming and other problems. They

Figure 6-42. 2009 Copenhagen conference

also agreed that the GHG emissions must be contained, and must not increase more than 2°C, which we believe is too high.

There was hope and excitement in the air. Finally, things will be done. But the largest change can be done only by changing the power generation to systems that generate less GHGs, and to limit the GHG emissions to 550 giga tons (GT) by 2050. This is close to the maximum that oceans, forests, crops, and plants can absorb without causing catastrophic global climate instability.

Sounds good and doable, but words alone don't do much good in practice, because in 2011, only two years after the Copenhagen excitement and in the midst of a global financial slow down, the world managed to emit a record level, 31.5 GT of GHG emissions. But the U.S. emissions decreased at that period by 1.8%, while China emissions rose 9.3%.

And this is just the beginning of a long battle to find a balance of the energy vs. environment issues. The developing countries are demanding increasingly more power. They feel cheated by the developed nations and are determined to catch up no matter what it takes. They plan to do this by burning as much coal as needed to produce electricity, which poses a great threat to the global climate.

Presently we are witnessing an annual increase of about 3%, at which rate in 15 years the total GHG emissions would far exceeded the 550 GT limit proposed in Copenhagen in 2009. At that point global climate will overheat to the point of no return.

The U.S. energy sector is entering a new phase of development, where technological advances allow the use of cheaper and less polluting fuels (natural gas and nuclear), which changed the predictions of the experts that reducing emissions would harm economic growth. While this is true in theory, it is no longer true for the U.S. Natural gas, solar and wind energy, advanced nuclear

power, batteries, and other energy storage solutions allow economic development in parallel with cleaning the environment.

We are also blessed with enough natural resources—including precious sunshine, wind, and water—so we can move in the direction outlined in Copenhagen by using these fuels and the related technologies. In addition, efficiency measures are another and maybe the best way to energy independence, by simply saving energy.

Each U.S. household consumes about 250 kWh of electricity daily, for heating, lighting, air conditioning, transportation, etc. At the same time Europeans and Japanese consume about half as much, so here is a chance to become like them and reduce our energy consumption by half. This, however, is not very likely, so we will be lucky to see a 10-20% energy reduction in the future.

Unfortunately, regulatory, legal, and financing obstacles block hundreds of billions of private sector investment in the more efficient renewable technologies and in implementing energy saving efficiency measures. The climate crisis is a reality, and every minute brings us closer to a time and place we don't want.

We rely on the government to attract private investors to implement new technologies and efficiency measures. With the government help, $1 trillion private investments into renewable generation, efficient distribution and consumption, and electric transportation over the next ten years would make the difference. Such an undertaking would bring a great revival in the U.S. energy sector and would create millions of new jobs.

On the international front, the U.S. could lead the world in the fight against energy shortage and increasing GHG emissions. If we all stand and work together to eliminate this threat, the world would be better, cleaner and more energy efficient place to live in. But first we need to resolve the internal energy-environment dilemma.

Fuel Transport

The transport of fuels—oil, natural gas, and nuclear materials from place to place around the U.S.—is regulated by a number of federal and state regulating bodies.

Each of these organizations has a clearly defined area of responsibilities, as follows:

The Department Of Transportation's (DOT) accident regulations are designed to promote public safety by identifying unsafe carriers and ensuring rapid responses to hazardous conditions. DOT trucking regulations are enforced by the federal motor carrier safety administration.

Hazmat carriers (including oil, petroleum products, natural gas and nuclear products and waste) must report to the DOT any accident involving a fatality, serious injury, or disabling vehicle damage. All carriers must keep a detailed record of any accident in an accident register for three years after the event.

DOT regulates shippers of hazardous materials, including radioactive material, and oversees vehicle safety, routing, shipping papers, emergency response, and shipper training requirements.

The federal motor carrier safety administration (FMSCA) under the department of transportation regulates the transportation of hazardous materials, including fuel, on the nation's highways. Transporters of fuel are required to follow specific registration, training, communication, packaging, emergency response, and security regulations to maintain public safety.

The pipeline and hazardous materials safety administration (PHMSA) is the agency in charge of ensuring transport safety in the U.S. The goals of PHMSA are to improve public health and safety by reducing transportation-related deaths and injuries and protecting people wherever they might be.

PHMSA aims to reduce the number of pipeline incidents involving death or major injury to between 26-37 per year and to reduce the number of hazardous materials incidents involving death or major injury to between 21-32 per year.

On the environmental front, PHMSA works to advance environmentally sustainable policies and investments that reduce carbon and other harmful emissions from transportation sources as needed to protect the natural environment, focusing especially on unusually sensitive areas.

PHMSA plans to reduce the number of hazardous liquid pipeline spills with environmental consequences to between 65-81 per year and reduce the number of hazardous materials incidents with environmental damage to between 44-64 per year.

PHMSA safety regulations ensure that infrastructure is assessed regularly and maintained in good condition. Strong safety programs help get products to market with minimal disruption, and make communities safer and more livable at the same time.

The nuclear regulatory commission (NRC) regulates users of radioactive material in 13 states (37 states regulate radioactive material users within their borders); approves the design, fabrication, use and maintenance of shipping containers for the most hazardous radioactive materials, including spent nuclear fuel; and regulates the physical protection of commercial spent fuel in tran-

sit against malicious acts.

The NRC requires radioactive materials shipments to comply with DOT's safety regulations for transporting hazardous materials.

The transport of the different fuels to different locations is done either by pipelines, or by road, water or air.

Pipelines

Due to the ease of operation, once the line is installed, pipelines are the preferred, safer, more efficient, and cheaper transportation method of liquid and gaseous fuels. They are used whenever possible or available, and there are a special type of regulations that dictate the proper use of these facilities:

The pipeline safety, regulatory certainty, and job creation act of 2011 was designed to examine and improve the state of pipeline safety regulation. The act reauthorizes PHMSA's federal pipeline safety programs through fiscal year 2015, provides the regulatory certainty necessary for pipeline owners and operators to plan infrastructure investments and create jobs, improves pipeline transportation by strengthening enforcement of current laws and improving existing laws where necessary, ensures a balanced regulatory approach to improving safety that applies cost-benefit principles, and protects and preserves congressional authority by ensuring certain key rulemakings are not finalized until Congress has an opportunity to act

This act changed existing pipeline safety laws and authorized the appropriation of funds to support the pipeline safety activities of PHMSA through 2015. Some of the amendments were in response to recent pipeline accidents, which required the U.S. Congress to take additional measures to ensure the safety of the 2.4 million miles of pipeline infrastructure crisscrossing the country.

The act also affects operators of facilities, and requires that PHMSA re-examine many of its regulations, to revise, expand, and strengthen them. Key provisions affecting hazardous liquid and gas pipelines address the possible expansion of IM requirements, establishing standards for leak detection, the expanded use of automatic or remote controlled valves, and the verification of gas pipeline records, including those in support of maximum allowable operating pressure (MAOP).

Note: In July 2010, a hazardous liquid pipeline ruptured near Marshal, MI, releasing an estimated 819,000 gallons of crude oil into the environment in the local creek and downstream river. In another incident in September 2010, a gas transmission line ruptured in San

Bruno, CA, resulting in multiple fatalities and extensive property damage.

These incidents raised a number of issues regarding PHMSA's safety regulations for liquid and gas transmission pipelines, including the effectiveness of PHMSA's IM regulations, and the ability of operators to stop the flow of liquids or gas as needed during a rupture. The accuracy of the records of buried transmission pipelines was also questioned.

Even before the passage of the 2011 act, and in response to these and other incidents, PHMSA was considering the related issues and had begun comprehensive reviews of its regulations. In two advance notices of proposed rulemaking (ANPRM), PHMSA sought public comment on the appropriateness of numerous changes to gas and hazardous liquid safety regulations. The passage of the 2011 act will likely lead to stronger pipeline safety regulations and reduced number of incidents and accidents.

Road Transport

Another transport method used widely for fuels transport is by road via trucks, trains, boats, and other vehicles. A number of regulations are in force when fuels and other hazardous materials are transported along the U.S. roads and highway systems.

Some of the pertinent regulations for transport of petroleum products and fuels, issued by DOT and other regulatory bodies, are:

* *49 CFR §173.8(a)* allowed the use of non-specification bulk packaging for the transportation of most hazardous materials (beyond just petroleum products) by an intrastate carrier until July 1, 2000. The remaining provisions of §173.8 are now limited to petroleum products. The use of non-specification cargo tanks (49 CFR §173.8(b)) or permanently secured non-bulk tanks (§173.8(c)) to transport petroleum products are both contingent on meeting certain criteria (§173.8(d)). Those requirements will be discussed after the non-specification cargo tank and secured tank provisions.

* *49 CFR §173.8(b)*, allows the continued use of non-specification cargo tanks, with capacities < 3500 gallons, for petroleum products provided items 1-5 of §173.8(d) are met (see below). In addition, after July 1, 2000 the Subpart E provisions "qualification and maintenance of cargo tanks" (49 CFR 180.401-180.417) were made a formal requirement (i.e. qualifications, inspections, record keeping etc.). An

exception to the provisions that address manhole assemblies (49 CFR 180.405(g) and 178.345-5) was allowed due the size of authorized tanks (< 3500 g).

* *49 CFR §173.8(c)* allows the use of non-bulk tanks for petroleum products provided the capacity is < 119 gallons and the tank is permanently secured to the vehicle and is protected against leakage or damage in the event of a turnover. As with the cargo tank provisions, after July 1, 2000 the permanently secured non-bulk tanks are subject to the formal subpart E "qualification and maintenance of cargo tanks" (49 CFR §180.401-§180.417) requirements (i.e. qualifications, inspections, record keeping etc.).

Another set of special regulations, issued by NRC, is in force for transport of nuclear materials and wastes.

NRC's regulations are contained in chapter I of title 10, "energy," of the code of federal regulations (CFR). Chapter I is divided into parts 1-199.

The following are the principal parts governing spent fuel transportation:

Part 71 establishes the procedures and standards for NRC approval of packaging and shipping procedures for fissile material and for a quantity of other licensed material in excess of a type A quantity.

Part 73 establishes requirements for the establishment and maintenance of a physical protection system, which will protect special nuclear material at fixed sites and in transit and at plants at which special nuclear material is used.

Regulatory guides are issued in 10 divisions and are intended to aid licensees in implementing regulations. The guides most applicable to spent fuel transportation are issued in division 7, transportation.

Rulemaking dockets is a government-wide, on-line database that includes NRC's public dockets for its rulemaking actions. The dockets include publicly available documents such as NRC-issued federal register notices, supporting documents, public comments, and other related documents.

The Utilities

The U.S. utilities are in charge of, and responsible for, the safe and efficient generation and then transmission of electric power around the country. Most transmission facilities in the U.S. are owned by individual utilities, including the federal power-marketing agencies, and some are jointly owned by multi-utility groups. In some cases, transmission lines are owned by independent entities other than utilities, which receive payment from all users of the transmission lines.

The U.S. Constitution reserves to Congress the power to regulate interstate commerce. Because power moves between states over transmission lines, FERC has authority over the pricing for most transmission services and has limited authority to override local authorities to provide for construction of lines that address the national interest, as deemed by a periodic U.S. Department of Energy assessment.

In some parts of the U.S., the lack of new transmission lines has hampered the development of renewable energy resources, because current transmission lines do not necessarily lie in areas that are most advantageous to renewable energy. Also, transmission pricing has generally evolved to serve base-load coal and nuclear projects; that pricing structure creates challenges for intermittent power sources like wind and solar that FERC is evaluating.

Public power entities such as the New York power authority, Arizona's Salt River project, North Carolina's Santee cooper, or the Los Angeles department of water and power *are not* under FERC jurisdiction. Federal power marketing authorities, such as the Bonneville power administration, the Western area power administration, and the Tennessee Valley authority are also self-governing, and fall outside FERC's general regulatory authority as well.

Finally, most of Texas and all of Hawaii and Alaska are outside FERC jurisdiction because they are not connected, or not tightly connected, to the interstate transmission grid. However, the entities not subject to direct regulation by FERC generally consider FERC policy and adhere to similar standards.

Several acts of Congress, including the energy policy acts of 1992 and 2005, as well as three key decisions by FERC guide current transmission regulation in the U.S., as follows:

Order 888 (1996) detailed how transmission owners may charge for the use of their lines, and the terms under which they must give others access to them. Order 888 also required utilities to separate their transmission and generation businesses, and to file open access transmission rates through which they provide non-discriminatory transmission service.

FERC intended for this separation to make it impossible for a utility to give its own power-generating plants preferential access to the company's lines. FERC also provided for the creation of separate transmission owning companies, generally known as *transcos*, which could build lines where local utilities would not.

Order 889 (1996) created an open access same-time information system (OASIS), through which transmission owners could post the available capacity on their lines, so all companies that wanted to use the system to ship power could all track the available capacity.

Order 2000 (1999) encouraged transmission-owning utilities to form regional transmission organizations. FERC did not require utilities to join RTOs, instead, it asked that the RTOs meet minimum conditions, such as having an independent board of directors. FERC gave these regional organizations the task of developing regional transmission plans and pricing structures that would promote competition in wholesale power markets, establishing the transmission system as a highway distribution system for that wholesale commerce.

Public Utility Regulatory Policies Act

Public utility regulatory policies act (PURPA) was enacted in 1978) as part of the national energy act. It promotes the safe and efficient use of domestic renewable energy. The law requires regulated electric utilities to buy electric power from other producers, if that cost is less than the utility's own avoided cost rate to the consumer.

NOTE: The avoided cost rate is the additional costs that the electric utility would incur if it generated the required power itself, or purchased its demand requirements from another source —if and when available.

This free market approach presented a number of investment opportunities and was significant government encouragement for the development of environmentally friendly, renewable energy projects and technologies. The law also created a market in which many non-utility (independent power producers) developed, while some other energy market players failed.

PURPA's implementation was left to the individual states, because needs varied, so a variety of regulatory regimes developed in states where renewable power resources were needed, available for development, or the generated power could be transmitted. Little was done, unfortunately, in many states where renewable resources were unavailable, where the demand growth was slower or previously met by advance planning.

PURPA promulgated the importance of cogeneration plants, which simultaneously produce electric power and steam. These plants are encouraged by the law because they harness thermal energy as steam that otherwise is wasted in electricity generators.

PURPA also enabled renewable energy providers to gain access to the energy markets, particularly in California and some other western states, thanks to aggressive actions on part of local governments and utilities.

Time has proven, however, that the addition of large amounts of renewable energy is costing the utilities a lot of money. In addition to access to free power grid use, the renewables, being variable and basically unreliable power sources, complicates the grid operation and increase its operating and maintenance costs. The utilities compensate for the loss by increasing the electric bills to residential and commercial customers, which is becoming very unpopular and is bringing a lot of questions. The regulators and the utilities will have to provide very good answers to these questions in the near future, or else Californians might force a change to the state's energy policies—again.

The U.S. Lobbying Machine

And while many people and energy companies are wondering what's coming next, there is a group in Washington, DC, that has clear goals and plans. This is the camp of elite lobbyists, paid for by the energy companies to protect their interests.

The U.S. energy sector runs primarily on fossils, with a mixture of renewable energy sources. The energy is provided by outside materials (coal, oil, and gas) and outside forces (solar, wind, geothermal, and ocean waves). Internally and secretly, however, many of the energy companies rely on other mechanisms and processes to achieve success and gain advantage in different areas of the energy markets. This is done quickly and most efficiently with the help of the omnipresent and omnipotent U.S. energy lobby machine.

Hundreds of lobbyists crawl in the halls of the U.S. Congress and slither down the corridors of the White House. Many of these people represent energy companies, and are paid by them. All coal, oil, and gas companies have troops of full time lobbyists, whose job is to promote the interests of their bosses no matter what, and at all costs.

Many large renewable energy companies (Solyndra and First Solar come to mind as the largest recipients of government finance favors) also have lobbyists knocking on the politicians' doors, asking for favors. The gas and oil companies head the list of lobbying dollars with over $120 million in 2009 alone, followed by the electric utilities with over $100 billion, and mining is steadily in third place with about $20 million. And in 2008 the lobbying expenses were at least 25% higher. What are these people lobbying for?

Most of these lobbyists don't have the necessary background to even understand what the technologies they represent do, nor do they understand the complexity of the energy markets, and yet, they proclaim loudly their full trust in their technologies, which are times too new and unproven to be put on the market. Nevertheless, through special deals and political favors and influences they were able to secure billions of dollars of taxpayers' money to the likes of Solyndra (half a billion dollars in grants) and First Solar (several billion dollars in loan guarantees).

But even with the fully dedicated and extremely efficient lobbying machine in place, many of the solar companies with active lobbying representation in Congress and the White House are no more. They all went down the Solyndra way.

Some of the remaining companies are struggling to keep afloat, and rely on their lobbyists even more than before. But a funny thing happened in Washington, DC, in 2012. The U.S. Congress and even the White House turned their backs on the renewables and their lobbyists. Oh, yes, DC politicians still wave the banner of green energy, energy efficiency, and energy independence, and still pat themselves on the backs for promoting cleaner energy technologies, but the fact is that most of the money and political effort now—and for the foreseeable future—goes into the fossils. Natural gas especially is promoted to the rank of an energy savior, that singlehandedly will bring us energy independence, clean environment, and even take the American dream to new heights.

So, what can be done to bring renewables back on the politicians' agendas, you ask? Not much...for now. Now we just have to wait to see what our next President will do, come 2016. Until then—drill baby, drill is the law and hope of the land.

What is missing in the U.S. energy sector? What has to be done to make it more versatile and self-sustaining? Here are some suggestions by the experts for the long-term success of the U.S. energy sector:

1. Lower the cost of capital for building sufficient power platform
2. Change tax law to attract private investment in the new power platform
3. Set reasonable renewable energy standards at the state level
4. Reform utility regulations to attract private investment
5. Lead the world by example in solving the climate crisis

Political Failures

No doubt we have experienced a lot of successes in the energy and environmental areas since the 1970s. Many, if not most, of these were as a result of decisive political and regulatory action. There have been, however, a number of serious glitches and failures that need to be remembered, recounted, and used as lessons of what not to do in the future.

In 1973 the long gas lines caused by the OPEC embargo forced the Nixon administration to look for alternatives and the solar race was on. Billions of dollars were pumped into companies and universities to invent and implement the solar solution. That didn't happen and the solar revival was short lived. The solar technology was not ready for the challenge, and as soon as the gas prices went down, the government subsidies dried up and solar was forgotten.

The politicians turned their attention to other energy sources, and soon the talks about the new energy revolution started anew; using different technologies and approaches this time. The Clinch River breeder reactor, the synthetic fuels corporation, the hydrogen car, and clean coal are but a few examples spanning several decades of costly and failed projects. Not a single one of these much-ballyhooed initiatives is producing or saving a watt or a whiff of energy, but they have managed to burn through hundreds times more taxpayer money than the ill-fated Solyndra.

An energy department report in 2008 estimated that the federal government had spent $172 billion since 1961 on basic research and the development of advanced energy technologies, including coal, gas, and nuclear. So, extrapolating this expense to our present 2013 era, and considering the $8 billion yearly subsidies to these industries, we are looking at over $200 billion spent thus far on supporting the daily operations and optimization of the conventional technologies.

What does Washington has to show for these investments? A lot of energy generation and increasing green house gasses (GHG) emissions. And should the government even be in the business of promoting particular energy technologies, once the basic research is done (which the government is best suited for, and where its efforts should be focused on and limited to)? But that is another subject.

Some economists, executives and financiers as well as energy secretary Steven Chu argued that the government must play a major role because certain technologies have non-financial benefits, such as producing fewer greenhouse gas emissions or easing U.S. reliance on foreign oil. The semiconductor industry is often held up as a model of how government money can help build a new type of economy.

But others argue that government attempts to lead the search for the holy grail of new or better energy tech-

nologies and approaches has been riddled by politics. And we saw our share of these during the solar boom-bust cycle of 2008-2012, when another flood of billions of dollars were spent on companies who promised a lot, but delivered none and went bankrupt in the process.

Note: Some points of the above discussion might seem unfair, but this is the reality of our capitalist society. We can blame governments and private interests for the solar and wind industry problems of late until the cows come home, but that won't help the situation any.

And since we are talking about unfairness, get this: between 2002 and 2008, renewable energy received total of $12.2 billion in government support, with $6 billion in direct spending and $6.2 billion in tax breaks, according to industry sources. At the same time period fossil fuel industries got $70.2 billion. $16.3 billion directly and $53.9 billion in tax breaks. And just think that the coal, oil, and gas companies are the adults on the energy block, fully capable of supporting themselves. And yet, the government is still supporting them—even when they have been recording record profits, some in hundreds of billions of dollars.

Corn ethanol, for example is still alive today only thanks to federal subsidies. It had benefited from $11 billion in tax breaks and $5 billion in direct spending during this time frame, but yet it is barely alive and still on life support.

From 1918 to date, the oil and gas industries have been getting $4.9 billion, and the nuclear $3.5 billion, in annual subsidies and other financial assistance. Subsidies for renewable energy started in 1994 at $0.35 billion annually, exactly 10 times less than the nuclear and 14 times less than the fossil industry.

Let's take a closer look at the failures of the not-so-distant-past, some of which could be used as a lesson of what not to do:

The Clinch River Breeder Reactor Project

The Clinch River Breeder Reactor Project (CRBRP) was conceived, designed and implemented by the leading nuclear brains and companies in the U.S. at the time. It was located on a 1,300-acre site inside the city limits of Oak Ridge, TN, but yet far enough from the population.

It was a joint effort of the U.S. atomic energy commission (AEC), the U.S. energy research and development administration (ERDA), the U.S. Department of Energy (DOE), and the U.S. electric power industry. The goal was to design and construct a next-generation sodium-cooled fast-neutron nuclear reactor.

It was intended to be a prototype of a new, superior class of liquid metal fast breeder reactors (LMFBR) in the U.S.. The project was first authorized in 1970, appropriated in 1972 and continued until the U.S. Congress terminated funding in October 1983. Thirteen years of wasted effort on an ill-conceived, and very expensive, idea, the likes of which we still see today. Just look at the multi-billion dollar national ignition facility (NIF) at the Lawrence Livermore national laboratory (LLNL).

It was supposed to demonstrate the feasibility of a fusion reaction, but so far it has been able produce only overdone popcorn with its 192 lasers—the most powerful laser facility in the world. It can evaporate an airplane, if it was placed properly within the target area, but there are no takers for that exercise. So, we end up with another big toy, sucking billions from the U.S. economy in annual O&M expense without much to show.

But, back to CRBRP: the work was done by a number of reactor vendors, with Westinghouse as the lead supplier, along with General Electric and Atomics International. There was also an impressive consortium of over 750 utility companies nationwide, and even more secondary vendors and technical consultants. The project costs went almost vertically up, and five years after its initiation, in 1977, the Carter administration terminated the licensing activity in an attempt to kill the project and cut its losses. The CRBR project entered an indecision phase and lay in semi-limbo for years, although most of the hardware was on site and ready to go. Finally, after a brief revival attempt in 1983, when the government and consortium attempted to find outside funding sources, the project was cancelled.

Mind you, over 70% of the equipment was delivered or ordered, and the site preparation work and licensing activities were almost completed. The environmental hearings were completed in March 1983, and the entire project was cancelled in October of the same year. There were six months of official existence—on paper.

AEC estimated that the Clinch River project would cost about $400 million of 1971 money, with additional $260 million contributed by private industry. Within one year, however, the projected costs had jumped to nearly $700 million. And by 1981 more than $1 billion of public money had been spent, while the estimated total cost to completion grew exponentially to over $3.0 billion. And yet another $1.0 billion were needed for handling the spent nuclear fuel at a special re-processing facility.

And as always, a congressional committee investigation in 1981 found evidence of contracting abuse, including bribery and fraud, which added to the total costs. The final estimate was that if the project were to continue, it would have needed over $8 billion to complete, a 20-fold increase.

The Synthetic Fuels Corporation

The Synthetic Fuels Corporation was established in 1980 by the U.S. government-funded synthetic fuels corporation act (which dates from World War II). The goal was to provide finances and technical support for the development, design, and construction of large-scale commercial synthetic fuel manufacturing plants of the coal gasification type. Thus produced fuel was then to be used to feed a gas turbine/combined cycle electric power generating system.

It was believed at high levels at the time that this is the most feasible alternative to imported crude oil, so about $85 million in 1980s money was authorized by the U.S. Congress for this purpose.

The objective of the newly created corporation was to partner with the oil and gas companies, to coordinate the production and marketing of domestically produced synthetic liquid fuels. The idea was to move research and development of synthetic fuels out of the DOE labs and put it in the hands of private companies or partnerships, which are more likely to produce tangible results in a short period of time. The initial goal was to produce about two million barrels by 1985.

The Great Plains coal gasification plant in Beulah, ND, was built with the support of the U.S. DOE as a demonstration of the synthetic fuels idea. It was supposed to produce two million barrels of synthetic fuel daily. Government politics and drop in oil prices in the early 1980s reduced the need for synthetic fuels and the corporation's existence was unjustifiable, and so the synthetic fuels dream and the synthetic fuels production plant lasted fewer than five years, until they both were abolished in 1985. The subject of these revolutionary fuels is still on the agenda, so the dream is still alive, albeit mostly on paper.

The Hydrogen Car

The hydrogen-powered car, which is supposed to revolutionize transportation, was the talk of the town back in the 1980s and 1990s. It is often brought out, dusted off, and presented as the savior of our internal combustion engine from time to time. A hydrogen car uses hydrogen for fuel, instead of gas or diesel. The hydrogen-powered engine converts the chemical energy of hydrogen into mechanical energy by burning hydrogen in the cylinders of an internal combustion engine. Hydrogen can be also used to react it with oxygen in a fuel cells, which can be then used to run an electric motor.

Hydrogen fuel, however, does not occur naturally on Earth, so it is not an energy source. It is, therefore, only an energy storage or carrier. Now it is made most often from natural gas or other fossil fuels, but can also be made via the renewable energy sources, such as wind, or solar. Since these sources are variable, the energy generated by them can be converted into liquid hydrogen, which can then be used to power cars. Wind-to-hydrogen conversion plants, using electrolysis of water could deliver large quantities, and with time the cost could be reduced enough to compete with the fossil sources.

The Bush Hydrogen Plan

President Bush unveiled a plan for a hydrogen-powered car in 2003 by proposing $1.2 billion in development and production costs. This was supposed to be a revolutionary, pollution-free car. A simple chemical reaction between hydrogen and oxygen would power a car, producing only water and no exhaust fumes. Bush predicted that within 20 years fuel-cell cars would dominate the roads and make our air significantly cleaner. This way, the U.S. would be much less dependent on foreign oil imports.

Mr. Bush even gave it a name, the freedom car, and seemed convinced that hydrogen-powered car is one of the solutions that we must pursue. His thinking (or that of his advisors) was that since hydrogen can be easily and cleanly extracted from water it is the ideal fuel. Using electricity generated by solar panels and wind turbines, he believed, would split water to hydrogen and oxygen. The hydrogen can then be stored in tanks and used later. When needed, hydrogen can be recombined with oxygen to produce heat and/or electricity. The electricity can be used to drive electric motors and power cars.

The skeleton in the closet, however, was that Bush had been working behind the scenes to ensure that the hydrogen would be generated by fossil fuels. He did not consider (or at least did not reveal it) that this method is potentially as dirty as any of the other fossil using power generators.

Using fossils would effectively eliminate the benefits offered by hydrogen use, and might be even worse, since hydrogen is just one more step in the fossil power generation process. Also, although fuel-cell cars are clean and emit nothing but water vapor, the process of producing the fuel cells uses large amounts of hydrocarbons that leave a large carbon dioxide footprint behind, which must be considered when comparing different technologies.

At the end, the budget that Bush submitted to Congress ignored renewable methods of producing hydrogen all together. More than half of all hydrogen funding in his budget was to be given to automakers and the energy industry. More than $22 million of hydrogen research for 2004 was to be devoted to coal, nuclear power, and natural gas, compared with $17 million for renewable sources. Overall funding for renewable research and energy conservation, meanwhile, was to be slashed by more than $86 million. How is cutting renewable energy sources and replacing them with fossils and nuclear a sustainable approach?

In 1999 the national hydrogen association (NHA), which was founded in 1989 by scientists from government labs and universities became quite famous. It was a Godsend for many small fuel-cell designers and electrolyzer makers, and others who supported the use of hydrogen. The group, however, was careful not to take a position on who would make the fuel or how. When the energy industry got interested in hydrogen, Shell, BP and Chevron executives joined the NHA board and used the association to lobby for more federal funding for research. They also pushed the government to emphasize fossil fuels in the national energy plan for hydrogen.

Automakers and energy companies then formed a consortium called the international hydrogen infrastructure group, whose hidden agenda was to monitor and influence federal officials in charge of developing fuel cells. The oil companies then bought up technology companies that were developing methods to refine and store the new fuel.

At that point Texaco invested $82 million in a firm called energy conversion devices, and Shell owned half of hydrogen source. BP, Chevron-Texaco, ExxonMobil, Ford, and General Electric have engaged many American energy scientists, and sponsored over $270 million to hydrogen research at MIT, Princeton, and Stanford. In this case, money helped to ensure that rich oil and gas companies will profit from millions of fuel-cell cars on the road—if and when their time comes.

Using federal research funding and resources to make hydrogen from fossil fuels enabled oil and gas companies to provide lower-priced hydrogen and to stretch pipelines all across the U.S. to transport it to a place where it can be used. The fact that a wind farm at that same place would do the same job was not even considered, nor was the fact that the pipeline and its contents will contribute to global warming by leaving behind carbon dioxide considered.

But none of this is a surprise, nor has anything changed now. Oil and coal companies still insist that they will be able to "sequester" the carbon permanently by a number of ways. The latest plans are to pump the poisons deep into the ocean, or in underground caverns. Such approaches, however, hold a very high risk, in addition to being a very complex, expensive, and simply unsustainable undertaking in the long run.

There are still many companies working to develop technologies that might efficiently generate hydrogen for cars and trucks. The benefit of using hydrogen as an energy currency is evident only when it is produced by renewable energy sources. If hydrogen is made without using fossil fuels, then the entire process is clean and would not contribute to carbon dioxide emissions.

If hydrogen is made with fossil fuels, the amount of energy used in the process is almost equal to the amount of energy to be generated by the newly bottled hydrogen gas. Another drawback of hydrogen use is its low energy content per unit volume, which requires the use of the heavy tanks, thus reducing further energy waste. There are also safety concerns related to very high storage tank pressure that is needed to keep the gas liquefied.

The production process inefficiencies, as well as complex storage, transportation, and filling of gaseous or liquid hydrogen in vehicles are additional problems to be resolved before hydrogen becomes universally accepted as vehicle fuel. And on top of that, there is a large investment needed in a new infrastructure as required to fuel vehicles across the country and the world.

After spending millions of taxpayer dollars, the hydrogen car and the hydrogen economies are still waiting their turn.

Clean Coal

Clean coal? There is no such thing as clean coal yet, nor will it happen any time soon. Coal is very dirty energy source no matter how you look at it, and very little can be done to clean it up without major effort, not to mention that cleaning it is prohibitively expensive, and doing so would mean raising power prices.

At the same time, however, we rely heavily on coal for providing reliable and cheap electric power. So, we must admit that we cannot get rid of coal now, nor for a long time to come, and that we have to find a way to live with it for the duration.

But we also should not close our eyes and hope that the problems will just go away. Instead, we need to be well informed and fully aware of the problems coal brings. The average coal-fired power plant burns 100 railroad cars of coal each and every day. At 100 tons each per car, this is 10,000 tons of coal burned every day by just one plant. Then think of the amount of toxic, climate warming smoke and small particles that go up the chimneys of the coal-fired power plants 24/7/365. Remember that each ton of coal generates almost three tons of toxic

gasses. The average plant would emit almost 30,000 tons of carbon dioxide and other gasses into the atmosphere daily. This is over one million tons of toxic gasses emitted annually from just one coal-fired power plant.

And then there are mountains of ashes and soot left behind after the burning is done. These have to go somewhere too, so they find their way into waste disposal sites and other places where they create another type of pollution. Just take a look at the air downtown Beijing, Mexico City, or Los Angeles on a summer afternoon.

Figure 6-43. Downtown LA smog

Would you like to breathe the thick, polluted Los Angeles air all day long, non-stop for several long months at a time, very similar in feel and taste to the thick smoke in Beijing, China? We are all trapped in this huge gas chamber called Earth, and the coal-fired power plants are injecting the poisons in it non-stop every day, day after day—for the last 100 years, and at least that many to come. Some of us are affected more than others, but we all feel and pay for the consequences one way or another.

While it is true that coal is not the only air polluter, it is by far the largest. Cleaning the gas and solid byproducts from coal burning is not easy, nor is it cheap. And although there are technologies, and even coal sequestration demonstration plants, retrofitting all coal plants would take a very long time and a lot of money. But even if it were possible, this is not a sustainable long-term solution.

Nevertheless, we need coal to generate large amounts of electric power for domestic and commercial needs, so the U.S DOE is involved in the work to develop carbon capture and storage (CCS) technologies, using several different methods. The last Bush administration spent about $2.5 billion on clean coal technology, which is a fairly small amount, compared with what is actually needed. The preliminary estimates are that at least $20-30 billion must be spent to make a dent in the environmental problems by introducing CCS technologies in coal-fired power plants.

In 2003, President Bush announced a new government-sponsored project, appropriately called future gen. It was supposed to build a near zero-emissions coal-fired power plant capable of producing hydrogen and electricity while using CCS technology. The project was cancelled and the DOE withdrew funding in 2008.

The DOE has funded a number CCS projects through its clean coal power initiative (CCPI) to date. Three rounds of CCPI funding later, one third of the projects have been cancelled or withdrawn. A lot of reports and presentations were generated during that time, but it is clear that, although there are some good and encouraging results, the final solution is still far in the future, technologically speaking. It is even further out in the future, financially speaking. This is one complex and expensive process, which will require a lot of money and effort to complete.

In 2009, President Obama signed the American reinvestment and recovery act, which allocated $3.4 billion for advanced CCS technologies development and demonstration projects. So, looking at all these efforts and the results thereof, we must conclude that the CCS technology is still in its infancy, and that it will need billions of dollars for full development, and many more billions and a lot of time for full implementation.

Even when all this is done, if ever, it is still not a complete nor a permanent solution to the problems at hand. The dangers are still there, since there is a limit to how efficient and safe the new sequestration technology could be, and/or how many power plants can afford it. There is also a limit to how many billions of tons of gas and soot we can store in or on the ground.

There must be a better way, and we know that there is. It is called *renewable fuels*, but their time—for a number of reasons—hasn't come yet, probably not until most of the coal and oil are gone.

Corn Ethanol

In 2008 a new star shone on the energy horizon. It was the corn-based bioethanol craze. The vast cornfields of mid-America would produce all the corn needed to supply all, or at least most, of our energy needs. Wait, not so fast! In 2010 overproduction of corn, to be used for bioethanol production, forced corn prices to jump nearly 90% on the consumer markets. This created a ripple effect around the country and even the world.

Nearly 5 billion bushels, or a third of the U.S. corn crops were used to make ethanol, encouraged by hastily approved by Congress mandate. This unexpected and unplanned boost in corn production and use was as a result of the politically driven mandate, requiring an increase of the use of biofuels from 6 billion gallons in 2007 to 36 billion gallons by 2017.

The EPA newly approved a blend of 15% ethanol is now mixed with gasoline, instead of the 10% standard blend that has been used for many years during the summer months in much of the country. And if everything is left as is, the corn ethanol's share will grow with time, which means that less corn will be available for food, driving the prices even higher. Ethanol receives a federal tax credit of $0.45 per gallon, which costs taxpayers about $6 billion annually. And then, there is a tariff of $0.54 per gallon on imported ethanol, which keeps out lower-cost ethanol from Brazil and other countries. Good place to be, you'd think, and this is what the corn farmers, the Congressmen, and the other proponents of corn-based bioethanol thought too.

We can kill several birds with one stone. The farmers get paid for producing lots of corn, the ethanol producers get their credits and other perks, the public gets cleaner and cheaper gas, and the country gains its energy independence.

But there are several quite serious problems with this plan:

- Ethanol produces more emissions of smog-forming nitrogen oxides and other pollutants. There is also increased danger of damaging the catalytic converters on cars. This is in addition to the increased fuel taxes at the pump and higher corn prices in the store.

- In most cases more energy is needed to make a gallon of ethanol than is contained in the same gallon of ethanol. So, in technical terms, ethanol is a net energy consumer, not a net energy source. There is an estimate that it takes over 130,000 Btu to make a gallon of ethanol, while the same one gallon of ethanol has an energy value of about 77,000 Btu. Knowing that a gallon of gasoline contains about 125,000 Btu, and considering the loss due to process inefficiencies, we can see that we need to use almost two gallons of gasoline to make one gallon of bioethanol. This is not the energy balance we need. Using wind and solar power might make this process much more cost effective and environmentally cleaner, but there is not enough of these power sources to go around yet. Maybe later in the century this would become a more viable and attractive alternative.

- Energy that is used to make ethanol is usually fossil fuel based. Fossil fuels run the tractors that plow the fields, the trucks that transport the corn, the electricity to drive the distillation equipment, and almost every thing else. So, while burning two gallons of gasoline, we also generate that much toxic gasses, in addition to whatever gasses the gallon of bioethanol emits during processing and burning.

- A major issue here is that a gallon of bioethanol contains about two thirds of the energy in a gallon of gasoline. Ethanol is 77,000 Btu/gallon, vs. 125,000 Btu/gallon of gasoline. This creates a number of problems. It reduces the miles per gallon we can get, and forces us to install larger fuel tanks to drive the same distance. Larger fuel tanks increase the weight of the cars, which in turn reduces the gas mileage even further.

- Because of all these problems eventually we might see increase of the cost of the fuel at the gas pump too.

- The rationale for the increased use of ethanol is to reduce our dependence on oil imports from the Middle East and South America. The results thus far, however, show very little savings.

- Corn ethanol, which is in existence exclusively because of federal mandates and subsidies, was allocated $11 billion in tax breaks and $5 billion in direct spending during the same time. If that is enough to keep bioethanol going, and what the future will bring is uncertain, but government politics must evolve to properly manage this natural resource, if we are to truly see any benefits from it.

Obama's Plan

In 2012, President Obama promised to make climate change a top priority in his second term., and rolled out his new plan for action during his 2013 state of the union address. In it he promised not to wait on Congress any longer, but instead to do as much as possible with the use of his executive authority. However, if new spending is needed for any part of this effort, it will depend on budget approval by Congress, which most likely will not fully fund the majority of the new tasks. As an example, the showpiece of the plan, EPA's regulation of carbon emissions from new and existing power plants, has already been in the works for a number of

years with very little progress to show. President Obama has issued a new memo to the EPA officials asking them to speed up the process, which he hopes to complete before ending his second term.

At the very least, the President's climate action plan highlights the enormous number of executive actions in the works and ties them together into a coherent package. It attempts to systematically mobilize all the tools of the executive branch to rapidly deploy clean energy solutions and more modern and resilient infrastructure, and advances very concrete, measurable, and immediate steps. It also builds on what's working, and focuses the nation's attention on how to move forward together without delay using all the tools at our disposal, according to insiders.

There are a handful of polices in the plan (albeit some are existing efforts) that could produce very good results, such as:

- *Renewable energy*
  Through the administration policies, the U.S. wind, solar, and other renewable electricity production doubled during the last four years, and a second doubling effort is underway through a suite of new policies, as follow:
  a. Issue permits for 10 GW of renewable energy projects (wind, solar, and hydro) on public lands by 2020, which is double the number of presently issued permits
  b. Install 100 megawatts of renewable energy systems on federally subsidized housing by 2020
  c. Install 20% renewable energy systems on federal buildings by 2020
  NOTE: The federal government owns a lot of buildings around the country, so these new initiatives will add substantial capacity, but will bring their own problems as well.

- *Energy efficiency*
  President Obama wants to double the U.S. energy efficiency by 2030. This can be done by:
  a. Establishing new efficiency targets for appliance standards and for energy use in federal buildings
  b. Cut CO_2 emissions by three billion metric tons by 2030 by tightening efficiency standards and policies. This is about half of the total energy-sector carbon emissions presently, so the bar is set quite high.
  c. A $250 million package will be managed by the Department of

Agriculture to help rural utilities implement energy efficiency programs

d. The Department of Housing and Urban Development will provide another $23 million for affordable housing efficiency programs.

e. Expand the better buildings challenge for multi-family housing

f. Work to increase energy data transparency through the green button initiative

g. Work with agencies to synchronize building codes for increasing energy efficiency

NOTE: Building energy efficiency initiatives have been around for a while now, and some of them are real success stories, so the new plan builds on the tools used, and on the lessons learned, in these areas.

* *Environmental data*

Transparency of energy data has been addressed many times in the past, but just now the administration is proposing the creation of a special databases for the environmental and climate science. An open platform will be established, where anyone would be able to access environmental and climate data to understand the government's actions, and to facilitate the public's participation in the activities.

The new global change research program will create tools for risk modeling, while the national climate assessment will include information to be used by local decision makers. New climate-resilience toolkits will be created to centralize the best practices on climate adaptation and mitigation.

These tools combined would represent the most comprehensive, transparent database of climate information ever created. It could be used to assess different climate risk scenarios, which would help avoid large disasters, and allow risk-free planning ahead.

* *Public financing*

The administration plans to work with national and international organizations, like ExIm Bank and the World Bank to stop financing coal mining and coal-fired power plants. The new plan also calls for new free-trade negotiations for environmental goods to break down trade barriers among different countries.

This part of the plan, however, depends fully on international cooperation. China and other countries have long-term plans to increase their coal-fired capacity several fold and nothing can stop them.

At the very least, this points out that we are now fully aware that energy generation and economic development should not be gained at the expense of the global environment. The counter-argument coming from the developing world is that they will do what we did for the last century, and will use as much coal and oil as needed to catch up with the U.S.

* The Keystone XL pipeline

Although the Keystone XL tar sands pipeline is not an official part of the President's climate plan, it is a major project and an important issue for the administration, so Obama promised to ask the State Department to complete its investigation, and reject the pipeline if there is a net increase in CO_2 emissions.

The State Department concluded during previous investigations that the Keystone XL pipeline would not cause net CO_2 increase. These facts are disputed by a number of environmental groups.

The major positive conclusion we can draw from the President's new plan is that, although each of the above mentioned points alone would not have any effect on the short term, and minimal effect in the long run, put together they present a concise and clear framework of the future the U.S. energy and environmental policies. It clears the way to energy independence, and clean environment—at least while Obama is in office.

Obama's Plan Implementation

President Obama's new plan addresses a number of factors not included in any agency reports. The most significant seems to be the carbon target of reducing 2005 levels by 17% in 2020, which would reduce U.S. total emissions to from 6,000 million metric tons per year (MMT/yr) to about 5,000 MMT/yr in 2020.

Since 2005, the U.S. carbon emissions were already reduced to about 5,300 MMT/yr in 2012. This 700 MMT/yr reduction in U.S. carbon emissions was due to a combination of factors, such as: fuel-switching from coal to gas, efficiency upgrades, and the economic recession.

But now, as the industry is ramping up again and the need for power increases proportionally on daily basis, reduction of the current level of U.S. carbon emissions would be nearly impossible. As a matter of fact, industry watch dogs predict that the U.S. total carbon emissions will increase to over 5,500 MMT/yr or more by 2020.

And to make things worse, all the new solutions to reducing U.S. carbon emission in Obama's new plan, such as fuel-switching from coal to natural gas, energy efficiency improvements, renewables contribution, and so forth, are already included in the most recent projections released in 2013. That narrows the areas of opportunities significantly and makes the projections seem unreasonably inflated.

Many newly suggested improvements, such as: heavy-duty vehicle efficiency standards, advanced bio-fuels developments, etc., are uncertain because of lack of track records, and technological and financial limitations. And even if some serious breakthroughs in materials, processes, or equipment occur, the affected technologies would be still very far from commercialization, since it takes many years and billions of dollars to bring new energy technologies to the market.

So, the most feasible approach to the 2020 carbon reduction target is possible only if we build upon and further develop some of the recent and proven successes in this area. The largest contributing factor towards reduced carbon emissions over the past five years has been fuels-switching from coal to natural gas. Natural gas power generation carbon emissions are only about 40% that of equivalent coal power generation, so this strategy would be best in achieving substantial carbon emission reductions by 2020.

Table 6-4. U.S. GHG emissions (in MMT/yr)

Power Source	2005	2012	2020*	2020**
Coal power	1,984	1,514	1,610	835
Natural gas	319	494	446	745
Other power	114	31	25	25
Power sector	2,417	2,039	2,081	1,605
Other sectors	3,582	3,251	3,374	3,374
Total U.S.	**5,999**	**5,290**	**5,455**	**4,979**

Note the difference in the 2020 projections in the two columns in Table 6-4.
*The first one assumes using coal-fired power plants (emitting 1,610 MMT/yr)
**The second one assumes using mostly gas-fired power plants (with only half of the coal-fired plants' emissions).

This shows that we can reduce the GHG emissions significantly by displacing coal with natural gas power generation capacity, which would give us emissions reduction of about 17% from 2005 levels. By doing this, the current coal power generation capacity would be reduced by 50%, while the natural gas power capacity would increase by about 75% in 2020.

Obama's latest climate policy is very hopeful about the future of natural gas and includes many strategies that could further reduce carbon emissions, and/or reduce the need for coal to natural gas fuel-switching. He envisions large increases in wind and solar power generation—50% or more—as one such alternative.

A most likely scenario, however, is for wind and solar power to increase only by about 20-25% by 2020.

More renewable power could be installed only through increased government based technical and financial support. If, however, we are able to double current wind and solar power generation by 2020, it would reduce natural gas power plant fuel consumption by an equivalent of 40-50 MMT/yr of carbon emissions by the same time.

In addition, increasing the efficiency of energy use in the residential and commercial sectors could reduce the coal power plant generation, thus reducing the GHG emissions by about 50-100 MMT/yr, depending on location, upgrade costs, energy-power costs, and the level of the new government subsidies.

To achieve all this, we need a lot of natural gas, since wind and solar cannot currently be used for base load power generation thus cannot replace the coal power generation capacity. Nor can it supply the level of required natural gas generation capacity needed to back up all variable renewable power sources.

Large-scale power storage is needed to solve this problem, but it is presently unavailable. If and when large-scale power storage becomes available, it will be very expensive, so we have to wait for it to become economically feasible, available and reliable. Only then would the now variable wind and solar power become able to displace fossil fuels as base load power generators.

Until large-scale power storage becomes available, natural gas will be used for base load and supply-demand power generation balances, stabilities and overall general power generation applications. Hydropower, geothermal, solar thermal, and nuclear can replace some natural gas capacity, but a broad range of economic, permitting, environmental impact and political barriers continue to hold back significant development of these lower-zero carbon alternatives.

The Key Issues

Now natural gas is the king of power generation in the U.S., which is a good thing, but remember that, as any other power source, natural gas brings some issues that cannot and should not be ignored:

- Natural gas is a fossil fuel, so there are limited quantities of it in Nature. The predictions are that it is going to be gone sometime later in the century at this rate of exploitation, and then it will be no more, so we need to plan ahead for that eventuality as well.

- Even though natural gas is cleaner than coal and oil, as far as CO_2 emissions are concerned, it still emits large quantity of GHGs during production and use. We need to monitor these emissions and their effects closely, because they are somewhat different from these emitted by the other fossils, and some unexpected consequences are to be expected.

- Large areas of land and surface and underground water bodies have been contaminated by the fracking fluids presently, the problem is growing, and it might become too big to ignore. If ignored, there is a danger that new policy restrictions and litigation might limit the use of natural gas, and/or increase the price above acceptable levels.

- U.S. natural gas production will increase by only about 1.5% per year by 2020, so this may not be enough to meet the increased needs for natural gas.

    NOTE: Increasing natural gas use, as needed to meet the 2020 goals, requires about 3.3 trillion cubic feet of natural gas per year *above* the present maximum production levels, which may not be sustainable or practical on the long run. This might even result in a very significant shortage of available domestic natural gas supply, and might create a need for imports even before 2020. Such a crisis could be avoided by further increases in fracking efficiency, adding more wind and solar power capacity, and increased energy use efficiency.

- A number of liquid natural gas (LNG) export projects were approved recently, which means that the administration is planning to increase the exports of LNG in the near future. The planned large scale fuel-switching from coal to gas would require all the gas we can get and more, so exporting LNG is inconsistent with the proposed climate policy carbon reduction target.

    Simple math shows that, as the 2020 target approaches, the domestic natural gas may not be enough, so we need to import it from abroad. At this point, the shutdown of existing LNG exports might be necessary to meet the domestic demand.

- Implementation of the large-scale coal to gas conversion, as well as adding more renewable power sources, require substantial capital and operating cost increases. As is always the case in supply-and-demand scenarios, the increased natural gas use might force changes in the marketplace, lead-

ing to serious gas shortages and/or substantial price increases.

This, in turn, would increase power costs, so the consumers might see 40-60% increase in their monthly power bills. That is a very bad news for all involved, which might lead to some unforeseen actions and situations, depending on the degree of discomfort to the taxpayers.

Obviously, the situation is complicated by a number of different factors playing different roles under different circumstances and at different locations, so only one thing is for sure now; there will be a lot of debates and battles on all levels in the near future, as the new policy actions are unrolled and executed.

NOTE: Mr. Obama is intelligent, eloquent, honest, involved and caring, but he is not a scientist, which is a serious handicap in this complex technology-loaded environment we live and work in now. Because of that, Mr. Obama relies on his advisers from the different scientific organizations and National Labs to tell him what the different technologies do and how they compare to each other. This is how, we believe, Mr. Obama got involved in the Solyndra mess—he simply followed the advice of his technical advisers from different institutions. They should've done much better job in analyzing the technology and the company's MO—both of which were out of the ordinary and bordering the ridiculous. And so Mr. Obama got a lot of criticism about his policies, the U.S. taxpayers lost over half a billion dollars from the failed Solyndra (plus several times that much from the other failed companies and projects) and the solar industry got another black eye.

This example should cause us to pause and ask, "Who is advising Mr. Obama on the complex issues of today? Is he listening to the right people? Are his advisors competent and knowledgeable enough to be able to consider, properly assess, and prioritize all the technical-administrative-financial aspects of today's energy-environment related issues, with their endless combinations and permutations?

Mr. Obama is once again intently listening to his advisors, while trying to make decisions on some of the nation's greatest and most urgent issues and projects: GHG reductions, coal-fire power plants closing, increasing natural gas production to switch the U.S. power generation away from coal, supporting wind and solar power, the Keystone XL power line, and so forth. If the advisors get it wrong, he will be wrong, too.

THE WORLD ENERGY AND ENVIRONMENT

All countries in the world have some impact on today's energy-environment puzzle, with some of them having much greater impact than others. A few countries are expected to have a very profound impact on the world's energy use and the related environmental impact. The U.S., China, and India are on the top of the list.

We've reviewed the U.S. portion in this puzzle, so below we focus on China, India, and some other counties.

China

Prior to the 20th century, China was a literal desert where deforestation and other poor agricultural practices had degraded major parts of the vast countryside and had depleted fish and wild animal populations. Pop-and-mom shops and many small factories were polluting the air, soil, and water. Fast growing population, frequent wars, and poor governance took a serious toll on the environment.

By the end of the 20th century, however, China's economy exploded when new government policies encouraged the privatization of agricultural and industrial enterprises. This was accompanied by a quick urbanization of the rural population and the development of more small rural industries.

With the influx of international investment, hundreds of millions of Chinese have been lifted out of poverty and China's economy grew at 8–10% annually. By 2005, China was the fourth largest economy and third largest exporting nation in the world, after the U.S. and Germany.

All this was accomplished at the expense of the environment. Water and air pollution, and soil degradation are now the predominant environmental issues that pose enormous threat to ecosystems and human health.

Air pollution in some large Chinese cities is beyond what we might call problematic; it is deadly. No wonder the number of people suffering from pulmonary and other respiratory problems has skyrocketed during the last two decades. Many people wear face masks to protect their lungs, but the micro-particles in the air are hard to filter, so many fall ill and even die from the constant toxic invasion.

But air pollution is only part of the grim picture. Driving from Hong Kong to Guangzhou, on the western cost of China, one sees a line of large factories belching thick brown-black smoke that is creating their own cloud system overhead. The land around some of these

Figure 6-44. Morning traffic a la China

is dotted with wet areas with green-brown chemicals bubbling below the surface.

Just recently, these issues have been made a priority by the Chinese government, and we see them being incorporated into policies and plans at the Central government level. The energy and environmental policies in China are changing quickly, creating new environmental institutions and practices. There is now decentralized environmental policymaking, implementation, and enforcement of the regulations. Private companies and organizations now have more rights and are taking responsibilities in environmental governance.

There is now new dynamics between the state, the markets (including the energy sector) and the society, all contributing and working together on managing the environmental issues. Political, technical, and administrative efficiency and legitimacy, however, are still major issues, and major obstacles in furthering the environmental policies. As a result there are still a number of very serious problems in China.

China's Energy and Environmental Regulators

There was a belief at one point of history that only capitalist societies suffered from environmental damage. And then China, which is still officially under a communist rule, saw itself mired in pollution from high above in the sky to deep down into the ground.

The beginning of the environmental politics in China dates to the first United Nations conference on the human environment in 1972, where a Chinese delegation took part and brought home the capitalist ideas about environment. As a result, the government's leading group for environmental protection was established in 1974. Equivalent agencies were created on the provincial level too, which basic function was to watch for and report environmental issues.

In 1983, environmental protection was declared a basic national principle in China and the government of China proposed key principles for environmental protection. This included the principle of prevention, control, and making the polluter responsible for pollution control.

A national regulatory framework was formulated, composed of a series of environmental laws, executive regulations, standards and measures (on all the major environmental sectors, starting with marine protection and water in 1982 and 1984 respectively).

In 1988, the leading group for environmental protection morphed into the national environmental protection agency, and in 1994 China laid out a broad strategy to achieve sustainable development. In 1996, China introduced its first five-year plan that included environmental protection, which made the environment a national priority.

In 1998 the national environmental protection agency (NEPA) was upgraded from a sub-ministry to a ministry level and its name was changed to state environmental protection administration (SEPA). SEPA has a wide range of responsibilities in ensuring cleaner production and pollution prevention.

In 2003, the national development and reform commission (NDRC) was created. It consists of the former state development planning commission (SDPC) and state economic and trade commission (SETC), which morphed into one, more efficient organization.

Presently, China has more than 20 environmental laws adopted by the national people's congress, in addition to over 140 executive regulations issued by the state council, as well as a series of sector regulations and environmental standards set by the state environmental protection agency (SEPA) and other government bodies.

The major regulating bodies are:

- The state environmental protection agency (SEPA) was established as a ministry in 1998, when the national environmental protection agency (NEPA) was upgraded from a sub-ministry to a ministry and its name was changed to SEPA.

  SEPA's role is:
  — To formulate the national policy, laws and administrative regulations for the environmental impact assessment of major economic and technological policies, development planning and key economic development plans and to formulate the national environmental protection plans; to formulate and monitor the im-

plementation of the national plan for pollution control and ecological conservation in key regions and river basins; and to organize the zoning of environmental functions of different regions.

— To coordinate and organize pollution prevention and control of key river basins at the national level; be responsible for the environmental supervision and management and administrative inspection of the environmental protection; and organize and undertake the examination of the enforcement of environmental laws and regulations at the national level.

— To formulate national standards for environmental quality and for pollutants emission and discharge and launch them according to the relevant procedure; be responsible for filing of local environmental standards; to organize the compilation and submission of the national report on the environmental quality and the issuance of the national report on the state of the environment and to release on a regular basis the report of the environment quality of key cities and river basins; and to participate in the development of a national program for sustainable development.

— To organize the development of environmental science and technology and important research projects and technical demonstration projects; to manage the national environmental management system and the certification of environmental labels; to establish and organize the implementation of the rule of accreditation for the qualification for environmental market access and to guide and promote the development of environmental industry.

— To be responsible for the environmental monitoring, statistics and information collection; to formulate the rules, regulations and specifications for environmental monitoring; to organize the construction and management of the national network of environmental monitoring and of environmental information; to organize the monitoring of the environmental quality and the supervisory monitoring of the pollution sources at the national level; to organize, supervise, and coordinate environmental education, publicity, and publication and to promote the participation of the public and nongovernmental organizations in the environmental protection.

Since its inception, SEPA and its affiliates have seen a rapid increase in bureaucracy. In 1995 the environmental agencies had over 88,000 employees across China, while in 2004 that number had grown to over 160,000 employees.

- The *national development and reform commission* (NDRC) is a management agency under the Chinese state council, with broad administrative and planning control over the Chinese economy. The NDRC's 26,000 regional departments study and formulate policies for economic and social development, maintain the balance of economic development, and guide the restructuring of China's economic system.

In more detail, the principal functions of the NDRC are to:
  — Formulate and implement macroeconomic policies
  — Monitor and adjust the performance of the national economy
  — Examine and approve major construction projects
  — Guide and promote economic restructuring
  — Coordinate the readjustment of China's industrial structure with development of agriculture and rural economy
  — Formulate plans for the development of China's energy sector and manage national oil reserves
  — Promote the western region development program, which calls for China's economic growth to include the poorer western provinces
  — Submit a national economic plan to the national people's congress on behalf of the state council
  — Manage China's strategic petroleum reserves

- *The bureau of energy* was established under the NDRC for: research of domestic and international conditions, to suggest energy efficiency policies, and to make system reform recommendations in managing the natural gas and coal reserves, and to regulate energy prices.

- *The national energy commission (NEC)* is a newly established agency to coordinate the overall energy

policies in China. It includes 23 members from different fields, such as: environment, finance, the central bank, the national development and reform commission, etc. The purpose of this new commission is to draft a new energy development strategy, evaluate energy security and coordinate international cooperation on climate change, carbon reduction and energy efficiency.

- The ministry of environmental protection (MEP) issues environmental policies and conducts environmental implementation and supervision. There are many environmental issues related to energy exploration and utilization, such as environmental impacts assessment of" energy construction projects and pollution during energy exploration and production. All of these issues are under the MEP's jurisdiction.

In 2003 the government of China introduced a new concept of environmental responsibility focused on humanism and attempting to achieve sustainable development and harmony between man and nature. The new concept also introduced the idea of coordinated socio-economic progress among various regions and with foreign countries.

Since then China has participated in a number of international environmental treaties, such as the convention on biological diversity and the millennium development goals. These treaties focus on poverty alleviation, environmental protection, and sustainable development of the countries involved and the world as a whole.

China's Energy and Environmental Regulatory System

China's environmental regulatory framework is vertically integrated through a four-tier management system on the national, provincial, municipal and county levels. The latter three levels are governed directly by their corresponding authorities in terms of both finance and personnel management, while SEPA is responsible for the formulation and enactment of the various environmental laws and regulations.

China's civil law system is focused on systematic legislation, within which there are six energy sub-systems, in addition to the basic energy law. These sub-systems are focused on coal, oil and natural gas, electricity, nuclear power, renewable energy, and energy conservation, although a basic energy law, oil law, a natural gas law, and a nuclear power law are still in the making.

Currently, there are four major energy legislative sub-systems, as follow:

- *The 1995 electricity law of 1993* is the first energy law, but because it was enacted during China's economic transition period, some of its provisions are out of date.

- *The coal law of 1996* was amended in 2011 to regulate the exploration, utilization, and production of coal. It also regulates the entire coal industry, so it is the most important ruling for the progress of the coal industry. It falls short in many areas due to the still immature regulatory system and enforcement. Licensing of mining operations requires nine permits and one license, issued by six different government agencies. The different agencies have different and uncoordinated requirements, which results in ineffective regulation.

- *The renewable energy promotion law of 2005* was amended in 2009 as the first renewable energy legislation in China. It is focused on developing renewable energy sources as part of the country's energy structure. It also aims to ensure consistent and reliable energy supply and at the same time control pollution.

    This law contains several key mechanisms: total amount control, mandatory grid connection, categorized electricity pricing, cost allocation, and special funds.

    In more detail:

    a. The total amount control provision specifies the government's development targets per each period of time, which promotes the efficient use of renewable energy.
    b. The mandatory grid connection provision requires all power grid enterprises to buy up all the renewable energy offered them, thus reducing the transaction costs for renewable energy.
    c. The categorized electricity pricing provision allows different types of renewable energy to set up their own prices, based on the prevailing average costs at their location.
    d. The cost allocation provision requires each energy region to allocate extra cost for generating renewable energy in a manner that is reasonable and fair, which avoids additional costs for the generators.
    e. The special funds provision addresses the problem of extra costs of renewable energy production by providing subsidies and other financial support instruments. This is especially helpful to renewable energy projects whose costs cannot be fully allocated to all market players.

- *The energy conservation law of 1997* is aimed at promoting energy conservation across the entire country. It is important in improving the efficiency and the economic benefits of energy usage. It is geared towards optimizing the enforcement and the related government authority.

    It also clarifies and emphasizes the market mechanisms and a number of incentive mechanisms, which are designed to assist the policies on energy conservation via finance, taxation, pricing, credit control, and government assistance, as well as the legal liabilities and penalties in case of incompliance.

All this sounds very clear and efficient on paper. But the energy and environmental picture in China is far from clear or efficient. The country is still in a peculiar transitional position, with one leg in communist-era ideology, and the other one in the capitalist enterprise. Invoking the proverbial *duck on ice* picture here. This is causing a number of discrepancies in the internal and foreign affairs of the country—including the energy sector and the related environmental effects.

A lot could be said about China's progress in all these areas, but one fact sticks out as a sore thumb: China's population and economy are growing very fast, which requires a lot of energy. And the Chinese government is determined to support the economical growth and increased energy use no matter what.

This in turn means that China will continue building new coal-fired power plants, which will continue to belch billions of tons of GHGs annually into the Chinese air and spread it around the world—environmental laws or no environmental laws.

China-US Relations

There is no country in this world that is more strategically important to the U.S. than China. Although both countries have totally different and even opposing governing systems—that of capitalism vs. communism—they depend on each other in many areas of their political and economic affairs.

Of these, the environmental issues are becoming a high priority. This is because China and the U.S. are the world's biggest polluters, where China's pollution is due to sheer numbers in population, while the U.S. pollutes because of its unmatched appetite for energy consumption and waste.

The U.S. and the European Union have actually reduced emissions at a great expense, and insist that China to follow the same clean air standards as the rest of the world. China's response is that, due to its millions of poor people and rapid economic growth, the proposed standard is unfair. And so, China is steadily increasing its emission levels in a significant way, and the plans are to increase them even more by the introduction of hundreds of new coal-fired power plants. China claims that this is a need to compete with the rest of the world and provide wellbeing to its citizens.

Whatever the case might be, the U.S. efforts in reducing GHG pollution and the results thereof have been nullified by the Chinese dependence on coal-fired power plants and other environmental discrepancies. Because of that China and the U.S. don't get along very well when it comes to energy and clean air policies.

At the 2011 UN climate change conference in Durban, South Africa, the world's biggest polluters hijacked the conference with ping pong-like politics and frustrated the rest of the world in the process.

And then in 2012 came the solar panels trade issue, where the Chinese are accused of dumping cheap solar panels on the U.S. and E.U. markets. Seven U.S. solar panel manufactures appealed to the U.S. international trade commission, who agreed that the Chinese are selling solar panels far below market value with the support of the Chinese government.

From coal-fired power plants to solar panels, the U.S. and China are on the warpath. But can the world afford a prolonged battle between these two giants? Would the global environment and the people in it survive an escalation of the anti-environmental activities?

As citizens of our small planet, and guardians of its precious resources and environment, we have the same goals, wants, and needs. And yet, we are two very different countries with the same problems, but involved in different and complex games of international politics, and the real victim is our fragile environment.

India

India's political and social systems, as well as its infrastructure are in a state of disrepair, for lack of better words. Trade disputes, complex tendering procedures, inefficient power and dilapidated road and transmission systems, dysfunctional governance especially on the state and local levels, and bribes—abnormalities reign,

while India is struggling to deliver to better the life of its citizens.

India still has the largest population living without any power of any country today, and a number of initiatives on the table are just sitting on the table. Solar was thought to have the potential to help reduce the energy discrepancy, but recent "please all parties" policies show that the government does not have the public's wellbeing in mind.

The overall energy situation in rural India is characterized by: the low quality of fuel; low efficiency of use; low reliability of supply; and limited access leading to lower productivity of land, water and human effort. All this ultimately leads to a low quality of life for the majority of the population and gradual environmental degradation.

Presently, lack of electricity severely limits working hours and opportunities for the socio-economic progress of millions of households in rural India. Nearly 700 million Indians still burn biomass as the primary source of energy for cooking in inefficient cooking stoves at home or at small business enterprises.

Indian rural energy scenario is characterized by:

- Dependence on biomass (fuel-wood, crop residue and cattle dung) and traditional cook stoves with low efficiency which emit smoke into kitchens, leads to a low quality of life for most rural women and nearly 300,000-400,000 deaths every year, according to WHO.

- Dependence on kerosene and wick lamps for lighting with uncertain supply of the fuel leads to low and intermittent lighting quality.

- Dependence on centralized grid electricity supply to low-load rural situations is characterized by fluctuating voltage, unreliable supply and a shortage of power in most parts of rural India.

Due to the dependence on the above items, rural India is still lagging behind, due to the various policies and their reach. The need for rural electrification is necessary to have a prosperous growth of the country, as majority of the population of the country resides in the rural areas.

The Energy and Environmental Regulators

The central electricity regulatory commission intends to promote competition, efficiency and economy in bulk power markets, improve the quality of supply, promote investments, and advise government on the removal of institutional barriers to bridge the demand/supply gap and thus foster the interests of consumers.

In pursuit of these objectives the commission aims to:

- Improve the operations and management of the regional transmission systems through Indian electricity grid code (IEGC), availability based tariff (ABT), etc.
- Formulate an efficient tariff setting mechanism, which ensures speedy and time-bound disposal of tariff petitions, promotes competition, economy, and efficiency in the pricing of bulk power and transmission services and ensures least cost investments.
- Facilitate open access in inter-state transmission
- Facilitate inter-state trading
- Promote development of power market
- Improve access to information for all stakeholders
- Facilitate technological and institutional changes required for the development of competitive markets in bulk power and transmission services.
- Advise on the removal of barriers to entry and exit for capital and management, within the limits of environmental, safety and security concerns and the existing legislative requirements, as the first step to the creation of competitive markets

Mandatory functions of the central electricity regulating commission are to:

- Regulate the tariff of generating companies owned or controlled by the central government
- Regulate the tariff of generating companies other than those owned or controlled by the central government specified in clause (a), if such generating companies enter into or otherwise have a composite scheme for generation and sale of electricity in more than one state
- Regulate the inter-state transmission of electricity
- Determine tariff for inter-state transmission of electricity
- Issue licenses to persons to function as transmission licensee and electricity trader with respect to their inter-state operations
- Improve access to information for all stakeholders
- Adjudicate disputes involving generating companies or transmission licensee in regard to matters connected with clauses (a) to (d) above and to refer any dispute for arbitration
- Levy fees for the purposes of the act
- Specify grid code having regard to grid standards
- Specify and enforce the standards with respect to quality, continuity, and reliability of service by licensees

- Fix the trading margin in the inter-state trading of electricity, if considered necessary
- Discharge such other functions as may be assigned under the act

Energy and Environment Regulations

The short-term energy policy of India is defined by emergency measures forced upon the government by the extreme energy deficit in the country, where frequent, and sometimes very large-scale, blackouts are the norm. In the long run, the government is looking at alternative sources of energy, especially nuclear, solar, and wind energy as permanent solutions to the rising energy problems.

India has the world's third-largest coal reserves, and presently over 70% of India's energy-generation capacity comes from fossil fuels, where coal accounts for about 40% of the total energy generation. Crude oil and natural gas follow at 24% and 6% respectively.

India has some fossil fuel reserves, but it is largely dependent on imports to meet its energy demands. The fast growth of electricity generation in India has been hindered by domestic coal shortages, due to inefficient operating and transport procedures and infrastructure. As a consequence, India's coal imports for electricity generation increased by 20% in 2012. At the same time the country imported over 175 million tons of crude oil, which amounts to over 80% of its domestic crude oil consumption and over 30% of the country's total energy imports. The estimates are that by 2030, India's dependence on imported energy will increase to 50-60% of the country's total energy consumption.

India has a growing, and yet immature, solar industry, which is expected to develop and grow substantially during the next decades. Current solar installations in India stand at 1,761MW with about 557MW installed in 2013. Since most of the concentrating solar power (CSP) projects that were due to be commissioned in 2013 were delayed, the forecast for the next year or two is flat, compared to 2012.

Solar policy uncertainty has been widespread, especially with the Jawaharlal Nehru national solar mission (JNNSM). Proposed rule changes have been far too many and too frequent. The current photovoltaic power vs. concentrated solar thermal power (PV/CSP) split and domestic content requirements are examples of this inadequacy.

The Indian government and the regulators are dictating the exact ratio of technology (PV vs. CSP), rather than allowing the market to select the most efficient and cost-effective technology for India. Policy makers have bowed to the CSP lobby and sliced the solar market pie to please everyone, disregarding the market realities of CSP costs that require intense sunlight and a lot of water, which is simply unavailable in these regions. If the developers were to select the best and most suitable, these projects would have likely been PV projects and thousands of homes could have been powered by now.

Figure 6-45. Solar power plant a la India

Solar's contribution to electrifying India is being held back by the complexities of the government's solar policies, but the growing energy needs are forcing new ways of thinking and doing. The official plans now call for adding about 20GW of solar power capacity by 2020—if the government finds a way to deal with the complexities of the solar industry.

India also has the world's fifth-largest wind power industry, with an installed capacity of about 12GW, and there are plans to add almost as much during the next decade as well.

Adding power via hydro dams has been on the India's political agenda, so the Narmada Valley development plan was created. Its goal is to build 30 large, 135 medium, and 3000 small dams to harness the waters of the Narmada River and its tributaries. The proponents of this very large plan claim that it would provide the large amounts of water and electricity that are required for further development of the country.

Opponents question the plan and believe that it is unjust and that the cost-benefit analysis is grossly inflated in favor of building the dams. The plan is based on unfounded assumptions of hydrology and seismicity of the area and the construction is causing large-scale abuse of human rights and displacement of many poor and underprivileged communities. Water and energy can be provided to the people of the Narmada Valley,

Gujarat and other regions through alternative technologies and planning processes, which can be socially just and economically and environmentally sustainable.

India's energy plans also call for a substantial increase of nuclear power from 4.2% presently to about 10% by 2040. There are five nuclear reactors under construction already, and plans are underway to construct 18 additional nuclear reactors by 2025 and more after that. This puts India near the top of the list of countries with active nuclear power plant development.

The rapid population and economic growth in India has created one of the world's fastest growing energy markets, which is expected to be the second-largest contributor to the increase in global energy demand by 2030. At that time India would account for about 20% of the rise in global energy consumption. Since almost half of this power is generated by coal and oil, the estimates are that India would also be one of the world's largest emitters of GHGs.

Obviously, India is a major player in the global energy markets and environmental debacle. How this game will play in the future is uncertain, but there will be no dull moments watching India struggle with its energy and environmental efforts.

The key energy and environmental regulations in India are as follow:

- *Water (prevention and control) act of 1974*
  The objectives of the water (prevention and control of pollution) act are to provide for the prevention and control of water pollution and the maintenance or restoration of the wholesomeness of water for use by the population. It established a board, which is in charge of carrying out the purposes for the prevention and control of water pollution, and assigned powers and functions to the board to accomplish the goals of the act.

- *The forest (conservation) act of 1980*
  This act provides for the conservation of forests and regulating diversion of forestlands for non-forestry purposes. When projects fall within forestlands, prior clearance is required from relevant authorities under the act. State governments cannot de-reserve any forestland or authorize its use for any non-forest purposes without approval from the central government.

- *Air (prevention and control of pollution) act of 1981*
  At the U.N. conference on the human environment held in Stockholm in June 1972, in which India participated, decisions were made for appropriate action to preserve the natural resources of the earth, which in-

cludes the preservation of the quality of air and control of air pollution. Thus it is necessary to implement these decisions as they relate to the preservation of the quality of air and control of air pollution in the country and world.

So, the *Air (prevention and control of pollution) act of 1981* was born for that purpose. The objective of this act is to provide for the prevention, control, and abatement of air pollution in the country, and for the establishment of board(s) in charge of carrying out the purposes of the act. The act assigned to these boards powers and functions related to all matters related to the act goals.

- *Environment (protection) act of 1986*

The environment (protection) act, established in 1986, was introduced as an umbrella legislation that provides a framework for the protection and improvement to the environment. The act and the associated rules require obtaining environmental clearances for specific types of new/expansion projects, addressed under environmental impact assessment notification of 1994, and for submission of an environmental statement to the state pollution control board annually. Environmental clearance is not applicable to hydro projects also.

SJVNL (Satluj Jal Vidyut Nigam, Ltd.) is responsible for conducting environmental impact assessments for all energy projects as a standard management procedure according to the environment (protection) act of 1986. SJVNL functions within the permissible standards of ambient air quality, noise levels, and all others as prescribed by national laws and international regulations.

- *Ozone depleting substances (regulation and control) rules of 2000.*

These rules were established for regulation and control of ozone depleting substances (ODS) and equipment under the Montreal protocol. The rules suggest certain control and regulation to be imposed on the manufacturing, import, export, and use of ODS compounds and the related equipment. The affected organizations are required to phase out all equipment that uses or generates ODS with the goal of totally CFC-free operation in the future.

- *The energy conservation act of 2001*

The act set the tone for the country's energy generation and energy efficiency agenda. It provides for the legal framework, institutional arrangement, and a regulatory mechanism at the central and state level to embark upon energy efficiency drive in the country.

The major provisions of act relate to: designated consumers, standard and labeling of appliances, energy conservation building codes, creation of institutional set up (BEE) and establishment of energy conservation fund.

The energy efficiency institutional practices and programs in India are now mainly being guided through various voluntary and mandatory provisions of the act, which was amended in 2010.

The key 2010 amendments of the energy conservation act of 2001 are:
- The central government may issue the energy savings certificate to the designated consumer whose energy consumption is less than the prescribed norms and standards in accordance with the procedure that is prescribed.
- The designated consumer whose energy consumption is more than the prescribed norms and standards shall be entitled to purchase the energy savings certificate to comply with the prescribed norms and standards.
- The central government may, in consultation with the bureau, prescribe the value of per metric ton of oil equivalent of energy consumed.
- Commercial buildings that are having a connected load of 100 kW or contract demand of 120 kVA and above come under the purview of ECBC under the act.

The Bureau of Energy E-fficiency of 2002

The bureau is an agency of the government of India, under the ministry of power, and was created under the provisions of the energy conservation act of 2001. Its function is to develop energy related programs geared to increase the conservation and efficient use of energy in India. The mission of the bureau of energy efficiency is to "institutionalize" energy efficiency services, enable delivery mechanisms in the country, and provide leadership to energy efficiency in all sectors of the country. The primary objective would be to reduce energy intensity in the economy.

The broader objectives of the bureau are to:
- Exert leadership and provide policy recommendation and direction to national energy conservation and efficiency efforts and programsf
- Coordinate energy efficiency and conservation policies and programs and take it to the stakeholders
- Establish systems and procedures that measure, monitor and verify energy efficiency results in individual sectors as well as at a macro level

— Leverage multi-lateral and bi-lateral and private sector support in implementation of energy conservation act and efficient use of energy and its conservation programs

— Demonstrate delivery of energy efficiency services as mandated in the EC bill through private-public partnerships

— Interpret, plan, and manage energy conservation programs as envisaged in the energy conservation act

— Provide a policy recommendation and direction to national energy conservation activities

— Coordinate policies and programs on the efficient use of energy with shareholders

— Establish systems and procedures to verify, measure, and monitor energy efficiency (EE) improvement

— Leverage multilateral, bilateral, and private sector support to implement the EC act of 2001

— Demonstrate EE delivery systems through public-private partnerships

• *The electricity act of 2003*

This act seeks to create a framework for the power sector development by measures conducive to and beneficial for the industry. The electricity act does not explicitly deal with environmental implications of activities related to power transmission. The applicable legal provision under this act is Section 68(1)—sanction from the ministry of power (MOP)—as a mandatory requirement for taking up any new project. The sanction authorizes Satluj Jal Vidyut Nigam, Ltd. (SJVN) to plan and coordinate activities as needed for the implementation of new projects.

The act enhanced mandates of regulatory commissions and other agencies in the power sector for the promotion of clean energy. Apart from these legislative measures, the Indian government has undertaken a wide range of policy initiatives to give impetus to renewable energy and energy efficiency.

• Hazardous wastes (management and handling) amendment rules of 2003

These rules classify used mineral oil as hazardous waste under the hazardous waste (management & handling) rules of 2003 that require proper handling and disposal. The affected organizations are required to seek authorization for disposal of hazardous waste from concerned state pollution control boards (SPCB) as and when required.

• *National electrification policy of 2005-2006*

The policy lays guidelines for accelerated development of power sector, providing electricity to everyone and protecting the interest of the consumers. The various innovative steps that central electricity authority (CEA) took to implement the policy on ground level are:

— Short-term and long-term forecasts for different regions of India. The short-term innovations consist of planning for the next five years in congruence with the feedback from the state governments. A long-term plan will give a 15-year perspective of the plan made by the CEA.

— State government's involvement in implementing the plan was a very efficient move done by the CEA. State government was involved in the planning and license distribution.

— Various institutions and agencies are also involved in demand forecasting and conducting studies at regular time intervals for knowing ground-level realities.

— Taking into account the various considerations like environmental impact, economic viability, energy security, etc., into account in the planning process

— Rural electrification was of prime importance.

— Taking care of the balance between the economic sustainability of power sector and making electricity affordable to the poorer population

— Introducing the concept of advance subsidy via state government along with a system to ensure the reach to the targeted beneficiaries

Additional laws and rules to be noted, as far as the energy and environment in India are concerned, are as follow:

— The rules for the manufacture, use, import and export and storage of hazardous micro-organisms, 1989

— Genetically engineered organisms or cells, 1989

— The manufacture, storage and import of hazardous chemical rules, 1989

— The hazardous wastes (management and handling) rules, 1989

— The 2-T oil (regulation of supply and distribution) order, 1998

— The bio-medical waste (management and handling) rules, 1998

— The public liability insurance act, 1991

— The national environment tribunal act, 1995

— The national environment appellate authority act, 1997
— The recycled plastics manufacture and usage rules, 1999
— Dumping and disposal of fly ash discharged from coal or lignite based thermal power plants, 1999
— Noise pollution (regulation and control) rules, 2000
— the municipal solid wastes (management and handling) rules, 2000
— The batteries (management and handling) rules, 2001
— The biological diversity act, 2002
— The national tariff policy, 2006

These are the major pieces of the institutional framework concerning the energy generation, energy efficiency, and rural electrification. The aim is to provide electricity to all households, quality and reliable energy at reasonable rates, and a minimum of 1 kWh per household per day.

Besides these policies, several programs and schemes have been set up to improve the rural electrification. Among others, the Rajiv Gandhi Grameen Vidyutikaran Yojana (RGGVY) scheme, the remote village electrification (RVE) program, and the Jawaharlal Nehru national solar mission (JNNSM).

The regulatory framework for rural electrification in India has been really dynamic and has known numerous amendments. However, in spite of these multiples initiatives, more than 18,000 villages still live without electricity and 300 million people do not have access to power.

The Trends

There are several trends worth noting in environmental management in India presently, as follows:

• *Environmental impact assessment*

Assessing environmental and social impacts prior to obtaining environmental approval from the authorities in India is mandatory in most project categories. Such assessments are required not only for newly constructed facilities, but also for new or upgraded operations in existing buildings.

• *Sustainability and regulatory compliance*

Indian companies are increasingly willing to meet world-class standards, which is translating into companies taking seriously the available sustainability so-

lutions and initiatives to improve their reputation, and from there the acceptance of their brand on the world markets. In addition, the India's environmental ministry advocates principles such as "green accounting," which furthers the drive to sustainability and global acceptance of India's commerce.

• *Environmental liability and cleanup*

Foreign investment has been a driving factor in revising the environmental liabilities associated with property transactions in India. Foreign companies would not take the risks of investing in India without proper risk assessment and management, which forces the local authorities and companies to respect and obey the minimum international rules and regulations if they are to obtain investment assistance from abroad.

• *Climate change*

India is on the bottom of the list of countries with good environmental plans, and even lower as far as compliance is concerned. Although there are regulations on paper, in reality the business activities are based on economic development rather than environment compliance.

Nevertheless, there is an increasing awareness about climate change, which is forcing a change of mind about the entire global environmental picture. This is augmented by predictions that India will be heavily affected by the rapidly changing global climate and future weather patterns. India is working on some of the clean development mechanism projects under the Kyoto protocol, but the situation is fluid and ever changing so it is not clear what the long-term results would be.

Case study: Policy Disconnect in Solar Development

Despite some successes and early growing pains in the solar energy field in India, there are a few signs to indicate that the lessons of the past have been learned. When Jawaharlal Nehru national solar mission (JNNSM) was first rolled out in 2012, the reverse bidding process was chosen so solar power could be procured at the lowest possible bids. The guidelines also state that developers must put in at least $2.5 million of their own funding in each project they develop.

The government is desperate for foreign investments for power projects, but at the same time they make wrong decisions and give the wrong signals by dictating how projects are to be built and where their equipment should be made. All this scares away investors and has made the international investment community wary.

Some of the efforts of late are geared towards protecting the domestic PV manufacturers, so India has entered into trade disputes with the U.S., China, Taiwan and Malaysia. The effort was dealt a blow when the WTO ruled against the Canadian province of Ontario's FIT program, which requires all solar projects to meet a minimum domestic requirement. The ruling sets a precedent, so it would be wise for India to settle its trade disputes in a swift and decisive manner once and forever.

However, domestic content requirement policies in India, like those that contributed to the delays experienced by solar thermal (CSP) developers, are still being pursued. There are also changes in the thin-film "loophole" in the domestic content requirement, which would hurt the global thin film PV industry in the long run.

NOTE: India implemented domestic content requirement some time ago, which put a limit on the percentage of imported solar cells and modules, but thin film PV modules were excluded. This explains the rapid growth of thin film PV installations in the country, but that loophole was closed and now the requirement applies to all future PV installations in the country.

In more detail: JNNSM's phase I batch I project power purchase agreements (PPA) was signed on January 10, 2011, for 610MW (140MW PV and 470MW CSP) power plants development. The PV projects were due to be installed by January 2012, with 130MW commissioned after months of delays and large fines. Ten megawatts have been cancelled because two project developers failed.

Only 50MW CSP are expected to be installed out of the original 470MW, while the remaining projects have been granted 10-month extensions, giving the developers a total of 38 months to complete, which moves these projects to a 2014 commissioning date, or later.

Phase II is targeted at 3.0 GMW of solar power through several batches. Phase II Batch I target goal is 750MW, but Instead of bidding for the lowest tariff, developers are now bidding for viability gap funding (VGF), under which developers sign a 25-year PPA to sell power at a fixed tariff of $0.10/kWh. In the case of accelerated depreciation, the tariff will be reduced by 10% to $0.09/kWh. The maximum limit for VGF is 30% of the project cost, or $500,000/MW, whichever is lower.

The problem is that with VGF most of the funding is upfront, thus there is no incentive to build the highest-performing projects. This is a discrepancy, mostly due to lack of environmental protection policies, which will play badly in India's immature solar energy market and very likely the global environment.

The total of 750MW of projects in phase II batch I will be spilt according to domestic content requirement,

where "part A" is an exempt, while "part B" is not. The total installations under phase II are set at 3.0 GW, which would include different mechanisms like VGF and/or bundling of power.

There is much added complexity in the already complex solar business in India, so the developers will have a hard time deciding between the JNNSM and the individual state policies. Presently only about 590MW has come from JNNSM projects, compared to approximately 1,200MW installed through various state policies.

The newly developed situation shows a disconnect between India's energy policies and the original goal of procuring solar at the most cost effective prices.

Europe

Europe is now one of the largest and most powerful political entities in this world…on paper. In reality the different states (countries) are having a difficult time adjusting to the new situation. Many of them have long history of wars, intrigues, and turmoil, some of which cannot be easily forgiven, let alone forgotten. And so today, a number of inter-state problems on different levels exist among the different countries.

On the energy and environmental protection fronts, however, the E.U. community seems united and working together toward the common goals of energy efficiency and cleaner environment.

The Energy and Environmental Regulators

The E.U. became a leader in renewable energy innovation and implementation during the 2007-2012, and was very successful in installing a great number of solar and wind power plants. Several regulating bodies coordinated the work, as follows:

- *The Commissioner for the Environment*

The commissioner for the environment is the member of the European commission responsible for E.U. environmental policy. The E.U. has made a number of environmental moves, partially in regards to climate change. Most notably, it signed the Kyoto Protocol in 1998, set up its emission-trading scheme in 2005, and is currently agreeing to unilaterally cut its emissions by 20% by 2020. (See: Energy policy of the European Union)

Other policies include: the natura 2000, a widespread and successful network of nature conservation sites; the registration, evaluation and authorization of chemicals (REACH) directive requiring safety testing on widely used chemicals; and the water framework directive ensuring water quality reaches higher standards.

- *The Council of European Energy Regulators*

The council of European energy regulators (CEER) is the voice of Europe's national regulators of electricity and gas for the E.U. member countries and internationally. CEER is a non-for-profit association, which facilitates the communications and cooperation among the different national regulators, helping them to work together and exchange best practices.

CEER's main objective is to facilitate the creation of a single, competitive, efficient and sustainable E.U. internal energy market that works in the public interest for the benefit of all people.

CEER works closely with and supports the work of the agency for the cooperation of energy regulators (ACER). ACER, which has its seat in Ljubljana, is an E.U. Agency with its own staff and resources. CEER, based in Brussels, deals with many complementary issues to ACER's work such as international issues, smart grids, sustainability and customer issues.

- *The Agency for the Cooperation of Energy Regulators*

The agency for the cooperation of energy regulators (ACER) was created in 2011 with the objective to assist and coordinate the completion of the internal energy markets of electricity and natural gas. ACER is an independent European organization working to foster cooperation among European energy regulators, and ensure the integration and harmonization of regulatory frameworks, as dictated by the EU's energy policy objectives, which are:

— A more competitive, integrated market, which offers consumers more choice

— An efficient energy infrastructure guaranteeing the free movement of energy across borders and the transportation of new energy sources, thus enhancing security of supply for E.U. businesses and consumers

— A monitored and transparent energy market guaranteeing consumers fair, cost-reflective prices and deterrence of abusive practices.

ACER is thus a central institution in the creation of a single energy market to the benefit of all E.U. consumers. In this respect, ACER and CEER have similar goals and work closely together on many complementary and not overlapping issues and projects.

- *The European Environment Agency*

The European environment agency (EEA) was established in 1994 as an agency of the E.U., whose task is to provide sound, independent information on the environment. It serves as an information source for developing, adopting, implementing, and evaluating environmental policy for the general public.

All member states of the E.U. are automatically members, but other states may become members too via agreements signed with the E.U. The EEA presently has 33 member countries and six cooperating countries, consisting of the 28 E.U. member states plus Iceland, Liechtenstein, Norway, Switzerland and Turkey.

The EEA is governed by a management board composed of representatives of the governments of its 33 member states, a European commission representative and two scientists appointed by the European parliament, assisted by a committee of scientists.

- *The European Environment Information and Observation Network*

The European environment information and observation network (Eionet) is a partnership network of the EEA and its member and cooperating countries. The EEA is responsible for developing the network and coordinating its activities, and works closely together with the national environment agencies or environment ministries in the member countries.

Eionet covers six European topic centres (ETCs) in the areas of air and climate change, biological diversity, climate change impacts, vulnerability and adaptation, water, land use, spatial information and analysis, and sustainable consumption and production.

The Regulations

There are a number of regulations and procedures in the E.U., most of which are in a constant state of development. Some of these are:

The E.U. commission for the environment proposed a list of initiatives, which were approved by the European council in 2007.

Key items in the 2007 proposal include:

— A cut of at least 20% in greenhouse gas emissions from all primary energy sources by 2020 (compared to 1990 levels), while pushing for an international agreement to succeed the Kyoto Protocol aimed at achieving a 30% cut by all developed nations by 2020

— A cut of up to 95% in carbon emissions from primary energy sources by 2050, compared to 1990 levels.

— A minimum target of 10% for the use of biofuels by 2020

— Ensuring that the energy supply and generation activities of energy companies should be 'unbundled' from their distribution networks to further increase market competition.

— Improving energy relations with the EU's neighbors, including Russia

— The development of a European strategic energy technology plan to develop technologies in areas including renewable energy, energy conservation, low-energy buildings, fourth generation nuclear reactors, clean coal and carbon captue.

— Developing an Africa-Europe energy partnership to help Africa "leap-frog" to low-carbon technologies and to help develop the continent as a sustainable energy supplier

A major goal of this effort is to limit global temperature changes to no more than 20°C above pre-industrial levels, which is the upper temperature limit needed to avoid out of control global warming.

• *The European Union emissions trading system (EU ETS)*, or the European Union emissions trading scheme, is the first large emissions trading scheme in the world. It was established in 2005 to combat climate change. EU ETS now covers more than 11,000 factories, power plants, and other installations in 31 countries. The installations regulated by the EU ETS are collectively responsible for reduce the EU's emissions of CO_2 by 50% and about 40% of its total GHG emissions.

A cap is set on the total amount of greenhouse gases that can be emitted by the participants and allowances for emissions are then auctioned off. These can then be traded. Installations must issue enough allowances for their emissions, and purchase allowances from others if exceeds the limit.

Other countries are following the E.U. example and are developing similar systems. For example, the Australia's trading scheme will be linked with the EU ETS in 2015. There is a plan to link it up with compatible systems around the world, thus forming a global carbon market.

• The European *climate and energy package* is a set of binding legislation, which was established in 2007. It aims to ensure that the European Union meets its ambitious climate and energy targets for 2020.

These targets, known as the "20-20-20" targets, set three key objectives for 2020:

— A 20% reduction in E.U. greenhouse gas emissions from 1990 levels

— Raising the share of E.U. energy consumption produced from renewable resources to 20%

— A 20% improvement in the E.U.'s energy efficiency

The targets set by E.U. leaders committed Europe to become a highly energy-efficient, low carbon economy, and were enacted through the climate and energy package in 2009. The E.U. is also offering to increase its emissions reduction to 30% by 2020 if other major economies in the developed and developing worlds commit to undertake their fair share of a global emissions reduction effort. The European Commission has published analysis of the options for moving beyond a 20% reduction by 2020 and assessing the risk of "carbon leakage," which is another major and growing concern.

The 20-20-20 targets represent an integrated approach to climate and energy policy that aims to combat climate change, increase the E.U.'s energy security and strengthen its competitiveness. They are also headline targets of the Europe 2020 strategy for smart, sustainable and inclusive growth. This reflects the recognition that tackling the climate and energy challenge contributes to the creation of jobs, the generation of "green" growth and a strengthening of Europe's competitiveness.

It is estimated that meeting the 20% renewable energy target could have a net effect of creating around 417,000 additional jobs, while getting on track to achieve the 20% energy efficiency improvement in 2020 is forecast to boost net employment by some 400,000 jobs.

The climate and energy package is comprised of four pieces of complementary legislation, which are intended to deliver on the 20-20-20 targets:

• *Reform of the E.U. (EU ETS)*, which is the key tool for cutting industrial greenhouse gas emissions most cost-effectively. The climate and energy package includes a comprehensive revision and strengthening of the legislation, which underpins the EU ETS, the emissions trading directive.

The revision applies from 2013, the start of the third trading period of the EU ETS. Major changes include the introduction of a single E.U.-wide cap on emission allowances in place of the existing system of national caps. The cap will be cut each year so that by 2020 emissions will be 21% below the 2005 level.

The free allocation of allowances will be progressively replaced by auctioning, starting with the power sector. The sectors and gases covered by the system will be slightly widened.

- *National targets for non-EU ETS emissions* are binding annual targets member states have taken under the so-called effort sharing decision, on binding annual targets for reducing their greenhouse gas emissions from the sectors not covered by the EU ETS, such as housing, agriculture, waste and transport (excluding aviation). Around 60% of the E.U.'s total emissions come from sectors outside the EU ETS.

The national targets, covering the period 2013-2020, are differentiated according to member states' relative wealth. They range from a 20% emissions reduction (compared to 2005) by the richest member states to a 20% increase by the least wealthy (though this will still requires a limitation effort by all countries). Member states must report on their emissions annually under the E.U. monitoring mechanism.

- *National renewable energy targets* are binding targets that member states have taken, under the renewable energy directive, on binding national targets for raising the share of renewable energy in their energy consumption by 2020. These targets, which reflect member states' different starting points and potential for increasing renewables production, range from 10% in Malta to 49% in Sweden.

The national targets will enable the E.U. as a whole to reach its 20% renewable energy target for 2020—more than double the 2010 level of 9.8%—as well as a 10% share of renewable energy in the transport sector. The targets will also help to cut greenhouse gas emissions and reduce the E.U.'s dependence on imported energy.

- Carbon capture and storage is the fourth element of the climate and energy package. It is a directive creating a legal framework for the environmentally safe use of carbon capture and storage technologies. Carbon-capture and storage involves capturing the carbon dioxide emitted by industrial processes and storing it in underground geological formations where it does not contribute to global warming.

The directive covers all CO_2 storage in geological formations in the E.U. and lays down requirements, which apply to the entire lifetime of storage sites.

Note: The European climate and energy package does not address the energy efficiency target directly. Instead, this is done more effectively through the 2011 *energy efficiency plan* and the *energy efficiency directive*.

The *energy efficiency plan* is a set of measures focused on creating substantial benefits for households, businesses and public authorities. It aims to transform the daily lives and generate financial savings of up to €1000 per household every year. It also should improve the E.U.'s industrial competitiveness with a potential for the creation of up to two million jobs.

The *energy efficiency directive* establishes a common framework of measures for the promotion of energy efficiency within the European Union to ensure the achievement of the 20% energy efficiency target by 2020 and to pave the way for further energy efficiency improvements beyond that date. It lays down rules designed to remove barriers in the energy market and overcome market failures that impede efficiency in the supply and use of energy, and provides for the establishment of indicative national energy efficiency targets for 2020.

2013 Update

All this sounds as a well-established path towards efficient energy management and environmental cleanup, right? Yes, but as we saw in many other cases, words are much easier to put on a piece of paper than it is to make things happen, especially if these things might require sacrifice and some pain to implement.

So, regardless of the regulations, the observers, etc., etc. energy and environmental measures, Germany and other E.U. countries have turned the dial back to the 19th century times, and are increasing the use of coal. They blame economics and rising prices as the reasons, but regardless, gas-fired power plants are being shut down, and coal power generation is expected to increase significantly in the near future.

So one has to wonder what good all these agencies, regulations, treaties, agreements, promises, plans, etc. are, if at the end we are going to pollute as much we want (or need).

This also means that no matter what the U.S. does, the global GHG emissions will increase, driven by E.U., China and India's increased use of coal for power generation.

Japan

Japan is going through major changes in its energy-environment scheme, so we won't spend too much time here.

The Energy Regulators

The mainstay of Japan's generation resources is nuclear energy. It accounts for 30% of the total amount of electricity generated in Japan, and the plans were to increase the share of nuclear energy to 40% or more—until the Fukushima disaster hit. Then things changed drastically.

Japan had plans to increase the share of renewable energy to 20% of the amount of electricity consumed by end users and nearly 10% of the amount of electricity generated by 2020, but was hesitating due to the problems such as unstable and variable power output, high initial cost, land (site) restrictions, regulatory problems, etc. This also changed after Fukushima. See update below.

The Nuclear Regulation Authority

A new and independent nuclear safety agency—the nuclear regulation authority (NRA)—was established and began operating in Japan in 2012. Its future, however, is already clouded by controversy. Approval of the five members of the NRA's governing commission was not obtained by the central government. At the very least NRA will make sure that none of Japan's shutdown nuclear reactors is restarted until and unless the NRA issues its own set of safety rules and applied them to restart decisions. This process will take at least a year, so Japan's nuclear future is on hold for now.

Also in 2012 Japan's cabinet backed down from a decision by the prime minister to phase out all nuclear reactors by 2030. The reason was the implacable opposition to the loss of reliable electric power by Japan's largest business federation, composed of heavy industry manufacturing operations. Some of these firms, which are also among Japan's largest employers, have threatened to take their operations offshore if the government doesn't authorize restart of the reactors.

And so, Japan is in the midst of real energy changes. Maybe something unexpectedly good would come from all this confusion and hesitation.

Oh, wait, it already had happened. Read on.

Energy Status Update

Before the 2011 meltdowns at the Fukushima Dai-ichi plant, Japan had all but neglected renewable energy, instead focusing on nuclear power. Fukushima shut down all 50 operable reactors, only a few of which have been restarted. The remaining shut downs are temporary, but the majority of Japanese remain opposed to nuclear energy.

Japan doesn't have many energy resources, so to compensate for the lost nuclear power companies and investors are racing to install solar panels at a rapid pace. As a result large solar power plants are popping all over the country as part of a rapid build-up has been compared to an "explosion." This boom in solar installations highlights Japan's desire to change directions.

The solar boom was actually sparked by an obscure government policy, implemented nearly a year ago, that guaranteed generous payments to anybody selling renewable energy, including solar power. This policy, or feed-in tariff (TiF), has made Japan into one of the world's fastest-growing users of solar energy.

The TiF obligates utility companies to buy electricity from renewable sources, such as solar, wind and geothermal at fixed prices. In most cases, the utilities buy the renewable-generated power from private individuals and companies. The TiF is fixed at an artificially high price at first, specifically to encourage start-up investments. The investors are small farmers, lumber companies and local governments, who also moonlight as little power-generation companies and sell their power to the utilities.

Under the terms of the tariff, they sell their renewable-generated energy to the local utility company at rates guaranteed for 20 years. The rates vary depending on the source, but solar is the most generous. When the tariff was first unveiled, sellers could get 42 yen per kilowatt-hour—about twice the rate in Germany and France. That rate for new projects was cut by 10% recently, but this is unlikely to the solar developers.

In 2013 alone Japan installed enough solar panels to provide the capacity of five-six modern nuclear reactors. In 2012 Japan's total solar capacity was 7.4 GW and almost doubled in 2013. This makes Japan the second-fastest growing solar market behind China. It is surpassed only by Germany and Italy in total installed capacity.

Japan installed over $20 billion worth of PV systems in 2013, up 82% from $11 billion in 2012, while at the same time the global market is still crawling at a tepid 4% pace. Germany still leads with the total number of units and capacity, however, with its 32,192 megawatts. Japan is now closer to the U.S.'s 8,069 megawatts at 7,429 megawatts, according to London-based BNEF.

The problem is that in all cases, renewables are several times pricier than nuclear power or fossil fuels such as coal, oil and gas. So in retrospective, the rising use of solar power means energy bills will rise, which will worsen Japan's still foundering economy. Japan always had the world's highest energy costs and if and when all 15 GW of solar projects come online, the power bills could increase 5% or more.

Nevertheless, most Japanese think that sacrifice is worthwhile, and believe that nuclear power is equally expensive with hidden costs of cleanup and compensation after an accident. Fossil fuels, on the other hand, release greenhouse gasses and must be imported.

Notes and References

1. California Global Warming Solutions Act, A.B. 32 (Cal. 2006), http://www.leginfo.ca.gov/pub/05-06/bill/asm/ab_0001-0050/ab_32_bill_20060927_chaptered.pdf.
2. California Public Utilities Commission, *Greenhouse Gas Emissions Performance Standard,* http://www.cpuc.ca.gov/PUC/energy/Climate+Change/070411_ghgeph.htm.
3. Lawrence Berkeley National Laboratory, *Renewables Portfolio Standards in the U.S.,* http://eetd.lbl.gov/ea/ems/reports/lbnl-154e.pdf.
4. Energy Information Administration, *California,* Apr. 1, 2010, http://tonto.eia.doe.gov/state/state_energy_profiles.cfm?sid=CA.
5. California Air Resources Board, *The California Low Carbon Fuel Standard Regulation,* http://www.arb.ca.gov/fuels/lcfs/1208lcfsreg_draft.pdf.
6. Cal. Exec. Order No. S-01-07 (Jan. 18, 2007), http://gov.ca.gov/index.php?/executive-order/5172/.
7. A.B. 1493 (Cal. 2002), http://www.arb.ca.gov/cc/ccms/documents/ab1493.pdf.
8. Rulemaking on the Proposed Regulations to Control Greenhouse Gas Emissions from Motor Vehicles, http://www.arb.ca.gov/regact/grnhsgas/grnhsgas.htm.
9. California Energy Commission, *California's Energy Efficiency Standards for Residential and Nonresidential Buildings,* http://www.energy.ca.gov/title24/index.html.
10. An act to add Section 25402.10 to the Public Resources Code, relating to energy, A.B. 1103 (Cal. 2007), http://www.leginfo.ca.gov/pub/07-08/bill/asm/ab_1101-1150/ab_1103_bill_20071012_chaptered.pdf.
11. Cal. Exec. Order No. S-20-04 (July 24, 2004).
12. A.B. 532 (Cal. 2007), http://www.climatechange.ca.gov/publications/legislation/ab_532_bill_20071013_ chaptered.pdf.
13. California Energy Commission, *2007 Appliance Efficiency Regulations,* http://www.energy.ca.gov/2007publications/CEC-400-2007-016/CEC-400-2007-016-REV1.PDF.
14. A.B. 1109 (Cal. 2009), http://leginfo.ca.gov/pub/09-10/bill/asm/ab_1101-1150/ab_1109_bill_20090413_amended_asm_v98.pdf.
15. *Environmental Economics.* The Environmental Literacy Council.
16. Jimmy Carter, "The President's Proposed Energy Policy," Address to the American People, April 18,1977.
17. *Photovoltaics for Commercial and Utilities Power Generation,* Anco S. Blazev. The Fairmont Press, 2011
18. *Solar Technologies for the 21st Century,* Anco S. Blazev. The Fairmont Press, 2013

Appendix A

Clean Air Act and Amendments.

1955 Pollution control act

1959 Reauthorization

1960 Motor vehicle exhaust study 1963 clean air act amendments

1965 Motor vehicle air pollution control act 1966 clean air act amendments of 1966

1967 Air quality act of 1967 national air emission standards act

1970 Clean air act amendments of 1970

1973 Reauthorization

1974 Energy supply and environmental coordination act of 1974

1977 Clean air act amendments of 1977 1980 acid precipitation act of 1980

1981 Steel industry compliance extension act of 1981

1987 Clean air act 8-month extension 1990 clean air act amendments of 1990

1991 Technical correction to list of hazardous air pollutants

1995-96 Relatively minor laws amending the act

1998 Amended section 604 re methyl bromide 1998 border smog reduction act of 1998

1999 Chemical safety information, site security and fuels regulatory relief act

2004 Amendments to §209 re: small engines

2005 Energy policy act of 2005 (amended §211 re: fuels)

2007 Energy Independence and Security Act of 2007 (amended §211, re: fuels)

Clean Water Act and Amendments.

1948 Federal water pollution control act

1956 Water pollution control act of 1956

1961 Federal water pollution control act amendments

1965 Water quality act of 1965

1966 Clean water restoration act

1970 Water quality improvement act of 1970

1972 Federal water pollution control act amendments

1977 Clean water act of 1977

1981 Municipal wastewater treatment construction grants amendments

1987 Water quality act of 1987

Ocean Dumping Act and Amendments.

1972 Marine protection, research, and sanctuaries act

1974 London dumping convention implementation

1977 Authorization of appropriations 1980 authorization of appropriations

1980 Authorization of appropriations 1982 surface transportation assistance act

1986 Budget reconciliation 1986 water resources development act

1987 Water quality act of 1987 1988 ocean dumping research amendments

1988 Ocean dumping ban act

1988 U.S. public vessel medical waste anti-dumping act

of 1988

1990 Regional marine research centers 1992 national coastal monitoring act

1992 Water resources development act

Safe Drinking Act and Amendments

1974 Safe drinking water act of 1974 P.L. 93-523

1977 Safe drinking water act amendments of 1977 P.L. 95-190

1979 Safe drinking water act amendments P.L. 96-63

1980 Safe drinking water act amendments P.L. 96-502

1986 Safe drinking water act amendments of 1986 P.L. 99-339

1988 Lead contamination control act of 1988 P.L. 100-572

1996 Safe drinking water act amendments of 1996 P.L. 104-182

2002 Public health security and bioterrorism preparedness P.L. 107-188 and response act of 2002

Solid Waste Disposal Act, Resource Conservation and Recover Act (RCRA)

1976 Law to control hazardous wastes, end open dumping, and promote conservation of resources

1980 Hazardous waste regulations

1981 First storage permit under rcra

1984 Hazardous and solid waste amendments of 1984,

1988 Standards for underground storage tanks

1990 Land disposal restrictions for hazardous wastes

1999 Revision of standards for air emissions from hazardous waste combustors

Insecticide, Fungicide, and Rodenticide Act and Ammendments

1938 Federal food, drug, and cosmetic act

1947 Federal insecticide, fungicide, and rodenticide Act P.L. 80-104

1954 Federal food, drug, and cosmetic act amendments

1958 Food additive amendments of 1958 (including the Delaney clause)

1964 Federal insecticide, fungicide, and rodenticide act amendments P.L. 88-305

1970 Transfer of pesticide residue responsibility to EPA

1972 Federal environmental pesticide control act P.L. 92-516

1975 Federal insecticide, fungicide, and rodenticide act extension P.L. 94-140

1978 Federal pesticide act of 1978 P.L. 95-396

1980 Federal insecticide, fungicide and rodenticide act amendments P.L. 96-539

1988 Federal insecticide, fungicide, and rodenticide

amendments of 1990   P.L. 100-532

1990 Food, agriculture, conservation, and trade act of 1990 P.L. 101-624

1991 Food, agriculture, conservation and trade amendments of 1991 P.L. 102-237

1996 Food quality protection act (FQPA) of 1996 P.L. 104-170

1996 Food quality protection act of 1996

2004 Pesticide registration improvement act of 2003 P.L. 108-199, division g, title V

2007 Pesticide registration improvement renewal act P.L. 110-94

Hydropower relicensing legislation

Some of the most significant laws affecting hydropower relicensing legislations are:

Federal Power Act

Section 4(e) authority. Federal land-administering agencies have authority under Section 4(e) of the federal power act (FPA) to require "mandatory conditions" for projects located on federal reservations under their jurisdiction. FERC cannot reject such "mandatory conditions" regardless of cost or the impact on other beneficial uses of the waterway. The term "reservation" lands is defined to include national forests, Indian lands, and any other lands "acquired and held for public purposes" (like wilderness areas), but not including national monuments or national parks.

FPA Section 18 authority. Under FPA Section 18, the Secretaries of the Departments of the Interior and Commerce can require "fishways" or specific conditions related to fish passage facilities at hydropower projects. FERC cannot reject these fishway prescriptions.

FPA Section 10(a) authority. Under FPA Section 10(a), FERC must give equal consideration to power and non-power values to provide the "best public use of the waterway." FERC must consider recommendations from federal and state agencies and Indian tribes, state fish and wildlife and water quality agencies

FPA Section 10(j) recommendations. Under Section 10(j) of the FPA, licenses must include conditions based on recommendations by federal and state fish and wildlife agencies for the protection, mitigation, or enhancement of fish and wildlife resources affected by the project unless FERC can find that they are inconsistent with the purpose of the project. Before rejecting any of these recommendations, FERC must show that it gave due weight to the recommendations and tried to resolve any inconsistencies.

Electric consumers protection act (ECPA) of 1986. EPCA amended the Federal Power Act by requiring that FERC give equal consideration to non-power values such as recreation, fish, and wildlife, when making hydroelectric project licensing decisions.

Energy policy act of 2005. EPAct 2005 allows a license applicant, or any other party to a licensing process, to propose an alternative FPA Section 4(e) and Section 18 to mandatory conditions placed on hydropower licenses by federal resource agencies (Departments of Interior, Commerce and Agriculture). If the secretary of an agency determines that the alternative meets the statutory environmental and resource protection standards, and the alternative provides significant cost or power savings, the secretary accepts the alternative. EPAct 2005 also allows any party to a licensing proceeding to call for a single, expedited trial-type agency hearing on disputed issues of material fact concerning mandatory conditions.

CWA Section 401 water quality certification. State water quality agencies also must issue a water quality certification stating that the project complies with water quality laws before FERC can relicense a dam. State water quality agencies essentially have mandatory conditioning authority through the section 401 water quality certification process.

National environmental policy act. Hydropower relicensing is considered a significant federal action that must undergo environmental review as part of the National Environmental Policy Act with FERC issuing an environmental assessment or environmental impact statement before issuing a hydropower license. NEPA requires analysis of alternatives but as a procedural statute it does not require FERC to choose a particular alternative.

Section 7 ESA consultation. Section 7(a)(2) of the ESA requires that FERC ensure that issuance of a license will not jeopardize the continued existence of endangered or threatened species or destroy or adversely modify to critical habitat. When an ESA species or critical habitat may be affected by licensing, relicensing or other related actions related to the project, FERC has to consult with the federal resource agency with relevant authority (i.e. the national marine fisheries service or the U.S. fish and wildlife service). This usually occurs between issuance of a draft environmental impact statement and a final environmental impact statement.

NHPA protections. The national historic preservation act requires FERC to consider the effect of a new project license on cultural resources eligible for inclusion in the national register of historic places. FERC must execute a programmatic agreement among relevant tribes and state agencies to protect historic properties at hydropower projects.

Recreation regulations. §2.7 of Part 18 of the federal code of regulations provides for recreational development at FERC licensed hydropower facilities. Licenses must provide "public access" to public waters. The regulations are vague, requiring only that the licensee make "reasonable expenditures" as part of an approved recreational development plan that provides public access to project waters.

Chapter 7

Economic and Legal Aspects of Power Generation and the Environment

*Green is the first socio-political movement in which
every single leader and spokesperson is filthy rich.*

—Julie Burchill

People in the U.S. live in the richest and most opulent society in the history of man. We have everything human beings could possibly need (all of us), wish for (some of us), and even dream of (few of us). Yes, we all have almost unlimited opportunities, and most of us hustle tirelessly day after day to maximize our chances to live the American dream. Some of us succeed, others not so much, but hustle we do—all of us, non-stop.

This hustling, however, and everything else millions of us do 24/7/365, requires energy—a lot of energy in different forms and shapes. Without the abundant and fairly cheap energy to which we have had unlimited access (until now), the entire bustling society would come to a screeching halt. Fortunately this it is not very likely to happen soon.

We have plenty of energy now, but using so much of it comes at a price. Excessive amounts of gaseous, liquid, and solid pollution are damaging the environment, and we are in fact killing ourselves in the process of improving our lives. It is a catch 22 of sorts—find the fuels; extract the fuels; generate power; use power; emit pollution; get sick.

One would think that there has to be a better and smarter way of doing what we are doing, but the *energy vs. environment* concept is a fairly new development, and we have not been able to fully appreciate and evaluate its benefits and negative consequences. Because of that, we have an excuse—for now. We know that, as Churchill said, "The Americans always do the right thing—after exhausting all the alternatives." This could not be any truer for the present generation. We see that things are not right. We see that pollution and social injustice—both mostly man-made—are all around us, so we are

now slowly waking up from the American dream hypnosis and are finally looking reality in the face. It will still take a while until we realize fully what's going on and decide to do the right thing, but we will—eventually. For now, however, we will just talk about it and will try all the easy alternatives first.

The major obstacle to doing the right thing today (as far as energy use and protecting the environment is concerned) is our unwillingness to sacrifice our personal well-being and comforts. This is why we burn millions of tons of coal, gas, and oil every day. We do it for the sake of the immediate comfort and instant gratification that we are so used to, although we know perfectly well that this cannot continue forever. We know well that if not tomorrow, then some day soon things will change drastically...for the worse.

We all know perfectly well that the fossils are in limited quantity, that very soon they will be no more, and that they are increasingly harming our environment and us. And yet, we close our eyes and continue to burn them in great quantities every day, non-stop, day after day, with no plans to even reduce the rate we are going at.

Making money NOW, today, is at the foundation of the capitalist enterprise, so it is the mighty buck that drives the energy and environment-related decisions of politicians and business officials. Nevertheless, there are signs of awakening and calls to do the right thing that can be distinguished now and then from the loud capitalist background noise.

We believe that Mr. Churchill was right; we only hope that it won't be too late for some of us and for the environment.

So, in this chapter we will take a look at the balance between moneymaking and the law on one hand, and energy and environment on the other. Energy prices (specifically gas, diesel, and electricity) have been for a long time, and still are, a major topic of discussion on all levels of business and domestic life. We are on the verge of a new era of energy development in the U.S., so the discussion is changing daily.

Energy Prices

Prices drive the energy business. The cheaper an energy product or service is, the more popular and successful it is. Coal, for example, has been the cheapest energy product for over a decade. Now, however, natural gas is shaping up as the new kid on the energy block, being cheaper and cleaner.

Figure 7-1 shows the relative prices of the fossil fuels during the energy crisis of 2008-2012. The fluctuating prices were caused and driven by rising crude oil prices and the related uncertainties with its production. Recently, natural gas has risen as the fossil fuel of choice in the U.S. and the world, which is once again changing the balance of the energy markets.

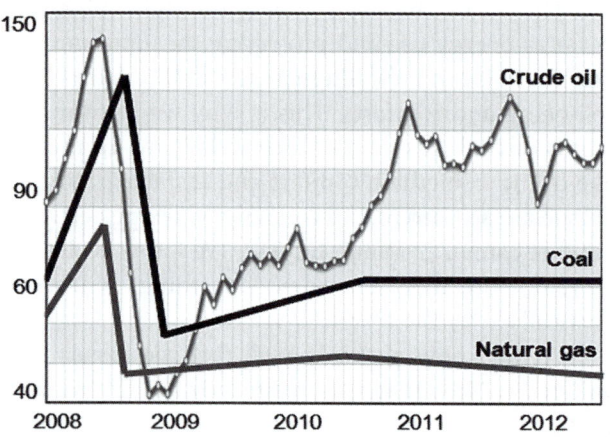

Figure 7-1. U.S. fossil fuels, comparative prices

The new hydrofracking technology opened new possibilities, so now enormous gas reserves are being exploited and a lot of new crude and natural gas is flowing around the country. This is bringing a number of changes and new trends in energy production and use. Recently the changes are reflected in coal-fired power plants' being converted to burning natural gas, and other changes are expected to utilize fully the new and abundant energy sources.

While we can clearly see the price fluctuations in Figure 7-1, the actual dollar per unit comparison is very difficult to do for a number of reasons. First, the physical properties of the different energy sources are so very different—oil is liquid, coal is solid, and natural gas is gaseous. Then, their heating values are quite different too, and to top it off the official market prices are expressed in different units: oil is given in dollars per barrel (42 gallons); the price of coal is in dollars per ton (1,000 kilograms); and natural gas in dollars per thousand cubic meters.

To get the real value in dollars of each energy source, we must know the actual application, its location, the type of process and equipment to be used as well as a number of other factors that might play a role in determining the actual and best values.

This is obviously a very complex picture from technical and economics points of view, which very few people have a good grasp of, and the complexity of which we will attempt to untangle in this text.

ENERGY ECONOMICS

When talking about economics and legal issues we must remember that there are people with titles such as economists, financial experts, lawyers, etc., whose sole (professional) goal in life is to put a value on all products and services. This includes evaluation and pricing of energy and environmental products and services.

Since we are not as qualified as most of them to discuss these subjects (just like they are not qualified to discuss the technical aspects), we will meet in the middle and will view the subjects at hand through the prism of our technical understanding of the energy-environment dilemma.

Energy generation and use is a huge and growing business, accompanied by a lot of pollution, which is creating another huge business in its wake—that of environmental protection.

Today, investments in telecommunications and information technology total $100 billion; while energy and utilities total over $300 billion. Adding environmental technologies and the related business transactions doubles the numbers, which makes these sectors a major part of the U.S. economy, with more capital expenditures than any other sector. They are also among the few with undeniable great future growth potential.

So like it or not, energy and environment are interrelated huge business. And this is how many economists and legal experts see it. As an example, just think of the BP Deep Horizon accident in the Gulf of Mexico. How many billions of dollars has BP made from its Gulf oil wells (energy business) before and after the accident, and how many billions it is still paying (environmental business)? Then think how many economists and legal experts were, and still are, involved in these business operations.

To begin with, let's clarify who the economists and legal experts are and what makes them tick. To be sure, they think and function differently than most of us "normal and average people." They see the world as a large ball made out of numbers and dollars, where a) everything has a value, and b) everything and everybody operates (supposedly) under the law.

If for some reason things go astray, as with the BP Gulf accident, then the economic and legal experts look for a way to:

1. Value each action in every step of the way to put a dollar number on it, and then

2. Figure out which of these actions were outside the law and what would that cost the violators.

Energy and environmental issues to these experts are simply market-based instruments represented by factors such as carbon taxes, cap-and-trade systems, fuel-economy standards, government subsidies, etc.; all of which have a value and price.

It is actually much better this way, because if one gets too involved in the action, emotion and sentiment might take over and fog up the uninhibited reasoning. Such fog would inevitably hurt the victims and the underprivileged, so we must thank our esteemed economists, financiers, and lawyers for their contribution in the process of clarifying, untangling and (partially) resolving the energy-environmental dilemma.

The economists and lawyers evaluate the activities in the different areas, including the political actions and regulatory policies on the basis of pragmatic consequences and in terms of the corresponding cost vs. benefit framework, although the *right vs. wrong* debate (and its ideology) is not a direct part of the economic, financial, and legal systems.

There is a joke out there that economists are against the death penalty primarily because it is too expensive and financially unjustifiable... This only confirms that to them it is much better to not get involved in the action, and only judge it for what it is from a healthy distance— unemotionally and professionally. Most lawyers have a slightly different view on the subject, which varies from person to person, but usually boils down to twisting the

law to the breaking point to protect their own (and their clients') interests.

Regardless of how imperfect economists, lawyers, and their actions might be, and how many bad examples we could find in history, economists, financial experts, lawyers, and legal experts are the gatekeepers of the capitalist system. Their major contribution to the preservation of our capitalist system functionality is their ability and drive to assigning dollar value to everything, and defending and preserving the laws of the Land.

These people have assumed the responsibility to provide clarity, as well as protect and keep everything moving in the right direction. This includes clarification (the economists) and protection (the legal experts) of the energy and environmental products and services, and the related infrastructures and markets.

In this chapter we will take a close look at the economics and finances of the different power generating products, technologies, and processes, as well as the economic effect these have on the environment and human health and well being.

Let's start with a quick look at the energy products and sources now.

Energy Generation and Use

As another clarification, in this text we use the terms *energy, energy generation, power,* and *power generation* interchangeably when describing the act of *electricity or heat generation and use.* By definition, however, energy is only contained in the energy sources (fossil fuels), which we burn to generate electric power. Because of that, it would be more appropriate to say that we are releasing the energy in the energy sources (the fossil fuels) by burning them as needed to generate electric power.

With all this said, we will continue using these terms interchangeably, except in cases where distinction is absolutely necessary.

In Figure 7-2 we compare the overall (lifetime) cost of construction and operation of power plants using different energy sources. It is obvious from the first glance that there is a big difference between the cost of coal and solar power plants, for example.

Please note that Figure 7-2 reflects the "lifetime" cost of using the respective technologies. In case of coal, for example, it includes everything from mining, transport, and burning coal, to generating, delivering, and using the electric power. Some, but not all, externalities, are also included in this estimate.

NOTE: Including *all* externalities would change the dynamics significantly in favor of the renewable technologies.

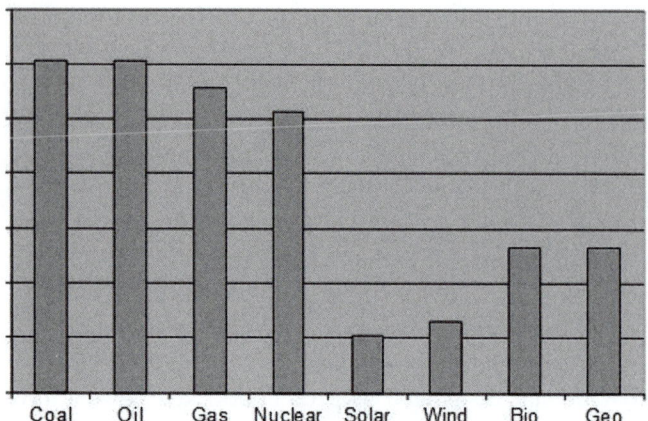

Figure 7-2. Lifetime cost expense of power generation by different technologies

Comparing the energy of the different energy sources to that of crude oil (a standard 42 gallon barrel) containing 1.7 MWh of energy, we see that 1,000 m³ natural gas contain 10.5 MWh of energy, while one ton of coal contains 6.5 MWh energy equivalent, and a kilogram of uranium contains the energy of 3,000 tons of coal. Thus, a $90 barrel of oil contains only 1/4 of the energy contained in $60 ton of coal, 1/6 of the energy contained in 1,000 cubic feet natural gas worth $40, and only a small fraction of the energy contained in one kilogram of uranium-235 worth several hundred dollars.

Mind you, the above numbers are the theoretical content of energy contained within the different energy sources, while the actual amount of electricity, or heat, produced while burning them will depend on a number of additional factors. The final heat output, or the efficiency of the heating capacity of the different fuels, depends (in addition to their own qualities and energy content) also on the type and efficiency of the equipment, the facilities and conversion processes involved.

The energy prices also reflect not only the actual energy value of the energy sources, but some other factors, such as ease and convenience of use. It is, for example, much easier, cleaner, and convenient to burn a kilogram of uranium than to transport and burn several thousand tons of coal; just to get the same amount of heat or electric energy. This is because uranium has much greater energy content than coal, which makes it much more convenient to use.

Also, on the surface it looks like solar power beats all other energy sources hands down, as far as initial construction and subsequent operation are concerned. But in reality, solar has a number of serious problems that simply disqualify it as a major power source—even

if the power generated by it were totally free.

Surprisingly, coal generates over 50% of the electricity used in the U.S. and even more around the world; even in the midst of all this talk about the harm of burning coal. Coal is not that cheap either, but it is always there and ready for use. This is its big advantage that will never go away...until all coal is gone, of course.

Coal use is actually increasing around the world, and with it more and more GHG gasses are emitted in the atmosphere daily. Why is that? Are we all blind, or stupid? Far from it! After considering all the options, analyzing all steps of the processes, and running the financial calculations, we have figured out that coal—regardless of the cost and everything else—is always there when needed, while sunshine and wind are here now, and gone in a minute or two.

We also have figured out that we have a lot of coal, while oil and other fuels are not as available, which also contributes to the reliability of coal as an energy source. Lately, however, gas has been replacing coal at a quick pace as large deposits are being explored and the price is going down, which is changing the energy dynamics in the U.S. and the world.

But this is still only the tip of the iceberg. Economists (the good ones) are knowledgeable enough to understand how the different technologies operate, and are familiar with their cradle-to-grave advantages and disadvantages.

Economists have realized that there is a large number of variables that need to be considered, so the lifetime cost, as important is it might be, is not the most important factor in their calculations. There are many other factors and variables to consider.

Let's look at what they see.

The Costs

Comparing the costs of the different power generating technologies is not easy, but we have to start somewhere, so Table 7-1 will serve this purpose for now. It shows the costs of the different technologies as far as their initial (capital) cost, the cost of operation and maintenance (O&M), and the levelized cost of energy (LCOE) are concerned.

The numbers in Table 7-1 show that there is a big difference in constructing a conventional combined cycle (CCC) gas-fired power plant vs. a solar CSP plant. This is because coal power is a well established technology, using readily available conventional equipment, while CSP is a relatively new technology, using specially designed equipment. There are a also a great number of other factors at play as reviewed in this text, and as

Table 7-1. Power generation costs (in $/MWh)

Fuel	Capital cost	O&M cost	LCOE cost
CCC gas	18	2	68
Natural gas	40	3	80
Hydro	77	4	90
Coal	65	4	100
Wind	83	10	100
Geo	77	11	100
Nuclear	90	10	115
Biomass	56	14	120
CCS coal	95	10	140
Solar PV	145	8	160
Solar CSP	210	40	250

detailed in our earlier books on the subject, see reference 18 and 19.

As a clarification:

1. While a coal power plant is much cheaper to construct than any solar plant, it uses millions of tons of coal, which makes it expensive to operate. Also, the new EPA GHG standards are impossible to meet by any coal technology, so no new coal plants will be built anytime soon in the U.S., regardless of the price.

2. There is another important factor that deserves special attention and evaluation—it is the variability of the renewable energy sources. It is important to understand that the conventional technologies (coal, gas, and oil) operate at 85-90% capacity, or basically they are available 24/7/365. At the same time, the renewables (solar and wind) operate at 20-30% capacity, or they are available only ¼-⅓ of the time.

3. It is also important to note here that:
   a. Solar is most efficient during the day, when electric power is most needed, and
   b. Combining solar and wind at some locations provides much higher capacity factor, thus their availability rate can be increased up to 75%.

If and when the above factors are managed to the full advantage of the variable power sources, and if and when energy storage becomes more efficient, wind and solar will then, and only then, become major sources of base load power in the U.S. and the world.

Presently coal and gas energy prices are the lowest (with externalities excluded) and are the standard of today's power generating industry. *Externalities* are the negative effects of coal use on the economic activity on a third party. When coal is mined, transported and burned to generate power, external costs include the impacts of air, soil and water pollution, toxic coal waste, the long-term damage to local and global ecosystems, and most importantly, their effect on human health and life.

If the total cost of externalities is included in the energy prices, however, then coal, oil and gas-fired, as well as hydro and nuclear power prices would be increased greatly—several fold in most cases.

The Initial Costs

Table 7-2 shows the relative cost to install, operate and decommission a solar power plant compared with a coal-fired one. Using coal's cost as a reference, or 1.0 unit, the relative levels of the cost and expenses for the solar technologies are derived from a breakdown of the different steps in their cradle-to-grave life cycle:

Table 7-2. Relative costs and expenses of coal vs. solar power generation

Task	Coal	Solar
Land & permits	1.0	0.6
Construction	1.0	0.2
Equipment	1.0	0.8
Installation	1.0	0.6
Operation	1.0	0.1
Maintenance	1.0	0.5
Supplies	1.0	0.1
Emissions	1.0	0.1
Solid waste	1.0	0.1
Carbon tax	1.0	-1.0
Decommission	1.0	0.2
Recycling	1.0	0.1
Waste disposal	1.0	0.2
TOTAL	13.0	2.6

It is obvious from Table 7-2 that the relative costs and expenses of coal power plants (taken as 1.0) are much higher when compared with solar power generation. This ratio, however, becomes irrelevant, and is even reversed, when some practical factors are considered, the most important of which are; subsidies, power availability, generated quantity, production variability, and reliability of the power generated by the different energy sources.

Solar and the other renewables are simply not—yet—as readily available in large quantities or as reliable as coal, oil, and natural gas power sources. Even with the glaring cost disadvantages shown in Table 7-2, coal-fired power generates the lowest price electricity, and is much more practical as a reliable power generator. There are a number of factors that make it the preferred power generator worldwide.

The important factors that make coal so important as a fuel must be well understood to get the entire picture, as follow:

1. Coal is abundant, readily available, and relatively cheap.
2. Coal has a high-energy value, which produces efficiently large quantities of heat and electricity.
3. Coal-fired power is constant, since the power plant can operate non-stop 24/7/365.
4. Coal-fired plants can also generate variable power if and when needed.

These factors do make coal the preferred power source for large-scale grid power generation, and because of that, coal is the backbone of the power generating system in the U.S. and most other countries. It provides the baseload, the one major and constant value of any power network. And since it can be produced in very high quantities, the coal-fired power prices are much lower and more stable than most other power generating technologies.

The negative externalities of coal-fired electricity generation, however, are estimated at several times the actual price of the electricity generated by coal itself. If this were put in dollar figures, coal-fired power generation would be the most expensive of all other technologies. But it is not...for now!

The Inequality

So how do we justify this inequality? Actually, we cannot, mostly because it is a fairly new subject, so we don't have a firm grasp on its intricacies. We are in fact just now starting to delve into that process, and here is where our economists, financial and legal experts, and their tools of the trade come in to help. They are feverishly trying to find the best fit for all possible scenarios and calculate the best ways to approach this huge problem that is growing and becoming more urgent by the day.

But regardless of what happens, we won't have a complete, standardized, and supported by all people (and countries) solution any time soon. Presently, a number of financial instruments, such as carbon taxes etc. are being tried as equalizers. Some of these are actually showing results in reducing the price difference among the different fuels and power generating technologies, but a number of controversies have developed around the strategies that do not allow a clear view and solution.

The energy vs. environment equation is very complex and far from being completely understood. It will not be completed anytime soon either, because some major players (China, India, Russia and other developing countries) are determined to go their own way. They will continue to build large numbers of new coal-fired power plants regardless of what the international community decides, or the consequences thereof.

They have their justifications, the major of which is that they demand the same level of development we have here in the West. And how can we argue? We have emitted most of the poisonous GHG gases that are causing the present climate changes during our 20th century furious industrial development and relentless chase of the American Dream.

And just recently other countries, some well developed like Germany, have also made a decision to ramp up their coal-fired plants. They also have a justification, mostly based on economic principles, and which totally ignores the environmental problems created by excess coal burning.

This makes it obvious that coal power will be around for a long time—regardless of the price. So, hang in there, solar and wind power; your time is coming, but it will take a while. And even then, you are still the new and weak kids on the block, so the older and proven technologies (the fossils) will dominate until the last piece of coal is mined, and the last drop of oil is pumped out of the ground.

All these abnormalities complicate the economic plans and mess up the financial calculations. Cost of fuels, transport, operating and maintenance (O&M), gas emissions, waste disposal, mines and power plants decommissioning, etc., etc. factors make the picture very complex. Some of these factors are changing with time as well, which brings further complications.

In the end, however, all these factors must be understood, sorted out, finalized, standardized and implemented globally. Then, and only then will we have achieved the ultimate balance of energy-cost-environment.

Our goal in this text is to shed as much light on the technical aspects of the complex energy-cost-environment in the open, to bring us all to a common denominator and allow us to start an intelligent discussion of all issues involved. Since economics and legal matters is the subject of this chapter, we will be looking at the energy technologies and issues at hand through their lens as well.

Let's start with the basics. In determining the economics of different energy sources, we use a number of financial formulas and techniques.

The major components of the energy economic picture are:

- Capital cost
- Operating cost
- LCOE

In more detail:

Capital Cost

The capital cost of any energy or environmental project consists of the specific construction cost (SC), the equipment cost, and the related labor tasks as needed to build the necessary infrastructure and start operation.

SC is the cost of building a plant, calculated in dollars per kW of capacity installed. Specific construction costs decreased from the beginning of the industry until about 1970, then doubled from 1970-1987.

The specific construction cost is a very important part of the overall cost system, and could easily be the subject of a separate decomposition study. Such a study would have a different scope from our intent to present the overall picture. Nevertheless, we can discuss the determinants of specific construction cost and in some cases provide numerical estimates of their impact.

The most important factors are:

1. Economies of scale
2. Add-on environmental controls
3. Thermal efficiency
4. Construction inputs in terms of prices and quantities

Economies of scale (the size of the project) usually lower the construction costs as unit capacity grows. This is due mostly to the fact that larger projects are better coordinated, and also because advanced ordering of large quantities of materials and equipment lowers the costs significantly.

Add-on environmental controls raise plant costs by an amount proportionate with the type and size of additions. These costs may decrease over time with increased engineering knowledge and technological advances, but are still a major part of plant costs.

Estimates show that sulfur scrubbers and cooling towers add about 15% and 6%, respectively, to the cost of plants. Besides raising plant costs directly by requir-

ing new equipment, there is evidence that pollution controls also raised costs indirectly by increasing the complexity of the plant, which now required greater planning and longer construction times. For example, adding new CCS emission controls will add major costs to new coal power plants and might contribute 60-80% increase of the total price tag.

Thermal efficiency can raise or lower the specific construction cost of a plant. This is because increasing the efficiency typically raises materials and construction costs, but may also increase the capacity of the plant. As the technologies mature, it may be possible to obtain a higher thermal efficiency for the same materials and building costs, which effectively reduces the final costs in the long run.

Varying price or quantity of construction materials and components during ordering affects plant costs accordingly. The quantities of materials and labor may decrease over time with the new technology developments, while changes in the national and global economies may also alter prices up or down, according to the developments at hand at the moment of ordering materials and components.

More specifically, capital costs of energy sources and power generators are considered to be those costs and expenses related to mines, drilling rigs, and power plants construction, equipment purchases and setup costs needed to put a project together and in operation.

As an example, the future of new coal-fired power plants is uncertain now, due to the increased EPA emission standards, which new coal-fired power plants cannot meet. But even if EPA lowers the standards, which is possible under a new administration, the capital costs of any coal-fired plant are extremely high, and have been best described as "soaring," "skyrocketing," and "staggering."

As recently as 2005, proposed coal-fired power plants were estimated to cost $1,500/kW, but the estimated construction costs of new coal plants have risen significantly since then. Now, the estimated costs of building new coal plants have reached $3,500 per kW, without financing costs, and are still rising. This means that a new 500 MW power plant would cost well over $2 billion after including the financing and insurance costs.

The cost increases have been driven by a worldwide competition for power plant design and construction resources, commodities, equipment and manufacturing capacity. And since there is no reason to expect that this worldwide competition will end anytime in the foreseeable future, the costs are expected to rise even more.

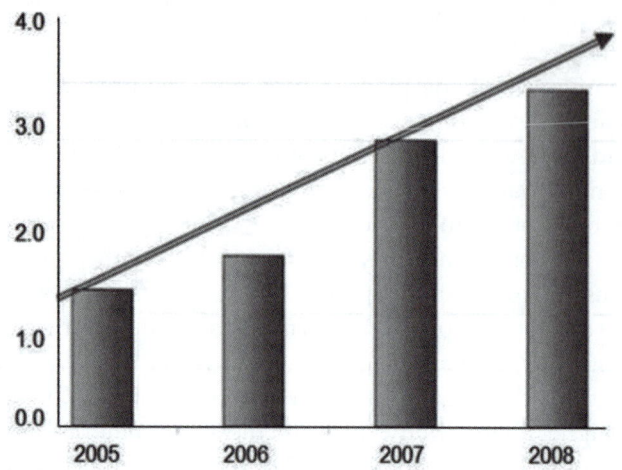

Figure 7-3. U.S. coal power plant cost increases (in $ billion)

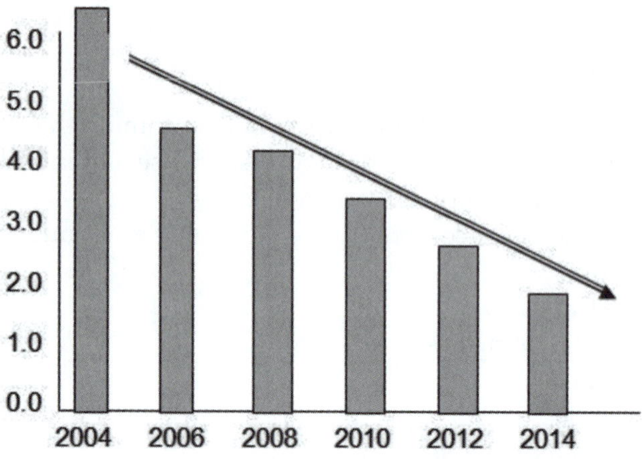

Figure 7-4. Solar power plants cost decrease (in $/Watt)

To make things worse, to meet the new EPA rules, new coal plants must be equipped with new carbon capture and sequestration (CCS) equipment, which is very expensive. To make things even close to impossible, this new CCS equipment is not even commercially available as yet. When it becomes available—most likely around 2025-2030—it will add 60-80% to the cost of building new coal-fired power plants.

It would be fair to say, then, that there will be no new coal-fired power plants built in the U.S. until then... if then. That, however, will not stop China, India and Russia from building hundreds of new coal plants on their territories, which totally defeats the purpose of the U.S. restrictions.

Many coal-fired power plants are being converted into gas-fired operation now, and many more are expected to be converted in the near future.

Nuclear plants in the U.S. are in a similar state of limbo since the 1980s, and their status is even more unclear since the 2010 Fukushima accident. There are plans for some new plants' construction, but those are mired in political and regulatory debacles and hesitation.

CS costs for wind and solar power plants, on the other hand, have been dropping significantly during the last several years.

Solar (PV) installation costs have been falling drastically lately, mostly due to millions of cheap Chinese-made PV modules flooding the world markets. Serious stagnation in the solar markets is also contributing to the low installation costs.

Due to the turbulence in the global solar markets, following the boom-bust cycle of 2007-2012, the PV equipment and installation costs might go in either direction.

Cost Breakdown

The installation, or specific construction cost (SC), of the different power generating technologies can be broken down as follow:

Nuclear power plant

Components	% of total
Equipment	17.5
Buildings	47.6
Engineering	15.9
Other costs	19.0
SC cost	**$6,100/kW installed**

Combined gas cycle power plant

Components	% of total
Gas turbine	14.0
Steam turbine	5.0
Buildings	58.0
Engineering	6.0
Other costs	17.0
SC cost	**$1,230/kW installed**

Combustion gas turbine plant

Components	% of total
Turbine	40.0
Buildings	40.0
Engineering	3.0
Other costs	17.0
SC cost	**$651/kW installed**

Pulverized coal-fired power plant

Components	% of total
Turbine	5.0
Boiler	9.0

Buildings	61.0
Engineering	8.0
Other costs	17.0

SC cost $2,890/kW installed

Carbon capture and sequestration addition

Components	% of total
CC equipment	100.0

CC cost $3,750/kW installed

NOTE: Carbon capture and sequestration equipment is to be added to the total cost of all new combined-cycle, fossil-fired power plants, as required to meet the new EPA requirements for drastically reduced GHG emissions.

Stand-alone biomass power plan

Components	% of total
Turbine	17.0
Boiler	23.0
Buildings	26.0
Engineering	15.0
Other costs	19.0

SC cost $3,830/kW installed

Geothermal power plant

Components	% of total
Well	26.0
Piping	8.0
Heat exchanger	2.0
Turbine	13.0
Buildings	26.0
Engineering	8.0
Other costs	17.0

SC cost $5,940/kW installed

NOTE: An enhanced geothermal power plant would cost an additional $4,000/kW installed.

Hydropower plant

Components	% of total
Reservoir	26.0
Tunnels	14.0
Turbines	16.0
Buildings	14.0
Engineering	7.0
Other costs	23.0

SC cost $3,500/kW installed

Ocean wave power plant

Components	% of total

Hydro-absorber	34.0
Power takeoff	28.0
Controls	2.0
Fixation	8.0
Engineering	10.0
Other costs	18.0

SC cost $9,240/kW installed

Ocean tidal power plant

Components	% of total
Hydro-absorber	15.0
Power takeoff	18.0
Controls	6.0
Fixation	27.0
Engineering	18.0
Other costs	16.0

SC cost $5,880/kW installed

Solar (PV) power plant (2012)

Components	% of total
PV modules	49.0
Structures	29.0
Inverters	8.0
BOS	7.0
Engineering	2.0
Other costs	5.0

SC cost $2,830/kW installed

Solar trough (CSP) power plant with energy storage (2012)

Components	% of total
Solar field	40.0
HTF system	9.0
Turbines	18.0
Heat storage	9.0
Engineering	8.0
Other costs	16.0

SC cost $7,060/kW installed

Solar tower (CSP) power plant with energy storage (2012)

Components	% of total
Solar field	38.0
Receiver	10.0
Tower	2.0
Turbines	14.0
Heat storage	6.0
Contingency	7.0
Engineering	8.0
Other costs	15.0

SC cost $7,040/kW installed

Wind power plant, onshore

Components	% of total
Wind turbines	68.0
Distribution	10.0
Construction	13.0
Engineering	4.0
Other costs	5.0
SC cost	**$1,980/kW installed**

Wind power plant, offshore

Components	% of total
Wind turbines	50.0
Distribution	12.0
Construction	27.0
Engineering	5.0
Other costs	6.0
SC cost	**$3,310/kW installed**

Wind power plant, floating platform

Components	% of total
Wind turbines	45.0
Distribution	13.0
Construction	30.0
Engineering	6.0
Other costs	6.0
SC cost	**$4,200/kW installed**

In summary, the estimated cost of the existing and most promising power generating technologies today is shown in Table 7-3.

Table 7-3. Initial cost of different power generating technologies (in $/kW installed)

Power plant type	$/kW
Combustion gas turbine	651
Combined gas cycle	1,230
Wind power, onshore	1,980
Solar (PV) power	2,830
Pulverized coal	2,890
Wind power, offshore	3,310
Hydropower plant	3,500
Standalone biomass	3,830
Wind power, floating	4,200
Ocean tidal power	5,880
Geothermal	5,940
Nuclear power	6,100
Coal with CC addition	6,640
Solar tower w/ES	7,040
Solar trough w/ES	7,060
Enhanced geothermal	9,010
Ocean wave power	9,240

Table 7-3 shows how different the initial costs of the different technologies are. These numbers do not reflect some peripheral, yet important factors, such as ease of obtaining permits and environmental resistance. They also do not indicate the added cost and complexities due to externalities such as accidents, negative effects on human health. and the environment.

O&M Costs

The operation and maintenance (O&M) costs of an energy system, or technology, reflect the day-to-day operations of a mine, drill rig, or a power plant. These costs are as significant as, and in some cases even more so than, the capital cost. O&M represents only about 10-15% of the total power generation costs of an average power plant, and there are other components included in the final equation that can increase the cost of O&M and the entire power production process significantly.

Operation and maintenance costs of any mine, drill rig, or power plant are actually part of a larger group, which we call production costs, and which can be separated in several sub-groups to encompass all cost elements of running the operation.

Production cost percentages of a coal, oil, or gas power plant operation are shown in Table 7-4.

Table 7-4. Production costs of a power plant

•	Fuel costs	60% of total cost
•	Day-to-day O&M	10%
•	Capital costs	10%
•	Depreciation	10%
•	Miscellaneous	10%

No doubt, fuel (thousands of tons of coal, thousands of gallons of oil, or thousands of cubic feet of gas) used on a continuous basis is the most expensive part of the operation.

As an example, the costs of a coal-fired power plant vary with a number of factors, the major of which are:

a) The cost of coal, because an average coal-fired power plant goes through 8,000-10,000 tons of coal daily, so any increase in the price affects the bottom line

b) The cost of labor and related expenses

c) The amount of power cycling (power reduction and increase cycles) the plant goes through daily. Power cycling is an unwelcome, but necessary part of power plant operations. It is needed to match the load demand, and is a major expense, because it is very expensive to shut down and restart a coal- or gas-fired power plant.

The boilers must be kept at a constant temperature to maintain efficient and cheap operation. A lot of time and fuel are needed to bring them back to normal operating temperature, after cycling (shutdown).

Power Cycling

Power cycling is a condition that is forced onto the power plant operators by the demand-supply ratio in the power grid. When the demand is low, the power plants are forced to reduce the power, or shut down altogether. Doing this is easy on the front end; just flip a switch or two and the entire plant goes down. But of course, the actual process is much longer and more complicated.

Bringing the plant to normal operating condition, however, is an even more complex and expensive procedure. In addition to the wear and tear on the equipment, and the long time needed to restart (heat) the boilers, power cycling is also dangerous, since it is associated with risks due to equipment malfunction and human errors.

The risk of personnel errors due to power cycling is multifaceted. It could create risks to human health and life, such as implosions, explosions, low boiler water level conditions, water induction into the turbines, low load instability, improper valve alignment, and other man/machine/electronics/and control interface problems during restarts.

The factors affecting cycling cost vary, but can be generalized as type of unit and its particular design, operator training and level of care, type of upgrades for cycling efficiency, overall O&M costs, system marginal energy and capacity costs, cost of new capacity, annual maintenance issues, and number and type of cycles in the past.

Excess power cycling is also hard on the equipment, which causes excess wear and tear, requiring additional repair and replacement expense. It is especially hard on the boilers, which experience a number of premature failures due to excess cycling—seals degradation, tube rubbing and damage, boiler hot spots, drum humping and bowing, down-comer to furnace subcooling, excess corrosion, expansion joint stress, and other expensive failures.

The turbines are also affected by excess cycling, which results in a number of failures such as water induction to turbine, increased thermal fatigue due to steam temperature mismatch, steam chest fatigue cracking, steam chest distortion, bolting fatigue distortion and cracking, blade and nozzle blockage, solid particle erosion, rotor stress and defects. Any of these conditions require a turbine shutdown and expensive repairs and parts replacements.

The total cost of power generation is usually significantly increased during each cycle due to excess maintenance/overhaul costs for parts and labor, forced outage rates, plant performance (efficiency) loss, overall system production cost increase, reduction in unit life expectancies, long-term capacity cost increase, and overall increase of emissions per kWh generated.

Nuclear power plants are very similar to any other power plants, but have some additional, and equally expensive, issues. Due to the overall complexity of nuclear plants' design, and the ever-present threat of nuclear accidents, we need to have a better understanding of their function.

Although cost is not the most important factor when analyzing a nuclear power plant operation, it is always taken into consideration to be compared with the competing technologies, as needed to extract best value of the particular situation.

Nuclear Power Plant O&M Specifics

Nuclear power plants are the most complex (and most dangerous) of all man-made and managed operations on Earth. They pack enormous power that can do miracles as far as power generation is concerned, but can also cause unspeakable damage and complete devastation—including loss of human life—equal to no other man-made contraption. Just ask the people at Chernobyl and Fukushima; they will tell you.

And yet, after a short hesitation after each nuclear accident, nuclear power plants are ramped up to full power, because we all need a lot of electricity to conduct our daily routines, and to run our energy-hungry commercial operations.

Following are some of the specifics of running a nuclear power plant.

Fuel Costs

This is the total annual cost associated with the "burn up" of nuclear fuel resulting from the operation of the unit. This cost is based on the amortized costs associated with the purchasing of the nuclear fuel—uranium material, its conversion, enrichment, and fabrication services, along with storage and shipment costs, and inventory (including interest) charges less any expected salvage value.

A typical 1.0 GW BWR or PWR nuclear power

plant, the approximate cost of fuel for one reload (re-placing one third of the core) is about $40 million. This amount of fuel and the resulting value is base on an 18-month refueling cycle.

The average fuel cost at a nuclear power plant in 2012 was 0.75 cents/kWh. Nuclear plants refuel every 18-24 months, which allows efficient advanced plan-ning, so they are not affected by fuel price volatility as much as coal, gas and oil power plants.

Fuel costs make up 30% of the overall production costs of nuclear power plants. At the same time, fuel costs for coal, natural gas and oil make up about 80% of the production costs.

Operations & Maintenance (O&M) Costs

The O&M annual cost of running a nuclear power plant is associated with the day-to-day operation, main-tenance, administration, and support of the on-going, non-stop activities. Here all costs related to labor, ma-terial and supplies, contractor services, licensing fees, and miscellaneous costs such as insurance, accidents, employee expenses and regulatory fees, as well as any other expenses are included.

The average non-fuel O&M cost for a nuclear pow-er plant in 2012 was 1.65 cents/kWh. This cost might in-crease significantly in a case of a minor accident. A major accident can put the entire plant out of commission... for good. Just ask the plant operators at the Fukushima nuclear plants.

Production Costs

Production costs are the combined O&M, fuel and all other costs at a power plant put together. Pro-duction costs are important in comparing the different technologies, because they reflect all steps and materials involved in the power generation. It has been estimated that nuclear power plants have achieved the lowest pro-duction costs as compared with the fossils; coal, natural gas and oil.

There are, however, several components in the production costs, which are not reflected in the general O&M expenses of the plant. Some of these are waste management and plant decommissioning costs that have a high price tag, but are hidden from view until the last moment.

Another hidden cost is that of additional safety and precautions taken on local, state, and federal levels for each nuclear plant. On top of that there is the linger-ing threat of nuclear accidents that incurs a number of additional expenses, the worst of which is an actual nuclear accident.

Waste Management Costs

In a addition to the tons of GHG emissions, all fossil-fired power plants generate liquid and solid waste, which must be stored or disposed of, one way or another. The fossil-fired power plants create on-site la-goons and piles of wasted materials, which are removed and disposed of from time to time.

Spent fuel and waste management (or lack there-of) in nuclear power plants is the Achilles heel of the nuclear industry. Presently, some of the waste fuel is transported to several outside storage facilities around the U.S. Most spent fuel, however, is stored on-site, with plans for long-term storage in limbo.

For this purpose, the nuclear power plants con-tribute regularly to the Nuclear Waste Fund, which has about $35.8 billion, $10.8 billion of which have already been spent on different (mostly failed) initiatives. The contributions amount to about 0.1 cent per kWh of elec-tricity generated at nuclear power plants plus interest. These payments to the Nuclear Waste Fund are included in the fuel costs.

However, with all this money on hand and with all the good intentions in mind, the U.S. nuclear industry has no reliable, permanent nuclear waste storage, nor are there any plans for building one. After Yucca Moun-tain was dropped, after spending billions, the nuclear waste issue hangs in thin air, where it will be for a long time to come.

Decommissioning Costs

After running without an accident for 40 years or more (or after a major accident) any power plant is shut down and decommissioned. Coal and gas power plants are simply demolished and the land is returned to its pre-construction status as much as possible.

Nuclear power plants are also demolished, but spe-cial efforts are required to decontaminate the equipment and land to return it to its previous condition. The esti-mates for this effort are about $300-600 million per plant.

Decommissioning and remediation of a nuclear plant includes efforts such as:
• Remediation of all radiological effects
• Used fuel disposal
• Overall site restoration costs

These costs average $300 million, $100-150 million and $50 million, respectively.

The estimates for the entire nuclear industry are in excess of $30-40 billion, or about $300-400 million per reactor. The catch is that the decommissioning costs are not included in the production, or any other, costs. Of the total $30-40 billion estimated to decommission all eligible nuclear plants at an average cost of $300 million, about ⅔ have already been funded.

The remaining more than $10 billion will be funded in the future, so not to worry—our nuclear future is free from additional costs from nuclear-plant decommissioning. We just have to make sure that we don't allow any Fukushima-like accidents, which could significantly alter the spreadsheet.

Levelized Cost of Energy

Levelized cost of energy (LCOE) is the price at which electricity generated from a specific source breaks even over the lifetime of the project. Keeping in mind that the break even price is a moving target, LCOE is just an economic entity—an assessment of the cost of the energy-generating system over its lifetime cycle, including capital investment, installation, O&M, fuel, and all other cost for the duration, with some externalities (but not all) included.

The inclusion of ALL externalities would require a brand new and much more complex equation. In this new equation, nuclear power, for example, would have to be taxed with billions of dollars of past, present and future damages to property, human health and death.

For now, however, LCOE is the best tool for calculating and comparing the costs of power generation by different sources.

LCOE can be defined in a single formula as:

$$LCOE = \frac{\sum_{t=1}^{n} \dfrac{I_t + M_t + F_t}{(1+r)^t}}{\sum_{t=1}^{n} \dfrac{E_t}{(1+r)^t}}$$

where

LCOE	=	Average lifetime levelized electricity generation cost
I_t	=	Investment expenditures in the year t
M_t	=	Operations and maintenance expenditures in the year t
F_t	=	Fuel expenditures in the year t
E_t	=	Electricity generation in the year t
r	=	Discount rate
n	=	Life of the system

Typically LCOE of a power generating plant is calculated over a 20-year lifetime and is given in dollars per kilowatt-hour, or megawatt-hour. The LCOE for a given energy source is highly dependent on the available (accurate) information and any (accurate) assumptions, such as financing terms and technological characteristics. For example, the assumption of the value of the capacity factor has significant impact on the calculation of LCOE.

A solar PV power plant may have a capacity factor as low as 10% depending on location, which would affect the LCOE negatively. At the same time, a nuclear plant could be in the 80-90% range. This is a big difference, and requires using reliable data and justified assumptions for achieving accurate LCOE results.

Table 7-5 reflects the conventional wisdom on the matter. Now, it is quite obvious that LCOE is a very complex variable, for which common wisdom would suggest using different measures and variables for the different power generating technologies. And yet it is applied equally and uniformly to all energy sources and situations—as different as coal in the depths of the Earth is different from the sunshine blasting at the Earth from above.

Here are some of the problems:

1. Electricity at different places and from different power generators sells at different prices, depending on the location, time of day and season, type of electricity (base-load, peak following, intermittent) and variables.

Table 7-5. LCOE of energy generation (estimates)

Plant Type	LCOE in $/kWh		
	Min.	Avg.	Max.
Conventional Coal	0.090	0.097	0.116
Advanced Coal	0.104	0.112	0.126
Advanced Coal w/CCS*	0.130	0.141	0.162
Natural Gas Fired			
Conventional CC**	0.062	0.069	0.881
Advanced CC	0.059	0.066	0.083
Advanced CC w/CCS	0.083	0.093	0.111
Combustion Turbine	0.095	0.132	0.164
Nuclear	0.108	0.113	0.120
Geothermal	0.085	0.100	0.114
Biomass	0.102	120.2	142.8
Wind, onshore	0.078	0.097	0.114
Wind, offshore	0.307	0.330	0.350
Solar, PV modules	0.122	0.157	0.246
Solar Thermal (CSP)	0.183	0.251	0.401
Hydro	0.058	0.089	0.148

*CCS - carbon capture and sequestration
**CC - combined cycle

2. LCOE cannot account for complex mechanisms, such as power plants that co-produce energy (electricity and heat) or chemicals and other products or services.

3. There are a number of discount rates, subsidies, and such that are (sometimes) not properly stated and included in the calculations. Some of these vary from time to time too, so an LCOE today is not the same as an LCOE tomorrow.

4. The units in LCOE calculations, usually currencies, are problematic since it makes it harder to compare between different countries, or between past cases. LCOE is divided by the price of electricity, so the units of normalized LCOE and the rate of return are not the same; one is dimensionless, and the other has units of time.

5. LCOE calculations hide the underlying nature of economics. In case of an LCOE value higher than the current electricity costs, the actual price of electricity would have to increase. In such a case, the calculation of the fuel costs, the labor costs, and the maintenance cost estimates will increase also, which will cause the LCOE to increase. Going back and forth like that, we get into a vicious cycle. The same is true if we add more plants, in which case the cost of electricity will keep increasing according to the amount of generated power, getting us into another vicious circle.

6. Perhaps the most significant variable, which is not even part of the LCOE calculations, is that of externalities. We continue ignoring that variable as if it does not exist, or as if it were going away tomorrow. But taking a close look at Fukushima and talking to the locals would reveal the true price of power generation. It would reveal a horrific situation that is difficult to describe in human terms, let alone put in dollar amounts or economic projections. It is a situation that is getting worse with time, and will be with us for years—perhaps centuries.

How and when would we be able to add this cost to the LCOE? Is it even possible? And yet, leaving it unaddressed is not the solution.

Alternative Cost Analysis

Nevertheless, LCOE is a valuable metric, because it allocates the costs of an energy plant across its useful life. This can give us an effective price per each unit of energy (kWh). This is like averaging the up-front costs across production over the entire life of the power plant.

LCOE gives a single metric that can be used to compare different types of systems—renewables, where the up-front capital cost is high and the "fuel" cost is near zero, to a coal power plant, where the capital cost is lower, but the fuel cost is higher. LCOE of different power generators can even be compared against the utility bills in \$/kWh.

Simplified LCOE-like Analysis

LCOE is too complex for some purposes, so instead, analyzing and comparing different levels of detail might be more useful in matching the level of complexity we are trying to accomplish.

Starting with the most basic assumptions is very useful in giving us a first glance idea of the difference between different energy sources and technologies. We can then expand by adding more detail and complexity until we get the answer that is most appropriate for our case. In more detail:

1. We start with the minimum amount of data and analysis that are needed to get simple LCOE-like numbers to compare the technologies. Here we need only to know:
    *   The system size, or the 'nameplate capacity' of the power system in question. This tells us how much power the system could produce when running at full power.
    *   The system cost, which is the cost to install the system expressed in \$/Watt.
    *   Watt-hours per watt-peak (Wh/Wp) is an extension of the nameplate (which only tells us how much power can be generated.) The Wh/Wp number gives us is how much energy we actually get out of our system over a period of time as compared to the nameplate number. For example, 100/90 means that 100 MW nameplate is producing 90 MW during a certain period of time. From this number we can also calculate the number of hours in a 24-hr cycle that the system was under full operation.
    *   Years of operation reflect the time from installation to decommissioning of our power plant. Most solar power plants are expected to operate and are warranted for 20-25 years of non-stop operation.

Using the above analysis we can get a good idea as to what to expect from a given power system, regardless of what technology is used. We just compare the system size to the system cost and then add the variable of how much power is expected for how many years.

Let's take for example two power plants—one is coal and the other a solar power plant.

Starting with the *minimum* level analysis:

Table 7-6a. Minimum analysis example

Variables	Coal	Solar
System size	100 MW	100 MW
System cost	$2/Watt	$2/Watt
Wh/Wp	100/90	100/25
Years	25	25

In this example, with everything equal, we see that the coal plant provides 90% of its maximum power, while the solar plant generates only 25% of the 100 MWp nameplate capacity, due to the variability of sunlight and nighttime powerdown state.

Also, the solar plant has more O&M expenses, further reducing profits, so if given a choice we would chose a coal plant for more reliable and profitable operation.

2. An added level of detail could include another set of assumptions and variables that are significant, but not always needed:
    *   Derating reflects the actual power generation, due to efficiency losses in the system—turbines, condensers, inverter, wire—which reduce the power by the time it enters the grid.
    *   Discount rate is the theoretical future value discounted against today's actual value of the system and the money used to pay for it. This number would be the same for all power systems, with rare exceptions.
    *   Government incentives drive the energy industries, and matter a lot. For example, there is 30% tax credit for renewable energies and dozens of state and municipal incentives, but much less for the conventional energies.

Adding these numbers to our minimum level exercise above, gives us the *medium level* analysis:

Now we see, with everything considered in 7b above, that solar benefits from a 30% tax break. This amounts to millions of dollars saved during the plant's

Table 7-6b. Added level of detail

Variables	Coal	Solar
System size	100MWp	100MWp
System cost	$2/Watt	$2/Watt
Wh/Wp	100/90	100/25
Years	25	25
Derating	**20%**	**20%**
Discount rate	**5%**	**5%**
Incentives	**5%**	**30%**

construction, so now we have to decide if the long-term inefficiency of the solar plant (expressed in dollars 25 years down the road) is more or less than a 30% savings that can be realized today.

3. To make the right choice we will need another set of variables:
    *   Degradation of parts and the system is expected to affect all components of any power plant. PV modules degrade much faster (0.5-1.0% per year), due to their physical characteristics. Coal plants degrade too, but at a much slower rate, most of which is absorbed by the maintenance cost.
    *   Operations costs include everything that is needed to run the plants for the duration—including fuel—and are different for different plants. In this case, coal plants require a lot of coal, while solar plants need no fuel.
    *   Maintenance costs include the equipment and labor needed to fix and replace power plant components. Coal power plants have a number of complex and expensive components, such as furnaces, turbines and generators, that need to be repaired and replaced periodically. Solar plants also need fixing and replacement of equipment—PV modules, inverters, wiring, etc., but at a much lower level of complexity and expense.

Adding these variables to the medium level exercise, gives us the *complete* analysis:

Now the picture gets more complicated with all these data piled up. Note that the units here are 0 to 1, which has no real value and is used only for comparative purposes.

With the degradation and operations cost awash, the maintenance costs are to be considered as a priority in this scenario, but will require full knowledge of the

Table 7-6c. All power plant details included

Variables	Coal	Solar
System size	100MWp	100MWp
System cost	$2/Watt	$2/Watt
O&M	$0.04/Watt	$0.08/Watt
Wh/Wp	100/90	100/25
Years	25	25
Derating	20%	20%
Discount rate	5%	5%
Incentives	5%	30%
Degradation	0.1	1.0
Operation cost	1.0	0.1
Maintenance	1.0	0.5

equipment and procedures involved and some guess work too.

Combining this last choice with the choices in 1 and 2 above, adds a level of complexity to the final decision. All variables need to be well understood and properly presented. Nevertheless, the number of choices is reduced to only 3-1 in each category, and although these are complex in nature, they can be resolved by simple individual evaluation and calculations, thus arriving at a plausible final choice and decision at each level of the analysis, as needed for the project design.

In conclusion, while LCOE is a valuable tool that covers the basics of power generation and its costs, it is not an ideal tool as far as comparing different technologies used under different conditions, and at different locations are concerned. Using the simplified cost calculation method above is also not perfect, but it reduces the complexity and eliminates some of the uncertainties contained in LCOE calculations.

We will, however, leave it to the economists to resolve these problems and come up with a more efficient method.

Power Plants Valuation

Power plants have an initial value based on the cost of materials and services during the design and construction phases. As the system's components get old, the value of the entire plant decreases until the end of its operation life cycle (30-40 years down the road) when the value is down to zero. Even worse, millions of dollars might need to be spent to demolish the plant's structures and decontaminate and restore the land to its original state.

There are several tools available to analyze and valuate the power plant during different stages of its operation, most of which are theoretical exercises. What is most important to owners and investors is the final number reflecting their return on investment (ROI).

ROI estimates are done during the plant's design stages and are basically the difference between all projected income and all foreseen expense for the duration, or:

$$ROI = I_T - E_T$$

where:
  I_T is the total income, and
  E_T the total expenses

The total income I_T includes:
- Total amount of sales (electric power, heat, and other products)
- Total amount of subsidies and incentives (during the construction and operation)
- Total amount of other money and goods received for the duration.

The total expense ET includes components such as:
- Total cost of design and construction,
- Total O&M expenses
- Total amount of other expenses (law suites, insurance increases, interest payments, etc.)

So far, everything seems clear and transparent, except there are items buried deep into the above formula's assumptions. Some are hidden behind complex technical operations, while some are purely financial functions and manipulations. Each of these could change the outcome and make the ROI go in whichever direction.

For example, solar modules failing at a higher rate than initially calculated, or an unforeseen increase in coal price or insurance premiums 5-10 years into the project (not included in the budget during design) could cripple the project and even force it into bankruptcy.

Here is where solid technical understanding of the technology on one hand, and thorough financial analysis must be applied. Expert technical and financial specialists working hand-in-hand during the design stages could and should foresee anything and everything to be expected to happen during the plant's lifetime. One missed or miscalculated variable could become the rock that overturned the car.

The Future Discount Rate

Power plants operate for many years, so comparing the real value of money now and at the end of the lifecycle is a convenient valuation method. It should not be used alone, but instead should be included in the comparative valuations of different technologies, locations, and timing schemes.

Discounting over time is used to value cost or benefit expected in the future, based on its present value and the present value of money. The discount rate is the annual rate at which dollar values are considered to change over time. It is a known fact that a dollar today is worth more than a dollar tomorrow after correcting for inflation.

For example, at a 10% discount rate, $1.00 today becomes $1.10 next year. Looking from the other side of the formula, $1.00 at this discount rate to be spent 10 years from now is worth only about $0.50 today.

Use of a discount rate in valuating environmental costs and benefits is a bit different and much more complicated. For longer time periods, the discount factor becomes much more dramatic. The present value of $1,000 to be received 50 years from now is only $87.20 at a 5% discount rate. And the present value of $1,000 to be received in 100 years is only $7.60 today. This would mean that, according to present value theory, it is not worth spending more than $7.60 today to avoid $1,000 worth of damages 100 years from now.

The problem is that no matter how we do it, it seems that we are basically saying that serious damages to future generations are less important than moderate costs today that might prevent these damages.

Discounting is essential if we consider the economics of, for example, taking a mortgage to buy a house or a loan to finance a business. The benefits of being able to own and live in the house starting today may well outweigh the future costs of paying interest on the mortgage over the next 20 years. Similarly, the income generated by the business investment can be compared to the annual payments on the loan.

In this case it makes sense to use the commercial discount rate, determined in current markets, to compare present benefits and future costs. Even so, can we say that a GNP gain today, or in the near future, outweighs major damage in the next generation? How should we evaluate broader environmental impacts that will continue over long periods of time?

In some cases, like that of a cost-benefit evaluation of a new coal mine project, the choice of discount rate may play a crucial role in the relative weighting of present and future costs and benefits.

There are actually three time periods of the mine cradle-to-grave lifetime that must be considered: the mine construction period, the period of active mine op-eration, and the period after the mine ceases to provide benefits.

During the construction period there are heavy costs, with little benefits (except temporary job creation and local revitalization). Once the mine starts operation, the benefits are tons of coal sold to power plants. In this period we pay two types of costs—operating and maintenance costs, and external environmental and social costs. As a matter of fact, the external costs begin long before the mine operation starts. During the 30- to 40-year expected lifetime of the mine, both actual benefits and costs are to be considered.

After the coal supply is depleted and the mine ceases operation, the environmental and social costs continue for a long time, and in some cases indefinitely.

The evaluation of net present value includes all of the above components, which must be discounted back to year 0. A number of complex formulas would show significant benefit during the 30-40 coal production years which are, however, overshadowed by the long-lasting damages to the local environment, and especially the wildlife and humans living nearby.

Economic Aspects of Power Generation and (or vs.) the Environment

Please note that environmental economics and energy are closely related, but only partially because there are many variables involved when talking about environmental issues. As a matter of fact, at a certain point the two part ways and in some instances they even contradict each other. This is where the energy and environmental experts of the legal industry get involved.

It is obvious, for example, that a coal-fired power plant operator would be penalized as the plant generates more power, which also emits more pollutants, which leads to a higher carbon tax. At the same time, a large solar power generator is increasingly rewarded as it increases power generation, which generates no pollutants at the point of use, although a lot of energy has been used and a lot of pollutants have been emitted at different times and locations during the manufacturing, transport and installation of the solar equipment.

So is it fair to consider rewarding the solar plant on the basis of what it is producing now, while totally disregarding the previous energy use and environmental damages? Is it fair to penalize the coal plant for emitting pollution today and ignoring the good it does by providing us with useful energy? If so, then why and how much? These are subjects that energy and environmental economists and legal experts are involved in.

Let's see who, when, and how this is done...

Basically, environmental economics is the study of the environment and related responses, uses and abuses evaluated through the lens of economics. Market failures, externality, or valuation methods are applied to environmental topics such as air pollution, fuel consumption, and alternative forms of energy.

One form of energy vs. environment evaluation today is based on the fact that we are taking too much from the earth (fossils), and hurting the environment in the process. Environmental economics is stepping in to find a balance between the usage and the damage on one hand, and obtaining the greatest societal benefit on the other.

The solutions and measures are often based on dollar amounts which one party has to pay for the benefit of another, but ultimately benefitting the society as a whole. The legal profession is involved in all this to ensure that the law is properly interpreted and followed, and that justice is done at the end.

Environmentalists and economists are trying (usually independently from each other) to determine the amount and value of the existing natural resources, and how to make sure that we all benefit from them without posing great risks to life on Earth.

Most natural resources used in every day life have been assigned a monetary value based on their availability, usefulness and use. The task now is to determine and establish a value on what we need to do to live comfortably and at the same time preserve the Earth for future generations.

The problem is that putting universal value on this key concept, and measuring everything with it, is almost impossible because it has a great value to some, while it is meaningless to others. To make things worse for economists, some of the natural events such as the value of clean air or water (which are taken for granted by most people) are intangible, and no one has figured out how to put a price tag on them.

This is causing a great divide in society. For example, we rely heavily on fossil fuels, which produce pollution that is harmful to all, but they are also a necessary part of life.

Different people look at this complex situation from different points of view. The environmentalists focus on the problems and insist on reducing the carbon footprint to the minimum. The pollution emitters (power plants and such) insist that this is a necessary evil, which helps the economy and should not be punished or eliminated.

The environmental economists are stuck in between, performing cost/benefit analyses to find the

middle ground and provide solutions. In some cases, they are willing to settle for mild environmental damage that brings great economic benefits, while other times they figure out that the damages outweigh the benefits. In all cases, there is someone or some group that disagrees, and this is where the legal experts step in to resolve the differences via court proceedings, arbitration, and counseling methods.

Environmental economists usually try to combine the opposing sides in the energy field, or find an acceptable compromise to work toward economic and societal advancement, keeping in mind the effect of all activities on the environment.

Figure 7-5 shows the daily cycle of economic activities and the related environmental impact, where the positive effects are represented by the input of solar energy and natural resources into the system. Pollution and waste heat generation represent the negative effects of the economic cycle.

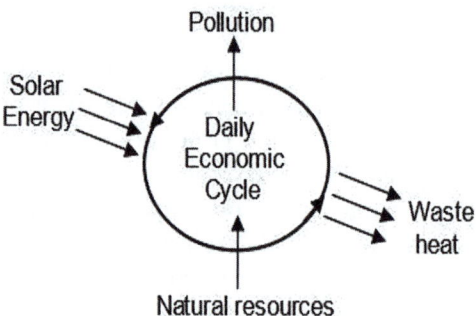

Figure 7-5. The energy-environment cycle

The lasting negative effects in this scenario are:
a) Gradual depletion of natural resources, which is only indirectly impacting us now, but which will become a major factor soon unless we find a way to control the complete depletion of fossil fuels.
b) Increase in pollution, which damages the natural environment and all life forms in it, including human life.
c) Increase in global temperatures, which is causing cataclysmic changes in some parts of the world.

The *environment* has a several-fold function:
1. It is a source of raw materials and services for human use, which can be interrupted by:
    a) Depletion of natural resources as humans use them quicker than they can be regenerated
    b) Increase of pollution affecting human activities to the point of extreme events and disasters

If any of the above points were reached, human activities would have to change drastically or cease altogether.

2. The second function is that of a life-giver and supporter. Without our environment there would be no life. Period. And then it supports life by providing and controlling the proper type, quality and quantity of critical life elements—air, light, water, and food to all living organisms, including humans. This function is the most important factor in all discussions of environmental issues. It is also taken for granted sometimes and ignored other times.

3. The environment also functions as a sink—a self-contained garbage disposal and storage bin in one—by absorbing and storing the natural and man-made poisons and waste byproducts in the air, soil and water. The sink and storage bin combination has its limits and stops normal function when the types and amount of pollution exceed certain levels in a given time period, or when the wastes exceed certain level of toxicity.

At such a point, the most critical components of the environment—soil, water, and air on which we depend daily—could become damaged, polluted, or poisoned. This is a critical point, which we are fast approaching. These issues must be resolved soon, before it is too late.

Modern environmental economics takes a broader perspective in framing environmental questions by incorporating laws derived from the natural sciences. A fundamental principle of environmental economics is that human economic activity is limited by the environment's carrying capacity and tolerance to change.

The *carrying capacity of the environment* is defined as the level of human and animal consumption of natural (non-renewable) resources, which the available natural resource base can sustain without complete depletion on one hand, and the capacity of the environment to absorb and store waste products on the other.

Environmental economists emphasize the importance of the different energy resources and their use, and especially the fossil fuels as related to the current economic systems. They also focus the pollution the energy sources generate as an unavoidable factor in all energy-related calculations.

The rapid growth of economic production during the 20th century required enormous energy inputs, and global economic systems will make even greater energy demands in the 21st century and beyond, thus energy availability and environmental implications of energy use are central issues for environmental economics.

For the human population, the issue is getting even more complex by the day. The issue of food supplies is certainly relevant as the world population grows toward a projected 10 billion by 2050. Ecological economists also point to energy supplies, scarce natural resources, and cumulative environmental damage as conditions and constraints on economic growth.

The problem is that the standard economic theories and practices are not aware of, or simply ignore, many of the key energy and environment related factors, and also that major structural changes in the nature of economic activity are required to adapt to the upcoming energy and environmental limits.

The environmental economists are focusing their attention on providing better understanding and valuation of the complex energy-environment dilemma of the 21st century, which we are trying to present in its utmost detail in this text.

So what is the proper way of accounting environmental costs?

Ecosystem Valuation

How do we put a value on the environment we live in and depend on? We must try, because if we don't things might get even worse. Valuation can be a useful tool that aids in evaluating different options to managing natural resources.

Our ecological resources and services are varied in their composition, so it is often difficult to examine them on the same level. If we, however, assign a value to each environmental resource or service (as hard as this might be) it can then be compared to any other similar resource or service.

The Basics

Value is generally defined as the amount of alternate goods a person is willing to give up to get one "additional unit" of the goods in question. An individual's preference for certain goods may either be stated or revealed. In the case of stated preferences, the amount of money a person is willing to pay for certain goods determines their value, because that money could otherwise be used to purchase other things.

Value may also be determined by simply ranking the alternatives according to the amount of benefit each produces. Revealed preferences can be measured by examining a person's behavior when it is not possible to use market pricing.

There are typically two ways to assign value to environmental resources and services—use and non-use. There are also approaches to measuring environmental benefits based on these defined values. When environmental resources or services are being used, it is easier to observe the price consumers are willing to pay for the conservation or preservation of those resources.

Market cost pricing is used when there are tangible products to measure, such as the number of fish caught in a lake.

Replacement cost can be calculated based on any expenses incurred to reverse environmental damage.

Hedonic pricing will measure the effect that negative environmental qualities have on the price of related market goods.

Non-use value is evaluated by employing contingent valuation through the use of surveys that attempt to assess an individual's willingness to pay for a resource that they do not consume.

A *cost-benefit analysis* requires the quantification of possible impacts of a proposed project. The impacts could be physical or monetary, but both must be calculated and included since a financial analysis that requires assigning dollar values to every resource evaluated is also performed. The process of environmental resource or service valuation provides a way to compare alternative proposals, but it is not without problems.

All valuation techniques encompass a great deal of uncertainty—flaws can exist in the methods of assigning value accurately due to a wide number of variables and it is difficult to compartmentalize and measure environmental and natural resources or services within an ecosystem that functions as an interconnected web.

Ecosystem Valuation

Ecosystem valuation is a method of assigning a monetary or other value to environmental resources, including their production, use of, or services provided by those resources. Environmental resources and services are particularly hard to quantify due to their intangible benefits and multiple value options.

It is almost impossible to attach a specific value to some of the experiences we have in nature, such as viewing a beautiful sunset. What is the value of the sunset itself, and how do we value the pleasure we get from viewing it? How do we valuate a forest that provides timber, fresh air, animal shelter and even beneficial environmental services by preventing hill slides and downstream flooding?

Resources that can be used for multiple purposes, such as a forest, must be valued in all aspects of their usefulness. The timber quantity has a certain value, while the prevention of hill slides onto neighborhood homes has a totally different value. Both can be expressed in dollars, but the quantity would vary according to the usefulness of the forest in each case.

The quantity of the different resource must also be taken into consideration because value can change depending how much of a resource is available. A small power plant generates a little smoke and the environment might not be harmful, at least not for a long time. A huge power plant, however, could destroy the local environment and hurt the locals in a very short time.

The small power plant's emissions are not valued very highly because the environment can be easily recover, even if it is damaged. However, if the pollution from the large emissions generator continues until the air becomes toxic to its surroundings, preserving clean air by preventing additional pollution is going to be increasingly valued.

In summary, ecosystem valuation is a complex process by which economists and regulators attempt to assign a value to natural resources, their production, use and the related services as provided by those resources. This is not easy, but it is the only way for policymakers to make decisions based on specific comparisons, typically monetary, rather than some other arbitrary basis. In recent years, the U.S. government has placed increasing emphasis on cost-effective environmental laws and projects in an attempt to establish a common measure by which to evaluate the alternatives.

Valuation Methods

Direct or indirect values of energy and environment do not provide precise dollar amounts from losses of properties and services, but we must agree that the assignment of "some" number is better than no number at all.

The assignment of "some" number, however, is still a complex and controversial undertaking—a lousy job, but somebody has to do it, and our tireless environmental economists are best suited to that effort. So what would they do? Where would they start?

Fortunately, they have an arsenal of tools and weapons that can be successfully used for this purpose. Successfully is highly subjective in this case, because no matter what number they assign, it will be questioned and disputed by one or another group. It's a thankless job, to be sure, so we do appreciate their efforts.

Following are some of the tools used for valuation of hard-to-value energy and environmental targets.

Cost-benefit Analysis and Valuation

Valuating the energy sector and the related social benefits and environmental effects is a difficult but needed endeavor. Different groups see it from different points of view, which makes the effort even harder. However, some see the environment as a priceless gift from above, and reducing it to monetary values is absolutely unacceptable. The other extreme insists on putting values on all ecological functions before the economic system gives them a zero value.

No matter what, we all agree that it is extremely difficult, and in some cases impossible, to conduct proper cost-benefit analysis. This is due to lack of sufficient reliable information, and also because certain elements, such as social, moral, and spiritual values are impossible to present as numbers of dollars.

Nevertheless, when properly used, cost-benefit analysis is a useful tool, while always keeping in mind that we are barely scratching the surface of the immense area of environmental responsibility and accountability. We should also realize that the methods are not set in stone and will slowly undergo gradual modifications and optimization, before becoming standards.

Presently, there a number of approaches that require polluters to pay dollar amounts corresponding to the amount of pollution emitted. These approaches are well received by some groups and rejected by others. Only time will tell who is right, who is wrong, and which approach will win the battle of universal acceptance.

Contingent valuation is basically a survey to determine how much people would be willing to pay to preserve their community and its environmental functions. The resulting estimate is their willingness to pay (WTP) that can be included in the *cost-benefit analysis* (CBA). The only problem here is that this method is almost always challenged by a group of people on one side of the issues at hand.

The hypothetical nature of the assumptions, when no actual money is involved often leads to unrealistic (very high or very low) valuations and unrealistic assumptions. Since respondents have limited knowledge of the actual science and technology of energy generation or environmental function, they tend to under- or over-estimate the real problems.

The *estimated willingness to accept* (WTA) is another approach, quite different from the more recognized *willingness* to pay (WTP) method. For example, when asked how much is an adequate compensation for the loss of picnicking, hiking, and fishing activities, most peoples' dollar estimates are much higher than the WTP

estimates for the same items. This leads to critics of the usefulness of the contingent valuation approach.

The disparity between WTP and WTA valuation is a problem, which has particular importance in the economic valuation of environmental issues. Unlike a more ordinary economic transaction such as the loss of land use, pricing the environmental effects involves serious ethical and philosophical considerations, in addition to the usual socio-economic considerations. This usually leads to the overwhelming question if the true value of environmental preservation can really be expressed in dollar terms.

For example, the public's WTP as needed to avoid the Valdez spill's wildlife damages was estimated at $2.8 billion, or about 75% of total cleanup and compensation costs. In other cases it was much lower, which means that society's willingness to pay to avoid environmental damages is significantly lower than the actual cleanup and compensation expenses.

It's not a precise science, and yet, the estimates, the valuation, and the related cleanup and restoration must be done, because this is the only way for our capitalist system to function properly. In fact, money helps a lot, as in the numerous cases of restoration of abandoned mining sites, cleaning water supplies, etc. Without that money, the mining area would be lost forever and the water supply would make many more people ill.

So we must thank environmental economists for making the effort to put a money value on things that we have a hard time putting a value on, but which we still need to survive.

Demand-side Methods

This valuation method is closely related to the way actual market decisions are made by valuing environmental products and services as they relate to the value of marketed goods and their availability. The price of a farm located next to a controlled conservation area is usually much higher than that of a comparable piece of land situated next to a dusty and congested road leading to a dirty and stinky oil rig.

In many cases, however, there is a bias in demand valuations—unless actual money is to change hands. Surveyed people often say one thing, when in reality they are not willing to put up real money in support. The inflated estimate is an example of strategic bias, where people attempt to bias the survey upward by stating an amount that exceeds the actual willingness to pay.

It has been determined that the disparity between WTP and WTA is usually found in non-marketed goods such as land preservation, where willingness to accept

(WTA) exceeds willingness to pay (WTP) by a factor of seven. In other words, people are often willing to place value on an environmental product or service that is seven times higher than what they are actually willing to pay for it.

Supply-side Methods

In contrast, the valuation on the supply side of the market is based on production function and engineering cost methods. Here more precise science plays a significant role since the goal is to evaluate the situation and determine the cost of restoring or preserving the environment via established products and services.

Building a waste-ash storage pond close to a coal mine would affect the forest and its pollution-absorption capabilities. If the forest is preserved, and building and operating the storage pond is unnecessary, thus avoided cost can provide an estimate of the value of pollution control services provided by the forest. We can easily make technical estimates of the facility and calculate the associated costs, which will give us the approximate value of the forest.

If an oil spill destroys a wetland, the responsible will be required to pay to restore it to its prior state, or to create a comparable wetland nearby. The cost estimates generated in such cases are typically significantly higher than those based solely on demand-side studies.

A combination of demand- and supply-side methods should be used to determine the best dollar value for environmental products and services. The usefulness of these valuations depends on our basic concept of "value," which consists of the purely economic value, and the broader concept of ecological value, which is very difficult to define.

In all cases value refers to what is important to humans, and is defined by our willingness to pay, or to provide substitutes. Some key environmental issues, such as climate change, are not possible to define in such terms. No matter how much money we pay, we cannot reverse global warming, because we don't even know what would work, nor do we have enough money to pay for the effort, even if we knew what to do—this is how big this problem is.

The potential and the limits of economic valuation of environmental costs and benefits is in question. There is a long list of environmental issues that cannot be valued, and some of them fall through the gaps. This makes the environmental economics models incomplete.

But when, how, and who would come up with the exact valuation of a human limb, or life? How do we value future events that may or may not happen, even

if we knew their magnitude and severity? How can we value the costs of tomorrow, if we are having problems valuing the costs of today? There are many questions in need of answers, so we thank our dedicated economists for working on all these issues.

Human Life Valuation

Just talking about valuating human life sounds like an inhumane and cruel way to deal with the most sacred thing on Earth. Human life is not for sale and that there is no price that can justify hurting, or taking it away. So how do economists value it, and why? Isn't anything sacred left? The environmental cost-benefit analyses force these questions and demand answers.

It might be easy for most of us to turn a blind eye on the subject, but ask a miner's wife whose husband has been killed in a mining accident. She will tell you that funeral expenses have to be paid on time, and that rent, utilities, and food bills are due every month in a household where income has been slashed to zero.

Some valuation is needed here to right at least some of the wrong. How much would she accept as a recompense for her husband's life? How much would the mining company be willing to pay? And how and who determines the actual amount?

On a broader scale, tighter control of coal-fired plants' smoke stacks may reduce the amount of cancer-causing chemicals and save some of the locals. The tighter controls, however, inevitably cause increased production costs. So the benefits are reduced cancer cases to the locals, who end up paying higher electricity rates. And the question again is, how and who will determine if the tighter controls are needed, and how to determine the rate increase if so needed.

The evaluation in this case requires reliable estimates of the reduction in cancer cases, in which case we would multiply that number by the cost of hospital care in each case to obtain a measure of total medical costs.

But if the evidence indicates that several deaths per year could be avoided, then how do we balance the lives saved with the increased production costs? A simple economic estimate of what an individual contributes in terms of production of goods and services to society might be one way (albeit unfair). This approach assigns a high dollar amount to the life of a CEO whose salary is in the millions, versus that of an hourly worker who is struggling to pay the rent.

Another approach is to consider the amount of life insurance and safety precautions taken in some cases, which will derive an estimated value in the range of several million dollars for a human life. No matter how we look at it, however, we cannot possibly capture the full value of human life. Instead what we are talking about is a compromise, which indicates an arbitrary value of what economists call a "statistical life." It is based on a demonstrated willingness and ability to pay a certain amount of money to avoid risks to life.

Again, that is not a perfect way to do things, but the option is to set the value of life at zero, which is wrong, or make it infinite, which is impossible. Taking the middle road, economists are deriving different solutions for different cases, which help the miner's wife to pay the bills and force the coal plants to enforce safety procedures and install pollution control devices.

The Environmental Externalities

The externality concept is a fairly new development, as far as the general public is concerned, but has been gaining popularity recently. It is basically a cost or benefit incurred by someone other than the buyer or seller (a third party), and the effect of it is not accounted for in the price the buyer paid initially. Additional costs paid later on (insurance, medical bills, etc.) might pay for part of the externalities eventually.

A positive externality provides a net benefit, such as improving the economic and social life in the affected areas. A negative externality results in a cost to a person or the society in general. Groundwater contaminated by hydrofracking is a great example of a negative externality since the locals are deeply affected and suffer from the effects. The cost of damaged property and health issues is not included in the price the buyers paid.

A major problem with coal is that its full costs are not reflected in its market price. Looking at the greater picture, we see that, although coal prices are low today, in the long run we are paying a much higher cost. The impacts on human and environmental health not reflected in the price of coal are the "externalities." Most of us benefit from the seemingly cheap electricity, but we eventually end up paying for the externalities in the form of medical bills, environmental cleanups, special taxes, etc.

A full cost accounting for the life cycle of coal, taking these externalities into account, shows the externalities and their effects as:

- Particulates and gasses causing air pollution
- Climate change from greenhouse gas emissions
- Toxic liquids and solid wastes polluting soil and water
- Increased illness and mortality due to mining pollution

- Loss of biodiversity worldwide
- Mudslide damage from mountaintop removal
- Surface and infrastructure damages from mine blasting
- Acid rain damage resulting from coal combustion byproducts
- Decreased property values
- Government coal, gas, and oil subsidies
- Cost to taxpayers of environmental monitoring and cleanup

The majority of the externality costs come from reduction in air quality, contribution to climate change, accidents, and other impacts to public health. The total cost of these externalities ranges from approximately 15 to 25 cents per kilowatt-hour (kWh) of electricity generated. This is a conservative estimate, because there are other externalities that are hard to impossible to account for—such as the added stress and discomfort to the lives of the locals confronted by the externalities.

An important fact here is that most of these external factors do not apply to most non-fossil fuel energy sources. On the other hand, some of the renewables have their own externalities, which are a new development that have not been fully evaluated and accounted for. Some of these are the noise and flickering that causes health problems to wind turbine neighbors, and the land grabbing in Africa due to the expansion of the use of biofuels.

Some solar PV modules, for example, contain significant amounts of toxic materials, and since there are millions upon millions of them spread all over the world's deserts, we can expect a large toxicity issue in the next few decades. These and many other externalities are unaccounted for, but they should not be ignored. Addressing them soon and putting them into perspective would be the right thing to do.

Quantifying Externalities

A closer look at the energy-environment externalities dilemma, we see that if, for example, a hydrofracking well pollutes a town's water supply, the cost of water treatment provides an estimate of real environmental damage that can be expressed in dollar figures. This, however, does not include less tangible factors such as damage to a local lake or river, or wildlife ecosystems.

The diagnosed health problems resulting from the local air or water contamination and the related medical expenses provide additional monetary damage estimates, which cannot account for some externalities like excess pain or the aesthetic damage to the locale. Contaminated water and dirty air are unpleasant, regardless of the health effects or costs, but it is not possible to put an exact dollar value on that aspect of life.

All the complexities presented by the above mentioned externalities are not easily converted into monetary rewards, but we need to assign some value to them and the environmental and health damage they cause. If we don't assign any value, then the society and market will automatically assign a 0 (zero) value of zero, simply because it is the easiest thing to do, and because none of these issues is directly reflected in quantifiable consumer products and services.

Different groups of specialists (environmental, energy producers, energy users, economists, legal experts) will describe and suggest various ways to put a monetary value on the externalities. They will all agree, however that no matter how many methods can be used, it all starts with obtaining the proper information. Such information is the foundation onto which the house of truth would be built. Because no house can stand for too long on a poor foundation, we must make sure that the information we are working with is precise, accurate, and sufficient.

Once that is done, we need to execute *cost-benefit analysis* (CBA), which in this case involves integration of economics into environmental facts and decisions through the use of economic techniques as needed to properly appraise the related projects, actions, policies, and their effects.

Actually CBA is used successfully to sort and analyze the information for proper decision and policy making. If a town's water supply is contaminated by fracking activities, the water assets become scarce, and the locals' attitude towards the drilling will change. They will start expressing their discontent and preferences for further action. These changes in people's attitude and behavior can be measured and expressed in monetary value, according to what is needed to restore the environmental quality and prevent further damage.

CBA is just a tool that is as useful as the user's skill allows, and since this is a new tool, the user has to be careful. There are always gaps in the information, which have to be filled with not-so-perfect data and values. Although it is better to input some imaginary values than to leave gaps unfilled, the input data must be based on some scientific principles. Data also have to be reasonable and open to discussion and changes.

In the power generation sector, the environmental goods (and damages) must be given the same weight as all other goods and services (power generation and use). We must always remember that when excess resources are allocated to protection of the environment, the resources spent on production of other goods and services will become more expensive, or their number or quality will be reduced.

The principle that economic efficiency is fundamental criterion for public investment and policy-making is fundamental in the use of CBA for economic analysis and decision-making tools. Although energy-related CDA methods are based on the principle that the benefits from the use of the scarce resources are maximized net of the costs of using them, we must also acknowledge that economic efficiency should not be the sole criterion in decision-making.

Distributional and competitive considerations can be rational justifications for deviation from the principles of economic efficiency as an absolute criterion for maximizing the welfare of society. Big obstacles here are the gaps that still exist in reliable environmental information and the accompanying uncertainty about prices and valuation estimates that can make the result of CBA tentative, to say the least. This is so because there are no markets, or ways to measure some environmental effects, so economists use alternative methods of valuation. This is a complicated process and often adds to the uncertainty and reduces the reliability of the outcome.

Nevertheless, since something must be done, we rationalize that this imperfect "something" is better than doing nothing. So we must embrace the short-term discomfort, while searching for perfection, for the benefit of having a standardized analysis and valuation system in the long run.

There are, at least on paper, three possible methods for reducing or eliminating environmental externalities:

- The existence of externalities is a justification for government intervention, usually in a form of new taxes
- The use of incentives to reduce environmental externalities— incentives allow flexibility in responding to problems rather than forcing a singular approach on all individuals
- Eliminating obstacles that prevent the market from functioning freely leads on its own to an optimal level of environmental protection and resource use

Goods and Use Values

There are various established ways to estimate values of goods and services, but there are no established ways to determine environmental benefits and damages, let alone assign a monetary value. So we use the established estimation and valuation techniques, at times in a modified form, for that purpose.

Use value is one of the types of valuation in use presently. In the case of hydrofracking, we see two types of use value:

a) Direct use value involves factors such as losses of producing farmland due to contamination. Here we see a direct relationship between the loss of the land and loss of economic value. The farmers simply will not get the crops they usually get, which will result in a monetary loss. This loss can be determined easily and accurately by comparing with the previous years' income. If the average past income is A, and the income from the contaminated land is B, then the loss is determined by simply subtracting B from A. The resulting dollar number is a fair account of the loss that can be put into dollar amounts. This amount, plus additional penalties, would be a fair remuneration for the farmers for losing use of their farmland.

b) Indirect use value is, for example, the loss (contamination) of a community park or lake that has no economic value per se. In this case, the loss cannot be represented as direct monetary loss, simply because there was no past income to show. In such case, groups use different criteria to measure and value the loss. The locals will remind us that they used to go to the park for relaxation, and swim and fish in the lake—the use of which is now lost due to the contamination. The environmentalists will emphasize the effect of the loss on the entire local flora and fauna, but in all cases a dollar number equal to the loss would be some random value assigned by an environmental economist.

c) Non-use value is, for example, the loss (extermination) of local species of birds that have no economic value. Here again, we will see several different groups stepping in, insisting on recompense for the loss. Although the birds have not contributed to any economic growth, they are part of the environment; therefore their loss will be felt. The locals might claim that the birds have helped in crop pollination, and their loss means crop reduction. The environmentalists would expand the loss to a loss on national and international level, but in both cases no actual dollar value can be assigned to the loss. So, here again we look up to the environmental economists to assign some dollar number. Any number is still better than no number at all.

In Figure 7-6 we have depicted the environment and the use values within it. No doubt, this is not a perfect way of evaluating the environment and the effects of human activities in it. Even if we get to a perfect and standardized way of doing these evaluations, there will still be gaps left in between.

The environment is too large and complex to be covered completely by our human ways of valuing the most invaluable thing we have. Nevertheless, we need to do something, so here we are…!

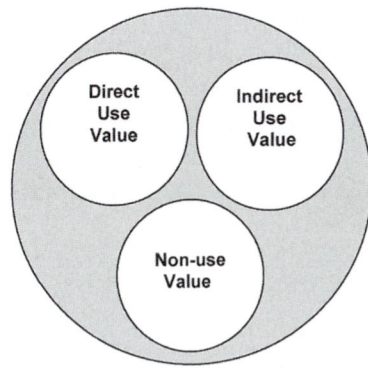

Figure 7-6. The use-value method of valuation

Carbon Tax

A carbon tax is basically a charge for the CO_2 gas emitted from the power station. It is a form of carbon pricing. Since carbon is present in every fossil fuel—coal, petroleum, and natural gas—and when they are burned some of it is released as carbon dioxide (CO_2). At the same time, the renewable technologies—solar, wind, and hydropower—do not emit much CO_2.

Figure 7-7. A coal-fired power plant

CO_2 is causing some global climate effects, so a tax on these emissions can be levied by taxing the carbon content of fossil fuels at any point in the product cycle of the fuel.

If properly designed and implemented, the carbon tax could be a potentially cost-effective means of reducing greenhouse gas emissions in the long run. At the very least, they help to remind us that the emitters of greenhouse gases must pay for the social costs of their actions, at least until we find a permanent solution. Carbon tax is a regressive tax, because it directly or indirectly affects mostly the low-income groups. The power generators pay the carbon tax by increasing their rates across the customer base, so the low-income class is disproportionately penalized.

A carbon tax is a tax on a transaction, rather than a direct tax that taxes income. A carbon tax also sets a direct price for carbon dioxide emissions, and usually results in higher power rates. In economic theory, pollution is considered a negative externality, a negative effect on a party that is not directly involved in a transaction, which results in a market failure.

Prices of fossil fuels are expected to continue increasing as more countries industrialize and add to the demand on fuel supplies. In addition to creating incentives for energy conservation, a carbon tax would put renewable energy sources such as wind, solar and geothermal on a more competitive footing, stimulating their growth.

Social Cost of Carbon

The *social cost of carbon* is a new concept, which defines the marginal cost of emitting one extra ton of carbon dioxide at any point in time. To calculate the social cost, the atmospheric residence time of carbon dioxide needs to be estimated. The impact of this ton of CO_2 on climate change must be then calculated and converted to the equivalent impact during the exact time this ton of carbon dioxide was emitted.

This time shift requires calculating the discount rate, which determines the weight placed on impacts occurring at different times and different locations. Under perfect conditions, the social carbon tax should be equal to the social cost of carbon and to the value of emission permits.

In reality, however, we live in an imperfect world, so the social carbon cost estimates are not complete. Presently, the amount of CO_2 pollution is measured by the actual weight (mass) of the gas emissions, or the actual weight of the carbon dioxide molecules in a ton of carbon dioxide. Alternatively, the pollution's weight can be measured by adding up only the weight of the carbon atoms in the pollution, ignoring the oxygen atoms. This unit is called a ton of carbon and is equivalent to four tons of CO_2.

A fully encompassing carbon tax is one that compensates for the social cost of carbon by fuel source, which can be expressed as the carbon dioxide production of the fuel source per unit mass or volume, multiplied by the social cost of carbon.

For example, gasoline, diesel and jet fuels produce around 20 lbs of CO_2 per gallon of burned fuel. An estimate for the total carbon tax would be in the order of $0.11-0.13 per gallon for each of these fuels.

Natural gas used for power generation would be penalized about $0.007 per each kWh electricity produced, while the carbon tax for coal burned at coal-fired power plants would be about $0.012—almost twice the tax amount charged for natural gas use. That, combined with the lower production cost of natural gas, and the higher efficiency of gas-fired power plants, explains the recent increase in its use for power generation in the U.S.

Estimates of the social cost of carbon are highly uncertain. There are some estimates of $40-80 per ton of carbon, which is actually more than the total cost of coal in most countries. The wide range here is due the uncertainties in the science of climate change and control. The climate sensitivity, the different choices of discount rate, different valuations of economic and non-economic impacts, treatment of equity, and how potential catastrophic impacts being some of the key uncertainties.

In all cases, the true value of the social cost of carbon is expected to increase over time as the population and use of fossils are increasing rapidly. The rate of that increase will be proportional to those increases.

Carbon Leakage

This is also a new concept, introduced recently to describe how the emissions regulation in one country (or geographic location) affects the emissions in other countries (or geographic location) that are not subject to the same regulation, but are yet affected. Carbon leakage could result in the increase in carbon dioxide emissions in one country as a result of an emissions reduction by a second country with a stricter climate policy.

Carbon leakage occurs when the emissions policy of one country raises local emission costs, then a neighboring country with a more relaxed policy may have a trading advantage. If demand for these goods remains the same, production may move offshore to the cheaper country with lower standards, and the total global emissions will not be reduced.

At the same time, if environmental policies in one country add a premium to certain fuels or commodities, then the demand may decline and their price may fall. Countries that do not place a premium on those items may then take up the demand and use the same supply, thus negating any environmental benefit.

The type and amount of leakage effects, therefore, could be negative by reducing overall emissions, or positive by increasing overall emissions. Also, short-term leakage effects are different from, and must be compared with, long-term leakage effects. An emission policy that sets carbon taxes in developed countries might lead to leakage of emissions into developing countries.

Border Adjustments, Tariffs and Bans

A number of policies have been suggested to address concerns over competitive losses due to one country introducing a carbon tax, while another does not. Such policies have been considered in an attempt to encourage some countries to introduce carbon taxes. These policies include border tax adjustments, trade tariffs and trade bans.

The border tax adjustments are basically additional taxes on imports from nations without a carbon tax. In extreme cases, these actions could result in trade bans or tariffs applied to countries refusing to implement carbon taxes.

Energy and carbon taxes have been implemented in some countries in response to commitments under the United Nations framework convention on climate change. In most cases, however, where an energy or carbon tax is implemented, the tax is implemented in combination with various forms of exemptions.

End of an ITC Era

The federal investment tax credit (ITC) has been the engine of the energy sector during the last several years, and attractive lure for investors in renewable projects. But like all good things, the ITC will be phased out in 2016, or maybe even sooner.

This represents 30% tax credit that has provided incentive for record-breaking investment in solar projects in the U.S. takes six years to receive fully. It kicks in as soon as the project has been completed and each of the six following years, the investor can take 15% of the full amount of the tax credit, provided that project is completed by December 31, 2016.

OK, so far so good. But come 2016 things will change drastically, especially for the solar companies and projects. How will then the U.S. solar firms manage without it? Will the industry drop all of a sudden in a credit abyss? Some are closing their eyes, hoping that the problem will go away. That the ITC will be extended…but that seems quite unlikely. So we basically have a four-year deadline to drive the costs down, to optimize the business structures, and to stabilize the other key policies, which are so important to solar's growth.

We cannot hope for solar to be in infancy forever, and come January 2017, it will have to stand up on its own, or risk to be put back in the closet and considered irrelevant…again! It is when the solar energy industry will have to justify the promises of cost reduction and its closeness to 'grid parity' will be put to the ultimate test." There is a chance that the ITC will be extended after 2016, albeit at a lower rate than the current 30%. Still, even a lower ITC would serve as a strong financial incentive when paired with a continued decline in PV module costs. But prices are this low because of the Chinese invasion of the PV markets. We cannot rely on that unsustainable phenomena to support the solar industry in the long run. Or can we?

Other factors outside of the PV cost curve will also have a great effect on competitiveness, namely: the price of natural gas, movements in state and federal regulations regarding carbon and renewable energy, changes to net metering regulations, and interest rate movements—all that on top of the ITC fluctuations, or in the absence of.

The only good thing that might come out of that is that by reducing or eliminating the tax credit, it becomes less important to the economics of a solar project, so that the risks associated with tax benefit recapture go down, or disappear all together. That alone could result in new pools of project capital entering the market to invest in solar projects. And other programs will most likely kick in, just like the clean path program, which is currently providing capital, credit and expertise for about a gigawatt of solar projects.

In all cases, replacing the benefits of a tax credit worth 30% will require some 30% improvements, or somehow replacement of the direct benefits lost by losing the ITC? That would be quite a tall order for any industry, let alone one in its commercial infancy. Some insiders think that replacing the ITC will amount to making a surprisingly small change in the finances of a project, provided that some positive change in performance (like reduced degradation or efficiency) is achieved. Over time, those slightly increased performance and efficiency would make up for the 30% upfront.

There is also a well-founded expectation that financing costs will come down with time. The solar industry is very young, so until now the finance industry has been loaning money based on an assumption of the risks associated with a nascent industry. But as more projects come online and begin performing as expected, perceived risk will decline, and bank rates will come down. It works all the time, and there is a good chance that it will work in the case of the solar industry too.

As more U.S. banks realize that solar projects with PPAs are very low risk projects, the interest for solar projects will decline. It's basically like buying a long-term CD that in addition to making money is producing energy. People would appreciate the benefits of buying something that provides such diversified and sizeable benefits. That change of attitude will also, over time, contribute to the stabilization of the solar industry in its effort to compete with the major energy generators.

Now let's take a look at the environmental side of things and see the role of economics and the legal system in the different cases:

Subsidies

There are a number of negative impacts of coal mining and burning, all of which have an economic cost. These range from the jobs lost by fishermen and farmers downstream of a coal mine, the health care costs of the people sickened by coal-fired power plant pollution, and to the cost of cleaning up spills of toxic coal waste.

Federal subsidies for fossil fuel and renewable energy production totaled approximately $72 billion for fossil fuels and $29 billion for renewable energy from 2002-2008. These include: foregone tax revenues due to special tax provisions; under-collection of royalty payments; and direct spending on research and development and other programs. Fossil fuel subsidies consisted primarily of tax breaks, such as the foreign tax credit and the credit for production of nonconventional fuels.

Direct government subsidies to nuclear energy companies and projects equaled $115 billion by 1999, plus $145 billion in indirect subsidies, such as R&D and other activities not directly related to the power generation cycle.

The U.S. federal energy sector subsidies affected approximately 75 programs/tax breaks, in the following major direct and indirect energy subsidies categories:

- Defending Persian Gulf oil shipping lanes
- Subsidized water infrastructure for coal and oil industry use
- Federal spending on energy research and development
- Accelerated depreciation of energy-related capital assets
- Under-accrual for reclamation and remediation at coalmines and oil and gas wells
- The ethanol exemption from the excise fuel tax

The IEA's world energy outlook 2008 annual report estimated that energy subsidies to oil, gas, and coal totaled $557 billion annually. The IEA estimated also that eliminating those subsidies would reduce global GHG emissions over 10% by 2050. The subsidies, however, are not going away, and they are on the increase in some countries, like China and India.

At the same period of time, the European energy subsidies totaled EUR 29 billion, mostly for coal production. These included: direct grants; preferential tax treatments, regulations and loans; trade restrictions; infrastructure investments; and uncompensated security and environmental costs.

The Canadian government subsidies for the oil and gas industry totaled CA$1.5 billion, or about CA$50 per capita. These analyses include: federal grants, tax benefits (such as the resource allowance and the accelerated capital cost allowance for oil sands), and government expenditures that directly support oil, gas and oil sands industries.

An U.N. study concluded that energy subsidies are widespread but vary depending on definitions, analysis methodologies, fuel type and location. It concludes that producer subsidies, usually in the form of direct payments or support for research and development, are most common in OECD countries, while most subsidies in developing and transition countries go to consumers—usually through price controls that hold end-user prices below the full supply costs. Fossil fuel and nuclear industries receive the majority of such subsidies, although OECD countries are increasing their support for renewable and alternative energy technologies.

"Renewable energy sector shouldn't receive government support, and if it can't stand on its own in the free market, it doesn't deserve to exist" is what we hear from the experts. But wait…as can be seen in Figure 7-8, fossil fuel's historical subsidies are like skyscrapers next to the renewables that look like a demolished building.

The lion's share of fossils in the subsidies jackpot is remarkable and does not include (nor even take into account) the massive indirect subsidies the oil and gas industry receive in unchecked and unaccounted for externalities, some of which wreak havoc on our health, our quality of life, and the potential viability of the human species after climate change is done with us.

For a long time oil and gas have taken the lion's share of subsidies allocated to the energy sector, and the financial support hasn't gone away yet. In fact, in many ways, it still trumps the fragile support for renewables, and is increasing in some aspects of the U.S. and global energy sectors.

For example, the oil and gas industries are benefiting tremendously from master limited partnerships

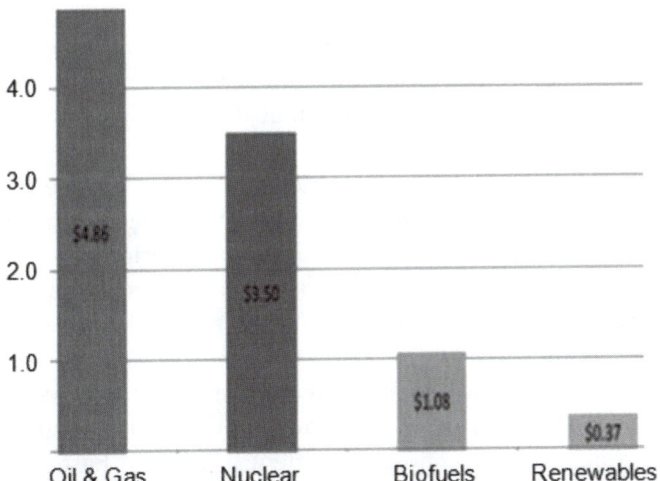

Figure 7-8. U.S. subsidies of different energy sources (in $ billion/year)

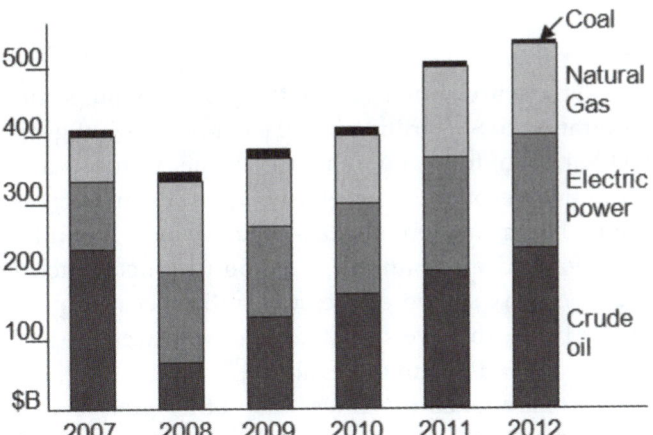

Figure 7-9. Global energy subsidies (in $ billion)

(MLPs) and real estate investment trusts (REITs), which represent two low-capital-cost ways of financing infrastructure that are now rapidly expanding in the financial services world.

None of these is available to renewable energy investors, and both cost less than the tax equity funds derived from solar investment tax credit (ITC) and wind's production tax credit (PTC). The U.S. government, for example, heavily subsidized natural gas production and use, starting with the combustion turbine that was developed for aircraft and later reapplied to the gas-fired energy generation sector.

There is a talk in the U.S. Congress about including the renewables in the MLP and REIT financing schemes, but talk is cheap, and the implementation of these acts into reality might take a while.

Global Pre-tax Energy Subsidies

Consumer subsidies include two components: a pre-tax subsidy (if the price paid by firms and households is below supply and distribution costs) and a tax subsidy (if taxes are below their efficient level). Box one describes the calculation of these two components. Most economies impose consumption taxes to raise revenue to help finance public expenditures. Efficient taxation requires that all consumption, including that of energy products, be subject to this taxation. The efficient taxation of energy further requires corrective taxes to capture negative environmental and other externalities due to energy use (such as global warming and local pollution).

The pre-tax subsidy estimates capture both those that are explicitly recorded in the budget and those that are implicit and off-budget. The evolution of energy subsidies closely mimics that of international energy prices. Although subsidies declined with the collapse of international energy prices, they have started to escalate since 2009. In 2011, global pre-tax subsidies reached $480 billion (0.7% of global GDP or 2% of total government revenues).

Petroleum and electricity subsidies accounted for about 44% and 31% of the total respectively, with most of the remainder coming from natural gas. Coal subsidies are relatively small at $6.5 billion.

Energy subsidies comprise both consumer and producer subsidies. Consumer subsidies arise when the prices paid by consumers, including both firms (intermediate consumption) and households (final consumption), are below a benchmark price, while producer subsidies arise when prices received by suppliers are above this benchmark.

Where an energy product is internationally traded, the benchmark price for calculating subsidies is based on the international price. Where the product is mostly non-traded, such as electricity, the appropriate benchmark price is the cost-recovery price for the domestic producer, including a normal return to capital and distribution costs. That approach to measuring subsidies is often referred to as the price-gap approach, and is used widely in analyses by other international agencies.

For example, the average pre-tax subsidies of some oil exporting countries in 2011 were as follows:

Table 7-7. Pre-tax subsidies for oil exporters

MENA	8.5% of GDP
Sub-Africa	5.5% of GDP
CIS	4.5% of GDP
Asia	4.0% of GDP
Latin America	2.0% of GDP

At a closer look the subsidies in Table 7-7 can be detailed as follows:

- The Middle East and North Africa region accounted for about 50% of global energy subsidies. Energy subsidies totaled over 85% of regional GDP or 22% of total government revenues, with one-half reflecting petroleum product subsidies. The regional average masks significant variation across countries. Of the 20 countries in the region, 12 have energy subsidies of 5% of GDP or more. Subsidies are high in this region for both oil- exporters and importers.

- Countries in emerging and developing Asia were responsible for over 20% of global energy subsidies. They amounted to nearly 1% of regional GDP or 4% of total government revenues, with petroleum products and electricity accounting for nearly 90% of subsidies. Energy subsidies exceeded 3% of GDP in four countries (Bangladesh, Brunei, Indonesia, and Pakistan).

- Central and eastern Europe and CIS accounted for about 15% of global energy subsidies, including the highest share (at nearly 36%) of global natural gas subsidies. Energy subsidies amounted to over 1.5% of regional GDP or 4.5% of total government revenues, with natural gas and electricity accounting for about 95%. They exceeded 5% of GDP in four countries (Kyrgyz Republic, Turkmenistan, Ukraine, and Uzbekistan).

- Latin America and the Caribbean made up over 7.5% of global energy subsidies (approximately 0.5% of regional GDP or 2% of total government revenues), with petroleum subsidies accounting for nearly 65%. Energy subsidies exceeded 5% of GDP in two countries (Ecuador and Venezuela).

- Sub-Saharan Africa accounted for about 4% of global energy subsidies. Energy subsidies amounted to 1.5% of regional GDP or 5.5% of total government revenues, with electricity subsidies accounting for over 70%. Total subsidies exceeded 4% of GDP in three countries (Mozambique, Zambia, and Zimbabwe).

- The only advanced economy where energy subsidies were a non-negligible share of GDP was Taiwan at 0.3% of GDP spent on electricity development.

In most economies, there are elements of both producer and consumer subsidies, although in practice it may be difficult to separate the two. The advantage of the price gap approach is that it also helps capture consumer subsidies that are implicit, such as those provided by oil-exporting countries that supply petroleum products to their populations at prices below those prevailing in international markets. The price gap approach does not capture producer subsidies that arise when energy suppliers are inefficient and make losses at benchmark prices.

Pre-tax subsidies are pervasive and impose significant fiscal costs in most developing and emerging regions. They are most prominent in Middle East and North Africa, especially among oil exporters. Given that energy consumption can be expected to rise as incomes grow, the size of subsidies could climb in regions where they currently account for a small share of the global total, such as sub-Saharan Africa.

Post-tax Energy Subsidies

These are much larger than pre-tax subsidies, amounting to $1.9 trillion in 2011—about 2.5% of global GDP or 8% of total government revenue. Virtually all of the world's economies provide energy subsidies of some kind when measured on a tax-inclusive basis, including 34 advanced economies. For some products, such as coal, post-tax subsidies are substantial because prices are far below the levels needed to address negative environmental and health externalities. The fact that energy products are taxed much less than other products also contributes to the high level of post-tax subsidies.

In MENA, for example, applying the same rate of VAT or sales taxes to energy products as other goods and services would generate 0.75% of GDP. Of the global total, pre-tax subsidies account for about one-quarter, and tax subsidies account for about three-quarters. The advanced economies account for about 40% of the global total. The top three subsidizers across the world, in absolute terms, are the United States ($502 billion), China ($279 billion), and Russia ($116 billion).

The Effect of Subsidies

Subsidies have a number of effects, some positive, and some negative.

The major effects of subsidies are as follows:

- Subsidies can discourage investment in the energy sector. Low and subsidized prices for energy can result in lower profits or outright losses for producers, making it difficult for SOEs to expand energy production and unattractive for the private sector to invest both in the short and long run. The result is severe energy shortages that hamper economic activity.

- Subsidies can crowd out growth-enhancing public spending. Some countries spend more on energy subsidies than on public health and education. Reallocating some of the resources freed by subsidy reform to more productive public spending could help boost growth over the long run.

- Subsidies diminish the competitiveness of the private sector over the longer term. Although in the short-run subsidy reform will raise energy prices and increase production costs, over the longer term there will be a reallocation of resources to activities that are less energy and capital intensive and more efficient (Box 4), helping spur the growth of employment.

- Subsidies create incentives for smuggling. If domestic prices are substantially lower than those in neighboring countries, there are strong incentives to smuggle products to higher-priced destinations. Illegal trade increases the budgetary cost for the subsidizing country while limiting the ability of the country receiving smuggled items to tax domestic consumption of energy. Fuel smuggling is a widespread problem in many regions around the world including in North America, North Africa, and the Middle East, parts of Asia, and Africa. For example, Canadians buy cheap fuel in the United States, Algerian fuel is smuggled into Tunisia, Yemeni oil is smuggled into Djibouti, and Nigerian fuel is smuggled into many West African countries (Heggie and Vickers, 1998).[10]

- Energy subsidies exacerbate the difficulties of both oil importers and exporters in dealing with the volatility of international energy prices. The balance of payments of many energy-importing countries is vulnerable to international price increases (IMF, 2008b). The adverse impact can be mitigated by passing through international price increases and by providing greater incentives for improving energy efficiency and lowering energy consumption (Dudine and others, 2006).

- Removing energy subsidies helps prolong the availability of non-renewable energy resources over the

long-term and strengthens incentives for research and development in energy-saving and alternative technologies. Subsidy reform will crowd-in private investment, including in the energy sector, and benefit growth over the longer term.

- The volatility of subsidies also complicates budget management. For oil exporters, energy subsidies accentuate macroeconomic volatility by increasing subsidies during periods of international price increases. Allowing domestic prices to rise with international prices can help cool off domestic demand during commodity booms and build up fiscal buffers for use during periods of declining prices. To offset concerns about the transmission of high international price volatility to domestic prices, some smoothing of price increases can be considered.

- The negative externalities from energy subsidies are substantial. Subsidies cause over-consumption of petroleum products, coal, and natural gas, as well as reduce incentives for investment in energy efficiency and renewable energy. That over-consumption in turn aggravates global warming and worsens local pollution. The high levels of vehicle traffic that are encouraged by subsidized fuels also have negative externalities in the form of traffic congestion and higher rates of accidents and road damage. The subsidization of electricity can also have indirect effects on global warming and pollution, but that will depend on the composition of energy sources for electricity generation. The subsidization of diesel promotes the overuse of irrigation pumps, resulting in excessive cultivation of water-intensive crops and depletion of groundwater.

- The over-consumption of energy products due to subsidies can also have effects on global energy demand and prices. The multilateral removal of pre-tax fuel subsidies in non-OECD countries, under a gradual phasing-out, would reduce world prices for crude oil, natural gas, and coal by 8%, 13%, and 1% respectively in 2050 relative to the no-change baseline. The reduction would be substantially larger if prices were raised to levels that eliminated subsidies on a post-tax basis. These spillover effects suggest that non-subsidizers would share the gains from subsidy reform, as well as extending the availability of scarce natural resources.

• Energy subsidies are highly inequitable because they mostly benefit upper-income groups. Energy subsidies benefit households both through lower prices for energy used for cooking, heating, lighting and personal transport, but also through lower prices for other goods and services that use energy as an input. On average, the richest 20% of households in low- and middle-income countries capture six times more in total fuel product subsidies (43%) than the poorest 20% of households (7%). The distributional effects of subsidies vary markedly by product, with gasoline being the most regressive (i.e., subsidy benefits increase as income increases) and kerosene being progressive. Subsidies to natural gas and electricity have also been found to be badly targeted, with the poorest 20% of households receiving 10% of natural gas subsidies and 9% of electricity subsidies.

Negative Subsidies Effects

Some of the simplest, and quite significant economic costs of coal come in the form of subsidies and tax breaks which are not reflected in the market price of coal. Also not include here are the estimated $4.8 billion in coal-related subsidies in the 2009 stimulus package. Coal mining and combustion projects require major investments, which are accompanied by a number of uncertainties and risks, the costs of which are often passed on to taxpayers via infrastructure subsidies and loan guarantees.

One example of extreme waste of money is the Healy clean coal plant (HCCP), which has cost the state of Alaska taxpayers nearly $300 million since the mid 1990s. And the plant has yet to produce any power in return. There are estimates that coal pays only 5% of its market value to the state of Alaska, even though the nominal rates are much higher.

A recent study in Kentucky determined that the government spends $115 million more on subsidies for the coal industry than it receives in taxes or other related benefits. In addition, the taxpayers also pay the costs of cleaning up environmental disasters caused by the coal industry. Cleanup of the recent coal ash spill in Tennessee is estimated to cost up to $1 billion, not including the costs of pending litigations. And since the cleanup at that site has been taken over by the EPA under the superfund law, most of that cost will be borne by the U.S. taxpayer, and very few would even know the total price they will end up paying.

The health impacts of coal pollution also have enormous economic costs, due to increasing health care costs and lost productivity. An Ontario government study es-

timated these costs as billions of dollars within Ontario alone. A similar recent study in West Virginia found that the cost associated with premature death due to coal mining was five times greater than all measurable economic benefits from the mining. How do you put a dollar number on these statistics?

Another growing issue is the fact that other major industries depend on the ecosystems coal mining destroys. Industries such as recreational fishing, commercial fishing, and tourism that are particularly relevant in a number of the affected states.

In Alaska, almost 55,000 direct jobs on full time equivalent basis are closely linked to the health of Alaska's ecosystems. These jobs make up more than a quarter of Alaskan employment base and produce almost $2.6 billion of income for Alaska workers. These 55,000 ecosystem-dependent jobs are threatened by oil production and transport, and mining operations, such as the Chuitna Coal strip mine, which could generate about 350 jobs. So how do we justify that project—and many similar such all over the U.S.—if the job-to-job ratio, and/or the economic benefits cannot justify the environmental damage to be done.

Negative effects on the economy, such as coal and oil projects present with their emissions, usually lead to worse health in the population. This in turn has a great impact on health care costs, compounding the negative economic impact. On the other hand, coal, no doubt, provides some benefits to society. It provides cheap electricity, which is a boon to the economy, therefore health is improved, and health care costs are lowered. While this additional health effect should indeed be considered, it should be applied after the economic impacts discussed above are considered and calculated.

Once the costs of pollution, global warming, and habitat destruction are added to the benefits of cheap electricity, the economic impact of coal may no longer be positive—especially in the most affected locations and among the most affected people.

We, however, must be fair and keep all these facts in perspective when discussing and analyzing the different pros and cons of fossil use and their effects.

Hi-tech Subsidies

Starting with the billions of dollars spent on nuclear research since the 1940s, we see the U.S. government spending enormous amount of money in the energy sector. In addition to nuclear, the coal, oil, and gas sectors have been beneficiaries of generous government subsidies, which are flowing unrestricted to this day.

While most of these subsidies produced some good

results, some of the money was wasted. Solyndra comes to mind as the most advertised example of hastily spent taxpayers money by bureaucrats who have no idea what energy does. But even worse is the advice given these politicians by scientists (at DOE, NREL and Sandia) who should know better.

How much of the subsidies go to waste, as in the now famous Solyndra case, is unknown. Most of the waste does not get publicized, and although there were many Solyndras since 2008, we just don't hear about them.

Many government projects, developed with good intentions become victim of poor planning, design, execution, and most often than not fall victim to a combination of these factors.

One such case is the multi-billion dollar NIF facility at the Lawrence Livermore National Laboratories, which hoped to demonstrate the next phase of nuclear power generation by producing a fusion reaction. After spending billions of dollars during 15 years of non-stop work by thousands of scientists and engineers, the goal was not achieved.

Case Study: NIF

This is a much less advertised example of a lot of money spent on not-so-productive projects. The national ignition facility (NIF) project. NIF is the world largest laser facility; the home of the world's most powerful inertial confinement fusion (ICF) research device, which is physically located at the campus of the Lawrence Livermore National Laboratory in Livermore, California. It is also the home of enormous spending hi-tech venture that very few people even know about.

The ICF device was originally intended to initiate a fusion reaction in a small target and eventually develop a way to bring it to a commercial-scale nuclear fusion power generation. The idea is to use a bundle of powerful lasers shooting at a small target, or to heat and compress a small amount of hydrogen fuel, to the point where nuclear fusion reactions would (hopefully) take place.

In addition to achieving fusion ignition with high energy gain, NIF is also supposed to support nuclear weapon maintenance and design by R&D of behavior of matter in nuclear weapons.

The NIF project was started in 1997, and scheduled for completion in 2002 at a total cost of $2.1 billion. A number of problems slowed progress, so not much was done until 2000, and after a number of additional glitches the NIF project was completed five years behind schedule at four times the initial budget estimates.

The dedication ceremony took place in May 2009,

and the first large-scale laser target experiments were performed in June 2009. The first series of "integrated ignition experiments," which tested the laser's power were completed in October 2010.

The initial calculation show that the 192-piece laser bundle is supposed to produce 1.2 MJ of energy, which would be enough to initiate a fusion reaction. These calculations now appear to be wrong, and almost twice that much energy would be needed to initiate fusion in a pea-size target. NIF's lasers are theoretically capable of delivering about 1.85 MJ, but there were technical problems when 1.4 MJ level was reached and serious overheating was feared to occur at higher levels.

But even if the full 1.8 MJ power were delivered, it might not be enough for igniting the reaction, although at that moment this would be actually about 1,000 times more power than the entire U.S. uses at the same time. After a number of additional trials, the project was officially terminated in September 2012 without even getting close to achieving fusion ignition.

Figure 7-10. NIF's laser bay during construction

The question now is: how much energy would be needed to initiate a reaction in a commercial reactor? We have to guess that if 2.0 MJ are needed to ignite a pea-size target, several times that much energy would be needed for a larger one. Can we even generate that much energy? And if so, then how much would the required equipment cost?

We fear we won't get proper answers any time soon. The NIF fusion ignition project is on the back burner, and the NIF lasers are now being used for materials research. NIF has been converted into the largest and most powerful research lab in the world.

It is now an expensive (nearly $10 billion) toy, which failed its initial mission, and, since it is not needed much for its other missions, it will be used by a number of scientists and engineers to play with. We are sure that much more funding will be approved sunk into NIF before its mission is officially declared "completed" and the facility is converted into a museum. Then, and only then, could the taxpayers hope for some return on their money.

NOTE: The author had a chance to work as a contractor during the construction of the NIF project in the late 2000s, and although the performance of most of the NIF scientists, engineers, and technicians was exemplary, the execution of the different tasks was a typical government work. Hesitation in decision-making, cost overruns, and endless (often pointless) paperwork dominated the daily routines.

One conclusion made at the time by many participants was that if the NIF project were managed and funded by private companies, it would've been finished at a record time and well within budget. This, however, will never be proven now that NIF has shown us that fusion is not in the cards—at least for now.

In our opinion, however, if private companies and investors were involved in NIF, it would've never happened. This is simply because even basic science tells us that even if NIF would've succeeded in initiating a small scale fusion reaction, the state-of-the-art today, including existing materials and equipment, would not allow commercial-scale fusion power generation. The awesome temperatures needed are beyond the capabilities of any known material or system to contain and put into practical use.

This case also confirms the fact that government money can, and is, used in very high-risk projects, which have no theoretical, let alone practical, solution to begin with. NIF is only one of these cases.

Speaking of waste, let's take a look at some of the most common energy wastes and pollution around us.

Fuel Waste

We live in time and age of wastes. From disposable everything to leisurely Sunday drive (averaging 50-100 miles), Americans are wasting fuel on a daily basis.

Some examples:

Car Travel

Let's take a look at this symbol of modern civilization, the reflection of the American dream: the large 300-horse power, 3,000-pound iron horse with one or two people riding in it.

How much power does a regular car-user consume?

$$Ed = \frac{Dd}{Df} \times Ef$$

Where:
  Ed   is energy used per day
  Dd   is distance travelled per day
  Df   is distance travelled per gallon of gasoline
  Ef   is the energy contained in unit of gasoline (about 30 kWh/gallon).

$$Ed = \frac{90 \text{ miles/day}}{20 \text{ miles/gallon}} \times 30 \text{ kWh}$$

$$= 135 \text{ kWh/day}$$

So our leisurely drive wasted about 4.5 gallons of gasoline, which could have generated 135 kWh (135,000 watt/hour) of electric power. This is more than what most people in the underdeveloped countries in this world use in a month—if fuel or electricity were available to begin with.

Add to this the energy costs and pollution emitted during the production of gasoline. There are estimates that making each unit of petrol requires an input of 1.4 units of crude oil and other primary fuels. So, during our leisurely Sunday drive, we have actually wasted 1.4 times more fuel of the global supply than what we've burned. Our total waste is then about 6.3 gallons, which could generate about 190 kWh of electricity.

Plane Travel

We all fly from place to place; some more than others. Let's assume one intercontinental flight per person in the developed world. How much energy does that use and what are the energy and pollution costs?

Let's take as an example a Boeing 747-400 that carries 65,000 gallons of fuel and 416 passengers. A round trip to Europe and back would be approximately 10,000 miles, during which flight about 2 x 60,000 gallons, or 120,000 gallons are used to propel the plane. Jet fuel has calorific value is about 38 kWh per gallon, so the energy cost of one full-distance round-trip on this plane would be equal to:

120,000 gallons x 38 kWh = 4.5 GWh

This is as much power as an average nuclear plant generates in 2-3 hours of full power operation.

If divided among all passengers, then we get:

$$\frac{120,000 \text{ gallons}}{416 \text{ passengers}} \times 38 \text{ kWh/gallon} = 10,900 \text{ kWh/person}$$

This means that just one international trip per year for each person on that plane has an energy equivalent greater than leaving 1.0 kW electric stove on; full blast non-stop, 24 hours a day, all year long.

Add to this the energy-cost and pollution emitted during the production of the jet fuel. There are estimates that making each unit of petrol requires an input of 1.4 units of crude oil and other primary fuels. So during our international flight, we actually wasted 1.4 times more fuel of the global supply than what the plane burned. Our total energy waste is then the grand total of about 15,000 kWh resulting from just one trip.

Now consider the GHG gasses emitted during the production of jet fuel, its transport to the airport and the related evaporation and additional emissions and other pollution from storage tanks, refueling trucks, and so forth.

Add to this the energy of manufacturing the plane, airport maintenance, and the pollution emitted during the entire port-to-port process. This will most likely double our energy cost and pollution estimates of our flight.

NOTE: Flying creates other greenhouse gases in addition to CO_2, such as water, ozone, and indirect GHGs, such as nitrous oxides. We can figure the actual carbon footprint from our flight (in tons of CO_2-equivalent) by getting the actual CO_2 emissions and multiplying them by two or three. When you multiply this amount by the thousands of flights every day around the world; the numbers you get will amaze you.

Cruise Ships

But the most unjustifiable waste of our precious energy resources is that of the cruise ship industry. Most adults in the developing countries take at least one 3-5 day cruise during their lifetimes. That amounts to millions of people boarding the ships to nowhere, circling the world's oceans aimlessly, and burning millions of gallons of fossil fuels.

The worldwide cruise industry is estimated at $29.34 billion for 2011, which is a 9.5% increase over the previous years. It is the industry with the fastest growth in the last decades, and with that its energy and environmental impacts grow too. Host communities usually bear some of the economic, environmental and socio-cultural effects deriving from ships and passengers' presence and related activities.

While there are some positive results from these activities, the negative environmental externalities are significant: large amounts of waste, erosion and degradation of vegetation; and degradation of historical and geological sites caused mainly by physical and visual impacts.

Further negative socio-cultural externalities can be produced too, since cruise passengers tend to "invade" the destination just for a few hours in a single day. This effect is particularly visible in small locations where cruisers compete for roads with the residents.

But the most obvious and constant negative result is waste of millions of gallons of diesel every year for an activity that is counter-productive and absolutely unjustifiable.

A large cruise ship, such as Royal Caribbean, burns close to 3,000 gallons of diesel per hour under full sail. Assuming a 50% lower speed, we get 2,000-gallons-per-hour that are needed to keep the ship moving and power supplied throughout its dozen of stories with high platforms and thousands of apartments, venues, and halls. A three-day cruise will then burn over 140,000 gallons, while a seven-day cruise will waste another 335,000 gallons.

With 3,000 people on board, we come up with a grand total of 112 gallons wasted by each person on a trip to nowhere—a trip that we make just because we can, and because everybody does it.

Multiplying these 112 gallons wasted by millions of people aimlessly cruising the oceans every year, we come up with a staggering number of millions of gallons of precious crude oil wasted. This number alone will tell us that we are quickly cutting the branch we are sitting on for no good reason at all.

Case Study: Cruise to Nowhere

Recently this author decided to check out the cruising phenomena personally by taking a weeklong cruise from San Diego, California, to Tijuana, Mexico. The actual air-distance port-to-port is 15 miles, with one stop at Catalina Island, which added 170 miles to the round trip.

So, we departed on a huge cruise ship with 3,000 passengers on board on a week's voyage to cover all 185 miles on our itinerary. The luxurious ship was travelling at a medium speed most of the time, which was decreased only when nearing a port.

There were five days at sea, or 120 hours sailing (with about 10 hrs. stop total at Catalina and Tijuana) at an average speed of about 20 MPH. At the end, the ship was under sail for about 110 hrs, which at 20 MPH would mean that we actually travelled 2,200 miles from start to end of the voyage. This also means that to travel the 2,200 miles between point A, B, and C only 85 miles apart, the great ship was going up and down the ocean expanse to pass the time.

At one occasion a passenger asked the captain where the ship is and how fast it was going. The captain's answer was, "I don't know exactly, because the ship is on autopilot." So it seemed that arriving at port A, B, or C was not the point. Instead, filling the time in between the ports was the goal.

So it seems that 3,000 souls on board spent a week on a ship headed to nowhere, on which nobody—even the captain—knew exactly where it was, or how fast it was going. All this was done at the expense of over 300,000 gallons of diesel, which emitted that much more pollution into the air and the ocean.

The cruise ship industry is here to stay, and millions of people will be wandering aimlessly the world's oceans until the last drop of diesel has been burned. Perhaps at that point, the great cruise ships will be equipped with electric engines, or more likely retrofitted to burn natural gas. In any case, the cruise industry is here to stay, and its significant positive and negative impacts must be included in all the energy and environmental calculations and estimates.

Emissions vs. Income

There are a number of theories on the relation between pollution and economic development. One of the most famous is the so-called Kuznets curve (see Figure 7-11), which represents the theory that economic inequality increases as a country develops its industrial complex.

As seen in the Figure 7-11, the SO_2 gas emissions rise as the income of the population increases. After a while, however, the inequality begins to decrease as the economy matures. During this economic development, the developing countries generate large amounts of pol-

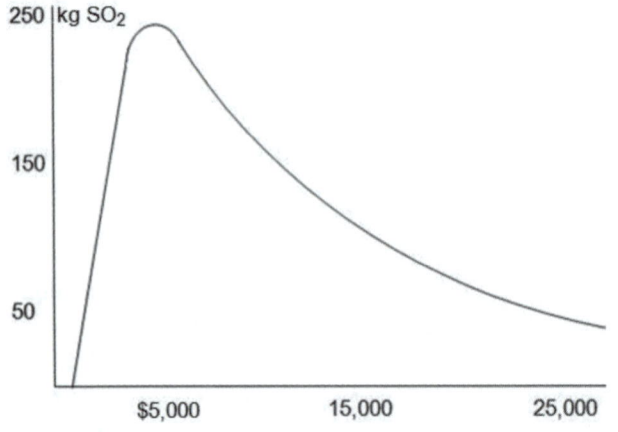

Figure 7-11. SO_2 emissions levels according to GNP per capita (in kg SO_2 vs. $ income)

lution, the amount of which shrinks as they approach economic maturity.

This phenomenon occurs because at low incomes, people tend to value development over environmental quality, but, as they achieve greater wealth, they are willing to devote more resources to environmental quality improvements. So, the developing countries tend to use highly polluting heavy industry in the race to catch up with the rest. Developed economies, on the other hand, rely on more advanced (albeit more expensive) and relatively clean technologies and services.

This is logical, because clean air and water provide benefits and an enjoyment that are income-elastic. As income increases above a certain threshold, which is different for different countries, individuals and society are willing and able to spend a larger share of their incomes on these goods. This reduces the pollution per unit of output and even decreases the total pollution with time.

We see the events of China now supporting this theory. China and India are now at the highest point of the curve, where economic development and acquiring goods is the top priority. That is why the Chinese are planning to build hundreds of new coal-fired plants. They need the energy to continue their rise as an economic power, regardless of the effects this might have on the environment. Hopefully, they will realize the problem and reduce coal burning.

This theory, however, cannot be applied for every single country, so it is contested by ecological economists, who believe that good environmental stewardship is possible at all times and at different levels of development.

Studies done on this subject are complex and contradictory, and the relevance of this curve seems to vary from case to case. One large factor is the location, because so much depends on whether the pollutants are local and people are essentially fouling their own environment, or if they are externalities generated by some far-away source.

In the case of SO_2 and particulates pollution, the damage is more evident. The pollution prices are near their marginal social costs, so turning points have been observed at relatively low-income levels. On the other hand, turning points are found at much higher income levels, or not at all, for pollutants such as CO_2—the damages from which are less immediate and less evident.

Other analyses show that rich and poor countries alike tend to reduce pollution relative to economic output over time, but that since developing countries grow at a rapid rate, their overall pollution grows rapidly with it. In rapidly growing middle-income countries, the scale effect, which increases pollution and other degradation, overwhelms the time effect. In wealthy countries, therefore, economic growth is slower, and pollution reduction efforts can overcome the scale effect. So, obviously, a fast-growing economy will produce more pollution despite technological advances.

Another recent study, using a number of different methods, finds evidence that the relationship between GNP and pollution exists in many countries, but that it is still a fragile concept. Only in a few cases, growing GNP and environmental damage evidence are absolutely undeniable.

As an example, a number of Latin American countries show significant evidence of the GNP-pollution relationship that is demonstrated by heavy deforestation. That is a result consistent with the theory that highly visible local conditions are the best evidence of this relationship. There is also an element of externalities here as well, since the large-scale deforestation is affecting neighboring countries and the entire world.

In all cases, the local environmental policies and institutional arrangements need to be accounted for to get a complete and accurate picture in each case. Scale, specific situation, and type of environmental degradation are the other set of variables that must be carefully examined when evaluating the relationship. Still it's clear that, particularly in China and India, economic growth is far outpacing improved environmental efficiency. Simply allowing development to take its course is insufficient, so other measures for environmental protection must be taken before it is too late.

Economy and Environment

The relationship between the local and national economies on one hand and the global environment on the other is two-directional. It all depends upon which side of the equation we are standing. If we are concerned with the ways environmental protection activities impact the overall economic performance, we see one thing. But if we are mostly concerned with how economic growth impacts environmental quality, then the picture looks quite different.

In this text we are mostly looking at environmental protection activities in the different areas of energy generation, and how they impact the overall economic performance, so let's look at how economic growth impacts environmental quality.

If we have to summarize it in one word, we'd say: significantly. More specifically, as people and nations get richer over time, the environmental quality in the area (directly), and around the globe (indirectly) change.

While the pattern follows some logic, the actual technical answers are not obvious.

Richer people usually use more energy and other resources and produce more waste and pollution. At the same time, however, a richer nation can afford to invest in renewable energy, install expensive pollution control equipment, and implement effective environmental policies.

Environmental quality is widely accepted as a normal good, which means that rich people will use more of it as their income increases, to protect the environment and themselves.

That brings the question of whether environmental quality is a luxury good, since spending on it increases disproportionately as income grows. While this may be the case with some higher income levels, it is merely a normal good at other income levels.

It seems logical that economic growth eventually provides the resources to reduce negative environmental impacts. There is clear evidence that, although economic growth usually leads to environmental deterioration in the early stages of the process, in the end the best—and probably the only—way to attain a decent environment in most countries is to become rich.

This notion that negative environmental impacts tend to increase initially as a country becomes richer, but then eventually decrease with further income gains, is known as the environmental Kuznets curve (EKC) hypothesis.

The EKC hypothesis proposes that the relationship between income and environmental impacts is an inverted-U shape, as in Figure 7-11, is based on actual data on sulfur dioxide emissions in the U.S. and Europe. The data show that per capita SO_2 emissions increase sharply with income up to a per-capita income of around $4,000, but then, as the income level increases, SO_2 emissions per-capita decline steadily. See Figure 7-11.

This is an encouraging result because the "turning point" occurs at a relatively modest income level. Thus, a moderate amount of economic growth can lead to substantial SO_2 emission reductions.

The Problem

The major problem here is that the EKC hypothesis, while accurate for SO_2 emissions, does not apply to all environmental impacts. Most importantly, the EKC hypothesis does not match the data on carbon dioxide emissions, which is the primary greenhouse gas. Any attempts to fit an inverted-U trend line through the CO_2 data fail. No turning point is to be found, and per-capita

CO_2 emissions continue to rise as per-capita income increases. See Figure 7-11.

A more sophisticated statistical analysis tested the EKC hypothesis for carbon emissions and concluded that, while it may be valid for some air pollutants such as SO_2, particulate matter, and nitrogen oxides, it does not seem to apply more broadly to other environmental impacts. Despite the new statistical approaches, there is no clear-cut evidence supporting the existence of the EKC for total carbon emissions, thus there is no relationship between economic growth and total pollution.

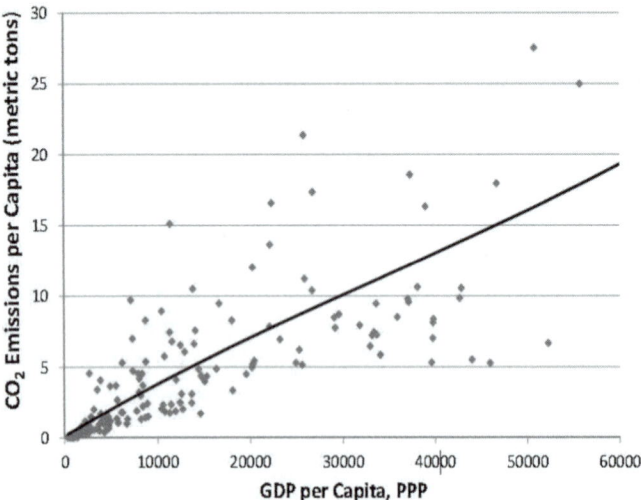

Figure 7-12. CO_2 emissions vs. income per capita

There is, however, an inverted U-shaped relation between urban ambient concentrations of some pollutants and income, but EKC is only a partial model of some types of emissions and concentrations.

In all cases, improvement of the environment is not automatic with income growth. It depends on a number of other factors, such as the types of policies and institutions. GDP growth creates the conditions for environmental improvement by raising the demand for improved environmental quality and makes the resources available for supplying it.

So, promoting economic growth as a vehicle for environmental remediation does not appear to be a means to solve the global warming, or other environmental problems.

Whether environmental quality improvements materialize with economic growth or not, and when and how, depend mostly on proper government policies, the activities of interested social institutions, and the functions of the energy, transport, and other pollution-prone markets.

But what does all that matter if we humans get to the point that we cannot even live on a planet that is changing drastically and out of control day after day in front of our eyes, a planet that makes life harder for millions by the day as a consequence of our mindless behavior, excessive depletion of fossils, and uncontrolled pollution of the environment to the point of no return?

Table 7-8 clearly shows what will happen if we do not change our ways…and soon! Because if we don't, all this talk about finances and regulations would become irrelevant. Once we reach the point of no return, only basic survival—finding fresh water to drink and clean air to breathe—would matter.

Maybe that will lay the foundation of another economy, and another financial system, where a glass of fresh water would be the measure of wealth, and where it would be worth its weight in gold…or more.

International Environmental Planning

The U.N. has a number of programs designed for and implemented in developing countries as needed to help them achieve the goals of the international community. Some of these programs are:

• Multilateral fund for the implementation of the Montreal protocol on substances that deplete the ozone layer is a financial mechanism established in 1991 to assist developing countries to meet Montreal protocol compliance targets. The fund facilitates the transfer of ozone-friendly technologies and financial assistance to developing countries so that they can phase out ozone-depleting substances (ODS). The Montreal protocol, adopted in 1987, has contributed to reversing the damage done to the ozone layer and is recognized as a global success story of global environmental protection. This is demonstrated by the massive reductions in the use of ODS worldwide since it came into force. The Montreal protocol had helped phase out over 95% of the ozone-depleting substances it set out to control.

• The environment and energy thematic trust fund gives seed money to innovative and catalytic initiatives which allow the United Nations to receive and quickly deploy resources into new business areas, thereby responding to new global or partner country demands. It supports the work within key result areas of the United Nations strategic plan that guides the work in the area of environment and sustainable development, such as: 1) environmental mainstreaming, 2) environmental finance,

Table 7-8. The effects of global warming

IMPACT	Temperature rise of 1°C would cause:	Temperature rise of 3°C would cause:	Temperature rise of 5°C would cause:
Fresh water supplies	✦ Glaciers in the Andes and other areas around the globe shrink and disappear. ✦ Over 50 million people are left without fresh water. ✦ Water supplies decrease 30% in Southern Africa and Mediterranean countries.	✦ Serious draughts occur in Southern Europe every 10 years of even more often. ✦ 2-4 billion people world-wide are left without water. ✦ Water supplies decrease 50% in Southern Africa and Mediterranean countries.	✦ Large glaciers in the Himalayas disappear all together. ✦ Quarter of the population in China, and surrounding countries, is left without fresh water supplies. ✦ Disease and death increase.
Food and agriculture	✦ A modest increase in crop yields is possible in some temperature regions. ✦ Crop yields in the tropics decrease significantly. ✦ 5-10% crop decrease in Africa.	✦ Crop yields increase at higher altitudes. ✦ Half a billion people are at risk of hunger. ✦ 20-30% crop yield decrease in Africa.	✦ Significant increase of ocean acidity and toxicity is blamed for reducing fish stocks. ✦ Warmer ocean waters change fish population habits and reduce fishing.
Human Health	✦ Reduction in mortality in high latitude countries. ✦ Quarter million die yearly from climate-related disease ✦ 50-60 million more people in Africans are exposed to malaria and other diseases.	✦ 5-6 million more people world-wide suffer from malnutrition, and 2-3 million more die from it. ✦ 80 million more people are exposed to malaria in Africa and many die from it.	✦ The number of climate-related diseases and death increase, putting additional burden on the health care and services systems, especially in the world's poorest countries and regions.
Coastal areas	✦ Increased damage from flooding in coastal areas. ✦ Flooding and inundation of low-lying counties, and permanent change of coastal areas. ✦ Forced evacuations of 10-20 million people from coastal areas.	✦ 200 million people subject to forced evacuation from low-lying coastal areas ✦ The numbers of people getting sick due to changing climate and living conditions increases.	✦ Ocean level rise is threatening major population centers in the U.S. and the West. ✦ New York, Tokyo, London, and others are on the evacuation list.
Ecosystems	✦ 10-15% of land species are facing extinction. ✦ 20-30% of all species face some change, or extinction ✦ Wild life risk is increased significantly.	✦ 40-50% of all wild life species face extinction. ✦ Half of the Arctic tundra is lost. ✦ Amazon forest collapse. ✦ Significant coral reefs loss.	✦ Uncontrolled world-wide wild-life extinction, coral reefs and glaciers loss. ✦ The entire human race is threatened by irreversible negative changes.

3) climate change, and 4) local capacity for service delivery.

- The global environment facility provides grants and concessional financing to assist countries to meet the costs of achieving their commitments under the global environmental conventions in biodiversity, climate change, and desertification, as well as supporting action on international waters and the phase-out of persistent organic pollutants. As a partnership between the implementing agencies of the United Nations and the World Bank, with the cooperation of seven nations, executing this program works to integrate action to generate global environmental benefits into the mainstream of country led development.

- The United Nations' green commodities facility is working to scale- up existing initiatives with companies, governments and others intended to help shift markets to drive the production and sale of green commodities. Green commodities are those produced and supplied in a manner that minimizes negative environmental impacts and includes bulk-traded products as well as more specialized niche varieties.

- Reducing emissions from deforestation and forest degradation is an effort to value the carbon stored in standing forests to create incentives for developing countries to protect forests. Financial flows resulting from this program will not only significantly reduce carbon emissions, but they can also benefit developing countries, support poverty reduction and help preserve biodiversity as well as other vital ecosystem services. Further, maintaining resilient forest ecosystems can contribute to adaptation to climate change.

Renewable Energy Country Attractiveness Index

Ernst & Young established a global quarterly publication in 2003 that ranks 40 countries by comparing the level of attractiveness of their renewable energy investment and deployment opportunities. It is called renewable energy country attractiveness index. The ranking in the index is based on several factors related to the global energy market and a number of technology-specific indicators, and several factors, including incentives, opportunities for projects and others.

In 2013, the 10th annual renewable energy country attractiveness index determined that the U.S. is the most attractive place in world for renewable energy, replacing China as the leader of the index in the previous years.

The global investment in clean energy grew to $269 billion in 2012, a five-fold increase since the renewable energy index inception. This shows that the renewable energy sector has moved from the fringes of the energy markets close to the mainstream.

"The sector now competes for investment with more traditional energy sources, where solar, biomass boilers, and mini wind turbines are allowing people to produce their own electricity, which is changing the way businesses and consumers think about energy," according to Ernst & Young. "Market fundamentals, such as energy demand growth, security of energy supply and the affordability of renewable energy (relative to other sources), feature as some of the most prominent drivers of renewable energy growth today. Our revised methodology allows us to analyze each market's investment attractiveness much more effectively by considering these factors and weighting them accordingly."

The U.S. achieved the highest overall score of 71.6 on the index, and China and Germany received slightly lower scores of 70.7 and 67.6, respectively. The U.S. success is due to factors such as: economic "macro stability," ease of doing business, and the bankability of renewables.

Obama's support for renewables and a permanent extension of the production tax credit (PTC) were some of the factors that raised the U.S. ranking in the index. In his 2012 state of the union speech, President Obama called for doubling the renewable energy generation in the country by 2020, while at the same time reducing oil imports to half of present levels.

He also called for a $2 billion energy security trust as needed to support clean energy research initiatives, in addition to the department of the interior drive to improve its permitting process for clean energy projects.

Another great factor for the renewables' success in the U.S. is the involvement of "big business," which is involved and increasingly involved and supporting the development and implementation of renewables energy sources.

U.S. business leaders are looking toward a smooth transition to unsubsidized renewable energy sources that can compete with the conventional such. Their competitiveness is based on extending while reducing, and ultimately eliminating, the PTC over time, which makes business sense and is supported by all parties, including the renewable companies and organizations.

Congress is considering extension of the master limited partnerships (MLPs) to renewable energy projects, which would make it much easier for the public and financial institutions to invest in the renewable projects.

In China, renewables are still a priority, but high barriers to entry for external investors, and other unfavorable financial factors placed China in second place. And yet, China's GDP is growing, the energy demand is increasing, and renewable energy manufacturing and use is a key to the local economies. These factors make renewables a good market for internal renewable energy investment. If and when China opens the doors to foreign investment, the growth renewables might bring China back to first place in the index.

Let's take a closer look at the economics of the different energy markets and their environmental effects.

COAL

Coal is indispensible as far as power generation is concerned, since it is responsible for more than 50% of the electric power we use. And yet, it is in the crosshairs of the environmentalists and governments now. At the same time, the energy and environmental economists are trying to resolve the situation by designing different financial instruments, as needed to keep everyone happy and move things to a successful end, or at least to an acceptable compromise.

We see a long and bloody battle ahead of us until any compromise can be reached.

GHG Pollution

Green house gasses (GHGs) are the major topic of discussion in the energy and environment related activities now. When discussing costs of producing and using coal, the actual price paid on the market is not the only number to be considered. Other factors, mainly pollution emitted during the production, transport, and burning of coal are major issues, which have also great, albeit hidden, costs.

These hidden costs were not an issue until recently, but are now getting more and more important and can be no longer ignored or misrepresented. Because of that, we need to take a very close look at all energy sources and compare their advantages and disadvantages, both as energy providers and pollution emitters.

Table 7-9 shows the actual amount of CO_2 emissions from the different power generating related technologies. CO_2 is considered a major GHG gas, and has been blamed for the climate warming of late. Obviously, coal is the worst polluter of the fossils, followed by diesel fuel—which is quite surprisingly followed closely by H2 powered fuel cells—most likely because the H2 gas was generated by fossil fuels. The CO_2 levels fall sharply

Table 7-9. CO_2 emissions from different power generators

Technology	Grams CO_2 per kWh*
Coal, conventional	1100
Coal w/CCS**	950
Diesel, oil	770
Fuel cell, H_2 gas	650
Natural gas	440
Nuclear	60
Geothermal	40
Biomass	30
Biogas	15
Hydro, river run	15
Hydro, dammed	10
Wind, onshore	25
Wind, offshore	15
Solar, PV modules	50
Solar thermal, CSP	20

* Including all cradle-to-grave emissions
**CCS - carbon capture and sequestration

when the H2 gas is generated by wind or solar energy.

Sulfur Dioxide

The clean air act allowed enhancements up to 20% of a power plant's total value to be done without the need to upgrade sulfur emission controls. Any additional upgrades had to comply with the new SO_2 requirements. This actually resulted in excessive sulfate aerosol pollution, which plays a major role in the environmental, and health impacts we've observed lately.

Removing sulfur, however, results in different environmental problems, namely the need to dispose of large amounts of sulfurous waste. For example, 33% efficient 1.0 GWe coal-fired power plant, burning coal with 3% by weight sulfur content and energy content of coal of about 30 MJ/kg, needs to burn about three GW of coal to produce its one GW of electric power. Three GW is 3,000 MW, or 3,000 MJ/s, so at 30 MJ/kg, our plant uses about 100 kg of coal per second, or a ton of coal is burned every 10 seconds and converted into heat, CO_2, SO_2, other gasses, ash and soot.

Our coal contains 3% sulfur by weight, so this amounts to 3 kg of sulfur content per ton, which amount is generated every second. In the scrubbers, $CaCO_3$ is used to neutralize the excess SO_2, so each sulfur atom is combined with one calcium atom and four oxygen atoms to make $CaSO_4$. The sulfur atomic weight is 32, calcium is 40 and oxygen's is 16, which means that for every 32 units of sulfur by weight, we get an additional 40 units from the calcium and 64 units of oxygen.

Or, in other words, for every one unit of sulfur we get 40/32 units of calcium and 64/32 units of oxygen. So our 3 kg/s of sulfur translates into 13 kg/s $CaSO_4$. This amount generated for 86,400 seconds (in the day) means that our 1.0GWe coal-fired plant produces 1,100,000 kg of $CaSO_4$ each day, or about 1,000 ton per day of $CaSO_4$ have to be dispose of.

Since the $CaSO_4$ is in a water-based slurry, we actually end up with about four or five times this mass, or about 4,000-5,000 tons of slurry is to be disposed of every day at our plant. This is about 1.5-1.8 million tons annually, or over 50 million tons of slurry generated and disposed of during the 30 years life of the plant.

Where does all this slurry go? How much does it cost to dispose of? The costs of its generation vary according to the scrubber technology used, so does the disposal, which cost is fixed. What is uncertain is what happens to the slurry that in many cases causes soil and water table contamination. These cases need to be investigated and the related costs considered, and calculated as externalities of the direct and indirect use value types.

Coal Sequestration

Coal has been blamed for major environmental damage, and while the extent of the damages is a subject of ongoing dispute, the fact that coal-fired power plants emit a lot of GHG gasses is unquestionable.

Figure 7-13 is a relative representation of the contribution of different power generating technologies to the ever-increasing GHG contamination. Obviously, coal is the largest emitter and something has to be done to limit the GHG emissions, and sooner the better!

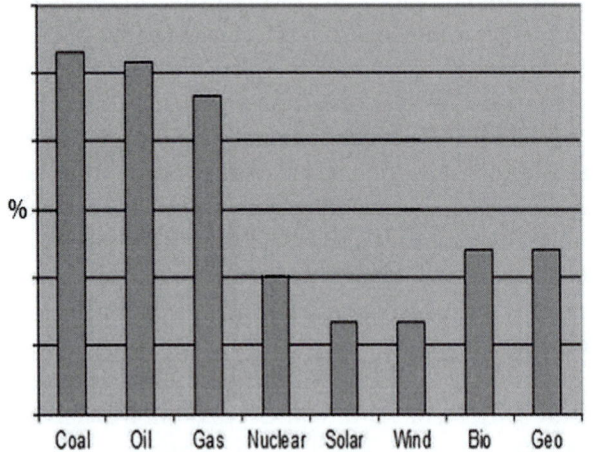

Figure 7-13. Carbon footprint of different power generating technologies

The solutions to the excess emission problems from coal-fire power plants are clear:

1. Switch the coal-fired power plants to non-polluting technologies
2. Reduce the pollution from the coal-fired power plants by installing carbon sequestration devices

The first option is being considered, and even implemented; many coal-fired power plants are converted, or to be converted soon, to gas burning. The second option, using carbon sequestration techniques, is under serious consideration, and is under intense research and development effort in the U.S. and around the world.

The U.S. Department of Energy (DOE), for example, is committed to spending over $575 million in an effort to test the efficiency of sequestering carbon generated from burning coal. According to the specialists, large-scale carbon sequestration is technically possible, but it could cost billions of dollars to develop and implement, and many more to operate and maintain every year.

The DOE effort will cover several pilot programs that are designed to test the feasibility of capturing and storing deep underground most of the carbon generated

from coal plants. The DOE is planning to cover about 60% of the total cost of the projects planned for development, while the private sector including the power plant owners and utilities will pay the rest of the bill.

How far this money will go in those larger than life projects is uncertain, but keep in mind that the Canadian and Chinese governments and companies have already spent several times this much money on similar projects, so the effort seems legit and fully feasible.

The DOE is also looking at huge, deep saline reservoirs near the pilot projects in 27 states and three Canadian provinces, which can store up to 100 years of the total carbon output generated in the U.S. Just three of these projects will be able to store over one million tons of carbon underground, doubling the amount currently being sequestered. This, however, amounts to only approximately 0.05% of the total carbon generated by coal power plants annually, so much more effort is needed to come closer to reducing the carbon footprint of the U.S. power generating industry.

The Carnegie Mellon electricity center published report, "Incentives for Near-Term Carbon Dioxide Geological Sequestration," outlines the potential and the cost for sequestering carbon while suggesting the government incentives are absolutely necessary to make it cost-effective for the power industry and the public.

According to the report, CO_2 can be safely sequestered indefinitely, but financial incentives are necessary to begin commercial-scale sequestration. The study also suggests that sequestering carbon on site at the emission sites is the only alternative, because the transport and sequestration costs are too high, at an estimated $5-$15 per ton of CO_2. This won't happen, so that will limit the possibility of underground sequestration since there are few such sites close to coal-and gas-fired power plants.

So, assuming that there are 1.2 billion tons of carbon to be sequestered in the U.S., and that each ton of carbon costs about $10 to sequester, then we end up with the grand total of $12 billion annual cost to be paid by the coal power industry (if everything goes well) for sequestration alone. This is a lot of money, which will increase the price of power generation significantly.

And these estimates might be a bit too optimistic, because in 2009 the OECD's international energy agency estimated $80-90 per ton of carbon capture, transport and sequestration, going down to $30-50 per ton by 2030.

Because of the high cost of sequestration, the coal industry is looking at a broad array of federal tax incentives and other vehicles to make carbon sequestration viable for the power companies and the public.

Some of the financial approaches that can help the carbon sequestration and other efforts during the transition period include:

- Continuation of the 15% enhanced oil recovery federal tax credit
- Enacting a federal CO_2 sequestration tax credit
- Enacting a federal investment tax credit for CO_2 pipelines
- Adding low-carbon emission coal facilities to the facilities eligible for the production tax credit
- Enabling tax-exempt financing for CO_2 sequestration infrastructure investments

Case Study: FutureGen, U.S.

In 2005 the U.S. DOE announced the $1.3 billion futuregen project, intending to design, build and operate an emission-free coal-based electricity and hydrogen production plant, with $250 million of the total to be provided by eight power companies.

The original plan was to build a coal gasification (IGCC) plant with additional water-shift reactors, capable of producing hydrogen and carbon dioxide. In addition, the development of ITM oxygen separation technology was part of the project.

About 700,000 tons of CO_2 per year, or about 60% of the U.S. total emissions would be separated from the exhaust gasses via membrane technology and then sequestered in nearby geologic formations. The hydrogen would be burned in a 275 MWe generating plant and in fuel cells.

Sounds complicated, no? The plan was later modified to 90% CO_2 capture and 330 MWe gross, or 240 MWe net power generation. This seems even more complex and expensive. The construction was to start in 2009 in Mattoon, Illinois, and the completed demonstration plant was to start operations in 2012.

The main hope was to validate the technical feasibility and economic viability of near-zero emission coal-based generation. Generating electricity with only 10% penalty for carbon sequestration, and producing hydrogen at $3.80 per GJ (or equivalent to gas at 12.7 cents per liter) was to be a very promising achievement for the coal industry and the entire power generating industry, not to mention the major effect on the environment with millions of tons of carbon stored safely in the ground caverns, instead of floating in the atmosphere, polluting it, creating global warming, and poisoning all of us.

Alas, it was not to be…at least not for now. In January 2008—even before the economic crisis started—the U.S. DOE announced that it would pull its funding for the project, expressing a number of uncertainties resulting in serious concerns over escalating costs. Increasing the plan from 60-90% levels of sequestration should have given DOE a warning signal about increasing costs, and maybe prevented the paper tower to be blown away.

The Obama administration reconsidered the project and work resumed where it was left two years before. The initial design, and the geological investigations produced a revised cost estimate, which the DOE approved and committed over $1.0 billion to as a public-private partnership. The work was under way with Industrial Alliance (FGA), Peabody, BHP Billiton, Rio Tinto, Consol Energy, E.On, and Exelon (tentative) joining the project.

And then in another twist, DOE abandoned the original futuregen plan in August 2010, and suggested retrofitting unit four of Ameren's existing coal-fired power plant in Meredosia, Illinois, with oxy-combustion. The new project was called futuregen 2.0, and was to become part of the clean-coal repowering program of the carbon dioxide storage network.

The retrofitted plant would burn pulverized coal to produce 140 MWe power while capturing over 90% of the CO_2 emissions. This amounts to 1.3 million tons of captured carbon annually, or nearly 40 million tons of carbon would be captured and sequestered (instead of being released in the atmosphere) during its projected 30 years of operation.

A pipeline would link the plant to the regional CO_2 storage hub to be sequestered in the Mt. Simon geological formations. The Ameren unit four would use B&W technology for oxy-combustion repowering of the plant, and FutureGen Alliance would focus on the pipeline and storage implementation effort. Other local CO_2 sources within a 100 miles range would be serviced too, so a total of 500 million tons of storage capacity was needed. Construction is due be completed in 2015 and in operation shortly thereafter, most likely by mid-2016.

Other carbon capture and sequestration projects are planned, or already underway, in the U.S. and in other parts of the world:

- Duke Energy Corp. in the U.S. is building a $3 billion, 618 MWe, IGCC plant at Edwardsport, Indiana ($4850/kW). This is a regulated plant, but Duke will not be asking the consumers to pay for more than $2.72 billion of its final construction cost, excluding financing.

- Summit Power Group's Texas clean energy project (TCEP) at Penwell, Texas, is a 377 MWe IGCC power plant burning coal with CCS, while capturing 90% of CO_2 and 90% of NO_x. It has $450 million commitment from DOE's clean coal power initiative toward its $2.4 billion cost, and is due to be completed and in operation in 2015. Of the 2.9 million tons per year of CO_2 captured, 83% will be used for enhanced oil recovery. Of the 377 MWe, 106 MW will be used to run the major project equipment on site, 16 MW will be used to compress CO_2, and 42 MW will be used to produce urea, leaving 214 MWe to be sent into the grid.

- The CCPilot 100+ project at Ferrybridge in West Yorkshire, U.K., has commenced operation. It can capture 100 tons of CO_2 per day from 5 MWe of coal-fired power plant. The operator is Scottish & Southern Energy in collaboration with Vattenfall and Doosan Babcock. It uses a post-combustion amine scrubbing process and is subsidized by the government. Vattenfall expects to apply experience from it to a much larger demonstration plant at Jaenschwalde in Germany, to operate from 2015.

- Scottish & Southern Energy and Shell U.K. agreed in November 2011, to build the first commercial-scale CCS demonstration project at Peterhead in the northeast of Scotland, at a cost of £1 billion. The project aims to design and develop a full chain, post-combustion CCS facility that will capture CO_2 from one 385 MW combined cycle gas turbine unit at SSE's Peterhead Power Station. It is planned that the CO_2 will then be transported to Shell's Goldeneye gas field in the North Sea (which will have ceased production) using, as far as possible, existing infrastructure. Some £1 from the E.U. and U.K. government is expected for the project. Earlier Scottish Power cancelled plans for a similar project at Longannet coal-fired power station.

- In Denmark a pilot project at the 420 MWe Elsam power plant is capturing CO_2 from post-combustion flue gases under the auspices of CASTOR (CO_2 from Capture to Storage). Flue gases are passed through an absorber, where a solvent captures about 90% of the CO_2. The pregnant solution is then heated to 120°C to release pure CO_2 at the rate of about one ton per hour for geological sequestration. The cost is expected to be $25-35 per ton of carbon.

- In Netherlands, E.On aims to capture 1.1 million tons of CO_2 per year from a 250 MWe coal-fired plant at the Maasvlakte in Rotterdam.

These are complex and very expensive efforts, so we must thank all participants and wish them the best of luck in this important undertaking.

The Other Coal Pollutants

Air emissions from coal mining and power generation operations are well-known pollutants that damage the environment and all life in it. The most dangerous of these are: coal sludge, coal ash, and other toxic waste materials (in form of liquids and solids)

Coal Sludge

After removing from the mine, coal is in big chunks which makes it difficult to handle and use. Because of that, it is crushed into smaller and uniform pieces and is then also washed to remove the soil and rock that may accompany it. These operations produce large amounts of coal sludge, or slurry, which is a messy liquid waste product. Most of the coal slurry is generated during the washing process at or near power plants, where huge amounts of water are used and then discharged as slurry.

Another form of liquid pollution is acidic mine runoff from the mines in a form of a liquid coal waste. It is formed as sulfuric acid forms when coal and coal dust are exposed to air and water. It is estimated that there are wastewater discharges containing toxic chemicals as mercury, arsenic, beryllium, cadmium, nickel, selenium, and some radioactive materials.

The coal sludge is usually disposed of by dumping it in specially constructed lakes made out of the solid mining refuse. The slurry dumps are used to store the liquid waste temporarily and until its removal from the site. These toxic waste collection dumps are usually located in valleys near the coal processing plants, and are constantly at risk of breaking open and spilling onto residential areas, or even worse, leaching into the groundwater.

Coal Solids

Millions of tons of solid coal waste are generated and removed from the mines each year. These solids are byproducts from dredging up land and its natural elements, which included many different chemicals, metals, and heavy metals.

The solids come from burning coal, which produces airborne compounds, known as fly ash and bottom ash (collectively referred to as coal ash). The ash, which contains large quantities of lead, mercury, nickel, tin, cadmium, antimony, and arsenic, as well as radioisotopes of thorium and strontium, is usually stored on location, near the power plants, until finally removed for permanent disposal.

Power plant gas scrubbers, used to remove sulfur dioxide from the smokestack gasses create a large quantity of solid coal waste too. The flue-gas desulfurization (FGD) process creates a wet solid residue containing calcium sulfite ($CaSO_3$) and calcium sulfate ($CaSO_4$). Solids like fly ash are usually added to stabilize the sludge for transport and landfill storage.

An average size power plant operating 30-40 years non-stop will generate 8-10 million tons of liquid and solid waste, most of which is highly toxic. There are great quantities of ash generated annually, with the estimates reaching 75 million tons in recent years, which is twice the amount generated 20-30 years back. The extremely large quantity of coal waste piling up non-stop around the country is considered as the nation's second largest waste stream after municipal solid waste.

Coal ash contains environmentally and biologically toxic elements, which are stored in very large quantities in unregulated coal waste sites. These sites are usually open to the elements and large amounts can be blown away by the wind or leach in the ground with the rains.

Coal waste is not regulated by the federal government, even though it has been established that power plants are the nation's biggest producer of toxic waste, surpassing industries like plastic, paint manufacturing, and chemical plants. The EPA has issued a list of the 44 "high hazard potential" coal waste dumps in 10 states, including 12 in North Carolina, 9 in Arizona, 6 in Kentucky, 6 in Ohio, and 4 in West Virginia.

The "high hazard potential" definition applies to coal ash storage sites at which a dam, or other waste storage failure is the most likely cause of the loss of human life. The report stops short of including an assessment of the likelihood of any such accidental releases.

Hexavalent Chromium

Drinking water contaminated with hexavalent chromium from coal is suspected to cause cancer, according to a report released by EarthJustice and the Sierra Club in 2011. It stated that there many health threats are associated with a toxic cancer-causing chemical found in coal ash waste, some of which are caused by hexavalent chromium.

NOTE: Hexavalent chromium (chromium VI) is a chemical compound of the element chromium in its +6 oxidation state. Inhaling hexavalent chromium is a recognized cause for human suffering, which can even result in cancerous conditions.

The report specifically cited 29 sites in 17 states where the hexavalent chromium contamination was found. The information was gathered from existing EPA data on coal ash and included locations in Alabama, Arkansas, Delaware, Florida, Illinois, Indiana, Minnesota, Massachusetts, North Carolina, North Dakota, Nevada, Ohio, Oklahoma, Pennsylvania, Tennessee, Virgina and Wisconsin.

Hexavalent chromium first made headlines after Erin Brockovich sued Pacific Gas & Electric because of poisoned drinking water from hexavalent chromium. Now new information indicates that the chemical has readily leaked from coal ash sites across the U.S. This is likely to open a new page in the Erin Brockovich's saga, because most coal ash dumpsites are not adequately monitored and the contamination from these is suspected to be widespread.

Coal Waste Disposal

Coal waste is most often disposed of in landfills or "surface impoundments," which basically are structures (or large holes dug in the ground) lined with compacted soil, or plastic sheets. These are very controversial and dangerous operations, because rain washes the contaminants towards the bottom of the deposit. Lining of any type does not last forever, and eventually the toxins collected at the bottom start leaching into the ground below. After 10, 20, or 30 years, the toxins that leach into the ground will sink deep enough to contaminate the local rivers, lakes or water table.

There are over 150 slurry and ash storage ponds at coal-fired power plants, and most of them are of the type that collapsed at the Kingston fossil plant in 2008. Indiana, Ohio, Kentucky, Georgia and Alabama are the states with most storage ponds.

About 20% of the generated ash—approximately 20 million tons—ends up in surface ponds, while the rest is dumped in landfills or is sold for other uses. There also are a number of studies showing that many of these storage ponds are contaminating the local ground water with toxic pollutants. There are reports of the contamination levels of toxic chemicals and metals like arsenic, cadmium, chromium, and lead being 350 times the allowable state limits. Prolonged use of water contaminated to such degree by these toxins can cause cancer, neurological disorders and other illnesses.

On December 22, 2008, a retention pond wall collapsed at TVA's Kingston plant in Harriman, TN, releasing a combination of water and fly ash that flooded 12 homes, spilled into nearby Watts Bar Lake, contaminated the Emory River, and caused a train wreck. Officials said 4-6 feet of material escaped from the pond to cover an estimated 400 acres of adjacent land. A train bringing coal to the plant became stuck when it was unable to stop before reaching the flooded tracks. Hundreds of fish were floating dead downstream from the plant. Water tests showed elevated levels of lead and thallium.

Originally TVA estimated that 1.7 million cubic yards of waste had burst through the storage facility. Company officials said the pond had contained a total of about 2.6 million cubic yards of sludge. However, the company revised its estimates on December 26, when it released an aerial survey showing that 5.4 million cubic yards (1.09 billion gallons) of fly ash was released from the storage facility. Several days later, the estimate was increased to over one billion gallons spilled. The TVA spill was 100 times larger than the Exxon Valdez spill in Alaska, which released 10.9 million gallons of crude oil. Cleanup was expected to take weeks and cost tens of millions of dollars.

Coal Externalities

This is the skeleton in the closet of the coal industry. In economic terms, an external cost, or externality, is a negative effect of an economic activity on a third party or the society in general. When coal is mined and used to generate power, for example, the external costs include the impacts of water pollution, toxic coal waste, air pollution, and the long-term damage to ecosystems and human health.

The list of such damages is long, and we cannot possible look at all items and cases in that list, so we will limit this writing to the very basics, as needed to underline the importance of this subject:

• Greenpeace released an analysis in 2008 showing that the global total cost of coal, including the externalities, was at least $450 billion annually and growing. This number was later on updated to $500 billion in 2011 by a Harvard study group, and now is most likely much higher.

The researchers arrive at these figures by looking at CO_2 and other pollution damages, and the damages, resulting in health costs from mining and power plant accidents, air, soil, and water pollution. The first report was released at the time when Industry Ministers from 20 big GHG emitting countries met in Warsaw with the world's climate-polluting industries, where was agreed that the relentless expansion of the coal industry is the single greatest threat to increasing the damages of the global climate change.

Coal is presently the most environment-polluting fossil fuel, responsible for one third to one-half of all CO_2 emissions, which are projected to increase to 60% of all emissions by 2030. Thus, reducing coal burning will benefit not only the global climate, but it also will reduce the other external impacts and the related costs which everybody else has to pay for.

In calculating the $450 billion annual global cost of coal figures, the focus was on the external costs of coal. This includes: the cost for rectifying damages attributable to climate change; human health impacts from air pollution; fatalities due to major mining accidents; and other factors for which reasonably reliable global data is currently available.

The above dollar number was derived by taking into account 90% of the global emissions and looking at the damages, which are projected to rise significantly, due to the impacts of climate change. With these changes, the total number of global cost of coal is likely to increase sharply—unless its use is reduced and/or the climate change is stopped soon enough.

The projected impacts of climate change include billions of people who will face water shortage, while others will be flooded by rising ocean levels. This also includes the hundreds of millions who will be threatened by food insecurity and hurt by exceedingly extreme weather events, such as storms, earthquakes, and tsunamis.

• There are, however, other specialists who insist that it is too late now. There are climate models showing that no matter what we do now—even if we stop all CO_2 and other GHG emissions immediately—we have already triggered a massive global warming and other environmental changes that can be reversed only by reducing the GHG gasses already in the atmosphere. Doing this is simply impossible to achieve, so no matter what we do, we cannot stop, let alone reverse the environmental damages.

But the negative impacts of coal are not only related to global climate change. Coal also pollutes local water resources, and dirties the local air, which causes black lung disease while large geographic areas are changed forever by blowing apart entire mountaintops. A dramatic increase of air pollution in China is a good example of such large-scale damages to environment and humans alike. Entire river systems and lakes are lost as a result in China and other countries as well.

• The new "clean coal" technologies have the potential to sharply reduce CO_2 emissions from coal-fired power plants, but the industry experts claim that the newly developed carbon capture and storage (CCS) techniques have their own problems that could lead to another set of dangers. The CCS technology is immature, unproven, and contains inherent risks. In addition, it comes with an enormous price tag and a long process and equipment development time period.

One thing everyone who is well informed on the CCS technology agrees on is that the global GHG emissions must start declining soon, and in best of cases the new CCS approach is in no position to play a significant role in making this happen for the above-mentioned reasons.

- Greenpeace insists for the world governments to see and agree on a "climate vision" that is to address immediately the threat of serious global emissions peaking by 2015. Developed countries must agree on immediate reduction targets in the 30-40% range, if any significant results are to be achieved before it is too late. How this is to be done and how much will be done, if anything at all, is still uncertain, but the talks continue—yes, we are still in the talking stages.

The Environmental Damage

There are a number of environmental changes of late, some of which are attributed to coal mining and burning. We cannot list them all, let alone discuss each in detail in this text, but here is a sample of what is happening and what could be expected to happen in the future.

Habitat Destruction

The majority of the coal mining in the U.S. is surface mining, which includes strip mining and mountaintop removal. In these cases, the original ecosystem which once was on the surface is destroyed and removed in the process of removing the surface dirt and then mining the coal underneath.

Mining destroys fish and wildlife habitat, which has rippling effects not only on their populations, but also on the local population that rely on them. In addition to the mine site itself, coal mining affects the surrounding areas too. Air pollution, wide spread coal dust, and mine runoff discharge into nearby water bodies. damages are the usual results from coal mining operations.

Coal dust particles, chemicals, and sediment from coal mining discharged in the local rivers and lakes can reduce life expectancy of fish, damage their immune systems, and suffocate fish eggs.

After the coal in the mine is depleted coal companies usually restore the surface to a certain level and plant vegetation in an attempt to restore the original ecosystem. This, however, is difficult and sometimes impossible, especially in wetlands areas.

It is very unlikely that any amount of effort or money could restore the environment and the wildlife in it exactly the way it was during pre-mining times. Because of that we must accept the fact that mining operations, if and when approved, will leave a permanent scar on the Earth's surface, which might take centuries to heal completely.

Health Effects

Mining and burning coal in coal-fired power plants releases a number of toxic pollutants, some of which rise in the air, and remain behind as liquid or solid waste materials and chemicals. These pollutants are responsible for a large number of illnesses and premature deaths to people directly involved in the industry, people who live nearby, and people worldwide.

Coal dust in mines and near storage and transport facilities contributes to serious respiratory illnesses such as asthma and Pneumoconiosis (black lung). Solid combustion wastes such as fly ash pollute groundwater near storage facilities, contaminating individual and community water supplies.

Airborne pollutants have a larger footprint. Despite air pollution regulations, toxic emissions (soot, sulfur dioxide, nitrous oxides) from coal-fired power plants are estimated to be responsible for thousands of deaths due to lung disease each year in the U.S. and Canada. A government study in Ontario found that the coal-fired plants in that province alone were responsible for an average annual total of about 660 premature deaths, 920 hospital admissions, 1090 emergency room visits, and 331,000 minor illness.

Coal combustion emissions released into the atmosphere contain nitrous oxides which are responsible for industrial and urban smog, sulfur dioxide which is the primary reactive agent behind acid rain, mercury which accumulates in the food chain, and large amounts of carbon dioxide which is the most important greenhouse gas contributing to climate change. Coal mining itself also releases significant amounts of methane, another extremely potent greenhouse gas. Coal mining is responsible for over 25% of the energy-related methane emissions in the US.

Coal combustion wastes (CCW) include ash,

sludge, and boiler slag left over from burning coal to make electricity. These wastes (120 million tons/year in the U.S.) concentrate toxins such as arsenic, mercury, chromium, cadmium, uranium and thorium. In addition, these wastes create an expensive storage problem "in perpetuity."

Coal-fired power plants are also a major source of atmospheric mercury, which accumulates in the food chain and can damage the developing nervous systems of human fetuses, as well as lead to reduced immune function, weight loss, reduced reproduction rate, mental defects and other neurological problems.

There are a number of health effects and illnesses attributed to the pollution released during coal mining, preparation, transport, combustion, and waste removal and storage.

Some of the negative coal-related health effects and illnesses in the U.S. are:

- Respiratory illnesses like asthma OCPD and such, caused by particulates, ozone, and sulfur dioxide emissions.

- Black lung from coal dust

- Congestive heart failure, caused by particulates and carbon monoxide emissions

- Non-fatal cancer, osteoporosis, ataxia, renal dysfunction, caused by benzene, radionuclides, heavy metals, emissions and waste materials

- Chronic bronchitis and asthma attacks caused by particulates and ozone emissions

- Loss of IQ, caused by excess air and water pollution

- Nervous system damage, caused by mercury releases in the drinking water

- Terminal cancer, caused by air and water pollution

- Reduction in life expectancy, caused by particulates, sulfur dioxide, ozone, heavy metals, benzene, and radionuclides emissions and releases

- Degradation and soiling of buildings caused by excess sulfur dioxide, acid deposition, and particulates emissions that can effect human health

- Ecosystem loss and degradation with negative effects on human health and quality of life, caused by excess emissions and releases of gasses, liquids, and solids.

- Global warming, caused by large quantities of carbon dioxide, methane, nitrous oxide, and sulfur dioxide emitted by coal-fired power plants

Coal-related Illnesses

Coal-fired power plants emit pollutants that may act as triggers to a number of medical conditions in humans and animals. These pollutants include sulfur dioxide, nitrogen oxides, and particulate matter. In addition, the carbon dioxide emissions from coal accelerate global warming, which is likely to increase the concentration in air of pollen from some plants, such as ragweed, and thereby contribute to the development of additional asthma and other conditions.

Chronic inhalation of coal dust causes several lung disorders, including simple coal-workers' pneumoconiosis, progressive massive fibrosis, chronic bronchitis, lung function loss, and emphysema.

We will review some of the most important illnesses related to coal mining and use, such as:

Asthma

Coal dust is one of the primary causes of asthmatic conditions for coal miners, people living and working next to coal mines, or living in areas with high pollution levels. There are a number of cellular actions, interactions, and conditions related to coal dust toxicity on human tissues, and the lungs in particular. The dust particles are known to cause lung disorders on cellular level like; macrophages and neutrophils, epithelial cells, and fibroblasts.

Inhaling coal dust particles induces cellular and non-cellular activities in the lungs, and may be involved in the damage of lung cells as well as some macromolecules including α-1-antitrypsin and DNA.

Recent studies with coal dusts show its effects on important leukocyte recruiting factors, such as: leukotriene-B4, platelet derived growth factora Coal dust particles also stimulate the macrophage production of various factors with potential capacity to modulate lung cells and/or its extracellular matrix.

In more practical terms, asthma is a chronic disease of the lungs characterized by inflammation and narrowing of the airways. Airway inflammation in asthmatics causes swelling in the throat that narrows a bronchial tree that has been previously sensitized to inhaled irritants, including many air pollutants. Exposure to an inhaled irritant causes further narrowing of the airways and the production of mucus that makes airways even narrower, a vicious and very dangerous process for all affected.

Patients with asthma experience recurrent episodes of dyspnea (shortness of breath), a sensation of tightness in the chest, wheezing, and coughing that typically occurs at night or early in the morning. This can lead to hypoxia (low blood oxygen level), hypercarbia (high blood carbon dioxide level), and respiratory acidosis (acidification of the blood caused by carbon dioxide retention) that may, in turn, cause cardiac arrhythmias and other medical emergencies.

During severe attacks, the lungs also fail to perform their task of exchanging carbon dioxide, produced by metabolic processes in the body, for live-giving oxygen. This, combined with other conditions, and the resulting panic, could prove fatal in some cases.

There are about 25 million asthmatics in the U.S., including 6-7 million children. The Centers For Disease Control And Prevention report that the number of persons with asthma increased by 84% from 1980-2004. More than half of the U.S. states report that 8.6% or more of their inhabitants have asthma. These high-asthma states are clustered in the Northeast and Midwest.

Oxidative Stress

"Oxidative stress" is the term used to describe the physiological state characterized by an excessive concentration of oxidizing free radical molecules. Oxidative stress, or the possibility that oxygen, or reactive forms of oxygen, to be toxic to certain cellular functions has been known over half a century. Research on the importance of highly reactive forms of oxygen, known as oxygen free radicals, in biological systems is ongoing, but we now know that some of these free radicals exert critical controls over normal cellular metabolic process and cellular signaling. This abnormality can cause tissue damage and illness.

Oxidative stress is usually created when oxygen ions, free radicals, or other reactive species are produced in excess of the body's ability to fight with remove these molecules. Genetic polymorphisms responsible for controlling the inflammatory response also increase an individual's susceptibility to the respiratory effects of ozone.

Studies have shown differences in the susceptibility to ozone (O_3, a form of reactive oxygen) that are due to polymorphisms (subtle differences in genes that control the expression of a trait) in the genes responsible for dealing with oxidative stress.

Thus, the probability that an individual will develop oxidative stress symptoms or illnesses depends on exposure to a trigger, such as ozone, and the individual's susceptibility to that trigger, i.e., a complex combination and interaction between genetic and environmental factors.

Our current understanding is that oxygen-free radicals are important contributors to the initiation and propagation of a several diseases, including: cardiovascular disease; pulmonary disease; atherosclerosis; hypertension; rheumatoid arthritis, diabetes mellitus; and neurodegenerative disorders such as Alzheimer's disease and Parkinson's disease.

Since coal-fired power plants emit large quantities of reactive oxygen, or ozone, we need to be aware of the conditions and consequences of living close to coal-fired power plants, or in cities with high ozone pollution levels.

COPD

Chronic obstructive pulmonary disease (OCPD), unlike asthma, which is a reversible condition, is permanent damage to the airway blamed on inhaling coal dust. It consists of a scary chronic obstructive airway condition characterized by a narrowing of the airway passages. Smoking tobacco is the most important risk factor for the development of COPD, and approximately 85% of all cases of COPD are attributed to that single, preventable cause.

Data that have emerged during the past several years have shown that there is a smaller but important link between air pollution, including pollutants produced by burning coal, and the subsequent development of COPD exacerbations.

Cancer

The National Cancer Institute estimates that in 2008 alone there were 215,020 new cases of lung cancer, the leading U.S. cancer killer in both men and women, with 161,840 deaths annually. Smoking tobacco, radon and other radioactive gases, second hand smoke, asbestos, arsenic, nickel compounds, and other airborne organic compounds have been identified as risk factors for developing lung and stomach cancer.

New data from several large epidemiological studies show that air pollution may also be a risk factor in these cases. Since air pollution is often as a result from coal-burning emissions, it is obvious that something has to be done quickly to reduce it.

Coal dust has also been blamed for the large number of lung and stomach cancer occurrences. Since coal miners are most affected by the coal dust and other coal-related illnesses, NIOSH's *criteria for a recommended standard—occupational exposure to respirable coalmine dust*, issued in 1995 recommends:

1. Exposures to respirable coalmine dust should be limited to one mg/m^3 as a time-weighted

average concentration for up to a 10-hour day during a 40-hour workweek

2. Exposures to respirable crystalline silica should be limited to 0.05 mg/m^3 as a time-weighted average concentration for up to a 10-hour day during a 40-hour workweek

3. The periodic medical examination for coal miners should include spirometry

4. Periodic medical examinations should include a standardized respiratory symptom questionnaire

5. Surface coal miners should be added to and included in the periodic medical monitoring

This is one of the tightest health specs, and best controlled mining work environment, in the world. Unfortunately, the GHG emissions from coal-fired power plants are not this easily controlled, so there are still many cases of coal-emissions related illnesses and death among miners and others affected persons in some areas of the U.S.

The situation is much worse in other countries, especially the developing nations, where the occupational exposure limits are lax, or non-existent. The air pollution in China, India, and other major countries is above any and all acceptable limits, and where coal-mining and burning-related illnesses and death are the norm.

The Economics of Coal Externalities

All of the impacts of coal have a direct and indirect economic cost, ranging from the jobs lost by fishermen downstream of a coal mine, to the health care costs of the people sickened by coal-fired power plant pollution, to the cost of cleaning up spills of toxic coal waste. And there are a number of other consequences—the list of which is too long to list here.

Some of the indirect economic costs of coal are in the form of subsidies and tax breaks which are not reflected in the market price of coal. For example about $4.6 billion in coal-related subsidies was introduced in the 2009 stimulus package. And on top of that, in the state of Kentucky, for example, the government spends $115 million more on subsidies for the coal industry than it receives in taxes or other benefits.

Coal mining and power plant operation are expensive projects, and often require major investments. The risks and costs of those investments are often passed on to taxpayers via different financial vehicles, such as: infrastructure subsidies and loan guarantees. For example, the Healy clean coal plant (HCCP) cost the state of Alaska and the federal government nearly $300 mil-

lion since its construction started in the mid-1990's and is yet is not produce any power in return. As a result of this, and other abnormalities in Alaska, the coal industry pays only 5% of its market value to the state, even though the nominal rates are much higher.

Taxpayers also pay the costs of cleaning up environmental disasters caused by the coal industry. These cases and the related expenses are not well publicized but many millions of dollars are spent on these activities every year.

Cleanup of the recent coal ash spill in Tennessee is estimated to cost up to $1 billion, not including pending litigation. Now that the cleanup at this site has been taken over by the EPA under the superfund law, most of this cost will be borne by the U.S. taxpayer. Congratulations, taxpayers, here is another gift from the coal industry.

The most serious impact of the coal industry is the air pollution, which has enormous economic costs through health care costs and lost productivity. Recent study by the government of Ontario estimated these costs in the billions of dollars within the state alone.

Similarly, the cost associated with premature death due to coal mining in the state of Virginia is five times greater than all measurable economic benefits from the mining industry. Measuring human death in terms of economic benefits is not easy, but our esteemed economists find the ways, and we agree that it is the best way to reflect the reality in our capitalist society.

A recent study found out that coal mining in the state of Illinois resulted in a net cost to the state of almost $20 million in 2011, even before including any externalities. Including the externalities would bring this number in the hundreds of millions dollars.

Another direct effect of coal mining is that it also hurts the ecosystems that other industries and population use and depend on. Recreational fishing, camping, commercial fishing, and tourism are important for the economy of most states. For example, there are over 55,000 full time jobs in Alaska that are closely related to, and depending on, the health of the state's fragile ecosystems. These jobs are over a quarter of Alaskan employment and produce over $2.5 billion of income in the state.

At the same time, the proposed Chuitna coal strip mine in the Cook Inlet, Alaska, would create 350 jobs, which will impact the 55,000 ecosystem-dependent jobs in a negative way. These effects will affect negatively the economy by leading to worsening the health of the population, which in turn impacts the health care costs, thus compounding the economic impact.

At the same time, it is undeniable that coal provides cheap electricity, which helps economic development and contributes to improving the health of the population, thus lowering the total health care costs. While this is true in theory, it has to be applied in the same equation with the negative economic impacts. When the total of all costs of air, soil, and water pollution, global warming, habitat destruction, and human health are added and compared with the benefits of cheap electricity, the overall economic and social impact of coal is negative by almost a two to one ratio.

$$\text{Economic benefit} = \frac{\text{Negative effects}}{\text{Positive effects}} = \frac{2}{1}$$

Could it be that the negative effects of coal mining and burning are twice as many and as serious as the positive? The coal industry proponents will surely argue with the above numbers, and the overall conclusions herein, so we just need to mention that using coal is not the only option.

So, even if the negative effects are not that great, the fact that coal is continuously emitting more and more air pollution is undeniable. The pollution in turn is causing illness and climate warming, which is also undeniable.

The other fact that needs to be considered in this context is that China, India and other large developing countries are planning to increase their use of coal mining and burning in the coming decades. That will cause an increase in coal pollution to levels we have never seen before.

What would that increase in GHG emissions will do to the health of the people and to the global environment is anyone's guess, but we venture guess that it won't be good…and might even have detrimental consequences to the people and Earth's tortured environment.

CRUDE OIL

Presently we use crude oil and its fuel derivatives (gasoline, diesel, and jet fuels) mostly for transportation, since the majority of electricity is generated by coal and natural gas. Many other products are produced from crude oil too; plastics, lubricants, fertilizers, medications, and chemicals just to name a few. Their prices are also dependent primarily on the price of raw crude oil.

Regardless of the price rise, the demand for crude oil is increasing, so are the production rates. This pattern will continue for the foreseeable future, but the natural crude oil supplies are decreasing fast. It won't take long before we see the bottom of the oil barrel and our precious crude oil gone forever. As that time approaches we will start witnessing the most incredible rise of the prices of any and all crude oil products.

Some areas of this world are gifted with huge oil supplies. Several countries in the Middle East, including Saudi Arabia, Iraq, Iran and others, have massive supplies of oil and are the world's leading oil exporters. Other countries like Russia, Venezuela and the U.S. have moderate oil supplies. Large oil fields discoveries in Texas in the last century resulted in a significant economic boom for the state and the surrounding regions. Recently, North America has become the world's second-largest oil producer.

On global scale, specialized oil interest groups like OPEC (the Organization of Petroleum Exporting Countries) monitor the oil supply of their members and control the exports as they see fit. This adds another factor in the uncertainty of oil supply and pricing. This is what caused the 1973 gas crisis in the U.S. when OPEC decided to "punish" Western nations for their support of Israel in the war in which the latter was attacked by Syria and Egypt.

The unexpected and unfairly imposed 1973 oil embargo resulted in a drastic upswing in oil prices and panic among the consumers in the U.S. and around the developed world. Gasoline prices in the U.S. rose fourfold from 30 cents per gallon to about $1.20 per gallon at the height of the crisis. And yet, $1.20 a gallon looks like a bargain now, so what's wrong with this picture?

We saw a glimpse of another tripling of prices at the gas pump in 2008-2009, when a gallon of diesel fuel at a truck stop in Bakersfield, California jumped to $6.75 a gallon overnight. Filling a truck gas tank was a traumatic near-$1,000 experience and a great hit to the pocket book of the drivers. Can this happen again? Yes, it can happen easily, since nothing in the Middle East, the U.S., or the world, has changed to a degree to warrant increased stability, or improvement in the attitude of the involved parties.

But even if the Middle East becomes a heavenly place of eternal peace, benevolence, and compassion, crude oil is a non-renewable source of energy and its supply is limited. Even in such unlikely case, very little would change at the rate we are pumping oil out of its primordial storage place.

Even the best OPEC attitude and the best of circumstances cannot change the fact that we are quickly running down the global oil supply. When it is gone, it will gone for good, never to return. Or rather, we can expect it to return after another few million years; while waiting for millions of animals and plants to fossilize and become liquefied, so that we can pump them out as crude oil again. Or not !!!

The awareness of the pending oil doom is increasing, but the demand and the daily use of oil is not decreasing. As a matter of fact there are enough data to confirm that oil use is increasing as the developing countries are demanding to share the comforts and all other economic benefits afforded the citizens of the developed world. And who can blame them?

Although it is hard to determine exactly how much oil is left in the world, governments are getting the idea that the end is near, so they and many businesses are looking into alternative sources of energy. Recently, the U.S. focused on natural gas, which is hoped to replace coal-fired power plants and even vehicles fuel, thus reducing the use of crude oil.

As the crude oil supplies dwindle, the short supply and other factors are making the demand increase, which will make the cost to go up along with it too. Wind, solar, bio- and geo-power are becoming important energy sources, which will have to take us through the transition from the dwindling fossil fuels (and crude oil in particular) to more sustainable energy sources.

Farewell, crude oil? Not so fast. There are unexplored supplies and newly emerged technologies that might extend the doomsday scenario by another 50-60, and maybe even 100 years. So for now we just have to get used to living with crude oil, accept it for what it is, and watch that it doesn't harm us more than is acceptable.

Crude Oil Use

Crude oil is a versatile and very useful product. We seldom see it in its natural shape and form—a stinky, yellow-brown-black gunk. And even less do we want to use it in its as-is form, for it is useless for all practical purposes. We, however, are crazy about its products, which vary from the gasoline we need to run our shiny cars, to the cosmetics we plaster on our faces hoping to look better, and the medicines we take hoping to live better and longer.

The list of byproducts from the crude oil refining and processing is quite long, so we will limit it to the most common; the once we know best and use daily. Some of these are:

Gasoline

Gasoline is the most common refined product, the bulk of which is used to fuel internal combustion en-

gines in the millions of cars and trucks we drive every day.

Diesel

Diesel is a slightly heavier product, used to power certain types of internal combustion engines, mostly heavier truck engine plants. It is superior to gasoline in its fuel economy and its ease of combustion. It is also known for its somewhat lower emissions.

Kerosene

Kerosene is used mostly for heating, lighting and the propulsion of jet planes. It is different than the standard jet fuel, and yet it is superior in several ways, including its higher freeze point. It can also be used to make diesel fuel.

Heating Oil

Heating oil is a low-viscosity fuel, most commonly used for burning in boilers and furnaces. About one-quarter of all crude oil is converted to heating oil for use in industry, and for heating during the winter months in some regions of the world.

Liquefied Gas

There are several kinds of liquefied petroleum gas. Propane and butane are some of the most commonly used fuels for outdoor grills and other portable appliances. These are also used in the manufacture of cosmetics, lubricants, medications, and other petrochemicals.

Residual Fuels

The heaviest fuels, which remain after most other fuels have been distilled, are residual fuels. These viscous fuels are used to power heavy machinery in boats, power plants and factories.

Asphalt

Asphalt, a byproduct of crude oil, is a black, molasses-like substance used primarily in the construction of roads, where is acts as a binding agent for hard particles.

Lubricants

Also known as mineral oils, lubricants are high-viscosity derivatives of crude used to reduce the friction between moving parts. There are a number of different types of petroleum-based lubricants, organized into three different categories based on their base chemical—paraffinic, naphthenic and aromatic.

Coke

Coke is a reside left after all the usual fuels have been distilled from the crude. It can be used as a form of charcoal briquette or in the manufacture of electrodes and dry cells.

Solvents

Crude oil is fed into special distillation columns where it is heated and refined into different solvents like benzene, toluene and xylene. These are used in many areas of the chemical industry, as well as in the manufacturing of cosmetics and medications, in addition to their use for cleaning machine parts.

Plastics

Plastics are perhaps the most significant development for the 20th century. Although we take them for granted, plastics—from a plastic grocery bag to a complex supercomputer frame—are all around us. Plastics are made from crude oil and natural gas by refining them into ethane and propane, which are then cracked into ethylene and propylene in high-temperature furnaces. Adding a catalyst converts these in a fluffy, powdered material. Thus produced polymer is melted again in the presence of additives and the melted final product (plastic) is cooled down and fed into a pelletizer that cuts the product into small pellets. The pellets can be melted and formed into different plastic products for use at the home or the industry.

Cosmetics

Crude oil and cosmetics seem unlikely partners, but they are closely related, since crude oil derivatives are the basic ingredients in many cosmetic products today. Cosmetics such as foundations, cleansers, and moisturizers often contain some type of oil. Fragrances in lotions, shampoos, and many other cosmetic products are composed of aromatic hydrocarbons, which are derived from crude oil. One popular chemical additive that carries moisture in cosmetics is propylene glycol. Yes, this is the same stuff that we use as antifreeze in our cars' radiators. Of course the function is different (or is it), but the material and its origins are surely the same.

Medications

Crude oil is also hard to imagine on the same shelf with the sterile medications in the neighborhood pharmacy. Nevertheless, some years ago crude was relished as the cure for a plethora of medical problems, both internal and external. Both the Native Americans and the early settlers found "Seneca oil" or "rock oil" an excellent curative for burns, bruises, and old sores, and especially as a liniment for various "rheumatick" complaints. Some people found the oil laced waters of Oil Creek in

Venango County a gentle but effective laxative, and later on the "American medicinal oil," which is pure crude oil came from a well in Kentucky, was prescribed by many doctors as a cure for a number of ills.

Now, crude oil derivatives, such as nitric and sulfuric acid, and many of the organic solvents from the oil refineries are used in the manufacturing process of many medicines. Some of the byproducts, such as acetylsalicylic acid (ASA) are used directly as active ingredient in many well-known over-the-counter pain relievers and other medications.

Crude Oil for Transport

But the use of crude oil and its derivatives for personal and business transport is by far the largest use of this commodity. Crude oil is used in the transport of crude oil (powering oil tankers), which determines the final price of the oil.

Table 7-10. Crude oil transport costs ($ per bbl.)

From	To	Cost
Caribbean	New York	2.46
Caribbean	Houston	0.90
N. Europe	New York	2.91
N. Europe	Houston	2.22
West Africa	N. Europe	1.60
West Africa	Houston	2.27
Persian Gulf	Houston	2.08
Persian Gulf	Japan	1.61
Persian Gulf	N. Europe	1.51

These figures, however high they might be, reflect only the direct cost of the transport service. The indirect—the externalities, such as oil spills and other transport accidents—are not included in this price. A cheaper way to transport oil is via pipelines, although the price would go up significantly if all related externalities are included in the final price.

Just mentioning Exxon Valdez brings to mind the chaos and devastation the broken oil tanker brought to the entire Alaska shoreline. Many year and mega-billions of dollars later, the horror of the accident and the agony of its effects are still present on the shoreline and in people's memories.

And speaking of the cost of crude externalities, we will only mention that some of the largest oil spills that were caused by offshore oil rigs failures. The 1969 Santa Barbara oil spill resulted from one such rig failing and belching millions of gallons of crude oil onto the pristine Santa Barbara-Ventura beaches. Many years later and millions of dollars spent on cleaning could not erase completely the marks the spill left in the water and on the beaches.

The 2010 Deepwater Horizon oil spill is the largest and most damaging by far of all previous oil spills. Its effects are still not completely accounted for. Lots of things went wrong during that time and a long time will go by before we fully appreciate the events and their aftereffects.

There is no point to quote settlement dollar numbers here, because they are astronomical, and hard to comprehend. But what is even harder to sort and account for is who gets how much and why. There is a lot of secrecy on all levels when it comes to post-accident payments. The oil companies decline to disclose the settlement amounts, and even the victims, who are most vocal during the legal action, become silent when settlements are discussed and negotiated. This leaves all of us wondering what happened, and what will happen next—hoping that we won't be the next victim.

NOTE: Companies that transport oil are required to pay $.08 per barrel into the oil spill liability trust fund, which is used by the U.S. government to respond to oil spills. But there's a catch and many companies are exempt from paying into the fund for their pipelines, when they carry oils and chemicals that are not classified as "conventional oil."

The controversial Keystone XL pipeline, which is scheduled to carry nearly 600,000 barrels of oil-like substance across the U.S. daily is also exempt for the same reason. That battle, however, is not over yet and is not clear who will win. Some changes might be the ultimate result of years spent in discussion, debate, and litigation on the issues at hand.

It suffices to say that we need crude oil, and that it has to be transported. We just have to accept that while we chose to operate this way, accidents will happen. There is no way around it, so we just have to make sure that we are prepared to handle them.

Once delivered to the refinery, the oil goes into large storage tanks (which also leak) and from there into the processing equipment to be refined into gasoline, diesel, and other solvents and chemicals.

Crude oil is made up of a mixture of many different hydrocarbons, so the first step in the refining process is to separate the different types from the mix. This is done by heating the crude oil in tall columns, during the course of which the different products are boiled off and extracted from the column at different temperatures.

The lowest temperatures in the distillation column is less than 360°F, which is where the lighter products (butane, naphtha, and low octane gasoline) are extracted, cooled down and stored for shipment or further processing. The yield at this stage is about 20% gasoline and about 50% residual crude.

At the next level of about 650°F, higher boiling point distillates (jet fuel, kerosene, home heating oil and diesel fuel) are extracted and sent down the pipes to storage containers.

There is residual oil left after all other components are extracted. It is the heaviest and least valued of the crude, and requires temperatures over 1000°F to extract some of the lighter products included in it, mostly gasoline. After all these steps, gasoline yields of around 60% of the total, and only about 5% residual is left to be discarded or used in some special applications.

Thus produced gasoline is sent for further processing, to remove the sulfur and other impurities. This process can also produce higher-octane gasoline, which costs more at the pump.

This entire process, however complex and energy hungry it might be, costs only $0.30-0.60 per gallon. The price might go up down with demand, production capacity variations and many other variables, including different taxes levied, seasonal changes and different blends required in the refining process.

Location also matters. The cost of processing a gallon of gasoline for the Virginia market will be less than for a gallon of gasoline sold at the pump in California. And this is not only due to longer transport routes. In California there are special state laws that call for specific requirements for lead content and other additives as well as unique gasoline formulations during the different seasons to prevent smog and other environmental considerations.

These extra requirements relate to higher refining costs that will be passed along in the higher pump prices. Also, since the quality of all crude oil varies widely, the level or ease (and cost) of refining depends a great deal on the quality of the crude. For example, west Texas intermediate has the most desirable characteristics for producing the lighter products like gasoline, while premium crude from Nigeria is easier to refine for middle distillates like home heating oil and jet fuel. In contrast, the refining of Saudi Arabian light will yield about 50% heavy-residual crude that must go through the more costly additional processing.

The U.S. Gulf Coast is the leader in oil refinery capacity in the U.S. and has the greatest concentration of state-of-the-art facilities in the world capable of refining the heaviest residual crude oils from all over the world. This region supplies refined products to both the East Coast (more than half of the gasoline, heating oil, diesel, and jet fuel) and to the Midwest (over 20%).

There are about 150 refineries in the U.S., with several idling periodically. The total operating capacity of the refinery fleet is around 17,500,000 barrels per day. The refineries yield about 42% gasoline, 28% home heating and diesel fuels, and 10% kerosene-based jet fuels.

Industrialized countries consume more crude oil than the rest of the world. The United States uses approximately 21 million barrels per day and leads the list of oil consuming nations. China follows with 7.3 million, Japan with 5.2 million, Russia 3.1 million, and Germany 2.6 million barrels per day.

Crude Oil Pricing

We all hate it when we hear that the price of a barrel of oil is going up. This usually means that we will pay—sooner or later—more at the pump and at the grocery store. But most of us do not know why a barrel of oil pumped out in Iran or Iraq determines the price of gasoline or diesel on the U.S. gas station pumps.

Simply put, it is because the barrel of oil—regardless where it was produced—is part of the global crude oil market, which determines the gasoline prices. About 70% of the gas price at the pump when we filled the gas tank today is derived from the price of the barrel of oil it came from. The rest is taxes, refining and transport charges. Because of that, when crude oil goes up in price, gasoline at the pump follows at approximately the same rate, but with a 4-6 weeks delay.

This is why we should not be surprised if the price of oil going is down today and yet the gas prices at the pump are rising, or visa versa. The gas price change is in response to what happened a month or more ago somewhere around the globe.

Crude oil in its purest form is of little use to anyone, so we refine it to produce useful products, such as gasoline and diesel fuels, as well as a great number of other chemicals, medications, fertilizers, and many other products. We need these products, which increases the demand for them. The high demand also contributes

somewhat to increase of their prices and with that, and depending on the supply, the price of crude oil might go up too.

We cannot control the price of oil, but why doesn't the cost of gasoline and diesel stay at a constant level? That's because crude oil is a "commodity." It is a product of certain quantity and quality, but that is basically the same no matter who or what produces it. It is just like any other commodities, such as corn, coffee beans, gold and copper.

The prices of all commodities are always in flux because they depend on worldwide supply and demand. When ethanol fuel started becoming a popular alternative fuel option in vehicles, the price of corn from which bio-ethanol is produced spiked uncontrollably, causing a number of other problems in the process as well. If an oil refinery shuts down for whatever reason, the normal supply of crude oil is reduced, which eventually causes the price of gasoline, diesel and many other products and services to increase. This is how the capitalist demand and supply MO manipulates and controls prices.

The international commodities market, on which crude oil is traded like any other commodity, also drives the crude oil prices up and down. At the commodity exchanges, large investors hedge bets on how much they think the price of oil will increase or decrease down the road. These large-scale bets and speculations over the price of oil also have a lot to do with how much it costs at certain periods of time too. The markets also take long time to respond at times, which complicates the picture and confuses the analysts.

By the end of 2008 crude oil prices spiked to over $150 per barrel (bbl). Gasoline jumped to over $4 per gallon at the pump, and diesel prices were seen as high as $6.75 per gallon in California. This somewhat scary and overly chaotic situation lasted 10-12 months and by fall of 2009 crude oil prices dropped almost three fold to around $65/bbl.

Why? There are several major drivers (in addition to the above discussed factors and abnormalities) that determine the price of crude oil. These are:

- Supply
- Consumption
- Financial markets
- Government policies

Economics 101 tells us that high supply means that the demand is low for whatever reasons. This also means that the prices are low. On the other hand, low supply usually increases demand and raises prices. Oil pricing, however, is well above and beyond the normal supply and demand rules and trends.

The way oil is traded on the financial market has a massive influence on its price. Speculators invest in oil futures, which are no more than bets on how much oil will cost at a later date. This affects how other people think oil should be priced and often contributes to mass hysteria that drives oil prices unreasonably high at times. This then affects how much oil the petroleum companies will release to the market, and all these components feed on each other adding more complexity and uncertainty to the system.

Government regulations are, willingly or unwillingly, also a big factor in setting oil prices. Tightening the rules on oil's sulfur content would raise the demand for sweet crude oil, which contains less sulfur. This in turn would increase the price of sweet crude oil, which is already less common than other types. Increased taxes on gasoline also affect the prices, and modify the public behavior, which might result in reduced driving.

As utilities switch to power sources like wind and solar energy, and as people drive more fuel-efficient cars, the demand for oil is going down in the U.S., but is increasing in other parts of the world, like India and China. This means that we are not going to see natural decrease in oil usage any time soon, and with that the oil supplies will continue to decrease rapidly, while its price goes up.

There are many other factors that determine how much a barrel of this precious commodity cost today, tomorrow, and even a month and year down the road. Weather, politics, economic developments, wars, accidents, sudden increase in demand factors also should be entered into the complex formula of the crude oil price structure. The gasoline and diesel price structure follows the crude oil price fluctuations with some up-down modifications and time lapses.

Nevertheless, the U.S. oil production is expected to rise by nearly 30%, to over 7.5 million barrels per day by 2020, which could lead to more stable prices and fewer supply disruptions for American consumers and businesses. But even more important, increased U.S. oil production will inevitably lead to a reduction in the more than $400-500 billion the country now spends each year to import foreign oil. This will cut the nation's annual trade deficit, thus keeping more money flowing through the domestic economy instead of sending it to the sheikhs in the deserts of MENA countries, or the revolutionary Hadji Babas in Iran.

Finally, being able to see the end of an oil imports era, and approaching energy independence, is the best news of the 21st century for America, and we are looking forward to seeing it through.

Oil Commodities Markets

What/who determines the price of oil? How much does a barrel of oil really cost? Oil prices go up and down daily and these numbers are used to set the prices at the pump and even dictate energy policies. They, however, fall short of explaining the complexity of the global oil markets.

Since it is impossible to synthesize the diversity of oil prices around the world, the oil industry uses benchmarks, which are a small number of carefully tracked prices at specially chosen locations. Some of these benchmarks are considered as industry standards and are used to set or compare all other prices of the different producers.

The most common crude oil benchmarks are:

• The Brent crude A benchmark is represented by crude oils produced in the North Sea. It is used to determine prices in Europe, Africa and the Middle East.

• West Texas intermediate is the price used for contracts traded on the New York mercantile exchange, and it is typically the price that the media has in mind in reports about oil.

The global oil market is the most important of the world energy markets because of oil's dominant role as an energy source, especially in the transportation sector. Understanding its function reveals the functioning of the global energy markets in general. Crude oil is an important commodity, which is traded like any other commodity. Contracts for its supply are traded through the commodity exchanges of the New York Mercantile Exchange and the Intercontinental Exchange.

Marginal Cost

The oil producers decide when and how much oil to pump out, depending (mainly, but not exclusively) on whether each additional unit of production will be profitable. Each additional unit (above the current production level) is a marginal unit. The cost of producing this additional unit is known as the *marginal* cost, and the price at which it can be sold is the marginal price.

Generally speaking, the *marginal price* is very important because it largely determines the behavior of producers and consumers, which in turn shapes the market for the duration. This principle is valid for all tradable commodities, including oil.

In our globalized world most countries are heavily dependent on foreign suppliers of energy products to operate efficiently. Globalization has leveled the world powers, so that a terrorist action in unstable countries like Nigeria, or Sudan, which are minor oil exporters, affect the world price of oil almost immediately. Usually we will see the action in Nigeria reflected in the higher price of gas we pay at the pump. This changes the marginal cost of oil, albeit temporarily.

Because of the influence of the uncontrollable marginal cost, sovereign nations do not have much control over the price of crude oil. Claims that energy independence will provide much needed control are no more than a wish that is void of substance. Oil is traded globally, so a supply disruption anywhere will affect energy prices throughout the world.

A good example of this is the wars in Iraq and Afghanistan, which have created, among other problems, a continual and substantial rise in the price of oil coming from that area of the world. Although the oil supplies have been relatively stable in recent years, the increased demand means that there is very little room for disruption in global supplies:

In a world where every single barrel counts, the actions of a terrorist group in unstable Nigeria or Venezuela could threaten the entire global energy security. The world exporters are pumping at nearly full capacity, so any interruption is critical and the global oil market cannot afford the smallest loss of exports from even the smallest producer.

This gives every marginal producer unprecedented power and greater geopolitical influence. This is one of the main reasons why energy issues are becoming more important by the day in discussions around the kitchen table, during debates in Washington, DC, and as well as at meetings on global level. Crude oil supplies and prices affect everything: driving to work, national economic policies, and international activities and relations.

Elasticity

Elasticity is a basic measurement of the response of supply and demand to price fluctuations. The supply or demand of a commodity (or any goods) is considered inelastic when price does not have a large effect on production or consumption. On the other hand, when the product price does have a significant effect, then the good's supply and demand are called elastic.

Elasticity is largely determined by the availability of the product, or its equivalent substitutes, and the reaction of the consumers. If the price of gasoline rose from $3 per gallon $3.30 per gallon, consumers will have to choose between reducing driving to save money, or paying the high price and continue driving the way they used to before the increase.

If many drivers are willing to reduce their driving routes, based on such a relatively small change in price, then the demand for gasoline is "elastic." If, however, this 10% increase in the price of gasoline did not cause drivers to change their driving habits, then the demand would be "inelastic."

Since there are no substitutes for oil, and people (especially in the rich countries) depend on driving their cars to work and anywhere else, then the demand for oil is thus thought to be generally inelastic. Lately, however, we have been witnessing signs of a change to a more elastic-like approach by the U.S. consumers, mostly due to the availability of alternative energy sources and alternative approaches (electric cars and such.) Nevertheless, these changes are minor, so much deeper structural changes would be needed to seriously impact the demand cycle profoundly and change it to being strictly elastic.

The inelasticity of demand even in the face of extremely high-energy prices in recent years has been quite obvious and even surprising. One way to explain it is by taking a closer look at the factors that drive high-energy prices. The price spikes during the oil crisis of the late 1970s were caused by restrictions to global energy supplies, so they were driven mostly by the supply factors. Presently, the high oil prices are due mostly to record demand, much of which can be attributed to the rise of an energy-hungry China and India. So the difference between 1973 and 2013 is critical—supply limitations in 1973, vs. record demand in 2013.

In the current demand-driven oil markets, the high prices have not been able to trigger corresponding decreases in consumption. As a matter of fact, the demand is increasing with total disregard to the supply issues and serious future limitations. This means that the days of cheap crude oil are over and that the high prices at the gas pumps are the norm now and forever.

There is a chance (albeit slight) that the elasticity of demand will gradually return to dominate the oil market. Unlike many other commodities, oil consumption has been inelastic and impervious to price fluctuations since the very beginning, or so it looks on the surface. In reality, prices always affect demand, even if the effect is not very significant, and even if it takes long time to manifest itself. This abnormality in this case is due to the fact that consumers—especially these in the developed countries—are determined to maintain the lifestyle they are used to and will drive as much as they want, whenever they want, for as long as possible.

Experience shows that oil consumption patterns will eventually be adjusted according to the higher global prices. This in fact might already be occurring, as oil prices have begun to level and even stabilize.

At the same time, OPEC and other oil producing countries are well aware of this abnormality, so they cut or add millions of barrels of oil per day depending on the demand and according to their abilities. For the first six months of 2012, for example, OPEC increased production by 1.4 million barrels a day, despite slumping oil prices at the time. This move was dictated by increased demand from China and other countries.

OPEC and the other oil producers moderate their actions driven mostly by fear that: a) oil prices might get too low and cut their profits on the short term, or b) that the higher prices might dampen efforts to improve the global economy, which might hurt their exports in the long run. Because of that, OPEC countries balance their exports to keep prices high enough, while continuing to add oil to the global market as needed to keep them running. They will continue doing this until they finally run out of oil, and then there will be no more OPEC. OPEC will then become OEPEC—Organization of Ex-Petroleum Exporting Countries.

For now, however, the global oil policy decisions depend on how the question of demand elasticity is viewed and approached.

Crude Oil Futures

Similar to the stock market, which involves trading investments in various companies, people also trade in a number of commodities (wheat, corn, pork bellies, gold and silver) at the global financial markets. These commodities include crude oil, whose importance as an energy source and trading commodity is increasing by the day.

The crude oil futures are traded in the New York mercantile exchange (or NYMEX), as well as the international petroleum exchange. People purchase futures of certain commodities, which are basically a sort of bet on whether the particular commodity will increase in price (or not) at a later date. Once locked into a futures contract, the buyer will get his or her commodity at that price, regardless of whether the market price has changed or not later down the line.

Commodity trading has been getting bigger than ever in recent years as a response to the dot-com crash of the early 2000s. As result, speculation has come to

shape the price of oil in a big way—and surely much more than ever before. We saw the abnormal and even scary increase of oil prices in 2008 to over $150 per bbl. There were no abnormal natural events, wars, or anything even nearly spectacular in the world at that time to justify any increase of prices. let alone the jump to unheard of high prices.

The 2008 oil price hike was partially as a result of the surprising effect commodity futures have on crude oil prices. It showed us that speculators who buy large amounts of futures can swing the price one way or another. A speculator who buys oil futures at higher than the current market price can cause oil producers to horde their oil supply so they can sell it later at the new, higher "future" price. This cuts the current supply of oil on the market and drives up both present and future prices. Thus $150 per bbl in 2008 and part of 2009.

While it may seem unfair that speculators have so much sway over the oil market, we all know that speculation is a significant part of any financial system, and stock investments are an act of speculation in and of itself. Dow Jones is based on speculation very close in nature to a gambling casino in Las Vegas. When buying stock, we are speculating on a company's future and the results of its future development.

Government regulation plays a significant role in keeping the speculators from going completely out of control. In the U.S., the commodity futures trading commission (CFTC) was established during the 1970s oil crises to head off speculation that artificially drove up the price of oil. Over the past few decades, however, the CFTC lost most of its regulatory power, especially during the economic boom of the 1990s.

As oil prices spike higher, Congress has shown more interest in allowing the commission to have increased oversight over oil prices. In any case, oil speculation is here to stay. It is legal and even encouraged by the authorities and the producers. It is the new way of looking at oil, so we better take a close look at it.

The New Direction...

The global oil financial markets drive the oil prices now, not the Arab sheikhs. Not any more! Got that? Most people are unaware of this important fact, so it must be remembered and used as a cornerstone in all oil decisions we make now and in the future. Also, the days of unlimited, cheap oil are over. A new oil future is awaiting us, so we need to jump into it with our eyes fully opened.

Several enormous changes rocked the oil markets lately, which created a number of problems, the impact of each of which will be felt for a long time…maybe forever.

Some of the changes in the crude oil industry are:

- Abnormally increased interest of new institutional and individual investors in commodities, and particularly the price of crude, which became the hottest game in town since 2008. Everyone is involved in it in one way or another and everyone wants to be a part of it.

Using commodity index funds and exchange-traded funds (ETFs), through dedicated energy hedge funds as well as individual futures accounts, the price of oil is now as easily investable as any stock or bond. This opens new opportunities to investors—even small ones—but complicates the already complex picture of oil demand, supply and pricing.

- Oil has only been available as an investment for a few years, but its share in the world's energy markets is increasing. As an asset class, oil has a lot of catching up to do, and a lot of new money yet to assimilate. But nevertheless, the asset-ization of oil is here to stay and is driving oil prices up and down according to the whims of the financial markets.

- There had been a rush for fresh financial innovation, so following patterns from similar derivative markets, the investment banks and energy marketers created and sold a whole new category of specialized and customized products to cater to every kind of energy client they could imagine. This includes financial products that would help mitigate risks from differing grades of crude, of transporting and refining crude, and from the output products from crude and their final sale. This created dozens of new markets, most of them over the counter and designed to be closed to most investors and accessible only to in-house traders of proprietary accounts. Commodity exchanges rushed to offer clearing of these side markets and get in on the new action.

- West Texas intermediate was the only traded crude product in the world some time ago, but now the exchange offers clearing on nearly 100 futures and derivative of derivatives on crude with even more numerous and complicated products offered in refined products and natural gas.

- While the opportunity for profiting from the sale and proprietary trading of this unnecessary diversity grew, so did the nominally traded market in oil, now 15 times greater than the amount of real physical oil. Got that? We now can trade a lot oil; most of which does not exist. The volume of the possible trade operations is 15-20 times larger than the actual amount of oil available at any time for sale or trade.

- The recent change from human driven trading on the trading floor, to a highly computerized, electronic virtual world of trading and price discovery destroyed many of the governors on price swings. The previous on-floor trading, which seems outdated and quaint now, provided as near to perfect a pipeline for orderly introduction of trade by forcing all the participants to transparently appear at one place to transact business. Now, open access of internet-based electronic platforms to oil trading has spurred massive increases in trading volume, but also created massive volatility, which leads to fluctuations and eventually to higher prices.

- The near $150 per bbl price in 2008 was driven and maintained at that unreasonably high level not by the oil sheikhs but by computer commodities traders, who were making money by driving the oil price up. And the price went up to the maximum possible level within days, making lots of money for some lucky people. It finally deflated, making lots of losers, also, almost overnight.

Gasoline Cost

Gasoline is what makes America move around the country. It is also one of the most profitable items on the oil companies' list of products. In the 1990s U.S. oil refiners made an average profit of 22 cents from each gallon of gasoline sold. By the mid 2000s, they were getting over 40 cents, and much more in California (due to special blends required).

The oil companies' profit margins fluctuate wildly among the different companies, from place to place, and from time to time. Since there are so many variables at play, precise cost breakdown of the different components in the total price of gasoline at the pump is difficult.

An estimate of the breakdown of the average cost at the pump for a gallon of gasoline is shown in Table 7-11.

Table 7-11. Cost of gasoline

Cost of crude oil	74%
Taxes	11%
Refining costs	10%
Distribution	5%
Total	100%

What Table 7-11 is trying to tell us is that the actual cost of crude oil is the major factor determining the price of gasoline at the pump. So it matters where the oil came from, and at what time. Oil coming from Iraq during the war activities would have added some extra charge. Crossing the Strait of Hormuz during the time of Iran's provocations in the area would have also added some cost to the oil price.

It also appears to be the only significant variable in the gasoline price structure. The other variables; taxes, refining, and distribution costs might vary, but by not much. And even if they do, their share in the total price is small, so we have to thank the oil producing countries for the high price we pay at the pump. This is a good reason to focus on energy (oil) independence. It is not the best solution, but it is the best of all possible choices.

In all cases, the oil companies that buy, refine and sell the gasoline will ensure a profit of $0.30-0.60 per gallon, or thereabouts. With all other variables in place, this profit margin is the only component of the price structure set in cement. Fair? Maybe…to a point. Just think that in 2008 Exxon reported a quarterly profit in excess of $40 billion—yes with a B—at a time when crude oil prices shot through the roof at over $150 per barrel. It was also the dark time of the global economy about to collapse, when millions were unemployed, and many more were losing their jobs daily. Fair? Maybe, depending on which side of the equation we sit.

NOTE: The U.S. oil companies claim that they have a reduced profit margin when the crude oil prices rise over $100 per barrel because it becomes increasingly difficult to pass the added costs to the consumer at the gas pump. Nevertheless, the oil companies have an obligation to their shareholders, not to their customers. They are mandated to increase profits as much as possible, but that is getting harder to do with crude oil prices so high.

In addition, when the price of oil increases, the consumption of gasoline in the U.S. usually falls significantly. So, when, for example, crude oil prices double, the wholesale prices for gasoline rise only about 30-40%. Since the crude oil price is the major component in the gasoline price structure, keeping the price at the pump

low eats into the oil companies' profits—or so they say.

What will happen in the future with the gas prices and oil companies' profits remains to be seen, but one thing is for sure—crude oil prices will continue going up and the gasoline prices will follow closely. Maybe not very close, but close enough.

The significant reduction in consumption in the U.S. reported lately is offset by the steadily increasing demand for crude oil from developing nations like China and India. And since the price at the gas pump depends on the cost of crude oil, and crude oil is traded on the global markets, the prices of both commodities in the U.S. will keep rising. How much and how long…we'll just have to wait and see.

Oil Rig Cost

Oil rigs are complex, custom made, structures. Land oil rigs are different from their offshore cousins, simply because they don't have to deal with deep water during installation and rough sees during operation. Most large, permanent, oil rigs are owned by large oil companies, but there are also many smaller, privately, owned oil rigs.

Specialized oil rig installation companies, who leave the site after a successful rig installation and drilling, install oil rigs. The cost of the installation is considered part of the overall cost of operation and is usually amortized for the life of the rig.

Table 7-12. Oil rig permitting cost (U.S. dollars)

Cost category	Cost $
NEPA / CEQA documents (EIS / EIR)	2,000,000
Execution plan preparation	100,000
Data collection and field surveys	60,000
Agency processing fees and staff time	65,000
Air & fisheries fees	100,000
Marine mammal fees	65,000
Mitigation and monitoring compliance	65,000
Total cost, each project / permit	**$2,555,000**

The cost of the offshore oil rigs is much higher and the land lease/purchase, permitting, and installation processes are much more complex and expensive, as is also the operation of an offshore rig.

A land oil rig could be installed and sold for as little as $1.0 million and up. Usually a lot up, when considering cost of the land, permits, and so forth.

For example drilling a swamp barge oil rig could cost from $10-100 million, depending on size and location. A jack up (shallow offshore) would be priced at $50-150 millions and more.

Offshore rigs also require special transport vehicles for a number of needs and services. A semi submersible, as used in deep offshore operations could cost $100-500 million. A drillship's cost varies from $250-500 million. Shore shuttles (small supply boats) vary from $1-10 million.

Renting some of these facilities and vehicles is an option in some cases, at equally stiff prices; a land rig, for example, could be rented for $10,000-20,000 per day, a swamp barge for $25,000-50,000 per day, jack up setup for $100,000-200,000 per day. The vehicles, unlike rental cars, cost a fortune as well; a shuttle boat might cost $5,000-10,000 per day, a semi-sub would set you back $100,000-300,000 per day, and a drill ship in the range of $250,000-500,000 per day.

Not a cheap enterprise. Imagine paying $100,000 per day, with everything going well until high seas, or a stupid mistake puts the operation on hold. How long can you be on hold while paying $100,000 per day? Because of this, and other similar complexities and intricacies, the entire cradle-to-grave process requires a thorough understanding of the elements and technologies, proper design and excellent management. Even the smallest mistakes are too costly to even factor in the designs, and some might put the entire project on permanent hold.

Another great expense is the daily operation of the oil rigs, where, again, off shore rigs are many times more difficult and expensive to operate. For example, the operation of a $200 million off shore rig in the Gulf of Mexico costs $40-60 million per annum. This includes the daily operational expenses for health and risk insurance, operational and maintenance labor, helicopters, supply boats, meals, entertainment for the personnel (yes, have to keep them all happy there, or else).

The expense numbers are not set in concrete. Instead they vary according to the workload and other conditions related to the rig operation, maintenance and other support services. And the expenses usually vary by going up, as does everything else.

And finally, there is another expense that might be quite significant. It is the end-of-life decommissioning, disassembly and disposal of the rig components. This is another multi-million dollar endeavor that has similar components of danger and risks, especially for offshore rigs.

There are many cases, however, where millions of dollars are spent only to find out that the well is not productive, or underproductive. In any case, it has to be abandoned and the rig disassembled, all of which is a great financial loss.

End of Life

Any and all oil wells reach a time in their lives when it is no longer profitable to operate them. This is the time when the production income does not cover the operating expenses, including taxes, insurance and other expenses.

This is the so-called "economic limit" of the well of oil or gas wells, which can be expressed as follows:

Oil Fields

$$EL_{oil} = \frac{WI \times LOE}{NRI[P_o + (P_g \, c \, GOR)/1,000] \times (1-T)}$$

EL_{oil} is an oil well's economic limit in oil barrels per month (bbls/month)

P_o, P_g are the current prices of oil and gas in dollars per barrels and dollars per MSCF respectively

LOE   is the lease operating expenses in dollars per well per month.

WI   is working interest, as a fraction

NRI   is net revenue interest, as a fraction

GOR   is gas/oil ratio as bbls/MSCF

Y   is condensate yield as barrel/million standard cubic feet

T   is production and severance taxes, as a fraction

In many cases, gas is found alongside with oil deposits, so it is useful to know what that means in economic terms.

Gas Fields

$$EL_{gas} = \frac{WI \times LOE}{NRI[(P_o \times Y) + P_g] \times (1-T)}$$

Where:

EL_{gas} is a gas well's economic limit in thousand standard cubic feet per month (MSCF/month).

P_o, P_g are the current prices of oil and gas in dollars per barrels and dollars per MSCF respectively.

LOE   is the lease operating expenses in dollars per well per month.

WI   is working interest, as a fraction.

NRI   is net revenue interest, as a fraction.

GOR   is gas/oil ratio as bbls/MSCF.

Y   is condensate yield as barrel/million standard cubic feet.

T   is production and severance taxes, as a fraction.

When the economic limit of a oil well is reached, it becomes unprofitable, and might even be a liability, at which point it is usually abandoned. Pipe and tubing networks are removed from the well and sections of well bore are filled with cement. The surface area around the wellhead is then excavated, and the wellhead and casing are cut off, a cap is welded in place and then buried. Sometimes the well bore is filled completely with cement, but this costly and unnecessary.

Abandoning the well and reconstructing the land is important and very much needed to isolate the flow path between gas and water zones from each other, as well as the surface, thus preventing future water or air contamination.

NOTE: Similar reasoning and calculations could be used to figure out the economic limit of coal mines and coal mining operations, but there are other variables in these cases that need to be considered, and which make the calculations much more complicated.

In most cases, when the economic limit of a oil or gas well is reached there is still a significant amount of material (oil, or gas) left in the original deposit. It is usually much harder and more expensive to extract, but the remaining quantity still might tempt the owners to defer total abandonment for a period of time, hoping that the oil price will go up, or that new, more efficient, recovery techniques will be discovered. In most cases, however, lease and insurance provisions and government regulations require quick abandonment, so the wells are capped quickly and the land brought back to its original state.

So, although in theory an abandoned well can be reopened and restored to production (or converted to injection service for supplemental recovery or for downhole hydrocarbons storage), this often proves to be difficult mechanically and not cost effective for now.

In the near future, however, as oil prices continue to go up, and as oil becomes scarcer, thousands of these wells will be restarted, which will create another set of price tariffs and will bring into the open a set of new environmental issues.

NOTE: The construction and operation cost of an oil well does not include the costs associated with the dangers of accidents, risk of explosion, or oil leakage. Some of these additional costs, partially covered by insurance and/or contracts, include the cost of protecting against major disasters, as well as the cost of mitigation of accidents and the related cleanup efforts; which could be significant and can put any operation in financial jeopardy.

In such cases, there are also hard-to-calculate costs of damage to the company's reputation and image. Just look what happened to BP after the 2010 Deep Horizon oil leak accident. Would they ever recover, regardless of the billions of dollars already paid and many more to be paid. And if they recover, it is only because they are such a large and rich company. So the question then is, can a small company recover from such a major disaster? Probably not!

Oil Rig and Well Decommissioning

After 20-30 years of operation, the oil transport and producing equipment gets old and has to be shut down and decommissioned. After many decades of use, oil rigs, gas wells, pipelines, oil tankers, refineries, oil storage tanks, and all the related equipment are usually a combination of dirty, rusty parts, components, and structures. A stinky, gooey mess, which has to be demolished, put apart, loaded on vehicles, and transported somewhere for storage or disposal.

The old site has to be cleaned up and brought up to its original condition as much as possible. Another messy, gooey, stinky, and dangerous job.

The first thing to do, before starting any of this work, however, is to apply for and obtain an official permit to do the decommissioning work. This is a lengthy and expensive process that has to be done according to federal, state, and local laws and regulations.

After the permitting process is completed, the actual decommissioning work starts. It is dirty, cumbersome, dangerous affair that is also very expensive.

Oil companies contract most of the equipment and services needed for the decommissioning process. Just take a look at Table 7-14 for the rates to bring in and use a heavy lift vessel as needed for decommissioning large oil rigs. A simple calculation shows that using the 4000-ton HLV for 200 days will cost nearly $100 million. And this is just to lease the vehicle as needed to decommission one single rig operating offshore in California' Pacific waters. Not an easy, or a cheap project.

Other costs pile on top of that too. The total costs for pre- and post-decommissioning side scan surveys, post-decommissioning debris removal, test trawling to ensure the area is clear of obstructions, and shell mound geotechnical and biological surveys, average $700,000 for platforms in less than 300 feet of water and double that amount for platforms at greater depths.

Shell mound (barnacles grown on the platform structure) must be removed prior to disposal. The shell mounds under some platforms can contain as much as 12,500 cubic yards of material. The removal of large amounts of shell mound material, particularly at the

Table 7-13.
Permitting fee for a oilrig-decommissioning progra

Category of installation	Fee $
- Small scale offshore installation. Any concrete or steel offshore platform or other installation including subsea with a weight of less than 10,000 tons.	130,000
- Submarine pipeline	130,000
- Multiple small scale offshore installation. Two or more concrete or steel offshore platforms or other installations including subsea each with a weight of less than 10,000 tons.	160,000
- Large scale offshore installation. Any concrete gravity based structure or steel offshore platform or installation with a weight of 10,000 tons or more.	260,000
- Combination of large and small scale offshore installation. Two or more concrete gravity based structures or steel offshore platforms or installations including subsea at least one of which (but not all) has a weight of 10,000 tons or more.	290,000
- Multiple large scale offshore installation. Two or more concrete gravity based structures or steel offshore platforms or installations each with a weight of 10,000 tons or more.	325,000
G) Revision (Section 34)	65,000

Table 7-14. Estimate cost of oilrig decommissioning.

Heavy Lift Vessel	Travel time	Setup	Day rate
500 ton HLV	100 days	$14.04 million	$156,000
2000 ton HLV	100 days	$18.36 million	$204,000
4000 ton HLV	200 days	$45.36 million	$252,000

deeper platforms, could involve a significant expense, including $220/cubic yard including disposal charge, or total of another $2.75 million just to remove and dispose of the barnacles.

The demobilization (disassembly) of the rig could add another $250,000-350,000 to the total cost of the decommissioning effort.

Scrap facilities in the Long Beach and Los Angeles area charge disposal costs of $384/ton, including site preparation, materials offloading of the cargo barges, materials handling, materials demolition, and materials scrap processing. This cost estimate does not include any scrap recycle value, or hazardous materials handling and disposal.

Reef enhancement, consisting of placing boulders or concrete around the base of the platform is a requirement in some cases too. The cost for placing a layer of

1-2 foot diameter rock in a water depth of about 45 feet average $60,000 per acre, including the cost of the rock itself, and transportation to, and placement at the site.

And then, there are costs related to additional labor, safety, and legal actions that add up very quickly to millions of dollars on top of all the other millions of dollars spent on the other steps of the process.

In other words, what we consumers need to remember from all this is that pulling up to the gas pump and complaining about the high gasoline prices is the easy part. The part that we don't see and don't appreciate, because we don't see nor smell the mess, takes place far away, deep in the oceans, or high up on the mountain tops. That is where the real work of bringing the gasoline to our gas pump starts and ends. And the people doing this work day and night are the ones who make it happen, and we should be thankful for their efforts.

Fuel Subsidies and Taxes

Fossil and renewable fuels have benefitted from influx of enormous subsidies through the years, which continue presently as well. On the other hand, the fuels have been exposed to taxation that varies from type to type and from location to location.

The problem is that there is lack of clarity on the subject, because the entire financial aspect of the different fuels is veiled in thin layers of foggy information or lack of information.

Fuels Subsidies

Recent estimates of the direct and indirect fossil fuel subsidies in the U.S. range from $14 to $50 billion annually. This includes some military spending on defending the international oil routes.

The breakdown of energy related U.S. government subsidies of several years ending at 2008 was as follows:

- $72.5 billion of fuel subsidies were allocated to the fossil industry, with $70.2 billion going to the traditional fossil fuels, and $2.3 billion spent on carbon capture and storage, $16.8 billion of fuel subsidies were allocated to corn ethanol development, production, and use projects, and 29.0 12.2 billion of fuel subsidies were allocated to the renewable energy sources, with $12.2 billion spent on the traditional renewable energy sources, and the rest used for R&D of new technologies.

The amount of government fossil fuels subsidies around the globe in 2012 alone was an astounding $775 billion (yes, with a B).

The breakdown of fossil fuels subsidies around the globe is as follows:

- $630 billion of fossil fuel subsidies were allocated to consumption subsidies in the developing countries alone. This number fluctuates widely with the price of oil from $409 billion in 2010, and $557 billion in 2008.

- $45 billion of fossil fuel subsidies were allocated to consumption subsidies in the developed countries, which is considered to be an average annual consumption subsidy.

- $100 billion of fossil fuel subsidies were allocated to the global producers, as cited in the June 2010 report for G-20 leaders from OECD, IEA, World Bank and OPEC. Here again, lack of total transparency is hindering getting a clear picture of the fossils subsidies.

In 2009, G20 leaders pledged to phase out fossil fuel subsidies, which was an historic commitment. Put on paper this was a great beginning, but which did not go very far, partially because it is not clear how much money the governments provide in fossil fuel subsidies. But the major problem is that politicians change their minds with the political winds, so whatever is promised today is no longer valid tomorrow…usually justified by unforeseen change in economic and political conditions.

Efforts to remove even small portions of those subsidies are constantly defeated in Congress, because it is generally assumed that keeping fuel prices low by subsidizes is beneficial to the economic development of the country. The low fuel price is credited with increasing employment, invigorating the general business activities, reducing property values, and increasing tax revenues. Another benefit credited to low fuel prices is helping the poor people, as an extra benefit that offsets some of the external costs.

These assumptions, however, are very often wrong. No doubt, that low fuel prices and subsidies do stimulate some—mostly fuel related—activities, such as fuel purchases and transport. These gains are small comparatively speaking, and the fuel subsidies often cause greater economic harm by:

a) Transferring wealth from fuel consumers to producers, since the producers benefit from receiving payment for their regular prices, while the consumers are eventually paying the price of the subsidies

b) Reducing overall transport system efficiency, which often leads to traffic congestion, accidents, higher road expenses, sprawl, and pollution emissions increases, as compared with higher fuel price conditions

Low fuel prices also cause increased vehicle travel, which we should remember, increases among the wealthy and much less in urban areas. Adding up to 5,000 annual vehicle-miles per person of the wealthy class only increases some of the above mentioned issues, and does not do anything to help the economy, especially that of the urban areas.

Economic benefits increase with higher fuel prices in some cases, particularly in oil consuming regions, where the fuels are imported. This is because higher fuel prices encourage people and businesses to think and operate outside the box by using resource efficient fuel consuming and transport options. This results in less wealth to be transferred to the oil producers, thus leaving more money in the local economy. This also could reduces transportation costs, increase employment, and invigorate the local business activity.

This can happen even in oil producing regions, as for example Norway, which is a major petroleum producer, and yet maintains high fuel prices. The high fuel prices in turn force the implementation of energy conservation policies, thus leaving more oil to export. As a result, Norway has one of the world's highest incomes, a competitive and expanding economy, a positive trade balance, and the world's largest legacy fund.

On the other hand, Saudi Arabia, Venezuela, and Iran subsidize the fuel to keep its price low and keep the masses happy, which, however, results in inefficient resource consumption, wasteful behavior, and relatively anemic economic development. In such and most other cases fuel expenditures are regressive, since they increase with income levels, so the overall equity impacts depend on how revenues (and subsidies) are used and the quality of transport options available.

Complicated picture of these subsidies, no doubt, the magnitude of which brings an obvious question, "Why are the world governments involved so closely in the fuels business, and why are they trying to control it?" The official answer is also obvious: "Fossils are the blood of the world's economies." But the more important question that remains unanswered is, "What will happen if the governments leave the energy sector alone and let it operate on its own in a true capitalist manner—with no outside assistance and control, complete with competition?" And the answer is silence.

Fuels Taxation

Many countries tax fuels directly for some applications; the U.K., for example, imposes direct taxes on vehicle gasoline and diesel fuels, which is adjusted to equivalent levels among the different fuels. The direct tax sends a clear signal to the consumer, but its use as an efficient mechanism to influence consumers' fuel needs to be revised for a number of reasons.

Some of the uncertainties about fuel taxes are related to the fact that in many countries fuel is already taxed to influence transport behavior and to raise other public revenues. The fuel taxes in most cases are used as a source of general revenue but since the price elasticity of fuel is low, increasing fuel taxation has a very slight impact on their economies. Under these circumstances, the role of the carbon tax is unclear.

A tax on vehicle fuel may counterbalance the "rebound effect" that has been observed when vehicle fuel consumption has improved through the imposition of efficiency standards. Rather than reducing their overall consumption of fuel, consumers have been seen to make additional journeys or purchase heavier and more powerful vehicles.

There is also enough evidence that consumers' decisions on fuel economy are not entirely aligned to the price of fuel. This can deter manufacturers from producing efficient vehicles, which have lower sales potential and bring lesser profits. Other broader efforts, such as imposing efficiency standards on manufacturers, or changing the income tax rules on taxable benefits, may be at least as significant.

If fuel taxes are used to finance services that benefit lower-income households, such as improved public education or transit, and if lower-income people have fuel-efficient transport options, then high fuel taxes are not necessarily regressive.

This reasoning is complicated by the diversity of the population, and the different socio-economic policies, but it leads to the conclusion that higher fuel taxes can be good and bad, depending on a number of factors. They can depress or support economic development depending on the combination of those factors. If implemented gradually and predictably, they could help to create more equitable transport systems. They can be even more beneficial if combined with policies that increase transport system efficiency and diversity, such as improved walking, cycling and public transit service.

But wait, walking, cycling and using public transit service is not part of the American Dream? Is that even possible? How many people living in the suburbs would get out of their comfortable SUVs and walk and cycle to work or to a concert, even if it were possible? Nope, not in America. Not today! We love our cars and will stand by them, and in them, until the last drop of oil, or until death do us part— whichever comes first.

Crude Oil Externalities

From economics point of view, **externalities reflect the cost** (of damage or benefit), which results from an activity or transaction, which affects a third, party uninvolved in the activity and who did not choose to incur that cost or benefit.

The cost of externalities is not easy to calculate, because they usually contain hidden costs: costs that have not been valued yet, or are simply hard to value in dollar terms. Nevertheless, there are a number of examples, which could be used as guidelines, or at least to compare similar cases in the future.

Some examples of externalities:

- Estimates for oil spill cleanup and damage costs in the U.S. average approximately $16 per gallon, or $670 per barrel. The range, however, varies wildly from $7 per gallon, or $300 per barrel, for the 1979 Ixtoc I spill in the Gulf of Mexico, to over $630 per gallon, or $25,000 per barrel, for the 1980 Exxon Valdez spill in Alaska.

These numbers reflect only the compensation costs, while many other damages are not compensated due to the complexity and the inherited difficulty to attribute costs to some damage types or locations. This is particularly true for small spills, including spills in international waters, or assessing damages to ecological services that lack legal status.

Some of the costs of these and most other, externalities are paid by the companies involved, but a significant part is paid directly by the taxpayers, and indirectly by the locals that are affected by the damages.

The major annual costs of petroleum production and use in the U.S., some of which are considered externalities are:

• Surface transportation	$91	billion
• Defense spending	83	billion
• National security	24	billion
• Climate change	16	billion
• Production externalities	1	billion
Total petroleum externalities	215	billion/year

If applied to the production levels, these would average about $14 of new taxes per barrel of crude oil. This breaks down to $0.33 per gallon for transport expenditures, and $2.96 per gallon for of external costs needed to pay for oil production and import services. This is almost $3.00 per gallon that needs to be added to the gas pump price to pay for all externalities. And these numbers are increasing by the day...

• In the late mid-2000s a federal report estimated U.S. petroleum import external economic costs, excluding military expenditures, to a total of $13.60 per barrel, with a range of $6.70 to $23.25, or about $54 billion annual cost to the U.S. economy. This phenomenon was further qualified as "a measure of the quantifiable per-barrel economic costs that the U.S. could avoid by a small-to-moderate reduction in oil imports."

The external costs per gallon and vehicle-mile from the extraction, distribution, and consumption of various fuels and vehicles for various time periods were estimated at:

• Car health damages totaling $36 billion
• All vehicles damages totaling $56 billion

NOTE: Electric vehicles and grid-dependent hybrid vehicles show higher damages than many other technologies if and when electricity is generated by fossil fuels, based on current emission control requirements.

The total externality of oil dependence of the U.S. economy has been estimated at $200-$250 billion annually in the mid 2000s, and a total of $10 to $12 trillion between 1970 and 2005. These costs are evenly divided between direct transfer of wealth (purchase money) from the U.S. to oil producing countries, the loss of economic potential due to oil prices elevated above competitive market levels, and disruption costs caused by sudden and large oil price movements.

These estimates do not include military, strategic or political costs associated with U.S. and world dependence on oil imports. They also do not include the constant risk of oil flow disruptions and/or price variations, which affect the U.S. economy and markets.

The U.S. Middle East military intervention external costs, as needed to maintain U.S. access to petroleum resources, average about $500 billion annually. These costs are in addition to comparable magnitude economic costs, thus bringing the total U.S. oil dependency to

about $1 trillion annually, significant parts of which are external costs.

Vehicular Externalities

Crude oil now is used mostly for transportation in fueling cars, tracks, planes, and ships. Let's take for an example the intense use of cars and trucks that results in a number of real costs at one time or another (property damage, accidents and air pollution), most of which are usually not included in the initial manufacturer's cost, or the cost of the fuels.

Some of these costs are included later in our taxes, insurance premiums, and court costs, all of which cover some of the damages, accidents, and casualties.

Nevertheless, all costs must be considered in the cradle-to-grave lifecycle of the car or truck in question, to get a full picture of the reality. Equally so, a major component in the case of environmental cost is its externalities, which must be brought to the market, accounted for and included in all economic analysis. This missing component, which reflects a major damage done to the environment by smoky cars' and trucks' exhaust pipes, has been ignored until now for a number of reasons, mostly a combination of ignorance, negligence, and greed.

The first problem we face in doing this is assigning a true and accurate monetary value to the environmental damages caused by the vehicles. Reducing complex environmental effects to a single dollar value is nearly impossible—especially at this early stage of development of the environmental economics sciences.

There is no clear-cut answer to this question. In some cases, economic damages may be identifiable, but not in others. For example, every year U.S. motor vehicles emit about 50 million tons of carbon monoxide, seven million tons of nitrogen oxides, as well as many tons of other toxins including particles, formaldehyde and benzene. At the same time, car and truck accidents kill more than 40 thousand people and injure more than three million others every year in the U.S. as well. These are serious external costs, most of which are not covered by manufacturer's warranty, personal insurance, or any other financial instruments, nor are they properly accounted in the costs of vehicles and fuels.

Additional external costs include natural habitat destruction from building roads and parking lots, as well as from activities related to vehicles, parts, oil, and waste water disposal. And then, even more abstractly, there are other costs associated with national security in securing petroleum supplies, noise pollution damage, and on and on the list goes.

A number of studies attempt to monetize the external costs of motor vehicle use by estimating the costs associated with global air pollution, crop losses, reduced visibility, national security, noise pollution, and so forth. The public sector pays some of these costs; others become external social losses, paid for by the government.

Assumptions of the total annual monetary and non-monetary externality costs of automotive externalities in the U.S. vary from $250 billion to $900 billion. Annual public sector costs for motor vehicle infrastructure and services are valued at $120 billion to $240 billion. Free-parking subsidies and cross-subsidies caused by congestion amounted to another $50-$100 billion per year.

A modified estimate of public sector externalities costs related to car use is as follows:

Table 7-15. Externality costs of vehicle use

Air pollution, human mortality	$300	billion
Air pollution, crops damage	15	billion
Pollution regulation and control	5	billion
Highway patrol and safety	8	billion
Highways and parking	200	billion
National security costs	7	billion
Other public sector costs	25	billion
Imposed travel delays	100	billion
Accident costs (pain, death)	50	billion
Productivity loss	150	billion
Noise pollution	15	billion
Water pollution	10	billion
Global warming	20	billion*
Other externality costs	35	billion

*A higher estimate of global warming costs, which are increasing exponentially, charged to vehicles could raise the estimates sharply.

An additional gasoline tax of $2.50 per gallon might be needed to internalize all the social costs, and even that won't be enough in many cases. To get closer to the reality, air pollution externalities should be internalized based on a vehicle's emissions levels rather than on gasoline consumption, or any other parameters.

And then there is another great number associated with health-related externalities brought upon by car and truck accidents around the country. There is an estimate from the 2000s of $400-450 billion spent on health issues and death from road accidents annually in the U.S. If added to the cost of gas, these numbers would represent additional $2.10 per gallon on top of the price at the pump.

No matter how we look at it and what we decide to do, we will not provide a complete, let alone perfect solution. Doing nothing, however, sends the wrong signal to the users and abusers—that the external costs are irrelevant, or that do not exist. This is why the efforts of our esteemed economists in this area are so important.

The Medical Externalities

The energy industry has been operated in a dangerous territory since the very beginning. Mining, oil and gas drilling, and fuel transport activities can be classified as dangerous—and in some cases extremely dangerous—operations. A lot of improvements have been made recently to reduce the environmental damage and avoid human illnesses and death resulting from these activities, and we do give the necessary credit to the industry for those efforts.

The case of the newly expanded gas fracking, however, stands out in its large-scale land use and huge amount of toxic chemicals used. The worst part of this is that we don't know the exact behavior and the negative effects of the large land mass combined with thousands of gallons of toxic chemicals pimped deep under the ground.

While the pumping itself might create problems by leaking toxic chemicals through poorly cemented well walls, the biggest problem is the uncertainty of what happens after that. Once the chemicals are pumped underground, the high pressure forces them in every crack and cranny that they can get into.

At the point when the liquid toxins leave the pressure pipe and are released in the underground they are on their own. There is no control over them whatsoever. They can go in any direction they want. Since the ground mass is porous they can travel miles through a path of less resistance. And since their main job is to make new cracks to push the gas out, they can make new paths and travel through them under the pressure and other forces acting upon them—again without any control from the ground crews.

Extensive and ever increasing use of vehicles in personal and commodities transport is also causing large medical externalities. In addition to using a lot of energy and emitting a lot of pollution during their manufacturing process, cars and trucks emit enormous amount of GHG gasses on the roadways, which make people sick and cause abnormal environmental phenomena, such as global warming.

As a matter of fact, most of the crude oil used now goes for fueling cars and trucks. And yet, most of the people in the world insist on having more cars and driving more miles. The car manufacturers around the world are ramping their production plants and encouraging driving in flashy commercials.

Cruise companies put huge ships, some as big as a small cities, in route to nowhere, pointlessly circling the world's oceans and burning millions of gallons of fossil fuels in the process.

Thousands of airplanes lift off every day criss-crossing the country and the world, burning many more millions of gallons of fuel. And there is no end in sight. We are all willing to drive a lot of miles, take cruises to nowhere, and go for an airplane ride whenever possible. We are basically acting as if there is no tomorrow. As if the fossils will last forever, which is absolutely not true, because we already see the bottom of the fossil's bucket. We are acting as if the fossils are not making us sick and killing us every day.

In economic terms, all these activities are costing us billions in health costs annually. Researchers have estimated that the health impacts by fuel type are:

- 19-45 cents per kWh for coal
- 8-19 cents per kWh for oil
- 1-2 cents per kWh for natural gas

Keeping in mind that the average retail price for electric power in the U.S. is about 9-10 cents per kilowatt-hour (kWh), then the coal and oil costs with added externalities (19-45 and 8-19 cents/kWh) are much higher than the typical retail price of electricity. The difference points to a very large cost of the respective externalities, which accounts fully for adverse climate and health impacts associated with fossil fuel usage.

Combining the average retail cost of electricity and the health impacts from fossil fuels brings the average electric bill 24-45 cents/kWh higher than it is today. This difference is to be used for alternatives such as energy efficiency and renewable technologies, as needed to avoid using fossil fuels.

A paper recently published by researchers at the U.S. EPA finds that full accounting for the health impacts of burning fossil fuels would bring the retail electricity price an average of 14-35 cents per kWh higher than the actual retail cost of electricity, or 24-55 cents depending on location. EPA also estimates that the hidden fossils-related health costs add up to as much as $886.5 billion of externalities expenses annually, which is about 6% of the U.S.'s GDP.

European NGO released a report recently, which found that emissions from Europe's coal-fired power plants cost the E.U. citizens up to $55 billion in health costs annually. This includes costs associated with medical costs, hospitalizations, medications, premature deaths, and reduced activity including working days lost.

In 2013 the international monetary fund (IMF) released a report calling for the end of $1.9 trillion in annual global energy subsidies. That includes $480 billion in direct subsidies to consumers and $1.4 trillion in the "mispricing" of fossil fuels. Mispricing is due to the fact that polluters are not forced to pay the full costs associated with fossil fuel combustion on climate change and public health.

According to the IMF, the biggest offender was by far the United States, with $502 billion in subsidies to energy companies, followed by China with $279 billion. Russia was third at $116 billion of subsidies to energy companies. Offsetting the impact of the energy subsidies in the U.S. would require new fees, or taxes totaling over $500 billion per year.

And as mentioned above, there are also a great number of health related externalities brought upon by car and truck accidents around the country. This amount is estimate at $400-450 billion spent on health issues and death from road accidents annually in the U.S. If added to the cost of gas these numbers would represent additional $2.10 per gallon on top of the price at the pump.

And yet, some of us don't even know that we are running out of fossils. Some deny it, but most of us don't care. So, we entered the 21st century with our eyes closed to the possibility of a fossil-less and car-less future, and not much is done, or planned to be done, to change that any time soon.

Drill, baby drill is still the predominant call in the America's energy sector. As things are going, that call will only get louder. While more drilling will supply us with enough oil and gas to power the economy and drive our cars for a while longer, it does not answer the fundamental questions of fossils depletion, and environmental congestion.

Actually, there are calls of reason also in the U.S., which demand reduction of fuel use and GHG emissions. As a matter of fact there is a noticeable reduction in oil imports and GHG emissions lately, as hydrofracking is providing more oil and as coal power plants are converted to gas.

However, even if this trend continues, which is not certain, it is still a drop in the global bucket as far as GHG emissions and global warming are concerned, because China, India and a number of other major polluters have no intentions of slowing down.

NATURAL GAS

Natural gas has become the king of energy in the U.S. And this is not a coincidence. It is a result of many years of research and development of new technologies for well drilling location and exploitation. The newest and most promising of them all is the hydrofracking process, which opened the spigot to untold quantity of natural gas and oil all over the U.S. and Canada.

So now natural gas is replacing coal in the power plants, and gasoline and diesel in cars and trucks. At the same time large quantities of oil are also produced via hydrofracking, which is contributing to a significant reduction in oil imports. The combination of oil and gas overproduction is also a sure path to our energy independence.

But every good thing has its negative side, and hydrofracking and its products are no exception. Read on...

U.S. natural gas production has been steadily increasing since 2005 due mainly to rapid growth in production from shale gas resources, using the newly perfected hydrofracking process. Now most of the natural gas consumed in the United States comes from domestic production.

The steadily increasing natural gas supply tends to dampen prices, and if the prices get too low, they can erode the incentive for drilling. This, in turn, eventually will result in decreased production and price increases. So the energy companies are following the supply and demand ratios closely, and are using it to play the pricing game.

Let's see how they do this.

Production Costs

Natural gas production starts at the well, with the first step being finding and drilling a deep hole in the ground as needed to access the gas reserves lying below.

Locating, permitting, and drilling a gas well is a long, complicated and very expensive process, which used to be reserved for the very brave and very rich. The game has changed lately and the gas drilling industry now has many new smaller players.

Still, one has to consider the high costs of drilling and operating a gas well now, which on the average are as follows:

Table 7-16 reflects the cost of securing well location, obtaining the necessary permits, drilling a large hole in the ground, installing the necessary equipment and taking the necessary steps to ensure safe and profitable hydrofracking operation. After the well is secured

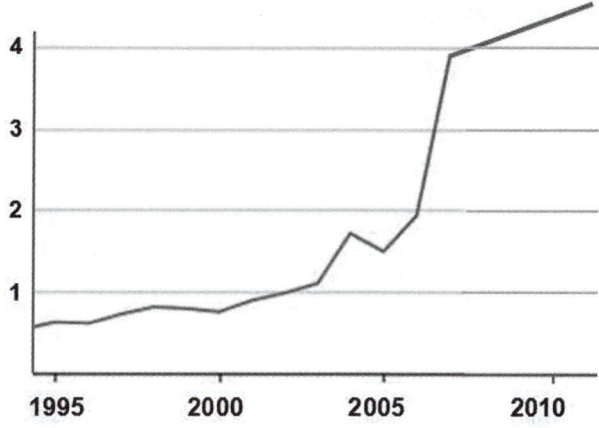

Figure 7-14. Gas well drilling prices (in $ millions)

and operational, the daily expense of running the operation goes down dramatically.

Table 7-16. Gas well costs break down

Task	Expenses
• Land acquisition and leasing:	$1,000,000
• Permitting:	25,000
• Vertical drilling:	660,000
• Horizontal drilling:	1,200,000
• Hydraulic fracturing:	2,000,000
• Gathering pipeline	500,000.
• Well completion	300,000
• Production to gathering:	550,000

Tables 7-17a and 7-17b give a more detailed breakdown of the drilling costs for different types of drilling operations.

It is obvious from Tables 7-17a and 7-17b that horizontal drilling is at least two times more expensive than vertical. This is because the drill equipment and the related drilling procedures are much more complex and expensive. This is also due to the fact that horizontal wells are usually several times longer than vertical ones. In most cases, the wells contain both; vertical well (to start with), which is then diverted into a horizontal drilling of a special well where the hydrofracking will take place. This process consists of several steps and they all add time and expense to the project.

The cost of gas well drilling and the related O&M expenses increase in parallel with the increase of gas production. There are a number of reasons for that, but growing demand and improving economic (and drilling support) conditions are the main factors to be blamed for the increases.

Table 7-17a. Vertical drilling cost estimates

VERTICAL DRILLING	
Surface Casing (fresh water): 16-3/4"	$19,500
1ˢᵗ Intermediate (coal string): 11-3/4"	$12,625
2ⁿᵈ Intermediate Casing: 8-5/8"	$51,500
Wellhead Equipment	$5,000
Float Equipment, Centralizers, Baskets, etc.	$11,750
Daywork Drilling	$225,000
Rig(s) Mobilization: All Rigs	$32,250
Fuel	$35,000
Bits, Reamers, Tools, Power Tongs	$50,000
Pit Liners	$24,000
Drilling Mud & Chemicals	$10,000
Drilling Miscellaneous (directional drlg, gyro)	$45,000
Cement Surface Casing	$15,000
Cement 1ˢᵗ Intermediate Casing	$10,000
Cement 2ⁿᵈ Intermediate Casing	$20,000
Trucking	$25,000
Mud Logging	$11,900
Engineering Consultant / Well-site Leader	$25,500
Miscellaneous Tools, Services & Rentals	$56,500
Haul Fresh Water for Cementing / Rig	$5,000
Vertical Drilling Subtotal	**$663,275**

Table 7-17b. Horizontal drilling costs

HORIZONTAL DRILLING	
Production Casing: 5-1/2"	$248,500
Wellhead Equipment	$25,000
Float Equipment, Centralizers, Baskets, etc.	$15,000
Daywork Drilling: Spudder, Intermediate & Horizontal Rigs	$209,000
Rig(s) Mobilization: All Rigs	$171,000
Fuel	$38,000
Bits, Reamers, Tools, Power Tongs	$4,000
Drilling Mud & Chemicals	$127,800
Drilling Miscellaneous (directional drlg, gyro)	$85,250
Cement Production Casing	$80,000
Trucking	$25,000
Mud Logging	$11,050
Engineering Consultant / Well-site Leader	$26,500
Miscellaneous Tools, Services & Rentals	$144,750
Haul Fresh Water for Cementing / Rig	$4,000
Horizontal Drilling Subtotal	**$1,214,850**

Immediately after the gas well is drilled, and the auxiliary equipment is installed and tested, the daily operation starts by injecting hydrofracking liquids in the hole and extracting thus displaced gas.

One very important and good thing about natural gas is that it can be used as is—with very little processing and refining—for burning in industrial type installations, such as gas-fired power plants. This also means that there is no further significant cost before sending the gas to the consumers.

There are number of ways to look at the costs to produce natural gas. The most direct way is to figure out what it costs to bring the gas out of the ground. A measure of the total cost to produce natural gas is its upstream costs, which include the major costs for finding and lifting.

Finding costs are the costs of exploring for and developing reserves of oil and gas and the costs to purchase properties or acquire leases that might contain oil and gas reserves.

Lifting costs are the costs to operate and maintain oil and gas wells and related equipment and facilities to bring oil and gas to the surface.

These costs are the easiest to estimate, because they are common in all underground exploration and exploitation industries.

Table 7-18. Natural gas production costs ($ per barrel of oil equivalent*)

Country	Lifting Costs $	Finding Costs $	Total Costs $
United States	12.18	21.58	33.76
Canada	12.69	12.07	24.76
Africa	10.31	35.01	45.32
Middle East	9.89	6.99	16.88
S. America	6.21	20.43	26.64

NOTE: The energy contained in 5,618 cubic feet of natural gas is equivalent to that in one barrel of oil.

These costs include the well construction too, but these numbers are not easily found, because a few producers reveal their actual well cost numbers. Instead, they usually include them in the finding and/or lifting costs.

A large producer gave an estimate of well drilling cost of $2.8 million in 2011. At the same time, however, this same producer showed over $2.2 billion in capital spending on 560 wells, which brings the cost per well to nearly $4.0 million per well. Go figure…but no matter how we look at it, drilling a gas well is a significant undertaking from any and all points of view.

Looking at the broader picture, we see the top 40 natural gas producers show roughly $130 billion capital spending in 2011 for a total of 16,000 wells drilled during that time. If these numbers are correct, then the gas industry wide average drilling cost is about $8.0 million per well. And of course, some wells cost more than others, but we'd be pretty close to the truth stating that the average cost to drill a new gas well is in the $2 to 10 million range—depending primarily on the type of well (vertical or horizontal drilling), location, technology used, and level of expertise of the technical personnel.

Natural Gas Prices

Natural gas prices vary with the energy markets, as any other commodity of this category.

Figure 7-15. Natural gas prices (in $ per MMBtu*)
* MMBtu is one million (thousand thousand) British thermal units.

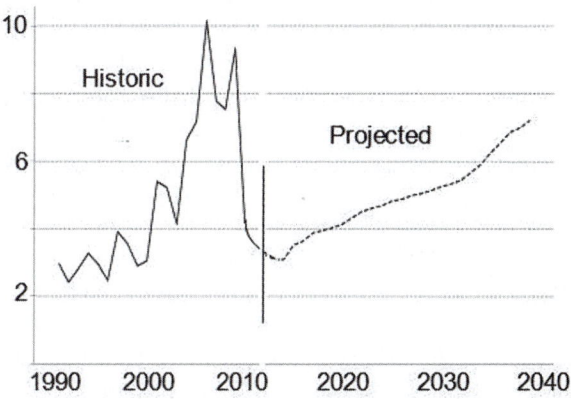

Using this nomenclature makes it hard to compare prices, so let's see:

- Burning 3412 Btu of natural gas (at 100% efficiency) would produce one kWh electric power

- One MMBtu, therefore, will generate the equivalent of 293 kWh electric power

- A barrel of crude oil (42 gallons) generates 1,700 kWh electric power

- Burning 1.0 gallon of crude oil would generate 41 kWh of electric power, so it takes 7.1 gallons of crude oil to generate the energy equivalent of 1.0 MMBtu natural gas

- Natural gas is about 3-4 times cheaper per energy value than crude oil

Here we go again with a new measurement unit of energy, specific for natural gas—the cubic foot.
- One cubic foot (cf) natural gas contains 1,027 Btu energy, or
- The equivalent of 0.33 kWh electricity generation, then
- About 130 cf natural gas contains the energy equivalent of a gallon of crude oil (138,100 Btus).

In addition:
- A gallon of liquefied propane contains 91,700 Btus,

or 2/3 the energy in a gallon of crude oil, and
- 1 kW of electricity contains 3,413 Btus.

The price advantage of natural gas gets even higher when the oil to gasoline processing costs is added.

Natural gas prices are relatively low and getting lower now because of the newly discovered gas fields and new techniques, but this bonanza won't last long. There are a number of reasons why natural gas prices are projected to go up.

One is that although natural gas fired plants generally have a cost advantage over renewables at low prices, renewable power costs are expected to decline over the coming decades. Since gas prices are likely to increase, the balance will be shifted in favor of the renewables. We just don't know when...

And there is another factor that might be of greatest importance to the future natural gas price structure. It is the fact that there are other costs in addition to the well finding, drilling, and O&M. These are the unspeakable, so called externalities, which represent the costs that are hidden (intentionally or unintentionally) or which are difficult to express in dollar amounts, which we review in more detail in this text.

A basic measure of the total cost to produce crude oil and natural gas is the upstream costs, which includes the entire process of finding and lifting (pumping) the gas.

Finding costs are the costs of exploring for and developing reserves of oil and gas and the costs to purchase properties or acquire leases that might contain oil and gas reserves.

Lifting costs are the costs to operate and maintain oil and gas wells and related equipment and facilities to bring oil and gas to the surface.

Table 7-19.
Costs for producing natural gas ($/bbl oil equivalent*)

Location	Lifting Costs	Finding Costs	Total Costs
U.S., average	**12.18**	**21.58**	**33.76**
On-shore	12.73	18.65	31.38
Off-shore	10.09	41.51	51.60
World, average	**9.95**	**15.13**	**25.08**
Canada	12.69	12.07	24.76
Africa	10.31	35.01	45.32
Middle East	9.89	6.99	16.88
S. America	6.21	20.43	26.64

Natural gas prices are a function—in addition to the varying production costs—of market supply and demand. Because of limited alternatives for natural gas consumption or production in most cases, even small changes in supply or demand over a short period can result in large price movements to bring supply and demand back into balance.

Major factors on the supply side that may affect gas prices include:

- Variations in the amount of natural gas being produced
- The volume of gas being imported and/or exported
- The amount of gas in storage facilities (referred to as storage levels)
- Increases in supply result in lower prices, and decreases in supply tend to increase prices

Factors on the demand side that may affect prices include:

- The level of economic growth
- Variations in winter and summer weather
- Oil price variations

Weather events have affected the normal U.S. natural gas production and have caused gas output to level off or even decline:

- In the summer of 2005, hurricanes along the U.S. Gulf Coast caused the equivalent of about 4% of U.S. total production to be shut in between August 2005 and June 2006.

- Hurricanes Katrina and Rita (Sept-Oct 2005)—disrupted up to 12.2-billion cubic feet per day (Bcf/d) in offshore natural gas production.

- Hurricanes Gustav and Ike in September 2008 disrupted up to 9.5 Bcf/d in offshore natural gas production.

- Winter-well freeze-offs in February 2011 disrupted up to 7.5 Bcf/d in natural gas production from Texas to Arizona, when water froze inside wellheads during extremely cold weather and blocked gas flows.

There have been several additional exceptions in the last several years when natural gas production leveled off during a period of falling spot natural gas prices. Some examples are:

- The economic recession and falling prices October 2008-September 2009 caused reduced industrial and manufacturing activity. Lower electricity use eased demand for natural gas as a feedstock and a power generation fuel and as a result natural gas prices fell sharply during the period.

- Supply overhang and falling natural gas prices during October 2011-Mar 2012 was caused by a warm winter that reduced heating fuel demand. There were also record high gas inventories during this time that resulted in a nearly 50% drop in gas prices. This discrepancy caused some energy companies to postpone new drilling and cut back on some existing operations.

Everything considered, the natural gas production has been increasing exponentially during the last 5-6 years. The overproduction has caused the gas prices to fall correspondingly, which in turn led to lower home heating and electricity prices for the duration. Retail home-heating prices for natural gas have fallen 21% in the Northeast, and retail electricity prices have also declined by about 2-3% over the past five years, because of lower costs for natural gas used to generate electricity.

According to the industry experts, the domestic natural gas production is expanding so fast that the U.S. is expected to become the world's largest producer of natural gas by 2015 and the world's leading producer of crude oil by 2017. This will eventually lead to a complete energy independence by 2035—barring any unforeseen socio-political events or natural disasters.

All this, thanks largely to the huge, newly discovered domestic reserves of oil and gas in shale rock, and the technology advancement that allows the efficient extraction.

These developments haven't yet been seen at gas pumps, largely because oil is a high-demand global product and its prices depends on the world markets fluctuations. So, we should not expect dramatic declines in oil and gasoline products any time soon, if ever, regardless of the price of natural gas, unless we can drive our cars with it.

Electricity may see production costs stabilize or decline in coming years, making their products more competitive on global markets. That is especially significant for some Northeast states, which have long struggled with high electricity and heating costs in the past, that have put them at a disadvantage. Lower and more stable energy prices will boost the U.S. manufacturing operations, which is good too.

On the other hand, any significant drop in the nation's trade deficit, caused by decreased fuel imports, accompanied by increased exports of U.S. products would certainly strengthen the U.S. dollar on currency markets. This, however, would make American-made products and goods more expensive in foreign markets, which would eventually hurt our manufacturing exports.

This phenomenon, called "Dutch disease," is a reference to the discovery of large reserves of underground gas in the Netherlands in the late 1950s. That gas find was an energy boon, but it also drove up the value of the country's currency, making its products more expensive to export and leading to a serious decline in manufacturing, loss of jobs and a mild economic slumber.

So, in all cases, there are pluses and minuses as far as the price of fuels is concerned. This is also true for the environment. All fossil fuels produce GHGs that contribute to global climate change, but natural gas emits less carbon dioxide than oil and coal, which are still the main fuel sources for U.S. electric power plants. The increased use of natural gas by power plants partially explains the 10% decline in carbon emissions in the United States in recent years, according to the U.S. DOE.

But the lower cost of natural gas makes it harder for emerging renewable sources, such as wind and solar, to compete. And also, as natural gas replaces coal, it could lead to the loss of thousands of jobs in the coal and the renewable industries. This will eventually cause disruptions and some redistribution of material and human resources.

The recent increase of production volume and low prices of natural gas has also led to significant increase of exports of this commodity. The rising exports of domestic gas supplies, which are sold at good prices, could also lead to higher prices for American consumers.

So, natural gas is bringing some new opportunities and hopes, but at the same time it is creating some problems that need to be taken care of. We hope that our esteemed economists will sharpen their pencils and find a long-term compromise soon enough.

The Hidden Costs

Like with many commodities, there are a number of hidden costs in the natural gas prices. Some of these hidden costs can be found in:

Production Rate and Quantity

One of the hidden costs in any production scheme of fossils is the decline in production with time, and natural gas is no exception. All gas and oil wells start with the burst of product and continue at maximum production level for several years. Eventually, the flow decreases; slowly at first and then more rapidly as time goes on.

It is very seldom, if ever, that a gas well would produce more during its 10th year of production than during the first year. Usually the production slows down and then it becomes harder and more expensive to produce enough gas to justify the operation costs.

The production rate of a gas well is defined by:

$$Pt = Po/(1+b*D*t)^{1/b}$$

where:

Pt is the production rate
Po is the initial production rate
D is the initial decline rate
t is the time of operation
b is a factor (subject to controversies)

From this formula, Arps (empirical decline) type curves are generated to estimate the future production rates. But the factor "b" is just an estimate. It is an almost arbitrary number that the specialists assign to each well.

So:

$b < 0$ is not possible
$b = 0$ brings the formula into an exponential decay,
$0 < b < 1$ unreasonably limits the cumulative production
$b = 1$ brings the Arps curve into a harmonic loop
$b > 1$ makes the cumulative production go to infinity

It is logical to assign a number greater than one to b, and then, no matter what the number is, we get a well that produces indefinitely. This, however, is far from the reality. Gas wells are like a rubber balloon; they can stay inflated for a long time, until finally starting to lose pressure. Or they can just go boom, with all the air let out.

In most cases, however, the decline in production is gradual, and the initial estimates of production rates are accurate. At the same time, the rate of decline of the well production is underestimated, while the total quantity of gas to be produced are typically overestimated. This is done on purpose, to make the well look better and attract more investors.

For example, a southwestern energy company claims that on the average, about 2.4-2.6 Bcf (billion cubic feet) of natural gas can be extracted from each of its wells. Industry publications, however, have disputed that claim by stating, "To put into perspective the claims of 2.4-2.6 Bcf gas production per well, consider the following: of the 742 operated wells completed, only 66 have produced more than 1.0 Bcf and none have produced more than 1.7 Bcf. Some wells have produced only 541 Mcf."

The USGS confirms these numbers again with the average wells coming in at 1.1 Bcf, which is significantly lower than the average 2.4-2.6 Bcf industry estimates.

So, it is obvious from this and other facts that we (and the specialists) don't know what exactly happens underground. And one doesn't have to be a specialist to figure out the large number of unknowns deep underground. The enormous pressures exerted by the hydrofracking liquids could create one-crack-too-many and send the gas into a new crack, in an unforeseen direction. Even in the best of cases, just one unforeseen large crack in the gas reservoir might drain the well into a river or lake. Or a large earthquake splitting the area into pieces and releasing the gas deposit somewhere in the ground or air.

The chemicals in the hydrofracking mix can also (unintentionally) eat through the layers of different materials underground and create a new path that could send the gas in a different, unplanned, direction.

This is not hard to imagine, albeit it is not very nice to talk about. And sure enough; the talks on this subject are limited due to "hard to prove" facts. And yet, there are gas and water fountains erupting in people's back yards, and gas is detected in the drinking water supplies in many locations. Could the gas going in unforeseen and unplanned directions be causing these abnormalities?

The well owners say, NO, this is not possible. The affected people say, YES, this is exactly what is happening. The reason for the disagreement is that it would be extremely expensive for the well owners to compensate for the damages. In some cases entire communities have been affected by excess air, soil, and water pollution, which means billions of dollars of damages. So, the fight will continue until the end.

Gas prices vary significantly, driven mostly by the demand cycles. For example, in 2012 the spot U.S. Henry Hub natural gas prices rose 65% from $1.80/MMBtu in mid-April to above $3.00/MMBtu. The reason given by the gas well owners and utility companies was increased power demand for air conditioning during the summer months, due to the heat wave across the country. This, however, has nothing to do with the production or distribution costs, which are the same no matter what the weather does. It is the old supply and demand trick that drives prices up and is used to make money by the energy companies.

Another unanswered question is that, regardless of the price of natural gas, it is in limited quantities, so how long will it last? The industry specialists predict at least 50 years of readily available cheap gas, but looking at the real world numbers at the present rate of use, and analysis of industry data, we would predict 25-30 years maximum.

In best of cases, no big problems would be encountered on the way, and the gas deposits would diminish slowly, allowing for price adjustments according to availability and difficulty of extraction. In worst of cases, unforeseen events, untold disasters, litigation and legislation would shorten the expectations, thus creating a serious natural gas glut and high prices.

Gas Rig Decommissioning

At the end of the useful life of the well, the equipment at the wellhead is disassembled, cleaned and transported for storing as needed to use in another operation, or properly disposed.

Above we discussed in detail the decommissioning process and costs of oil rigs, and since the process and the expenses are similar, we would refer the esteemed reader to the oil rigs decommissioning section in this text above.

The cost of gas rigs and power plants end of life decommissioning must be always included in the initial construction and operation designs and estimates. The cost could be significant and is usually rising with time—especially since these facilities are used decades at a time.

Gas Transport

Once gas is extracted it can be either stored or immediately transported. Storing it is difficult, because very large vessels are needed for relatively small amounts of gas. Compressing natural gas into a liquid state is used in some cases, for it reduces the volume and makes it more transportable. This, however, is a very expensive procedure and is used only in cases where price is not the object, or the gas has to be liquefied for transport.

Usually, natural gas pumped from the well is sent into pipes to the processing plant, and then for transport and distribution to power plants and populated centers for residential and commercial use. The efficient and effective movement of natural gas from producing regions to consumption regions requires an extensive and elaborate transportation system. In many instances, natural gas has to travel great distances to reach its point of use.

A complex network of pipelines, designed to quickly and efficiently transport natural gas from its origin, to areas of high natural gas demand, has been built and is in use in the U.S. There are three major types of pipeline systems—the gathering system, the interstate pipeline system, and the distribution system.

- The gathering system consists of low pressure, small diameter pipelines that transport raw natural gas from the wellhead to the processing plant. High sulfur and carbon dioxide contents in sour gas require special gathering pipe, due to its corrosive properties.

- Intrastate pipelines, on the other hand, transport natural gas within a particular state.

- Interstate pipelines carry natural gas across state boundaries, and in some cases clear across the country.

- Distribution pipelines actually deliver the natural gas to the retail customers, including commercial and residential natural gas users.

The transport equipment and procedures are the same for all types of pipelines.

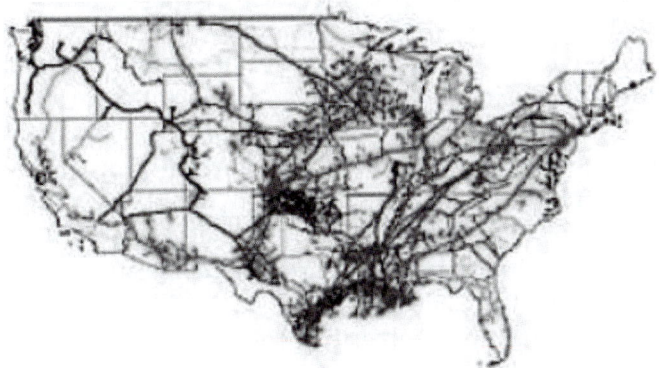

Figure 7-16. The national gas pipelines

Just like the national highway system, the national pipeline system crisscrosses the country in whichever direction. And just like the highway system, it consists of a number of elements. Some of these are:

- Transmission pipes
- Valves
- Compressor stations
- Metering stations
- Control stations

All these components have a specific role to play in the proper, safe, and efficient delivery of gas to the point of use. The entire system costs a lot of money to design, construct, operate and maintain.

Safety

The gas companies are making an honest effort to ensure the safety of the lines, and their record on the average is good. The pipelines are inspected be a number of means, ranging from periodic visual inspection to running inspection devices (pigs) inside the pipes.

In addition there are a number of other safety precautions and procedures in place to minimize the risk of accidents. It has been said that the transportation of natural gas is one of the safest ways of transporting energy, mostly due to the fact that the infrastructure is fixed, and mostly buried underground.

There were in excess of 100 deaths per year associated with electric transmission lines in 2009, while no deaths were associated with transmission pipelines, and 10 deaths were associated with distribution systems.

Some of the safety precautions associated with natural gas pipelines, taken by the gas companies, the regulatory and other agencies, include:

- Aerial patrols ensure the safety of construction activities and monitor the routing of the pipelines, especially in residential areas.

- Leak detection equipment is periodically used to check the pipelines for leaks, especially in areas where the natural gas is not odorized.

- Pipeline markers are placed on the surface above pipelines paths to indicate the presence of underground pipelines, and to reduce the chance of any interference with the pipeline.

- Routine gas sampling of the gas in the pipelines ensures its quality and level of acidity, which is used to prevent corrosion of the interior of the pipeline and limit flow of other contaminants in the pipes.

- Preventative maintenance is an important tool for testing of valves and the removal of surface impediments to ensure proper pipeline inspection and its overall safety.

- Emergency response teams that train for the possibility of a wide range of potential accidents and emergencies, and are ready to respond accordingly at any time accomplish emergency response.

- The one call program is a program instituted in all 50 states. It provides excavators, construction crews, and anyone interested in digging into the ground around a pipeline with a single phone number that may be called when any excavation activity is planned. Unauthorized construction and digging is the primary threat to pipeline safety, according to the industry specialists, so the "one call" program can help by alerting the pipeline company to flag the area, and send representatives to monitor the digging. The national three-digit number for one call is "811."

NIMBY

The latest, and very important development in the increasing hydrofracking activities is the not-in-my-back-yard (NIMBY) movement originating mostly in small towns and villages in the U.S. and around the world. In the U.S. the feds are washing their hands of the responsibilities, while taking full credit for the progress of and encouraging, hydrofracking, so they have transferred the responsibility to the state governments. While most of the states are happy to add a new industry with the related jobs and money influx, many small town folks in the affected by the new activities locations are standing up and saying, NO, NO, NO. No more!

There is actually a real war going on in parts of the U.S. that most people know nothing about. It is a battle between a coalition of great powers (the gas industry) and a fragmented insurgent movement led by small towns' people. It is a secret war being waged in the shadows of the gas wells, while most of us go about our everyday life unaware of it.

People's lives in those small towns have been seriously affected in a number of ways by the local gas and oil fracking wells so they are fighting back in a big way. Recently their plight has been heard and supported by the 99% army of farmers, factory workers, physicists, chemists, journalists, teachers, librarians, innkeepers, brewery owners and engineers.

- The State of New York—of all places—is on the forefront of this movement. The small town of Middlefield, NY became one of the first towns in the U.S. to use the humblest of tools it has available at its disposal in the fight against big business. Its zoning ordinances were modified and adopted as needed to control and stop fracking as needed.

This had been unthinkable until recently—an im-

possible task to be accomplished by ordinary people residing in small towns. This, however, is another example of the fact that when American people get pushed against the wall hard enough, they will push back. And push back a number of NY state towns did.

In 1981, the state of New York exempted gas corporations from New York's constitutionally guaranteed home rule under which town ordinances trump state law. In 2011, however, Ithaca lawyers helped to overturned that gas-cozy law by establishing that towns can use their zoning powers to keep out unwanted new comers—even if the state has the power to regulate the industry development. Since then, a cascade of bans and moratoria—more than 140 in all—have protected towns all over New York from high-volume fracking well drilling. Democracy at its best!

- Another small town, Caroline, a small hamlet in Tompkins County with population of 3,282 was the second town in the state to get 100% of its electricity through wind power. It was one of the most recent to pass a complete fracking ban and no wells have been drilled nearby.

An overall feeling of mistrust of the federal government started with the exempted of fracking from the clean water and air acts. How can this action be explained other than exception made for protecting Big Business interests. It also shows that the Federal and state governments did not have the interests of the small town people in mind doing this.

So the local governments took the fight into their own hands, although it is bringing a lot of distress to their fragile structure and challenges their limited functions. Town governments whose leaders are paid $500-600 a month to carry their part-time duties are keeping the towns afloat, and are now all of a sudden unexpectedly finding themselves at ground zero for human rights and climate change. This is a fight between David and Goliath, which David must win.

The town of Caroline implemented two years pre-ban work, after replacing the pro-drilling members of the town board with fracking opponents, in addition to public education forums and a six-month petition drive. No door was left without a knock or two by the residents opposed to unsafe shale gas extraction (ROUSE) members.

Most people were opposed to the expansion of gas drilling in the area, but were either afraid to speak out, or did not know how to voice their opinion. These folks were the silent majority—71% of the participants signed a fracking ban petition—and then a final debate between drilling opponents and proponents took place. The vote that followed overwhelmingly endorsed the ban, and then the town board ruled four to one in favor.

- In another case, XTO, a subsidiary of Exxon-Mobil Corporation, applied to the Delaware River Basin Commission (DRBC) for a water-withdrawal permit. A quarter of a million gallons of water were needed every day for its hydraulic fracturing operations. Within days, there were 7,900 letters of outrage, and on June 1, 2011, hundreds of citizens, organized by grassroots anti-frackers, packed a hearing room as a result of which the Delaware River Basin Commission indefinitely tabled the XTO application. While just a grassroots victory, this case also serves as a warning about how determined both sides are to move forward their agenda.

- In May 2012, a town board passed resolution pledged that the town of Sanford would take no action against fracking, while awaiting the decision of the DEC. There was no prior notice, and the town folks had to read about it in the local papers.

In June, a headline in the town of Sanford paper read, "Local Officials in Eligible Communities Approve Pro-Drilling Resolutions," complete with a map of towns that had passed such resolutions. The subscript under the map read, "Joint Landowners Coalition of N.Y. (JLCNY)." The JLCNY is the state's grassroots gas industry ally, whose stated mission is to "foster... the common interest... as it pertains to natural gas development." Gas drilling supporters represent the organization in Sanford.

During the summer several citizens requested that the board rescind the resolution and conduct a referendum, but their request was denied. By the end of August, 43 towns in the region had passed resolutions modeled on one appearing at the JLCNY website, stipulating that at the local level "no moratorium on hydraulic fracturing will be put in place before the state of New York has made it's decision." It was later on revealed that the moratoriums were as a result of contacts between gas industry operatives and town officials.

Demonstrations against Cuomo's fracking plan, which drew thousands to Washington, DC, and Albany and elsewhere in New York, included pledges to commit sustained acts of civil disobedience should the governor carry out plans to open the Pennsylvania border area of the state to fracking.

At the end of September, The New York Times announced that Cuomo had retreated from his previously announced plans. The state's grassroots movement was credited for his change of mind. The NY governor will confront an increased political challenge in the coming months. In the end, he will either please gas-industry supporters or his Democratic base—which will affect his political carrier.

Superstorm Sandy swamped parts of the state later on and in addition to flooding problems, the locals saw a danger of the fracking chemicals getting into the water table. There is a history of floods turning millions of gallons of fracking wastewater for which there is no safe storage into streams of poisons that wash into waterways. The battle intensified...

- In 2013, anti-fracking laws passed in two New York towns were upheld by an appeals court, which rejected arguments by a dairy farm and a Norwegian energy company that the bans are superseded by old state law.

An appellate panel of the New York State Supreme Court in Albany, NY, ruled in May 2013, that drilling bans in the towns of Dryden and Middlefield don't conflict with state regulations for the oil and natural gas industry. This is a great victory for the small people.

The state law seeks to protect the right of the general public, not just the owners of oil and gas properties," a goal which is realized when individual municipalities can determine whether drilling activities are appropriate for their respective communities," the court said.

The bans are aimed at stopping hydrofracking, and stopping millions of gallons of chemically treated water from being pumped underground. They also mark a new level of frustration and determination by the general public to put an end of uncontrolled and unenforced drilling all over their lands.

- In summary, serious environmental battles are still raging about the mountaintop removal in West Virginia, deep-sea drilling in the Gulf of Mexico, and the tar sands in Alberta, Canada, but fracking has brought the fight closer to home—and is focused in upstate New York, where the line is drawn by the city leaders.

The decision to ban fracking in many small towns, was not made because people hate the idea of cheap gas fracking, but rather by the real fear of long-term negative impacts of fracking on health and the environment. Fear that the locals felt when they realized that neither the Federal nor State governments, nor the fracking companies have their interests in mind. Instead, they all had their own reasons for allowing the fracking, which usually impacted the locals negatively.

So, the battle continues by many small towns continuing to develop local anti-fracking measures and *might get worse...before it gets any better.*

Case Study: Fracking Town, USA

While on the subject of environmental externalities and valuation, let's pay a visit to our virtual location that exemplifies these terms and conditions. Frackingtown, USA, is a small town somewhere in the mountains of Kentucky. Its 5,000 citizens are small farmers and store owners. One stoplight, one restaurant, one park, one police car, and one city hall building were the major attractions of Frackingtown...until 2008. Then things changed very quickly.

It all started with a dozen large drilling rigs moving into the nearby fields and an army of workers digging for gas and oil. The scene in and around the town changed drastically. The most noticeable change was the never-ending line of huge trucks going up and down main street day and night. The trucks were full of water, sand, and different chemicals, which they dumped at the rigs and then started their way back just to repeat the cycle. Another line of trucks would load the waste chemicals coming from the rigs to be carried away for disposal or reprocessing at a distant location.

Hundreds of new people moved in the town too, which created an economic boom. Some of the locals were paid large sums of money for the use of the land, which increased the prosperity of the region. New restaurants, grocery stores, and motels opened and a number of new housing developments popped up around town too.

It was easy to see that the fracking rigs had been a boon to the little town. The good times flowed for a couple of years, until one morning Mr. Johnson awoke to a large sinkhole in his back yard that had swallowed the storage shed with everything in it. The next morning, the hole was filled with bubbling green and brown liquids. A week later, a geyser shooting a 10-foot stream of similarly colored liquid appeared in the middle of the newly remodeled city park.

The mystery liquids started oozing out of many other places too, and soon the citizens were becoming concerned, if not alarmed. The locals suspected that these phenomena must surely have something to do with the new fracking rigs a mile or two away, but they were assured that this was not possible. The problem must be somewhere else, according to the expert opinion of drilling specialists that attended the town meetings.

However, the problem was becoming more obvious by the day and people began to notice that their tap water had a chemical smell. Walking around town, one could also notice the sulfurous smell of leaking gas at almost any street. And there was continuous noise from the compressors in the distance, which was as loud as a locomotive idling nearby.

One day Mr. Johnson's house was almost burned when he struck a match to light his pipe close to the running kitchen sink. There was something like natural gas in the running water that filled the kitchen sink and blew up when the flame of his lighter got too close.

Up to this point the problems were limited to these inconveniences, which the authorities and the rig owners denied having anything to do with the drilling and fracking activities. Nevertheless, they had agreed to look into the holes with bubbling liquids in the ground, and provide clean water to the affected households, at least for a while.

And that should've been the end of the story, but then Mrs. Johnson woke up one morning with horrible headache and chest pains. She has been relatively healthy until then, so Mr. Johnson didn't know what to do. The pains were getting worse, so he finally called the ambulance. The tests revealed increased levels of toxicity in her blood, but the origin could not be identified.

The drilling rigs owners denied any and all responsibility for this and all other cases, and the government officials support their claims. So at least for now Mr. and Mrs. Johnson, and the entire Frackingtown community are on their own. But Mr. Johnson is taking his case to court, asking for a multi-million dollar reimbursement for his property damages, water contamination, and his wife's health issues. The rig owners will be fighting the lawsuit, which will most likely end up in a small monetary settlement—as so many similar case in the past.

And that will be the end of that one...until another local citizen gets fed up, or hurt enough, to bring another law suit...followed by another...and another...

Polish Anti-fracking Woes...

The anti-fracking battles are not limited to small towns in the U.S. There are equally serious activities in Europe too. One of the best examples is Poland, which has the European Union's biggest reserves of natural gas. The total technically recoverable reserves in the country are approximately 187 trillion cubic feet, 33% more than those of America's Marcellus shale.

Recent estimates show that there is enough natural gas to last at least 50 years, which would free Poland from a century-long dependence on Russia for energy. There are numerous problems to achieving that goal, however. Exploiting the deposits will require the agreement of the local farmers, some concerned ethnic groups, environmentalists and the tourism industry. They are convinced that hydrofracking will pollute their air and water and are putting a fight against it.

Although Conoco-Phillips, Chevron Corp. and Polish gas companies are willing to spend over $5.0 billion to tap into natural gas more than three miles below the surface, due to the resistance in 2012 about 25% fewer wells were completed than forecast by the environment ministry. Some projects were delayed and some cancelled as a result.

In the summer of 2012, a tanker truck moving drilling liquids between two sites overturned on a traffic circle near Bytow, Poland. While there were no injuries or immediate environmental damage, 424 cubic feet of drilling mud, the fluid used to help boreholes go deeper into the ground, and containing some biocide, was released into a nearby river.

The chemical is potentially dangerous for the environment and human health, which highlighted the risk to the environment and the lives of those dependent on the land and the waters within. "Exploration has just begun and the mud has already spilled," said a local official, "so what will happen when the scale is much bigger?" The concern is that while one or two wells can be controlled, hundreds or thousands of them and the related activities would be hard to keep under complete control.

Even farms that are protected by the European Union's natura 2000 biodiversity program are concerned about potential water contamination from drilling. The toxic chemicals under tremendous pressure can travel undetected underground long distances and contaminate land miles away.

Nevertheless, Poland's environment ministry expects 309 wells to be completed by 2021. Each of these wells would cost as much as $15 million. How many wells will be drilled in the midst of this controversy is unclear, but both sides are determined to continue the fight, so the battle will continue for a long while.

People in the region have emotional ties to their land, which they've owned for generations, For them, the value of an old home with a shack and surrounding land is much higher than any market estimate. The other big problem is that in Poland, land ownership means that the owners are entitled to only two feet of soil under the surface. Anything below that level belongs to the government.

This outdated law is a reminder from the communist era, where the gas reserves are government property and the land owners have nothing and get nothing. Nada…zilch! And although there might be millions of gallons of fuel under their crops, the farmers are not entitled to any of the benefits.

On top of that, the farmers and land owners know who will "benefit" from the negative effects of fracking under their lands. Air and water contamination, and a number of other ills, will be shared equally by the people living in the affected areas. The government gives them the right to sue the fracking companies for damages, but once damage is done, lawsuits won't help return the people's health, or the land, to their original state.

So who can blame them for not agreeing to let the fracking companies and the government make money at their expense?

For this and other reasons, things are not looking good for the fracking companies in Poland. In June, 2012 Exxon Mobil, the world's biggest energy company by market value, pulled out of Poland, citing "disappointing" results from its first wells. In October, Talisman Energy Inc., another energy giant, decided to exit Poland to focus on shale in North America.

And the battle in Europe is expanding. There are numerous embarrassing anti-fracking protests in France, the Netherlands, the Czech Republic, Bulgaria and part of Germany. As a result, there were some form of restrictions on hydraulic fracturing put in place in these countries in response to public concerns and protests mirroring those led by U.S. activists.

As the anti-fracking movement in Europe grows, the Polish government decided to effectively outlaw the anti-fracking dissent. A new legislation was proposed that would effectively eliminate the possibility of organized opposition, making it a crime. The movement is already operating in a climate of fear, so the new proposal only makes things worse.

The new laws state that protesters will be able to participate in demonstrations over fracking only if they have been in existence for over 12 months. This in effect will ban any community groups and organizations that have been recently affected from participation in the movement and will be unable to participate in an important decision making processes that directly affect them.

Are such laws to follow in other parts of Europe? …the U.S.? We would not be surprised, taking into account the size of the fracking activities, the might of the gas and oil companies involved, and the importance of natural gas to the governments.

The recent developments in natural gas discovery and extraction are opening a new page in the global energy sector. High volume and lower prices bring positive and negative developments, and we just have to wait and see what the final results would be.

One thing is for certain; natural gas is here to stay and will shape our future for some time to come. Another thing is for certain too; the battle between the gas producers and the affected communities will continue and will even escalate with time.

Natural Gas Externalities

Although gas drilling and exploitation have a number of positive effects on the local economy by creating jobs and wealth, it of course contains hidden and at times questionable indirect and induced* effects and the associated costs. These include the perceived and actual damages done at the gas well site, and the related activities, to the:

- Local environment (land, water, and air)
- Local property values
- Local wildlife
- Local human population
- The negative global effects

NOTE: The direct effects are obvious, clearly observable damages caused by the gas well drilling and operation. Examples of these effects are air and water contamination, and human illnesses.

The indirect effects are represented by a number of additional economic activities of (or effects upon) the value chain network, which are mainly caused by the gas well drilling and operation. These are different from, and in addition to the direct effects. The results from these effects can be positive or negative.

The induced effects are a different set of additional economic activities of (or effects upon) other, unrelated, firms and households that are also caused by the gas well drilling and operation and its direct and indirect impacts. These effects can also be positive or negative.

For example, 2009 estimates of direct spending on the Marcellus Shale industry in Pennsylvania were approximately $3.8 billion. This includes the direct costs of well drilling, O&M etc. expenses that are reflected in the books.

An additional $1.6 billion of expenses have been attributed to *indirect* spending by other industries on goods and services. The combined direct and indirect effects generate approximately $1.8 billion in *induced* effects, which result in economic benefits for the local area. The overwhelming conclusion in this case is that each $1 spent by the gas industry generates $1.90 in gross output and sales in the state and the country.

For example, gas well owners pay royalty payments for the land they are renting or leasing. This way, the local land owners could get bonanza payments for their (sometime otherwise useless) land of over $50,000 annually for leasing each 100 acres to the drilling operations.

What is harder to estimate is the negative effects, which are either hidden, or which presence is delayed by months or years.

The External Costs

One of the biggest problems with natural gas—and especially its production and transport now—is the accidental release of contaminants into the air, soil, and water. The size and cost of these types of contamination have not been determined, but a fierce battle is raging across the U.S. and the rest of the world that is intended to stop or at least tightly regulate hydrofracking.

The cost of this battle to the gas industry, and the entire U.S. industrial complex is unknown, but it is significant. Legal action, delaying or stopping well drilling projects, and other related anomalies cost money and will have to be accounted for sooner or later.

Another great cost in the natural gas production and transport is from legal action resulting from accidents. Just like spilled oil, spilled gas can cause serious damage. The difference is that in some cases, the damage is immediate. Spilled (leaked) natural gas mixed with air and exposed to an open flame will explode and burn very hot. It would destroy anything in its path within minutes.

This is the case of the 2010 natural gas pipeline explosion in San Bruno, California that killed eight people, injured 66, and destroyed 38 houses. Property damage of about $220 million was assessed, but how about the other losses—including the loss of human life. The $2.5 litigation is the largest penalty ever levied by a state regulatory body in the U.S.

The largest penalty under federal pipeline safety laws thus far is $101.5 million for an August 2000, explosion on the El Paso natural gas pipeline in New Mexico. Twelve people camping under a concrete-decked steel bridge that supported the pipeline across the river were killed instantly and their three vehicles destroyed. Two nearby steel suspension bridges for gas pipelines crossing the river were extensively damaged. Property and other damages or losses totaled nearly a million dollars, and resulting in $101.5 million in punitive damages awards.

The Fracking Facts...

Fact 1. The toxic fracking liquids enter into the Earth's depth under very high pressure and strictly via controlled process. But then, they are released into porous ground without much, if any, control from above, because at this point any control that the process crew had is lost. The chemicals are free to act on their own and can travel in whichever direction they (not the ground crew) want.

Fact 2. At the point of release from the delivery pipes the chemicals are on their own and move around according to the particularities of the local geological formations. This way they can enter into the water table, and eventually flow up and break through the surface. There is no way to control their movement under the ground. This fact cannot be disputed!

Fact 3. What we know for certain is that there are increasing numbers of cases of fracking liquids and gasses showing up in places where they don't belong and where they have not been present before. This fact cannot be disputed!

Fact 4. Any intentional or unintentional contact with these liquids and gasses by humans or animals would lead to some negative health effects. Common sense tells us that the effects of any contact with toxic fracking liquids, or any petroleum products, would range from a skin rash to cancer, depending on the chemicals type, concentration, and length of exposure. This fact cannot be disputed!

Fact 5. A number of researchers in veterinarian medicine have looked into this problem and a number of cases in several shale states have been investigated. The conclusions are that livestock had often experienced neurological, reproductive and gastrointestinal problems after being exposed to fracking fluids either accidentally or incidentally.

NOTE: Some of the most dramatic cases thus far have been the death of 17 cattle within an hour after being exposed directly to hydraulic fracturing fluid. In another case 140 cattle exposed to fracking wastewater after an impoundment was breached, of which 70 died and the remainder produced only 11 calves with only three survivals. There are also many other deaths reported as a result of poisoning of animals accidentally getting into the fracking fluids.

The exposure symptoms usually result in neuro-

logical symptoms and weight loss in horses, problems with dairy goats reproducing, and abnormalities in dogs. In some farms, adult animals suffered abnormally high miscarriages or stillborn births after the animals had been accidentally exposed to fracking fluid.

The health issues and death of animals as a result of exposure to fracking fluids only confirms that the fracking chemicals are:

a) Where they are not supposed to be

b) That they are dangerous to all life forms, including humans.

The above facts are supported by a large body of research and it all leads to a very real conclusion; that there is a danger brewing in the fracking fields of the U.S. and that we must take all possible precautions to ensure the safety of the locals and the environment.

Nevertheless, the fracking industry, supported by government authorities, claims that any and all accidents and incidents related to fracking, and any and all assumptions made as a result of these are not based on any scientific merit. Instead, they claim, the opposition is using unverifiable, anecdotal information to fit predetermined set of results all of which conflicting a number of studies on the same issue done by the industry.

This brings to mind the claims of the tobacco industry some years ago, when they blamed the users of their products for the high incidence of lung cancer cases. Just like in those days, the present day oil and gas industry attributes the health problems to a mass hysteria that has swept the nation. According to industry representatives most of the claims are anecdotal, since no study has been definite enough to offers any clear evidence supporting the notion that fracturing is making people sick.

Representatives of oil and gas companies usually claim that they take health claims seriously, and we have to believe that they mean that...to an extend. They claim that they would respond to any medical reports or scientific data showing a direct link between fracking and human health, but they would not respond to anecdotal accounts.

And since all claims are "anecdotal," according to their measure of anecdotal vs. non-anecdotal accounting, there is no real problem for now, and as far as they are concerned there would be no real action—probably until a very large disaster is documented and recorded showing a direct link between fracking and human health.

In one of the affected states, the state oil and gas commission plans to study whether oil and gas pollution affects health, but it will take years before any reliable information is available. The health-risk assessment phase of the study won't begin until January 2016. It will probably take another two-three years to complete the study, so by 2020 we might have some results. Until then…tough!

Many people are not willing to wait any longer, so as a result a number of lawsuits have been filed that blame the fracking operations and their chemicals and byproducts for health-related abnormalities and death, and blame the drilling companies for the property damage and the related health problems. For more info on the subject visit the FrackCheck WV website (2).

We can only hope that we don't have to witness another tobacco-, or asbestos-like gruesome large-scale disaster, and the end of such a high visibility issue of national and international importance. But as things are going, we would not be surprised.

NUCLEAR POWER

Nuclear power has been on and off the energy of choice since the mid-20th century. It has been mostly on the off side for the last 30+ years for a number of reasons. No doubt Three Mile and Chernobyl nuclear plants' disasters had a lot to do with the slow down in nuclear power development. But there are other reasons, one of which is the difficulty in permitting and the high cost of building new nuclear power plants.

Another reason indirectly impacting the growth of the nuclear industry is the lack of permanent storage for thousands of tons of spent fuel, which are presently piled up in temporary storage in nuclear plants' back yards, and other temporary storage facilities. How long can the ever-growing amounts of spent nuclear fuel and wastes be stored like that before a permanent depository is found is a serious question that needs to be answered before the nuclear industry can spread its wings again.

Problems or not, nuclear power is still providing over 20% of the basic electric power load in the U.S. It is still the most reliable and cheapest source of energy available. Nevertheless, looking at only aspect of this awesome power doesn't make it justice. Instead, we need to look at all aspects of the nuclear power generation cycle to make conclusions of its total usefulness and future.

Despite the promising economic figures of nuclear plants, there are risks and uncertainties that must be considered. Those are primarily public acceptance of long-term operation, national policies on energy and

Figure 7-17. U.S. electric power generation sources

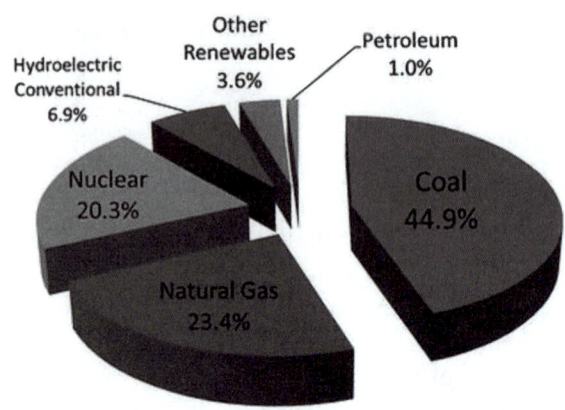

security concerns. Countries that have decided on long-term nuclear power use have done so through a license renewal process or through periodic safety reviews and upgrades as dictated by the respective national nuclear energy regulating bodies.

As the world grapples with excess carbon generation and GHGs reduction programs, the utilities must keep the electricity flowing. They have no choice but to keep the base load levels steady as needed to counterbalance the intermittent power coming into the grid from the variable sources like wind and solar. Nuclear is a major baseload power source, so shutting it down is out of the question.

But around 289 reactors across the world are over 25-years-old, and only 45 new units have been connected to the grid between 2000 and 2011—none in the U.S. This imbalance has created an unprecedented trend towards life extension and operating license renewal. Although not a perfect solution, without life extensions, generally, nuclear capacity will fall dramatically in the next decade, especially if no new nuclear plants are built for whatever reasons.

Cost of Nuclear Plants

Nuclear power plants permitting, construction, and operation are complex and expensive undertakings. Billions of dollars are needed to design, construct, equip, and start up even the smallest nuclear plant. The costs and expenses can be divided in several groups, as follows: capital costs, financing costs, construction costs, operating costs and decommissioning costs.

* Capital costs consist of the bare plant cost, also known as engineering-procurement-construction (EPC) cost; land; cooling infrastructure; administration and associated buildings; site works;

switchyards; and project management. This also includes the more uncertain costs of permitting and licensing, tax and cost escalation and overall inflation.

- Owner's costs (which include any of the above costs) may also include transmission infrastructure, and overnight capital cost, which is the EPC plus owners' costs, excluding financing, escalation due to increased material and labor costs, and inflation.

- Construction costs are also called "all-in cost," can add escalation and interest during prior to and construction, to the overnight cost. Construction is expressed in the same units as overnight cost and is useful for identifying the total cost of construction and for determining the effects of construction delays and overruns.

The construction costs of nuclear power plants are always significantly higher than for coal- or gas-fired plants because of the use of special and more expensive materials, in addition to much more sophisticated and equally expensive safety features and back-up control equipment. Although these extras contribute to increase in the long-term nuclear power generation cost, once the plant is built, the cost variables are minor to none.

Extended construction periods will put the project over budget, and will push up financing costs, as we have seen on several occasions in the past, when they have gone spectacularly high. Construction times in Asia seem to be much shorter, where for example the construction of 1.3 GW Japanese reactors, built in the mid-1990s, took little over four years. Now the Japanese EPCs estimate four to four and a half years maximum for a typical plant completion today. Unfortunately, the Fukushima disaster put an end to many such plans. It also put the Japanese nuclear industry in reverse, so it is not sure if and when it will recover any time soon, if ever.

Overnight cost, in general terms, is the partial cost of the construction project, calculated without the usual interest incurred during construction, which is as if the project was completed overnight. Or, it is also interpreted as the present value cost that would have to be paid as a lump sum up front, to completely pay for a construction project. For power plants, the unit of measure typically used is $/kW (dollars per kilowatt).

If, for example, the overnight cost of a nuclear plant is $2,000/kW, a 1000 MW plant would have an overnight cost $2 billion. This excludes the interest on the $2 billion

spent during construction, which would be calculated separately, and added as an additional cost.

- Financing costs depend on a number of factors and conditions. These, in addition to the level of manageable risk, include the rate of interest on debt, the debt-equity ratio, and (in a regulated cases), how the capital costs are recovered. There is usually also an allowance for a rate of return (ROI) on equity, or risk capital.

- Operating costs include operating and maintenance (O&M) expenses plus fuel. Fuel cost figures include used fuel management and final waste disposal. These costs are usually external for other technologies, but are internal for nuclear power, since they have to be paid or set aside securely by the utility generating the power. The cost is usually passed on to the customer in the actual power tariff.

The fuel storage and disposal, contributes up to 5-10% of the overall costs per kWh (the fuel cost is less in case of direct disposal, rather than recycling or reprocessing.) The U.S. used fuel program (valued at approximately $26 billion) is funded by a 0.1 cent/kWh levy.

Cost Examples

Some examples of nuclear power plants costs as of 2008 (no newer plants have been built ever since, although several are in planning and permitting stages):

The cost for two new AP1000 reactors built at Turkey Point site built by Florida Power & Light were estimated at $3,108 to $4,540/kW, including cooling towers, site works, land costs, transmission costs and risk management. With finance charges, the total cost goes to $5,780 to $8,071/kW, or $6.6 and $9.3 billion for the entire facility, respectively.

The cost for two new AP1000 reactors in Florida, built by Progress Energy, was estimated at $5,144/kW for the first unit, and $3,376/kW for the second. Or total cost for the entire plant estimated at $9.4 billion. Adding the cost of the land, plant components, cooling towers, financing costs, license application, regulatory fees, initial fuel for two units, owner's costs, insurance, taxes, escalation, and contingencies, brings the total to over $14 billion.

Similarly, two new AP1000 reactors at the Virgil C. Summer Nuclear Generating Station in South Carolina would cost $9.8 billion, which includes forecast inflation and owners' costs for site preparation, contingencies, and project financing.

Two new AP1000 reactors at Duke Energy Carolinas' Lee site were estimated to cost $11 billion, including other owners' costs, but excluding finance and inflation estimates.

Two new AP1000 reactors at the Bellefonte site were estimated to cost $2,516 to $4,649/kW for overnight capital cost, or a combined construction cost of $5.6 to 10.4 billion. The total cost ranging between $9.9 to $17.5 billion).

Two new AP1000 reactors built by Georgia Power Company were estimated to cost $14 billion plus $3 billion for transmission upgrades.

The construction cost estimates for new nuclear power plants in the U.S. are very uncertain and have increased significantly in recent years. Companies that are planning new nuclear units are currently indicating that the total costs (including escalation and financing costs) will be in the range of $5,500/kW to $8,100/kW or between $6 billion and $9 billion for each 1,100 MW plant.

These new cost estimates are far higher than the industry had previously predicted. For example, as recently as the years 2000-2002, the industry and Department of Energy were talking about overnight costs of $1,200/kW to $1,500/kW for new nuclear units. This range of estimated overnight costs suggested total plant costs of between $2 and $4 billion per new nuclear unit. The MIT future of nuclear study in 2003, increased the estimated prices of new nuclear plants to $2,000/kW, not including financing costs.

However, the estimated costs for new nuclear power plants begin to increase significantly starting in about 2006-2007.

For example:

- A June 2007, report by the keystone center estimated an overnight cost of $2,950/kW for a new nuclear plant. With interest, this figure translated to between $3,600/kW and $4,000/kW.

- In October 2007, Moody's investor services estimated a range of between $5,000/kW and $6,000/kW for the total cost of new nuclear units (including escalation and financing costs) but acknowledged that this cost estimate was "only marginally better than a guess."

Also in October 2007, Florida Power & Light ("FPL") announced a range of overnight costs (i.e., no escalation or financing costs) for its two proposed nuclear power plants (total of 2200 MW) as being between $3,108/kW and $4,540/kW. FPL also estimated the total cost of the project (including escalation and financing costs) as being between $5,492/kW and $8,081/kW. These estimated costs translated into a projected total cost of $12.1 billion to $17.8 billion, for just two 1100 MW plants.

NOTE: Calculations of power generating costs use levelized costs of energy (LOE) formulas, which reflect the average costs of producing electricity including capital, finance, owner's costs on site, fuel and operation over a plant's lifetime, with provision for decommissioning and waste disposal.

It is important to note here that capital energy cost figures quoted by reactor vendors, or other interested parties, usually reflect only the EPC costs, because the owner's costs vary hugely for a number of reasons, including whether a plant is built on a Greenfield (new installation), or at an old site, replacing an old plant.

Cost of Nuclear Materials and Services

It has been estimated that approximately 10,000 tons of earth have to be moved in the process of obtaining the equivalent of one ton of uranium. And this is only one part of the complex and expensive process of obtaining nuclear fuel.

The cost of one kg. uranium, processed to UO_2 reactor fuel grade can be broken down as follows:

Starting with uranium ore, approximately nine pounds of U_3O_8 ore are needed to obtain one kg. of reactor grade UO_2, so at $150 per kg for the ore, we get:

Uranium ore	$1,350
Conversion	100
Enrichment	1,100
Fuel processing	250

Total:	$2,800 per kg. reactor fuel

Assuming that under normal operating conditions one kg of enriched uranium UO_2 generates about 360 MWh electrical power, the fuel cost then is approximately $0.0078 kWh, or less than a tenth of penny per kilowatt/hour. This reduces the cost of nuclear to about 10-15% of the retail price of electric power in the U.S., vs. 80% for coal and oil generated power. This means that the cost of nuclear fuel is several times lower than the cost of coal, or oil fuels used for generating the same amount of electricity. The different fuels' emissions and waste disposal expenses complicate and change this balance, as we will see later in this text.

NOTE: These estimates are based on published 2011-2012 reports on prices of goods and services in the U.S. Theoretically speaking, and at 100% efficiency, one kg. of pure UO_2 can generate many times more electricity than 360 MWh, but considering the dilution ratios of the fuel mix and process inefficiencies, the estimate of 360 MWh is used as an average here.

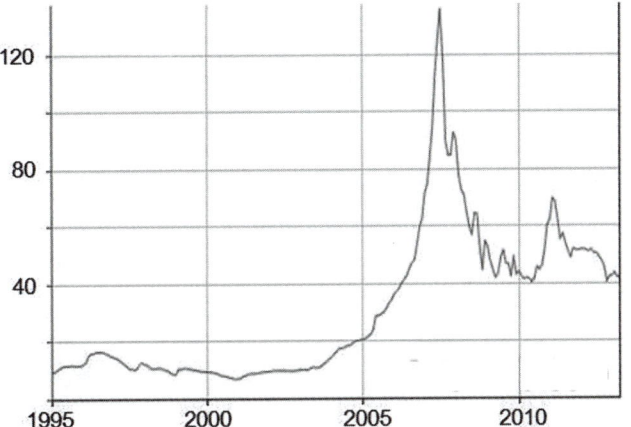

Figure 7-18. Uranium prices (in \$/lb of UO2).

The U.S. imports the major part of its uranium. Prices paid for uranium (U3O8) during the 1970s were higher, \$43/lb-U3O8. The import price dropped to \$32.90/lb-U3O8 in 1981 and down to \$12.55 in 1990 and to below \$10 US\$/lb-U_3O_8 in 2000. Uranium prices reached an all-time low in 2001, down to \$7/lb, but has since rebounded strongly.

In 2007 the price of uranium on the spot market rose to \$113.00/lb. This is very close to the all-time high (adjusted for inflation) in 1977—the high point of the uranium bubble of 2007. The extreme price increase has led to a trend in expansion in current uranium mining operations, including construction of new mines, re-opening of old mines, and a spur in new prospecting.

Construction and Operations Cost Overruns

Cost overruns have been, and still are, a major obstacle in the progress of the world nuclear industry. There are many reasons—most of which have nothing to do with the projects themselves—but they all contribute to extreme delays and cost overruns.

As an example, there were serious cost overruns for the Darlington nuclear generating station in Canada, largely due to unscheduled delays caused by policy changes and other outside interferences. This case is often used by opponents of new reactors to overemphasize the problems, which in some cases were caused by them.

Construction of Darlington power plant started in 1981 at an estimated cost of \$7.4 Billion, and finished in 1993 at a cost of \$14.5 billion. 70% of the price increase was due to interest charges incurred due to delays im-

posed to postpone units three and four, 46% inflation over a four year period, and other changes in financial policy. No new nuclear reactor has since been built in Canada, although a few have been and are undergoing refurbishment.

In the U.K. and the U.S., cost overruns on nuclear plants contributed to the bankruptcies of several utility companies. In the U.S. such losses helped usher in energy deregulation in the mid-1990s that saw rising electricity rates and power blackouts in California.

The U.K. began privatizing utilities in the 1990s, but its nuclear reactors were so unprofitable that they could not be even sold. Eventually in 1996, the government gave them away. And then the company that took them over, British Energy, kept on losing money so it had to be bailed out in 2004 to the tune of 3.4 billion pounds.

The Other Issues...

Nuclear power plants are different from all other power plants and facilities, for they are associated with nuclear bombs, terrorism, accidents, loss of life, etc., which are negatives that are hard to overlook. They need to be carefully guarded against attempted sabotage and possible theft of nuclear material. Terrorist attacks are usually executed with the goal of causing a nuclear incident, rather than just interfering with the plant's operation.

The security costs of protecting the physical plant from outside attacks, as well as ensuring the internal security (screening and supervision of workers and contractors) are considerable.

Nuclear reactors contain a core of highly radioactive fuel, which is kept under control by a complex cooling system which is also significantly contaminated. The complexity and the danger of accidents surrounding this cooling system requires the investment of considerable resources in keeping it running properly and safely.

While a break in any component of a conventional power plant can be fixed without large environmental or health effects, in nuclear power plant, even the slightest malfunction is a cause of great concern. So, extraordinary effort and money is spent on preventing and fixing any and all malfunctions.

Especially after the 2011 Fukushima nuclear plant accident, the public is no longer willing to perceive industrial risk as it used to in the early days of nuclear energy. Instead, nuclear plant operators now are expected to operate the plant with the highest possible safety standards. This, in most cases, means the most complex and costly designs and O&M procedures, which will in turn make nuclear power scarce and prohibitively expensive.

Spent Fuel Disposal

There is another critical issue that is hindering the development of the world's nuclear power industry. All nuclear plants produce radioactive waste and pay a lot of money for storing, transport, and disposal of the waste materials. In the U.S. a surcharge of a $0.001 per each kWh generated is automatically added to the electricity bills in nuclear power generating areas. In Canada, about 1.0% of the total electrical utility bills are charged in areas that use nuclear power to fund nuclear waste disposal.

There are a number of temporary nuclear waste storage facilities around the U.S., so when nuclear plants run out of storage space for their nuclear wastes, they ship them to these facilities.

Some of the U.S. temporary nuclear waste storage facilities are:

- Energysolutions Barnwell operations, located in Barnwell, South Carolina. Barnwell is licensed by the state of South Carolina to receive wastes in Classes A-C classes, and accepts waste only from the Atlantic compact states (Connecticut, New Jersey, and South Carolina).

- U.S. ecology, located in Richland, Washington, is licensed to receive wastes in the A-C classes and accepts waste only from the Northwest and Rocky Mountain compacts.

- Waste control specialists (WCS), LLC, located near Andrews, Texas, is licensed by the state of Texas for Classes A, B, and C waste, and accepts waste from the Texas compact generators and outside generators with permission from the compact, WCS

- Energysolutions Clive Operations, located in Clive, Utah, is licensed by the state of Utah for Class A waste only, and accepts waste from all regions of the United States.

The disposal of low-level waste costs around $3,000/m³, while the disposal of high-level waste cost is between $75,000/m³ and $300,000/m³ depending on the particular waste and its location.

NOTE: There is about 80% low level and 20% of high level waste generated around the world. Each nuclear reactor produces roughly 12 m³ of high level waste, and 3-4 times that amount in low-level waste, annually.

The mentioned storage sites are classified as temporary nuclear waste storage facilities, although the definition of "temporary" is somewhat fluid, and due to the lack of permanent storage, the nuclear wastes will remain there forever, or at least for a very long time.

As can be seen in Figure 7-19, there are large amounts of nuclear wastes generated by the world's nuclear power plants. This reveals the biggest problem that has been, and still is, plaguing the world nuclear industry—there is no way to store the nuclear waste out of the way in permanent manner. Amazingly enough, after all the advancements of the nuclear technology of late, there is not one single operating permanent nuclear waste disposal site anywhere in the world.

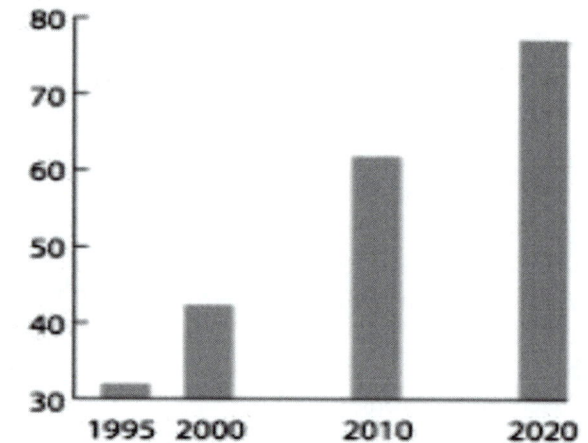

Figure 7-19. Global Nuclear waste (in thousands metric tons annually)

In 2009, the U.S. DOE cancelled the Yucca Mountain nuclear waste repository, which was designed to handle all U.S. civilian nuclear waste. There are presently no plans for permanent disposal of the nuclear wastes, so the nuclear plants are required to keep the increasing amounts of nuclear waste on the plant premises indefinitely. An expensive undertaking…

In 2002 Canada created a nuclear waste management organization to oversee long-term disposal of nuclear waste. Later on, in 2007, Canada implemented the adapted phased management procedure for long-term management, which is subject to change based on technology and public opinion, but currently largely follows the recommendations for a centralized repository as first extensively outlined in by AECL in 1988.

It was determined that following these recommendations would safely isolate the waste from the biosphere. The location has not yet been determined, but it is expected to cost between $9 and $13 billion CAD for construction and operation for 60–90 years, employing roughly a thousand people for the duration.

Funding is available and has been collected since 1978 under the Canadian nuclear fuel waste management program. Very long-term monitoring requires fewer staff, since high-level waste is less toxic than naturally occurring uranium ore deposits within a few centuries. Yet, it is not certain when, if ever, this project will be started and completed.

Onkalo Permanent Storage

The most advanced waste nuclear depository project is the Onkalo spent nuclear fuel repository, which presently under construction in Finland. It is a deep geological repository designed for the final disposal of spent nuclear fuel. Based on the KBS-3 method of nuclear waste burial, developed in Sweden, the Onkalo facility's constructions plans are divided into four phases:

- Phase one was focused on excavation of the large access tunnel to the facility, spiraling downward to a depth of 1,380 ft.

- Phase two continued the excavation to a final depth of 1,710 ft. The characteristics of the bedrock were studied to adapt the layout of the repository.

- Phase three marks the construction of the repository, which is expected to begin around 2015, after the completion of the initial investigation and the design plans.

- Phase four, the encapsulation and burial of areas filled with spent fuel is projected to begin around 2020.

Figure 7-20a shows the overall design of the facility with its multiple streets and alleys.

Figure 7-20.b shows a detail of the actual deposition sites, where the canisters will be deposited and buried forever.

Once in operation, the Onkalo disposal process would involve putting several fuel assemblies into a large boron steel canister and enclosing it into an even larger copper capsule. The sophisticated and expensive coffins full of radioactive nuclear materials will be shut close and welded via special robot-welder once and forever. They will be then loaded on special remotely controlled transport cars, equipped with robotic arms, and delivered to their final destination.

The robotic arm will lift the canister and drop it (gently) into its cement grave. The robot arm would then wave one final goodbye to the canister and its contents,

Figure 7-20a.
Onkalo long-term nuclear waste disposal facility

Figure 7-20b. Detail of the buried nuclear waste capsules

before the hole is plugged up with a cement cap. This way thousands of canisters will be put to sleep deep underground for thousands of years, entombed in thick walled cement graves deep underground.

A lot of expensive materials and equipment are involved in this complex process, but it seems the only way to ensure the security and safety of such a large quantity of very dangerous nuclear waste materials, at least until a better, safer, and cheaper way to dispose of nuclear waste is discovered, tested and implemented.

The estimated cost of the Onkalo project construction is about $1.0 billion, which includes construction, encapsulation, and operating costs. We are sure that the cost will double and triple with time, and we might be looking at $10 billion price tag before the project is complete. And yet, it is still much less than the almost $100 billion price of the now abandoned in mid-stream Yucca Mountain nuclear waste disposal project.

The Onkalo repository is designed to accept all spent fuel waste generated in Finland for around one hundred years, at which point the final encapsulation and burial will take place. After that, the access tunnel will be backfilled and sealed and the entire area will be converted into a wilderness, intended to make us forget the monster asleep underground. Will we forget…? Will we follow the Onkalo example…?

There are also proposals to bury nuclear waste deep in the ocean floor. The idea is to create specialized teams of deep ocean floor drillers, who would be able to drill large boreholes in the abyssal mud and clay of the ocean floor at special locations.

Cylindrical shafts, hundreds of feet deep, and spaced hundreds of meters apart would be drilled following special safety procedures. Several canisters containing the nuclear waste would be carefully lowered in these holes, separated by mud and clay deposits.

Thus entombed canisters would last thousands of years before decomposing and releasing their deadly content. At that time, the mud surrounding the canister would cling to the radioactive materials and prevent them from seeping into the ocean waters. There are tests showing that the radioactivity escaping the decomposed canisters would not travel more than few meters even after 100,000 years in the muddy grave.

But for all of us—not familiar with ocean bottom mechanics and mud-traveling-radioactivity—these plans are suspiciously lacking of data. For that reason alone, we must be cautious and allow more time for the science to develop and provide some proves that this method would not cause an even greater disaster.

Decommissioning of Nuclear Plants

Many U.S. and world nuclear plants are old and near the end of their useful lives. Some of them are undergoing refurbishing and recertification to extend their operation beyond the design time limit. Eventually, however, old nuclear plants have to be eventually shut down and decommissioned.

The process of decommissioning a nuclear reactor can only take place after the appropriate license has been granted, pursuant to the relevant legislation and local laws. As part of the licensing procedure various documents, reports and expert opinions have to be written and delivered to the competent authority, e.g. safety report, technical documents, environmental impact study, etc.

Decommissioning costs represent about 5-10% of the initial capital cost of a nuclear power plant, but when discounted, they contribute only a small percentage to the investment cost and even less to the generation cost. For example, in the U.S. the decommissioning costs average to 0.1-0.2 cent/kWh, which is about 5% of

the cost of the electricity produced.

Decommissioning and land remediation is a complex and expensive undertaking. The dismantling of the equipment (reactors and such) could cost from $5 million to $10 million. Handling and removal of the fuel could cost another $5-10 million alone. The entire plant decommissioning could be in the range of $25 million to a $1 billion, depending on the level of contamination and the corresponding decontamination effort needed.

In some cases there is an additional charge for a long-term upkeep of the area, which could be up to $10 million annually. If these costs were not foreseen and estimated in the overall operating budget of the plant, the owner is faced with many legal problems and uncertain financial future.

Once a nuclear facility is decommissioned properly, there is no longer danger of radioactivity in the area. At that time, and after official inspection and certification, the area and the owner of the plant is released from regulatory control, and is no longer responsible for the nuclear safety of the area.

In the U.S. the estimates now for decommissioning a nuclear reactor average $325 million per reactor. The decommissioning of Connecticut Yankee nuclear power plant cost over $400 million. The Shoreham nuclear generating station in New York, which cost $7 billion to be build was decommissioned shortly thereafter at a cost of $400 million. Who paid for it? You and I, of course.

Several other nuclear plants were decommissioned—Connecticut Yankee, Connecticut; Yankee Rowe, Massachusetts; Maine Yankee, Maine; Big Rock, Michigan, and the Trojan nuclear plant in Oregon (in 2006). The costs of these end-of-life projects are similarly high, and the U.S. taxpayer is also paying for that work too.

In France, decommissioning of the Brennilis nuclear power plant, a fairly small 70 MW power plant, went up to over $600 million, which is about 20 times the originally estimated costs, and the work is still underway… On top of that, and despite the huge investments in securing the dismantling process, radioactive plutonium, cesium-137 and cobalt-60 leaked out into the surrounding lake. This complicated the situation and is increasing the costs even further. Dismantling came to a halt, with only the reactor block, the heat exchangers, and various nuclear waste remaining in place at the site. This will remain a work in progress for a while longer at a great expense.

In the U.K., decommissioning of the Windscale advanced gas cooled reactor (WAGR), a 32 MW prototype power plant, cost over $130 million.

In Germany, decommissioning of Niederaichbach

nuclear power plant, a 100 MW power plant, amounted to more than $160 million.

Decommissioning Funds

In Europe there is considerable concern about the funds necessary to finance final decommissioning. In many countries either the funds do not appear sufficient to pay the financial decommissioning, and in other countries the funds are being used for activities other than decommissioning, putting the funds at risk, and distorting competition with parties who do not have nuclear decommissioning funds available.

Currently the European commission is looking into this issue. It is estimated, that during the next two decades, the dismantling of the 150 nuclear reactors in Europe will cost around €150 billion, with an average cost of one billion for reactor.

Similar concerns exist in the United States, where the U.S. nuclear regulatory commission has located apparent decommissioning funding assurance shortfalls and requested 18 nuclear power plants to address that issue.

International Collaboration

Organizations that promote the international sharing of information, knowledge, and experiences related to nuclear decommissioning include the international atomic energy agency, the organization for economic co-operation and development's nuclear energy agency and the European atomic energy community. In addition, an online system called the deactivation and decommissioning knowledge management information tool was developed under the United States Department of Energy and made available to the international community to support the exchange of ideas and information. The goals of international collaboration in nuclear decommissioning are to reduce decommissioning costs and improve worker safety.

Ships, Mobile Reactors, Military Reactors

Many warships, and a few civil ships, have used nuclear reactors for propulsion. Former Soviet and American warships have been taken out of service and their power plants removed or scuttled. Dismantling of Russian and American submarines and ships is ongoing. Marine power plants are generally smaller than land-based electrical generating stations.

Although these power plants are much smaller and somewhat different from the large nuclear power generating plants, they have similar problems. They are similarly expensive to construct, require highly quali-fied labor, and are subject to most of the civilian nuclear energy rules and regulations.

One big difference is that their decommissioning is much easier and less expensive. The Russians, for example, used to simply bury their mobile nuclear reactors in the deep ocean expanse. We would not be surprised if they still do that. Why not? This is the quickest, most efficient and cheapest way to get rid of the stuff...a la Russian.

Nuclear Externalities

The U.S. nuclear power plants produce over 50 billion kilowatt-hours of electricity annually, which is over 20% of the total utility-generated power in the country. This means that U.S. is heavily dependent on nuclear power, regardless of its enormous expense, radiation pollution, the threat of a nuclear accident, nuclear terrorism, and the nuclear waste issues.

The nuclear power advocates believe that there are scientific solutions coming to these problems soon, but in most cases they are not paying for the nuclear plants. It is us, the taxpayers that have been paying as much as the federal government wants us to. We are in fact willingly or unwillingly major stockholders in nuclear power. It is amazing, but after half of century the nuclear industry still depends on government bailouts, insurances and subsidies.

Nuclear power is cheap because of those subsidies and incentives. It costs residential consumers an average of 8.0 cents per kWh of electricity, while industrial users pay only about half that. Not bad, you say and we agree, but the actual cost of nuclear power would be much higher still if it was not for the federal subsidies, which also pay for the "externalities."

We know by now that externalities are hidden charges where some people bear costs that they are not paid or compensated for. Here, the decision-makers do not pay for the additional costs, and don't even take them into consideration in deciding how the resources shall be allocated.

The power plant owners have no reason to produce benefits that they don't get, nor to cut back on costs that they don't pay for. So, if there are 'external' costs of any sort we can expect to get charged for things we are not responsible for, all of which makes the energy markets to be inefficient.

Externalities in the nuclear power business have been estimated by the Greenpeace's, *The Economic Failure of Nuclear Power*, a 1993 study, which estimated the federal expenditures for nuclear power until 1990 to be over $97 billion. This is many billions of dollars spent on research, development, regulation, construction costs, uranium enrichment, and for contributions to the Nuclear Waste Fund. These funds, however, did not pay for the environmental destruction caused by nuclear accidents and other real and perceived damages.

There are many other externalities and costs that we don't hear much about. The Shoreham nuclear generating station in New York was finished in 1988 at a cost of $7 billion, only to be decommissioned shortly thereafter without ever producing a single watt of electricity. And because one of the reactor cores was turned on for a test, the decommissioning cost an extra $400 million. Who paid for it? You and I, of course.

And then, many nuclear plants in the past were completed with 500-700% cost overruns, while others were just abandoned because they were too expensive. Who paid for these? You guessed it.

The subsidies hide the true cost and create an underestimation of the true cost of nuclear power. But why are the feds so much into covering up for nuclear? A study by the nuclear information and research service and U.S. public interest research group found that by 1992 only three members of the Senate and seven members of the House have *not* benefited from money donated by the nuclear industry's Political Action Committee campaign contributions. Any questions?

When general electric was unable to obtain accident insurance for their reactors, Congress responded with the Price-Anderson indemnity act, which limited the liability of the nuclear industry in case of a major nuclear accident to $12.6 billion. Any amount above that will be paid by the U.S. taxpayer. The same law also indemnifies nuclear plants if an accident is caused by operator error, even it is by negligence.

The nuclear industry is obligated to maintain only $7 billion of insurance under the act, while there are estimates that a major nuclear accident could cost as much as $15 billion. A meltdown would cost $56-314 billion for remediation and recompense, not including the cost of the facility itself. And this was in the light of the NRC's estimate of a 45% chance of having a meltdown in the near future. So the question is no longer if, but where and when.

And of course, the nuclear waste is a big issue as well. The nuclear repository at Hanford, Washington, is already leaking, with a third of its 177 underground storage tanks leaking toxic chemicals and radioactive waste. In response, the locals have filed a number of lawsuits.

Yet another externalized cost of nuclear power is the cost to our health. Uranium mining, enrichment, and

nuclear accidents affect our health by contaminating our environment with cancer-causing radioactive particles.

ExternE is a major European study of the external costs of various fuel cycles, focusing on coal and nuclear, ExternE, shows that in clear cash terms nuclear energy incurs externalities amounting only about one tenth of the costs of coal. This is before the costs of any major accidents are accounted for. In these cases—such as Chernobyl and Fukushima nuclear disasters—the externalities well exceed any other.

The external costs are defined as those actually incurred in relation to health issues and environmental damage. These costs are quantifiable, but are presently not built into the cost of the electricity. If these costs were in fact included, the E.U. price of electricity from coal would double and that from gas would increase 30%. And even these costs do not include the external costs of accidents, global warming and other factors.

NOTE: In the nuclear plant case, things are complicated further by a very important factor that is not included in the external costs. It is the external cost of environmental damage, and pain and suffering caused by nuclear plants' accidents. These costs are hard to even estimate, let alone put a harder number on the effects. How do you estimate the cost of human health damages and death caused by the Chernobyl accident? Or Fukushima?

These accidents caused a complete devastation of a large land mass, and its animal life, crops, water sources etc. And unlike other accidents caused by power generators, due to nuclear radiation, which lasts long time, the area is rendered useless for many, many years—perhaps forever.

But the most important and irreconcilable damage is the thousands of animals and people that have been made ill and killed as a result. How do you estimate the cost of a human life? Thousands of them? Or the pain and suffering of over a million after Chernobyl?

If these enormous costs are somehow compiled and spread over the entire global nuclear industry, it may in fact prove to be the most expensive and dangerous energy source in use now. So, while the impacts of global warming can be classified as "inter-generational," the impacts of the nuclear accidents and waste cycle debacles are better described as "inter-civilizational" in addition to being inter-generational.

The nuclear power industry points to global warming as an argument, and a good reason, for its renaissance. This might be true, assuming that the problems of, a) nuclear accidents, and b) disposing of spent nuclear fuel will be solved sometime in the near future. Unfortunately, this is not the case, because these assumptions were made by nuclear energy proponents fifty years ago. If we haven't solved these problems during the past half century, what makes us think that we will be more likely to do so in the next one?

Nuclear power has an Achilles heel or two, consisting of:

1. Nuclear power is an awesome source of power when under control, but it is even more awesome when out of control. In such cases, it devastates anything and everyone in its path. No excuses, no exceptions, no mercy! Full and permanent devastation of large areas is left behind, accompanied by loss of life, in addition to heavy contamination of even larger areas. Chernobyl and Fukushima are the unwilling witnesses to this awesome power, and what it is capable of doing within very short span of time.

2. Nuclear fuel wastes remain hazardous for hundreds of thousands, and as much as a million years. Since human history goes back only about 10,000 years, this means that the radioactivity of the spent nuclear fuels and waste materials will be dangerous at least 100 such periods of time.

Thus far, no successful implementation of permanent disposal option for nuclear waste is available, although some plausible solutions have been proposed. Thus we will leave the unresolved externality of nuclear energy production for future generations to worry about, a task for future civilizations to solve. This is the most blatant transfer of the most expensive part of the cost of the nuclear fuel cycle to future generations and civilizations to deal with. We must pause and wonder what they will think of us.

3. There is also a real damage done by the nuclear power plants to the environment presently, where most significant of these are the aquatic impacts associated with cooling water withdrawals and heat discharges common to most steam electric generating facilities.

Aquatic impacts from even one facility can be staggering, and according to the EPA, "impingement and entrainment at individual facilities may result in appreciable losses of early life stages of fish and shellfish (e.g., three to four billion individuals annually), serious reductions in forage species and recreational and com-

mercial landings (e.g., 23 tons lost per year), and extensive losses over relatively short intervals of time (e.g., one million fish lost during a three-week study period)."

These impacts can be reduced and even eliminated by implementing closed cycle cooling systems, but this is not on the industry's agenda—yet.

4. In addition to the risks and potential dangers of accidental reactor meltdown and release of radioactivity during normal operation, there is also a real danger of nuclear proliferation and terrorism. Rogue nations, as well as many terrorists and criminal organizations are working towards obtaining nuclear weapons and using them against the civilian population of large cities in the U.S. and Europe. These risks are inseparable from any scheme of nuclear energy production and waste disposal, and must be entered in the power generation and use equations.

5. There are also other environmental and public health costs of nuclear materials, facilities, spent nuclear fuel and radioactive wastes that the nuclear energy industry prefers to keep hidden, not fully account for, and externalizing them. All this is done with the full knowledge and support of the world's governments, so it is not something that will change anytime soon. So the big question, "Who is going to pay for the piling externalities?" remains. And unless and until it is answered in a way that is satisfactory to all parties involved, the long-pending nuclear renaissance seems to be just a mirage. Thus, nuclear power will remain as an unwelcome substitute for any of the known power generation sources.

No doubt, the impacts of global warming would be tremendous, with millions of people displaced and dead. Nuclear power on its best behavior contributes significantly to reducing the air pollution, but the possibility of misbehavior on its part nullifies these benefits, and makes nuclear power even more dangerous, uncontrollable and longer-lasting. Yet, nuclear power is here to stay; we just have to be more careful in its use.

BIOFUELS

Using biofuels seems to be a no-brainer. They are "green," safe and cheap...with some conditions attached. There is no question about the sustainability of biofuels, as far as environmental and social impacts are concerned, but there are some unresolved technical and economics issues. These must be resolved before they become competitive with gasoline and diesel fuels.

Types of Biofuels

We divide the biofuel technologies now into:

1. Conventional biofuels;
   a) Sugar- and starch-based ethanol
   b) Biodiesel
   c) Biogas
2. Advanced biofuels
   a) Cellulosic bioethanol
   b) Advanced biodiesel

Conventional Biofuels

The sugar-to-ethanol process uses sugar crops such as sugarcane, sugar beet and sweet sorghum. The sucrose obtained from these is then fermented to ethanol, which is further processed. This is the most efficient process, because of the ease to produce sucrose—which is the goal of most biofuels.

The starch crops (corn and such) require an additional step, consisting of the hydrolysis of starch into glucose (sucrose cousin). This step alone requires much more energy and chemicals than the entire sugar-to-ethanol process.

The economic value of the starch-based feedstocks and processes is heavily influenced by the value of their co-products, such as dried distiller's grains with soluble (DDGS) and fructose. These byproducts are critical in most cases, since they add value and bring revenue to the processing plant.

NOTE: A bushel (approximately eight gallons) of corn produces 2.8 gallons of ethanol, 16 lbs. of high-protein distiller grains, and 17 lbs. of CO_2.

The final production costs, and with that the final product price, depend heavily on the feedstock prices. Since these prices are volatile, especially lately due to economic abnormalities and draught, the production costs also vary greatly. As a result, the price of biofuels is unstable too.

There are efforts to increase the production efficiency and reduce the related expenses by implementing more effective amylase enzymes, decreasing the ethanol concentration costs and enhanced use of the co-products

Advanced Biofuels

Ligno-cellulosic feedstocks are the foundation of advanced biofuels. The abundance and low price of the feedstock (agricultural wastes and grasses) is what makes this technology especially attractive. There are, however, a number of technical, logistics, and economic hurdles to jump over before this process is established as a major fuel competitor.

Advanced biofuels are produced via biochemical conversion of the cellulose and hemi-cellulose components of biomass feedstocks into fermentable sugars. As noted above, feedstocks like sugarcane contain large amounts of sugar in form of sucrose that can be simply squeezed out of the stalks. The sugar making process is that easy.

The sugar conversion process is more complex with corn and other starchy crops, because an additional step is added.

The advanced biofuels processing requires even more steps, due to the low quality of the feedstock, which requires several additional and expensive steps. It takes several steps to convert the difficult-to-digest cellulose into sugars. Once the sugars are extracted, they are fermented into ethanol, similar to the conventional biofuels.

Theoretically speaking, cellulosic ethanol has the potential of exhibiting the best energy balance, GHG emissions and land-use requirements, as compared with the starch-based biofuels. There large-scale advanced biofuels producing plants that are geared to demonstrate the feasibility of this technology.

Advanced Biodiesel

Biodiesel is an important transportation fuel, thus its process optimization is receiving a special attention. There are presently several processes under development that aim to produce fuels with properties similar to diesel and kerosene. In most cases thus produced biodiesel would be blended with fossil fuels in some proportion, as needed to be fully compatible with different diesel engines.

The advanced biodiesel fuel production uses different feedstocks and processes than the bioethanol and the other biofuels. The most promising advanced biodiesels are:

- Hydro-treated vegetable oil (HVO), which is produced by hydrogenating vegetable oils or animal fats. The first large-scale biodiesel production plants are already operating in Finland and Singapore, but the process has not yet been fully commercialized.

- Biomass-to-liquids (BtL) diesel is produced by a two-step process. In the first step, the biomass is converted to a syngas, which rich in hydrogen and carbon monoxide. During the second step, the syngas is cleaned and catalytically converted through a special chemical synthesis into a number of hydrocarbon liquids, containing synthetic bio-diesel and bio-kerosene fractions.

Recently, several novel biofuel conversion processes have been developed, to produce synthetic diesel fuels. Some of these are:

• The use of a micro-organisms such as yeast, heterotrophic algae or cyano-bacteria that turn sugar into alkanes, which are the basic components in the gasoline, diesel and jet fuel composition.

• The transformation of a variety of water-soluble sugars into hydrogen and chemical intermediates using aqueous phase reforming, and then into alkanes via a catalytic process.

• The use of modified yeasts to convert sugars into hydrocarbons that can be hydrogenated to synthetic diesel.

Thus far, however, and despite the promise, and all the money and effort spent, none of these processes has been developed to the point of successful use in a large-scale production operation.

The Biofuels Finances

There are now differential tax systems in use that reflect the differing external costs of different fuels, that allows some "green" fuels to successfully co-exist in markets today with the fossil fuels that are less expensive. It makes sense to realize the additional values of "green" fuels through such differential tax systems, geared to promote their use.

But this comes at a cost, and there are limits to how much it can be justified, so biofuels must find a way to move toward cost parity with fossil-based fuels in the longer term—without most of the additional perks they enjoy now.

A taxation system based on the environmental and energy performance of individual fuel types, including a carbon tax, is already implemented in some countries as one way of placing a dollar value on biofuels' environmental and societal contribution, and of reducing gaps in competitiveness with fossil fuels.

The biofuel production costs are different depending on size of the production plant, the technology and feedstock types and costs. Detailed data on biofuel

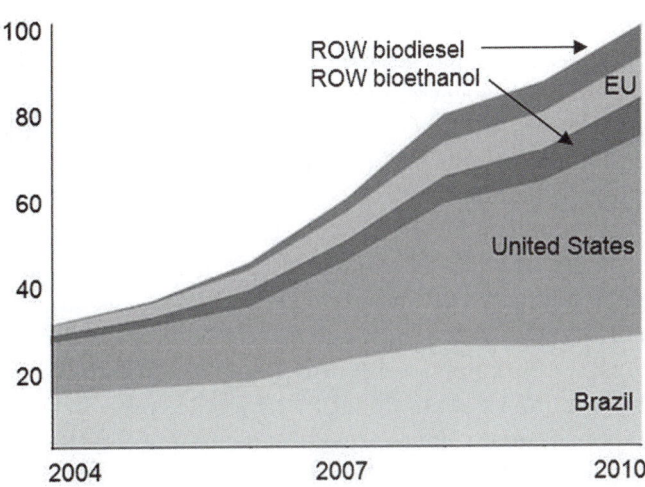

Figure 7-21. Worldwide biofuels production (in billion liters)
*ROW means rest of the world

production costs are not available, mostly because the information is usually confidential. And even more importantly, there are not many large-scale production plants, so it will take a while to gain experience and generate reliable production data.

There is no question that the production volume of biofuels around the world has been increasing at a fast pace. While the growth in the past has been concentrated in a few countries, like the U.S., Brazil, and a handful of others, now the number of countries is rapidly increasing. This is due to government mandates in Canada, some E.U. countries, Australia, Indonesia, China, India, and a number of South American (Argentina, Bolivia, Chile, Colombia, etc.) countries.

The Current Situation

Operating under the suggestion that biofuel production could (eventually) encourage rural economic development and alleviate poverty, biofuel subsidies in 2006 amounted to over $11.0 billion in the leading OECD producing countries. The largest biofuel programs are in the U.S., the EU, and Brazil, but many developing countries are also implementing or considering similar policies to encourage domestic biofuel production

The U.S.

In the U.S., federal and state ethanol programs were initially aimed at supporting farm prices and farm incomes. The ethanol industry, including corn farmers, has received federal support since the 1970s (e.g., farm subsidies, tax and non-tax incentives, and import tariff). Later the rationale for these programs shifted to environmental quality, and more recently to energy security/independence and reduced GHG emissions.

Federal subsidies have ranged from $0.40 to $0.60/ gallon and are currently at $0.45. When state programs and subsidies for start-up and investments are included, the total subsidy is estimated to range from $1.15 to $1.45/gallon.

In the past decade Federal legislation has established a schedule of renewable fuel production targets, the most recent being the energy independence and security act of 2007, which sets targets for renewable fuels consumption (increasing from 9 billion gallons in 2008 to 36 billion gallons in 2022). There are proposals for more aggressive targets, such as increasing the share of biofuels within the fuel portfolio to 20-25% by 2020.

The volumetric requirements by renewable fuel type were adjusted in 2010 under the revised renewable fuels standard (RFS2), and currently the U.S. corn ethanol capacity is approximately 13 billion gallons annually, including idled capacity. Actual annual biofuels production is in the 7-8 billion gallons range.

Currently, there are 124 biofuels refineries in the US., and 76 more are under construction and seven are being expanded. These refineries convert corn and some other crops into ethanol. Today, ethanol accounts for about 3-4% of total gasoline consumption in the U.S., reflecting an increase from about 1.0% in 2000. This recent increase is primarily due to recent policies of replacing MTBE (methyl tertiary butyl ether) with ethanol in more than 20 states. Such blended gasoline contains 6-10% ethanol in volume. Most ethanol is used for such blending.

A small amount of ethanol (about 0.3% of total) is used as E85 (fuel with 85% ethanol content) in flex-fuel vehicles that are capable to handle E85. The share of E85 is expected to remain below 2% of the annual fuel mix by 2030. There are several reasons for the market for E85 to remain limited, with importance of corn and other energy crops for use as food being one of the major factor.

The total mandate of 36 billion gallons by 2022 requires cellulosic ethanol production to rise from 0.1 billion gallons in 2010 to 16 billion gallons. At the same time the corn ethanol production is to rise to 15 billion gallons, and an additional five billion gallons of non-cellulosic "advanced" biofuels including a minimum of one billion gallons of biodiesel (primarily soybean-based).

Brazil

Ethanol production for sugarcane in Brazil dates back to the 1930s. The Brazilian government began in 1975 a "pro-alcohol" program to produce ethanol from cane biomass using quotas, fixed prices, and subsidized loans.

It takes seven times less energy to produce an equal amount of ethanol from sugar cane, and half as much land, than from corn crops. Use of water for irrigation of sugarcane, however, is doubled and tripled as compared with that needed for corn crops.

Natural conditions such as soil quality and rainfall render sugar cane production in Brazil lowest cost in the world, further reducing the cost of ethanol production.

Between 1997 and 1999, sugar and ethanol prices were deregulated and flex-fuel vehicles introduced so that consumers could choose what fuel to use. Presently all commercial grade gasoline in Brazil is blended with 20-25% ethanol.

The total national production in 2008 was 6.5 billion gallons, exceeded only by the U.S. in recent years.

Europe

Europe had a late start in the biofuels race. It was not a priority until several countries started producing biofuels in response to concerns about energy security in the mid-1990s. Russia kept its hand on the energy spigot of Europe, and since dealing with Russia is as bad as dealing with an hungry polar bear, the E.U. saw a number of renewable energy proposals put forward in the early 2000s.

A biofuel target for 2% of transportation fuel by 2005 and 5.75% by 2010 was established in 2003, only to be abandoned in 2005 when it became clear that production would fall 1.4% short of the 2% target. In 2006, the E.U. replaced quantitative targets with a strategy aimed at continued promotion of biofuels in the E.U. and developing countries, support for research into second-generation biofuels such as cellulosic ethanol and exploration of opportunities for developing countries to produce biofuel feedstocks and biofuels.

In 2009, a new E.U. mandate was established that calls for 10% biofuel content in transportation fuels by 2020. Although the E.U. mandate is 10% by 2020, the increasingly critical energy situation on the continent is forcing a revision of the biofuels 2020 target is 20% and even more.

The Biofuels Costs

The main cost factor of most biofuels production now is the type and price of feedstock. It accounts for up to 75% of the final production costs. The advanced biofuels that use ligno-cellulosic biomass sourced from energy crops, waste and residues, benefit from a lower feedstock cost factor in the 25-40% range. In this case, capital costs are the major factor with as much as 50% of production costs.

In addition, using co-products such as dried distillers' grains with solubles (DDGS), glycerine, bagasse, lignin or waste heat can reduce biofuel production costs by up to 20% depending on the fuel type and use of co-product. This case is exemplified by some of Brazil's major sugar-mills, which sell bioelectricity produced from bagasse at the plant, and which represents 10-20% of the total plant income. This is 10-20% profit from waste products, used to generate power instead of paying to be hauled away. This is the direction that biofuels will follow in the future, for it makes a lot of economic sense.

In some special cases, such as the production of soy biodiesel from soybeans, the biodiesel is a by-product and benefits from co-production advantages.

Table 7-20. Production cost for different biofuels (in cents/gallon)

Stock	1	2	3	4	5	6
Corn	40	10	2	10	3	-12
Sugarcane	30	15	3	2	2	-28
Cellulosic	15	20	20	4	10	-12
Soy oil	70	15	5	2	5	-2
Palm oil	55	15	5	1	5	-2
Jatropha	50	15	5	1	5	-2

Legend:
1—Feedstock price
2—Capital cost
3—Process chemicals
4—Energy used in the process
5—O&M
6—Co-production credits (secondary income)

Table 7-21. Biofuel production plant costs

Cost Centers	1	2	3
Financing	3.0	0.7	2.6
Operating cost	1.6	1.1	1.5
Land development	5.6	9.9	2.4
Plant construction	65.0	55.0	120.0
Working capital	9.5	3.5	7.0
Transport/stock	2.0	2.0	2.0
Fire/Water Supply	2.0	1.5	1.3
Contingency	2.7	3.4	5.0
Total	$91.4	77.1	141.8

Legend:
1—Costs for a 100 MLY* corn-ethanol production plant (in $ millions)
2—Costs for a 200 MLY sugarcane-ethanol production plant (in $ millions)
3—Costs for a 100 MLY cellulosic-ethanol production plant (in $ millions)
*MLY is million liters annual production

Obviously, there are differences in the construction and some other areas of the different types of plants. What is not reflected here is the fact that making bio-ethanol from sugarcane is much simple and cheaper process than making it from corn. This is due to the fact that sugarcane contains high quality stock that is easily converted into ethanol.

Cellulosic-ethanol production is the most difficult and most expensive, because it requires a lot of time, energy and chemicals. And then, over 30 billion gallons of water are needed to process corn into biofuels annually. This can be done in some areas, but most areas (agricultural lands and processing facilities) around the world are in areas with limited water resources, which is causing another set of problems that will only increase in the future.

Since Brazil has ideal conditions for growing sugarcane, due to abundant rains and other water supplies, it benefits from the much higher quality and cheaper feedstock. As a result, Brazil has been producing very large quantities of bio-ethanol since the 1970s, and a significant part of it is exported.

As Figure 7-22 suggests, the future of biofuels is bright, but yet uncertain. Their development depends on too many factors to be able to predict with some degree of accuracy. Technological and economic developments, as well as the price of the other energy sources will be the main factors in the future development of biofuels.

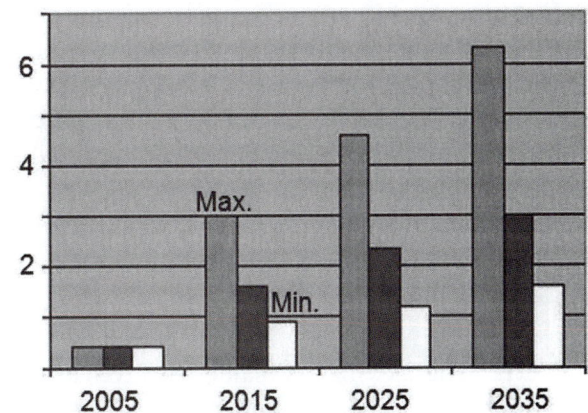

Figure 7-22. Min-max biofuels demand estimates (in TWh)

Biofuels and Transportation

Biofuels are the most convenient (if not the only possible) substitute for fossil fuels in the transportation industry. Their use in other energy sectors is also possible, but using them as substitutes for gasoline and diesel makes most sense and it seems that it is where the emphasis is now.

The energy industry estimates the biofuels production to increase by 2030 to around $2.75 trillion. This is less than 7% of all transportation fuels, which are estimated at $45 trillion for the same time period. Later on, by 2030, the biofuels production is expected to ramp up considerably, reaching about $9.0 trillion, vs. total cost of transport fuels of about 60 trillion, or about 15% of total spending on transport fuels for the period.

Biofuels are shaping up, at least on paper, as a major factor in replacing crude oil in the transportation sector. This is very important step in the path to energy independence, but there are a number of serious problems related to the quick expansion of biofuels crops around the world, some of which we discuss below.

Biofuels Externalities

The production and use of biofuels has been advertised as an economic engine for some developing countries. Is it?

Consider this in light of the facts that:

- In Mexico, the corn for fuel programs caused loss of agricultural workers' income, consolidation of the tortilla industry, excess urban migration, and increased poverty.

- In East Asia, increased use of corn for fuels caused growth of the livestock industry, accompanied by more meat consumption, which in turn leads to a number of health complications.

- In Africa, corn for biofuels was transformed into a battle for land. Land grabbing for expansion of the biofuel crops by governments and multi-national companies caused forced resettling of entire populations. The diversion of corn crops from the kitchen table of the masses to the gas tanks of the rich also created untold misery. This was a huge global problem that resulted in riots, hunger for millions, and in death from starvation in some cases.

NOTE: The fact that the same resources are used for production of both food and biofuel crops creates a disequilibrium in the food-energy systems. If the demand for one of the products (biofuel crops in this case) is rising, the price of other (food crops in this case) will also rise.

During the last boom-bust biofuels cycle of 2007-2009 there was a sharp increase in the demand for biofuel crops. As a result, the food crops acreage decreased quickly and with that the food became scarce, forcing its price to rise accordingly.

A bushel of corn (approximately eight gallons) produces approximately 2.8 gallons of ethanol.

Filling a 25-gallon gas tank with pure ethanol requires over 450 pounds of corn, which contains enough calories to feed one person in Mexico or Africa for an entire year.

The production and use of biofuels is classified as renewable, clean, and green technology. Is it?

In addition to the alcohol, a bushel of corn also produces 16 lbs. of high-protein distiller grains, which can be used for animal feed, or for protein enrichment of foods. This is the good thing…

The bad part is that that same bushel is also responsible for the emission of 17 lbs. of CO_2 during its lifetime. This amount multiplied by the billions of bushels of corn produced world wide every year, puts corn—and by extension, corn ethanol—among the major GHG polluters.

During the recent ethanol boom and bust cycle, the price of corn increased from $2.25 per bushel in summer 2006 to $4.25 in February 2007, and has been up and down (mostly up for a number of reasons) ever since. Corn prices have risen and fallen many times in the past, but now the bio-ethanol pressure will keep them high for an extended period this time around.

Substituting corn for other commodities such as soy is also causing an increase in the price of these commodities. In developing countries, the food versus fuel trade-off is even more critical.

There are winners and losers in this battle for more energy sources, but the problems will only grow. The price of gasohol for the rich people will go down, while the food prices for the poor will increase.

Energy use and GHG Pollution

- A lot of energy in form of electricity and heat are used in the production of biofuels. Starting with the growing crops, a lot of diesel fuel is used by the agricultural machinery working the fields.

- Millions of tons of nitrogen-rich fertilizer is used in the corn production too, which also requires a lot of fossil energy to be produced, transported, and spread onto the fields.

- Biofuels crops are also water-intensive. Over 30 billion gallons of water are needed annually to grow crops and process them into biofuels. Some countries, like Brazil, are blessed with lots of rains and other water sources, but this is not the case in most other countries.

- In addition to using a lot of fossil fuels and water, the biofuels processes are polluting as well. Carbon emissions analysis for biofuels show that the carbon life cycle assessment (LCA) depends greatly on the type of technology, and types of fossil fuel used.

Considering all these facts we see that:

- Using corn ethanol results in a 20% reduction in CO_2 emissions per MBtu (million British thermal units) when substituting for gasoline.

- The reduction is 40% for biodiesel from U.S.- and Europe-produced corn biofuel, and 78% for Brazilian-made sugarcane.

- Increasing biofuels production increases the price of food, by diverting the wheat, soy, and corn production from production of food to filling the gas tanks.

- Given the increased tax relief and other incentives for farmers producing biofuels, a situation might occur in which more fuel is used than is produced, an obvious misallocation of resources.

These abnormalities result in some major, unforeseen and unwanted developments, such as:

- Subsidies for biofuels lead many farmers to switch to corn.

- Fewer food crops (like soybeans and wheat) lead to higher food prices.

- Higher soybean prices lead Brazilian soybean farmers to expand, displacing cattle ranchers.

- Cattle ranchers are forced to clear new pastures out of the Amazon.

- The deforestation of the Amazon rainforest and other world forests alone most likely outweighs any and all the positive externalities which biofuels were supposed to bring. The removal of millions of trees decreases the plants number and their overall CO_2 consuming potential, thus driving the world's CO_2 to higher levels faster.

Positive externalities associated with biofuel production

- The main positive externality is the fact that the vegetation growth process leads to decrease in the amount of CO_2 in the atmosphere.

- Increased transport needs can be met by usage of the biofuels, aka 'green' fuels.

- Production of biofuels from sugar beets uses less fuel than it produces, therefore it could easily meet the increasing demand for fuel.

Summary

The cost (and the future) of the biofuels depends on several factors that are (at this time) still uncertain. A number of scenarios are possible; some are plausible and others not so much.

The major factors that determine the future of biofuels are:

- At crude oil prices above USD 120/bbl, advanced biofuels will reach cost-competitiveness.

- Valuing CO_2 savings at around $50/ton would enable most biofuels to reach cost parity.

- Government assistance and regulatory changes might accelerate biofuel production and use.
- New technological discoveries might lower the biofuels production down to cost parity.

The future of biofuels is bright, and the only question is when exactly will it happen? The use of transport fuels by 2030 are estimated at $40-50 trillion, or roughly 7-8% of all fuel spending. The use of transport fuels post-2030 is estimated at $60 trillion, or about 15% of the total spending on fuels at the time.

At the same time, the estimates for conventional and advanced biofuel use by 2030 are in $2-3 trillion per annum. Post-2030, biofuels production is expected to ramp up to about $10 trillion.

These are still only estimates, and there are still a number of uncertainties, as described above.

All data on biofuels need to be compared to similar data if diesel and gasoline fuels were used instead.

- By 2030, the use of biofuels would lead to incremental costs of $100-250 billion above the cost of the gasoline/diesel replaced. This is equivalent to between 0.2% and 0.5% of total fuel costs, with advanced biofuels accounting for the major share of these costs.

- By 2050, total incremental costs for biofuels are estimated to be at around $300 billion (plus additional expenditure for advanced biofuels of $400 billion), resulting in $100 billion of fuel cost savings (compared with use of fossil gasoline/diesel)—when conventional biofuels are used.

- Provided that oil (and energy in general) prices are within reason, thus having limited impact on feedstock production and transport, advanced biofuels could be produced at lower costs than their fossil counterparts. Incremental spending on advanced biofuels could be $500-600 billion less compared with use of fossil fuel, and total fuel cost savings could add up to $1 trillion annually.

• And equally importantly, with the increased use of biofuels, the GHG emissions would be significantly reduced as well. This alone is a great step ahead in ensuring the health of our Earth and its inhabitants.

SOLAR ENERGY

Solar energy generation has been around—on and off—for almost half a century. Actually, until recently it was mostly off, shoved back in the closet after a number of attempts to compete with its more powerful cousins, the fossil fuels. During every energy shortage or economic slow-down since the 1970s, solar was pulled out of the closet, dusted off and pushed on the world arena with expectations that exceeded the technology's ability.

Inefficient government policies, accompanied by greed, negligence, and ignorance on part of unscrupulous corporations only interfered with the proper development of the solar technology and its implementation. The last boom-bust cycle started with the economic slow-down and abnormal oil prices rise of 2007-2008.

Energy panic gripped Washington and billions were thrown at anyone who had the word "solar" in the company logo, or painted over their shop door. Thousands of people and companies changed their titles from mechanic, electrician, plumber or roofer to "solar" specialist, or installer. Most of these people have not even heard about solar before, let alone are they specialists in anything solar, but a quick on-line course would bring them up to speed and then they can go around and work on solar projects.

The results of this hoopla became quite obvious in 2010-2012, when hundreds of the new "solar" companies went out of business and thousands of people ended up in the unemployment lines. The end result was another black eye for the solar industry and billions of taxpayers' money wasted around the world in the hasty rush to the new gold mine, which was not to be found.

And yet, there is a difference this time. Solar is not going back in the closet for a change. It is still limping from the last fiasco, but is showing signs of improvement. If there is a lesson from all this it is the fact that

the energy sector is a complicated puzzle of complex technologies, laws, regulations, competition, problems, and more problems.

Solar power is in the middle of this puzzle, positioning itself to be a great potential competitor to the other energy sources, but yet weak and feeble to face them mano-a-mano right now. So, solar power is here to stay, but its steps are guarded and measured so that it does not step on the toes of its bigger and older cousins—the fossils.

Economic Evaluation of Solar Energy Technologies

Since money and profits are the bottom line in the energy, and any other industry in the 21st century capitalist system, below we take a closer look at what makes solar tick and how it measures financially and legally in the energy markets.

Let's start with some of the basics used to evaluate solar and the other power generators.

Economics 101

The text below is an overview of the procedures involved when developing the key financial elements of a solar product or installation.

The key financial elements are:

1. Net present value (NPV)
2. Total life-cycle cost (TLCC)
3. Revenue requirements (RRs)
4. Levelization (LCOE)
5. Annualized value (AV)
6. Unadjusted and modified internal rate of return (IRR),
7. Simple payback (SPB)
8. Discounted payback (DPB)
9. Benefit/cost (B/C) ratios
10. Savings/investment ratios (SIR)

The descriptions and formulas in this section can be used to compare specific alternative investments and projects economics on individual basis. However, the analyst should be aware that, when comparing alternatives, different measures may not always provide the same answer.

For example, simple payback requirements reject an alternative that, while having a longer payback period, has strong long-term returns.

These, nevertheless, are important tools when considering investment opportunities, or analyzing an alternative energy project.

Having full understanding of the subjects at hand

and utilizing the formulas properly might make the difference between success and failure.

Here is a description of the subjects we consider most important, and absolutely necessary, for a basic economic evaluation and analysis of solar projects, which MUST be done—properly and thoroughly so—before anything else is even considered (1):

Net Present Value (NPV)

The NPV of a project is one way of examining costs (cash outflows) and revenues (cash inflows) together. A NPV analysis can be composed of many different cost and revenue streams. The analyst must know the form of the different streams (current or constant dollars), so the correct discount rate can be used for the present value analysis. (1)

Alternatively, the cash flows can be adjusted to reflect the form of the discount rate.

The formula for NPV can be expressed as:

$$NPV = \sum_{n=0}^{N} \frac{Fn}{(1+d)^n} = F_0 + \frac{F1}{(1+d)^1} + \frac{F2}{(1+d)^2} + \ldots + \frac{FN}{(1+d)^N}$$

Where:

NPV = Net present value
Fn = Net cash flow in year n
N = Analysis period
d = Annual discount rate.

Total Life-cycle Cost (TLCC)

TLCC analysis is used to evaluate differences in costs and the timing of costs among alternative projects. TLCCs are the costs incurred through the ownership of an asset over the asset's life span or the period of interest to the investor.

Only those costs relevant to the decision should be included in the analysis. TLCC analysis considers all significant dollar costs over the life of the project. These costs are then discounted to a base year using present value analysis.

Any revenue generated from the resale of the investment is also discounted to the base year and subtracted from present value costs.

The formula for calculating TLCC is as follows:

$$TLCC = \sum_{n=0}^{N} \frac{Cn}{(1+d)^n}$$

Where:

$TLCC$ = present value of the TLCC
Cn = cost in period n: investment costs include fi-
nance charges as appropriate; expected salvage value; nonfuel O&M and repair costs; replacement costs; and energy costs
N = analysis period
d = annual discount rate.

Revenue Requirements (RRs)

RRs are often calculated in regulated industries, such as the electric power markets, for a firm (utility) as a whole. The discussion here is directed toward the revenues required to cover the costs associated with a specific project, rather than a firm.

The RR is the total revenue that must be collected from customers to compensate a firm for all expenditures (including taxes) associated with a project. It is actually no different than the before-tax revenue required of the TLCC outlined earlier.

The RR economic measure is recommended as an appropriate measure when evaluating a regulated investment. The general decision rule for utilities is to choose the alternative for which the present value of the multi-period investment revenue requirement is the lowest (assuming the services provided are identical). Businesses apply the RR method to project costs over an investment's useful life. Because RR is normally the basis on which regulated investments are defended, it is the recommended measure for evaluating such investments.

RR is not recommended fosr economic evaluation when deciding whether to accept or reject an investment because RR provides no frame of reference for what are acceptable or unacceptable costs and benefits and returns are not addressed.

The formulation of the revenue requirements approach is:

$$RR = TLCC = \frac{1 - (T * PVDEP) + PVOM(1-T)}{(1 - T)}$$

Where:

RR = revenue requirements
$TLCC$ = total life-cycle cost
I = initial investment
T = income tax rate
$PVDEP$ = present value of depreciation expenses
$PVOM$ = present value of operating and maintenance expenses

The Levelized Cost of Energy (LCOE)

LCOE allows alternative technologies to be compared when different scales of operation, different investment and operating time periods, or both exist. For example, the LCOE could be used to compare the cost of energy generated by a renewable resource with that of a standard fossil fueled generating unit.

The LCOE can be calculated using the following formula:

$$\sum_{n=1}^{N} \frac{Q_n * LCOE}{(1+d)^n} = TLCC$$

$$LCOE = TLCC / \left\{ \left[\sum_{n=1}^{N} (Q_n / (1+d)^n \right] \right\}$$

LCOE = levelized cost of energy
TLCC = total life-cycle cost
  Qn = energy output or saved in year n
   d = discount rate
   N = analysis period

It is important to note that if the system output (Q) or savings remains constant over time, the equation for LCOE can be reduced as follows:

$$LCOE = (TLCC/Q)(UCRF)$$

Where:
  TLCC = total life-cycle cost
     Q = annual energy output or saved
  UCRF = the uniform capital recovery factor, which is equal to $\dfrac{d(1+d)^N}{(1+d)^N-1}$

The shortcut methodology for estimating the before-tax-revenues-required LCOE requires the assumptions that the project not only have constant output, but also constant. O&M and no financing. If these assumptions can be made, the shortcut can be used with the application of the following formula:

$$LCOE = \frac{I * FCR}{Q} + \frac{O\&M}{Q}$$

Where:
  LCOE = levelized cost of energy
     I = initial investment
   FCR = fixed charge rate, in this case the before-tax revenues required FCR
     Q = annual output
  O&M = annual O&M and fuel costs for the plant.

NOTE: The comparisons between the costs of renewable and non-renewable types of power genera-

tion usually focus on the cost per MWh, based upon an assumption of uniform load factors and a standard discount rate to translate capital expenditures and O&M costs into a single cost; the so called "levelized cost per MWh," or LCOE.

Unfortunately, in economic terms, these comparisons are faulty. one MWh generated at 12 p.m. in April in Arizona (when all heating and cooling is switched off), for example, is simply not the same product as one MWh power generated at 2 p.m. in the middle of July (when all air conditioners are on at full blast).

The utilities are well aware of this discrepancy, so the cost of this commodity when needed most reflects a corresponding supply-demand surcharge. The price of electricity in Arizona is 3-4 times higher during the day hours of the summer months (from 1:00-8:00 p.m. May-September), than the price of the same amount during noon hour in the winter months.

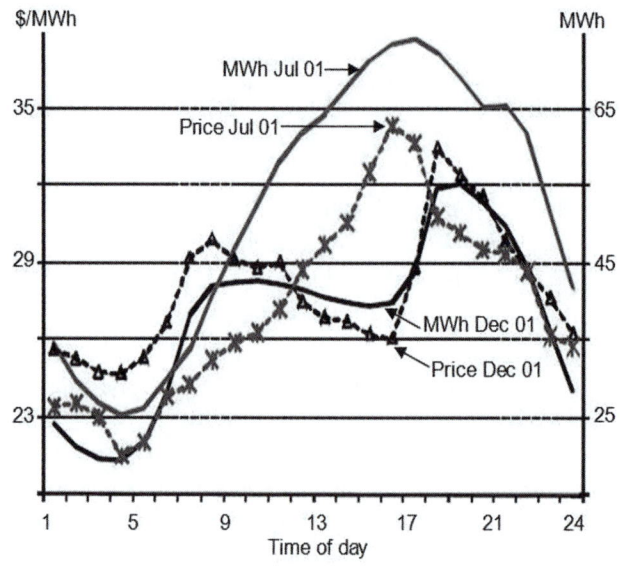

Figure 7-23. Electric system demand and prices, California

In this example of actual numbers, we see that the power generation and the price are several fold higher mid-day in July (due to excess air conditioning use), vs. much lower power generation and prices mid-day in December, when all heating and cooling is off.

LCOE, therefore, could be useful for comparing dispatchable power generation technologies that are used to meet base load demand only. Using LCOE for any other comparisons is simply misleading and full of assumptions and errors.

Annualized Value (AV)

The annualizing process transforms a swing of cash flows (Fn) into equivalent annual streams. Cash flows are discounted to their net present value and then annualized by multiplying the present value of the cash flow by the uniform capital recovery factor (UCRF); i.e., $[d(1 + dy]/[(1 + d)'' - I]$.

This is similar to the annualization of required revenues in the revenue requirements subsection and can be done with a single equation that combines the NPV and capital recovery factor calculations.

$$NPV = \sum\nolimits_{n=1}^{N} F_n /(1+d)^n$$

$$AV = UCRF * NPV = UCRF * \sum\nolimits_{n=1}^{N} F_n /(1+d)^n$$

Where:

NPV = net present value
AV = annualized value
Fn = cash flow in period n
UCRF = uniform capital recovery factor
d = discount rate.

This formula can be simplified if the cash flow Fn is escalating at a constant rate ΔP:

$$NPV = \sum\nolimits_{n=1}^{N} [F_o (1+\Delta P)^n] /(1+d)^n$$

$$= F_o \sum\nolimits_{n=1}^{N} * k^n$$

$$= F_o [k(1-k^n)/(1-k)]$$

$$AV = UCRF * NPV$$

$$AV = UCRF * F_o [k(1-k^n)/(1-k)]$$

Where:

F_o = cash flow to be annualized
ΔP = rate of escalation
k = $[(1 + \Delta P)/(1 + d)]$

The Internal Rate of Return (IRR)

IRR for an investment that has a series of future cash flows (Fo, F1, ... Fn) is the rate that sets the NPV of the cash flows equal to zero. The IRR analysis allows for the comparison of a wide variety of investment activities. However, IRR is not recommended when evaluating investments in which further investment after return is required because downstream investments are improperly discounted and multiple positive PRR values can occur.

IRR is commonly used for accept/reject decisions, allowing a quick comparison with a minimum acceptable rate of return (hurdle rate). IRR is not recommended when selecting among mutually-exclusive alternatives because the values of differing investment sizes are not considered (an investor will choose to invest more in an alternative with more favorable returns).

This shortcoming may be corrected by applying IRR on an incremental basis. IRR is also not recommended when ranking projects because IRR implicitly assumes reinvestment of returns at the IRR.

The viability of a project is usually assessed with IRR by comparing the IRR of the project with a "hurdle rate" that represents the IRR of the next best alternative (the opportunity cost of capital).

IRR also has the advantage that it can be used to directly compare the after-tax return on readily available financial instruments, such as bonds, thereby providing the investor with a quick qualitative assessment of the project.

IRR equals the rate for which:

$$0 = NPV = \sum\nolimits_{n=0}^{N} \left[F_n /(1+d)^n \right]$$

Where:

NPV = net present value of the capital investment
Fn = cash flows received at time n
d = rate that equates the present value of positive and negative cash flows when used as a discount rate.

Modified Internal Rate of Return (MIRR)

For projects of different scale and lives, it is possible for different ranking criteria, such as NPV and IRR to produce conflicting results because of differing reinvestment assumptions.

The NPV method assumes reinvestment at the discount rate, whereas the IRR method assumes reinvestment at the IRR rate.

The modified internal rate of return (MIRR) accounts for varying reinvestment rates and should be used in these circumstances. MIRR is calculated by assuming that all cash inflows received before the end of the analysis period are reinvested at the discount rate until the end of the analysis period.

The terminal (future value) amount at the end of the analysis is then discounted back to the base year. The discount rate that will equate the present value (in the base year) of the terminal amount to the present value of all investment costs is the MIRR.

The formula for calculating MIRR is as follows:

MIRR = solution for "r" in the following equation:

$$MIRR = r, where \sum_{n=0}^{N} \frac{F_{n_n}}{(1+d)^n} = \sum_{n=0}^{N} \frac{F_{p_n}(1+d)^{N-n}}{(1+r)^N}$$

Where:

MIRR = r, modified internal rate of return

Fnn = net negative cash flows at time n

Fpn = net positive cash flows at time n

d = rate of return of reinvestment

N = life of investment.

Simple Payback (SPB)

SBP is a quick, simple way to compare alternative projects. It is relatively easy to utilize and as such is a very popular financial tool. Simple payback is the number of years necessary to recover the project cost of an investment under consideration.

SPB is commonly used and recommended when risk is an issue (i.e., significant uncertainties are present) because SPB allows for a quick assessment of the duration during which an investor's capital is at risk.

SPB is not recommended when evaluating alternatives involving financing and tax features because their inclusion complicates the analysis and loses the advantages of simplicity.

SPB is also not recommended for selecting among mutually exclusive alternatives because the values of differing investment sizes are not considered; for example, an investor will choose to invest more in an alternative having more favorable returns.

This shortcoming may be corrected by applying SPB on an incremental basis. When ranking projects, SPB is not recommended because it ignores returns after payback.

The SPB can be expressed as the first point in time at which:

$$\sum n^* \Delta I_n \leq \sum n^* \Delta S_n$$

Where:

SPB = minimum number of years required for the non-discounted sum of annual cash flows net annual costs to equal or exceed the non-discounted investment costs

ΔI = non-discounted incremental investment costs (including incremental finance charges)

ΔS = non-discounted sum value of the annual cash flows net annual costs.

The Discounted Payback Period (DPP)

DPP is the number of years necessary to recover the project cost of an investment while accounting for the time value of money.

DPB is recommended when risk is an issue (i.e., significant uncertainties are present) because DPB allows for a quick assessment of the duration during which an investor's capital is at risk.

DPB is not recommended when evaluating alternatives involving financing and tax features because their inclusion complicates the analysis and loses the advantages of simplicity.

DPB is also not recommended when selecting among mutually exclusive alternatives because differing investment sizes are not considered (i.e., an investor will choose to invest more in an alternative with more favorable returns).

This shortcoming may be corrected by applying DPB on an incremental basis. When ranking projects, DPB is not recommended because it ignores returns after payback.

DPB can be expressed as that time in which:

$$\sum n[\Delta I_n / (1+d)^n] \leq \sum n[\Delta S_n / (1+d)^n]$$

Where:

DPB = minimum number of years required for the discounted sum of annual net savings to equal the discounted incremental investment costs

ΔI = incremental investment costs

ΔS = annual savings net of future annual costs (i.e., AS equals the incremental energy costs, incremental nonfuel operation, maintenance, and repair costs, incremental repair and replacement costs, minus the incremental salvage costs)

d = annual nominal discount rate

Benefit-to-cost (BIC)

BIC analysis is conducted and B/C ratios are derived to ascertain whether, and to what degree, the benefits of a particular project exceed the costs. Such analyses are more frequently performed for projects that involve the public interest. They range from direct government investments in public works (such as infrastructure, parks, or public power projects) to private investments by utilities in which the impacts on the ratepayers, investors, and the environment all may have to be considered to determine if the action is appropriate.

Because B/C ratios are commonly used when evaluating investments from a societal perspective, they are recommended for use when evaluating projects in which social costs prevail.

BIC ratios are not recommended when selecting among mutually exclusive alternatives because the values of differing investment sizes are not considered; i.e., an investor will choose to invest more in an alternative with more favorable returns.

This shortcoming may be corrected by applying B/C ratios to the incremental benefits/costs of the alternatives. predominate, particularly from a public policy perspective.

BIC ratios can also be used when ranking projects if benefits predominate, particularly from a public policy perspective.

The mathematical formula for B/C ratios is:

$$B/C = [PV(\text{all benefits})]/[PV(\text{all costs})]$$

Where:

PV (All Benefits) = present value of all positive cash flow equivalents

PV (All Costs) = present value of all negative cash flow equivalents.

Savings-to-investment Ratio (SIR)

A variation of the B/C ratio, known as the savings-to-investment ratio (SIR), is used when benefits occur primarily as cost reductions. Although SIR is basically a B/C ratio, there is a computational difference. B/C ratios are typically calculated with dl benefits in the numerator and all costs in the denominator.

In the calculation of SIR, only the principle investment costs are included in the denominator. All other costs are subtracted from the benefits in the numerator. This, in essence, makes the numerator a measure of net savings.

The formula for the calculation of the SIR is as follows:

$$SIR = PV(NS)/PV(IRS)$$

Where:

SIR	=	savings investment ratio
PV(NS)	=	present value of net savings of the activity (i.e., total savings minus all incremental operation and repair costs not directly attributed to incremental investment costs)
PV(IRS)	=	present value of the sum of incremental investment costs plus incremental replacement costs minus incremental salvage values.

Now we know the financial factors in play, and what is required to fund, install and operate a solar power plant. Assuming that we have done everything right and the plant is up and running properly, let's take a close look at the day-by-day operation from a financial point of view.

Subsidies and Taxes

The status of government subsidies, taxes and investments, related to renewable energy sources and projects for the 2012-2018 time period is as follows:

Production Tax Credit (PTC)

Applicable for wind, geothermal, landfill gas, trash combustion, open-loop biomass, closed-loop biomass, hydropower and wave tide:

- The PTC provides a tax credit for the production of electricity from renewable sources and the sale of that electricity to an unrelated party.
- Credit amount is:
  —2.2 cents per kWh for wind, closed-loop biomass and geothermal
  —1.1 cents per kWh for other renewable energy resources.
- Available for facilities placed in service before January 1, 2014 (2013 for wind)
- Available for a 10-year period beginning the year the facility is placed in service

Investment Tax Credit (ITC)

Applicable for solar, geothermal, qualified fuel cell or micro turbine property, combined heat and power systems, small wind, geothermal heat pumps and PTC-eligible facilities placed in service after 2008 and before 2014 (2013 for wind).

- The ITC provides a credit for qualifying energy property
- The ITC for any taxable year is the energy percentage of the basis of each energy property placed in service during the taxable year
- Credit amount is:
  — 30% of eligible costs for fuel cell, solar, and small wind property
  — 10% of eligible costs for combined heat and power, microturbine property and geothermal heat pumps
- The ITC is generally available for eligible property placed in service on or before December 13, 2016.

Grant in Lieu of PTC and ITC

Applicable for tangible personal property or other

property that is an integral part of a qualified facility (as defined by the PTC and ITC rules):

- The American recovery and reinvestment act (ARRA) enacted a new grant program which provides a cash grant in lieu of the PTC or ITC
- ARRA permits PTC or ITC projects to elect a grant of up to 30% of costs of construction of PTC or ITC energy property in lieu of tax credits
- Projects must begin construction before 2012 and submit a grant application no later than October 1, 2012
- Projects must be placed in service before their PTC or ITC credit expires:
  — PTC expires in 2014 (2013 for wind)
  — ITC expires in 2017.

Renewable Portfolio Standards (RPS)

These standards generally place an obligation on electric supply companies to produce a specified fraction of their electricity from renewable energy sources and enumerates mechanisms that are permitted to achieve compliance, such as renewable energy credits (RECs).

Currently no federal RPS legislation has been enacted.

A total of 29 states and the District of Columbia have an RPS. The states include Arizona, California, Colorado, Connecticut, Delaware, Hawaii, Illinois, Indiana, Kansas, Maine, Maryland, Massachusetts, Michigan, Minnesota, Missouri, Montana, Nevada, New Hampshire, New Jersey, New Mexico, New York, North Carolina, Ohio, Oregon, Pennsylvania, Rhode Island, Texas, Washington and Wisconsin.

Armed with the financial basics, we will now take a close look at what happens during the long-term operation of solar power plant, and what is needed to ensure its financial success.

Practical Example

Keeping in mind what we have learned and discussed thus far in this text, we will apply this wealth of knowledge and understanding in taking a close look at a practical example of a (virtual) PV power plant, operating for 30 years in the Arizona desert.

Pre-construction Considerations

We've reviewed the key aspects of present-day PV technologies and their applications in this text. Now we will review some of the key considerations used to design, finance and operate a PV power plant in the Arizona desert using real-world conditions.

Our brand new PV plant is 100 MWp and is to be installed in an appropriate location in a U.S. desert. This particular location has 300 days of full sunshine and averages six hours per day full output. The average solar insolation is 900 W/m².

So for the duration we estimate, and should expect:
—Total solar insolation per m² per day = 6 hrs/day x 900 W/m² = 5.4 kWh/m²/day
—Total solar insolation per m² per year= 300 days x 6 hrs/day x 900 W/m² = 1,620 kWh/m²/year

This means that we can expect ~1,620 kWh sunlight to fall on each square meter of that location during the entire year. Or, if we had 100% efficient technology we could produce 5.4 kWh from each square meter of land each day, and 1,620 kWh from each square meter during an entire year.

This sounds quite good, BUT:

1. There is no such thing as 100% efficient PV technologies—not yet! So we'll use 15% c-Si PV technology for this example.
2. We also cannot cover 100% of the land with modules, so we need much more land for inter-row spacing to avoid shading from adjacent modules.
3. 300 days per year with 6 hours per day full sunlight are averages we use here (Arizona desert), based on average summer-winter sunlight utilization, and the related weather variations.
4. There are additional uncontrollable variables, which vary wildly from hour to hour and day to day—even in the deserts—so the numbers could change drastically in one or the other direction.

Keeping in mind the above factors, we will try to get the best estimate for the operation of this new PV installation.

We start with the theoretical calculations, which go something like this:

A 100-MWp (nameplate) power installation will require 100 MWp of PV modules, fixed-mount or on trackers. Assuming that the modules are 200 Wp each, we'll need 500,000 modules to generate 100 MWp DC electric power.

If we are using trackers, the number of modules to obtain the 100 MWp nameplate rating would be the same, but the daily and annual energy output will be greater. Tracking modules produce more power during the early and late hours of the day simply because by tracking they receive more sunlight than fixed-mount modules all through the day. Only around noon do both types have almost the same power output.

NOTE: The nameplate number of 100 MWp is arrived at by considering the maximum output of the modules at STC (25°C module temperature and 1000 W/m² insolation) as measured by the manufacturer. In reality this power output will be reached only around the noon hour (thus the designation of peak power) every day. Keep this in mind, because it is an important variable, which is ignored (intentionally or unintentionally) sometimes.

15% efficiency means that each square meter covered with these PV modules will generate 150 Wp DC power (at STC). Since we are using STC numbers to design the plant, this means that we need ~667,000m² (165 acres) of active area (area covered by PV modules). Adding 50% space between the rows of fixed-mounted modules, we end up with minimum ~330 acres of land needed to install a 100-MWp power plant.

Usually, however, we need much more than that, to compensate for shade-free operation, adding access roads, abatement, etc. systems, so a typical plant size would be in the 500-600 acres range, which comes to approximately 5-6 acres per 1.0 MWp installed.

And this is when using c-Si, or any 15-16% efficient modules. The land usage increases proportionally when the modules' efficiency is lower. i.e., a 100MWp power plant using 9-10%-efficient thin-film PV modules will need additional land. Several such power plants have been installed lately on 10-12 acres land per 1.0 MWp installed.

PV modules mounted on trackers would need less land, depending on their configuration and plant design characteristics (location, installation specifics, etc.) As a rule of thumb, 15% c-Si modules mounted on trackers are expected to generate 15-20% more power in the desert. This difference might be even greater under cloudy conditions, but estimates for such conditions are hard to make due to the great variability of sunlight intensity.

Using CPV technology using high concentration solar cells with 40% efficiency changes the calculations, to where—everything considered—we could get much more power from an acre of desert land. We are taking a closer look at the CPV technology in the previous chapters of this text, so we only need to mention here that although CPV cells need to be mounted on trackers, which are expensive to build and operate pieces of equipment, the final financial outcome might be still better.

Most utilities prefer using Watts AC in their calculations, instead of Watts DC, which changes the calculations. To do this, we need to track the power delivered to the grid back to the PV modules. In our case, 100 MW AC power would mean adding at least 20 MWp to the original 100 MWp DC modules to compensate for the losses from the modules to the grid (wires, inverters, transformers etc.), if we are to provide 100MWp AC to the grid at peak hours. The rest of the estimates would parallel the increased number of modules and power generation capabilities.

With all of this figured out, we find an appropriate land in an acceptable location (sunny climate and cooperative utility) and negotiate a purchase or lease with the owners. Then we finalize the calculations, and obtain pre-construction financing.

Several million dollars would be needed for pre-construction financing, as needed to:

a) Design the plant and pay the expenses (engineering services, etc.)
b) Generate official electro-mechanical drawings of the installation
c) Secure the land via lease or buy option
d) Obtain building and interconnect permits, PPA, etc.

We estimate that $4-5 million pre-construction finance would be needed to complete all of the above tasks on a 100MWp PV power plant in central California.

After months of meetings, stacks of forms, payments, etc. we get a construction permit and a PPA and construction finance ($450-500 million were needed to build a 100MWp fixed mount PV power plant in the U.S. during 2011-2012). Then we proceed with the installation of fixed-mounted modules (or on trackers) on the site.

When everything is ready to go, we flip the main switch ON and start measuring the output during different times of the day.

PV Plant Operation, 30 Years Scenario

Here is a close, albeit hypothetical, look at the day-by-day operation of a PV plant operating in the SW U.S. deserts during 30 years of non-stop operation under blistering desert sun, sand, and rain storms and everything else the desert throws at us in its usual, most unorthodox and inhospitable ways.

NOTE. The operation in any other geographic area would include many more fluctuations and irregularities, due to bad weather (clouds, rain, snow, etc.). So we can think of this example as an "ideal case," which can be used as a foundation for other projects, after extrapolating for the additional variable of each case.

The only exceptions of the "ideal" case scenario in this case are the facts that, a) extreme heat reduces the power output significantly, b) extreme heat tends to shorten the life of the PV modules and BOS, while, c) wild fires, flash floods, sand, rain and hail storms and other desert phenomena can damage the installation.

So, with all this understood and kept in mind, we flip the power switch ON, and our new 100 MWp PV power plant starts generating power, sending it into the grid.

Great, but let's take a very close look at what's going on in the field:

Day 1

It's noon on a bright and sunny mid-summer day in the desert, bathing our brand new 100 MWp power plant with its generous, unobstructed, sun rays. Solar insolation 900 W/m², air temperature 120°F. Since the modules' output was measured at STC (25°C module temperature and 1000 W/m² insolation) we get our first surprises:

a. Because typical solar insolation at high noon in the desert is ~900 W/m² instead of the theoretical 1000 W/m² (which was used for the nameplate calculations of the modules and the power plant), we see that we have lost nearly 10% of the modules' output. Instead of 100 MWp, we are getting 90 MWp DC power output as a first measurement.

b. Then we notice that the output starts going down quickly. This cannot be. Yes, it can! The modules start heating up under power, and with the help of the hot desert noon sunshine the temperature inside the modules could reaches 150, 160, 170, even 180°F and higher.

Under these conditions internal resistance increases and other things happen (remember the 0.5% power drop for each degree C increase of temperature), so that we could lose another 10-20% of the power output during the most productive hours of the day.

Now our 100 MWp power system is producing only 80 MWp during the noon hour.

c. While we are busy making these measurements, DC power is running through the wires, combiner boxes, inverters and transformers and finally flowing into the electric grid. When we measure the actual electric power going into the grid, we find that it has dropped another 8-10% due to conversion and resistive losses in the equipment between the PV modules and the grid.

The higher the ambient temperature, the higher the DC to AC conversion losses. So we are now down to 70-75 MW AC power generated during the noon hour and sent into the grid.

d. When the sun starts going down, the power output will go down proportionally until no more power is generated by the system when the sun goes down. As the sun starts going down, the modules will cool off some, so the power reduction is not linear.

e. The cycle starts again the next day with a gradual increase of power output as the sun goes up, until the modules reach their maximum output. In the afternoon hours the output levels drop gradually as the sun goes down, and level at zero during the night.

NOTE: Using trackers will complicate the comparative measurements, but we should assume that the same type PV modules, installed on trackers, would generate the same amount of power at noon as the fixed-mount modules. During the hours before and after the noon hour, however, the tracking modules will generate 10-20% more power than their sitting fixed cousins, due to better orientation towards the sun and better absorption of sunlight.

Temperature extremes and tail-ends have different effect on tracking PV modules, which complicates the otherwise simple scenario. It suffices to say, for the sake of this exercise that the end effect is 10-20% higher DC power output from the trackers.

Money Talk

Now let's look at the bottom line of that first day of operation. During the noon hour of day #1 we generated 75 MWp AC power, or 75 MWh (75 MW per hour) went into the grid. We actually generated that much power during each hour from 10:00 a.m.-4:00 p.m. on that summer day in the desert. This is a full six hours of maximum power production.

After that (from 4:00 p.m.-8:00 p.m.) the generated power goes down with the sun. The same is true for the hours from 6:00 a.m. until 10:00 a.m. that morning, when the generated power went from zero to maximum as the sun was rising.

So, during that day we had six hours of full power generation and eight hours of partial power generation. These eight hours would average the equivalent to ~3 hours of full power generation. So that day we had a full nine hours of full power generation (6 hours of full power and three hours average from the rest of the day)—or—9 hours x 75 MWh = 675 MWh AC power was sent into the grid.

This is 675.000 kWh, for which the utility company will pay us $0.15/kWh, or a total of $101,250.00 for one day of power generation.

Over 365 days, this is $36,956,250.00 gross annual income. Not bad, but we don't have 365 days of full sunshine even in the deserts, and most winter days don't produce even half this amount of energy. Because of that, we usually average the annual power production to 300 days annually at 6-7 hours per day. So, this would bring our annual gross income to somewhere in the $20-25 million range.

NOTE: $0.15/kW payback is another variable that is controlled by the utilities. We have seen PPAs from $0.09 to 0.23/kWh, depending on the location and the utility (they have their own ways to determine energy costs).

The utilities also pay different amounts for power generated during different times of day during different seasons. This complicates things even further, but basically it means that we can get a higher return during the peak demand hours of the summer (1-8 p.m.) and much less in the winter when the peak hours are 5-9 a.m. and 5-9 p.m., at which times there is not much sun.

How much of the gross income is profit will depend on the financing package(s), but there is a good chance of ending up with a good profit the first year of operation, and maybe the next several years too...keep on reading.

Year #1

One year has gone by since the first day of operation. At noon of the anniversary, and under the same weather conditions, we notice that the power output is 1-1.5% lower than this time last year. We look at the manufacturer's spec sheet and see that it predicts ~1% drop of power each year. If the loss is less than 1%, we are good and operation continues.

If the output loss is higher than 1%, however, we need to negotiate with the manufacturer and obtain a replacement for the failing modules. But the warranty is often not clear if any replacements can be done during year #1. Also, how do we justify a plant shutdown as needed for the replacement of the failing modules, if an agreement is reached at all?

A day or two of shutdown will result in several hundred MWh loss in production, which is even greater than the power loss of over 1% that we are experiencing. Tough decision...

Money Talk

If we average our power generation (summer and winter months) to six hours/day and consider 300 full sunshine days per year, we get 300 days x 6 hours/day x 75 MW AC = 135 MWh/year. This is 135,000 MWh x $0.15 = $20.25 million in gross income expected during the first year. At this rate, the investment would be repaid in ~20 years.

Adding the different subsidies, incentives, carbon credits, and perks the plant might be repaid in 10 years and maybe less—if everything works as planned. This is a big "if." Hoping that everything goes this way for the duration is a bit of a stretch, because things usually do not go as planned, and we are yet to discount the expenses from the gross income. Read on.

Year #5

The power output from several hundred modules and several inverters has dropped significantly during the last several years and something must be done. The inverters are under warranty for now, so all we have to worry about is the lost power generation during a 2-3 day maintenance shutdown for their upgrade. Unless there is a stipulation in the inverters' warranty agreement, we have to eat the loss.

The failing modules, however, have to be removed and replaced, which will take several days and maybe weeks depending on the quantity. This is gross profit that will fall while the operating expense remains constant. Did we include this loss in the initial plant O&M budget?

Using trackers would cause an additional headache to the plant managers at this time, because some of the moving parts, such as bearings, motors, as well as sensors and controllers need to be upgraded or replaced. This is additional expense and more time of useful power generation lost.

This activity and the related expense must have been anticipated during the power plant design stages as well. If proper maintenance and replacement of failing equipment is not done on time, then the trackers just might stop tracking and things will only get worse.

Money Talk

$20.25 million was generated during the first year, dropping down 1% annually every year thereafter, so now we are at least 5% short on power generation and gross income, in addition to the above mentioned loss of time. This means that the 75 MW AC peak power generation we got during year number one, is now down to 71 MW AC power generation at peak hour. That also affects the bottom line, so now we get ~$19.00 million annual gross income.

And some other things have gone wrong; additional maintenance and replacement of hardware and equipment is needed, which will cost us at least another $1 million. Basically, our power generation and revenue are now down an additional 6-7%, putting the gross annual income at $18 million. Considering inflation, and that we are five years in the future, $18 million might be even less.

Year #15

Many modules show greater than 20% loss of power output now. Several inverters are failing and their long-term warranty has expired too. Critical decision time. What is better, shutting down the plant to replace the failed modules (provided the manufacturer is still around and will honor the warranty) or continuing to operate like this for a while longer? What if the warranty is no longer an option, due to whatever reasons? Who is going to pay for the replacements?

Do we replace the inverters now or later? This is a major expense so, unless it was provided for in the plant operation budget, it just won't happen. And 15-year old inverters operating in the desert are a gamble, even with the best maintenance.

Money Talk

Now things get serious. The power output has been dropping 1% every year and we are getting 15% less (or even less could be expected for a number of reasons) than the first year of operation. Our 100 MWp DC power plant is pumping only 64 MW AC power into the grid. Our gross income for the year is also down to ~$17 million at best.

Also, this is the time when capital equipment replacement and major maintenance work are must be done (projected, or not) the sum of which could vary from $5 million to $15 million (if a number of inverters are to be replaced).

This might be catastrophic on its own, if proper budget and other measures were not taken in the beginning, because without these the power plant is faced with a major revenue loss.

Year #20

The scenario is even worse now, much worse than for year #15. A proper plant operations budget and management would make the difference between success and failure at this point.

Have we thought of this beforehand? Were we aware of all possibilities and did we provide for each accordingly? The answers to these questions will determine if the PV power plant will remain in operation or go into bankruptcy proceedings, thus converting another 500 acres of desert land into a junkyard.

Money Talk

At this time the power output has dropped at least 20%, so we are down to ~60 MW AC power generation, and $16 million in gross income annually. Is this enough to pay the bills?

In addition, and even worse, all manufacturers' warranties have expired and we are totally depending on luck and good performance insurance, if any.

Any major failure of, or damage to, large numbers of PV modules or inverters means that we'll have a hard time recovering—even if there is adequate insurance coverage and modules/inverters replacement options (due to lost power generation).

Adequate budget and efficient management will now be the key to success. Any short cuts, or inadequacies in the budget, will cost us dearly…and worse.

Year #30

The power output is down over 30%, so our 100 MWp power plant is now producing less than 50 MWp, everything considered. All warranties have expired, maintenance costs are increasing, and it is time to shut it down for good.

The plant now goes into the final stage of its life cycle—decommissioning. Who will remove the PV modules and the supporting structure? Who will load the metal waste on trucks and pay for its transport, recycling and disposal? Who is going to bear the extra cost of handling, recycling and disposing of the remains as hazardous waste (in case of toxic TFPV modules)? Who is going to return the land to its original state and decontaminate it as needed?

Obviously, recycling is expensive, but so is waste disposal of hazardous products. One is paid in advance by the manufacturers (if they are still around), while the latter is paid for later on by somebody else.

And there are many other costs during the decommissioning of a solar power plant. For example, the support structures have to be removed, the land leveled and returned to its original state. These are very expensive processes that must be done properly and efficiently. Hopefully we have allowed for this effort in our preliminary planning, design, and budget calculations. If not, there will be a lot of toxic junkyards in the deserts 20-30 years from now.

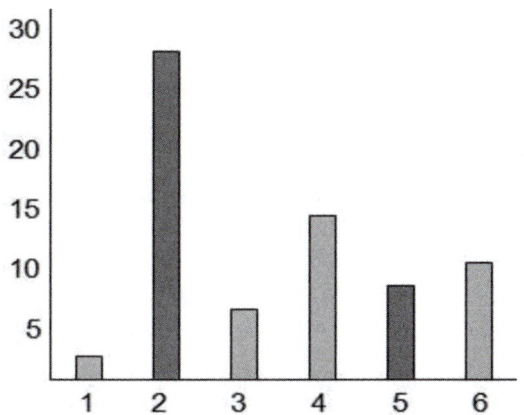

Figure 7-24. Cost of recycling and disposal (in cents per Watt)
Legend:
1. Non-hazardous disposal
2. Hazardous disposal
3. Smelting (large scale)
4. Smelting (small scale)
5. In-house recycling of CIS and CdTe modules
6. In-house recycling of silicon PV modules

And speaking of toxic waste management, that is an extremely expensive proposition, which is also taken very lightly by the manufacturers and project managers. They have some money for the decommissioning of the modules, but disassembly, sorting, packing, loading, transporting, recycling, hauling the waste away is very expensive now day, and will be several times more expensive 20-30 years later.

Disassembly and recycling of millions of toxic modules would be a sight to see, and as a result of the scale of this undertaking many large-scale TFPV projects will end up with broken banks! And we have not even considered here a number of potential lawsuits, due to the toxicity of the modules, and related damages, during the operation and decommissioning stages.

Money Talk

This, in our opinion, is where many PV power plants would be in shambles. With power generation and revenues decreased by 30%, increasing failures and maintenance costs, and pending decommissioning, recycling and land restoration expenses, most managers and owners would prefer the easy way out. Unless, of course, all this has been foreseen and taken care of ahead of time.

But we really don't see much of a worry about this last period now. There is not much talk about the last stages of PV installations. It is not on the agendas, so very little effort and planning is put into it. It is the stepchild of the industry, where the new shiny modules get all the attention.

This stage is also when and where winners and losers will be separated, new lessons learned, and a precedent for future work established at the expense of failed installations and broken dreams. Here is where the surviving technologies and operators will be proven adequate and safe for this use, and where proper initial planning and design will be verified and used as a standard for the PV industry to follow.

The above scenario is neither the best nor the worst of cases. Things might go much better if we had a capable team consisting of experienced specialists in the different areas of the project development, and if proper planning, plant design, installation and operation (including provisions for the above mentioned issues and activities) have been specified and implemented.

Things could go much worse too, if we rushed into it to beat the government subsidy deadline, and used technologies that were dirt cheap at the time, without considering (or knowing) their long-term performance characteristics.

We have seen examples of both cases in the U.S. and around the world through the years, and since there are no long-term examples for comparison, we must wait for time to sort things out and separate the winners from the losers.

**Summary of the Issues,
Discussed in the above Example**

We have seen a number of issues, which we need to keep in mind and consider in cells, modules and power field design and use. These issues are partly responsible for the uncertainty in the PV industry, lack of investments for, and failures of, PV installations today.

Some of the Reasons for Failure

1. PV module manufacturers usually guaranty 80% output by the 20th year and stop there. This means an average 1% reduction in produced power every year up to year 20, leaving uncertain losses after year 20—which is when PV modules are nearing their end-of-useful-life stage and when they start deteriorating and failing at even faster rates.

2. Some insurance coverage can be obtained to cover damage and performance deficiency of PV power plants, but we are not sure that adequate insurance can be purchased for the period after year 20, which is just around the time when many PV plants become profitable. Or, if such insurance exists, can we even justify or afford its price?

3. The yearly power decrease represents a minimum 1% annual loss of revenue—1% loss the first year, 2% the year after, 10% by the 10th year, 20% by the 20th year (in best of cases) and a whopping 30% loss or more during the 30th year of operation, if the plant is still operational at all. And this is big "if," with no guarantee whatsoever.

   NOTE: Long-term field test results show that regardless of the manufacturers' claims, most PV modules lose ~1.3-1.5% or even more power annually. There is no way to prove this with new modules, so using the field tests as the most reliable long-term test numbers available, we calculate 13-15% power and revenue loss by year 10, 26-30% loss by year 20 and a staggering 39-45% power loss by year 30.

4. PV modules also lose 0.5% power per degree C above STC (25°C); i.e., PV modules exposed to the blistering Arizona desert sun will heat to over 85°C in the summer. This is 60°C over the STC value. The modules, therefore, will lose 30% of their power output during the 4-6 most productive hours of the day. This phenomenon is also a well-kept secret that we don't hear many people talking about. This is a significant loss, however, which should be addressed during the power plant design stages.

5. An equally serious loss, which cannot be easily estimated and is often overlooked or underestimated, as discussed above, is the loss from various total field failures. There are many reasons for PV modules to fail shortly after installation and manufacturers usually offer 2-5 years materials and labor warranty, which is good enough in most cases.

   Developers of large-scale PV power plants should, however, also consider negotiating a post-warranty failure warranty with the manufacturers. Such a warranty, or special performance insurance is needed, because there are a number of manufacturing conditions that might cause premature field failures, many of which were discussed in the previous chapters.

6. Designers, customers and investors must understand the issues we are discussing herein and obtain assurance from the manufacturers that the PV modules will not degrade excessively, and fail prematurely. Purchasing performance insurance might be another way to ensure a plant's survival.

We need to know what exactly would happen in the field during the first year, during year 5, 10, 20, and have a clear idea of the measures to be taken in each and every case. We, the technical personnel and consultants, should provide the most realistic theoretical analysis and best-worst scenarios estimates based on actual experience and scientific data, backed by field measurements and tests. This is a lot of work, some of which has not even been started yet, but it has to be done, and done right to provide efficient and trouble-free, long-term operation.

So, at the end of the first day we get an unpleasant surprise, which only grows with time…and by year 15-20 the surprise grows even bigger. It is clear that we are not getting the performance we expected from the newly installed plant and are losing money. And around year #30 things start falling apart?

Using highest quality PV modules and BOS components, proper project planning, strong all encompassing budget, and excellent performance insurance are the solutions. This, however, is not what we see now. Front end gains is the priority in most cases. Reliability and longevity are either not well understood, or non existent.

In most cases end-of-life decommissioning and recycling, as well as the related hassles and expenses, is like talking about funeral arrangements during a wedding. At any time something can go wrong. What else can go wrong? Here is an example.

Hazardous Materials Use

Recently large-scale solar power plants have been popping up in the deserts. Some of them operate properly and are becoming a standard of efficient power generation, some not so much. But how about the environmental side of things? What do we expect, or not expect, from them during 30 years of in-sun operation in world's most ferocious deserts.

For example, there is a dangerous trend of installing large quantities of CdTe PV modules on thousands of acres desert land in California and Arizona. But wait—CdTe PV modules are a new product that has never been proven efficient and safe for desert operation. And even more importantly, each of the millions CdTe PV modules installed in the U.S. deserts contains 8-9 grams compounds of the toxic, carcinogenic heavy metal cadmium. So what do we expect to happen?

To get a better idea of the issues related to the toxicity of CdTe modules see below excerpts from an environmental report (C.9 hazards and hazardous materials) issued by the San Luis Obispo County planning commission) on a large-scale project, proposed to contain over 9.0 million CdTe modules spread over 4,000 acres desert land in California—on top of the San Andreas fault line, no less.

Good planning? You be the judge. It is, however, easy to see the bias (mixed with ignorance on the subject) in the report writing; the major issues are addressed, but very superficially discussed, and usually dismissing the dangers of any toxic cadmium contamination as remote, although there is absolutely no scientific evidence to support the claims and bias in these conclusions:

C.9.3.4 Impact Assessment.
Topaz Solar Farm Project (14)
Hazardous Materials Related to Cadmium Telluride PV Module Technology

The PV modules panels proposed for use at the proposed project site contain cadmium telluride (CdTe), which is formed when elemental cadmium (Cd) is reacted with tellurium (Te), and also contains a smaller amount of cadmium sulfide (CdS).

The total onsite quantity of cadmium telluride in the modules would be approximately 123.0 tons and cadmium sulfide would be 2.45 tons. Therefore, the total amount of cadmium and tellurium that is fully encapsulated within the modules at the site would be approximately 59.5 tons and 65.4 tons, respectively.

The solar modules, based on various testing data (NGI, 2010b; SAL, 2010; Steinberger, 1997), exceed both the state's total threshold limit concentration (TTLC) of 100 ppm for cadmium and the soluble threshold limit concentration (STLC) of 1.0 ppm for cadmium (SAL, 2010). The TTLC is a total composition analysis that does not factor in the potential for release.

The U.S. EPA has classified cadmium as a probable human carcinogen ("Group B1;" EPA, 2000). Cadmium telluride and cadmium sulfide, the two compounds of cadmium used in the solar modules, are currently regulated within the group of cadmium and cadmium compounds. CdTe appears to be less toxic than elemental cadmium in terms of acute exposure, but the highly reactive oxidizing surface of CdTe when in quantum dot form can damage cell membranes, mitochondria, and cell nuclei.

Tellurium compounds are highly toxic and teratogenic (causative of birth defects); exposure can also cause intensely bad breath and body odors, and in higher doses can cause chronic effects to the liver and acute effects to the digestive tract, such as nausea and constipation.

The solar panels, based on various testing data, exceed both the state's total threshold limit concentration

(TTLC) of 100 ppm for cadmium and the soluble threshold limit concentration (STLC) of 1.0 ppm for cadmium.

The module cost includes the recycling costs, so that the end user has already pre-paid for modules to be recycled and it would cost them nothing more to do anything other than recycling the modules through First Solar.

Some of the studies performed to determine the environmental impacts of CdTe module technology raise questions about the economic and technical viability of CdTe module recycling and whether cadmium should be used in a "green" technology.

Hazardous Materials During Construction

There is a small chance that panels broken severely during installation could release CdTe particles or flakes into the environment during panel removal and off-site transport. Removal and off-site transport of broken panels would therefore pose a significant risk to on-site personnel and members of the public at the visitor center and in residences surrounded by the project.

Mitigation measure HZ-1.7 would require that broken panels be collected by personnel wearing protective respiratory gear and placed in air-tight containers for offsite shipment to reduce the potential for broken panels to pose a health risk to project personnel and members of the public.

Hazardous Materials During Operation.

Out of the approximately nine million modules to be installed onsite, it is expected that approximately 36,000 modules would break during the three-year construction period and an average of 2,880 100 modules would break on average each year during operations; and 72,000 2,500 modules (0.80 0.03%) would break during project operation over the 25-year module life.

In the event of a broken module, the amount of cadmium and tellurium that would be available for release would be much less than the six and 6.6 grams, respectively, that are contained in each module; only the CdTe located along the fracture lines would have the potential to be released from the solid CdTe and CdS film matrices of the modules.

It is possible that very small amounts of cadmium could leach out of a broken module if the cadmium were exposed to natural precipitation that has a low pH. Testing results of CdTe module leaching potential (NGI 2010b; SAL, 2010) indicate that CdTe has a greater potential for leaching if exposed to low pH liquids, which could occur if CdTe is exposed to low pH rainwater (acid rain). These studies and tests have shown that leaching from the module material, particularly Cd, is strongly dependent on pH conditions. While Cd leaching at the material's intrinsic pH is low due to sorption/precipitation, a lower pH may cause substantial leaching. Thus, CdTe film that is exposed to natural precipitation in the environment that has a low pH (pH<6) could exhibit substantial leaching of Cd and Te.

Other site specific and PV module design factors that have been considered are as follows:

- Each module contains approximately six grams of cadmium; modules are normally completely encapsulated so exposure of Cd to the environment could only occur from broken/fractured modules; and only 108,000 2,500 modules are expected to break over the life of the project. This represents a total project life release potential of 33 lbs of cadmium, if the panels were finely ground and exposed to low pH liquids.

- The applicant has proposed a module collection and recycling program, as part of the project description that will be subject to county inspection and enforcement, which will limit the potential exposure time of any broken modules to the elements.

- The breakage pattern for the modules, due to their design including a strong laminate material, is similar to safety glass which will crack but not shatter. This would keep the very thin CdTe- and CdS-containing surfaces encapsulated under the expected module breakage scenarios and would significantly reduce the potential for environmental exposure of the very thin CdTe- and CdS-containing surfaces.

- The applicant completed an ambient air sampling analysis of broken module handling in 2010 and found that all of the airborne cadmium concentrations, including those from a personal air sampler for the worker handling the modules, were at least ten times below First Solar's internal action level of $1.0 \, \mu g/m^3$ and at least 30 times lower than OSHA's action level of $2.5 \, \mu g/m^3$. This sampling analysis is conservative in comparison with potential outdoor exposures since it was conducted in an enclosed warehouse.

- The active footprint of the project would be approximately 4,100 acres, so under worst-case conditions, where 33 lbs of cadmium (the maximum amount of Cd expected to be able to be released over the life of the project) were mixed evenly with the top foot of soil under the project area that would increase the cadmium concentration in the soils by approximately 0.22 parts per billion (ppb), or if a single panel (4 feet by 1.97 feet) were to release its entire six grams of cadmium the surface soil at a depth of one foot, assuming all the cadmium is mixed evenly in the first foot of soil, would have its average cadmium concentration increased by 17 ppm.

- Acid rain is not considered a concern in the area of the Carrizo Plain (BLM, 2009), due to the remoteness and low level of development in the area. However, normal rain, due to the absorption of CO_2 forming carbonic acid, has a pH of approximately 5.6. Additionally, if future development, with emissions of nitrogen and sulfur compounds (NO_x and SO_x), in the area increases then the concern regarding acid rain, or acid fog, could increase.

- Rainfall in the area averages approximately seven to nine inches per year, and is sporadic, infrequent, and undependable, which would limit the initial leaching potential of Cd from broken modules, if inspected properly and removed quickly after being severely damaged, and would also limit the movement of Cd through the soil column into underground aquifers.

- As described in the groundwater study, groundwater levels in area wells are between 10 and 40 feet below ground surface.

NOTE: This report reviews a number of issues, and ends up with more questions from scientific and socio-economic nature than it answers. And while it addresses (albeit very superficially) some of the key issues, most of them remain unanswered as far as the efficiency and safety of the long-term CdTe modules operation in the desert is concerned:

A number of assumptions were made in the report that simply lack scientific proof and merit. Assumptions made without scientific proof are just that—assumptions—they cannot and should not be used to justify poisoning thousands of acres, even if the chance is very small. This is especially true when the report is issued by government authority, financed by taxpayers' money, and when discussing real danger affecting the lives of the locals.

In more detail:

1. Large quantities of products containing toxic materials, spread over very large areas is not something that we can justify as a scientific experiment, especially when human health and life are concerned.

2. Even if small percentage of modules are broken (1% of 9.0 million modules is still a great number; over 90,000 modules), or catch on fire, or if in any way release their toxic contents into the air, soil and water table, the impact on the local environment and life forms in it would be tremendous. Nearby population centers, shallow water table, heavy winds, mixed with large amount of toxic materials contained between the fragile glass panes on top of the ready-to-blow-any-day San Andreas fault, is a hazmat nightmare and something that has to be thoroughly evaluated and not just superficially estimated and dismissed as "negligible."

3. It is obvious that this report was done in haste and issued under duress. It was done to meet a deadline, without enough effort to evaluate the risks properly and justify using toxic cadmium materials in such a very large project...in the desert...on top of San Andrea active seismic fault, no less.

4. Why are we exposing the locals and the environment to such real danger using unproven and untested product for desert operation on such a large scale?
   a. 120 tons of poison of any kind, let alone carcinogenic, heavy metal cadmium, spread evenly over 4,000 acres is something that should make us pause and take a very, very close look at what we are doing and why we are doing it this way.
   b. Do we have to use cadmium at all? Isn't there any other way of doing this?

Well, it is too late now. The work at the topaz solar farm is well under way and it is hailed as an example of large-scale solar power success. Although we do agree that it is success in terms of the conventional way of thinking, we fear that it (and many other CdTe and SIGS power fields in the deserts) will become major environmental disasters in the not very distant future.

Solar Failures, 2013 Update

Financiers jumped head first in the game during the last solar boom-bust cycle of 2008-2012, the tail end of which we are still witnessing. Most of the newcomers did not even know what a solar module looks like—let alone know what it does, or what its problems might be. In the end, they lost lots of money, many companies went broke, many people lost their jobs, and the solar industry got another black eye and a bloody nose.

The difference this time, however, is that due to a number of technological, political and regulatory developments, solar is now in a much more favorable position that even before. It is still a minor contributor to the world's power generation, but its chances for growth in the future are now much greater than any time before.

Nevertheless, let's not forget the lesson of the past.

In our book, *Solar Energy for the 21st Century*, published by The Fairmont Press in 2013, we describe the hundreds of solar companies' failures from 2008 to 2012. Each of these companies has a story to tell; a story that ends up with a shutdown or a sale of a promising technology, and hundreds of people losing their jobs.

This is a list of companies that have filed for bankruptcy, significantly reduced personnel and operations, sold-out, closed down, or somehow showed significant weakness during the 2008-2012 solar boom-bust cycle.

1	3S Soluciones	27	BrightSource
2	A123 Systems	28	Calyxo
3	Abound Solar	29	Centrotherm Photovoltaics
4	Advent Solar		
5	AE Polysilicon	30	Con Edison's Hixville Plant
6	Aero-Sharp		
7	Alamosa	31	Concentrator Optics
8	Aleo Solar	32	CSG (Suntech)
9	Amonix	33	Day4
10	Ampulse	34	Diehl
11	Amtech Systems	35	ECD
12	Applied Materials, Solar Div.	36	Energy Innovations
		37	EPV Solar
13	Applied Solar	38	Evergreen Solar
14	AQT Solar	39	First Solar
15	Arise Technologies	40	Flexcell
16	Arise Technology	41	G24i
17	Ascent Solar	42	Gadir Solar
18	AstroPower	43	GE Solar
19	Ausra	44	Global Solar Energy
20	Azuray	45	Global Solar Energy
21	Azure Dynamics	46	GlobalWatt
22	Beacon Power	47	GreenVolts
23	Blue Chip Energy GmbH	48	Helianthos Solar
		49	HelioVolt
24	Bosch	50	HelioVolt
25	BP Solar	51	Hoku
26	Bright Automotive	52	Inventux

53 ISET
54 Isofoton
55 Konarka
56 Konarka
57 LDK Solar
58 LSP Energy
59 Maricopa Solar
60 Masdar PV
61 Meier Solar Solutions
62 MiaSolé
63 Moree Solar Farms
64 Nanosolar
65 National Semiconductor, Solar Magic
66 NetCrystal
67 NovaSolar
68 NuvoSun
69 OCI, Korea
70 Odersun
71 Oelimaier
72 Oerlikon
73 Optisolar
74 Pairan
75 Phoenix Solar
76 Photovoltech
77 Photowatt
78 Pramac
79 Q-Cells
80 Ralos New Energies AG
81 Ready Solar
82 REC
83 Recurrent Energy
84 Renewable Energy Corp ASA
85 Satcon
86 Scheuten Solar
87 Schott Solar
88 Schuco International
89 Sempra U.S. Gas & Power
90 Sencera
91 Senergen
92 Sharp Solar
93 Siemens, Solar Div.

94 Signet Solar
95 Silicor Materials
96 Siliken
97 Skyline Solar
98 Solar Array Ventures
99 Solar Dawn
100 Solar Milenium
101 Solar Power Industries
102 Solar Systems
103 Solar Trust
104 SolarDay
105 SolarDay
106 Solarhybrid
107 SolarWatt
108 SolarWorld
109 Solasta
110 SolFocus
111 Soliant
112 Solibro
113 Solon Energy
114 Soltecture
115 Solyndra
116 Sovello
117 SpectraWatt
118 Stirling Energy Systems
119 SunConcept Group
120 SunFIlm
121 SunPower
122 Suntech
123 Sunways
124 SV Solar
125 Tessera Solar
126 Thomson River Power LLC
127 Timminco Ltd.
128 Trony Solar
129 Twin Creeks
130 Unisolar
131 Vestas
132 VHF Technologies
133 Wakonda
134 Willard & Kelsey. Solar Group
135 Wurth Solar
136 Xtreme Power

All these cases are detailed in our previous book, *Solar Technologies for the 21st Century*, published by The Fairmont Press in 2013, so we don't feel that it is necessary to repeat the facts here. It took an entire chapter to do that, so repeating it would be a bit too much.

Nevertheless, the list is not complete without the latest failures in the solar industry, as follows:

The Solar Companies' Failures Continue…

Every industry has gone through growing pains at the very beginning of its existence. Sometimes the grow-

ing pains go away, but sometimes they grow bigger and sharper and bad thing happen then to the companies and their employees. The solar industry went through a spectacular boom-bust period during 2007-2012, which is subsiding, but the repercussions of which are still resounding throughout the global solar and wind industries.

In our book mentioned above, we review the failures of hundreds of solar, wind companies, and renewable energy-related companies in the U.S. and abroad. Now, the echo of the failures is still heard in the board rooms, more failures are been reported often, and many more are expected in the near future.

Since the publication of our book in March 2013, several other solar companies showed signs of failing, or failed all together.

Some of the most recent failures are:

Aleo Solar

Aleo Solar was founded in 2001 in Prenzlau, Germany, as a PV modules manufacturer. The company went public in 2006, with Bosch as a majority stock holder since 2009. In return, Aleo Solar owns 9% of the Bosch Solar CIS Tech GmbH, headquartered in Brandenburg.

Blaming deteriorating market conditions in Europe for another set of disheartening financial figures, Aleo Solar reported revenue of €68.3 million in the first six months of 2013. This is revenue decreased by 58.9% compared to the first half of 2012 (€166.4 million). Earnings before interest and taxes (EBIT) came in at -€29.3 million, and the EBIT margin was -42.9%. Earnings per share amounted to -€2.54.

The worsening financial situation of the company is blamed on low PV demand in its core European markets, particularly in Germany where only 1,500 MW of new capacity was installed in the first five months of the year compared to 4,400 MW in the same period in 2012. Cuts to government subsidies for solar in Italy, Greece, and Belgium have also led to a decrease in demand, only partially offset by substantial increase in business in the United States.

At the same time, selling prices dropped by around 25% compared with the first six months of 2012. And to top it off, Aleo is also contending with the departure of its major shareholder, Bosch, from the solar business and its decision to liquidate all its solar assets. This combination of unfavorable events has forced Aleo to start talks with potential buyers but no takers as yet.

NOTE: The Bosch Group holds a 90% majority shareholding in Aleo, the balance is free float. Altogether there are about 1,600 small shareholders. They are all anxiously awaiting the developments of the Aleo saga, which we predict won't end up well for all parties involved.

Asola Solarpower GmbH

Asola Solarpower GmBH was established in 2001 as a manufacturer of monoand poly-crystalline photovoltaic modules for rooftop, roof-integrated and building-integrated systems, glass-glass modules, bifacial and colored cells, and other solar products.

Asola Solarpower GmbH experienced serious financial difficulties during 2012-2013 and filed for insolvency with the Jura District Court in January, 2013. A court appointed administrator was in charge of monitoring the company's operations and its restructuring plan. A strategic realignment was agreed by the creditors committee and was initiated immediately.

The initiated steps proved to be accurate in light of the European anti-dumping investigation, launched against Chinese photovoltaic imports. Asola's business operations were running unchanged while the company was looking for a way out of the financial difficulties.

The management was talking about its hopes for efficient redevelopment via a realigned business plan, but this is what we hear from the managers of most sinking solar companies. Like the captain of a sinking ship trying to avert a mass panic, they project positive attitude while the water is rising up to their necks, in the hope of avoiding the unavoidable.

The blame for insolvency proceedings has been blamed on high restructuring costs, oversupply of PV modules, increasing Chinese competition, and a declining European market. Asola's restructuring plan was designed to account for the newly altered conditions, and to restructure the company strategically, operationally and financially. These are the right words, and maybe the right plant too, but Asola's real hope was for a rich daddy to come along and swallow it together with its problems.

And sure enough, the Shanghai-based STGCON with offices near Munich, acquired the insolvent Asola Solarpower in June 2013. The management was able to keep the company afloat in the turbulent solar waters, navigating among the wrecks of hundreds of other solar companies until the knight in shining armor finally showed up and relieved them from their problems.

Now, the once proud Asola Solarpower GmBH is another Chinese company struggling to make it in the world's solar markets. Asola, under Chinese management, will continue to manufacture and sell solar modules while focusing on the development of prototypes and production of special, non-standard module applications, including the automotive business.

Bosch Solar

Bosch Solar Energy has been in trouble for a while, struggling to compete in the crystalline silicon PV cells and modules field. The global supply glut, and increased competition, interfered with Bosch's plans by depressing the prices and flooding the market with cheap (mostly China made) PV modules, to the point to where Bosch could no longer compete without going deeper in the red.

Bosch followed its partner, Aleo Solar which filed for bankruptcy earlier in 2013, and decided to start shutting down the manufacturing of ingots, wafers, cells and modules. This action is planned for execution in early 2014, at which time Bosch would account for $3.1 billion in losses from past, current, and potential activities.

This is not very surprising to those who follow the industry, because in 2012 Bosch sustained a loss of over one billion euros due to changing market conditions, which will not improve any time soon. Bosch was unable to adapt to the changes and offset such enormous and unrelenting price pressure in an increasingly difficult marketplace.

Bosch's management made a number of changes to the company's MO by reducing manufacturing costs significantly in 2012 and other improvements, but even that wasn't enough to compensate for the 40% fall in market prices.

Bosch's management looked carefully into every aspect of its solar business and considered the latest technological advances, and all possible additional ways of reducing costs, including partnerships, but, unfortunately, none of these possibilities offered a solution that would be economically viable over the long-term.

When market conditions change as fundamentally as they have in this industry, Bosch and many others were forced to face the consequences. But, although the decision to shut down the solar business seems reasonable and understandable, it is one of the most revealing.

It shows several problems that are common for the latest solar boom-bust cycle:

1. Bosch got in the solar energy products manufacturing business by inertia, drawn by the lucrative market opportunities in the solar sector during 2007-2009. Large demand for solar products plus generous government incentives and subsidies opened the doors for Bosch and countless other companies to enjoy the free ride while it lasted.

2. When the market conditions deteriorated and the government goodies disappeared, Bosch, and many like it, saw themselves inadequately prepared to survive in the new reality.

3. If Bosch with its immense resources and reputation cannot compete against the cheap Chinese imports, then who can?

4. It is not only Bosch that is in this peculiar situation. Most solar companies, with very few exceptions, are currently either swimming in, or getting into, the red. Those who made it thus far unscathed are the lucky ones and most of them have a very good chance for a long-term success.

Cel Celis

Cel Celis is a Spanish solar manufacturer, who following the trend of failures had suspended the production operations at its San Roman de Bembibre factory. Some of the 100 workers on payroll were given maintenance or other duties, hoping that production will resume in the near future, while the destiny of the rest is unclear.

In the summer of 2013, Cel Celis filed insolvency proceedings at the commercial court of Leon, in northern Spain, amid reports that the company is in $39.3 million of debt. The major problem is immediate cash flow issue resulting from the Castille y Leon's regional government failing to provide $6.5 million in subsidies as promised in a 2010 agreement.

And although there is no financial contingency plan to deal with the shortfall, the company officials insist that restructuring of the company would take place, instead of a closure of facilities or liquidation. We have seen this happening at many other failing companies before, where company officials say whatever they are supposed to say to keep the boat afloat a bit longer.

Given the current economic situation in Spain, with 25% unemployment (and 50% among young people), as well as slowing in the solar markets, and the government's lack of support for the solar industry, the future of Cel Celis is uncertain even under best of circumstances.

Centrosolar

In its 2012 financial results, Germany-based Centrosolar noted that it has used up half of its share capital, driving the need for restructuring. This is mostly due to sales deteriorating from €2.2 million in 2011 to negative €12.6 million in 2012. Wow, this is a big change for a small company.

The company also sold 100% of its glass division, Centrosolar Glas GmbH, which brought major losses in 2012, to Belgian company Dukatt NV for a very small prices, according to inside sources. This move is expected to reduce the company's debt by €14 million.

Further denting Centrosolar's bottom line is a nagging restructuring plan approved in February that has resulted in considerable non-recurring expenses in connection with legal and consultancy services. Personnel cutbacks also ate into the bottom line, although the company has set aside €4.1 million to meet the anticipated overall cost of restructuring. The group included an additional €500,000 in restructuring expenses in its first quarter operating costs.

A sure indicator of the poor status of the company is its share drop, from the highest of $10 in 2008 down to $0.25 per share in mid-2013. And things might just get worse yet. The board and the shareholders approved a simplified capital reduction of 25:1, under which the number of shares merged from 20.4 million to 814,000. With all this going on, we have to wonder what's next for this once-promising solar company.

Conergy

German manufacturer and developer Conergy has started insolvency proceedings at the district court of Hamburg after plans to include a new strategic investor in the company were thwarted by one of 10 existing creditors. The insolvency filing is expected to protect its manufacturing operations and workers and pay for three months of operation, while it seeks renewed agreements with creditors and potential new investors under court protection.

Unexpected payment delays on one of the large-scale PV projects had resulted in liquidity issues for its module and mounting systems manufacturing operations in Germany, forcing the company to seek creditor protection. The company has presented two concrete concepts on the investment by investors to the lenders, but they repeatedly could not reach an agreement on a timely implementation of the proposal. Left without a solid capital structure, Conergy Group could not continue normal operations, thus the insolvency filing.

Conergy is not alone in shifting emphasis to a greater dependence on the PV project (design, installation, and O&M) business, which requires greater level of capital, but has greater profitability over component sales in the long run.

The continued expansion downstream depends on strategic new investors providing sufficient working capital for the projects' business. So new blood (with lots of money) was the only solution.

Alas, in the summer of 2013, the U.S. based investor Kawa offered to buy most of Conergy AG's global sales operations—only two weeks after the insolvency filing.

Kawa acquired two of Conergy's German entities; Conergy Deutschland GmbH and Conergy Services GmbH, in addition to the its subsidiaries in North America, Singapore, Thailand, Australia, Spain, Italy, France, Greece, Cyprus and Britain.

In a surprise move, Conergy's production subsidiaries, Mounting Systems GmbH and Conergy SolarModule GmbH, were not part of the transaction. That means goodbye to Conergy's production capabilities all together, unless another knight in shining armor rides in to save them some time soon.

Gehrlicher Solar

Gehrlicher Solar AG is a German photovoltaic corporation, based near Coburg, Germany, with administrative headquarters in Dornach. Gehrlicher Solar AG is a system integrator, in charge of planning, building, financing, maintaining and operating large-scale photovoltaic power plants and rooftop systems.

It is also a wholesaler for solar modules, inverters and complete photovoltaic systems, while offering its own components of the GehrTec family of products. Gehrlicher Solar had 250 employees in Germany and a turnover of $415 million in 2011. It was also one of the 20 largest EPC providers in 2012. Its sister company, Gehrlicher Solar Management holds 25 funds for investment in solar energy, and its U.S. subsidiary, Gehrlicher Solar America, had a 400% growth in revenue in 2012 with sales totaling $74.1 million at the time. Its Brazilian subsidiary recently completed the installation of a PV system on a football stadium in Bahia.

The good times, however, are now gone and in the summer of 2013 Gehrlicher Solar became just another German firm to file for insolvency. Coincidently, the filing was done on the very same day as fellow manufacturing and engineering, procurement and construction (EPC) company Conergy announced that it had filed for insolvency. Small world...

Challenging conditions in Europe are squeezing EPC firms, with many looking to exploit emerging, overseas markets. Domestic competitors in the U.S., Asia and Latin America have also joined a market that was previously dominated by European firms. European companies formed seven of the top ten EPC companies in 2010, but this figure has now fallen to just four. The 30 largest operators in the world make up just 26% of the global market.

The dramatic change in the EPC landscape in 2012 confirms that the industry remains incredibly fragmented, and that there will be many additional changes—mostly not that good—in the future.

Hoku Solar

Hoku was a subsidiary of Tianwei New Energy Holdings, a Chinese manufacturer of polysilicon, wafers, cells and modules, and an affiliate of China South Industries Group Corporation (CSGC)—a large Chinese conglomerate with nearly 200,000 employees.

Hoku started out as a specialized fuel cell membrane and materials company in Hawaii, and then decided to follow the crowd by jumping in the solar business as polysilicon manufacturer. At the same time it also tried solar installations in its home state of Hawaii with reported $1.6 million revenue in 2013. Jack of all trades, master of none, it seems...

The big troubles started in 2012, when the firm's stock was delisted from the Nasdaq. At the same time, when the solar business was in a free fall, Hoku focused on the long-suffering $700 million polysilicon plant in Pocatello, Idaho—since it had already received $280 million in prepayments from Hanwha SolarOne, Tianwei New Energy, Jinko Solar, and Suntech for polysilicon to be delivered between 2012 and 2016. Hoku actually has been planning to build the Idaho factory since 2008, when polysilicon prices were much higher, but it took its time in doing so.

The 2012 polysilicon market prices went way down, so the company was having difficulty paying the Idaho plant electric bill. At that time the CFO and CEO resigned, emphasizing Hoku's lack of direction, and poor technological differentiation in silicon manufacturing and in fuel cells. Hoku simply flowed with the currents without a solid strategic business plan. It just went along the established route of following the crowd, going public, while paying high salaries to its underperforming executives. This lack of solid direction and significant technological differentiation is what brought many solar companies to their knees at the time.

Now Hoku is over $1.0 billion in debt to 30 creditors, but not to worry; its mother company, CSGC, is a rich company and will figure something our to get out of this embarrassing situation of world proportions.

Komax Solar

Komax Solar was a solar equipment manufacturer, a subsidiary of the large Komax Group, which has two other business units; Komax Wire, Komax MedTech, with sales primarily in Europe.

After completing a strategic review and releasing financial figures earlier this year, Komax Group said the risk potential of Komax Solar was "not compatible" with the group's objectives.

Komax Solar cut jobs in June 2012, and again in January 2012, reducing its staff by over 50%. The reasons given were a 90% drop in product orders due to overcapacity and loss of customers due to a number of reasons.

Komax Solar operations were in the red even back in 2009 and 2010, making it a relatively easy decision to exit the solar industry as the backlog got almost fully depleted over the past 18 months and new orders were few and far between.

Komax's debut in the PV equipment supply chain consisted of four phases, according to the management:

- Phase I, 2006-2008, showed strong order intake as Asia Pacific and European module suppliers added capacity, many from a very low megawatt installation base
- Phase II shortly thereafter, during the brief economic downturn when there was a short lull in PV capacity investments
- Phase III, 2009-2011 were the glory days for Komax, as Chinese c-Si module suppliers added significant new capacity, and Komax was able to sell a lot of equipment
- Phase IV, the final days of the company, represents the over-capacity, investment-reset period where new-order intake dropped to very low levels and profitability was not feasible, nor expected.

NOTE: These phases are characteristic for the developments during the last solar industry boom-bust cycle, where many companies followed a similar path, including the final stage.

The Komax Group pulled out of the solar industry in the summer of 2013 by selling its module assembly equipment design and manufacturing arm, Komax Solar, and is looking for a suitable buyer, although it will continue to honor contracts and maintain equipment it has already sold.

Nanosolar

Nanosolar is the symbol of what happened and what went wrong during the last solar boom-bus cycle of 2007-2012. At one point Nanosolar was hailed as the best thing that ever happened to the solar industry, and its stock was valued at $2 billion for a while, and over $450 million in international investment since its start in 2002.

Nanosolar's contribution to the solar industry is that it was able to sell its feeble and unproven technology to a long list of famous investors, such as OnPoint Technologies, Mohr Davidow Ventures, Ohana Holdings, Family Offices, AES, the Carlyle Group, French utility EDF and Energy Capital Partners, Lone Pine Capital, the Skoll Foundation, Pierre Omidyar's fund, GLG Partners, Beck Energy, Grazia Equity, Benchmark Capital, Google, Larry Page, and Sergey Brin. What does this tell us about the savviness of the investors?

What does this say about the future of solar thin film PV? The answer is clear; not much good is to be expected at least for some time to come, although some companies are still hanging in there for dear life. Unfortunately, unless things change dramatically in the energy field, they will not be able to hang on for very long…

Following 70% layoffs of its staff, a low-valuation financing in 2012, and other struggles, Nanosolar is selling off its German fully automated PV panel assembly factory to a Swiss investor at undisclosed price. At the same time it is selling off its solar production and manufacturing equipment and all related capital assets at its factory in San Jose, California.

The Swiss investor is buying Nanosolar GmbH, which is the CIGS module manufacturing division of Nanosolar created in 2008 in Luckenwalde, Germany. This factory the Swiss investor plans to use to make c-Si solar modules, but the rest is a trade secret. As part of the sale, Nanosolar GmbH will be able to continue making CIGS PV modules.

As is becoming a habit for company officials, a Nanosolar official stated, "We are very excited about this new strategy for Nanosolar GmbH. With our highly automated module manufacturing line and our proven experience of high quality module production we can offer our customers premium products tailored to the new era of grid parity installations.

According to the newly adopted strategy, Nanosolar GmbH plans to grow its market share and workforce considerably in the future. Any bets?

If Nanosolar was not able to make it on its own, what makes the investor sure that he can beat the odds? Will he join the long list of losers in the Nanosolar saga, instead?

Panasonic

Panasonic is one of the pioneers of the solar sector; developing solar cells since the early 1980s. By 1987 Panasonic was mass producing solar cells that were widely used in calculators and other applications.

In 2012 Panasonic received the corporate innovation award from the institute of electrical and electronics engineers (IEEE)—given only to companies that have shown major advances in applied electro-technology—for developing, optimizing, and successfully commercializing its high performance hetero-junction solar technology (HIT). Today, HIT cells have the highest conversion efficiency of nearly 22% in mass production, and Panasonic produces about 6.0 GW of HIT solar cells every year for the Japan, Europe, and America's solar markets.

What a portfolio of successes—until the summer of 2013, when Panasonic revealed a long streak of failures. As a result of changing market conditions, the PV manufacturing division announced closure of its PV module manufacturing facility in Hungary, to consolidate its manufacturing operation in Japan and Malaysia. The plant was opened just recently and 550 jobs are now gone.

This move is in response to the decline and growth of PV markets in Europe and Asia respectively, and particularly the changes of late in post-Fukushima Japan, and the fierce competition by cheap Chinese PV modules.

Panasonic already trimmed down its manufacturing operation the US, ending wafer manufacturing at its Oregon plant in June, 2012.

Since the Poland solar modules manufacturing plant is the company's only solar European module manufacturing facility, it plans keep its PV module manufacturing capacity at 900MW a year. Panasonic is not a low price manufacturer, so the unfair Chinese competition will be a great hurdle for Panasonic solar operations.

The only question now is, what is Panasonic going to do next; will it be able to keep the 900 MW production capacity going, and expand it in the near future?

Refusol

And yet another German solar company (inverter manufacturer) hangs on the fringes of failure. Refusol Holding GmbH confirmed that an agreement with Advanced Energy has already been signed, so the U.S. company has acquired Refusol's three-phase string inverter line, which is expected to complement its central inverter products.

Advanced Energy paid around €59 million cash for Refusol, after assuming €9 million of debt and reducing net working capital by €1.8 million. Another €10 million could also be paid out in both cash and Advanced Energy stock, if special conditions are met.

While the combination of the two companies' 2012

businesses makes them the world's third largest inverter supplier, due to a "relatively fragmented" supplier base, their combined global market share, based on 2012 revenues, is estimated to be just over 5%.

Refusol is no more, and now it remains to be seen if it would not be the proverbial stone tied around the neck of Advanced Energy, sinking it in the turbulent solar waters. Let's hope not...

Solar World

SolarWorld is/was the largest Germany-based solar manufacturer and distributor, who was not spared by the solar tsunami of late. It saw heavy losses grow in the face of intense competition from China, which has sent prices for PV panels plunging as much as 75% since 2009. SolarWorld has been at the forefront of U.S. and European efforts to impose anti-dumping duties on Chinese manufacturers.

The first signs of SolarWorld throwing the towel came, or rather changing strategy, came in the summer of 2013, when it laid off 14% of its work force and suspended silicon crystal and wafer manufacturing at its Hillsboro, Washington, production plant.

SolarWorld AG, however, has a rich partner; Qatar Solar Technologies (QSTec), that is willing to help with a much needed capital investment of €35 million. An agreement with the Qatar group was reached, in which it holds 29%, as well as with a majority of its creditors on the future structure of the company.

As part of that plan, QSTec would acquire 30% of SolarWorld for €35 million following a share increase. In addition, QSTec is expected to buy a convertible bond that would bolster SolarWorld's status by as much as €200 million. SolarWorld CEO contributed €11 million of equity capital into the company in exchange for about 20% of the company's shares.

With all this said and done, SolarWorld's ship is upright and ready for battle...again. It failed once, however, and since the global solar situation has not changed much, and the competition is more fierce than ever, the activities at SolarWorld seem similar to rearranging the deck chairs on the Titanic. We will be watching.

Solen AG

Solen AG, was established at the beginning of the latest solar boom-bust cycle in Cologne, Germany, and operated through its global subsidiaries. Solon manufactures and supplies independent solar energy systems for solar plants worldwide in a form of vertically integrated and planned, developed, and sold PV systems for ground-mounted, roof-mounted, and roof-top integrated solar energy systems.

Solen AG also planned and delivered turnkey installations for institutional and private investors, and provided various other services, including the installation of solar-energy systems, purchase and trading of modules and components, acquisition of solar-energy sites, project planning and ready-to-use installation, and project sale to individual investors or investment funds.

In the spring of 2013 Solen stalled, and although there were some indications that Solen was in trouble, the failure was startling. In the beginning of 2011 Solen's stock fell bellow a dollar per share, and soon after that it became apparent that it would not be able to repay the more than €2 million interest accumulated on the loan. And sure enough, it was unable to repay it on time.

€2 million doesn't seem like a lot of money for a global contender, but meetings with creditors designed to decide on a moratorium failed because of lack of interest and participation. Without a feasible recourse, the board turned for help to the district bankruptcy court. So, Solen AG filed for insolvency at the Meppen, Germany, district court in April, 2013, although it went on doing business as usual.

By doing this, the board intended to continue to run the Solen's businesses until a solution is found. The sharks are circling the quickly decaying body of Solen AG, so it is up to the board to decide on the options. All requests and offers, as well as the decisions, were evaluated by an insolvency administrator appointed by the court, with a corporate reorganization as a priority.

Solen had a good thing going on in Italy, but the delay of the sale of a large PV project there added to the burden and accelerated the events leading to the bankruptcy. There were also some profits coming from Solen's subsidiaries in the U.S. and the U.K., but they were simply not enough to cover the interest of more than €2 million for the loan creditors.

The total debt amounts to more than €27.5 million, which is a lot of money for a relatively new company. So the question here is, "Who is crazy, those who got the loan money or those who gave it away?" How do you give $27 million to a company that is Jack of all trades and master of none? A company that is all over the place, operating mostly on loans? Lesson learned?

The Chinese solar manufacturers are also experiencing great difficulties now. And maybe much more than their foreign counterparts.

Sunergy

Another of the Chinese giants, solar cell and module maker, Sunergy Co Ltd has been reporting a number of consecutive quarterly losses—seven at the last count. The reason given is that the PV modules prices and demand are weak, which means that most Chinese solar companies have been unable sell their products and turn a profit.

The Chinese ignored the proverbial wisdom, "Don't cut off the branch you are sitting on." Instead, they kept on cutting the prices (the only branch they were able to sit on), and now many of them are sitting on the ground, while others are headed that way. Due to a steep fall in panel prices, caused by excess capacity and the loss of subsidies in the top market, Europe, the PV panel market dried up.

A large portion of China Sunergy's revenue comes from European markets, with Germany accounting for nearly 30% of total revenue in 2012, while Italy accounted for nearly 15%. And the problems continue, and got even worse as the European Union imposed restrictions and duties on Chinese made solar panels and components, similar to, but more generous and flexible than, those imposed by the United States in 2012.

So now Sunergy and most of the other Chinese solar manufacturers are turning their attention to their home market and Japan. Japan seems to be the main target, due to growing solar markets that is developing as a result of government subsidies for solar power in the wake of the Fukushima disaster.

The discrepancy between the internal needs and wants on one hand, and the reality in China on the other, are increasing, because although the government plans to double its installed solar power capacity in 2013, the state-owned banks that propped up the ailing solar industry have become very cautious about lending money to losing companies.

Sunergy's net loss widened to $70.5 million in 2012, from $49.6 million in 2011, while the revenue fell 51% to $54.4 million. The company stock is down 20%, so borrowing more money would not be easy.

Once mighty Sunergy, Suntech, and a number of other Chinese solar manufacturers are exiting the global arena and are shrinking back in the Motherland. This is actually for the best, because Chinese business MO is still stuck in the Middle Ages. Chinese representatives showed amazing arrogance, ignorance and negligence to detail during the good days of 2008-2010, when they thought that they can dominate the world solar energy markets by dumping large quantities of low-price PV modules in the U.S. and Europe.

They were actually successful to a point, mostly due to greed on part of American and European developers, who saw low prices as a key to success and riches.

Now things have changed and the Chinese manufacturers can no longer sell their products overseas, so they are moving the game back home, or close by.

We just have to wish them best of luck, hoping that they have learned a lesson or two from their last attempt to invade the world's energy markets. But based on previous experiences this is not very likely.

Sunselex

Sunselex was founded in 2008 from the original company Leitramm Solar GmbH, operating as a full-service provider in the area of planning, design, construction, assembly, operation and maintenance of photovoltaic open space and roof facilities, including exchange of the respective components.

The company with its head office in Munich has branches near Leipzig and in Kaufbeuren, Germany, as well as subsidiaries in Spain, Switzerland, and Italy. To date Sunselex has an installed capacity of over 1.0 GW around Germany and the world.

A bright future was envisioned in Switzerland by the ambitious company management, but it became one of the latest victims of the shift in solar energy market currents. The desolate solar PV market situation in Germany, according to Sunselex executives was the main reason for the failure.

Despite efforts to cut costs, including workforce reduction, the management was forced to pull out of that market all together and file for insolvency in August, 2013. An interim insolvency manager of the German office would be liaising with the Swiss sales and distribution office with a view to handing over much of the business and assets to Sunselex in Zurich.

Sunselex is pulling out of the German energy market, while its international subsidiaries will not be adversely affected by the insolvency. The Swiss branch of Sunselex is expected to reposition the firm to have more involvement in emerging markets for PV such as South Africa, the Middle East and north Africa, central and south America and the U.K. This includes a joint venture (JV) in South Africa, Sunselex-Romano.

So it seems now that the German solar market is in a down spiral, which may last a long time.

Suntech

Suntech Power International (a subsidiary of Suntech Power Holdings), based in China, has resorted to court proceedings in Switzerland to stop bankruptcy proceedings filed by creditors. It was granted a provisional moratorium for two months on creditor claims for payment by the court in Schaffhausen, Switzerland.

The provisional moratorium was intended to allow more time to restructure the existing, primarily intercompany debt. In the meanwhile it is business as usual at Suntech.

The slide down hill and eventually into insolvency, started in 2009, when some customers related to the Suntech's founder that they couldn't pay their bills. The non-paying customers amounted to nearly 30% of Suntech's business, but the company booked the sales as revenue anyway. Business a la China, is what this is, no doubt. It is a wide-spread secret that everyone knows about. This also amounts to about $720 million of fraud and $540 in bond default.

Suntech's machinations were discovered by the U.S. SES, which by the way, is does not recognize this type of favoritism a la China as legitimate MO. So, SES squeaked, because Wall Street investors funneled $1.28 billion into Suntech, including the bonds and $742.6 million of stock sales in 2005 and 2009.

But finally in March 2013 Suntech received a notice of default on the $541 million bond payment and agreed with almost two-thirds of the holders to extend the due date. The U.S. investors are faced with big losses, no doubt.

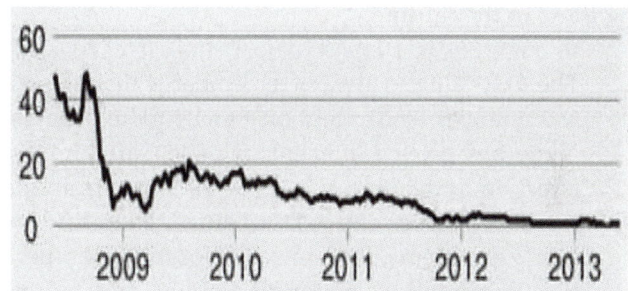

Figure 7-25. Suntech stock.

This is what a losing stock looks like. This is a drop from $50 in 2008 to $0.50 in 2013, a 100-fold drop in five years. Actually, the stock dropped long before that, as early as in the beginning of 2009, but most people did not notice it in the midst of the big solar hoopla and the promises of lots of money floating around at the time brought out.

There were many other companies that had a similar faith during that time period. First solar comes to mind, where its stock dropped from above $350 in 2008 to below $12 in 2012. This is actually only a 30-fold drop as compared with Suntech's 100-fold drop in the same time frame.

Suntech's Chinese Wuxi subsidiary entered bankruptcy proceedings too, shortly after Suntech defaulted on repayment of a $541 million bond. The Schaffhausen bankruptcy court has appointed a representative to investigate the possibility of restructuring Suntech's European operations. The story will take long time to develop fully. Lots of players and activities...

In March 2013, Suntech also closed its production plant in Arizona, which was supposed to be its flagship that was to take Suntech into the great expanse of the U.S. solar market. With the flagship sunk, Suntech's flotilla would have a hard time navigating the choppy waters of the huge U.S. energy market.

In Summary

There are many different reasons for the failures during the boom-bust cycle of 2008-2013, and we have taken a fairly close look at some of them, as well as the related issues in our book on the subject, *Solar Technologies for the 21st Century*, where an entire chapter is dedicated to the hundreds of failed company at the time.

Just looking at the large number of companies that have gone under, those that have been, or still are under serious distress, would give us an idea that something big and almost uncontrollable took place.

So then, keeping in mind the mistakes and failures of late, what do we need to be aware of, to avoid repeating these in the future?

1.   The first thing to always remember is that all solar technologies—no exception—are work in progress. None has proven efficient, reliable, safe and cost effective in the long run. They all suffer from materials, components, performance, reliability, and safety problems. Annual deterioration, temperature degradation, materials fatigue, and failures under extreme weather conditions are some of the most common problems.

2.   The immaturity of the solar products is reflected in the real danger of failure while operating non-stop under adverse conditions such as high winds, dust storms, lightning, brush fires, hail, blistering desert sun, and excess moisture. These, and a number of other similarly serious dangers, have been ignored for the most part thus far, due to ignorance, negligence or greed. It suffices to say, however, that any of these natural, or man-made disasters could cripple a solar power field, and put it out of commission temporarily or even permanently.

3.   Many companies rushed to put their products on the market—before they were ready. This is a viola-

tion of the basic marketing laws and most of these companies paid for their mistake, or greed. Solar technology is complex to design, manufacture and use. Each step of the process must be perfectly executed, tested, and certified. And then improved, tested and certified again and again—well before large quantities are manufactured for large-scale deployment.

4.   Something that we don't see every day (at least not that obviously so often) is the atrocious, if not criminal, behavior of some failing solar companies officials. Many of them made misleading statements, hid important facts, and continued doing so until the very end, or until found red handed.

5.   We also must remember that government funding has its limits and must be administered carefully and used wisely. Just mentioning Solyndra, which is actually only the tip (and most visible part) of the 2008-2012 fiasco iceberg, brings back the government ignorance and negligent hastiness in issuing grants and loans despite the technological inefficiencies of Solyndra and many of the benefiting (and ultimately failing) companies, and the combination of other factors that brought the company down and caused thousands of people to lose their jobs.

6.   But most importantly, solar energy generation depends on sunshine availability. Unfortunately, even the sunniest places in this world have periods of time—during a day or a season—that the sun is hidden behind clouds. And, of course, no sunshine is available during night time, which is most of the time. At those times solar is useless, and sits idle, or produces very little power.

This puts solar (together with wind power generation) in the category of variable and unreliable energy sources. This alone would delay their development into a world-level power generator until and unless an efficient energy storage media is found.

There is no doubt that the older and well-established energy sources (the fossils) are still alive and doing well, thank you, but things have changed. The fossil supporters on one hand and the budding and fragile renewable energy technologies on the other are now locked in a serious battle.

We have seen this trend several times since the

1970s, but this time is different. Solar is now established, albeit fragile, competitor, that is determined to stay and do well. This won't happen overnight, the battle will go though many stages, many more companies will fail, but solar will survive one way or another. It is our 21st century energy future.

The battle right now is based on the cost of energy generation, which seems to be a moving target. Solar is a different type of energy source, and must be treated differently. Many of the principles involved in the solar business don't even understand the way solar REALLY works, so we all must be much better educated to make the right decisions for solar power generation and use in the future.

This includes understanding the inherent risks of solar power, some of which are quite serious:

Operational Risks

When considering economics of a renewable energy project, we must include all of the factors discussed above, and any and all additional issues that might (or might not) pop-up during the 30 years of non-stop operation. There are a number of risks associated with the use of PV modules during the long-term field operation. These risks are augmented in large-scale fields operating under extreme climate conditions (extreme desert heat and high humidity).

Some of the major risks associated with the operation of PV modules, as far as the profitable and safe operation of these is concerned, are as follows:

Low Power Output

Low power condition (lower than expected) could be caused by a number of abnormalities. The worst case, and what is most frequently the case of low power condition, are defects in the modules, such as improper soldering, micro-cracks in the cells, lamination problems, frame materials and design problems.

Poor installation, bad weather, or a combination of the above factors also could cause lower than expected conditions$_+$.

Power Loss (Heat)

Excess heat, such as the 120+ days in the desert, causes all PV cells and modules to decrease power output in proportion to the heat levels. An average power loss of 0.5% per degree Celsius is accepted as the norm.

This means that a module operating at high noon in a hot desert day could lose 30% of the power it generated in the morning.

Power Loss (Time Degradation)

All PV modules degrade with time. That is to say that as they weather, they change in a way that causes them to lose power gradually and consistently. An average 1.0% power loss per year is accepted as the norm.

This means that a 100 Wp PV module will generate 90 Wp during year #10, 80 Wp during year 20, and 70 Wp during year 30.

The actual long-term field tests with c-Si and thin film modules show much greater excursions as time goes by—especially in desert regions, as is to be expected.

Premature Failure

Premature failure of PV modules (the modules failing shortly after installation, and before the expected EOL) could be caused by a number of factors, some of which are outlined in one above.

Excess power loss, high annual degradation and other unusual incidents are often early symptoms of premature failure.

Electrical Shock

Electrical shock is caused by short circuits, and insulation failure in the modules, overheating, bad frame and connectors design, faulty inverter, poor installation, and so forth.

Electrical shock is easy to prevent by making periodic electrical measurements of the modules and strings.

Physical Injury

Physical injury (personnel cuts, falls, etc.) are most often caused by bad frame design and manufacturing, where sharp edges and other imperfections could cause serious harm by cutting people's hands and bodies.

Faulty racking systems could also harm people by collapsing, or by other abnormal behavior. Improper handling of heavy objects (inverters, frame elements etc.) is another source of personal injury dangers.

Poisoning

Many PV modules contain toxic materials, Pb, As, Cd, etc. Although these are mostly contained within the modules, trace amounts (remaining from the manufacturing process) could be adhered to the modules surface. Upon contact, these toxins could cause skin rashes and internal poisoning.

With the large number of modules installed at each site—millions upon millions in large-scale fields—and with the increased number of CdTe and CIGS modules installed in these, the danger of poisoning increases proportionally.

Fire

Fire danger is the obvious and most dangerous long-term risk. Individual PV modules could catch on fire upon overheating—especially when operating under extreme climate conditions. Once fire has started in one point of the module, it will spread quickly through the entire module by burning the EVA and other plastic components.

When one module starts burning, the adjacent modules in the string start overheating due to the flames. This and increase of the internal resistance in the modules might ignite many of them too. In worst case the fire can then jump from string to string and engulf the entire field.

Solar Storms

Intense solar storms are getting more frequent and stronger lately. Sky-watchers in the North get a treat from the aurora borealis, or northern lights, which are caused by the solar storms at their peaks. The lights occur across much of the northern tier of the U.S., as far south as Oregon in the West, Illinois in the Midwest, and the Mid-Atlantic states in the East.

On March 10, 2006, NASA issued a solar storm warning for unusually strong solar activities (solar flares) during 2012. In June of 2010 NASA reinforced their original 2006 warning, telling the public to get ready for something new and unexpected—a solar storm.

NASA spokesman said, "We know it's coming but we don't know how bad it's going to be, however, the next solar maximum should be a doozy." NASA expects the sun storm to be in full swing sometime in 2012-2013, but they don't know exactly when, how strong, or long it will be.

March 8, 2012. Massive solar storm (flares) were expected about seven a.m. ET, according to the Space Weather Prediction Center in Boulder, CO, who predicted the storm to last about a day. On the "G1-G5" scale of geomagnetic storm intensity, with G5 being the worst, this storm was G3, considered to be a "strong" one.

July 12, 2012, another massive solar storm was observed, with strong energy field traveling towards the earth at a high speed. The effects of the high energy stream hitting the earth were expressed in increased intensity of the Northern Lights, which could be observed all the way in Central and Southern U.S. No damages were reported during this storm.

In August 2013 a solar storm of unprecedented power nearly missed the Earth. Had it hit us head on, it might've caused the greatest damage the Earth has seen

for a long time.

These storms have the potential to trip electrical power grids, although power companies around the world are usually alerted in advance for possible outages. Solar storms can also disrupt GPS systems or make them less accurate. Power grids, communications and satellites could be knocked out by a massive solar storm in the next two years, scientists warn.

Experts say the sun is reaching a peak in its 10-year activity cycle, putting the Earth at greater risk from solar storms.

NASA reports that the current increase in the number of solar storms is part of the sun's normal 11-year solar cycle, during which activity on the sun ramps up to the solar maximum, which should peak in late 2013, and since we are the season for these now, similar solar storms will occur every month or two for the next few years.

"The sun is waking up from a deep slumber, and in the next few years, we expect to see much higher levels of solar activity," says Richard Fisher, head of NASA's Heliophysics Division. "At the same time, our technological society has developed an unprecedented sensitivity to solar storms." "We know it is coming but we don't know how bad it is going to be. It will disrupt communication devices such as satellites and car navigations, air travel, the banking system, our computers, everything that is electronic. It will cause major problems for the world."

The National Academy of Science confirms that a very large solar storm could start any day now.

What NASA and NAS are not telling the general public is what to expect and what to do to prepare and protect from the potential sun storm damage. And most of us have no idea what they could be doing to prepare for a sun storm.

Major news agencies and talk radio are covering this slow developing story, spilling details here and there as of exactly what NASA's warning actually means. They speculate that If NASA and the other scientists are right, the physical and economic damage to the U.S. alone would be many times greater than hurricane Katrina. And the worst part, unlike expecting a hurricane, we simply don't know what to expect. We don't know what will happen during, nor what the short and long-term effects from a super solar storm on the Earth's populace.

If the earth gets a direct hit by a solar storm producing x-class solar flares, (coronal mass ejection or CME) it can potentially cripple the world in a number of ways. To start with every electronic device will malfunction or will stop working. Many of them will be damaged and in need of repair or replacement.

So just imagine...in one single blink of an eye all cell phones, computers, cars, trucks, planes, trains, ships, computers, GPAs, TV, radio, medical equipment, and everything that has a battery or is powered by electricity will stop working. Even if the effect is short-lived, a minute or so, even then the damage would be tremendous. And the flares would damage many essential pieces of equipment, which won't come back online for a long time, further complicating and aggravating the situation.

There might be electric power blackout in most of the world for days or many months on end. The banking system, the hospitals, airports, harbors, gas stations, and the New York Stock Exchange will be all shut down. Credit cards will be worthless and only cash, silver and gold would be accepted.

No question, it will be a real nightmare if the earth takes a direct hit from a super CME, thus changing billions of lives forever. Far fetched...maybe!!! But it is a possibility, and we see solar flares often—some of great magnitude—so it is quite likely that one of these will hit the earth fast and furiously some day.

Solar Storm Risks

So let's imagine a hot summer day at our large-scale solar field; our 100MWp PV installation in the Arizona desert is under full power. It is noon time, the PV panels are "cooking" and a lot of power is sent into the grid. All of a sudden, the intense energy blasts sent by the sun several days ago hits our PV field and the sensors in the field show instantaneous increase of the solar insolation from the usual 900 W/m^2 to extraordinary 3000 W/m^2, accompanied by extreme amounts of UV and IR radiation.

Even if the flare lasts only several seconds, the power field will be incapacitated. The system has enough fuses and breakers to protect it from overload at different section of the field, but a sudden, powerful and all encompassing overload—which the system designers were not even thinking possible—would cause a serious damage to the different electrical components, including the PV modules.

PV modules and inverters will be overloaded, breakers will be thrown off, fuses will burn, but not until some damage from the powerful surge is done in the milliseconds it takes to trigger the safety systems. Some modules and inverters might burst into flames from the overcurrent and overheating, and strings of PV modules might catch on fire.

All electronic equipment will be incapacitated by the blast, thus no power, or any other, controls or communications would be operational, which would leave the plant equipment vulnerable to further damage. And if the flares continue, more damage to the equipment—proportional to the strength and length of the solar storms—will be done as well.

A long enough sun flare would certainly cause a lot of damage to the PV modules, inverters and transformers, as well as any other electric and electronic equipment and the wiring in the site. Fire started in one part of the plant might propagate throughout the field and eventually ignite the entire field.

A total loss! This is the worst case scenario to be expected after a very strong solar storm of long duration. But is this possible? And what can we do to protect the field and our selves from such a tragic eventuality?

There are a number of measures that can be taken to double and triple the safety mechanism of the plant equipment. Such redundancy, however, is expensive, so not many people would even think of it.

The insurance, if we have one, would not cover "acts of God" in most cases, so we are on our own here... unless we are clever enough to somehow have such events covered by the insurance policy, as unlikely as this might be.

The millions of dollars, and thousands of hours, spent on the plant's planning, design, permitting, installation and operation would be for nothing and we still may owe lots of money to the banks (if the banks survive the solar storm too).

Such monstrous solar storms don't happen every day, but one big one is all it takes to wipe out a great portion of the active PV fields in the affected areas. So, planning and designing redundant protection for super solar storm attacks must be on the agenda.

All parties involved must be aware that there is—albeit very slight—possibility of a super solar storm hitting the earth, and badly damaging our power field sometime during its 30-years operation.

So in addition to getting surprised by the deteriorating performance of the modules, and the increased cost of the operation, we could also be even more surprised and even badly hurt (financially) by their abrupt field misbehavior and failures.

What can be done to eliminate the surprise?

How about insurance? It might be the best, if not the only, way to recover from a serious damage. This is America, after all; everything and everybody is insured. So why not the power field and its output? The modules are basically insured by the manufacturer to produce the specified power for 20 years. But how about unexpected and unforeseen events—excess clouds, equipment failures, natural disasters, etc. Including solar storms?

Enter the world' insurance industry…

Performance Insurance

This is a new concept, which albeit discussed in the past, and even partially applied in some cases, was never fully implemented in one single project. It is now, however, becoming a prerequisite, in our opinion, for starting (and for sure financing) new solar projects.

So, we are now looking at the newest branch of the U.S. insurance industry, performance insurance of solar power plants.

It is like the knight in shining armor coming to save the PV industry from its problems. Or is it…? This type of insurance is too new for us to assign it an exact place and role in the 21st century, but our long experience shows that it is one (if not the only) way to fill the gaps between quality, performance, and profits.

We know what to expect from the PV manufacturers, installers, and operators, so before jumping into the abyss of insuring PV fields—and especially large-scale installations—we need to meet the other part of the equation—the insurance companies.

The Basics of Insuring Property and Persons

Insurance companies world-wide are in the business of allocation of risk as their primary concern. People buy insurance to protect against financial damages or loss of property or persons. Insurance underwriters provide insurance to protect against potential damage or loss based on the associated risks.

Risk, as far as the insurance companies are concerned, is, "The chance of loss to the person or entity that is insured." Simple, but in each situation, the actual risk depends on a multitude of factors, such as what is being insured, what events might occur, and how likely each occurrence might be.

The insurance companies assess the total risk they are covering for any particular situation and determine the likelihood that they will have to make a payment if that risk becomes an actual loss. The annual insurance premium payment is determined based on the potential for the risks to become actual losses. For insurance companies to be profitable, the premiums they receive for insuring against losses must be greater than the actual payouts in the event of losses occurring.

The three main types of insurance companies are:
a. Insurance brokers
b. Insurance underwriters, and
c. Reinsurers

Underwriters, brokers, and re-insurers all play important roles within the insurance industry and are vital to the U.S. economy.

Brokers, just like the name suggests, are the intermediaries (salesmen) between the underwriters and the customers. As agents of the underwriters, their role may sound trivial, but they are responsible for finding the customers, negotiating the deals and in the process they come up with new and unique products, which are useful to all involved.

Industry-specialized brokers work with renewable energy product manufacturers, facility developers, and project finance clients to create unique product offerings and the necessary underwriting support that are not well-covered by traditional insurance. The goal of an industry-specialist or consultative insurance broker is to strategically partner with clients and provide innovative, responsive, and cost-effective solutions that mitigate the risk and uncertainty of renewable energy systems.

Insurance underwriters, on the other hand, are the companies that actually have the money to pay the customers when legitimate claims are made. They approve the deals negotiated by the brokers, and formulate the payment estimates designed to cover their risk. All terms of the deal are outlined in a binding contract which is approved by the underwriters. They also define the price and risk allocation terms under these contracts through a multitude of processes, including research, engineering analysis, risk modeling, contractual negotiations, and modification of pre-existing underwriting forms.

Insurance underwriters are specialized in different areas of the economy, which allows them to gain expertise in a particular area, which leads to a better understanding of the risks involved. This allows customers to receive best possible insurance premiums and faster turnaround on the creation of an insurance policy for liability and property, depending on the project location, size and other conditions.

Working together with the insurance brokers, the underwriters are gaining more understanding of the intricacies of the renewable energy business, since it is quickly becoming one of the major areas of their business with great growth potential in the near future, as well.

Basically speaking, the process of establishing insurance policies begins with developers or project owners identifying the risks that they need or want to cover and looking for an insurance broker to put their needs into an insurance package.

The insurance broker (industry-specialist preferably) might have suggestions for what to cover, how and how much. After a preliminary agreement on the type and size of insurance coverage needed, the brokers present the underwriting company they are working for with an outline of the insurance products that interest this particular client.

The clients, on the other hand, are presented with the range of policies, premiums, and terms of coverage from which to choose. Once the customers decide which policy they want, the broker returns to the underwriter to complete the policy formation process, a contract is designed and signed, and the insurance policy, and all its conditions, takes effect. The project and the people are then protected by the terms of insurance policy for the duration of the contract.

NOTE: We did not discuss the role of reinsurers, because these are specialized insurance industry type of insurance companies that provide risk management, and even insurance, for the insurance contract issued by the insurance underwriters.

The insurance industry is being significantly affected by the current economic downturn, new regulation requirements, and increased losses to policyholders. In the context of these large-scale forces shaping the insurance industry as a whole, the insurance market for PV systems is evolving and maturing rapidly.

The addition of the renewable energy market insurance options to the portfolio of insurance products, has not made the insurance company executives lives any better. Needless to say investments in PV products and projects are often viewed by underwriters as quite risky for two main reasons: 1) The technologies are newer (i.e., most systems do not have a long history of operational data); and, 2) There are fewer installations relative to other technology deployments (e.g., the real estate or the automobile).

Insurers use the "law of large numbers," which says that "the larger the group of units insured, the more accurate the predictions of gain and loss will be." And although the solar technologies have been in existence since the 1950s, their deployment at a significant level occurred much later, so the numbers are not that large.

Since 2007 new commercial on-grid installations increased to more than 1,500, which statistically speaking is not a large number. Not enough solar installations have been in place for long enough for underwriters to feel they can accurately predict what the losses associated with them would be. The experiences with some of these fields have not been very reassuring either, so all this fuels the uncertainty of the insurance industry.

On top of that, data of the different projects, products, installation and operation are not readily available, which complicates the process. Insurers have access to data on only projects that they insure, so the more insurers there are, the less data each insurer has.

Another major factor that adds to the complexity of insuring solar installations is the typical involvement of many parties, including installers, developers, investors, lenders, and insurance companies in each project. And typically, each party to the transaction attempts to minimize the risks it assumes while defining the recourse available in case a risk event occurs and leads to actual losses. In many cases, insurance products can be used to mitigate and manage the allocations associated with complex contractual arrangements.

Until the recent growth in the PV market, demand for PV system coverage was not adequate to encourage insurance underwriters to develop PV-specific products. If the upward trend of new PV installations continues, there will be a great demand for insurance products for PV. This growing market of new solar installations, which is being driven by state policies, federal incentives, and corporate responsibility, represents a possible market opportunity for insurance underwriters.

So let's look at the solar insurance from our perspective.

The Insurance Issues

In this text we've discussed the major technical, administrative, and financial issues facing the solar industry. We determined that long-term performance and longevity are some of the most important, albeit least discussed, issues in any PV undertaking with any of the existing PV technologies. And looking at the data in some long-term desert tests we can't help but wonder how anyone could put a positive spin on the results and accept the risks associated with 20-30 years of in-sun operation of these modules...especially in the world's deserts. We obviously don't know much about the different possibilities during such a long time exposure to such unforgiving climates. At the very least, we should take a very close look and estimate the extremes.

The long-term field tests are conclusively assuring us that the risks are real and are warning us of the potential and serious long-term physical deterioration, power degradation, failures and other dangers.

The lack of convincing test data, plus negative data from a number of field test studies, point to major obstacles in the early stages of the PV projects' financing, because investors are concerned with the lack of reliable scientific or test data that can convince them that the risks associated with long-term on-sun operation are well-known and manageable.

Enter the insurance industry…again!

A number of insurance companies do offer conditional performance guarantees designed to put the risk factors on a level ground which would make potential customers and investors more comfortable. PV performance insurance is a new field and like the PV industry it is equally un-standardized and unregulated thus far. In some cases, coverage is available to all participants—manufacturers and distributors of PV modules, integrators, utilities, customers and investors, while in other cases it covers only certain segments of the PV cycle, such as PV modules' efficiency and performance only.

Different insurance companies cover different types and percentages of the risks related to PV products and services. That might be just enough to eliminate the majority of risks, but we'd advise customers and investors to take a close look at the guidelines and definitions of the coverage in each policy before making a final decision. This is new thing and we all need to be careful.

Nevertheless, this is an encouraging development that might be just what is needed to bridge the gap of financing PV projects today and in the near future. Proper performance insurance fills the gap between quality, longevity and profitability of PV modules and projects, so it might be the key to providing acceptable levels of risk management, thus increasing the customers' and investors' confidence in solar installations.

One serious catch: the insurance companies would favor the more established manufacturers (at least for now) who produce better quality PV products. But there are a lot of PV project owners and investors who prefer to use the "cheap" Asian-made PV modules. So how would the insurers determine which of these have acceptable performance risk? How do insurers know what a better performance is to begin with?

What do they know about longevity, let alone assessing the risks associated with it? Because of its importance, these questions and the entire solar performance insurance sector needs special attention, so let's take a closer look at the characteristics and conditions of providing "performance" insurance.

To mitigate the performance and longevity risks of PV modules, insurers must have a good idea what these are. Since they are not specialists in the solar field, and since there are many risks in all areas of the cradle-to-grave life span of modules, they will need to create a "PV products performance insurance" technical team, which would consist of a number of technical specialists

with varying areas and degrees of responsibilities.

Expertise

As an example of a team of experts, as needed for the success of both; the insurer and insured, we'll suggest the following additions to the insurance company's professional team:

1. Materials specialist, in charge of evaluating the type and quality of the all process materials and chemicals used for making the modules in each of the insured projects.

2. Front end process engineer, in charge of determining the quality of each step of the solar cells manufacturing operations.

3. Back end process engineer, in charge of evaluating the PV modules assembly process.

4. Quality control engineer, in charge of determining the quality procedures of each process step and the final product.

5. In addition, a group of other specialists is also needed to ensure the integrity of the PV project's installation and operation. These specialists should be able to evaluate the project's design, structure, land, interconnect, and other aspects and issues related to the modules' installation and operation.

NOTE: Actually two separate technical teams are needed to cover all aspects of PV modules manufacturing and use—one team consisting of c-Si cells and modules manufacturing and use specialists, and the second of TFPV modules manufacturing and use specialists. This is needed because the materials, processes, installation and operation of these different types of PV technologies are quite different. Therefore, the different tasks and responsibilities are not interchangeable.

The Tasks

These specialists' and engineers' tasks would be to, a) obtain the most recent and reliable information on the manufacturer, the materials and products to be used, and, b) analyze and summarize the risks in the respective areas.

The goal is to arrive to conclusions in the key areas of interest, as follows:

1.   Supply chain management and quality
2.   Manufacturing process execution
3.   Quality control verification
4.   Efficiency evaluation under local climate conditions
5.   Performance evaluation under local climate conditions

   a.   Temperature coefficient verification

b. Annual degradation verification
6. Longevity under the local climate conditions
    a. Early mortality estimate
    b. Useful life estimate
    c. End-of-life measures
7. Toxicity and safety evaluation
8. Land and interconnect evaluation
9. Evaluation of political and regulatory issues in the local area

After completing these tasks, the technical team members would make a thorough and detailed report on each material and process step in the cradle-to-grave life span of the modules and estimate the level of quality, efficiency, performance and longevity of the final product and the entire project.

With all this done, the insurers will have a very good idea what they are dealing with and will have a better chance to calculate and mitigate their risks. It is possible that within several years of this thorough due diligence, a pattern would emerge that can lead to standardizing the entire insurance process. Actually, it is most likely that several patterns would emerge—patterns related to different manufacturers (established vs. new companies), different locations (hot desert vs. cloudy climates), different technologies (c-Si, vs. TFPV, vs. HCPV), and several combinations of the above.

Short of that, the insurers are working with their eyes closed, so rolling a die would be the only worse thing they could do. While the insurance business is full of uncertainties and risks, mitigating the risks in the chaotic solar frenzy is only logical.

Sorting and sifting the low quality players and technologies would prevent disasters and save money for all involved. This is not an easy task and some serious knowledge, professionalism and hard work is needed before obtaining a good handle on the situation.

We hope that the insurance companies involved in providing performance insurance to the solar products business will be able to understand and successfully tackle this fascinating but risky business venture.

"The insurance industry doesn't work this way," some might say. Maybe, but the insurance industry has no experience with long-term PV installations either, and is far from being a specialist in all areas of PV products manufacturing and use, so it needs to take a very close look at all options (including the above suggestions) before jumping on the solar bandwagon, or else, it might end up in a mess of its own and up to its neck in risks, problematic issues, and unresolved cases. Just saying...

If everything is properly set, solar project installers, owners and investors would have a choice of insurance protection, which could vary from full, unconditional coverage to a minimal coverage required by law.

1. Manufacturers who use their own PV modules to build PV power plants may not need or want performance insurance*, although they still might choose a level of conventional insurance coverage to protect the plant from natural and manmade disasters.

2. Another class of customers using the highest quality PV modules available may also decide to skip insurance coverage altogether for obvious reasons.

3. Most of the other players, however, especially those using cheap PV modules, will be able to choose a level of coverage as they see fit. This way the gap between uncertain quality, deteriorating performance, and reduced longevity will be at least partially closed and the PV plant will survive unpredictable events, including excess performance degradation and failures.

NOTE: There is a difference between "performance" and regular insurance coverage required by state or federal law. Performance insurance in this text refers only to covering the amount of energy lost with time due to poor product performance, or other factors affecting the overall performance and yield.

Nevertheless, there is some overlapping of conditions and issues when talking about any type insurance for power plants, so the utmost care must be used when designing or signing insurance contracts.

There are still major challenges in this newly developed (or rather developing) solar and wind energy fields, so not many (if any) insurance companies would be willing to provide adequate long-term insurance to projects using these technologies.

As an alternative, mid- to large-size renewable energy developers and manufacturers (or projects) concerned about the overall cost of insurance and product warranty conditions and premiums may have the option of establishing a captive insurance company (hereafter referred to as "captive"). Such enterprises are common with fortune 500 companies , which have successfully used them for a long time.

A captive subsidiary established with the parent company (or project) explicitly as a risk mitigation arm is intended to maintain control of the operation—including any accidents, underperformance and other issues.

Like traditional insurance companies, the insured (the solar project) pays a premium in exchange for coverage as outlined in the policy. And like any insurance company, the captive should be managed in such a way that it avoids and somehow does not absorb all the losses of the insured.

This could be an attractive alternative to buying insurance from a traditional underwriter, since insurance premiums for plant construction and operation are limited in scope and way too high in price. Insurance premiums of 25% of a system's annual operating expense, and 0.25%-0.5% of the total installed cost of the facility, have been reported.

Based on NREL's system advisor model (SAM), a one MW system located in Phoenix, AZ, with a total installation cost of $4.5 million would have an annual insurance cost between $11,500 and $22,500. This means that our 100 MWp at the same location, and insured under the same conditions might pay close to $1.0 million annually in insurance fees alone for incomplete coverage (full performance coverage is not provided). This is a large chunk of the profits no matter how you look at it, so a better alternative is needed.

The higher premiums in most cases are due to the solar industry's turbulent childhood; with its maturing technologies, imperfect business models and evolving applications—most of which are not fully established and standardized.

On top of that, most insurance companies lack expertise and investment strategies as needed to manage actuarial capital and the related risks in the solar industry. So the combination of all these factors drives prices unreasonably high. At least for now...

The Challenges

The challenges of this captive enterprise, therefore, are numerous and serious, as follows:

a. The captive may lack the actuarial expertise needed to assess risks, especially for the uncertainties associated with innovative technologies, their financial structures, conditions and issues.

b. Setting up a captive includes, among other things, transaction costs (feasibility study costs, organizational costs, actuarial fees, business plan costs, permitting and PPA costs, management fees, legal fees, audit fees, and taxes). These costs could be staggering—in the millions of dollars for significant-size projects.

c. Costs to establish a captive range from about $50,000-125,000 or more, depending on the captive's com-

plexity. This means that developers would need to determine the minimum project risk (and optimum operating conditions) that would make a captive worthwhile.

d. Determining where to establish the captive is tricky too, because not all states have regulations conducive to establishing such a venture. Developers must research state and local code to determine possible locations. Vermont is the most common state for captive domiciles, and foreign countries may also be used.

e. A major claim event or series of claims could be costly, so the possibility of such an event must be entered into the equation to make a proper decision.

The View from the Top

The insurance executives' view of the solar industry in general is somewhat limited for a number of reasons, some of which we discussed already. Their view of the solar business in general is as follows:

1. Manufacturers cannot ensure the long-term efficiency and reliability of their product.

2. Developers do not know exactly what coverage they need.

3. Broker's understanding of the solar technology ensures proper coverage.

4. The solar PV market is a maturing industry, but it is not yet mature.

5. Lack of established standardization and regulations is of great concern.

6. The solar PV industry has excellent fundamentals (e.g., strong product demand, declining input costs), but there are still a number of uncertainties and risks.

The View from the Bottom

On the other side of the equation, the opinion of the solar industry about the insurers is also somewhat skewed, as follows:

1. Insurance policies are not affordably priced.

2. Insurance companies sometimes lack the background knowledge of solar PV technologies.

3. Insurance premiums could go down if the insurance industry had better data and understanding about system operation and historical data.

4. Insurance brokers are considered the 800-pound gorilla in the room.

5. If brokers aren't educated on the technologies and risks, then the underwriters won't be either.

6. Some brokers pretend they understand solar technologies and place policies that do not fully cover what needs to be covered.

For example, in a famous case, one insurer asked about the use of molten salt in the PV system, which is relevant for solar CSP, but not for PV, thus revealing the severe lack of understanding of the business in this particular case.

The Negotiations

Solar project insurance negotiations usually go along the lines of the general insurance business, as follows:

1. General liability—covers for death or injury to persons or damage to property owned by third parties (not the policyholder)

2. Property risk insurance covers damage to or loss of policyholder's property, such as theft, natural disasters, transit of goods etc.

3. Additional policies, such as environmental risk insurance, business interruption, contractor bonding, etc.

4. We will add here performance insurance. The long-term performance of the equipment is a major issue we are concerned with during 30 years of non-stop operation. We must have some assurance (and insurance) that whatever happens to or with our investment (power generation) is protected against any unforeseen events—including and above the manufacturers' warranties.

Summary

Project performance (and any other type of) insurance might be the solution to successfully using any type of PV modules and products, including those of unknown quality—as is the case quite often now.

The European and Japanese solar markets are more mature than the U.S. solar market, with most of the growth in PV capacity in Europe has occurred in Germany, which was the world leader in cumulative installed capacity in 2010-2011. Spain and Japan also have robust PV markets.

The maturity of the European PV market gives European insurance companies more experience underwriting renewable energy generation systems than the U.S. market. Because of Europe's greater experience with solar PV installations, some U.S. insurance companies use loss data from Europe to project probabilities of future losses and risk in the United States.

Provided that the insurance companies are well aware of the risks and accept them (for a price, of course) most PV power plants with adequate performance insurance coverage will survive the test of time.

Without adequate performance insurance, however, many PV plants of type three mentioned above may experience serious problems in the deserts and other harsh climate areas during long-term exposure to the elements.

Solar Risk Insurance

As a confirmation of the positive developments in the area of *performance insurance coverage*, and to free us from our worries and hypothesis about field failures, several companies are actively looking into it, and some are taking immediate actions as follows:

LDK Solar Risk Insurance Package

LDK Solar and Solarif introduced a new type of insurance package for PV systems in the summer of 2012. It is a full insurance package, including "all-risk insurance," with the related warranty and inherent defect insurance.

The all-risk insurance is for all components of PV systems (including BOS), while LDK Solar power and product warranties cover their PV modules.

LDK Solar's manufacturing process was audited by Solarif and the insurance is covered by German insurer HDI Gehrling. The insurance package consists of full coverage of all products sold on the European continent, including compensation in case of production loss during warranty exchange and transportation, and all other costs related to module replacements per warranty conditions.

This, to our best knowledge, makes LDK the very first PV company to introduce such innovative, complete, and much-needed insurance solution, which sets new standards for the PV insurance industry.

Nevertheless, we see a number of problems with this first attempt to cover the long-term performance of PV components, starting with the financial health of the participants.

Solar manufacturers have varying degrees of short- and long-term debt as well as cash levels, and these vary from day to day with the market fluctuations and according to companies' activities, so it is hard to get a good picture of the situation, let alone predict the future.

But at a quick glance of the financial results of 2011

we see that LDK Solar had (and still has) $1.2 billion long-term debt, and $2.2 billion short-term debt. This is a lot of money owed to banks, suppliers, governments, etc. Other Chinese solar companies, like Trina Solar and Yingli Green Energy show much better results. During the same period they had $383 million and $0 in long-term debt, and $343 million and $1.1 billion in short term debt, respectively.

So there is a big difference in the bottom line for sure. And although it is hard to predict what will happen, we don't see LDK as a healthy company, and things are not looking any better for them in the near future either. On top of that LDK is a Chinese company, that is dependent on its communist government whims, so if they decide to shut down LDK (as it happened to 50% of the Chinese solar manufacturers) nobody can stop them. So what will happen then to the full insurance package? We don't know what the small print says, so we have to wait and see.

Nevertheless, this is a good example and a good start in the right direction. This type of full insurance coverage, we believe, is what is needed badly now, and is a solution for securing investments in PV projects. It is the make-it-or-break-it for large-scale solar installations in the U.S. and Europe.

Not withstanding the high price of such insurance, we see it as the missing link that hindered development of solar projects thus far in the U.S. in particular. It is also absolutely the best (if not the only) way to ensure power plants' long-term profit. It is how business will be done in the near future, and for sure during the latter part of the 21st century. There is simply no other, or better, way!

In another case, Assurant, Inc. and GCube Insurance Services, Inc., both insurance industry veterans, have partnered and have created a new insurance for commercial-scale solar projects. The insurance package covers solar installations between 100 kW and 3.0 MW in size. In addition to the standard property and liability insurance, the new insurance package offers an unique warranty component at a project-specific level.

The new warranty concept addresses the concern that the manufacturers typically offer 25 years of insurance, usually handled by a company that has been in business for at least 4-5 years. The new package brings experience and capital to reassure the financiers that it can stand behind the warranty. Also, the project developer has the option of warranty management coverage as long as the project's property and liability coverage remains with the original insurer.

This new insurance instrument is a huge value-added, because it is really the only one with warranty management available in the market. The warranty management will be done through the manufacturers and the O&M providers, similar to the way auto insurance providers use mechanics and body shops.

NOTE: No question, this is the path of the future. And while we do not question the ability of these insurance companies to make money, we only wonder how much expertise they actually have in the solar power field, and if they have full understanding of the risks they are taking.

On the other hand, we wonder if the potential insured parties would be able to afford the insurance premiums (which won't be cheap, for sure) without breaking the bank.

No question, there is a large gap between the insurers and the insured right now, which again points to the immaturity of the solar industry. We do hope that with time the gap will be narrowed down to an acceptable level for the benefit of all parties involved.

Time will tell, but we clearly see the companies in the above described cases clearing a path into the future, which everyone will follow during the 21st century. The path is not going to be short, nor easy, but is one that provides most security and reliability to the solar power generation industry.

ReneSola 25-year Performance Insurance

As another confirmation of the need and feasibility of performance insurance, ReneSola, a China-based manufacturer of solar wafers and modules, signed a solar products performance insurance agreement with PowerGuard Specialty Insurance Services, who specializes in insurance for solar and other alternative energy companies and products.

The new coined agreement, PowerGuard, provides conditional insurance and warranty-related coverage for ReneSola's PV products for 25 years. This insurance will provide an edge for ReneSola to offer its products with high degree of confidence and to increase its market share to include customers with varying risk-management profiles.

This type of insurance addresses the customers needs for reliable long-term operation, and reduces the difficulties that are often encountered by solar project developers, installers and operators. It will also allow ReneSola to focus on their area of expertise, thus increasing the quality of their products.

PowerGuard is a good example of the things to come. The PowerClip warranty product has been particularly popular, with the likes of China Sunergy, Lightway Green New Energy, and SunEdison having all adopted the protective cover during 2012.

The Practical Solar Insurance Aspects

With the economic and technical fiascos of solar companies and projects of late, investors and customers alike are getting more and more suspicious and careful about putting money in solar companies and projects. The fact that the world's PV modules manufacturers have been (and still are) sitting on 50% surplus is one indicator of the issues at hand. The spontaneous failure of solar companies and projects of late has increased the level of uncertainty, which similar to what happened several times in the past, is threatening the very existence of the solar industry.

Things are getting so bad that customers and investors are asking PV modules installers to provide an insurance from reputable insurance companies. Several such companies are involved in the solar insurance game now.

These companies cover warranty claims even if the solar panel maker goes out of business. And this is becoming the accepted modus operandi, if not the only way that solar companies, even the large ones, can sell their products on the U.S. and E.U. markets.

Warranty Claims

Warranty claims resulting from manufacturing defects appear to be one of the biggest expenses facing PV module makers. There were recently a number of news stories of such claims eating up profits at solar companies. I.e. First Solar has received more than 5,000 warranty claims since 2008, mostly due to manufacturing defects, field failures, rejects, and other quality deficits. Over 5,000 unhappy customers. and that many projects to spend resources and money at.

Industry experts report that First Solar has paid around $150 million in warranty claims thus far, which have resulted from defects that cause the thin film PV modules to fail in hot desert climate. Additional $35 million have been allocated as a reserve for covering future failures.

While $150 million is drop in the bucket for a company that can get $4.5 billion from Uncle Sam, the failed modules cause chaos in the solar fields, resulting in lost revenue and embarrassment for the owners.

Did First Solar officials and their friends at DOE and the White House, know that the CdTe PV modules have not proven to be reliable for operation in hot desert climate? Did they hear the official statements that CdTe PV modules degrade and fail prematurely under extreme heat?

Just think, the CdTe PV modules have been in mass production only 4-5 years, with most of the larger installations in cloudy Europe. The large-scale desert installations of CdTe PV technology in the U.S. deserts started just couple of years back. Proven track record? Nope. None! But it appears that the "new normal" of only a couple of years lab testing is good enough for the DOE to issue billions of dollars in loans and loan guarantees for product that may, or may not, live up to the expectations.

There are also other similar reports of major field failures of PV modules made by other world-class manufacturers. Most of these, however, have been taken care of quickly and silently, thus not allowed to spread throughout the media. Such problems are expected to grow in the future, and get worse as the manufacturers down-scale, or go into bankruptcy under the uncertainty of the present day economic situation.

Most manufacturers do not use third-party insurance. The major reason for that is that most insurers don't have enough confidence in the PV products. They also lack sufficient cash reserves to cover larger claims, as expected in many cases in the near future.

So, in our opinion, the warranty claims will keep coming in ever increasing number, but the solutions will get fewer and far between. The imbalance will be too much to handle for some companies and projects, so we won't be surprised if some of them fail and go bankrupt.

Quality of the Manufacturers

What can we expect when buying from different quality manufacturers, while considering adding performance insurance to our large PV project? Let's see:

Poor Quality Manufacturers

Buying poor (or uncertain at best) quality Chinese PV modules made by government subsidized, hastily put together, flight-by-night operations, using cheap materials and unqualified labor was wide spread in the U.S. and Europe until recently. Not a wise move, and we are still to see the full range consequences in the near future.

This is the worst case scenario, where unpredictable quality of the PV products (modules and BOS components) will shock U.S. with low performance and prematurely failing modules and projects.

In such cases, the risks are enormous and extremely expensive to mitigate (if at all possible). And we dare say that there are many such cases, because during 2007-2011 most wanna-be solar installers and specialists purchased and installed the cheapest PV junk they could find.

Driven by greed and blinded by lack of expertise, they bought large quantity of PV modules, the only requirement for which, in addition to the lowest price, was that they look shiny enough. They then slapped these toys as hastily as they could on every roof they could find, Now, how will these modules perform? How long would they last? These questions were very seldom asked and are now becoming irrelevant, because most of the wanna-be installers are gone and never to be found.

So we have to wish best of luck to the PV installations owners, who were gullible enough to allow their roofs to be covered with untested Chinese junk made and installed by flight-by-night operators.

And we feel even more for the large-scale solar power fields owners who used the same untested Chinese modules. Many of them will be put through the stress test of their lives, together with the modules. We hope that, for their sake, we are wrong and the modules will perform efficiently and flawlessly for 30 years.

Medium Quality Manufacturers

In case of below-average or intermittent quality of the PV products (PV modules and BOS components) the risks are lower, but still unpredictable. So the risks still need to be evaluated and mitigated, and the problems corrected; be it through warranty, negotiations with the manufacturers or via insurance claims.

Since in most cases the manufacturers are of some reputation, they will agree to cooperate. This makes things much better, but some additional expense (lost power generation revenue. module replacement modules transport and installation, etc.) is expected to be paid by the customer.

Excellent Quality Manufacturers

The quality of the PV products (PV modules and BOS components) in this case is good to excellent, which is ensured via thorough understanding, and or direct inspections and tests, of the manufacturing process. Here some of the risks, inherent to PV products are still present, but they are monitored and controlled by the customer and a third party, with the full cooperation of the manufacturer.

In all cases some long-term performance insurance will save us a lot of effort and money in the long run. So, how much could the insurance industry help the suffering of the solar industry? This is yet an unknown (or rather still developing) factor, but we suspect that there will be some good examples, as well as some "quick buck" deals that will give another black eye to the solar industry and its insurance counterparts.

Nevertheless, the evidence of late points to the fact that solar power plants of the 21st century will be either self-insured, or insured by a third party.

One way or another, customers and investors are awaking to the fact that the impressive, big-name labels on the shiny PV modules and inverters do not ensure their long, trouble-free life (especially in the desert), and do not guarantee profits during the long and difficult trip. So, the insurance industry, in our opinion, will have a decisive, if not the last, word in the world's solar energy game in the 21st century.

Certification (Performance) Insurance

And speaking of insurance, here is a new, different, more elaborate and reliable way to test and certify PV modules. It is a brand new service offered by a few companies, who claim to thoroughly check and test the three key aspects of the modules' quality, namely: a) overall performance, b) individual cells' quality, and c) level of workmanship.

These factors basically do reflect the performance and reliability of PV modules, so the new tests would determine how good a PV module is, but also how a manufacturer is able to produce good PV modules on a large scale in mass production mode.

The tests are done via the conventional test methods, but a more thorough check and evaluation is also undertaken. And what is even more important here, and something that is simply not done in any enterprise thus far, is that 100% of the modules are tested in some way to avoid gaps in individual modules, and batch performance.

The results are then sorted and reported as follows:

Performance [Weight 34%]

Performance shows mainly the power output of a module, but power alone is not entirely representative of a module performance.

A module with higher efficiency will reduce the cost of the BOS (balance of system) by reducing the land use and the number of structure elements.

Under this category is evaluated the power output of each module, based on the result of a flash test at the standard testing conditions (STC) but also at low irradiance to evaluate the power output in less sunny day.

Also, the lot tested is evaluated as a whole or lot homogeneity as PV modules in the field will be grouped together to produce electricity and the weaker one will affect the power output of all the other PV modules.

Also evaluated under this category is the ability for the manufacturer to provide PV modules with positive tolerance on power, which the buyers appreciate.

Cells Quality [Weight 30%]

The performance is evaluated at the time of testing, but users of PV modules want to get a high power output from their modules for the longest time possible.

A solar cell containing cracks may perform correctly at the moment, but with transportation, mechanical stress, and climate constraints, cracks and other cell defects will spread in the cell with time and result in a cell that does not produce any more electricity.

Under this category, the quality of the cells themselves is evaluated, or more exactly their electroluminescence picture.

Workmanship [Weight 36%]

Under this category is grouped the quality related to the making of the PV modules.

Assessment includes the visual appearance of the PV modules but also the safety to the user and the packaging as well as the quality of the sealing, construction and other parameters.

The workmanship score indicates the quality of the work that has been performed to produce the PV modules.

Additional Performance Insurance Factors

The mark given to each panel is the result of a thorough and detailed testing, during which the following factors are checked and tested step by step:

Positive Tolerance [Weight 5%]

A higher score is given to manufacturers providing PV modules with a positive tolerance for their PV modules.

This seems to be easy, but the output will later be evaluated against this positive tolerance.

Output Against Nominal Value [Weight 12%]

The power output is determined by a flash test under STC (25°C, AM=1.5, 1000W/m^2).

To show the ability of the manufacturer to produce quality PV modules on a mass production scale, we take into account the average power of the lot, the minimum and the consistency (homogeneity in power) of the whole lot.

Efficiency [Weight 6%]

To save cost of the system and space, the PV modules need to provide the maximum of power in a smaller area.

A higher score is given to modules with a higher efficiency.

Efficiency at Low Light [Weight 6%]

Modules are expected to perform well in sunny weather but also during less sunny days.

The power output is therefore determined under low irradiance (25°C, AM=1.5, 400W/m^2) to evaluate its performance under these conditions.

Inefficient Area [Weight 10%]

Appearing as black area under EL test, these areas of the cells do not produce power and reduce the power output of the module.

Another risk is heating of these areas resulting in hotspot (burns on the modules)

I-V Curve Appearance [Weight 6%]

When natural sunlight is simulated through a flash test machine, the response from the module in terms of current and voltage is well defined.

Bumps and accident in that curve show some problems in the function of the solar cells or the module itself.

Cracks [Weight 10%]

Cracks in solar cells are a threat to the reliability of the PV modules with time. Cracks in cells are identified under electroluminescence test.

Pollution [Weight 5%]

Processing issues during solar cells manufacturing might result in less efficient area which in turn can results in hotspot problem or lower output of the cells.

These defects are identified under electroluminescence test.

Soldering Defects [Weight 5%]

Processing issues during solar cells manufacturing might result in less efficient area which in turn can results in hotspot problem or lower output of the cells.

These defects are identified under electroluminescence test.

Packing [Weight 5%]

If packing is not always considered as a major item by manufacturers, it crucial to protect the PV modules during long transportation and, of course, is user-friendly.

Marking [weight 3%]

Required by IEC standards and mandatory to enter

European or U.S. market, marking must include specific information and be legible.

Construction [Weight 3%]

Under this category are taken into account both the design of the PV, modules' construction and the quality of the assembly.

Dimensions [Weight 5%]

Installers are basing their structure and installation on the dimensions of the PV modules.

Dimensions such as length, width, skew, and compliance of mounting holes are measured.

Frame Assembly [Weight 5%]

Poor docking of the frame elements can result in sharp edges, putting the user at risk.
The presence of these sharp edges and quality of the work is evaluated.

Sealing [Weight 5%]

For the PV module to perform for more than 20 years, the encapsulation of the cells and the sealing must be waterproof to prevent moisture from entering and corrode the inner elements.

Cells Layout [Weight 3%]

Spacing between cells and between strings is important to avoid any risk of short circuit inside the modules.

A minimum distance between the electrical conductors and the frames must be respected to avoid electrical shock risks.

Stringing [Weight 2%]

To perform accurately, the cells must be correctly connected to each other. The conductors have to be well-soldered and properly laid to ensure good conductivity in time.

Component Appearance [Weight 3%]

As end users are more concerned with the visual appearance of the products they buy, cosmetic defects are taking a higher importance in the choice of the PV modules.

Components such as glass, frames, junction box, and cables are evaluated.

Components Usage and Function [Weight 2%]

When tested against IEC standards, the PV modules are a combination of different components.

Taken separately, some components might seem equivalent, however, the combination of all these components might not work properly. This is the reason why it is mandatory for the manufacturers to respect the use of the specified components.

The function of these components such as connecting function of connectors is also evaluated.

In conclusion, the test labs involved in this type of thorough checks and tests are looking for a set of product issues related to the overall performance and reliability, as follows:

Performance Estimates

One of the major aspects of the solar products and projects is their ability to deliver the expected power for the duration. We can only estimate what will happen during year number 20, allowing for an ample room of error that gets even larger by year number 30.

The maximum power determination is performed according to IEC 60904. Even though IEC 61215 requires the output power determination to be performed on class B sun simulators, AAA class equipment should be used to obtain the most accurate and reliable results.

The tests are performed in a controlled environment, to guarantee that the tests are performed in conditions as close as possible to the standard test conditions (STC). During this test we not only control the output power, but also check each electrical characteristic as well as the shape of the IV curve to identify any intermittent malfunction of some solar cells.

Individual Cells Quality

One guarantee that the modules will perform well over time is that the solar cells are free from defects such as cracks and pollution. Those defects are invisible to the naked eye.

The most efficient way to detect this type of defect is to use the principle of electroluminescence: In practice, the solar cells are transforming the light (photons) that they receive into electricity. The solar cells also have the reverse property.

When subject to a current, the semi conductors will emit light through the emission of photons.
The electroluminescence equipment is using this property to perform an x-ray-like picture of the module where the dark areas show the less efficient part of the cells.

Workmanship

As a lot of operations remain manual during the production, the quality of workmanship can vary considerably from one module to another.

The quality of workmanship will not only affect the appearance of the module, which has become a criterion of choice for the end users, but it can also affect the safety of people installing the products or the reliability of the products over time.

We perform a thorough inspection of the construction, focusing on the dimensions the quality of sealing, the components used and the packaging.

The final performance tests (flash tests) are done via solar simulation tests. IEC 60904-9 defines three categories of sun simulators—A, B and C (A being the best class) based on three different criteria:

Temporal Instability

To be accurate, the measure has to be performed with a stable irradiance (light sent to the module by the simulator) during the whole period of testing (the time to take the entire I-V curve).

The temporal instability refers to the difference between the maximum and the minimum irradiance in percentage. The lower the instability, the better.

Spatial Non-uniformity

Equally, the irradiance provided by the sun simulator shall be the same all over the testing area.

The spatial non-uniformity refers to the difference of irradiance between various points of the testing area. The lower the non-uniformity, the better.

Spectral Match

As the natural sunlight is composed of different wavelengths, to provide a good evaluation of the behavior of the module in the field, the sun simulator shall be able to recreate the composites of the natural light.

In nature, different wavelengths of light will participate in a certain proportion of the irradiance.

The spectral match is the ability of the sun simulator to provide irradiance similar to the natural light for given wavelength ranges or its deviation from the reference irradiance for different wavelengths.

Summary

In summary, lab tests done by qualified labs using thorough, sophisticated, 100% checks and testing of the product, using the best equipment and procedures available today, is a step forward in the battle for efficient and reliable product, which must withstand 30 years of extreme heat and humidity.

If all PV modules coming to the energy markets are tested this way, we will have to take back most of what has been said thus far about suspected poor quality of modules and PV installations, and the related future PV modules failures.

Unfortunately, this type of testing is:

a) Not done by 99.9% of the manufacturers

b) Although 100% thorough check and testing routine, as described above, would increase significantly the long-term reliability and durability of the PV modules, there is still a chance that many modules would fail with time, due to latent problems created during the manufacturing process—many of which are not noticeable at first glance.

This is simply because there are dozens (if not hundreds) of different materials and process steps with many combinations and permutations of different conditions, which affect the performance and quality of the modules. Not ALL of these can be checked and tested even with the most vigorous and thorough test methods available today. The key word here is, TODAY.

Today we simply do not have the technology, the know how, and even the will, needed to take a very close look at the inner workings of PV modules—especially during their actual under-load field operation, which is the most relevant part of their function. If we are able to do that, we would be able to see the actual performance issues, and even predict their long-term behavior and potential failure mechanisms.

This, however, is today! The way things are going today, this ain't gonna happen any time soon. But we are absolutely sure that it will be a routine operation later on in the 21st century, when engineers, equipped with special equipment, will be able to see **in real-time** exactly what is going on **inside** of each and every module operating in their power plants. This way, they would be able to correct any and all problems in a timely fashion and avoid expensive and embarrassing surprises.

This is a dream today, of course, so until then, we would at least hope that more modules are checked and tested as described above.

The Future of Performance Insurance

A report on the subject was issued by Bloomberg's new energy finance in August 2013, which estimated that the renewable energy industry could be spending three times as much on performance insurance by 2020. If and when fully implemented across the entire energy industry, such insurance would mitigate risks to projects and convince investors that the renewables are here to stay and fighting for a equal place in the energy markets.

The report looked at six of the world's leading markets for solar and wind—Australia, China, France,

Germany, the United Kingdom and the United States. Based on different factors and scenarios, Bloomberg estimates that insurance premium volumes in these markets will increase from $850 million today to $1.5-$2.8 billion by 2020. The likely drivers for this increased demand is the growing industry scale and growing interest in the sector from more risk-averse investor groups.

New global renewable power capacity by 2030 will grow to more than $2 trillion in total investment, of which 75% (900 GW) of capacity additions will be in the solar and wind sectors. Most of these developments are expected in the already mentioned major global markets, where the demand for risk management is growing as owners and developers of renewable energy projects are looking into new financing options. Of special interest are large groups of institutional investors such as pension funds and other large money managers.

Wind and solar projects are technologically complex, and are exposed to adverse weather effects through the duration. Physical damage to the projects' infrastructure, unplanned delays, and unavoidable downtimes are the norm, which can significantly reduce the returns on investment.

There are also construction and operational risks as well, and changing market conditions, with the government subsidies and incentives going away. The new risks are many, including balancing charges, curtailment due to grid constraints, counterparty risk, possible retroactive policy changes, and power price volatility.

Project owners are finding ways to manage these risks internally, but are also looking for third-party services to assist them in their choices as new insurance products are developed.

Convincing them of the advantages of renewable energy requires also a new and better way to assure them that all risks of wind and solar are accounted for all through the life of the projects. According to the new Bloomberg report, this is doable and is happening already:

"The analysis conducted for this report shows that the demand for risk management solutions will grow, partly because the renewable energy sector will simply get bigger, but also because of increasing uncertainty affecting power markets in general. As the renewables mature and become part of the mainstream energy industry, they will need to evolve from an innovative sector where risks are taken on the chin, to one where returns are predictable and there are fewer surprises" according to Bloomberg new energy finance, which issued the report:

"Insurance is not a silver bullet. But by mitigating the risk in the construction phase and improving the consistency and surety of revenues during operation, insurance can help improve the return on investment for renewable energy projects. This, in turn, would allow the sector to attract the scale of investment necessary to put the world's energy mix on a more sustainable footing," according to the Swiss Re Corporate Solutions, which commissioned the report.

In more practical terms, all the talk about performance insurance is directly related, and boils down to ensuring the quality of the final product by strict control of the down-stream materials, processes and labor during manufacturing. The first step in the ensuring quality performance in the field during 25-30 years of non-stop operation is making sure that the renewable energy products are of the highest quality possible.

The quality battle starts at the beginning of the manufacturing process with obtaining and maintaining the quality of all incoming process materials and components used in every production step. Most of these commodities come from third party suppliers that we call the supply chain, which is a critical part of ensuring the quality of the final product.

So let's take a look at the problems with the PV modules supply chain:

Supply Chain Quality and Costs

Volume, cost, and quality fluctuations of raw materials and consumables in the solar industry is a major subject that needs an entire book of its own to be fully explored. We chose to include the supply chain issues under the subject of performance insurance because they are of utmost importance to the final quality of the product.

Nevertheless, the issues are not easy to detect, and some will reveal themselves months and years after installation, so we need to know what we are looking for in the supply chain materials, if we are going to discuss and negotiate performance insurance.

The key materials, part of the solar industry's supply chain are polysilicon, metals, plastics (encapsulants), gasses, exotic materials, glass, etc. Here is a discussion on some of the key materials in the supply chain:

Polysilicon

Polysilicon is a key material that is needed to manufacture c-Si solar cells, and although it is an abundant material in nature, it has been, and still is, a bottleneck in the solar photovoltaic energy industry explosion. The high initial capital and technical requirements of polysilicon production plants means that only large size (over 1,000 tons per annum) production can be economical, effective and competitive. This also means that only large enterprises with government help (which is the case in Asia) can undertake the huge risks and compete in this area.

The gap between demand and supply has been and still is huge in Asia. The total demand in 2005 was 2,825 tons while the supply was only 130 tons. A number of new polysilicon production plants closed the gap somewhat, but PV has been growing about 30% per year lately, and since this growth is faster than anticipated, a temporary shortage in silicon feedstock occurred. With the projected slowdown of the PV industry during 2011-2013, the gap might be closed. In the midst of this, polysilicon prices dropped significantly from \$400/kg in the 2008 spot-market to \$30/kg in 2010.

The quality of the silicon feedstock material is of major concern. Just think how the 130 tons of silicon produced in 2005 has grown to over 30,000 tons today, with plans to reach 90,000 tons in the near future. Instead, however, the volume is going down due to lack of demand. All this is causing shockwaves in the industry, which must have some (most likely negative) effect on the product quality.

On top of that, some of the silicon production plants still use outdated Russian equipment and processes, while others are copying Western technology, so production is growing and prices are going down, but what about product quality? Do all production facilities have proper equipment, processes and qualified labor? Who controls the process and product quality? How do they do it?

This is the black box in the Asian PV industry, and we have no access to the details; we just have to assume that what we are buying is of good quality.

Metals

Huge quantities of silver, aluminum, copper, and other metals, as well as plastics and many chemicals are needed to produce millions upon millions of PV modules as demanded by the solar markets. Large amounts of silver metal are used for providing good ohmic contact between the inside of the cell and the outside circuitry of the PV modules and for reflective backing for mirrors in thermal solar plants.

According to the VM Group in London over 1,000 tons of silver were used for making PV modules in 2011 worldwide. This is over 1.0 million kilograms of silver, an amount projected to triple by 2016. Nearly 3,000 metric tons of silver will be used for making PV modules worldwide every year at that time.

If we add that much more silver metal for coating heliostat mirrors and use in the semiconductor and other industries, we end up with some very large numbers.

So the question here is, "How much silver will be left in the world in 10, 50 and 100 years from today if we use it at this pace?"

Silver is a precious metal, the price having gone sky-high lately from \$4.00/ounce several years ago to nearly \$50.00/oz. in 2011. As things are going, prices will continue to rise. What will that do to the price of PV modules?

Similarly, the price of copper and aluminum metals has sky rocketed lately, and although there are large deposits of these left on Earth, the increased prices will play a significant role in PV modules' use on the world's energy markets.

The quality of these metals is an issue that has no simple answers. The metals are used in different forms—sheet, soldering wire, paste, dust, etc.—and there are issues at every step of their manufacturing process. One cost-saving measure resulting in a contaminated batch of silver paste, for example, could make several thousand PV modules fail immediately, or within a year in the field.

Encapsulation Materials

A number of materials, mostly of organic nature, are used in the PV modules manufacturing process. Many of these materials were originally developed for application in laminated windscreens and laminated architectural glass.

Encapsulants play a key role in the development of photovoltaic modules. Current and future innovation in formulations will lead to modules with longer useful lives and increased energy conversion efficiency. These advances will result in reduced cost per watt for the module maker and end module user.

EVA is an established material for this purpose, but polyvinyl butyral (PVB) is gaining favor in certain segments of the photovoltaic market. PVB is typically provided to a module maker as a resin-based sheet that can be trimmed to fit a given application. While it has been in use for decades in laminated glass applications, recent technology developments have made it a material of choice for certain PV module designs, including many thin film technologies.

The development of formulas with strong edge stability and chemical compatibility provide module designers with a material that improves both manufacturing processes as well as long-term module durability. This, however, does not answer the question of long-term reliability, because no matter how good the newly developed compounds are, they have not had a chance to be thoroughly tested, thus present a serious performance risk.

On top of that, the quality of the materials encapsulants are made is paramount to their performance in the field. A small amount of contamination in a production batch, for example, could make a large number of modules fail during testing or after short time in field operation.

And, honestly speaking, there is no way to check, let alone enforce, the high quality of the materials the resins are made, because the manufacturers claim proprietary materials and processes, thus they would not allow anyone to witness the manufacturing process or the supply chain documentation.

The same is true for the other materials and components in the supply chain. So, there are no simple answers, and we need to find the best way to figure out what we are dealing with. This is done on case-by-case basis, and whatever results we get are entered in the overall performance formula.

Thin Film PV Modules

Thin film modules manufacturing is a fairly new industry that grew too fast before having a chance to prove its efficiency and reliability. And as a matter of fact, as a result, most of the solar company failures during the 2008-2012 boom-bust cycle were due to thin film companies jumping into the market too fast with inferior and unproven products.

In its present state, thin film modules require a number of rare and exotic raw materials, such as cadmium, tellurium, arsenic, indium gallium, selenium, etc. Some of these are already in limited supply and it won't be long before they are depleted altogether. And if so, then how and why do we qualify these as "renewable? These materials are getting depleted into oblivion, their prices will go up with time, according to the supply and demand ratios, and we must do something before we end up on the ugly side of town.

The quality of the thin films per se is less of an issue, due to the sophisticated deposition processes and the related quality control procedures. The problems arise from improper execution of some intermediate steps, such as substrate surface cleaning and preparation, deposition process abnormalities, and such.

This, however, is a complex subject, which we review in other books, see Reference 18 and 19, so it suffices to say that the product quality of the thin film PV modules is harder to measure and less of a concern than their overall stability and reliability in long-term operation in the deserts—which condition is related mostly to the natural behavior of materials and their specific operational characteristics.

In addition, some of the thin film materials are toxic, which adds an additional element of uncertainty and increases the risks associated with thin film modules failing under uncompromising climate conditions.

Long-term Field Tests

What are the consequences of poor quality? What happens if the product is not designed properly, contains poor quality materials, or if the labor quality is poor? Unexpected and unforeseen field failures are most likely to occur, the type and quantity of problems proportional to the design, materials, and labor quality issues during manufacturing. What happens to our profit margins in such cases?

While the results from laboratory tests (done at the manufacturers' and certification labs) are important, what happens under actual load conditions in the field is totally different. Very different.

The actual results depend on many factors, so keep in mind that:

1. The results from tests under the extreme heat in the Arizona desert sun or the high humidity in South Florida, for example, would be drastically different from those under the cloudy skies of Portland, ME, or Berlin, Germany.

2. In all cases, field failures and degradations increase exponentially as time goes by, especially when operating in extreme heat and humidity climates.

Thin film PV modules are exceptionally vulnerable to the effects of heat and moisture during long-term field operations, because their packaging (the PV modules' body) usually consists of two glass panes joined together with plastic adhesives. No matter how resistant to UV and IR radiation any plastic is, it is no match for the persistent blistering sunlight and suffocating humidity in some areas of the world.

Although most thin films used in thin film PV modules are fairly chemically inert and mechanically sturdy under ideal conditions, they are nothing like that when exposed to high temperature and humidity. Elevated temperature tends to increase the tension and stress in the thin films and their inter-layer boundaries.

In the deserts, for example, the entire thin film package within the PV modules goes through daily cycles of extreme heat during the day and extreme cold during the night. During each cycle the thin films expand (with heat) and contract (with cold). This creates internal stress in the thin films and even more so in their inter-layer boundaries. Day after day, cycle after cycle during 25-30 years exposure to the elements would cause some damage.

The plastic encapsulants that protect the thin film structure from the elements, are actually much more fragile and much easier affected by the heat-cold cycles and the UV radiation. Any plastic left unprotected in the desert will disintegrate within months, and the same thing happens to the encapsulants.

At that point, small cracks and develop in the plastic materials, which eventually allows moisture to penetrate into the module itself. And when it does, the thin film structure is highly vulnerable to corrosion and other chemical reactions which could destroy it and its ability to generate electric power.

The field tests in Table 7-22 show the average annual degradation of different PV modules from different manufacturers operating in moderate mid-west U.S. climate. Most of the results from c-Si PV modules are actually quite encouraging, but notice also that most of the manufacturers whose products show good results are reputable, well-established companies who have been in the solar business for a while now and have figured out how to make a high-quality product. In contrast, most new manufacturers have not had a chance to work out the process bugs and conduct long-term field tests to prove the reliability of their products.

Again, remember that these tests were done under moderate climate conditions. Now let's go to the desert…

Long-term Desert Field Tests

As a confirmation of the facts and issues discussed in the previous chapters, a research study published in the fall of 2010 (12) confirms the presence of major issues in PV modules operating under harsh desert conditions. The study describes the results from long-term scientific tests done with PV modules operating in an official desert test field for a number of years (ranging from 10-17 years).

NOTE: To our knowledge, this study is the largest-ever evaluation of the long-term performance of production-grade PV modules under desert conditions.

The study was done at one of the most prestigious PV test sites in the world—APS's STAR solar test facility in Phoenix, Arizona, where most world-class PV modules manufacturers send their

modules for long-term testing, so we would not be surprised if the tests include some famous names.

The work was supervised by one of the world's most reputable PV specialists, Dr. Govindasamy Tamizhmani (Mani) from the Arizona College of Technology and Innovation, and president of TUV Rheinland, Tempe, Arizona. Dr. Mani's team carefully and thoroughly visually inspected, tested electrically and IR measured each module in the nearly 1,900 PV modules batch.

The final results from the long-term tests in the Arizona desert are shown in Table 7-23. Amazingly, almost 100% of the nearly 1,900 PV modules tested in that study showed some sort of visual deterioration. Some were more impacted than others, but the overall conclusion was that a large percentage of PV modules exposed to constant sunlight and heat in the deserts deteriorate beyond the manufacturer's warranty within 10-17 years of operation.

Many of the tested modules show average 1.3-1.9% annual power degradation, which translates into 23-33% total power loss for the duration (some only 10 years). This, extrapolated for the extended time of use, is well above the manufacturer's warranty of maximum 20% degradation in 20 years.

Interestingly enough, significant EVA encapsulation discoloration and delamination was observed on many modules, even those that were exposed to the sun only 10 years. Solar cell discoloring (due to a number of

Table 7-22. Annual degradation of PV modules

Manufacturer	Module Type	Exposure (years)	Degradation Rate (% per year)
ARCO Solar	ASI 16-2300 (x-Si)	23	-0.4
ARCO Solar	M-75 (x-Si)	11	-0.4
[not given]	[not given] (a-Si)	4	-1.5
Eurosolare	M-SI 36 MS (poly-Si)	11	-0.4
AEG	PQ40 (poly-Si)	12	-5.0
BP Solar	BP555 (x-Si)	1	+0.2
Siemens Solar	SM50H (x-Si)	1	+0.2
Atersa	A60 (x-Si)	1	-0.8
Isofoton	I110 (x-Si)	1	-0.8
Kyocera	KC70 (poly-Si)	1	-0.2
Atersa	APX90 (poly-Si)	1	-0.3
Photowatt	PW750 (poly-Si)	1	-1.1
BP Solar	MSX64 (poly-Si)	1	0.0
Shell Solar	RSM70 (poly-Si)	1	-0.3
Würth Solar	WS11007 (CIS)	1	-2.9
USSC	SHR-17 (a-Si)	6	-1.0
Siemens Solar	M55 (x-Si)	10	-1.2
[not given]	[not given] (CdTe)	8	-1.3
Siemens Solar	M10 (x-Si)	5	-0.9
Siemens Solar	Pro 1 JF (x-Si)	5	-0.8
Solarex	MSX10 (poly-Si)	5	-0.7
Solarex	MSX20 (poly-Si)	5	-0.5

factors) was observed on most cells too. Since the oldest modules in this study were made in the mid-1990s, we must assume that encapsulation and cell manufacturing processes have improved some to reduce the defect ratio during the last 10-15 years.

Still, we have no proof of such progress, so it becomes another unknown that needs our attention when dealing with PV modules destined for desert applications.

In summary, testing revealed that browning in cell center was almost 100%, encapsulation issues followed as a distant second, followed by frame seal deterioration, hot spots, broken cells and glass, etc. Many of these defects are serious enough to cause power loss and eventually lead to total failure, be it due to optical interference, electrical resistance, overheating, mechanical disintegration, or any combination of these.

This is simply not supposed to happen, in such large numbers at such an important site. We must ask, "What caused the problems? Was it materials quality (silicon, metals, EVA, glass), the manufacturing process (diffusion, metallization, encapsulation), or some special combination of these that was primarily responsible for such a large number of defects and failures?"

In any case, this study confirms the unfortunate reality that PV modules of any type and size are prone to

rapid deterioration and failure under harsh desert conditions. Although we cannot predict future performance and overall condition of modules during years 20, 25 and 30, the logical assumption is that the deterioration processes will continue at the same rate, and even faster in some cases. Because of that, we must conclude that each module type and size must be very well designed and properly manufactured with high quality materials and proper processes to be given a chance to survive the desert elements.

NOTE: The reasons for the above described defects and the related explanations and justifications are too numerous to launch into at this point, but references and explanation to many of them can be found in the previous chapters.

Italy Field Test

Another set of long-term field tests, albeit with a reduced number of modules and under different climatic conditions, was conducted by the institute for energy, Ispra, Italy. The test field is located in northern Italy, so climate conditions are much different from those in the Arizona desert, causing the field inspection and test results to be somewhat different as well:

Table 7-24. Long-term field test in Italy

32%	1-5%
25%	10-20%
24%	5-10%
8%	20-30%
6%	30-50%
3%	75-100%
2%	50-75%

Summary

What can we learn from the above long-term test in a non-desert area?

- 50% of the modules show yellowing after 10 years, and 98% after 20 years of in-sun operation, with 78% showing excessive yellowing.

- 74% of the modules show delamination after 10 years, and 92% after 20 years.

- 76% of the modules show sealant infiltration and 22% have noticeable signs of hot spots.

- The average annual degradation of connected modules is ~1.0%, while that of modules left in open circuit mode was only 0.6%, showing the negative influence of current flow and additional temperature increases.

Table 7-23. Long-term testing in the Arizona desert.

Module	Module Count	Modules Affected
A—Mono-Si (17 years; glass/polymer)	384	
Browning in cell center	384	100.00%
Frame seal deterioration	384	100.00%
Hot spot (IR Scan)	4	1.0%
B—Mono-Si (12.3 years; glass/polymer)	1092	
Encapsulant delamination	2	0.2%
Browning in cell center	1092	100.0%
Hot spot (IR Scan)	2	0.6%
C—Poly-Se (10.7 years; glass/glass	171	
Broken cells	47	27.5%
Encapsulant delamination	55	32.2%
Hot spot (IR Scan)	26	15.2%
White material near edge cells	2	1.2%
White material browning	56	32.8%
D—Poly-Si (10.7 years; glass/polymer)	48	
Browning in cell center	37	77.1%
Hot spot (IR Scan)	4	8.3%
E—Mono-Si (10.7 years; glass/polymer)	50	
Bubbling substrate	33	66.0%
Browned substrate near Jbox	50	100.0%
F—Poly-Si (10.7 years; glass/polymer)	120	
Discolored cell patches	6	5.0%
Backsheet bubbling	1	0.8%
Browned spots on backsheet	2	1.7%
Metalization discoloration	22	18.3%
Frame seal deterioration	15	12.5%
Hot spot (IR Scan)	4	3.3%
Total Modules:	**1865**	

- Glass-glass modules also had a greater degradation, most likely due to excess temperature levels during operation even at this location.

- High level power losses (>20%) are attributed to series resistance increase, while moderate power losses (<20%) to optical properties degradation.

NOTE: These results are not as dramatic as some other field tests we've seen (probably due to the moderate climate and good construction—Arco c-Si modules), but are still significant and another confirmation of the fact that PV modules will perform as well as they are made.

Extrapolated to the finances of our 100 MWp power plant, the average power degradation and failures shown in the above long-term field tests represent a major income loss from year number 10 on. And the question remains, "Can we afford even moderate power and product losses like this?"

The field test results prove that c-Si technology, if properly made and used, can be a viable and reliable energy source and that some of the major and well-established manufacturers have achieved reliability.

Keep in mind, however, that most of the above tests (except one) have been conducted 10-12 years max), so the conclusions reflect only a fraction of the time, stress and abuse all PV modules will experience during 30 years of non-stop exposure to the sun and the elements. And it has been proven that extreme climate conditions have detrimental—and usually quickly accelerating—effects.

We need to always assume that power degradation after 10-15 years of non-stop operation will increase somewhat erratically and perhaps drastically, which might result in catastrophic developments in some cases.

So, we must know by now that the financial health of any solar installation largely depends on the quality of the products involved. Cheap products used to save money usually will result in mid-long-term failures.

Rremember, many of the Asian PV modules manufacturers are too new in the field that they do not have the necessary experience, let alone the background of successful installations, long-term field tests etc.

This means that those who buy their products will most likely be surprised when after 5-10 years of non-stop operation, the modules start failing one way or another.

This also means that we are volunteering to play the role of guinea pigs in the solar field lab. We wish the best of luck to those who voluntarily or involuntarily have assumed this position, and would like to warn those who are thinking about it to think twice…or thrice.

Thirty years' exposure to intense sunlight is a long time for a poorly made PV module to endure the torture it will be submitted to day after day. Inferior materials will fail, disintegrate, and otherwise stop functioning, which will bring the entire module and eventually the entire installation down.

And speaking about quality issues, we must emphasize that quality will be priority #1 in the design and implementation of solar power generation in the 21st century. So we need to start with thorough understanding all technical characteristics and the related issues of solar materials, processes, and products. Only by knowing exactly what we are talking about will we be able to make the right decisions.

External Impacts and Costs

All power generation has some external cost, which is a cost (or benefit) which results from an activity or transaction that affects a third (otherwise uninvolved) party who was not part of the activity, and did not choose to incur that cost or benefit.

The "external" costs of PV plants' setup and operation are defined by monetary quantification of the socio-economic and environmental effects and damage they inflict now (and in the future), to a local area, a nation, and the world, during their cradle-to-grave life cycle.

Although we think of solar as "green," "clean" and "safe" it is far from that in many cases. There are serious damages to the land and the surrounding environment in most cases. Sometimes real estate values and even human health and well-being are affected.

These effects and the related damages could be expressed in dollars per kWh generated, for lack of better way, and should account for all materials, procedures, and events from cradle to grave. Included in these calculations are environmental effects, human health, materials production, effects of use and disposal (materials, gasses, chemicals) on agriculture, noise, audio and visual pollution, ecosystem effects (acidification, CO_2 damage), and all other effects. Thusly obtained numbers could be used to provide a scientific basis for legislative and regulatory policies, energy taxes and incentives, and global warming policy adjustments.

ExternE Project

The "ExternE (13) project, addressing these issues in detail, was introduced and funded by the European commission to develop a methodology to calculate the external costs caused by energy consumption and production. This is another far-thinking program of the E.U. community, which, along with their RoHS program, makes them far superior in this area when compared to the almost vacuum of such considerations in the U.S. and other developed and developing countries.

The ExternE project defines costs as the monetary quantification of the socio-environmental damage, expressed in eurocents/kWh, with the possibility of providing a scientific basis for policy decisions and legislative proposals such as subsidizing cleaner technologies and energy taxes to internalize the external costs. It looks at all energy-production technologies using a methodology developed for this project that allows the various fuel cycles to be compared. An outline of the initial results for the PV fuel cycle, starting with a very small sample of PV systems, shows that the results are not consistent and require more work.

There has been pressure from the PV industry for the PV fuel cycle to be re-done using a larger sample of more representative systems, but this is still in the making. So, one of the earliest publications from this project by Baumann, et al. is still valid. In this article the author outlines the basic assumptions and requirements of the methodological framework for the quantification of external costs and compares the environmental effects of different energy technologies, including renewables and the conventional technologies of coal, oil, nuclear, and natural gas.

Basically, PV systems must be designed and manufactured with long-term environmental concerns and considerations in mind, which must include:

1. Manufacturing materials and procedures, including the production and use of MG and SG Si, thin-film metals and chemicals, glass panes, metals frames, gasses, chemicals, and other process supplies

2. Solar wafers and cells manufacturing processes

3. Module encapsulation and framing processes

4. Evaluation of direct and indirect processing energy (including transport, storage, etc.)

5. Gross energy requirements of input materials (supply chain and internally generated products and byproducts)

6. Allocation schemes used in the calculations

7. Separate thermal energy, electrical energy, and "material energy" calculations

8. End-of-life recycling and disposal calculations (including transport and storage)

There are a number of dislocated efforts in the above areas, but no uniform, standardized method

presently exists that is capable of capturing all environmental factors into one, all-encompassing methodology. Such a methodology is needed to account for the effects of the above concerns on the PV manufacturing processes and long-term use of the related PV products.

A key factor to be considered when evaluating solar modules is their energy use and overall impact on the environment:

Lifetime Energy Balance

Lifetime energy balance (LEB) is the energy used during the PV products manufacturing, transport, installation, and operation, compared with the power they generate during their useful lifetime. LEB is an important factor, which needs to be kept in mind when analyzing and calculating the energy benefits from a PV power plant. LEB basically tell us how much energy we save by using PV energy generating sources.

The solar cells and modules manufacturing process starts with melting and purifying sand in huge, dirty, dangerous, and energy-guzzling furnaces. The produced metallurgical grade (MG) silicon is crushed in huge mills and further purified in a complex network of chemical and electric equipment, again using enormous amounts of natural resources and energy. The product at this point is solar grade (SG) silicon of varying purity, the quality of which depends on the raw materials and process quality.

The SG silicon is crushed again and melted again in large furnaces at high temperatures for a very long time. Thus produced ingots of mono or poly silicon are sliced into thin wafers onto which the solar cells will be built. The wafers are cleaned, baked, fired several times, and coated several more times until finally a solar cell emerges at the end of the line. They are then sorted, lined up, and vacuum-bake sealed into the module frames, then transported to the location. The next time these PV modules are transported will be at the end of their life cycle, going to the crusher.

All this requires energy, materials, and resources. Fortunately, the production equipment and processes are very efficient these days, but even so, making a solar cell and module is an energy-consuming undertaking.

The LEB Equation

Consider this equation for lifetime life energy balance (LEB):

$$LEB = \frac{E_{prod} + E_{trans} + E_{inst} + E_{use} + E_{decom}}{E_{gen}}$$

Where:

E_{prod} = energy used during production of materials, wafers, cells, and modules

E_{trans} = energy used to transport materials, modules, and BoS to PV site

E_{inst} = energy used to assemble and install the PV power plant

E_{use} = energy used to operate the PV power plant

E_{recyc} = energy used to decommission, transport, and recycle the PV field

E_{gen} = energy generated during the life of the PV power plant

In all cases, Egen must be much higher than the sum of the other sources of energy used for the system to be an effective energy source.

The term "energy payback" describes this "energy in-energy out" ratio and is what we will have to consider when designing, pricing, and justifying a PV system. Or in other words, how long do we need to operate a PV system before we recover the energy used, and pollution generated, during its manufacture, transport, and operation before it is decommissioned?

There are energy payback estimates ranging from one to four years for different technologies; more specifically:

- 3-4 years for systems using current multi-crystalline silicon PV modules

- 2-3 years for current thin-film PV modules

These estimates, however, vary from product to product and from manufacturer to manufacturer. Cost of energy (crude oil in particular) also has a great effect on the estimates, so these numbers must be adjusted periodically. The ever changing socio-economic situation in different countries is another great factor and we expect that the present-day economic slow-down and worldwide financial difficulties will drastically reshape these and most other estimates as well.

Lifetime CO_2 Balance

Similarly, a system's lifetime CO_2 balance (LCB) is a factor that takes into consideration the CO_2 used during the manufacturing and use of PV components vs. the amount of CO_2 saved by using the PV components instead of coal- or oil-fired power generation.

The solar wafers, cells, and modules manufacturing processes generate significant amounts of CO_2 and other harmful gasses, which must be taken into consideration when talking about the advantages of PV technologies over the conventional energy sources.

The LCB Equation

Consider this equation for lifetime CO_2 balance (LCB):

$$LCB = \frac{C_{prod} + C_{trans} + C_{inst} + C_{use} + C_{decom}}{C_{save}}$$

Where:

C_{prod} = energy used during production of materials, wafers, cells, and modules

C_{trans} = energy used to transport materials, modules, and BoS to PV site

C_{inst} = energy used to assemble and install the PV power plant

C_{use} = energy used to operate the PV power plant

C_{recyc} = energy used to decommission, transport, and recycle the PV field

C_{save} = energy generated during the life of the PV power plant

In all cases, C_{save} must be much higher than the sum of the CO_2 generation sources for the system to be an effective energy source. Nevertheless, and regardless of the LCB ratio, the PV plant will receive carbon credits for the CO_2-free power generated during its lifetime.

Here again, we have seen estimates that the total quantity of CO_2 generated during the cradle-to-grave cycle of PV components is compensated within 2-4 years of CO_2-free PV power generation, by reducing CO_2 emissions as compared to conventional power generators.

In all cases, solar power generation is much less energy hungry and polluting than the conventional energy sources (fossils, nuclear, etc.). Due to the increased pollution new financial vehicles were developed to fight against it. One of these is the carbon tax.

Carbon Tax

A carbon tax is a new taxation imposed on carbon (CO_2 and such GHG gasses) generating facilities. It is usually determined by the carbon content in the fuels used in these facilities.

Carbon is a component in every hydrocarbon fuel (coal, petroleum, and natural gas), which upon burning generate and emit these harmful gasses (CO_2 mostly). CO_2 is a heat-trapping "greenhouse" gas (GHG), and scientists have proven its potential negative effects on the climate system upon release in the atmosphere.

Since GHG emissions are related to the carbon content of the respective fuels, a tax on these emissions can be levied by taxing the carbon content of fossil fuels at any point in the product cycle of the fuel.

Other, non-combustion energy sources, such as wind, sunlight, hydropower, and nuclear do not burn, and therefore do not emit CO_2. So, the carbon taxes offer a potentially cost-effective means of reducing GHG.

From an economic perspective, carbon taxes are a type of Pigovian tax. They help to address the problem of emitters of greenhouse gases, not facing the full (social) costs of their actions.

Carbon taxes are also regressive taxes, in that they disproportionately affect low-income groups, because they pay un-proportionally large portion of the tax. I.e., most U.S. utilities charge all their customers a surcharge to cover the expense for introducing new energy sources, such as solar and wind. The poor cannot afford solar, but are yet taxed for the fact that some rich person has installed solar on house roof and is benefitting from the subsidies and reduced power bills.

A number of countries have implemented carbon taxes related to carbon content of emitted gasses. The problem is that most GHG related taxes are levied on energy products and motor vehicles, rather than on CO_2 emissions directly.

Many countries and large users of carbon resources in electricity generation, such as the U.S., Russia and China, are resisting carbon taxation, so we see its future as a come-again, gone-again phenomena. It remains to be seen if carbon tax will survive, and if it does in what form.

Solar Investment and Financing

The 2008 financial crisis and the lingering economic recovery have significantly affected the development of renewable energy projects, and investors, developers, and consumers are still feeling repercussions. Federal stimulus funding through the American Recovery and Reinvestment Act of 2009 (ARRA) offered short-term relief, but ARRA programs are nearing their end. Renewable development in California will then rely on traditional financial markets and project finance strategies under uncertain economic times.

Consumer education, renewable technology advancement, and generous financial support have enabled market growth during these troubled economic times. However, when compared to other infrastructure dependent sectors, such as transportation, renewable energy development is still a young asset class.

Renewable development does not enjoy the same technological, financial, and marketplace advantages afforded to traditional infrastructure with more mature supply markets and support structures in place.

Key Financing Issues

Key financing issues facing renewable technologies and efforts to address those issues, include:

- Financing challenges, specifically funding gaps that occur during the research and development (R&D) and early commercial stages that can affect project development.

- The role of private and public investment in energy-related R&D, including "angel" and venture capital investors, universities investment in research, and the role of power purchase agreements and financing instruments, like debt and tax equity, in resolving barriers to renewable development.

- Efforts underway to address financing challenges for utility-scale renewable projects including supporting technology innovations and reducing significant capital requirements through tax incentives, accelerated depreciation, and loan and bond financing programs.

- Efforts underway to address financing challenges for distribution-scale renewable projects, including case studies to illustrate technologies and finance programs in use.

- Efforts to finance renewable development in neighboring states and internationally.

- Financing renewable energy—from research and development to project deployment—is dynamic and capital-intensive. Each stage of development requires significant resources, and financing gaps must be addressed for emerging technologies to move to commercial maturity in a timely manner.

Development of Renewable Technologies

Successful development of renewable technologies includes five stages:

- R&D generates ideas and tests intellectual property. If developed successfully, intellectual property can leverage needed funds further along the development continuum. Nevertheless, R&D is a high-risk stage for potential investors given high failure rates.

- Demonstration/proof-of-concept builds the company, designs and tests prototypes, and further develops intellectual property needed to demonstrate the feasibility of an idea or technology.

- Pilot facility moves the technology out of the laboratory to the field where data and results are quantified to improve the prototype and to provide technical information to potential investors. In this phase, companies also begin to market the technology.

- Early commercial enables a company to demonstrate the viability of its technology at scale and prove that manufacturing and power generation can be economically scaled.

- Commercial maturity is the widespread adoption of a technology, when it is commercially proven, sold, and distributed at scale.

The inherent uncertainties in R&D can make it difficult to obtain financing, and significant capital is required in the early commercial stage to address technology performance issues and regulatory risk. These two key financing gaps can affect the ultimate development of a renewable project as described as follow:

Financing Research and Development—Financing Gap 1

California is endowed with abundant natural resource assets. These assets lend themselves to renewable development but first require research and development, resource assessment, and use impacts. As such, California requires public and private investment in research and development that differs from the other states due to its variety of renewable resources.

A recent American enterprise institute report indicates that, despite a clear innovation imperative, neither public nor private sectors currently invests the resources required to accelerate clean energy innovation and drive down the cost of clean energy.

Private firms do not invest adequately in new technologies for various reasons, including the higher price of clean energy technologies, knowledge spillover risks from private investment in research, inherent technology and policy risks in energy markets, the scale and long time horizon of many clean energy projects, and a lack of widespread clean energy infrastructure.

R&D externalities and challenges can lead to financing gaps and less than socially optimal technology innovation. The International Energy Agency estimates that globally, solar and wind energy technologies face an annual R&D shortfall of between $2.68 billion and $6.28 billion. To a large extent, knowledge is a public good. In economic terms, it is non-excludable and non-ap-

propriable because it is difficult for owners to establish enforceable property rights or to dole out usage rights to particular individuals. Because almost anyone can access the knowledge developed in R&D and a private firm cannot monetize all the public benefits and spillovers of its R&D, private companies tend not to invest in the level of R&D that is most beneficial to society.

Patents help reduce this concern but generally offer limited protection for intellectual property rights. The underinvestment in R&D can be further exacerbated for clean energy technologies because the positive environmental attributes of these technologies, like greenhouse gas emission reductions, may not be adequately valued in the market.

Other R&D challenges increase risk due to the high variance of the distribution of expected returns, the specialized and sunk (and as such not transferable) nature of the asset, and intangibility. Uncertainty and intangibility make financing through capital markets difficult since investors typically want some certainty of return on their investment. Information asymmetry, where one party has better information than another, can exacerbate uncertainty since a technology developer is in a better position to assess the potential of a technology than investors, so investors will require bigger return to address this uncertainty.

These challenges—and given that startup markets are decentralized and involve multiple firms—contribute to a financing gap for R&D, particularly energy-related R&D. Although overall R&D investment in the United States has grown annually by 6%, investment in energy-related R&D is about $1 billion less than a decade ago. The private sector's share of energy R&D investment has also declined to 24% from nearly half in the 1980s and 1990s, with total private sector energy R&D less than the R&D budgets of a few large individual biotech companies.

Corporate R&D spending (reinvestment) can be a significant driver of new technology development.

However, according to the National Science Foundation, corporate R&D spending as a percentage of domestic sales in 2008 was 25% for communications, 15% for software, and only 0.3% for energy, which is spent primarily on technology improvements and not on new technology development. This underinvestment in the renewable energy sector affects the development of next generation, lower-cost technologies and illustrates the important role of the public sector in accelerating the demonstration of new clean technologies in the absence of private funding.

Apart from private and public sector investment

trends, venture capital investments continue to increase and are still on the same scale as private R&D investments by large companies. Venture capital firms' contribution to innovation is especially important since studies have found that, in general, venture capital investment is three to four times more effective than R&D at stimulating patenting.

The biggest private sector participants in R&D are "angel investors"—an individual or a network of individuals that provide capital to startups in exchange for ownership equity or convertible debt. Angel capital fills the gap between seed funding—usually provided by the startup members and friends and family—and venture capital, and typically ranges from hundreds of thousands of dollars to less than $2 million.

After declines of 26.2% in 2008 and 8.3% in 2009, total angel investments in the United States in 2010 increased 14% over 2009 to $20.1 billion. According to a study by the University of New Hampshire's center for venture research, the clean tech sector received about 8% (about $1.6 billion) of those investments. The study also reveals that angel investors have lessened their interest in the startup stage of technological development, with seed or startup capital decreasing in 2010 by 4% from 2009.

The financing gap for energy related R&D may also persist at the roof of concept stage as companies continue to require capital for applied research and pre-commercial growth and activities. The most active private sector participants in this stage are angel investors and venture capital (VC) firms. VC firms invest the financial capital of third party investors in enterprises that are too risky or too complex for the standard capital markets. Targeted investments are early stage and high potential startups that have already received seed investments and have a technology and idea beyond the initial R&D stage.

Venture capital investments in clean tech companies have increased, with $3.98 billion invested nationally in 2010. Investments in the first quarter of 2011 were $1.14 billion, a significant increase from the $743.3 million of venture capital invested during the first quarter of 2010, with California accounting for 56% of total investments.

California perennially tops the list of regions receiving venture capital. Unlike other regions of the United States, California is home to more than one venture hub—Silicon Valley in the north, San Diego in the south, and a burgeoning new corridor in Orange County. In addition, California-based venture backed firms and their investors have worked consistently with state policy makers to ensure that young, innovative startups and their technologies have the opportunity to grow and succeed within the state's larger business climate. These factors have led to nearly $200 billion in venture investment in California since 1970.

Historically, federal and state governments have played a pivotal role in funding research and demonstrating high-risk technologies through direct procurement. The federal government is the primary source of funding for basic research across all sectors, providing some 60% of funding; the second largest source of basic research funding comes from academic institutions. Universities conduct the majority of basic research in the United States (55% in 2008), with business and industry conducting less than 20%.

The state funds research primarily through the state and private universities. The University of California research system received more than $4.3 billion in total research funding in fiscal year 2009-2010, produced more patents than any university in the nation, and secured $8 in federal and private dollars for every $1 in research funding provided. In addition to directly funding energy research, the university system contributes to technology transfer and the overall development of the state's expertise in renewable generation technologies.

In addition to universities, the energy commission's public interest energy research (PIER) program funds public and private entity research and has a significant role in supporting renewable technologies. The PIER program has also seed funded incubators such as the Sacramento area regional technology alliance (SARTA) and the environmental business cluster. Fostering R&D through such organizations as SARTA, CleanTECH San Diego, CleanTechOC, Clean Tech Los Angeles, Silicon Valley Leadership Group, Greenwise Sacramento, and the Bay Area Council accelerates the growth of renewable energy technologies and provides economic benefits that accrue to local communities.

The state's innovation hub (iHub) initiative stimulates partnerships, economic development, and job creation around specific research clusters through state designated iHubs. The iHubs leverage assets such as research parks, technology incubators, universities, and federal laboratories to provide an innovation platform for startup companies, economic development organizations, business groups, and venture capitalists.

Financing Early Commercial Development—
Financing Gap 2

Another financing gap occurs at the early commercial stage of development. Early commercial can be defined as one of the first three to five deployments at a scale that generates revenue and within the size range consistent with a company's long-term rollout plan. In this stage, companies and technologies face the convergence of high capital needs and scarcity of capital. Significant capital is needed to finance projects to demonstrate the viability of a technology at scale, as well as to prove that the manufacturing and power generation can be economically scaled.

There is a significant difference in installed renewable capacity between the residential and commercial sectors for early commercial technologies that can be attributed to: 1) greater federal tax benefits and accelerated tax depreciation provided to commercial systems, 2) the larger commercial project size, and 3) the appropriate project finance structure. Small-scale renewable systems, often found on residential and small commercial properties, have limited financing options and must resort to using established financing tools such as equity loans and cash combined with applicable public programs. Other options include leases, small scale power purchase agreements, and on bill financing.

New financing opportunities, such as third party models, open up for community scale systems. Partnering with an investor such as project developers and other organizations can also take advantage of tax and depreciation benefits through various partnership structures and power purchase agreement models to reduce costs. Utility or large-scale renewable projects are most commonly financed by a combination of equity and debt. Financing options include corporate balance sheets, use of debt (loan guarantees), equity (federal section 1603 cash grants), 360 and asset depreciation.

The U.S. Partnership for renewable energy finance indicates where several emerging renewable technologies are currently or are anticipated to be at this early commercial juncture in the next three years. In particular, concentrating solar-power towers, advanced solar manufacturing, and energy storage will encounter financing gap 2. These technologies are seeking approval for U.S. Department of Energy loan guarantee program funding, which could be leveraged for additional private capital.

Funding for traditional renewable technologies such as solar PV, wind, and geothermal could also advance these technologies in the market.

Traditionally, private equity, debt, and tax equity markets have served as options to firms in the early commercial stage. However, since the financial crisis, these options are either impractical given economic conditions, depend on government incentives to function well, or do not provide sufficient returns for investors.

Finance options and structures have evolved in response to the patchwork of incentives and the preferred choice depends on several factors such as return and yield rates, presence of a tax investor, cash and financial position (balance sheet financing), exit strategies, and risk-adjusted mitigation measures. Financial innovations are increasingly reducing investment barriers such as high upfront costs, technology and performance risk, and low tax credit appetite. These mechanisms allow investors to extract maximum value from myriad local, state, and federal support programs.

Financing gap two poses a challenge for equity investors such as angel investors, venture capital firms, and other early stage investors accustomed to traditional technology companies' speedy and relatively low-cost paths to commercialization. Capital requirements for renewable energy projects can be tens to hundreds of millions of dollars, depending on size and technology, for a single project. This is beyond the capacity and appetite of the great majority of VC firms.

Renewable projects also rely heavily on project finance, which is not the traditional business model used by VC firms. Project financing relies on the complex management of project risks, mitigation strategies, legal and commercial structuring, significant debt financing, and coordination with a variety of stakeholders, including contractors, large industrial partners and potential customers.

Lastly, private equity firms, particularly VC firms, anticipate higher equity returns than those expected from renewable energy projects.

Bankability

Bankability, or the perceived ability to show financial stability and marketing ability to get a bank to finance a solar company or a project, is a new phenomena, which, in our opinion, is totally misunderstood and misused.

A typical financial structure for a any solar company or project, including large companies and large-scale projects (over a few MW) is the so-called "non-recourse project financing," and we have seen through the years that banks and other lenders often refuse to finance companies or projects for a number of reasons on the basis of this structure. So how could "bankability" change that?

More often than not the banks refuse financing because they don't understand or dislike certain technology, or the project, or one aspect of it. And sometimes they simply don't like the company, the management, and some parts of the information they are given. And there are no rules to follow on implementing or changing these sentiments.

This perception, which at times overflows into an established behavior, is what the myth of "bankability" is based on. It is supported and "cemented" by the perceived necessity of the manufacturers to show "bankability," and by doing this to get on the banks' "bankability" lists.

But, as anything perceived, such lists do not even exist—at least not officially so—and there are no strictly defined rules or processes for establishing "bankability." Furthermore, most of the reputable and experienced banks do not even want to work with such lists for good reason. Instead, most often they work on case-by-case, location-by-location and company-by-company bases.

So "bankability" is a term that we think should be sent where it came from—in some manufacturers' imagination—and be put back to rest, since it is not something that a company or a product can claim officially.

And, in our opinion, even if they somehow achieve such status, there is no way for them to keep and maintain it for a long time, due to ever-changing character of the solar industry and the related markets. For example, a large company with lots of money and a respectable pipeline of solar projects could claim "bankability" and no one would argue with that label. The banks, however, might have a different label and things could go either way.

Applied Materials, Solyndra and First Solar come to mind as examples of such rich and promising companies that could have been labeled "bankable" (we just made that term), but even they could not use that title indiscriminately, or maintain it forever.

Case in point, Applied Materials is one of the largest semiconductor manufacturers in the world. They had no problem getting financing for their jump into manufacturing production equipment for the thin film solar industry. That, however, did not last long, and their "bankability," at least as far as financing any solar projects is concerned now under serious question.

Solyndra might've been where the term "bankability" came from. Solyndra was a master in pushing their "bankability." With half a billion dollars of Obama money, they were an example of ultimate "bankability." What could be better than this? A never-ending flow of free money, there for the asking. Life couldn't be better for them, or could it?

Solyndra simply misunderstood their role, so instead of being the manufacturer, they fell in the role of a spender and misused whatever financial power and government sponsored "bankability" they had. They

got carried away in the spending spree and run themselves out of business due to unwise moves and actions. And until the last day, they still had the label of "bankability" attached to their name. And until the last day Obama and Dr. Chu believed in them, and banks were willing to lend them money…because of their "bankability," or connections…?

First Solar, as one of the most successful solar products manufacturers and power field developers in the world is another case of dubious "bankability." Actually several years ago they could've, and did, use the label of "bankable" company to describe their financial status.

Due to a number of reasons, however, their stock collapsed from over $300 in 2007 down to $14 in July, 2012. First Solar also down-scaled in June 2012 by shutting overseas plants and laying off 2,000 people. Nevertheless, at the same time they secured a multi-billion dollar loan guarantee from the U.S. government, so their "bankability" is ensured by U.S. tax payers money at least for now.

First Solar still has lots of money and a good pipeline of projects, but their "bankability"—without the generous government financial assistance—is under question for a number of reasons. And things will get only worse for them and the entire thin film PV industry from here on, so "bankability" is not what these companies should count in the long run. Efficient, durable and safe product is the key.

Solar Financing Today and Tomorrow

U.S. solar projects have historically been bankrolled by some combination of energy sector players, banks, and the federal government, but the landscape is rapidly changing. New business models are emerging with an emphasis on third-party financing. New investors, including institutional players, are entering. And new financing vehicles such as project bonds and other securities are being assembled to tap the broader capital markets. (19)

There is an ongoing evolution of U.S. solar financing—where the market is today, where it is heading, and what's behind this important transition, and namely:

- Maintaining U.S. solar deployment growth will require substantially more investment. Asset financing for U.S. photovoltaic (PV) projects has grown by a compound annual growth rate of 58% since 2004 and surged to a record $21.1 billion in 2011, fuelled by the one-year extension of the Department of Treasury cash grant program. But funding the next eight years of growth (2012-20) for U.S. PV deployment will require about $6.9 billion annually on average.

- Traditional players are taking a smaller role. Regulations, primarily in the E.U., are curtailing banks from providing long-term debt as easily as previously. In the U.S., the Department of Energy loan guarantee program's expiry has meant less direct federal government support.

- New models are emerging. Distributed generation is driving innovation and creating new models for solar deployment. Few homeowners can afford the upfront cost of a solar system, giving rise to third-party financing models, which allow them to 'go solar' with little or no money down. These models also give investors a diversified opportunity to back solar.

- New investors are taking interest. Institutional players such as insurance companies and pension funds seek stable, long-lived assets to match long-term liabilities; some utilities may seek solar portfolios to offset revenue loss from distributed generation. On the development side, infrastructure funds could achieve targeted returns by bringing these projects to fruition.

- New vehicles are taking shape. Such structures aim to make solar project investments more liquid by allowing developers to tap the capital markets. Options include project bonds, solar real estate investment trusts (S-REITs), public solar ownership funds (yieldcos), and others.

- The cost of capital will fall. Solar equipment prices have dropped by more than half since the start of 2011, but financing costs matter too. New financing vehicles and new investors across the solar project lifecycle—development, construction, commissioning, and then long-term operation of assets—will cause the costs of equity, debt, and even tax equity to migrate down.

- This is happening now. Institutional investors have bought solar bonds; publicly listed renewable asset funds exist; solar portfolios are poised for securitization; and pension funds have shown willingness to buy and own renewable assets.

- Policy could accelerate change. Surveyed investors seek stronger SREC programs, new standards, more flexible tax credits, and sanctioned high-liquidity vehicles such as S-REITs.

U.S. Solar Financing

U.S. commercial and utilities solar power plants are poised to attract over $20 billion of investment by 2016. Insiders report that the utility scale solar power market in the U.S. will attract $20.5 billion of investment by 2016. The report claims that solar power is "emerging from the shadow of conventional energy in the U.S."

In the past, confidence in the U.S. utility scale solar market has been demonstrated by major investments in projects by large investors as Warren Buffet's mid-American renewables. Other large institutional investors like MetLife Insurance and Citi have also expressed interest and have supported large-scale solar power plants development.

The market has been given another vote of confidence, in the form of a report showing that solar is taking a major slice of new energy capacity in the U.S. market, with that share set to grow. Frost & Sullivan released its "Analysis of the U.S. Utility Scale Solar Power Market" report in 2013, disclosing that utility scale solar attracted $1.91 billion of investment in 2011, and is expected to grow to $20.5 billion by 2016. While this is possible, it is not very likely for a number of reasons, some of which we review in this text.

Utility scale solar continues to be dominated by photovoltaics, in the data analyzed in the report, however Frost & Sullivan notes that CSP development share is increasing. This strong outlook and solid investment performance to date are in part due to renewable portfolio standards (RPS) in certain states, including California.

A press release in 2013 announced that the higher adoption rates for photovoltaics promoted by the RPS requirements have not led to a big increase in investment figures. So, the solar investment has not gone up much recently, although the average selling price of solar PV modules continues to decline.

Analysts also note that restrictions to project financing could result in the near term, due to uncertainty that cash grants for solar development may not be extended much longer. To fund these projects, banks and investors must be confident that a power plant will operate long enough to return their investment, so in all cases well-established project developers using proven technologies will have an advantage in obtaining financing before their smaller competitors.

This is only part of the picture, though. There are other critical parties and factors involved, such as the regulators, the utilities, the technologies, and the global investment community. They all have an equal say so in the future of the different energy sources.

The U.S. utilities, for example, are increasingly concerned with the variability of wind and solar power. They did not see it coming until recently, although they had plenty of warning, but after finding out that it is continuously and permanently affecting their bottom line, they are now fighting against solar and wind proliferation. Where this battle will lead is uncertain at this point, but one thing for sure is that the utilities will win, as they always do.

Nevertheless, a report issued in the summer of 2013 by a major financial institution claims that the utility scale solar power market in the U.S. will attract over $20.0 billion worth of investments by 2016. The conclusion is that solar power is emerging from the shadow of conventional energy in the U.S. and will walk and run on its own pretty soon. Let's hope they are right…

Case Study: Macho Springs

NOTE: The following is a case of extremes, which might be either too extravagant to repeat, or might be the new way of doing business. It all depends on many factors, and since we are in the beginning of the 21st century solar game we just have to take it all in stride and learn as we go.

In the summer of 2013, a planned solar power plant; the 50-megawatt Macho Springs solar plant in New Mexico obtained a 25-year PPA from El Paso Electric Power. And with that, the New Mexico's largest solar power plant will be built on 500 acres of state trust land in Luna County, NM.

So far so good, another solar project in the desert… but this one comes with a twist. The Macho Springs project's PPA price is two-three times lower than the normal. That is not a small difference, which puts the profitability and the success of the entire project under question.

We usually do not hear officially about PPA prices of different projects, but keeping track of the industry for a long time we know from reliable sources that the PPA contracts are usually 10-15 cents per kWh of AC power sent into the grid for the duration of the contract. In most cases this price, everything considered, is just enough for the solar plants to show profit after 10-15 years of operation.

In this case, the PPA price was disclosed by mandate and was set at $57.90 per MWh AC. This is 5.79 cents per kWh, which is the lowest PPA price ever for any solar power plant that we know of. It is less than half of the normal PPA price in the U.S. (which is much lower than other countries) and which is very close to the price of electricity generated by a coal- and gas-fired power plants in the U.S.

The good news here is that the project is eligible for New Mexico's state production tax credit (PTC), which will add about 2.5 cents per kWh to the plant revenue. We estimate from the original source that this incentive averages to about 2.7 cents per kWh, but only for the first ten years.

So, a quick calculation shows:

The first 10 years of normal operation at the PPA price plus added incentives, or total of 8.49 cents per kWh (everything included), which is still lower than the low-end PPA out there, will bring about $10,152,000 annually.*

The next 20 years (normal operation without incentives) at a PPA of 5.79 cents per kWh will bring about $6,948,000 annually.

NOTE: This estimate uses a daily average of eight hours per day in-sun operation and 300 full sun-days per year, both of which are typical for the desert regions of the U.S. Southwest, considering long summer and short winter days.

INCOME

First 10 years revenue = $101,520,000 (at 8.49 cents per kWh)
Next 15 years revenue = $104,220,000 (at 5.79 cents per kWh)

a. 25 years income* = $205,740,000 (theoretical)
*This is the theoretical total income from selling freshly generated DC power—before any losses and conversion to AC are taken into consideration.

LOSSES

1% annual degradation = -$2,057,400*
10% DC-AC conversion = -$20,517,000†
Unscheduled O&M loss = -$5,000,000

b. 25 years' losses= -$27,574,400
*An average 1% annual efficiency degradation of the PV modules is expected as they get older, which combined with bad weather estimates, averages to about 15.5% total loss of power for the duration—if the plant is in full operation. Major problems and unscheduled shut downs of long duration could bring the revenues way down and through the entire calculation off by a large margin.
†This solar power plant generates about 50 MWp of DC power at noon in a full sunshine day. Thus generated power travels from the PV modules into wires, distribution boxes, more wires, and goes into an inverter to be converted into AC power. Thus converted AC power is sent into transformers and conditioning and control equipment to bring it to the grid high voltage, and synchronize it with the grid frequency. There are losses at each step of this travel path. The losses are greater with increased temperatures, due to increased resistance of the wires and the other components.

EXPENSES

Construction cost = -$175,000,000 ($3.5/Watt from
                                            previous projects)

O&M expense* = -$37,500,000 ($1.5 million annually from previous projects)

Decommissioning† = -$10,000,000

c. 25 years expense = -$202,500,000

*O&M expense includes daily supervision and labor, periodic maintenance, equipment repairs and replacement, insurance, loan repayment, PV modules recycling, plant decommissioning, and all other tasks and expenses related to the proper and efficient technical and financial operation of the solar plant for the duration.

†After 25-30 years operation the plant is old and tired and at that time the PV modules have to be disassembled, during which process they have to be handled and processed as hazardous waste, due to the presence of toxic cadmium heavy metal in them. All structures and equipment will be removed too, and everything will be loaded on tracks and trains and taken for disposal or recycling.

The land then has to be returned to its original condition by special decontamination and restoration procedures. Somebody has to pay for all this work, but at this point it is not clear who that is.

d. ROI after 25 years operation = -$34,334,400 (a-b-c)

NOTE: A major expense around year 10-15, when modules, wiring, and inverters, transformers, controllers, etc. electronics have to be replaced might add significant cost to the operation. A great number of PV modules are also expected to fail under the desert sun, which might bring the entire project solidly and even further in the red.

There might be some added revenue from carbon avoidance and other perks for solar, but these are hard to estimate and in any cases do not represent a large number, so they would not alter the final numbers much.

So, in best of cases, this means that after 30 years operation without any huge disasters, the plant will be in the red by nearly $84 million. It won't be able to operate for much longer either, due to aged equipment, so the operation must cease (if it had not already done so)…in a bankruptcy court, most likely.

There is no doubt that the new plant will revive the local economy (300 temporary and a dozen or more permanent jobs will be created), but the numbers do not indicate a financially strong solar project.

We also believe that this particular case showcases a number of additional problems:

1. CdTe PV modules are not designed, nor successfully tested to withstand the blistering desert sun for 25-30 years of non-stop operation, and there have been thousands of such modules failing and being replaced in the recent past only within months from installation. Because of that, we foresee large additional expense in replacing failed PV modules with time.

2. CdTe PV modules used in this project also contain compounds of the toxic, carcinogenic element cadmium which has not been proven safe for large-scale, long-term operation under desert conditions. If the cadmium misbehaves and escapes its shiny prison cell, we will be faced with a serious environmental disaster of unknown type and proportions, which would at the very least mean another large expense in cleaning and decontaminating the air, water table and the land mass.

3. The PPA with the NM PUC is for 25 years, so it is unclear what will happen after that. The plant might be able to continue operation under the present PPA conditions, or not…?

4. At the end of the 25 years, over 600,000 CdTe PV modules (and the related hardware) must be taken down, packed up as hazardous waste, loaded on trucks and transported to a recycling facility for recycling and disposal as hazardous waste.

This is another lengthy, labor intensive, and very expensive process, which begs the question, "Who is going to do all this work and who will pay for it?" What if the manufacturer and owner of the project is no longer available, or able, to do this work and pay for it?

In summary, undertaking such a borderline financial operation might mean a number of things, the most probable of which is that the owners do not plan to stick around until the end of this contract.

In that case, the owners will do one of the following:

a. Sell the plant soon to someone who somehow can make profit

b. Squeeze as much as they can during the first ten years, and then file for bankruptcy

c. Run the plant into the ground and as long as possible, and then abandon it

d. Complete the PPA terms and incur heavy losses—possibly $40-50 million all considered, in our estimate

There might be other complications and additional expenses during the 25 long years of this project too, which the thin profit margin just won't be able to support. So this project just might happen to be one of the best examples of how not to do solar projects in the U.S. deserts.

Not possible, you say? Oh, yes, possible, we say! We have seen a number of such half-cocked ventures in the solar and other areas of the energy industry in the

U.S. and abroad. Making a buck today is the ultimate, and some cases only goal of the capitalist enterprise. Tomorrow either never comes, or comes at the expense of others.

Case Study: Financing with Bonds

Utility scale solar power generation is a different and growing game. The utilities support it, and it is enjoying much more popularity and quicker development than the distributed solar and other renewable energy sources. Until recently the financing of these projects was done the conventional way, but this is to change now.

In April, 2013 Soitec (CPV equipment manufacturer and solar project developer) finalized a bond of about $85 million to be used to finance a portion of a 44 MWp CPV plant in South Africa. This is the first ever publicly-listed project development bond issued to finance a CPV solar power plant. It is also only the third bond ever issued to finance a solar installation anywhere in the world.

This bond will be listed on the bond market to allow institutional investors, such as pension fund or asset managers to consider investing in it, hoping for a stable return over time.

Solar projects are typically financed through a mix of debt and equity. Debt investors get their money back plus interest, and equity investors get a share of the project and make money through any profit that the project generates.

Equity investors in some countries can also take advantage of tax credits or other financial incentives offered by governments that support renewable energy development. For this deal, the company issued the bond to cover the debt portion of the project and partners have already been identified to finance the equity portion.

The 44 MWp Touwsrivier project will be located on South Africa's Western Cape, and site preparation has begun by fencing and ground preparation. Some modules and systems have already been shipped to the site, where Soitec will source the 1500 modules from its German and U.S. manufacturing centers. The installation work will be done by Group Five, the EPC partner on the project.

Soitec's solar bond has an 11% fixed return and reaches maturity in 2029. Moody's gave the Soitec bond a rating of Baa2.za. Baa2, however, is just above a C rating, with C being junk. A low rating but still considered investable, according to the specialists. It's also important to note that ratings differ from market to market, so comparing a rating designed for the Johannesburg stock market with one designed for the U.S. market isn't apples to apples.

High-yield bonds are inviting to money managers because of the potential returns they offer. But Soitec's 11% return and Baa2.za rating indicates that, while attractive, it definitely comes with some risk. With interest rates so low, money managers would be very interested in a bond offering an 11% return, after considering the risks.

Some of the risks are that Soitec's CPV technology has never been used in a project as big as this, the company could always go out of business, or the equipment could fail. O&M costs could be greater than anticipated, or any number of other unforeseen issues could arise. This simply means that, with so many variables and uncertainties, investing in this bond could be called "speculative."

As the solar industry continues to mature and investors become more comfortable with solar power projects, expect to see greater use of solar bonds for project development in 2013 and beyond. This new financing mechanism couldn't have come soon enough, since the solar power plant market is the fastest growing market segment in the PV industry. In retrospective, the traditional project financing relies on just one or two banks, until now market growth has been limited.

In countries with an active bond market and a strong solar resource, solar project financing with bonds is a viable path. The U.S. and Europe are good candidates for this type of transaction, since financial instruments that bring more capital to the solar market are exactly what the industry needs.

With PV module prices at record lows, developers are actively seeking capital to execute new solar projects in regions all over the world. Issuing bonds like Soitec's to cover a portion of the project could be a good way to get more money into the sector, and financial institutions across the world are starting to take note.

For example, in the U.K., Foresight Group recently announced that it had issued a $93 million solar bond, which has been used to refinance its existing portfolio of solar assets located in Kent, Somerset and Wiltshire. This is the largest solar bond to date in the U.K. and is a further endorsement of the low-risk profile of operating solar power plants, according to Foresight Group. The company said it plans to deploy another $387 million into new large-scale ground-mounted solar projects in the U.K. over the next year.

Warren Buffet's mid-American energy holdings issued its first utility-scale solar project bond in March 2012 to help finance the 550 MW topaz solar farm in San Luis Obispo County, California. Mid-American energy holdings initially issued bonds worth $700 million, then upped them to $850 million once they proved popular. One month later the holding company announced plans to issue another bond because the first one was oversubscribed by $400 million. The bonds, which will reach maturity in September 2039, will yield a 5.75% return rate.

2013 Update: Solar Financing

Regardless of the problems in the global solar sector, there's have been a lot of good news in 2013. In the first quarter of 2013, for example, the U.S. installed over 720 MW of solar energy, which is over 48% of all new electric capacity in the country. And then by mid-2013 the U.S. exceeded the 10 GW mark for installed solar PV capacity, and yet solar is only 0.1% of the total U.S. power generation. So how do we move the solar industry forward?

Financing seems to be the answer—or is it? Most experts agree that state and federal subsidies and incentives have been largely responsible for the expansion of the U.S. solar market lately. Now that these are mostly gone, or at least questionable for the long run, new creative financing options are emerging. Some of these are leases, REITs, MLPs, and PACE programs, to name a few, and yet most of the estimated $100 trillion of capital in worldwide markets is still not available to fund renewable energy projects. This is mostly because the solar products are not liquid tradable, and as a consequence many of the conventional financing models haven't yet been used for solar.

How do we enable this access? One example is the national renewable energy lab (NREL) with their open solar performance and reliability clearinghouse (oSPARC), also SunShot-powered, that aims to build an open-source database of solar projects and to standardize documents and other solar project elements for a quick access, comparative studies and analysis. This will enable new investors to understand and evaluate the risks involved in the solar asset class, since this is a fairly new, untested, and unproven asset class. As such, it has to go through at least one complete life cycle, which is absolutely necessary for getting its vital signs and all other needed information. Without that, solar is facing excess skepticism and scrutiny, which is not unusual for a new product or service.

Other problems, such as lack of standards, lack of enough performance data, generally unpredictable systems etc. factors have been on people's radars ever since Solyndra, and other high visibility solar companies failures of the recent past. Uniform standards are usually one of the (many) keys to building confidence in

a product or service. Another NREL initiative, solar access to public capital (SAPC), has a goal of standardizing documents and best practices.

Solar delinquencies is a new area of concern, which occurs when owners cannot pay the bills of their solar installations. Although such delinquencies on residential and commercial solar projects are rare, the challenge is that there are not enough data to show convincing data for a typical 20-year residential solar lease cycle. This situation usually cannot be covered by insurance either, so it is a gap in the process that needs attention and solution.

In the end, financing for the renewables is coming slowly into place as each and every part of the puzzle is falling into place after significant time and effort. Unfortunately, there are still many pieces missing, or misplaced. Only when all pieces are in place, can consistent policies that promote investing and expansion of the industry be expected.

The puzzle of tracking data, assessing risks, creating and enforcing standards, and other tools that serve everyone, including customers, is complicated. It is necessary, doable, and the work to its completion is underway. With all this going on, and with so much left to do, only one (and very important) thing is clear—the financial world is getting interested in solar.

And it is not just the smaller community banks, which have been more involved in smaller solar projects. As the projects grow larger and larger, and the amounts of money increase, the puzzle gets more complete by the day, and as a result the financial industry as a whole will get seriously involved soon enough.

NOTE: Many subjects discussed above can be applied to the other renewable power sources. Because of that, we will not repeat them from here on, but advise the esteemed reader to keep this in mind and refer to the solar section above if and when needed to get more information, or to clarify a subject matter.

WIND POWER

Wind power is a significant electricity generator in a number of places in the U.S. and around the world. It has a number of undisputed advantages, but is also troublesome in some ways, as we will see below.

Wind Turbine Economy

Wind turbines and wind power plants come in many shapes and sizes, and are installed in different places, operating under different conditions. As such, there is no general guideline on their cost, so we would generalize that the total costs for installing a commercial-scale wind turbine vary significantly depending on the type and number of turbines used, cost of land and equipment financing, purchase agreement conditions, construction contracts, the location of the plant, O&M conditions, and a number of other, equally important factors.

Cost components also include a number of tasks and disciplines, such as wind resource assessment and site analysis expenses; construction expenses; permitting and interconnection studies; utility system upgrades, transformers, protection, and metering equipment; insurance; operations; warranty; maintenance and repairs; and legal and consultation fees. Taxes, subsidies, and incentives also impact heavily the project economics.

NOTE: We discuss all these subjects in full detail in the other chapters, so it suffices to say that there are a large number of technologically and logistically complex, difficult (and expensive to deal with) issues at each step of the cradle-to-grade lifetime of wind projects.

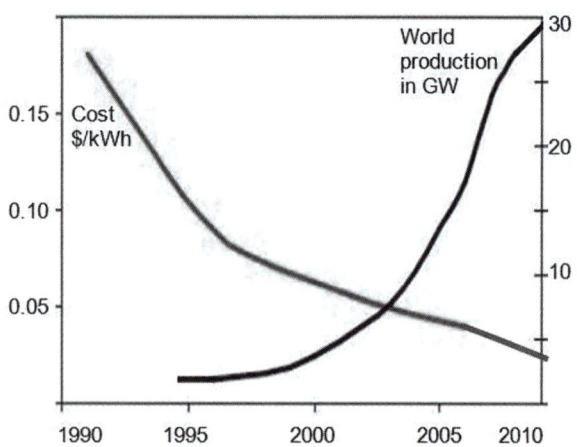

Figure 7-26. Wind turbines cost and production levels

The costs for a utility scale wind power plant in the past were quite high, but have been dropping steadily lately, as wind turbine production has been increasing. For example, in 2012 the cost of a large wind turbine was in the range of $1.6 and $2.2 million per MW of nameplate capacity. This includes all manufacturing, construction and installation costs, except for some special conditions and local ordinances, which might complicate the calculation and increase the final cost.

The majority of utility-scale wind power plants planned for installation today use wind turbines averaging 2.0 MW in size that cost roughly $3.5-$4.0 million installed. This is roughly $2.00/Wp installed, which is

in range of coal, gas, and nuclear power plants initial costs, and about 2-3 times cheaper than any type of solar installation.

Smaller wind farm fields or residential scale turbines vary in size and price, but are usually more expensive per kilowatt of energy produced. For example a 100 kW wind turbine cost roughly $5,000-$8,000 per kilowatt of installed capacity, Or this amounts to $5-8 per Wp installed. A much smaller, 10 kW wind turbine might cost $60,000-$80,000, depending on the type, size, and cost of installation.

And speaking of costs, what we see today is that wind and solar power are what they are, and not much improvement in efficiency and overall performance or price is foreseen at least for a decade or more. So, where does this leave these energy sources, in comparison to the conventional forms of power generation (the fossils)? This is the six million dollar question that the energy industry is tackling, but the complexity of which does not offer any easy answers.

As can be seen in Table 7-25, a wind turbine operates in the range of 22-39% capacity, which means that it is idle, or is underperforming, most of the time. At a 22%-35% capacity factor it would generate 3.3 to 5.5 GWh electricity annually. If the wind turbine operates 100% of the time, however, it would then generate over four times as much energy, which gets very close to the fossils generators performance and costs.

Table 7-25.
Power generation estimates for a 1.8 MW wind turbine

Wind speed	Capacity factor	MWh/year power gen.
6.0 m/s	22%-25%	3,320-3,500
6.5 m/s	27%-30%	3,920-4,190
7.0 m/s	31%-34%	4,500-4,880
7.5 m/s	35%-39%	5,150-5,540

The four-fold increase of idle time for the wind turbines, combined with the fact that in many cases and locations wind is most active at night—when electric power is not needed—means that the wind power is highly variable and unreliable power source. At least from the utilities' point of view.

What the utilities see in wind power plants is a power source that:

1.   Idles most of the time, which translates in waste of money for maintenance and additional operating costs

2. Generates most of the electricity at night, when it is not needed and yet requires attention and unnecessarily engages operating resources

3. Varies with wind availability and velocity, which makes the generated power level or sequence unpredictable, and which requires special attention and additional resource use (personnel and peaking power use)

4. Wind power cannot be relied upon during the most critical peak times during the day when most power is used

All this translates into money that could be better spent on other power generating options. Or can it? At 10 cents per kW sold on the retail market, our average 1.8 MW wind turbine generating 3.3 to 5.5 GWh annually would show $332,000-$554,000 income per year, depending on the actual times operating under the different wind speeds.

Of course, we also need to subtract all costs associated with the turbine initial cost, interest, taxes, land lease, and O&M expenses. Still, not bad for a 1.8 MW wind turbine that cost about $3.5-4.0 million to install. At this rate it would pay for itself in 10-12 years—unless some major accidents, repairs, or parts replacements (which are very expensive) double the cost at that time. That is, if utilities are willing to put up with its unpredictable and unreliable power delivery schedule, and they seem to be less and less willing to do that, as we see later on in this text.

Solar has a similar problem, in that it is inconsistent power generator, since it depends on the sun to generate power. No sun, no power, and that's bad for all involved.

And of course, coal, gas, nuclear, hydro, geo, and bio-fuels do not have this problem. They are available at all times and perform 100% of the time or as needed and when needed. Because of this abnormality alone, wind and solar power generation are under scrutiny by the utility companies. And as the capacity of wind and solar power generators increases, the utilities will be complaining even more of the adverse effects caused by these variable power generators.

A combined solar-wind power generation, however, makes a lot of practical sense, because solar matches the power needs during the day, and wind will provide the rest at night. Both, wind and solar, would benefit tremendously by the addition of energy storage, however, which will reduce or eliminate the variability, and provide power for night time use too.

As a matter of fact, we don't see any of these power sources growing as utilities favorites until such energy storage is available.

Wind Power Misinformation

There is still some intentional and unintentional misinformation floating around that is creating some confusion on the subject of wind power generation. Take for example, an U.S. utility announcing that it intends to spend $1.0 billion on an offshore wind farm, capable of supplying 200,000 households with electricity, and create 100 permanent jobs. What do they really mean by these numbers?

1. The quoted cost usually includes the wind turbine components and their installation, but that's it. It usually excludes the cost of providing the high power lines and substations that are needed to connect to the national grid. Since most wind farms are usually in remote locations, far from substations and power grid lines, the additional cost of running miles of wires underwater and building new substations could easily exceed the cost of an entire wind power project.

   NOTE: We don't hear these details very often, because the utilities have monopolized the power distribution business and—intentionally and unintentionally—are used to providing partial information in as they see fit format. Just think, if in the above example the utility announced that it would spend additional $200 million for new power lines and grid connection as needed to provide electricity for 200,000 homes.

   This immediately leads to the quick realization that this amounts to $1,000 per home and that somebody has to pay this amount back. Who would pay most depends on the demographics, but in many cases, the majority of the additional costs are usually paid by disadvantaged customers who can barely afford the monthly bills.

2. Saying that the wind farm will provide electricity for 200,000 homes does not specify how much electricity will be provided and for how long. To get a complete picture we must know if the houses that will be powered use 2, 5, or 10 kWh daily, weekly, or monthly. These numbers and designations make a big difference. And here again, the customers that use most power will benefit, vs. those that are on the other side of the economic balance sheet.

The poorest among us always get charged disproportionately more than the rest. Fair?

3. And finally, supplying 200,000 homes with electricity from the new wind farm is a misinformation in another way too. There is simply no way to hook up the generated power directly into the homes, as needed to supply exclusively for them…unless some rich and very determined soul spends enormous amounts of money for special modifications that would provide power to these particular 200,000 homes. And additional millions of dollars to provide power when the wind is not blowing.

This is simply impossible, mainly because such an undertaking would require massive and expensive energy storage, which is not possible with the present state of the art. No such feat could be accomplished now. Maybe sometime in the future…

For now, however, we need to remind the utilities that instead of saying that they would power 200,000 homes with the power generated by the wind farm, they must say that the wind farm will be providing electric power equivalent to powering 200,000 homes. There is a huge difference in these statements.

The utilities have a way of providing partial and misleading information, and presenting it in a rosy light. This partially due to the newness of the renewable energy sources, but partially it is intended to keep the customers and the investors happy, lest they panic by the high numbers or the consequences of these large undertakings, and lead a revolt against the utility. This is how it is going to be until and unless the entire industry is well standardized and regulated. For now the utilities make the rules and create the advertisement with misleading information.

Cost Re-evaluation

In this case the utility is planning to spend $1.0 billion, which means that the wind power plant is somewhere in the 400-500MW size (at $2.0/Wp installed). But probably the nameplate number is lower, because off-shore installations are much more expensive. So for the sake of argument, let's say that they are building a 360 MW power plant, consisting of 200 wind turbines, of 1.8 MW size each, which is lot of turbines to install on the ocean floor. But we now also have 100 trained professionals to worry about. These are the people who will run the facility for the next 30 or more years.

At an average salary of $50,000 this is about $5.0 million in salaries annually, which is actually $10.0-15.0 million when all benefits, taxes, etc, expenses are added every year.

Then there would be equipment and materials needed for the O&M operations, as well as payment on loans, more taxes, insurance, replacement of major components, and who knows what additional expenses for the duration.

It's complicated…so let's see how our 360 MWp off-shore wind power plant with 200 wind turbines of 1.8 MWp size fares during -30 years operation in the sea.

Day 1

It is early in the morning, the seas are relatively calm, wind is at steady three to five MPH ground speed, and the inauguration ceremony is underway. The governor of the state cuts the ribbon and turns the key of the new wind power plant on.

The giant windmills swirl lazily their long, powerful arms in the air, driven by the much higher wind speed 200 feet above the ocean surface. The power plant instantly starts injects 360 MW AC into the national power grid—not in the 200,000 homes as the utility company advertised.

A peaking* power plant somewhere in an adjacent state detects the power influx and slows down its turbines near idle. The 200 windmills are working at maximum capacity and at this rate the plant owner counts on a steady return. Later on that afternoon the wind speed slows down and the wind turbine blades stop. The peaking power plant fires its boilers quickly and goes back to maximum power generation. These on-and-off cycles repeat several times every day.

The customers do not see or feel the changes, and the national grid power is kept at a constant power level, except that the peaking power plant has wasted several tons of coal to keep it at a slower power generation capacity while the wind power plant was generating enough power. There is also wear and tear on the equipment to consider as the peakers cycle so often.

NOTE: A peaking power plant, or peaker, is usually a fossil-fired power plants that runs only during high power demand, like in a hot Arizona afternoon. Since peakers supply power only occasionally, and yet they run constantly, the power supplied by them is at a much higher price than the normal base load power provided by constantly running nuclear, hydro, or fossil power plants.

Year 1

Our 360 MWp wind power plant has been operating normally most of the time, with no exceptional issues or unresolved problems.

At an estimated 3,300 to 5,500 MWh annual electricity generation per turbine, the power plant's 200 turbines could generate 660-1,100 MWh power during the first year of operation. At 10 cents per kWh sold on the retail market, this is approximately $66-110 million gross income annually. A lot of money...if all goes well and without any major problems.

Subtracting all yearly expenses, we get (an estimate):

Loan interest on $1.0 billion	-$30 million
State and federal taxes	-5 million
Land lease, etc. expenses	-5 million
Labor expenses.	-10 million
O&M expenses	-5 million
Subsidies etc.	+5 million
Total yearly expense	**$50 million**
Total yearly income	$66-110 million
Average yearly income	$90 million

No major repairs and parts replacements were needed this year.

Averaging the estimated gross income to $90 million, we end up with $40 million net profit for the first year of operation. Not bad ! And yet, we will need 25 years of this performance for the plant to be free and clear.

Year 5

Our 360 MWp wind power plant, which operated normally during the first couple of years developed some technical problems, which forced shutting down several turbines during severe storms and as needed for scheduled maintenance and parts replacements. Each of these outages reduces the output significantly, and all of them put together represent a large chunk of money lost.

The initially estimated average gross income of $90 million is now $70 million, so we end up with only $20 million net profit during the fifth year of operation. Still not bad, but now it will take 40 years of this performance for the plant to be free and clear.

And again, no major repairs and parts replacements have been needed thus far.

Year 10

Here is where things start going wrong. Several turbines had to be shut down for major repairs, which not only reduced the total amount of generated power, but also required some major expenses for replacement of major parts—bent blades, worn out generators and failing gear boxes and controls.

And now our 360 MWp wind power plant with initially estimated average gross income to $90 million is now showing $50 million gross profit, so we end up with $0 net profit during the 10th year of operation. This is no good, but the power plant is still a feasible entity that generates electricity as always, so we will just have to keep our fingers crossed.

Year 20

After another 10 years of operation, the turbine shut-downs for repairs, storm damage, corrosion, major parts replacement, boating accidents, lawsuits, mishaps, and so forth, our wind power plant is now old and tired. Subsidies and other financial support mechanisms would most likely keep it afloat for another 10 years, but the profit-making scenario is all but an unfulfilled dream now. And could be much worse too, depending on the extent of damage done by the whims of the ocean weather in high seas.

Is this possible? Very much so. Since we don't have much experience with large-scale off-shore wind power plants, it remains to be seen how much of the above scenario could happen, where, when, and how. In our opinion, many off-shore wind power plants would experience similar destinies, with some fairing much worse than others.

The U.S. is behind the off-shore race and this may be a good thing, because this way we can learn from those who are ahead of us—mostly E.U. nations—and avoid the expensive mistakes they make. Tricky, eh?

Wind Power Intermittency

A number of arguments are sometimes made by the specialists to suggest that the intermittency and lack of load-following capability of wind power and other renewable technologies should not be regarded as a serious constraint on their application. These arguments are full of faults, which seriously affect the real economics of wind power in several areas of wind power generation.

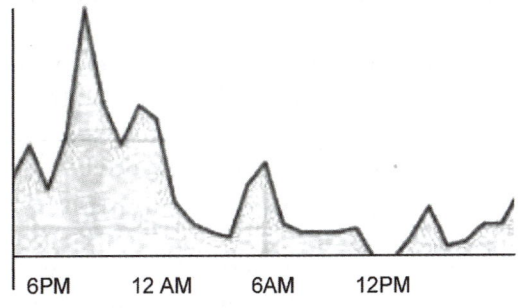

Figure 7-27. A 24-hour wind availability example.

It is obvious from Figure 7-27 that a windmill would be going very slowly, and idle significant part of the time. This is a major problem, which could be resolved only by:

a) Combining wind power with other power sources, such as gas or solar, and by
b) Adding energy storage means to the wind power plant, where excess power is stored for use during no-wind scenarios.

Power Storage

The biggest problem of wind and solar power generation is the variability of their energy sources—wind and sunlight. Windmills pretty much sit idle if there is no wind, or if the wind is not up to certain speed, which could take most of the day. The negative impact of intermittent generation can be offset if there is sufficient energy storage to assist the windmills in providing power 24/7.

In practice, this problem could be solved by:
1. Building large storage facilities adjacent to the wind farms, where excess power is stored for use during no-wind times. The energy could be stored in mechanical (flywheel) or electrical (batteries) form. Building these storage facilities is an expensive proposition, which also means that the wind farm must be several times larger than the demand, since it needs to not only supply enough power during peak hours, but also needs to generate excess power to be stored for later use.

2. Hydro plants with storage reservoirs including pumped storage is another solution. In this case, the water is pumped up in the reservoir during times of full wind, and then let down the hill into a water turbine to generate power during windless times.

3. Combining wind and solar, which compliment each other in a 24-hour power production cycle as needed to match the power grid requirements.

So, this means that additional storage would be very expensive in systems with large amounts of intermittent generation. The marginal value of storage is also high when there is a large difference between the marginal costs of generation for base load (e.g. nuclear plants) and peak generation (e.g. gas turbines). In some European countries investing in added energy storage was found practical and profitable, but only if and when it is possible and acceptable for at least 30 years.

The introduction of additional renewable generation capacity does not change the constraints that limit the amount of storage. So, storage will remain the weak point of the renewable power generators for the foreseeable future.

So combining wind power with other power sources, like hydro and solar is the best alternative for its expansion in the near future.

Alternative Energy Storage Options

There have been a number of alternatives to energy storage suggested and explored recently that all have elements that show promise, but none of them has been proven technically capable and cost-effective enough for large-scale implementation.

Some of the alternative energy storage methods are:

Power Pooling

Pooling of power is actually a type of energy storage that can be used on demand. Pooling advocates insist that while winds may be insufficient to generate enough power at one single wind farm, there is sufficient wind for substantial generation from a large, dispersed set of wind farms across the state or the country. While this is so, this also assumes that we could generate and transmit energy capacity equal to several times the level of demand served by wind power alone.

In other words, we need to build many more wind farms in different areas, the total capacity of which is much greater than the power demand. This way only part of the wind farm fleet needs to be operational to meet the total demand. The rest will idle until wind conditions allow normal operation, at which time other wind farms would shut down due to shifting winds. So the cycling will go day and night. Theoretically plausible, but practically impossible solution, due to high initial cost and excess O&M expenses.

Grid Storage

Storing large quantity of excess power in the power grid is an exciting possibility—and probably the only immediate solution—for the renewable power generators to achieve a broader recognition as base load providers. Then, and only then could they even start competing with the fossils.

The best chance for grid energy storage is the up and coming smart grid. The existing power grid was designed a century ago to have the generation sources respond on-demand to user needs. In contrast, the smart grid will be designed to vary usage demand with production availability from intermittent power sources such as wind and solar. The power loads will be controlled and switched on and off as needed by the utility during peak hours. The cost per kilowatt will also dynamically vary between peak and non-peak periods to encourage turning off non-essential high power loads.

Unfortunately grid storage is only a dream for now. And a very expensive dream it is, which will take many years to implement fully. Even if and when the technological issues are resolved, and the money is allocated, the smart grid will take decades to become available for daily use. At that time, wind and solar will become even more competitive, but for now we just have to figure a way to keep them alive.

So in the end, and at least for now, all these methods of energy storage are works in progress. Some of them seem practical enough, but their cost is very high and the technology needs more work, so we hope the new generations will figure out a way to reduce the cost, and find better ways to store energy

HYDRO POWER

Hydropower is one of the oldest, cheapest and most reliable means of power generation available now. It provides a major part of the U.S. base load and is important as ever. As a matter of fact, its importance is increasing, because it is the only unchanging (and unchallenged) component of the U.S. and global electric power networks.

The major, and maybe only problem now is that the U.S. and the world are maxed out in terms of hydropower availability, and not many additional hydroelectric plants can be build now.

In the early 1900s, hydropower was the dominant source of the country's electricity generation, as a result of a number of massive federal hydropower projects such as Hoover Dam in the Southwest and Grand Coulee Dam in Washington state.

In the 1940s, hydropower accounted for 42% of electricity production in the U.S. But by the latter part of the century, developers had tapped the most mountainous regions, mostly in the Northwest, whose steep inclines supply the strongest river flows and permit more cost-efficient projects.

Today there are 80,000 dams in the U.S., but only 2,400 have functioning hydropower plants, which provides about 10% of U.S. electricity generation. With fossil prices decreasing, new hydropower doesn't look economically viable. Instead of building new dams, which are expensive and take years to complete, developers

are adding generators to existing dams that have none and are expanding hydroelectric plants at others.

The construction expenses in all cases are very high; nearly twice those of wind, solar and coal, but the overall long-term expenses are much lower, since there are no fuel costs, and no expensive maintenance is needed.

Another advantage is the growing number of states with renewable energy mandates. Although most states don't consider existing hydroelectric plants part of the package, the new capacity is recognized and appreciated. Since 2005, utilities also get a tax credit for adding new power, though hydro gets half the benefit afforded solar, wind and other renewables.

As a matter of fact, hydropower is not officially recognized as renewable power in the U.S., so there is a fight now in Congress to change its status to that of renewable energy source.

Hydropower Costs

Hydropower is different from the rest of the power generators in that the power plants usually consist of massive structures that are property of governments, thus subject to different rules and benefitting from a number of privileges. Since a dam and its reservoir are so big, a number of special permits and authorizations are needed.

Although it is considered one of the most reliable and cheapest power sources, hydropower is limited by the number of dams that can be constructed, by the climate variations, and by changes in the dam reservoir and structure. In the end, hydropower generation depends on the river flow, which is function of the local and global climate variations. Because of that, we cannot rely on hydropower as an inexhaustible and 100% reliable source of energy.

Also, except for China and a few other countries, the number of hydropower installations are at a peak level. That fact combined with the great environmental devastation caused by damming rivers means that not many more large dams can be expected to be constructed in the future. This makes hydropower a finite and somewhat fragile energy resource.

Construction Costs

Large dam construction is a case of an extreme construction project of great dimensions. The size and duration of such a project is equivalent to building an entire city, and the costs are close to that too. For example, the construction of Hoover Dam took nearly five years and cost about $175 million in 1931 dollars, or close to

$2.0 billion in today's money. The actual dam structure cost $60 million, while the rest was used for the building related infrastructure. It took about 16,000 men and women, and total of 4.4 million yards of concrete to build the 730 feet tall dam, housing a powerhouse with 17 generators in 10 acres of floor space.

The 6.6 million ton, 1,250 feet wide structure created a large lake in the Arizona-Nevada desert and produces over four billion kWh annually from 17 generators, totaling 2.0 GWp power output at maximum load. The amount of generated power varies with the seasons and the height of the reservoir, and is sent for use in California, Nevada, and Arizona.

The dam has paid for itself by now, but the construction took the lives of nearly 100 workers, and inundated large desert area in the upstream, which will never be the same. The downstream ecology, as well as the wildlife and people living in it, were drastically affected as well.

In contrast, one of the largest dams in the world, the Three Gorges Dam in China cost nearly $40 billion. It, however, is much larger and much more sophisticated than the Hoover Dam, and most other dams in the world. Its effects on the up- and down-stream environment, however, are proportionally much more devastating.

Smaller dams are much easier to finance and construct. For example to build a small dam that needs no full-time personnel to operate, we need a number of steps and costs.

Table 7-26 shows an example of the steps and the minimum costs to build a small dam. There would be some significant additional costs too, such as a transmission line and connection to a power grid substation. At $1.0 million per mile, plus the cost of substation modification or upgrades, these additional costs could easily exceed the cost of the entire project.

Table 7-26. Small dam construction costs

Steps	$ Cost
Initial hydrology analysis:	20,000
Breach analysis:	20,000
Geotechnical analysis:	60,000
Permits, PPA, etc.:	150,000
Engineering design:	90,000
Construction management	150,000
Construction cost:	1,500,000
O&M annual cost:	75,000

Even if money were not a problem, building any

type and size of dam is getting much harder to do in the U.S. and Europe for reasons that include lack of suitable sites for dams and tightening environmental restrictions and conditions.

The production cost of hydropower generation is low compared to the other technologies, mostly because once built, it does not need fuel and has no excess O&M expenses.

Table 7-27. Cost of different technologies

Technology	Cost	
	Present $/kWh	Future $/kWh
Large hydro	3-5	3-5
Small hydro	3-10	3-8
Geothermal	12-20	8-15
Wind turbines	5-13	3-10
Biomass	5-15	3-12
Combined cycle	8-11	5-8
Tidal power	8-15	6-10
Wave energy	8-20	5-15
PAFC fuel cells	10-20	5-15
Thermal solar	12-18	4-8
PV solar	25-55	5-15
Geothermal	12-20	5-15

External Costs

There are additional, hidden costs when dealing with large dam structures and reservoirs. These are the external costs that are accumulated as a result of damages caused by building and operating power plants and dams. Although it is much less than other externalities (coal, for example), there is still a significant hidden cost that has to be considered and added—one way or another—to the cost of doing business of the hydropower generators.

Table 7-28 shows the estimated external costs of the different power generating technologies. Note that the external costs for hydro power vary, mostly depending on the areas affected by river damming and water storage construction, are one of the lowest.

Up- and down-stream communities are affected in different ways. The up-stream communities are usually totally wiped out by the flooding waters, while the down-stream communities are affected by reduced water flow and suffer slow death. In case of dam failure they get flooded, so life below a hydro dam is quite different and far from normal.

To the affected people, the externalities are as high with the deterioration of their lifestyle, increased stress,

Table 7-28. External costs of power generators

Technology	Cost $/kWh	
Hydro	0.50	
Coal	4.00	
Crude oil	3.20	
Natural gas	1.60	
Biomass	0.80	
Nuclear	0.40	(accidents excluded)
PV solar	0.30	
CSP solar	0.50	
Wind	0.15	

and even loss of life. How to put a dollar number on human suffering of one population, for the sake of ensuring the comforts of another, is one of the questions economists are struggling with.

Fortunately, there are no plans for any large hydro power projects in the U.S. for now and the near future. So our economists don't have to worry about finding answers. China and other countries, however, are looking at hydro power as a significant energy source in the future, so their economists will be busy answering the questions raised by large-scale hydro power construction for a long time to come.

China Hydro

Hydropower is a key energy resource in China, and China is one of the few countries that is planning a major expansion of its hydro resources in the near future. This is one of the ways the Chinese government hopes to meet its energy objectives. In 1950, China had only 23 large dams, not including small-scale, private dams used for irrigation. In 2013 there were over 85,000 dams, half the number of such dams in the entire world, which includes 22,000 dams higher than 50 feet. China also holds many records on hydropower generation, and has the greatest hydropower potential of any country on Earth. The estimated total capacity is approximately 380 GW. China has the largest overall dam reservoir capacity, and the dam with the highest ship lift.

But at what cost? The Three Gorges Dam on the Yangtze River operates the world's largest hydroelectric station, with an installed capacity equivalent to approximately fifteen large nuclear power plants. The Xiaowan dam on the Lancang-Mekong River, which was completed in 2010, at about 900 feet height is the world's highest arch dam.

The Three Gorges Dam, alone, displaced an estimated two million residents from thirteen cities, 140 towns, and 4,500 villages. An additional 50,000 people will be resettled during the hydropower dam development on the Nu-Salween River. Many more will be also displaced by development on the Lancang-Mekong River and other hydro projects.

This creates a number of problems, such as widespread community disarticulation, loss of livelihood, and resentment in the affected communities. Dams are also causing a lot of environmental problems by changing the flora and faun of the up- and down-stream areas. The change in natural water flow pattern disrupts the natural flood patterns necessary for the cultivation of rice. Dams also trap sediments rich in minerals and nutrients, and disturb the productivity of downstream floodplains and fisheries that rely on seasonal flows. The sediment also will shorten the life of the dams if not taken care of, which is a difficult undertaking. These changes create real economic and food security problems for the people living in downstream areas.

China Hydro Finance

There are two classifications of hydropower projects—the large and medium-sized (over 50MW), and the small-sized (below 50MW), built either by a) government funds, or b) state-owned enterprises (SOEs). The government funds are provided to private enterprises through state-owned assets supervision and management entities. The SOEs are large enterprises such as Huaneng Group, Datang Co., Huadian Power International Co. Ltd., Guodian Co. and Power Investment Co.

Recently, private companies and foreign investments are beginning to show intense interest in funding China's hydropower projects, due to their nature of stable returns, and low maintenance cost, and may benefit from numerous preferential governmental policies. Also, hydropower plants have alternate means of income such as the sale of certified emission reductions (CERs).

An investment into a large or medium-sized hydropower project would cost between $60 and 120 million. A number of active foreign investors in this sector include Hong Kong CLP Holdings (HKCLP) and the AES Corporation. HKCLP's core business is in Asia's power industry, where as AES Corporation, which holds a hydropower station in Hunan province, is a U.S.-based independent power producer that has been working in China's power industry since the 1990s.

Hydropower project permitting and construction in China is a very complicated and pricey process. The financing and investment procedures are also complicated, and could be divided into the following phases:

1. *Pre-investment verification* phase consists of a series of approvals and permits. This involves a lot of meetings, hands shaking, bribes, etc., etc. business in China type of transactions. They are nothing like what we think about business here in the West. After obtaining all the related approvals, if lucky and rich enough, an investor can legally submit its application of a hydropower project for project verification.

The following approvals are increasingly important:

- Review comments on environmental impact statement, to be approved by the ministry of environmental protection, which has the authority to stop any project lacking proper environmental impact statement.
- Seismic hazard assessment
- Cultural relics investigation of the project

2. *Investment verification phase* is obligatory pursuant to the decision of the state council on reforming the investment system that all projects constructed on major rivers and projects with the total installed capacity of 250 MW or more are subject to the approval of the national development and reform committee (NDRC). All other hydropower projects are a subject to approval by the local development and reform committee. All hydro projects valued at over $100 million are to be approved by the NDRC. Those below this investment threshold, not constructed on a major river, and are below 250 MW capacity, are subject to approval and verification by the local development and reform committees.

3. *Post-investment verification* phase includes several approvals that are additionally required for the hydropower station after the formal verification of the project is completed. Nothing in China is quick, easy or straightforward. An example is a permit on conversion of agricultural land into land for construction (if applicable). Pursuant to the PRC land administration law, if an agricultural land is proposed to be occupied for construction purpose, the examination and approval procedures regarding the conversion of agricultural land into land for construction purposes is required.

So China is on the way to significantly increasing its hydropower generating capacity. This will help with resolving some energy problems, but it also brings a number of serious issues related to environment integrity and human life protection. We will be watching closely...

GEOTHERMAL

Geothermal power generation is one of the oldest heating technologies, which has seen a new surge in the years of late. There is a good reason for that, since this is a viable renewable technology, but the progress of this type of energy won't be quick, cheap, or simple. There is a lot of work to do still on making sure that geothermal power is used properly and efficiently.

Geothermal Costs

Development of geothermal resources has been promoted at the U.S. federal level through RD&D investment policies. RD&D investments from the public sector are correlated to increased patent numbers, which is a good indication of private-sector investment in technology development. The public-sector funding for geothermal demonstration is critical, but has been variable. It is needed especially for larger electricity installations because they need extensive siting and permitting processes. The public-sector involvement can reduce risk of failure of the projects undertaken with its financing and technical support.

As Figure 7-28 suggests, geothermal power development was put on the backburner for the last 20 years, but now there is a new influx of federal money into it, so we expect great things in return in the near future.

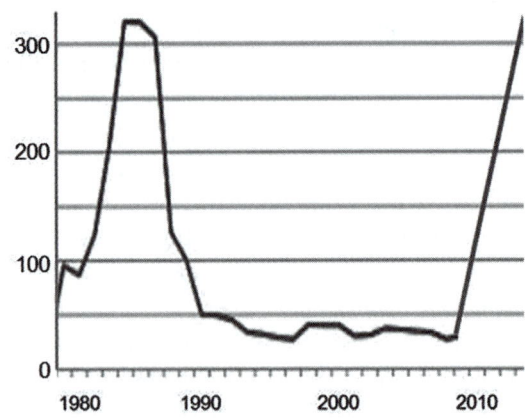

Figure 7-28. U.S. government funding of geothermal R&D (in $ millions)

Construction Cost

An economically competitive, large-scale, geothermal power plant can be constructed at a capital cost of $3,000-3,500 per kilowatt installed. The cost of a new geothermal power plant is usually higher than that of a comparable natural gas facility, but in the long run the two come to a similar bottom line.

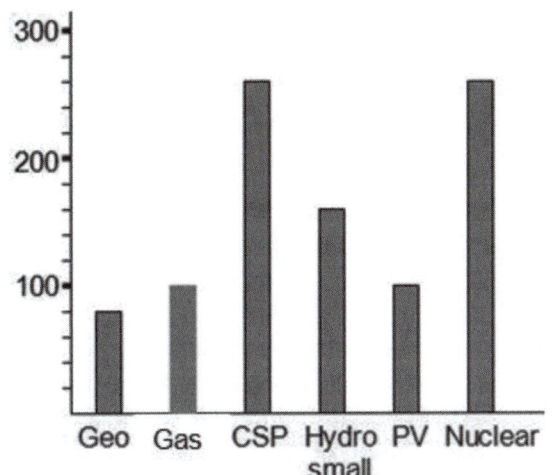

Figure 7-29. Construction costs of different technologies (in $/MWh)

This is because while natural gas construction costs account for only one third of the total price of the facility, the cost of the fuel over the life time of the facility represents two thirds of the cost. In contrast, the initial construction costs of a geothermal facility represent two thirds of the total costs, but there is no fuel cost to consider; only O&M costs for the lifetime of the facility.

The initial investment for a geothermal power plant is higher, because of the high expense of well digging and infrastructure required, but even then they are still economically comparable over a long-term operation.

Industry specialists estimate the levelized generation costs for a 50 MW geothermal binary plant at $92/MWh and $88/MWh for a 50 MW dual flash geothermal plant. Over the lifetime of the plant these costs can be competitive with a variety of technologies, including natural gas.

CEC estimates natural gas costs at $101/MWh for a 500 MW combined cycle power plant (but $586/MWh for a 100 MW simple cycle plant.) At the same time, the cost for new geothermal projects ranged from $60-80/MWh, including the production tax credit. The cost for individual geothermal projects, however, varies significantly depending on a series of factors, the most important of which is that the costs of power projects change over time with changes in political, social, and economic conditions.

Of critical importance here is the fact that the fossil fuels (natural gas included) get scarcer by the day, which raises their prices. In contrast, a properly chosen geothermal power source is consistent and the price of its "fuel" won't change with time, or socio-political conditions.

Geothermal projects, however, are site-specific, thus the cost to connect to the electric grid is critical, quite significant, so it varies from project to project. Also, it matters a lot if the project is the first in a particular area, which impacts both risks and costs. Since to fully explore a geothermal resource a developer is required to lease the rights to 2,000 acres or more, the land acquisition and leasing varies a lot, and usually adds to the initial cost.

Challenges to leasing and permitting vary from project to project; especially on federal lands. These factors include:

- Capacity of the resource
- Temperature of the resource
- Chemistry of the geothermal water
- Heat source depth and permeability
- Size of the power plant
- Geothermal power plant technology
- Federal and state environmental policies
- Federal, state and local incentives
- Local and global market opportunities
- Financing options and cost
- Time delays in exploration and construction

In all cases, a major impact on geothermal power cost is the local, regional, national, and global competition for commodities such as steel, cement, and construction equipment. Geothermal power is competing against other renewable and non-renewable power development, such as building construction, road and infrastructure improvements, and all other projects that use the same commodities and services. Until equipment and plant inventories rise to meet the increase in demand for these commodities and services, the costs will well above the inflation levels.

Small Home System

A small residential geothermal system is estimated to cost around $45,000 installed. This is a large investment as compared to solar installations, but the price is only a small piece of the entire project puzzle. Excavation of the ground loops and several hundred feet of pipe, are the major part of the cost. This is one time expense that never needs to redone, even if the other system components (pumps, etc.) will need replacing after 20-30 years.

Homeowners also get 30% income tax credit for the entire system cost, including parts and labor, or about $13,000 in our case. Also, subtracting the cost of a complete high-efficiency conventional heating and cooling system (if this is a new home construction), we end up with an actual out-of-pocket cost of just over $7,000 for the entire geothermal system.

The average savings from home and water heating, as well as fewer equipment repairs, could save $1,500 each year, plus an average annual increase of 4% for the duration (to account for steadily rising utility prices. Calculated over 20 years of life for the system, a homeowner could save over $40,000.

Geothermal Finance

Geothermal power was the government's favorite for a while in the 1980, but fell out of grace until recently. Now it is back on the priorities list with an influx of feds money for geothermal research and project support.

In addition, geothermal power benefits from a number of government programs as follows:

- The DOE's geothermal technologies program currently funds R&D and technical assistance for exploration and development. Cost-shared drilling for exploratory wells helps geothermal projects become economical and draw in developers.

- Since 2005 the federal government has offered a production tax credit (PTC) for geothermal electricity production. The PTC provides a significant subsidy—1.9¢/kWh for 10 years for geothermal plants that are placed in service before the expiration of the credit program.

- The federal government implements several grant and loan programs for which geothermal electric systems are eligible. Geothermal projects can receive tribal energy program grants and U.S. Department of Agriculture rural energy for America program (REAP) grants. Additionally, the federal government provides loan guarantees for renewable energy projects, including development of geothermal resources.

- Non-Tax Incentive ARRA Funding provided $338 million for geothermal research and demonstration, as well as funding for innovative exploration techniques. It is too early in the implementation of this ARRA funding to determine impacts of the policy.

- Validation of innovative exploration technologies EISA section 613 addresses the demonstration of innovative site characterization and drilling exploration technologies. The goal of this $100 million FOA, which closed in 2009, is to reduce the high

level of risk during early stages of geothermal project development by funding the validation of innovative exploration activities to locate undiscovered geothermal systems and increase the reliability of site characterization to prioritize target sites for energy production.

Some of the key areas of interest in further geothermal research are:

- Geothermal energy production from low-temperature resources, co-produced fluids from oil and gas wells, and geo-pressured resources. The goal of this $50 million FOA, which closed in 2009 is to demonstrate the technical and economic feasibility of geothermal energy production from these non-conventional geothermal resources.

- Geothermal data development, collection, and maintenance. EPA 2005 section 931(a)(2)(C) includes authorization for continued data submission to the national geothermal data system (NGDS) with the goal of developing, collecting, and maintaining data for all 50 states for the NGDS to make geothermal data available to the public and reduce the risk associated with initial stages of geothermal development. The $30 Million FOA closed in 2009.

- Enhanced geothermal systems (EGS) demonstration, $90 million funding is for the further scientific exploration of the technologies and strategies necessary for achieving the potential of EGS.

- EGS research and development analysis is a $80 million program with a goal of making EGS a major contributor to baseload generation.

- IRS clean energy renewable bonds are open to public entities willing to participate in clean renewable energy bonds (CREBs). These bonds were primarily used for solar projects, but the reason for a lack of geothermal projects is unknown. It is possible that there is a lack of knowledge of the program in the geothermal community.

- State tax incentives: Fifteen states offer one or more tax incentive(s) that can be applied to geothermal development.

- Non-tax-related state financial incentives: Sixteen states and the District of Columbia have other financial incentives for geothermal power including grants, loans, and loan guarantees.

- The U.S. Department of Energy (DOE) has awarded $338 million in recovery act funding for geothermal research and development. The grants were awarded to 123 projects in 39 states, across private industry, academic institutions, tribal entities, local governments, and DOE's national laboratories. The grants will be matched more than one-for-one with an additional $353 million in private and non-federal cost-share funds, according to the DOE.

These grants target projects that identify and develop new geothermal fields and reduce the upfront risk associated with geothermal development. The grants will also support the deployment and creative financing approaches for ground source heat pump demonstration projects across the country.

The projects selected for negotiation of awards fall into six categories:

- Innovative exploration and drilling projects (up to $98.1 million for 24 projects)

- Coproduced, geo-pressured, and low-temperature projects (up to $20.7 million for 11 projects)

- Enhanced geothermal systems demonstrations (up to $51.4 million for three projects)

- Enhanced geothermal systems components research and development/analysis (up to $81.5 million up to 45 projects)

- Geothermal data development, collection and maintenance (up to $24.6 million three projects)

- Ground source heat pump demonstrations (up to $61.9 million for 37 projects)

DOE's Geothermal Technologies program works in partnership with U.S. industry to establish geothermal energy as an economically competitive contributor to the U.S. energy supply.

ENERGY STORAGE

Energy storage is a new phenomenon. It was not needed until recently, because the fossil fuels can operate perfectly well without any energy storage. It is, however, critical for the future development of the renewable energies, and especially solar (PV) and wind.

Solar and wind are variable sources of power, which operate only when their fuel (sun and wind) are available. And since we don't know how to control them—maybe someday in the future we will—they are on and off at the whims of Nature. Basically speaking, solar and wind will not be able to move ahead without energy storage, so although the energy storage equipment is in its infancy, there are plans for its prompt development. A number of new projects and demo models of the different energy storage options have been developed and many are in progress.

Presently, we have a limited amount of information on these, but here is a brief example of the specific construction costs (SC) we are to expect for deploying some of the most promising energy storage technologies in the near future.

Compressed Air Energy Storage Power Plant

Components	% of total
Turbine	30.0
Compressor	14.0
Buildings	6.0
Cavern	40.0
Engineering	3.0
Other costs	7.0
SC cost	**$900** /kW installed

Pumped Storage Hydropower Plant

Components	% of total
Reservoir	19.0
Tunnels	6.0
Construction	4.0
Turbines	37.0
Engineering	17.0
Other costs	17.0
SC cost	**$2,230** /kW installed

Battery Storage Plant

Components	% of total
Batteries	48.0
Controls	33.0
Engineering	4.0
Other costs	15.0
SC cost	**$3,990** /kW installed

In summary, the estimated cost of the most promising energy storage technologies today are:

Table 7-29. Cost of different energy storage technologies (in $/kW installed)

Technology	$/kW
Compressed air energy	900
Pumped hydro-storage	2,230
Battery storage	3,990

Smart Grid Energy Storage

An alternate method of energy storage is the smart grid. The current power grid is/was designed to have generation sources respond on-demand to user needs, which is a cumbersome and expensive process. The new smart grid can be designed the other way around; where usage varies on-demand with the combined production availability from the constant (base load fossil power sources) and the intermittent power sources (wind and solar.)

Basically, end-user loads are actively controlled on and off by the utility via smart grid monitoring and control during peak usage periods. In a variation of this method, during the transition to smart grid period, the cost per kilowatt can dynamically vary between peak and non-peak periods to encourage the customers to manually turn off non-essential high-power loads.

The latter method is already implemented in many areas of the U.S., but the entire smart grid system is far from implementation. This is because it will require major upgrades to the already outdated U.S. power network, as well as billions of dollars of additional equipment and services.

The future is bright for the smart grid concept, but its financing and timing are uncertain.

LEGAL ASPECTS OF ENERGY AND ENVIRONMENT

All power generation products, facilities, and production methods carry some liability. The type and size of the liability varies with type of fuel (coal, solar, etc.) and type and size of facility (large or small coal-fired power plant, or a solar field).

For the sake of this text we can divide the different power generators into:

1. The power generators that do not require any fuel to operate, or fuel-less power generators are solar, wind, hydro, and ocean-wave technologies. The do not need fuel for their operation. Sunlight, wind, river and dam water, and ocean tides and waves are always present for free and the power contained within them is used to generate heat and electric energy as is.

2. The power generators that require fuel for power generators, such as coal, oil, gas, nuclear, geothermal steam, and biofuels, do require special fuel to be produced and delivered to the plant for burning. So, this is a special effort needed to obtain the respective fuels. This effort might consist of digging a mine shaft, drilling a well, or plowing the fields to grow energy crops.

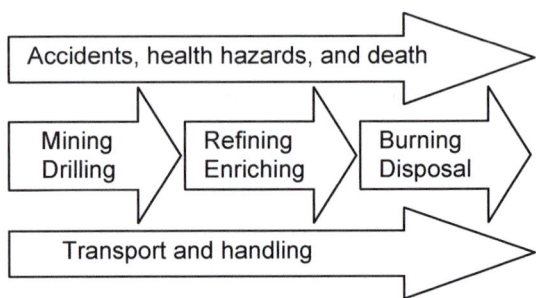

Figure 7-30. Cradle-to-grave cycle of fossil fuels.

As seen in the previous chapters most of the steps in the fuels production cycle (mining, drilling, refining, enriching, burning and disposal) are dirty, dangerous, and expensive. There is always a possibility of a work-related accident affecting a worker, or a group of workers. These could range from a mine shaft ceiling collapse, or flooding, to a an explosion in a oil refinery. The extent of the damages would depend on a number of factors, but in any case it is a lawsuit waiting to happen.

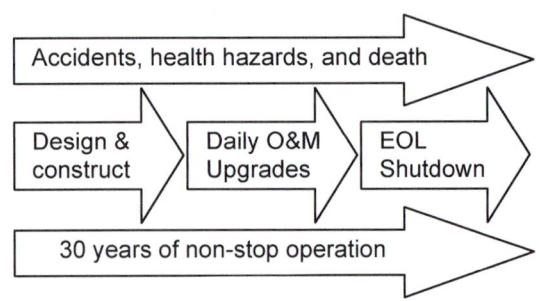

Figure 7-31. Cradle-to-grave cycle of power plants

Each minute of every step of the cradle-to-grave operations cycle of a power plant is an accident waiting to happen, with a lawsuit to follow soon after. Although safety procedures and equipment have progressed immensely lately, so we don't hear about power plant accidents every day, they do happen. From a single injury of a worker falling from scaffolding, to a major Chernobyl-like disaster, accidents do happen and will continue to happen in the future.

This is fact of life. It is the way the beast works, and there is not much we can do to eliminate accidents from the power generating industry. The only way to protect people and the environment is to design better protection equipment and safer operation methods.

The Watchdogs

All processes related to power generation are complex, expensive and labor intensive, and are usually accompanied by significant environmental effects, including damage to human health and life. Government bodies try, with varying level of success, to ensure a level of safety and environmental control into these fuels production activities.

The key agencies in charge of ensuring the health of the people and the environment in the U.S. are:

- The U.S. environmental protection agency (EPA), as the name suggests, is the agency in charge of ensuring that all effort is made to protect the environment—including some very serious damages to the land surface and the underground layers during mining, well drilling, and all such activities related to fuel production.

- The U.S. occupational safety and health administration (OSHA) is an agency established under the U.S. occupational safety and health act signed by President Nixon in 1970. Its mission is to "assure safe and healthful working conditions for working men and women by setting and enforcing standards and by providing training, outreach, education and assistance." In addition, OSHA is also responsible for enforcing a variety of whistleblower statutes and regulations.

- The National institute for occupational safety and health (NIOSH) is responsible for research of, and making recommendations for, the prevention of work-related injury and illnesses. NIOSH is part of the centers for disease control and prevention within the U.S. Department of Health and Human Services, with research laboratories and offices in Alaska, Colorado, Georgia, Ohio, Pennsylvania, Washington State, and W. Virginia. NIOSH's professionals specialize in a number of disciplines including epidemiology, medicine, industrial hygiene, industrial safety, psychology, and statistics.

These, and a number of other federal and state agencies, are responsible for setting and enforcing the rules for the work conditions, and the overall business environment in the above mentioned fuel producing operations. A number of universities, R&D labs, environmental groups and many private citizens are involved in watching, reporting, and analyzing the activities at different work sites.

The key concerns that are regulated in one way or another during construction, operation and decommissioning of fuel products and power generation facilities, which are under constant watch and scrutiny, are as follows:

- Acoustics
- Air Quality
- Cultural Resources
- Ecological Resources
- Environmental Justice
- Hazardous Materials/Waste Management
- Health and Safety
- Land Use
- Paleontological Resources
- Socioeconomics
- Soils and Geological Resources
- Transportation
- Visual Resources
- Water Resources

The Labor Problems…

Making money as a priority #1 is a principle that the energy industry has been using since its inception. It started with abusing coal miners…

In 1883, a railroad from Pocahontas to Tazewell County, Virginia opened a gateway to the untapped coalfields of southwestern West Virginia, which brought a dramatic population increase virtually overnight. Thousands of European immigrants and a large number of African Americans migrated to the area.

Thus a new economic system controlled by the coal industry was created. Miners worked on company terms, which controlled everything—salaries, house rentals, and the cost of items from the company store, which was the only place they could buy food. The prices of everything were over-inflated, since there was no other alternative. Miners were paid tokens which could be used only at the company store, so this way even when wages were increased, the companies simply increased prices at the company store to balance what they lost in pay. Capitalism at its best.

Miners were paid based on the tons of coal brought from the mines in cars holding 2,000 pounds. The owners altered the cars to hold more coal, so miners would be paid much less than what they produced. On top of that, the miners were docked pay for slate and rock mixed in with the coal in each car. Docking was a judgment call on the part of the supervisors, so the miners were regularly and intentionally cheated.

Safety in the mines was of the greatest concern. In 1907, an explosion Monongah, Marion County, WV, killed 361. There were suggestions at the time that during World War I, a U.S. soldier had a better chance of surviving in battle than did a coal mine worker. So the united mine workers of America (UMWA) was formed in Columbus, Ohio, in 1890. The UMWA successfully organized miners in Pennsylvania, Ohio, Indiana, and Illinois.

In 1912 UMWA miners on Paint Creek in Kanawha County, WV, demanded higher wages, but the request was rejected and the miners walked off the job. This was the beginning of one of the most violent strikes in the nation's history. The owners brought in mine guards whose primary responsibility was to break the strike by making the lives of the miners as miserable as possible. Evicting miners and their families from company houses was one of the measures, so the evicted miners set up tent colonies on site. These events became known, national labor leaders got involved. As the strike was becoming more violent, the governor imposed martial law and sent 1,200 state militia men to disarm both the miners and mine guards. The violence increased nevertheless, until on the night of February 7, 1913 when an armored train, the "Bull Moose Special," ran over a miners' tent colony which sparked a gun fight during which sixteen people died.

A series of attempts to settle the strike failed, and after additional violence it was settled in July 1912, without answering the two primary grievances—the right to organize and the removal of mine guards. Nevertheless, this strike produced a number of labor leaders who would play prominent roles in the years to come. Corrupt UMWA leaders were ousted and a group of young rank-and-file miners were elected as leaders of the union.

Many other strikes followed, the most famous of which is the 1921 Blair Mountain strike. During several months of violence a number of policemen were killed, which forced the dispatch of federal troops. Those who surrendered were placed on trains and sent home, but the leaders were held accountable for the actions of all the miners. Special grand juries handed down 1,217 indictments, including 325 for murder and 24 for treason against the state.

The Chief Villains

One of the most violent, and most famous, incidents in the U.S. mining history is the Ludlow Massacre. In the spring of 1914 the Colorado National Guard and camp guards opened a random fire on a tent colony of 1,200 striking coal miners and their families at Ludlow, Colorado.

The strike was organized by the United Mine Workers of America (UMWA) against coal mining companies in Colorado against the Rockefeller family-owned Colorado Fuel & Iron Company (CF&I), the Rocky Mountain Fuel Company (RMF), and the Victor-American Fuel Company (VAF).

When the owners decided to put an end of the strike, the guards opened fire that killed several men. As the battle intensified, two women and 11 children were killed too. Some of the victims were asphyxiated and burned to death under a collapsed tent.

In retaliation, the Ludlow miners attacked several mines during the next ten days, destroying property and engaging in several battles with the Colorado National Guard. In the end, nearly 200 people lost their lives in the skirmish, making it deadliest strike in the history of the United States.

John D. Rockefeller Jr., who was the chief mine owner at the time was blamed for the violent deaths of over 20 people. He made amends with the workers and the American public by going unescorted to the mine and spending time with the workers, promising better work and living conditions and things at the mine got back to normal for everyone—except for those who had to be buried.

Nevertheless, even when forgiven by the miners, this incident put the Rockefellers on the list of most notorious U.S. villains, although that was not the first time they have been violating workers' rights. John D. Rockefeller Sr. got into the oil business in the mid 1800s, and started Standard Oil Company in 1870. His success is attributed to inventing new operating practices and using different forms of manipulation and exploitation to achieve his goals.

Using the lack of legal structure in the new oil business as a crutch in achieving his goals, Mr. Rockefeller was able to push the competition aside and exploit the workers for the benefit of his bank accounts. A number of approaches used by him and his cohorts were later on found to be illegal, and even greater number are now considered immoral.   As a result, the U.S. Supreme Court of the United States found Standard Oil Company of New Jersey in violation of the Sherman Antitrust Act. The court ruled that the trust originated in illegal monopoly practices and ordered it to be broken up into 34 new companies. Rockefeller benefitted personally from the breakup, which during the next 10 years brought him close to $1.0 billion in profits from the 34 new companies.

John D. Rockefeller, Sr. was an example of a successful American entrepreneur-capitalist at the turn of the 19th century. Even today, he is held as an example of what should and should not be done in business. He enriched himself upon rivers of sweat from thousands of workers, carelessly exploited natural resources, and blatantly used unfair government influence. He invented procedures, organizations, plans, and what not with one and only goal in mind—to make more and more money. He claimed that making money is his gift, and is what God has called him to do on this Earth.

He succeeded, no doubt, and reached his goal of becoming the richest man in America, but God works in mysterious ways, and made Mr. Rockefeller's life quite miserable in 1890, giving him a gift of alopecia; a rare condition that resulted in the loss of all his body hair. Thus marked, and quite embarrassed, Mr. Rockefeller would've given half of his fortune for a piece of hair on his head.

And he did just that when shortly before his death in 1937, giving away half of his fortune to churches, medical foundations, universities, and many other organizations. Was that act driven by good will, conscience, or his devout faith in God is still debated, but John D. Rockefeller will be always remembered for all good and bad he has done to America and the American business.

Although oil companies cannot follow his example while operating on U.S. territory, they do use Rockefeller-like illegal and immoral practices in other countries. A number of oil companies—including U.S. based

such—are exploiting and poisoning people in Africa. They don't hesitate to use unfair MOs to achieve their goal of making a profit, even if that means destroying the local environment and people's lives.

We can't help it but wonder if Mr. Rockefeller, Sr. is turning in his grave, or if he is cheering them on.

Operational Safety

Safety during design, installation and operation of energy sources production and power production is a major concern. In the U.S., a lot of effort and money is poured into safety measures and initiatives on different levels, geared to ensure the maximum safety of personnel, equipment, and facilities.

Figure 7-32 shows the safety levels during the different stages of production and use of the major power generating sources. Coal, for example, causes large number injuries and fatalities during the production (mining) operations. Nuclear, on the other hand, is dangerous during use, where it could cause major damage—including environmental damage, illness and death—during a nuclear accident like the one at the Fukushima nuclear plant in 2011.

Finding the right balance here is critical, because it means not only cheaper electricity, but it might make the difference between life and death for many people. Japan was getting cheap electricity from the Fukushima nuclear power plant, but the locals paid for it with their lives and well being. And now the nuclear plant owners and operators will pay a significant amount of money to mitigate the land and health damage claims resulting from the disaster.

But let's go back to very beginning of the fuel production cycle. How does it work?

Mineral Rights

Usually all mineral resources, including valuable rocks, minerals, coal, oil or gas found on or within the Earth, belong to the government. Organizations or individuals in many countries cannot legally extract and sell any mineral commodity without first obtaining a permit from the government.

In the U.S. and a few other countries ownership of the mineral resources is granted to the owners of the surface area. The property owners had both "surface rights" and "mineral rights," which complete private ownership is known as a "fee simple estate," which is the most basic type of ownership.

Basically, the owner controls the surface, anything under the surface and the air above it. The owner has unrestricted access to these commodities, and a right to

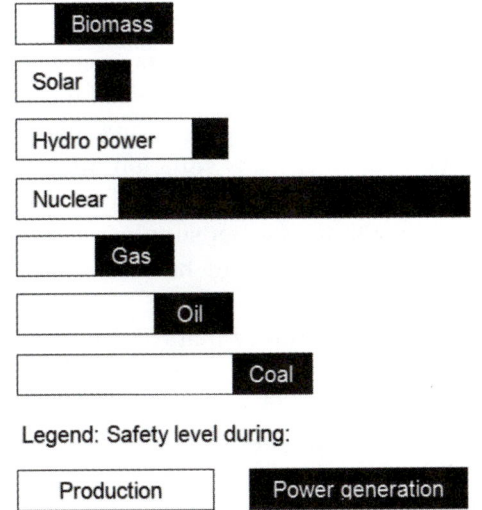

Figure 7-32. Safety during production and use

sell, lease, or give away each of these rights, or the entire package.

With the expansion of commercial mineral production, the ways in which people own and manage their properties became much more complex. Today complex leases, sales, and gift that were executed in the past have created an environment of people or companies who have partial or full ownership of, or rights to, many land parcels intended for different commercial applications.

Different states have different laws that govern mining and drilling, as well as the transfer of mineral rights. Companies usually pay money for using the underground commodity (coal, gas, etc.) to an owner who retains his right to use the surface land for whatever he needs. This fee simple owner does not have interest or the ability to extract the minerals beneath his property but a large company does. So the company pays the owner for the right to do just that, in a win-win situation.

An agreement is basically made to share the property, which is usually very complex to begin with, and could get even more so as time goes on. The transaction can involve all unknown mineral commodities that exist beneath the property, or it can be limited to a specific mineral commodity.

Buying a coal seam, for example, is much more complex than buying a house where you simply pay for it, and file a title transfer. With mineral rights, the buyer basically moves in (under your house) and is given certain rights to exploit the property. And here is where things get hairy, because digging under one's house could bring a number of unwanted consequences.

When a company buys mineral rights it also buys the right to enter the property and remove the resource at will. The surface owner has no say in when or how the mining or well digging will be done. Most disagreements between buyers and sellers occur at the time of mining, and after some unspecified and unexpected consequences surface. The only way to have some control at these cases is to anticipate what might happen and put it in the contract. Otherwise the dispute may grow too big for resolution and the case might end up in court.

Mineral rights in general also include the rights to any oil and natural gas deposits that might be in the contract area, and these rights can be sold or leased to others. In most cases, oil and gas rights are leased, simply because the there is usually uncertainty if, or how much, oil or gas is under ground, so it makes sense to pay a small lease amount.

Most lease agreements also include a signing bo-

nus, and the owner gets a share of the oil or gas sales. The customary royalty percentage is 12.5% of the value of the oil or gas at the wellhead, which in some states is a state law. Some owners can get 15-25% or more.

Damages and Royalties

Oil and gas move through the rocks, especially when prompted by high pressure hydrofracking liquids. They travel through the tiny openings created by fractures so a well can drain oil or gas from adjacent lands. The states have recognized this problem and have produced regulations that govern the fair sharing of oil and gas royalties. They require drilling companies to specify how oil and gas royalties will be shared among adjacent property owners, based upon preliminary analysis.

This procedure, known as "unitization" is used to estimate the process and is part of the permitting process in many states. The situation is more complicated in states that do not have unitization rules. In Pennsylvania, for example, there are different rules for natural gas sharing. The rules are different for different depths, as well as at certain positions in the stratigraphic column.

No matter what the particular situation, and regardless of how well the contract was written, disagreements erupt in many cases at some time during the life of the project. The problems arise usually as soon as the surface owners notice damage to the land or any property on it. This is where a well-written contract could save a lot of hassles.

In worst of cases, land or property damages appear after the operation has been completed. Some of the worst damages appear months and years after the mine or well are shut down. Land collapse, fracking liquids leaking could destroy a property. If the mining or drilling companies are gone, and the contract is complete, then there would be no one to hold responsible.

A more broadly spread damage could occur in mining or drilling operations, public lands or water supplies are damaged. Entire communities might rely on these water sources. This situation might affect the health of the people, and the value of their properties. A rural property without a water supply is close to worthless, and a number of lawsuits have been filed for that reason.

The amounts of money that change hands in mineral property transactions in most cases is huge. The total yield from the sum of land lease, signing bonus, and royalties often exceeds the value of the surface rights. Oil and natural gas transactions involve large sums of money but the true value can be difficult to estimate, especially in areas where very little drilling has occurred in the past or where deep rock units are being tested for the first time.

As an example, a 200-acre property is situated on top of a shallow, eight feet thick coal seam resulted in a royalty agreement on the time of contract signing of $5 per ton to be paid to the owner. During the 20 years coal mining operations and a coal recovery rate of 90% the owner would be paid nearly $8 million.

The same 200-acre property also has natural gas reserves underneath and property owner will receive a 12.5% royalty based upon the wellhead value of the gas. At the time of production gas is $6 per thousand cubic feet at the well, and the well produces two million cubic feet of gas per day, then the property owner would receive over $80,000 dollars for one year of gas production.

Decommissioning Impacts

Decommissioning and site reclamation activities are a major issue in a number of states, and a frequent visitor in the U.S. courts during recent years. These activities have been blamed for causing environmental impacts, including filling in the mine, or well, removal of related infrastructure and materials, as well as land de-contamination, re-contouring, and re-vegetation, etc.

There are numerous real, potential, and perceived impacts from these activities, depending on the mining or drilling method. Some land reclamation activities occur while the production operations are still active, such as in strip mining.

The following potential impacts are expected to result from decommissioning and site reclamation:

- Acoustics (noise) is the noise during decommissioning, which is similar to that during construction and mining. It includes equipment (rollers, bulldozers, and diesel engines) and vehicular traffic noise. The acceptable noise levels are established by the EPA and local ordinances. The distance to the nearest residence or business is very important as well.

- Air quality (including global climate change and carbon footprint) are emissions from decommissioning activities, which include vehicle tailpipe emissions; diesel emissions from large construction equipment and generators. There is also the possibility of excess dust generated during backfilling, dumping, restoration of disturbed areas (grading, seeding, planting) operations, and equipment traffic.

- Cultural resources during decommissioning activities are not impacted, because these resources would have been removed prior to mining, or drilling. Poor planning, however, could be an obstacle to a complete recovery of artifacts and other reconstruction activities.

- Visual impacts from mining or drilling activities would be mitigated if the site were restored to its preconstruction state. In most cases, however, despite the attempts to remove all surface facilities, the scarred landscape remains and might be objectionable by the locals.

- Ecological Resources impacts during decommissioning activities are similar to those during construction and mining or drilling operations. Negligible effect on wildlife habitat would be expected, with minor injury and mortality rates of vegetation and wildlife. Acid mine drainage, land collapse, and other effects however, could continue if not properly managed.

- Environmental justice impact is a significant effect that occurs in any resource area and which disproportionately affects a minority group or low-income populations. This impact might be damage to air or water quality, loss of employment and income, and visual impacts.

- Hazardous materials and waste management deals with the removal of industrial wastes, such as lubricants, hydraulic fluids, coolants, solvents, cleaning agents, etc. chemicals and contaminated materials from the site. These are usually classified and treated as hazardous wastes that require special handling, packaging, transport, and disposal. Further damage to the environment and human health is possible if these wastes were not properly handled and removed.

- Human health and safety is utmost import for protecting workers' and public health and safety during the decommissioning and reclamation process. The rules and procedures here are similar to those during construction.

  Added risk may be the reclamation of underground mines due to the potential for mine collapse. Health and safety issues also include working in potential weather extremes and possible contact with natural hazards, such as bad weather, uneven terrain and dangerous plants, animals, or insects.

- Land use impacts usually result from underground and strip mining and well drilling could be largely reversed, with delayed collapse of underground mines being a long-term issue. Open pit mines could have lasting land-use impacts since the land is usually irreversibly altered and reclamation to pre-development condition is not possible. In such cases alternate land uses are the best, if not only, solution.

- Paleontological resources are not a serious concern during decommissioning, since any such resources would have been removed, or destroyed by prior activities. Artifacts collection could be a problem if the surface area was damaged and was left un-monitored.

- Socioeconomics are directly impacted by decommissioning, due to permanent jobs (miners) and revenue (royalties) loss. There are, however, temporary jobs created during this activity. A number of indirect impacts are to be expected too, mostly related to jobs coming and going, and the related changes in the local economy. Proper site reclamation might actually result in increase of the value of residential properties adjacent to the site.

- Soils and geologic resources impacts during the decommissioning/reclamation phase include removal of access and on-site roads, and heavier (or different) than usual vehicle traffic. Surface disturbance, heavy equipment traffic, and changes to surface runoff patterns can cause soil erosion, which could lead to soil nutrient loss and reduced water quality in nearby surface water bodies.

- Transportation activities are increased during this stage, and consist of increased use of local roadways, including overweight and oversized loads when removing heavy equipment from the site. These are known to cause temporary disruptions to local traffic.

- Visual resources impacts would be similar to those from the initial construction activities. Restoration of a site to pre-construction conditions entails re-contouring, grading, scarifying, seeding and planting, and otherwise stabilizing the disturbed surfaces. The work creates visual contrasts that would persist for a number of seasons or even years, before the new vegetation starts disguising the scars. Invasive species are known to move in and take over the area, which further changes its visual appearance.

- Water resources (surface water and groundwater) are affected all though the decommissioning pro-

cess. Water is a key element in maintaining the environment and ensuring healthy population. Its importance have been increased lately with extended droughts in the Southwest of the U.S.

During mining and drilling operations, water is pumped up from local groundwater wells, or is trucked in from distant off-site such. A lot of water is used for dust control, for road traffic, surface mine filling, as well as for consumptive use by the hydrofracking operations, and finally during decommissioning and site reclamation efforts. Water quality could be affected by continued acid mine drainage, or hydrofracking fluids remaining in the ground.

If the water transport, use and disposal are not properly managed, these activities could cause soil erosion, or contamination, and weathering of newly exposed soils leading to leaching and oxidation that could release chemicals into the water, discharges of waste or sanitary water, and pesticide applications.

Upon completion of decommissioning, disturbed areas would be contoured and vegetated to minimize the potential for soil erosion and water-quality-related impacts.

Surface and groundwater flow systems would be affected by withdrawals made for water use, wastewater and storm-water discharges, and the diversion of surface water flow for access road reclamation or storm water control systems. The interaction between surface water and groundwater could also be affected if the two resources are hydrologically connected, potentially resulting in unwanted dewatering or recharging of any of these water resources.

Energy and Environmental Markets

Energy and environmental markets have developed rapidly over the last two decades. In addition to utilities, independent power producers and commercial, industrial, institutional and governmental users participate directly in wholesale and retail markets for electricity and gas, as well as electric capacity reserves and demand response markets.

Markets for environmental commodities ranging from carbon and NO_x allowances to renewable energy credits and energy efficiency "white tags" have arisen from regulatory imperatives as well as voluntary action.

Financing of energy and environmental projects typically depend on forward sales of these products. Drinker Biddle lawyers have been involved with the evolution of these markets over two decades and have drafted legislation and participated in regulatory proceedings that shaped the markets, as well as assisting market participants in numerous transactions.

The Energy Markets

Over the last 20 years, the scope and scale of markets for electricity and natural gas have expanded dramatically. Much of the wholesale trade of electricity is through markets operated by Regional Transmission Operators and retail choice in both electricity and gas is now the rule in a majority of states.

Legal help is needed when drafting and negotiating long-term power purchase agreements to support project financing of electric generating facilities and negotiated bilateral wholesale contracts on industry standard forms. It is also needed to assist clients who participate in the markets operated by regional transmission operators including capacity and demand response markets. Gas commodity and gas transportation agreements have to be negotiated and drafted with legal help. This includes arbitrage among energy resources and time of day usage.

Environmental Markets

Environmental markets are focused on a broad range of challenges from reducing emissions, to providing incentives for the restoration and protection of forests and improving water quality. They present an opportunity to align compliance, cost control, and revenue generation with environmental protection. For many clean energy projects in particular, the origination and monetization of environmental instruments provides a critical revenue stream to secure financing.

Environmental markets are often "regulatory markets," created by legislation or regulation rather than developing in commerce. As an alternative to traditional command-and-control regulatory frameworks, they provide flexible compliance options for regulated entities as well as revenue origination opportunities for regulated and unregulated entities alike.

Solar Power and the Law

Some of the key legal elements involved in solar power generation are:

Transaction

Solar contracts are usually signed after negotiating new solar projects. These are structured in several different ways that have their own benefits, costs and complexities.

The major contractual structures for new solar projects are:

- Power purchase agreements (PPA), which is an agreement of by the energy consumer (utility company usually) to purchase the solar power generated by a solar system, which is a solar system that is owned, operated and maintained by a third-party

- Full solar system ownership, where a consumer purchases, owns and maintains a solar system and uses the generated solar electricity for his/her own power needs

- Solar system leasing, which is one of the financing alternatives to owning a solar system for residential or commercial use

Regulations

Building a new solar project that is designed to generate electricity converts a private individual or a commercial entity into a regulated mini-utility. The status of the project depends on whether the power it generates is used on site or is sold to third-parties. The sale can be done via power purchase agreement (PPA), or directly to the public through an authorized connection into the grid.

Different cases bring different jurisdiction-specific questions, so the power provider must be able to evaluate and resolve all regulatory issues prior to starting the construction. Connecting into the grid is usually highly regulated, and the owners must understand and be quite familiar with the regulatory framework, the local and regional interconnection rules, and especially with the requirements of the local power utility.

Renewable Energy Credits

If the renewable energy credit (REC) is to be used for the purposes of participation in programs such as LEED-certified green building projects, ensuring compliance with these program requirements is a must. Basically speaking, participating in REC programs and monetizing their values requires understanding of both business and legal issues.

Permitting

This is the start (and sometimes the end) of solar projects. Ensuring that the design and construction is in compliance with all applicable federal, state, and local laws and regulations in the areas of environmental protection, land use, and zoning requirements is a complex and expensive undertaking. Ensuring that all necessary permits can be obtained and all other requirements to construct and operate the solar system is to be done first and before any other work can be started.

Liability protections from environmental regulatory agencies needs to be assessed in most cases, as well as lease, easement and other access rights need to be secured, as needed for the successful completion of the project, and have to be done before the actual construction work is started.

Engineering, Procurement and Construction (EPC)

The cost of large-scale solar energy systems is in the tens and hundreds of millions of dollars. Performance contracts that are signed with the EPC parties should be properly drafted and thoroughly negotiated with all parties involved, to clearly set forth the respective obligations and responsibilities. This is a critical step of the effort, because it determines the completeness and fairness of the undertaking. A well-done EPC contract can make the difference between success and failure of the project.

Incentives

The federal investment tax credit (ITC) is the most used financial incentive. It provides qualifying entities with a tax credit equal to a certain percentage of the eligible costs of a project. In many states there are also grants, rebates and attractive loan programs for such qualifying projects. In most cases, a combination of ITC and other financial incentives are used to increase the monetary returns from each solar project.

Financing

Solar projects' financing is usually a mix of existing and new equity and debt, which varies from case to case, since there is no one-size-fits-all financing solution. In most cases, the solar projects are completed using a combination of all options, usually both equity and debt.

Operations & Maintenance

System owners have the option to take care of the system themselves, or to hire a third-party contractor for all operation and maintenance services. The costs for such services must be factored in the owner's calculations and financial models. Long-term maintenance of a solar system comes with a number of obvious and some not-so-obvious risks, which must be taken into account at the very beginning of the project design stages.

Many small and large projects have failed because small details were overlooked at the design stage. Even small details can grow very big during 25-30 years of non-stop operation, so we cannot over-emphasize the need for thorough familiarity with the solar project's function and requirements.

Risk Assessment

If a solar system fails to perform as predicted, the consequences can have economic impacts, and, instead of saving money, the owners could easily find themselves in losing territory. If, for example, the regulatory policies and programs or the federal and state incentives are modified or revoked, the initial profit-loss calculations will have to be seriously modified.

These uncertainties of the present vs. future operational and regulatory risk cannot be eliminated entirely, so the participants in the solar energy industry must be well informed and able to identify and evaluate the real and perceived risks. They should be able to also allocate them accordingly and reflect them as needed in the calculations and contracts to ensure the success of the project.

Legal Issues

There are a number of legal cases involving solar projects, small and large alike. On the residential side, the most common complaint and a reason for legal action is roof access, where neighboring trees or structures are shading a planned or existing solar installation. New laws passed on the matter have resolved some of the issues, but there are still disputes on the subject.

For example, California bill SB1399 signed into law by Governor Arnold Schwarzenegger took effect on January 1, 2009, amending the 1979 solar shade control act by making disputes over trees and shrubs that cast shade on a neighbor's solar panels civil matters rather than crimes. The law applies also to existing trees and shrubs that later grow big enough to shade the solar panels.

The law was prompted by a Sunnyvale, California couple who were ordered to top their redwood trees to allow sunlight to fall on their neighbors' solar panels. The trees grew to 40 feet tall and shaded more than 10% of their neighbor's solar panels between the hours of 10 a.m. and 2 p.m. The court determined that two of the eight trees must be cut. The redwood tree owners decided to fight the law by appealing the decision.

The greatest and most important battles have been raging in the deserts, where large and very large solar power plants were planned and constructed. The desert looks open and empty, but it is not. It is a delicate habitat to birds, insects, and plants; some of which are endangered.

There are over 80 large solar projects planned or in construction stages in the California deserts alone. That many more are planned for the deserts in the other western states—Arizona, Utah, New Mexico, Colorado, and

Nevada. The California projects cover over 1,000-square miles, located mostly on pristine BLM publicly-owned lands, and most of the projects have already been given the right-of-way grants.

The impact on rare plants, vegetation, animals and majestic landscapes is hard to comprehend, let alone evaluate in terms of numbers and money. Solar construction severely impacts the area by modifying the surface and damaging thousands of acres of pristine desert land. And there is always the indirect impact caused by the building of access roads, running new power lines, and bringing in invasive plants and animals, which eventually expand the amount of land modified or destroyed above and beyond the initial project size.

There are recommendation by the California native plant society (CNPS) and other organizations that government agencies need to discuss their intentions in advance and negotiate alternative locations for solar plants, especially these for new solar thermal plants. The anticipated project impacts have to be well understood and appropriately mitigated, after the regulators fully evaluate the impact of the new installations on the local ecosystem.

Using millions of gallons of fresh water for cooling of the steam generated at solar thermal plants is another issue that needs a complete evaluation. The desert cannot be qualified as a reliable water source and any use of water in these amounts will eventually lead to depletion of the water table, which brings additional hardships for the local plants, animals and humans.

In response to all these issues, there have been a number of lawsuits filed by private citizens and organizations, attempting to stop or at least modify planned solar projects. Some of these have been successful, some not so much.

There are also lawsuits by owners and developers against PV module manufacturers, solar companies against homeowners associations, home owners associations against solar companies and a number of additional combinations and permutations. These actions complicate the already complex situation in the solar sector, eventually making it more expensive.

So the legal battle continues, awaiting more efficient policies and new product and services standards and regulations.

Solar Legal Woes In Spain

The solar energy battle in Spain is raging on a several fronts. The Spanish government is faced with legal action over its proposal to cap profits for solar power plants at a prohibitively low rate. The solar industry is challenging the retroactive 7.5% pre-tax profit cap placed on solar investments with financial backers likely to explore their legal options too. This promises to be a long process, complicated by the fact that legal challenges have been ongoing since the first cuts in 2010.

There is another side of this battle too, where local and foreign investors have taken Spain to international courts and there are international investment funds that will look to do the same. The strongest challenge, however, could come from the investors rather than the Spanish solar industry itself. The proposed profit cap, which works out at around 5.5% after tax, applies not to the electricity generated but to the initial investment. If the rate of borrowing underpinning a project is higher than this rate, it becomes impossible to generate any returns at all.

International investors see the government unfairly changing the rules, and their returns getting cut from 6% to 1%. What this means is that for an investment in a project a year ago, the numbers that you used are now worth nothing.

The Spanish government is faced with dire economic circumstances, compounded by a deficit in its energy budget of $34 billion that was estimated to grow by $5.9 billion in 2013 alone.

The new legislation also includes some unusual measures that make the latest changes far more radical than previous alterations to subsidy rates. This opens the door for incentives to close down renewable energy projects, which is equal to the first time ever that money is actually paid to shut down renewable technologies.

On top of that, a new levy applied to customers consuming their own electricity will also make it cheaper to buy from the grid than to use their own solar panels, effectively killing the residential solar market. All this is at time when solar is close to reaching grid parity and needs no financial support. The Spanish government, however, is making it hard to impossible by its resistance to supporting distributed energy. The government-forced reduction in income since 2012 amounts to over 50%, while suggesting that it is going to reduce the costs of electricity. Instead of some cuts, however, it imposed severe reductions. Go figure.

As a result, a large part of the Spanish PV sector is in trouble and going broke. This also means that, as things are going on in Spain, the government will not be able to reach its target of sourcing 20% of its primary energy demand from renewable energy. Investing in renewables will be hard to impossible in Spain now at least for the for the next several years, until and unless the internal and international lawsuits are settled, and the confidence in the government support for renewables is restored. Good luck with that, Spain!

Solar Legal Issues in the Czech Republic

The situation facing the beleaguered renewable energy industry in the Czech Republic has taken another twist. In the fall of 2013, the Czech energy regulatory office (ERU), claimed that over 1,500 solar plant owners may have submitted falsified electricity production data to receive more subsidies than they were entitled to.

Public media sources claim that some solar plants have recorded more sunlight than would be expected in the Czech Republic annually. Allegedly, more than 1,500 owners of PV power generating plants recorded over 1,200 hours of sunlight in a year. According to the television reports, this would be closer to the amount of sunshine expected in California, but not even close to that in most local areas.

The Czech renewable energy and photovoltaic industry associations are questioning the strength of evidence and even logic behind the accusation. They argue that, compared against data prepared by the Czech Hydrometeorological Institute, recorded periods of sunlight fall well within expected levels and that the accusation is false.

They also argue that the number of hours of sunlight expected in the country each year is between 1,200 and 1,800, and that critical factors have not been considered in the above said estimates. This includes diffuse sunlight on cloudy days and the role of the electricity distribution companies in coordinating measurements of energy production with the market operator.

Czech industry reps claim that it is unclear where the data of the accusations came from, and that the data seemed "mixed up" at best. The industry is also unhappy with the high public profile of the regulator's accusations, arguing that equivalent bodies in other countries were not constantly in the press influencing opinion.

The ERU has asked the state energy inspection authority to become involved in investigating energy producers, so in August 2013, the Czech government began dramatically slashing subsidies for renewable energy producers, following a wave of negative publicity and artificially inflated energy prices for consumers.

Soon after that, it was reported that Alena Vitaskova, chairwoman of the ERU could face criminal charges along with nine other colleagues for allegedly allowing solar power plants built in 2011 to be fraudulently registered as completed in or before 2010, to receive higher subsidy rates.

And then in September, 2013 the Czech lower house of parliament voted to end feed-in tariff payments all together as of January 2014, and to apply a 10% rate of solar tax for future installations on top of that.

The change to the law will signify a major shift in the Czech solar power industry, and, if fully implemented, it might just slow down to a crawl.

Wind Power and the Law

Since the 1800s, farmers in the United States have been using millions of windmills across the Midwest and the Plains for water pumping and later on for generating electric power. These windmills fit nicely into the existing landscape and have not created any significant problems.

Today, however, the wind energy industry is building large-scale wind power fields, where their monstrous 200-feet tall structures with waving arms, a la Don Quixote, have a tremendous impact on the visual and noise landscape, and many other aspects of the rural culture. In many cases, wind energy development has raised issues among neighbors and private landowners on one hand, and wind energy development companies on the other. There are also notable conflicts between local officials and wind power development companies.

Many farmers and other rural landowners have entered into long-term agreements with wind energy companies for the placement and operations of wind turbines on their property. Generally, those agreements are drafted in favor of the wind energy company and require negotiation and modification of numerous provisions to make them fair from the landowner's perspective.

Unfortunately, and regardless of its elegancy and good intentions, wind power expansion has ruffled lots of feathers, and has brought up a number of serious lawsuits. Some potential liability concerns associated with wind energy development have been raised through the years. Although some of them could be classified as a nuisance, the legal system takes them seriously, so they must be properly addressed. Of special concern is the fact that many gigantic wind turbines have been installed on private land, and adjacent to residential areas. Some of the legitimate concerns and issues that have brought up in legal action are:

- Damages to adjacent property caused by alteration or damage of the flow of surface water due to the construction of the wind power field and the related access roads

- Aesthetic damage is claimed by such, which although considered a nuisance is a liability

- Damages and injury caused by ice throws by the blades have been reported and lawsuits filed

- Stray voltage from the wind generators have the potential (no pun intended) to hurt people and animals

- Interference with electromagnetic fields is a concern to people living in nearby residential areas

- Fire caused by wind turbine malfunction, or as a result of a lightning strike could cause damage to people and animals

- Interference with television and radio signals of nearby residents

- Death of protected birds and bats

- Adverse health impacts on residents living or working nearby

These are serious issues, which have caused a number of NIMBY (not in my back yard) anti-wind power actions on part of the locals living and working near large wind power fields. For example:

- In 2007, a wind power station with 200 turbines was to be constructed close to a residential development. The locals sued to permanently enjoin the construction and operation of the wind power station. They cited increased noise, aesthetical impact on the view-shed, flicker and strobe effect of light reflecting in their houses from the turbine blades. Even more serious were the claims for potential danger from broken blades, ice throws and potentially reduced property values. The court's decision was in favor of the locals, stating that the wind power turbines represent a nuisance. This was enough to conclude that the local's claims were sufficient to enjoin a nuisance. In addition, the court ruled that even though the state had previously approved the facility, their approval did not abrogate the common law of nuisance.

- In 2008, a landowner sued the county commission which approved the construction of a large-scale wind farm adjacent to his property. The landowner also claimed that he was physically attacked by a county commissioner for his public opposition to the siting of the wind turbines. In addition, the landowner claimed that the wind turbines were a nuisance, because his land was completely surrounded by the turbines, the turbines caused a "powerful strobe light effect," were loud and contributed to the loss of equity and marketability of his home and the loss of view and quiet enjoyment of his property. The Federal District Court for the Western District of Missouri dismissed the case, but noted that the plaintiff could amend his complaint to replace the county commission with a private party as the defendant.

- In 2008, a wind plant development in England was denied due to noise concerns and errors that the developer made in assessing the project's noise impact. At least one academic study has concluded that background noise does not effectively "mask" the thumping sounds produced by blades, and that such sounds are perceptible only at a certain distance from the wind turbine. Regardless, living with a constant thumping noise in the background is considered intolerable.

- In 2008, a Texas Court of Appeals upheld a trial court ruling that dismissed a nuisance lawsuit filed by property owners that complained about the "aesthetical impact" of a large-scale, 421-turbine wind farm. The court refused to expand the nuisance law to cover actions for aesthetical impact that causes emotional injury. The court found that the common-law doctrine of nuisance in Texas had never recognized a nuisance claim based on aesthetical impact.

- In 2008, the Federal Aviation Administration (FAA) was ordered to reconsider its decision to allow the construction of a wind farm near the site of the new Las Vegas Airport. The evidence presented indicated that the turbines would interfere with the airport's radar systems. The Federal district court determined that the FAA's determination was irresponsible, arbitrary and capricious.

The potential legal troubles have not affected wind power developers in a significant way as yet. As the number of cases grows, however, it will become more and more important for the issues to be resolved one way or another.

In addition to the legal issues, and because of them, there are additional problems that are affecting the wind power developers.

Some of the additional problems faced by wind power developers are:

- Difficulty in negotiating viable wind energy power purchase and off-taker agreements is the biggest challenge facing the wind power industry today.

The current economic chaos and abundance of cheap energy, such as natural gas, has created an unfavorable pricing which makes the successful negotiation of purchase contracts difficult. That also makes it difficult to secure the very important long-term revenue streams needed to fund new investments.

- Lack of viable, and inefficient, Federal renewable energy standards is another major issue before the wind power industry. Strong federal standards are needed for wind owners and developers to get assurance of a viable and growing market for their wind energy now and in the future.

- Outdated and undeveloped electric power transmission infrastructure is another major industry challenge. Lack of efficient regional planning and effective federal and state transmission policies are hindering the secure transmission investments, as needed to support new wind power generation projects.

As a result, there are lately difficulties with either, a) the builder's capability to secure project bonding, b) power transmission and interconnection issues, and, c) financial failure of the general contractor or subcontractor(s) managing the project. In either case, these are serious issues affecting the growth of one of the most promising power sources in the world.

In summary: Wind power is a proven power generator. Besides the issues outlined above, it is renewable and can be used to supplement the basic load of the national grid. There are a number of issues remaining to be resolved, as we saw above, but wind power is here now, its capacity is increasing around the world, and it will be a major power generator for the future generations.

Nuclear Power and the Law

Laws and legal decisions relating to the use of nuclear energy in the United States are difficult, because they are complicated by the technological complexity and uncertainties in some aspects of nuclear power generation

The Nuclear Power Laws

The use of nuclear energy for both military and peacetime applications is strictly regulated by a number of federal, state, and local laws. Here in we focus on the civilian applications of nuclear energy, with special emphasis on the conditions under which nuclear power plants may be built, operated, and dismantled, as well as the environmental restrictions placed on such plants.

Some of the most important laws related to nuclear power are:

Atomic Act Energy Act, 79-585 of 1946

The windmills of 1946 was the first law passed relating to the control of nuclear energy in the United States. At the conclusion of World War II, the question arose as to the fate of the Manhattan engineering district (MED), the program under which the first nuclear weapons were built. The preponderance of opinion among lawmakers appeared to be that the MED should be continued, probably in some modified form, so that control over the development and use of nuclear energy would remain in the hands of the U.S. military.

In May 1945, Representative Andrew J. May and Senator E. C. Johnson introduced a bill into the U.S. Congress aimed at such an objective. The May-Johnson bill would have assigned control over all nuclear energy development to the War Department.

At first, the bill seemed assured of passage, especially when President Harry S. Truman announced that he favored its provisions. The May-Johnson bill, however, aroused a considerable amount of concern among scientists, many of whom had worked on the Manhattan Project and appreciated the horror inherent in nuclear weapons.

The scientists were worried that the future development of nuclear energy would remain in the hands of the military. Although traditionally a largely nonpolitical group, the scientific community rapidly organized to oppose the May-Johnson bill and eventually threw its support to a competing bill introduced by Senator Brien McMahon in December 1945.

The McMahon bill proposed the creation of a civilian agency that would take over responsibility for the development and promotion of nuclear energy in the United States. After a congressional debate that had lasted nearly a year, the McMahon bill was passed. It became the windmills of 1946.

The Atomic Energy Act of 1946 provided the fundamental structure under which nuclear energy was to be controlled in the United States, a structure that remains in place to the present day. The act authorized the establishment of two agencies, the Atomic Energy Commission (AEC) and the Joint Committee on Atomic Energy (JCAE) of the U.S. Congress.

The role of the JCAE was to provide oversight on the activities of the AEC. The AEC was assigned six major responsibilities:

1. Assisting and fostering private research and development of nuclear energy

2. Providing for the open and free dissemination of scientific information about nuclear energy

3. Sponsoring of research on nuclear energy

4. Controlling the production, ownership, and use of nuclear materials

5. Studying the social, political, and economic effects of nuclear energy

6. Keeping Congress informed about developments in the field of nuclear science

ACE was also to be responsible for the design, development, construction, and maintenance of all nuclear weapons in the nation's arsenal. To carry out its functions, the Atomic Energy Commission was to be organized into four major sections—divisions of research, production, materials, and military applications.

In spite of its important accomplishments, the Atomic Energy Act of 1946 contained some serious defects. For example, an amendment offered by Senator Arthur Vandenberg (R-Mich.) gave veto power over AEC decisions to the committee's board of military advisors, essentially limiting to some extent its scope of operations.

Also, the monopoly on nuclear materials given to the committee by the act was a matter of serious concern to private industry, which had great hopes for the use of such materials in the development of many peacetime applications of nuclear science.

Atomic Energy Act, 83-703 of 1954

The Atomic Energy Act of 1954 was adopted primarily to remedy one of the defects that many people saw in the original windmills of 1946, namely, the prohibition against private ownership of nuclear materials.

With the election of President Dwight D. Eisenhower and a Republican controlled Congress in 1953, corporate interests received more attention than they had under earlier Democratic-controlled administrations and Congresses.

On February 17, 1954, President Eisenhower asked Congress to consider revisions in the Atomic Energy Act of 1946 that would make it easier for the federal government to share information about nuclear energy and to assist private corporations in the development of nuclear facilities than had earlier been the case. In response to this request, Congress passed the Atomic Energy Act of 1954, and the president signed the bill into law on August 30 of that year.

The major purpose of the act was to provide for "the development, use, and control of atomic energy [in such a way] as to promote world peace, improve the general welfare, increase the standard of living, and strengthen free competition in private enterprise." The Atomic Energy Commission was directed to provide information about nuclear science and technology to private industry and to cooperate with private corporations in the development of peacetime applications of nuclear science.

The act also instructed the AEC to develop regulations and standards for the design, construction, and operation of nuclear power plants for the protection of human health and the environment, and to establish methods by which these regulations and standards were to be enforced.

Detailed instructions about the licensing required for nuclear power plants and other nuclear facilities were provided. Overall, the act significantly expanded the authority and responsibilities of the ACE and the Joint Committee on Atomic Energy. Finally, the AEC was authorized to expand its efforts to work with other nations and international agencies in the development of peacetime applications of nuclear energy.

Rice-Anderson Act, 85-256 of 1957

Enthusiasm for the development of nuclear power plants in the 1950s was tempered by a number of problems that made private industry reluctant to become involved in such construction. Among the most important of these problems was the legal liability a company would face in case of an accident at a nuclear facility. A study conducted by researchers at the Brookhaven National Laboratory in 1956 (WASH-740) concluded that, in a worst-case scenario, 3,400 people would be killed and 43,000 injured in case of a nuclear accident. In addition, property damage could reach as much as $7 billion.

Few, if any, private companies were willing to accept this level of risk in the construction of a nuclear reactor. In addition, the amount of insurance from private companies (even high-risk takers, like Lloyd's of London) available to cover a company's liability in case of a nuclear accident was far too low. The best terms available capped limits at $60 million for liability and an additional $60 million for property damage.

Under these circumstances, the U.S. Congress became convinced that the development of nuclear power in the U.S. was going to be possible only if the federal government itself assumed all or most of the financial responsibility for accidents that might occur at a facility.

As a result, it passed a piece of legislation authored by Senator Clinton Anderson and Representative Melvin Price that absolved private companies from all legal liability for any accidents that might occur at a nuclear power plant.

In addition, the Price-Anderson bill allocated $500 million to a fund designed (along with the $60 million available from private insurers) to pay the victims of any such accident. The legislation included an expiration date of 1967, 10 years after its adoption.

As expiration of the original Price-Anderson Act approached, Congress adopted an extension to the legislation in 1966. This extension maintained liability protection for nuclear power plants in essentially the same form as the original act, although it did make some minor adjustments in provisions for liability and payments in case of an accident. The act was amended again in 1975 (for 12 years) and 1988 (for 14 years).

As the latest extension was about to expire, Congress took up yet another amendment to the act in 2001. Although the latest extension has not yet been approved, a temporary continuation of Public Law 85-256 was passed by the Congress in 2003.

One of the most significant changes included in the 1975 and 1988 amendments was a shift of primary liability in case of an accident from the federal government to private industry. A fund to cover costs of such an accident was created and paid for by a tax on nuclear power plant owners.

Over time, the value of that fund has increased; today it amounts to more than $10 billion, an amount that would be increased to nearly $11 billion if the 2001 amendment passes.

Private Ownership of
Special Nuclear Materials Act, 88-489 of 1964

One of the most serious concerns of legislators in their early debates over the peacetime applications of nuclear energy was the ownership of nuclear materials. With the experience of the first two fission bombs fresh in their minds, public officials worried that these materials might fall into the wrong hands and be used for weapons production.

Under both the Atomic Energy Act of 1946 and the Atomic Energy Act of 1954, therefore, ownership of nuclear materials was restricted to the U.S. government. As reasonable as this policy may have been from a security standpoint, it proved to be an impediment for industry in the development of nuclear power plants and other facilities. The industry began lobbying almost immediately after World War II, then, for the right to own nuclear materials on their own.

Slowly, government officials and legislators were won over to this position and, in 1964, the Congress passed the Private Ownership of Special Nuclear Materials Act, which allowed private companies to purchase and own nuclear materials.

Energy Reorganization Act, 93-438 of 1974

One of the fundamental criticisms that had long been aimed at the Atomic Energy Commission was the inherent conflict in two of its major responsibilities— promoting the use of nuclear power in the United States while adopting and enforcing standards that ensured the safety (and, hence, the cost) of nuclear power plants. In trying to carry out these two somewhat conflicting roles, the AEC was often accused of siding too often with the nuclear industry and too often ignoring the safety problems associated with reactors.

In 1974, the U.S. Congress dealt with this problem by abolishing the AEC and reassigning its responsibilities to two new agencies—the Nuclear Regulatory Commission (NRC) and the Energy Research and Development Administration (ERDA).

The former agency was charged with the regulatory functions previously carried out by the AEC. It was assigned the task of regulating the:
1.   Design, construction, and operation of nuclear reactors
2.   Research on nuclear materials
3.   Safety and safeguard functions related to nuclear energy

The latter agency was given the task of promoting research and development on nuclear power. ERDA remained in existence for only three years. In 1977, it was abolished as a separate agency and its functions were transferred to the new Department of Energy, created by the Department of Energy Organization Act of 1977. Some critics have suggested that the goal of the 1974 Energy Reorganization Act was never adequately achieved since the NRC continued to have relationships too closely tied to the nuclear power industry to allow it to carry out its regulatory tasks adequately.

Nuclear Waste Policy Act, 97-425 of 1982

The third in the federal government's trio of acts designed to deal with the nation's nuclear waste problems was the Nuclear Waste Policy Act of 1982 (NWPA), fashioned to deal with high-level wastes. The act charged the Department of Energy with responsibility for developing a plan by which the federal government would develop an underground repository for the permanent storage of high-level wastes.

The act also set out a time table for the selection, testing, approval, and opening of a site for the nuclear waste depository. According to that timeline, the first wastes were to be delivered to the storage site no later than January 31, 1998.

As with the LLWPA, the NWPA has been largely unsuccessful in solving the problem it was drafted to handle. The selection of a site (Yucca Mountain, Nevada) was accomplished, and extensive research on the site has been conducted. But, largely as a result of unexpected environmental problems and the fervent opposition of the state of Nevada and a number of environmental groups, progress in construction of the waste repository has gone forward only very slowly. In 2004, development of the site was delayed once again when the Federal Appeals Court for the District of Columbia ruled that the Department of Energy's plans for ensuring the safety of stored wastes for a period of 10,000 years was inadequate.

The court ordered DOE to modify its plans to extend the period of time during which the buried wastes could be considered to be safely entombed. Unfortunately the Yucca Mountain plan was abandoned in 2012.

Coal Mining Laws and Regulations

The coal industry is very likely the most regulated in the energy sector. Federal legal requirements apply to many specific activities associated with coal mining. A number of federal laws, regulations, and executive orders apply to coal mining activities. For the most part, state laws and regulations do not apply to coal mining on tribal lands. The extent to which the federal requirements apply to specific coal mine projects on tribal lands depends upon the nature of the project, its location, and size.

Some of the federal laws and requirements that apply to specific activities associated with coal mining are:

Acoustics
• Noise Control Act

Air Quality
• Clean Air Act

Cultural Resources
• American Indian Religious Freedom Act
• Antiquities Act
• Archaeological and Historic Preservation Act
• Archaeological Resources Protection Act
• Executive Order 11593: Protection and Enhancement of the Cultural Environment
• Executive Order 13007: Indian Sacred Sites
• Executive Order 13175: Consultation and Coordination with Indian Tribal Governments
• Executive Order 13287: Preserve America
• Historic Sites, Buildings, and Antiquities Act (Historic Sites Act)
• Illegal Trafficking in Native American Human Remains and Cultural Items
• National Historic Preservation Act
• Native American Graves Protection and Repatriation Act
• Theft and Destruction of Government Property

Ecological Resources
• Bald and Golden Eagle Protection Act
• Clean Water Act
• Endangered Species Act
• Executive Order 11988: Floodplain Management
• Executive Order 11990: Protection of Wetlands
• Executive Order 12996: Management and General Public Use of the National Wildlife Refuge System
• Executive Order 13112: Invasive Species
• Executive Order 13186: Responsibilities of Federal Agencies to Protect Migratory Birds
• Federal Insecticide, Fungicide, and Rodenticide Act
• Fish and Wildlife Coordination Act
• Migratory Bird Treaty Act
• National Wildlife Refuge System Administration Act
• Noxious Weed Act
• Rivers and Harbors Act
• Wild Free-Roaming Horses and Burros Act

Energy Resource Development
• Surface Mining Control and Reclamation Act
• Tribal Energy Resource Agreements

Environmental Justice
• Executive Order 12898: Federal Actions to Address Environmental Justice in Minority Populations and Low-income Populations

Hazardous Materials & Waste Management
• Comprehensive Environmental Response, Compensation, and Liability Act
• Emergency Planning & Community Right-to-Know Act
• Executive Order 12856: Federal Compliance With Right-to-Know Laws and Pollution Prevention Requirements

- Federal Insecticide, Fungicide, and Rodenticide Act
- Hazardous Materials Transportation Act
- Pollution Prevention Act
- Resource Conservation and Recovery Act
- Toxic Substances Control Act

Health & Safety
- Emergency Planning & Community Right-to-Know Act
- Executive Order 13045: Protection of Children From Environmental Health Risks and Safety Risks
- Federal Mine Safety and Health Act
- Occupational Safety & Health Act

Land Use
- Air Commerce and Safety Act
- Farmland Protection and Policy Act
- Federal Land Policy and Management Act
- National Trails System Act
- Rivers and Harbors Act
- Soil and Water Resources Conservation Act
- Surface Mining Control and Reclamation Act
- Wild and Scenic Rivers Act
- Wilderness Act

National Environmental Policy Act
- National Environmental Policy Act

Paleontological Resources
- Antiquities Act
- Paleontological Resources Preservation
- Theft and Destruction of Government Property

Soils & Geological Resources
- Farmland Protection and Policy Act
- Soil and Water Resources Conservation Act

Water Quality
- Clean Water Act
- Safe Drinking Water Act

Patents

The different renewable energy technologies continue to grow, which is evidenced by the number of patents filed and issued during the last several years.

The granting of patents by the United States Patent and Trademark (PTO) is often cited as a measure of the inventive activity and evidence of the effectiveness of research & development investments. Patents are considered to be such an indicator, because to be awarded

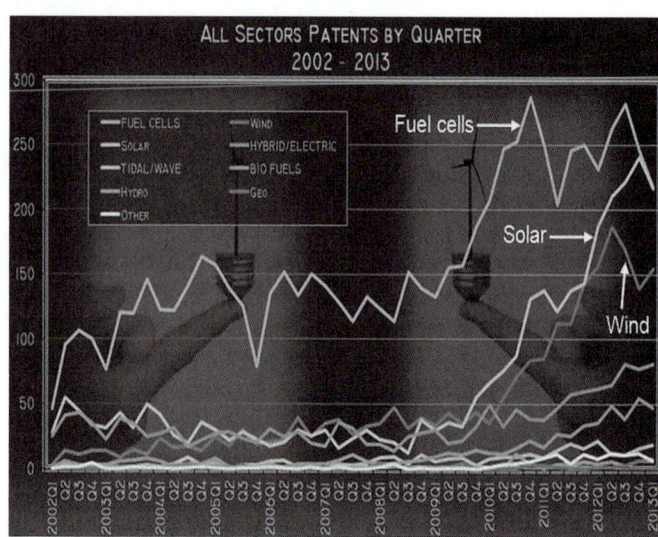

Figure 7-33. Patent filing for different energy technologies

a patent, it requires not only the efforts of inventors to develop new and non-obvious innovations but also successful handling by patent counsel to shepherd a patent application through the PTO. Thus, the granting of a patent is an indicator that efforts at innovation have been successful and that an innovation had enough perceived value to justify the time and expense in procuring the patent.

The Clean Energy Patent Growth Index (CEPGI), published quarterly by the Cleantech Group at Heslin Rothenberg Farley & Mesiti P.C. provides an indication of the trend of innovative activity in the clean energy sector from 2002 to the present. Results from the first quarter of 2013 reveal the CEPGI to have a value of 738 granted U.S. patents which is down 45 relative to the fourth quarter total of 783, but is up 44 over the quarter from one year prior. GM was granted the highest number of clean energy patents for the first quarter.

The CEPGI, shown in Figure 7 tracks the granting of U.S. patents for the following sub-components: solar, wind, hybrid/electric vehicles, fuel cells, hydroelectric, tidal/wave, geothermal, biomass/biofuels and other clean renewable energy.

In more detail:

Fuel cell patents edged solar patents by one in the first quarter of 2013, but fell 28 to 218 relative to the fourth quarter of last year. This one patent difference is the smallest differential on record and suggests that solar patents are poised to pass fuel cell patents. This difference further suggests that investments in solar technology R&D are reaching a pinnacle despite the slew of bankruptcies and consolidations in the solar industry.

Wind patents jumped 15 to 155 but still trailed solar patents (217) which fell 24 compared to the fourth quarter of 2012. Since the start of 2012 a once slim gap between solar and wind patent grants has opened up into a more than 50 patent gulf. As recently as quarter four of 2011 had these two technologies tied. Hybrid-electric vehicle patents led the rest of the field with 81, up three from the fourth quarter of 2012.

Tidal patents were up three to 19 while biofuel/biomass patents dropped seven relative to the fourth quarter to 48. Hydroelectric patents remained at seven. Geothermal patents were up one compared to the fourth quarter of 2012 resulting in eight granted patents in the first quarter. Other alternative energy patents dropped six to 7.

GM, driven by its fuel cell (34) and hybrid/electric vehicle patents (8), took the quarterly crown from 2012 annual winner Toyota. GM also topped all others in fuel cells. Toyota trailed GM by nine and had 25 fuel cell patents, seven HEV patents, and one biofuel/biomass patent. Twenty-one wind patents blew GE into third place along with six solar patents, one fuel cell, one HEV and one other patent. Mitsubishi also was led by its wind patents (18) followed by HEV and solar, both at three. Honda and Samsung tied at 22 granted clean energy patents with Honda receiving patents in fuel cells (15), HEV (5), solar (1) and biomass/biofuels (1). Samsung had 16 fuel cell and six solar patents tying GE and Sunpower for the quarterly lead in solar patents.

Vestas tied Mitsubishi in wind patents behind GE at 18 patents with wind being the only technology in which it was granted clean energy patents. Ford had 14 HEV patents leading all others in this category along with a single solar patent. More wind patents were granted to Repower (12) while Panasonic had 10 fuel cell patents and one solar patent. Hyundai followed in 10th place with four fuel cell and seven HEV patents granted.

Japan has been leading non-U.S. holders of U.S. clean energy patents and individual U.S. states with 151, which was a decrease of 26 compared to the fourth quarter and was up one patent over the same quarter a year before, to again claim the quarterly geographical clean energy patent crown.

California took second place with 82 clean energy patents, which was 16 less than the fourth quarter and up 12 over the first quarter of 2012. Germany (72) jumped 14 patents compared to the fourth quarter and took third place—followed by Michigan (68) which

jumped 17 patents due to GM and Ford's contributions described above.

Korea edged New York by three and had 43 clean energy patents in the first quarter, down 15 compared to the fourth quarter while New York dropped 14. Taiwan (25) edged Texas (22) and Massachusetts (16) topped Colorado (14). Connecticut, Canada and France all had 12 granted clean energy patents in the first quarter of 2013. New Jersey and China tied with 10 such patents.

Notes and References

1. *The True Cost of Coal*, http://www.greenpeace.org/international/en/publications/reports/cost-of-coal/
2. *FrackCheck* WV http://www.frackcheckwv.net/impacts/the-human-story/
3. http://www.eia.gov/naturalgas/
4. Koplow, Doug, 2009, Measuring Energy Subsidies Using the Price-Gap Approach: What Does It Leave Out? IISD *Trade, Investment and Climate Change Series* (Winnipeg: International Institute for Sustainable Development).
5. Laan, Tara, Christopher Beaton, and Bertille Presta—Strategies for Reforming Fossil-Fuel Subsidies: Practical Lessons from Ghana, France and Senegal, *The Untold Billions: Fossil-Fuel Subsidies, Their Impacts and the Path to Reform*
6. Nordhaus, William, 2011—Estimates of the Social Cost of Carbon: Background and Results from the RICE-2011 Model, NBER Working Paper No. 17540 (Cambridge: National Bureau of Economic Research).
7. National Research Council (NRC), 2009—*Hidden Costs of Energy: Unpriced Consequences of Energy Production and Use*, Committee on Health, Environmental, Other External Costs and Benefits of Energy Production and Consumption, (Washington: The National Academies Press).
8. Sterner, Thomas, 2012, ed., 2012, *Fuel Taxes and the Poor: The Distributional Effects of Gasoline Taxation and Their Implications for Climate Policy*
9. Alghamdi, A.A., Radwan, A.M. 2005. *Decommissioning of Offshore Structures: Challenges and Solutions*. Department of Mechanical Engineering, King Abdulaziz University. Jeddah, Saudi Arabia
10. Byrd, R. 2008. Article *Offshore Platform Decommissioning: Tales from the Gulf of Mexico*
11. California Energy Commission. 2010. *West coast LNG prospects and proposals*. http://www.energy.ca.gov/lng/documents/3_WEST_COAST_LNG_PROJECTS_PROPOSALS.PDF.
12. *Performance Degradation of Grid-Tied Photovoltaic Modules in a Desert Climatic Condition* by Adam Alfred Suleske, ASU, Tempe, Arizona
13. *The ExternE Project*. http://www.externe.info/externe_d7/?q=node/6
14. *Hazards and Hazardous Materials*—SLO County Planning Commission http://www.google.com/search?q=C.9.3.4+Impact+Assessment.+Topaz+Solar+Farm+Project&hl=en&sourceid=gd&rlz=1Q1GGLD_enUS473US474
15. *Photovoltaics for Commercial and Utilities Power Generation*, Anco S, Blazev. The Fairmont Press, 2011
16. *Solar Technologies for the 21st Century*, Anco S Blazev. The Fairmont Press, 2013

Chapter 8

Energy and Environmental Markets

The ultimate test of man's conscience may be his willingness to
sacrifice something today for the future generations whose words of thanks
will **not** *be heard by us...*

Gaylord Nelson

The 1970s started with a loud energy and environmental bangs. The U.S. and the world were on the threshold of a new trend of energy scarcity and adverse global climate for which they were not prepared. The Arab oil embargo put America in the awkward and very dangerous position to depend on the whims of a handful of unfriendly Saudi Arabian sheikhs. Was this the end of the American Dream? It surely seemed so then to all of us sitting in long lines for hours at gas stations all over the country.

To top it off, a major global *cooling* was coming our way at a fast pace for which we were not prepared either. A fast approaching gasification period was upon us, where the entire Earth's surface would soon be covered by ice, and humanity would be no more.

The scientists were sure, and who would dare doubt them? Imagine the horror... The scientific reports were convincing, and the common belief at the time was that some chemicals and changes in Earth's orbit were the dominant cause of the mid-20th century irreversible cooling cycle.

Human activity, and especially the use of aerosols, was identified as a big problem, and drastic measures were taken, which led to the extinction of the aerosol cans as we knew them then. Then came the extinction of Freon, which was widely used in air conditioning and refrigeration systems until then.

The Earth's orbit was a much more complex matter to understand and eliminate as a concern. Even if we understood it, however, there was not much we can do to restore the Earth's orbit. But even if we knew how to do it, we would not dare take any drastic actions for fear of the unknown. Further change in the orbit, nevertheless, would surely continue the cooling trend, which would be detrimental to the Earth's climate and humankind.

The scientists warned us that drastic climate change would force global economic and social adjustments, and it seemed that everyone was confused on the matter, especially political leaders, who hesitated to take any positive action to compensate for the climatic change or to delay its effect.

The warnings were quite stern; the average ground temperature in the Northern Hemisphere had fallen by 0.5°F from 1945-1968. There had been a large increase in snow cover around the world, very possibly due to a measured decrease of over 1.0% in the amount of sunshine hitting the globe.

The reason for the reduced sunshine was the increased frequency of natural events, like volcanoes and such, but also, and increasingly so, due to overuse of fossils. Cars and fossil-burning plants were blamed for emitting some gasses that were very likely causing some of the changes.

The media reports quoted famous scientists declaring that the temperature decline has taken the planet about a sixth of the way toward the Ice Age average. The world agricultural system was under imminent threat. The worst example was in Britain, where the cooling trend had already shortened the growing season by two weeks. That could lead to unprecedented food shortages and even catastrophic famines.

Radical warming solutions and plans were suggested and some emerged as winners. Increasing the global temperature to the point of melting the arctic ice cap to achieve some long-term stability was the goal. One possible way of achieving all this was the idea of covering part of the Earth with black soot. That was guaranteed to raise the temperature gradually and permanently. The debate continued for a long time, and lots of other, similarly wacky ideas were presented and discussed, but very few concrete, practical, actions to rectify the matter were taken. And so we went through the 1970s; wondering not how but when the global freeze would affect us...scary times those were!

Fast forward to the 21st century—today we are still in a panic mode, but the trend has reversed. We now have enough energy, so we no longer depend on the Arab and other volatile nations for our energy supplies. And the Earth is no longer cooling down, but…wait… it is now getting too warm, too fast. The plans for covering it with black soot were abandoned, but instead it appears now that the black soot had invaded us, and is now the cause of all that ails the Earth and the humanity. The black soot and other stuff in the air, soil and water is overheating the Earth, causing major disasters with many more and much worse to come.

And surely, we have choked the atmosphere we live in with carbon emissions as a result of burning fossil fuels to heat and cool ourselves during different seasons. By so doing, we have apparently turned our tender planet into a greenhouse, and the air pollution we have created traps too much of the sun's warmth, preventing it from escaping back into space.

The average global ground temperature has risen over 1.0°F over the past 100 years, and the warming trend is accelerating by the day. Scientists predict that the abuse of our environment is so great and irreversible that the Earth will be again in the hot state it was 60 million years ago, at which point we all will die.

Let's fast forward 250 years in the future…

- Laughter in the auditorium: "Yes it was a marketing scam. That was the way some clever people scared everyone to sell their ideas and the products they had for sale." End of story.
- Or else, there would be total silence in auditorium, because it is empty…with all people on Earth dead and gone.
- Most likely, however, there would be a compromise, where the new generations would have found a way to live without fossils, using solar, wind, and ocean energies to power everything. The only reminder of the fossil's past would be the ruins of thousands of coal and gas power plants. The greatest benefit of this change would be pristine environments and healthy people.

Let's take a look now at some of the present and future issues and opportunities:

INTRODUCTION

The generation and use of energy have created enormous opportunities for many creative individuals and companies in the past, and could offer many more now and in the future. Huge markets have opened, where energy-related products and services are made, sold and bought in great quantities. Billions upon billions of dollars change hands daily around the globe in fuel and other forms of energy sales. And as the global needs increase, so do those markets. As a matter of fact, with the population explosion during the last several decades, and the substantial progress of the 21st century's science and technology, the energy-related markets are expanding.

At the same time, we see the development of environment-related markets around the globe too. Since energy generation and the peripheral products and services emit toxic gasses and liquids, people and companies are now buying and selling environment-related products and services too. Although those products and services are not as well-defined as other market commodities, they are shaping as major market drivers in the 21st century.

To clarify the picture, we need to define the energy and environmental markets as follows:

The energy market is a sector of the U.S. and global economy that creates goods, services and jobs primarily related to: the production of fuels; generating electric power and heat; and their residential and commercial uses.

Some of the key segments of the energy market are:

- Fossil fuels production (coal mining, gas and oil drilling); their transport, storage, and use
- Renewable energy technologies; their manufacturing, transport, and use
- Production equipment manufacturing (i.e.,, mining, drilling, and solar cells manufacturing equipment)
- Power plant construction, operation, maintenance, and decommissioning
- Power generation, distribution, and use
- Financial and legal services related to the above

The energy generation and use create a different set of opportunities for creating goods, services and jobs in the area of environmental protection. We call those _environmental markets_.

Some of the key areas of the _environmental markets_ are:

- Carbon tax
- Carbon (emissions) trading
- Pollution-free industries:
  — Renewable technologies

— Natural gas conversions
— Carbon capture and storage
— New equipment and processes
- Electric cars
- Performance and liability insurance
- Investment opportunities
- Environmental legal services

Let's take a closer look at the energy and environmental markets.

THE ENERGY MARKETS

The energy market is the area—or rather several areas—of the U.S. and world industry and technology that deal with the creation, support, and use of energy goods, services, and jobs. Although, officially speaking, the energy market is commonly referred to as the market that deals strictly with the supply and trade of energy, usually electric energy and heat.

We will, however, allow the inclusion of some supporting and peripheral markets into this general category (i.e., production equipment manufacturing; construction, financial, and legal service), because without these, the energy market simply won't be there. Or at the very least, it won't be of the shape and size we know it today.

As mentioned above, in the very broad sense of the word the energy and energy-related market can be divided into a number of segments, as follows:

The key segments of the *energy market* are:
- Fossil fuels production (coal mining, gas and oil drilling), their transport, storage, and use.
- Renewable energy technologies; manufacturing, transport, and use
- Production equipment manufacturing (i.e., for mining, drilling, and solar cell manufacturing)
- Power plant construction, operation, maintenance, and decommissioning
- Power generation, distribution, and use
- Political action, financial and legal services related to the above

Fossil fuels generate a major part of the energy (heating and electric power) that we use on daily basis here in the U.S. and worldwide. The most commonly used fuels today are: coal, oil, gas, nuclear,* and biofuels. The other power generating technologies: hydro-, geo-, ocean-, solar, and wind do not require any fuels, so they will be reviewed separately.

Nuclear power generation is usually not included in the fossil power category, but uranium ore and most other nuclear fuel precursors are mined as ores from the Earth's depths. Because of their fossil-like origins and limited quantities, we would classify nuclear fuels as "fossil fuels," at least for the purposes of this text.

NOTE: A detailed description of the production, transport, and use of the different fuels could be found in the previous chapters of this text, so here we will only take a brief look at their markets and the related activities.

Power Generation Market

One of the most important and largest markets in the U.S. and the world is that of *electric power generation, distribution, and use.* This is a huge market that includes an enormous network of mines, drill sites, power plants, land and water vehicle fleets, distribution lines, and millions of jobs around the world.

The market activities include all operations related to the cradle-to-grave power generation, its distribution, and use. That includes: coal mining, oil and gas drilling; transport activities; production equipment manufacturing; power plant construction, operation, and maintenance; power distribution and use; and finally, decommissioning of the facilities and disposal of the equipment at end-of-life.

Technologically complex, labor intensive, and expensive sets of events, involving thousands of facilities and millions of people in the U.S. and around the world, are fully responsible for bringing us human comforts and propelling the world economies on daily basis. That is what the *energy markets* are and it is what they do—at the expense of disturbing our environment. Catch 22? Yes! It is something that we cannot live with, but cannot live without, either.

We take a much closer look at the technological aspects of the different technologies and procedures involved in the energy market operations in other chapters of this text, so here we review only their market aspects.

These are large markets, arranged in different categories; each with a set of sub-markets within the respective energy market category.

NOTE: We use the terms *energy and power* somewhat interchangeably in this text, simply because they have almost the same meaning in most cases. Nevertheless, the term *energy* (as in energy resource) is used when the energy is not quantified and usually describes the energy content and the potential to generate electric power, heat and other forms of energy. Once the potential energy is used, as in burning in a furnace to generate electricity, we then call it *power,* as in 1.0 MW electric power was generated and used.

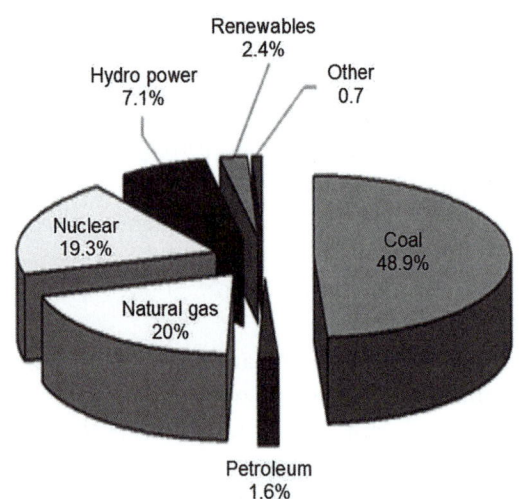

Figure 8-1. Power generation in the U.S. (2010-2011)

In 2012 the U.S. coal-fired plants produced about 1,500,000 GWh of electric power, vs. 2,100,000 GWh. That was almost 60% of U.S. power produced by coal-fired power plants in 2008, which means that coal power is being steadily replaced now by other fuels, such as natural gas, wind, solar, biofuels, and other. There are about 600 coal-fired power plants in the U.S. today (vs. 650 in 2001) with about 1,500 turbines and generating units, and a total of 339 GW nameplate capacity.

At the same time, there are over 2,300 coal-fired power plants in China, generating over 30% more electricity than their U.S. counterparts. In addition to suggesting that the Chinese power plants are almost 50% less efficient than those U.S., those numbers also tell us that the Chinese power industry produces equally higher GHG pollution. This ratio is increasing even more, because the Chinese are building hundreds of coal-fired plants every year and there are no plans to slow down their proliferation.

Globally, there are currently proposals for 1,200 new coal-fired power plants to be build immediately in 59 countries. China and India together account for 76% of the new coal plants projects, while the U.S. is seventh on the list with 36 proposed coal-fired power plants.

The new reality, however, points to a shift in direction in the U.S., where no new coal-fired plants will be built any time soon. This is due to new EPA restrictions, implemented in 2013, which make it impossible for new coal-fired power plants to meet the new emission standards. China, India, and other developing countries,

however, have no such restrictions, so they are ramping up the construction of new coal-fired power plants as one way of continuing their economic development and supporting the increasing population.

If all of those power plants are built as scheduled, it would represent almost four times increase of the current capacity of all coal-fired plants in the United States. This, however, doesn't mean that all proposals will be approved and that all coal plants will be built any time soon, and we are sure that many won't be built ever. Nevertheless, that number and the intentions behind are reflection of things to come and a confirmation that coal is not going away any time soon.

We know that coal-fired power plants are the largest contributor to the greenhouse gas emissions that cause climate change. We also know that we must be reasonable and must consider at least 80% of the world's proven oil, coal and natural gas reserves as almost depleted, and leave them in the ground, unburned. That is needed to ensure that future generations have some fossils, and to avoid the release of excess GHGs to warm the planet above the internationally agreed upon limit of two degrees Celsius.

We also know that even though 167 countries that are responsible for more than 87% of the world's carbon dioxide emissions signed the 2009 Copenhagen accord and endorsed the two-degree target, it is still too much of an increase in such a short period of time. And on top of that, it is now becoming clear that even that lenient target won't be achieved, so we need to be ready for greater temperature increases and more spectacular climate changes in the near future.

On a positive note, many U.S. coal-fired plants are old and ready for retirement. Since no new coal plants can be build in the U.S. (in addition to the new trend of conversion to natural gas) that will bring the number of coal-fired power plants in the U.S. significantly down in the near future.

The bad news is that, whatever the number of decommissioned power plants in the U.S., it will be offset several times by thousands of new coal plants built around the globe in the near future. fact suggests that the net effect of GHG emissions will increase uncontrollably for the foreseeable future. China and India will make sure that that happens.

And even more surprising is the new trend in Germany and some other developed countries, where coal is coming back as a most reliable and economically-feasible power generation option. There are plans in those countries for gas-fired power plants to be converted back to coal burning. That is not a move in the right direction, so let's hope that it is only temporary and that it won't spread around the world.

U.S. Power Generation and Use

The U.S. is one of the world's largest energy consumers. We were actually in second place in terms of total use in 2010 and seventh in energy consumption per-capita. This, however, does not include the huge amount of energy used in other countries (China in particular) in the production of goods exported for use in the U.S. Including those in the energy calculations brings the U.S. way ahead of any country in energy consumption.

During the same time the energy generation and consumption in the country was as follows:

Table 8-1. U.S. energy generation and consumption

Energy generation:

- 28% from petroleum (used mostly for personal and commercial transportation)
- 25% from coal (used mostly for power generation)
- 25% from natural gas (also used mostly for power generation)
- 12% from nuclear power
- 6% from large hydroelectric dams
- 2% from wind power, geothermal and solar energy

Energy consumption:

- 40% as electric power generated by:
  —51% coal
  —21% nuclear
  —17% natural gas
  —9% renewables
  —2% crude oil

- 29% in transportation used as:
  —95% crude oil
  —3% renewables
  —2% natural gas

- 21% for industrial operations used as:
  —42% crude oil
  —40% natural gas
  —10% renewables
  —8% coal

- 10% for residential and commercial use in form of:
  —78% natural gas
  —18% crude oil
  —2% renewables
  —2% coal

The energy consumption in the country increased much faster than the energy production during the 20th century so now the difference is met through imports, mostly crude oil for transportation purposes:

Table 8-2. World energy consumption (in PWh in 2008)

Source	U.S.	World
Oil	11.71	50.33
Gas	6.50	31.65
Coal	6.60	37.38
Hydro	0.84	8.71
Nuclear	2.41	8.14
Renewables	0.95	1.38
Total	**29.26**	**138.41**

The U.S. per-capita energy consumption has been consistent from the 1970s to date, with the average of 334 million Btus used per person from 1980-2010. Although the U.S. population has been increasing, the energy demand has remained constant because the energy used to support the increase in U.S. consumption has been shifted to other countries.

In contrast, the world average of energy use is about 75 million Btus per person, nearly 5 times less than the energy use per capita in the U.S.

The Country of California

No, this is not a misspelling. In many respects, California is a separate and large country. It is much larger in territory and wealth, including power generation, than most of the countries in this world. California has many state and local laws that dictate the energy and environmental projects, some of which are changing the way energy was used before. New approaches and trends in power generation, distribution, regulation, and use have been implemented, and many are under way, or planned.

California is switching to natural gas and renewables with unprecedented speed and unwavering determination. So, in 2013 coal power generation is down to 1%, which is partially responsible for the drastic reduction in carbon emissions from power generation. Over 22% reduction was recorded in 2011, countering increases from other industrial sources and helping drive state-wide plant emissions down 5.6%.

Emissions from the electric power generation sector in the state was 34.9 million metric tons in 2011, down from 44.6 million in 2010. The total reported emissions

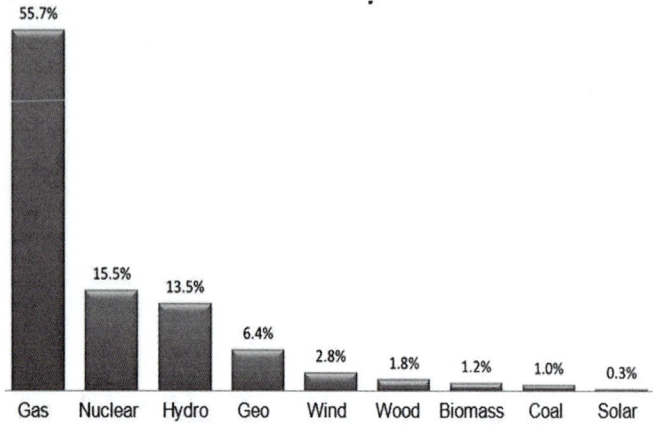

Figure 8-2. California energy generation

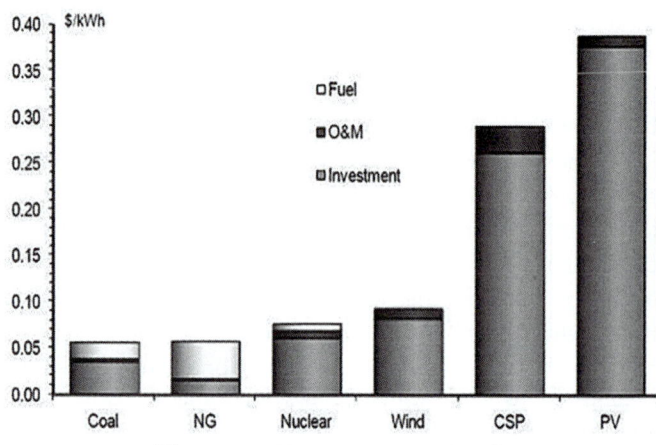

Figure 8-3. Energy cost per kW/h

were 111 million metric tons, down from 117.6 million during the same period. Those are emissions from stationary sources only, and do not include emissions from the transportation sector, which actually have gone up.

The reductions reflect mostly decreases from electricity-generated emissions, due to increased gas and renewable generation. There is significant increase in hydro, solar, wind, and nuclear power generation, which, combined with some decrease in consumption, accounts for the overall GHG reduction.

Although there is a definite inequality in the different stages of the different energy sources, as seen in Figure 8-3, the significant switch to less polluting energy sources is plausible. It had won California the title of the most advanced state in renewable power implementation in the country.

The California Energy Supply and Demand

California has been relying more and more on gas, and so more than half of the electricity generation in the state is done by gas-fired steam turbines. That is nothing new, since the ratio has been steady, but the actual use of natural gas has increased about 25% during the last decade in response to the increase in demand. And that trend is expected to continue for a long while.

In 2011, California had total of 71 GW of electric power generating capacity; 45 GW of the total was natural gas-fired power plants. Hydro was distant second with about 13.5 GW, and nuclear with 4.5 GW generating capacity. Only natural gas-fired installations have shown a definite increase during the last decade.

The renewable capacity also grew, but a much slower pace. Solar and wind were at 0.6 GW and 4.0 GW respectively, and other renewables followed at about 2 GW. Although the number of the renewable installations is increasing, so is the total generating capacity, thus the

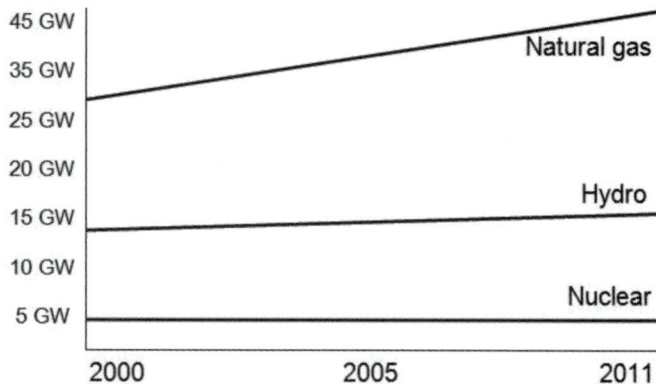

Figure 8-4. California electricity generation capacity

overall ratio of active generation capacity remains the same.

The actual electric power generation, however, shows different ratios. Again in 2011, natural gas produced 91 TWh electricity, while nuclear and hydro shared the second place with 36.5 TWh power generation each. Renewables were close at 33 TWh, which is a dramatic change in the overall energy picture. The renewables produced over 14% of the state's electricity in 2011, vs. only a fraction a decade ago.

Obama's Energy Security Trust

In his 2013 State of the Union address, President Obama called on Congress to create an energy security trust fund (ESTF), which would create new energy markets complete with new technologies, thousands of new jobs that ultimately will reduce or eliminate the painful spikes in gas prices.

The President's plan is build on an idea that has bipartisan support, including industry experts, leading CEOs, and other key players. ESTF is focused on the goal of reducing oil use for transportation by shifting

America's cars and trucks to alternative fuels.

The funding for the energy security trust will come from energy projects and will be invested in research that will make future technologies cheaper and better. The proposed ESTF will fund the advances that will allow us to run cars and trucks on electricity or home-grown fuels, and on the technologies that will enable us to drive from coast-to-coast without using any oil.

The energy security trust will provide $2 billion over a 10-year period, which will be primarily used for critical, cutting-edge research focused on developing cost-effective transportation alternatives. The bulk of the funding will be provided by revenues from federal oil and gas development and will not add any addition-al costs to the federal budget.

Those investments will support research into a range of technologies, such as advanced vehicles that run on electricity, homegrown biofuels, and domesti-cally produced natural gas. They also will help fund a small number of real-world experiments that try differ-ent transportation techniques in cities and towns around the country using advanced vehicles at scale.

In each of the last four years, domestic production of oil and gas has gone up and our use of foreign oil has gone down. While America uses less foreign oil now than we've used in almost two decades, there's more work left to do in this area to achieve greater energy se-curity, which requires developing new energy supplies and new technologies that use less oil.

The proposed secure energy trust will ensure American scientists and research labs have the support they need to keep our country competitive and create the jobs of the future.

Good idea? Our government at work...again. But we have seen the results from a number of such noble attempts, which resulted in disasters when the ball was dropped without a notice, due to shifting government priorities. What is different this time? How much can we rely on the proposed ESTF?

Who believes that the oil and gas companies will dip into their pockets and hand out $2 billion? Who wants to bet that if they do, then rising gasoline prices will get hit with a new tax (to support the ESTF) at a time when American's can least afford it. "The only way we're going to break this cycle of spiking gas prices for good is to shift our cars and trucks off of oil for good," Obama said. "It's not just about saving money. It's also about saving the environment. But it's also about our national security."

Obama's administration plans also intend to accel-erate oil and gas permits to raise production. Back we

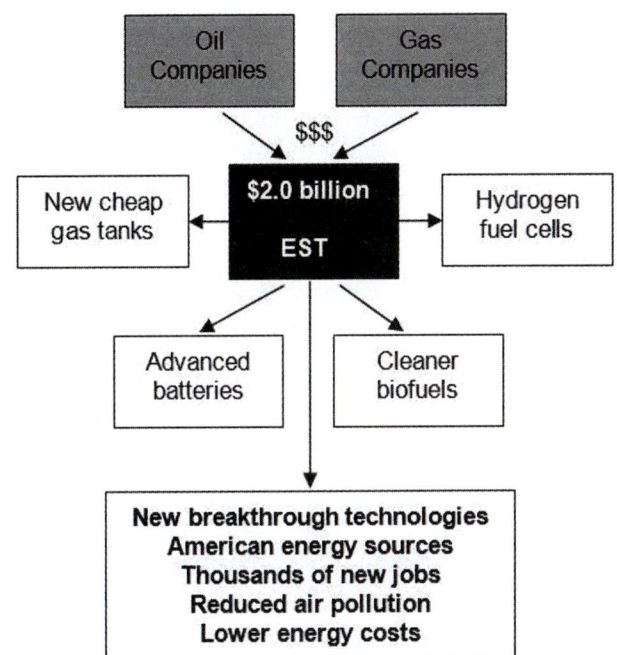

Figure 8-5. Obama's Energy Security Trust

are at the old and familiar, "Drill, baby drill," but more and faster this time. So, royalties for mining and energy development added up to $12 billion in 2012, according to the office of natural resources revenue, which is $1 billion more than in 2011 because of increased natural gas fracking on public lands.

So, that initiative seems geared to addressing the global climate change, but counts on expanding U.S. oil and gas production for raising revenue for the develop-ment of low-carbon technologies, a catch 22 of sorts.

In the best of cases, however, the ESTF proposal fixes only part of the problem. While U.S. vehicle-relat-ed emissions are substantial, reducing them —even to zero—is not going to change much the global climate change picture. Coal-fired power plants in the U.S. and around the world—and especially those in China, In-dia, Russia, and many other developing countries—will make sure that is so.

The political economy of the trust is also question-able, because by designing the trust as a tax on oil pro-duction that is specifically destined to reduce gasoline for the U.S. vehicle fleet, the initiative essentially asks oil producers to pay to diminish their largest market. That is another Catch 22, which the oil companies have en-countered before and are used to dealing with, and this time is no different.

Instead, to get real answers to the global climate challenge, we should strike a larger bargain that will get the entire energy industry support. That is the only way to make a meaningful impact on carbon emissions in the U.S. and around the world.

As an example, Norway is using income from oil production to fund the transition away from oil. Instead of using royalties, however, the oil companies are paying a corresponding carbon tax. The proceeds fund a wide range of initiatives, including $2 billion to expand public transport and facilitate the transition to electric cars. And all that in a country that can fit several times in the U.S., and has hundreds of times fewer natural and other resources.

World Energy Use

As we are looking around for solutions, and going back and forth on our promises for cleaner environment, the world's population and its needs for energy, including the consumption of coal, gas, and crude oil is growing dramatically. It is projected to increase by almost 50% of present levels by 2035. The growing demand is driven by the needs of a global population that is projected to increase 25% by the same time, and by the desire of developing countries to improve the lifestyle of their people and grow their economies.

Because of that, most of the energy use growth is in developing countries, such as China, India, and a number of other Asian and South American countries. Energy demand from ramping up economic output and improved standards of living likely will put added pressure on energy supplies, while at the same time adding millions of tons of GHG pollution into the atmosphere.

The energy demand in China alone is expected to increase by 75% by 2035. The response of the oil and gas companies, of course, is, "Drill, baby drill." Although the use of renewables is expected to triple over the next 25 years, the increase in power output won't be enough to offset the fossils use and related damages.

It's quite obvious by now that the world will depend on fossil fuels for at least 50% of its energy needs for a long time to come—or at least until there are no more fossil fuels to burn. So, the fossil use will increase as needed to fuel the developing global economies, and continue to emit excess pollution—regardless of what the international agreements say.

The new technologies and the increase of domestic production have helped the U.S. reduce its crude oil imports significantly. The developing countries, however, are increasing their imports, so the supply and demand balance is still in favor of demand, while the supplies are decreasing by the day.

Fueled mostly by fossils, the U.S. economy is surging ahead, using twice as much energy per capita as the

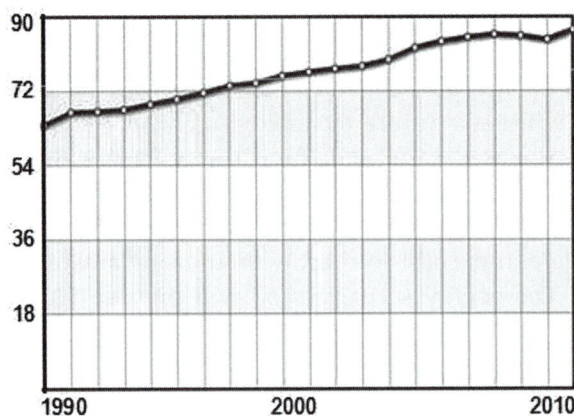

Figure 8-6. Global oil consumption in million barrels per day

entire 27 countries in the European Union combined, 10 times more than China, and 20 times more than India.

The theoretical energy available for power generation in 2008 was 144,000 TWh, while the total end use was about 98,000 TWh. That means that 46,000 TWh, or almost 1/3 of all available energy at the time, was simply wasted in inefficient equipment and processes. That is a major problem that has to be addressed in a timely fashion, and factored in all energy and environmental calculations and future assumptions.

A major part of energy is lost during the power generation through the inefficient burning of fuels (coal, gas, and oil), and the respective cooling cycles. Nuclear power generation, for example, wastes nearly 70% of its energy on water cooling systems, so from a total of 8,283 TWh generated in 2008, only 2,731 TWh were used and paid for.

Similarly, a lot of energy is wasted in cooling steam turbines in coal-, gas-, and oil-fired power plants. Some solar power generators, such as solar thermal power plants, also waste a lot of their energy for water-cooling. The losses vary across the various energy sources, depending on technology and processes used. In all cases, it amounts to a lot of fuel and money wasted. The waste ranges from 20-50% for the different power plants and technologies.

And to make things worse, all the power generation and waste issues translate into excess emissions of gasses, liquids, and solid wastes, accompanied by heat emissions, all of which pollute the air, soil, and water tables around the world. That opens doors to opportunities for developing new, smarter, less wasteful, and less polluting power generation, distribution, and use technologies.

We will now take a closer look at the markets created by the production and use of fossils, followed by those of the renewable and other technologies.

FOSSIL ENERGY MARKETS

Coal

Coal mining is one of the oldest industries in the world. It is characterized by a well-known and established product and related processes. The choice of mining method is determined largely by the geology of the location and type of the coal deposits.

All coal comes from two different types of mines: underground and surface. Underground mines are used when the coal is deep in the sediment and surface mines are used when the coal is near the surface. Underground mining currently accounts for a bigger share of world coal production than opencast mining, although in several important coal- producing countries, surface mining is more common. For example, surface mining accounts for around 80% of production in Australia, while in the U.S. it is used for about 67% of production.

There are two main types of black coal: thermal coal, also called steaming coal, and metallurgical coal, also known as coking coal. The quality of the coal varies with the mine and the location of the reserves. Coal from Wyoming has lower energy content, but has low relative sulfur content (which is considered a serious polluter). Reserves of thermal coal in the U.S. that are used mostly for power generation and heating, are much larger than those of metallurgical coal, so the industry is oriented toward thermal coal production. The ratio of underground vs. surface mines has remained stable over the past decade.

Different types of coal have different uses. Steam coal, also known as thermal coal, is mainly burned in coal-fired power generation plants. Coking coal, known as metallurgical coal, is mainly used in steel production.

The U.S. Coal Mining

Coal mining was a huge business in the U.S. during the 19th and 20th centuries and still is, but there are some difficulties lately. That is reflected in significant reduction in coal production in the U.S., and the diminishing of its contribution to power generation (where it is replaced by natural gas).

The coal market is going through a major shift; in the U.S. the demand for coal is diminishing. To compensate for losses in the U.S. energy market, the coal companies are finding overseas markets for their coal and are exporting large quantities. That is a new phenomenon, which is quite controversial, because on one hand we boast reducing GHG emissions as a result of reducing the amount of coal burned, while on the other we are exporting massive amounts of to be burned somewhere else. The net effect to the GHG emissions is absolute zero, and we must account for that in the environmental statistics and formulas.

The total coal production in the U.S. has been over 1 billion tons annually until 2012, when it dropped to just slightly under that number. The coal production in 2013 is also down, most likely due to competition from the rapid drop in natural gas prices after 2010, and the subsequent conversion of coal- to gas-fired power plants.

In 1987, Wyoming became the largest coal producing state in the U.S. using strip-mining exclusively. Wyoming's coal reserves total about 69.3 billion tons, or 14.2% of the total available U.S. coal reserve. West Virginia and Kentucky are distant seconds in total coal produced. Texas is the state with most coal use, followed by Illinois.

The demand for coal is driven primarily by its use as a fuel for power generation. Presently, metallurgical coal is at a high demand, as companies are rushing to meet the demand for steel. Emerging economies are increasingly using metallurgical coal, and the demand will increase over the next five years. Coal for electricity consumption is also expanding in some parts of the world, as consumers and businesses increase their production and energy use.

Global Coal Mining

Coal is still a very big business globally. There are about 36,000 coal-related businesses around the world, employing over 4 million people, and generating over $1 trillion in annual revenue. Since 2000, global coal consumption has grown faster than any other fuel. The five largest coal users are China, USA, India, Russia and Japan, which account for over 75% of total global coal use.

The biggest market for coal is Asia, which currently accounts for over 67% of global coal consumption, although China is responsible for a significant portion of this. Many countries do not have natural energy resources sufficient to cover their energy needs, therefore need to import energy to help meet their requirements. Japan, Chinese Taipei, and Korea, for example, import significant quantities of steam coal for electricity generation and coking coal for steel production.

Coal demand across Southeast Asia is expected to double by 2020 to over 250 million tons, which is a cause of concern that the growth of coal-fired power generation is undermining the efforts by many countries to rein in global GHG emissions. A major (and increasing) part of the imported coal to those countries comes from the U.S.

Table 8-3. Global coal production in million tons (2011)

Country	Yearly
China	3,471
USA	1,004
India	585
Australia	414
Indonesia	376
Russia	334
S. Africa	253
Germany	189
Poland	139
Kazakhstan	117

China is the world's largest coal consumer, using coal for over 2/3 of its energy production. The demand for coal has been growing lately and is expected to rise steadily even more until at least the end of the decade. India is a major competitor in that area, and is expected to become the world's largest thermal coal importer in coming years due to mining and transport bottlenecks and stagnant domestic natural gas output.

Japan is in a energy conundrum, where the solution (for now at least) is coal. Tokyo Electric Power Co., the operator of the Fukushima nuclear power plant, is using about three times more coal in 2013 than a year earlier in an effort to offset lost production from idled nuclear reactors. Japan has no coal, so guess from where the coal will be imported? The U.S., of course.

Australia will also benefit from exporting mountains of coal, since its mining sector has been hit by falling prices and softening demand. So the construction of new coal-fired power plants in Southeast Asia is very exciting news to the coal companies there. Australian thermal coal exports are expected to rise to 183 million metric tons, with a steady growth of 7% annually for the foreseeable future.

Coal is widely used around the globe and its prices fluctuate on daily basis, depending on the demand and other local and global conditions. The global demand for both thermal coal and coking coal has increased during the past five years as some emerging economies have shown rapid growth. As the global economy normalizes and the power generation is satisfied, steel production is expected to increase, thus boosting demand for coking coal. The emerging technologies that enable burning low-sulfur coal will also increase demand for thermal coal in Western markets, while at the same time keeping coal's environmental impact under control.

Coal Transport

Coal is transported via trucks, barges and trains around the U.S. and on large ocean vessels internationally. About 70-75% of the coal mined in the U.S., however, is transported via train to, and used at, U.S. based coal-fired power plants.

Specialized, large train configurations are used to transport the mined coal from the mines to the coal processing facilities and to the coal-fired power plants. Trains of 100 railroad cars, 100 tons each are the norm, and are shuttling back and forth hundreds of miles each way day and night between the mines and the power plants.

In 2011, for example, 700 million tons of coal was transported: 110 million by trucks, and 100 million by river barges, and most of the rest by coal trains. About 60 million tons of coal is moved by conveyor belts servicing mine-mouth power plants located up to 10 miles from the mine.

This is a significant increase over the total of 20 million tons of coal transported in 1970, and 180 million in 1980. The cost of coal transportation is increasing proportionally too. At an average of $11-16 per ton, it makes 15-20% of the total wholesale cost of coal in most cases today. Since the cost depends on the distance travelled, a dollar-per-net-ton-mile measure is used, which varies with location and other conditions.

The average transportation cost has increased 2-3 fold during the last decade too, which is an added burden to already burdened coal industry. Presently, barge transport is the cheapest mode of coal transport, followed by rail and truck transport. Conveyor transport is the most expensive because of the high cost of energy and maintenance needed to keep it going.

As we use and export greater amounts of coal from more remote locations, coal transportation is becoming an increasingly important concern from cost, energy, and environmental standpoints. And as distances increase, the long distance hauls contribute to cost increases, so transportation cost at times can greatly exceed the mining cost. The railroad infrastructure is getting old, and coal train accidents are not unusual, which is an additional and expensive problem to deal with too.

Coal is also stored at the mine-mouth, at the rail transport nodes, or as an emergency supply. Coal supply is often placed in "dead storage" in a compacted and sealed pile that is not susceptible to dusting during high winds. That way the air pollution due to coal dust is minimized.

The emergency coal storage pile is used only when the normal supply is depleted. It consists of coal layers of 12-inch deep coal layers that are compacted to a 25-foot high pile with bulk density of about 70 pounds per ft^3. Thermocouples are placed throughout the pile to monitor hot spots and prevent spontaneous combustion. The outer surface of the pile can be sprayed with an organic polymer-crusting agent to prevent dusting or rain erosion. This way water runoff contains little contaminants, which, together with a waterproof base, prevents water seepage into the ground.

There were attempts made in the past to move coal from the mine to the power plants via pipeline. This has been attempted on several occasions, and it requires the coal to be pulverized and suspended in large quantities of water. Thus produced coal-water slurry was pumped into a steel pipe and delivered under pressure hundreds of miles away to the point of use, usually a power plant. Here the coal-water slurry had to be processed to remove the water before it could be burned in furnaces.

One such case was a 275-miles long, 18-inch diameter, steel pipeline stretching from a coal mine in northern Arizona to a power plant on the Nevada border. About 5 million tons of coal suspended in water was moved every year, using millions of gallons of fresh water to push the pulverized coal slurry through the pipe.

Entire lakes, 3,750 acre-feet (over 1 billion gallons), of fresh water were needed for this operation every year. Enormous energy was also needed to pulverize the coal and run the huge pumps that pushed the coal slurry along its long route. But the experiment didn't last long, because water is a precious commodity in Arizona, and the locals shut down the pipeline amidst intense protest and lawsuits. A number of similar projects were started and discontinued around the U.S. in the 1970s and 80s.

Coal Use

Around the globe, coal is used primarily for electricity generation and steel production. Until recently, coal accounted for nearly half of the power generation in the U.S. Its use is diminishing now, being replaced by natural gas as new gas deposits are found all over the U.S.

Coal production has stabilized in certain regions of the world, and yet, the overall coal production has expanded faster than the global GDP. The industry's main product, thermal coal (used in power generation),

is constantly under threat from environmental concerns, yet coal production is forecast to expand in line with world GDP by 2020. Coal production and imports by developing countries are growing particularly strongly and expected to dominate the world's coal markets.

The rapid development of new gas fracking techniques, as well as the increased shale oil production is threatening the coal mining around the world. The switch to gas-fired energy in the U.S. had more than doubled its coal export capacity, pushing coal prices down and raising a question over new coal mining developments in Australia and many other countries. The new gas capacity has, almost overnight, taken a significant share of the world's energy markets, and some of this will be at the expense of coal mining operations.

In the US, export constraints have kept coal prices low, fostering a renaissance of energy-intensive manufacturing and a switch by power plants from coal to gas. Today, however, the U.S. has more and cheaper energy, and the demand for coal is diminishing, so coal exports will most likely increase. This will also make the U.S. a major competitor to the present coal exporters.

As a matter of fact, the U.S. exported 63 million tons of cocking coal in 2012, which is 25% more than the estimates. While the U.S. coal exports will most likely go up and down, depending on demand and freight costs (which is a major constraint), it is shaping as a major coal exporter to be feared by the competition.

Coal has many important uses worldwide. In addition to its use in electricity generation, large quantities of coal are used in steel production, cement manufacturing. Around 6.6 billion tons of hard coal and 1 billion tons of brown coal were used worldwide in 2012.

Coal is also used by: alumina refineries, paper manufacturers, and the chemical and pharmaceutical industries. Several chemical products are from the coal and by-products of coal. Refined coal tar, for example, is used in the manufacture of chemicals, such as creosote oil, naphthalene, phenol, and benzene. Ammonia gas recovered from coke ovens is used to manufacture ammonia salts, nitric acid and agricultural fertilizers.

Thousands of different products have coal or coal by-products as components: soap, aspirins, solvents, dyes, plastics and fibers, such as rayon and nylon.

Coal is also an essential ingredient in the production of specialist products, such as:

- Activated carbon—used in filters for water and air purification and in kidney dialysis machines
- Carbon fiber—an extremely strong but light weight reinforcement material used in construc-

tion, mountain bikes and tennis rackets

- Silicon metal—used to produce silicones and silanes, which are in turn used to make lubricants, water repellents, resins, cosmetics, hair shampoos and toothpastes

Gasification Processes

Gasification process is a new approach that could help coal retain its place as an efficient and less-polluting fossil fuel. In conventional coal-fired plants, coal is often pulverized and burned with excess air to produce complete combustion. This results in very dilute carbon dioxide at the rate of 800 to 1200 g/kWh.

Coal gasification, instead, converts the coal to burnable gas with the maximum amount of potential energy from the coal being in the gas.

In integrated gasification combined cycle (IGCC) the first gasification step is pyrolysis, from 400°C up, where the coal rapidly gives carbon-rich char and hydrogen-rich volatiles in the absence of oxygen.

In the second step, the char is gasified from 700°C up to yield gas, leaving ash. With oxygen feed, the gas is not diluted with nitrogen.

The key reactions in this process are:

$$2C + O_2 = CO$$
and the water gas reaction:

$$C + H_2O \text{ (steam)} = CO + H_2 \text{ (syngas)}$$
which reaction is endothermic.

Thus obtained syngas can then be burned in a gas turbine, and the exhaust gas from it can then be used to raise steam for a steam turbine, hence the "combined cycle" in IGCC—denoting more efficiency of the fuel.

In gasification, the O_2 supply is much less than required for full combustion, so as to yield CO and H_2. The hydrogen has a heat value of 121 MJ/kg, or about five times that of the coal. That makes it very energy-dense fuel, which ensures efficient burning process.

However, air separation plant is needed to produce oxygen for the reaction, which plant unfortunately consumes up to 20% of the gross power generated by the IGCC plant.

To achieve a much fuller clean coal technology in the future, the *water-shift reaction* will become a key part of the process so that to produce:

$$2C + O_2 = CO, \text{ and}$$
$$C + H_2O = CO + H_2, \text{ then the}$$
$$2CO + 2H_2O = 2CO_2 + 2H_2 \text{ (water-shift reaction).}$$

The products are then concentrated CO_2, which can be captured, and hydrogen. There is also some hydrogen from the coal pyrolysis, which is the final fuel for use in the gas turbine.

Overall thermal efficiency for oxygen-blown coal gasification, including carbon dioxide capture and sequestration, is about 73%. Using the hydrogen in a gas turbine for electricity generation is efficient, so the overall system has long-term potential to achieve an efficiency of up to 60%.

Coal Prices

The recent rise and fall in coal prices was quite predictable following the turbulence of the global energy. See Figure 8-7. When coal prices skyrocketed, major exporters such as Indonesia and Australia increased output. China followed by focusing on its own coal industry's efficiency, while at the same time the Chinese electricity demand dropped. A wicked combination of falling demand and massive supply increases created a vacuum that sucked coal prices back to normal levels.

And now as the American coal industry keeps on dreaming about increased exports, three of the six export terminal proposals were cancelled and the expectations were lowered—not a pretty picture for the investors in the failed terminals.

On top of that, global analysts are sounding the alarm about coal prices falling even further due to a peak in Chinese and Asian coal imports. This would be followed by a long-term decline, so China and Asia might not be the salvation for the coal market that the coal companies were hoping for until now.

There are also estimates by major financial institutions that the global coal markets are expected to remain

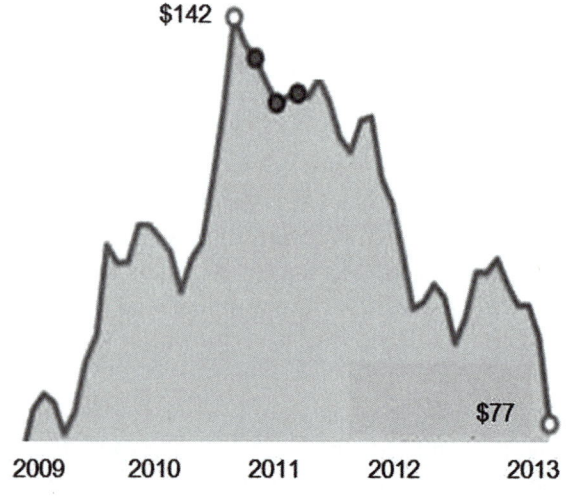

Figure 8-7. Coal prices (in $/ton)

oversupplied for a decade, thus the window for thermal coal investment is closing quickly. What this means for the U.S. coal exports is that the planned 100 million tons of annual Northwest exports could reasonably be lowered to 30 million tons. This is less than a third of the capacity of the proposed export facilities still on the drawing board.

Coal is still a primary fuel in power generation, and will remain so for the distant future. Its use, actually, is increasing in several parts of the world—Asia mostly. A new trend is developing lately, where even developed countries are increasing the use of coal for electric power generation.

This phenomena is surely going to affect the coal availability and prices in the near future. We cannot foresee how this will develop exactly, since there are many factors and uncertainties involved, but one thing is for sure; coal prices will rise with time.

Coal Exports

Coal exporting is a big business, and now as coal in the U.S. power plants is being steadily replaced by natural gas, the coal industry is looking at coal exports as the next step to progress and profits. In 2011, U.S. coal exports totaled 107 million short tons, the highest level in over 20 years.

Coal exports accounted for nearly 10% of total U.S. coal production and supported the employment of thousands of U.S. workers. The economic contribution of coal exports includes also activities and employment related to downstream transportation providers that move coal from mines to ports, as well as the port services that prepare and load the coal for shipment abroad. Many other businesses are supported by coal export activity, all of which contribute to profitable economic activity

Ernst & Young LLP was commissioned by the national mining association (NMA) to estimate the economic contributions of coal exports in the U.S. in 2011. The analysis considers the current economic contribution of coal exports to the U.S. economy and provides estimates for each state.

Some of the key findings are:

- The U.S. coal industry produced nearly 1.1 billion tons of coal in 2011, of which 974 million short tons were used domestically and 107 million (10% of total production) were exported abroad. While in 2007 exports totaled 55 million short tons of coal (5% of total production).

- The U.S. coal exports accounted for 8.4% of world seaborne coal shipments, up from 5.7% in 2007.

- 107 million short tons of coal exports supported 141,270 total (direct, indirect, and induced) jobs to the U.S. economy, or 1,320 jobs for every million tons of coal exported.

- Each million tons of exported metallurgical coal supported 1,460 employees, and 1,050 employees per million tons of exported steam coal.

- Direct employees of coal-export related businesses (coal mines, transportation companies, port and port services firms, and coal-exporting ships) earned an annual average of $96,100 in wages in benefits, compared to the U.S. average for all employees of $64,500 in 2011.

- 25,130 (18 percent) of the total 143,440 U.S. coal mining jobs were related to coal export production, and supported $5.4 billion in total gross value added.

Update: In 2009, Pacific Rim coal prices were rising fast and continued doing so for the next two years. That was due in part by temporary surging demand from China for imported coal. The U.S. coal exporters saw a great business opportunity, and hatched plans for six different coal export terminals in Washington and Oregon states to service the Pacific Rim coal market, and the related export routes.

Bad timing! The coal price surge came and went with the oil prices bubble. So, it seems in retrospective that all six proposed export projects were launched after coal prices had already peaked. Prices kept on falling after that, from the 2011 high stabilizing in the $120-$130/ton range for nearly a year. A then the Australian benchmark coal prices fell below $100/ton.

As a result, three of the six coal export terminal projects were cancelled recently.

This development was also predictable. The developers launched the export terminals projects just at the time when the Pacific Rim coal bubble was starting to deflate. Regulatory hurdles, community opposition, and cash crunches, combined with coal price declines and global oversupply put a big question mark over those projects and the plans of their developers.

And then, as the proverbial straw that broke the camel's back, there is a storm brewing at Cherry Point, just north of Bellingham, WA, where the largest coal export terminal in North America is planned to be built. The plan calls for nearly 500 large cargo ships loaded with coal travelling the inlet waters every year. That is about two large cargo ships that are loaded with coal and sent on their way across the world every day.

The railroad and road traffic, the dust, the air, soil and water pollution are too much for the locals to take, so there is a debate on the benefits vs. the damages, an a big battle, all the way to the U.S. Congress, is raging on the issues. How will it end is the six million dollar question, the answer to which will decide the future of U.S. coal exports, at least those from the U.S. Northwest.

In summary, we see coal as an important commodity, and an even more important fuel now and in the future. It is the backbone of the world's power generation, steel, and other major industries. More than half of the world's electric power is generated by coal, and its use is increasing. When all other fuels and substitutes are exhausted, coal will still be here, due to its immense supply.

Unfortunately, coal is also the main reason we are in a panic mode as far as our increasingly contaminated atmosphere and warming climate are concerned. It is the evil we cannot live with or without, which is the biggest catch 22 ever!

There are many solutions for cleaner burning coal on the horizon, but none of them are conclusive, or feasible, at this time, so lots of work remains to be done in this area. Most of the proposed solutions, such as carbon storage and sequestration, are cost-prohibitive for most cash-strapped developing nations, so we do not see much improvement coming our way from new ways to burn coal.

Does that mean that we have to give up and get used to living in polluted air and even changing climate? On the positive side of things, coal is opening the doors to new markets and new opportunities, where scientists and companies are invited to develop new technologies for more efficient coal burning and better carbon emission controls.

Coal is here to stay, make no mistake about it. Our choices are to either curse, embrace, or control it. Cursing and embracing are easy and we know who is doing it, while controlling, which is what is needed most in the long run, is the hard part, but that is what we need to focus on for the future wellbeing of our planet and its inhabitants.

NATURAL GAS

Natural gas has been around for a long time too, going up and down in volume and price according to the whims of the world energy and financial markets.

Lately, however, it got a major facelift thanks to a newly developed equipment and techniques for deep horizontal drilling This new process, hydrofracking, has opened the possibility of extracting enormous amounts of natural (shale) gas from places that were unthinkable just a few short years ago.

While hydrofracking is capable of extracting gas from solid rock formations miles deep in the ground, a new surge in gas exploration is extracting huge amount of gas from existing coal beds (so called coal bed gas) using similar techniques.

The combination of hydrofracked and coal bed gas exploration had significantly increased the production levels and dropped the prices significantly. The U.S. now produces almost 50% more natural gas than a decade ago, and there are prospects of producing even more in the future. The large production quantity, together with lower pricing has converted the U.S. into a major user and exporter of natural gas and gas products.

Gas Cost

Natural gas prices are driven by supply and demand conditions, but are often linked to the price of crude oil and petroleum products. Natural gas prices in the U.S. had historically followed oil prices, but in recent years have decoupled from oil and are now trending somewhat with coal prices.

The current surge in oil and gas exploitation in the U.S. due to increased hydrofracking activities has resulted in lower gas prices in the U.S. This has led to plans of Asian countries to import gas. Since natural gas has to be exported as liquefied natural gas (LNG), which is much more expensive, due to complex and expensive pressurizing and transport process, the future of LNG exports are still under discussion and negotiations.

The cost of natural gas is driven by the demand, which depends on the following main factors:

- Climate and weather conditions
- Demographic variations
- Economic growth
- Local fuel competition
- Storage capabilities, and
- Export conditions

In more detail:

- Weather impacts natural gas demand and supply, where especially cold winter temperatures increase the demand for space heating in commercial and residential buildings in some areas of the U.S. and around the globe.

There is also an increase of use in the summer months, where residential and commercial air conditions increase the demand for electricity.

Inclement weather also impacts the supply of and demand for natural gas in indirect way. When, for examples, major hurricanes approach the Gulf of Mexico, offshore natural gas platforms are shut down as workers evacuate. That reduces the production, which could be temporary, or permanent when hurricanes cause severe destruction to production facilities. This has happened several times during the last decade alone.

In addition, power lines are often knocked down during storms, thus interrupting the flow of electricity produced by natural gas, which can result in significant reduction in demand for a while in the affected area.

- Changing demographics affect the demand for natural gas, where increased population movement to the southern and western states, which are characterized by warmer weather, could in effect cause a decrease in demand for heating in the winter. This, in turn, could increase the demand for cooling in the summer.

- The state of the economy of a specific area or country has a considerable effect on the demand for natural gas for the duration. In a booming economy, output from the industrial sectors generally increases, and the demand for gas increases too. When the economy is slowing down, the demand drops. For example, during the U.S. economic recession of 2001, natural gas consumption by the industrial sector fell by over 6%.

- Supply and demand conditions affect the natural gas prices in a number of ways. The price can affect the demand for certain consumers, and particularly those consumers who can switch to other fuels, such as solar or wind. Also, when natural gas prices are extremely high, electric generators may switch from using natural gas to using cheaper coal or fuel oil. This leads to a decrease for the demand of natural gas, and a drop in its price.

- North America maintains large natural gas reserves (storage), which competes with the normal uses of gas such as heating and power generation. When the storage levels are low, they send a signal to the market that the supply is diminishing and that the gas prices will be rising. And visa versa, when storage levels are high, gas prices are expected to drop.

- Increasing natural gas exports represents another market. Increasing competition among fuels and countries also affects the global energy prices. When demand for natural gas overseas increases, domestic prices tend to rise, and visa versa. Capitalism, you know.

Table 8-4. 2012 U.S. natural gas prices (in \$/1,000 ft³)

Wellhead Price	3.35
Imports Price	3.93
By Pipeline	3.84
As Liquefied Natural Gas	5.22
Exports Price	4.15
By Pipeline	3.88
As Liquefied Natural Gas	11.76
City gate Price	4.79
Residential Price	9.75
Percentage of Total Residential Deliveries included in Prices	95.8
Commercial Price	8.11
Percentage of Total Commercial Deliveries included in Prices	68.6
Industrial Price	4.72
Percentage of Total Industrial Deliveries included in Prices	17.3
Electric Power Price	4.36

NOTE: The energy equivalent of natural gas is as follows:
1,000 ft³ natural gas is equal to 0.1725 (about 1/6) barrels of oil
1,000 ft³ natural gas is equal to 8.25 gallons of gasoline.

So, one conclusion we can draw from those numbers is that the energy contained in a unit of natural gas is 6-8 times cheaper than that in oil. Oil, and gasoline in extension, are much more convenient for use in transport vehicles, thus the price difference is erased for the benefit of convenience, which is why we don't see much natural gas in use in transport vehicles for now.

Also, coal has higher energy content than natural gas per dollar amount, but the convenience of transport and use of natural gas nullifies that advantage.

A ton of coal costs \$35-70 (depending on grade and region), and has an average energy content of 9,000-

13,000 Btu.

At the same time, the amount of fuel used to generate one kilowatt-hour (kWh) of electricity is as follows:

- Coal = 0.00053 Short Tons or 1.07 lbs., or 1,007 lbs. of coal
- Natural gas = 0.00798 Mcf (1,000 cubic feet), or 8,000 cu. ft. natural gas
- Residual fuel oil = 0.00185 barrels, 0.08 gallons, or 1.85 barrels, or 80 gallons of crude oil
- Converted into dollars the cost of generating the same amount of energy (about 1.0 MW) contained in the different fuels is:
  — Coal = $35-70
  — Gas = $30-40
  — Oil = $180-220

Obviously, natural gas is the way to go as far as the price per unit energy generation is concerned, but there are other complex technical, logistics, and financial factors to consider too, as we discuss in this text.

The tendency in the U.S., regardless of the price difference is toward: 1) Using natural gas for electric power generation, thus replacing coal and all other fuels and sources; 2) Using crude oil (gasoline, diesel, and jet fuel) for all transportation needs, and 3) Reducing the use of coal for power generation and finding new markets for it, such as export overseas, and for metallurgical and other industrial applications.

The primary drivers for using gas in power generation are:
1. Convenience of use (solid, vs. liquid, vs. gaseous), where gas is most convenient
2. GHG emissions (natural gas is less polluting than the rest)
3. Demand and supply driven by seasons, location, and price

As Figure 8-8 demonstrates, natural gas prices are at historic lows and are predicted to stay at that level for some time to come. If everything goes as planned, natural gas will become the preferred fuel for power generation and many other applications in the near future. It is estimated that it will dominate the use of coal by a factor of 2, and the use of crude oil by 1.5 by 2050.

Gas Transport

Gas from the wellhead to the refinery, or consumer, is most conveniently transported via pipelines.

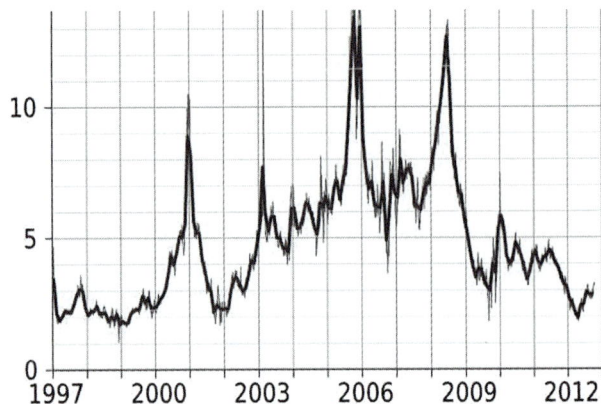

Figure 8-8. Natural gas price fluctuations (in $/1,000 ft³)

Sometimes trucks, trains, and ships are used to transport liquefied natural gas products too. Pipelines, however, are the preferred and prevalent method for transporting gas.

There are three major types of pipelines for transporting gas: the gathering system, the interstate pipeline system, and the distribution system. The gathering system consists of low pressure, small diameter pipelines that transport raw natural gas from the wellhead to the processing plant. If natural gas from a particular well has high sulfur and carbon dioxide contents (sour gas), then a specialized sour gas-gathering pipe is used. Sour gas is corrosive, thus its transportation from the wellhead to the sweetening plant must be done carefully.

Pipes can be from 6-48 in diameter and hundreds to thousands of miles long. Compressor stations, placed at 40-100 mile intervals along the pipeline keep the pressure high, as needed to help move the gas along. Here scrubbers and filters capture any liquids or other unwanted particles from the natural gas in the pipeline.

The gas flow and the integrity of the system is controlled by centralized gas control stations, which collect, assimilate, and manage data received from monitoring the compressor stations along the section of the pipeline under their control. Flow rate, operational status, pressure, and temperature readings are used to assess the status of the pipeline 24/7 in real time.

The safety of natural gas pipelines is ensured by:

- *Aerial patrols*, where planes are used to ensure that no construction activities are taking place too close to the route of the pipeline, especially in residential areas. Unauthorized construction and digging is the primary threat to pipeline safety.
- *Pipeline personnel on the surface* who check for leaks periodically use gas-detecting equipment.

- *Pipeline markers and signs* indicate the presence of underground pipelines to the public, as needed to reduce interference with the pipeline.
- *Gas sampling* in the pipelines ensures the gas quality, and indicates corrosion of the interior of the pipeline and the influx of contaminants.
- *Preventative maintenance* consists of testing of valves and the removal of surface impediments to pipeline inspection.
- *Emergency response* teams are trained to handle potential accidents and emergencies.
- *One Call program* exists in 50 states and provides anyone planning to dig around a pipeline with a phone number, 811, to call first. This way the pipeline company can flag the area, or send representatives.

Pipelines are the most practical and safest method of transporting oil and natural gas. While there are in excess of 100 deaths per year associated with electric transmission lines, according to the DOT's Office of Pipeline Safety, in 2009 there were no deaths associated with transmission pipelines, and 10 deaths associated with distribution systems.

Nevertheless, gas line accidents during construction activities when accidental gas line ruptures cause explosions and hurt people. Aging gas lines also break occasionally and cause damage.

Natural Gas Exports

The abundance of natural gas and quickly dropping prices in the U.S. has created a new market. Actually it is an old market that is now being expanded. It is export of natural gas abroad, mainly to Asia. To be exported, however, natural gas must be liquefied at cryogenic temperatures to achieve an energy density (and volume) that justifies the high processing and shipping costs. This process requires building complex liquefaction installations, which are expensive to build and operate.

Large profits are expected from those budding markets, but the opposition is also on the rise. In its ranks are some heavy lifters like Nucor and Dow Chemical, Huntsman Chemical, Celanese, Alcoa and the American Public Gas Association. They have issued reports and warnings that large-scale exporting of natural gas at world prices will eventually lead to increase of its prices up to international levels, which will put the U.S. manufacturing and economic revival at jeopardy.

The major oil companies are leading the export drive, since most of them have already large positions in the U.S. gas sector and some also have grandiose expansion plans in mind. The argument here is that free market forces will protect against price increases, so the government should stay out of this business. Increasing world natural gas supplies and a rapid build-out of liquefaction plants will create a global buyers' market on their own, according to the big oil guys.

Each facility has to be reviewed and approved by the DOE, which is the only thing slowing down the U.S. natural gas exports. So, there is already a move in Congress to remove DOE's authority, to allow approvals to move even faster. The oil and gas industry has activated its lobbying machine in an attempt to bypass, or at least shorten, the permission process. Three projects have already been approved, and 25 more are in the queue. At least half of those are at advanced stages and approval is just a matter of time.

There are studies and reports on both sides of the debate, and so the battle continues. Nevertheless, the Obama administration has made natural gas a priority, and although exports are not included in his plan (at least not at the huge scale they are planned now), they are inevitable. Only time will show how much natural gas will be exported.

Natural Gas Use

To be used as a fuel, natural gas must first undergo processing to remove impurities and water (especially from coal bed gas), to meet the specifications of useful fuel. The main product of the refining process is methane gas, while by-products include ethane, propane, butanes, pentanes, and higher molecular weight hydrocarbons, hydrogen sulfide, carbon dioxide, water vapor, and small amounts of helium and nitrogen.

But the most significant development has been the conversion of natural gas into a major source of electricity generation through the use of cogeneration, gas turbines and steam turbines. The huge production volume and low prices have contributed to the conversion of a number of coal-fired power plants to natural gas-fired.

Natural gas has a number of additional advantages, as follows:

1. It is well suited for a combined use with wind and solar power plants and for alimenting peak-load power stations functioning in tandem with hydroelectric plants.

2. It is also very convenient for use in grid peaking power plants and some off-grid engine-generators because of the ease of start-up and shutdown.

3. Particularly high efficiencies can be achieved by combining gas turbines with a steam turbine in combined cycle mode.

4. But the greatest advantage of natural gas is the fact that for an equivalent amount of heat, burning natural gas produces about 30% less carbon dioxide than burning petroleum and about 45% less than burning coal. A coal-fired electric power plant emits around 2,000 pounds of carbon dioxide per MWh electricity generated, or almost double the amount of carbon dioxide released by a natural gas-fired electric plant for the same amount of power generation.

Combined cycle power generation using natural gas is currently the cleanest available source of power using fossil fuels, and this technology is widely and increasingly used as natural gas can be obtained at increasingly reasonable costs. Locally produced electricity and heat using natural gas-powered combined heat and power plant (CHP or cogeneration plant) is considered energy efficient and a rapid way to cut down on carbon emissions.

Because of the wider use of natural gas for electric power generation, and due to its higher carbon efficiency, carbon dioxide emissions in the U.S. have fallen significantly lately, as evidenced by the fact that the emissions in 2012 were at a 20-year low.

Natural gas is also used as a cleaner and cheaper alternative to gasoline and diesel used for transport vehicles. In 2012 there were over 16.5 million natural gas vehicles around the world. Pakistan was on top of the list with 3.1 million natural-gas-powered vehicles, followed by Iran with 2.9 million, Argentina 2.1 million, Brazil 1.7 million, India 1.5 million, and China 1.2 million. The U.S. had less than a million natural gas powered vehicles during that time, but their number is increasing, and we estimate it to double by 2015.

The energy efficiency of natural gas powered engines is equal to that of gasoline engines, but lower compared with modern diesel engines. Gasoline vehicles converted to natural gas have low compression ratios, which results in a 10-15% reduction of power. Engines especially designed for natural gas use have a higher compression ratio and are much more efficient.

Israel's Gas Future

Just recently, Israel discovered a treasure-trove of natural gas on its territory. And it is so much that it might lead Israel towards energy independence before many other nations, to the point that Israel is now even planning on exporting natural gas in the near future.

Only 55 miles off Israel's Mediterranean coast, the immense Tamar natural gas reservoir was discovered recently. It was quickly developed and started flowing gas in 2013. A second gas field in the area is almost twice as big, and should be pumping gas by 2016. That would be enough gas to supply Israel's power plants with reliable fuel for decades and decades to come. But that is not all. There are also huge oil deposits near the gas fields, which represent an economic miracle.

The Israelites are on their way to energy independence, which has been their Achilles heel since the beginning of the new state.

It has been a long time in the making, though, since a small Israeli company began drilling for oil and gas onshore in 1991. With the help of another small Texas company, Noble Energy, the work proceeded slowly and it took considerable engineering to get the job done.

Five wells were drilled during this time; some were more than three miles below the seabed in waters too deep for a normal production platform. The effort almost broke the small companies, but it paid off in the end. The Tamar platform weighs 34,000 tons and is 290 meters high.

The huge platform and its base were built in Texas and were transported more than 8,000 miles to the Mediterranean. Upon arrival, the base was plunged into the sea and the platform was placed on top of it. All that work, from conception to operation, took just about four years.

Success followed and the first Tamar platform started producing a lot of gas in the spring of 2013. The estimates are that over the life of Tamar's gas reservoir, Israel will save over $100 billion in fuel imports. Long steel pipes laid to shallower waters more than 90 miles away transport the gas to land, comprising the longest platform-to-land "tie back" in the world.

Fifty people work on the platform around the clock today. Here water is separated from the gas, which is then sent onshore to be filtered once more. The treated gas is then sent to multiple gas-fired power plants around the country to be converted into electricity as needed to feed Israel's electric grid.

Using gas instead of coal or oil is also good for the environment. 40% of Israel's electricity is fueled by gas, which is much cheaper, and much cleaner, than oil. Burning natural gas saves the country 17 million metric tons of CO_2 emissions annually, which is equal to parking all cars in Israel.

There is also good news on the political side too. Israel now can expand exports into Palestine and Jordan. New trade relationships are expected as well with countries like Turkey and others in the area. That would renew and intensify the economic relationships between Israel and its neighbors. Better Arab-Israeli relations is even a greater achievement than the gas deposits.

But as any good things, there is a problem. A big one. The new gas and oil reserves and the related infrastructure will have to be protected from jealous neighbors and ill wishers.

Israel already spends 20% of its budget on defense, far more than most other nations. The new platforms, sitting vulnerable at high seas, will add to the expense.

Figure 8-9. The new natural gas platform at Tamar.

The government has plans to export much of the new gas, which has ignited protests. The government's believes that it can generate billions in new revenues, but the opposition claims that the government action lacks the necessary parliamentary approval, and so there are court challenges on the matter.

All this is also affecting the volatile politics of the region. To complicate things further, the newly discovered gas and oil reservoirs extend into international waters off Syria and Lebanon. Israel's maritime border with Lebanon is in dispute, so experts worry that maritime border disputes could erupt.

The Natural Gas Problems

The increased natural gas production around the world is a good thing, no doubt, but there are some not-so-good aspects of the production and the use of natural gas. To start with, there are a number of reported serious environmental damages done by hydrofracking in the U.S. and abroad.

Methane gas is leaking in the water supplies around the gas drilling sites and is creating the *flaming water* phenomenon, where people are able to light their faucet water on fire. Hydrofracking chemicals are also showing up in the drinking water supplies, and even in people's backyards.

This situation is causing an ongoing controversy, accompanied with a number of law suites and a spike in the environmental movement geared towards stopping the hydrofracking activities.

On the user end, natural gas produced about 5.3 billion tons of CO_2 emissions in 2008, while coal and oil produced 10.6 and 10.2 billion tons respectively. The estimates for 2030 show that natural gas would emit the major part of the CO_2, or 11 billion tons a year, with coal and oil emitting 8.4 and 17.2 billion respectively—assuming demand increase of about 2% a year.

But the worst part is that natural gas is a very bad greenhouse gas, which is 20 times more potent than carbon dioxide as far as climate change is concerned. A ton of methane in the atmosphere traps as much radiation, and does as much damage, as 20 tons of carbon dioxide, although it remains in the atmosphere less time before fully oxidized to CO_2.

The biggest danger lies in coal bed gas (methane) not captured by coal bed methane extraction techniques, in which case it is simply lost into the atmosphere. EPA estimates global emissions of methane at 3 trillion cubic feet annually, or 3.2% of global production. Direct emissions of methane represented 15% of all global anthropogenic greenhouse gas emissions in 2008.

Another great danger lies deep below the ocean floors in the global permafrost. It is where millions of tons of methane gas are trapped in ice formations. The trapped ice-methane is stable enough under the high pressure and freezing temperature of its original bed, but as the global temperature rises, the danger of its melting is increasing.

Once defrosted, the methane gas will escape from the ice embrace and will float up into the atmosphere. Since there are millions upon millions of tons of this mixture around the world, the danger is real and unavoidable under the present circumstances.

No doubt, natural gas is not going away any time soon, and is promising to show us the way to energy independence. Due to the immense size of its development, it is also showing us a way to environmental disaster, unless something is done to control the development and reduce the uncertainty of the hydrofracking activities.

Natural Gas to Coal Conversion Issues

Although many coal-fired power plants have been converted from coal to natural gas, a closer look reveals that most of those "conversions" are actually complete replacements rather than partial retrofits. The switch to natural gas can be done by: a) retrofitting existing coal-fired units to burn natural gas; b) by closing the coal plants and building new gas-fired plants. Presently, virtually all the turbine conversions of coal to natural gas are actually replacements by new gas-fired units.

The reason is mostly because of economics. Switching all U.S. coal-fired generation is simply not feasible, since it is much more cost-effective to construct new gas-fired units than to retrofit the existing old and outdated coal-fired units to burn natural gas.

The other major reason for those conversions, in addition to availability and cost, is that natural gas combustion produces almost 45% fewer carbon dioxide emissions than coal. It also emits lower levels of nitrogen oxides and particulates, and produces virtually no sulfur dioxide and mercury emissions.

This means that natural gas does not contribute significantly to smog or acid rain formation, which are major, increasingly detrimental issues related to coal-fired power generation. On top of that, natural gas boilers do not need scrubbers as required for coal-fired power plants to reduce SO_2 emissions, so the initial investment is reduced, as is the amount of toxic sludge generated by coal plants.

With all this said, natural gas is still a fossil fuel, and although its carbon content is lower than that of coal, it still releases significant amounts of harmful CO_2 into the atmosphere when burned. Also very importantly, during extraction from shale CO_2 is released into the atmosphere and the local soil and water table. Sometimes this leads to serious environmental damage and is affecting human health and wellbeing.

There are estimates of global methane leakage of about 3 trillion cubic feet annually, or 3.2% of global emissions, while the total methane emissions represented about 14% of all global anthropogenic greenhouse gas emissions in recent years.

With this in mind, we must be watching carefully the development of the natural gas industry.

In 2012 natural gas power generation in the U.S. matched the power generated by coal. Coal and natural gas generation provided approximately 60% of the total U.S. power generation capacity. The competition is just now starting, and promises to be fierce.

Following is a list of existing, in progress, and proposed coal-to-gas conversion projects in the U.S.:

- Alabama: Gadsden and Barry Steam Plants
- Alabama and Tennessee: John Sevier Fossil Plant and Widows Creek Fossil Plant
- California: Mt. Poso Cogeneration Plant
- Colorado: Arapahoe Station, Cameo Station, and Valmont Station
- Delaware: Dover Municipal Power Plant
- Florida: Scholz Generating Plant
- Georgia: McDonough Steam Generating Plant, Mitchell Steam Generating Plant, and UofG Physical Plant
- Hawaii: Hu Honua Station
- Illinois: The Eastern Illinois University Power Plant, and University of Illinois Abbott Power Plant
- Indiana: Gallagher Generating Station, and Jasper 2 Power Plant
- Kentucky: Big Sandy Plant Units 1 and 2
- Louisiana: Big Cajun II Power Plant
- Massachusetts: Somerset Power Generating Station
- Minnesota: Black Dog Generating Station, Riverside and High Bridge Plants
- New Hampshire: Schiller Station
- New Jersey: Howard Down Generating Station
- New York: Cornell University Central Heating Plant
- North Carolina: Progress Energy plants, Lee, Sutton, Cape Fear and Weatherspoon
- Ohio: R.E. Burger power plant, Big Sandy Plant Unit 1, Muskingum River Plant Unit 5, Conesville Power Plant, Muskingum River Plant, Tanners Creek Plant
- Oregon: Boardman Plant
- Pennsylvania: Penn State University to Convert Plant to Natural Gas
- Texas, Welsh Power Plant
- Utah: Utah Smelter Power Plant
- Virginia: Dominion to convert Altavista, Hopewell, Clinch River Plant and Southampton
- Washington, DC: Capitol Power Plant
- Wisconsin: Bay Front Station, Blount Street Station, Capitol Heat and Power Plant, and Charter Street Heating Plant, Stoneman Generating Station, Valley Power Plant, and Waupun Correction Central Heating Plant
- Ontario, Canada: Thunder Bay, Lakeview, Atikokan, Lambton, and Nanticoke. Shutting 4 coal plants, and considering conversion for the remaining 11 plants

CRUDE OIL

Oil is the most important commodity on the world energy markets, simply because of its dominant role as an energy source and an energy standard—especially in the transportation sector, where it has no competition. The supply and demand of oil determines its price, and influences the energy markets function in general.

Oil is a commodity, and large contracts for its supply are usually traded through the major commodity exchanges such as the New York Mercantile Exchange and the Intercontinental Exchange.

Due to the extreme importance of oil, the energy market is constantly trying to balance the oil supply and demand on one hand, and the relation of oil to the other energy sources, on the other. There are two important concepts in the supply and demand function in global energy markets. Those are the *marginal unit* and *elasticity*.

Crude Oil Prices

Oil prices, although very critical for the overall function of the entire energy market, are extremely volatile. If we see that oil is selling for $100 per barrel today, we know that it is just a temporary number, determined by the moment-to-moment supply and demand ratio and other temporary factors, such as commodity trading variation.

The price alone does not explain the complexity of global oil markets, and since it is impossible to synthesize the diversity of oil prices around the world, economists usually refer to benchmarks, which are small number of carefully tracked prices that are considered industry standards and against which all other prices can be compared.

The two most common crude oil benchmarks are *Brent Crude* and *West Texas Intermediate*. Brent Crude is oil "sourced" from the North Sea and is the benchmark against which prices are set for oil coming from Europe, Africa and the Middle East. West Texas Intermediate is the price used for contracts traded on the New York Mercantile Exchange and is typically the price that the media uses when reporting about oil and oil prices.

The marginal unit is each unit that is produced in addition to, and above, the current production. The cost of producing this unit is known as the marginal cost, and the price at which it can be sold is the marginal price. That is extremely important, because it largely determines the behavior of producers and consumers, thus shaping the entire market.

The price of crude oil is determined by the mate-rials and processes involved in its cradle-to-grave process, which involves all expenses from pumping it from the ground, transporting and refining.

Table 8-5. 2011 gasoline price structure

Process step	Cost
Raw materials	= $2.62*
Distribution	= 0.33
Taxes	= 0.39
Refining	= -0.07†
Total (2011)	**= $3.27/gallon¶**

*The raw materials (crude oil) prices are dictated by the global oil markets.
†The gasoline refining process produces other goods which are sold at profit.
¶There might be other fees and local taxes on top of that.

Crude Oil Transport

Crude oil and refined products are transported across the water in barges (around the U.S.) and oil tankers (around the world). On land, crude oil and its products are moved from one place to another via pipelines, trucks, and trains.

Pipelines are the most efficient method to transport crude oil from the wellhead to the processing facilities. From there they are moved to refineries and tanker loading facilities. The finished products—gasoline, jet fuel and diesel fuel—are then moved to the local distribution facilities via pipelines or trucks and trains.

The pipeline may have many collection and delivery points along route. Booster pumps located along the pipeline push along the oil. The pipeline may handle different types of products, and its operation is scheduled according to type and destination. Storage facilities are usually located along the pipeline to ensure smooth continuous operation.

Batching is used to move two or more different liquids through the same pipeline, usually in a series of batches. The adjoining batches mix where they come into contact. That mixed stream may be sent to refinery for re-refining, sold as a lower-valued product such as a mixture of premium unleaded gasoline with regular unleaded gasoline, or sold as mixture.

Crude oil tankers are used to transport crude oil from fields in the Middle East, North Sea, Africa, and Latin America to refineries around the world. Product tankers carry refined products from refineries to terminals. Tankers range in size from the small vessels used to transport refined products to huge crude carriers. Tanker sizes are expressed in terms of deadweight (dwt) or cargo tons. The smallest tankers are general purpose, which range from 10-25,000 tons and are used to transport refined products.

The large range and very large crude carriers (VLCC) are employed in international crude oil trade. The size of tanker that can be used in any trade (commercial voyage between a port of origin and destination) is dependent on the tanker's length and loaded depth and the size of the loading and unloading ports. Very large ships are used because they reduce the cost to transport a barrel of crude oil.

Crude oil and refined products are stored in storage tanks for shipment to other locations or processing into finished products. There are four basic types of tanks used to store petroleum products: 1. *Floating roof tank*—used for crude oil, gasoline, and naphtha; 2. *Fixed roof tank*—used for diesel, kerosene, catalytic cracker feedstock, and residual fuel oil; 3. *Bullet tank*—used for normal butane, propane, and propylene; 4. *Spherical tank* used for isobutane and normal butane.

Oil Tankers

Occasional oil spills are the other big headache of the world's oil industry. There have been 9,350 accidental spills that have occurred worldwide since the 1970s. Most spills result from routine operations such as loading cargo, discharging cargo, and taking on fuel oil. About 91% of the operational oil spills are small, resulting in less than 7 metric tons per spill. On the other hand, spills resulting from accidents like collisions, groundings, hull failures, and explosions are much larger, with 84% of those involving losses of over 700 metric tons.

The size of land and life damage and their long lasting effects from some of those accidents are so great that they are impossible to minimize, let alone excuse or forget. Just mentioning Exxon Valdez, or BP Deep Horizon rings the alarm bells almost as loud as mentioning a pending nuclear accident.

Oil spills from oil tankers account for 12% of all dangerous chemical spills, while the major cause of ocean oil pollution is industrial waste at over 60%. Tanker accidents contribute 5% and tanker operations account for 7% of all oil spills. Other shipping accounts for 14%. The Exxon Valdez is blamed for being the world's largest oil spill, but it actually is only the 52nd biggest spill. The spills during the Iraq war constitute the largest uncontrolled release of crude oil.

Not so long ago, oil tankers discharged their dirty ballast water (oil mixed with sea water) into the ocean prior to refilling with fresh oil. That is no longer allowed, thus eliminating a major global pollution source.

U.S. tankers are constructed and operated under strict regulations. New tanker design requires separate ballast and oil cargo tanks. New ships also have double-hull construction in accordance to the oil pollution act of 1990. Double-hull construction is required on new ships built after 1993.

These new and improved vessels represent about 15% of the world's tanker fleet. Superior communication networks of telephone, telex, and satellite systems are now used to navigate and control the tankers' operations. Automatic collision avoidance systems track ships' movements and alert personnel to an obstruction on its course. The ship crews also follow strict safety procedures, thus ensuring safe trips and minimizing the chance for spills.

Normal oil transport causes some pollution, most of which is air pollution from oil tankers', trucks', or train engines' emissions. Pollution and other damages from cargo fires, or vessels breaking or sinking, are another set of serious concerns. Large ocean tankers often burn low-quality fuel oils, such as bunker oil, which are highly polluting, and a health risk for humans exposed to their fumes.

Ship fires very seldom result in a loss of the entire ship and its cargo, because modern ships are well equipped with specialized firefighting gear and techniques. Oil fires on water or on solid ground are difficult to put out, and could burn for days or weeks. To ensure the safety of the local residents, those operations usually require mass evacuations, due to dangers to human health caused by toxic liquids and smoke.

Crude Oil Use

Crude oil reserves deep down in the ground are of different quality and contain a number of impurities. To make the "as is" oil suitable for use in vehicles and for the manufacturing of different products, the crude is refined. During the refining process different fractions are obtained in the following approximate ratios: 47% gasoline, 23% diesel and heating oil, 18% other petrochemicals, 10% jet fuel, 4% liquefied petroleum, 3% asphalt.

Or, from each barrel containing approximately 42 gallons crude, we get the following:

The main use of crude oil is as a transportation fuel and to make it into other products. There are many products that are derived from crude oil, but fuels including gasoline, diesel fuel, jet fuel, bunker fuel and kerosene, are the main final products. Those fuels provide power for the internal combustion engines in cars, trucks, boats and trains, and are also used to generate electricity. Crude oil is also used to make fertilizers and pesticides,

Table 8-6. Crude oil content and fractions

19.4 gal. gasoline

10.5% fuel oils (diesel)

4.3 gal. jet fuel (kerosene)

2.2 gal. coke

1.8 gal. still gas

1.7 gal. residual fuel oil

1.5 gal. liquefied gasses

1.4 gal. road oil (asphalt)

1.1 gal. raw materials for petrochemicals' production

0.4 gal. lubricants (motor oils and greases)

0.4 gal. other petrochemicals

plastics, waxes, tar, sulfuric acid, asphalt, petroleum coke (solid fuel) and paraffin wax, synthetic rubbers, cosmetics and perfumes, industrial solvents, and in liquid fuels such as butane and propane, which are used in special commercial applications (and in home grills).

Transportation Uses

A major use of crude oil is as a fuel for transportation vehicles.

Transportation fuels are the major component of the U.S. energy portfolio. Of the 20 million barrels of petroleum consumed each day in the United States, 68% is used in the transportation sector. It is what moves most of our cars, trucks, ships, trains, and agricultural and other machinery.

Since 1990, much of the increased fuel consumption can be directly attributed to the growth in sales of light duty trucks and SUVs. Alternative fuel programs re-

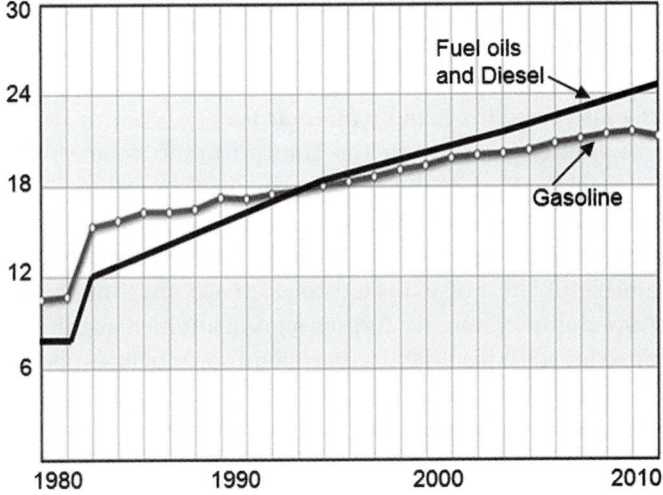

Figure 8-10. Crude oil fuels used for transportation in the U.S. (in millions barrels/day)

ceived significant attention and investment in the 1970s, but lost ground every time the price of petroleum-based fuel declined.

NOTE: The fossil energy on and off trend preceded and dictated each of the solar energy boom-bust cycles, including the last one (2008-2012). The difference is that this time the boom cycle was very well funded, and the bust cycle is somewhat more extended time-wise than the previous cycles.

To make up the difference between the oil that we consume and the oil that we produce domestically, we increased our dependency on imported foreign oil, which rose from 30% of our supply in 1970 to over 50% today. At an average of $100 bbl, we are spending over $1.0 billion every day on oil imports.

The use of oil is increasing world-wide as well, in response to the growing demand for oil associated with the rapid industrialization of China, India, Russia, and other developing countries with combined population of close to 4 billion people.

The Automobile

Everyone between the ages of 16 and 106 drives a car or truck in the U.S. This is becoming so in most other parts of the world too. Driving a motor vehicle incurs not only direct costs but also external, social, costs. The fuel taxes and other taxes that we pay in higher healthcare costs cover some of the external costs, while the entire situation is snowballing into decreased environmental quality and higher personal taxes.

In the U.S. alone, motor vehicles emit about 50 million tons of carbon monoxide, 10 million tons of nitrogen oxides, as well as other toxins including formaldehyde and benzene every year. At the same time, motor vehicle accidents kill 40-50 thousand people and injure more than 3 million. Those numbers have to be multiplied several times when considering those events on global scale. And on top of that there are additional major external costs, such as natural habitat destruction from building roads and parking lots, vehicle and parts disposal, noise pollution, and other costs related to securing petroleum supplies.

The external costs of air pollution, crop losses, reduced visibility, national security, noise pollution, and so forth are paid by the public sector, but many other become external social losses, never to be recovered of compensated. Total annual monetary and nonmonetary externality costs have been estimated to as high as $900 billion.

Annual public sector costs for motor vehicle infrastructure and services are estimated at about $200 billion. Free-parking subsidies and cross-subsidies (damages paid by third party) caused by congestion amount to $50-$100 billion per year. Total public sector and social costs are estimated at over $1,000 billion per year. Including the estimate of global warming costs could raise those figures even further.

Table 8-7. Automobile related costs

Public Sector Costs (in $ billion)

Highways and parking	$150
Pollution regulation and control	5.0
Highway patrol and safety	7.5
National security costs	5.0
Other public sector costs	20.0

Externality Costs (in $ billion)

Human mortality and morbidity	$400.0
Accident costs (pain, death, loss)	50.0
Imposed travel delays	135.5
Global warming	50.0
Loss of visibility	35.0
Damage to crops and forests	10.0
Noise pollution	15.0
Water pollution	10.0
Other externality costs	40.0

The above numbers are estimates derived from averaging several studies. It is difficult to verify those numbers, but their magnitude alone shows that there are a lot of activities in many areas where automobiles are involved. This is creating new markets to be tapped by oil companies, refineries, entrepreneurs, engineers, insurance companies, and lawyers.

These markets will grow in the future, until there is no more oil. As we slowly approach that point of no return, the there would be significant modifications and rearrangement of the global energy markets, including those related to the automobile. When and how this is going to happen is uncertain now, and we don't expect it to be any time soon. Nevertheless, we should get a good understanding of what this would mean and get ready for it.

Industrial Uses

Global warming or not, crude oil is, and will be, on top of the list of energy sources and consumer goods manufacturing. In addition to their wide and unrestricted use in transportation, crude oil fuels are used to generate electricity in special applications (peaker power plants) and in consumer goods production. Different petroleum based fuels are also widely used in domestic and commercial heating during the winter months.

The most common distillation fractions of petroleum are fuels that are used in a number of sectors of the world economy. Fuels used in different industrial applications include: LPG, butane, gasoline, jet fuel, kerosene, fuel oil and diesel fuel.

The products (hydrocarbons) produced from crude oil distillation can be mixed with non-hydrocarbons to create other end products for use in different industries. Some of the resulting compounds are: alkenes (olefins) which are used to make plastics or other compounds, lubricants (light machine oils, motor oils, and greases), wax used in the packaging of frozen foods, sulfuric acid (produced as a waste product), bulk tar, asphalt, petroleum coke (used in specialty carbon products or as solid fuel), paraffin wax, and other aromatic petrochemicals to be used as precursors in the production of different chemicals.

Crude oil products are widely used in agriculture as well, where they have increased the productivity dramatically. This increase is due largely to the increased use of energy-intensive mechanization (using oil based fuels), and the application of oil-based fertilizers and pesticides. Amazingly enough, nearly all pesticides and many fertilizers are made from crude oil derivatives. Who knew? Because of that, we need to add those critical for food production products to the list of endangered species, because without them (once the fossils are gone) the world might experience severe scarcity of food crops and other unprecedented maladies.

Of the 20 million barrels of petroleum consumed each day in the United States, over 30% are used for industrial applications. Almost everywhere we look around us we would see products made out of petroleum based materials. Every branch of the world economy also depends heavily on their use.

Here, just like in the transportation sectors, the long-term effect of their use in chemical processing and burning for power generation create enormous emissions, resulting in global warming. And similarly, the emissions are not expected to decrease any time soon. As a matter of fact, we foresee significant increases in industrial activities that use petroleum products, especially in developing countries like China and India, which will add to the already high emission levels.

Crude oil is a very versatile product. After refining and separating the different components in the crude oil, we end up with a number of products, which are used in many areas of our lives, such as: gasoline, diesel fuel, heating oil, jet fuel, bunker fuel, fertilizers and pesticides, different types of plastics, synthetic rubber and fibers (polyester, nylon, acrylic), dyes, paints, detergents, photo film, food additives, different medicines, candles, and many, many more.

The approximate breakdown of crude oil use in the U.S. is as follows:

- Transportation 65%
- Industrial 25%
- Residential 4%
- Electricity 6%

During peak years, the U.S. consumes over 20 million barrels of crude oil every single day. This equates to approximately 20 barrels of crude oil per person annually. China is second, with approximately 10 million barrels a day, but only 2 barrels per person annually. This means that Americans use at least 10, and as much as 20 times (compared with India) more crude oil than any nation on the face of this Earth.

The crude oil production is lagging in comparison, where Saudi Arabia produces only 10 million barrels daily, followed by Russia with 10 million and the U.S with 8 million. Iran, China, Canada, Mexico and U.A.E. follow with 3-4 million barrels daily production.

The global use of oil is broken down as follows:

Asia	30%
USA	25%
Europe	19%
Middle East	7%
South America	6%
Russia	5%
Canada, Mexico	5%
Africa	3%

A close look at those figures reveals that we are consuming as much oil as we are producing. The immediate question then is how long can we keep up this pace? And the obvious answer is—not for very long. Crude oil is getting harder to find and pump out, and will eventually run out. If not in 20 years, in 30, or 50, or even 100, people will not have even one drop of oil left unless we do something to change the trend. But what can we do?

We believe that the first step is to get people fully educated and informed about the materials and processes used today, and the issues those bring. Then, and only then, will we be able to get a complete picture of the situation and start looking into ways to change it, thus preventing impending doom.

The Environmental Impacts

Most of the oil is imported from fragile or even hostile countries, where the oil production leaves a significant footprint on the local and global environment, due to the lack of environmental and safe procedures. But the environmental impact is felt most heavily in the populated centers, where CO_2 and other toxic gasses from vehicle exhaust is creating smoke and smog with serious health consequences.

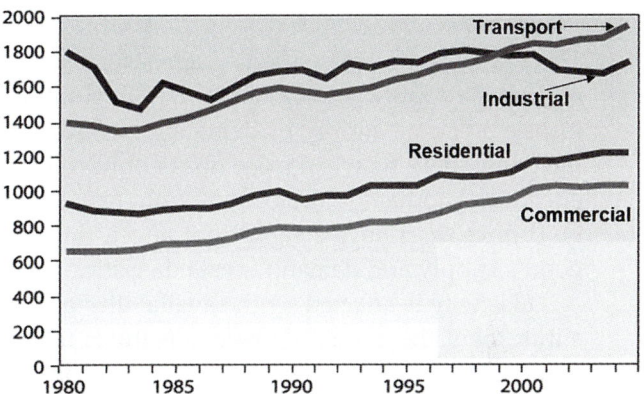

Figure 8-11. U.S. CO_2 emissions by use sector (in million tons/year).

It is easy to see that transportation is the major emitter of pollutants, approaching 2 billion (yes, with a capital B) tons annually. The total quantity of CO_2 gasses emitted in the atmosphere is nearly 3 times that amount. About 5-6 billion tons of GHGs emitted into our atmosphere every year is a huge amount, which increases with every passing year and has to be accounted for somehow.

Where does all this poison go? Some of it ends up in people's lungs and other places, where it causes damage according to the extent of exposure, while some of it stays up in the air, causing all kinds of uncontrollable environmental changes and damage.

The long-term effects of the enormous emissions are also causing global climate warming, which can be reversed only by reducing the emissions to a bare minimum, which, as things are going, is not going to happen any time soon. At least not until we pump the last drop of oil from the ground. But by then it might be too late. We will have damaged our planet and its fragile environment so badly that there will be no going back.

Oil Effects

Oil is a global commodity, where most countries are heavily dependent on oil imports. Where suppliers are already operating at peak capacity, the marginal unit of production might come from anywhere in the world. Globalization made the world more transparent and leveled the playing field to the point where most activities of even minor oil exporters (often in unstable countries) have profound effects on the oil prices around the globe.

Because of this, even the most powerful nations on Earth cannot control the oil prices. This in turn is affecting the energy security of even the most advanced societies.

Some of those oil-specific effects are:

- *The elasticity* of the oil markets is a measure of how responsive supply and demand are to fluctuations in price. The oil supply or demand is considered relatively inelastic when price does not have large effects on production or consumption, respectively. If price does have a significant effect, then the good's supply and demand is called elastic.

  Elasticity is affected by the availability of substitutes, but there are no direct substitutes for oil. Some of the indirect substitutes are too expensive. Because of that, and at least for now, demand for oil is inelastic. Much deeper structural changes are needed to impact demand and to change the oil's demand status to elastic.

  In the present oil market, high prices are largely a function of record demand, much of which can be attributed to oil glut in China. Oil is used mostly for transportation, and as the world population increases, more transport is needed, thus the demand for more and more oil will increase as well. Since there is no cheap substitute for oil (at least for transportation needs) the high demand for oil will keep prices high. Since there is no foreseen decrease in consumption, unless some serious changes occur soon, the days of cheap oil are over and that we need to get used to expensive oil energy.

- Another major factor contributing to the oil price variations, are the *oil market speculators*, who have been quite successful in driving and keeping price of oil and gasoline higher than normal. The U.S. government is looking into it, and President Obama wants to boost funding as needed to step up regulators' surveillance of energy futures traders. He also insists on increased civil and criminal penalties tenfold for those found guilty of manipulating prices. He is urging the market regulators to deploy new technology to control the prices, but there is no indication that this will result in any meaningful changes any time soon.

With all this said, oil is here to stay and will be used as always, at least until we pump every drop from the ground, and no price or environmental concerns will slow this process down. And since we have at least 50 years of oil reserves left, we will have to get used to the ups and downs of the energy markets, driven by oil supply and demand and varying prices.

The largest proven oil reserves in the world are in Saudi Arabia, which has about 260 billion barrels in oil reserves, followed by Iran and Iraq with approximately 120 billion each, and Kuwait, Venezuela with about 100 billion each, the U.A.E. with 55 billion, and the rest of the oil producing countries with 10-20 billion each. Those countries also produce the largest amount of oil for export.

The largest consumer of oil today is Asia with 30% of total global consumption. China is the largest oil consumer in the region, but its economic rise is slowing down, which brings a reduction in the use of oil. If this trend continues, and if it affects other countries, we will very likely see some changes in the global oil market, where supply exceeds demand. The reduced demand might also bring us much lower oil prices by 2015.

The U.S. is next on the list of big oil users with 25%, and Western Europe follows next with 19%. The other consumers are the countries in the Middle East, South America and Eastern Europe that use about 5% each, while Africa is the tail end with 3% oil consumption.

The U.S. estimates were 10 billion barrels in oil reserves until recently, but that number has increased significantly with the advent of new hydrofracking techniques. Add to this the enormous quantity of oil flowing from Canada, with much more projected in the future, and the U.S. is now looking at a period of plenty of oil, which is bringing us near to energy security.

Terrorism

The total world oil production amounts to approximately 80-100 million barrels per day. About one-half of this quantity is moved by oil tankers on fixed maritime routes. The global economic downturn of 2008 reduced the world oil demand, and the volumes of oil shipped to markets via pipelines and along maritime routes.

There are several chocker points around the world, through which large quantities of oil float daily and which are under constant threat of terrorism. By volume of oil transit, the Strait of Hormuz leading out of the Persian Gulf, the Strait of Malacca linking the Indian and Pacific Oceans, Bab-el-Mandeb at the entrance to the Red Sea, and the Strait of Gibraltar at the exit from the Mediterranean Sea, are the world's most strategic and most dangerous chokepoints.

The oil tankers crossing those chokepoints are exposed to political unrest in the form of wars or hostilities and vulnerable to theft from pirates, and terrorist attacks. All this can lead to shipping accidents, resulting in disastrous oil spills and or blockage of the waterways. The blockage of a chokepoint, even temporarily, can lead to substantial increases in total energy costs.

Over half of America's oil is imported, so terror organizations like al-Qaeda and its affiliates see the disruption of oil transportation routes as one of the ways to hurt the U.S. and its allies. And sure enough, disruption of scheduled oil flow through any of those routes could impact negatively the global oil prices.

Several attacks against oil tankers in the Arabian Gulf and Horn of Africa have been planned in the past, starting with June 2002, when a group of al-Qaeda operatives suspected of plotting raids on British and American tankers passing through the Strait of Gibraltar were arrested by the Moroccan government. In October of the same year, a boat packed with explosives rammed and badly damaged a French supertanker off Yemen. al-Qaeda claimed responsibility for that attack, and for plans to seize a ship and crash it into another vessel or into a refinery or port.

The terrorists' goal is to cut the economic lifelines of the world's industrialized societies, but such attacks would also weaken and perhaps topple some of the Gulf oil monarchies. This would have even greater and long lasting effect on the world's oil supplies and transport routes.

There are approximately 4,000 tankers crossing the world's oceans every day. Each of those slow and vulnerable giants can be attacked at the narrow passages, where a single disabled or burning oil tanker and its spreading oil slick could block the route for other tankers.

This constant threat and the increased risks contribute to further increase in oil prices. Insurance carriers are raising the premiums to cover tankers in risky waters, as evidenced by the fact that the insurance for oil tankers entering Yemeni waters tripled since the attack in Yemen a decade ago.

A typical supertanker with two million barrels of oil on board would pay about $450,000 instead of the usual $150,000 for insurance of the ship alone. The cargo requires a separate and equally expensive insurance policy each trip. This adds about 15-25 cents a barrel to the cost of the oil.

Even the best insurance cannot ensure completely the safety and reliability of our energy supply under those conditions. The only way to achieve energy independence, therefore, is to eliminate the need to import and transport oil across the globe. This, however, is not going to happen any time soon, so the new situation has created a new niche market for individuals and companies that provide insurance and ensure the physical safety of the oil tankers.

Some oil tank owners are resorting to placing security personnel on board, especially when crossing pirate-infested international waters. This measure, in addition to equipping the tankers with special equipment, is one of the services that is expected to grow. The number of complexities of those services, as well as their costs, will increase as the pirate attacks are on the rise, at least until we figure a way around it.

The Hubbert's Peak

As far back as 1956, Mr. Hubbert proposed that the global fossil fuel production would follow a roughly bell-shaped curve. The highest point in the curve is the highest level of fossil production, and it is where crude oil production is at its peak. After that point is reached, the production levels would slope down, going to zero within 30-40 years.

This curve and the logic behind it later on became known as the Hubbert's peak theory. The highest point on the Hubbert's curve denotes peak oil, or the time when oil production is at its maximum volume. It is basically a scientific projection of the time when future petroleum production (whether for individual oil wells, entire oil fields, whole countries, or worldwide production) will eventually peak and then start a slow decline at a similar rate to the rate of increase before the peak as those reserves are exhausted.

Considering all past oil discovery and production data, a Hubbert's curve that attempts to approximate past discovery data can be used to provide estimates for future production, as follows:

$$Qt = \frac{Qmax}{1 + AB^{-bt}}$$

The year of maximum annual production (peak) Tmax then is:

$$T_{max} = \frac{1}{b} \ln(a)$$

This is were the cumulative production Qt reaches half of the total available resource:

$$Qt = Qmax / 2$$

Where:
   Qmax is the total recoverable crude oil
   Qt is the cumulative production volume
   a and b are constants

Hubbert's peak oil theory accurately predicted the peak of U.S. oil production at a date between 1966 and 1970, based on data available at the time of his publication in 1956. Using the same data, Hubbert predicted world peak oil in by 2006. That date came and went, but the global peak oil date is still debated and seems to be shifting further into the future.

This is because Mr. Hubbert had a fairly limited amount of data, which considered only the easy ways of obtaining oil, without advanced technologies and new discoveries, as we know them today. As time went on, new oil reserves were found and the new technologies, such as hydrofracking, shale, tar sands, are now pumping oil from places that were unknown to Mr. Hubbart and even unimaginable at the time.

Nevertheless, recently oil reserves have become more difficult to extract and the alternatives are too expensive for some companies and the developing countries. According to the International Energy Agency (IEA), production of conventional crude oil peaked in 2006, as predicted by the Hubbert's model.

Since then, however, things have changed to where now we don't know where exactly the oil peak is going to happen.

The Energy (Oil) Transition

Everything considered, we know that since virtually all economic sectors rely heavily on petroleum, and since its supply is limited, a peak will occur sooner or later. It will eventually lead to a partial or complete failure of the energy and other sectors within a very short time period.

In 2007, the U.S. GAO issued a report that provided an urgent call for action due to eminent reduction and approaching collapse of global oil supplies. The report reaffirmed that peak oil is real and inevitable by 2040, which might be followed by a quick decline in world oil production without warning. New and more efficient exploration methods and production techniques allow new discoveries and improved production, which might delay the peak oil estimates, but oil is finite resource, so whether it is 2040, 2050, or 2060, its end is eminent. Rising demand for oil from developing countries shows sharply increased risks of significant disruption to oil supplies, too.

For now, however, the U.S. fossil fuel industry (oil, gas, and coal) is encouraged to grow. It is good for the country and it is good for all of us, the TV commercials proclaim, so in the short term we are looking at more consumption of crude oil and other fossils, accompanied by more damaging carbon emissions.

Due to its priority status the fossil industry has been receiving subsidies since the very beginning at the tune of over $72 billion in subsidies between 2002 and 2008, according to the Environmental Law Institute.

The nuclear industry gets significant subsidies also, but the exact number is only a guess, for it is part of the national security package, and as such it enjoys special privileges and favors.

The renewable energy industry has been getting subsidies on and off through the years, depending on which direction the political and energy winds blew. Lately, however, it has been receiving massive amounts of subsidies too. The proponents claim that the renewables are more deserving to receiving subsidies than the fossil fuels, because the renewables are much more versatile and environmentally friendly, thus they are good for the environment, our energy security, and for a number of other reasons, including fuel diversification.

In 2009, the G20 agreed to phase out energy price subsidies in principle, which alone could result in a 10% drop in global GHG emissions by 2050. These, however, are only words, while in reality many countries are increasing the subsidies and the use of fossil fuels today.

While officially agreeing to reduce subsidies and cut emissions, most governments are in fact encouraging fossil fuel use and expansion by increasing the subsidies, which will lead to quick depletion of the natural resources and an increase of GHG emissions.

This is a new phenomenon, where not only China and India, but also developed countries like Germany, are building new coal-fired power plants and are switching from gas to coal at the same time.

These new developments go against all international agreements and all efforts to clean the environment. As a result, the global GHG emissions are projected to increase in the future, if this trend continues.

This will eventually lead to:

1.   A world-wide economic stagnation and collapse, which if no decisive measures are taken might be as bad as the U.S. recession in the 1930s, or

2.   If enough smart people and countries decide on a radical solution, it might lead to a speedy and or-

derly transition to 100% renewable energy within a very short time. In best of cases, experts predict that at least a decade is needed for a drastic transition.

The transition from A (fossil economy) to B (fossil-less economy) is not easy to design, let alone agree among the nations. The ultimate choice of what is the best way to get from A to B will most likely be different for different areas of the world, and can be influenced by many factors and variables.

It is impossible to foresee what will happen in the long run, because of the complexity of the energy sector and the large number of variables, but in the short term we see a number of practical things taking place:

• In the people transport sector, which uses the most crude oil, free shuttle buses running frequently along the most travelled routes may persuade many to leave the car home and take the bus. This won't happen in America any time soon, because of the American mentality and the way life is structured here. In many other countries, however, most people would take the free bus service even if they had access to cars and other means of personal transportation.

• Safe designated bicycle lanes and parking racks at both ends of traffic areas, may persuade many to ride a bike to work. Again, not many Americans would take this option, but the numbers would increase in the developing countries.

  NOTE: Some European cities even have free public bicycles programs, where people ride a bike from one point to another and leave it at designated racks for others to use. There are also inexpensive bike rental systems where users can pay by the hour using a credit or debit card.

• Parking space availability and price often determines the choice of transport too, where the car-alternative options become more attractive with price increases. City planners in some European cities are rationing the use of private cars in city centers by making parking scarce and expensive. With a few exceptions, Americans do not obey this rationale for a number of reasons, one of which is that they have no other choice but drive a car from their distant suburban residences. For example, most of the residents of big, congested cities such as New York, London, or Tokyo do not drive cars, for lack of parking and congestion of inner-city traffic.

• Road congestion is another big factor, for which there are dual occupancy lanes and other measures that help traffic flow. In many European cities there are special dedicated bus lanes, where buses run at normal speed while traffic is stuck in a jam. This option is available in some places in the U.S. as well, but it will be a long time before it becomes a standard, due to the Americans' love affair with the automobile and the lack of well-developed mass transit systems.

Anyway, a change in the way we look at and use crude oil and its products is coming our way. Our choice is to ignore it (and the upcoming the Hubbert's peak and its effects) until it hits us in the head, or to start planning ahead of time. This is the right time to plan ahead for the transition, because when the inevitable comes it might be too late for any plans or actions.

Things might change eventually, but for now the planning ahead option is on the back burner.

Power Plants Construction and O&M

The dynamics of fossil-fired power plants has changed lately. Because coal has been largely blamed for a major increase in GHGs releases, the construction of a large number of new coal fired power plants in the U.S. has been either delayed or cancelled. This is not the case in other countries, and as a matter of fact, the construction of new coal-fired power plants in China and India is rapidly increasing. Nevertheless, the global tendency is to use less polluting technologies.

In all cases, the construction of a large coal- or gas-fired power plant is a huge undertaking. Power plant construction is a large industry, where a number of different companies play some role in the different stages of the plant planning, design, permitting, construction, installation, testing, certification, operation and maintenance, and decommissioning stages.

The design of a coal-fired power plant is very different from that of a gas-fired plant or an oil-burning power plant. On the other hand, the design, construction and O&M of a wind, or solar, or biofuel power generating plant is a totally different animal.

While some engineering and construction companies are large enough to handle many tasks in any power plant project, the majority of smaller companies are specialized in some areas of their expertise. They can handle some smaller aspects of the entire process, such as: electrical, mechanical, chemical processing, or safety.

At the same time, the design and construction of a wind or solar power plant is quite different and equally complicated from a number of points of view. Selection of the location, for example, is more critical than in any other case, as is the proper installation of the power generating equipment. While, for example, a coal plant can be installed anywhere, installing a solar plant under the always cloudy and rainy skies of Seattle, WA, would produce totally different results than installing the same plant under the blistering Arizona sun.

There is a big difference also in the operation and maintenance of the different power plants, the proper execution of which is critical for their overall performance, efficiency and profitability. Coal-fired power plants, for example, are busy and noisy places, with trucks and railroad cars coming every minute for unloading, and there is dust and smoke all over the place. Inside the plant, there are dozens of engineers and technicians supervising the transport of the coal, its processing and proper burning.

On the other extreme, a solar power plant is a lonely place. There are only a few workers here and there, doing some light maintenance from time to time. There is minimum of noise, dust, and hardly any pollution can be detected.

And yet, let's not forget that coal plant can produce maximum power non-stop 24/7/365 for many years, while a solar power field produces power part of the time, and only if there is sunshine. Also, thousands of acres of land are needed to generate power comparable to that of a coal-fired power plant. To produce 1.0 GWp of solar power, we need to install millions of solar panels on an area of 5,000-10,000 acres, while a coal plant that is located on 10 acres of land can produce the same amount of power.

And then, time comes when the plant has to be shut down, decommissioned and the land brought back to where it was prior to the plant installation.

Summary: The fuels production, equipment manufacturing, plant construction, operation, and decommissioning are energy- and labor- intensive processes. There is a lot of air, soil, and water pollution emitted during those stages as well. Because of that, the entire cycle, and all related steps, must be taken into consideration when evaluating any aspect of power generation and use. Putting all pieces of the puzzle together is the only way to get a complete picture of what we are dealing with, because looking at just one segment is not good enough, and might be misleading.

For example, coal-fired power plants emit a lot of black smoke during power generation. At the same time, solar power fields are clean and quiet for most of their useful life. When taking a closer look, however, we see a

lot of similarly black smoke and other pollutants coming out from the silicon melting furnaces, and lots of dust raised by the large trucks bringing sand for melting—all those activities are needed to make solar and wind products. In addition, there are also a number of steps in the solar and wind equipment manufacturing schemes that are energy and labor intensive, and emit all kinds of air, soil, and water contaminants.

Mines and Drill Sites Decommissioning

Another big industry serving the energy sector consists of companies involved in decommissioning coal mines, and gas and oil rigs and wells. This is a complicated business from logistical, financial and environmental points of view. A mine is considered officially closed when the coal extracting activities have ceased completely, and final decommissioning and mine land reclamation have been completed.

Closure planning is not formalized in many countries, nor has it been standardized around the world. This less than perfect situation often leads to unintended consequences that have the potential to become larger than life if not adequately managed.

Coal mines and drill sites closure planning actually starts from day one of the project and continues throughout the life of the mine or drilling operation. It starts with conceptual closure plans and budget estimates during design and permitting stages way before mining or drilling has started. This is followed by periodic checks and updates throughout the life of the operation, ending with a final decommissioning plan.

In all cases a detailed closure and decommissioning plan is submitted to the EPA two years prior to mine or drill site closure. The plan describes in detail the reclamation objectives and specific reclamation and closure activities for the open pits, waste rock disposal facility, tailings storage facility, water storage facility, mill and process plant, sediment control structures, storm water management structures and all ancillary facilities. Final grading and contouring schemes are to be also detailed for all aspects of the project area.

In more detail, specific reclamation objectives to be included in the Plan include:

- *Legal Compliance* statement is needed to meet all statutory requirements.

- *Landform Stability* ensures that land is left in a stable condition that minimizes long-term environmental impacts and does not compromise proposed post mining land uses.

- *Eco-system Re-establishment* requires reclaiming as much of the affected area as possible to a condition where its pre-mining usage can resume and ensuring the eco-system function is representative of this land-use. The primary pre-mining uses include cropland, livestock grazing and small residential development.

- *Water Quality* is a requirement that ensures that the quality of water discharged from the reclaimed mine area meets standards for the immediate downstream use.

- *Public Safety* is needed to ensure that reclaimed land is physically safe for people to access and does not pose a human health risk.

- *Infrastructure* requirement calls for decontamination, decommissioning, salvage or demolition of all structures on the site according to the terms of the mining agreement. Those include facilities, ancillary equipment and buildings.

- *Biodiversity* requirements ensure that the biodiversity of the mining area is maintained at pre-disturbance levels or improves.

- Monetary provisions must be also set up in respect of decommissioning and restoration obligations that arise from production activities, where the cost should be expensed and not capitalized, since it does not give rise to any future economic benefits.

In addition, the decommissioning work might take place 30-50 years down the road, when money would have a totally different value, so current money value is to be used, but extrapolated for future money devaluation.

Complex and expensive work effort...

As Figure 8-12 shows, decommissioning costs are rising; from $4 million to nearly $12 million per site, or about 15% annual increase. Extrapolating to present times we might find out that we need $30-50 million for decommissioning services per site. And going 50 years in the future the cost might reach $100 million in today's money. This is due to rapid increase in energy and labor costs, as well as tightening regulations and safety procedures.

The most practical and widely accepted approach, if sometimes only on paper, is that of progressive reclamation, which is conducted over the life of the mine or drill site by partially closing and decommissioning parts of the mine or well that are no longer in use. This method reduces the reclamation burden at the time of final closure.

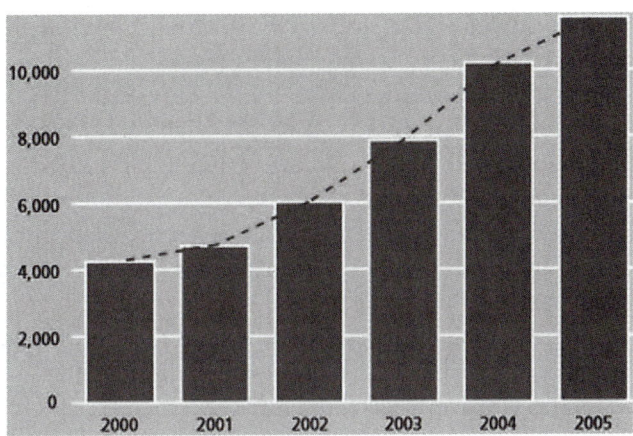

Figure 8-12. Decommissioning costs (in $ millions)

For that purpose some mine shafts are capped by a large concrete plug around 3 feet thick that is placed over the shaft to cover it and stop fatal accidents from occurring. Some mines are capped using large metallic grills, usually on deep level shafts. This way the airflow through the deep tunnels helps prevent subsidence.

Similarly, portions of drilling wells can be filled and capped as time goes on and as parts of the well are no longer producing enough oil or gas.

There are several aspects of mine- or drill-site closure:

- *On-site closure* planning is focused on environmental rehabilitation and returning the land to a reasonable condition, including vegetative and wildlife recovery measures. A large part of this is generating an offset against the high cost of environmental remediation, which in certain cases can exceed the value of the mined coal or produced gas.

- *Off-site closure* is focused on local livelihood, which is a more complex issue.

In all cases, mine- and drill-site closure is expensive, complicated and controversial issue that very often has negative connotations and equally bad results for some of those involved.

NUCLEAR POWER

Nuclear power is different from the rest of its cousins, and is the most expensive and difficult to deal with. It is like the genie in the bottle. The bottle is small, but the impact of its content is tremendous. One day it can provide power for an entire city, and wipe out all the inhabitants in a split second the next day.

Just ask the Fukushima folks—they experienced its mighty fury on their own backs, where their bright, nuclear-powered future was converted into a total devastation in one split second. High levels of radiation will keep the area deadly and closed for generations to come, something that no other force on Earth can do so cruelly and thoroughly!

Uranium is the fuel most often used in nuclear reactors, and all most of us see of it is the shiny metal in the fuel rods, which power our lives, but which have to be disposed somehow, somewhere, some time in the future.

A closer look takes as where it all actually starts—in a dark, dusty mine somewhere in Kazakhstan, Canada, or Australia, which are the top uranium ore producers today, which together account for 63% of world uranium production.

Namibia, Russia, Niger, Uzbekistan, and the U.S. also produce uranium in excess of 1,000 tons per year. Worldwide production of uranium is over 50,000 tons annually, and the known uranium ore resources that can be mined today at current costs, and at current rate of use, are estimated to last about a century. New deposits and new materials for nuclear power generation are estimated to extend the availability of nuclear fuels another century.

Naturally occurring uranium is 99.2745% uranium-238, with uranium-235 (the energy producing isotope) making up about 0.720% of the bulk, and uranium-234 filling in the remainder at less than 0.0055 percent. World total uranium production is about 80 million pounds annually.

Thousands of tons of uranium ore are dug out and extracted from the ground and transported for processing. Here the uranium ores are pulverized to a uniform particle size and treated with harsh chemicals to extract the uranium from the dirt by chemical leaching. The milling process commonly yields dry powder-form material consisting of natural uranium, "yellowcake," which is sold on the uranium market as U_3O_8.

- One ton of natural uranium can produce more than 40 million kilowatt-hours of electricity. This is equivalent to burning 16,000 tons of coal or 80,000 barrels of oil.
- 1 kWh electricity generated by coal emits 1,000 grams of GHGs, natural gas 500 grams, while nuclear power emits less than 10 grams of GHG for equal amount of power.
- 104 operating U.S. nuclear power plants produce

over 20% of U.S. electricity.
- 441 nuclear plants around the globe supply about 16% of the world's electricity.

So as a confirmation of our *genie in the bottle* analogy, uranium-235 contains, and can produce, as much energy as 3,500 tons of coal. Assuming that only 0.01-0.2% U-235 can be obtained from the average uranium ore, which then has to be enriched as needed to sustain a chain reaction, we see that we need to dig out and process 1-6 tons of uranium ore to obtain 1 kilogram of enriched U-235—a lot of digging in a dirty, dusty mine shaft full of radioactive contamination.

The global uranium resources that are economically recoverable at a price of about $60/lb. are enough to last over 100 years at current consumption. As the consumption increases, however, as is the case in some countries (China, India), then the supply will be depleted sooner. In all cases, uranium, and nuclear power in general, will not be an option sometime in the 22nd century and beyond.

Uranium oxide ore price on the world market varies, starting at $2.00/lb. in the early days of nuclear power, but is now stabilized at $35-40/lb. About 20 tons of U-235 are used in each reactor, which means that 60,000-120,000 tons of uranium ore have to be dug out, transported, and processed to fill one reactor, at a price of $2 million, which will produce power for 6-9 months.

On the other hand, think how many tons of coal would be needed to generate the same amount of power—if one kilogram of U-235 generates as much power as 16 tons of coal. Amazed? Confused? Yes, we all are. There are too many factors to consider, and too may pros and cons to make an educated decision on any of these.

The benefits of using nuclear power are quite clear; just look at the thousands of tons of coal (and GHGs) we save every year by using nuclear instead of coal power generation. The picture, however, is fogged-up by the enormous destructive power of that much uranium in one place, and the uncertainties this monstrous combination brings. Just ask the people at Fukushima; they will tell you a horrific story.

So the debate continues, and with it the hesitation of some countries to use and expand nuclear power.

Nuclear Fuel Transport

The genie in the bottle sometimes has to be transported. For obvious reasons, this process is very tightly controlled via special licensing and other strict regulations and measures. Over 20 million radioactive material packages are shipped around the world each year, but only about 5% of those shipments are nuclear-fuel related.

International regulations for the transport of radioactive material have been issued by the International Atomic Energy Agency (IAEA), and have been adopted for use by most countries. Regulatory control of shipments of nuclear material is independent of the material's intended use or application.

Uranium oxide concentrate, or yellowcake, is transported from the mines to conversion plants in 200 liter drums packed into normal shipping containers. No radiation protection is required beyond having the steel drums clean and within the shipping container. To and from enrichment plants, the uranium is in the form of uranium hexafluoride (UF6), which is barely radioactive, but has significant chemical toxicity. It is in special containers, which also function for storage.

Uranium fuel assemblies are manufactured at fuel fabrication plants, and are made up of ceramic pellets formed from pressed uranium oxide that has been sintered at a high temperature (over 1400°C). The pellets are placed into long, hollow, metal rods, which in turn are arranged in the fuel assemblies, ready for introduction into the reactor.

Different types of reactors require different types of fuel assembly, so when the fuel assemblies are transported from the fuel fabrication facility to the nuclear power reactor, the contents of the shipment will vary with the type of reactor receiving it. In Western Europe, Asia and the U.S., the most common means of transporting uranium fuel assemblies is by truck. A typical truckload supplying a light water reactor contains 6 tons of fuel. In the countries of the former Soviet Union, rail transport is most often used. Intercontinental transports are mostly by sea, with occasionally transport by air.

The annual operation of a 1000 MWe light water reactor requires an average fuel load of 27 tons of uranium dioxide, containing 24 tons of enriched uranium, which can be transported in 4 to 5 trucks.

The precision-made fuel assemblies are transported in packages specially constructed to protect them from damage during transport. Uranium fuel assemblies have a low radioactivity level and radiation shielding is not necessary.

Fuel assemblies contain fissile material and criticality is prevented by the design of the shipping packages, (including the arrangement of the fuel assemblies within it and limitations on the amount of material contained within the package), and on the number of packages carried in one shipment.

Nuclear fuel cycle facilities are located in various parts of the world and the handling and transport of nuclear materials generated in those is a subject of the greatest public concern. The procedures for transport of nuclear materials are designed to ensure the protection of the public and the environment, where special procedures are followed during routine transactions and during accidents.

The amount of nuclear fuel used for power generation is much smaller than the amount of any other fuel, which reduces the volume of shipments. This in turn reduces the conventional risks and environmental impacts associated with fuel transport. Nevertheless, the stigma of great danger surrounding the genie in the bottle cannot be equated to its size.

In the U.S., the Nuclear Regulatory Commission is in charge of this process, and everything else related to the safety of nuclear materials.

This is done by the issuance of guidance documents that are used by the licensees and other stakeholders to ensure the safety of the transportation of those dangerous materials, and to prevent theft and any other unforeseen incidents and accidents.

Some of those documents are: the Standard Review Plan For Transportation Packages For Radioactive Material (NUREG-1609), the Standard Review Plan For Transportation Packages For Spent Nuclear Fuel (NUREG-1617), and Classification of Transportation Packaging and Dry Spent Fuel Storage System Components According to Importance to Safety (NUREG/CR-6407).

In the U.S. about 1.0% of all 300 million packages of hazardous material shipped each year contain radioactive materials. About 250,000 shipments contain radioactive wastes from U.S. nuclear power plants, and 25-100 packages contain used nuclear fuel, spent or not, are packed in specially designed, robust 125 ton type B casks.

Rail or ships usually transport the casks, containing about 20 tons of spent nuclear fuel each. The casks and the transport vehicles are especially designed and built to survive serious accidents. Although there are a number of such accidents to report, there has never been any accident in which a type B transport cask containing radioactive materials has been breached, or any radiation leaked.

Health Effects

All types of mining are dangerous in terms of accidents, illness, and even death. Uranium ore mining is especially dangerous, because uranium emits radon gas. Radon is produced during the radioactive decay of uranium, so underground uranium mines usually have very high concentrations of radon. The health effects of high exposure to radon are a particular problem in the mining of uranium, where high numbers of lung cancer illnesses and deaths have been identified in epidemiological studies of uranium miners.

In Russia, and some of the Eastern Block countries, political prisoners and death row inmates were sent to dig out uranium in the past. Many of them never made it out of the mines, and many of those who did were suffering from lung cancer.

Lung cancer has been the major cause of death among uranium miners around the world in the near past. Presently, ventilation and other measures have been implemented to reduce radon levels in most modern mines. The average annual exposure of uranium miners has fallen recently to very low levels, but it still remains an issue for those who are currently employed in affected mines, and especially for miners employed in the past.

Another problem is that uranium sites are very difficult to clean once operations have stopped. Hundreds of abandoned mines remain as they were during the last day of operation, thus presenting serious environmental and health risks in the local communities. The EPA, in concert with other organizations, has been working on resolving the issue, but there are still hundreds of abandoned mines with unresolved final status. Those still emit radiation, contaminating the environment and harming wildlife and humans—and the situation is much worse in other countries.

But the biggest problem by far (in addition to the fear from nuclear accidents) is the lack of proper storage facilities and processes. There are thousands of tons of spent nuclear fuel stored "temporarily" in the back yards of nuclear plants in the U.S. and around the world, awaiting disposal in a permanent storage. The waiting has been going on for over half a century, and there is still no concrete solution (no pun intended) in sight. This and other issues are hanging over the nuclear industry like the proverbial dagger over our heads. What's next, nobody knows.

Nuclear Terrorism

Nuclear terrorism is a new phenomenon and a reflection of the new complexities arising from unresolved global conflicts. It could mean the detonation of a nuclear bomb containing fissile material by terrorists, or a sabotage of a nuclear facility, or the detonation of a radiological device, also called dirty bomb. Nevertheless, the term nuclear terrorism is not officially defined and could mean any, or a combination, of the above activities.

According to the 2005 United Nations International Convention for the Suppression of Acts of Nuclear Terrorism, nuclear terrorism is an offense committed if an entity unlawfully and intentionally "uses in any way radioactive material ... with the intent to cause death or serious bodily injury; or with the intent to cause substantial damage to property or to the environment; or with the intent to compel a natural or legal person, an international organization or a state to do or refrain from doing an act."

James Bond and others superspies have used suitcase size nuclear weapons, and it is hypothetically possible for terrorists to acquire such, or larger, nuclear weapons, but the threat thus far remains verbal. Nevertheless, the U.S. and other nations are taking the necessary precautions in the form of national nuclear counterterrorist efforts. This involves assessing the interest and capabilities of terrorist groups in acquiring and employing nuclear weapons; addressing vulnerabilities with respect to the storage of those materials; developing and improving means of detecting nuclear weapons or material in the possession of terrorists; and identifying the source of such items through nuclear forensics and attribution.

Recently the U.S. National Security Archive posted 40 documents produced by a range of U.S. and other government agencies that concern assorted aspects of the current U.S. nuclear counterterrorism effort, and provide details of earlier investigations into the threat of clandestine nuclear attack.

Some items of particular interest are:

A Defense Science Board report (Document 8) which discusses Project SCREWDRIVER (1950-52) and the resulting Project DOORSTOP (1953-70), where the objective was to detect any attempts by Soviet Bloc diplomats to smuggle nuclear material into the U.S.

An after-action report (Document 4) of the 1998 ERRANT FOE exercise, which identifies issues concerning the effort to disable a terrorist device as well the mission, capability, "deployment trigger," team size, and composition of NEST components.

The existence of a yearly Defense Intelligence Agency report—Postulated Threat to U.S. Nuclear Weapons Facilities and Other Selected Strategic Facilities.

Creation of the "SIGMA 20" nuclear weapons data category—to protect information about data on improvised nuclear devices (Document 12).

The report (Document 17) of a radiological survey of Washington, D.C., in preparation for the nuclear detection efforts conducted before and during the 2009 Presidential inauguration.

A description of the potential terrorist tactic (Document 15) of employing a radiation exposure (or emission) device.

The pre-9/11 conclusion of the Defense Science Board (Document 8) that "current nuclear forensics capability is inadequate to support timely response."

The efforts by the Domestic Nuclear Detection Office to create a Global Nuclear Detection Architecture (Document 13)(Document 37)

These documents, and the related actions clearly show that we are ready to confront any type of nuclear threat on our doorsteps.

METHANE HYDRATE

Methane hydrate is a new phenomenon on the world's fossil energy markets, referring to huge amounts of solid clathrate hydrate deep in the ocean floor and in the permafrost in which methane gas is trapped. This is an unusual type of formation within the frozen crystal structure of water, forming a solid similar to ice. They are usually found in the shallow marine geosphere, but could occur both in deep sedimentary structures and form outcrops on the ocean floor.

Methane clathrates are also present in deep Antarctic ice cores, which scientists drill out looking for a record of the history of atmospheric methane concentrations through the millennia. This record is a valuable source of information for global warming research, along with that of oxygen and carbon dioxide.

Methane hydrates form by the migration of methane gas escaping from the depths of the Earth along geological faults. During its way up, the gas encounters cold ocean water, which causes it to precipitate, or crystallize on contact.

It is estimated that the world-wide sedimentary methane hydrate reservoir contains close to 10 times the currently known reserves of conventional natural gas. This is a potentially important future source of fossil fuel. There are, however, a number of problems:

—The deposits are too dispersed for economic extraction, since small quantities here and there would not justify the great expense involved in locating and extracting them.

—Detection, location, and estimation of viable reserves is difficult, due to their awkward and remote locations, which add uncertainty to the process and make it very expensive.

There is no technology presently for safe and economic extraction of methane gas from the hydrate deposits.

—Ongoing research and development of this technology aiming for commercial-scale extraction are ongoing, but are in the very early stages. Japan and China have plans to study natural gas hydrates and develop the extraction technology.

There is an estimate of a potentially economically recoverable large reserve in the Gulf of Mexico, containing approximately billions of cubic feet of methane gas. To extract the gas, however, specialized equipment is used to drill into the layers to depressurize the hydrate deposits. This causes the methane gas to separate from the ice and float freely. It can then be collected and pumped to the surface for further processing and use.

Extraction of methane gas from shallow on- and off-shore deposits is possible, but the major reservoirs are offshore and deep under the ocean floor, where their extraction would be much more difficult and expensive. The key to success with this future energy sources is to get the extraction costs down to that of the existing energy sources.

And then, if and when viable and cost-effective extraction technology is developed, there is another problem. A big one! Methane is a powerful greenhouse gas. It has short atmospheric half life of about 7 years, but its global warming potential is greater than any other gasses. Sudden release (intentionally or unintentionally) of large amounts of methane gas from clathrate deposits could accelerate the climate warming.

Methane hydrate, similar to nuclear power, is the genie in the bottle. It could do miracles if properly used and controlled, but it could also destroy us if abused or if out of control.

There are events in the Earth's history that are linked to release of large amounts of methane from the permafrost. Scientists are also predicting that there is a good chance for the methane clathrates in the present permafrost regions will be released slowly during the global warming cycle we are in.

Measurements during the last decade have shown that there are millions of tons of methane gas being released from the permafrost due to the warming ground. Concentrations in some regions of the permafrost have been measured at 50-100 times above the normal.

Large enough releases in the future might unleash

excess feedback forces, which may cause runaway climate change that cannot be controlled, and effects of which would be devastating to the global environment and life in it. Human intervention in an attempt to recover those frozen assets might accelerate this process, thus making the methane hydrates the most powerful and dangerous weapon on Earth.

RENEWABLE ENERGY MARKETS

The renewable energy markets include the entire cradle-to-grave cycle of renewable energy products (solar, wind, bio, geo renewable power generators) products and services, as well as their deployment and use in the U.S. and around the world.

The actual global renewable energy markets have gone through three different generations of development and deployment:

- *Gen one* renewable technologies are already mature and economically competitive technologies and equipment exist that are used for the production of heat or electric energy from biomass, hydroelectricity, and geothermal power and heat.

- *Gen two* renewable technologies are market-ready (or almost ready), some of which are being deployed today, including solar heating, PV, wind power, solar thermal power, and advanced forms of bioenergy.

- *Gen three* renewable technologies are still in R&D mode, and need some more time and effort to make a big splash in the global energy markets. Those include advanced biomass gasification, exotic PV technologies, biorefinery technologies, hot-dry-rock geothermal power, methane hydrates, fuel cells, and advanced ocean energy.

The renewables markets have grown significantly lately, and exceeded $250 billion in investments in 2011. Almost that much was invested in 2010, although things are slowing significantly lately. The U.S. alone has spent over $100 billion in the development of renewable energy technologies recently, and 3 million jobs today (most of which are in biofuels) depend on renewable technologies.

Price is the key determining factor in using any and all energy sources, and so wind, hydro- and bio-power generators lead the pack today as follows:

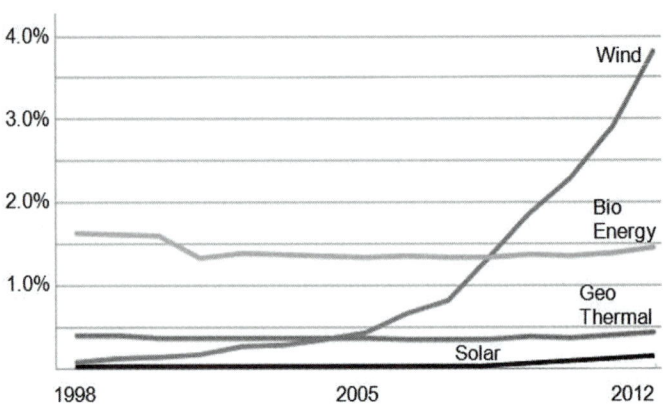

Figure 8-13. Share of renewables in the U.S.

Table 8-8. U.S. energy costs, 2012
(in cents

Hydro	3-10
Geothermal	4-10
Biomass	5-12
Wind	5-15
Solar thermal	12-20
Solar PV	15-25

In 2011, there was 41 GW of new wind power capacity, 30 GW of PV, 25 GW of hydro-electricity, 6 GW of biomass, 0.5 GW of CSP, and 0.1 GW of geothermal power added globally. In 2012, renewable power generation accounted for around half of all new power generation capacity (including the fossils and nuclear) added globally.

Solar energy generation is expected to dwarf all other energy sources by 2050, when using the free energy of the sun will produce most of the world's electricity. As confirmation of the trend, global PV installations in 2012 were about 30 GWp, and are expected to grow to 55 GWp by 2016. The 3.3 GW in the U.S. in 2012 will increase to over 8 GW during the same time.

Presently, however, the solar and wind industries are still recovering from the great losses during the last renewable energy boom-bust cycle of 2007-2012. Billions of dollars were spent during that time by the U.S. and world governments on supporting the development of new and existing renewable technologies, which only caused a collapse of hundreds when the support was dropped in 2011-2012.

The remaining companies and projects are struggling, and although some progress is clearly seen in California and some countries, the reliability of the renewable energy sources, and their ability to stand on their own, is now questionable.

Table 8-9. Total global solar power generation (to be completed)

| Country | INSTALLED SOLAR ENERGY CAPACITY (MWp) | | | | | | Projected | |
	2007	2008	2009	2010	2011	2012	2015	2020
Germany	1,100	1,500	3,800	7,200	7,500	6,000	4,000	6,500
Spain	560	2,500	75	850	500	650	1,200	2,000
Italy	75	420	550	4,200	9,200	4,500	4,500	5,000
France	55	150	250	700	1,500	1,500	3,750	4,200
Japan	201	230	480	975	1,500	2,500	2,200	4,500
China	70	110	175	580	2,800	4,500	6,000	5,000
India	10	15	30	80	1,500	300	900	4,500
USA	207	342	480	975	2,100	3,300	5,200	7,500
World	Balance	Balance	Balance	Balance	Balance	Balance	Balance	Balance
Annually	~2,800	~5,600	~7,500	~16,250	~27,500	~32,000	~28,000	~30,000
Total	~9,550	~15,150	~22,650	~38,900	~65,000	~77,000	~140,000	250,000

Nevertheless, the unprecedented, albeit short-lived, growth of renewable companies and projects helped a number of related companies to increase their production and develop new products and services. During 2007-2010 many small and large companies added one or other type of "solar" to the signs over their doors, and to their commercial ads. Anybody who could hold a screwdriver was given a title of a "solar installer" and was sent on the roofs to install solar panels.

Well, those days are over now. Most of the "solar" were removed, taking entire companies down with them. Most of the "solar installers" are now doing other, non-solar, jobs, or are reminiscing about the good old days of solar in the unemployment lines.

Most of the solar manufacturers and the supporting companies are suffering from reduced production volumes and extremely competitive prices of energy products and services. The future looks bright for a number of large companies that were able to withstand the subsidies tsunami and remain competitive in the following price pressure from Chinese manufacturers.

The drastic drop in PV module prices is blamed for the collapse of the solar industry during 2010-2012, but there are many other factors, which we discuss in more detail in our books on the subject (see references 20 and 21).

We will take a closer look at the solar markets, since they are the most flexible and the fastest developing area in the energy sector.

Solar Market Segments

The solar energy market is the most promising alternative energy source in the long run. In 2012, there was an estimated 93.0 TWh generated from solar, about 0.41% of total global electricity generation, which was

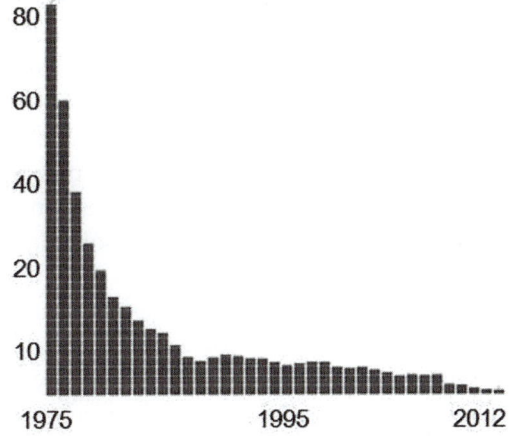

Figure 8-14. PV module prices (in $/Watt)

a 58% increase over the power generation in 2011. The trend, nevertheless, is projected to slow down, due to the complexity and expense related to construction and operation of solar power plants.

We divide the world-wide solar industry and the related markets into several segments, where the technologies suitable for commercial and utilities applications today, and presumably for the rest of the 21st century, are:

1. Solar thermal technologies:
   a. The flat plate water heater
   b. The Stirling engine dish
   c. Parabolic troughs
   d. Power towers
   e. New and exotic solar thermal technologies

2. Solar photovoltaics technologies:
   a. Crystalline silicon PV modules

b. Thin film PV modules
c. HCPV trackers
d. New and exotic PV technologies

Solar Thermal

Also called concentrated solar power (CSP), this promising technology relies on concentrating sunlight onto receiver assemblies, where transfer liquid is heated to very high temperature. The liquid is then used to heat buildings directly, but more often it is used to generate electric power. Transferring the heated liquid to a powerhouse, where it is used to create steam, which in turn activates a turbine to generate electric power, does this. The electric power is sent into the grid, while the steam is cooled down (a great waste of energy) and recycled.

Commercial concentrated solar power plants were first developed in the 1980s in the U.S. The 354 MWp SEGS CSP installation, located in the Mojave Desert of California, the 280 MWp Solana Generating station, and the 250 MWp Agua Caliente Solar Project, both in Arizona, and the 221 MWp Charanka Solar Park in India, are the world's largest photovoltaic power plants. Other large CSP plants include the 150 MWp Solnova Solar Power Station and the 150 MWp Andasol solar power station, both in Spain.

One of the principal advantages of concentrated solar power is that it allows for energy storage, which ensures power generation during cloudy days and at night. This way one of the greatest handicaps of solar energy, its variability, can be overcome by providing 24-hour power output. This output can be scheduled to meet demand requirements, which is a great help to the power grid operators.

The Solana Generating Station in Arizona, for example, is designed to provide six hours of energy storage. When properly used, it can be scheduled to provide power to the grid 24 hours every day, something that cannot be done with photovoltaic power generators... for now.

Nevertheless, photovoltaic power generation is more flexible, and easier and more convenient to use. PV modules can be installed in small quantities on individual house roofs, or in larger numbers for large-scale power generation. CSP, in contrast, makes sense only in very large-scale commercial operations—over 50 MWp. Smaller installations are not economically feasible.

CSP is also limited in terms of technological developments and improvements, contrasting with dozens of new photovoltaic technologies that were developed during the last decade alone, and where many existing technologies underwent major facelifts in terms of efficiency improvement and cost reduction.

Because of that, photovoltaic technologies are the solar power of the future, and that is why we dedicate much more space to them in this text.

The Technologies

There are a number of solar thermal technologies, with the main being: a) solar water heaters, b) trough concentrators, c) power tower, and d) Sterling engine. The latter three are also called concentrating solar power (CSP) technologies. The solar thermal industry is focused on the design, manufacturing, installation, and operation of those technologies. In the process it is opening the doors to a number of other industries and creating new energy and other markets. In more detail:

Just like above, each of those technologies needs production equipment and materials for the manufacturing of the final products, which then have to be transported and installed on house roofs (solar water heaters), or in large-scale solar power fields, usually in the deserts.

Some companies own and operate thus installed power fields, while in most cases the fields are sold to a new owner, who is in charge of the operation and maintenance of the equipment for the duration.

California led the new PV installations with 1,033 GW in 2012. Arizona was second with 710 MWp new installs and New Jersey was third with 415 MWp—not bad for a state with little sunlight. It is a confirmation, just like the incredible growth of solar installations in cloudy Germany, that where there is a will, there is a way.

A number of trends dominated and some even strongly shaped the U.S. solar markets in 2012:

• As a result of the global solar bust, many PV manufacturers had to live with reduced margins, which forced many less mature technologies and less-competitive facilities around the world to shut down. The remaining companies, however, tightened their belts and found ways to stay on their feet, thus resulting in a more robust solar industry.

• Large-scale solar is finally becoming a reality with the first wave of truly utility-scale solar coming on-line in 2012. Eight of the ten largest PV projects operating today were completed in 2012, but most of them were products of the generous DOE loan guarantee program. The trend is continuing, with more than 4.0 GW of utility solar projects currently under construction. And even though the easy DOE money is gone now, another 8.0 GW of projects with PPAs in place are expected to start construction soon.

- The U.S. utilities are beginning to see problems with the sudden influx of large-scale solar and wind power into their distribution networks. Due to the variability and other technical problems with wind and solar, the utilities are looking at increased O&M expenses and additional difficulties, so they are now looking for ways to manage the new situation. It appears that a new and serious battle is about to start on the large-scale power fields.

- The China-U.S. trade dispute resulted in the introduction of high tariffs on Chinese solar cells and modules. The final impact of this decision is uncertain, but for now the Chinese module shipments to the U.S. have dropped significantly, as have the PV prices. The ongoing dispute in Europe could change the scenario and result in new tariffs. The short effect of those activities may not be beneficial to the U.S. solar industry, but in the end it will provide some stability and outline clearly the path for the industry to take in the near future.

- The newly introduced and expanded, third-party-owned (TPO) approach, swept the country resulted in increased residential solar leases. Through it power purchase agreements (PPAs) gained further popularity and as a result TPOs PV systems accounted for over 50% of all new residential installations in most major residential markets. Arizona topped the list with 90% of TPOs. A number of new companies entered this market to add new approaches to the business model. It is widely expected that the TPO residential solar market will grow to nearly $6.0 billion market by 2015.

- Another revolutionary and very important trend of late is the diversification in, and the introduction of, new project financing. There are now a variety of new ways to finance solar projects, some of which have been already introduced already, but need to be scaled up, while others are working their way to becoming a reality in the near future. Solar real estate investment trusts (REITs), crowd funded solar projects, securitized solar assets, and solar inclusion in master limited partnerships (MLPs) are some examples of those new trends to watch for in the future.

- The newest, and maybe most important, trend in the U.S. is the decision of the Lancaster, California city council, which unanimously approved changes to the city's zoning code that requires housing developers to install solar with every new home they build in the same way that they must meet minimum parking space and other building requirements.

If a housing tract is built in phases, each phase must meet the requirement, while multifamily developments can meet the requirement with a rooftop system or a system on a support or shade structure. As an exception, builders have the option to meet the solar energy generation requirement off-site by providing evidence of purchasing solar energy credits from another solar-generating development located within the city.

There is no doubt that solar is coming to the U.S. in a big way. This time it intends to stay, and we believe that it will.

Photovoltaics

The major PV energy technologies of today are:
- Crystalline silicon PV modules
- Thin film PV modules
- HCPV trackers
- New and exotic PV technologies

We will take a look at the different types that form the PV power generation market and can be divided into:
- Residential
- Commercial
- Utility segments

Each of those segments uses all types of PV modules and general setup, but in different quantities and for different purposes.

- The *residential PV market* participants are usually homeowners, who can afford a $2,000-5,000 down payment to install a PV array on their roofs. The size of those installations vary from 1-5 kWp in size, which is not enough to run the entire household, but saves some money in the long run by selling power back to the local utility.

- The *commercial PV market* is dominated by small businesses, which have available roof space and money to install PV arrays in the 10-100-kWp range. Those could be restaurants, Laundromats, or office building owners, whose aim is to reduce the energy bills by selling power back to the utilities.

• The *utility PV market* is quite different. It usually refers to the installation of large-scale power fields by contractors, which are then operated by the utility companies. Those fields range in size from 100 kWp-500 MWp, and are usually installed in the deserts.

The utilities also purchase power from a number of residential and commercial PV power generators, so this is a different market that is driven by a different set of rules and regulations. Both markets create lots of headaches to the utilities, and for a number of technical and financial reasons are still suffering from growing pains and are undergoing changes.

The world PV installations exceeded 100 GW in 2012, which is a great achievement that guarantees the further growth of this technology in the future.

In 2012 the U.S. PV installations grew 76% over 2011. A total of 3.3 GWp of PV modules were installed, with an estimated market value of $11.5 billion. Each market segment (residential, commercial, and utility) grew, while the overall markets in most U.S. states expanded as well.

At the same time, PV modules and installed prices for PV systems fell 27% during 2012 and at least 13% in each market segment. Nearly 83,000 homes installed solar PV, and cumulative PV installations in the U.S. surpassed 300,000. Most of those developments were in California, followed by Arizona.

The U.S. Solar Market

The U.S. solar market went through a period of rapid progress during the latest solar boom-bust cycle of 2007-2012. It is still growing, but at a slower rate and with some uncertainty of the future developments.

The solar market growth of late has been impressive. See Figure 8-15. If it continues going at that rate, we could be running the entire country on solar before long. This is not going to happen, however, due to changing political, financial and other conditions.

The major growth is recorded in the utility scale solar power installations. This sector is growing and is expected to continue growing in the near future, but at a slower pace.

Part of the reason for the ramped up solar activities of late was the drastic reduction of prices of PV modules and other components, as shown in Figure 8-16. This

was also a temporary situation, and now we expect the prices to increase somewhat before stabilizing in 2015-2016.

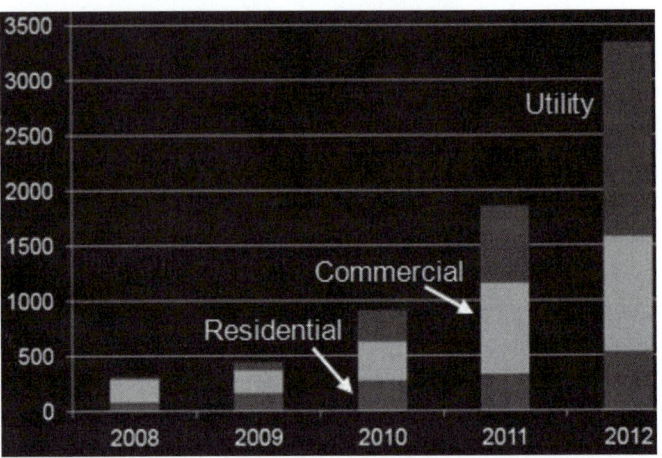

Figure 8-15. U.S. PV installations (in MWp)

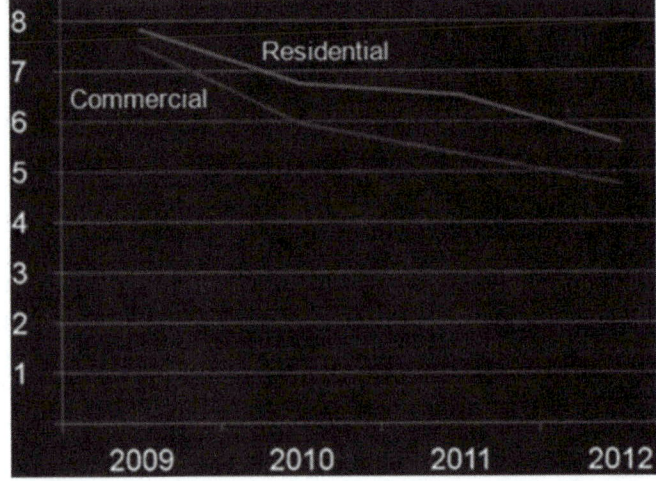

Figure 8-16. U.S. PV installations cost (in $/Watt installed)

U.S. 2013 Update

Solar installation rates in the first quarter of 2013 beat all previous records; residential and utility market segments registered highs with 164 MW and 318 MW respectively, reaching a record of 723 MW in the first quarter of 2013. This represents a 45% decline from the last quarter of 2012, but a 33% increase from the first quarter of 2012.

The total installations forecast for 2013 in the U.S. was about 4.5 GW, which is one of the highest, and that is mostly due to increasingly bullish expectations for the residential market across a number of states. The cumulative operating PV capacity in the U.S. now stands at about 8.0 GWp.

The residential market has grown consistently during the last several years, independent of seasonal effects. It had a 53% growth in 2013, compared with 2012, while the commercial sector had a slow start in 2013, down 20% on both a quarterly and annual basis. About 18% growth in the commercial sector (down from 29% in 2012) is forecasted for 2013, with stronger growth to be seen in 2014-2016.

The utility PV market is expected to have another record year with 2.3 GW installed, followed by a slowdown in 2014.

Residential system prices fell 15.8%, from $5.86/W to $4.93/W in 2013, while non-residential system prices fell 15.6% year-over-year from $4.64/W to $3.92/W. Utility system prices declined from $2.90/W to $2.14/W in 2013.

There were 24 large-scale utility projects completed in the first half of 2013, ranging in size from 1 MW to 80 MW. Four of the five largest projects were the early phases of larger projects to be completed over the next two years. The five largest projects were commissioned in California, of course.

California's residential market recorded a breakthrough volume of installations without subsidies (but with the help of ITC), where 13.2 MW of residential solar was installed outside the California solar initiative program. Those are solar's first baby steps. It is just now showing us its ability to compete in residential markets in some locations with just the ITC.

The challenges to the new solar revival in the U.S., and especially in the quickly growing California solar market, include political and regulatory discrepancies and the associated risks over:

- Net energy metering
- Changing rate structures
- The availability of project finance

The utility companies are trying to change the solar game by modifying the metering rules and the rate structure, which will impact the future development of solar in the country.

The unofficial estimates are that the distributed power generation market (mostly residential rooftops) will require over $50 billion in investments by 2018. This is far above all project finance provided to date, so it is not clear where this money would come from.

California Solar

California is setting new records for solar generation, and breaking them as soon as they are advertised.

Take a look at how dramatically the solar generation records are being broken in the Golden State:

According to Figure 8-17, California achieved new solar power generation records in 2013 as follows:

- January 1, 2013, a new record of 1,122 MW
- January 2, 2013, a new record of 1,235 MW
- May 23, 2013, a new record of 1,872 MW
- May 24, 2013, a new record of 1,897 MW
- August 9, 2013, a new record of 2,570 MW

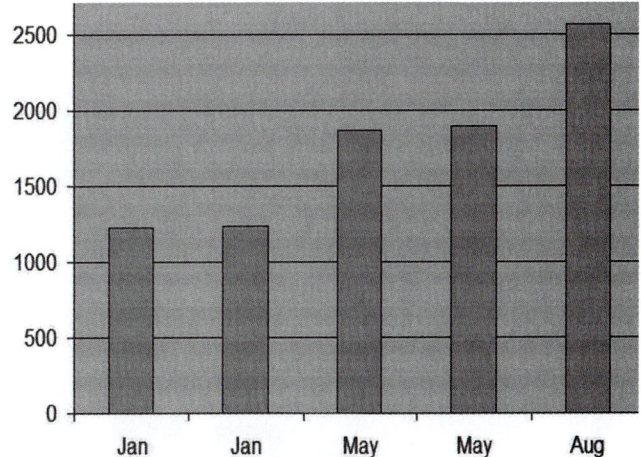

Figure 8-17. 2013 California solar installations (in MWp)

The total utility-scale renewable energy output including wind, biomass, geothermal and hydro in August peaked to nearly 9.0 GW in the some afternoons. This roughly coincided with peak demand of 32.6 GW, meaning that renewables peaked at over 27% of demand.

This also translates to utility-scale solar generation peaking at 8.3% of the total demand. This is a new record both in terms of total output and percentage of demand met by PV and CSP, surpassing a series of records set in late July 2013.

One important thing to remember here is the fact that, unlike Germany, the California solar generation data does not include "behind the meter" residential and commercial PV systems. Those are currently not centralized, so their output is not measured, nor added to the total. If added, the total number would be much higher, since there is more than 1.0 GW of behind the meter solar power systems in California. This means is that the peak solar power generation record has jumped 69% from 2012.

The new wind record was set at about 4 MW also in August 2013.

The California electrical energy demand is expected to increase 20% by 2020, which is a significant increase that will require new power generation capacity. Most of this capacity is expected to come from natural gas-fired power plants, with a significant help from the renewables.

Figure 8-18 shows the difference in price for power generation by the different sources in California. Obviously coal and gas are the cheapest overall energy sources—from the initial fuel production to the final power generation steps. With the increased abundance of natural gas reserves and reduced prices, we expect it to dominate the energy markets in California and the U.S. for the next several decades.

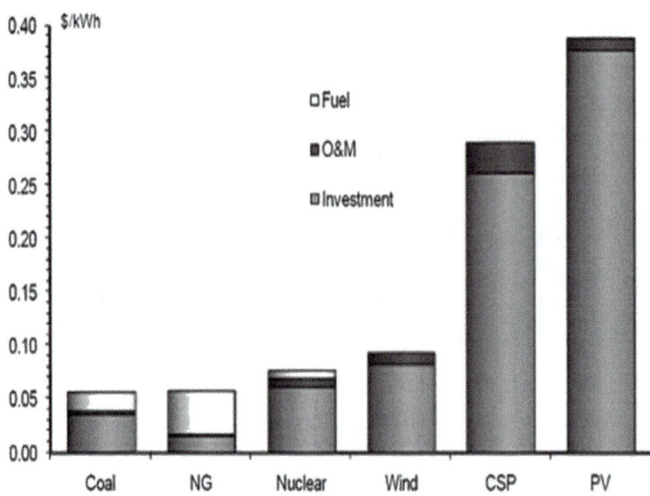

Figure 8-18. Energy cost per kW/h (2010)

Taking a closer look, we can see that solar and wind do not need any fuel to run, since the natural forces of the sun and the wind power them. They do, however, require some expense in operations and maintenance (O&M), which adds to the final price tag.

What this tells us is that the different energy sources and technologies have different advantages and disadvantages, and so should be used in different areas and different applications, when and where appropriate. One single energy source, no matter how attractive it might seem, cannot provide all the power we need, so we need a balanced approach.

This versatility creates versatile energy sources and energy related markets.

Figure 8-19 shows the different levels of GHG emissions during the different stages of fuels production (coal mining) or product manufacturing (solar modules) and use of the major power generating sources. Coal, for example, generates the most GHG while burning during power generation. Solar, on the other hand, uses a lot of energy and emits the most GHG during its manufactur-

ing process (silicon ingots, wafers and cells manufacturing processes are extremely energy hungry.)

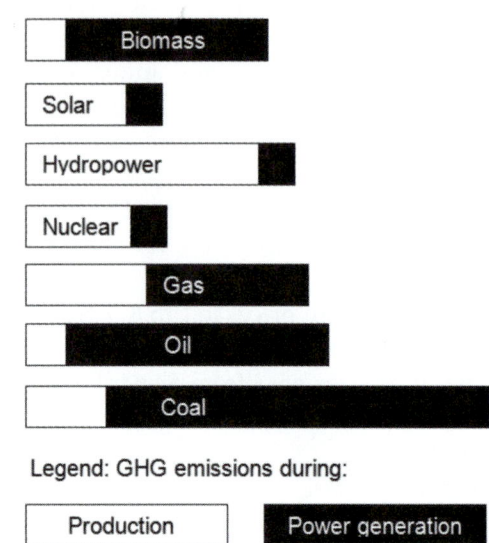

Figure 8-19. GHG emissions during production and power generation

Here again, we need to find a balance between the fuel production and the equipment manufacturing on one hand, and the actual power generation processes on the other.

The utilities are also unhappy, because the need for more electricity is creating a number of discrepancies. For example, the use of the grid is increasing with the increase of solar and wind power generation, and the utilities are stuck with the bill to maintain the grid and to take care of the fluctuations and outages created by the variable power provided by solar and wind generators.

Despite the many benefits that wind and solar bring, the California utilities are getting quite worried about their long-term impact on the grid and their bottom line and are beginning to fight for their rights. As the renewables use in California is growing, we expect to see some drastic changes in the way they (solar and wind power especially) are used in the near future.

California's Net Metering Revolution

Bill AB327 was passed by the California senate, which was a big victory for solar and a confirmation that solar is recognized as a major power source.

In essence, bill AB327:

• Repeals the limitations on increasing the electric service rates of residential customers, including the rate increase limitations applicable to electric service provided to CARE customers. Instead it but would require the California Public Utilities Commission (CPUC) to establish rates for CARE program participants, as needed to ensure that low-income ratepayers are not overburdened by monthly energy expenditures.

- Requires that increases to rates and charges in rate design proceedings, including any reduction in the CARE discount, be reasonable and subject to a reasonable phase-in schedule relative to the rates and charges in effect prior to January 1, 2014.

- Authorizes CPUC to approve new, or expand existing, fixed charges. That is as defined, to allow an electrical corporation for the to collect a reasonable portion of the fixed costs of providing service to residential customers.

- Imposes a $10 limit per residential customer not part of the CARE program, and only a $5 per month limit for participants in the CARE program. Those rates will be adjusted according to the annual percentage increase in the Consumer Price Index.

- Allows the CPUC to authorize the utilities to offer residential customers the option of receiving service pursuant to time-variant pricing and to participate in other demand response programs.

- Prohibits the CPUC from requiring or permitting an utility from employing mandatory or default time-variant pricing, as defined, for any residential customer, except that beginning January 1, 2018, the commission may require or authorize an electrical corporation to employ default time-of-use pricing to residential customers, subject to specified limitations and conditions.

- Requires a large utility with more than 100,000 service connections in California to provide net energy metering to additional eligible customer-generators in its service area through July 1, 2017. It also requires CPUC to develop a standard contract or tariff for eligible customer-generators with a renewable electrical generation facility that is a customer of a large electrical corporation.

- Requires the large utilities to offer the standard contract or tariff to an eligible customer-generator beginning July 1, 2017, or when ordered by CPUC,

and there is no limitation on the number of customers.

Generally speaking, AB 327 is the first sweeping rewriting of utility ratemaking policy since the 2000-2001 energy crisis. It basically redefines California solar net metering and residential electricity rate structures, and represents the brightest hope for ensuring a stable solar growth.

The bill is supported by the big IOU utilities that have long argued that changes like those are needed to align electric rates with the economic realities of serving the changing needs of the state's customers. If the utilities are happy, then everybody is happy too.

The solar industry welcomed the new bill as well, and is now girding themselves for the upcoming challenge of shaping the new changes to state policy, which could either boost or hinder California's solar future. Many solar advocates plan to take an active role to assure that the CPUC's rules for net metering contracts are transitioned to the new regime to protect their value. This is to protect the solar customers from the midstream changes.

The opposition sees AB 327 allowing changes to residential energy rate structures that could harm the growth of rooftop solar PV and the overall energy efficiency. The Sierra Club, for example, is opposed to flattening of high tiered rates for big residential electricity consumers, as well as rules that would allow utilities to seek flat fees of up to $10 per month to cover fixed grid costs. According to their representatives, "AB 327 is a powerful reminder of the extent to which utilities influence public policy to the benefit of their shareholders and the detriment of working families. It's disappointing that so many legislators walked away from their constituents' interest. They've now saddled Californians with up to $120 a year in new charges on their electricity bills."

Who is right and who is wrong is unclear, since this is a very complex and quickly developing situation, but a future battle field is shaping even now. The field will be divided into winners and losers soon enough, as it usually the case after major policy changes, and so we just have to wait and see what will happen next in the great state of California.

For now, however, solar is on its way to becoming a major power source. It will not be stopped this time, unlike what happened many times before. Solar is here to stay…at least in California. Unfortunately, most other states are not that lucky.

Let's examine Arizona—the solar capital of the world—as an example.

Arizona Solar...or Not

The solar revival in Arizona started with a loud bang of activities...mostly lots of talks, hopes, and expectations in public meetings, in the media, and around corporate conference tables. The general consensus in the 2007-2009 period was that Arizona is to be the future solar capital of the world.

After a number of false starts, the solar industry in Arizona is in a world of pain today; it is hurting from a number of aggressive policy decisions made by the state's energy commission. Those actions are supported by the local utilities, and according to some insiders, are instigated by the utilities.

What happened, and what is expected in the future, is short of amazing:

- In January 2013, the Arizona Corporation Commission (ACC) surprised the local solar industry with an unannounced $38.3 million hit, designed to eliminate performance-based incentives (PBIs). Those incentives were provided to small to medium commercial solar system buyers by the state's two investor-owned utilities (IOUs). Lifting the incentive started a period of hesitation and indecision as far as new solar installation plans were concerned.

- Shortly thereafter, again unexpectedly, ACC drastically reduced the upfront incentives (UFIs) provided by the IOUs to residential solar system buyers. This initiated a hesitation cycle in the local solar residential market too.

- Arizona Public Service (APS), one of the state's largest utilities, was scheduled to reduce its PBIs for commercial systems to $20.8 million during 2013. Tucson Electric Power (TEP) was scheduled to go to $10.5 million. Instead, both are now near zero.

- And then, as if all this were not enough, a scheduled $400,000 allotment for APS UFIs was cut to $100,000, while at the same time another scheduled $1.7 million set-aside for TEP UFIs was cut completely.

- The APS residential UFIs were scheduled to go to $6.96 million in 2013, but instead were cut to $2.65 million. In addition, the TEP's residential UFIs were cut from $1.46 million to $744,000.

- The UFIs were paid at the rate of $0.10 per watt, while the PBIs (based on competitive solicitations) fell to about $0.05 - $0.06 per kWh during the same time.

All those unexpected and unjustifiable changes brought the commercial solar market in the solar capital of the world to a virtual standstill. The reductions sucked the life out of it and it is now on life support.

Now the solar project plans are coming to a screeching halt, where only projects with previous incentives and still in the backlog are in development. Commercial projects lined up with 2012 incentives will be completed by the end of 2013, but the solar companies cannot start any new commercial systems, such as for churches and municipalities, that do not qualify for the federal investment tax credit (ITC).

So, the solar industry is basically being forced to focus on niche opportunities where solar can compete with utility power without any incentive.

The only good news now is the fact that we are able to talk about solar opportunities *without any incentive*s and any other financial support. This was impossible to imagine just a short while ago, and confirms the undeniable progress of the solar industry's cost-cutting efforts. It also highlights the misguided approach of the ACC and the Arizona utilities in attempting to cut the solar industry's legs off at the most inopportune time.

We all know very well that subsidies are used in all energy industries, and especially those in need of further development to reach the critical scale of operation without subsidy. This is the case of coal, oil, gas, hydro- and nuclear power.

Solar is expecting the same treatment, but now it seems that it won't get it, but guess what? It seems to have outgrown that need ahead of schedule and in the near future will be able to survive without subsidies. This is true at least for some solar (like residential in California). In Arizona, however, the ACC decided to cut support for large-scale distributed solar, which is a bit too early for this still- developing branch of the Arizona's solar industry, and it will be hurt the worst.

The ACC commissioners decided on the cuts because they hope to reduce the Renewable Energy Standard and Tariff (REST) premium added to Arizona ratepayers' utility bills needed to fund solar. The REST premium is capped at $4.00 per month, so the PBI cuts will save APS ratepayers no more than $0.06 per month. The customers will save virtually nothing, but will nevertheless continue paying for the expenses of the large-scale solar plants owned by the utilities.

So, whom is ACC helping? The regulated monopolies, at the expense of the ratepayers, by shutting down a competitive market that was bringing meaningful cost reductions to Arizona, the solar-capital-of-the-world-wanna-be, where their only and most competitive advantage is the abundance of sunshine.

ACC action is one more step backwards for Arizona's commitment to economic development, free markets and the expansion of clean energy resources. This will hurt Arizonans a lot, especially at this time of financial challenges, problematic water supply, and the shutting down of coal-fired power plants.

Desertec...or Not!

Internationally, Desertec was considered one of the most promising developments in renewable technologies implementation. It was supposed to include many GWs of solar and wind fields installed in the North African deserts, powering the E.U. group of countries.

It seemed like a brilliant idea to use the abundant sunshine of the deserts to provide power to countries with much less sunshine and land availability. This would also benefit the North African countries by providing power and jobs to them.

Well, the dream is over, or almost over. The Desertec Foundation has announced the termination of its partnership with the Desertec Industrial Initiative DII GmbH after "many irresolvable disputes between the two entities in the area of future strategies, obligations and their communication, and, last but not least, the managerial style of DII's top management."

The supervisory board and the board of directors of the foundation agreed to decouple from the industrial initiative at an extraordinary board meeting, which took place last June 27, 2103.

The Desertec Foundation, which is the main idea- and name-giver for the Desertec concept, said in a press release that it wants to avoid being dragged into the maelstrom of negative publicity about the management crisis and disorientation of the industrial consortium. The dispute at the management level has already led to resentment among the partners of the Desertec Foundation and it negatively affected their reputation and trust.

The project was hit hard earlier when two of its largest members and supporters, Siemens and Bosch, announced that they were leaving the project. Then Spain refused to sign a declaration of intent to connect high voltage lines between Morocco and Europe through Spain, a key component to bringing energy from North African deserts to Europe.

Now the future of the Desertec project is in limbo. The increasing unrest in that part of the world further adds to the uncertainty, so for now we just have to con-sider Desertec a good idea that is not going to happen any time soon.

Challenges and Opportunities

Looking beyond to identify the important, but not necessarily obvious, new battlegrounds, industry opportunities, and new global markets in the renewable (and especially the solar) industries, we see:

Bottlenecks for Utility-scale Solar

With slow standards development partly to blame, utility project developers have indicated that the primary bottlenecks for large-scale PV in the U.S. (in addition to the barriers put lately by the utilities) are actually related to interconnection rather than project finance. This is a good sign, as the next wave of utility procurement will come in states where installations are driven by project economics, rather than legislated renewable obligations.

Timelines will vary, but we expect non-RPS utility projects before the ITC expiration. As a result, project developers are targeting individual utilities where economics may be favorable rather than looking toward state RPS programs.

Storage and Advanced Grid Integration Technology

In addition to utilities' concerns about the economic impact of PV, they also express concerns about the perceived technical impacts of PV on the grid, which add to the utilities' economic impact concerns. There is also a very slow and inconsistent development of grid integration standards, which can result in higher testing and operating costs. Quickly learning from painful lessons in Germany and Italy, inverter manufacturers are shipping product with advanced grid interactive features like ride-through, remote on/off, and reactive power latent in expectation of forthcoming requirements and standards. In some stringent regimes, like Puerto Rico, significant amounts of storage have been required.

However, the overall outlook for storage-based distributed PV systems appears to be complicated by: a) the immaturity of the energy storage technology; b) by inverter manufacturers' reservations about the growth in storage; and c) by some commercial PV developers using various non-traditional storage applications to secure the old and capture the new revenue streams.

Net Metering and Rate Structure Debate

The threat that solar PV poses to current utility business models is one of the most discussed topics by the specialists lately. In a post-subsidy solar industry, the utilities are taking different tactics to address the growing role of PV, but many utilities have a mortal concern driven by distributed generation.

In North America, net metering is the next major battleground in the industry, and the rhetoric surrounding the debate has become highly charged. A more significant cause for concern is the prospect of utilities using rate design as another mechanism to constrain the growth of distributed generation. It's more subversive, but just as impactful.

Third-party vs. Direct Ownership in U.S. Residential Markets

At a high level, the conversation always comes back to the debate over which is the most analogous market for solar: television, cars, satellite TV, or a power plant. The Arizona market is expecting a reversal in third-party-owned residential systems as recovering home equity enabled more families to realize federal and local incentives. More specifically, the cost of tax equity represented a hidden cost to the industry and ultimately to the consumer.

While the "math is correct," solar is ultimately a service industry and most are better served by third-party-ownership models.

Customer Acquisition and the Importance of Solar Marketing

Regardless of the nature of ownership, the increasing maturity on the industry marketing front is obvious. Customer acquisition costs and strategies are about to get more attractive. Service providers need to add much more value beyond the solar panel to compete within the industry and with other purchases.

One place where solar marketing may overstep is in perpetuating "tiers" of module manufacturing. If the industry could do away with the idea of tiers, we would be better off, since there is only a very loose correlation between performance and tiers.

Product Innovation as a Cost Driver

Of course, marketing solar as a service becomes simpler as the cost of solar energy declines, and that will be the result of product innovations that drive lower prices and increased reliability. Inverters and balance-of-systems markets point to numerous cost-saving avenues, with merits and limitations of decentralized architectures. EPC and Balance-of-Systems need more integrated designs and components that shift labor from the field to the computer and factory. With BOS costs in the crosshairs of the industry, savings of even a few cents per watt can strongly influence project viability.

Temperance in New PV Markets

The declining cost of solar has opened new non-incentivized markets, although the cost-competitiveness of solar with the existing electricity supply does not mean that solar, both large-scale and distributed, will start appearing everywhere. Not only are there technical hurdles to overcome, especially in developing countries, but also the creditworthiness of off-takers is often subpar. In this case, developers are looking to regional banks for financing, but the regional banks are unfamiliar with solar. It's a catch-22.

Furthermore, local content mandates in regions like Saudi Arabia and India may pose obstacles to near-term end-market growth, as most emerging markets do not have a robust supply chain, which could raise bankability issues.

Challenges Operating in Asian Growth Markets

The importance of local knowledge and partnerships in the Asian markets is paramount. Otherwise successful American and European companies are "dead on arrival" when they try to enter new markets without a true understanding of the local business and regulatory environment. In some countries, like China, even operating between provinces is challenging. Moreover, while the growth of the Chinese market looks promising, operating in the market is less exciting.   Partnering with state-owned entities in China usually means a much lower profit margin. And the payment terms are horrific. There are competitors out there willing to not take any payment for two years, and sometimes it is four years before they get 100% of the payment.

Despite numerous headwinds throughout the industry the opportunities in the marketplace still exist. The business models and technology alike are still evolving and maturing, but a path toward a global post-subsidy reality, or at least subsidies on par with competing industries, is quickly emerging.

THE MOST PROMISING SOLAR TECHNOLOGIES

There are a number of renewable technologies that sound too good to be true, and some are. Others, however, hold the promise of impacting the solar industry positively, and those are the ones we review here to give the reader a glimpse in the future.

Background

A new phenomenon is taking a shape around the world—the tendency to use highest performance solar cells and modules. This condition is due primarily to lack, or high cost, of land available for solar installations.

The other, equally important consideration in preferring high performance PV products is the fact that higher performance solar cells and modules are of relatively higher quality. This means that they will be much more reliable during daily operation, and will last for the duration without problems, even in harshest climates—something that cannot be said for a number of different solar cell types.

This preferential treatment will become more pronounced during the 21st century. And as a confirmation of this deduction, Japan announced in the summer of 2012 that it will spend over $10 billion on solar installations—giving priority to cells and modules that are in the above mentioned "high performance" class.

It so happens that Japanese manufacturers, such as Sony, Sanyo, Sharp, Mitsubishi, manufacture most of the high performance solar cells and modules, so there might be some bias in this preference.

Nevertheless, the fact that a major player in the solar market is drawing a line based on higher efficiency (and by association higher quality) is a major push in that direction, and we expect the trend to continue and grow with time.

There are types of solar cells and modules, which use the standard materials and process sequences with some modifications, just enough to give them different (hopefully superior) qualities. One thing to note here is that when evaluating such technologies and devices, one must keep in mind that changing (even improving) one parameter alone is not enough. For instance, if the efficiency is increased at the expense of extreme sunlight degradation, then the "improvement" is worthless, and must be either abandoned or changed in a way that does not negatively affect the rest of the operating parameters of the final device.

The type of cells we are discussing here falls into the category of "most promising" and "high-efficiency" solar technologies, simply because they are more efficient than the standard lot o f similar materials and processes, and contain an element that promises high efficiency, improved reliability, or a lower price.

Some of those most promising and best performing technologies are:

HIT Solar Cells

The Hetero-junction with Intrinsic Thin layer (HIT) solar cell is composed of a single thin crystalline silicon wafer, usually 4" or 5" square, sandwiched between two thin films of amorphous silicon (a-Si).

The structure of the HIT cell enables an improvement in the overall output by reducing recombination loss, which is the loss of electrical current that occurs when an electron and a hole (carriers) generated by impinging photons within the solar cell combine and disappear.

This effect is achieved by surrounding the energy generation layer of single thin crystalline silicon with high quality ultra-thin amorphous silicon layers.

Several manufacturers have developed special technologies for cleaning the energy generation middle layer and protecting it from damage during construction of the surrounding layer, with the result being an increase in the open circuit voltage from 0.718V to 0.722V. This also improves the efficiency and reliability of the solar cell by avoiding the usual problems related to doped and fired silicon solar cells.

This type of solar cell would be more expensive to produce, but might provide the much needed solution to the problems c-Si and TFPV modules encounter when exposed to extreme desert temperatures. Such cells theoretically would exhibit less heat sensitivity and power degradation, but, we have not seen any proof of that happening as yet.

HIT cells have improved efficiency, over 22% in lab tests and around 19% in mass production, mostly due to the good a-Si:H/c-Si/a-Si:H hetero-interface of the HIT structure, which enables a high Voc (well over 0.7 V). This also results in much better temperature coefficient and better heat handling properties (theoretical values).

In order to reduce the manufacturing cost, numerous technologies are in R&D mode presently, with the goal to further improve the efficiency, and especially to increase the Voc of HIT solar cells, with the aim to achieve up to 25% efficiency in the near future.

The commercial modules have the following key electrical and performance properties:

Cell Efficiency (n%)	19.7%
Module Efficiency (n%)	17.0% (under load)
Max. Power Voltage (Vpm)	55.8V
Max. Power Current (Ipm)	3.59A
Open Circuit Voltage (Voc)	68.7V
Short Circuit Current (Isc)	3.83A
Temperature Coefficient (Pmax)	-0.29 %/C
Temperature Coefficient (Voc)	-0.172 V/C
Temperature Coefficient (Isc)	0.88 mA/C

It looks good, yes. The key questions here, as related to the major issues surrounding the use of solar cells and modules, remain:

1. No doubt that the additional a-Si films improve the efficiency of the devices, but do they also improve the device quality and performance characteristics? What if those films misbehave under blistering desert sun? What if, with time, they cause increased resistance, overheating etc. anomalies, which lead to reduced efficiency and maybe even failures?

2. Surely, the additional materials and labor add to the final cost of the device. Is the added cost justified by the marginally higher efficiency? How about the added uncertainty? Does it have a price too?

Bifacial Solar Cells

The bifacial solar cells could be a modification of the HIT model, or some other design that basically utilizes both surfaces to collect sunlight and convert it into electricity.

While there is some benefit in using both surfaces, we see it as quite limited, and basically confined to a niche market, such as fences, car-ports and similar structures that have two open sides.

The power that could be generated from the shaded side of a PV module is quite limited. Special modifications and white paint of the surrounding surfaces can be done to increase the reflected sunlight, but that also is expansive, impractical, and more expensive in most cases.

This condition was confirmed by installations done by Solyndra (which tubular panels also was touted as "bifacial"). Entire roofs were painted white, as needed to reflect more sunlight. While that increased the power output, it was not enough to justify the initial expense and the continuous maintenance. On top of that, with time the roofs got dirty and their reflectivity decreased, thus eliminating the slight advantage of the white surface.

And so, the bifacial technology is: a) too new, thus not proven reliable as yet; and b) it comes at a higher price, which in most cases cannot be justified by a marginal increase of electric output.

And so, although we don't doubt the practicality and flexibility of bifacial solar technologies, we see them filling only small-market niches. We do not foresee them as major participants in the large-scale PV power generation of the 21st century.

Buried Contact Solar Cells

The buried contact solar cell is another high efficiency commercial solar cell, this one based on a metal contact formed inside a laser-formed groove in the front surface. The buried contact technology has many advantages and avoids the problems of conventional solar cells related to the old screen-printed contacts method. This allows buried contact solar cells to have performance up to 25% better than commercial screen-printed solar cells.

A key high efficiency feature of the buried contact solar cell is that the metal is buried in a laser-formed groove inside the silicon solar cell, which allows for a large metal height-to-width aspect ratio of the contacts, which improves the device's operational characteristics, since a large metal contact aspect ratio allows a large volume of metal to be used in the contact finger, without having a wide strip of metal on the top surface. This allows a large number of closely spaced metal fingers, while still retaining a high transparency of the front surface.

For example, on a large area device, a screen-printed solar cell may have shading losses as high as 10-15%, while in a buried contact structure, the shading losses will be only 2-3%. Those lower shading losses allow higher level of photon collection (more photons hit the active surface), and low reflection (less photons hit the metalized front surface areas), which contributes to higher short-circuit currents

In addition to good reflection properties, the buried contact technology also allows low parasitic resistance losses due to its high metal aspect ratio, its fine finger spacing, and its plated metal for the contacts.

The emitter resistance is reduced in a buried contact solar cell since narrower finger spacing dramatically reduces the emitter resistance losses. The metal grid resistance is also low since the finger resistance is reduced by the large volume of metal in the grooves and by the use of copper, which has a lower resistivity than the metal paste used in screen printing.

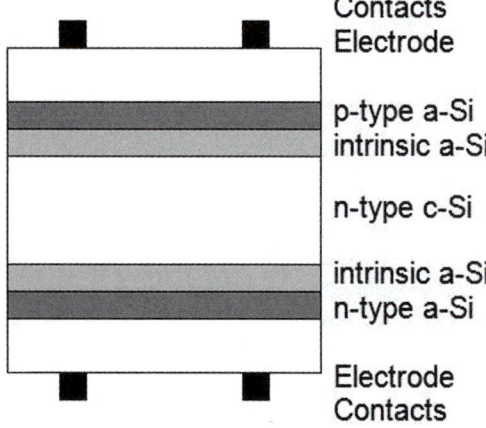

Figure 8-20. Bifacial solar cell

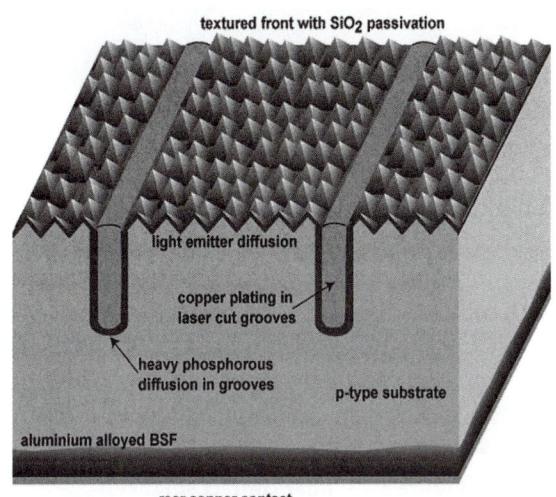

Figure 8-21. Buried contact solar cell (3)

The contact resistance of a buried contact solar cell is lower than that in screen printed solar cells due to the formation of a nickel silicide at the semiconductor-metal interface and the large metal-silicon contact area. Overall, those reduced resistive losses allow large area solar cells with high FFs.

When compared to a screen-printed cell, the metallization scheme of a buried contact solar cell also improves the cell's emitter. To minimize resistive losses, the emitter region of a screen-printed solar cell is heavily doped and results in a "dead" layer at the surface of the solar cell. Since emitter losses are low in a buried contact structure, the emitter doping can be optimized for high open-circuit voltages and short-circuit currents. Furthermore, a buried contact structure includes a self-aligned, selective emitter, which thereby reduces the contact recombination and also contributes to high open-circuit voltages.

The efficiency advantages of buried contact technology provide significant cost and performance benefits. In terms of $/W, the cost of a buried contact solar cell is the same as a screen-printed solar cell. However, due to the inclusion of certain area-related costs as well as fixed costs in a PV system, a higher efficiency solar cell technology results in lower cost electricity. An additional advantage of buried contact technology is that it can be used for concentrator systems of up to 50x concentration.

PERL Solar Cells

There are several types of solar cells that can be built on silicon substrates, but which require much more expensive materials, sophisticated equipment, and elaborate processing. The passivated emitter with rear locally diffused cell (PERL) is one of those devices.

It is a fairly recent development of a solar cell design that uses micro-electronic techniques as needed to produce solar cells of high efficiency, up to 25% in the PERL case.

Thinner silicon wafers (solar cells) are used in this design, to optimize the efficiency, with 50 μm thick cells having the highest efficiency. Using such thin wafers in production is impossible due to breakage, so a compromise in the 150-200 μm wafer thickness area must be used.

One characteristic of this type of solar cell is the improved texturing of the active front surface area, which is done in the shape of inverted pyramids. If the base size of the inverted pyramid texturing is increased, then the effective surface area increases, which in turn increases absorption in the silicon structure. So a lot of effort is put in the optimized size and shape of the pyramids.

Bigger texture structures (> 10 m) increase the optical absorption and also the resulting cell efficiency. Using conventional chemical texturing the maximum achieved base size of the pyramid is around 9 m. So, optimizing the pattern size is best done via photolithography methods, similar to those used in the semiconductor industry. This lithographical process adds an additional processing step, which has several advantages that are worth the additional effort and expense.

Placing the metal contacts on top of the pyramidal structure is also critical and requires careful consideration and precise execution. The contact placement will determine the path the carriers will travel to reach the contact, so the position of the contacts is critical for the overall electricity generation process. Properly executed front metal contact lines could be as thin as 2 microns, which would reduce the front surface shading to about 3% of the surface area. The reduced contact area reduces the total recombination at its proximity, which contributes to higher Voc of the device.

The passivated emitter is the high quality oxide deposited at the front surface of the cell, which significantly lowers the number of carriers recombining at the surface. The rear of the cell is locally diffused only at the metal contacts areas, to minimize recombination at the rear while maintaining good electrical contact.

A major advantage of the PERL solar cell is the improved surface passivation of the front and rear cell areas via thermally grown oxide, and the respective dopants, which significantly reduces the emitter saturation current, thus leading to improved open-circuit voltage (Voc above 0.7 V). This also reduces the recombination levels

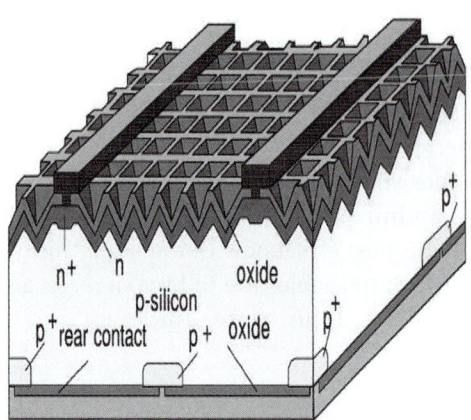

Figure 8-22. PERL solar cell

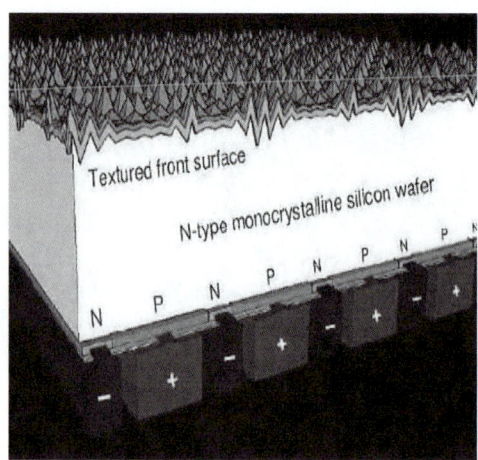

Figure 8-23. Rear contact solar cell

at the contact regions, due to suppressed minority concentration in those areas. PERL cells can reach 25% efficiency, but commercial types operate in the 19-20% range.

The PERL solar cells have not been proven reliable for large-scale operation under different environmental conditions. This, combined with their complex manufacturing process and higher cost, will have to be tested by time and location before this technology is fully established as major competitor in the world's energy markets.

The PERL solar cells seem to be suitable for some special applications, such as solar powered vehicles and space applications, so we foresee their number increasing as time goes by.

Rear Contacts Solar Cell

Rear contact solar cells eliminate shading losses altogether by putting both contacts on the rear of the cell. By using a thin solar cell made from high quality material, electron-hole pairs generated by light that is absorbed at the front surface can still be collected at the rear of the cell. Such cells are especially useful in concentrator applications where the effect of cell series resistance is greater. An additional benefit is that cells with both contacts on the rear are easier to interconnect and can be placed closer together in the module, since there is no need for a space between the cells.

Efficiency of over 23% has been achieved with this cell design. Those types of solar cells usually cost considerably more to produce than standard silicon cells, and are typically used in specialized applications, such as solar cars and for space exploration.

Passivated Rear Point Contacts Solar Cell

This type solar cell is even more specialized, due to its complexity, and although we don't see its use as

such in the near-term energy markets, we do believe that some of its features (materials and processes) will be used in the future for developing new technologies. This alone is enough to put it in the category of most promising technologies for the 21st century use.

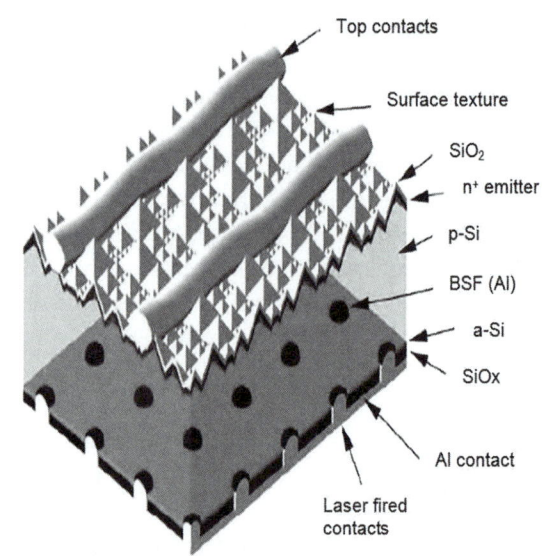

Figure 8-24. Passivated rear point contacts solar cell

Efficiencies of over 22% have been reached with those cells, but due to their complexity and higher cost, their use is limited.

Selective Emitter Solar Cells

The "selective" emitter design solar cells concept uses laterally different emitter doping, which consists basically of:

1.   High doping under the front side metallization for low contact resistance between contact metal and semiconductor interface

2.   Lower doping between the contact fingers for a better short wavelength response due to less Auger recombination as well as improved emitter passivation

Unfortunately, most of those designs are very complex as far as the process is concerned, due to a number of masking steps required for achieving proper selective diffusion or emitter etch-back.

In particular, such existing concepts are hard to implement into industrial production of solar cells. Nevertheless, several different approaches designed for industrial production are currently under development, and some are already being transferred to the industry.

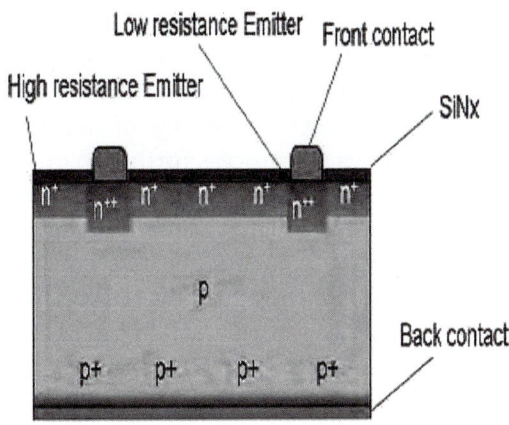

Figure 8-25. Selective emitter solar cells

A number of organizations are developing solar cells with this type of selective emitters, which allow the use of thinner emitters as needed to improve the short-wavelength spectral response.

We do foresee the use of this technology also limited to niche markets, but its components are valuable instruments in the battle for higher efficiency, reliability, and cost effectiveness, which can be successfully used in the development of other solar technologies in the near future.

Intermediate Band

This is intermediate band nitride thin film semiconductor material, which might be an alternative to the multijunction designs for improving the power conversion efficiency of solar cells.

The intermediate-band solar cell is a thin-film technology based on highly mismatched alloys. The three-bandgap, one-junction device has the potential of improved solar light absorption and higher power output than III-V triple-junction compound semiconductor devices.

Efficiencies of over 20% have been demonstrated.

Quasi-mono Crystalline Silicon Technology

A brand new, proprietary "super large quasi-crystalline silicon ingot casting" technology was developed by a number of manufacturers, and recently approved by a group of experts.

The new method addresses some of the issues of polycrystalline silicon ingot casting waste and cost. When implemented and proven, this technology will have a huge impact on the entire crystalline silicon industry and the energy markets. It could be used as a substitute of the more expensive mono-crystalline silicon, while providing similarly good performance.

Polycrystalline silicon has much lower efficiency than monocrystalline silicon, but it is much cheaper and efficient to produce: $20/Kg polycrystalline silicon castings per batch vs. the $60/Kg batch of Czochralski (CZ) process monocrystalline silicon—not to mention the related complexity of the latter process.

Because of this inequality, polycrystalline and monocrystalline silicon have similar costs *per Watt*, and their share in the energy markets is approximately 50:50.

The intent of the "super large quasi-crystalline silicon ingot casting" is to reduce further the polysilicon casting costs—down to $10/Kg (vs. approximately $25/Kg for making single crystal silicon presently).

The problem here is that no matter what process is used, the CZ single crystal process produces silicon that reaches 18.5% efficiency, while polycrystalline silicon cannot exceed 14-16%. This difference is enough for the CZ to be the material of choice in some applications—regardless of the cost. This difference cannot be changed, because the laws of physics and chemistry, as well as the nature of the semiconductor materials cannot be changed, so that polysilicon used for making solar cells will always be less efficient.

So, the claim that the efficiency of the newly developed quasi-crystalline silicon produced by this new ingot-casting technology is comparable to monocrystalline silicon, with efficiency over 18% has to be seen to be believed. And if it reaches that efficiency, then the resulting material cannot possibly be poly- or even quasi- silicon; rather it is simply single crystal silicon, or a variation thereof at best. Nevertheless, the increased efficiency at a lower cost is good enough to put it on the market in a very short time.

"This technology uses polycrystalline silicon ingot casting technology to produce products with the quality of monocrystalline silicon. It's like producing a product worth $25 for the cost of a $10 product," according to company representatives.

They're presently at least 45 quasi-crystalline casting furnaces in operation in China, which, under full operation, represents production capacity of over 300 MW/year. Not a small thing, and if the predictions are correct, it also represents a breakthrough, and maybe even a disruptive, new technology that could take the markets by storm.

There is presently a broad range of commercially available quasi-mono silicon PV cells with efficiencies from 16%-18.4%, so the new technology seems to be working as predicted thus far. If the cost is low enough, and if it proves to be reliable in field operations, then we have a different and successful product, which will make a significant difference in the bottom line and will help China achieve the goal of reaching grid parity by 2020.

Nevertheless, we must persist with our claim that only single crystal silicon can be that efficient. This simple matter of physics, and there is simply no way for any other silicon to be that efficient, unless the laws of physics have been somehow changed too.

Since we don't believe that the Chinese can do that, we must insist that no matter what the new product is called, and how it is made, if it reaches 18% efficiency it has mono-crystalline structure. Anything short of that would not be able to achieve this high efficiency.

Nevertheless, we'll be watching the developments with the Chinese manufacturers and their new quasi-mono crystalline silicon. It seems too good to be true, but you never know.

Granular Silicon

This is a new method in the arsenal of polysilicon production techniques. It was developed over the last 15 years and shows much promise, mainly in reducing costs and improving yields, while maintaining the usual quality.

Granular polysilicon is produced by decomposing silane (SiH_4) in a fluidized bed reactor. Small seed particles are introduced and a silane/hydrogen mixture is then fed into the reactor. The silane decomposes around the seed particles increasing their average size to approximately 1,000 microns.

The granular polysilicon particles are then withdrawn from the reactor and packaged in drums in a completely enclosed system to maintain purity.

This is a continuous production process, with a number of advantages over the conventional batch methods, based on $SiHCl_3$ chemical vapor deposition (CVD) production process.

The fluidized bed SiH_4 CVD reactor benefits from both a lower operating temperature for the decomposition of SiH_4 to Si and H_2 as well as a higher throughput from its continuous operation.

Lower energy consumption, as compared to the Siemens process, continuous production process (as compared with the conventional batch processes), and a very consistent product quality with low variability are the advantages of this process.

Granular polysilicon can be also transported more easily from a storage container to a crystal puller in an enclosed system. It can be poured into a crucible, eliminating the laborious and tedious tasks of manually stacking silicon chunks of various shapes and sizes with sharp edges and jagged corners.

In 200 mm standard hot zone designs, using an external hopper, the poly can be fed into the liquid pool created from melting an initial charge of chunk polysilicon, which facilitates the process further. With this new approach, manufacturers have been able to achieve up to 40% larger charge size than possible with an all-chunk cold charge.

It is also possible to reduce the thermal stress on the crucible wall and improve crystal growth yields.

Additionally, optimal combinations of chunk and granular polysilicon fed through a feeder system can be used with great efficiency in the larger, 300 mm hot zone furnaces.

Large charge and multiple recharges of the granular polysilicon production process is a great advantage. This material removes the limitations on charge size in large, complex hot zones and provides for replenishing the melt for another "pull" as the just-completed crystal cools in the removal chamber of the crystal growth furnace.

With a two-crystal recharge process, crystal pulling costs can be reduced by as much as 40% overall, while the throughput can be increased as much as 25% overall.

Manufacturers have commercialized the recharge process for 150 mm, 200 mm, and 300 mm products, and intense research and development of granular polysilicon have resulted in robust and proven processes that benefit silicon wafer manufacturers.

These benefits will not only help silicon suppliers internally, but should also enable them to provide a higher quality product to solar cells and semiconductor manufacturers.

So, this is another promising, and possibly disruptive, product for the 21st century PV manufacturers to use in the battle of optimizing processing techniques and reducing cost.

Super Monocrystalline Silicon

This is a new purer type of silicon with more perfect crystalline structure, and less impurities. This type of material is close to the "perfect" silicon, whatever that might be...

In the solar cells case, it exhibits reduced phonon-phonon and phonon-electron interactions, which are responsible for the transport of the active species within the silicon material.

The "super" qualities of the purer silicon, and the related phenomenon, increase certain transport properties, resulting in 60% better room temperature thermal conductivity than natural silicon.

The issues, of course, are cost of materials and labor, and the durability of the finished devices. Since the very title, "super," is somewhat all-encompassing, and since there are a number of ways to look at the material quality, the manufacturing of such a product (which has been going on for decades), we hesitate to predict the readiness and usability of such superior materials in the 21st century, but the promise is still great and should not be overlooked.

Obviously anything "super" is more often than none a good thing, but producing material that is super in one category does not make it automatically "super" for all practical purposes.

And finally, we need to remember that the quest for better silicon dates from the mid-20th century, and that semiconductor companies (whose very existence depends on very pure silicon) have been, and are, spending a lot of money and making a major effort in this area. So the battle continues—and we must be ready for surprises.

Roll-to-roll TFPV

Roll-to-roll process is reviewed in the "High Efficiency Technologies" category not because it produces high efficiency solar devices, but because the manufacturing process is of the highest efficiency possible today.

The process consists of coating the substrate material from a roll. The process can be conducted at a high speed and relatively low temperatures. Thus it is inexpensive, fast, and less energy intensive than the other PV technologies.

Another advantage is that it can be produced using existing coating and printing equipment, and thus does not require construction of a new facility. This simplifies the manufacturing scale-up and significantly lowers capital and labor costs as compared to the previous generation solar cells.

Compared with the competing PV technologies, the roll-to-roll process:

- Is non-toxic and is environmentally friendly
- Significantly lowers capital cost for new plant construction
- Uses less energy
- Offers low cost retrofit of existing facilities

Several world-class companies are developing and using this process, which we believe will become a major competitor in several niche energy markets in the 21st century.

III-V PV Cells

There are several technologies that fall in the gap between the most promising and exotic, technologies but weigh on the side of most promising only because they are theoretically promising. In most cases, some good results have been shown as well, but generally speaking those technologies have not been fully proven—yet.

Some of those "semi-most" promising solar technologies to watch for in the 21st century are the so-called "III-V PV devices. Those are PV technologies based on the deposition of thin films of the III-V materials. Those devices are divided into single- and multi-junction devices as follows:

Single-junction III-V Devices

A number of compounds such as gallium arsenide (GaAs), indium phosphide (InP), and gallium antimonide (GaSb) have adequate energy band gaps, high optical absorption coefficients, and good values of minority carrier lifetimes and mobility, making them excellent materials for making high efficiency solar cells. Those materials are usually produced by the Czockralski or Bridgmann methods, which provide high quality materials with increased efficiency and reliability, but at a higher price.

After silicon, GaAs and InP (III-V compounds) are the most widely used materials for single-junction (SJ) solar cells manufacturing. Those materials have optimum band gap values (1.4 and 1.3 respectively) for SJ conversion of sunlight. The construction of solar cells made of those materials is similar to the regular single-junction c-Si solar cells we discussed elsewhere.

The major disadvantage of using III-V compounds

for PV devices is the high cost of producing the materials that they are made of and the related manufacturing processes. Also, crystal imperfections, including bulk impurities, severely reduce their efficiencies, so that only very high-quality materials could be considered. Too, they are heavier than silicon, which requires the use of thinner cells, but they are weaker mechanically, so their design requires a delicate balance of thickness vs. weight.

The combination of high efficiency, high price, crystal imperfections intolerance, and mechanical weakness makes those devices useful for limited applications, where efficiency and overall behavior is more important than price. Thus they are not widely used in the general PV market, but still can be found in some important niche markets.

Multi-junction III-V Cells

Single-junction PV devices convert only a portion of the sunlight (with photons just above the band-gap level of the semiconductor material). The problem is that photons with lower or higher energy do not generate electron-hole pairs and are lost as heat, which is also detrimental to the cells, reducing their efficiency and deteriorating them over time.

One way to solve this problem and to increase the efficiency of the PV devices is to add more junctions, thus creating multi-junction (MJ) solar cells. By selecting materials, properties, number and types of junctions, and manufacturing processes designed to capture the majority of sunlight photons, we can reach very high efficiencies.

Thus far, multi-junction solar cells made primarily using the III-V compounds have clearly proven that by minimizing thermalization and transmission losses, large improvements in efficiency can be made over those of single-junction cells. Those devices find use in generating power for space applications and in concentrator systems. They show great promise for high efficiency and reliability under harsh climate conditions, such as those in the deserts.

Future development of multi-junction devices using low-cost thin-film technologies is especially promising for producing more efficient and yet inexpensive devices. Cost reductions will also be significant when thin-film technologies are directly produced on building materials other than glass, because many materials such as tiles and bricks can be substantially cheaper than glass and have much lower energy content.

The devices in this group are gallium arsenide-based, germanium-based, and CPV solar cells.

Gallium Arsenide Based Multi-junction Cells

High-efficiency multi-junction cells were originally developed for special applications such as satellites and space exploration, but at present, their use in terrestrial concentrators might be the lowest cost alternative in terms of $/kWh and $/W. Those multi-junction cells consist of multiple thin films produced via metal-organic vapor phase epitaxy. A triple-junction cell, for example, may consist of the semiconductors GaAs, Ge, and GaInP2.

Each type of semiconductor will have a characteristic band gap energy which, loosely speaking, causes it to absorb light most efficiently at a certain color, or more precisely, to absorb electromagnetic radiation over a portion of the spectrum. Semiconductors are carefully chosen to absorb nearly all of the solar spectrum, thus generating electricity from as much of the available solar energy as possible.

GaAs-based multi-junction devices are some of the most efficient solar cells to date, reaching a record high of 40.7% efficiency under "500-sun" solar concentration and laboratory conditions.

This technology currently is being utilized mostly in powering spacecraft. The demand for tandem solar cells based on monolithic, series-connected, gallium indium phosphide (GaInP), gallium arsenide GaAs, and germanium Ge p-n junctions is rapidly rising. Prices are rising dramatically as well.

Twin-junction cells with indium gallium phosphide and gallium arsenide can be made on gallium arsenide wafers. Alloys of In.5Ga.5P through In.53Ga.47P may be used as the high band gap alloy. This alloy range allows band gaps in the range of 1.92eV to 1.87eV. The lower GaAs junction has a band gap of 1.42eV.

In spacecraft applications, cells have a poor current match due to a greater flux of photons above 1.87eV vs. those between 1.87eV and 1.42eV.

This results in too little current in the GaAs junction, and hampers the overall efficiency, since the InGaP junction operates below MPP current and the GaAs junction operates above MPP current. To improve current match, the InGaP layer is intentionally thinned to allow additional photons to penetrate to the lower GaAs layer.

In terrestrial concentrating applications, the scatter of blue light by the atmosphere reduces photon flux above 1.87eV, better balancing junction currents. GaAs was the material of the highest-efficiency solar cell, until recently, when Germanium-based MJ cells capped the world record at 41.4% efficiency.

Indium Phosphide Based Cells

Indium phosphide is used as a substrate to fabricate cells with band gaps between 1.35eV and 0.74eV. Indium phosphide has a band gap of 1.35eV. Indium gallium arsenide (In0.53Ga0.47As) is lattice-matched to indium phosphide with a band gap of 0.74eV. A quaternary alloy of indium gallium arsenide phosphide can be lattice-matched for any band gap in between the two.

Indium phosphide-based cells are being researched as a possible companion in the manufacturing of gallium arsenide based cells. The two, but different materials can be either optically connected in series (with the InP cell below the GaAs cell), or through the use of spectra splitting using a dichroic filter.

The efficiencies of those types of cells are in the 15-20% range.

A variation of this technology is the Indium gallium phosphide (InGaP), also called gallium indium phosphide (GaInP), which is a hybrid *semiconductor*, composed of *indium*, *gallium* and *phosphorus*.

It is used mostly for fabricating high-power, high-frequency electronics and LEDs of different colors. But its use in the manufacturing of high efficiency *solar cells* used for space applications is growing.

Ga0.5In0.5P is used as the high energy junction on double and triple junction photovoltaic cells grown on *GaAs* substrates. GaInP/GaAs tandem solar cells have shown efficiency of over 25% under AM 0.

A different alloy of GaInP, lattice-matched to the underlying *GaInAs*, is utilized as the high-energy junction GaInP/GaInAs/Ge triple junction photovoltaic cells.

One of the greatest problems of the GaInP grown by *epitaxy* is its tendency to grow as an ordered material, rather than a truly random alloy, as required in some cases. This changes the bandgap and the electronic and optical properties of the material, which makes the manufacturing process quite complex and expensive.

We see those cells taking place in some niche markets (space mostly for now), but due to manufacturing complexity and unproven performance characteristics, they will not be deployed any time soon in large quantities on the ground-based utility energy markets.

The presence of varying quantities of toxic materials in those devices must be considered when planning their use in large quantities as well.

Germanium-based Single- and Multi-junction Cells

Germanium (0.86eV band gap) is a semiconductor material, with properties far superior to other substrate materials used for PV cells and modules. It is ~40-50%

more efficient than silicon and has a much lower temperature coefficient. It is several times more expensive than silicon, too, but with new superior slicing techniques, it can be cut into very thin wafers, saving a lot of material. This, combined with its higher efficiency and less degradation than silicon, could put it on the competitors' list within the next few years.

Germanium-based solar cells have been used mostly for space applications, but a number of manufacturers have geared up for mass producing them for use in high concentration PV (HCPV) and other high efficiency applications.

III-V Cells Research Trends

Current research on high-performance III-V multi-junction thin film devices focuses on several major challenges:

1. Determining high-bandgap alloys based on I-III-VI and II-VI compounds and other novel materials for the top cell

2. Considering low-bandgap CIS and its alloys, thin-film silicon, and other novel approaches for the bottom cell

3. Studying the difficult task of integrating the thin-film tunnel junction (interconnect) with the top cell. This work includes understanding the role of defects, how they affect the transport properties of this junction, and the diffusion of impurities into the bulk material

4. Fabricating a monolithic, two-terminal tandem cell based on polycrystalline thin-film materials that requires low-temperature deposition for several layers

5. Avoiding deterioration of the top cell when fabricating the bottom cell if a low-bandgap cell is fabricated after a high-bandgap cell with a superstrate structure, such as CdZnTe

6. Avoiding temperatures and processes that could damage the CIS bottom cell if a high-bandgap cell is fabricated on top

Tandem Cells

One way of increasing the efficiency of a solar cell is to split the solar spectrum into different sections and use a different solar cell that is optimized to capture each section of the spectrum. This can be done with tandem solar cells.

Tandem cells are basically stacks of individual cells with different energy thresholds each absorbing a different band of the solar spectrum. Those are usually connected together in series with the ultimate goal to engineer a new type of solar cell that is more efficient than the existing technologies. Such material could be "engineered" using a number of methods, including the use of quantum dot nanostructures of silicon in a silicon based dielectric matrix.

The confined energy levels in the quantum dots will increase the lowest absorption edge of the material compared to bulk silicon. If the quantum dot density is high enough the wave functions of the quantum dots will overlap to create true super lattice mini-bands and increase the effective band gap of the material.

Non-silicon materials have been used in tandem configurations with great success as well, and some of those have produced the highest conversion efficiency to date.

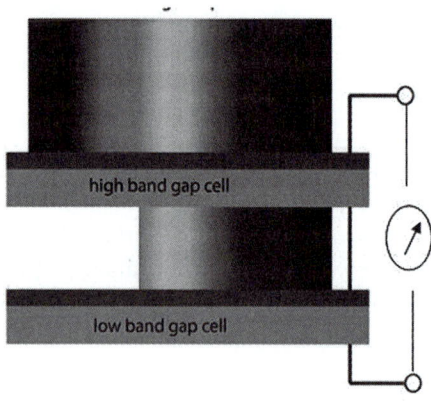

Figure 8-26. Tandem cell structure.

Tandem cells are two or more solar cells (and two p-n junctions) stacked on top of each other. The top cell absorbs high energy photons, while the bottom cell collects the photons with lower energy. Since those are usually lost in single cell, single junction devices, the efficiency of tandem cells is significantly higher under different light conditions.

The cells are connected in series and stacked in the direction of the incident light. The top most solar cell usually has the highest band gap and the bottom most solar cell has the lowest band gap.

Each solar cell (band gap) is designed to target a small portion of the incident solar spectrum for most efficient absorption and conversion to electricity.

The absorption profile for the stack is step-wise,

with no overlap or gaps in the absorption between any of the solar cells in the stack. Or, each solar cell absorbs light greater than its own band gap but does not absorb photons with energy greater than the solar cell above it in the stack.

Each solar cell also absorbs all incident photons with energy greater than the cell's band gap and is transparent to photons with energy below the band gap. Each photon produces exactly one electron hole pair upon absorption.

Tandem solar cells can either be individual cells, or connected in series. Series connected cells are simpler to fabricate but the current is the same through each cell, so this contains the band gaps that can be used.

The most common arrangement for tandem cells is to grow them monolithically so that all the cells are grown as layers on a single substrate, and where tunnel junctions connect the individual cells.

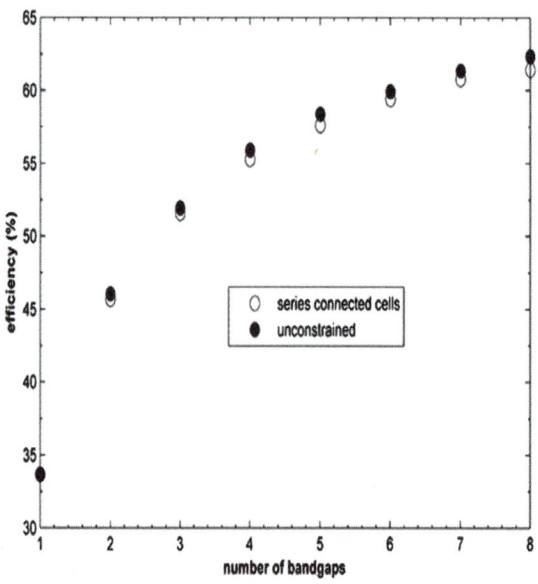

Figure 8-27. Theoretical efficiency of an ideal stack of solar cells vs. the number of band gaps under ideal solar conditions (AM 1.5D and diffuse radiation excluded).

"Unconstrained" tandem solar cell stack here means that each solar cell is connected to a separate electric circuit, and is basically free to operate unrestricted and unhindered at its maximum power point at all times. In the case of "constrained" solar cells, those are connected in series, with any mismatch in the output current of each cell needing to be minimized for optimum operation.

The constrained tandem stack is the preferred configuration for all practical purposes, despite the slight current matching restriction. The advantage of this type of arrangement is that only two electrodes are needed for the whole stack, instead of a pair of electrodes from each cell, which complicates the manufacturing and usage of the devices and is simply impractical.

It has been proven that the band gap sensitivity of the constrained tandem solar cell stack is greater than that of the unconstrained stack. This is because the constrained case means that the output current of the solar cells in the tandem stack needs to be matched. Or, any change in one of the band gaps can reduce the efficiency of each other cell, and hence the effect on the overall efficiency is large.

The maximum theoretical efficiency for a two-junction tandem under the AM1.5G spectrum and without concentration is 47%. At the peak efficiency, the top cell of such a stack has a bandgap of 1.63 eV and the bottom cell has a bandgap of 0.96 eV.

As the number of band gaps increases, the efficiency of the stack also potentially increases. In reality, increasing the number of cells in the stack will increase its efficiency to a point—depending on the materials' properties and process parameters—but eventually the efficiency will start decreasing, due to interference and because the stack gets so thick that the extraction of electrons is impeded.

The tandem solar cells are complex devices, and are also quite expensive, so their use is restricted to use in specialized applications. One of the most practical applications of this technology is their use in concentrated tracker assemblies. In such cases, the tandem solar cells follow the sun all day long, thus getting maximum sunlight, which is then converted into electricity most efficiently in the different bandgap materials in the cells.

Tandem solar cells made out of different materials have reached the highest conversion efficiency of any commercial solar cell to date. Tandem cells made out of III-V type (non-silicon) materials are over 43% efficient under 500x concentration. This is a great achievement, so we predict that tandem cell technologies have a great future, and will be widely used on the energy markets of the 21st century.

III-V Type Solar Technologies

The III-V type cells and modules, for which efficiencies have risen even higher (up to 43.7% in summer of 2012), are used in special applications. While they may become the technology of choice in the future, their use is limited today.

We do expect them—short of another disruptive technology popping up out there unannounced—to be the technology of choice by the end of the century. That, however, remains to be seen, because to achieve such high efficiencies (and to justify their significantly higher cost) the III-V type cells must be used in conjunction with tracking devices, which is a complex and expensive proposition. Because of that and because of our inability to make reliable and cheap trackers, their use is quite limited today. Let's hope that the future generations would find better and cheaper ways to make those cells and trackers, as needed to build and use very efficient solar conversion equipment.

Research Trends

Current research on high-performance multi-junction thin film devices focuses on several major challenges:

1. Determining high-bandgap alloys based on I-III-VI and II-VI compounds and other novel materials for the top cell

2. Considering low-bandgap CIS and its alloys, thin-film silicon, and other novel approaches for the bottom cell

3. Studying the difficult task of integrating the thin-film tunnel junction (interconnect) with the top cell. This work includes understanding the role of defects, how they affect the transport properties of this junction, and the diffusion of impurities into the bulk material

4. Fabricating a monolithic, two-terminal tandem cell based on polycrystalline thin-film materials that requires low-temperature deposition for several layers

5. Avoiding deterioration of the top cell when fabricating the bottom cell if a low-bandgap cell is fabricated after a high-bandgap cell with a superstrate structure, such as CdZnTe

6. Avoiding temperatures and processes that could damage the CIS bottom cell if a high-bandgap cell is fabricated on top

Miniature Solar Cells

Miniature solar cells are a special branch of the solar industry. They are specialized, very small, PV devices, based on high-performance semiconductor materials.

They could be shaped as a single cell, or a monolithic string of several solar cells. When exposed to sunlight, or bright artificial light, the energetic photons (optical energy) activate the miniature cell, or array, and generate low output voltage. Some of those cells are capable of generating floating source voltage in the 2-6V range, and have current sufficient to drive and power CMOS ICs, logic gates and other electronic components and devices.

These solar cells have small niche market in commercial applications for small and portable electronics.

Some could be used for providing wireless power and take advantage of the clean power generation without harmful EMI/RFI generation.

Such cells or arrays could also provide power for small LED screens or displays, or "trickle charge" for batteries and other power applications.

There is still some skepticism as far as the efficient and reliable operation of very small solar cells, not to mention the high prices, so it remains to be seen how this branch will develop.

CPV and HCPV Technologies

Concentrating photovoltaics (CPV) is a branch of the PV industry that uses special cells, optics and tracking mechanisms. Several companies with contracts and financing from the U.S. Department of Energy developed it in the 1970s.

Early CPV systems used silicon-based CPV cells, which had a problem with elevated temperatures. Those were later replaced by GaAs-based multi-junction cells, which have much higher efficiency, but still suffer from the effects of high temperatures.

At first GaAs CPV cells were made by using straight gallium arsenide in the middle junction. Later cells utilize In, Ga and As, due to the better lattice match to Ge, resulting in a lower defect density.

CPV Solar Cells

The result of the 30 years of CPV cells development effort is a complicated stack of crystalline and thin film layers, with different band gaps that are tailored to absorb most of the solar radiation. Those compound semiconductor solar cells have been shown to be more robust when exposed to outer space radiation and extreme climate conditions on earth.

These cells take advantage of the successes achieved by the new materials, such as Germanium, GaAs, as well as the development in the processing of III-V semiconductors and multi-layer (tandem) structures in the semiconductor industry.

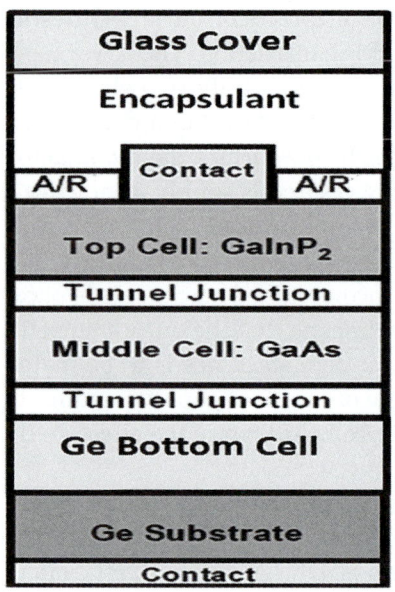

Figure 8-28. CPV solar cell

Since each type of semiconductor has a different characteristic band gap energy, it then allows the absorption of light most efficiently at a certain wavelength, hence absorption of electromagnetic radiation over a specific portion of the spectrum.

The hetero-junction devices, consisting of layers of various cells with different band-gaps are tuned for utilizing the full spectrum. Initially, light strikes a wide band-gap layer producing a high voltage; therefore using high-energy photons efficiently and enabling lower energy photons transfer to narrow band-gap sub-devices, which absorb the transmitted infrared photons. Gallium arsenide (GaAs)/indium gallium phosphide (InGaP) multi-junction devices) have reached the highest efficiency of over 43%.

Originally those cells were fabricated on GaAs substrates however, to reduce the cost and increase robustness and because it is reasonably lattice-matched to GaAs, germanium (Ge) substrates are being used more often.

The first CPV cells had a single junction much like the Si p–n junction solar cells. Later on, using their ability to introduce ternary and quaternary materials such as InGaP and aluminum indium gallium phosphide (AlInGaP), dual and triple junction devices were grown to capture a larger band of the solar spectrum, thus increasing the efficiency of the cells.

CPV Technology

The CPV cells are mounted under special (Fresnel) lenses, which concentrate and focus sunlight on the cells at 100 to 1000 times its original intensity. This is a lot of sunlight falling on a small area, but that way it allows high efficiency and reliability, better land utilization, and other benefits.

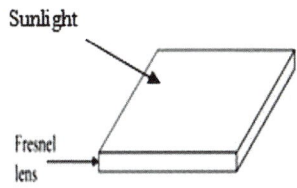

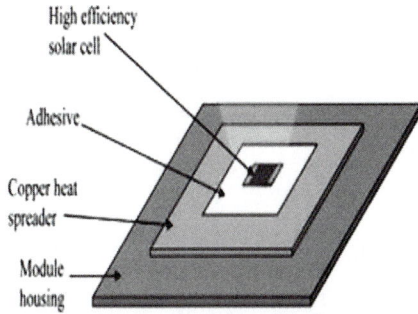

Figure 8-29. CPV assembly

Cell-lens packages are assembled into large modules, which are mounted on trackers that track the sun precisely through the day, providing the most power possible.

Efficiencies of 30-32%, measured in the grid, are obtainable with those devices.

HCPV Technology

High concentration PV (HCPV) technology is a variation of the CPV technology, but it uses much higher sun concentration ratios—in the 100-1000 times range.

It was developed in the 1980s and tested in small-scale projects during the 1990s. It was, however, put on the shelf soon thereafter, so it is still waiting to be introduced and proven in field operations. Several manufacturers have installed capacities, but they seem to be still mostly in the development stages.

HCPV systems are designed and built for operation under extreme desert conditions. They operate at 50-1000 times concentration of sunlight with over 42% efficiency at the cell. Efficiency in the grid is lower, of course, but still at least 2-3 times higher than any of the competing PV technologies. The CPV solar cells are made out of germanium, or GaAs, which are superior semiconductors that are not affected by temperature extremes. They are also made via sophisticated and precise

semiconductor processes, which make them durable and reliable for long-term operation. The optics are made out of glass and silicone, which are also unaffected by sunlight and temperature extremes.

HCPV modules are mounted on trackers that have a number of moving parts, control mechanisms, and electronics that need regular maintenance and tuning for optimum performance. This requires highly trained personnel and increases O&M expenses.

We can only hope that with its 40% or more efficiency, which is increasing with time, HCPV technology will become an active participant in the energy markets of the U.S. and the world in the near future. HCPV holds great promise of high efficiency (over 60% in the near future), combined with reliability of quality hi-tech components suitable for large-scale generation of electricity in the deserts.

The quickly increasing efficiency of multi-junction solar cells for CPV applications is the most exciting development in the solar industry. The maximum efficiency records have been increasing recently from: 41.2% in 2011, to 42.3% in 2012, and in 2013 the new world record of 44.7% efficiency was set. This is not surprising, since the maximum theoretical efficiency of some multi-junction cells is over 80%.

HCPV Tracking Systems

As mentioned previously, HCPV systems use very accurate two-axis tracking, and this, combined with other sophisticated components, makes HCPV the most efficient, reliable technology to date. Its operation, however, is quite complex for use in today's energy mar-

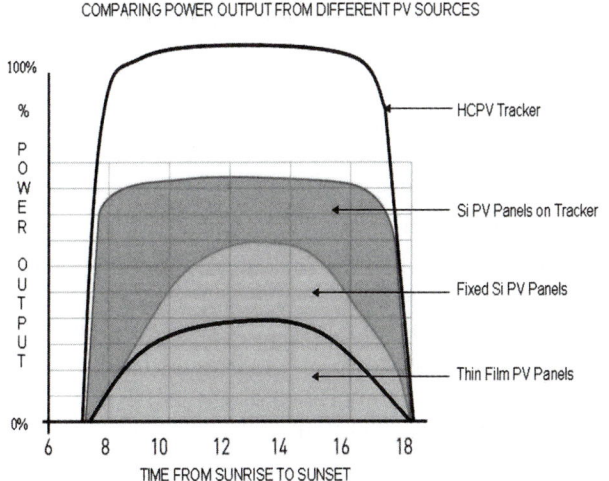

Figure 8-30. Efficiency of the different PV technologies

ket as we know it, so it will take a while but HCPV technology will eventually find its place in energy markets.

HCPV is especially efficient, because in addition to over 42% efficient CPV cells, it tracks the sun extremely accurately—0.01% accuracy—which allows it to capture every single sun beam coming down from sunrise to sunset. The problem is that if there is any cloud cover or haziness in the sky, HCPV optics cannot handle the diffused light going through them, and the efficiency drops quickly and significantly. Basically, HCPV systems can be used only in bright, hot desert areas, where other technologies have a hard time surviving the harsh elements.

But HCPV is a complex technology and some work is still to be done before we see HCPV trackers installed in large quantities in the world's large-scale PV power plants. At that point the equipment costs can be reduced significantly by placing large orders for materials and components.

With time the technological issues will be resolved, and we clearly see CPV and HCPV technologies as the primary choice for installation and use in large-scale power plants, especially those in desert regions, during the latter part of the 21st century.

Achievements of PV Companies

One of the most encouraging facts of late is that there are performance records across the board for every photovoltaic material type: crystalline silicon, a-Si, CdTe, CIGS, CIS, GaAs, and triple-junction CPV cells.

Many of those were not expected, and some were considered unachievable just several short years back. Nevertheless, the efficiency numbers keep rising and the prices are going down for now. How far the efficiency and price envelopes can be pushed remains to be seen, but we see a lot of envelope stretching with time.

Here are some recent record-setting results:

Abound Solar (now bankrupt)

Abound Solar was a manufacturer of cadmium telluride PV modules, with planned production of 82.8-watt modules at its Longmont, Colorado factory. This represents a 12.2% aperture efficiency to be produced on existing production equipment.

The mass production of 82-watt modules was scheduled to begin in the second half of 2012, but unfortunately Abound Solar shut down and filed for bankruptcy before achieving that goal.

NOTE: Abound Solar, and several other high profile companies, were setting records in many areas and yet they went bankrupt. This begs the question of how

important records are and where the line should be drawn. If so many companies spend enormous time and resources on setting records and still go bankrupt, then a middle line must be found to balance record setting and staying afloat.

Alta Devices

Alta Devices' most recently produced a GaAs-based solar panel has a 23.5% efficiency, as verified by the National Renewable Energy Laboratory (NREL). This seems to be another world record, but no other details are available, so we have to assume that this was done in their pilot phase.

Alta's process allows the manufacturing of layers of thin GaAs films that are flexible and measure only one micron in thickness, which has advantage in a number of niche markets.

First Solar

First Solar holds the world record for CdTe PV module efficiency with a 14.4% total area efficiency. This achievement comes six months after First Solar hit a CdTe solar cell efficiency of 17.3%. Both records were set at the Perrysburg, Ohio factory. In the summer of 2013 First Solar set another record of 18.7 efficiency*.

NOTE: Another record—the best in the world for CdTe PV technology by one of the leaders in the global solar energy. But what does it mean with the backdrop that each of the CdTe modules contain 8-9 grams of the toxic, carcinogenic heavy metal cadmium?

These frameless, all glass modules have not been proven efficient or safe for long-term desert operation, where excess IR and UV radiation will attack the modules and blister the thin films inside non-stop for 25-30 years. And yet millions upon millions of those unproven PV modules have been installed in the U.S. deserts. What if…?

MiaSolé

MiaSolé is a CIGS thin-film PV manufacturing company, which was third in CIGS panel production in 2011, behind Solar Frontier's 400 MW and Solibro's 66 MW.

MiaSole announced a 17.3% efficient modules, while the manufacturing process for 14% efficiency is in production.

Solar Frontier

Solar Frontier is a CIGS/CIS manufacturer with 400 megawatts of modules shipped in 2010. The newly recorded 17.8% aperture area efficiency on a 30-centimeter-square CIS-based PV lab module is a new record for a "fully integrated sub module" manufactured at the Solar Frontier's factories at commercial production scale.

Kunitomi, Japan

Kunitomi recently demonstrated a new CIGS module at 14.5% aperture efficiency, equivalent to a 13.3% module efficiency.

Solar Junction

Solar Junction is a developer of multi-junction cells for high-concentration photovoltaic (HCPV) applications. Working with Semprius, it has an agreement to deliver multi-megawatts of epitaxial wafers to the market.

Semprius holds the world record of CPV solar module efficiency using Solar Junction's III-V multi-junction solar cells based on lattice-matched dilute nitrides. The firm recorded a module efficiency of 43.3%.

SoloPower

SoloPower is a CIGS startup building flexible solar panels in a roll-to-roll electroplating process, has an NREL-measured aperture area efficiency of 13.4%, but the module efficiency is significantly less than that.

The practical application and value added for flexible modules in general is that there is less hardware required to install and the installation is easier. At least according to the manufacturers, but the claim has yet to be proven in actual life.

SunPower

SunPower has been manufacturing and selling high efficiency cells and modules during the past several years. Their back-contact crystalline silicon cells (which move the metal contacts to the back of the wafer, thus maximizing the working cell area, and eliminates redundant wires) have been in production since 2005.

Consistent improvements in efficiency have been demonstrated with each successive generation of commercialized cells, reaching Gen 3 cell efficiencies of over 23%.

Suntech

Suntech's Pluto cell technology achieved a 20.3% efficiency for a production cell using commercial-grade p-type silicon wafers. The new technology is a combination of different elements, which, when combined, improve cell efficiency. Now, 21% efficiency is targeted in the near future. The improvements include surface patterning, improved metallization, improved front metal contact dimensions, changes in dopant concentration at the emitter, and improved high-temperature performance.

These are, however, expensive processes, and the new product is not yet in full production. It is, instead, a premium product, offered at premium prices.

Fraunhofer Institute

Researchers at the Fraunhofer Institute have made an impressive advance in the area of high concentration photovoltaics (HCPV) with a 44.7% efficient solar cell. This is over twice the maximum efficiency achieved by traditional photovoltaic cells.

It took three years of research for the experimental cell to leapfrog the competition on its way to breaking 50% efficiency, which researchers expect to reach in the not-too-distant future. The new multi-junction cell utilizes four individual solar-absorbing sub-cells to transform sunlight into useful electricity. The sub-cells are made out of different semiconductor materials and stacked on top of one another. Each sub-cell absorbs a slightly different range of the solar spectrum, where the entire group absorbs most of it.

HCPV uses lenses to focus the sun's rays onto smaller solar cells, which allows for much higher efficiencies, while taking up much less space per generated power unit.

The researchers have managed to increase efficiency over one percentage point in just four months of work, and expect to surpass 50% efficiency in the near future.

Global Solar Markets Shakeout

Solar energy was brought in and out of the closet during several solar boom-bust cycles since the 1970s. The latest such cycle (2007-2012) was exceptional in that solar and wind were initially propped up financially by the U.S. and foreign governments to achieve a world-class status. They were expected to help greatly with ensuring our energy independence, reducing GHG emissions, and creating jobs.

This rise from the ashes, however, was short lived for the solar industry. Instead, it was badly hurt by changing regulations, reduced financial assistance, and lately by a trade war between the U.S., the E.U. and China. On top of that, the U.S. utilities are waging a war on wind and solar too, blaming them for disrupting the normal grid operations and costing them a lot of money, mostly due to the variability of the solar and wind energy sources. And so, many Chinese, U.S., and European solar companies are going under.

In the U.S., the fossil fuel companies have been trying to kill any measure proposed to help the industry through such things as renewable energy standards (RES), and feed in tariffs (FITs).

Cheap shale gas from fracking has also taken its toll on both wind and solar, as falling gas prices make a tough situation even more difficult for start-up companies and large multinationals alike. Extreme austerity measures in the E.U., for example, have seen FIT programs pared back in Spain, Greece, Eastern European countries, and elsewhere.

And the worse is yet to come, since there are predictions that the growth in the solar market will slow down during the next several years instead of expanding it dramatically, as needed to address the issues of the day.

The story of the recent and ongoing solar PV's "shakeout" leads to the conclusion that market competition is getting in the way of the urgently needed transition to renewable and low carbon energy systems. Falling prices should accelerate the trend towards renewables, but when private investors see falling prices they also see falling profits and panic sets in. In such case investments fall and demand guarantees in form of power purchase agreements and other such instruments to avoid long-term risk.

The decrease in investment in renewable energy in 2012 and the challenging policy environment is causing a serious production surplus of modules and wind turbines. Nevertheless, judging by the investment levels in renewables, which fell 12% in 2012, investments are still around the $200 billion level for a third time in a row. This, however, has not even scratched the surface of CO_2 emissions reductions, which are still headed firmly upward.

Wind and solar are not dead (but on life support for now); accounting for 5% of electrical power generation globally, and about 2% of all energy consumed.

How do we get solar and wind back on the world stage for good? This cannot happen without the decisive move away from liberalized energy markets and the continued support for expansion of fossil fuels.

One way is for the public sector to take charge of the expansion of solar, wind, and other renewable low carbon technologies. The public sector can borrow capital more cheaply than private companies; it can issue bonds; it can recover up-front costs for renewable energy in a variety of ways without shareholders demanding almost immediate returns. Long-term investments are not only possible, they are essential if the energy transition is going to actually happen.

The example of Germany is more than spectacular. Germany is now de-privatizing its power generation sector, while at the same time it has been accelerating the deployment of wind and solar power. As a result, this relatively small country, with population of 81 million (1% of world population) and sunlight matching only that of the U.S. Northeast (less than 10% of sunlight available in Arizona), has 32% of the entire global solar PV market. How could this happen?

Falling PV module prices are seen as a good thing over the long-term by some, because that will eventually increase demand as consumers realize that solar and wind power can be affordable if properly done—technologically and financially.

The bankruptcy of major solar PV companies is not just a bump in the road and a short delay in the effort to low-carbon economies. The problem is that even if the solar industry rebounds, as we expect it to do in the near future, the damage is already done. The reputation of those technologies has been hurt and it would be hard for many of them to recover.

The speed and scale of the deployment of solar and wind is way short of the levels demanded by climate change calculations. And as things are going, it would become more difficult to speed up or increase the scale of solar and wind power development in the shadow of the current shakeout.

On top of that, the world fossil-based power plants are being built every day in gigawatt size, while most renewable companies and projects are still stagnating in the megawatt size at best. As the fossils increase in size, the GHG pollution and its adverse effects multiply by the day.

We are entering the energy transition period, believe it or not, and the world desperately needs to survive while looking for the best ways to move forward. More public intervention, increased long-term public investment, and democratic control are the key elements needed for the survival and expansion of the renewable technologies.

This also requires cooperation from all involved, as well sharing of skills sets and knowledge. Many variable and complex factors are involved in this puzzle, and we are now in the initial stages of putting it together. Its final resolution might take many decades, but we have no other choice, but work on it day after day.

The process starts with educating the masses and putting all energy technologies and environmental effects under a common denominator. This is not easy, but is absolutely necessary in the long run, and is the focus of this writing.

And the failures of the past? They, like somebody said, could be looked at as the fire that forges the steel. At the very least, we can learn from them and make sure we don't repeat the mistakes of the past.

WIND ENERGY MARKETS

The wind energy industry has been going through the ups and downs of the energy sector during the last several decades, but has seen a sharp rise since 2004. In 2007, its best year yet, the wind industry installed close to 20 GW worldwide, an increase of 31% compared with the 2006 market. The U.S., China and Spain led the progress at the time, bringing the total global installed wind power capacity to about 95 GW.

The top five countries in terms of installed capacity were Germany (22.3 GW), the U.S. (16.8 GW), Spain (15.1 GW), India (7.8 GW) and China (5.9 GW). The ratio is changing today, with China foreseen as pulling ahead of the pack by 2020.

Table 8-10. Global wind power capacity in 2012 (in GW)

Country	2012	Total	%
China	12,960	75,324	26.7
United States	13,124	60,007	21.2
Rest of world	6,737	39,853	14.1
Germany	2,145	31,308	11.1
Spain	1,122	22,796	8.1
India	2,336	18,421	6.5
UK	1,897	8,845	3.0
Italy	1,273	8,144	2.9
France	757	7,564	2.7
Canada	935	6,200	2.2
Portugal	145	4,525	1.6
World total	**44,799**	**282,587**	**100%**

NOTE: In 2013, the global wind power installation exceeded the 300 GW mark.

In terms of economic value, the global wind market in 2007 was worth about $37 billion in new generating equipment, and attracted $50.2 billion in total investment. Europe was the leading market for wind energy and new installations represented 43% of the global total.

The U.S. was the second largest wind power market in terms of cumulative installed capacity base and annual capacity addition in 2012, but the economic slowdown and the nation's lack of long-term policy certainty have caused a 43% drop in installations.

By the end of 2012, the nation recorded annual wind power installations of 13.1 GW, and reached a cumulative installed capacity of 60 GW. The experts predict that growth in U.S. wind power installations will slow to 2020 given the possible, and perennially anxiety-inducing, expiration of the Production Tax Credit (PTC) after 2013.

The extension of the PTC is a political decision, so it's difficult to predict what will happen. If it is not extended, that will impact the market significantly, especially due to the low cost of natural gas for power generation found in the U.S. presently.

But in any case, the U.S. wind market will not fall to zero, as there are other support mechanisms for wind in the U.S., including the state-based renewable portfolio standards which require increasing proportions of electricity consumed to be renewable. Wind will benefit from the state standards, no doubt, but it is unclear where, when, and how much exactly.

Installed capacity is one thing—it shows how much power could be produced—if the wind turbines were working non-stop day and night. This is never the case, however, so the actual win-power generated electricity is much less. It depends on a number of factors and variables such as: wind and equipment availability, grid operation, and use efficiency.

Table 8-11.
Wind-power generated electricity in 2012 (in TWh)

Country	TWh	%
United States	120.5	26.2
China	88.6	19.3
Germany	48.9	10.6
Spain	42.4	9.2
India	24.9	5.4
Canada	19.7	4.3
UK	15.5	3.4
France	12.2	2.7
Italy	9.9	2.1
Denmark	9.8	2.1
Rest of world	67.7	14.7
World total	**459.9**	**100%**

It is obvious from Table 8-11 that the U.S. leads the world in the amount of generated electricity, even though China has the largest installed wind capacity. This is actually a significant lead—about 35% everything considered, which shows that the U.S. is serious about wind power. That is due to superior conditions in the U.S., as far as the efficiency of operation and use of wind power and the grid are concerned.

The problem in this case is that a number of wind power plants were installed in areas where they do not have full access to the national grid, so the generated power is partially used, or not used at all.

In 2010, wind energy production was over 2.5% of total worldwide electricity usage, and growing rapidly at more than 25% per annum. The monetary cost per unit of energy produced is similar to the cost for new coal and natural gas installations.

In 2011, Denmark generated more than a quarter of its electricity from wind, and 83 countries around the world are using wind power on a commercial basis.

China is the most ambitious of all wind game players; the government plans to order its electrical companies to source up to 15% of all of its power using wind turbines by 2020.

Presently there are about 200,000 wind turbines generating electricity around the world. There are documented 13,600 wind farms around the world, with over 270 GW of power generating capacity. There are also about 950 off-shore wind projects with over 280 GW generating capacity.

In April 2013, California set a record in wind power production with 4.2 GW peak power produced at a time when the entire California power system used 24 GW of electricity. This means that wind provided about 17.5% of the entire power needs of the state at the time... but for a short while.

In the first part of 2013, the U.S. wind-power generated capacity totaled 60 GW, or 5% of the total nation's energy production capacity. Another 135 GW of potential wind production awaits development and connection to the grid, according to industry data, while the U.S. DOE reports suggest that by 2030 about 20% of America's energy could be generated by wind.

Unfortunately, there hasn't been a lot of investment in the grid for the last two decades, and its overall expansion is hindered by lack of grid lines in the areas of the country where there are a lot of wind resources. The grid was built a long time ago to service coal, nuclear and hydropower plants without wind power energy in

mind. Since wind power plants are located in remote areas, and operate intermittently, it is difficult and expensive to get the electricity from those rural areas into the national grid.

On the other hand, U.S. government subsidizes the fossil fuel industry to the tune of $12-50 billion annually. Similar investment in clean energy would put the renewable energy markets on their feet, ensure our energy independence, and speed up the fight against climate change. In reality, however, this is not possible, since without sufficient political will, the abundant natural, renewable resource will remain under-utilized a while longer.

Regardless of all difficulties and obstacles in the way, the global wind power industry is growing, and its future looks bright. According to new studies, about 4 million turbines installed at strategic places around the world, could provide 7.5 terawatts of energy annually, which is about half of the estimated power necessary to run entire world's power grids in the future.

But, of course, this is not easily done, since there are problems, such as the need for over 10 million acres of land and thousands of miles of new transmission lines, which require major investment. Where would the birds and the land animals that now live on those 10 million acres go, and where the money for the land and the lines be found? Those are the questions for future generations to answer.

The idea of half of the world's energy being provided by wind power is a bit far fetched, but doable at its extreme, so the reality is somewhere in between, and the choice is ours. We must agree that wind is not the most reliable energy source...for now at least. Sometimes it blows, sometimes it doesn't. So yes, there are reasonable concerns about the use of wind power as a reliable energy source, but it can be very successfully used in combination with other sources, such as solar-, hydro-, or ocean-power, and combined with energy storage.

The Wind Future

In 2012, Greenpeace International and the Global Wind Energy Council released a bi-annual report on the future of the wind industry. It shows that wind power could supply up to 12% of global electricity by 2020, creating 1.4 million new jobs and reducing CO_2 emissions by more than 1.5 billion tons per year, more than 5 times today's level.

By 2020, the IEA's new policies scenario suggests that the total wind power capacity would reach 587 GW, supplying about 6% of global electricity. The GWEO moderate scenario suggests that wind could reach 759 GW, supplying 7.7-8.3% of global electricity supply. The advanced scenario suggests that, with the right policy support, wind power could reach more than 1,100 GW by 2020, supplying 11.7-12.6% of global electricity, and saving nearly 1.7 billion tons of CO_2 emissions. And by 2030, wind power could provide more than 20% of global electricity supply.

With over 300 GW installed capacity in 2013, wind power is a major source of clean power. Wind is a major contributor to emission reductions, and needs no fresh water to generate electricity. This alone is a unique, and very useful, attribute, which only wind and solar (PV) power possess, and which makes them attractive options for power generation in an increasingly water-constrained world.

Wind power is an indigenous energy source, which could be particularly useful to countries short on natural resources and burdened with large fossil fuel import bills. Wind power is now competitive in an increasing number of markets, even when competing against heavily subsidized conventional energy sources. In addition, wind power provides a number of environmental and social benefits: zero CO_2 emissions, zero water use, and no air or water pollution and no additional cost.

No doubt, wind energy is useful and practical, so it is going to play a major role in our energy future, but for wind to reach its full potential it needs help. The level of uncertainty surrounding the wind technology is still great, so the specialists foresee several different scenarios for the wind industry in the future.

Technologically speaking, wind is intermittent and unreliable power source, so the utilities are rethinking their acceptance of wind power in their power generation mix. New technologies, such as large-scale energy storage, are needed to stabilize wind power generation.

The energy storage technologies, however, will not be available or economically feasible any time soon, so the only way to remediate the wind's intermittency is to combine it with other power sources, such as solar, hydro, and others.

Financially speaking, wind power is subject to governmental policies and regulations, and since both the global political and financial sectors are still in turmoil, wind's future is full of uncertainties and risks. The long-term success of the wind industry requires stable, long-term policy, sending a clear, and very much needed, signal to the investment community that it has the governments' support. Without these, wind will be limping along until the critical moment when its use would become absolutely necessary.

Nevertheless, wind is here to stay, and one way or another we will see great developments in this area in the near future.

Europe Wind

During the latest solar boom-bust cycle of 2007-2012, most European leaders took pride in thinking that they lead the way toward the era of renewable power generation and low-carbon emissions. Now the game has changed, and they seem more worried about the cost of the fuels.

Between 2005 and 2012, gas prices fell by 66% in America, while at the same time rising 35% in Europe. All this means that while the U.S. is forecast to become a net exporter of energy in the next few decades, Europe's dependence on foreign fuels and electric energy will only grow.

This, of course, threatens Europe's competitiveness and increases the worries that energy-hungry European factories are packing up and fleeing to the U.S. So, confusion is reigning among European leaders, who don't know how to handle the developing and ever changing energy market.

It seems that they would have to rely on others to provide energy when it is needed at home, instead of focusing on how to produce it. The major problem here is that, despite the benefits, a deeper market would create winners and losers, and will surely require expensive cross-border infrastructure.

And the most difficult to manage aspect of the problem is the growing web of national incentives: power companies may trade even more energy in wholesale markets, but German taxpayers, for example, do not want to subsidize French or Polish companies.

On Sunday, June 16, 2013, Germany's solar panels and wind turbines were humming at their peak and generated a record 60% of Germany's electricity, but it was on a slow weekend afternoon. France and Belgium were also generating lots of nuclear power at the time that could not easily be cranked down, so for several hours during that remarkable afternoon, power generating companies had to pay customers to take their surplus power.

Negative wholesale prices have become more common as European countries turn to renewables. Germany is a particularly interesting example in its forced shutdown of nuclear power. This, and the addition of a lot of renewable power have changed the way power companies do business.

At times Germany generates too much power, as during that afternoon, while at others it sucks power from nuclear plants across the border in France, Poland, and other neighbors. And German customers still are faced with the risk of blackouts when the sun does not shine and the wind does not blow.

Germany, nevertheless, is shaping as the leader of the pack today—energy and otherwise. As Europe's biggest energy consumer and largest producer of renewable energy, its power grid would be at the heart of any upgraded pan-European network. Inevitably, Germany will have the last say-so in any and all gas and electricity distribution plans.

Many of the German neighbors, such as Poland and the Czech Republic, however, are starting to complain that power surges from Germany are playing havoc with their grids too. This is a strange, unexpected, and unplanned for, consequence of subsidized renewables.

Another unexpected and unwanted effect is that now governments have to pay the power companies to produce electricity from fossil fuels to ensure that back-up power is available. All this because the sun doesn't shine some of the time and wind doesn't blow the rest of the time.

Now Europe is switching to burning more heavily polluting coal instead of the cleaner and more flexible gas, because coal is cheap, the gas market is far from liquid, and the carbon-emissions system is broken.

Another oddity is that Germany pays some of the lowest wholesale prices for electricity in Europe, yet at the same time offers some of the highest retail prices. Consumers are forced to pay a number of unusual charges, such as: network fees, taxes, and ever-growing charges for subsidizing renewable energy projects.

The German energy system also encourages heavy users, making them exempt from some charges. And while politicians are in disagreement about how to proceed, they are in total agreement to keep the energy system going as is.

Abandoning the renewables is not a solution, as the Spain case shows. Spain has huge renewable power from sun and wind, so much so that now government subsidies are putting a large hole in the country's ailing economy. Spain, however, cannot sell much of this bounty because there is no adequate distribution network to its neighbors.

If all of the different European grids were linked up properly, like in the U.S., they would form a large integrated energy market. In such case, the peaks and valleys of power demand and supply could be easily handled.

This, however, would have required forward thinking, where, for example, instead of installing solar panels in cloudy Germany, they would be much more efficient in sunny Greece. It is the same with wind power generation, which could be concentrated in the windiest parts of the continent, instead of here and there far from the grid.

Cross-border co-operation has been discussed since the creation of the European Union, but full integration is far off. Eastern Europe still has "energy islands'." Done properly, an integrated E.U. energy market could favor the transition to renewable power, enhance security and promote cheaper energy. This is not the case now, so E.U. customers will have to suffer the consequences.

What does all this mean for European wind power? It simply puts it in a very disadvantageous position. Wind power plants are small in size and built in remote locations, usually far from the power grid. This causes fragmentation of the wind industry, making it inefficient and the generated power expensive.

As we enter the era of cheap gas, and until Europe integrates its power grid, wind power will grow, but much slower than in the past.

China Wind

China is entering a new phase of serious plans for reduction its carbon footprint and increasing electricity production in rural areas. According to the specialists, China has doubled its cumulative wind capacity each year between 2006 and 2011, growing at a compound annual growth rate of 76%.

China, with number two market the U.S. and top markets Germany, the U.K., Italy, Spain and India, accounted for 74% of global installed wind capacity in 2012.

China's plan has been focused on two goals: a) to support the development of a Chinese manufacturing base for wind turbines and other equipment, which can then be exported, and b) to connect more renewables to the grid to reduce carbon emissions from electricity generation.

The progress of the Chinese wind power related equipment manufacturing and increased exports are a testament that the latter goal has been achieved, where several Chinese manufacturers are now global players and Chinese wind products exports are unrivaled.

China's growth began to slow in 2012, however, as some aspects of the nation's wind power strategy have proved challenging. China is having a problem connecting wind power plants into the grid, thus it has been unable to fully accommodate the already installed wind capacity. This is especially serious in remote areas where wind yields are at their highest.

Wind power plants' output is often disconnected from the transmission system when supply exceeds demand or there is system congestion. This is a major economic dysfunction and disincentive for any wind project, so only the most favorable projects would get financed, usually with a lot of government help.

China's wind slowdown might continue until the power grid infrastructure is upgraded to integrate existing and new wind generation, which might take several years, or even decades. This will certainly limit the size of the Chinese market compared to previous highs.

This unexpected obstacle in the internal wind power development is forcing the Chinese wind equipment manufacturers to focus on increasing their exports to keep the production plants doors open, so we should be looking for some significant price competition and even price wars globally over the next few years.

In summary, the growth in the major wind power markets is expected to slow down by 2020 as emerging markets from the Asia-Pacific region and South and Central America gain significant market share. The growing Asia-Pacific wind power market, led by India, China and other emerging countries such as Korea, Thailand and the Philippines, will continue to drive growth, while budding wind markets in Argentina, South Africa, the Philippines, Ukraine, Brazil, Korea and Mexico are projected to expand rapidly by 2020.

EQUIPMENT MANUFACTURING MARKETS

Many different pieces of equipment are used in the production of fossil fuels, and in their conversion into heat, or electric power. Those are designed and manufactured by a number of companies, which have a large supply chain of parts and consumables that are used daily in their operations.

Fossils Fuels Production Equipment

Coal mining is the most intensive fuel producing business, in terms of size and volume, today. Presently there are about 2,500 coal-related businesses in nearly 500 categories globally, generating approximately $90 billion in annual revenue. While the coal mining in the U.S. is slowing down, thus reducing the demand for mining equipment, China, India and other developing countries (along with some developed) are projected to account for over 75% of all mining equipment purchases in the next several decades.

Mining drills and breakers are the fastest growing equipment segment, which reflects their universal use for breaking through the ground and subsurface materials. Crushing, pulverizing and screening equipment post the second strongest demand, which are widely used in both surface and underground mining. Although demand for surface mining machinery is growing at a slower rate, they will continue to account for the largest single share of equipment demand in the future.

While the major part of the coal, oil and gas markets are in the production and sale of the fuels by coal, oil and gas companies, there are many other industries involved in the process of bringing those products to market. Some of the other key players are: equipment manufacturers and other supply chain participants; the power producers, who use the fuels to generate power; and power distributors, who sell the power to the public.

The equipment manufacturers are usually large companies that design and make the equipment and the supplies used in coal, oil, and gas production operations, which heavily depend on specialized equipment for efficient and profitable operation. The equipment manufacturers, on the other hand, depend on the fuel producers to buy their equipment and services, and to supply replacement parts for subsequent maintenance work—a perfect win-win situation.

A number of construction and engineering companies are also involved in different stages of field exploration, construction and maintenance of coalmines and drill sites. Although most of those companies are not directly involved in the mining or drilling process, together, they represent a large chunk of the U.S. and global economies and also use a lot of heavy-duty equipment.

As we saw in the previous chapters, mining, drilling, and transport equipment for the most part consists of very large pieces of machinery and structures, such as cranes, oil tankers, trucks, draglines, diggers, and train cars used in those operations. The equipment used in power generating plants is also very large and very expensive.

The fossils fuel production, transport, and use supports the large equipment manufacturing industry, consisting of a very large number of equipment and parts manufacturers. The variety and volume of products made by those companies in size, weight and money is tremendous, and is the foundation of one of the largest global niche markets.

Thousands of tons of steel, plastics, and other materials, miles of wires, and a lot of electro-mechanical components are used to make the energy production equipment. The energy used, and the pollution emitted, during the manufacturing and transport of those huge pieces of machinery is significant as well. We cannot look at a coal mine, an oilrig, or any power plant without thinking of what it took to make, transport, install, and maintain all the pieces of equipment used in those operations.

Renewables Production Equipment

At the same time, most of the renewables do not require any fuel, except biofuels, which need biomass. Instead, the renewable companies manufacture products that are used for generating electricity. For example, wind power companies manufacturer large wind turbines, while solar energy companies manufacture PV modules, or troughs for thermal conversion. In all cases, those companies purchase the production equipment that is used to make their products from third-party vendors. This equipment is then used to make the final products—wind turbines, solar modules

The production equipment in most renewable energy manufacturing operations is not that large, but it is quite complex and expensive. One exception, where very large pieces of equipment are used, is in the large furnaces and earth moving equipment needed for producing silicon material from sand. Another exception to keep in mind is the very large equipment used in the initial mining and processing of some of the minerals used in making the components of the renewable energy products.

In addition to silicon, large quantity of glass, aluminum, steel, silver, copper, cadmium, tellurium and other minerals and chemicals are also needed in the renewables' manufacturing processes, all of which are mined and processed using large pieces of machinery. The transport of the materials and the finished product also requires large vehicles.

All in all, manufacturing the equipment and vehicles needed for energy production is a big business, spread over several market niches and general market areas. The production equipment manufacturing industry, serving the energy sector is quite large and provides work for thousands of people. Many of those companies are totally dependent on orders from coal, oil, and gas fuel producers, as well as from wind and solar energy manufacturing companies, power plants, transportation and other companies involved in the process.

ENERGY STORAGE

Energy storage is basically a way of diverting electric power from its original destination (the power grid or home use) into a device or a system of devices where it could be stored and kept until needed. This is one of the critical elements that is badly needed for stabilizing the wind and solar power variability.

Energy storage is shaping the future of solar and wind power generation, since they are inconsistent and unreliable sources of power, which is very inconvenient for the utility companies. Even in the deserts, where the maximum amount of sunlight on Earth is found, there are hours and entire days of hazy skies, clouds, and storms. During those times, even the most efficient solar power generators sit idle.

The power grid senses the reduced power input and reacts in ways the utility companies don't like. Peaker power plants, fueled by fossil fuels ramp up in response to compensate for the lost power, and it costs the utilities a lot of money every time a peaker plant is started.

Wind power has a very similar problem, and because of that abnormality, the utilities are increasingly standing up against wind and solar power generation. So, unless and until large-scale energy storage is a proven, efficient, and cheap, solar and wind will be looked at as inferior energy sources.

Falling FITs and PV module prices, rising energy prices, the desire for energy independence, and the drive towards reduced emissions are helping the development and implementation of energy storage, but it is still in the design and test stages.

Battery Storage

Storing solar power in batteries is an attractive concept to homeowners and commercial operators who want to be independent from the grid and save money from rising prices in the process. The high cost of the batteries, and the complications involved in setting and maintaining them, however, has proven the battery power storage concept to be impractical and uneconomical in most cases. This is especially true for large-scale energy storage for now.

The rise of grid power prices, and new policies and incentives that boost solar installations are starting to shift that equation in favor of energy storage for solar. Germany is the world's biggest distributed solar PV market that might be the first to enter into a wholesale shift to battery-backed solar energy storage, despite the high cost and integration challenges involved.

The Germans have accepted the fact that battery storage and photovoltaic energy are a good fit for residential and commercial applications, and so the use of those is increasing. The Germans, and most other Europeans' life style can be easily modified to reduce power use as needed for battery backup.

Prior to Germany's FIT reduction, almost all solar PV in the country was off-grid, which required the solar installation to have battery storage to provide power during cloudy days or at night. The additional costs for storage batteries was a bottleneck for off-grid deployments. The introduction of FITs in early 2000s changed all that. German solar power operators were finally able to sell their solar power back to the local utilities at guaranteed prices that exceeded the retail electricity prices. At that point, very few people chose to install battery energy storage, except if living in remote locations.

In 2008, for example, German utilities paid up to $0.80 per kWh generated by a residential or commercial solar installation. Not many people got rich from that, because there is very little sunshine in Germany, but still it made sense to install solar on one's roof, and so many people did.

Today, however, the FITs in Germany and most other European countries are almost gone, while the electricity prices are going up, so the situation is reversed, and energy storage is attractive once again. Once the solar FIT price is less than the price of electricity, it makes sense to use as much of it as possible directly. If the price of the energy storage is right, then it makes sense to store the electricity for later use.

The German solar industry is looking to find ways to continue to grow and profit amidst the slow decline of FIT prices. The era of high FIT prices was all about making money, while the new reality of falling FITs and PV module prices has shifted the emphasis to saving money.

The demand for energy storage options in Germany is heard by the industry and some companies like Solar Battery, a privately funded German startup, founded in 2008, which has a software package that is designed to integrate PV modules, lithium-ion batteries, and home energy management systems into an efficiently working unit. The package was successfully tested it in 2010, and now there are over 1,300 such systems installed in German homes and businesses.

These systems cost about $13,000 for a 4.5 kWh energy storage system, and about $21,000 for a 10 kWh system, he said. This is a lot of money for couple of hours of added energy storage, which very few people can afford, but as equipment prices go down and utility bills rise, the technology will reach the point that it is more affordable.

This is not an acceptable option for an American home or business, which can blast through 4.5 kWh in a matter of minutes, but because the typical German home uses far less electricity than the typical U.S. home; 4.5 kilowatt-hours is enough to keep the power on at minimum level all night long.

No matter how you slice it, however, the battery storage approach is not accepted in the U.S., where everything is bigger and requires much more power. It would be a long time before batteries can power half a million 5 ton air conditioners during Arizona's summer season 24 hours a day, non-stop for 6 months, so battery power is not coming here any time soon.

Large-scale energy storage is still way in the future too, so the battery storage market in the U.S. is limited for now and for some time in the future.

The utilities are nevertheless interested in energy storage, because: a) they need to add new solar installation business, but b) they also want to integrate the distributed solar power into the grid, which is not possible without energy storage. This is actually the holy grail of electric utilities, where efficient, large-scale, commercial viable energy storage would solve some of their biggest problems related to the expansion of the variable renewable energy sources, like wind and solar.

And so, although for now energy storage is only a dream of utilities and wanna-be manufacturers, there are examples of some progress in the area. For instance, Eos Energy Storage is now working to deploy its energy storage technology with major utilities in the U.S. and Europe. Their new Aurora energy storage system is a 1 MW, low-cost, zinc hybrid cathode battery the size of a 40-foot shipping container. If successful, the new technology could supply power to the grid for around $160 per KWh, compared to between $400 and $1000 per KWh for current battery technologies. The company also has smaller units, 2 kW sub-modules the size of a washing machine.

The ultimate goal is to produce a battery with a reliable 25-year life cycle that can be integrated into the utility grid at a price equivalent to a combustion gas turbine. Then, Eos, or anyone else, would be in a position to change the way utilities think about the variable renewable resources. It is also the only way to make them change the way they do business.

Their Genesis program intends to deploy iterations of the energy storage technology in 2014, including utilities representing more than 300 GW of power generation and 76 million customers in 70 countries. The program represents a major step in bringing viable energy storage to the grid, which could radically change not only systems for meeting peak demand and the economics of intermittent renewable technologies as well.

Energy storage can solve also another problem,

which is related to distributed solar power. The power generated from lots of rooftop solar installations at the noon peak power times usually leads to local electricity market prices dropping significantly. Similarly, excess wind power at times of reduced usage can drive the electric prices down to nearly zero.

Eliminating this problem is only possible with the implementation of grid-connected energy storage systems with central control. Solar Battery is working on the development of such a system with a group of 29 German local utilities and regional energy firms, involving about 700 homes connected to a single distribution circuit. The results from this effort might make the difference to speed up seamless solar integration in the power grid.

In Germany, there is a government program to subsidize PV-connected energy storage that deals with the distributed network problems, but the program has proven to be very cumbersome, which has limited its usefulness and its future is uncertain at best—not a good start for the energy storage technology in the most promising place for its development and implementation.

Similar energy storage integration programs and projects are under development in California, where companies like Tesla and SolarCity, and Silent Power and Hanwha are working on solar-battery combinations for residential customers. Others are working on commercial-scale or utility-scale storage for solar-grid integration, which is a more difficult and far more expensive proposition.

Mostly due to increased government funding, energy storage technologies are seeing serious returns on investments in the U.S. and around the world with distinctly focused industries taking shape in Europe, North America, and Asia.

Presently, 633 advanced energy storage projects encompassing 865 separate systems are in operation or under development worldwide. An amazing 38 new projects were added just in the first half of 2013, but both technologies remain fragmented in use and applications in each region.

France's Alstom leads all vendors with 19% of total market share, closely followed by Germany's Voith with 16%, and America's Gridflex with 13% of all present day projects.

UK Battery Storage

One of the world's largest, and first for the U.K., large-scale battery energy storage projects was completed in the summer of 2013, and connected to the grid by the Scottish Hydro Electric Power Distribution (SHEPD). The Kirkwall Power Station battery storage consists of about 2 MW capacity lithium-ion technology, manufactured by Mitsubishi Power Systems, Europe and Mitsubishi Heavy Industries. This type of battery energy storage has been already installed and tested successfully at Nagasaki, Japan, where it ran continuously and without any major problems over a two-year period.

The Kirkwall Power Station in Orkney is expected to demonstrate that the trial battery storage will prove efficient and reliable enough to be used for storing excess renewable energy that would otherwise go to waste. Thus stored energy can then be used as needed to send power to the grid.

This battery storage project is still considered to be research into the viability of using batteries for electricity storage. It is an important subject, so there is a lot of effort and money going in it. It is likely to become even more important to help balance the variable output from renewable forms of generation as the energy industry moves to a largely low-carbon electric generation mix.

The use of a 2 MW battery is not the solution to the current constraints of the Orkney distribution network, but it is a glimpse in the future of energy storage, where batteries could provide a cost-effective way of freeing up capacity on the network to help facilitate new connections of low carbon generation.

Ofgem's Low Carbon Networks Fund is funding the trial, as if to show that energy storage has a wide support and a bright future. The British islands are projected to generate significant amounts of renewable energy, but variability of the sources and lack of sufficient grid capacity is a problem that has to be solved first.

Battery storage is shaping as one of the most important approaches to finding a solution to those problems, and ensuring that the limited energy resources are used most efficiently. So, the new 2MW battery storage is not considered a short-term solution, but rather the work on it and the results thereof will be used to design the next steps in the energy storage technologies development.

Efficient and reliable energy storage is key for the future of solar and wind power, since variability and wasted energy are the major reasons to denigrate those promising industries. How the 2MW storage would be expanded to accommodate the growing market is uncertain as yet, but the residential PV storage capacity in the U.K. is projected to reach over 3.0 GW by 2020, so an energy storage solution is absolutely needed.

California Energy Storage

California is shaping the way solar and wind energy are to be used in the future. Now, prompted by the utilities worries about the variability of solar and wind power generation, California is taking the next step in the development of the new technologies by proposing a sharp rise in energy storage to better integrate renewable power with the rest of the grid.

Enter California's Governor Jerry Brown, "We can't just rely on sunlight, we've got to bottle it." This is a new twist in California's already crowded and complex energy field, which comes in response to the mandated 30% of renewables mix in the state's electricity supply by 2020. The proposal has started a new technology race that has already attracted a number of venture capitalists, large-scale battery makers, and a number of companies.

The 30% renewables target by 2020 is forcing the energy storage issue with the goal of implementing energy storage of up to 1.3 GW by 2020, enough to power more than a million homes. That proposal, if and when implemented, will have an immediate and lasting impact on the national grid energy storage market, which will soar to installations worth $10.4 billion in 2017 from just $200 million in 2012.

The California proposition, however, is much more expensive compared with building new gas power plants. The estimate is $1 to $3 billion will be needed to install so much storage. Where is the money coming from, since there are significant risks that those storage technologies will not deliver on their promises? Many projects might fail and bring financial ruin to their investors and the taxpayers who are always on the hook.

A natural gas-fired plant costs about $1,000 per kilowatt to build, while a battery-based energy storage system has a breakeven capital cost of $1,684 per kilowatt in 2013. The costs will go down with mass production, but the reliability issues won't be resolved any time soon.

We must note here that gas-fired power plants will need gas for fuel for the duration, while energy storage uses excess energy, which also costs money, but is available once the design is implemented. Nevertheless, the O&M costs of the present day gas-fired and battery energy storage (if proven reliable enough in the long run) technologies are quite close.

And let's not forget the bitter lessons from the past, as far as energy storage is concerned. A number of companies have been struggling to prove that energy storage is reliable and cheap enough. Storage battery maker A123 Systems and flywheel maker Beacon Power LLC were two of the first and most high profile companies, who used U.S. government funds to develop their projects. Unfortunately, both of them ended up filing for bankruptcy after spending the DOE money.

Now both are reinventing themselves under new ownership. A123 is now a Chinese company, after being sold for $257 million to the U.S. unit of Chinese auto parts maker Wanxiang. It is still making grid-scale batteries.

Beacon was bought by Rockland Capital for $30.5 million, and is presently working on a new project in Pennsylvania...again with government financial support.

The benefit of energy storage is that it enables utilities to avoid building power plants or new transmission lines to meet peak demand, by simply providing extra power for a few hours a day. But are the high storage cost and the risks worth it, even if all benefits are considered is still uncertain and the debate continues.

So, the bottom line for the practicality and usefulness of energy storage is: a) price of grid electricity, vs. b) FIT prices, vs. c) battery prices.

Significant changes in any of those variables could alter the direction of the technology drastically whichever way. The utilities will have the last word on this issue as well.

Energy Management

Energy management for residential customers using smart thermostats is the talk of the town. There are iPhone apps that can be used to control the smart thermostats remotely from anywhere on Earth. Isn't this just dandy? Sitting at a table in a London bar, you can whip out your iPhone and dial a new setting for your home A/C system in Arizona to a temperature that is more comfortable for Pooch. What a useful gadget. Or is it?

This is what home energy management is shaping up to be today. When thermostats become a subject to a hi-tech discussion, you know things are changing, and sure enough, residential demand response has become a necessary part of the demand response strategy in many areas of the U.S.

Consumer energy management is also a hot topic among energy specialists and utilities, where peak load demand and supply has risen to a priority level. It is also the lowest-hanging fruit in the commercial and industrial sector, so full attention is paid to it.

The utilities are hesitant about the approach they need to take as far as managing the customer's home energy needs and usage, but some are taking it head on.

For example, the Sacramento Municipal Utility District has a pilot project with tens of thousands of customers, the result of which is expected to be a new way of doing business with residential customers.

At the same time, Portland General Electric is testing a new smart grid home appliance standard, using their employee's water heaters as guinea pigs. It also has a customer portal, EnergyTracker, and is adding increased capabilities to it; in effect abandoning in-home displays as nearly worthless for energy efficiency management. Their use is now limited to that of an educational tool only.

The new programs require new ways to reach into the home, such as Wi-Fi, ZigBee, Z-Wave or broadband. In addition, integration of legacy systems with new platforms is needed.

A number of companies working with the utilities, such as Tendril, AlertMe, EcoFactor, Simple Energy and EnergyHub, have a number of options. Those range from leveraging smart thermostats that customers have already bought, or using telecom providers to get into the home energy game, to bringing energy management to a game-like status. Those offer a variety of options for use by the utilities and their customers.

Segmentation is the key to deploy the right approach to the right people, so the utilities and their cohorts are working hard on dividing and conquering the population. The game is just starting, so there are both challenges and promises in the way utilities plan to reach and impact the way residential customers use their energy.

And speaking of utilities, they are driving (or trying to) not only the home energy markets, but also many other areas of energy generation, transmission, and use. Let's see…

THE UTILITIES

The utilities dictate, directly or indirectly, the way things are done in the energy sector. They make and break the rules, and operate in a way that is much less than democratic or fair, and yet we need them. Without the utilities there would be no power every time we flip the light switch, or air conditioning unit on. Life would be quite different without the utilities running the power plants and distribution lines that deliver this precious commodity to our front doors.

So, while we admit our dependence on electric power and the utilities, we also need to protect our rights. It all starts with understanding how the utilities operate, which we have dedicated large portions to in our previous books on the subjects at hand; see references 2.

The U.S. Utilities Status

The utilities industry (yes, there is such a thing as utility industry) has been changing lately—faster in some areas and much slower in others, as dictated by the regulatory changes, supply-demand factors, price volatility, and more importantly the new competition. The new competition is from energy sources that were but ignored in the past: solar, wind, bio-, and geo-powered systems and installations.

Until recently, the large regional monopolies ran the whole show without any interference. They controlled everything from the way that power was generated all the way down to retail supply. Recently, however, the industry structures that once led the electricity industry has been going through a slow disintegration. It is slowly breaking down into several separate (supplier related) segments.

The new utility industry segments are:

* *Power Generators*, are the electric power systems and power plants that generate electrical power. Large utilities continue still build and operate such plants, but a growing number of independent "merchant generators" build power capacity. This development is done on speculative basis or is based on acquired utility-divested plants. Those independent companies market their output at competitive rates in unregulated markets.

* *Grid Operators* determine the way power is distributed via regional and distribution networks. They also sell access to their networks to retail service providers. This aspect of the industry is heavily regulated and very expensive, so those network operators form an oligarchy of natural monopolies. Breaking into this business and duplicating the existing network operations is simply not possible, because it would be very expensive, redundant, and extremely risky. No takers thus far…

* *Energy Traders* buy and sell energy futures and other derivatives. Those traders and marketers have created a complex system of "structured product." One of the useful functions of those participants in the energy market is that they help the utilities and businesses that use a lot of power secure a dependable supply of electricity at a stable and somewhat

predictable price. Traders usually wager on the direction of power prices to increase their returns.

- *Energy Retailers* are the choice of services that are now available in most U.S. states. Now consumers can choose from a number of retail service providers. In a number of states the power grid is open to third party providers, so many such companies are entering the market, and buying power at competitive prices from transmission operators and energy traders. The energy retailers can then sell thus acquired power to the local end users. Those services are often bundled in competitive packages with gas, water and even financial services included.

- *Energy Price Regulation* is also changing today, where wholesale electricity prices are no longer set by regulatory agencies. Instead, they are mostly free to fluctuate with supply and demand, which introduces a variable that is no longer under the control of regulators or the utilities (which was basically one and the same in many cases in the past). This in turn significantly increases the risk of uncontrollable price increases.

Average electricity costs in the U.S. are in the $0.08 to $0.40 per kWh, depending on location and season. In the Arizona summer days, for example, power bills vary from $0.05/kWh during normal hours, to over $0.35/ kWh during summer peak hours.

Under the right conditions, the power bills could very quickly go sky high as dictated by the supply-demand market conditions. This creates a price risk that is a full-time headache for the utilities. For assuming some control over pricing in the increasingly deregulated energy market, forwards and futures options provide the tools to help hedge against unexpected price swings.

As with anything else, however, those tools can help avoid short-term risks and losses, but they are helpless in the long run. A major disaster, such as shutting down all nuclear power plants in the U.S., for example, could jack up energy prices permanently to levels that are even hard to imagine today.

As the use of electric power increases, expecting 355 GW of new electric generating capacity (more than 40% currently supplied) will be needed by 2020 to meet growing demand. Upward consumption growth is almost guaranteed over the long run, but the short-term fluctuations of the energy market increase the risk. This is because the demand for electricity fluctuates on

a daily and seasonal basis. An unusually mild winter, for instance, can moderate consumption and reduce revenues. This makes estimating the appropriate level of investment in power generation capacity a difficult task.

The Players

Several agencies are in charge of regulating the activities of the publicly owned utility companies, but very little regulation is forced on the independent operators.

The publicly owned utilities are regulated by:

- *The Federal Energy Regulatory Commission (FERC)* regulates the U.S. electricity industry, which oversees rates and service standards as well as interstate power transmission, and most any activities related to power generation, distribution, and use.

- *California Public Utilities Commission (CPUC)* regulates privately owned electric, natural gas, telecommunications, water, railroad, rail transit, and passenger transportation companies in California. The CPUC main goal is to protect consumers and ensure the provision of safe, reliable utility service and infrastructure at reasonable rates, with a commitment to environmental enhancement and a healthy California economy.

- The *Public Utility Holding Company Act* was enacted during the Great Depression and was designed to prevent industry consolidation. The act's repeal would evoke a wave of mergers among publicly traded utility companies, and so for now it is set in cement.

The Tools of the Trade
- *Power Purchase Agreements (PPA)* is a contract entered into by a power producer and its customers, and independent power generators. PPAs require the power producer to take on the risk of supplying power at a specified price for the life of the agreement—regardless of price fluctuations.

- *Load* is the amount of electricity delivered or required at any specific point or points on a system. The load of an electricity system is affected by many factors and changes on a daily, seasonal and annual basis. Load management attempts to shift load from peak use periods to other periods of the day or year.

- *Megawatt Hour (MWh)* is the basic industrial unit for pricing electricity, equal to one thousand kilowatts of power supplied continuously for one hour. One kWh equals 1,000 watt hours. One kWh = 3.306 cubic feet of natural gas. An average household uses 0.8 to 1.3 MWh/month, depending on location and season. The use is much higher in the Northwest during cold winters, and the Southwest during hot summers

The Fight

As a confirmation of the changing situation, and the continuing efforts of - to control the situation by manipulating their customers, Arizona Public Service (APS) recently proposed a drastic overhaul of net energy metering (NEM) policy in its service areas.

NOTE: Current NEM policy credits solar homeowners at a full retail rate for the energy they send back to the grid when panels produce more than a solar home consumes, which helps Arizona residents stabilize their utility costs.

The plan is to replace consumer-friendly NEM practices with more favorable to APS options.

APS has proposed two options:

- Add a charge of $50-$100 to solar owners' monthly bills for—get this—'use of the grid', and/or

- Credit solar homeowners for the electricity they generate at the wholesale rate. **NOTE:** The wholesale rate is about third to a quarter of retail.

Both options mean that any financial benefits for solar owners would be eliminated. And as usual, those who would be hurt the most is the middle class, whose sole purpose of installing solar on their roofs was to save money on rising monthly electric bills.

If the proposal is approved, it would signal an end to rooftop solar installations in Arizona, so the battle is just now starting in the Southwestern desert. The proposal is so important to APS that they are using tactics that have not been seen in Arizona for a long time. APS is using fake grassroots movement, consisting of front groups 60 Plus and Prosper HQ, to launch TV ads in support of the APS demands. Using outdated scare tactics and financial figures that have been publicly denounced, the groups appear to be blatantly misrepresenting the truth to the public.

There is also an anti-APS proposal resistance movement, consisting of the solar advocacy group Tell Utilities Solar won't be Killed (TUSK). TUSK has launched an ad in opposition to the proposed changes to the existing NEM policy. TUSK claims that the proposal is a slap in the face to APS's own customers. There are also other Arizona NGO and civic groups who are getting involved in the fight by applying pressure directly to a number of government agencies.

By ignoring the benefits of rooftop solar for all of its customers, APS sees it only as a threat to its bottom-line and is determined to eliminate it at any cost. This is so important to APS, that even if they don't succeed this time, they will try again and again until finally getting what they want. From previous experience, we know that the utilities always win, so we would be surprised if APS does not win in the long run.

In another example, Maryland's regulators are working on a provision that allows state utilities to bill customers—get this—for an electricity outage, even if it is not their fault. So imagine for a moment; the power goes out, all customers are in the dark for days or weeks, and when it is all over, they are forced to pay for the blackout.

In response, the Maryland Public Service Commission (PSC) deemed the charge applicable only for the first 24 hours of an outage. The fee kicks in for any storm with more than 100,000 outages, or 10% of a utility's Maryland service territory, whichever is less.

A severe storm stuck numerous Maryland electric customers in the summer of 2012, resulting in many long-lasting outages. The affected people suffered in stifling heat and misery, while living without power, in addition to spoiled food in the hot refrigerators. And when it was over the customers got a bill for living without power for several days or weeks.

Even if the amount was quite small (this time), it is still hard to explain to people why do they have to pay for suffering without power, or who is going to reimburse them for the suffering and spoiled food.

The utilities' explanation is that since they cannot control the weather, they deserve to be reimbursed for unexpected revenue losses. While this makes sense, the principle of paying for a service that is not working is not accepted in the U.S. and this alone should be enough to prohibit the fee from being assessed during an outage. Customers should not be punished for damages not caused by them.

ENERGY FINANCE AND LEGAL MARKETS

The 2008-2012 boom in renewable energy generation resulted in a significant increase in manufacturing and deployment of solar, wind and other alternative power generating technologies. Recently, however, those same technologies went through a bust cycle, which created a number of opportunities for financial institutions and legal firms to get involved in the frenzy that accompanied the closure or take-over of many companies.

Finance

Financing energy companies and projects has been, and still is, a big business. Billions of dollars are spent annually around the globe to finance the conventional energy projects—fossil and nuclear power plants, and distribution lines. New power plants are built in most developing countries, while upgrades of existing facilities are ongoing in the developed world.

But this all is business as usual. The most unusual, and somewhat more interesting part of energy projects' financing was the recent renewable energy boom-bust cycle of 2007-2012. Finance companies jumped at the opportunity to make money that was supported by large government subsidies and overly generous incentives.

The focus in the renewable and alternative energy sector was on power plant construction and acquisition, energy infrastructure projects, energy services, energy equipment manufacturers, power transmission and services, the smart grid, and recently on energy storage. Those different subjects took their turn on the center stage, had their 15 minutes of fame then went away.

First on the stage were the biofuels, which were supposed to reshape the way the world uses energy. It didn't take very long for the increased use of biofuel crops to create a worldwide disaster, complete with high food prices, hunger, and land grabbing, so now the biofuels are back on the back burner. Not defeated, but put in their place.

Then came solar, and we were told that we can power the entire world with only a piece of the Arizona desert. Solyndra's debacle proved us wrong. Solar, like a puppet propped up by government subsidies and unreasonable expectations, collapsed and is still on its knees. Hundreds of solar companies went bankrupt, billions of taxpayers' dollars were wasted, and thousands of people are unemployed as a result.

Wind was another favorite, and governments, VCs and other investors on R&D and deployment of wind turbines spent billions of dollars. In the U.S., billions of taxpayer dollars went to Chinese and other foreign wind turbine manufacturers, as part of Obama's economic recovery programs.

Now confused governments and rich (but poorly informed) VCs are spending billions of dollars on smart grid, energy storage, and other equally risky projects, which—even if developed as needed and on time—will not solve the energy and environmental problems. Other, more basic programs need to be designed and implemented to use properly and efficiently the available energy resources. Such approach, however, is not in the cards as yet. Money making is...

Lately, the political focus and the finance and investment trend were changed to investment in the new kid on the energy block—hydrofracking. Oil and gas drilling in the U.S. and parts of the world is taking over the energy sector and promises to be the thing that will ensure once and forever our energy independence, while at the same time cleaning the environment.

This is all good, but we are now back where we started a century ago—"Drill, baby drill" is the new motto of governments and investors with a hydrofracking twist, and it is what we'll be living with for a long time.

The Finance Industry

The focus of the finance industry is on pinpointing the best possible match between capital resources and asset acquisitions, business growth, and exploration and development. The array of transaction advisory services provided by a number of financial institutions is endless, but is usually focused on:

- Acquisition advice and screening
- Energy investment analysis
- Business plan review and peer group analysis
- Risk mitigation strategy
- Strategic and business planning
- Finance analysis and capital structure advice
- Company valuation
- Technical support and trend assessment
- Country risk assessment
- Energy market research
- Due diligence
- Capitalization and deal structure
- Opportunities screening and negotiation

The financial services and financing schemes include:

- Equity finance
- Senior financing
- Second line financing
- Mezzanine debt
- Bridge and project finance
- Volumetric production payments

Those are some examples of creative and thorough financial services offered today in the energy sector.

Environmental Finance

This branch of the energy sector promises to grow faster than any other that we have witnessed in the past. Wells Fargo & Company, for example, announced a record $2.8 billion in loan commitments and tax equity financing in 2011, which they provided to businesses and projects related to the environment. That brings Wells Fargo's total environmental financing and investments to $11.7 billion since 2005, which is when the company first announced a dedicated environmental financing commitment. We have to assume that by the end of 2013, Wells Fargo's environmental finance and investment portfolio will increase to over $15 billion. That's not a small chunk of change, even for a giant like Wells Fargo.

So what did they do to achieve this remarkable progress in the relatively new and risky energy and environmental markets? As an example, in 2011 Wells Fargo provided the following loans and investments to environmental markets:

- Approximately $450 million in tax equity deployed to solar photovoltaic projects, doubling total investment in the sector to more than $900 million

- Approximately $200 million in wind project tax equity investments, increasing total wind investment to date to more than $1.6 billion

- Over $1.5 billion in loans to LEED®-certified commercial buildings and community development projects

- More than $150 million in loans to commercial banking, and community banking clean-tech customers

A seemingly well-balanced investment portfolio, with billions spent on activities that favor clean tech companies and projects, and at the same time can help clean the environment. We don't know what the results from all those investments are, but must assume that all parties are benefiting one way or another.

Energy Efficiency Finance

Energy-efficiency is the new game in the energy sector that promises to be a big game soon. It includes (and often consists exclusively of) upgrades and improvements that require funding. Some upgrades require little capital investment, while others need a lot of capital. Small or inexpensive projects are usually paid by means of personal finance, which keeps the payback period low and return on investment high.

For larger projects, however, financing is often the only way to pay for the upgrade. For this purpose there are a variety of financing mechanisms available. Strategic energy efficiency investments are a hedge against the certainty of higher utility bills that cannot be controlled, so this business will grow with time.

In all cases, upfront costs are a major barrier to implementing energy efficiency projects in homes and businesses. An important goal of efficiency policies and programs is to help minimize those upfront project costs so property owners are encouraged to invest in energy efficiency improvements and retrofits. Several financing strategies are being pursued to achieve this goal, many of which are available to all interested.

Various entities offer many types of financing for energy efficiency upgrades, including utilities, federal, state, and local governments, and energy service companies (ESCOs). In addition, private equity entities have become increasingly interested in funding packages of energy efficiency projects. The success and prevalence of the financing programs, however, has ebbed and flowed over the past few decades, due to their complexity and challenges for which resolutions are still evolving.

A brand new branch of the energy efficiency financing is adding risk insurance to solar and wind projects that guarantees their output. Depending on the arrangement, this service can cover different types and levels of failure to produce the contractual amount of energy, due to a number of factors and variables—from manufacturing defects to weather phenomena.

Financing this option might be one of the ways to eliminate some of the risks of operating solar and wind power plants. Those energy sources are variable by nature, but also suffer from man-made and nature caused problems. Weather it is a manufacturing defect or a severe storm that interrupts the operation of a solar or wind power plant, the operators are guaranteed some return for the duration of the interruption. Not a cheap way to do business, but a most needed now and until solar and wind become more reliable energy generators.

Better understanding of the energy generation and distribution aspects of the business and the related effective financing opportunities are critical for improving energy efficiency in homes and businesses. Energy education of investors, financiers, utilities, and policymakers, including comprehensive surveys of the energy efficiency financial landscape and the latest innovations in financial structures and models is needed for achieving the energy efficiency goals.

We believe that this text provides a glimpse towards those goals, and hope that it could be used to clarify the issues on the subject.

Federal and State Financial Assistance

Although the surge of government handouts is mostly over, there are still a number of grants, loans and financing opportunities available for many energy projects.

Some of those are the:

- ENERGY STAR Resources—include financial products and services to small businesses interested in making energy efficient upgrades. There are also special offers and rebates on ENERGY STAR qualified products such as: office equipment, electronics, appliances, and lighting products in many areas.

- The alliance to save energy, financing energy efficiency is a database of over 60 energy efficiency funds and programs operating throughout the world. Local government commissions' funding opportunities is a program of federal, state and local financing and project assistance programs for improving the energy efficiency of buildings.

- Small business financing—grants, loans and venture capital program offers financial assistance for a new or expanding business, including SBA and other government-backed loans, grants, and venture capital. The Office of Small Business Development Centers (SBDC) offers free services to help small firms develop conventional loan applications for loans backed by the SBA. The Small Business Association of Michigan operates a web site open to all small businesses throughout the U.S. that need assistance with energy efficiency and energy management.

- The Department of Energy (DOE) loan guarantee program authorized by EPAct2005 provides loan guarantees for clean energy technologies, but it never awarded funds for energy efficiency projects. Legislative proposals have been advanced to expressly add energy efficiency in the authorization language for this program, but there are no results thus far.

- The U.S. Department of Energy (DOE), office of energy efficiency and renewable energy's financial opportunities offers grant opportunities for busi-

nesses developing energy efficient technologies. At the same time, the DOE's industrial technologies program is the lead government program working to increase the energy efficiency of U.S. industry. It helps research, develop, and deploy innovative technologies that companies can use to improve their energy productivity, reduce carbon emissions, and gain a competitive edge.

- The Clean Energy Deployment Administration (CEDA) is an independent administration within DOE to manage a new clean energy investment fund. It issues direct loans, letters of credit, loan guarantees, and other debt instruments to encourage the commercialization and deployment of clean energy, including energy efficiency projects.

- Many of the funding mechanisms of the American Recovery and Reinvestment Act (ARRA) are routed through the state energy offices, such as the energy efficiency and conservation block grant program. State revolving funds, such as the lone star fund in Texas, have proven to be successful in financing energy efficiency upgrades in a number of states.

- Property-assessed clean energy (PACE) bonds are an example of municipal clean energy financing which allows property owners to finance energy efficiency retrofits through financing added as a special assessment on the homeowner's property tax bill. PACE financing provides long-term financing that can be transferred along with the sale of the property.

More than twenty states have passed laws authorizing the establishment of PACE programs, and DOE allocated ARRA funding for PACE projects in a number of states. Federal mortgage underwriting agencies (Fannie Mae and Freddie Mac) raised questions about the impact of PACE programs on mortgage stability and have declined to underwrite new PACE projects, which has had the effect of "freezing" the program at its present state.

In other words, this is a new area—a new energy related financial market—that is doing quite well, thank you, in some areas and for some people and businesses, while failing for other areas and people. No doubt those programs will further develop and grow with time, and although their benefits are hard to predict, it is for certain that they will help us in our drive towards managing our energy use, which is one way to ensure our long-term energy independence.

Energy Financing for All (4)

"Energy for all: financing access for the poor" is an excerpt from the World Energy Outlook report of 2011, presented by the International Energy Agency. It is focused on the critical issue of financing energy access for all people in this world. Most of the finance structures are geared to providing access to money and services to those who can afford them.

Very little, if anything, is geared to helping those less fortunate among us to obtain energy for everyday use or for powering small business enterprises. This opens the opportunity of creating a new energy market that has not been tapped thus far for a number of reasons.

The report estimates that in 2009, $9.1 billion was invested globally in extending access to modern energy services. While providing such services to the world by 2030 is achievable, the annual investment to do so must be increased to more than five-times existing levels to make energy accessible to all, and the extra spending must be matched by public-sector reforms.

The report concludes that five actions are essential to transforming the situation:

1. The adoption of a clear and consistent statement that modern energy access is a political priority and that policies and funding will be reoriented accordingly. National governments need to adopt a specific energy access target, allocate funds to its achievement and define their strategy for delivering it.

2. Mobilize additional investment in universal access, above the $14 billion per year as assumed in our central scenario, the new policies scenario. All sources and forms of investment have their part to play, reflecting the varying risks and returns of particular solutions. All need to grow.

3. Private sector investment needs to grow the most, but significant barriers must first be overcome. National governments need to adopt strong governance and regulatory frameworks and invest in internal capacity building. The public sector, including multilateral and bilateral institutions, needs to use its tools to leverage greater private sector investment where the commercial case is marginal and encourage the development of replicable busi-

ness models. When used, public subsidies must be well-targeted to reach the poorest.

4. Concentrate an important part of multilateral and bilateral direct funding on those difficult areas of access, which do not initially offer an adequate commercial return. Provision of end-user finance is required to overcome the barrier of the initial capital cost of gaining access to modern energy services. Operating through local banks and microfinance arrangements can help create local networks and the necessary capacity in energy sector activity.

5. Make provisions for the collection of robust, regular and comprehensive data to quantify the outstanding challenge and monitor progress towards its elimination.

International Investment

World banks have reached record levels of investment in the clean energy sector, exceeding the $100 billion year mark in 2013 for the first time in history. Overall, 26 financial institutions had invested $425 billion in the renewables and clean energy sector since 2007.

Investment in solar power products and infrastructure is also on the increase, from about $2.5 billion in the 2007-2009-time period to nearly $10.0 billion during 2010-2012. The European Investment Bank recently invested $230 million in several solar projects in Latin America, while India is preparing a $7.9 billion investment designed to improve its power grid, needed to get ready for use by an increasing number of solar installations. The World Bank, KfW, and the Asian Development Bank are the principal investors in this undertaking.

Financing of renewables projects and energy efficiency and transmission infrastructure was up almost 20% in 2012; KfW of Germany, the China Development Bank, and the Brazilian Development Bank were on top of the list.

The year 2013 brought an additional 15% growth in development bank financing. The long term shows potential for an even bigger investment increases when other institutions become more comfortable with the fairly new sector and get fully involved.

Not surprisingly, a collective switch away from investment in coal power is underway by the development banks, which promises to bring higher investment levels in the renewables and clean energy sectors. This is a major move away from the fossils and vote of confidence for the renewable technologies. If this trend continues, we will see major solar power development around the world in the near future.

Legal Aspects of the Energy Markets

Legal firms are involved in many activities related to energy generation and the respective environmental issues. The major political and legal issues (these are often hard to separate) presently are:

- *The Keystone pipeline* is still the largest political confusion that involves a number of legal issues and pending law suites. The choice for the decision makers is between two major classes of people and ideologies—these of labor and environmentalism. Whatever the final political decision, the legal battle will begin and be in full force, which will likely delay the project.

Actually the legal battle is gaining speed as we speak. For example, TransCanada Corp., the company proposing the project, has hired two Washington lobby firms, and its subsidiary employs a third. Alberta, Canada, has just hired two firms to push the project. One will lobby for the pipeline, while the other will handle PR issues through the employ of a member of Obama's election campaign. Another participant in this coalition was a congressional liaison for Kerry's presidential run, and a relative was Kerry's campaign manager.

The Canadian Association of Petroleum Producers, another supporter of the project, employs a former U.S. ambassador to Canada as a lobbyist. Opposing the project is a new group founded by a Democratic strategist with strong ties to both Kerry and Obama.

Politics and legal action are inseparable, we say. And we stick by it!

- *Natural gas vs. everything and everybody*. Really! Despite the amazing proliferation of new gas wells, 55% of Americans say they are unfamiliar with the term, down from 63% a year ago. Although the majority still do not seem to know or worry much about gas fracking, the deluge of media attention to this controversial extraction technology is likely responsible for the increased awareness.

Nevertheless, increased awareness is not synonymous with increased public approval. Among those familiar with hydraulic fracturing, only 41% support it; down from 50% a year ago. Also 66% of Americans insist on a greater government oversight of the fracking process, up from 56% earlier in 2012.

NY drilling opponents are trying to ban drilling with whatever it takes, while Ohio and other states are worried about earthquakes. In response, the gas industry is in a full-fledged offensive that looks like an election campaign, "Pick me, pick me!"

2012 signaled the rebirth of the natural gas drilling industry in the U.S. and many countries.

The big oil and gas giants are getting ready for the biggest battle ever. It will be a battle on all fronts, and until the very end. Exxon, Shell and BP on one hand and entire countries like China are looking to take big piece of the action shale exploration plays in the energy sector.

The EPA and some environmentalists are playing the "cleaner gas" card, and amazing job and revenue benefits are hitting states like PA and OH, so the battle will continue to grow and expand on the political and legal fields.

2012 also brought us the question of the continued persistence of the low prices for natural gas. It is critical for the willingness of the utilities to switch to gas for a number of reasons, but on the other hand, the low prices will continue to pinch drillers, who in many cases are getting more for the crude in the shale wells. Regardless of the price, increasing scrutiny of gas production and use will remain key issues for now.

- *Offshore oil drilling is back* after couple of years of uncertainty. It is now here to stay…for now, together with bringing lots of jobs, and ensuring our economic recovery. The Western Gulf oil and gas lease sale attracted more than $337 million in high bids in 2012, and more are planned or underway. Overall Gulf energy activity could create over 200,000 new U.S. jobs, pending Federal commitment to running an efficient permitting system.

- *Offshore wind got the administration's commitment to renewables*, with the Atlantic Wind Connection taking a major place in the negotiations. It is a massive offshore transmission project that will be essential to establishing an infrastructure for new offshore wind projects and the jobs they will create. The big players like Good Energies and Google support them, but there are many opposed. The legal battle is just starting.

- *The coal problem is gaining importance* on political and legal levels too. Environmentalists are also gaining ground with the help of new and proposed EPA rules. Coal is suffering under the pressure of outside forces such as financial markets and low gas prices. On the global level it won't matter much, as developing countries continue to use coal in record numbers, so many U.S. companies are exporting more. Nevertheless, affordable energy in many parts of the country that rely on coal are truly being threatened, as are jobs and the economic activity in the affected regions.

- *Ethanol,* or at least the plans and expectations for it being a major fuel are now history (almost). It played a major role in the energy plans until recently, and caused a number of political and legal shockers of the last several decades, but now it is settling down as one of the additives that will be used at reasonable levels and prices.

Congress did not renew either the 45-cent-per-gallon tax credit for corn-based ethanol or the 54-cent-per-gallon tariff on imported ethanol. This confirms the political will to keep ethanol in its place as one of the humble additives.

Amazingly, the ethanol industry gave up quietly and without much fight. Cellulosic ethanol is one of the bright stars on the ethanol's horizon, but it is woefully short on its requirements, so it remains on the back burner for the future generation to resolve. Instead, we will be looking into increased imports from the Caribbean and Brazil.

- *Solar support slumped post-Solyndra,* but the solar industry survived the toughest part of the conundrum and is on the way to recovery.

The solar industry achieved record growth in 2011 thanks mostly to utility-scale projects, a strong residential market, and effective policies. The plummeting price of solar panels didn't hurt either. Grid-connected PV installations in 2011 and 2012 grew as compared to the previous years.

The loss of the 1603 treasury grant program caused a hesitation, but the solar industry will likely be stronger in the near future because of increasing demand.

Nevertheless, there were hundreds of solar manufacturing and solar-related companies that closed, went bankrupt, or were acquired by larger entities. This created a large field for legal actions, and many legal firms in the U.S. and abroad were involved in the closures and other activities.

- *Nuclear Renaissance* is a term that we hear a lot lately, but talk is cheap, so now is the time for the

nuclear renaissance to "put up or shut up." Many promising projects fell apart due to low demand, lack of financial support, high risk, or market regulations.

The nuclear uncertainties, like Yucca Mountain and Fukushima, are certainly affecting the size of the long-term expansion of nuclear power. Right now, however, all eyes are on the utilities with the most nuclear assets, and on the hope that tougher EPA regulations on coal plants will help bring nuclear back.

The legal action was revived when EPA's cross state air pollution rule was stayed by the DC Circuit Court and California's LCF standard was blocked by a District Court in Fresno. The GHG is a big shot in the arm for the legal activities in the U.S., because establishing and enforcing GHG rules for everything and everybody is not an easy task.

There are significant unintended consequences with all actions to be taken; so going through the political and legal barriers will take much longer (and will be much more expensive) than anybody thinks.

Making plans or predictions is very hard, mostly because of the difficult political and legal situation the energy and nuclear sector in particular are in. One uncertainty that we should always remember is that another Fukushima-like accident, or any such unforeseen event of great consequences might change everything overnight.

But for now, we just have lots of coals in the fire and nuclear fuel in the reactors, so we are looking forward to very interesting (from political and legal points of views) months and years ahead.

From a marketing point of view, we see a number of great opportunities that the perceived energy generation problems and the hoopla around environmental issues related to these, have offered to many people and companies. This has opened the doors to billions of dollars of energy and environmental "goodies" and services markets.

As we discussed, with the new energy generation, use, and saving approaches and methods, carbon trading, environmental taxes, environmental legal action, pollution fighting, air cleaning, new medical methods, renewable energy, and electric cars, new ideas and plans are all around us. Those have created some of the new energy markets that we review in this text.

The newly discovered, and yet to be fully explored, environmental markets offer new and very lucrative opportunities, and so everybody who knows anything about it is rushing to cash in.

And speaking of the environmental markets, below we look closer at this fairly new, and still in development, phenomenon.

THE ENVIRONMENTAL MARKETS

As we mentioned in the beginning of this chapter, the environment-related markets are in their infancy. They are just now defining their territory and modus operandi. Nevertheless, there are a number of fairly well defined products and services that we will take a close look at.

Some of the products and branches of the environmental market are:
- Carbon trading
- Pollution-free industries
  — Renewable technologies
  — Natural gas conversions
  — Carbon capture and storage
  — New equipment and processes
- New transportation modes
- Performance and liability insurance
- Environmental legal services
- Public health services

The concept of environmental markets is a fairly new one that has a number of dimensions that can be understood and interpreted in a number of different ways. The environmental markets are very similar to the traditional commodities markets, except that their products and services are closely related to the environmental effects caused by different commercial (mostly energy related) activities.

Usually, there are several market groups: a) producers, or sellers, who generate the products and services, b) consumers, or buyers, who need and use the products and services, and c) intermediaries*, who help bring the products and services to the market

NOTE: The intermediaries are indirectly involved in the process, but are very important group because they often have the power of repackaging the market instruments. They do this as they see fit to meet market demands, and, of course, to meet their own needs too.

In a simplified form, the average environmental market works like this:

- *Buyers* are required to buy credits by law, because they are involved in some type of environmental damage. The buyers could be: utility companies, project developers, public works, or different agencies who need to have an environmental permit to participate in the market activities.

- *Sellers* sell credits because they are usually involved in activities that help the environment, or simply because they are qualified to do so. Sellers could be private or institutional entities, such as; banks, environmental organizations, farmers, timber producers, wind and solar farms those entities do not need permits and can sell as much as the buyer is willing to buy.

- *Intermediaries*, like in all trades, are entities that are willing and able to assist in the transactions. An intermediary could be any institution that can provide services, such as financing, crediting, or project delivery. Some of the large finance institutions are getting in this game too, and that will bring the environmental market to a new dimension and a much higher level. We only hope that it won't also push us closer to another—this time environmental—cliff.

The environmental markets function through direct transactions between buyers and sellers with the intermediaries assisting. The regulators are also involved through approval of the buyer's environmental permits, which limits the number of credits for sale. The direct market transactions are known as "over-the-counter" deals, but as the market mature, it incorporates additional market services, typical to all markets, such as aggregation, third-party verification, brokerage functions and internal financing.

As a matter of fact, some environmental markets, such as the Chicago Climate Exchange, have already matured to where they operate as the traditional stock and commodity exchanges. They have many buyers and sellers executing transactions simultaneously, using a wide range of market services, such as clearinghouse functions, as needed to facilitate transactions and to guard against defaults.

Carbon Trading Markets

The major issue with all types of energy generation is the carbon emissions during the related manufacturing and power generation operations. Carbon emissions are of great concern, as far as the environment is concerned, and, since capitalism can make business out of anything, we now have carbon market. It is basically a place where carbon emitters pay for their sins...because they are forced into it by political will and social righteousness.

The cost of energy produced from the different energy sources is hard to generalize, because of the great diversity of products and uses.

Table 8-12. Fuel prices and CO₂ tax (in Europe, 2011)

Price	Coal $/ton	Crude $/ton	Gas* $/ton**	CO2 $/ton
High	80	70	60	35
Middle	60	50	40	15
Low	40	30	25	4

    * Natural gas and biogas
    ** Ton coal equivalent

Please note that the CO_2 avoidance concept (or pay as you continue to generate CO_2) is in full force in some countries, which means that the cost of electricity is inversely proportional to the pollution generated by the energy source. That means that using a ton of coal might cost $80 for the cost of coal, plus $35 paid as carbon tax.

All this creates new carbon-related market, where the emitted carbon is the unit of measure.

As a clarification of the different fuels and their measurement units:

Table 8-13. Energy in different fuels

Fuel	Energy Content
1 ton coal	= 29.31 GJ/ton
1 ton oil	= 41.87 GJ/ton
1,000 m³ gas	= 38.3 GJ/ton
1 MWh any fuel	= 3.6 GJ energy

This means that one-ton of coal or oil contains enough energy to generate 10 MWh of electric power. This, however, is far from the reality, where inefficiencies at the different process steps significantly reduce the actual electric power output. The type and quality of the fuel on one hand, and the equipment type and quality on the other determine the efficiency drop.

Low quality coal, for example, would produce much less power than high quality, and combined cycle power generators would be much more efficient than the classic steam turbine setup. Low quality fuels and equipment also tend to emit more GHG gasses.

Emissions Trading

Emissions trading is the newest, most promising (and most confusing) of the budding environmental markets. For example, since July 2012, Australia has had in place carbon pricing scheme, or a "carbon tax," which is also known as "Emissions Trading Scheme (ETS)"

with a fixed price. There are now plans to move to an ETS with a floating price.

So, what are the differences between those two?

An ETS works by setting a cap on emissions and requiring emitters to hold a permit for each ton of CO_2 that they emit. The level of the cap determines the number of permits available. If emitters don't already hold a permit, they must either cut back on their emissions or buy a permit from another emitter, who must then cut back. This means that a cost is imposed on emissions, equal to the price of buying or selling a permit.

But it's not actually the price that causes the overall cuts in emissions. The cap determines the level of emissions, and the required cuts in emissions cause the price. That is, permits have a value because they allow you to avoid making cuts in emissions.

In the coal power plant case, for example, the smoke is generated in place A, blown by the wind to place B, where mitigation of some sort is needed. It finally settles in location C (most likely the higher atmosphere) where we cannot do much about its effects.

In most cases, however, the mitigation is not easy to assess since it is not location based, but in all cases the power plant at place A will be required to buy credits equal to the smoke emissions it generates—regardless of what happens to them, and the damage they cause, in the future.

Most buyers in today's environmental markets participate because they are required to purchase credits to fulfill environmental regulations. The "credits" are used, rather than more tangible assets, because they are a most convenient trading tool for the environmental market needs.

Each market has a different type of credit, which generally represents a unit of an environmental resource, such as an acre of restored wetland, a pound of nitrogen removed from a stream, or a ton of carbon dioxide kept out of the atmosphere.

Emissions trading is shaping as one of the largest businesses of the century, and the opportunity has attracted the big guys too. Without wasting any time, they became specialists on the subjects of energy and environment, and are now leading the way into the newly developed markets in those areas.

A number of companies and organizations, such as the Environmental Markets Association (EMA), Evolution Markets, 3Degrees, and many others are involved in supporting energy and environmental markets with GHG cap-and-trade initiatives, and in developing the emissions trading market.

Enter the big guys…

The Environmental Investment Market

In any capitalist society, money making is the goal and focus of any activity. The environment, and the related issues, are shaping as a new money making opportunity, which is still in its infancy. Investing in the poorly regulated environmental activities seems like a risky enterprise, but that won't stop the rich and daring from trying their luck.

FTSE is leading the pack here with the headline index within the FTSE Environmental Index Series; the FTSE ET50 Index. It is comprised of the 50 largest pure-play environmental technology companies, by full market capitalization, globally. Previously known as the Impax Environmental Technology (ET50) Index, calculated by Impax Asset Management, the index is designed to measure the performance of companies that have a core business in the development and operation of environmental technologies.

- *FTSE Environmental Technology Index Series*—measures the performance of companies globally whose core business is in the development and deployment of environmental technologies, including renewable & alternative energy, energy efficiency, water technology and waste & pollution control.

  Forming part of the overall FTSE Environmental Markets Index Series, the FTSE Environmental Technology Index Series requires companies to have at least 50% of their business derived from environmental markets and technologies (as opposed to at least 20% for the FTSE Environmental Opportunities Index Series).

- *FTSE Environmental Opportunities Index Series*—measures the performance of global companies that have significant involvement in environmental business activities, including renewable & alternative energy, energy efficiency, water technology and waste and pollution control.

  Forming part of the overall FTSE Environmental Markets Index Series, the FTSE Environmental Opportunities Index Series requires companies to have at least 20% of their business derived from environmental markets and technologies (as opposed to at least 50% for the FTSE Environmental Technology Index Series).

  The investment products based on the FTSE Environmental Markets Index Series appeal to a broad range of institutional and retail investors who are looking to:

- Invest in environmental technology sector via an investable and transparent FTSE index

- Maximize environmental growth opportunities within their portfolios

- Invest in companies that are best placed to succeed in a future low- carbon environment

- Support the growth and development of environmental markets

Investing in the environment sounds like a noble undertaking, but the problem here is that, a) the majority of investors do not understand the issues at hand, and, b) are not as interested in the environment as they are in their bottom line. This begs a number of questions that have no answer presently.

The biggest danger here is that lack of understanding and protecting self-interests can lead to conflicts of interest, if, for example, one has to chose between solving an environmental problem vs. making money for personal gain. How many investors would chose losing money to mitigate an environmental problem? So, in fact, investing in the environment is gambling with the most precious commodity on Earth—our environment.

The fact that we can treat the environment as a *commodity* should give us a pause and force us to take measures that ensure putting the environmental issued *above and beyond* all personal or corporate interests.

The Big Guys

It is impossible to imagine any area of our lives without the guiding hand of the financial gurus, and the environment is no exception. So, the big guys are entering the environmental arena with a big splash:

J.P. Morgan's Environmental Markets Trading Desk, through the acquisition of EcoSecurities in 2009, is one of the leading market makers in exchange-traded and over-the-counter (OTC) environmental products. Those include: European Union Allowances (EUAs), Certified Emission Reductions (CERs) and Verified Emission Reductions (VERs).

There are options and investor structures available for each of those commodities, designed to help clients in managing their exposure to environmental risk. This is an environmental products trading platform on a global scale, designed to support interested companies' ability to manage risk across all areas of environmental involvement at dynamic pricing.

EcoSecurities was created in 1997 to provide environmental (carbon-related) guidance to companies interested in reducing GHG emissions. Its involvement in the development of the global carbon market to date consists of: developing the first clean development mechanism (CDM) project registered under the Kyoto Protocol—the NovaGerar Landfill project, Brazil in 2004; structuring the first CDM component for the first project in the world to receive CERs—La Esperanza Hydro project, Honduras in 2005; and development of 12 CDM approved methodologies since 2001

EcoSecurities also become the first carbon project developer in 2010 to successfully register 200 projects with the CDM executive board. Using this expertise, J.P. Morgan is well qualified to take advantage of the environmental problems of, and provide solutions to, companies involved in those markets.

The Environmental Markets Group (EMG) at Goldman Sachs coordinates and oversees the environmental markets transactions. This is done by providing guidance on environmental issues, develop training and resources, and engage with interested parties as needed to strengthen Goldman Sachs' environmental efforts.

EMG is also working with transaction teams in conducting environmental, social, and governance reviews across all areas of the environmental business selection. This is a tool to manage risks, better serve the interests of the clients and yield greater benefit for the environment and broader society.

EMG also manages the center for environmental markets, which conducts independent research with partners to explore and develop public policy options and tools for creating market-based solutions to environmental challenges.

There are a lot of activities undertaken to create more efficient and liquid markets for environmental products and services through market making activities. This is Big Business…

The big guys are planning for big business…maybe the biggest ever! They see the environmental issues as a big marketplace, and a great money making opportunity. Who better to tap into it than the financial gurus of Wall Street.

How did those people became specialists in environmental issues so quickly, and how do they know the right answers to the most important questions? It suffices to remember that those are the same people who brought us the devastating financial crisis of 2008, so we should not expect any answers.

When so much money and power are involved, the big guys don't feel responsible for answering to anybody, nor do they need anybody's advice. They know how to make money from both sides of any issue and will find the way to make money on the expense of the environmental issues and all involved as well. All we can do is watch…

America is just now getting out of the economic disaster those same people created in the mid-2000s, so we can only hope and pray that we will be able to avoid another disaster created by their seemingly good-willed intervention in dealing with the environmental markets.

We have seen time after time how good intentions become predatory activities when a good chance to make an extra buck presents itself. We have also seen how the big guys deal with the little guys, just because they can. So, we should watch closely and try to control their actions this time.

California's Emissions Trading

California adopted an emissions-trading program after efforts to pass a national cap-and-trade plan failed, and has hailed its effort as a model for the rest of the world, even as carbon prices in the U.S. Northeast and Europe declined.

The *country* (equivalent) of California is the world's ninth-largest economy and is heavily involved in the electricity generation and carbon trading markets. A grand total of $23.1 million carbon allowances were available for 2013 at $10.09 each, which generated $233.3 million at a minimum price of $10.

NOTE: Edison International bought all of the state's carbon permits (and more) in the state's first auction in the fall of 2012…by mistake. Edison unintentionally bid for twice as many carbon allowances as were for sale. Edison, the state's second-biggest power utility, submitted a proposal to buy 21 times more allowances than it wanted. This shows that carbon trading is a new business, run by first-timers, so mistakes do and will happen.

The Federal energy regulatory commission is monitoring California's emissions-trading program to see if it affects U.S. West Coast power markets. Among other things, the commission will be tracking California permit trading, allowance derivatives trading, and the results of the state's carbon auctions.

The costs that companies incur to comply with California's emissions program may soon contribute to the establishment of market prices in California and other parts of the Western U.S. The overall effect on electricity prices in the region is still to be seen, but it is expected that the prices will eventually rise to cover the additional expense by the utilities. That is another confirmation that this is a new and budding business with many variables and even more players.

That is a complex undertaking without a precedent, and since there is a lot at stake, some players will make mistakes, while others will use and even misuse the opportunity to make an extra buck.

Cap and Trade

Cap and trade is another environmentally and economically sensible approach to controlling greenhouse gas emissions, which are the primary drivers of global warming. The *cap* sets a limit on emissions, which is lowered over time to reduce the amount of pollutants released into the atmosphere by the targeted industries. A cap sets a maximum allowable level of pollution and penalizes companies that exceed their emission allowance. The cap is measured in billions of tons of carbon dioxide (or equivalent) per year. This number is set based on scientific research and experience, and covers all major sources of pollution.

The cap should limit emissions economy-wide, covering electric power generation, natural gas, transportation, and large manufacturers. Emitters can release only limited pollution, using permits or *allowances* that are distributed or auctioned to polluting entities. One allowance is issued per ton of carbon dioxide, or CO_2 equivalent heat-trapping gases. The total amount of allowances is equal to the cap. A company or utility may only emit as much carbon as it has allowances for, which is an effective economic incentive to pollute less.

The *trade* creates a market for carbon allowances, helping companies innovate to meet, or come in under, their allocated limit. Some companies will not be able to reduce the number of permits, so trading gives them a choice to buy and sell allowances, leading to more cost-effective pollution cuts, and incentive to invest in cleaner technology.

Unlike with some pollutants, all CO_2 goes into the upper atmosphere and has a global effect. So it doesn't matter whether the polluting factory is in San Francisco, Boston, or Beijing; by reducing its pollution the total global emissions will be reduced. If a company is able to cut its pollution easily and cheaply, it can end up with extra allowances, which can then be sold to other not so fortunate companies. This provides a powerful incentive for creativity, energy conservation and investment, and an additional revenue stream.

While companies may exchange allowances with each other, the total number of allowances remains the same and the hard limit on pollution is still met every year. This way the industry can plan ahead and gradually reduce the annual cap. Companies can plan well in advance to reduce the number of permits by reducing pollution, thus less global warming pollution will be emitted in the long run.

Clean Development Mechanism

The clean development mechanism (CDM) is defined in Article 12 of the Kyoto Protocol, and allows a country with an emission-reduction or emission-limitation commitment under the Kyoto Protocol (Annex B Party) to implement an emission-reduction project in developing countries. Such projects can earn saleable certified emission reduction (CER) credits, each equivalent to one ton of CO_2, which can be counted towards meeting Kyoto targets.

The mechanism is seen by many as a trailblazer, since it is the first global, environmental investment and credit scheme of its kind. It also provides a standardized emissions offset instrument, CERs for use around the world.

A CDM project activity might involve a rural electrification project using solar panels, or the installation of more energy-efficient boilers. The mechanism basically stimulates sustainable development and emission reductions, while giving industrialized countries some flexibility in how they meet their emission reduction or limitation targets.

Some of the restrictions and requirements for CDM projects are as follows:

- The project must provide emission reductions that are additional to what would otherwise have occurred.
- The projects must qualify through a rigorous and public registration and issuance process.
- Approval is given by the designated national authorities.
- Public funding for CDM project activities must not result in the diversion of official development assistance.
- The mechanism is overseen by the CDM executive board, answerable ultimately to the countries that have ratified the Kyoto Protocol.

CDM started operational in the beginning of 2006, and has already registered more than 6,000 projects, including more than 100 programs of activities (PoAs), 25% of which are in Africa. CDM is also expected to produce CERs amounting to more than 4 billion tons of CO_2

equivalent in the first commitment period of the Kyoto Protocol, 2008–2012 (that data were not available at the time of this writing).

RECs Market

Renewable Energy Certificates (RECs) is another instrument designed to reward the use of renewable energy sources. It represents the property rights to the environmental, social, and other non-power qualities of renewable electricity generation.

A REC, and its associated attributes and benefits, can be sold separately from the underlying physical electricity associated with a renewable-based generation source. This means that, for example, a grid-tied solar or wind power generator produces both electricity and RECs. Both of those entities can be sold together or separately at the point and time of generation.

RECs basically serve the role of laying claim to and accounting for the associated attributes of renewable-based generation. The REC and the associated underlying physical electricity take separate pathways to the point of end use. As renewable generators produce electricity, they have a positive impact, reducing the need for fossil fuel-based generation sources to meet consumer demand. RECs embody those positive environmental impacts and convey those benefits to the REC owner.

RECs provide buyers flexibility in procuring green power across a diverse geographical area, and in applying the renewable attributes to the electricity use at a facility of choice. This flexibility allows organizations to support renewable energy development and protect the environment when green power products are not locally available.

One REC is created for every 1.0 MWh of electricity sent into the grid.

If the electricity and the associated RECs are sold to separate buyers, the electricity associated to this REC electricity is no longer considered "renewable" or "green." The REC product, therefore, is what conveys the attributes and benefits of the renewable electricity, and not the electricity itself.

The primary REC attributes are that it represents: a renewable fuel source, emissions of the renewable generation, geographic location and vintage of the generator, and eligibility for certification or RPS. The secondary REC attributes include: avoided amount of emissions, and power price stability provisions.

RECs ownership and the right to make environmental claims are verified by two methods: 1) REC contracts and audits of the chain of custody, and 2) through the REC tracking systems*.

NOTE: A regional certificate tracking system is an electronic database that is used to track the ownership of RECs, much like an online bank account. It issues a uniquely numbered certificate for each MWh of electricity generated by a generation facility registered in the system. It then tracks the ownership of certificates as they are traded, and retires the certificates once they are used or claims are made based on their attributes or characteristics. Since each MWh in the REC system has a unique identification number and can only be in one owner's account at any time, this reduces ownership disputes and the potential for double counting.

Both of those methods help the buyers avoid double counting and claims, and ensure against fraud, but the REC tracking systems provides greater transparency, when tracking RECs from their point of creation to their point of final use.

Pollution-free Industries

We need to mention here some pollution-free, or relatively pollution-free industries and products. Those are the hope of our energy future, so we need to be fully aware of what they offer, in addition to renewable power.

Renewable Technologies

Although the renewable energy sources have been hailed as clean and green, that is only partially true. All energy sources have some impact on our environment. Fossil fuels (coal, oil, and natural gas) do substantially more harm than renewable energy sources, including air and water pollution, damage to public health, wildlife and habitat loss, extreme water use, land use, and global warming emissions.

Nevertheless, we must keep in mind that there are some significant environmental impacts associated with producing power from renewable energy sources such as solar, wind, geothermal, biomass, and hydropower. The type and intensity of environmental impacts varies from technology to technology, as well as the geographic location of their use, in addition to a number of other factors.

In more detail:

Solar Power

The environmental impacts associated with solar power include the pollution created during the manufacturing and transport of the solar panels and BOS. Large amounts of toxic gasses and chemicals are emitted into the atmosphere, soil, and water during the manufacturing of silicon and thin film materials, and the related solar cells and modules.

There are a number of hazardous materials used in the manufacturing processes as well, which impact the environment and the people involved in manufacturing.

After that, during installation and use, there is damage to large areas of land, which includes wild habitat loss, the use of large quantities of water, and the uncertainty of some toxic materials used to manufacture solar cells and modules. The environmental impact and damage vary greatly depending on the technology used and the location.

Wind Power

Like solar power, the wind provides a tremendous resource for generating clean and sustainable electricity. Harnessing power from the wind is one of the cleanest and most sustainable ways to generate electricity, as it produces no toxic pollution or global warming emissions. Wind is also abundant, inexhaustible, and affordable, which makes it a viable and large-scale alternative to fossil fuels.

Despite its vast potential, there are a variety of environmental impacts associated with wind power generation that should be recognized and mitigated. The use of great amounts of land is one of the most important environmental issues related to wind power farms installation and operation. Wild life habitat is affected, as are the people who live nearby. The large propellers kill birds, and people get sick from the noise and upset from the visual pollution.

Geothermal Energy

The most widely developed type of geothermal power plant, also known as hydrothermal plants, are located near geologic "hot spots" where hot molten rock is close to the earth's crust and produces hot water that can be used for heating and electricity generation. There is no way around it, because there is no way to relocate them anywhere else.

In some regions enhanced geothermal systems, or hot dry rock geothermal, which involve drilling into the earth's surface to reach deeper geothermal resources, can allow broader access to geothermal energy.

The environmental impacts differ depending on the conversion and cooling technology used, but in all cases those impacts are much less than most other power generating technologies. Lately a new technology, known as enhanced geothermal systems (EGS) has been used in some areas. This technique uses lower-temperature areas by fracturing the rock with high-pressure water, which is similar to the controversial "fracking" process in the natural gas industry. The only difference at this point is that EGS uses only pure water and none of the toxic chemicals that have raised water-quality and health issues with natural-gas fracking. But, there is some evidence that EGS produces small earthquakes. So here we go again—electricity or earthquakes?

Biomass for Electricity

Biomass power plants are similar to fossil fuel power plants since they use combustion of a feedstock to generate electricity. Because of that, biomass plants have similar problems with toxic air emissions and water use as fossil fuel plants. The only difference is that the feedstock of biomass plants can be sustainably produced, while fossil fuels are non-renewable.

Sources of biomass resources for producing electricity are diverse, including: energy crops (like switch grass); agricultural waste; manure; forest products and waste; and urban waste. Both the type of feedstock and the manner in which it is developed and harvested significantly affect land use and life-cycle global warming emissions impacts of producing power from biomass.

In all cases, the GHG and toxic gas emissions from those plants parallel those from fossil power plants, so the real-time environmental damage is quite significant, regardless of the justifications.

Hydroelectric Power

Hydroelectric power includes both massive hydroelectric dams and small run-of-the-river plants. Large-scale hydroelectric dams continue to be built in many parts of the world, but it is unlikely that new facilities will be added to the existing U.S. fleet in the future.

Instead, the future of hydroelectric power in the U.S. will likely involve increased capacity at current dams and new run-of-the-river projects. Unfortunately, there are serious environmental impacts at both types of plants. The most important of those is the large area destruction that is needed during the construction of a hydro dam reservoir. Millions of acres of land, villages, and cultural artifacts are inundated, and thousands of people are relocated.

The land, and everything on it, is lost forever. How bad that is depends on which side of the question you are.

Hydrokinetic Energy

Hydrokinetic energy is the energy produced by wave and tidal power. It encompasses an array of energy technologies, many of which still in the experimental stages or in the early stages of deployment. While actual impacts of large-scale operations have not been observed, a range of potential impacts can be projected. We can easily envision fish and large ocean animals caught in, or killed by, the mechanisms of those technologies. In all cases, the sheer presence of large equipment in the ocean will change the environment, but it is too early to tell in what ways, so we need to give those technologies some time before making judgment calls.

Coal-to-gas Conversions

The design, construction, operation, and maintenance of coal-, gas-, or oil-fired power plants are the oldest electrical generation businesses in the world. Recently the construction of new coal-fired power plants has been on hold, and another trend is shaping up as the most promising for the foreseeable future. It is the conversion of coal- to gas-fired plants.

Coal-burning facilities have dropped down to 10% of total new capacity in the U.S. in 2013, down from 18% in 2009, according to the U.S. Energy Information Administration reports. Gas, at the same time, is up to 82% of new capacity in 2013 from 42% in 2012. This is one of the fastest energy market conversions ever.

There are several conversion options that are suitable for different applications. Some of those are:

1. Coal-to-gas fuel switch by modifying the existing boiler
2. Coal-to-gas fuel switch for the existing boiler, and the addition of a new gas turbine to the existing boiler cycle. This can be done by:
    a. Addition of a cycle to the existing system
    b. Hot wind box repowering
    c. Combined cycle repowering
3. And, of course, the best and most expensive option is building a totally new combined-cycle gas plant, and decommissioning of the existing coal plant.

Each of those options has advantages and disadvantages, in the areas of cost and operational considerations, and since no two plants are identical, the solutions vary according to the needs. A coal-to-gas conversion averages $40-50 million, while building a brand new gas-fired plant is several times this amount. So there are lots of things to consider.

In most cases, the key force in the decision making process (at least in the beginning) is regulatory, in terms of emissions and as an offset for a new unit. In addition, fuel costs, the age of the plant and the need for greater power output also play critical roles in determining the type and timing of the switch.

Regulatory forces are somewhat foggy, and a wide range of rule changes and legislative efforts are up in the air—some of which could have a far-reaching impact on coal-fired plants operation, but in all cases, some form of CO_2 controls will be enacted in the near future. Those controls could be part of a cap-and-trade system (similar to previous allowance programs for SO_2 and NO_x) or they might take the form of gradual reductions to meet increasingly stricter goals.

There will certainly be some additional regulatory controls placed on power plant emissions, such as the New Source Review and offsets for other emissions regulated by state and federal laws, on one hand, while the utilities are factoring in the future need for electrical power generation, because of market demand projections, or to replace an old power plant, on the other.

The combination of the above factors is good justification for considering a timely switch—not to mention that the price of natural gas has dropped and it is becoming the preferred fuel for baseload power generation, due to plentiful supply and reduced demand from other industries.

Natural gas prices have been falling fast, and are down to about $4 per 1.0 million Btus, which is helping gas to capture an ever-increasing share of power generation. Gas prices, however, are much more unstable and sensitive to short-term changes in supply and demand than coal prices. So while current economic conditions favor natural gas usage in the short term, the potential price volatility must be factored into major decisions as well.

Since most of the existing coal plants in the U.S. are getting old and ready for retirement, and using the global warming debate as a cover, a number of utilities are playing the "green card" too, and choosing door #3 above (scrapping the old coal-fired monster and installing brand spanking new gas-fired plant.) This way they kill 2 or 3 birds with the same stone. Clever, eh? It works! For now…

There is another problem with the fast invasion of the energy industry by natural gas. It is the fact that most owners (the local utilities usually) are expecting their neighbors (their customers) to pay for the conversions. Fair, you say? Maybe, but it is the poorest members of our society that are hurt most by this movement. So it remains to be seen if all this switching won't get us into another energy revolution.

Carbon Capture and Storage (Sequestration)

The atmosphere today contains on the average over 450 ppm of CO_2 (equivalent), which in some places is above the concentration where negative impacts of the global warming trend of climate change would occur. Those levels are increasing rapidly, due to the quick rise of fossil burning and their emissions.

Even the best intentioned approaches, such as the transition to renewable energies, or reduction in demand will not happen overnight, so fossil fuels (and coal especially) will continue to play an important role in the energy portfolio for some time. Since we will not be able to reduce coal consumption, if left unattended, atmospheric CO_2 could increase quickly, so we have to find new ways to get rid of it and stop it from going into the atmosphere.

The best possible way to reduce CO_2 emissions in the atmosphere and avoid the negative impacts of higher atmospheric concentrations of GHG is to avoid emitting the CO_2 into the air in the first place, which can be done by capturing the gas before it is released.

Present technologies allow CO_2 to be captured easily at stationary sources and injected underground for long-term storage in a process called geologic sequestration (GS). This type of CO_2 capture and geologic sequestration is one of several options, in addition to using energy efficiency and renewable energy to avoid CO_2 emissions. This method has the potential to reduce climate change mitigation costs and increase flexibility in achieving greenhouse gas emission reductions.
There is enough capacity worldwide to permanently store as much as 1,100 gigatons of CO_2 underground. Considering that worldwide emissions of CO_2 from large stationary sources is estimated at approximately 13 gigatons per year, if properly implemented, this approach would give us 80-90 years of CO_2-free power generation.

The scientists have confidence in the viability and safety of this approach, which is supported by the extensive experience with CO_2 produced through natural processes that has been retained in underground geologic formations for hundreds of millions of years. The addition of multiple trapping mechanisms would reduce the mobility of CO_2 underground over time, thus further decreasing the risk of CO_2 leaking to the surface.

Approximately 95% of the largest stationary sources of CO_2 emissions, such as coal-fired power plants in the U.S., are within 50-100 miles away from a potential GS sites. Considering the large storage capacity in the United States, GS has the potential to contribute significantly toward meeting the goals of the nation's climate policy.

For that purpose, the federal government is supporting the development of a wide range of GS-related activities, and we just have to hope that this approach proves feasible and can be implemented in the near future.

There are facilities for sequestration that exist today, though none of them at the required scale, nor have they yet demonstrated acceptable risk. From this we have to accept that there is a tradeoff between the risks of large-scale carbon sequestration and the risks of global warming impacts.

Unfortunately in 2011, American Electric Power canceled its large carbon capture and sequestration project, which was considered one of the best pilot tests of CO_2 sequestration. The equipment was installed on a large coal-fired power plant, captured carbon dioxide, and permanently stored it underground in deep rock formations and saline aquifers.

The pilot plant shutdown was driven mainly by the fact that the U.S. utilities are under increasing pressure to switch from coal to natural gas because of new federal regulations on coal. Because of that, counting on carbon capture and sequestration as a savior for old coal plants will have to wait a while longer.

We, however, cannot wait and must look into other ways to deal with GHGs. Besides point-source removal discussed so far, CO_2 can be removed from the atmosphere in a variety of other ways. U.S. forests and croplands already sequester over a million metric tons of carbon equivalent, after accounting for both gains and losses in carbon. This current amount of sequestration in forests and croplands offsets approximately 12% of total U.S. CO_2 emissions from the energy, transportation and industrial sectors.

Additional land-use and management changes can maintain and enhance those carbon sequestration levels in the U.S., reduce emissions of other greenhouse gases, and thus help address the climate change problem.

Making biochar is another way to reduce GHG emissions. It is essentially an inverse coal process, where coal-like material (biochar) can be created by pyrolysis of biomass and other materials. It is actually charcoal, which primary use is not for fuel, but for bio-sequestration or atmospheric carbon capture and storage.

Charcoal is a stable solid that is rich in carbon content, and thus, can be used to lock carbon in the soil. Biochar is of increasing interest because of concerns about climate change caused by emissions of CO_2 and other GHGs.

There is also a direct, but novel, way of carbon sequestration by capturing it directly from the air, processing and storing it underground. This method removes carbon dioxide from ambient air by carbon dioxide scrubbing. It is a different approach to removing CO_2 from the stack emissions of large point sources, such as fossil fuel fired power stations.

And finally, large-scale growth of special bacteria can help the CO_2 sequestration process. The bacteria can be genetically modified to trap CO_2 faster, and then keeping it underground for thousands and millions of years.

China and India

Similar efforts are underway in other countries too, but the problem here is that no matter how successful the CO_2 sequestration and storage efforts are, and even if we are able to completely capture and sequester CO_2 from all coal-fired plants in the U.S. and Europe, we are faced with a big problem. It comes from the enormous, uncontrolled and ever increasing use of coal in China, India and other developing countries, where sequestration would not be possible, and is not enforceable for now.

And as we continue the new technology development efforts and spent billions in the process, there is an inevitable certainty that no matter what we (in the U.S. and the E.U.) do just won't be enough to compensate for the ever increasing smoke from coal-fired plants across the world's oceans.

New Transportation Modes

Crude oil is almost exclusively used for fueling transportation—cars, trucks, boats and trains. Since oil prices are rising and the GHG emissions from transport vehicles are increasing, it makes sense to look into other forms of transport, or at least new types of fuels for the transport industry.

The electric car is one of the approaches, where electric power generated by a coal, nuclear, or solar plant somewhere in the country is used to charge the batteries of a car or truck at a different part of the country. Or it could be that the electric car charge comes from a solar or wind farm; then the power is almost free from fossils, thus cleaner and cheaper. In any case, it might seem that we are only shifting the problems from one pocket to the other, but it is much more complicated than that.

Let's take a closer, unbiased look at electric vehicles.

Electric Cars

Electric cars have been surrounded by a mystery since the very beginning, and have a special meaning and designation in the U.S. and Europe. A person driving an electric car is thought out to be smart, considerate and head and shoulders above the rest. Lately, however, the mystery is being reduced to a sales gimmick, which car companies use to attract unsuspected, and often ignorant, people with promises of saving money, and with an additional bonus of saving the environment in the process.

What the new, proud owners of electric cars don't know is that they are inheriting the problems of an immature technology, which come with a number of headaches. They are not told that although the car runs clean, the electric energy it uses is far from it. It was generated somewhere else by burning dirty coal. And while, by using electricity to charge the car's batteries did not contaminate the local environment, it did contaminate the environment around the power generating plant. There is no free lunch, remember? So the net gain, if there is any, is reduced to transferring the responsibilities from one place, and person, to another.

So let's see what will happen if most of us buy electric cars. Come 5:00 PM, everybody arrives at home, and the first thing they do is plug the electric car battery charger into the wall socket, and go to watch the nightly news. The sun goes down at the same time, and there is no wind to speak of, so solar and wind generators are down.

With millions of electric cars plugged in at the same time at this hour of the day the peaker power plants will kick in, and our total electric bills will travel upwards with them too. The probability of blackouts will increase significantly, and they might start rolling faster than we can imagine.

While no one can argue that electric cars have the potential to do a lot of good for the air and the planet, they also push utilities toward a reckoning with the so-called smart grid. Our national electric grid at its present state is already stretched to the limit. It is simply not designed to handle the load.

Power Grid Effects

As more governments encourage the use of electric cars through mandates, tax breaks, and other mechanisms, utilities will need to figure out how to deliver power to those cars reliably and efficiently, and without cutting further into already razor-thin profit margins.

This is not an easy task when you consider that providing more power at night (which is not the case today) is only part of the problem. The utilities also must create and service an electric version of the gas station network that has been in place for over 100 years.

The grid will be forced to get smarter...at a small, several billion dollars worth, charge. And overseas the situation is even more complex. For example, in Germany the government has set a 2022 deadline for shutting down all nuclear power plants, which until recently provided nearly 25% of the country's power generating needs. In Japan, lingering concerns about the safety of nuclear power following the tsunami-related meltdown at the Fukushima Daiichi facility, have resulted in the ongoing shutdown of almost all the country's nuclear power sector.

The likely replacements for nuclear (and coal, oil, and natural gas), solar and wind power, are as unreliable and anxiety-inducing to the current electric grid as are electric vehicles. Neither provides what the grid is designed for: predictable flow.

With wind power generation, utilities may have only a day or even just a couple of hours' notice to confirm whether generating capacity will meet or exceed power needs. Some of the time, the wind may blow when it is not needed, so utilities will need storage solutions for excess energy that they can feed back into the grid when the wind dies down and power demand picks up. At the same time, nobody can predict where and how long the sun will shine, so the utilities are totally relying on an unreliable power source.

Sounds like a disaster in the making, right? Well, we over-exaggerated the situation to a worst-case scenario, so let's not forget that renewables and electric vehicles are in their infancy. They, nevertheless, represent great opportunities for new revenue, new markets, and even for new business models for the respective industries, which today are still in their infancy. They are still stuck in low-margin commodity land, but will eventually emerge as winning industries.

Although it is unlikely that EVs will take over the world, we do believe that they will eventually account for 10-15% of vehicle sales volume in the developed countries. As a matter of fact some governments (i.e., Germany and Ireland) have already set those goals. For the utilities, this new activity represents an opportunity to open a new and very large market.

The most profitable new business opportunities may come from building new service stations and operating the charge points that EV owners will need to use to recharge their batteries and otherwise service their cars. Those charge points are a challenge for now. As another case of immature technology, they are few and between, the technology is not proven and the cost is high. In Europe, it costs over $15,500 just to install a single public charging station. And then there are the costs of maintaining and operating those charge points.

The Power Companies

Energy companies are looking at a variety of strategies for defraying charge point installation costs or adding revenue streams as a result of increased use of the national power grid—including the effects from increased use of EVs.

Several examples of such strategies are:

- Collaboration with businesses where drivers don't mind waiting— Restaurants, retailers, shopping malls. etc. are prime candidates.

- Managing electric car fleets to provide car sharing—Utilities could take on the management of corporate and rental electric car fleets, just as some of them provide other solutions for power management.

- Partnering with technology companies—This will speedup the proper and efficient installation and operation of networks of charging stations.

- Adding electric car charge and service to conventional gas stations—This is the easiest solution, since the infrastructure is already in place and adding charging components would add more business.

- Using the charge station for advertising—displays and selling advertising space could bring additional income.

The Smart Grid…again

A decisive factor in this development on the EV industry in the long run would be the development of the smart grid. Only with a well- developed smart grid would we be able to cope with the demands of millions of consumers plugging their cars into the grid at the same time, either in their homes or at public charging points. In all cases, the utilities will have to find a way to manage the extra demand with smart grid systems that can intelligently allow EVs to draw from the grid during periods of low energy demand, such as during the overnight hours.

Utilities could allow users customers to recharge their EVs at any time, but provide financial incentives so that it is less expensive to recharge a car (or run any major electric appliance) during low-demand periods.

In any case, as attractive as it might sound, this is immature technology, and many questions surrounding EVs, and the related subjects, are still unanswered. But EVs are here to stay, and they are getting more reliable and cheaper by the day. As governments boost incentives and mandates for EV development, more utilities are getting interested. They, and many other companies in the field, are testing the logistics and economics of EV usage.

The 21st century is a time for bold experimentation, where the EVs, smart grids, and the renewable energy technologies are growing in importance and promise to bring us, among other things, a new and exciting utility-transportation system that is environmentally safe as well.

Nevertheless, EVs are one alternative on the table that won't go away, so let's look at it. EVs date back to the mid-19th century, when electricity was the new miracle that provided a level of comfort and ease of operation that could not be achieved by the gasoline cars of the time.

Presently all electricity powered cars and trucks, trains, planes, boats, motorcycles and scooters, and spacecraft are considered EVs. There are plans for developing and using electric tanks, submarines, and lighter unmanned vehicles

There are three basic types of electric vehicles, depending on the power source: a) directly powered from an external power filling station, b.) powered by stored electricity obtained from an external power source, and c.) powered by an on-board electrical generator, such as an internal combustion engine (a hybrid electric vehicle) or a hydrogen fuel cell.

The EV Issues

As any other technology, EVs are not perfect. They have a number of technical issues that need to be resolved, such as:

Charging Stations

EVs need periodic charging, which depending on the travelled distance could vary from 2-3 hours to 2-3 days. The charging can be done from conventional power outlets, if there is access to such, or from dedicated charging stations at different locations. The charging process takes hours, which is very inconvenient in the midst of a long trip. Most often, however, EVs are charged overnight which provides enough charge for normal everyday usage.

The widespread use of EVs within large cities, EV users can plug in their cars while at work and let them charge throughout the day. This extends the commuting range and eliminates the often associated with EVs range anxiety (the fear of the batteries running out of juice in the midst of a heavy city traffic, on the highway, or in some remote location.)

A new development is a recharging system that avoids the need for a charge cable. One such systems, called Curb Connect features special electrical contacts built into curbs. A specially equipped EVs parking at this curb charging point makes contact with the curb contacts, which become energized and start charging the batteries.

Another possible, and more convenient, solution for daily recharging is an inductive charging system, which does not require cables. Here the EV drives by, or over, a special inductor, which transits the charge via inductive force and charges the batteries. But this method is much slower than conventional plug-in charge points.

For EVs that are used for short distance travel the "rapid charging" system is available in some European cities. It is capable of bringing the batteries charge from 20 to 80% within 20-30 minutes.

Battery replacement is another possible alternative, although presently no OEMs have any plans to produce such vehicles. Battery swapping would require standardization of products and procedures across all EV platforms, models and manufacturers. Swapping also requires many times more battery packs to be ready and available at all times in the system. Those are complications that won't be resolved any time soon.

Electromagnetic Radiation

Most high performance electrical motors emit electromagnetic radiation, and there have been claims associated with a number of human ailments. Those claims, just like those associated with windmill propellers, are unsubstantiated, except in some extreme cases of high exposure levels. There is a way to shield electric motors properly with a metallic Faraday cage, which might reduce some, but not all of the related problems.

The Grid

The electric grid is limited to how much power it can provide, and if millions of EVs to be plugged in the grid, the demand might exceed the capacity of grid. The increased demand for generation and transmission would require new generating capabilities and would increase the GHG emissions too. In the U.K., for example, the high-voltage electricity transmission system would be able to manage the demand of about a million EVs, but the local distribution networks in cities like London would struggle to balance the grids if many more EVs are plugged in at the same time.

The U.S. grid is assumed to have sufficient existing power plant and transmission infrastructure to handle many EVs charging at the same time, assuming that most charging would occur overnight, using the most efficient off-peak base load sources.

It is also estimated that the overall energy consumption and emissions when using many EVs would diminish because of the higher efficiency of EVs over the entire power generation and distribution cycle. This opens a number of possibilities and new markets for those new technologies.

Pollution

Many, if not most, EVs are purchased by people who are concerned with energy efficiency and the environment. To them, driving an EV means saving money and helping the environment at the same time, a win-win situation, no doubt! Saving money aside, however, how much do EVs contribute to saving the environment? Just think—they need electric energy to charge the batteries, which is equal to the amount of energy provided by gas or diesel fuel as needed to move the vehicle the same distance.

Where does this energy come from? Unless it is generated entirely by solar panels on top of the EV's owner house, it is produced mostly by fossil fuels. And since 99% of city dwellers do not have solar generators at home (and even if they did, the sun doesn't shine at night when most charging is done), then a coal- or gas-fired power plant several hundred miles away is generating the power needed to charge the EVs.

Coal- and gas-power plants provide the majority of the power in this world for now, and that won't change any time soon. So, the electricity produced by the fossil fuel power generators at point A is used to charge EVs at point B. The GHGs and other pollution created at point A stays there, with some of it blown all over the place. Point B benefits from the energy generated at point A without the environmental problems created there.

So the EV owners see clean electricity coming into their EVs and feel happy that they are helping to clean the environment. In reality, however, we need to factor a number of operations, especially the energy lost and pollution created during:

- Mining and drilling the fossil fuels
- Transporting the fossil fuels to the power plant
- Burning the fossils and turning the power plant turbines to generate electricity
- Transmission of the electricity from point A to point B
- Energy lost during the charging process

If all those factors are taken into consideration, we'd see that in most cases it would be much more efficient and less polluting to use gasoline or diesel engine, instead of using fossil fuels to generate an equivalent amount of energy to charge an EV.

This, however, does not mean that we should abandon the EVs all together. It is only a reminder that we should not jump blindly on the bandwagon of environmental sentimentalism. We must always consider the big picture, and remember that all technologies have their special place in the world's energy and environmental battles. They all should be given enough consideration and used properly.

Safety

High voltage used in EVs carries some safety risks. Because of that the U.N. has adopted the first international regulation (Regulation 100), addressing the safety of electric and hybrid-electric cars. This is to ensure that EVs with a high voltage electric power train are as safe as conventional cars and trucks. The E.U. and Japan are working on the incorporation of the new U.N. Regulation 100 in their respective rules on technical standards for EVs.

Nevertheless, the concern about the safety of EVs, their charging systems and batteries is not going away. EVs must meet the same safety standards as conventional vehicles, so there are already standards for functional safety, such as ISO 26262 and IEC 61508, as well as for charging systems, such as UL 2202, UL 2251 and UL Subject 2594. There are also third party tests for batteries, and chemical and mechanical components that can be performed to validate and certify the safety of the different EVs.

Case Study

In 2010 the National Highway Traffic Safety Administration (NHTSA), a U.S. federal agency, opened an investigation after concerns about Chevy Volt batteries causing fires in a crash. As a result of the investigation, GM offered replacement with any GM car to Volt owners while the federal investigation was taking place. GM was also prepared to recall all Volt cars and buy-back, repair, or replace them if and when recommended by the investigators, or if the owners so wished.

The investigation was closed in 2012 with NHTSA releasing a report stating that the Chevy Volt does not pose greater danger than any other vehicle. The fires leading to the investigations occurred only during NHTSA controlled crashes, including simulated rolling of the vehicles. In contrast, 184,000 conventional vehicles caught fire on U.S. roads in 2010. At that time GM reported that only around 250 Volt owners had requested either a loaner vehicle or a potential buyback.

It seems that EVs are quickly jumping over the barriers in their path to wider acceptance, and with the total cooperation of the manufacturers are becoming integral part of our lives.

> *There are millions of large commercial trucks crisscrossing the U.S. from coast to coast, consuming billions of tons of diesel annually. Those trucks spend about 1/3 of their time on the road idling at truck stops and rest areas with their engine running so that the drivers can listen to the radios and use heaters and A/Cs. Shutting down the engines during non-operation could save the U.S. over a billion gallons of diesel annually.*

Environmental Finance and Legal Services

According to industry sources, between now and 2030, if we are to reduce greenhouse gas emissions by half by 2050, $550 billion per year is needed for clean energy investments. Approximately 50% of those funds will be required in developing countries. Furthermore, at least $86 billion will be required annually for adaptation to climate change by 2015.

Big business and many financial and law companies have seen the opportunity and have jumped willingly in the boiling pot of environmental financial and legal activities. Those include:

- Consulting firms specializing in servicing clients with complex environmental restoration and remediation projects

- Underwriters of environmental insurance and environmental liability insurance

- Legal, financial, transactional services to municipal entities and companies involved in water/wastewater, solid waste, energy, real estate and construction projects

- A full range of risk management related products

- Advising on initial launch and all financial and legal growth stages of clean tech companies

- Identifying appropriate financing sources, and initiating, assisting and supporting the relationships

- Management of environmental risk efficiently via environmental risk products

- Management of project development, financing, construction, and implementation

- Advising on Section 45/48 PTC/ITC tax election, and eligibility for Treasury 1603 programs

- Drafting land options and lease terms along with easement agreements

- Advising developers and builders on all phases of green building projects life cycle

- Preparing corporate operating agreements or asset acquisition documentation

- Advising on insurance coverage and supply chain contracts

- Guiding environmental review and permitting processes at the state and federal levels

- Providing expert finance, performance and liability insurance counsel

- Advising on employment matters involving independent contractors and direct employees

- Evaluation and prosecution of intellectual property rights

- Defending projects and permits in judicial and administrative forums

- Legal services to clients with local, regional, national and international operations

NOTE: As with the conventional commodities markets, there are also rules and regulations that products must meet to be bought and sold in the marketplace. The biggest difference here is that the environmental markets are frequently driven and controlled, by federal, state, and local regulations. Those federal and state agencies typically set the market rules either through approval of individual transactions, via local regulations, or through market-wide requirements.

There are a number of laws that require compensation for damage to the environment and mitigation for damages, which serve as the foundation for legal action.

Since on-site mitigation is often not possible, as is the case of smoke emissions from a coal-fired power plant, more effective ways to compensate for environmental damage have been devised. Those *more effective* and other *alternative* ways of approaching the issues at hand is what fuels the growth of the environmental markets and the growing need for legal services.

Legal services are required in many cases to mitigate discrepancies and disagreements when the environment and people's health are negatively impacted. Lung cancer caused by the smoke of a nearby coal-fired power plant, water contamination from a fracking well, or illnesses caused by a nuclear plant accident, are primary examples of the need for legal intervention.

There is lots of work to be done, right? Yes, and a lot of money to be made, and the battle is just now starting.

Internationally, the United Nations Development Program (UNDP) leaders believe that if environmental management is treated not as a constraint but as an opportunity, it can become part of the solution. If policies, skills and incentives are developed to encourage investments in environmentally-friendly and climate-friendly businesses such as energy efficiency, renewable energy, sustainable transportation, and greening of commodity supply chains, not only can environmental challenges be addressed but new economic opportunities and millions of new jobs can be created.

In financial terms, the UNDP is one of the largest brokers of environmental grants in the developing world, having disbursed $1.58 billion directly and leveraged over $3 billion in co-financing from public and private sources to support sustainable development during 2004-2007.

Unfortunately, development assistance by itself can do very little to close this gap. Official development assistance (ODA) presently provides only about $10 billion per year for climate change-related activities, only a small percentage of what is required, and that is declining.

U.S. ENERGY AND ENVIRONMENTAL STATUS

The U.S. is presently the world's largest user of energy and respectively the largest polluter. But things are changing; China, India, Russia and other large nations are increasing their populations disproportionately, with which the demand for electric and heating power increases dramatically.

The increase of power generation increases the emissions proportionally as well, and since there are no controls to limit them, the health of the locals will suffer, along with the global environment. Climate warming under those conditions is inevitable.

People around the world demand increased comforts, and so the number of cars, home appliances and the use of other energy using conveniences is increasing. With the population and energy demand increases, the negative effect on the environment is expected to increase as well.

Millions of new cars will be added on the already crowded roads. Millions of new homes and dozens of coal power plants are planned all around the world. The air and soil pollution from those activities, com-

bined with those of the energy generators is promising to bring us new, and more serious challenges as far as air pollution and climate warming are concerned.

In the U.S. the major energy and environmental issues and those that shape the respective markets, are as follows:

Air Pollution

A brief glimpse at today's energy-environment situation reveals that the U.S. is considered the world's largest user of energy per capita, and respectively, the largest polluter. CO_2 emission from fossil power plants is blamed for 80% of the pollution.

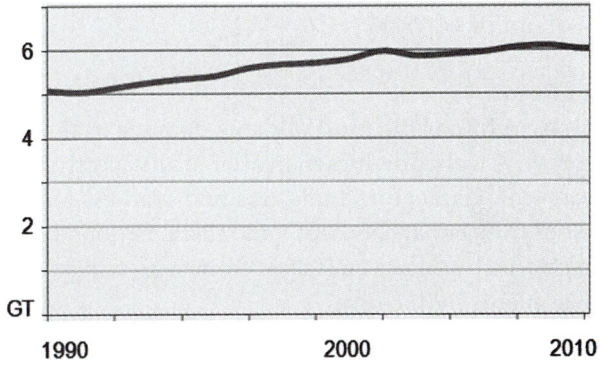

Figure 8-31. Annual U.S. CO_2 emissions (in GT)

CO_2 emissions are still growing, but a change is coming, where natural gas is replacing coal, thus generating the same amount of power at lower CO_2 emission rates. This is good, for there would be less coming from the exhaust stack of the power plants, but there is a problem at the front end of the gas production process. Large areas of land have been contaminated, and as the business increases, so do the contaminated areas.

So it seems that we have chosen to trade air pollution for land contamination. The end result is still being tabulated and we will not know the results any time soon. Let's hope that they won't be as bad as some think they will be.

The key to dealing with air pollution is to understand its causes and effects, and track changes in the environment. Officially, the EPA, state governments and individual companies do that. Air and water samples are collected on regular basis and are tested for changes in pH, chemical content, and other variables. The results are analyzed and the effects on the environment are calculated and documented.

In case of testing for acid rain damage, for example, materials and structures containing marble, steel, bronze, copper, and other materials that can be damaged by exposure to acid rain are observed and tested. The goal is to gain a complete understanding of the effects of the acid rain causing agents on our surroundings and on human health: primarily sulfur dioxide (SO2); nitrogen oxides (NO_x); and particulate matter.

To solve the acid rain problem, we need to understand how it damages the environment. We also need to understand what changes could be made to the air pollution sources that cause the problem. The answers to those questions help leaders make better decisions about how to control air pollution and therefore, how to reduce—or even eliminate—acid rain.

Because there are many solutions to the acid rain problem, we have a choice of which option or combination of options is best.

Acid Rain

Acid rain is the most obvious damage to the environment. A walk downtown in almost any Northeastern city reveals damage to buildings and statues' features. Most of this damage, except vandalism, is done by acid rain created by excess emissions from coal- and gas-fired power plants in the area.

Acid rain is a growing problem that is defacing our national treasures, so it is attracting more attention and is creating its own market niche.

Clean Up Smokestacks and Exhaust Pipes

Almost all the electricity that powers modern life comes from burning fossil fuels such as coal, natural gas, and oil. Acid deposition is caused by two pollutants that are released into the atmosphere when fossil fuels are burned: sulfur dioxide (SO_2), and nitrogen oxides (NO_x). Coal accounts for most U.S. SO_2 emissions and a large portion of NO_x emissions. Sulfur is present in coal as an impurity, and it reacts with air when the coal is burned to form SO_2. In contrast, NO_x is formed when any fossil fuel is burned.

There are several equally complex and expensive options for reducing SO_2 emissions:

- Using coal containing less sulfur
- Washing the coal before burning
- Using scrubbers to chemically remove SO_2 from the gases leaving the smokestack
- Using catalytic converters to reduce NO_x as in car exhaust
- Switching from coal to natural gas, which emits much less SO_2 than coal
- Using power generating technologies that do not burn fossil fuels

Certain approaches will also have the additional benefit of reducing other pollutants such as mercury and carbon dioxide (CO_2). Each of those options, however, has its own costs and benefits; there is no single universal solution. Understanding the main benefits, the accompanying "co-benefits," and the related costs is very important in seeking cost-effective air pollution reduction strategies.

Nevertheless, elimination of acid rain-forming gasses is the basis of the development of special markets, as follows:

- R&D of new equipment and methods for reducing emissions from fossil-fired power plants
- Manufacturing of emission reduction equipment
- Mitigation of damages, resulting in new services and jobs creation and
- Financing and legal service opportunities

Environmental Damage Mitigation

Acid deposition penetrates deeply into the fabric of an ecosystem, changing the chemistry of the soil and streams and narrowing—sometimes to nothing—the space where certain plants and animals can survive. Because there are so many changes, it takes many years for ecosystems to recover from acid deposition, even after emissions are reduced and the rain pH is restored to normal.

For example, while visibility might improve within days, and small or episodic chemical changes in streams within months, chronically acidified lakes, streams, forests, and soils can take years, decades, or even centuries (in the case of soils) to heal. Nevertheless, people can help bring back lakes and streams more quickly. This sometimes requires the intervention of legal experts, and financial backers.

Large-scale acid rain mitigation procedures, such as in lakes, have been tried in some countries like Norway. They are very expensive and involve adding large quantities of limestone to acidic lakes to neutralize the acid effects. This process, called liming, has not been used very often in the United States, due to expense and because it is considered a short-term remedy in only specific areas.

Sure enough, it cannot solve the broader problems of changes in soil chemistry and forest health in the watershed that are caused by acid rain. Nor does it address materials and structures damage, nor risk to human health. And yet there is damage done to properties and people, so something has to be done, which is where the finance and legal professionals create new market opportunities for their respective disciplines.

The Future

The U.S. Congress created the Acid Rain Program in 1990, but its expectations are far from met. Assessments done by EPA and others show that acid rain is still harming the environment, and is on the increase in some areas. Congress may have to consider additional ways to reduce emissions that cause acid deposition, such as additional emission reductions from known sources, or new methods to reduce emissions from other sources, like energy efficiency and alternative energy. That opens the door to new energy and environmental markets, such as those using alternative energy and energy efficiency optimization technologies.

Alternative Energy Sources

The best solution for reducing acid rain in all cases is using other sources of electricity besides fossil fuels. This includes nuclear power, hydropower, wind energy, geothermal energy, and solar energy. Nuclear and hydropower are used most widely in the U.S., but wind, solar, and geothermal energy presently are rising.

Some types of energy are more expensive to produce than others. Nuclear power, hydropower, and coal are the cheapest forms of energy today, but advancements in technologies and regulatory developments may change that in the future. All of those factors must be weighed when deciding which energy source to use today and which to invest in for tomorrow.

Natural gas is the preferred energy source today in the U.S., but it, as all sources of energy, has environmental costs and benefits. The final tally is not completed as yet, so we are watching closely and calculating the benefits and the costs.

All those technologies are part of the huge energy market, with its different branches, where new opportunities are created daily in many areas. Implementation of cost-effective mechanisms to reduce emissions and their impact on the environment are also integral part of the energy market, and will continue to evolve.

Personal Action

Each American is an energy guzzler and a huge source of pollution. The sooner that we realize it and agree that something has to be done about it, sooner we will be able to face and solve the problems at hand. Taking personal action, as individuals, we owe Earth our active participation and support of the environmental battle.

Although it seems that there is not much one individual can do to stop the pollution, when multiplied by several hundred million even a little help becomes significant.

If all individuals reduce their contribution to the problem and become part of the solution, then we get closer to solving the immediate problems. We all can contribute directly by conserving energy, since energy production causes the largest portion of the acid deposition problem.

For example, the contribution of each person in the environmental battle could, and should be, to:

- Turn off lights, computers, and appliances when not in use

- Use energy-efficient appliances, and only if and when absolutely needed

- Keep the thermostat low in the winter and high in the summer

- Insulate the house the best that is possible

- Carpool, use public transportation, walk, or bicycle whenever possible

- Buy vehicles with low NO_x emissions, and properly maintain them

- Most importantly, be well informed and participate in the solution activities

THE GREAT GAS GUZZLERS AND POLLUTERS

As discussed above, it should be our responsibility to save as much energy as we can, because there is enormous waste of energy everywhere we look. This is especially true in the in the developed countries, with the U.S. leading the pack. The U.S. is the largest energy waster of all.

Here is a list of the most obvious energy wastes combined with environmental damage today:

The U.S.'s Standing Army

Yes, we have a huge *standing army*; a large military machine, similar to what the Romans had 2,000 years ago, and which occupied half of the world. The British Empire followed in their steps during the 18th, 19th, and all the way into the 20th centuries. We now keep the tradition alive with our military bases and their culture spread all over the world.

NOTE: The U.S. is the only country in the world today with an active standing army, which occupies most of the world. This is a huge machine, comprised of over 250,000 solders and officers (and their families) spread over 700 U.S. military bases in 110 countries around the world. Wow…

The U.S. military bases are built at strategic, and often environmentally sensitive, locations, with the purpose of defending American interests and keeping peace around the world. At least this is how the official version goes. It is not up to us to decide if this is good or bad, but we know that the combined energy usage of all U.S. military bases is greater than that of many countries in the world today. And so are the air, water, and soil pollution those bases generate during their daily operations.

The U.S. military bases are huge businesses, equipped with the latest and best technologies available; buildings, structures, facilities, planes, tanks, trucks, cars, boats, motor vehicles, and equipment that use enormous amount of electrical energy and fossil fuels. The solders live in those compounds with their families, thus nearly a million Americans are living and serving overseas. Those people drive around on different tasks daily, and fly back and forth to the U.S. periodically, which increases the overall pollution even further.

When we talk about inefficiency, we need to remember the U.S. military bases as an ultimate example of absolute inefficiency—logistically, financially, energy and environmentally speaking. No other country in the world deploys thousands of solders and moves them around the world—together with their spouses, kids, dogs, cats, cars, and all their belongings, household furniture, and everything they own—and houses them in all-paid-for (by the tax-payers) secure accommodations on the bases. How can you even talk about efficiency of the average solder on the base?

On top of the inefficiencies, the huge overseas U.S. bases—the facilities, equipment, and people—on them have been known to destroy large areas of the local environment. The reported damages range from devastation of large virgin forests, farmland, and even entire settlements during construction, daily operations, which continue even after they are closed down.

During construction, the land is bulldozed and built without any regard for its future use. During operation, there is 24 hours movement of planes, tanks, trucks, cars, and other military and civilian vehicles, with loud noise, dust, and smoke covering the place and affecting the lives and health of the locals.

Respect for the environment of host countries simply doesn't seem to be a priority for the U.S. military, according to media reports, and there are a number of examples to confirm this sad reality.

Just to mention a few:

- In the Philippines, for example, the U.S. Military Inspector General admitted that the bases "took advantage of the lax regulatory climate." A Department of Defense spokesperson stated that the U.S. had no environmental obligations there because its policy was to be in compliance with local environmental laws, and the Philippines had none, despite the fact that the Filipino environmental statute book was contained in three volumes at the time.

- The U.S. military bases in Panama closed in 1999 after impacting the environment in a number of ways. They created an enclave in the canal area, distorting development by creating double standards: one relatively "pristine" and wealthy area, and another that was poor and environmentally exploited.

The military activities also left behind toxic and dangerous materials such as conventional and chemical munitions (some unexploded and left behind unattended on the old firing ranges. This rendered large areas of land around the bases unusable, because the presence of unexploded munitions and chemical weapons does not allow the land to be reclaimed for farming or resettlement.

The U.S. military simply does not feel responsible for the widespread pollution from the bases in the region: polluting the local ecosystems, damaging biodiversity, and depleting fish stocks. The severity of the environmental impacts on Panama has brought together the peace movement with mainstream environmental organizations like the Sierra Club and others.

- Greenpeace has made the U.S. base at Thule in Greenland the target of one of its campaigns, with its ships observing the dumping of hundreds of barrels of waste and piles of metal without protection. They also measured the results of high levels of toxic Polychlorinated Biphenyls (PCBs) and radioactive material from tests and accidents, including the crash of a nuclear bomber, which released plutonium.

Such pollutants are absorbed from the environment by shellfish and are concentrated when fish, birds and land carnivores eat them, resulting in birth defects, cancers, and other diseases in the animals of this formerly pristine environment. Similar loss of biodiversity is reported from Guam and Okinawa, due to chemical pollution and the introduction of alien species to the island by military ships and planes.

- In developed countries where the enforcement of environmental legislation is stronger, such as Germany and Italy, the U.S. military has been held responsible and prosecuted for illegal disposal of toxic waste. The bases have been forced on a number of occasions to correct the environmental damage, or pay for it. The "polluter pays" principle is enforced in the rich countries, but not so much in the developing world, which has no political clout with Washington.

NOTE: Regardless of the number of military bases, their activities, and the billions of additional dollars spent on propping up fragile governments, the overall results are quite disappointing:

- The U.S. doesn't have many friends out there
- Most of the Arab world—the most sensitive area of the U.S. foreign affairs—is at war
- In most cases, America is blamed for anything bad happening in the world.

These factors are a warning signal that new ways for keeping the world's peace are needed. Closing the military bases might be a good step in that direction, which will also reduce the amount of energy used and pollution emitted by Americans around the world.

Commercial Transport

Commercial transport in the U.S. is the life-blood of the nation's commerce. Eighteen-wheelers, trucks, trains, and ships carry passengers and commodities around the countries 24/7. This is huge business, regulated by federal and state laws, which require commercial vehicles to be registered when traveling on any public highway or road in the United States. All types and sizes of commercially used motor vehicles have a DOT number.

We need to note here that the national interstate road system was actually designed and constructed after the WWII with emergency military purposes in mind. Its use was later on authorized for personal and commercial traffic use, which is the primary use today too. This explains some of the laws that stipulate certain uses for our roads and highways.

Small businesses that are susceptible to those newer laws include:

—Commercial vans, SUV's, pick up trucks and other medium sized vehicles, such as the ones commonly seen for plumbing, locksmith and construction. Other vehicles include various sized dump trucks, box cargo trucks and any vehicle pulling a trailer used for commercially transporting cargo.

—Rental trucks are considered commercial vehicles when used for business purposes, but not when used for private use, such as moving household items from place to place.

Today there are over 250 million registered passenger motor vehicles in the U.S.

Of these, approximately:
- 200 million are light duty vehicle, short wheel base (cars, pickups, and vans)
- 40 million are light duty vehicle, long wheel base (small trucks and larger pickups)
- 8 million are vehicles with 2 axles and 6 tires (cargo trucks)
- 2 million are trucks, combination type
- There are also over 8 million motorcycles in the U.S.

Over 30% of all vehicles are 10 years old or older.

The number of motor vehicles has been rising by an estimated average 3.69 million each year since 1960 with the largest annual growth between 1998 and 1999 and between 2000 and 2001, during which times the number of motor vehicles in the U.S. increased by eight million each time.

NOTE: The largest percentage increase ever was between the years of 1972 and 1973 when the number of cars increased by 5.88%. This was just before the Arab oil embargo and might be indicative of a change in the American psyche, which resulted in more cautious approaches to buying and using motor vehicles.

Americans drive an average of 13,500 miles each year, which comes to over 2.5 trillion miles annually. In recent years, however, several factors have influenced the way Americans drive. Higher fuel prices, economic and environmental concerns, and employment challenges have resulted in significant changes to the automotive industry and the U.S. driving statistics.

Driving is an important part of the U.S. economy and a major influence on American culture, which means that Americans drive many thousands of miles every year more than people in any other country.

Some statistics:

- American men drive considerably more miles than American women: over 16,000 miles per year for men, vs. 10,000 miles for women across all age groups.
- Americans between 35 and 54 years of age drive over 15,000 miles per year on average, while those

over age 64 average about 7,500 miles annually.

- Women over the age of 65 drive the least of any age group, averaging about 5,000 miles annually, most likely due to generational differences and the high rate of retirement of women.

- Men aged 35-54 drive the most miles, logging an average of 19,000 miles annually, most likely due to work-related car travel.

- 16-19-year-old American teenagers drive about 7,500 miles annually. Teenaged boys drive slightly more than teenage girls, with 8,200 miles vs. 6,900 miles on the average.

The average driving miles per state per year is as follows:
- Wyoming with 21,821 miles
- Georgia with 18,920 miles
- Oklahoma with 18,8891 miles
- New Mexico with 18,369 miles
- Minnesota with 17,887 miles

States with the fewest miles driven annually are:
- Alaska with 9,915 miles
- Washington, DC with 10,045 miles each year
- Hawaii with 11,104 miles
- Connecticut with 11,595 miles, and
- Massachusetts with 11,759

The Semis

A semi-trailer truck is a large vehicle that consists of a towing engine, known as a tractor in the U.S. and truck in many other places, attached to one or more trailers. Those vehicles carry *freight*, also known as *semi, tractor-trailer, big rig, or 18-wheeler* in the United States; or *transport* in Canada; *prime mover* in Australia; and articulated lorry, or artic in the U.K.

A semi-trailer is usually attached (hinged) just forward of the rear-most axle of the towing unit. This way a large portion of the weight of the trailer is carried by the heavy-duty prime mover. This makes both tractor and semi-trailer very different in design and operation than a rigid truck and trailer combination, or any other vehicle.

Today there are an estimated 2 million semis (eighteen wheelers and other trucks with trailers) crisscrossing the American highways. This represents just 4% of all registered vehicles, but over 7% of all vehicle miles traveled.

These large (largest in the world) vehicles are allowed to carry 20,000 pounds on a single rear axle, and

34,000 pounds maximum on tandem rear axles. Longer combination vehicles (LCV) types include triples, or three 28.5-foot trailers hooked together, with maximum weight up to 129,000 pounds; and turnpike doubles, consisting of two 48-foot trailers with maximum weight up to 147,000 pounds.

Large cargo trucks and semis get about 5-6 miles per gallon of diesel, although different trucks get fuel economy in a range from 4-8. Going up a steep hill, a truck's mileage might drop down to about 2.5 mpg, while going down the same hill will raise it to more than 25 mpg. New fuel-economy standards that take effect beginning in 2014 will require semi trucks with a sleeper cab to get 7.2 mpg on level roads. Not an easy, but achievable, task.

Thousands of semis travel non-stop along the U.S. highways. Travelled distance has been increasing steadily with time: from about 60 billion miles in 1970, to over 100 billion in 1980, and nearly 300 billion miles in 2009.

This is a lot of driving: a lot of miles, a lot of money, a lot of fuel, and a lot of pollution.

NOTE: Semis stop periodically to refuel and for the drivers to rest. During those times the engines are kept running. Overnight idling by sleepers and long-duration idling during workdays amounts to over **2 billion gallons of diesel** fuel wasted every year by semis' and work trucks' idling.

Air Travel

The global emissions have been rising non-stop during the last 50 years, which is what happens when fuel is cheap and GHG emissions are totally free. Because of this inequality, very few people and companies are looking into ways to save energy—let alone reduce GHG gasses emissions.

A good example is the fact that commercial transatlantic flights—which are a huge fuel consumer and GHG emitter—can reduce their fuel consumption by roughly 2% by making small modifications in operating procedures. Flying at optimal altitudes for maximum efficiency rather than arbitrary altitudes set by air traffic controllers is one of those small ways, which requires some education of the involved personnel and no technological improvements or investment.

This is basically a *zero pain with 2% gain* plan with no takers.

The current traffic levels in the key transatlantic market call for 50,000 two-way flights annually, each one using 50 metric tons of fuel on the average. So, a 2% saving adds up quickly to about a grand total of 50,000 tons jet fuel saved annually. In monetary terms, this is over 150 million dollars saved by the air companies annually. Still there are no takers...

Similar savings can be had in other markets. Less fuel burned means less GHG emissions, which are especially damaging when released at high altitudes. The question is why such trivial measures were not explored until now? The answer is that airlines began to pay serious attention to their fuel consumption only after recent rises in the cost of jet fuel, beginning in 2008 when oil prices approached nearly $150 per barrel for the first time.

They became even more interested in fuel consumption only after the European commission began talking about putting restrictions on GHG emissions associated with air transportation, believed to represent roughly 3% of global GHG emissions.

Two observations:

- If energy costs are small, they escape attention
- Regulations are needed to prompt energy conservation on of all sizes and on all levels

Airplanes

Airplanes use special type of aviation fuel, which consists of petroleum-based compounds. It is generally of a higher quality than fuels used in most other applications, such as power generation, heating or road transport. Aviation fuel also contains special additives to reduce the risk of icing, explosion due to high temperatures, and a number of other properties.

The aviation fuels today are types of petroleum based mixtures, when used in piston and Wankel rotary engines, while jet turbine engines use special jet fuel A or A-1, which is also used in diesel-type aircraft engines.

The Boeing 747 type airplanes have four engines, which consume jet A or jet A-1 fuel. The smallest, 747-100 carries a maximum of 48,445 gallons of fuel, while 747-200, and 300 each carry 52,410 gallons. The largest of the bunch, 747-400, carries 57,285 gallons.

This corresponds to maximum range of 6100, 7900, 7700, and 7260 statute miles respectively for each 747 model.

NOTE: While fuel capacity is calculated in gallons, fuel consumption is calculated in pounds.

Flight plans for Boeing 747-200 or 300 allow for 2200 pounds of fuel to be used for taxi and up to take off. An additional 33,000 pounds of fuel are used during take off and climbing to cruising altitude. On the average, the aircraft consumes 28,000 pounds of fuel per hour during the first half of the flight.

After that it lightens as a lot of fuel is burned and at the end of the trip, the fuel consumption drops to about 21,000 pounds per hour, while descending and landing consume the least fuel, around 6000 pounds.   W h e n most of the fuel is gone, the aircraft consumes only 1000 pounds of fuel, less than half of what it needed to taxi before take off. There is always a reserve of 25,000 to 40,000 pounds left in the fuel tanks to allow for emergency maneuvers if and when necessary.

So, a 747-400 on a 10-hour transoceanic flight burns:

- 2,200 lbs during taxiing
- 33,000 lbs during take off and climb to cruising altitude
- 140,000 lbs (28,000 lbs. during each of the initial 5 hours)
- 105 lbs. (21,000 lbs, during each of the following 5 hours), and
- 6,000 lbs. during final decent, landing, and taxing, or 286,200 lbs. total fuel burned during one 10-hour flight.

This is almost 42,000 gallons of fuel burned during one single flight. Jet fuel A and A-1 weigh 6.84 pounds per gallon.

At the same time, airplanes exhaust hot gasses, which are considered serious pollutants (GHGs) of several types. The pollution is created at the airport during fueling, takeoff and landing, and also while the aircraft is in flight. The principle emissions are carbon dioxide, nitrogen oxide and water.

Particulate emissions (usually in form of sulfur compounds) act as nuclei for cloud formation which reduces the amount of sunlight reaching the Earth, while at the same time increases the greenhouse effect, which is blamed for the increase in global warming.

Noise is one of the biggest complaints of people living under an approach route to busy airports.

There are also increased GHG emissions during fueling and taxiing, which is when engines exhaust composition changes and cause increased hydrocarbon emissions, all of which also contribute to photochemical smog.

At times aircrafts are forced to dump fuel into the air to reduce fire hazards. No doubt, this procedure is accepted as absolutely necessary for passenger safety, but it still contributed to significant hydrocarbon levels increase. Any driver of land-based vehicle dumping fuel anywhere would be severely punished, which is not the case with pilots.

Mass Transport

There are many forms of mass transport today that use huge quantities of fuel and emit enormous dust and GHG pollution. In addition to airplanes, we use millions of trains, buses, taxis, ferries, boats, cruise ships to transport goods and people from place to place. They all contribute to the demise of the fossils and damage the environment.

Buses

Buses are the most widespread form of local public transport in the U.S., where more than 1,000 inter-city and suburban bus companies operate services to around 15,000 cities and towns, the vast majority of which have no other public transport services.

The bus network covers around 280,000 miles of roads, on which some 350 million passengers are carried annually. Each region has its own bus companies providing local town and country services.

There are two main kinds of bus service in the U.S.: urban bus services and long-distance buses.

The urban bus services consist of local city, suburban and rural bus services that are provided by a number of local bus companies. Many cities also have other types of buses, like trolley buses, operated electrically from overhead wires. The New York City Transit Authority (NYCTA) operates the world's largest fleet of buses. About 4,400 public buses move nearly 700 million people per year on routes not served by the subway system, such as cross-town (East-West) routes and outlying areas. This is a lot of driving non-stop 16-20 hours every day.

Long-distance buses transport people to all major U.S. cities and are the cheapest and most popular form of public transport in the U.S., particularly among the poor, the car-less, the eccentrics, and many other interesting types. Greyhound is the largest provider of intercity bus travel, with over 2,300 destinations and 13,000 daily departures across the U.S.

There is not enough data to put all this into gallons of fuel used and GHG gasses emitted, but it is not hard to imagine that the numbers would be staggering.

School buses are an unconventional mode of transportation, which only very rich countries can afford. Every day in the U.S., nearly 500,000 buses make estimated 10 billion student trips every year, transporting about 26 million children to and from schools and school-related activities. This is over half of the country's student population transported by school buses that are leased or purchased by school districts. About 40% of school districts use school bus contractors to transport students, while in Canada they are used almost universally.

A school bus gets 4-5 miles per gallon, so an average daily 50 miles stop-and-go trip per each bus would use about 10 gallons of diesel. All school buses will then burn 5,000,000 gallons of diesel in one day. In a year this would come to over 1 billion gallons of diesel used to transport students.

Trains

Railroad companies in the U.S. are generally separated into three categories based on their annual revenues: Class I for freight railroads with annual operating revenues above $346.8 million (2006 dollars); Class II for freight railroads with revenues between $27.8 million and $346.7 million (in 2000 dollars); and Class III for all other freight revenues.

In 1900, there were 132 Class I railroads. Today, as the result of mergers, bankruptcies, and major changes in the regulatory definition of "Class I," there are only seven railroads operating in the U.S. that meet the criteria for Class I. As of 2011, U.S. freight railroads operated about 140,000 route-miles of standard gauge in the U.S., which makes it the world's longest national railroad network.

NOTE: Trains are huge bulks of metal, carrying huge amounts of weight. Each car weighs more than 50 tons empty and could easily carry that much or more cargo. A typical train in the U.S. West hauls well over 10,000 tons. And yet our average train gets about 400 miles per gallon per ton, which is about 5-10 miles per gallon of diesel to propel an entire 100-car train. Amazing…

U.S. railroads still play a major role in the nation's people moving, and even more in freight shipping. Trains carried 750 billion ton-miles by 1975, and 1.5 trillion ton-miles in 2005. In the 1950s, the U.S. and Europe had roughly the same percentage of freight by rail, but by 2000, the share of U.S. rail freight was 38% while in Europe only 8% of freight traveled by rail. In 1997 U.S. trains moved 2,165 billion ton-kilometers of freight, the E.U. trains moved only 238 billion ton-kilometers of freight.

All this equates to millions of gallons of diesel used, and lots of GHG and dust emissions.

Water Transport

To this we could add millions of private and commercial boats dashing over the nation's waterways. There were close to 17 million privately owned and operated boats in 2000 in the U.S. alone. Most of those have some sort of a gas or diesel engine for propulsion.

Adding to this number thousands of commercial boats, including fishing, cargo, oil tankers, and cruise ships, and we get another huge number of engines that use millions of gallons of fuel and emit that much GHGs into the atmosphere.

Personal Transport

But the greatest fuel guzzler is the personal transport vehicle, which is blamed for increasing pollution in most world capitals and major cities. There are over 200 million personal use cars, trucks and vans in the U.S. alone. Worldwide, those vehicles are in excess of 1 billion and their number is growing daily. Just take a look at the big picture: millions of people wake up every day and jump into their cars and trucks, headed to work or some personal or business activity. The amount of fuel burned and pollution emitted every day is mind- boggling!

If each of those vehicles burns only a gallon a day... you get the picture.

Figure 8-32. Los Angeles fog and smog

Living in some major cities in this world is becoming increasingly hazardous. And the problem is not only in China or India. Thick smog covers the downtown and the surrounding areas of all large cities in the U.S. as well. Los Angeles looks just like Beijing during some summer smog-filled days.

The toxic gasses and particles in the smog cover, the majority of which is caused by personal transport vehicles, are harmful to people—especially those with compromised immune systems—so we are faced with a variety of health issues and deaths as a result.

The total amount of fuel (gas and diesel) used by all those guzzlers on daily basis is mind-boggling. The pollution that comes with it is overwhelming. Looking at all this one doesn't have to be a scientist to figure out that:

1. Using this much fuel will come to an abrupt end some day, when the oil deposits are depleted

2. Emitting this much pollution will overwhelm the natural environment sooner or later

The only rational conclusion then is that we are blindly rushing towards a fossil-less future—if we survive the environmental damage we are causing.

THE WORLD ENERGY AND ENVIRONMENTAL STATUS

There are several developments of late shaping the present and future of energy use and our environment. The key developments are:

1. Switching from coal to natural gas power generation—the real thing?
2. Nuclear power decrease—talk or reality?
3. Renewables (solar and wind) power generation increase—temporary?

Gas vs. Coal

Switching from coal-fired power generation to natural gas is the biggest thing ever in the power generation sector. Huge gas discoveries and low prices, combined with reduced emissions and now regulations, have made coal-fired power plants obsolete.

Due to EPA's lowering the emissions limits, no new coal power plants can be built in the U.S. This regulation, which probably will be duplicated around the world, transformed the battle of the giants (gas vs. coal) into a slaughter, where coal has no chance.

Coal-fired power plants presently generate about 43% of the electric power, while natural gas-fired power generation is only about 22% of the mix. If everything goes according to the plans, and no major disasters befall the industry, the ratio is expected to reverse by 2035. At that time, natural gas will generate over half (53%) of the nation's electricity, where coal will settle to a distant second place with about 20% of the mix.

The Nuclear Dilemma

Nuclear is the most reliable, cleanest and cheapest energy source on one hand, yet a merciless killer on the other. We need it, we want it, and at the same time we

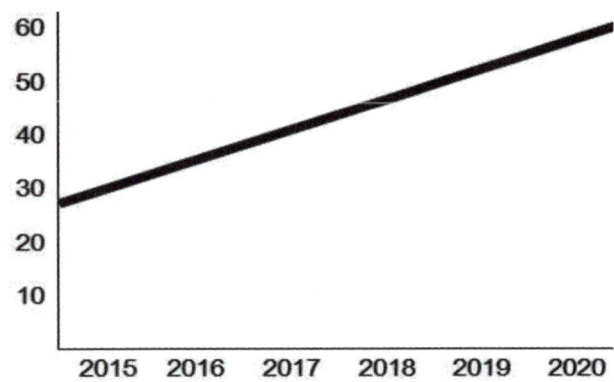

Figure 8-33. Coal-fired power plants retirements (in GW)

are scared to death of it. Some governments are shuttering their nuclear facilities, while others are building new nuclear power plants. But most are hesitating, so the future of nuclear energy is uncertain.

Nuclear power generation is also expected to diminish by a factor of two by 2035 from 18% presently down to 9% by that time.

<u>The Renewables</u>

European PV installations have been estimated to fall by more than 6 GW in 2013 compared to 2012. Those installations are 3 GW lower than previously predicted due mostly to anti-dumping duties against Chinese module manufacturers. The European commission's 11.8% duty on Chinese solar imports accounts for 1.3 GW of that total.

Nevertheless, and despite this dramatic fall, global solar installations grew at a double-digit rate to 35 GW in 2013 driven by a surge in demand in Asia. This is up 11% from 2012.

The analysts predict that the E.U. duties on Chinese PV modules, as well as other factors, will accelerate the decline in European installations, with the biggest falls occurring in Germany and Italy. The decline is actually caused by a shift from Chinese to non-Chinese made PV modules, since the higher tariffs prevent dumping of cheap Chinese products.

Competition is what drives the markets to develop, with the U.S. as a good example. Here the number of installations boomed after tariffs on Chinese PV modules helped the U.S. solar industry come back to a level playing field. A number of competitors, including global ones, came into the American market.

Despite the huge fall in European demand, the global PV market grew in 2013, with solar installations hitting 35 GW, up 11% from 31 GW in 2012.

Asia remains the driving force for this growth, with installations in the region predicted to exceed 15 GW for the first time, thus accounting for 45% of global demand. This will make the Asian market larger than the European for the first time.

China and Japan account for the majority of this growth and will become the two largest markets based on volume, with Japan leading in terms of revenue.

For a first time no European country ranks among the top three top markets, and the 10 top ranking countries are evenly balanced across the world. The bottom ranked emerging markets are not expected to provide support amid waning demand in Europe, but they still added about 6.0 GW in 2013, up from 3.4 GW in 2012. This amount, however, is made up by more than 60 countries globally. The solar installations in those regions will grow to 9 GW in 2014 and to more than 16 GW in 2017, highlighting the need for solar companies to focus on emerging markets—and more importantly on picking the right ones.

China Today

Since launching its first five-year plan (FYP) in 1953, China's five-year plans have been both a blueprint for the immediate future and a showcase of the political economy of the day. Important as each plan has been, the evolution of the process has been neither smooth nor trouble free.

In the early years of the People's Republic, successive plans revealed some very different priorities within the ruling party and, on occasion, the tensions of other events: there was a hiatus between the second and third plans, for instance, from 1962 to 1966, following the Sino-Soviet split. The first plan had been drawn up with Soviet advice, and stressed large-scale construction, rapid heavy industrialization under increasing state control, and the beginnings of agricultural collectivization. In many respects, the plan was successful, with rapid growth in iron and steel output, mining and energy.

Although the gains had been huge, some critics were beginning to voice concern over the unsustainability of this model of rapid industrialization and the government's emphasis on GDP growth above every other factor. The 10th FYP included some environmental targets: to increase forest coverage to 18.2%, to raise the urban green rate to 35%, and to reduce urban and rural pollutants by 10% compared to 2000.

The government's prime concern for the 12th FYP (issued in 2011) is the related question of re-balancing a society that has suffered from a severely uneven distribution of the benefits of growth. To meet its ambition of encouraging domestic consumption, the government needs to raise the share of the national income enjoyed by ordinary people.

One aspect of the plan that could have profound effects is the ambition to move small farmers into rural conurbations of up to 250,000 people, allowing for a better delivery of services and more efficient farming. Due to differences in development of different areas of the country, the plan may have unpredictable results.

The new 2011-2015 plan includes binding targets on resource and environmental protection, including:

Energy—16% cut in energy consumed per unit of GDP, 17% cut in carbon emitted per unit of GDP, and a boost in non-fossil fuel energy sources to 11.4% of primary energy consumption (it is currently 8.3%). An estimated 40 GW of nuclear and some hydropower will be added; 70 GW of wind power and 5 GW of solar plants are in the plan too.

By 2015, total energy use will be limited to the equivalent of 4 billion tons of coal.

NOTE: both the nuclear and solar estimates were revised in 2012. The nuclear plant permitting was suspended until further notice after the Fukushima disaster. Solar power will be increased logarithmically to offset some of the nuclear energy losses, and to accommodate the large surplus of PV modules from Chinese manufacturers.

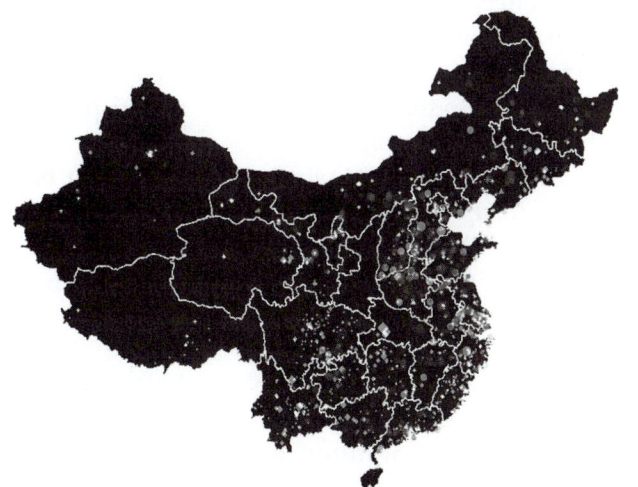

Figure 8-34. China's power plants and CO_2 emissions distribution (light areas)

Pollution—There is an 8% reduction target for sulfur dioxide and chemical oxygen demand, and a 10% reduction target for ammonia nitrogen and nitrogen oxides that come mainly from China's dominant coal sector. There will also be a focus on cutting heavy-metal pollution from industry.

As they say, "A picture is worth a thousand words," just looking at the Figure 8-35 makes you feel like the end of the world is coming. But this is actually downtown Beijing, with the most prosperous Chinese economy.

Figure 8-35. China's killer smog

- Water—water intensity (water consumed per unit of value added industrial output) will be cut by 30% by 2015

- Forestry—forestry cover will be boosted to 600 million cubic meters to cover 21.66 forested lands

- Climate—carbon taxes and carbon trading "may" be introduced, but no definite decisions have been made as yet

- Government investment in form of subsidies, grants, and loans (a la communist China) is projected to increase to 3 trillion Yuan. Most of it will go into pollution control and cut the release of major pollutants

- 35,000 km of high-speed rail will be build to connect cities over 500,000 inhabitants

- Overall, the plan's goal is to achieve average GDP growth of 7%— this is less than the present day 9-10%. It also will provide for equal distribution of benefits to alleviate the social inequality, and protect the environment.

- 36 million low-income housing units will be constructed, or renovated

- 45 million jobs will be created in urban areas, and keep unemployment below 5%. Pension schemes will cover all rural and 357 urban residents

- Population growth will be limited to 1.39 billion people and life expectancy will be increased by one full year

- Seven strategic emerging industries will be supported (a la communist China) via tax breaks, and other benefits; biotechnology, new energy, high-end equipment manufacturing, energy conservation and environmental protection, clean-energy vehicles, new materials and next-generation information technologies. Those are expected to contribute 8% to the GDP (from 5% today)

So, China willingly enters the green (r)evolution. How far those measures will be taken, and how successfully they will be implemented during the new 5-year plan remains to be seen. In the long run, it remains to be seen as well how long the Chinese Communist government can retain its stronghold on the people, and what will happen if it fails to do so. What would a new, non-Communist government do? In any case, and everything considered, we must look at China as another great natural disaster waiting to happen.

Hundreds of new coal factories are planned and under construction all around China, and their smoke will make the already bad air in the large cities even worse. Millions of new cars are clogging the already overcrowded streets, billowing toxic gasses non-stop. All this is a prelude to an upcoming crisis, which is just now beginning...

Speaking of energy and resources use, abuse, and waste, we cannot ignore the amazing new development of the so-called "Chinese ghost towns." More than 20 new large towns are built in China every year, where apartments and condominiums are erected to house millions—but no one lives there. Those are entire communities, complete with huge shopping malls, hospitals, parks, kindergartens, and uninhabited facilities.

Imagine the amount of natural resources and energy used to build those monstrosities. Imagine 50-60 million workers going to work every day, building and maintaining those monuments of inefficiency and waste.

People are buying those never-to-be-lived-in empty dwellings at an amazing rate. Some people own 5-6 properties, which they will never live in, and may even never visit. At the same time, the displaced folks are pushed into the overcrowded urban shantytowns. With this, the inequality increases daily; those who need housing cannot afford it, and are left living on the streets, while those who can afford it, have chosen to hoard as much as they can with the hope of future benefits.

The Chinese government is the prime designer, coordinator, and investor in this unsustainable reality. But there are signs lately that the contractors and investors are running out of money, so the construction has

Figure 8-36. China ghost town

slowed down in some places and stopped completely in others. The real estate bubble has grown so big, that it is very likely to collapse under its own unmanageable weight.

This is one the largest, most unusual, and awkward real estate booms the world has ever seen. If not properly controlled and contained, it might eventually result in the biggest real estate disaster the world has ever seen too. The effects of such an event would be dramatic for the Chinese political, economic, and social systems, but those who will suffer most are the middle-class Chinese who bought into the illusion of a new reality, presented by the Chinese government.

A version of the "Arab Revolution" might be ignited in China, leading to weakening and even falling of the Communist government. In any case, this would be a cataclysmic event, the reverberations of which would be felt all around the world—including in the U.S.

China Solar

China is set to lead the world in renewable energy generation in the near future, with a target of 35 GW of installed capacity for solar power generation by 2015. This requires 10 GW to be added each year until 2015, which is a four-fold increase from the 8 GW of capacity installed as of the end of 2012, and 14 GW higher than a previously stated 2015 target of 21 GW.

The revised target is an attempt to combat changes in the newly developed market conditions, including a glut of domestically produced PV equipment in China, lack of energy, and other problems China is facing today.

The state council referred to overcapacity issues as

"severe." Falling government subsidies and trade disputes including high anti-dumping and anti-subsidy tariffs on Chinese solar products to the U.S. have also had a serious impacts.

The European commission also imposed anti-dumping tariffs and restrictions to Chinese made solar products.

The state council offered to support the Chinese domestic industry with measures aimed at stimulating growth, including elimination of outdated production capacity and the promotion of small-scale solar power generators. It has also vowed to make subsidies more efficient and to free up the market from bureaucratic buffers, including access to cheap land and greater encouragement of mergers and acquisitions.

The insiders claim that China would struggle to meet the target because of the absence of infrastructure to meet intermittent energy capability and a lack of funding for solar subsidies; nevertheless, most believe that 21 GW by 2015 is a more achievable target than the state council's wished-for 35 GW.

In a desperate move to save face and to prevent more solar company failures, the Chinese government decided in the summer of 2013 to limit the construction of new solar products manufacturing facilities. The move is intended to also cut down excess capacity within the country's ailing solar industry.

The new decision targets new solar manufacturing plants that are intended to "purely" expand capacity, which will not be permitted. This will most likely bring about industry consolidation, and will encourage healthier companies to absorb assets from distressed firms rather than build new capacity.

Actually, the government has been pushing for consolidation within the solar industry for a while now, but progress has been quite slow. Many struggling tier-2 and some tier-1 manufacturers operate at massive losses and large debt loads, propped by government subsidies. Now the government will have to allow some of those firms to fail, to bring about more mergers and acquisitions within the sector.

On the other hand, the manufacturing facilities held by failing companies are likely to be less sophisticated, which may not be ideal for manufacturing high quality cells and panels. This is a problem, since many of China's top solar firms have been increasingly focusing on high value markets like Japan, Australia and the United States, where the quality and efficiency of panels are paramount. This would potentially require solar firms to invest in further developing the facilities that they acquire to bring them up to world-class standards.

In all cases, this will not happen without active government intervention.

We will watch...

China Expansion...or Not!

This is the latest development of the solar boom-bust cycle, the tail end of which we witnessed in 2013. Things were quite different 2-3 years ago, when the Chinese invasion of the U.S. and E.U. solar markets was going full blast. Some Chinese companies decided to take advantage of the situation and went even further in their intention to take over the global solar markets—they started opening manufacturing facilities in the U.S. and EU.

One such effort was by Suntech, China, which initiated a new solar modules manufacturing facility in January 2010, in Goodyear, a suburb of Phoenix, AZ. Amidst great fanfare, many local and state politicians and businessmen, headed by Arizona Gov. Jan Brewer celebrated the China-based solar company's plans to expand in Arizona.

They were foreseeing great things for Suntech and the state's solar industry. The factory was supposed to be a symbol of the budding China-U.S. cooperation, and was supposed to bring economic prosperity to the region and to the local solar development, while pumping thousands of solar modules into the solar market.

The plant started operations in the fall of 2010 with 70 employees, and was designed to manufacture 30 MW of solar modules annually. The plans were to scale up to 120 MW within a year or two. According to Suntech's officials at the time, having a facility in the U.S. would also reduce the time, costs and greenhouse gas emissions associated with shipping panels from overseas.

Figure 8-37. Suntech's Arizona operations

The Goodyear factory ramped up to a production volume of 50 MW solar modules in 2011 with total of 107 employees, but things went downhill shortly after that. Suntech's timing was exquisitely bad. It seemed as if at the time everyone was rushing to expand solar manufacturing capacity and, although demand was growing for a while, it was not at a pace sufficient to support the expanding manufacturing capacity of hundreds of Chinese manufacturers.

And then came the solar trade disputes between China and the U.S. and the budding cooperation became a bloody war. This was followed by a solar glut, which put many companies out of business. Suntech, mired in huge debt, started cutting expenses and operations all over the place. Even back home in China, Suntech and most other solar companies were (and still are) in a world of hurt.

So, finally after a two-year struggle and almost exactly three years in the local headlines, Suntech, Goodyear fell victim to the quickly changing situation, uncontrollable solar markets whims, and is no more. The company officials blamed the unpredictable solar markets, but it was actually the overly ambitious and overly subsidized Chinese solar industry strategies that brought the company down.

China's ambition to remain the world's #1 manufacturer of solar modules is still alive, but the overseas expansion tendencies have been reduced to internal struggle for survival. Expansion now, and for the foreseeable future, is possible only locally—in China and the surrounding countries.

As if to confirm the end of Chinese dominance of the world's solar markets, an Italian court ordered the seizure of 37 solar parks constructed by companies associated with Suntech's Global Solar Fund. The Court of Brindisi, Italy, ordered also the seizure of feed-in tariff payments made to the same companies due to improper collection of FiTs.

This development will be a further blow to Suntech, which is undergoing major financial restructuring after a bond default forced its Chinese subsidiary, Suntech Wuxi, into bankruptcy earlier in 2013...not a good year for the Chinese solar-leaders-wanna-be companies.

India

India is facing a serious coal shortage, which might even get worse, reaching 20% by 2015. The domestic production is leveled at approximately 800 million tons for the duration, while the minimum coal demand is 1 billion tons for the same time. The failure to reach the target was confirmed in 2012 when the over 100 million tons of monthly coal production that was planned was not achieved, and was actually leveled at only 35 million tons monthly.

Coal India, the government mining, is planning to add 180 million tons to its annual production by 2016-17, thus increasing total production to 615 million tons, compared to 435 million tons in 2011-12, but this is not certain, and even if it happens, it is still not enough.

India is the world's third largest coal producer, and imported more than 100 million tons during each of the previous years. Imports have more than doubled from about 50 million tons in 2007-08, and are now forecast at nearly 200 million tons for the future.

So, India will import 15-20% coal on a cost plus model for the fore-seeable future. But this is only one of the problems. Another major issue is the transport of such large quantities of coal from the mines to the power plants, which could be many hundreds of miles away.

The Indian railroad infrastructure is antiquated and thus inadequate for transporting more than 50% of the coal going to the power plants. Because of that, trucks are carrying millions of tons of coal to the power plants on India's roads, a messy, inefficient, and expensive business that creates another set of environmental and safety issues for the Indian government and the locals to deal with.

Figure 8-38. Coal transport a la India

The state-run Coal India Ltd. has proposed a solution to solve the country's coal shortage. They have suggested expanding the mining in the Indian forests in a big way. "Our future growth has to come from forest areas," according to S. Narsing Rao, Coal India's President. But will it? Probably not...

Mining in forest areas has been a controversial subject in power-starved India. Environmental concerns forced a ban on mining in those areas in 2009, but the decision was overturned recently. So now mining in forest areas is technically allowed, but getting approval to mine coal in those areas is very difficult. Delays in environmental clearances, among other bureaucratic and infrastructure hurdles, are a burden for Coal India, which meets more than 80% of the country's coal requirement, making it crucial to India's economic growth.

More than half of India's total coal resource of 285 billion tons falls in forested areas. However, delays in environmental clearances prevent companies from realizing their output potential. Getting a green light to mine in forest areas can take as long as four years under the present regulations, which has led the industry to demand a more effective system to secure clearances.

Most of India's coal-based power stations have been operating at a low level of coal stocks to generate electricity. The coal shortages, which became significantly worse over the past couple of years, threaten long-range plans to increase generating capacity. The government intends to raise capacity by 44%, to 288 GW, by 2017, most of which will come from new coal-fired plants.

The coal shortages, including the stagnant coal production and rising prices over the past two years, are the main reason of the frequent power cuts, some of which affect the entire country.

In conclusion, India is buried up to its eyebrows in coal. The only preoccupation of India's government is how to meet the coal quotas to generate enough power for its fast-growing population. Energy efficiency and environmental issues are not on the agenda, and won't be on it for a long time to come. So, in the meanwhile India will be adding new coal-fired plants as fast as it can. It will be also blasting millions of tons of toxic gasses into the air, and dumping many more millions of tons of toxic liquids on the ground.

Desertec

The Desertec Foundation, the Trans-Mediterranean Renewable Energy Cooperation (TREC) and the National Energy Research Center, Jordan, developed the Desertec industrial initiative (DII) as a concept in the late 2000s. Scientists, and energy and environmental experts from Europe, the Middle East, and North Africa (EU-MENA) put their heads together to come up with a plan to create a global renewable energy program based on the concept of generating electric power in the deserts. The North African deserts are exceptionally suitable for generating wind and solar power for local use and for transferring the excess through high-voltage DC transmission lines for use in European countries.

DII was also supposed to take into account land and water use in its plans and to provide an integrated solution to food and water shortages in the coming decades. Building and powering desalination plants to provide freshwater to the MENA region was also in the original plan.

Scientific studies demonstrated that the desert sun in MENA countries could be used to generate a lot of power as needed to meet the rising power demand, and could reduce GHG emissions across the region. A new study called desert power 2050 was published in 2012, which confirmed that the MENA region would be able to meet its power needs by using wind and solar power. Excess power would be also generated and exported to Europe, thus creating an export industry with an annual volume of more than €60 billion.

This way DII would kill two birds with one stone; it would create thousands of jobs and provide plentiful power to MENA countries, while at the same time saving about €30/MWh for some European consumers.

It is a wonderful idea, no doubt! But like many other such ideas where many participants are involved, it is not easy to agree on the path to take, let alone take and implement difficult decisions. So, DII is now going through growing pains. In the summer of 2013, bad things started happening, leaving us wondering if this is the end, or a new beginning for DII.

- First, in the fall of 2012, one of the principal members and full shareholder in DII, the Siemens Group, did not renew its membership in the initiative.

Siemens has been supporting DII in the past with its technical expertise, and took over Israel-based solar thermal manufacturer Solel Solar Systems in 2009, which was one of the founding members of DII. The initiative was not implementing any specific projects, so Siemens decided to sell Solel as part of its austerity program. No buyer was found, so in the summer of 2013, Siemens decided to exit its solar business all together.

Siemens' exit from the DII project is a heavy loss of a major German technology partner and investor for DII.

- Around the same time, Bosch, another German industrial giant, bailed out of the DII. Bosch claimed that economic conditions do not allow a continuation of its membership in the venture. This marks the second German company to leave the consortium within the space of a month or so.

- Then, one of DII's principal members; the DESERTEC Foundation terminated its partnership with DII due to irresolvable disputes between the two entities in the area of future strategies, obligations and their communication, as well as the managerial style of DII's top management.

So, the supervisory board of the foundation decided to decouple from the industrial initiative, but the dispute at the management level escalated and has already led to resentment among some of the partners.

Update 2013

Presently, the DII consists of 21 companies and 36 partners, including France, Germany and Italy. Its short-term goal (and the first actual project) is to build a solar thermal (CSP) power plant in Morocco with an electricity generation capacity of 500 MW. That is the power equivalent to about half of a modern nuclear power plant, to be generated mostly from solar and wind energy.

That's not bad as a first project, but we have learned a lot from similar projects in the U.S. and Europe, so here are the problems facing the Morocco thermal solar project:

- High costs are expected to hinder the financing of the project. The cost is estimated at €3.5/watt for the installation, plus another €0.50/watt cost for high voltage transmission, plus O&M cost too. That is a lot of money, considering that solar PV already costs less than that to install, and its O&M costs are almost nothing. On top of that, solar PV technology is projected to decrease in price, which—everything considered—might bring it to half of the CSP technology price by 2020.

- The political turmoil in the MENA region has been going for several years now and seems to be growing. The success of the DII project depends on full cooperation and unprecedented coordination among more than 40 countries in Europe and MENA. The principal countries, Algeria, Morocco, Egypt, and other MENA countries, are politically unstable and socially volatile, so the concerns about the future of any projects undertaken on their territory are legitimate.

- Terrorist attacks and rogue regimes are to be expected in the MENA region. The power plants and transmission lines would become a terrorist target, thus increasing the O&M cost of the generated electricity. The possibility of rogue regimes taking control of MENA countries and the DII projects is another serious concern.

- Water issues related to solar thermal plants operation are also serious. CSP uses lots of water, which in desert areas just is not available. Dry cooling can be used, but it raises the initial and O&M costs of CSP projects too much. Using seawater is not practical, because it requires building the CSP plants very near the coastline, which is not ideal for CSP technology and might result in significant loss of efficiency.

- Ecological and cultural issues are expected to be heavily impacted by the use of millions of mirrors. Desert wildlife would be endangered, as we have already seen happening in the U.S. deserts. There are also cultural issues with some of the Muslim countries, who have a problem dealing with non-Muslim countries. This is a serious concern, the effects of which cannot be fully appreciated and estimated before the project is finished and operational.

- Energy dependence is Europe's Achilles heel. It is held hostage by the Russian gas baron's whims and massive oil imports. Depending on DII for electric power is no different, since it will only replace one form of energy dependence with another.

- Management anomalies are holding the DII project back. The exit of several major partners throws a shadow of a doubt on the entire undertaking. DII also needs massive subsidies by European countries, about which the taxpayers won't be very happy.

In summary, while the DII project sounds like the best solution to both MENA and the E.U. problems, its location and present political and economic conditions in the region do not promise a successful long-term venture. No doubt, some work will be done in the area and we just have to watch and see, but unless some drastic changes take place soon, we see DII lingering for a while, idling a bit longer, and then disappearing all together until better times come to the MENA region.

Europe's Coal Conundrum

There is new development in Europe that is hard to explain, let alone justify, in terms of environmental effects.

While the U.S. is shutting down coal-fired power plants, or retrofitting them for natural gas fuel, Europe is doing the opposite. There are many idling gas-fired power stations, which is holding back Europe's consumption of the natural gas fuel. This anomaly is due mostly to competition from the renewable energy sources (wind and solar), and rising prices of natural gas imports. The use of coal-power generation is increasing significantly in the E.U., and with it the GHG emissions are on the increase as well. If this trend continues, the E.U. will become just like China.

The share of natural gas in Germany's electricity output fell by 2.3 percentage points to 11.3% in 2012 from a year earlier, according to insiders. The estimates are that the total demand will drop another 3.5% to 550 billion cubic meters in 2015, according to the International Energy Agency.

The switch from gas to coal in Europe is a very serious retrograde step from a climate change perspective. It is worst in Germany, where building new coal power stations is underway, thus locking the country in excess GHG emissions for another generation.

RWE AG (RWE) is Germany's second-largest utility and largest GHG emitter, with an increase of 11% more GHG gases in 2012, mostly due to increased coal-fired power generation. That way the utilities ensure their profitability at the expense of carbon emissions. The situation has been encouraged by the collapse in carbon permits to record lows, cutting the cost of burning coal, thus allowing the utilities to switch back from gas to coal.

Under the new conditions, operating gas-fired power plants—new or existing—is not profitable, regardless of how clean, efficient and good for the climate and the country they may be. The utilities are not willing to run plants at a loss. As a matter of fact, turning the situation around will require more natural gas-fired power plant closures.

European utilities also need to shut down about 30% of all fossil fuel fired stations to counter increasing production from renewable sources—mainly wind turbines and solar. As a consequence, natural gas-fired power plants are getting shut down first.

Electricity output from French gas-fired plants dropped 24% in 2012, and the utilities plan to close or mothball 10,000 MW of capacity across Europe, mostly gas plants. Centrica Energy Plc. is considering permanently closing at least one gas-fired facility in the U.K. this year. EON has already withdrawn two gas plants from the grid, reserving them only for periods of peak demand. RWE, where plants are operating near half their capacity, will idle two units for six months in 2013.

Germany…Back to Coal?

After almost a decade on the forefront of energy efficiency and environmental consciousness, Germany is reverting to the old ways of coal-burning. It is hard to believe, but true; a new trend is shaping up in Germany and some of the E.U. countries, and coal is making a great comeback.

Three years ago, Germany's largest utility spent $523 million building the EON SE's Irsching-5 in Bavaria, a natural gas-fired power plant. In the summer of 2013, the company closed the plant because it's losing so much money.

EON SE's Irsching-5 in Bavaria operated less than 25% of the time in 2012 as slumping power prices made burning natural gas unprofitable by record margins. As Europe's weak economy holds back electricity demand, cheaper coal, requirements to buy renewable energy and the collapsing cost of carbon permits are undercutting gas-fired plants.

The pattern is repeated throughout Europe as utilities, including France's GDF Suez SA and Centrica Plc., mothball gas plants. The impact is both environmental and commercial. Switching to coal increases emissions while it lowers profit for gas plants, which generate almost a quarter of European power. This also shrinks the market for suppliers led by OAO Gazprom. Russia's Gazprom lost its position as Europe's largest gas supplier to Norway in 2012 as shipments of Russian gas dropped significantly

Gas-fired plants in some areas are idling three days out of four, which puts the industry in crisis, since there is justifiable (but dangerous) overcapacity. This caused the difference between the cost of fuel and the price paid for the power generated to reach a record low in the summer of 2013. The so-called spark spread for the month ahead fell to as low as minus $23.87 per MWh.

Gas plants are also unprofitable in France, the Netherlands, Spain and the Czech Republic, while in the U.K. they're barely breaking even. At the same time new, or retrofitted, coal-fired power plants are profitable in every European market, as coal prices drop.

What happened with the plans for GHG reduction, which were led by Europe—and Germany in particular—until recently? Now Europe, led by Germany, is changing direction and will certainly lead the world in increase of GHGs.

European Solar

Europe has the world's largest number of power plants and capacity of solar power generation. Concentrated solar power (CSP) plants have a total installed capacity of nearly 2.0 GW as of the end 2012. Approximately 3.4 million m^2 of solar thermal collectors (solar water heaters) were installed in the E.U. at the same time, for an installed base of nearly 30.0 GWth.

But both markets are facing difficulties worldwide. The experts predict a global total of 8.0 GW in 2015, 12.0 GW in 2017, and about 20.0 GW in 2020. This is a drastic reduction of previous predictions of nearly 150 GW installed in 2020.

CSP installations had a banner year in Europe in 2012, when 17 new plants with a capacity totaling 802.5 MW came online. The number of projects under construction in 2013 is significantly smaller. Europe's solar thermal (solar water heating) market fell 5.5% in 2012 from the previous year. The main reasons for this downturn are pressure from the PV sector and a government moratorium on new solar power generation. This, combined with drastic subsidy cuts for new solar projects and a 7% tax on energy generation, has crippled the solar market.

Europe CSP

Spain was the world's number one market for CSP as well as solar water heating. Spain added 802.5 MW in 2012 for a total capacity of nearly 2,000 MW, which generated over 5,100 GWh during the year. Of the total 42 plants, 37 were parabolic trough plants, three were power tower plants and two use linear Fresnel collectors.

Capacity additions included a number of significant projects such as: Termosolar's 22.5 MW Borges CSP facility, coupled to a biomass generator and running 24/7; and Novotec's 30 MW Puerto Errado 2, currently the largest Fresnel plant in operation.

Spain's largest developer, Abengoa Solar, was a 20% owner of Abu Dhabi's 100 MW Shams 1, and is building a 150 MW plant in South Africa, a 280 MW plant in the U.S., and a 470 MW hybrid solar-gas plant in Mexico.

2013 began well for Spain too, with two 50 MW plants from NextEra Energy, Termosol 1 and 2, coming online, bringing the nation past the 2.0 GW installed capacity mark with 2053.9 MW of total installed capacity. Six more parabolic trough plants are currently under construction, as well as three new plants using parabolic dish technology.

And then came the February's energy reform, which put an end to the boom. That forced most CSP developers to turn to other countries for new projects. Jobs in the sector dropped from 28,885 in 2011 to 17,862 in 2012.

Italy is now set to develop a full-blown CSP sector given its highly attractive FIT in effect as of December 2012. Licensing applications for over 200 MW in Ital-

ian projects have been filed by companies such as Enel Green Power and Energogreen, most of which will use parabolic trough technology with molten salt as the heat transfer fluid.

France's CSP sector is going slowly, with construction on the first industrial-sized demonstration facility, while Solar Euromed's 12 MW Alba Nova 1 in Corsica still on hold. A July 2012, tender also resulted in CNIM's 9 MW project at Llo in the Pyrenees Orientales, which EurObserv'ER estimates will be commissioned in 2015. Areva Solar is the only French company active on the international market and claims 300 MW of operational or under-construction CSP projects.

Slowing growth is taking its toll on the industry, pointing to a restructuring phase. As a result, Siemens exited both the CSP and PV markets in 2012, only three years after buying Israel's Solel Solar Systems Ltd, and after only 300 MW of completed projects.

German parabolic trough receiver manufacturer Schott also restructured its CSP business, closing its 400 MW U.S. plant; the company said that the move was designed to improve its chances of winning major contracts in the Middle East.

Most European nations are drifting further and further away from meeting their initial and maybe overly enthusiastic solar goals. For example, Spain's target of 3048 MW by 2015 will be lucky to reach 2386 MW, and only if all planned projects are commissioned. France's 2015 target of 203 MW will be cut to 21 MW at most. Portugal, Greece and Cyprus have also set targets, but sector takeoff in those countries is on hold with nothing planned before 2015.

Italy is the only country set to keep up the solar flame, with the first projects to be commissioned in 2015.

Europe Solar Water Heating

The European solar water heating market contracted for four consecutive years, ending up at 3,395,420 m² of glazed solar collectors in 2012, a 5% drop from 2011. The E.U. solar water heater market fell by 1.2 million m² during the last four years. This is mostly due to the increased use of PV modules and efficient heat pumps, which have put pressure on the sector, especially in Germany where PV dominates the domestic solar energy market.

Germany installed more than 1 million m² solar water heaters per year, had a slight market pickup in 2011, which faded in 2012. Recession conditions in Spain, Italy and Portugal, which resulted in a construction sector crash, are hindering solar water heating development. Austria enjoyed increased incentives, but did not show any progress in this area, while in the U.K. the solar market contracted significantly.

The French market is holding steady thanks to development of the multi-occupancy sector. Greece, Poland, Hungary and Denmark are also seeing increase due to a rise in gas and heating oil prices.

The German Renewable Energy Act

In the summer of 2013, the European Commission sharpened its focus on Germany's Renewable Energy Act, due to possible violations of European Union competition regulations. German companies that have profited from incentives could be forced to pay back millions in back payments. The investigation into Germany's controversial renewable energy subsidy policy is said to favor energy-intensive domestic companies over European rivals.

The Renewable Energy Act was originally introduced in 2000, but was later amended in 2009, and again in 2012. It is aimed at subsidizing renewable energy companies and projects, providing feed-in incentives and promoting the development of renewable energy technologies by mandating an energy surcharge from electricity consumers.

The problem for the European Commission is a loophole in the legislation that provides energy-intensive companies with an exemption from the levy due to the possible threat of increased international competition, which may actually prove a competitive disadvantage for most European rivals.

The law has also forced private consumers and SMEs, which do not qualify for the discounts, to pick up the bill for exempted companies. The commission had received a complaint from a German association that represents private consumers and small and medium-sized enterprises regarding the reduced surcharge for energy intensive companies.

A preliminary investigation is underway, where the EC is looking into the complaint, specifically the reduced surcharge for energy intensive undertakings as well as support for renewables under the new financing system introduced in 2012. The E.U. is examining whether those measures constitute state aid in the meaning of the treaty and whether, if so, they comply with applicable state aid rules and other treaty provisions.

Germany's renewable energy law has allowed a wide range of companies, from brown coal mining facilities to public transportation companies, to obtain exemptions from having to pay the renewable energy surcharge. In some cases, companies only have to pay 1% of the surcharge.

The E.U. Commission has come to the conclusion that rebates for energy-intensive businesses violate European competition law and is focusing on the economic advantages that the law has had for German companies and whether the exemptions are not only protecting them against competitive disadvantages, but whether they might also be providing an edge over rivals from fellow E.U. member states.

The investigation could lead to companies not only losing future entitlements, but also having to pay back millions already obtained through the exemptions. The rules that determine who can benefit from the discounts are vague and have resulted in questionable practices, such as the exemption of some public transportation companies, including Berlin's BVG and the MVG in Munich, which clearly do not face international competition in Germany.

For example, Vattenfall Europe Mining, a subsidiary of Swedish giant Vattenfall, which operates several coalmines, has also benefitted from the surcharge exemption, prompting many to question the stated goals of the renewable energy law, because coal is largely considered to be a global climate enemy number one.

Spain

The Spanish government has announced a series of cuts to renewable energy subsidies totaling €2.7 billion ($3.5 billion) as part of widespread reforms to its energy policy. Solar energy producers, already hit hard by previous rounds of tariff cuts, could be further damaged by the latest reforms.

The country has a deficit of €26 billion ($33 billion) as a result of regulated electricity prices' failing to catch up with rising costs of energy. This year's deficit alone is estimated at around €4.5 billion ($5.9 billion).

The Spanish government's latest reforms will see a new system of financial returns introduced for renewable energy installations under which investors will be guaranteed "reasonable profitability" of 7.5% over six years for their investment. In addition to the subsidy changes, regulated electricity tariffs will go up by 6.5%, which translates to a 3.2% jump in customers' total bills.

Prior to the announcement, it was speculated that the government would seek to gain €900 million ($1.2 billion) through increased consumer bills and would cover no more than €900 million from its own pockets.

The Spanish PV association UNEF said it was unable at this stage to estimate precisely what effect the proposed changes would mean for the liquidity of solar installations, but said it was unlikely the proposals would "not have a strong impact" on the sector.

The most recent energy sector reforms passed in Spain is the fourth time that a sweeping set of retroactive changes has rocked the country's solar energy industry. This new royal decree law, passed in the summer of 2013, modifies billions of Euros worth of renewable energy contracts. When those are added to the previous retroactive measures, the insolvencies across the sector will increase dramatically.

The $3.5 billion retroactive cost cut for the renewable energy sector have left project developers, manufacturers, and consumers reeling.

The major problem is that legislators in Spain are trying to address the crumbling economy and the rapid growth of the electricity system deficit, which now stands at €26 billion. The deficit was created over the last fifteen years as the costs of generating electricity have risen faster than what utilities can lawfully recover. The cause of all this is primarily due to the fact that the government limits the amount by which electricity prices can increase, while at the same time throwing billions of euros at wind and solar power generation.

Spain encouraged private investment in wind and solar power partly to meet binding E.U. climate and energy targets, partly to improve its energy security, and partly to encourage the development of new economic sectors.

While FITs are proven to be the most cost-effective means of accelerating investment in renewable energy, the Spanish FITs were extremely generous, so they are partially responsible for the present debacle. The biggest problem, however, is that the government, through regulations dating back decades, prevented utilities from recovering the true costs of the electricity system through higher rates.

Spain tried to have it both ways: it set out to transform its electricity system, but went around it the wrong way and simply failed to establish credible mechanisms to pay for it.

- *Lesson one:* The tragedy of the Spanish situation is that a policy mechanism based on providing long-term investment certainty, which has proven uniquely successful at scaling-up renewable energy investment worldwide, became a victim of policy and regulatory uncertainty. That resulted in imposing unsustainable costs on ratepayers, a lose-lose situation.

- *Lesson two:* FITs are a powerful mechanism for attracting investment in renewable energy, and accelerating the transition to a cleaner and lower carbon power sector. They provide long-term,

performance-based contracts for electricity that is generated from renewable energy sources, which helps to attract private investment, and engages the customers, businesses and investors directly in the transformation of the electricity system. FITs have been implemented in over 80 jurisdictions around the world, and despite all the criticism, they remain one of the most widely used renewable energy policies.

- *Lesson three:* A comprehensive policy to scale-up privately financed renewable energy investment is needed, but a credible, long-term mechanism to ensure that those costs are recovered over time must be established as well. Ensuring that the overall framework has the broad support of the customers and that it will be robust to changes in governments and overall economic conditions is essential.

- *Lesson four:* A fundamental transition in the energy system can only be sustained if it is built on a sound financial footing, and if it has the broad support of the customers. Customers' consensus is tested in Spain and even in Germany, while the different parties finalize their positions for continuing the fight during the new administration.

Owners of solar power plants in Spain, which has more than 4.0 GW of installed capacity, will be hit hard with months of uncertainty concluding with the government's definitive changes. Consumers will also be hit hard with increased levies on self-consumed solar energy that is now so high that many will pay more for the electricity they generate themselves than they would for the regular grid power.

In summary: The Spanish government is faced with dire economic circumstances, compounded by a deficit in its energy budget of $34 billion, on top of which it will still spend as much as $10.5 billion a year on renewable energy subsidies, even after the latest cuts.

Can Spain afford all this and remain a viable member of the European Union? We will just have to wait and see. Only one thing is for sure now; the Spanish renewable energy sector (wind and solar) is badly damaged and will suffer for a long time. Many Spanish companies and projects will fail in the future, but at least, we have the lessons the Spaniards left us, so let's hope that those lessons are not repeated.

United Kingdom

A report presented to the U.K. Parliament estimates that the spare power generation capacity is expected to fall from 14% in 2012 to 4% over the next 3-4 years.

Tough environmental targets, financial instability and ageing power stations are what contribute most to the predicted energy shortage. The dangers ahead for the U.K.'s electricity generation capacity are serious and reflect widely held concerns within the energy industry.

There are a number of additional uncertainties in the U.K.'s energy future. For example, the EU's large combustion plant directive (LCPD) sets a legal limit on the level of emissions allowed by plants built before 1987, but their operational hours (limited to 20,000 between 2007 and 2015 if they opt out of the directive) are running out fast. Most of those power plants are expected to close before 2015.

At the same time, the uncertain economic outlook and inefficient policies and other measures affect the demand for electricity.

EU-based environmental legislation aimed at reducing carbon footprints has a side effect, reflected in the closure of coal and oil-fired power stations in some countries. Apart from potentially increasing unemployment, closing those stations before the renewable energy sector has caught up may also result in a countrywide shortage of energy.

Amazingly enough, the U.K.—despite its poor sunlight availability—has a good number of solar power installations; **about 230,000 solar power projects were recorded in the U.K. in 2011. The** total generating capacity in the country was about 750 MW, which rose to over 1.0 GW in 2012. Solar power use has increased very rapidly in recent years as a result of reductions in the cost of photovoltaic (PV) panels, and the introduction of a FIT subsidy in 2010.

In 2012, the government said that the sun, which represents over 22.0 GW of installed solar power capacity by 2020, would power 4 million homes across the U.K.

A poll in the summer of 2013 revealed that the British public is seven times more likely to welcome a local solar farm than a gas fracking field. The survey asked respondents to rate which one local energy development they would prefer to be sited nearby: 40% chose a solar farm, 25% chose a wind farm, 10% a nuclear power station, and 6% shale gas fracking.

Two thirds of the respondents support the development of either good quality solar farms. The level of public support rose to 71% after the STA's recent 10 commitments for solar farms were described. Just 5% of people indicated that they opposed the development of all solar farms.

Iceland

Iceland is an idyllic, postcard-picture-perfect, land: land of ages, old virgin ice caps, and unshaken traditions (like the one that allows only government-approved names to be given to newborn babies). It is a land far away from the crowded continents and from global warming. Or not!

A large piece of land around Mount Hengill, approximately 30 km from the capital is a very busy place. Roads, drills, pipelines, and a large powerhouse mark the area of the site of the large Hellisheiði geothermal power plant. The plant generates electricity from free steam, compliments of Earth. This means cheap electricity for the locals. Or not!

Not so fast—almost all of the electricity is used for powering aluminum production.

Geothermal energy is commonly praised as a "green" alternative to environmentally unfriendly power sources such as fossil fuels, coals and nuclear energy.

As a result of "the development of what were once thought to be non-viable resources, more and more public and private entities are looking into geothermal power as part of their strategy to mitigate global warming while still meeting growing energy demands.

In a promotional text for the geothermal energy exhibition at Hellisheiði, the plant is said to be a "striking example of how geothermal energy is harnessed in a sustainable manner in Iceland and a showcase for the rest of the world." Additionally, Reykjavík Energy has not hesitated to say that the "general public opinion of exploiting the geothermal resources in the Hengill region is positive."

Only about ten kilometers away from the plant is the small town of Hveragerði, wherein one gets to hear a completely different story. The locals cannot accept the fact that that the plant will be permitted to continue polluting the atmosphere. The local health authorities are encouraging the locals to start taking magnesium and iodide supplements to counteract the health impacts of the power plant's sulphur (hydrogen sulphide) pollution. It seems that the pollution is of such quantity that the human body needs those two materials to resist the effects, according to them.

Recent inspections make it clear that the sulphur pollution not only reaches Hveragerði, but also to Reykjavík, and often goes far above Icelandic and international standards. In the case of Hveragerði, the quantity of polluting materials in the atmosphere is such that the town should be considered within the plant's dilution area (the area in which residential homes are not permitted).

Iceland also has several active volcanoes, which erupt from time to time, creating havoc in trans-oceanic air travel and spewing millions of tons of lava and suds in the skies.

Iceland is alive and boiling in deadly (natural and man-made) fumes and liquids. Far from idyllic, but those things cannot be seen on the postcards, so Iceland will keep its virtual status of an "idyllic" land for a while longer.

Saudi Arabia

Saudi Arabia has one of the largest oil reserves in the world, and is the world's top oil exporter and producer. Its proven oil reserves amount to 18% of global reserves, or over 260 billion barrels. Proven natural gas reserves in Saudi Arabia are over 250 trillion cubic feet. The entire Saudi Arabia's economy is petroleum-based. Oil accounts for 90% of the country's exports and nearly 75% government revenues. The oil industry produces about 45% of Saudi Arabia's gross domestic product, against 40% from the private sector.

Saudi Arabia has a per capita GDP of $20,500, and its economy is still very dependent on oil in spite of on-and-off diversification efforts in a number of areas, especially the petrochemical sector.

The 2009 global production reached 29 billion barrels of oil, and 110 trillion ft³ of natural gas. Saudi Arabia is one of the world's largest crude oil producers, pumping over 10 million barrels of crude oil per day. Most of the produced oil is exported but domestic use is increasing, where oil is primarily used for electric power generation. That use is expected to increase with time.

Table 8-14. Saudi Arabia's energy balance

Year	A	B	C	D
2007	6,412	4,606	175	358
2008	6,734	4,796	187	389
2009	6,145	4,324	199	410
2010	6,258	4,551	219	446

A is total energy production in TWh
B is total energy exports in TWh
C is total electric power generation in TWh, and
D is the CO_2 emissions in million tons per annum

One thing is very obvious in Saudi Arabia: the electric power generation and the CO_2 emissions are increasing significantly every year.

Saudi Arabia has realized that the oil reserves are finite and a day is coming when there will be no more. Because of that the government is looking into the alter-

natives—solar power being one of the most promising. Saudi Arabia is blessed with a lot of sun too, which is also a curse, because a lot of power is needed to keep buildings cool in the summer.

Recently, Saudi Arabia started planning a round of procuring roughly 600 MW solar power (PV and CSP) projects at several sites. The introductory round featured a request for proposal (RFP), which is an exciting milestone in what looks to be a very promising solar market in the country. The plan, however, has a number of points that are questionable. For example, it requires the bidding projects to have at least four hours of energy storage capacity. This immediately eliminates PV installations, since there is no PV technology presently that can provide that much energy storage.

Project revenues will be taxed at 1% for training local employees and 1% for local research and development projects related to renewable energy in Saudi Arabia. Also, local content and economic development are also evaluated, and in this case, PV modules (usually imported) are valued at 50% less than racking, wafers, and inverters in local content ratings (some of which are local products).

Japan

Fukushima changed the way Japan, and the world, looks at power generation. Nuclear is now in doubt, and that is creating a new culture in the energy sector.

The March 2011, earthquake and tsunami crashed the Japanese economy and with it the belief that nuclear power can be safely used to power the world's second largest economy. Pushed by a wary citizenry, Japanese officials shut down most of the nation's nuclear plants in 2011 until they can be proven safe for operation.

This is a long, tedious, and expensive process, which has led to power shortages in Japan, and a growing energy ascetic among the population. During the hot summer days, the air conditioning in homes and buildings is set at an uncomfortably high setting. This is partly because people realize that there isn't a lot of capacity, and that brownouts and blackouts could follow.

For now fossil fuels, such as imported liquefied natural gas and oil are replacing the shut down nuclear plants. Japan has no fossil fuel reserves to speak of, and the renewables (mostly hydroelectricity) are a relatively small part of the mix, so imported fossil fuels produce 90% of the nation's electricity now.

Aside from renewable energy, Japan has few indigenous energy resources, so the high cost of importing fossil fuel is putting pressure on electricity prices. Four utilities: Kansai Electric Power, Kyushu Electric Power,

Tohoku Electric Power and Shikoku Electric Power, have requested rate increases since late 2012, and more are likely to do so. They simply have no other way to make ends meet.

The major factor behind the recent applications for electricity rate increases is the growing demand and fuel import costs, resulting from the energy deficit caused by the shut down nuclear power plants. The only reasonable way to bring down energy costs on the short term is through energy efficiency and conservation. In the long run, importing low-cost liquefied natural gas from the U.S. and liberalizing its utility industry are the preferred methods to meet the energy demand and lower costs.

There are also a number of solar projects planned in the overall energy mix, but they are not considered cost-cutting measures for now. They will help with providing more needed electricity, but are actually adding to the electricity rates because of the FiT.

The utilities cover the cost of the FIT, which is available to all renewables (solar, wind, small and medium-scale hydroelectricity, geothermal power and biomass) through a surcharge paid by all customers. So far, the FiT costs are low: approximately $1.3 billion in 2012, which is about 1.6% of Japan's total electricity cost. They are, however, expected to rise as more solar and wind power plants are built and the FiT is increasingly employed.

Solar is not at grid parity in Japan without incentives. So the nation's push for more solar is viewed not as an economic play, but as a way to bring safer, cleaner and more indigenous resources to the nation. Japan needs power now, today, and solar can be built fast, much faster than any other power generator.

Solar is the obvious choice for the Japanese, since it is fast and efficient enough and Japan just doesn't have many alternatives to electric power generation. Now the Japanese have also learned that there is nothing more hazardous than nuclear power, so going to clean safe solar is no brainer. And since solar prices are falling, while all other prices are rising, makes solar heaven-sent.

PV system prices dropped in 2012 14% to $3.10/Watt installed for projects over 1.0 MW, and will likely continue to fall, as Japan imports or makes more modules. At the same time, the FiT will most likely keep Japan's energy prices high as compared with other countries.

Japan is planning to add 6.0 to 10.0 GW of photovoltaics in 2013, much of it from large-scale projects. This is a big leap for Japan, because just before instituting the FiT in 2012, the nation had only 0.8 GW of large PV from about 40 installations. Twenty-year contracts

now get $0.40 per/kWh generated, but it was dropped down by 10% in April 2013. Still, the incentive remains one of the most attractive in the world right now, even with the 10% cut.

Wow, Japan, slow down! We have seen this kind of rush several times before. Every time, it crashed when the incentive disappeared or something else affected the energy markets. Take a look at Spain, where the euphoria of 2008 is now woeful with a broken solar market.

Japan may be in the midst of their first boom and bust cycle, which we have witnessed in the U.S. time after time. Or maybe things are different this time—at least in Japan? Maybe, but there are several problems; one is that Japan doesn't have much land or climate for efficient for solar installations, which certainly will limit the amount of total solar power generation in the country.

And don't forget that all it takes is for the government to allow opening all nuclear plants again for solar to go into a full bust mode, just as it happened in Spain recently, but for different reasons.

Vietnam

Vietnam is looking at hydropower as one of the solutions to its energy problems, and is doing this in a hasty manner. A report by the ministry of industry and trade show indicates that Vietnam has 1114 hydropower projects nationwide, including 217 projects now under the construction and 309 other projects being planned.

Hydropower specialists express concern that the hydropower development program has a lot of problems. It was designed without regard to the proper exploitation of the limited water resources. There seem to be an underestimation of the impacts of the hydropower plants on the up- and down-stream currents, and the people living around them.

As a result, and unlike other hydropower plants in the world, Vietnam's hydropower plants are neither clean nor as cheap as expected. And sure enough, there were problems at the Song Tranh hydropower plant, in addition to a break of the Dak Rong 3 hydropower plant's dam, causing problems downstream.

People around the Song Tranh hydropower plant are concerned because of the continual earthquakes that threaten to break the dam without a warning, and could kill many of them at any time. This is a serious situation that has become a hot topic for discussion at the highest government levels.

Under the current regulations, investors are responsible for the safety of the dams that they finance, which does not allow state agencies to control the quality of hydropower plants. Surveys have found that many hydropower plant investors fail to register their hydro projects, and lack proper plans to exploit and develop the water natural resources.

On the other hand, local authorities are authorized to control the quality of small and medium hydropower plants, but they have no funding, nor experienced engineers, for this effort. As a result, the local authorities simply approve the projects and do not control their quality.

World scientists have changed their view about hydropower plants, finding out that this is not a source of clean energy as was previously thought. It is also not as cheap as thought, since it only benefits the investors, who pay only for the construction, but are not held responsible for any social and environmental problems.

As a result of the dam construction, thousands of people had to relocate to resettlement areas built by the hydropower plants investors. The new housing arrangements are brick and cement structures of poor quality, where the locals, who are used to living in wooden houses, are most uncomfortable living in. Many people have abandoned their resettlement homes and have set up wooden houses in the nearby forests.

For example, the Pachepalanh resettlement area in Dong Giang District was built only two years back, but already is in need of repair. All the 257 households who relocated there to make way for the A Vuong hydropower plant said that they don't even have cultivable land and are in constant fear of mountain landslides.

At the end of the 20th century, Quang Nam Province was covered with thick green forest, but over the last ten years vast areas have been denuded, ever since the state permitted hydropower projects to be built. At least 10,000 hectares of forestland has been taken over by hydropower plants. Of them A Vuong Hydropower Plant swallowed 1,000 hectares, Song Tranh 2 and 3 plants devoured more than 2,600 hectares. So far none of the investors of the operating hydropower plants has offered to help with replanting the denuded areas.

In another example, Song Con 2 hydropower plant's dam was raised by 1 meter to increase the power generation. This modification is affecting hundreds of households, who have cried for help because they have lost land.

The volume of water in the reservoir was increased, which left 108,000 square meters of agriculture production land under the water. That had forced the local farmers to leave their old rice fields and move to higher ground. The soil in the new areas is not good enough for cultivation, which has caused hunger.

Bangladesh

Bangladesh...? Amazingly enough this dot on the global map country is now the largest off-grid power user. Not much, mind, you, but still the largest. This is the best-kept secret of today, or the people involved just don't like shouting about it. Bangladesh has quietly become the world's biggest domestic off-grid solar user.

Over the past decade, since the Bangladesh government launched a rural electrification program supported by the World Bank and other international aid bodies, the number of off-grid installations in the country has rocketed. In 2002, there were 7000 installations; today that figure has exploded to nearly 2 million and counting, with average installation rates now topping 80,000 a month.

Bangladesh is a classic example of a country that could really benefit from micro-renewable generation technologies such as solar. Around half the predominantly rural population still lacks access to electricity. While off-grid generation technologies are not seen as particularly well suited to the high energy intensity countries of the West, in Bangladesh, where electricity demands at the moment are relatively modest, they are ideal.

The explosive deployment of off-grid solar in Bangladesh has been helped by a combination of two factors: the dramatic fall in the price of small PV systems and a well organized micro-credit scheme that allows even those in relatively impoverished areas to cover the up-front costs of installing a system.

One of the leading players in Bangladesh's off-grid solar revolution is Rahimafrooz Solar, a Dhaka-based company that manufactures and installs PV systems. They use micro-credit to finance solar and it has brought the reality of domestic electricity within the reach of millions of Bangladeshis.

Micro-credit works as follows: a typical customer makes a 15% down payment, and then the balance would be paid over a period of 24-36 months. A typical system in the countryside would be 50W, and is used to power LED lights, a black and white TV connection, a mobile phone charger, and usually has a four-hour (battery) back up for night use. The cost of an entire system would be $300, with $8-10 monthly payments.

This relatively modest power generation, which would be a laugh in the U.S., makes a big difference to the local people's lives: clean energy that makes money, and serves a part of the population that didn't have energy access.

Because the Bangladesh off-grid program is relatively mature, it has spawned a local supply chain. All equipment is manufactured locally. This creates local jobs and keeps costs down, and benefits the local economy.

- *Lesson one:* Although developing a local supply chain has been a key part of the success of the Bangladesh program, other countries should not get too hung up on localization, at least initially. An initial pilot phase is a key, building it to over 50,000 installations, and then focus on the localization, which happens best at increased volume.

- *Lesson two:* There are many ways to obtain best efficiency from solar. A customization of the systems is needed to fit the local customers best. For example, Bangladesh uses south-to-south solar installation models, vs. the traditional north-to-south, especially suited for its bottom rural energy access needs.

So thank you Bangladesh for teaching us new ways to use solar.

Regardless of its relative advances in solar energy deployment, Bangladesh is one of the most polluted countries in the world. Air pollution from brick kilns, home cooking (both using coal and wood as fuel) and traffic congestion is increasing and, together with heavy pollution of the local rivers, is contributing to health issues and death among the population.

Dhaka City, the capital of Bangladesh was documented as one of the world's most polluted cities in 2012. How solar fits in this entire picture is hard to tell, but we are obviously entering a new phase of energy vs. environment development, where the balance of those two variables is not under our control.

Africa

President Barack Obama's $7 billion initiative to bring power to the African people was launched officially with great fanfare in 2013. Amazingly enough, the program has already leveraged $9 billion from private industry. It is designed to add more than 10.0 GW of cleaner, efficient electricity generation capacity over five years. 20 million more households and commercial entities will be electrified from the grid, distributed generation, or mini-grids. The target countries at the present are: Ethiopia, Ghana, Kenya, Liberia, Nigeria and Tanzania.

Some of the largest companies in the world already are recruited to participate in the program. For example, General Electric has committed to bring online 5 MW of new, affordable energy in Tanzania and Ghana. Symbion Power is to invest $1.8 billion to develop 1.5 GW of new energy projects in Africa over five years. Both companies have signed a joint agreement to develop an additional 400 MW natural gas power plant in Tanzania that will take a small amount of the country's as yet untapped reserves.

It seems then that cleaner energy in White House terms includes natural gas, hydro and some wind. Solar is somewhere on a back burner. Still, at the very least it will achieve a reduction in coal-fired electricity. South Africa, which is the most advanced African economy is 93% powered by coal, though the government is planning to push for 1.45 GW of solar to be build by the end of 2014.

Africa needs a lot of power to grow its economy, keep water sources clean, to educate children, and to reduce deaths from cooking over burning dung and other solid fuels. More than 75% of the population of Sub-Saharan Africa has no access to electricity, which number rises to over 85% of those living in rural areas.

While we all agree with Obama's plan, we see the obvious lack of provision for solar installations, even though distributed (house roofs) solar power generation seems a most natural choice for countries that have 325 sun days every year, and no grid infrastructure to speak of outside major cities.

Distributed generation would be most useful in those countries, as is the example of Bangladesh above. Even the International Energy Agency estimates that universal energy access by 2030 can only be achieved if more than half of new connections are from distributed (solar mostly) energy sources. And yet, solar doesn't really get much support under the Obama's plan.

Only $2 million has been allocated for the U.S. African development foundation (USADF) to launch the off-grid energy challenge and provide grants of up to $100,000 to African-owned and operated enterprises to develop proven technologies for off-grid electricity in rural areas.

Before the natural choice, solar, starts to gain real traction, Africa seems to be geared towards getting fossil fuel energy embedded in the grid infrastructure. As a matter of fact, some of the announced projects were well under way even before power Africa was even announced.

Mini-grids would be most suitable for power generation in Africa. They could be sized around 10 to 50 kW as needed to meet the basic needs of lighting, cooking and mobile phone charging. However, Africa's solar energy development is not in Obama's plan...

Under the present conditions, the solar future of Africa does not appear to be in America's best interests, so it can be achieved only with private financing. And amazingly enough, the appeal of investing in Africa is real since returns can be robust. As an example, one of the Tanzania's hydro projects has a 60% return on investment.

Notes and References

1. U.S. IEA, *Transport, Energy and CO_2. Moving towards mobility*, OECD/IEA, Paris.
2. U.S. *IEA, Medium Term Oil and Gas Markets 2010*, OECD/IEA, Paris.
3. PVCDROM, C.B. Honsberg and S. Bowden, www.pveducation.org, 2010.
4. http://www.worldenergyoutlook.org/resources/energydevelopment/energyforallfinancingaccessforthepoor/
5. Natural gas hydrates; Overview by Steve Dutch. http://www.uwgb.edu/dutchs/Petrology/Clathrate-0.HTM
6. Henriet, J.P., Mienert, J., 1998; Gas hydrates: relevance to world margin stability and climate change, London: The Geological Society, *Geological Society special publication* no. 137, 338 p.
7. Holder, Gerald-D (editor); Bishnoi, P. R. (editor), 2000; Gas hydrates; challenges for the future. *Annals of the New York Academy of Sciences. 912; New York Academy of Sciences*. New York, NY, United States. Pages: 1039.
8. Paull, Charles K. (editor); Dillon, William P. (editor), 2000; Natural gas hydrates; occurrence, distribution, and detection. *Geophysical Monograph 124*, American Geophysical Union. Washington, D.C., United States. Pages: 315.
9. Haq, Bilal U., 1998; Gas hydrates; greenhouse nightmare? Energy panacea or pipe dream? GSA Today. vol. 8; 11, Pages 1-6. Geological Society of America (GSA). Boulder, CO, United States.
10. Smelik, Eugene A.; King, H. E. Jr., 1997; Crystal-growth studies of natural gas clathrate hydrates using a pressurized optical cell. *American Mineralogist*. vol. 82; 1-2, Pages 88-98.
11. DOE, *National Hydrogen Energy Roadmap*, 2002. http://www.google.com/search?q=National+Hydrogen+Energy+Roadmap&hl=en&sourceid=gd&rlz=1Q1GGLD_enUS473US542
12. Energy and Environment, http://www.multi-science.co.uk/ee.htm
13. Energy and Climate Change, http://www.whitehouse.gov/energy/
14. UN Development Program, http://www.undp.org/content/undp/en/home/ourwork/environmentandenergy/overview.html
15 International Energy Agency, http://www.iea.org/
16. Energy + Environment, http://www.energyandenvironment.com/
17. U.S. Energy Information Agency, http://www.eia.gov/countries/
18. China Energy Group, LBNL, http://china.lbl.gov/
19. Europe's Energy Portal, http://www.energy.eu/
20. *Photovoltaics for Commercial and Utilities Power Generation*, Anco S. Blazev. The Fairmont Press, 2011.
21. *Solar Technologies for the 21st Century*, Anco S. Blazev. The Fairmont Press, 2013.

Chapter 9

Future Power Generation
And the Environment

Then I saw a new heaven and a new earth, for the
first heaven and the first Earth had passed away...
—Revelation 21:1

We started this book with the beginning of the world, so it seems appropriate to complete it with a look at the end of the world, as we know it. One thing we all agree on is that, as everything else, this world will eventually end someday, somehow. We just don't know when and how exactly this will happen. The "end of the world" also has a different meaning to different people, which complicates the subject even further.

Generally speaking, those of us who believe in the Bible are convinced that it is the only place where one can find the real answers on this and most other subjects. And so, these people are going through it page by page looking for hints to allow them to figure out (or at least guess) when and how this world will end.

A number of "prophets" have come out in the past predicting the "end" as they saw it in the Bible, but they all—without exception—were wrong and went down in history as "quacks" and false prophets. As a matter of fact, the Bible itself says that we are not supposed to know when and how the world will end, and that it will sneak upon us as a thief in the night. Because of that, most true believers are not looking for any signs, but instead are focusing on what comes after the end of the world—whenever and whatever that might be—which simplifies things significantly.

For people who do not believe in the Bible, however, things are much more complicated. Due to the uncertainty and mystery the end of the world concept is wrapped in, they need to find a plausible answer to unwrap at least some of the uncertainty and the mystery.

And so, they look at the scientists, who usually also have no idea as of when and how the world will end, but yet make up some wacky hypothesis that does not hold water. And since there is no other source of information on the subject, these people continue looking, but not finding the answers. It is a very frustrating situation to be in, for sure!

We cannot offer any answers either, but instead provide a lot of information and data from different sources, in an attempt to fill some of the blanks, while remaining impartial as possible on all issues. For this purpose, we take information from all possible sources and filter it through our scientific knowledge and real-life experiences to present as unbiased account of all facts and the probable consequences as possible.

This chapter starts with a short description of the near misses of the past, where the world was at a critical point during or after a great disaster. We then move onto the present developments in the energy and environment sectors, and finally complete each subject with impartial conclusions and educated predictions of possible developments in the future.

And now, back to the end of the world...

END OF THE WORLD...PART 1

Sunday morning, May 14, 1935... A beautiful, warm sunny day over the Great Plains, covering parts of the states of Colorado, Kansas, Montana, Nebraska, New Mexico, North Dakota, Oklahoma, South Dakota, Texas, and Wyoming, as well as the Canadian provinces of Alberta, Manitoba and Saskatchewan.

Thousands of people went to church that morning thanking God for the good weather and the prospects of another bountiful harvest. It was just another beautiful Sunday afternoon in the Great Plains. Leaving church, the people were making plans for a peaceful afternoon, with picnics and outings to nearby parks.

It was not to be. Soon after noon, a huge dark cloud appeared from nowhere, covering a large area of the Great Plains all of a sudden. The cloud of dust grew and moved quickly to overtake large area with a dense plume of fine dust and sand, sending people running for cover. Blackness and dust blackness covered the plains at a great speed, and many people thought that this was the end of the world, as the Bible predicted.

That was Black Sunday of the now infamous Dust Bowl of the 1930s, which is still remembered as one of the worst days of the 10-year drought. This long lasting drought is one of the worst in the U.S. history, killing many, and sickening many more. It deprived thousands of jobs and daily sustenance and forced countless numbers of people to move away.

The dust cloud blew over most of the plains that day and raised the greatest dust cloud ever seen. The dust travelled thousands of miles in all directions, and even deposited a layer of dust on the desk of the President of the U.S. It was as if God were reminding men of who is in charge, reminding them that things have gone wrong and need to be made right...

This worst environmental disaster in the U.S. history was caused by reckless technology use, compounded by people's ignorance, negligence, greed, and disregard to Nature's laws. Several years of severe droughts, combined with poor farming methods lifted the dust up in an instant and wiped out the American Dream that took dozens of years to build, thus putting millions on their knees.

Figure 9-1. The Dust Bowl of the 1930s

The technology and cultivation methods were designed for high productivity and for making a quick buck during the time of the war and the Great Depression. The methods lacked sensible, let alone scientific, thinking. Those were methods that were imposed by the capitalist way of business, focused on making profits, while disregarding some of the basics. These, and many other similarly haphazard methods of the capitalist enterprise, have brought many such disasters before and after.

Extensive, deep plowing of the topsoil of millions of acres in the Great Plains in the 1920s had displaced the natural deep-rooted grasses that kept the soil in place by trapping moisture, which allowed the soil to withstand high winds even in drought periods.

Thousands of small tractors and harvester-combines converted the dry grasslands, which receive no more than 10 inches o rainfall per year, into a cultivated cropland emporium. But then the 10-year drought started. Without natural anchors to keep the soil in place, it dried and turned into dust. The high winds took it and blew it away every which direction. For 10 long years people run away, hid in their dusty houses, breathed dusty air and ate dusty food. This turmoil made many sick.

Millions of acres of farmland were damaged, and hundreds of thousands of people were forced to leave their homes, migrate to California and other states, and look for better economic conditions. The once proud and rich farmers of the Great Plains now owned no land, and had no income, so many became migrant workers who traveled from farm to farm to pick fruit and other crops at starvation wages.

In the 1940s, things improved. Lessons were learned. People got smarter, and implemented better, more scientific methods for cultivation and the Great Plains blossomed once again. Technological advances allowed a lot of water to be pumped for irrigation, so that the crops no longer depended on rainwater. Because of all this innovation and expertise, today the Great Plains are the most productive area of the U.S. Again...

...But wait; didn't we just go through that? Did we already forget the lesson of the Dust Bowl debacle? High productivity and the latest technology may not be the best for the area and the people who live there, especially if overused and without proper forward thinking and planning.

The Great Plains now depend on the water table underneath for irrigation. Water is pumped up from thousands of wells and is sprayed over millions of acres. Crops that do not belong in that area are once again grown. Water, however, is limited, but there are no plans to slow down or change the practices.

Fast forward 20-30 years of this accelerated crop production, and there would be no more underground water to speak of. The Great Plains might get into another Dust Bowl—again. Is that possible? Yes it is! Nature does not change her laws to accommodate people's desires, or their unreasonable behavior. When the water is gone, so will the bountiful crops; the disturbed soil will dry up and will blow away once again, creating another Dust Bowl.

END OF THE WORLD...PART 2

April 26, 1986 was just another beautiful spring day in the Russian city of Prypiat, close to the Dnieper River, adjacent to the border with Belarus. Kids were playing in the playgrounds, while their mothers were knitting nearby, discussing quietly the new development in Russia. They were all unaware that reactor number four of the nearby Chernobyl nuclear plant, where their husbands worked, was going into a test mode when it experienced a sudden and unexpected power surge.

This was not the first time that the reactor misbehaved, so the engineers executed an emergency shutdown, as per the plant's safety procedures. This time, however, the reactor responded with an exponentially larger spike in the power output. This abnormally large, uncontrollable power surge led to an explosion that ruptured the reactor vessel, followed by a series of high-pressure steam explosions.

The explosions and the power surge events exposed the graphite moderator of the reactor to air, thus causing it to ignite. A large flame of high-temperature fire leaked inside and out the reactor housing and sent a plume of highly radioactive gasses into the surrounding air.

The fire continued and expanded, increasing the amount of emitted gasses over an extensive geographical area, including the city of Pripyat and beyond. For several days, the killer gas plume drifted over large parts of the western Soviet Union and northern Europe.

Figure 9-2. The disabled Chernobyl's reactor 4 today

The total damages of the accident are still unaccounted for, but over 350,000 people were evacuated and resettled from the most severely contaminated areas of Belarus, Russia, and the Ukraine. About 60% of the fallout landed in the nearby provinces of Belarus. Millions of people in Russia, Eastern and Northern Europe were hurt, or otherwise directly affected.

There are estimates that among hundreds of millions of people living in the broader geographical areas that were directly or indirectly exposed to radioactive contamination from the disaster, nearly a million cancer cases and deaths occurred from 1986-2008.

Agricultural crops and industrial enterprises were badly contaminated, and many were shut down. The world was alarmed and many people were scared. At the same time, the Russian government tried to hide the truth about the accident, which only increased the concerns about the safety of the Soviet nuclear power industry, as well as nuclear power in general, slowing its expansion for a number of years and forcing the Soviet government to become less secretive about its procedures.

The government cover-up of the Chernobyl disaster was a "catalyst" for glasnost, which paved the way for reforms leading to the Soviet collapse. Russia, Ukraine, and Belarus have been burdened with the continuing and substantial decontamination and health care costs of the Chernobyl accident.

The environmental consequences of the accident estimate a global collective dose of radiation exposure from the accident "equivalent on the average to 21 additional days of world exposure to natural background radiation."

Individual doses were far higher than the global mean among those most exposed, including 530,000 local recovery workers who averaged an effective dose equivalent to an extra 50 years of typical natural background radiation exposure each. Estimates of the number of deaths that will eventually result from the accident vary enormously. Disparities reflect both the lack of solid scientific data and the different methodologies used to quantify mortality—whether the discussion is confined to specific geographical areas or extends worldwide, and whether the deaths are immediate, or in the short-term or long-term.

Thirty-one deaths are directly attributed to the accident, all among the reactor staff and emergency workers, and the total confirmed deaths from radiation were estimated at 64 as of 2008.

The eventual death toll could reach 4,000 among those who were exposed to the highest levels of radiation (including more than 200,000 emergency workers, 116,000 evacuees and 270,000 residents of the most contaminated areas). These figures include some 50 emergency workers who died of acute radiation syndrome, nine children who died of thyroid cancer and an estimated total of 3,940 deaths from radiation-induced cancer and leukemia.

END OF THE WORLD...PART 3

On March 11, 2011, a major earthquake shook the eastern coast of Japan. A 15-meter tsunami hit and disabled the power supply and cooling systems of three Fukushima Daiichi reactors. All three cores partially melted during the next 2-3 days, causing an uncontrolled nuclear accident. It was rated 7 out of 10 on the International Nuclear Events Scale (INES), due to high radioactive releases over the days following the disaster.

The great east Japan earthquake with a magnitude 9.0 at 2:46 p.m. on Friday, March 11, 2011, did considerable damage in the region, and the large tsunami it created caused even more property damage. The earthquake was centered 90 miles off the shore of the city of Sendai in Miyagi prefecture on the eastern cost of Honshu Island (the main part of Japan), and was a rare and complex double quake with a severe duration of about three minutes.

Eleven reactors at four nuclear power plants in the region were operating at the time and all shut down automatically when the quake hit. Subsequent inspection showed no significant damage to any from the earthquake. The operating units which shut down were Tokyo Electric Power Company's (Tepco) Fukushima Daiichi 1, 2, 3, and Fukushima Daini 1, 2, 3, 4, Tohoku's Onagawa 1, 2, 3, and Japco's Tokai, totaling 9377 MWe net. Fukushima Daiichi units 4, 5 & 6 were not operating at the time, but were affected. The main problem initially centered on Fukushima Daiichi units 1-3. Unit 4 became a problem on day five.

The reactors proved robust seismically, but vulnerable to the tsunami. Power, from grid or backup generators, was available to run the residual heat removal (RHR) system cooling pumps at eight of the eleven units, and despite some problems they achieved "cold shutdown" within about four days. The other three, at Fukushima Daiichi, lost power at 3:42 p.m., almost an hour after the quake, when the entire site was flooded by the 15-meter tsunami. This disabled 12 of 13 backup generators on site and also the heat exchangers for dumping reactor waste heat and decay heat to the sea. The three units lost the ability to maintain proper reactor cooling and water circulation functions.

Electrical switchgear was also disabled. Thereafter, many weeks of focused work centered on restoring heat removal from the reactors and coping with overheated spent fuel ponds. Hundreds of Tepco employees and some contractors, supported by firefighting and military personnel, undertook this. Some of the Tepco staff had lost homes, and even families, in the tsunami, and were initially living in temporary accommodations under great difficulties and privation, with some personal risk. A hardened emergency response center on site was unable to be used in grappling with the situation due to radioactive contamination.

A total of four reactors were completely destroyed and nearly 3.0 GWe power capacity is lost forever, in addition to the extensive damage to the plant infrastructure and the immediate area. By week three, adding cooling water stabilized three reactors (units 1-3), but there was no proper heat sink for the removal of decay heat from the active fuel.

By July 2011, the reactors were being cooled with recycled water from the new treatment plant. Reactor temperatures had fallen to below 80°C at the end of October, and official "cold shutdown condition" was announced in mid-December, 2011. The immediate danger was over, and now the cleanup and stabilization effort is underway.

With the cooling somewhat under control, the efforts were directed to prevent further release of radioactive materials, particularly contaminated water leaking from the three units in the surrounding area and into the ocean. The radiation effects have been noticed on land and in the deep ocean, so the immediate area is considered radioactive. A number of proposals for containing the contaminated water from leaking into the ocean are under evaluation, but no feasible solution is in sight. The radiation in the area is stabilized but is still not under full control, and the uncertainty continues to play a role in the political and economic decisions in the area.

During the earthquake, Japan moved a few meters east and the local coastline subsided half a meter. The tsunami inundated about 400 square miles of land, resulting in a human death toll of over 19,000 and much damage to coastal ports and towns. Over a million buildings were destroyed or partly collapsed, and thousands of cars, trucks and other vehicles were destroyed.

Three Tepco employees at the Daiichi and Daini plants were killed directly by the earthquake and tsunami, but there have been no fatalities from the nuclear accident. There have been no deaths or cases of radiation sickness from the nuclear accident, but over 100,000 people had to be evacuated from their homes. Most of them are still away and many will never return to their former homes.

This is how the *beginning of the end* looks like. When we voluntarily cut off the air we breathe, and the water we drink, both of which are critical to life support—and Nature sending tsunamis our way that kill people—then the rest is irrelevant. It matters very little if you are dirt poor or have a large bank account, if you have no water to drink or air to breathe, or if you are unfortunate enough to be irradiated by a damaged nuclear reactor.

In all cases, we as a species are guilty for allowing such major disasters. And even worse than that is the reality that we are doing very little to change the situation. We keep building coal-fired power plants that will increase the pollution further, and nuclear power plants that might blow up in our faces some day.

This is the path we have chosen; we are willing to take the risks in our never-ending thirst for more energy, more things, and increased comfort. Lessons learned? Maybe… And there are many, many other examples of nuclear mishaps and near misses. Although not all of them are as serious, they are signs of problems that we are experiencing. And even more importantly, they are examples of serious man-made problems.

END OF THE WORLD…21ST CENTURY

We don't know exactly how this world would stop existing, so we can only guess. One can form a fairly plausible scenario of the end of the world, judging from the results of our accelerated activities during the last century.

Just spend a week in Shanghai, China, or Bombay, India, and you might get a glimpse of what could happen by the end or this century. Or the next…

The air in Shanghai is—just missing, replaced by dense clouds of smog (Shmog, as they call it). The locals judge how bad the daily pollution is by how far down the street they can see an approaching car. The scientists measure the air pollution by the number of micrograms of PM10 and PM2.5 (particles measuring less than 10 and 2.5 micrometers respectively) per cubic meter. Those particles are caused by dust or emissions from vehicles, factories, construction sites and coal combustion.

Fine particulates (PM2.5) are the most dangerous, for they can penetrate lungs and enter the bloodstream, making them the most detrimental to health. Chronic exposure to these, as is the case in Shanghai and many other cities in Asia, leads to an increased risk of lots of nasty things, particularly heart disease and lung cancer. China's capital, Beijing, has the worst air pollution

due to its geographical location. Shanghai is by the sea, which helps to clear the air rapidly, while Beijing lies in a valley surrounded by mountains, so the air remains over the city most of the time.

Figure 9-3. Shanghai air pollution (shmog)

Prolonged exposure to extreme air pollution leads to premature death, and we now know that over half a million Chinese die prematurely each year from ailments caused by indoor and outdoor air pollution. We also know that a decrease of 10 micrograms per cubic meter in a city's fine-particulate concentration was associated with an estimated increase in life expectancy of approximately 0.6 years. All things considered, we calculate that people living in Beijing would theoretically die 5-6 years younger than people living in Los Angeles, America's most polluted city.

This, however, does not apply to the officials and party members. China is a Communist system, so the privileged are privileged in every want and need. Many of them have their own private air supply devices; special types of air-purifiers, which are installed in their homes and offices. So obviously, some of us will survive no matter what.

Bombay also has bad air, but that problem has been surpassed by a bigger, and much more urgent one—a lack of water. The water supply situation in Bombay is critical, with the level of supply so much below demand that water use is restricted and reaches emergency proportions during certain periods, especially when the monsoons fail.

Bombay is also one of the noisiest cities in the world also, and suffers from serious air pollution, both from noxious industries and automobile emissions. Although there has been substantial progress in the public transportation system, traffic congestion in the metro-politan area is on the increase.

More than 2 million Bombay residents have no sanitary facilities, and most sewage collected in Bombay—residential and industrial—is discharged untreated or partially treated into creeks or coastal waters. Attempts to relocate industries outside the island city are under way, but that is only a dent in the industrial pollution, which remains an extremely serious problem.

That is not an isolated case; there are many more—some much worse—cases of water scarcity and their number increases by the day. There is a severe water shortage in many parts of the world. Even in oil-rich Arab countries, drinking water is not available locally in some large populated centers, so it is delivered daily in trucks from distant locations. And worst off of all are millions of people in a number of countries, such as Sudan, Venezuela, Ethiopia, Tunisia, and Cuba who are forced to consume mostly untreated and contaminated water on daily basis.

If we continue in the path of destruction we have taken now, it won't be too long before we enter one of the darkest periods in human history. Literally. We use so much fossil fuel and emit so much toxic gasses that pretty soon we will run out of fossils, if we don't suffocate from their emission prior to that.

One of the immediate effects of the increase in greenhouse gasses emissions is the increase of global temperature.

Figure 9-4 reflects the possible scenarios of global temperature rise. The current atmospheric CO_2 concentration is around 380 ppm, or 430 ppm when considering the contribution of other greenhouse gases. The increase thus far has been gradual, and we'd expect it to continue that way, as reflected by the solid line on the graph. This scenario is based on a number of factors that counteract the negative effects of the GHGs and keep the environment at a relative balance.

The dashed line in the graph in Figure 9-4, however, represents a scenario when the GHG concentration and a variety of other factors, overwhelm all counteracting actions, and the Earth's climate gets out of control. The temperatures in such a case might rise to extreme levels, and a number of natural disasters would follow in return.

At the end, the magnitude of actual warming and other effects will depend upon the level at which atmospheric concentrations of CO_2 and other greenhouse gases are ultimately stabilized.

The scientists' projections suggest that stabilizing greenhouse gas concentrations at 450 ppm CO_2 would

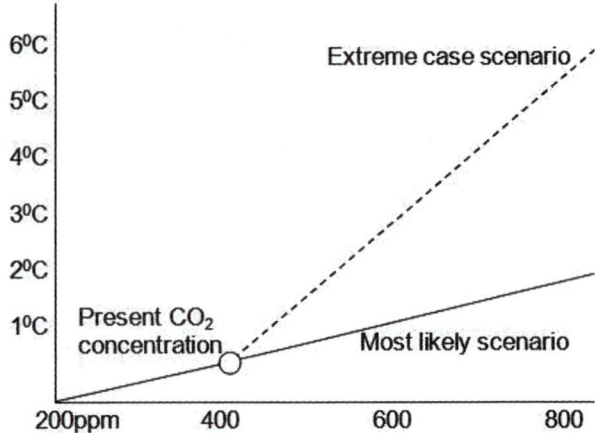

Figure 9-4. Global temperature vs. CO_2 levels forecast

be 90% likely to eventually result in a temperature increase between 1.0 and 3.8°C, with a small probability that the rise could be significantly more than this. With current greenhouse gas concentrations in the atmosphere at 400 (430) ppm CO_2, and steadily rising, stabilization at 450 ppm would be extremely challenging. As we will see later, even stabilization at 550 ppm CO_2 would require dramatic policy action.

A quick look around us shows that we are now doing exactly what the 1930 farmers in the U.S. and the Russian nuclear engineers in 1986 did—we are developing and implementing different technologies in very large-scale projects, without having tested their safety properly, and without taking proper precautions.

And we are still digging large holes in the ground, and pumping millions of gallons of toxic chemicals into the Earth, to push oil and gas to the surface. What these large caverns and chemicals will do now and later is unknown, although there are already serious indications of great environmental damage in the affected areas. And yet, we keep on digging great holes, and pumping large quantity poisons into the ground.

Such were the lead and asbestos proliferation cases, which we (the scientists and principals at the time) knew from the very beginning that might be dangerous to humans. And yet, we stuffed lead pipes and asbestos in the walls and attics of millions of homes, schools and commercial buildings, all the time knowing that those present some danger. And yet, very little was done until it was too late, and thousands of people got ill or died as a consequence.

Nuclear power plants have popped up all over the world during the last 50 years, and more are planned, even though we know that an accident at just one of them can, in a split second, wipe out entire regions and populations.

And then, thousands of coal-fired power plants and millions of oil-burning vehicles are turning our world into a frying pan with their smoke, dirt, and heat, and yet we are indiscriminately increasing their use by the day.

Renewable energy sources are doing their part in cleaning the environment, while at the same time are contaminating it. Mountains of sand are moved and melted to make raw material needed for manufacturing of solar cells. Several train compositions full of metals, such as silver, copper, and aluminum are also dug out and processed annually for making solar cells, PV modules, wind turbines and other renewable energy equipment.

And lately, exotic and of limited quantity materials, such as arsenic, cadmium, selenium, and tellurium have been used making millions upon millions of PV modules. And as if this were not enough, some of these materials, like arsenic and cadmium, are highly toxic—yet we are covering millions of house roofs and thousands of acres in the deserts with these questionable and unproven for large-scale, long-term operation in these regions.

It is becoming obvious by the day that these activities won't slow down any time soon. Only a disaster of world proportions, something like a combination between the Dust Bowl and Chernobyl on steroids encompassing a large area of the world, might make us reconsider and maybe even stop their use. Then, and only then, will reason and compassion prevail and it is then that the great minds will come up with a new approach to energy generation and use.

So, our goal here is not to prescribe a recipe for stopping all the harms we are doing to Earth and ourselves with the energy technologies, but rather to expose the problems and give the esteemed reader enough information on both sides of the issues at hand, to be able to decide how to deal with the present situation and what can be done to improve it.

What could the future problems and their consequences be? Let's take a quick walk into the future…

The Possible Scenarios

"The environment is everything I am not," said our famous friend, Albert Einstein half a century ago, as a warning of the environmental problems we have been creating ever since. With these seven words, he declared that he is integral part of everything that surrounds him. Things have changed dramatically since his times, so that today one doesn't need to be a genius to be fully aware of everything around us, and what an integral part of our lives and our future survival the environment is.

We are bombarded daily by bad news about contaminated soil, dying trees, water shortages, weather problems, and even the bad quality of the air we breathe. Is it really that bad? If it is, why? And is there anything we can do to change things? These are questions we are asking and tackling in this text, focusing on the role and the effects of energy generation on the environment and their future interactions.

We need to assume from the onset that these effects, as multi-faceted and complex as they might be, are generally speaking not good. But just imagine…yes, scientists are allowed to imagine—not surprisingly the most imaginative genre of literature and movie making is called "science fiction."

One can argue also that science does not mix with fiction, but let's imagine, nevertheless, life in year 2150. Crude oil deposits are long gone, coal and natural gas are near depletion, and so are rare and exotic minerals and materials. What would life look like in this natural resources depleted society?

Let's look at two extreme cases:

Best Case Scenario

The new generations have found a way to eliminate or bypass the use of oil and all other natural resources, replacing them with new man-made, abundant and cheap materials. As a consequence, there is no danger of shortages, prices are low and the environment is clean. Life is better than ever. I don't believe that anyone today can foresee how this could happen, but it could happen, if the new generations are smarter and more capable than we are.

One way they could've done that is to stop the indiscriminant use of natural resources for producing energy and other, not absolutely necessary, activities and things. They would have been maximized the use of solar and wind energy and other energy producing sources like hydropower, ocean wave and tidal power. Exploiting the limitless methane hydrates would certainly provide enough energy for a long time, while they tune up the energy transition.

They would've been smart enough to prioritize and compartmentalize the use of scarce natural resources for manufacturing only most important items and life-supporting medications, while relying on other materials and processes for everything else. Either that, or else, they'd be living in dark and untold misery…

Worst Case Scenario

Wow! We can spin around and paint a very bleak picture here. But even keeping it within reason, we still see a society wrapped in darkness and misery...unless we change the way we exploit and waste the precious energy resources.

The year is 2150. Things have gone bad during the last century. The fossils are gone, hydro is running out of water, and solar and wind energy sources have not been as efficient and reliable as promised, and are not producing enough energy. The infrastructure is decrepit and in need of total overhaul, but first the money is going mostly to support the race for optimization of the existing energy sources and R&D and implementation of new energy sources. Energy is in high demand, but it is nearly unavailable, and where and when available it is extremely expensive.

Because of indiscriminant use of natural resources during the century, the environment is badly contaminated and the climate has changed drastically. People's health has been negatively affected and extreme weather conditions—boiling summers and freezing winters—make life even more miserable, and take many lives. Many coastal communities, cities, and entire countries, are under water. At the same time deserts have taken over thousands of acres of previously producing agricultural lands.

Plastic bags cost $1,000 each. Gas is at a whopping $100 per gal. Charging an electric car costs $50 a day. Mass transport is scarce and costs $10 a trip (all these estimates in 2013 prices). Medications and cosmetics are astronomically high and unavailable as well. Air conditioning and heating are used only in emergencies, and in schools and hospitals. The thermostats are turned way down in the winter and way up in the summer. Special energy police teams are looking for violators of the energy use laws, and are arresting the violators. Energy laws dictate the use of energy in an uncompromising way, and rule the land!

We can go on and on in the depths of the pending energy gloom and doom. An entire new book could be written, and a number of movies made, on the subject of energy in the 22nd century. Can it happen? Absolutely! But who wants to live in such a place? And yet, this is one of the options we are promising our children and grandchildren.

In all cases, we can expect the effects of increase and accumulation of carbon dioxide (and other poisons) in the Earth's atmosphere to produce a number of negative effects. Some of the most obvious, and some of which are already occurring, are the:

- Loss of land area, including beaches and wetlands, to sea-level rise

- Loss of species and forest area, including coral reefs and wetlands

- Disruption of water supplies to cities and agriculture

- Health damage and deaths from heat waves and spread of tropical diseases

- Increased costs of air conditioning

- Loss of agricultural output due to drought

In addition to these effects, there are some other, less predictable but possibly more damaging effects, including:

- Disruption of weather patterns, with increased frequency of hurricanes and other extreme weather events

- A possible rapid collapse of the Greenland and west Antarctic ice sheets, which would raise sea levels by 12 meters or more, drowning major coastal cities

- Sudden major climate changes, such as a shift in the Atlantic Gulf Stream, which could change the climate of Europe to that of Alaska

- Positive feedback effects, such as an increased release of carbon dioxide from warming Arctic tundra, which would speed up global warming

Let's take a look at the details of the possible effects of climate change.

At 1°C temperature increase, we could see:

- Small glaciers in the Andes disappear, threatening water supplies for 50 million people

- Modest increase in yields in temperature regions

- At least 300,000 deaths each year from climate-related diseases

- Reduction in winter mortality in high latitudes and increased damage from coastal flooding

- At least 10% of land species facing extinction and increased wildfire risk

At 2°C temperature increase, we could see:

- Potential water supply decrease of 20-30% in some regions (southern Africa and the Mediterranean)

- Declines in crop yields in tropical regions (5-10% in Africa) 40-60 million more exposed to malaria in Africa

- Up to 10 million more people exposed to coastal flooding 15-40% of the species potentially face extinction

At 3°C temperature increase, we could see:

- Serious droughts in southern Europe every 10 years; 1-4 billion more people suffer water shortages

- 150-550 million more people at risk of hunger

- 1-3 million more people die annually from malnutrition potentially

- Up to 170 million more people are exposed to coastal flooding

- 20-50% of the species potentially face extinction

- Possible onset of collapse of the Amazon forest

At 4°C temperature increase, we could see:

- Potential water supply decrease of 30- 50% in Southern Africa and Mediterranean

- Yields decline by 15-35% in Africa

- Some entire regions are out of agricultural production

- Up to 80 million more people exposed to malaria in Africa

- Up to 300 million more people exposed to coastal flooding

- Loss of half of Arctic tundra

- Widespread loss of coral reefs

At 5°C temperature increase, we could see:

- Large glaciers in Himalayas possibly disappear, affecting ¼ of China's population

- Increase in ocean acidity possibly reduces fish stocks

- Further disease increases and substantial burdens on health care services

- Sea level rise threatens major cities such as New York, Tokyo, and London

- Significant extinction of wildlife and human populations across the globe

At 6°C temperature increase we could see additional, unpredictable, but excessive and even critical increases in all of the above categories in all world's regions. This would be the point of no return, because even if we wanted to and had a way to change things, the environment would be so modified by then, that nothing could return it to where it was during the pre-industrial days.

Maybe this is our destiny and there is nothing we can do to change it. And sure enough, there is a chance for the global warming to bring some positive, and even beneficial, outcomes in some cases and some areas of the world that might include:

- Increased agricultural production in cold climate areas

- Yields likely to peak at higher latitudes

- Lower heating costs in cold climate areas

- Fewer deaths from exposure to cold in the cold areas

- Less frequent and lesser intensity floods in flood-prone areas

The present situation is very complex and dynamic—lots of moving parts—to be able to make an educated guess of events for even the very near future. Any separate event in one part of the world could trigger an avalanche of events capable of changing the people's lives in the immediate area and around the globe.

Just look at the Fukushima accident, where an earthquake turned into a tsunami, which turned into a nuclear power plant destroyer that took only minutes to convert large populated areas into uninhabitable wasteland forever, killing many and evicting thousands of people from their homes.

The contamination and debris from the accident is now spreading around the world, and the final consequences and results are still to be tabulated.

What if a second nuclear plant on the other side of the Japanese island explodes too? And a third…? What would the combined results from such a series of disasters be? Would that be the end of Japan? The world?

We can only guess the answers to such ominous questions, but let that be a reminder that this is a fragile world with fragile environment, populated by fragile people, living in a very narrow life-supporting zone, and even narrower comfort zone. Many things can disturb our comfort zone and even affect our life-supporting zone.

With the risk of getting some things wrong, we will nevertheless dare to take a peak into our energy and environmental future, so let's go on this long and daring journey.

THE FOSSILS' FUTURE

There is no doubt that our present and near term future, are completely dominated by fossil fuels. Coal, natural gas, and crude oil will be driving our economies and vehicles at least for the next 20-30 years and maybe even longer. So what are we to expect during that time? How about after that? These are serious questions that we are addressing in this text in the hope of providing some answers.

So now, we will take a close look at the present and future of the major fossil fuels: coal, natural gas, and crude oil. We will then review the other energy sources: nuclear, and hydropower, ending with the renewables: solar, wind, bio-, geo-, and ocean-power technologies.

NOTE: Each of these fuels and the related technologies have a number of advantages and disadvantages, which we need to understand and consider in any energy-environment related discussions and decisions.

Just because an energy source has a lot of energy—as is the case with coal and nuclear power—it cannot, and should not, be considered as the only solution to all our energy problems.

On the other hand, just because an energy source doesn't have enough power and is intermittent—like solar power—it should not be disregarded as a viable power generator.

Instead, we should explore any and all possible opportunities to use all available energy sources and develop new sources that could provide the best possible mix of energy and environmental solutions for the future.

But first things first—let's try to figure out the present and future role of the different energy sources and the related power generating technologies in light of the present day economic and environmental crisis.

COAL

Coal is no doubt a national treasure of great value that had contributed immensely to the development o the world's most advanced economy. Coal is certain to continue playing a major role in the U.S. and world's energy future for several key reasons.

- It is the lowest-cost fossil source for base-load electricity generation, even taking into account the fact that the capital cost of a supercritical pulverized coal combustion plant (SCPC) is about twice that of a natural gas combined cycle (NGCC) unit.

- In contrast with other fossil fuels, coal resources are widely and equally distributed around the world between developed and developing countries.

Table 9-1 shows the available and recoverable coal reserves, as well as the estimated increase of coal use by 2030, around the world. The U.S. is undisputed leader in coal quantity and quality, and in the amount of its production and use. These numbers alone show that all the talk about reduction of GHG emissions and cleaning the environment are just words. There is no doubt that coal will be around until the last piece is dug out and burned.

Table 9-1. Coal reserves and heat value

Country	2010 BT*	2030 BT	Heat value**
U.S.A.	275	350	20,400
Russia	180	220	19,000
China	130	50	19,900
India	110	160	16,400
Australia	95	110	20,300
Africa	55	110	21,000
Other	180	200	20,000

*Billions of tons
**Average heat value of different coals in thousand Btus per ton. This value determines the quality and price of coal from different locations.

Coal use in the U.S. has been steadily decreasing, but this is not the case in other countries, which will bring us closer to the day when there will be no more coal. That will also bring us closer to the moment when the air that we breathe will be saturated with toxic gasses, and when life on Earth won't be healthy—or even possible.

Coal effects

The major disadvantages of coal come from the adverse environmental effects that accompany its mining, transport and combustion. Coal combustion results in greater CO_2 emissions than oil and natural gas per unit of heat output because of its relatively higher ratio of carbon to hydrogen and because the efficiency (i.e., heat rate) of a NGCC plant is higher than that of a SCPC plant. In addition to CO_2, the combustion-related emissions of coal generation include the criteria pollutants: sulfur dioxide (SO_2), nitrogen oxides (NO and NO_2).

Table 9-2 shows that coal is the worst polluter by far, which is one of the great concern of the 21st century. As the world develops its energy, needs change and so does the environment.

The countries that are not members of the Organisation for Economic Co-operation and Development (OECD), the developing economies, for example, consume less energy than OECD, the developed countries, but are projected to surpass them by 2030. An even more dramatic picture holds for coal consumption. The non-OECD economies consumed about the same amount as the richer group until recently, but are projected to consume twice as much by 2030.

The global CO_2 emissions follow a similar pattern. The non-OECD economies emitted less CO_2 than the mature ones from the turn of the century until recently, but because of their heavier dependence on coal, their emissions are already surpassing those of the more developed countries.

Emissions generated by coal burning are even more dramatic; the growth rates for energy and emissions by 2030 will exceed 2%, with emerging economies increasing at a rate about three times that of OECD countries. Emissions of CO_2 follow the same pattern.

Coal's contribution to total CO_2 emissions had declined to about 37% early in the century, but is projected to grow to over 40% by to 2030. Clearly any effort of individual countries to constrain substantially the total CO_2 contribution to the climate change cannot succeed until the total global contribution from this source is reduced. How and when is the question?

Coal is widely accepted as a great energy source, but a major contributor to the anthropogenic greenhouse effect at the same time. Its use is not going to diminish, so the best option is to "clean" it by reducing its emissions.

There are several options for reducing carbon emissions from combustion of fossil fuels. Among the most important are:

- Improvements in the efficiency of energy use, including transportation and electricity generation

- Expanded electricity production from nuclear, hydro- and other such sources

- Switching to less carbon-intensive fossil fuels, like natural gas

- Increased use of renewable energy such as wind, solar and biomass

- Continued combustion of fossil fuels, especially coal, combined with CO_2 capture and storage (CCS)

Figure 9-5. Coal-fired power complex...CO_2 galore...

Table 9-2. CO_2 emissions from different energy sources

Plant type	CO_2 Emissions in grams / kWh
Lignite, power	1153
Bituminous coal	949
Lignite, heat	729
Hard coal, heat & power	622
Natural gas, power only	428
Natural gas, heat only	148
Biogas, heat and power	409
Hydro power	40
Nuclear power	32
Solar power, PV	30
Solar power, CSP	25
Wind energy, on-shore	24
Wind energy, off-shore	23

Carbon Capture and Storage

If additional CO_2 policies are adopted, it is not likely that any one path to emissions reduction will emerge. Instead, all will play an important role in proportions that are difficult to impossible to predict today. As far as using clean coal in the future is concerned, the wide application of the CCS techniques is the only solution.

The importance of CCS for climate policy is underlined by the projection for coal use if the same CO_2 emission penalty is imposed and CCS is not available. In case of limited CCS application, for example, the coal use by 2050 would be reduced by almost 30%, but that would still increase global CO_2 emissions by about 15%.

Since it is clear that coal will continue to be used to meet the world's energy needs, the successful adoption of CCS is critical to sustaining future coal use in a carbon-constrained world. More significantly, considering the energy needs of developing countries, this technology may be an essential component of any attempt to stabilize global emissions of CO_2, much less to meet the climate convention's goal of stabilized atmospheric concentrations.

This conclusion holds true even for significant levels of expansion of nuclear and other power generation, and for implementation of policies stimulating the other approaches to emissions mitigation. So it is easy to conclude that if carbon capture and sequestration is successfully adopted, increased coal use in the future would not increase the CO_2 emissions, and emissions control scenarios are projected to grow as the technologies are optimized.

There is no way of stopping the planned coal-fired power plants increase in China, Russia, India, and some European countries. Forcing them to implement CCS technologies, however, is more feasible. This, in our opinion, is the only feasible option the world has for keeping GHG emissions lower while coal use is expanding during the next 20-30 years.

The Issues

Our estimates and suggestions, however, assume that CCS will be available, proven socially and financially, and environmentally acceptable, if and when an agreement is reached on imposing a charge on CO_2 emissions. A fully functional CCS option, unfortunately, is not available in this sense today.

Many years of development and demonstration will be required to prepare for its successful, large-scale adoption in the U.S. and elsewhere. Hasty attempts at CCS implementation in the face of urgent climate concerns could lead to excess cost and heightened local environmental concerns, as already seen in several such attempts. The failures would potentially lead to long delays in implementation of this important technology.

That underscores the need for CCS development work now at a scale appropriate to the technological and societal challenge. The task during the next several years, therefore, is to explore all components of efficient CCS development—including the issues of the different carbon capture technologies and CO_2 storage—in a search for the most effective and efficient path forward.

Once the acceptable solution is found, the work towards mass production and implementation would start. That would be another long and difficult road, but in the face of the alternatives, it is well worth the effort. The new CCS technology won't be simple or cheap, so initial capital costs and additional O&M expense will need to be justified and forced upon the GHG emitters. There is simply no other choice, if we want to stabilize GHG emissions at the projected increase of coal burning in the near future.

In addition to GHG emissions, coal mining is causing hardship in a number of different ways too. Many abandoned mines dot the countryside in many states and countries. Some of these have done so much damage that the area in some cases has turned into a wasteland.

Case Study: Centralia, PA

Centralia, PA, is a small coal-mining town in the backwoods of Pennsylvania. Things were not different from those of any small mining town until 1962, when a fire started in a mine right beneath the town. The fire spread, which made it impossible to put out. Amazingly enough, the fire is still burning deep under downtown Centralia.

It seems that members of the volunteer fire company cleaning up the town landfill, located in an abandoned strip-mine pit, set the dump on fire and let it burn for some time. This had been done before, but this time the fire was not fully extinguished upon completion of the cleanup. An opening in the pit bottom allowed the fire to enter the abandoned coalmines beneath Centralia and ignite the remaining coal in some of them.

It was not until 1979, however, that the problem became evident in rising temperatures underneath the city streets. Wide attention to the fire began to increase, culminating in 1981 when a 12-year-old resident fell into a sinkhole 4 feet and 150 feet deep that suddenly opened beneath his feet. The boy was pulled out as a plume of hot steam, saturated with lethal levels of carbon monoxide, blew up from the hole.

Giving up on extinguishing the fire, in 1984, the U.S. Congress allocated $42 million for relocation of the locals. Most of the residents accepted buyout offers and moved away, but a few families opted to stay despite warnings from Pennsylvania officials.

In 1992, Governor Bob Casey invoked eminent domain on all properties in the borough, condemning all buildings in the town. A subsequent legal effort by residents to have the decision reversed failed. Soon after that the U.S. Postal Service revoked Centralia's ZIP code and in 2009, Governor Ed Rendell began the formal eviction of the remaining Centralia residents.

Today very few homes and buildings remain standing, being demolished by the authorities or Nature. The small town now looks like an abandoned field with streets. There are warning signs, indicating danger of underground fire, unstable ground, and carbon monoxide. Smoke and steam is coming from the now abandoned Pennsylvania Route 61, from the hilltop cemetery, and numerous cracks in the ground scattered about the town.

Figure 9-6. Warning signs in Centralia, PA.

A number of lawsuits went back and forth, and now some former Centralia residents believe that the state's eminent domain claim was a plot to gain the mineral rights to the anthracite coal beneath the borough. Its value is believed to be in the hundreds of millions of dollars, although the exact amount of coal is not known.

The beginning of this theory can be traced to the old municipality laws of the state, according to which, when the municipality can no longer form a functioning municipal government, or when there are no longer any residents, the entity legally ceases to exist.

At that point, the mineral rights, which are owned by Centralia, and are not privately held, would automatically become the property of the state of Pennsylvania. The state then can sell the right to, or use, the mines as it sees fit, making millions of dollars in the process.

Centralia is one of the many different ghost towns in the U.S., many reminders of the glory days of coal. The small ghost town of Centralia was also an inspiration for the film adaptation of the video game Silent Hill,

and other movies like *Nothing But Trouble*.

Knoebels Amusement Resort, in nearby Elysburg, features The Black Diamond, a dark ride/roller coaster based on the theme of a haunted coal mine. Near the end of the ride, trains pass a swirling, fiery vortex. Although this resembles popular depictions of the gates of hell, a sign identifies the location as Centralia.

The underground fires in and around Centralia are still burning and may continue to do so for 250 years. The Centralia mine fire extended beneath the town of Byrnesville, Pennsylvania, a few miles to the south, and forced its abandonment and the evacuation of its residents as well.

Coal Exports

The U.S. coal industry is experiencing a slowdown due to reduction of coal use, caused by economic slowdown in the short term, and many conversions of coal-to gas-fired power generation in the long run.

To compensate for the loss of the U.S. market, the coal industry is turning to the world coal markets. The hunger for high quality coal is growing, and many developing countries are ready to consume any amount of coal they can get. Enter the U.S. coal industry.

Washington's Cherry Point is the newest planned coal export depot with a capacity of unloading 20 coal trains (with 100-115 cars each) and loading their contents on barges every day.

What this boils down to is a controversy of great proportions. We are sharply criticizing China, India and other countries for increased use of coal-fired power generation, while we are willingly exporting millions of tons of coal to them at the same time. What's wrong with this picture…?

And then, there is serious damage to the local environment. Every day an estimated 200,000 to 230,000 tons of coal are to be loaded at the mines, transported several hundred miles down to the export terminal, unloaded from the trains and the coal is to be loaded again on transport ships for long voyages across the world's oceans.

Particles and GHG gasses from the coal and the trains' diesel engines will invade the pristine valleys of the Washington coastline. Serious contamination of the local air, soil, and water is expected, and so a battle is raging between the locals and the coal companies.

The local Lummi tribe is opposing the granting of a permit for the proposed Gateway Pacific coal export terminal at Cherry Point, because the related activities would interfere with fishing and disrupt an important cultural site. The move could derail the project, since the tribe has a strong position, based on treaty rights. There are a number of precedents where the U.S. Corps of Engineers has refused to process permits on other projects that tribes said would violate treaties. This will force the involved parties to reassess the plans for the export depot.

The project is one of three in the Northwest proposed to ship coal from Montana and Wyoming to Asia. The others are on the Columbia River at Longview and Boardman, Oregon.

In summary, coal is here to stay. The U.S. is a major producer of high quality coal, and although coal use in the U.S. is decreasing, it will not affect the total amount of coal mined in the country. As a matter of fact, increased exports might even increase the coal production significantly in the future. The U.S. coal industry is preparing for it by building new export terminals in several key coal export areas of the country.

While we cannot blame the coal industry for trying to survive, this situation is a good example of the controversial power generation vs. environmental pollution conundrum today. It exemplifies the proverbial case where the left hand doesn't know (or doesn't care) what the right hand is doing.

While the U.S. proudly announces decrease in coal-fired pollution, it is equally proudly producing and exporting large quantities of coal to be burned somewhere else in the world. The result from this action is net zero pollution decrease, or even worse—more pollution around the globe.

NATURAL GAS

Natural gas resources in the U.S. and the world are abundant. The mean remaining resource base is estimated to be 16,200 Tcf, with a range between 12,400 Tcf (with a 90% probability of being exceeded) and 20,800 Tcf (with a 10% probability of being exceeded). The mean global projection was 150 times the annual consumption in 2009, where, with the exception of Canada and the U.S., this estimate does not include any unconventional supplies.

The global gas supply base is relatively immature, where outside North America only 10-15% of the estimated ultimately recoverable conventional resources have been produced to date.

Natural gas production in the U.S. has traditionally been associated with the Southwest region and the Gulf of Mexico. However, significant production also takes place in Alaska and in the Central region. In the

case of Alaska, the vast majority of the gas is associated with oil production on the North Slope. Due to the lack of an export mechanism, this produced natural gas is re-injected into the wells to enhance recovery from the oil fields. This gas, however, is not wasted and could be recovered some day when technological and economic conditions allow, or in emergency situations.

Small volumes of liquefied natural gas (LNG) are exported from Alaska to Japan, which will very likely increase in the future as prices go up and Japan needs more gas.

There are producing gas wells all around the U.S., with a clear dominance of the Southwest, Gulf of Mexico and Central regions. The dynamics of the production levels across these major regions have differed appreciably over the past decade. In the Southwest, the largest gas producing region.

According to industry analysis, the natural gas remaining resources in the U.S. have almost doubled since the 1990s. This shows the power of technology development, and confirms the large uncertainty inherent in all natural resource estimates

Although the global resources are large, the supply base is concentrated geographically, with an estimated 70% located in only three regions: Russia, the Middle East (primarily Qatar and Iran) and North America, including unconventional gas. By some measures, global supplies of natural gas are even more geographically concentrated than oil supplies. Political considerations and individual country depletion policies play at least as big a role in global gas resource development as geology and economics, and dominate the evolution of the global gas market.

Over the past two decades, the global production of natural gas has grown significantly, rising by almost 42% overall from approximately 74 trillion cubic feet (Tcf) in 1990 to 105 Tcf in 2009. This is almost twice the growth rate of global oil production, which increased by around 22% over the same period.

Much of the gas production growth has been driven by the rapid expansion of production in areas that were not major gas producers prior to 1990. This trend shows that growth in production from regions such as the Middle East, Africa, Asia, and Oceania has significantly outpaced growth in the traditional large producing regions, including North America and Eurasia (primarily Russia).

In addition to demonstrating the overwhelming scale of the U.S. and Russia compared to other producing countries, the numbers illustrate the very significant growth rates in other countries. The substantial growth of new gas producing countries over the period reflects the relative immaturity of the gas industry on a global basis outside Russia and North America, the expansion of gas markets and the rise in global cross-border gas trade.

Between 1993 and 2008, global cross-border gas trade almost doubled, growing from around 18 Tcf (25% of global supply) to around 35 Tcf (32% of global supply).

Most of the world's gas supply is transported from producing fields to market by pipeline networks. However, the increase in global gas trade has been accelerated by the growing use of liquefied natural gas (LNG), which is made by cooling natural gas to around -162°C by pressurizing it.

In its liquid form, natural gas has an energy density 600 times that of gas at standard temperature and pressure and it can be readily transported over long distances in specialized ocean-going vessels.

Shale Gas

The revolutionary techniques for exploration of the new shale deposits represent a major contribution to the resource base of the U.S. One of the problems, however, is that there is considerable variability in the quality of the resources, both within and between shale layers. This variability in performance contributes to substantial differences in the average well performances at different locations.

Shale gas deposits extraction is not a "manufacturing process," where wells are drilled on a regular basis. In contrast to conventional oil and gas exploration, where each prospective well is evaluated on an individual basis, the shale gas production occurs within a highly variable and unpredictable subsurface environment.

Another major issue of shale production is the amount of hydrocarbon liquid produced along with gas. Some areas contain wet gas with appreciable amounts of liquid, which can have a considerable effect on the breakeven economics—particularly if the price of oil is high compared to the price of gas.

The liquid content of a gas is often measured in terms of the "condensate ratio," expressed in terms of barrels of liquid per million cubic feet of gas (bbls/MMcf). For example, at a liquids price of $80/bbl and a condensate ratio in excess of approximately 50 bbls/MMcf, the liquid production alone can provide an adequate return on the investment, even if the gas has

no market value. In other cases, the liquid could break even, with the gas content bringing the profit margin.

These factors create an interesting dynamic in the U.S. gas supply and demand chain. Natural gas prices were driven to low levels by 2010, primarily as a result of the abundance of relatively low-cost shale gas. Meanwhile oil prices, determined by global market forces, have remained high.

This has led producers to seek liquid rich gas reserves, such as certain areas of the Marcellus or the Eagle Ford play in Texas, where condensate ratios can be well in excess of 100 bbl/MMcf. These reserves then enable more gas production, even at low gas prices, thus putting further downward pressure on gas prices.

Hydrofracking

Hydraulic fracturing is used to facilitate the production of oil and natural gas from low permeability formations. The process has received significant attention recently in relation to its use in shale formations, where it promises to bring great quantities of oil and natural gas.

Hydraulic fracturing creates hundreds of thousands of jobs, bolsters national security by decreasing our dependence on imported energy, and even can have environmental benefits because hydraulic fracturing often is used to produce natural gas, the cleanest burning of all fossil fuels.

The skeptics raise several environmental concerns, including a fear that hydraulic fracturing can threaten underground sources of drinking water. The problem is that fracture fluids are based on several chemicals, such as acids, gels, organic and inorganic compounds, water, oil, petroleum products, and very often all of the above.

Each of these additives is designed to serve a particular function in the overall process—usually geared to increase the efficiency of the process. None of these, however, is designed for the safety of the environment or the local people, and since most of these chemicals are toxic and harmful to the environment and human life, we end up with some extreme cases of property and health damages.

Friction reducers are used to lessen the resistance of the fluid moving through the casing; biocides to prevent bacterial growth; scale inhibitors to prevent buildup of scale; and proppants, such as sand or ceramic beads to hold the fractures open.

It is the use of such additives that has raised one of the concerns about hydraulic fracturing, since some of them—benzene, ethylene glycol and naphthalene—have been linked to negative health effects at certain exposure levels. Some of the additives, such as sodium chloride, potassium chloride and diluted acids, present low to very low risks to human health and the environment. When used in large quantities, however, they can damage the environment and life in it.

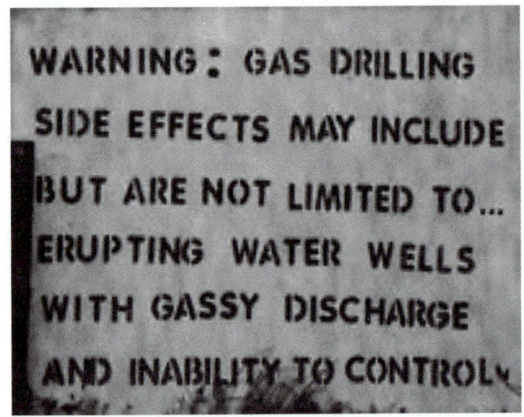

Figure 9-7. Warning sign by a gas-drilling site

The ultimate fate of hydraulic fracturing fluids returned to the surface often is determined by the availability of treatment and disposal technologies such as on-site or municipal treatment facilities and injection wells. Underground disposal via injection wells is the most common method of disposal for used fracture fluid. Treatment in municipal wastewater facilities also is sometimes conducted, provided the fluid will not cause the facility to violate a drinking water standard.

The unrecovered treatment fluids are trapped in the fractured formation via various mechanisms such as pore storage and stranding behind healed fractures, thus isolating them from ground water…in theory.

Several studies, and neighbors' reports, however, show that depending upon the design of the well and the underground formation dynamics, 30-70% of fracturing fluids could return to the surface through the well or ground pores and crevices.

Ground and water table contamination resulting from the flow back of fracture fluids returned to the surface is usually caused by failures of key barriers of protection, such as casing strings and cement sheaths. Once that happens, the fluids are free to flow in whichever direction possible.

The use of hydraulic fracturing appears likely to continue unhindered, but regulations, some of which have already been strengthened, will likely further address environmental and health concerns.

The effect of the new regulations is hard to predict, but we expect fierce court battles soon, before any major changes take place. The gas industry is very powerful

and getting even more so by the day, and is unlikely to roll over and die because of some regulations. Time will tell…

Present Status

Fracking brings with it the potential for spills, blowouts and well failures that contaminate groundwater supplies. Cleanup of drinking water contamination is so expensive that it is rarely even attempted. In Dimock, PA, Cabot Oil & Gas, for example, reported having spent $109,000 on systems to remove methane from well water for 14 local households, while in Colorado, cleanup of an underground gas seep has been ongoing for eight years at a likely cost of additional hundreds of thousands of dollars.

The provision of temporary replacement water supplies is also expensive. Cabot Oil & Gas reported having spent at least $193,000 on replacement water for homes with contaminated water in Dimock, Pennsylvania.

Fracking can also pollute drinking water sources for major municipal systems, increasing water treatment costs. If fracking were to degrade the New York City watershed with sediment or other pollution, construction of a filtration plant would cost approximately $6 billion.

Toxic substances in fracking fluid and wastewater—as well as air pollution from trucks, equipment and the wells themselves—have been linked to a variety of negative health effects.

The National Institute of Occupational Safety and Health recently warned that workers may be at elevated risk of contracting the lung disease silicosis from inhalation of silica dust at fracking sites. Silicosis is one of a family of dust-induced occupational ailments that imposed $50 million in medical care costs in the U.S. in 2007.

Residents living near fracking sites have long suffered from a range of health problems, including headaches, eye irritation, respiratory problems and nausea—potentially imposing economic costs ranging from health care costs to workplace absenteeism and reduced productivity.

Fracking and associated activities also produce pollution that contributes to the formation of ozone smog and particulate soot. Air pollution from gas drilling in Arkansas' Fayetteville shale region imposed estimated public health costs of more than $10 million in 2008.

Fracking converts rural and natural areas into industrial zones, replacing forest and farm land with well pads, roads, pipelines and other infrastructure, and damaging precious natural resources.

Fracking strains infrastructure and public services and imposes cleanup costs that can fall on taxpayers. The truck traffic needed to deliver water to a single fracking well causes as much damage to local roads as nearly 3.5 million car trips. The state of Texas has approved $40 million in funding for road repairs in the Barnett shale region, while Pennsylvania estimated in 2010 that $265 million would be needed to repair damaged roads in the Marcellus shale region.

The need for vast amounts of water for fracking is helping to drive up demand for new water infrastructure in many regions of the country. Texas' official state water plan calls for the expenditure of $400 million on projects to support the mining sector over the next 50 years, with fracking projected to account for 42% of mining water use by 2020.

In addition, the oil and gas industry has left thousands of orphaned wells from previous fossil fuel booms. Taxpayers may wind up on the hook for the considerable expense of plugging and reclaiming wells that will become orphans in the future. Cabot Oil & Gas claims to have spent $730,000 per well to cap three shale gas wells in Pennsylvania. If they, or others, do not complete the job, the taxpayers will end up with the bills and the consequences.

Fracking can also undercut the long-term economic prospects of areas where it takes place. A 2008 study found that Western counties that have relied on fossil fuel extraction are doing worse economically compared with peer communities and are less well prepared for growth in the future. This is due to a number of factors, most of which vary from location to location. The fact is that excess fracking activities change the face of a town and the local area, usually for the worse.

The Future

We saw above that there are a number of negative aspects of hydrofracking. Nevertheless, it is now an established method of oil and gas production, which is supported by the U.S. government. We will not be able to stop it no matter what happens, because it serves the national interests.

Similar to the building of a large hydro dam, which requires the resettlement of thousands and the destruction of entire populated centers and cultures, the large-scale development of hydrofracking is on national importance. Isolated incidences of soil and water contamination cannot stop a national undertaking of such great importance.

And yet, we need to consider the affected people,

because the number is growing. There are a number of convincing documentaries on the web, which we recommend to the esteemed reader. They clearly show some of the problems related to hydrofracking and its effects on the locals.

And since the hydrofracking is expanding quickly across the nation, we need to look at the larger picture too, to see if we can avoid the problems from spreading and becoming a national agenda.

We can and should make some changes to the way things are done. One doesn't need to be a genius or a scientist to figure out that some simple modifications to the process could be very beneficial to the locals and the environment as a whole.

For example, one sure thing to solve the contamination problem is for drillers to use non-toxic chemicals to replace the toxic concoctions used today, and the nature of which they are not even willing (or required) to reveal. This is not very likely to happen any time soon, however, because the fluids used today are very effective and companies take pride in their proprietary formulations. And since under capitalism the property rights are fully protected, we do not see any changes in the chemical disclosures. We are also not aware of any movement to develop new, non-toxic drilling fluids.

At the very least, however, the drillers could add chemical tracers into their fracking fluids so that if a nearby domestic well is contaminated, that tracer will show up in the well water. This way the affected people will know for sure whether the well is contaminated from the hydrofracking operations or perhaps from some other source, like an unrelated underground storage tank leaking, or some surface contaminants are getting into the groundwater.

This way there would be no doubt and the locals will have a 100% confident solution to their water and soil contamination problems. Yes, but that will also be a sure proof of guilt, thus it is not likely to happen either.

In the broader scenario, affected citizens, cities, drillers, and oil and gas companies should gather baseline data on water quality from wells before hydrofracking begins, which would be compared with after-drilling test results. That method has been very helpful in some cases, like the Pavillion gas field, where multiple potential sources of contaminants have been found in domestic wells. The Pavillion field is just one of multiple sites now being studied by the U.S. Environmental Protection Agency (EPA) to learn about past and future effects of hydro-fracking on groundwater.

Disposing of the used hydrofracking fluids is another issue that needs attention and complete resolution. A similar pre-fracking science approach, as that described above, is used in some areas to evaluate the effects of disposing of fracking fluids by injecting them deep underground.

In Ohio and Texas, this disposal method has been the prime suspect in the recent activation of old, dormant faults that have generated clusters of low intensity earthquakes. So in North Carolina, as well as other places where fracking has been proposed, some scientists are scrambling to gather as much pre-fracking seismic and other data as possible.

Anti-fracking Movement

The future of natural gas looks bright, but it will not be smooth. There are people who have been hurt by the increased drilling and hydrofracking activities, who will not give up until some acceptable solutions are found. An anti-fracking movement is growing in the U.S. and abroad. The specific agendas of anti-fracking groups vary according to local priorities and group composition. Public consultation is critical in France, for example, while rural conservation issues dominate in Australia.

The global anti-fracking movement can be divided into several broad camps:

*   Those desiring a better deal from the gas industry

*   Those advocating further study into the environmental and economic impacts of unconventional gas development

*   Those demanding a complete ban on hydraulic fracturing

*   Those demanding tighter regulation of gas development

We can expect some dramatic developments in the future. While most people are not opposed to hydraulic fracturing per se, their agenda is to strike an acceptable deal with the gas industry for ensuring safety of people and their property, better economic opportunity, fair taxation, and proper compensation.

The anti-fracking movement discounts the overly rosy industry projections of economic growth and employment. U.S. and foreign activists are concerned that labor will be imported and profits exported, leaving local communities to bear the long-term environmental and public health costs of the industry.

In the U.S., the movement takes the form of sectional opposition to energy companies from Texas and Oklahoma dominating the industry in Pennsylvania

and New York. In France, Bulgaria and Czech Republic, this sentiment has manifested as specific opposition to foreign involvement in the industry, on top of general opposition to hydraulic fracturing. In South Africa, anti-fracking activists wonder how uneducated, unskilled local labor forces are supposed to benefit from hydraulic fracturing.

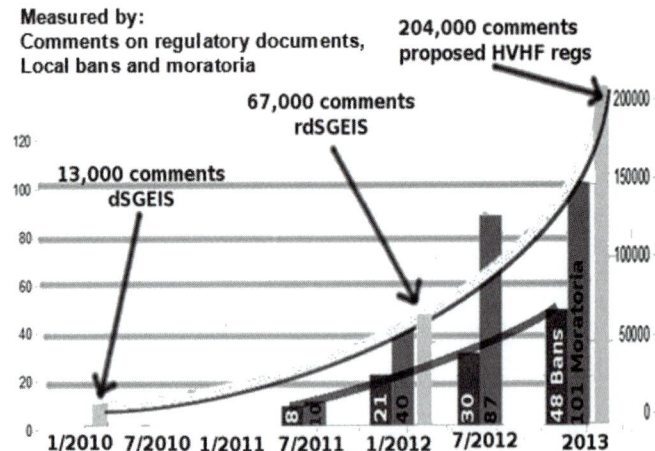

Figure 9-8. The anti-fracking movement results in New York state.

The anti-fracking movement is growing fast in some places of the U.S. and abroad. The exponential increase of complaints and other actions in New York state demonstrates the fact that people are getting increasingly aware of the problems. At the very least, they require more information on the processes and materials used—before the drilling activities start.

Obviously, the New York government officials have heard the citizens' complaints and so now there is a moratorium on hydraulic fracturing in the state. It states that if and when the state permits hydraulic fracturing as a means to extract natural gas from the southern tier's Marcellus shale formation, drilling will be allowed only in communities that are fully informed and officially agree to allow the practice and its consequences. Fair, no?

While this is not an argument for prohibiting unconventional gas development, such concerns will continue to drive demands for increased local control, which in turn will increase the risks to the investors. On the other hand, the anti-fracking movement's efforts for obtaining a better deal revolves around the tax structure of the unconventional gas industry. At one level, this reflects animosity towards the incentives and exemptions often provided to attract investment.

The anti-fracking movement in Pennsylvania, for example, has questioned the state's low taxes on unconventional gas development, calling for both a severance tax (i.e. based on volumes extracted) and royalty rates in line with those in other parts of the country. At another, it reflects a desire for increased taxes to compensate for the social costs of unconventional gas development.

Local impact fees in parts of the U.S. are envisioned as being a way for municipalities to recoup the costs of maintaining public roads degraded by truck traffic or funding emergency response capacities. The tax structure is also perceived as a bulwark against unconventional gas development full stop, as opposition to tax exemptions for liquefied natural gas (LNG) exporters and support for carbon taxation suggest.

In many cases the anti-fracking movement overlaps with direct compensation claims by individuals or communities against companies, seeing itself as a counterweight to the energy industry's political clout and legalities. Prominent U.S. anti-fracking groups, for example, took in similar cases in the U.S., environmental groups such as EarthJustice and the Delaware Riverkeeper Network have involved themselves in litigation against gas companies, filing briefs in support of residents seeking compensation. In these cases, getting a better deal from the gas industry concretely implies maximizing direct settlement compensation. Yet, as in many cases, monetary settlement—rather than conceding the debate and fuelling anti-fracking sentiment—may be the least costly course of action for the gas companies and their investors.

So it seems that the battlefield lines are drawn along economic and environmental concerns. We have seen only the beginning stages of the battle, which appears to be growing larger in size and fiercer in nature. Peoples' lives and properties are at stake, and so they are willing—and in some cases forced—to fight against perceived injustices done by fracking activities.

Neither party has any intentions to give up the fight, so the only question is how long and how large the battle will grow. There is no answer to that question, so we will be witnessing some very interesting events developing through the years to come.

In summary, the natural gas industry is expected to grow significantly in the U.S. and abroad, albeit slower, during the next several years and even decades. Regardless of the good news, natural gas has inherited problems, which cannot and should not be ignored:

- It's supply is limited, regardless of the misleading abundance of the recent developments

- It is also emitting large quantities of GHG emission

- Even more importantly for the short term is the fact that hydrofracking is damaging the environment and is making people sick

These are important factors, which should make us slow down and think about what we are doing. We are in a hurry to totally exhaust a precious and irreplaceable natural resource…just because it is there and because we can. It is end time to think what will happen 20, 30, 50 years down the road when natural gas is no more? What then?

In the meanwhile, we need to consider that although it is less polluting than coal, natural gas is still a ferocious GHG emitter. Increasing its use for power generation will fully compensate for the reductions, and we might even end up emitting more GHGs than coal-fire power plants.

And finally, looking at the present situation, we see a number of unwanted consequences. The leaking gases have contaminated people's homes, back yards, parks, and water supplies and chemicals, causing a number of property and health damages.

Due to the amazing speed of development and huge number of fracking sites, we cannot even estimate the number and size of the present damages, let alone envision those of the future. One thing is for sure though—we have not learned the lessons of the past, where sloppy regulators and greedy developers allowed large-scale debacles. Lead and asbestos materials were allowed for use on a large scale in the U.S. in the recent past, resulting in countless property damages, illness and death for thousands.

We are obviously headed in that direction with hydrofracking, and so this is the time to educate the public and ensure open discussion about basic and efficient safety precautions with the developers in each case—before the drilling starts.

CRUDE OIL

The Earth's circumference is 40,075 km, so imagine wrapping a large, 48" diameter pipe around it. Each meter of the pipe contains 273.4 gallons, so the entire pipe would contain approximately 11.0 billion gallons of oil. A lot of oil, you'd say. Yes, it is, but get this; the world uses about 85 million barrels (42 gal. each) every single day. This is over 3.6 billion gallons crude oil used daily, so every three days we use all the oil in our virtual 48" pipe that we had wrapped around the Earth.

Or even better, imagine pure crude oil running down Niagara Falls. Every 6.6 hours of full flow would be how much oil the world uses daily, which is a 9,000 acre-feet lake full of crude oil.

However, as things have been going lately, the Niagara Falls of crude oil has been increasing, but the source is slowly drying. One and two miles deep oil wells are things of the past, because most of the oil well levels today are much lower. The Saudi's oil tank is approaching empty, so they are forced to dig wells up over 10 kilometers (6 miles) down into the ground. Recently Shell set a world record of 12,376 meter (7.7 miles) deep well in Russia. This is 15 times the height of the world's tallest skyscraper in Dubai.

How long will it be before we run completely out of oil, if we use so much of it? That is the question of the day. Trying to imagine life without oil is difficult; it is something we prefer not to think of, so we will leave it for the next generations to figure out. Good luck, next generations!

Peak Oil

Peak oil is a term used to describe the point in time when the maximum rate of petroleum extraction is reached. It is assumed, on the basis of all we know on the subject, that at that time the rate of production is expected to level and eventually enter a terminal (and unpredictable) decline.

This seemingly insignificant term, that most people have not even heard, let alone care about, is used to describe something remarkable that is inevitably going to happen. Or it might even be here now. In any case, it is a significant moment in time that we simply do not know much about.

Peak oil will have the combined seismic economic shock wave effect of all disasters of the past, resonating in every corner of the globe. Some professionals in the oil industry believe that the *oil peak* is happening now. Others think that it started in 2007, or 2010 and other dates. The World Energy Council forecasted it as "after 2010" which could mean anything and anytime, but since it did not say "after 2015," we need to presume that they really mean anytime "shortly after 2010," which is just about now.

Other scientists forecast the *peak oil* to occur at any time between 2010 and 2020, while Shell Oil has put a date of 2025, or later. Some say it will never happen, as the technology improves and we are able to get oil from places we could not even dream before. You be the judge!

In all cases, we need to be aware and well educated on the matter, because it will have profound impact on

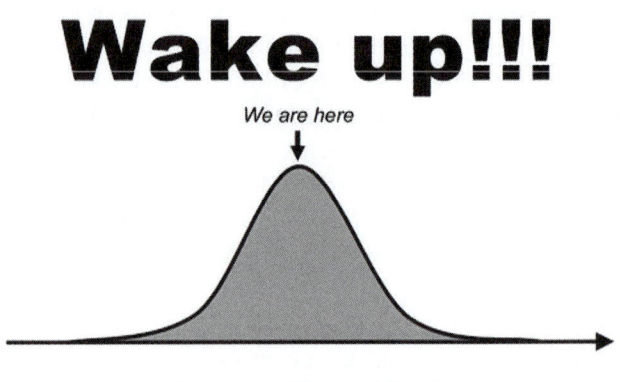

Figure 9-9. This is no joke. Peak oil is here to stay!

our lives. A 2005 study, *Peaking of World Oil Production, Impact, Mitigation and Risk Management* by Robert L Hirsch warns us that:

1. When world oil peaking will occur is not known with certainty. A fundamental problem in predicting oil peaking is the poor quality of and possible political biases in world oil reserves data. Some experts believe that peaking may occur soon. This study indicates that "soon" is within 20 years.

2. The problems associated with world oil production peaking will not be temporary, and past "energy crisis" experience will provide relatively little guidance. The challenge of oil peaking deserves immediate, serious attention, if risks are to be fully understood and mitigation begun on a timely basis.

3. Oil peaking will create a severe liquid fuels problem for the transportation sector, not an "energy crisis" in the usual sense that term has been used.

4. Peaking will result in dramatically higher oil prices, which will cause protracted economic hardship in the U.S. and the world. However, the problems are not insoluble. Timely, aggressive mitigation initiatives addressing both the supply and the demand sides of the issue will be required.

5. In the developed nations, the problems will be especially serious. In the developing nations peaking problems have the potential to be much worse.

6. Mitigation will require a minimum of a decade of intense, expensive effort because the scale of liquid fuels mitigation is inherently extremely large.

7. While greater end-use efficiency is essential, increased efficiency alone will be neither sufficient nor timely enough to solve the problem. Production of large amounts of substitute liquid fuels will be required. A number of commercial or near-commercial substitute fuel production technologies are currently available for deployment, so the production of vast amounts of substitute liquid fuels is feasible with existing technology.

8. Intervention by governments will be required, because the economic and social implications of oil peaking would otherwise be chaotic. The experiences of the 1970s and 1980s offer important guides as to government actions that are desirable and those that are undesirable, but the process will not be easy.

And we need to be also aware that after *oil peak*, there will be *gas peak*, and then *coal peak*. It is only logical that after such intensive use, sooner or later these otherwise enormous supplies will end. They cannot last forever, although we wish they did, so we need to be at least aware of the consequences, and do something about it.

The Future of Crude Oil

Crude oil is usually refined into different products, which are then used in different applications.

Table 9-3. Crude oil products

Product	% of total
Gasoline	51.4
Fuel Oil	15.3
Jet Fuel	12.3
Still Gas	5.4
Coke	5.0
Residual Fuel Oil	3.3
Liquefied Gas	2.8
Asphalt, Road Oil	1.7
Other Products	1.5
Lubricants	0.9

The major use of crude oil products is for transportation. Transportation fuels (gasoline, diesel, and jet fuel) make over 2/3 of the total use of crude oil. The rest is used to make a large number of useful products, which we use on daily basis.

The U.S. refineries process billions of gallons of crude oil daily, which process emits millions of tons of GHG gasses and other pollutants. The refining (and pollution) is done nonstop 365 days of the year, with some minor interruptions.

Oil Burning Pollution

Crude oil products propel billions of vehicles: cars, trucks, boats, trains, and airplanes. These vehicles emit millions of tons of CO_2 and other GHG gasses, which are the leading cause of global warming. Diesel vehicles are the worst offenders, which are responsible for nearly 80% of vehicle-related particulate matter pollution, and the U.S. is the world's highest producer of these gases.

Seaports are another huge source of air pollution, because ships burn large quantities of fuel even when they are not moving. As a result, people who live and work near seaports are among the highest cancer risk populations. Airports fall in the same category, where the huge airplane metal bodies are moved around at the expense of tons of jet fuel and tons of GHG emissions. There are ways to reduce pollution. For example, ships can use shore-side power instead of idling at the docks and airplanes can move more efficiently during taxiing, but such practices are mostly ignored.

So what can we expect in the future? The U.S. EPA, which develops regulations and programs to reduce airborne toxins from transportation, cites several keys to reducing harmful emissions:

*   Using lower carbon fuels

*   Using emissions reducing technologies

*   Improving vehicle technology

*   Traveling fewer miles

*   Careful driving and car maintenance

Those things are easier said than done: Using lower carbon fuels requires understanding of the problems at hand, lots of money, and willingness to change, none of which is likely to happen any time soon. The technology is improving slowly, so we do not expect any great break-through in new vehicles soon. And travelling fewer miles is synonymous to American psyche with taking our freedoms and dreams away. Not possible!

Some simple changes, however, like driving carefully and keeping cars in good mechanical shape are more likely solutions to be accepted as fuel-saving measures.

The EPA also suggests the use of renewable fuels (such as electricity) and alternative fuels (such as natural gas) as a partial solution. This, however, is not likely to happen soon on mass scale, due to the high cost of electrical and alternative fuel vehicles.

It is not clear how much emissions would be saved by electric and alternative fuel vehicles, because: a) electric vehicles use electricity produced by fossil-fired power plants, and b) natural gas powered vehicles also emits GHG gasses, some of which are even more dangerous than these emitted by gasoline and diesel powered vehicles.

So what is the solution for future use of crude oil and its derivatives?

Oil Spills

We have witnessed a number of large oil spills through history, some of which are fading from our memory, so here is a refresher:

The world's largest oil spills:

Gulf War, 1991, Kuwait, over 250 million gallons of crude oil were spilled as Iraqi forces retreated from Kuwait during the first Gulf War. On their way out, they opened the valves of oil wells and pipelines to slow the advance of American troops.

Figure 9-10. Gulf war intentional oil spill.

This mindless action resulted in the largest oil spill ever. Some 250 million gallons of crude oil flowed into the Persian Gulf and flooded the surrounding land. The resulting oil slick spanned an area of the size of the state of Maine.

The coalition forces sealed off some of the open pipelines using smart bombs, but the full recovery effort had to wait until after the war. 25 miles of booms, skimmers, and vacuum trucks were deployed in the gulf, mostly to protect the water intakes for desalinization, as well as for industry and power plants' safety. About 60 million gallons of oil was recovered during that effort.

Ixtoc 1 Oil Well, 1979, Bay of Campeche, Mexico, over 140 million gallons of crude oil were spilled when an oil well collapsed after a pressure buildup sparked an explosion. During the next 10 months, about 140 million gallons of crude oil spilled into the Gulf of Mexico from the damaged oil well.

Mud and steel, iron and lead balls were dropped down in the well shaft in an attempt to shut the flow off. Some of the oil burned when it reached the surface and some evaporated. Dispersants were then sprayed over 1100 square miles of oil slick in the ocean. On the Texas side of the gulf, skimmers and boomers were placed in the water to protect the bays and lagoons of the barrier islands.

Atlantic Empress, 1979, Trinidad and Tobago, West Indies, 88.3 million gallons were spilled during a storm, when two full supertankers collided off the coast of Tobago in the Caribbean Sea during a stormy night accident. This precipitated the largest ship-caused crude oil spill in history.

The crippled vessels began to leak their crude and one of them caught fire. It was later towed to shore, where its remaining cargo was recovered. The other tanker, still ablaze, was towed out to sea until it exploded 300 miles offshore. There were 26 crewmembers killed in the disaster and nearly 90 million gallons of crude was dumped into the sea.

Firefighting was a major effort during this accident, after which dispersants were used to treat the oil spills.

Fergana Valley, 1992, Uzbekistan, 87.7 million gallons of crude oil were spilled from an oil well, and although its remote location did not get much press at the time, it remains as the largest inland spill ever.

There were no attempts to clean the spill, because the ground quickly absorbed the oil and there was nothing left to clean.

Nowruz Oil Field, 1983, Persian Gulf, 80 million gallons of crude oil were spilled after an oil tanker crashed into the Nowruz field platform in the Persian Gulf and knocked it down. The well infrastructure on the ocean floor was badly damaged and started leaking. Due to the ongoing war activities, however, it was left unrepaired for over seven months, so about 65,000 gallons a day were spilled into the ocean.

The Norwegian company, Norpol, was contracted to stop the leak and clean the spill. Miles of booms and skimmers were used to stop the oil spread.

ABT Summer, 1991, offshore Angola, 80 million gallons of crude oil were spilled when an explosion aboard a fully loaded tanker, ABT Summer, disabled the vessel and caught fire 900 miles off the coast of Angola. The body was damaged and its entire payload leaked into the ocean. Drowning in the growing oil slick, approximately 80 square miles in size, the oil tanker burned for three days and finally sunk still leaking oil.

It is impossible to determine how much of the oil sank or burned off; most of the spilled oil was broken up by high seas with little costal damage due to the tanker's remote offshore location.

Castillo de Bellver, 1983, Saldanha Bay, South Africa, 78.5 million gallons of crude oil were spilled due to a fire onboard the oil supertanker Castillo de Bellver about 70 miles northwest of Capetown, South Africa. The tanker was abandoned and drifted offshore until it eventually broke in half. The stern sank into the deep ocean, while the bow section was towed away over deep ocean waters and it sunk.

The coastal damage was minimal and only some minimal dispersant spraying was used to prevent further coastal contamination.

These are only a few of the spills that made history, but there are other, smaller spills that created great environmental damage. The 1969 coast of Santa Barbara oil spill, the 1989 Exxon Valdez oil spill, and the 2010 Gulf of Mexico's Deep Horizon oils spill come to mind as examples of oil spills causing great environmental damage and economic hardship.

In summary, we need oil, so it is here to stay until the last drop on Earth is pumped out and burned. We are also well aware of the dangers and willingly, or unwillingly, taking the risks associated with drilling, pumping, transporting, and using crude oil and its derivatives. As a consequence, we will very likely witness many more oil accidents and spills in the future. We have learned how to prevent them from occurring and how to clean up after these that are unpreventable. We can only hope that there won't be too many of them in the future.

But that is only part of the problem. In addition to increasing prices, we will also witness huge increases in GHG gasses coming from the ever increasing number of vehicles on the roads, in the waters, and skies. How will all this end is uncertain, but for now we will keep pumping and using as much oil as we need and more.

There is not much the esteemed reader can do to control the development of the events in this sector, but understanding the issues will give us the best answers. Making educated decisions in our daily lives—at home and at work—is a good start. Getting involved in organized actions to control the oil production and use is another way to contribute to the health of Earth and its inhabitants.

NUCLEAR POWER

Nuclear power has gone up and down on the priority lists of energy and political officials since its inception in the 1950s. Nuclear energy was back on top of the policy agendas of many countries, with projections for new build similar to or exceeding those of the early years of nuclear power. This signaled a revival in support for nuclear power in the West that was diminished by the accidents at Three Mile Island and Chernobyl and also by nuclear power plant construction cost overruns in the 1970s and 1980s, coupled with years of cheap natural gas.

The nuclear industry has been dormant or in decline for some time in the Western world, while nuclear capacity has been expanding in Eastern Europe and Asia.

Globally, the share of nuclear in the world's electricity has shown a slight decline from about 17-13.5% since the mid 1980s, though output from nuclear reactors actually increased to match the growth in global electricity consumption.

The March 2011 Fukushima accident changed everything. It set back public perception of nuclear safety significantly, despite there being no deaths or serious radiation exposure from it.

The complications from Fukushima's disaster were serious and kept on coming. The increased uncertainty forced several governments to shut down most of their nuclear power plants, as if awaiting a larger disaster.

The advent of shale gas has adversely changed the economics of nuclear power in places such as North America as well. And so now the energy industry, including nuclear power, is going through serious changes.

Figure 9-11. Fukushima nuclear reactor explosion

So what is driving the nuclear power rise and fall cycles, and what can we expect in the future? The first generation of nuclear plants was justified by the need to alleviate urban smog caused by coal-fired power plants. Nuclear was also seen as an economic source of base-load electricity, which reduced dependence on overseas imports of fossil fuels.

Today's drivers for nuclear building have evolved mostly around the issues of increased energy demand. Global population growth in combination with industrial development will lead to a doubling of electricity consumption by 2030. Besides this incremental growth, there will be a need to replace a lot of old generating plants in the U.S. and the E.U. over the same period.

In addition, an increasing shortage of fresh water calls for energy-intensive desalination plants in some parts of the world, while electric vehicles will increase overnight (base-load) demand. In the longer term, hydrogen production for transport purposes will need large amounts of electricity and high temperature heat as well, which is best supplied by nuclear power.

Increasing energy demand, plus concerns over climate change and dependence on overseas fossil fuels supplies are coinciding to make the case for increasing use of nuclear power. China, for example, is planning a huge increase in nuclear capacity to 80 GWe by 2020, and India is planning to add 30 new reactors by 2020.

The Issues

In addition to the threat of Fukushima-like nuclear accidents, the nuclear industry has to deal with a number of other problems, such as:

Uranium fuel supply is an issue that most nuclear nations are forced to deal with. For that purpose, two major new Canadian uranium mine projects are coming into production in the next few years, and Australian, Namibian and Kazakh mines are all expanding their operations.

Recent developments and the forecast of greater demand for uranium have increased the market price for the commodity to levels that make new mining ventures attractive, though the market has softened following the Fukushima accident. The actual spot price has little effect on production costs for nuclear energy, but it has led to a renewed interest in uranium deposits that were not profitable to mine with previous price levels in the two decades before 2003

Processing issues, such as enrichment of the uranium ore are dealt with by introducing efficient centrifuge technologies, which are replacing the older energy-intensive diffusion techniques. Several such processing plants are under construction in France and the U.S. E.U.-based Urenco and Areva are building plants in the U.S. to replace an obsolete plant here, and Russia is playing an increasing role in supplying enrichment services to the West. A new Australian process based on laser excitation is under development by GE-Hitachi in that country.

The nuclear waste disposal issue is still lingering without a final solution, but recently it is finding an acceptance in Finland and Sweden, where the people have accepted the local construction of permanent disposal sites for nuclear waste, while the international cooperation in the field of nuclear waste storage is growing.

Advantages and disadvantages of Nuclear Power

Along with the number of serious issues, as discussed above, there are some advantages to using nuclear power in the future:

• Security of supply is a re-emerging topic on many political agendas, as interrupted deliveries of oil and gas, and elevated prices, are always possible for different reasons. Naturally occurring uranium is abundant, and offers large energy yield from each ton, which makes nuclear power attractive from an energy security point of view. Several years' supply of nuclear fuel is easy to procure and store for use at relatively low prices.

• Climate change and the dangers and effects of global warming have contributed to a widespread awareness that the use of fossil fuels need to be reduced and that they are to be replaced by low emission sources of energy, such as solar, wind, hydro, and nuclear power. While the focus today is on renewables, they are not ready for the task, and nuclear power is the only readily available large-scale alternative to fossil fuels for production of continuous, reliable supply of electricity, capable of meeting base-load demand.

- The energy economics are also in favor of nuclear power, where increasing fossil fuel prices are confirming the superiority of stable nuclear power prices. A number of studies show that nuclear energy is the most cost-effective of the available base-load technologies, except when natural gas prices are too low. Nuclear power also benefits from the carbon emission reductions that are encouraged through various forms of government incentives and emission trading schemes.

- Future price increases of fossil fuels are certain. That will ensure a longer-term advantage of uranium over fossil fuels, which promises much more stable future pricing, and lower impact than the increased fuel prices will have on the final electricity production costs. A large proportion of those costs are in the capital cost of the plant. The insensitivity of nuclear power to global fuel price fluctuations offers a way to stabilize final power prices in deregulated markets. In addition, new nuclear plant construction costs are down too, as shown in China, which further increase the competitiveness of nuclear energy.

- Public acceptance is a major issue, which has been also going up and down with the political situations and the events at hand. During the early years of nuclear power, there was a greater tendency among the public to respect the decisions of authorities licensing the plants, but this has changed for a variety of reasons. No revival of nuclear power is possible without the acceptance of communities living next to facilities, the public at large, and the politicians they elect.

The Future of Nuclear

The future plans show that globally 1,200 to 2,000 GWe of nuclear capacity is possible by 2050-2060, increasing to over 10,000 GWe by the end of the century; compared with today's approximately 400 GWe total global nuclear power generation. Of course, most of this increase (more than 80%) will be in countries that already use nuclear power. And most of it will also depend on what will happen during that time. One or two more Fukushima-like disasters might put the entire nuclear industry on its knees, or worse.

In the U.S., there are 12 license applications to the Nuclear Regulatory Commission (NRC) for new nuclear plants construction, as well as operating licenses under review for about 20 new nuclear power reactors. So, no matter how good things look for nuclear power in the U.S., there will be no new nuclear capacity at least until 2020 or beyond. And again, even the smallest unresolved problem could put the nuclear industry in limbo again.

The ongoing and unresolved technical problems at the San Onofre nuclear plant in California opened Pandora's box, and the discussions continue. Although the issues seem mundane and not threatening enough to trigger a public outcry, we need to remember that the devastating Chernobyl accident started with an unexpected and unexplained power surge caused by one single malfunctioning component.

The good news is that U.S. technology, operation, and safety protocols are far superior to that of the Soviets. One of the main reasons for the lack of new builds in the U.S. has been the extremely successful evolution in operation and maintenance and safety strategies.

> *O&M procedural changes and optimization techniques have increased utilization of the U.S. nuclear power plants drastically. They alone have increased the total nuclear power output in the country to equal that of adding almost 20 new 1.0 GW plants to the U.S. nuclear fleet.*

This is actually a very good example of how efficiency could rival, reduce, and even substitute for fuel increases.

The U.S. is home to more commercial nuclear energy reactors than any other country—104 to be the exact (35 boiling water reactors and 69 pressurized water reactors.) But that number is unlikely to leap past 108 in this decade, or even the next. As things are going, with natural gas increasing in importance and having lower prices, the U.S. nuclear power generation might even decrease.

The precursor to increased demand for nuclear energy in the U.S. is an equally increased demand for electricity in general. Low natural gas prices paired with economic uncertainty is putting things into perspective for the nuclear industry, where four new reactors will be added to the grid by 2020, but a fifth might be pushing it.

Things can change if the U.S. The EPA includes nuclear as a part of its state clean energy standards. This, however, is not going to happen soon, because the EPA is focused on addressing clean energy standards with the coal and gas industry on the priority list for now.

While each nuclear power construction project in the U.S. is massive in scale, the U.S. nuclear sector is going to focus largely on its progress as a nuclear technology exporter, both for products and personnel. And with each export, the market brings unique set of challenges.

The U.S. can export its nuclear technology abroad and at the same time make new projects at home more attractive. That necessitates creating new standardized construction methods, which need to happen in the near future in order for nuclear to re-take its place as a leading power provider at home and around the world.

A $350 million thorium reactor research in China; space-based nuclear power; and a sliver of hope that a comprehensive U.S. nuclear waste legislation bill will be up for discussion soon, are keeping the nuclear flame burning. The next several years promise to bring technological change and eventful government decision-making.

Nuclear Power Around the World

While the U.S. electricity supply and demand ratios are not currently in the nuclear sector's favor for increased power production, on the other side of the world the situation could not be more different.

There are presently over 60 new reactors under construction around the world, with only three in the U.S. In addition, there are about 475 nuclear reactors planned, or proposed, to be build around the world in the near future, 25 of which are in the U.S. and 170 in China. India and Russia are in second place with about 60 new reactors planned each.

Hasty responses to the Fukushima accident in Japan and Europe changed the nuclear power's prospects some, but it didn't last too long. Most countries with established nuclear programs need to replace the old reactors and build new, while at the same time another 25 countries are either considering or have already decided to make nuclear energy part of their power generation capacity. Nevertheless, over 80% of the expansion in this century is expected to be in countries already using nuclear power.

Presently, there are over 60 nuclear reactors in construction around the world, with another 150 or more planned to come online during the next 10 years. More than 200 are further down the pipeline, and with that

the global nuclear industry is moving steadily towards a bright future—regardless of the problems.

Europe as a whole is presently the world's largest nuclear power producer.

Table 9-4. E.U. nuclear reactors

Country	Number of nuclear reactors
France	58
Russia	33
U.K.	16
Ukraine	15
Sweden	10
Spain	8
Belgium	7
Czech Rep.	6
Finland	4
Hungary	4
Slovak Rep.	4
Bulgaria	2
Romania	2
Netherlands	1
Slovenia	1
Total	171

With 171 active nuclear reactors, the E.U. community, including CIS, leads the world in the number of nuclear reactors and quantity of generated nuclear power. The U.S. is second with 104 operating nuclear plants. Japan follows distant third with 50 nuclear power plants.

Germany agreed to extend the operating lives of its nuclear plants, reversing an earlier intention to shut them down, but has put this on hold following the Fukushima accident. The nuclear program is now under evaluation, but Germany doesn't have too many energy options, so moving ahead without nuclear would be difficult to impossible.

The U.K. government endorsed the replacement of the country's ageing fleet of nuclear reactors with new nuclear builds, and now four 1,600 MWe French units are planned for operation by 2019. An additional 6,000 MWe are proposed for construction in the near future as well.

Finland and France are expanding their nuclear power generation with the 1,650 MWe EPR from Areva, 40 of which will eventually replace all present French units.

Sweden has abandoned its plans to prematurely decommission its nuclear power, and is now investing heavily in several plants life extensions and upgrades.

Hungary, Slovakia and Spain are all implementing or planning for life extensions on existing plants.

Poland is developing a nuclear program, with 6000 MWe planned, and is also involved, with Estonia and Latvia, in a joint project with established nuclear power producer Lithuania.

Several countries in Eastern Europe are firmly on the nuclear power generation path. Romania and Slovakia are currently constructing new power plants, while Bulgaria, the Czech Republic, Romania, Slovenia and Turkey have firm plans to build new nuclear power plants.

Russia plans to double its nuclear capacity to 43 GWe by 2020, using its world-class light water reactors. Construction of a large, fast breeder unit has been prioritized, and development proceeds on others, aiming for significant exports as well. A new floating nuclear power plant is under construction, and is to be delivered in the near future.

Argentina and Brazil have commercial nuclear reactors generating electricity, and additional reactors are under construction.

Chile has a research reactor in operation and is also working on the infrastructure needed to build and operate commercial nuclear reactors.

Canada is quietly stepping up its nuclear capacity. Overall, things are looking good for the nuclear industry there. The Ontario government is refurbishing and restarting four old reactors, which will add 25 years to the overall operating lifetime of each reactor. This seems like the first step in the plan to expand the Canadian nuclear power generation. In 2008, Darlington was selected as the site for two large new nuclear reactors operated by OPG to come on line in 2018. Unfortunately, the plans have stalled due to a number of reasons, but Canada still has the intention to build some 3,500 MWe of new capacity in the near future.

Alberta is considering using nuclear power to extract oil from its northern deposits of oil sands, so Atomic Energy of Canada Limited (AECL) is developing new designs of its CANDU reactors. It is also bidding for exports of the advanced version of these reactors.

Nuclear facts: A gallon of bottled water weighs about 8 lbs. Uranium metal in a gallon bottle weighs over 150 lbs. Worldwide, there are 441 nuclear power plants that supply about 16% of the world's electricity.

China has plans to increase nuclear generating capacity to 70-80 GWe and even more by 2020. China has completed construction and commenced operation of 10 nuclear power plants within the last few years, and some 30 reactors are under construction. These include the world's first four Westinghouse AP1000 units and a demonstration high-temperature gas-cooled reactor plant. Another 51 units are planned, with construction due to start within three years. The plans call for the new power plants to use mostly local designs.

India has a target to construct 20-30 new reactors by 2020 as part of its national energy policy. These include light- and heavy-water reactors as well as fast reactors. Seven power reactors are under construction or almost so, of both indigenous and foreign design, including a 500 MWe prototype fast breeder reactor. This will take India's ambitious thorium program to stage two, and set the scene for eventual utilization of the country's abundant thorium for fuel reactors.

South Korea has plans or has placed orders for 12 new nuclear power reactors. It is also involved in intense research on future reactor designs.

Vietnam intends to have its first nuclear power plant operating in 2017 with Russian help and a second soon after with Japanese input.

Indonesia, Thailand, and the Philippines are planning nuclear power programs.

Bangladesh has approved a Russian proposal to build its first nuclear power plant.

Kazakhstan has abundance of uranium and is working closely with Russia on the development of a small reactor for its own use and for export.

The United Arab Emirates is planning to build four 1450 MWe South Korean reactors at a cost of over $20 billion and is collaborating closely with IAEA and experienced international firms.

Jordan and Egypt are also moving toward employing nuclear energy for power and desalination.

South Africa is committed to plans for further conventional nuclear power reactors.

Nigeria has sought the support of the International Atomic Energy Agency to develop plans for two 1000 MWe reactors.

Alternative Nuclear Power

There are a number of ways to generate nuclear power. The low-hanging fruit has been gathered already, so now it is time to attempt the harvest the harder to reach realms of alternative nuclear power. Here are some examples of what could happen in the future.

Thorium Research Project

Jiang Mianheng, son of former Chinese President Jiang Zemin, is spearheading a thorium power project for the Chinese National Academy of Sciences with a start-up budget of $350 million. There are already 140 PhDs and scientists working full-time on thorium power at the Shanghai Institute of Applied Physics, with staff projected to increase to 750 by 2015.

NOTE: Nuclear reactors can use only certain fissile isotopes to make energy. The three most practical ones are:

- *Uranium-235*, purified from naturally occurring uranium ore, which is what most nuclear power plants use today

- *Plutonium-239*, transmutated from Uranium-238, which is also produced from naturally occurring uranium ore and could be used for nuclear weapons

- *Uranium-233*, transmutated from Thorium-232, which is produced from naturally occurring thorium ore

Thorium-based nuclear power is basically a nuclear reactor modified to use the element thorium.

A thorium fuel cycle has a number of potential advantages over the predominant uranium fuel cycle. This includes: much greater abundance of thorium on Earth, superior nuclear fuel properties, and reduced nuclear waste production.

Thorium fuel, however, suffers from much higher thorium fuel production and processing costs, and lacks weaponization potential. Nevertheless, scientists now believe (and the Chinese are banking on it) that thorium is key to developing a new generation of cleaner, safer nuclear power. According to a the industry specialists, the overall potential of thorium-based nuclear power is to provide 1000+ years of quality, low-carbon electricity, thus ensuring the uninterrupted transition to renewable energy sources, and significantly contributing to solving the negative environmental impacts of fossil fuels.

China is determined to make a breakthrough in nuclear power and they have the talent to make a more than decent attempt to achieve it. China badly needs and is looking feverishly for new energy solutions, since it is in desperate need of clean, reliable electricity. It has to be homemade because of political tensions from neighbors, such as Vietnam, Japan and the Philippines, which leaves the growing residential and commercial population vulnerable to energy imports and looming black outs.

If China has the talent and the deep pockets to pay the thorium research bill, then perhaps this could be their moment to find the answers to the uncertainties

still hovering over thorium for use in commercial reactors. It is also this level of determination to find a solution that could help the U.S. Department of Energy reconsider its position on thorium-based reactors. It then could have a piece of a potentially lucrative market that it first researched and developed into a reactor at Tennessee's Oak Ridge National Laboratory in the form of a molten salt-based reactor. News reports have surfaced that the U.S. is already interested in collaborating with the Chinese thorium project.

So it looks like a thorium rector race has at least started, where Chinese, Americans, Norwegians, Japanese, British, and Russians are looking to find the keys to using this precious material. There are different reasons for this race, ranging from ensuring power security, boosting commercial export revenues, providing environmental safety, and also pure, old politics. No matter what the reasons, however, thorium nuclear power might offer a solution to the greatest questions of today related to energy and environment.

Recovery from seawater

Uranium ore reserves are limited and estimated to last about 80-90 years, thus nuclear power is not a renewable energy source. Because of that, there are efforts to extract it from other sources. Rocks like granite, which contain minute amounts of uranium have been considered, but the process is cumbersome and very expensive.

Extracting uranium from seawater seems doable, and there are a number of efforts in that area. The uranium concentration in seawater varies, but averages about 3.3 mg uranium per m^3 of seawater. This is a very small amount by all means, but the quantity of this resource is huge, so even a small portion of the uranium in seawater could provide fuel for nuclear power generation for a long time.

A number of methods have been tried to extract uranium from seawater, including using a uranium-specific nonwoven fabric as an absorbent.

NOTE: The Takasaki Radiation Chemistry Research Establishment of the Japan Atomic Energy Research Institute is doing research in this area. The scientists there have produced uranium adsorbent by irradiation of polymer fiber. It has a functional amidoxime group that selectively adsorbs heavy metals, and, as the performance of such adsorbents is improving, so is the yield. Uranium adsorption capacity of the polymer fiber adsorbent is high, approximately tenfold greater in comparison to the conventional titanium oxide adsorbent.

Extracting uranium from seawater uses uranium-specific nonwoven fabric as an absorbent, where three collection boxes containing 350 kg of absorbent fabric produce 2 lbs. of yellowcake after 240 days of submersion in the ocean. The cost of this production method is about $150/lb.

A new absorbent material, called HiCap, developed in 2012, outperformed previous best adsorbents five to seven times. HiCap also effectively removes toxic metals from water, so it might have a dual use. It is possible that this and other efforts will bring the cost of getting uranium from sea water down to acceptable levels, thus significantly extending the time that we can use nuclear power for generating electricity.

The major cost of nuclear power is in the construction and operation of the power station, so the fuel's contribution to the overall cost of the electricity produced is relatively small. Because of that, even a large escalation in fuel price will have relatively little effect on the generated electric power's price. For example, a doubling of the uranium market price would increase the fuel cost for a light water reactor by 26% and the electricity cost about 7%, whereas doubling the price of natural gas would typically add 70% to the price of electricity from that source.

If the price becomes very high in the distant future, however, then extraction from sources such as seawater and other materials containing traces of uranium might become economically feasible.

Microbes in Nuclear Power?

A possible and exciting future direction is to use microbes to clean up nuclear wastes and again improve prospects for nuclear power plants. Microbes can influence green energy prospects beyond biofuels. For example, engineered microbes may someday play a role in mitigating the damaging effects of wastes from nuclear power, a carbon- neutral energy source. The U.S. is not building nuclear power plants in part because of their huge capital costs, but also because of questions surrounding their safety and that of the radioactive waste materials that they produce.

What do microbes have to do with this? Little now, but researchers are identifying microbial species that survive in environments with high amounts of ionizing radiation. For instance, the gram-positive bacterium Deinococcus radiodurans can withstand 5,000 Grays (Gy, or Joules/Kg). About 2.5-5 Gy is enough to kill a human.

These and other bacteria can reduce and immobilize heavy metals such as chromium and uranium. If Deinococcus radiodurans or other bacteria can reliably clean up nuclear wastes, perhaps this capacity will make nuclear fission more acceptable to the general public again. In this way, bacteria might be used to improve the safety of this nonbiological energy technology, while also changing attitudes surrounding its use.

With progress in basic and applied microbial research, researchers in these fields should be thinking of novel ways that their work might be used to solve global problems.

International Technological Cooperation

International cooperation on many of the issues related to nuclear power, energy security, climate change, nuclear safety and non-proliferation is increasing, since they are global in type, dimension, and size. This has prompted several initiatives to be taken as needed to promote international cooperation in research, use, and trade of nuclear power.

NOTE: Global cooperation is becoming crucial in the nuclear energy sector, so the recently signed a memorandum of cooperation confirms the willingness of governments and companies to work together on resolving nuclear power issues and optimizing the related processes. The memorandum cosigners also agreed to implement concrete projects to help alleviate the consequences of the Fukushima Daiichi nuclear accident.

The memorandum was signed during a three-day Fukushima ministerial conference on nuclear safety, and included arrangements to promote cooperation in two key areas: one on radiation monitoring and remediation between the IAEA and Fukushima Prefecture, and the other on human health between the IAEA and Fukushima Medical University.

For this purpose, a training center will be built in Fukushima Prefecture to help reinforce emergency preparedness and response activities, supported by the government and the prefecture. An IAEA response and assistance network (RANET) capacity building center will be designated, with IAEA radiation monitoring equipment to be deployed in case of need and to provide training in emergency preparedness and response in Japan and the wider Asia Pacific region.

This framework will use the international community's experience and expertise in the related areas of the process of reconstructing Fukushima. Thus gathered knowledge will be then disseminated to the rest of the world.

A major advantage of this and other such initiatives is that countries with an established nuclear industry can, through formal international collaboration under IAEA auspices, assist developing countries to gain access to advanced nuclear technologies, thus helping them to address poverty without emissions of greenhouse gases.

For example, France and Japan have set up joint government-industry schemes to help to set up structures and systems to enable the establishment of civil nuclear programs in countries wanting to develop them, and will draw on those countries' expertise to assist.

As another example, generation IV international forum (GIF) and the international project on innovative nuclear reactors and fuel cycles (INPRO) are two long-term research projects where leading scientists from a dozen countries join forces in the effort to develop future reactor designs.

GIF is a U.S.-led grouping set up in 2001 which has identified six (now seven) reactor concepts for further investigation with a view to commercial deployment by 2030. This effort is expected to improve plant safety and economics and at the same time reduce proliferation risk.

INPRO is focused more on assessment methodology for the needs of developing countries.

There are already examples of the globalization of the nuclear industry at the commercial level. Recently three major Western-Japanese alliances have formed to dominate much of the world reactor supply market:

- Areva with Mitsubishi Heavy Industries

- General Electric with Hitachi

- Westinghouse became a 77% subsidiary of Toshiba (with Shaw Group 20%).

Nuclear power equipment manufacturing and installation are also getting international cooperation. Several of China's reactors use technology from Canada, Russia, France, and U.S., while China itself assists countries like Pakistan to develop their nuclear programs.

Nuclear power is a necessity in our energy-hungry societies. It is the evil in disguise; the genie in the bottle that can be used to do miracles, but which can in a split second wipe out properties and mercilessly kill hundreds and thousands of innocent people.

It is clear that we just have to be much more careful with the genie and what we wish. With some caution and luck we should be able to harness nuclear's awesome powers for generations.

2013 Update: San Onofre Nuclear Plant

San Onofre nuclear plant in Southern California is a collective ownership between SCE, SDG&E and

the city of Riverside. Unit 1 reactor was started in 1968 and operated until 1992, when it was shut down and dismantled. The plant now has four generators, two per reactor, with 9,727 alloy tubes each.

The old nuclear plant has been in operation over 40 years, but has been experiencing problems, which have increased the uncertainty and risk surrounding it. The problem is the steam generators, which were installed during a $670 million overhaul in 2010. The generator tubes circulate hot, radioactive water from the reactors, which then heats the non-radioactive water surrounding them, thus creating steam, which is used to turn turbines to make electricity. It was discovered during the maintenance work that many of the tubes are so badly eroded that they could fail and possibly release radiation.

Figure 9-12. San Onofre nuclear plant

As a result of this and other abnormalities, San Onofre has been idle since January 2012, when a small radiation leak led to the discovery of unusual damage to the hundreds of eroded tubes carrying radioactive water. Questions also arose over changes to the replacement generators, which were 23.6 tons heavier than the original with hundreds of new tubes added as part of design changes. Some unusual vibration has been noticed as well, that had added to the uncertainties and worries of the public and the industry watchdogs.

The owners insisted for a long time that Unit 2 of the plant could be safely restarted, but lingering uncertainty lasting over 18 months was too much, so now the troubled San Onofre nuclear power plant is closing. The decision to shut down the old nuclear plant on Highway 5 was made in the summer of 2013 after a long battle over whether the twin reactors could be safely restarted with millions of people living nearby.

The owners agreed to retire the twin reactors because of uncertainty about the future of the plant, which faced a tangle of regulatory hurdles, investigations, and mounting political opposition. With the reactors idle, the company has spent more than $500 million on repairs and replacement power, in addition to the millions spent since 2010 on the renovation.

San Onofre powered nearly 1.5 million homes in Southern California, so it is not clear now where the extra power to replace the loss from San Onofre will come from. There is also the danger of wildfires or other disruptions in the distribution network that could cause power shortages.

Southern California electricity customers will be required to increase energy efficiency and conservation during peak usage, while upgrades to transmission and generation resources are planned and underway.

San Onofre was a victim of faulty redesign and failing equipment, so it could no longer operate safely. The modifications were unsafe and posed a danger to the eight million people living within 50 miles of the plant, so San Onofre nuclear plant will be permanently shut down and safely decommissioned. It hopefully won't become a long-lasting liability for the California community.

In summary, nuclear power is the most intensive energy source known to man. The amount of energy contained in just one pound of uranium is equivalent to that in thousands of pounds of coal and gallons of oil. Nuclear power is an awesome force.

Like the genie in the bottle, when properly used and controlled, nuclear power can power entire cities. However, when it is let out of the bottle and is out of control, it can devastate large areas in minutes and kill thousands of people without showing any mercy. Unlike other energy sources, the contaminated areas are converted into wastelands virtually forever. Nothing will grow there for centuries, and humans will be kept out of the areas for the duration as well.

Nuclear power generation is very complex technologically, even when under control. Once out of the control, however, nuclear power's unmatched force is well beyond human understanding and ability to put back under control. And this is the greatest, if not the only, thing that stops nuclear power from taking over the energy sector.

Because of that, nuclear power is always on the priority lists of governments and utilities.

HYDROPOWER

Hydropower is another awesome, albeit limited and less dangerous, power suitable for generating electricity. Its limits have been reached in many countries—including the U.S.—where all (or most) suitable rivers have been already dammed, and where no new large dams are planned for the near future.

Hydropower generated from damming rivers supplies about 1/5 of all world's electricity. There are about 900 GW of river electricity generated, or planned, worldwide. More than 60 countries get over half of their electricity from hydropower.

The world's total technically feasible hydro potential is estimated at 14,370 TWh/year, of which about 8,082 TWh/year is currently considered economically feasible for development. About 700 GW (or about 2600 TWh/year) is already in operation, with a further 108 GW is under construction. Most of the remaining potential is in Africa, Asia and Latin America.

Table 9-5. Global hydropower (in TWh/year)

Continent	A	B
Africa	1750	1000
Asia	6800	3600
North America	1660	1000
South America	2665	1600

A is the technically feasible potential
B is physically and economically feasible potential

Table 9-6. Hydropower in different countries

Country	A	B
China	652.1	196.8
Canada	369.5	89.0
Brazil	363.8	69.1
United States	250.6	79.5
Russia	167.0	45.0
Norway	140.5	27.5
India	115.6	33.6

A is annual generation in TWh/year
B is installed capacity in GW.

Hydropower Status

Increasing the global amount of hydropower and predicting how well the existing hydropower capacity will fare in the future is becoming more difficult. Climate change is affecting rivers' volume and flow, so predicting stream flow by taking records of past flow to predict power generation and designing dams is no longer feasible.

In Australia, for example, the government study has found that average surface water availability in the country's Murray-Darling river basin could shrink by as much as 34% by 2030. It could, however, also rise 11%, according to the same study. A guessing game...

In tropical and mid-altitude rivers, water sources are already flowing less or drying up altogether. Significant changes in the stream flow of a third of the world's large rivers have been recorded recently, with 6% less freshwater flowing into the Pacific and 3% less making it to the Indian Ocean. However, at the same time, drainage into the Arctic Ocean rose by about 10%, most likely due to faster melting glaciers and snow cover.

The abnormal river flow already has reduced or even shut down power generation in existing dams, during times when their reservoirs drop below critical levels. As a result, many drought-stricken countries are suffering periodic blackouts and electricity rationing. These countries are forced to stop relying on hydropower and to quickly develop other forms of energy generation to compensate for unreliable hydropower.

World climate models show that mid-altitude areas are expected to experience reductions in river flow and lower hydropower output. In Southern Africa, droughts will cause decrease of hydropower capacity of over 70 GWh per year by 2050. Afghanistan, Tajikistan, Venezuela, and parts of Brazil are likely to be among the most affected as well.

In contrast, Northern Europe, East Africa, and Southeast Asia will probably see a boost. This way, Norway and other far north countries, where river runoff is likely to increase, have a chance to adapt quickly by adding more turbines to already existing dams, and build new ones to use extra flow.

In the U.S., where droughts are also expected to continue and get even worse, special measures are taken to prevent an electric power generation decrease. Hoover Dam, for example, will be swapping the existing turbines for new, more efficient ones, designed to work more efficiently at lower water levels.

To date, the U.S. already has developed only 20% of its hydropower potential. Although hydropower is non-polluting, construction of new facilities is highly controversial because of environmental and social impacts. The best location for plants is often in mountainous or rainy areas where ecosystems are fragile and often protected. Yet, new hydropower projects do not necessarily

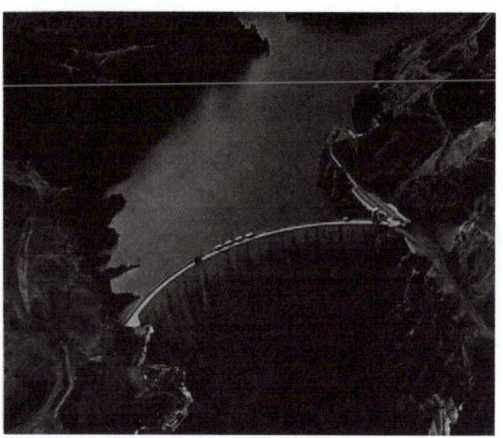

Figure 9-13. River dam

require extensive construction, since for example, only 2,400 of the total of 80,000 dams in the U.S. are used for energy generation. Dams and hydropower plants are also very expensive to build, even in rich countries. New technology along with upgrades in current power plants will eventually increase power generating efficiency, which is the only way ahead for providing enough power without disrupting more lands.

Regardless of the future events, a number of dams are being built in Brazil, China, and India that cause unrest among the environmentalists and the local communities that the new dams are affecting.

Most countries in East Africa, where runoff is expected to increase, will not be able to take advantage of the increase, because they just don't have the capacity, infrastructure, resources, or political will to develop new hydropower resources. In Africa, only about 7% of the economic potential for new hydro projects has been developed, so getting Africa closer to the level of hydroelectric development in the U.S. or Europe—70% and 75%, respectively—would provide a vast resource for the continent. While such high levels might be the best trade-off between deployment using hydropower and preserving some rivers in a natural state, this cannot happen overnight, nor can it happen in the midst of political and financial debacle the continent is going through.

In all cases, hydropower is now a victim of its older cousins—the fossils—because climate change is making it unpredictable as a base power resource for the future. The challenge of predicting how a hydroelectric dam will perform in the years to come, and the ability of a developing country to keep it up and running, is making this energy resource a riskier, and perhaps in some cases unpalatable, investment choice.

Dam-free Hydropower

Using the power of ocean waves and tides, as well as river current, for electric power generation is a variation of the conventional hydropower. It is also referred as "dam-free," or damless hydropower. The interest in the dam-free technologies is growing, but they remain technologically challenging, and politically and financially challenged.

The difference between a dam-based and a dam-free hydropower is the presence or absence of a dam. The same water current can be used to turn the turbines of each type to generate electricity. Damless hydropower uses only the natural flow of the river, ocean waves or tides to produce electricity.

Such turbines can be installed on the bottom, or on the surface of the water body and are low head installations with very minimal environmental impact.

Well-made damless turbines are designed so that the blades turn slow enough to allow fish to escape, and therefore do not affect the fish migration the way dams do.

Another important advantage of damless hydropower is that the turbines can be site-based and optimized for performing in certain unique situations. Each power plant can be studied on a site-by-site basis for optimal performance.

The Federal Energy Regulatory Commission (FERC) plays an important role in the establishment of damless hydropower in the future. The same challenges of federal and state approvals that apply to the existing dams, apply to the new damless technologies, so FERC has the final word.

Presently, however, the U.S. government is focused at other renewable sources of energy like wind and solar, so it may be overlooking the contributing potential of hydroelectricity. In the end, government support and private investment into damless hydro will determine its destiny, and its development into a feasible renewable and clean alternative for power production in the U.S.

The U.S. Federal Power Commission conducted the first studies for application of damless technologies as early as 1924. The northern border area of the U.S. state of Maine and the southeastern border area of the Canadian province of New Brunswick were chosen as most suitable for this project. Nothing came of the study and it is unknown whether Canada had been cooperating with the U.S. Federal Power Commission on this effort.

The international commission in April 1961 issued a report titled, "Investigation of the International Passamaquoddy Tidal Power Project" produced by both the U.S. and Canadian Federal Governments. The resulting data on the benefit to costs ratios showed that the project was beneficial to the U.S. but not to Canada.

A 1977 study by Nova Scotian and New Brunswick Governments (Reassessment of Fundy Tidal Power) was designed to determine the potential for tidal barrages at Chignecto Bay and Minas Basin at the end of the Fundy Bay estuary.

There were three sites determined to be financially feasible: Shepody Bay (1550 MW), Cumberline Basin (1085 MW) and Cobequid Bay (3800 MW). These were never built despite their apparent feasibility.

Like the other renewables, damless hydropower is usually left in the closet in times of prosperity, but brought out in emergency cases…just to be shoved back in the closet when the economic fortunes change for the best again. We do not see this situation changing any time soon, so dam-free hydropower will remain an R&D project for university scholars to tackle in their spare time.

China Hydropower

Hydropower is a very important energy resource in China, where two classifications of hydropower projects predominate: a) large and medium-size hydropower plants, over 50MW, and b) small-size hydropower plants, below 50MW. The different categories have different applications, and use different financing vehicles

The main investment vehicles for the large hydropower plants in China are:

1. Government funds, which are channeled through state-owned assets supervision and management entities
2. State-owned enterprises (SOEs), which include the major players are Huaneng Group. Datang Co., Huadian Power International Co. Ltd., Guodian Co. and Power investment Co.
3. Private companies are just now beginning to show intense interest in funding for hydropower projects, and are involved in the smaller hydro projects
4. Foreign investments, due to stable returns, low maintenance cost, and numerous preferential governmental policies. Hydropower plants promise high basic ROI. Lately, these investments look even better by the additional income such as the sale of certified emission reductions (CERs)

Investment Regulations

Construction of a hydropower project in China is a complicated process, which can be divided into the following phases:

1. *Pre-investment verification phase*, where a series of checks and verifications, some in need of approvals, are required. After obtaining all the related approvals, an investor can legally submit the application of a hydropower project for project verification. Over the past few years, the following approvals have become increasingly important for the construction of a hydropower project:

    a. Review comments on environmental impact statement, i.e., the ministry of environmental protection issued a stop order for the construction of the hydropower project on Jinsha river because it lacked this statement approval. This would act as a cautionary tale for the necessity of acquiring this approval

    b. Seismic hazard assessment

    c. Cultural relics investigation of the project

2. *Investment verification phase* and approval of the projects investment phase is pursuant to the decision of the state council on reforming the investment system, according to which the projects constructed on major rivers and projects with the total installed capacity of 250MW or more are subject to the approval of the national development and reform committee (NDRC), and other (smaller) projects are subject to the approval of the competent local development and reform committee.

    A hydropower project is within the range of encouraging classification of the catalogue of industries for guiding foreign investment, a project where if the total investment is over $100 million, it shall be approved by the NDRC. Those that fall below this investment threshold are subject to approval and verification upon the local development and reform committee's examination provided that the project has an installed capacity below 250MW and is not constructed on the major rivers.

3. *Post-investment examination and verification phase* is conducted after the formal verification of the project, where several additional approvals are required for the hydropower station. For example, during this phase the emphasis is on approvals that tend to be neglected in practice, such as a permit on the conversion of agricultural land into land for construction (if applicable), which is pursuant to the PRC land administration law. If agricultural land is proposed to be occupied for construction purpose, the examination and approval procedures regarding the conversion of agricultural land into land for construction purposes is always required.

The Future of China's Hydropower Projects

Upon the notification to improve the small-sized hydropower and hydropower for rural electrical progress, the Chinese government is recognizing the fact that large hydropower projects will be few and between in the future, so it is encouraging small-sized hydropower projects to improve construction in the rural area that will meet power requirements.

Substantial subsidies have been granted for small-sized hydropower projects, with the possibility of further policy support in the future.

In summary, hydropower is a significant energy source. It is also renewable and clean, but is severely limited in a number of ways. First, it depends on climate conditions; dry climate countries would have a hard time obtaining much energy from dammed rivers. This is the case in Southwest U.S., where several years of drought have decreased the reservoirs' levels and are threatening to reduce the generated power significantly if the drought continues.

Hydropower is also limited in additional capacity, because most of the large hydro dams around the globe have been built and there is not much capacity left to be captured in the future.

There are plans by China and other countries to build more dams, but the majority of these are small to medium size. It is also unclear how many of these can be build, because the creation of a large water reservoir required in most cases is a complex socio-economic problem that takes many years and a lot of money to resolve.

So, while hydropower will remain a major energy source worldwide , very little capacity increase is possible at least for the foreseeable future.

SOLAR POWER

Solar, in its different shapes and forms, has been around for over half a century. It has gone thorough a lot of good and bad things during that time. One of the best things is that solar has been, and still is, benefitting from the achievements of the most advanced technology in the world, that used by the semiconductor industry.

The semiconductor industry has been always a step or two ahead of the world's technologies, and several miles ahead of the solar technology. Billions of dollars have been spent on semiconductor equipment, processing development, and optimization during the last several decades. The result of these efforts is a sophisticated and almost perfect industry that makes thousands of different semiconductor devices of unparalleled quality. Its products are used in all sectors of our lives and have drastically changed the way we do things.

The solar industry uses the same materials, equipment, and processes as these used in semiconductor processing facilities (Fabs). This includes the brainpower, where thousands of engineers have been shuttling between the semiconductor and solar industries through the years—including this author.

Mono- and poly-silicon solar cells, SIGS, CdTe, Ge, GeAs, multijunction cells, nanotechnology, organic photovoltaics, and solar products, are byproducts of semiconductor research and development. This has given the solar products manufacturing a shot in the arm at the critical times and has led to the superior state of the art they enjoy today.

Just think of the experience and advantages that the semiconductor industry offers:

- It all started in 1947, when William Shockley developed the theory of a p-n junction and a junction transistor (which is the foundation of solar cells' operation). Then John Bardeen at Bell Telephone Lab developed the actual bipolar transistor, which is what solar cells are, during the same year.

- Soon, large corporations got involved in developing and fabricating semiconductor devices. With that came a race for new and better materials, equipment, and processes.

- The race among the semiconductor manufacturers since the 1960s was fierce, which contributed to the quick development of today's state-of-the-art semiconductor industry. The race is still on, and billions of dollars are still spent on R&D and tests of new equipment and processes every year.

- The solar industry simply uses the advances of the semiconductor industry and chooses which piece of equipment, or entire production line, is most suitable for its needs and uses it for making solar cells. Experienced engineers and technicians are "borrowed" from the semiconductor industry to reduce the learning curve and ensure the quality and cost-efficiency of the final product.

And so, today:

- Both industries use the same raw materials, from the most commonly used silicon, to the most exotic cadmium, indium, and selenium materials

- Both industries use similar, and sometimes identical, process equipment: ingot pullers, wafer slicers, wafer cleaning and surface preparation, p-n junction creation, thin film materials deposition and metallization, packaging, and quality control and testing.

- Both industries use the same type of professionals: engineers, technicians and operators, some of whom have special education and experience, and most undergo special training for specific jobs.

- Both industries rely on optimizing the existing equipment and processes, and discovering new, more efficient, and cheaper ways to manufacture the final products.

- Since the semiconductor industry is light years ahead of its solar cousin technologically and logistically speaking, the exchange of innovation is a one-way street—from the semiconductor to the solar sector. Any time a solar engineer needs a new material, equipment, or a process s/he simply turns to the semiconductor materials, equipment, or process specialists at universities, national labs, or manufacturers. It is that simple and easy, which is a huge advantage.

Another big advantage of the solar industry is that most of its products qualify as " renewable," "clean," "green," and "eco-friendly." They need no fuel to operate and generate very little GHG during on-sun operation—how much is another question that we addressed in the previous chapters. For the most part, however, we cannot even compare the great amounts of pollution emitted by a coal-fired power plant with that of a solar power plant of the same nameplate.

But the solar energy products manufacturing and solar power generating industries have big problems too. Some of these are:

- All solar devices are variable electric power generators, because they depend on the availability and intensity of the sun. If there is little sunshine, there is little power generated, and if there is no sunshine, there is no power at all. This makes solar impractical for use in many areas of the world.

- Using energy storage is one way to solve the variability issue, but the technology is immature, unreliable and too expensive, which puts solar in a great disadvantage. That issue needs to be solved first before solar can truly compete with the conventional power generators.

- The solar devices require large land areas to produce significant amounts of electric power. For each MWp of power produced, 5-10 acres of land are required. A 500 MWp solar power generating plant would require 5,000-10,000 acres of land, which for all practical purposes is a lot of land to work with. At the same time, a 500 MW gas-fired power plant could be squeezed into a 5-10 acre site. This is a big and very serious difference, no doubt. This alone, makes solar power impractical for use in many locations.

- Some solar technologies, such as CSP and energy storage using turbines, use a lot of water for cooling purposes. Since these are usually located in the desert areas, where water is getting increasingly scarce, their future hangs in the balance.

- All solar technologies use precious, rare or exotic materials. Many of these materials are getting depleted and more expensive, which puts the future of some solar technology in doubt.

- Solar power plants have a 20-30 years useful lifespan, after which they need to be shut down and decommissioned. The expense of this step will increase with time, due to transport, disposal and recycling fees increases. Some PV modules contain toxic materials, which require special hazmat-type handling, transport, and recycling, and waste disposal procedures. As time goes on, these steps will increase significantly in price, which possibility needs to be taken into consideration in the early days of plant design and financing.

- The major problem facing solar power generation today is the low price of the conventional (fossil) fuels. This makes it hard to impossible to compete with them directly. This discrepancy has forced governments to establish mandates and provide subsidies for solar power development. This support, however, is unsustainable in the long run, so new, alternative ways need to be found to reduce the price discrepancy and equalize the energy prices.

The U.S. Solar

Solar power in the U.S. is the gift and curse of the energy sector. It is amazingly always available when more energy is needed, but awkwardly useless when the need is gone. After the latest solar

boom-bust cycle of 2007-2012, solar came strong in many states, and then went away quietly in some. Whatever the case might be, solar is going strong in a dozen of states in the Union, and although some of them are starting to lag, others are ramping up.

Table 9-7. Solar in the U.S.

States	A	B	C
California	2,901	1,033	76
Arizona	1,097	710	167
New Jersey	971	415	110
Nevada	403	198	146
Colorado	270	40	52
N. Carolina	230	132	23
Massachusetts	198	129	30
Hawaii	191	109	137
New Mexico	190	24	11

A is total installed capacity in the state
B is solar installations in 2012
C is solar capacity per person (in Watts)

Presently California and Arizona hold the solar flame alive, mostly due to the fact that there is a lot of sunlight and demand for electricity in these states. New Jersey is third in the race, and since it has only 1/3-1/4 of the sunlight of California or Arizona, its success is mind boggling, and that needs to be attributed to successful political action and wider social acceptance.

These states represent about 1/4 of the total U.S. population and less than 20% of all U.S. electricity consumption, yet they generate about 85% of America's total solar energy capacity. These states are very different demographically and politically, but have one thing in common: they have all used smart policies, that if they were implemented in other states, could help America get 10% of its electricity from solar energy by 2030.

The U.S. had 7,500 MW of solar (PV) installations in 2012, which is three times more than in 2010, and ten times more than in 2007. in the last quarter of 2012 alone, 1,300 MW of solar capacity was installed, which is more than the total solar power capacity the U.S. had installed in its entire history up to 2010. Amazing!

The latest solar boom-bust cycle that brought failures and slowdown of solar activities around the world caused a slight hesitation in the U.S. too, but did not slow down the U.S. solar industry's progress much, especially in California.

Today, solar power represents nearly half of all the new electric generation capacity installed across

Figure 9-14. Solar installation

the country. At the same time, the U.S. also became one of the three countries around the world to exceed the 10,000 MW solar power generation mark.

This also brought work to 120,000 Americans in 2013, or about 15% more than the previous year. Over half of these workers are solar system installers, and employment in that employment grew 20% in 2012 alone. Unfortunately, there were failures and slowdowns in the solar manufacturing sector, where a number of solar companies shut down or sold out. And then came the serious competition from cheap Chinese imports, which caused a trade war and another hesitation in the world solar markets. Analysts now predict that the U.S. solar industry will be fully recovered by 2015, and employment in the solar sector will rebound at the same time.

Small and large solar power plants also help in reducing pollution by replacing power generated by fossil-fired power plants. Solar emits 95% less pollution than coal-fired power and 90% less pollution than natural gas. It also helps the grid during peak hours, thus reducing the need to start peaker power plants and the need for long-distance transmission, since there is a lot of local generation near demand centers that generate the most power when demand is highest. Win-win situation…or is it? We will see below that the utilities are not happy with this arrangement, so things might change in the future.

The solar development, however, is concentrated in several U.S. states. Why are some states so successful and many are not? One common factor among the solar champion states is the availability of sunshine, as in the Southwest states. Another factor is the successful use of important state and government policies, such as: renewable energy standards, local interconnect policies, net metering, and creative financing options. This has allowed several Northern states—where sunshine is not as abundant as in Death Valley—to install a great number of solar power plants, despite the sunshine deficiency.

The government policies, when successfully implemented, have been a driving force in the solar power proliferation in the U.S. and the E.U. In more detail:

- Mandatory minimum requirements, as dictated by the renewable energy standards (RES) are followed, where a certain percentage of the utility's power needs to come from renewable sources by 2020, and some have a specific solar portion that sets specific targets for solar installations within the RES.

- Interconnection is a major issue in the U.S., so the successful states have implemented strong interconnection policies that cut through red tape, which help expedite the review and approval process of connecting new solar systems to the grid.

- Strong net metering policies are a common denominator in these states, where consumers are paid retail electricity rate for any excess power sent back into the grid. This shortens the payback time and increases ROI for residential and small-business customers.

- Financing is another obstacle for solar in the U.S., so these states have designed and implemented more flexible financing mechanisms to help pay for new solar installations. Those include solar leasing, on-bill financing, virtual net metering, third-party power purchase agreements, and property-assessed clean energy (PACE) financing.

The Solar Revolution

The recent solar trade war between the U.S. and China led to a bumpy, even catastrophic, ride in the last quarter of 2012 alone for some manufacturers. But at the same time, it created a boon to installers and customers. The solar industry is recovering from the hardships of late and is expected to grow. Like any growth, though, there are pains, which in the solar industry translates to company failures, consolidations, and bankruptcies.

While failures and bankruptcies are disruptive to the industry growth, consolidations help maintain the equilibrium of the industry. The PV modules oversupply that has been hurting the global solar industry is changing as the Chinese government rules and policies evolve. The days of easy credit to any mom-and-pop shop with a "solar" name are over, and only the top-tier manufacturers have access to credit lines. This is forcing many to consolidate or to retract all together.

In 2012, the size of the global solar products supply was twice the demand, and although capacity (in China mostly) is still on the rise, demand is catching up and even relatively increasing. The market is also spreading over new areas of the globe, which levels the different market segments. Markets are getting more diversified, with utility-scale installations getting priority in most countries. Diversified markets demand flexibility in terms of size and type of installation, financing, and policies, so this is where the future efforts will be focused.

A full equilibrium and stabilization of the solar industry is expected to return by 2015, when increasing demand and stable supply (at reasonable prices) will bring normal working conditions. The U.S. demand for solar power is expected to exceed 60 GW by 2020 and to double by 2030. At the same time, China, Japan, and India are planning to add much more solar power to their growing energy demand. The experts agree that solar is entering a new phase, steadily moving toward a more sustainable way of business.

California is leading the way in many respects, but the state response to the growing demand for power is feeble compared to the challenge. The state government has promised to remove all obstacles and help the state to move to a true renewable and sustainable America as leader of the solar world.

This leadership, combined with favorable conditions for solar development promises a bright future for solar in the state. California's example will be followed by a number of other states, so it remains to be seen how successful solar will be in meeting the goals set for 2020.

One state that is not planning to follow the California example is the solar capital of the world—Arizona. The state bureaucrats and the local utilities have a different idea of what solar should be in the state, so we expect to see some battles on the solar front there. Keep on reading…

Case Study: Lancaster, California

Lancaster is bringing the U.S. distributed solar energy into new and uncharted territory. The city fathers resolved that all newly constructed single-family homes built in 2014 and beyond need to include a fully functional solar system that is plugged into the grid.

The resolution states, "The purpose of the solar energy system standards is to encourage investment in solar energy on all parcels in the city, while providing guidelines for the installation of those systems that are consistent with the architectural and building standards of the city."

That means that all newly built single-family family homes on lots larger than 7,000-square-feet need to have a 1kW system at a bare minimum. The minimum for rural homes on lots greater than 10,000 square feet is 1.5 kW.

Lancaster is one of the sunniest places on Earth, so it is not surprising that it leads the state in solar generating capacity. But using the law to mandate solar installations is a new, bold move that is certain to make a mark in the way solar business is conducted in the state, the country, and the world. Is Lancaster's management getting overly ambitious in aiming to become the "solar capital" of California, and even the "solar energy capital of the world?"

This actually might not be too far from the mark, since there have been already several major photovoltaic-related developments in the city during the recent past. In 2010, Lancaster partnered with SolarCity and launched a new and quite successful solar financing program—appropriately called Solar Lancaster—for homeowners and small-businesses. The 1.45 MW program is available to private homeowners and small businesses, and a number of city buildings, such as the city hall, the performing arts center, Clear Channel Stadium, churches, schools and more. It is expected to generate about $1.5 million annually through 2017, and then $800,000 per year for the next 20 years.

It is easy for Lancaster managers to say and do, as they are blessed with over 300 days of strong and steady sunshine, a high altitude, and thousands of flat roofs. Solar installations and the related investments seem logical in this place, which also has several utility-scale solar power plants, including eSolar's groundbreaking Sierra Sun Tower with its 24,000 mirrors.

But how can other cities and states follow this example, if they are not as blessed with strong, abundant sunshine most of the year? They need to figure it out… Americans are good at that!

The Obstacles

As already discussed, there are a number of serious obstacles in solar industry's path to success. The major challenges to the U.S. solar industry have been in the areas of:

• Reduced government funding for solar
• Cheap Chinese imports
• The changing role of the utilities

Government Funding

The latest solar boom-bust cycle started in 2007-2008 with a flood of money from governments all over the world. The fuel behind the incredible development of the solar industry of late was generous government subsidies, loan guarantees, and incentives thrown at the solar industry.

Billions of dollars were spent on propping up failing U.S. companies and projects. Many more billions were spent on products imported from Chinese, European and other overseas manufacturers. Generous PPA contracts and amazing TiF prices dominated the solar market.

For example, in the fall of 2008, a small-size commercial PV installation in Germany could have been installed for $1.50/Watt (after all subsidies and incentives). The same installation could then bring $0.80 for each kWh it generated. The situation in the U.S. was quite similar, although not as extreme as that in Germany.

Nevertheless, that is all in the past. The generous subsidies and incentives are now history in most European countries, and are running out in the U.S. too. The U.S. solar industry is now faced with a future that lacks much needed financial help from the government. Will it be able to cope with the new situation…?

Chinese Imports

In 2012 the U.S. imported about $3.1 billion worth of solar cells and panels from China, up from $600 million two years earlier. Chinese solar manufacturers such as Suntech Power Holdings, Yingli Green Energy and Canadian Solar have been flooding the U.S. market cheap PV modules, solar cells, and wafers during the last several years. They also continuously and persistently kept the price below that world average, thus virtually eliminating any chance of competition by local companies.

That all but crippled the U.S. solar industry. The flood of cheap products caused hundreds of companies to file for bankruptcy, consolidate, or shrink in size. As a result, in the summer of 2013 the U.S. international trade commission (ITC) voted 6-0 in favor of duties of about 31% in the case filed in 2012 by SolarWorld Industries America, the largest U.S. solar panel maker.

SolarWorld accused the Chinese competitors of selling solar products below cost in the U.S., while receiving government subsidies to do it. With the ITC decision, the U.S. Commerce Department issued a five-year anti-dumping and countervailing duty orders on those imports.

In response, Beijing launched an anti-dumping and anti-subsidy investigation on imported U.S. and South Korean solar-grade poly silicon and other raw materials. China's Ministry of Commerce also imposed duties on solar-grade poly silicon imported from the E.U. over alleged dumping.

The trade is not over, and in its wake the U.S. solar industry is expected to go though and overcome many additional hardships.

The Utilities

Amazingly enough, the U.S. utilities that have been the greatest supporters of solar are now turning against it. It appears that they have been watching with increasing concern as millions of solar panels have sprouted across the nation's rooftops.

Finally, breaking the deafening silence, the utilities are crying "wolf" and are fighting hard to slow the spread of solar installations, especially the small PV installations on home and business rooftops. The battle among energy executives, lawmakers, regulators, and customers across the country is just now starting, but is already red hot in California and Arizona. We predict that the battle in different states will go through several cycles, which makes foreseeing the end quite difficult.

The utilities are alarmed by what they see as an existential threat to their core business, and are trying to roll back government incentives aimed at promoting solar energy and other renewable sources of power. Some are even insisting on rate increases to pay for additional expense caused by the thousands of solar power installations. According to their battle call, the future of the entire U.S. electricity generating and distribution industry is at stake.

Rooftop solar installations depend on government incentives and mandates, which have been the main reason for their proliferation in states like California and Arizona. They also depend on the utilities' good will and assistance in the permitting, installation, and operation of the small, private PV electricity generators. If one of these factors is missing, the entire solar industry might collapse overnight.

On one hand, the government subsidies and incentives are decreasing and some will be cut totally in the near future, which will cause the solar industry to limp for awhile until finding a different MO. On the other hand, although the total of these generators countrywide account for less than 0.25% of the nation's power generation, the utilities are seriously concerned that these power sources threaten their ability to maintain the nation's grid. This hinders their efforts to operate properly and profitably. They are also afraid that it might be too late to salvage the situation, if efficient measures are not taken immediately.

In Arizona, the country's second-largest solar

market, the state's largest utility, APS, is pressuring the Arizona Corporation Commission (ACC), which sets the utility rates, to reconsider the generous residential credit allowed for solar installations. APS also insists on imposing new fees on customers—which happened only months after the ACC eliminated a commercial solar incentive.

At the same time, in North Carolina and other states, the utilities are pushing for a new set of charges for solar customers, needed to pay for the additional expense from solar installations.

California's Solar Battle

California is where the hottest battle is raging. California is the nation's largest solar market and is where some of the most aggressive subsidies have been implemented. California is also the home of the most ambitious greenhouse gas reduction mandate in the nation, which calls for 33% of energy to come from renewable sources by 2020.

The utilities seemed agreeable with the role of solar and wind in achieving the goals, but things did not go as planned. They obviously miscalculated, or overlooked, some crucial details. And now the battle is centered on a credit system called "net metering," which pays residential and commercial customers for excess renewable energy, which they generate and sell back to the local utilities. Net metering was implemented in 43 states, the District of Columbia and four territories, which offer some other form of the incentives too.

While some states keep the credit in line with the wholesale prices that utilities pay large power producers (a few cents per kilowatt-hour), in California, those payments are much more generous. This is because they are tied to the daytime retail rates customers pay for electricity, which include utility costs for maintaining the grid.

The utilities are not happy with the way solar and wind are using their resources, the way they increase the O&M expenses, and reduce their profits.

It is obvious from Figure 9-15 that the love and hate feelings have been building for a long time—at least since 1995 to be exact. Amazingly enough, PG&E has been one of the fervent supporters of solar in the state, with many MW of large-scale solar installations. It is known for its encouragement of new solar installations, so it is surprising that they would use such strong language so early in the game.

San Diego Gas and Electric (SDG&E) is not much behind in this battle. It raised the rates for some households and most businesses, or about 25% of SDG&E customers will have to pay higher bills for energy they use.

The Public Utilities Commission approved the rate hike in 2013 per the utility's request. The rate hike is needed to help pay for energy (and monetary losses) from renewable sources, since it is more expensive than electricity produced from natural gas.

Pacific Gas and Electric Company   925 L Street, Suite 990   Thomas H. Willoughby
                                               Sacramento, CA 95814   Manager
March 20, 1995   916/446-5206   State Governmental Relations
                                               Fax 916/446-7315

The Honorable Al Alquist
California State Senate
State Capitol, Room 5100
Sacramento, CA 95814

Oppose SB 656

Dear Senator Alquist

PG&E strongly opposes the CAL-SEIA sponsored SB 656.

SB 656 is a bold scam by the solar power industry to force our electric customers to subsidize the sale of expensive residential photovoltaic systems.

Under SB 656 an electric utility would sell electricity to a homeowner, when his photovoltaic system did not fully supply the needs of the home. Conversely, when the home's system generated excess electricity, the utility would purchase it.

The mischief—and the ratepayer rip-off—is in the accounting mechanism which SB 656 mandates for such transactions.

Figure 9-15. PG&E letter protesting solar industry's "bold scam"

Despite an increasing use of renewable energy sources like wind and solar and changes in the way households receive energy, the way energy rates are calculated has stayed the same. It seems then that a rate reform is needed and inevitable, to meet California's greenhouse gas reduction goals and to keep all parties happy.

Until then, however, all three major utilities in the largest solar market in the country estimate that to operate properly and profitably, they need additional $1.5 billion a year starting immediately. This hike is blamed on revenue lost to solar customers, and the burden of which they plan to shift that to non-solar customers. Huh?

It is not clear yet if their estimate of such great annual loss is true, since there are studies that show that the net metering credit system can result in net savings for the utilities. It would be interesting to see what will happen if they are proven wrong. We wonder what their excuse would be then, and what would PG&E call the solar industry then.

Nevertheless, the California utilities have appealed to lawmakers and regulators to reduce the credits and limit the number of people who can participate in solar installations.

The utilities don't seem to agree on some of the major points of the debate. SCE's Gary Stern said recently that distributed solar means less need for new transmission, thus less expense, while PG&E's David Rubin said solar users work the grid more intensively than non-solar customers, which causes undue burden and additional expenses. Go figure…

This fight is very important to both sides, and there are a lot of misunderstandings and confusion on the major issues. There are also not enough data on the use of net metering, which allows both sides to make premature conclusions. All this promises that the battle is not going to be easy, or brief. It will very likely follow the familiar back and forth pattern with appeals from both sides after every decision.

Who will win in the end will determine the future of solar in California—and eventually in the country.

Arizona's Solar Battle

Over the past several years, Arizona has become one of the fastest growing solar markets in the U.S., due mostly to a strong state policy framework and excellent market fundamentals. In February 2013, however, Arizona's solar incentive program was severely curtailed

and uncertainty now surrounds the future prospects of the state's solar industry, leaving many wondering what the impact of these cuts will be.

These incentives, both production-based and upfront, were part of the state's renewable energy standard and tariff (RES), which sets out to have the state procure 15% of its electricity from renewable sources by 2025. Utilities in Arizona, which are legally mandated to comply with the RES, succeeded in using these incentives to reach and even exceed their intermediate RES targets.

Just like in California, the Arizona utilities are concerned with the adverse effects of many small solar installations on their MO and bottom line. Their stocks and profits are up in today's market, but their anticipated growth is decreasing because solar is complicating their O&M procedures and making them more expensive.

Solar and energy efficiency initiatives are also keeping the overall energy consumption down, so to keep the stock price and the profits up, they are trying to stop, or at least modify, solar power generation.

Just as in California, net metering is also the culprit here. The utilities cannot oppose solar directly because it will hurt their stock prices and overall profit margin. Instead, they say officially how much they love it, while behind closed doors they are actually against solar and for sure against net metering.

But solar without net metering is unsustainable, so they are in fact stabbing the solar industry in the heart while embracing it for show and tell purposes. Cold-blooded murder is what this looks like. Net metering is the lifeblood of distributed solar power generation. It requires the utilities to reimburse home and business owners at retail rates for the electricity they send to the grid. The utilities are now beginning the fight, as Figure 9-15 shows. It is now still behind the scenes, but the gloves will come off soon enough, and the battle will escalate on all levels, including the courts.

The utilities claim that net metering:

a. compromises utility financials, due to additional costs for grid maintenance and lost revenue from solar power generation

b. shifts costs for solar to non-solar ratepayers, which is actually their idea. APS claims that net metering is not a revenue issue or a profitability issue, but a cost-shift issue.

c. The utilities "rate-base" assets they purchase, so they can charge their customers at "cost plus 10% return." But when the customers put solar systems on their roofs, the utility's revenues are significantly reduced. So APS is advocating for a policy change allowing it to pay for lines to new homes, a cost historically covered by housing developers.

APS is willing to pay $10,000 per home for 700,000 homes because they can profit from rate-basing the new lines. This is basically forcing the existing customers to pay for the new customers. That is a massive cost-shift worth billions of dollars, which APS calls cost sharing, although only they will profit from it—at the expense of the customers.

Simply put, the utilities see their customers who own solar installations as mini-competitors. And while the utilities make profit when they own solar installations, they cannot profit under the net-metered solar method. All this is a subject of concern, because there are thousands of mini-competitors, and the number is increasing by the day, so the combined effect is serious erosion of their bottom line.

We know that some utilities are losing money, so we need to be sympathetic to their plight too. We need their services, and are willing to work with them, but we should not allow them to disregard the benefits of solar and make it carry the major part of the energy inequality burden. The solar industry is too fragile as is, so this additional burden might just break its back.

Instead, a compromise needs to be found to where all parties work hand in hand searching for the best way to proceed without overburdening the customers and killing the solar industry. Utilities could be less profitable but still alive and well, while helping solar and wind, thus all surviving as credit-worthy entities.

Texas Solar Battles

It took several years of hard work to get net metering policies in 43 states, and now there is an onslaught of utility-backed measures to dismantle them. In addition to the net-metering fights in California and Arizona, we are witnessing an attack from the San Antonio, Texas municipally owned utility, CPS Energy (CPS). CPS has plans to discontinue net metering, which will effectively eliminate solar as a customer option. This action will stop all developments in distributed solar generation.

CPS suggests replacing net metering with a new tariff called "SunCredits." It is essentially a feed-in tariff (FiT), but priced very low at the utility's marginal cost of existing generation. It allows also a penny or two for extras and incidentals. Sun Credit is to go into effect for all new solar customers and all current commercial solar energy users in November 2013. Residential solar customers are the exception; for they have been given

ten-year extension in use of net metering.

With this move, CPS is changing the solar game's fundamentals by making solar users mini-solar wholesale generators. They now need to sell all their resources to the utility, which basically takes away the right to reduce the electricity bill by using solar energy on their roofs. This is like getting a used car, but paying the price of a brand new one.

The price that CPS offers now to the new miniwholesale generators is far less than the actual cost of solar generation. SunCredit tariffs simply ignore all advantages and benefits of rooftop solar generation, and credits solar customers 5.6 cents per kilowatt-hour for their solar production. This is nearly 50% less return than net metering with its 12.8 cents per kWh.

This means that a 5.0 kWp PV system in San Antonio, Texas will generate on the average about $2.24 per day for the owner under the new tariff. This is hardly worth the trouble of installing the system, even if it were free. But this tariff makes absolutely no sense after spending $20,000-25,000.

On top of that, CPS has the right to change this price every year as they wish. This makes long-term solar investment a risky proposition.

This approach disregards all advantages and benefits solar bring to the table. CPS is not giving any value to the future stream of benefits of solar systems that are on-line for 25+ years. The utility appears to be asking is, "What costs would we have avoided last year if we had sold fewer kilowatt-hours due to our customers using solar energy?"

It is unclear what capacity value CPS is assigning to solar, and if it is crediting it for providing a fuel hedge against rising natural gas and other power generation costs. It is also unclear where all this is going, but from previous experience we know that if the utilities don't succeed in getting there completely, they will try again…and again! This is their game and they will dictate the rules…

In conclusion, the U.S. utilities are faced with a dilemma—solar, or no solar. With solar they can achieve the goals and the mandates ahead of them, but solar is creating problems that are affecting the bottom line. So what shall it be?

It is clear from Figure 9-16 that distributed energy resources (DER) and energy efficient initiatives are changing the picture and are forcing the utilities to change their MO. The utilities blame DER for revenue loss, which is forcing them to increase the rates as needed to maintain a healthy profit balance. But this is also forcing the customers to re-evaluate the energy they

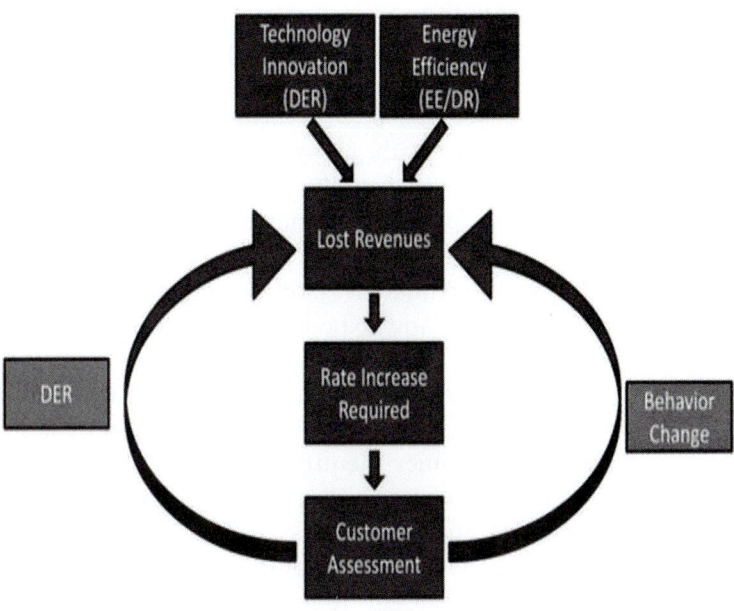

Figure 9-16. The utilities dilemma with DER.

generate and use.

Generally speaking, DER PV is a relatively tiny slice of U.S. electricity, less than 1%. For that reason, utility investors aren't paying much attention, despite the risks that a rapidly growing level of DER present. The issues are not currently well understood and are not being discussed by the investment community, nor have they been factored into the valuation calculus reflected in the capital markets.

But the immediate problem is that this almost insignificant 1% is concentrated in a small handful of utility districts, primarily California and Arizona, so the trouble for these utilities is already here and needs to be addressed before they become too big to handle and spread all over the country and the world.

U.S.'s Solar Future

The U.S. had record PV installations in 2012, about a 75% increase over 2011, or total of 3,313 MW of PV power. An estimated market value of $11.5 billion was added, and all market segments, from small residential to large-utility scale, grew in many U.S. states.

PV system prices fell nearly 30% in 2012 and about 83,000 homes installed solar PV, which brings the cumulative PV installations in the U.S. above 300,000.

The global oversupply caused manufacturers' margins to remain depressed, and less competitive companies and projects went bankrupt or were sold in 2012.

Residential solar leases and power purchase agreements (PPAs) continued to gain popularity throughout 2012. Third-party-owned systems accounted for over 50% of all new residential installations in most major residential markets, with Arizona topping 90%. New vendors entered the space to provide unique twists on the business model or to offer ancillary services such as customer lead generation. The experts predict that the third-party-owned residential solar market will maintain its momentum and become a $5.7 billion market by 2016.

Eight of the ten largest PV projects operating today were completed in 2012, some of which were recipients of the DOE loan guarantee program. This trend continues with more than 4.0 GW of utility solar projects under construction and more than 8.0 GW of projects scheduled to begin construction.

Diversification in project financing is now entering the solar markets too. The groundwork for a variety of new ways to finance solar projects has been laid, where some that have been introduced already need to scale, while others will become a reality for the first time by 2014. Examples are: the solar real estate investment trusts (REITs); crowd funded solar projects; securitized solar assets; and solar inclusion in master limited partnerships (MLPs).

PV Technology Forecast

1. *Si PV efficiency is expected to increase as follows:*
   2015 — Single-crystalline: 21%
   — Multi-crystalline: 17%

   2020 — Single-crystalline: 23%
   — Multi-crystalline: 19%

   2050 — Single-crystalline: 25%
   — Multi-crystalline: 21%

2. *Si consumption is expected to be reduced as follows:*
   — 2015 to 5 grams/Watt
   — 2020 to 3 grams/Watt
   — 2050 to 2 grams/Watt

3. *Key R&D areas for the near future are:*
   2015 — New Si materials and processing methods
   — Improved cell contacts, emitters, and passivation

   2020 — Improved device structures
   — Productivity and cost optimization

2050 — Wafer equivalent technologies
     — New device structures with novel
       concepts

4. *Thin film PV efficiency is expected to increase as follows:*
2015 — Thin film Si: 10%
     — CIGS): 14%
     — CdTe: 12%

2020 — Thin film Si: 12%
     — CIGS: 15%
     — CdTe: 14%

2050 — Thin film Si: 15%
     — CIGS: 18%
     — CdTe: 15%

5. *Manufacturing aspects*
2015 — High rate deposition
     — Roll-to-roll manufacturing
     — Packaging

2020 — Simplified production processes
     — Low cost packaging
     — Management of toxic materials

2050 — Large high-efficiency production units
     — Availability of manufacturing materials
     — Recycling of modules

6. *Key R&D areas for the near future:*
2015 — Large area deposition processes
     — Improved substrates and transparent
       conductive oxides

2020 — Improved cell structures
     — Improved deposition techniques

2050 — Advanced materials and concepts
     — Standardized equipment and procedures

The Future

What can be done to achieve America's full solar energy potential? To start with, a lot of work is needed. At the very least, utilities need to agree to support solar during these trying times. Without their support, solar cannot continue to grow. The solar industry, on the other hand, needs to accept the fact that it is immature and in need of a lot of help. As such, it needs to cooperate with the utilities, instead of fighting with them. Fighting will get us nowhere...plus the utilities are too rich and pow-

erful to fight with.

At the same time, solar is fully dependent on governmental help for now and the foreseeable future. For solar to prosper, the U.S. government should lead by example. To start with, government offices should cut their energy costs by installing solar PV on government buildings, the federal government should continue to fund tax credits, support research and development to develop new technologies and smooth renewables-to-grid integration, and expedite solar development on public lands.

State governments should encourage utilities to invest in solar through their role as utility regulators, implement consumer-friendly rate structures, maintain or expand RES targets and support investments in smart grid modernization.

Local governments should support solar rights laws that allow residents to install solar on their properties, implement PACE programs, provide feed-in tariffs, and adopt solar-friendly zoning rules.

Full cooperation on all levels and efficient coordination by the leading institutions and organizations are needed to ensure that solar does not go back in the closet as it did many times since the 1970s.

Update 2013: White House Solar

As in response to the calls for installing solar PV on government building roofs, the chief government residence is getting solarized...again. After three years of hesitation, negotiations, and bargaining, the White House now has about 40 PV modules on its roof as a sign of the President's commitment to renewable energy. The retrofit also includes installing updated building controls, variable speed fans, and other efficiency measures.

Great, right? We need a sign from the President to assure us that we are headed in the right direction. But this is not the first time we got a sign like that. Solar equipment has graced the White House's roof several times before. As early as 1979 President Jimmy Carter had 32 solar water heaters modules installed to provide hot water, but President Ronald Reagan removed them in 1986. Then in 2003 President George W. Bush installed (on an adjacent building) a photovoltaic system and two solar thermal units to heat the White House swimming pool.

As early as 2010, then DOE Secretary Chu said, "This project reflects President Obama's strong commitment to U.S. leadership in solar energy and the jobs it will create here at home. Deploying solar energy technologies across the country will help America lead the global economy for years to come." This was just several months before Solyndra went bust, proving that this is not as easy as the secretary thought.

Figure 9-17. The White House gets solar panels…again.

Nevertheless, once again the country's most powerful address will be drawing some power from the sun…until the next President removes the solar stuff from the roof as we speed down the road not taken.

The new White House solar project is a part of an energy retrofit that will improve the overall energy efficiency of the building. It is also hoped to demonstrate that historic (old) buildings can use solar energy and energy efficiency upgrades.

The new installation is estimated to pay for itself in energy savings over the next eight years. Not so fast… Let's do the math to see what is the White House and the taxpayers are getting: 40 PV modules of average 200 W power is about 8.0 kWp installed. Figuring out the bureaucracy inefficiency, additional security procedures, and other work time lost in the negotiations, we estimate that the entire project cost at least $50,000 for the installation and about $500 annually for maintenance.

The bottom line is that after 30 years (if the modules survive that long on the White House roof) the project will have cost the U.S. taxpayers about $65,000. Now let's see how much the taxpayers get in return. Under the mostly cloudy DC skies, the White House solar installation would generate an annual average of 10,000 kWh electricity the first year, which is probably less than tenth of the total power used in the most important building in the world.

Thus generated power can be sold to the local utility at about $0.10/kWh, which means that the new solar installation will bring in about $1,000 income the first year. The efficiency of the PV modules drops about 1% every year after that, so during the 30 years of the project lifetime, we'd expect about 250,000 kWh of electricity to be produced. At $0.10/kW, this is about $25,000 income. Subtracting the 30 years worth $15,000 maintenance expenses leaves us with $10,000 income from sold electricity for the 30 years of operation.

Some of the modules, inverters, and wiring, equipment usually needs to be replaced with time, so we'd assume an additional expense of $5,000. This leaves us with $5,000 total income for the 30 years operation, which means that the new White House solar installation will need to be in a non-stop and non-failure mode over 300 years to break even.

But when you apply various tax subsidies and incentives from the federal, state or local governments, which the White House is no doubt qualified for, the repayment time could be cut in half—to about 150 years. Most likely, however, a new President will take down the old and dusty PV modules within the next decade.

Nevertheless, now we have a sign from the President, who supports solar and wind, assuring us that we are going in the right direction. Signs are good…the direction, however, is not that clear.

And there are other obstacles to the solar industry development. Some are in the most unexpected places— like the sunniest place in the world—Arizona…

Arizona Update…

Arizona is the solar capital of the world…at least on paper. In fact, it is one of the sunniest places on Earth, and deserves to be the solar capital, but alas this is not going to happen, if the local utilities have anything to say about it.

One of the local utilities, Arizona Public Service, which was in full support of solar developments in the mid-2000s, is now against it and is trying to kill net metering in Arizona—and rooftop solar with it.

APS is openly unhappy with the present situation and is trying to change the rules to have a negative effect on solar growth in the state. This is a shortcut to profit from solar power. Instead of looking into innovate ways to operate, APS is blaming the solar industry for reduction in its revenue.

Now, however, APS's long-term financial forecasts cite solar energy—and particularly that generated on rooftops—as competition that could impact its profits. But instead of trying to figure out a long-term solution, APS is putting a lot of effort toward convincing the Arizona corporation commission to change the rules so its shareholders will continue to see generous dividends.

APS did and still does enjoy a healthy profit margin from its operations. Its profits have increased by more than 50% since 2008. About 400 MW of solar are working in the Arizona fields every day to increase APS's profits by generating clean and cheap energy.

APS is trying to fix the game now by rigging the system so it doesn't have to pay fair market value for the excess electricity that rooftop solar customers send back to the grid, which is the essence of net metering that APS is trying to eliminate. Net metering negatively impacts APS's bottom line they are not willing to take a loss.

APS is spending a lot of money on public awareness campaigns and TV commercials that show a distorted picture of the situation, and are as confusing as the APS strategy is. APS's managers also believe that they have strong connection with, and influence over, the Arizona corporation commission (ACC), which has jurisdiction over the pricing structure. If this is so, then it is cronyism, which is not allowed in the public sector.

Although it is possible for the ACC to side with either the APS, or the customers, it is also very possible that whatever happens, APS will not stop the battle until it wins. If not this time, next!

APS executives, who initially embraced net metering, could not adapt to the changes it brought, so they chose to eliminate it. Or as somebody said, "Now that they have missed the solar boat, they want to sink it."

The APS bosses, who have been around for a long time and are set in their ways, don't want to bother understanding that what's good for APS isn't necessarily good for their customers. They also don't want to recognize that this is not the solar industries', or the customers' problem. Instead, it is a problem facing APS and its shareholders. Making it a statewide problem might only worsen things for APS and its customers.

APS's efforts to crash the future of solar power in the state will have profound consequences for the future of the solar capital of world. It might even make solar homeless in the sunniest state of the country.

The Solar Panel Problems...The Beginning

Recently, many solar panels covering a large warehouse roof in East Los Angeles began to fail in groups. The installation was less than two years into its expected 25-year life span, so this was a great surprise for the owners. Coatings, designed to protect the panels from mechanical or thermal damage, simply disintegrated or peeled off.

Other defects caused several fires that caused some additional damage and forced a two-year system shutdown. These problems cost hundreds of thousands of dollars in lost revenues, and the repair costs were added

on top of that. Not a good start for solar in the most promising region of the U.S., if not the world.

This, however, is not an isolated incident. Many testing labs, developers, financiers and insurers are experiencing similar problems. This ultimately means that the nearly $80 billion global solar industry is facing a quality crisis at the most inopportune time—just as solar panels are on the verge of being accepted and are facing a widespread adoption.

How bad this problem is anyone's guess, since there are no industry figures about the number defective solar panels, or the type of the different defects. On top of that, when defects are discovered, confidentiality agreements often keep the manufacturer's identity secret, making accountability in the industry almost impossible. In most cases, we hear about the problems only when they are on a large scale, or have affected an important installation.

This situation will change soon, we predict, because at stake are billions of dollars of investment and financing of solar installations. The main reason people invested in solar panels was with the expectation that they will last and more than pay for themselves over a quarter century. Failing within a short time after installation put a large hole in this expectation and in the public's confidence in this technology.

The quality concerns started emerging shortly after a surge in solar construction in the U.S. and the E.U. Solar panel generating capacity exploded from 80 MW in 2002 to 7.3 GW megawatts in 2012, enough to power over 1.2 million homes. And yet, the rapid growth of solar—with half the total capacity installed in 2012 alone—means that any significant performance problems and defects will not show up for years.

There is no question that corners were cut during the solar boom-bust cycle of 2007-2012. Millions of cheap Chinese solar panels were purchased and installed without checking or testing them. They have been the preferred product of most developers for a long time just because they were cheap.

There were also millions of thin film solar panels installed, despite the fact that this technology has not been even around for more than a few years. Nevertheless, the panels were cheap, so the developers didn't hesitate. Billions of dollars of government loan guarantees propped up some of the manufacturers and their projects too.

The quality...? Well, we will worry about that later...and later is now! But worrying won't do any good. The hassle is ahead and only serious work and lots of money and effort will rectify the situation.

The solar developer, Dissigno, has had significant solar panel failures at several of its projects.

The product quality poses a long-term threat, but quality of solar panels is not something you can see. Also, materials and process used in the PV modules change daily, and manufacturers do not provide any information. All this makes solar panels a "black box" product, which we blindly install on our roofs and in the deserts.

And things are getting worse now in China as oversupply and extremely low prices are forcing some shortcuts in materials and labor. Inspectors have observed that in 2012-2013 even the most reputable Chinese solar companies are substituting cheaper, untested materials and are using unqualified labor.

Some have shut down their production lines and subcontracted some of the production steps, including modules assembly to smaller mom-and-pop shops where they have no control over quality. There are shortcuts being taken, even by some of the more reputable companies. A lot of new companies started up in recent years without adequate standards in place. Some of these companies use cheaper and unproven materials, including some whose use-by date had expired.

Over 215,000 Chinese-made PV modules evaluated by a Shanghai laboratory in 2011 and 2012 found that the defect rate had jumped from about 8% to over 13%. In one case, an entire batch of modules from one name-brand manufacturer listed on the New York Stock Exchange proved defective.

Another U.S. company discovered defect rates of 5.5-22% during audits of 50 Chinese factories during 2012-2013. Even some Chinese manufacturers acknowledge that quality has become a problem.

In 2011, at a year-old Australian solar plant, testing

confirmed that substandard materials were causing the Chinese-made modules' protective coating to degrade.

A review of 30,000 installations in Europe by a German solar monitoring firm found 80% of the recently installed solar panels were underperforming. Testing of six manufacturers' solar panels at two Spanish power plants in 2010 found defect rates as high as 34.5%.

In the Netherlands, claims had risen 15% recently, and an inspection of a solar plant in Britain in March 2013 revealed that 12% of the newly installed Chinese-made modules had failed. Other solar developers and installers have experienced quality problems too, and their number is increasing.

Non-Chinese manufacturers have had quality problems as well. The defective solar panels installed on the Los Angeles area warehouse, for instance, were made by an American manufacturer, but the company identity cannot be disclosed because of a confidential legal settlement.

First Solar, one of the U.S.' biggest manufacturers, was forced to replace several hundred thousand thin film modules recently, and has set aside $271.2 million to cover the costs of replacing defective modules made in 2008 and 2009.

One solution to these problems is a comprehensive insurance policy offered by some manufacturers, or independent insurance companies. Some large developers and customers have established their own testing laboratories as well.

Nevertheless, we will not know what to expect while the solar industry operates behind closed doors. The public will be buying black boxes and kept blindfolded until it is allowed full access to the solar manufacturers' defects data. Solar is supposed to be the cleanest and greenest of all energy technologies. How could it be so, if it continues selling black boxes?

China Solar

The cost of producing a conventional crystalline silicon (c-si) solar panel continues to drop. Between 2009 and 2012, leading "best-in-class" Chinese c-Si solar manufacturers reduced module costs by more than 50%. And in the next three years, the big manufacturers like Jinko, Yingli, Trina, and Renesola, are on a path to lower costs by another 30%.

Future cost drops from Chinese crystalline silicon solar producers will not be as steep as recent years, but they will still be significant.

It is obvious from Figure 9-19 that the future cost reductions will be much less than in previous years, but there is still potential for significant cost reductions.

Figure 9-18. Solar panel with internal and external damage

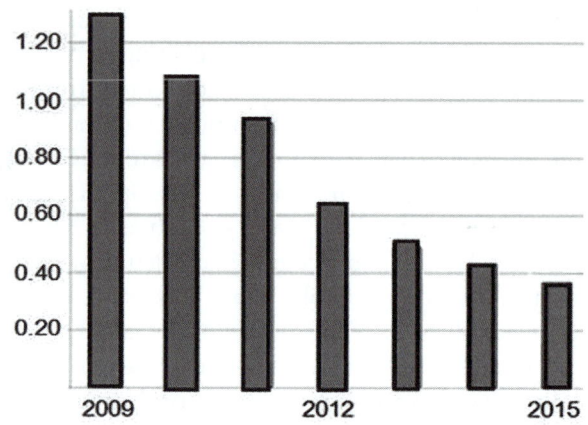

Figure 9-19. Chinese PV modules prices in $/Watt

Going below $0.40/Watt is a considerable achievement, which will be welcomed by the Chinese solar industry, and will serve as a guide for the global community.

There are still many new and promising developments in the crystalline silicon PV manufacturing sector. These include new ingot and wafer sawing techniques, making thinner wafers, using new conductive adhesives, and building frameless modules achievements that allow companies to continue reducing the manufacturing costs, which will shave more pennies off the cost of each solar panel.

However, new approaches need to be developed to reduce the installed cost of solar, since it is getting harder to realize cost reductions in manufacturing alone. New BOS materials and structures, improved construction techniques, more efficient inverters, etc. activities are expected to reduce the overall cost of solar installations to make more accessible to residential and businesses customers.

China's Solar Future

China is planning on a 10-gigawatt solar market in China soon, but this might be too optimistic. Different market forces are in play, and while some make sense, a closer look reveals the stark communist reality still dominates all spheres of business in the country. It operates in much different ways than what we are used to, or expect to see. China is a place where only companies with very good relationships to the communist government can survive.

This is so, because China is still a centralized communist state, where the decisions are made by the Central Communist Party leaders, who then authorize the local communist party leaders to decide on the execution of the different polices—including which solar company to support and which to let die.

How sustainable this arrangement is, remains to be seen, but the consequences are clear—you need to be an obedient communist to get support and favors from the government. Outsiders, without connections and unfamiliar with the way of the communist provinces have little chance of success in China.

There are opportunities for some specialized technology or service companies, who can offer a better mousetrap that can squeeze a bit more margin. And yet, you have to have a local strategic partner work through that partnership. This sounds like a normal and fairly easy concept, but going through the process and succeeding in China is close to impossible for Western companies.

If it is difficult for a developer from Oregon to do business in New York, it would be totally impossible for them to do any business in China, unless they make friends on high places. Partnering (through bribes mostly) with the right state-owned entity or local company is the only way to do business there. You really need to know who your partner is, because they can easily put out of business, or worse.

It takes many years, a lot of money, and a long-term focus to establish a foothold in China's changing solar business sector. And even then, there is no guarantee that you would be successful. Even in best of cases, it won't be business as usual, for there are much lower margins and horrible payment terms.

The competition in China works in a different and very much Chinese way. Some companies are working without payments for years, and it might take many more years to get 100% of the payment; just to secure the project. Westerners do not work that way, so as a consequence they are outbid or simply excluded from most projects.

There is presently oversupply of PV modules, so there are no longer central government subsidies. Instead, these have been channeled through the China Development Bank and pushed to developers. The system works the same way, but the channels are different. Those outsiders who had connections in the old system and have figured a way to work in it, now need to find new contacts and figure a way to survive in the new system. Not an easy task!

In all cases, obtaining project permits and successfully developing projects in China is almost impossible for outsiders.

But from the Chinese government's point of view, the people are employed and China is moving toward 10-11% renewables goal. They already have many solar power plants that are actually generating power. This is unlike most of the wind power plants that are not connected to the grid.

The Chinese solar industry is projected to reach global grid parity in the near future, when it would be cheaper to have rooftop solar to generate electricity instead of buying it. At that point China's solar industry will see a serious upswing.

But for now the Chinese solar industry is just buying time, as needed to survive the next 3-4 years, until the new and larger opportunities will open. This all raises a question about the Chinese government commitment to solar. Obviously, their huge investment in solar was not triggered by environmental concerns, so it all boils down to energy security and employment.

Today, the political and economic winds in China and around the world are changing, so the Chinese Central Party could chose a different direction at any time. And so solar is hanging in the balance today, but we have seen that the Chinese leadership is technology-savvy, and science and engineering are a priority in the country. They have established a clear a strategy as reflected in their five-year plans, so unless something drastic gets on the way, China will stay fully committed to solar and wind for the foreseeable future.

Chinese Inverters

PV module producers are feeling intense pressure in the solar market, but they are not alone. Manufacturers of all other components used in solar installations are hurting too. Inverter manufacturers are also in the midst of a looming shakeout, enduring the continued shifts in global demand and strong downward pricing trends.

Inverter prices have fallen lately, and are expected to fall further by over 10% annually during the next few years. Starting with $0.35/Watt in 2010, down to $0.22/W in 2012, and expected to get as low as $0.14/W by 2016. Some companies struggle to keep their costs in line with pricing, but this is getting harder to do, so consolidation and bankruptcies will increase before leveling out by the same time.

For now the solution is consolidation, but pricing is forcing even deeper changes and is expected to drive the entire sector. The major problem facing the global inverter manufacturing community is the low prices of Chinese inverters.

The cost of a Chinese made inverter is almost half of the cost of a comparable American-made inverter. So how do you compete with such an abnormal difference?

Why such a large gap? There are several reasons for that.

The cost of raw materials and labor are the main reasons for the price discrepancy. Materials are much cheaper in China and so is labor. The cost of procuring materials and components in China is much lower than in America, but the quality of the products vary. Some leading Chinese inverter manufacturers are using European suppliers for major components like power modules, so the final product costs are higher in such cases. On the other hand, the difference in procurement costs is forcing leading Western inverter manufacturers to buy Chinese-made components. Major firms like Advanced Energy, Schneider Electric, and SMA manufacture their sub-assemblies in China and India respectively.

Direct labor is much more expensive in the U.S., and all this brings a number of complications, which contribute to much higher costs. The U.S. and E.U. inverter manufacturers have more stringent testing requirements, which add utility-integration and labor costs for U.S. companies. China's testing standards are much less strict than America's, thus using less labor, which is another factor that keeps costs lower. This, however, means that the quality is inferior and that the developers should expect more field problems and expenses during field operations if quality suffers. Solar panel manufacturers are finding that out the hard way today.

There are also the additional costs needed for certification and testing to various grid support policies between different utilities throughout the U.S., which leads to higher costs for U.S. manufacturing.

Also, American central (large field installed) inverters are usually located outdoors, while in China they are often housed in containers. As a result, Chinese products have substantially lower costs associated with weather, cleaning and cooling. That, in addition to the lower cost, makes them the preferred product in some installations.

These factors are putting pressure on higher-cost Western firms and are eroding the market share of leading manufacturers. However, quality still matters, so SMA, Power-One, Schneider Electric and other established Western manufacturers will be around and fighting. Price matters too, but the low-cost competitors will be forced to prove their reliability and bankability first. So the battle rages on…

Australia

Australia is setting another new and unusual precedent by electing a new prime minister mostly on his promise to scrap the tax on carbon polluters, along with his other controversial plan to stop asylum seekers from reaching the nation's shores by all means possible. Nevertheless, his first priority is to repeal the carbon tax on Australia's biggest industrial polluters.

This is the first time in human history that a government's rise and fall is attributed primarily to energy policy. The outgoing labor party was doomed by years of party instability and bickering, but its decision to renege on an election promise by implementing the carbon tax was the straw that broke the camel's back. Most Australians blame the carbon tax for steep increases in their power bills and they decided to retaliate by dumping the government this presidential election.

Australia's new prime minister, Tony Abbott, once dismissed evidence of climate change as "absolute crap." Now he has disbanded an environmental agency set up to provide independent information to the public, and sacked its head, the internationally renowned scientist and author Tim Flannery.

That happened on day two of his premiership, so it seems that this issue has a high priority on his agenda, or it is the most troublesome, so it had to go first. Environmentalists, academics and many in the wider community are aghast. This flies in the face of the scientists who have been claiming that Australia is the world's driest inhabited continent, thus most vulnerable to climate change, as evidenced by more frequent and severe bushfires and floods.

The new prime minister, however, does not buy that and has made clear that it intends to make steep cuts to spending—including solar and wind—in a bid to return the Australian budget to a surplus. This means that solar will have to wait for better days in Australia too. The money saved will be reallocated to fund road projects and other large projects.

Europe

2013 brought exciting events in the U.S. and Europe. Several polls were conducted by research companies in 2013 of over 500 PV installers and residents of all 27 E.U. member states, most of whom were from Germany, Italy and France. The findings show that the overall consumption of Chinese solar products between 2009 and 2012 increased by 200% for PV modules, 90% for solar cells and 30% for silicon wafers. There was a slight decrease in solar products demand in 2012.

On the overall, although the consumption increased, the market share of European manufacturers decreased during that period. Chinese exporters took advantage of the growing consumption in the E.U. and kept on lowering prices to increase their market share.

The average import price of Chinese made PV modules decreased by 65%, solar cells dropped by 45%, and the average import price of silicon wafers decreased by 50%.

That resulted in damages to the E.U. solar industry, and so the Union imposed increased import duty rates on the Chinese imports. This led to increase of the overall prices of solar products, which in turn resulted in reduced PV installations in the short term.

Duty rates for Chinese companies that cooperated with the EC investigation are shown in Table 9-8.

Table 9-8. E.U.-imposed import duties on Chinese solar companies, summer of 2013

Chinese Company	Duty
◆ JingAo Solar ◆ Shanghai Jinglong Solar Energy	58.7%
◆ Jiangxi LDK Solar Hi-Tech ◆ LDK Solar	55.9%
◆ Trina Solar	51.5%
◆ Wuxi Suntech Power ◆ Luoyang Suntech Power ◆ Suntech Power ◆ Wuxi Sun-Shine Power ◆ Zhenjiang Ren De New Energy ◆ Zhenjiang Rietech New Energy	48.6%
◆ Jinzhou Yangguang Energy ◆ Jinzhou Rixin Silicon Materials ◆ Jinzhou Youhua Silicon Materials ◆ Jinzhou Huachang PV Technology ◆ Jinzhou Jinmao PV Technology	38.3%
◆ Yingli Energy	37.3%
◆ Companies with special considerations	47.6%
◆ All other Chinese solar companies	67.9%

Many European downstream companies are the hardest hit by the duties, so they have been advised to diversify in the relevant skill areas to benefit from the increased demand in the neighboring sectors of the energy industry.

Germany

Germany leads the world with 34.5 GW total installed solar power by the summer of 2013. The PV installations increased by almost 8.0 GW in 2012, and solar PV provided 18 TWh of electricity in 2011, or about 3% of total electricity needs of the country.

According to the official estimates, and If all goes well, Germany solar power generation is projected to satisfy 25% of the total electricity use in the country by 2050. The government has a goal to produce about 35% of its electricity from renewable sources by 2020 and 100% by 2050. 1/4 of that power generation is expected to come from solar installations.

But Germany has less than half of the average sunshine of any location suitable for profitable solar power generation. At the same time, most of Germany—coastal and mountain areas—are simply too cloudy and too foggy for decent solar power plans. This leaves only a small part of the country available for profitable solar power generation. This, however, is not a very large area, and is crowded with agricultural and other business activities. So, solar in Germany has serious limitations from above and from inside the country.

Solar also comes at a high cost under these circumstances. The solar installations have to be much larger and more expensive, if expected to produce significant power, due to the limited sunlight, which reduces the PV modules' efficiency.

And also there are the FiT costs, which amount to over $18 billion annually (and growing) for wind and solar installations. The FiT cost is spread across all ratepayers with a surcharge of 4.6 ¢/kWh, which is approximately 15% of the total domestic cost of electricity used.

So, is the government plan too ambitious for a country with limited sunshine and other renewable resources, and increasing financial difficulties? Not very likely, and so recently the German government started to increase the use of coal-fired power plants around the country. It seems that Germany is taking the easy way out… at least for now.

We can only hope that this is a temporary solution to the country's energy and financial problems, and that Germany will continue to rely on the renewables for a permanent solution.

Italy

Italy is another example of amazing solar developments. As a relative newcomer, it rose quickly to be ranked among the world's largest solar power generators in a very short time spam. The installed PV capacity in the country in 2011 was nearly 12.75 GWp with 330,200 plants in operation and total energy production of 11,000 GWh. This was nearly 3.5% of the total energy demand in the country of 332.3 TWh at the time.

In retrospective, the installed solar capacity tripled in 2010 and nearly quadrupled in 2011, as compared with previous years. Amazing growth…

In 2012 the installed capacity grew even more to nearly 17 GWp. This in fact forced several gas-fire power plants to operate at half of their nameplate capacity during most of the day. The solar sector also provided employment to about 100,000 people, albeit most of it was temporary employment during the design and installation stages of the numerous power plants development.

In 2013, Italian solar power added 20% more share of the energy mix. By mid-summer the solar power plants generated total of 14,000 GWh. In comparison, hydropower generated about 33,000 GWh, wind generated 10,000 GWh, and geothermal about 3,000GWh during the same time.

But 2013 also proved to be the year that marked the beginning of the end for Italy's solar power industry. The problem started when Italy stopped FiT payments in the first week of July for a number of reasons. Solar plants depend on the FiT payments to repay the debt and continue operation. Without it, future solar power projects might be at risk of being dropped.

Under the previous $8.8 billion program, Italy added some 17 GW of solar power capacity to the grid, but unresolved economic problems are plaguing the fragile Italian economy, and might prevent further funding from being made available.

And then there is the ongoing—and maybe even more serious—issue of mafia connections. Isn't that exactly what the solar industry needs…?

The Italian government acquired 43 wind and solar energy companies, 98 properties, and 66 bank accounts in the spring of 2013. The total worth of these companies, properties, bank accounts, and projects is estimated at nearly $2.0 billion. Unfortunately, this action was not as a result of a public scheme designed to ensure the Italian energy future, or rein in carbon emissions. Nope, instead it was a court-ordered action to seize the assets as a result of an organized crime investigation.

The Italian courts are charging the Sicilian mafia groups with using solar to launder money they have made from extortion, drug sales and other illegal activities for the Sicilian Mafia and its fugitive, Matteo Messina Denaro, who is believed to be the Mafia syndicated Cosa Nostra's head boss.

This also sets another record in Italy and the world. It is the largest ever seizure of Mafia-linked assets. Now, did you get this? Translation, please: the largest every seizure of *Mafia-linked solar assets*.

Isn't this exactly what the solar industry needs now? That will be another black eye for a long time to come.

We need to congratulate the Italians for inventing a new way of solar deployment, using mafia connections to set world records. The other good news here is that by this unprecedented court action, the Italian public has become the collective owner of some serious renewable energy generation capacity.

The only problem now is that this incident, along with other accusations of impropriety by Italian and foreign solar companies, puts a big shadow over the future of the Italian solar industry.

Spain

Spain is in the news lately for another phenomena in the solar sector. It is expressed in protests outside a Barcelona prison against what they called the "criminalization" of domestic solar energy use. This is provoked by a number of major changes to the Spanish solar landscape that have been announced in 2013.

But the one that draw most attention was the plan for fines of up to $40 million for people consuming solar energy not generated within the country's oligopoly of energy companies. This is a direct attack on people who produce their own energy, which prevents people from contributing to Spain's energy independence and reducing emissions to avoid climate change.

Recent changes to electricity bills added a large levy to electricity customers using power from their own panels that would make electricity from the national grid cheaper. Anyone caught using solar panels that are registered for those tariffs will be subject to the multi-million euro fines.

Solar investors were also hit with a cap on profits that has already triggered a legal challenge . The proposed profit cap, which works out at around 5-5.5% after tax, applies not to the electricity generated but to the initial investment. If the rate of borrowing underpinning a project is higher than this rate, it becomes impossible to generate any returns at all.

Several Spanish organizations have decided to declare themselves "guilty" of using solar energy for the generation of electricity for the sake of defending the right of all citizens to use renewable energy for their own needs and to fight climate change.

The Spanish government is faced with dire economic circumstances, compounded by a deficit in its energy budget of $34 billion that was estimated to grow by $5.9 billion in 2013 alone. The changes in the solar energy use were implemented to reduce the growing budget imbalance.

The government estimates that the changes to its energy policies would save it $3.6 billion every year. While this is true, it will also kill Spain's distributed power generation industry. Not a good way for solar

expansion in the sunniest country on the European continent.

The UK

The U.K. is a good case for solar use under restricted conditions. The average solar insolation in the U.K. is only about $120/m^2$, due to clouds, fog and other weather conditions predominating across the country. So basically, whatever sunlight comes down to roofs' level is diffused. Diffused sunlight has different properties and in such cases, short of total obstruction, it makes little difference in which direction the PV modules are pointed—they will generate little power.

One strange fact is that if the average solar energy falling on square meter of south-facing roof in the U.K. at noon is roughly $110W/m^2$, while a flat roof would get about $100W/m^2$. This goes against the basics of normal solar insolation, but it is not very surprising for this location, due to the diffused solar energy reaching the roofs, thus there is a very small difference between a tilted roof facing south and a horizontal roof.

The U.K. solar situation is so very different from other solar markets. Compare their $100W/m$ solar radiation with Arizona's sunlight intensity on a south-facing roof that can be as much as $1,000 W/m^2$. A flat roof, however, would see less than half that much energy (which almost nothing) in the early morning and late evening hours.

And yet, believe it or not, the U.K. managed to complete 230,000 solar power projects by 2011. This brought the total installed generating capacity of the

Figure 9-20. Can't see the solar panels for the usual fog

country to 750 MW at the time. In 2012, the installed capacity reached 1,000 MW.

In 2012, the U.K. government estimated that over 4 million homes would be solar powered by 2020. This represents about 22 GW of installed solar power capacity by 2020. That is quite impressive for a country with dismal amount of reliable solar insolation.

One great advantage of U.K. solar installations is the fact that the PV modules need no washing. There is enough rainfall all through the year that does a good job in keeping the modules clean at all times.

But what is the solar future in the U.K.? For now it looks quite bleak. The future might bring more surprises and solutions, but for now we are not going to hold our breath.

Africa

Africa has abundant solar radiation of between 4 kWh and 6 kWh/m2, but it also has the world's lowest electricity access rates, where most of the countries experiencing daily power outages, which create a lot of problems and unnecessary expense.

Large-scale solar power projects are especially suitable for deployment in many African countries, the presence of which could transform the life of their population. The fast-rising populations and proportionally increasing energy use are forcing the African governments to look at new energy sources...and the sun power is the most plentiful, and most accessible way to achieve that.

60% of the world's fastest growing economies are in Africa, and they all require energy at a pace that the world has never seen before. Most developing countries in Africa have no natural resources, nor do they have money to buy the needed supplies and equipment to generate power with fossils. They have to find a way to provide power to their economies, so solar, wind and other renewables are becoming more attractive by the day.

South Africa is setting the pace in the new era of renewables on the continent, but a number of small and large projects are being undertaken across the continent, as more countries are looking to the sun to help them get into the 21st century.

For example, in 2013 Mauritania completed Africa's biggest solar PV plant; a 15 MW facility designed to generate about 10% of the country's energy. Morocco started work on the construction of a 160 MW concentrated solar power technology plant near Ouarzazate as part of the country's efforts to produce 2.0 GW of solar energy by 2020. Ghana is planning a 155 MW solar power plant at a cost of $400, which will be fully operational by the end of 2015.

Planning is good, but as with anything else, there are problems, and Africa is still far from exploiting a major part of its massive solar energy resources. And so presently oil and gas-fired power plants account for over 80% of Africa's total power generation, Nuclear power accounts for about 2%, hydropower for 16%, while all other renewable sources account for just 1%.

But financing, or rather the lack thereof, is the biggest problem in Africa's solar path. Higher up-front capital costs, long payback periods, and a lack of solar-project experience (solar technology and financing) limit access to project funding.

Experts blame the African governments for a lack of awareness about the current price competitiveness of solar technology. This, coupled with inefficiencies of their regulatory system and the utilities, is preventing most African countries from scaling up their solar power generation.

Inadequate policies and a lack of political commitment have been also identified as barriers to serious solar development. And so, African governments need to change their attitude and thinking that solar is too complicated and expensive.

According to UNEP, Africa's power sector needs over 7.0 GW of new generation capacity every year to meet the growing energy demand. This, however, can happen only if and when stronger commitments and effective policy measures are taken to reverse current trends of stagnation. If this is not, done, the report concludes, half the population of sub-Saharan Africa will be without electricity by 2030. This will delay the development of many of the newly developing economies, and will cause hardship to millions.

Case Study: South Africa

South Africa now boasts the world's fastest growing clean energy investment? Jumping from a few hundred million dollars to $5.7 billion, South Africa recorded the world's highest growth in renewable energy investment in 2012, according to the U.N. Environment Program (UNEP).

This spectacular surge is led by investments in solar power projects as South Africa is aiming to reduce its dependency on coal, which generates over 85% of its electric energy. To achieve that, the country has set an ambitious target of generating 18 GW of renewable energy by 2030.

This has attracted investments, including $12 million from Google, which has spent more than $1 billion in renewable energy projects in the U.S. and Europe in recent years. Many other investors are looking into investing in South Africa because of its favorable climate and.

In summary, solar has been shyly poking its head out of the closet where it was shoved after its short debut following the 1973 energy crisis. This happened on several occasions later on as well, but every time it was given a nose-bleeding blow by governments and big business, and back in the closet it went.

This time is somewhat different. Tings have changed drastically in solar's favor since 2008, when billions of dollars were thrown at the solar industry in an attempt to make solar a major energy generator. The last several years moved solar in the forefront of our fight for energy independence and cleaner environment. The public now knows that using solar makes a lot of sense so they won't let go easily of the idea.

And now, although the government money is mostly gone, solar has enough inertia to stay up on its own feet and continue the fight for a chance to compete with the fossils. This won't be easy, as a matter of fact, solar is already back in the closet in some countries, and more might follow in the near future—a trend that might go on for a long while. The capitalist system makes it hard to compete with established moneymakers, regardless of what benefits the new wanna-be competitor might bring.

So, solar is here to stay, but barely hanging on the ledge for now, with much brighter horizons shaping up in some countries—including the U.S.—and even brighter later on in the century, when:

a) The fossils will be fully or nearly depleted, and new energy sources will be needed
b) More efficient, reliable, and cheaper devices and technologies will be developed
c) The need for cleaner, eco-friendly energy technologies will increase to a critical point

The future of solar looks bright, but we still have a number of serious obstacles to jump over before solar becomes a major energy source.

WIND POWER

Wind power has been relevant, if not a major, power source in the U.S. since the very beginning. It was widely all across the nation for pumping water and providing electricity for residential, agricultural, and small business needs. Its resurgence in the 1980s, especially in

California, was due to generous power purchase agreements (PPA) with the local utilities, which needed more power and for which they were willing to pay. A number of large wind power plants were build close to the coast, where some of them operate successfully even today.

In the 1990s, however, the wind market was affected by the expiration, or forced re-negotiation, of the once attractive PPAs. California's utilities, Southern California Edison and Pacific Gas and Electric, were no longer willing to pay for wind power. At the same time, much of the existing wind power plants were getting old and expensive renewal was needed.

The rescue came in the early 2000s, prompted by the "green power" initiatives in California, Colorado, Texas and many other states. The U.S. wind power generating capacity increased quickly 1999, with a much broader geographical base this time.

New wind power plants were installed in the U.S. at that time, including a cluster of Zond Z-40 turbines in southwest Texas, a wind plant of 46 Vestas machines in Big Spring, Texas, a 10-megawatt wind plant in Northern Colorado, a number of plants in the upper Midwest, and the refurbishing of several wind power plants in California. The U.S. had over 2.0 GW of new capacity, due primarily to the fact that the cost of energy generated by large wind turbines installed in utility-scale power fields dropped from about \$1.00/kWh in the early 1980s to under \$0.05/kWh by the early 2000s. The cost dropped even further by the mid 2000s to about \$0.025/kWh with the new large wind plants coming on line at the time.

The capital costs of the large wind turbines dropped below \$800 per installed kW, which is lower than the capital costs of any other type of power plant at the time.

The Issues

The major difficulty with wind power is its variability. Although wind turbine power plants are cheaper to install, their low capacity factor, relative to coal and other fossil-fueled power plants is very low.

NOTE: *Capacity factor* is the ratio of actual energy produced by a power plant to the energy that would be produced if it operated at rated capacity for an entire year.

Capacity factors of normally operating wind power plants are in the range of 0.20-0.35. This means that they idle 65-80% of the time, compared with 0.50-0.75 capacity factors for gas-fired power plants. Advanced wind turbines provide higher efficiencies due to better rotor loading made possible by improved rotor design, shedding of fatigue loads provided by teetered hubs and flexible structures, and other innovations such as variable speed operation. Reduced weight and advanced material usage, combined with the high reliability of the new wind technologies are the most important factors in the cost equation.

The solution to the wind power's variability is energy storage. "This is very important, because according to the utilities ...wind power will only be accepted as a mainstream supply when its variability and connectivity to the grid is resolved. The utilities demand 24-hour power delivery and since wind does not blow 24 hours a day, energy storage is the only way to eliminate this weakness.

The already mentioned concepts and technologies will be further improved, and new concepts could eventually revolutionize wind energy conversion technology. The combined effort of governments, regulators, and private companies is pointing towards a bright future for wind power generation.

The Wind's Future

Wind energy promises to become the most cost effective source of electrical power in the U.S. and a number of other countries. In fact, it already has achieved this status. We saw in the previous chapters that the actual life cycle cost of fossil fuels—everything included— is certainly far more than the current wholesale rates.

This fact combined with the threat for eventual and imminent depletion of the fossils means rapid price rise, which will surely result in economic global backlash. Considering the environmental and political costs of fossil fuels use that are increasing by the day, we need to give wind power due credit.

A number of European manufacturers have commercialized turbines with more conventional rotors, but featuring such important innovations as low speed generators and complete variable speed systems incorporating advanced power electronics. GE Energy adopted the European design and has been using it successfully in the U.S.

One of the innovations, for example, is the addition of a hinge at the nacelle-tower attachment, allowing the turbine to "nod" up and down in response to turbulence and wind shear. This configuration offers substantial reductions in rotor and drivetrain loads and in control system costs.

New and unusual wind turbine designs, like the vertical axis model might provide solutions for some applications, like for small residential power generation.

Based on experience with other technologies, and

Figure 9-21. Vertical axis wind turbine

our view of the future of energy generation, we foresee full commercialization and deployment of wind power generating technology increasing at a rate we cannot even imagine today. Wind is a major power generator in some countries, and will become so in many others in the very near future.

The U.S., U.K., China, Germany, Spain, Italy, Ireland, Denmark, India, Russia, France, Greece and Portugal are the countries offering the most potential for wind growth by 2015 and beyond. China is believed to lead the pack by becoming a model for others to move their renewables industries forward.

Africa, most of Asia, and Latin America do not appear to be offering much short-term wind opportunities.

On the long run, the same countries, led by China, the U.S., and U.K. are offering by far the greatest wind opportunities, with Spain and the Scandinavian countries also in the top ten.

Africa, India, and Latin America also appear as areas where wind power will emerge on the longer-term.

Wind currents contain mighty power, 99.9% of which is wasted presently. Harnessing that immense force might mean the difference between darkness and light for the future generations. It might be also the difference between choking in toxic gasses and breathing clean air.

China Wind Power

Major Chinese wind manufacturers, such as Goldwind, Sinovel, and Ming Yang struggled through inventory clearing losses, similar to those China's solar panel manufacturers had to endure during the solar bust cycle of 2011-2012. That was followed by a tough period of adjustments, but now the wind industry is back on its feet, thanks to the helping hand of the Chinese government.

The long-term plans of China's largest wind developers, supported by the government policies and financial handouts, reflect a renewed commitment to wind power implementation in the country. The government is back to promoting the domestic renewable energy market development.

The new policies are designed and implemented, and are expected to counteract outside forces that have hurt China's wind and solar sectors. This includes additions to the government's 2013 targets for solar of over 10 GW and wind over 20 GW, complete with streamlined access to government subsidies. The plans for the future are even more grandiose.

The energy developers did much better during the hard times, mostly due to existing pipeline of projects that were not affected by the global turbulence in the energy markets.

Table 9-9.
China total energy project developers (in GW)

Company	2012	Total
Datang	9.3	34.1
Longyuan	10.5	28.8
Huaeng	9.7	28.2
Guodan	5.4	23.7
GD Nuclear	4.6	21.6
Huadan	5.4	19.5
CPI	3.8	16.5
Shenhua	4.0	16.1

The wind installations slowed down in 2012 as compared with prior years, and yet China's wind developers' pipelines remained optimistic about the sector. The major problem, however, remains to be policy challenges that might halt the overambitious wind development plans.

But the big power producers appear to appreciate the benefits of wind power, and enticed by higher profits than their conventional generation businesses will most likely continue to invest heavily in wind power. The estimates are for the China's installed wind capacity to reach and exceed 300 GW by 2020.

This figure is higher than any previous forecasts and only underlines the Chinese market's path of rapid growth, despite significant challenges that have slowed expansion over the past year or two, eroding the profits across the industry. On the other hand, the wind pipeline estimates may be underestimating the growth potential of some promising developers and projects,

because the energy industry development targets tend to favor China's well-established Big Five power producers.

In any case, supportive government policies, an attractive concessional program, and the availability of low-cost financing from government banks are the main reasons for the growing wind power market in China to date. However, the growth might slowdown in the near future, due to insufficient infrastructure, low quality wind turbines, and the persistence of questionable pricing policies in some areas of the country.

And so, under a best scenario, we might see wind power development numbers in excess of 300 GW by 2020. It is, however, also quite likely that the numbers would be quite lower for the above mentioned reasons, which are part of the Chinese reality today.

In summary, wind is a renewable, clean and green power, which is widely available all over the world. Yes, it has problems, but it is free and abundant in many areas of the U.S. and the world. Overcoming the technical and other obstacles is a matter of effort and time, and now, although wind can no longer rely on government money for its support, wind power has enough inertia to stay up on its own feet and continue the fight for a chance to compete with the fossils.

This fight won't be easy, and as a matter of fact, wind is on the decrease in some countries, and additional cuts might follow in the near future. The major problem in the U.S. is lack of interconnection points close to the major wind channels. This is slowing the introduction of new wind power capacity in the country, and the trend might go on for a long while.

This in addition to the competition with the established power generators, which is part of the capitalist system, where the established money makers dominate the markets for as long as they can, regardless of who the competitor is.

So, wind is here to stay, and while going through some growing pains, it has the promise of brighter future. Things will improve a lot in the future, when:

a)   The fossils will be nearly depleted, and new energy sources will be needed

b)   More efficient, reliable, and cheaper devices and technologies will be developed

c)   The need for cleaner, eco-friendly energy technologies will increase to a critical point

Wind meets all these requirements, so after overcoming some of the initial obstacles, it will become a major power generator.

BIOMASS AND BIOFUELS

Conventional biofuel technologies include well-established processes that are already producing bio-fuels on a commercial scale. These bio fuels, commonly referred to as first-generation, include sugar- and starch-based ethanol, oil-crop based biodiesel and straight vegetable oil, as well as biogas derived through anaerobic digestion.

Typical feedstocks used in these processes include sugarcane and sugar beet, starch-bearing grains like corn and wheat, oil crops like rape (canola), soybean and oil palm, and in some cases animal fats and used cooking oils.

Advanced biofuel technologies are conversion technologies, which are still in the research and development, pilot or demonstration phase, commonly referred to as second- or third-generation. This category includes hydro treated vegetable oil (HVO), which is based on animal fat and plant oil, as well as biofuels based on lignocellulosic biomass, such as cellulosic-ethanol, biomass-to-liquids (BtL)-diesel and bio-synthetic gas (bio-SG).

The category also includes novel technologies that are mainly in the R&D and pilot stage, such as algae-based biofuels and the conversion of sugar into diesel-type biofuels using biological or chemical catalysts.

It all starts with biomass, which can take many forms and shapes, as we see in Table 9-10.

The Problems

There is a general agreement that biomass fuel is renewable energy resource, however, it is not correct to claim this at present. This is due to the occurrence of some unsolved environmental problems during planting, growing, harvesting, transport and use of biomass fuels, as well as utilization of biomass waste products, when considering the complete life cycle assessment.

There is lack of generally accepted terminology, classification systems and standards worldwide about biomass and biofuels, which lead to some serious misunderstanding during the investigations. Analytical and representative sampling problems associated with biomass also occur and some of them have been discussed.

There is a huge amount of data about the biomass in numerous project reports, scientific proceedings or Internet; however, the use of such information is insecure because the data are not peer-reviewed.

The common practice is to avoid the complete description of biomass used (as samples or feedstock), their place and manner of collection, as well as storage and processing conditions. For instance, the use of biomass specification such as wood, fuel wood, firewood, forest or agricultural residue, bark, straw, grass, manure, coppicing or dedicated energy crop and short rotation coppice or crop, do not bring sufficient information for the real identification and characterization of a particular type of biomass. Additionally, the exact fuel status of the samples studied, namely as collected (har-

Table 9-10. Types of biomass groups, sub-groups, and varieties

Biomass groups	Biomass sub-groups, varieties and species
Wood and woody biomass	Coniferous or deciduous; angiospermous or gymnospermous; soft or hard; stems, branches, foliage, bark, chips, lumps, pellets, briquettes, sawdust, sawmill and others from various wood species
Herbaceous and agricultural biomass	Annual or perennial and field-based or processed-based such as: • Grasses and flowers (alfalfa, arundo, bamboo, bana, brassica, cane, cynara, miscanthus, switchgrass, timothy, others) • Straws (barley, bean, flax, corn, mint, oat, rape, rice, rye, sesame, sunflower, wheat, others) • Other residues (fruits, shells, husks, hulls, pits, pips, grains, seeds, coir, stalks, cobs, kernels, bagasse, food, fodder, pulps, cakes, others)
Aquatic biomass	Marine or freshwater algae; macroalgae (blue, green, blue-green, brown, red) or microalgae; seaweed, kelp, lake weed, water hyacinth, others
Animal and human biomass wastes	Bones, meat-bone meal, chicken litter, various manures, others
Contaminated biomass and industrial biomass wastes (semi-biomass)	Municipal solid waste, demolition wood, refuse-derived fuel, sewage sludge, hospital waste, paper-pulp sludge, waste papers, paperboard waste, chipboard, fibreboard, plywood, wood pallets and boxes, railway sleepers, tannery waste, others
Biomass mixtures	Blends from the above varieties

Table 9-11. Advantages and disadvantages of biomass

Advantages	Disadvantages
Renewable energy source for natural biomass	Incomplete renewable energy resource for biomass fuel with respect to the complete life cycle assessment. Complex fuel processes.
CO2 neutral conversion and climate change benefits	Miss of accepted terminology, classification systems and standards worldwide
Commonly low contents of ash, C, S, N, and trace elements	Insufficient knowledge and variability of composition, properties and quality
Normally high concentrations of volatile matter, Ca, H, Mg, O, P	Commonly high contents of moisture, Cl, K, Na, Mn, and some trace elements
Great reactivity during conversion	Low energy density
Mitigation of hazardous emissions (CH4, CO2, NOX, SOX, trace elements) and wastes separated	Potential competition with food and feed production
Capture of some hazardous components by ash during combustion	Possible soil damage and loss of biodiversity
Huge availability and relatively cheap resource	Odor, potential emission and leaching of hazardous components during disposal
Diversification of fuel supply and energy security	Possible hazardous emissions during heat treatment
Rural revitalization with creation of new jobs	Potential technological problems during heat treatment
Potential use of oceans and low-quality soils, and restoration of degraded lands	Regional availability
Reduction of biomass-containing wastes	Great collection, transportation, storage and pre-treatment costs
Cheap resource for production of sorbents, fertilizers, liming and neutralizing agents, building materials, and for some synthesis or recovery of certain elements and compounds	

vested), as received, air-dried (at ambient temperature) or oven-dried (at specific temperature up to 105°C) basis is also very often not reported which is a serious omission.

Some studies include peat as biomass resource, but peat is fossil fuel. Additionally, it should be always considered that significant part (occasionally dominant) of contaminated biomass contains other non-biomass products and. Hence, contaminated biomass (semi-biomass) should be considered separately.

The systematic and complete data from simultaneous proximate, ultimate and ash analyses, as well as from phase, mineral and trace elements analyses for the biomass varieties and their products are missing or they are very scarce.

It is commonly accepted that the concentration and behavior of elements such as Ca, Cl, K, Na, P, S, Si and heavy metals (more precisely trace elements) are mostly responsible for many technological and environmental problems during biomass processing. However, the experience from the studies of other solid fuels shows that the actual reasons for such problems are most likely connected with the abundance and behavior of modes of element occurrence (specific phases or minerals) in biomass and biomass products.

Most studies used the data from ash yield (shortly ash) or the bulk chemical composition of ash to explain mineral matter, mineral composition, minerals, inorganic matter or inorganics, which is not fully correct and can lead to confusion. Furthermore, the inorganic matter in biomass has generally been divided into two classes, namely inherent (or intrinsic) and entrained (or extraneous, adventitious, extrinsic, added, dirt) materials. However, the actual inorganic matter in biomass could be divided into detrital (terrigenous) and authigenic genetic classes, which are more informative, well known and accepted for the solid fossil fuels (SFFs).

Many findings about the behavior of organic and inorganic matter during biomass heating are based only on theoretical equilibrium and stoichiometric calculations of chemical data. These indirect investigations may be quite unrealistic for actual predictions of phases in a multicomponent (polycomponent) system under non-equilibrium conditions. Such calculations can be used only as a subsidiary prediction procedure of the real and direct (input, output) phase studies of the systems.

Sequential chemical fractionation is mostly used to distinguish the speciation of elements in biomass fuels and their ashes. However, this indirect procedure cannot be applied to identify the actual modes of element occurrence. Leaching alone has many limitations and can be used only as preliminary information for some possible associations of elements. Other direct methods applied for coal and coal ash should be used for such a purpose.

The problems related to biomass ash utilization are only at an initial stage of investigation and they need further clarification. For instance, there is no doubt that biomass ashes contain plant nutrients, namely some compounds of Ca, Mg, Na, K and P, that have to be re-cycled back to the soil. However, the problem is if these compounds occur in accessible (bioavailable) forms in the ash. There are indications that significant propor-tions of the above nutrients are present as water in-soluble phases (glass, silicates, phosphates), while other dangerous trace elements are highly mobile impurities in surface enriched salts on ash particles.

In this case the fundamental questions is what amount of accessible (water-soluble) or non-accessible (bound into glass) nutrients and how much bioavailable or non-bioavailable trace-element contaminants will be returned to the biomass cycle with these ashes? Further-more, washing of alkali-rich biomass fuels prior to their use may reduce some technological and environmental problems. However, such future large-scale washing may create new environmental concerns related to the fate of alkali metals, Cl, S, P, and some hazardous trace elements leached from biomass.

There is a strange acceptance that biomass ash does not contain toxic metals like in the case of coal ash. However, certain results for biomass ashes are very disturbing. For example: maximum concentrations of elements such as As (243 ppm); Ba (0.37%); Cd (657 ppm); Cr (0.17%); Cu (0.24%); Hg (7.3 ppm); Mn (4.7%); Mo (114 ppm); Pb (5.0%); Sb (264 ppm); and Zn (16.4%) were detected in some biomass ashes, particularly filter fly ashes. These concentrations are much greater than in coal ash and they even have a unique resource recovery potential. Additionally, the trace elements in biomass ash tend to occur in much more mobile and hazardous compounds than in coal ash. Systematic studies about the trace elements in biomass and biomass products are also only at an initial stage of investigation.

Regulations exist in some countries that specify the limiting and guiding values for the contents of Ca, Cl, K, N, S, and some trace elements (Cd, Co, Cr, Cu, Ni, Pb, V, Zn) in biomass fuel or ash in respect of their unrestricted use. However, the bulk concentrations of these elements are less informative than the abundance of their modes of element occurrence.

There are quite limited data about the exploration of the impact of biomass varieties during their blending with other solid fuels.

Current State

In the U.S. ethanol is primarily produced from corn, and accounts for about 9-10% of the volume of all gasoline sold. Microbe-assisted processes are already used to produce some fuels, with the most prominent example being the ethanol fuel produced by sugar-fed yeast. This still amounts to a small portion of the overall

Table 9-12. Phase composition of biomass

Matter	State and type of constituents	Phases and components
Organic matter	Solid, non-crystalline	Structural ingredients, namely cellulose, hemicellulose, lignin, extractives, others
	Solid, crystalline	Organic minerals such as Ca–Mg–K–Na oxalates, others
Inorganic matter	Solid, crystalline	Mineral species from phosphates, carbonates, silicates, chlorides, sulphates, oxyhydroxides, nitrates, and other mineral classes
	Solid, semi-crystalline	Poorly crystallized mineraloids of some silicates, phosphates, hydroxides, others
	Solid, amorphous	Amorphous phases such as various glasses, silicates, others
Fluid matter	Fluid, liquid, gas	Moisture, gas and gas–liquid inclusions associated with both organic and inorganic matter

Table 9-13. Biomass formation process, time, and place

Formation process	Place of formation	Time of formation	Formation mechanism
Natural	Authigenic (formed in biomass)	Syngenetic (during plant growing)	Generated by biogenic processes of growing plants (photosynthesis, diffusion, adsorption, pinocytose, endocytose, exocytose, hydrolysis, precipitation, others)
		Epigenetic (after plant died)	Originated by natural processes after plants died (evaporation, precipitation)
	Detrital (formed outside biomass, but fixed in/on biomass)	Pre-syngenetic (before plant growing)	Pre-existing and finely dispersed mineral grains (commonly < 1 µm) introduced into the plant by water suspensions during syngenesis (endocytose)
		Pre-syngenetic, syngenetic or epigenetic	Pre-existing and fine-grained particles (normally < 10–100 µm) introduced by water and wind on plant surfaces and fixed in pores, voids, and cracks
Anthropogenic	Technogenic (formed outside or inside biomass and fixed in/on biomass)	Post-epigenetic (during and after plant collecting)	Natural and/or industrial components (dust, materials, additives, contaminants, others) introduced in biomass during collecting, handling, transport and subsequent processing

biofuels production, but hold a great promise.

Corn-produced ethanol has an energy balance of 2.3, which means that a certain volume of this fuel generates 2.3 times more energy than that used to produce it. At the same time, sugarcane-based ethanol has a higher energy balance that ranges from 5 to 10. The higher energy balance is due to the fact that sugarcane plants contain large amount of sugar, which makes the extraction and conversion processes much more efficient and cheaper than all other energy crops, including corn.

Corn and sugarcane ethanol conversion processes, however, are NOT carbon neutral. They all require a lot of fossil materials, such as; fertilizers, and fuel for farm and process equipment and transport of materials. Nevertheless, corn ethanol is officially considered a renewable fuel, because it reduces greenhouse gas emissions from fossil fuels it replaces by about 20%. At the same time sugarcane ethanol is classified as an "advanced" biofuel, since it reduces greenhouse gas emissions by about 50%.

Sugarcane-produced ethanol is a primary fuel in Brazil, where official mandates require 20% ethanol content in all gasoline sold around the country. These programs have been in place for decades and do reflect some progress in efficient energy use; it is still not clear if producing ethanol this way saves energy and reduces carbon dioxide emissions.

From energy balance point of view, however, we see that neither type of ethanol can power all vehicles because it has a lower energy density than gasoline. It basically produces much less energy per unit volume during combustion. Alcohol is also soluble in water, and diluted alcohol (since it cannot be separated) is a problem for internal combustion engines. Diluted alcohol is also incompatible with the currently used hydrophobic liquid fuel infrastructure.

Sugarcane ethanol is superior to corn ethanol, mostly from economic point of view. Unfortunately, unlike Brazil, the U.S. land and climate are not easily adaptable for producing sugarcane. The solution to the biofuel problems might be in using microbes as needed to improve the existing, or develop new, biofuel types to make them compatible with the present infrastructure for handling liquid fuels, and providing new feedstocks for liquid fuel production, in addition to corn and sugarcane.

The Future of Biofuels

Biofuels today are predominantly produced from corn and sugarcane feedstocks, also called energy crops. They, however, are not ideal for this purpose, nor are they carbon neutral. Because of that, the scientists are looking into other crops, methods, chemicals, enzymes, and microbes that can improve yields, carbon neutrality, and sustainability of the energy crops.

Ethanol by itself is not a solution to the energy problems, simply because it is not an ideal replacement for gasoline. Its chemical and thermodynamic properties are inferior to those of gasoline, and it is not made in

Figure 9-22. Fueling with biofuel...not!

a carbon-neutral way.

Because of that, new ways and techniques are needed to improve the properties and yields of a variety of more complex fuels. This can be achieved with the help of different microbes, where increasing the diversity of microbial energy sources, combined with some creative engineering, the new fuels can meet the quality and quantity requirements, and help us overcome the fossil energy addiction.

The Future Technologies

And so, the first step in getting to the next level of energy production and use is to develop new biofuels that are compatible with our industrial-scale infrastructure for handling and distributing liquid fuels. To this purpose, scientists are looking into developing microbial processes that can be engineered to produce such types of liquid fuels.

Ethanol-producing yeasts cannot process nutrients other than sucrose from sugarcane and starchy components from corn feedstocks. So, to increase the feedstock variety, microbes need to be able to process other carbon sources than the sugar-based components, such as sucrose from sugarcane or glucose from cornstarch. Presently, the focus is on the corn leaves and stalks, switch grass and other such cellulosic materials.

This would significantly increase the ethanol production per unit land area, since this way much more ethanol could be produced per unit of corn. This is needed to make biofuel production efficient and economical, and to get it closer to carbon neutral status.

Newly genetically engineered versions of Escherichia coli and other microbes, for example, can produce different types of fatty acids, alcohols, alkanes, aromatic compounds, biofuels that in theory can replace the fossil fuels (gasoline, diesel oils, and jet fuel.) Some of these compounds have been already produced in the lab; all the scientists have to do now is figure out how to use the microbes to produce these fuels on industrial scale.

The techniques used to increase biofuel yields from bacteria involves genetically "knocking out" some genes and "over-expressing" other genes to drive production of specific compounds from a given carbon source.

A new approach is tried, where enzymes are engineered onto molecular "scaffolds" in bacteria, using proteins or RNA type scaffolds. Thus the selected pathway intermediates are elevated and substrates can channel directly between enzymes, which increase the final yield. Pathway intermediates no longer interact with other enzymes, in such cases, thus preempting unwanted side reactions, including potentially lowering toxicities.

Using this technology, E. coli bacteria can be used for production of biofuels and a number of other products, including Hydrogen. Special arrangement of proteins (such as ferredoxin and hydrogenase used together) can increase the overall production of hydrogen nearly 50 times.

Biofuels production efficiency is expressed as a percentage of the maximum theoretical yields achievable, compared with as if 100% of carbon and energy sources available to the microbe were converted into biofuel. By this measure, yeasts produce ethanol from sugar at greater than 95% of the theoretical yield.

Biofuels also have different chemical characteristics and toxicity levels, thus the number of enzymes required in their production, and the actual methods vary. The emphasis currently is on increasing yields of advanced biofuels, to increase the quantity, which is needed for the biofuels to be able to compete with ethanol on the energy markets.

Biomass

Biomass is the fuel that attracts the least attention for it is mundane every day stuff that often consists of waste products. There is no excitement, no dangers, no media exaggerated scandals to remind us of its importance. And yet, it is the most important fuel used in great quantities by millions of people around the world.

Biomass, in the form of firewood and crop remains, is some of the largest energy source (fuels) in the world. This type of fuel has been used for centuries, and is still used quietly and unnoticed by most of us on daily basis on all continents.

Biomass is used as cooking fuel, paper making and for manufacturing of different chemical feedstocks. Its use for power generation has been limited to burning wood and crop remains until recently, but today a number of biofuel processes have been developed to convert biomass into biofuels.

Ethanol derived from corn and sugarcane is the most famous of the biofuels, and we have dedicated enough space for it in this text. Because of that we will limit this section in stating that it is another large industry with equally large, and expanding, market.

The biomass power generating industry in the U.S. consists of approximately 11 GW of summer operating capacity, mostly by burning biomass (sugarcane, corn stalks, and urban wood) for supplying power to the grid. This type of biomass produces about 1.5% of the U.S. electric power albeit on seasonal basis.

Just like the genie in the bottle, biomass can produces benefits, but is also quite dangerous when released. Worldwide air pollution in the form of carbon monoxide, carbon dioxide, nitrogen oxides, volatile organic compounds, particulates and other pollutants are generated by biomass burning at levels that are much higher than those from all traditional fuel sources put together.

On combustion, the carbon from biomass is released into the atmosphere mostly as carbon dioxide (CO_2) in great quantity, because the amount of carbon stored in dry wood, for example, is approximately 50% by weight. This means that about half of the mass of all biomass (firewood and all) burnt by millions of people around the globe daily goes up in smoke and accumulates in the atmosphere.

Black carbon is another dangerous pollutant created by incomplete combustion of biomass, which is considered as the second largest contributor to global warming. A giant brown haze that periodically covers large areas in South Asia is attributed to uncontrolled large-scale biomass burning.

Biomass is considered to be a renewable product, since the plant matter used as a fuel can be replaced by planting for new growth, but biomass from forests takes very long time to recapture the carbon stored in it.

In recent times, massive deforestation has reduced the carbon storage capacity of the world forests, so the renewable character of the world's forests needs to be reviewed.

The Issues

There are a number of issues affecting the evaluation of biomass as a viable solution to our energy problem. Some of these are: a) the effects of the farming and production of biomass, and b) the effects of the factory conversion of biomass into usable energy or electricity.

There are as many environmental and economic benefits as there are detriments to each issue, which presents a difficult challenge in evaluating the potential success of biomass as an alternative fuel. For example, the replacement of coal by biomass could result in a considerable reduction in net carbon dioxide emissions, but on the other hand, the use of forest wood and other cultivated plant material for fuel may mean unwanted and detrimental to the environment deforestation of large land areas.

Extended deforestation and widespread clear cutting can lead to groundwater contamination and irreversible erosion patterns that could literally change the structure of the world ecology. Although tree plantations have considerable promise in supplying an energy source, actual commercial use of plantation-grown fuels for power generation is limited to a few isolated cases.

Supplying the U.S. energy needs, for example, would require an area of over 1.0 million square miles, or roughly 1/3 of the area of the 48 states. There is no way to do this for a number of good reasons, so obviously biomass cannot replace our current dependence on coal, oil, and natural gas. It, however, can complement the energy mix.

In all cases, new technological innovations are needed for efficient, less polluting, and cost-effective conversion of biomass into usable energy. Government support is critical for this to happen any time soon, and only then we may have a successful form of alternative energy from biomass. But this won't happen while worldwide prices of coal, oil and gas are relatively low. And so, although it is currently used daily by millions around the world, biomass energy is clearly not capable of being a substantial part of the world's energy generation. For now…

The Industrial Process

The industrial-scale processes to produce biofuels from cellulosic feedstocks depend on chemically and enzymatically treating the feedstocks, which is quite expensive. Using E. coli in the production of biofuels from corn leaves and stalks, switch grass, and other plant matter can be done after treatment with ionic liquid, such as l-ethyl-3-methylimidazolium acetate. E. coli can be engineered also to produce and secrete cellulases and xylanases that degrade the plant materials, thus avoid a separate step of treating thee feedstocks with enzymes.

A more direct approach is that of avoiding the need to break down the complex hydrocarbons in plants. One way of doing this is for photosynthetic microbes to use the plants as a feedstock.

As an example, genetic manipulations of the photosynthetic cyanobacterium Synechococcus Elongatus can, under certain conditions, increase its carbon fixation and sucrose production rates. Synechococcus can grow in water with light as its only energy source, so in practice it could be grown on lands that are not useful for producing food crops.

Modifying Synechococcus to express a sucrose permease from E. coli and to knock out a few genes, which are normally involved in storing sugars as glycogen, can induce this strain to produce sucrose at several times higher rate than the carbohydrate production rate of corn or sugarcane. The problem is getting these microbes to producing sucrose at high rate, as needed for large-scale production.

The further development of any of these compounds and processes will eventually allow increased yields from corn and sugarcane crops, as well as mass production of biofuels form cellulosic materials. The combination of these methods would guarantee the biofuels a well-deserved place in the energy markets.

Another approach is getting engineered microbes to take up electrons from an electrode to fix carbon and produce biofuels. This system could then be plugged into a solar panel, or a wind turbine where it could generate electricity as a carbon neutral energy source.

Converting the energy from renewable sources into liquid fuels is a good way to store energy from the variable and unpredictable solar and wind power generators. Thus stored energy can then be used to generate power, when required by the variability of these sources. Or, the liquid can be used to power automobiles and trucks.

As an example, bacterium Ralstonia eutropha has been used to produce isobutanol and 3-methylbutanol. It does not take electrons directly from the electrodes, but instead uses the produced at the electrode formate as a carbon and an electron source.

Another example is bacterium Shewanella, which can also take electrons directly from electrodes, thus reversing the natural tendency of the bacteria to donate electrons to iron as they grow. Shewanella can survive on electrodes in which electrons are flowing into the bacteria, so if these electrons can be used to support Shewanella growth, it would be possible to divert some of this energy into fuel production.

EU Biofuels Roadmap

Biofuels in liquid and gaseous form derived from organic matter (biomass) could play an important role in the energy security and reducing CO_2 emissions in the transport sector of the E.U. countries. The estimates are that by 2050, biofuels could provide nearly 30% of total transport fuel and contribute in particular to the replacement of diesel, kerosene and jet fuel.

At the same time, the projected use of biofuels could avoid emitting over 2.0 gigatons (Gt) of CO_2 and other GHG gasses per year—if and when produced sustainably. To meet this vision, most conventional biofuel technologies need to improve conversion efficiency, cost and overall sustainability. In addition, advanced biofuels need to be commercially deployed, which requires substantial further investment in research, development and demonstration, and specific support for commercial-scale advanced biofuel plants.

Support policies should give incentives to the most efficient biofuels in terms of life-cycle greenhouse-gas performance, and be backed by a strong policy framework, which ensures that food security and biodiversity are not compromised, and that social impacts are positive.

This includes sustainable land-use management and certification schemes, as well as support measures that promote "low-risk" feedstocks and efficient processing technologies.

Meeting the biofuel demand in Europe would require around 65 exajoules (EJ) of biofuel feedstock, occupying around 100 million hectares by 2050. This poses a considerable challenge given competition for land and feedstocks from rapidly growing demand for food and fiber. There is also a need for additional 80 EJ of biomass for generating heat and power for everyday needs.

With a sound policy framework in place, it should be possible to provide the required 145 EJ of total biomass for biofuels, heat and electricity from residues and wastes, along with sustainably grown energy crops.

Trade in biomass and biofuels will become increasingly important to supply biomass to areas with high production and consumption. A roadmap looking specifically at the use of bioenergy for heat and power will be produced earlier, which could trigger investments and mobilize biomass potentials in certain regions.

Scale and efficiency improvements will reduce biofuel production costs over time. In a low-cost scenario, most biofuels could be competitive with fossil fuels by 2030. In a scenario in which production costs are strongly coupled to oil prices, they would remain slightly more expensive than fossil fuels.

Total biofuel production costs from 2010 to 2050 in the E.U. roadmap range between $11 trillion $13 trillion. At the same time, the marginal savings or additional costs compared to use of gasoline/diesel are in the range of only +/-1% of total costs for all transport fuels.

Europe is looking at biofuels as the transition vehicle to energy independence (at least in the transportation sector), and for partially cleaning the environment. A lot of work is left to do, and a lot of problems are to be overcome, but the Europeans don't have many energy choices, so biofuels are definitely in their future.

Table 9-14a. Milestones for technology improvements

Milestones for technology improvements	Dates
Demonstrate reliable, commercial-scale production of cellulosic-ethanol, BtL-diesel, HVO and bio-SG.	2010-2015
All biofuels to reach >50% life-cycle GHG-emission reductions.	2015-2020
Demonstrate economically feasible production of algae-derived biofuel and other novel biofuel routes.	2020-2030
Integrate biofuel production in innovative biorefinery concepts.	2015-2025

Table 9-14b. Milestones for feedstock and sustainability

Feedstock and sustainability

Milestones for feedstocks and sustainability	Dates
Increase biofuel production based on "low-risk" feedstocks (*e.g.* wastes and residues) and through yield improvements.	2010-50
Reduce and eventually abolish tariffs and other trade barriers (*e.g.* logistical) to promote biomass and biofuel trade.	2010-20
Improve biomass potential analysis with better regional and economic data, including from large-scale field trials.	2010-30
Enhance biomass cascading and use of co-products through integration of biofuel production in biorefineries.	2010-30
Continue alignment of LCA methodology to provide a basis for sound support policies.	2010-20

Biomass and Biofuels Markets

Trade in biomass and biofuels can be successfully used as a vehicle to mobilize currently untapped biomass resources. This in turn could trigger new investments in biomass-rich regions by providing access to international markets. Biomass and biofuel trade are growing, driven by increasing and volatile oil prices, and by policies promoting use of biomass and biofuel for energy generation

For example, growing biofuel demand in the U.S., the European Union and Japan has led to considerable flows of Brazilian ethanol into these markets. At the same time vegetable oil and biodiesel from the U.S., Latin America, and South East Asia is also traded on the international markets. Around 3.0 million tons of bioethanol, as much biodiesel, and approximately 4-million tons of wood pellets have been traded around the globe every year recently.

Biomass and biofuel have become global commodities over the last decades, and yet the related industries and markets are still immature. They face a number of serious barriers, such as tariffs that need to be reduced to create stable industries and reliable market conditions.

In the short term, biomass and biofuels trade will include conventional biofuels and feedstocks, but after 2020, ligno-cellulosic feedstock trade is likely to grow rapidly and supply large advanced biofuel plants in coastal locations. If everything goes as predicted and expected, pelletization, pyrolysis or torrefaction will very likely become increasingly important since they increase the energy density and thus tradability of ligno-cellulosic feedstocks and residues.

This, however, will require a lot of work and money for research and pilot plants trials. There is presently an increasing awareness of the importance of these products as renewable energy sources, so we just have to hope that they will become fully mature and will be able to compete with the more established fuels.

Case Study: 2nd Generation Biofuels

DuPont is currently engaged in two major projects to commercialize advanced biofuels, which constitute the development of the 2nd generation of such fuels. The first project is a 30 million gallon per year corn stover-fed facility in Nevada, Iowa. The second project is a joint venture with BP called Butamax Advanced Biofuels, which also utilizes corn stover treated with a mild caustic pretreatment process to produce iso-butanol (i-BuOH).

The corn stover-fed facility in Iowa can process 5 and 6-carbon sugars, where i-BuOH yield is expected to be around 75 gallons per ton. This process could eventually compete with crude oil at $70-$80 per barrel, and about 3-4 billion gallons of corn stover i-BuOH annual production in the U.S. alone. Corn stover seems to be one of the easiest feedstocks to process, and as a byproduct of ethanol production, it is readily available.

The capital cost of the first facility is estimated at about $7/gallon of capacity, or about $200 million. This cost is certainly higher than comparable costs for a corn ethanol facility, which combined with the issues of the blend wall and current overcapacity in the ethanol market, makes the challenges ahead of the second generation biofuels quite serious.

The second project also utilizes corn stover and a mild caustic pretreatment process to produce isobutanol (i-BuOH) from genetically modified (GM) organisms. The GM organism is actually yeast modified specifically to make i-BuOH, which has an octane advantage over n-BuOH, and is simply a better fuel. Isobutanol is very similar to normal butanol, since it has the same numbers of the same kinds of atoms, except that they are arranged differently. This gives it slightly different and somewhat superior properties.

This process is similar to the process for making corn ethanol, but ends up with i-BuOH instead of ethanol. The major differences in the two processes are in the organisms used for the fermentation, in addition to differences in the separation processes.

One problem with the new technologies and the resulting biofuels is that the approval process for allowing a new fuel to be blended into the national fuel blending system could be prohibitively long and expensive. The commercialization plans for these advanced fuels cannot start prior to obtaining the EPA approval.

And then, even if approval is granted, a route into the national fuel supply for the new products is not easily available. DuPont might find the way quicker than the rest, since they have deep pockets and are well into the approval process, but not for new comers attempting to commercialize a new fuel blend.

In summary corn and sugarcane feedstocks are used today for biofuels production, but they are not ideal for that purpose for a number of reasons. They are also not carbon neutral. That leads to an increased emphasis on using other crops and microbes to improve yields and sustainability, which can be done by using novel ways to use engineered microbes, and finding new, more abundant and cheaper feedstocks (such as cellulosic materials) to produce biofuels.

For example, new ways to treat crop stalks and other cellulosic plants can be integrated into efficient production processes, to simplify the conversion into usable fuels, which would allow mass production at reduced operational expenses, and ultimately lower biofuel costs.

Newly developed synthetic biology techniques, such as scaffolding of metabolic enzymes, allows the development of Escherichia coli, and other such microbes, to produce fatty acids, alcohols, alkanes, aromatic compounds, and hydrogen, some of which can be used as biofuels.

Co-culturing yeasts with some photosynthetic microorganisms will eventually enable bypassing a number of extraction and conversion steps, which is one way of efficient and cost-effective production of biofuels.

FUTURE TECHNOLOGIES

Yogi Berra might have been referring to the future of the solar industry when he reportedly said, "It's tough to make predictions, especially about the future." That, however, never stops people from trying! Looking back at the many predictions about the solar industry, it's instructive to see how they stacked up to reality.

For example, some 100 years ago Thomas Edison said, *"I'd put my money on the sun and solar energy. What a source of power! I hope we don't have to wait until oil and coal run out before we tackle it."* Even then, in the complete darkness of the early 20th century, he could see and fully realized that the sun's power is a formidable force, which we take for granted. He also suspected that we just might wait until coal and oil run out before we seriously consider using sun's power.

How right he is! Although we are fully aware of the pending doom of fossil fuels, we are not putting much effort in finding the substitutes. Actually, the effort is sporadic, to say the least. There are lots of words, meetings, agreements (on paper) but no results.

Solar and wind were taken out of the closet several times since the 1970s…every time under duress… Every time under the threat of higher oil prices, and every time they were shoved back in the closet as soon as the threat was reduced or eliminated.

Although the last time—during the renewables boom-bust cycle of 2007-2012—solar and wind were allowed and even encouraged to spread their wings and show us what can be done. This time too was a short lived glimpse into what it could be IF…

And now, we will take a short glimpse into the future…the very distant future.

The oil companies and other large energy-related

interests are back in control, and the digging and pumping is once again intensified. Back to the old and quite familiar, "Drill baby, drill," we go.

Yes, Mr. Edison, you were right. We will wait until every drop of oil is pumped out of the ground, and the last trainload of coal is mined, before we start the real energy transition. Until then we will just talk, negotiate, and fake interest in renewables while making money from fossils.

Capitalism at its finest. The only hope is that when that time comes we will be given enough time to design and properly execute an efficient energy transition, before the world is plunged into darkness, irreversible economic decline, or worse.

Still, our energy future could be saved and looks fascinatingly possible. Let's take a quick look on the positive side of things to see what to expect in the 21st century and beyond:

Methane Hydrates

One of the greatest amount of energy resources are yet to be discovered and explored; methane hydrates, also called hydrocarbon clathrates, and hydrocarbon hydrates are important intermolecular compounds that occur naturally in submarine continental margins and regions and predominantly in the Arctic permafrost.

They are also expected to occur within medium-to large sized icy moons of the outer solar system and in the polar regions of Mars. It has become increasingly evident that naturally occurring gas hydrates are important components of the shallow geo-sphere and are of societal concern in at least three major ways: resource, hazard and climate.

Two main reasons make gas hydrates attractive as a potential resource.
- *First is the enormous amount of methane that is apparently sequestered within clathrate structures at shallow sediment depths within 2000 m^2 of the Earth's surface.*
- *Second is the wide geographical distribution of the gas hydrates. It was mentioned that the energy potential of methane hydrates is considerably greater than that of the other unconventional sources of gas, such as coal beds, tight sands, black shales, deep aquifers and conventional natural gas.*

The resource potential of marine gas hydrate is yet to be fully assessed and ascertained, but considering the possibility of enormous gas reservoirs, gas hydrates will continue to attract attention until their development po-

tential is measured. Methane hydrates are considered a major potential source of hydrocarbon energy and could be important in meeting natural gas demand in the future. The hydrates and any free gas trapped below the hydrate stability field may provide a significant hydrocarbon resource in the future. (5)

Natural gas hydrates are a curious kind of chemical compound called a clathrate. Clathrates consist of two dissimilar molecules mechanically intermingled but not truly chemically bonded. Instead, one molecule forms a framework that traps the other molecule. Natural gas hydrates can be considered modified ice structures enclosing methane and other hydrocarbons, but they can melt at temperatures well above normal ice.

At 30 atmospheres pressure, methane hydrate begins to be stable at temperatures above 0°C and at 100 atmospheres it is stable at 15°C. This behavior has two important practical implications:

First, it's a nuisance to the gas company. They have to dehydrate natural gas thoroughly to prevent methane hydrates from forming in high-pressure gas lines.

Second, methane hydrates will be stable on the sea floor at depths below a few hundred meters and will be solid within sea floor sediments. Masses of methane hydrate "yellow ice" have been photographed on the sea floor. Chunks occasionally break loose and float to the surface, where they are unstable and effervesce as they decompose.

The stability of methane hydrates on the sea floor has a whole raft of implications.

First, they may constitute a huge energy resource. Second, natural disturbances (and man-made ones, if we exploit gas hydrates and aren't careful) might suddenly destabilize sea floor methane hydrates, triggering submarine landslides and huge releases of methane. Finally, methane is a ferociously effective greenhouse gas, and large methane releases may explain sudden episodes of climatic warming in the geologic past. The methane would oxidize fairly quickly in the atmosphere, but could cause enough warming that other mechanisms (for example, release of carbon dioxide from carbonate rocks and decaying biomass) could keep the temperatures elevated.

Methane Hydrates Status

The Department of the Interior's U.S. Geological Survey (USGS) and Minerals Management Service (MMS) has reported the U.S. gas hydrate resources. However, USGS estimate of undiscovered technically recoverable gas hydrates in northern Alaska probably represents the most robust effort to identify gas hydrates that may be commercially viable sources of energy.

Despite a lack of a production history, the USGS report cites a growing body of evidence indicating that some gas hydrate resources, such as those in northern Alaska, might be produced with existing technology despite only limited field testing.

Methane hydrates are widespread in sea sediments hundreds of meters below the sea floor along the outer continental margins and are also found in Arctic permafrost. Some deposits are close to the ocean floor and at water depths as shallow as 150 m, although at low latitudes they are generally only found below 500 m. The deposits can be 300–600 m thick and cover large horizontal areas.

A nearby deposit nearly 500 km in length is found along the Blake Ridge off the coast of NC at depths of 2000–4000 m. Gas hydrates trapped in the marine sediments require multifaceted, extensive efforts to bring them into world energy balance. Government organizations, laboratories, and the oil industry have recently taken up projects to explore gas hydrates in the Indian offshore areas. However, participation from the academic institutions is negligible due to a lack of collaboration among them.

There should be greater involvement of researchers from academic institutions to intensify efforts in the exploration of gas hydrate horizons. Besides, the country needs more sophisticated drilling vessels with deep penetration drilling devices and a repository to store sediment cores [34]. Efforts to explore the development of gas hydrate resources are already underway in energy resource poor countries such as Japan and India.

Most methane hydrate deposits in the U.S. are located in the Alaskan Outer Continental Shelf. Additional deposits are onshore in northern Alaska, the Gulf of Mexico, and on the western and eastern outer continental shelves.

The USGS estimates 200,000 trillion cubic feet of methane hydrate in the U.S. alone, compared to the estimated 1,400 trillion cubic feet of recoverable natural gas reserves and reservoirs. Or, the U.S. has almost 150 times more methane hydrate deposits than natural gas.

If these deposits are properly and safely exploited, then the U.S. has enough energy supplies for the next several centuries. That is a big "if," which could actually result in an environmental disaster on an unprecedented scale.

Worldwide estimates of methane hydrate deposits reach the overwhelming number of 400 million trillion ft³—far outdistancing the 5500 trillion ft³ of proven worldwide gas reserves.

The USGS estimates that there is twice the amount of carbon to be found in methane hydrate deposits as there is in all other fossil fuels combined. However, this estimate is made with scant information, and could very well be wild speculation. There are better data for the existence of methane hydrates in certain locations. Mappings by the USGS of offshore North and South Carolina reveal the possible existence of a 1300 TCF methane hydrate deposit. If this is true, and if it could be extracted safely, it would represent a 700% increase in the current natural gas deposits in the US. At current consumption rates, this would be a 70-year reserve of natural gas.

Globally, the amount of gas hydrate to be found offshore along continental margins probably exceeds the amount found onshore in permafrost regions by two orders of magnitude, according to one estimate. With the exception of the assessments discussed above, none of the global gas hydrate estimates is well defined, and all are speculative to some extent.

One way to depict the potential size and producibility of global gas hydrate resources is by using a resource pyramid. The apex of the pyramid shows the smallest but most promising gas hydrate reservoir, which may host tens to hundreds of TCF. The bottom of the pyramid shows the largest but most technically challenging reservoir. Sandstones are considered superior reservoirs because they have much higher permeability than shales, which can be nearly impermeable. The marine shale gas hydrate reservoir may host hundreds of thousands of trillion cubic feet (TCF), but most or all of that resource may never be economically recoverable. It is likely that continued research and development efforts in the U.S. and other countries will focus on producing gas hydrates from Arctic and marine sandstone reservoirs.

USGS issued a resource assessment of Alaska's gas hydrates, estimating that 85.4 TCF of natural gas can be extracted, which is an amount that could heat more than 100 million average homes for more than a decade. That does not mean that commercial production of these resources is imminent, but it does suggest a vast natural gas resource trapped in Alaska's gas hydrates.

At the same time, the USGS assessment indicates that the North Slope of Alaska may host about 85 TCF of undiscovered technically recoverable gas hydrate resources. According to the report, technically recoverable gas hydrate resources could range from a low of 25 TCF to as much as 158 TCF on the North Slope. Total U.S. consumption of natural gas is about 25 TCF. Of the mean estimate of 85 TCF of technically recoverable gas hydrates on the North Slope, 56% is located on federally managed lands, 39% on lands and offshore waters managed by the state of Alaska, and the remainder on native lands.

The total area comprised by the USGS assessment is 55,894 square miles, and extends from the National Petroleum Reserve in the west to the Arctic National Wildlife Refuge (ANWR) in the east. The area extends north from the Brooks Range to the state-federal offshore boundary three miles north of the Alaska coastline. On February 1, 2008, the MMS released an assessment of gas hydrate resources for the Gulf of Mexico. The report gives a statistical probability of the volume of undiscovered in-place gas hydrate resources, with a mean estimate of over 21,000 TCF.

The MMS report estimates how much gas hydrate may occur in sandstone and shale reservoirs, using a combination of data and modeling, but does not indicate how much is recoverable with current technology. The report notes that porous and permeable sandstone reservoirs have the greatest potential for actually producing gas from hydrates, and gives a mean estimate of over 6700 TCF of sand stone hosted gas hydrates, about 30% of the total mean estimate for the Gulf of Mexico.

Even for sandstone reservoirs, however, the in-place estimates for gas hydrates in the Gulf of Mexico likely far exceed what may be commercially recoverable with current technology. The MMS is planning similar in-place gas hydrate assessments for other portions of the U.S. Outer Continental Shelf (OCS), including Alaska.

Models of gas hydrate stability for the northern Gulf of Mexico continental slope address basic problems of gas hydrate geology. Resource estimation is based on assessment of the volume of the gas hydrate stability zone and concentration in sediments. Total volume of gas trapped in gas hydrate in the Gulf is estimated to be 100 times less than previously predicted. However, structurally-control led accumulations of gas hydrate on the rims of salt withdrawal basins could be economic in the future. Bacterial gas hydrates in salt withdrawal basins are unlikely to represent a significant energy resource because they are disseminated.

A field located in permafrost terrain on the eastern margin of Russia's West Siberian Basin, the Messoyakha field, was developed as a conventional gas field and has produced continuously from 1970-1978 and thereafter intermittently, primarily in the summer to accommodate regional industrial demand. As is normally the case, reservoir pressure declined as a consequence of production. However, the reservoir pressure remained substantially higher than normally expected.

A 100-m thick methane hydrate zone is located 700 m beneath the surface, and the apparent difference between the actual and predicted pressure decline behavior has been attributed to recharging of the reservoir with gas derived from pressure decline-induced decomposition of the natural gas hydrates in this overlying layer. In 1990, the gas evolved from it reportedly comprised nearly half of cumulative field production, although some investigators have expressed doubt that gas hydrate production actually occurred. Scientific field studies of natural gas hydrates have been carried out in Canada for many years by the geological survey of Canada and by a number of universities.

In December 2003, the Canadian Mallik 2002 Gas Hydrate Production Research Well Program partners (including the USGS and the DOE) publicly released the results of the first modern, fully integrated field study and constrained production test of a natural gas hydrate accumulation. The Mallik 2002 gas hydrate production testing and modeling effort has, for the first time, enabled rational assessment of the production response of a gas hydrate accumulation.

Project-supported gas hydrate production simulations have shown that under certain geologic conditions gas can be produced from gas hydrates at rates exceeding several million cubic feet of gas per day.

Methane hydrates are found in the Nankai Trough located offshore from Japan. The Nankai Trough runs along the Japanese Island, where forearc basins and accretionary prisms developed extensively and BSRs (bottom-simulating reflector) have been recognized widely. High resolution seismic surveys in 1997, 2001 and 2002 and drilling the Nankai Trough wells conducted by the Ministry of Economy, Trade and Industry (METI) have revealed the subsurface gas hydrate widely distributed at the depth interval from 200-270 mbsf.

There have been major drilling campaigns in the Nankai Trough offshore Japan in 2004, and in several widely spaced sites offshore India in 2006. Unlike the U.S.-led efforts, these programs had the specific objective of assessing the fossil fuel potential of gas hydrate. Resource estimates from these campaigns are not in the public domain, and therefore this summary does not draw on, nor necessarily apply to, those areas. However, these programs serve in some respects as models of national resource assessment.

The national project of methane hydrate development in Japan (MH21) started in 2001. Worldwide, only a few dozen boreholes have been drilled to assess marine hydrate resources. Most of these boreholes were drilled offshore in Japan in 2004, and offshore in India in 2006. Comprehensive reports of these campaigns are not yet in the public domain, so there is little public record available to assess the efficacy of exploration paradigms. Thus the main technology barrier is the lack of validated means of reliably finding significant marine gas hydrate resources. A multi-site geological and geophysical exploration program, followed with a multi-site drilling campaign, is needed to accelerate the assessment of marine gas hydrate as an energy resource.

The national energy authorities of Japan and India are conducting the most significant offshore drilling campaigns directed to finding economically significant gas hydrate deposits. The results of these campaigns are not in the public domain. China has recently announced a \$100 million program of hydrate exploration. The state-owned oil companies of Malaysia and Korea have signaled their intention to explore for hydrates in their territorial waters.

Gas hydrates potential in the Black Sea is investigated as a source of methane. The Black Sea is the world's most isolated sea. The Black Sea is a unique energy-rich sea. It abundantly contains gas hydrates and hydrogen sulfide (H2S) as methane (CH_4) and hydrogen source, respectively. The Black Sea is the world largest water body containing hydrogen sulfide and its hydrogen sulfide layer that begins about 200 m below the surface. The concentrations of H2S differ from 1.5 -2.3 mL/L in the Black Sea at depths of 200–1500 m. The Black Sea has suitable conditions (pressure and temperature) for the formation of natural gas hydrates. On the other hand, anaerobic but hydrogen sulfur containing conditions of Black Sea, starting at a depth of 200 m from sea level, makes it more suitable for hydrate formation.

Methane seepage is extremely intense on the shelf and on the slope of the Black Sea. Methane hydrates can form in the Black Sea at water depths exceeding 580–700 m. One of the first reported observations of gas hydrates in marine sediments was from the Black Sea. The area of the Black Sea that is suitable for gas hydrate formation is evaluated at 288,100 km2, representing about 68% of the total Black Sea or almost 91% of the deep-water basin. Methane has discharged into the Black Sea and the global ocean via fluid flow through submarine mud volcanoes. The areas of active fluid venting and mud volcanism were investigated in the Black Sea below the oxic zone at depths varying between 800-2200 m.

The Black Sea is located strategically with its surface area of 423,000 km^2 and a maximum depth of 2212 m, making it the largest anoxic water basin in the world.

Figure 9-23. Black Sea's strategic location

Freshwater river inflow resulted in lower surface water salinity (17.5–18.5‰), whereas the salinity of deep water is 22.3%. Currently, the Black Sea is the largest anoxic water body on the planet and represents the closest contemporary analog to past sulfidic oceans.

The Black Sea has a layered structure where only the upper 150 m is oxic, whereas the main water body is anoxic. Methane seepage is extremely intense on the shelf and on the slope of the Black Sea. The methane content increases from the water surface towards depth; in the central Black Sea, the concentration has been measured at 0.036 lM (micromole/L) in the 150 m surface layer, increasing from 5.1 to 13.9 lM at 250 and 550 m, respectively, reaching the plateau value to the bottom.

The Black Sea is an important potential energy source so the research continues with growing expectations.

Methane Hydrate Properties

Oceanic methane hydrate and associated gas deposits have been formed due to gas flow in the sediments, and the subsequent development of a gas–fluid interface. This is the cause for the methane to be concentrated in one place—probably the coldest spots in the gas flow. The remainder of the gas flow has been most likely dispersed near its source of production without any significant concentrations of either natural gas or hydrate.

Methane hydrates have unique properties that are quite different from any other energy sources. They are stable under low temperatures and high pressures. The hydrate stability zone in marine environments is a function of the water depth, the seafloor temperature, and the geothermal gradient. Any changes to the temperature and pressure, both at the surface and in the area adjacent to the hydrate, will affect the thickness of the stability zone.

Although temperature and pressure are the main controls in the formation of gas hydrates and the thickness of the hydrate stability zone, other factors such as gas chemistry and gas availability will also alter the thickness and location of the hydrate stability zone.

Methane hydrate has a very high concentration of methane gas. One m³ block of methane hydrate in its frozen state can release about 160 m³ of gaseous methane upon melting.

The growth and stability of the free-gas zone (FGZ) beneath gas hydrate related bottom-simulating seismic reflectors (BSRs) is investigated using analytical and numerical analyzes to understand the factors controlling the formation and depletion of free gas. Gas forms across a thick zone because the upward fluid flux is relatively low and because the gas-water solubility decreases to a minimum of several hundred meters below the seabed.

Methane sI hydrates that are much more stable at 1 atm and 268.2 K than any previously reported. Extraordinarily stable natural gas sII hydrates at 1 atm and 268.2–270.2 K are reported for the first time. Test innovations that achieved ultra-stabilities give insight into hydrate self-preservation mechanisms.

The resulting hydrate stability window is 268.2-270.2 K at 1 atm. Methane sI, as well as natural gas sII, hydrates exhibit only minimal decomposition upon reducing confining system pressure to 1 atm in the 268.2–270.2 K stability window. Total gas that evolved after 24 h at 1 atm in the stability window typically amounted to less than 0.5% of originally stored gas, and this ultra-stability was shown to persist when the test was allowed to run 256 h before terminating.

The entire methane sI or natural gas sII hydrate mass remains stable during pressure reduction to 1 atm, whereas previous reports defined hydrate anomalous stability for only about 50% of fractional hydrate remnants. At pressures and temperatures outside the hydrate stability range, melting and decomposition of gas hydrates will occur.

Decomposition will result in the release of water and methane gas but it requires heat input. As decomposition occurs, the released gas and water create a volume expansion. If the heat transport and the pressure change processes are fast compared with pore pressure dissipation processes, the excess pore pressure and reduction in effective stress can be estimated.

The decomposition of gas hydrates can stem from any change in the pressure and temperature regime in the hydrate stability zone and results in a significant volume change. In the natural environment, the importance of the pore pressure generated by hydrate dissolution and dissociation depends on the temperature increase rate and on ratio of thermal diffusivity to hydraulic diffusivity. For a slow rate of temperature increase and a thermal diffusivity of 2–3 orders of magnitude higher than the hydraulic diffusivity, the excess pore pressure generated by both hydrate dissolution and hydrate dissociation is expected to be low.

However, during exploitation, hydrate dissolution and dissociation may significantly alter the structure and mechanical properties of the marine sediments and the subsequent softening and decrease of the shear strength is probably the main driving factor of sediment deformations and slope instabilities.

Methane in hydrates is derived from both within the hydrate stability zone (HSZ) and more importantly from the great thickness of sediments below. Both shallow, biogenic gas derived mainly from bacteriological decay of organic matter buried along with the sediment, and deeper sourced, thermo genic gas produced by thermal cracking of higher density hydrocarbons, have been found within hydrate deposits. The biogenic methane is usually dominant.

The requirement for sediments rich in organic carbon explains the suitability of continental margin sediments. Methane formed from either biogenic or thermo genic activity will tend to migrate upwards, and be trapped as hydrate within the HSZ or as free gas beneath it. Once trapped as hydrate, the methane will tend to stay concentrated in the HSZ.

Impacts of Methane Hydrates on the Greenhouse Effect

Today's world is facing two environmental problems: global warming and air pollution. Both of these are linked to the heavy use of the fossil fuels. Global consumption of fossil fuels is staggering and is increasing at an alarming rate. The quadrupling of oil prices in the 1970s and rapid increase in recent years, the growing awareness of energy-related pollution, and the possibility of climate change have all contributed to a re-evaluation of energy use.

Among the fossil fuels, natural gas (methane) is the least responsible for CO_2 emissions. Liquefied petroleum gas (LPG) causes higher CO_2 than that of natural gas. Methane gas, contained in methane hydrate deposits, however, is a very powerful greenhouse gas.

Warmer Arctic temperatures could result in a gradual melting of gas hydrates below permafrost, and warming oceans could cause gradual melting of gas hydrates near the sediment-water interface. Although many news reports have presented this as a potential catastrophe, USGS research has determined that gas hydrates are currently contributing to total atmospheric methane and that a catastrophic melting of unstable hydrate deposits is unlikely to send large amounts of methane into the atmosphere any time soon. And yet, the danger is there for us to assess and contain, instead of disregarding it. It is too big to be ignored!

Methane hydrates sediments are sensitive to temperature and pressure changes. They can rapidly dissociate with an increase in temperature or a decrease in pressure. This dissociation produces free methane and water, the huge quantity of which needs to be considered as a great risk of large quantity GHG gasses in the atmosphere.

The conversion of solid sediment into liquids and gases will create a loss of support and shear strength. That can cause submarine slumping, landslides, or subsidence that can damage production equipment and pipelines. The process can escalate to unimaginable size with untold damage to the environment, while also bringing devastation to coastal areas. This is a nightmare scenario, which, as unlikely as it might seem, needs to be taken into consideration when doing anything close to disturbing the sleeping giants.

Possible Effects of Methane Hydrates on the Climate Change

Hydrates may affect climate because when warmed or depressurized, they decompose and dissociate into water and methane gas, one of the greenhouse gases that warms the planet. Methane is a greenhouse gas. Discharge of large amounts of methane into the atmosphere would cause global warming. It has been well documented that methane levels in the atmosphere were lower during glacial than during interglacial periods. In fact, methane is many times more effective as a greenhouse gas than is CO_2.

Therefore, if the flux of methane into the atmosphere from dissociating hydrates is sufficient in quantity, this methane can cause global warming. Specifically, as the Earth warms, increasing bottom water temperatures could cause gas hydrate disassociation in many marine shelf locations. This gas hydrate disassociation would cause further warming due to the greenhouse effects of the gas that is released, such as methane releases from hydrates into the atmosphere if the sea level drops, and sea-level rise causes relatively warm ocean water to cover cold Arctic strata.

The resulting breakdown of stable gas hydrates within the sediment releases gas into the atmosphere. Methane releases from hydrates into the atmosphere if the sea level rises. The dissociation of gas hydrates during de-glaciation has therefore been linked to the ending of ice ages during the last few millions of years.

During formation of large polar ice sheets, the sea level falls, reducing the pressure on the ocean margin gas hydrates. The shallower gas hydrate deposits become unstable, and release methane into the atmosphere, which caused warming and the ending of the ice age. This scenario remains questionable, however, because almost certainly the permafrost had hydrate reservoirs much larger than now during the glacial periods when permafrost regions were much more widespread than they are now.

Analyzing methane concentrations in polar ice cores might check the scenario of large pulses of methane into the atmosphere. The methane peak concentrations in the atmosphere would not remain for long, because methane has an atmospheric residence time of only about 10 years before being oxidized to CO_2.

The time resolution of ice core sampling has until now not been enough to resolve such short-term peaks.

In addition, gas hydrate dissociation has been suggested as the cause for oceanic anoxia and massive extinctions of marine biota at the end of the Permian; oxidation of the methane within ocean waters could have used up a large part of the dissolved oxygen in the oceans.

A much better documented possible episode of massive hydrate dissociation occurred during a short-term warming event occurred at the end of the Paleocene. Oil and gas wells drilled through permafrost or offshore to reach conventional oil and gas deposits may encounter gas hydrates, which companies generally try to avoid because of a lack of detailed understanding of the mechanical and thermal properties of gas hydrate-bearing sediments.

However, to mitigate the potential hazard in these instances, the wells are cased to separate and protect the well from the gas hydrates in the shallower zones as drilling continues deeper. Unless precautions are taken, continued drilling may heat up the sediments surrounding the wellbore, causing gas from the dissociated hydrates to leak and bubble up around the casing.

Once oil production begins, hot fluids flowing through the well could also warm hydrate-bearing sediments and cause dissociation. The released gas may pool and build up pressure against the well casing, possibly causing damage. Some observers suggest that exploiting the gas hydrate resources by intentionally heating or by depressurization pose the same risks as drilling through gas hydrates to reach deeper conventional oil and gas deposits.

Climatic conditions during the latest Paleocene are characterized by a geologically brief time interval of rapid and profound global warming. Carbon isotope records across the latest Palaeocene thermal maximum (LPTM) display show a remarkable delta 13C excursion of at least 2.5 per mil that occurred within 100 years.

Thermal dissociation of marine gas hydrate and release of massive quantities of CH_4 to the exogenic carbon cycle appears to be the only plausible explanation for this geochemical perturbation. Methane, after carbon dioxide, is the second most important greenhouse gas in the atmosphere and has caused dramatic climate shifts in the past several million years.

The characteristics of the isotope anomaly suggest a massive and abrupt input of carbon to the ocean-atmosphere from an external reservoir greatly enriched in 12C, such as methane gas hydrates, followed by a gradual return to earlier conditions. The LPTM represents a geologically brief time interval characterized by profound global warming and associated environmental change. The LPTM is marked by a prominent negative carbon isotope excursion (CIE) interpreted to reflect a massive and abrupt input of 12C-enriched carbon to the ocean–atmosphere reservoir, possibly as a result of catastrophic gas hydrate release, on time scales equivalent to present-day rates of anthropogenic carbon input.

The LPTM corresponds to important changes in the global distribution of biota, including mass extinction of marine benthic organisms. The dinoflagellate cyst record indicates that surface dwelling marine plankton in marginal seas also underwent significant perturbations during the LPTM.

Methane hydrates hold the danger of natural hazards associated with sea floor stability and the release of methane to ocean and atmosphere, and gas hydrates disturbed during drilling pose a safety problem. Continental slope instability caused by hydrate decomposition is suggested as a trigger mechanism for underwater landslides and tsunami generation. If large volumes of methane are stored in marine reservoirs, they may significantly influence the sedimentary environment in which they occur.

The formation and subsequent decomposition of gas hydrates within the sediments affect the physical properties of the sediment as well. Changes in pressure and temperature will decompose solid gas hydrates to gas and water, which may lead to sediment instability and failure.

The abundance of methane in the Earth's atmosphere in 1998 was 1745 ppb, up from 700 ppb in 1750. In the same time period, CO_2 increased from 278 to 365 ppm. Today it is reaching levels above 400 ppm in some parts of the world. There is a large, but largely unknown, amount of methane in methane hydrates in the ocean floors. The estimates, however, are that there are several times more methane hydrates on Earth than all gas and oil reserves combined.

The Earth's crust contains huge amounts of methane. Large amounts of methane are produced anaerobically by methanogenesis. Other sources include mud volcanoes, which are connected with deep geological faults, and livestock from enteric fermentation.

Methane has 21 times the global warming potential as the same mass of carbon dioxide. Anthropogenic inputs, such as rice paddies, livestock, and biomass combustion, contribute 71%, the largest proportion, to the atmospheric concentration.

Methane concentrations have doubled from 850 ppb to currently approximately 1750 ppb over the last 150 years. Natural sources, such as wetlands and termites, contribute approximately 29%, along with other small sources. It is assumed that the release of methane from marine hydrates during climatic maxima and minima has played a significant role in climate change.

The Earth has witnessed several intervals of climate change, typified by lowering and rising in sea levels due to rapid cooling and warming. Because several of these time intervals are characterized by major inputs of carbon into the ocean and atmosphere, and because the change in pressure and temperature conditions during those times may have reduced the stability of gas hydrate reservoirs, it is believed that the release of methane from marine hydrates has played a significant role in warming the Earth's climate.

During the formation of gas hydrates, methane and water become immobilized within the sediment pore spaces. Because of the presence of these solids, the sediment cannot become consolidated because the water cannot be expelled, increasing overburden as more sedimentation occurs. Cementation of the sediments does not occur when pore spaces are filled with hydrates rather than with water, from which minerals such as calcite can be precipitated. Gas hydrate rich sediments are thus cemented by the hydrates, which may occupy much of the sedimentary section, but which are not stable when the temperature rises or the pressure falls. This may lead to problems during continued sedimentation and further burial of the gas hydrates; the hydrates will become buried so deeply that the temperature will increase according to the regional geothermal gradient.

The hydrates will then no longer be stable, and will disintegrate into a liquid water and gas mixture. The basal zone of the gas hydrate becomes under-consolidated, possibly over-pressured because of the release of the methane, leading to the development of a zone with low shear strength where failure could be triggered and massive landslides could occur. With the landslides, more gas could escape.

Gas hydrates are a significant hazard for drilling and production operations. Gas hydrate production is hazardous in itself, as well as for conventional oil and gas activities that place wells and pipelines into permafrost or marine sediments.

For activities in permafrost, two general categories of problems have been identified:

1) Uncontrolled gas releases during drilling

2) Damage to well casing during and after installation of a well

Similar problems could occur during offshore drilling into gas hydrate-bearing marine sediments. Offshore drilling operations that disturb gas hydrate-bearing sediments could fracture or disrupt the bottom sediments, which would compromise the wellbore, pipelines, rig supports, and other equipment involved in oil and gas production from the seafloor. Problems may differ somewhat between onshore and offshore operations, but they stem from the same characteristic of gas hydrates: decreases in pressure and increases in temperature can cause the gas hydrate to dissociate and rapidly release large amounts of gas into the well bore during a drilling operation.

The Earth's atmosphere has a large number of sources and sinks for methane including gas hydrates, which exist in metastable equilibrium with the environment. This equilibrium is affected by natural changes in pressure and temperature. The amount of methane that is trapped in gas hydrates is perhaps 3000 times the amount in the atmosphere and this enormous quantity of methane is available for release with catastrophic consequences for global climate.

The rapid climate change in the past from the glacial to interglacial is indeed attributed to the huge release of methane from gas hydrates. Some of the models linked these observations with climatic change caused by hydrate decomposition or vice versa. Accordingly, glaciation and sea level fall will reduce hydrostatic pressure on the sediments of shelf and slope at mid-lat-

itudes, thereby destabilizing hydrates and consequently releasing methane into the atmosphere.

The methane so released will cause rapid warming, which will lead to dissociation of hydrates in the permafrost regions and shallow continental margins of the high latitude regions, a positive feed back causing further warming. Consequently ice in the higher latitude will melt, thereby increasing sea level. This rise in sea level will in turn increase the hydrostatic pressure on the sediments of shelf and slope at mid-latitudes, initiating negative feedback that will inhibit further release of methane from hydrates.

Submarine sediment slumping or sliding occurs when huge piles of unstable sediments build up. In some cases movement of these sediment slumps or slides can possibly be caused by the decomposition of gas hydrates and the resulting expansion or release of gas. In the continental slope area, continued sedimentation may lead to burial of hydrated sediment to such a depth that the hydrates are no longer stable and that they dissociate into a liquid–gas–water mixture. The dissociated hydrates create a zone of weakness in the sediment where slope failure could be triggered by further gravitational loading or earthquakes.

These changes, though of long duration, may have caused solid sediment to become gas-cut mud and resulted in mud diapers, mud volcanoes, or mud slides flows, depending on sediment composition and bottom topography.

Methane hydrates are located in the shallow submarine geosphere, which is a finely balanced system in equilibrium with all its components such as sediment, pore water, fluid flows, pressure, temperature, overlying water, and hydrate. Removal of any one component of this equilibrium may destabilize the whole system and lead to irreparable damage. The destabilizing factors may be either natural or exploitation perturbations. Studies have indicated that methane hydrates have the potential to affect global climate and the geological environment at a catastrophic scale.

Methane Hydrates' Future

The world's first commercial production of useful methane gas from methane hydrate sites has a history of almost 20 years. The site is located at Messoyakh, Russia, where the methane hydrate is mined directly from the permafrost. During the last two decades, ocean exploration has revealed an abundant fuel source of methane hydrate (MH) stored in deep ocean sediments. The majority of methane in ocean sediments has a biogenic origin, as a by-product of marine biogeochemical processes that includes photosynthesis and oxidation. The rest of the known methane from deposits has a thermo genic origin.

Photosynthesis is a sequence of reactions that convert sunlight into chemical energy, which then is used to build an organic molecule (a sugar) from inorganic molecules (CO_2 and water). A by-product of photosynthesis is oxygen gas. The chemical bonds of sugar hold chemical energy that can be used by cells to do work. Oceanic phytoplankton in the euphotic zone (from the ocean surface to the depth where sunlight is attenuated to 0.1% of its surface intensity) accounts for almost half of all photosynthesis on Earth. Phytoplankton is also the primary producers of the marine food chain. More complicated molecules, living tissues, marine zooplankton and animals are built on this foundation. After the marine animals die, their tissues decay (by bacterial decomposition) into dissolved organic matter and small molecules such as CO_2 and methane (CH_4).

The oxidation of methane is a several-step process that produces CO_2, water, and energy at a rate of 195 Kcal/mol of methane. An important difference between the two reactions is that the energy used in photosynthesis is sunlight energy in ocean water, whereas the energy released in oxidation is chemical energy and heat that is transferred via biomass, eventually being deposited into the seawater that supported the life in the first place. The rate of oxidation of methane depends on the population of methane oxidation (aerobic) bacteria and the amount of dissolved oxygen in seawater. Therefore, some percentages of methane broken apart from dissolved organic matter will not oxidize. In the deep-sea's cold and high-pressure conditions, that portion of methane is locked up in methane hydrate. Methane hydrate is usually found in the ocean sediments on the sea floor of the continental shelf/slope (at a depth range of 350–1200 m. A small fraction of methane hydrate resource is also found in the polar permafrost. Methane hydrate is an ice-like crystalline; its molecular structure is similar to ice except that there is a methane molecule trapped within the hexagon/pentagon cage of ice. Methane hydrate exists in metastable equilibrium with its marine environment and is affected by changes in pressure and temperature. When it dissociates (due to either lowering pressure or rising water temperature), the ice cage melts and the methane gas escapes.

Methane hydrate is an ideal fuel that burns and produces some CO_2, but no other air pollutants. The amount of methane that is trapped in hydrate is perhaps 3000 times the amount contained in the atmosphere. The chemical energy stored in all known methane hydrate

deposits is estimated to be twice that of all other fossil fuels combined. Thus it is, in principle, most desirable to develop the technology to exploit this enormous energy source.

But methane hydrates could be also at least partially responsible for the present day global warming. There are huge amounts of these fossils deposited deep under the ocean floor. As the global climate temperature increases, the dissociation of oceanic methane hydrates increases. The process is accelerated by fluctuations in ocean currents and shifts in major warm current systems, such as the Gulf Stream migrating towards the continental slope of the northeastern U.S. and Canada.

The dissociative forces cause outgassing of the surface layers of the methane hydrate deposits, which is accompanied by the release of huge volume of microscopic methane bubbles into the ocean waters. Methane oxidation bacteria and other microbes will convert the bulk of CH_4 into CO_2 and generate heat. Both the CO_2 and any residual CH_4 will escape into the atmosphere, while the heat warms the interior ocean (predominantly at intermediate depths). The warmed oceans will then evaporate more water vapor into the atmosphere, thus augmenting the enhanced greenhouse effect. This will cause further temperature increases, which will then accelerate the dissociative processes further, thus creating a non-stop chain reaction, the final result of which is environmental disaster.

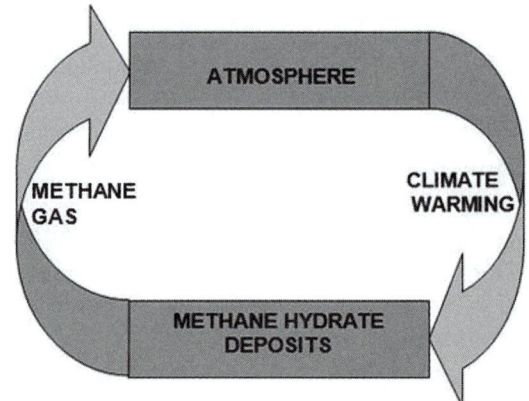

Figure 9-24. The vicious cycle

The noticeable melting of the ice cap and glaciers disappearance, caused by the gradual climate warming, might be one of the most significant events of the 21 Century. There are billions of tons of methane hydrates locked into the permafrost and deep into the world oceans. These fossils have been kept locked in their watery-icy grave through the centuries by the low temperatures prevailing deep down below the ocean floor.

As warmer ocean currents hit the deposits, the methane hydrates will thaw slowly at first, with a small release of methane gas in the water and the atmosphere. As a matter of fact, we might be at that first stage already, for there are signs of increased methane outgassing in some places around the world.

But as the climate continues to warm, the speed of thawing of the permafrost will increase, and that is when things will get very dangerous. At some point of the out-of-control climate warming cycle, the chain reaction will enter a non-reversible and quickly accelerating speed, where the permafrost will melt at an ever-increasing pace.

At such a time, the methane hydrate in the mountains will start collapsing and releasing immense amounts of methane gas. The resulting reaction cannot be stopped, and it will keep accelerating until all methane hydrates are completely dissociated and evaporated into the atmosphere. That would surely mark the end of the world…

Conclusion

Gas hydrates are crystalline solids that form from mixtures of water and light natural gases such as methane, carbon dioxide, ethane, propane and butane. Methane was the dominant component among other hydrocarbon gases in the sediments. Gas hydrates are ice-like crystalline solids formed from mixtures of water and natural gas, usually methane. They occur where pressure, temperature, gas saturation and local chemical conditions combine to make them stable.

Methane gas hydrates are of interest primarily for three reasons:

1) Gas from hydrate may be a new clean energy source. It is now recognized that there are huge amounts of natural gas, mainly methane, tied up in gas hydrate globally. Methane gas hydrates are potential energy resources.

2) NG hydrate may play a role in climate change. Methane is a strong greenhouse gas, so its escape to the atmosphere from natural gas hydrate could result in global warming.

3) There are important production problems. Gas hydrate is a hazard from shallow gas release in conventional hydrocarbon exploration and from seafloor instability, especially in the Arctic and in deep water where hydrate is stable.

Sub-seabed methane within the continental margin sediments is produced primarily by microbial or thermogenic processes. In the microbial process, bacteria in an anoxic environment decompose organic debris into methane by a complex sequence (methanogenesis). Organic matter is composed of carbon, hydrogen, and phosphorus in the ratio of 106:16:1, and decomposition results in production of methane.

Methane hydrates are located in the shallow submarine geosphere, which is a finely balanced system in equilibrium with all its components such as sediment, pore water, fluid flows, pressure, temperature, overlying water, and hydrate. Removal of any one component of this equilibrium may destabilize the whole system, leading to irreparable damage. The destabilizing factors may be either natural perturbations or those associated with exploitation of resources.

Studies have indicated that methane hydrates have the potential to affect global climate and the geological environment at a catastrophic scale. Methane hydrates are common in sediments deposited in high latitude continental shelves and at the slope and rise of continental margins with high bio-productivity.

High biological production provides the organic matter that is buried in the sediment, which, during early diagenesis and after exhausting oxygen, sulfate and other electron acceptors, eventually generates methane through fermentative decomposition and microbial carbonate reduction.

The properties of sediment-hosted gas hydrates are strongly determined by texture, structure and permeability of the sediment and the mode of supply of methane.

In conclusion, we now know about the existence of large amounts of methane hydrates and their properties, which leads to the conclusion that they might be a significant part of our new energy future—or at least that of the future generations. This is a comforting thought, which beats the alternative of leaving no energy sources at all for those following us, leaving them in complete darkness and an energy-deprived existence.

The use of methane hydrates as an energy source, however, is a complex and expensive process. Presently, we have no technology or process that is efficient and safe enough to warrant large-scale development of this huge energy resource. There are also the safety issues surrounding large-scale explorations deep under the ocean floor, where forces that we are not that familiar with could unleash a global disaster.

What this tells us is that there is hope, a great hope that we needs to approach very carefully. Any hasty move might result in costly and irreversible damages.

Space Power

On the extreme opposite of the deep ocean floor, we see power that can be extracted from deep space.

This new source is especially welcomed now when we expect a 50% increase in worldwide electric generating capacity, from 4,650 GW presently to just over 7,000 GW by 2030.

These estimates do not include the additional power that may be required to enable:

- Replacement of obsolete or environmentally unacceptable facilities
- Wide-spread adoption of plug-in hybrid or fully electric vehicles
- Desalination of seawater on a large scale
- Substantial economic growth in poor nations

Even if a decisive action to reduce the cost of renewable sources, especially wind and solar, is undertaken, it will still involve greater expense and consumption of coal, nuclear energy and natural gas during the transition stages.

The presently installed cost of a large array designed to feed power to the utility grid is about $2,000/kW installed. Because of nighttime, daily and seasonal variations and weather, the average intensity of sunlight is less than 280 watts/m^2, even in the high solar radiation Arizona desert.

The real installed cost, spread to a 24-hr cycle, is then about $7,000/kW. And even then, a complete utility-scale system also requires extensive energy storage to compensate for the variations in sunlight and night, plus long-distance transmission lines to deliver power from the desert to load centers.

When all these costs and inefficiencies are added, the cost of our large power plant rises to nearly $15,000 for each kW delivered to the load. The cost will fall further, but this is still far from competitive with fossil fueled power plants (prior to including the external costs). In all cases, the solar contribution to electric utilities, worldwide, will be less than 1.0% of the total consumption by 2030.

So what do we do? How about taking the solar modules up into space, where the sun shines non-stop 24/7/365 and the intensity of sunlight is 1,360 W/m^2, which is 40% greater than on Earth, so there is no variability to be concerned with.

But how do we do this?

The best location is geostationary orbit (GSO, 35,800 km above the equator), where a satellite remains fixed relative to terrestrial sites. The principal components of a power satellite are a large solar array and a microwave transmitter that beams power to an Earth-based receiver called a rectenna (a contraction of "rectifying antenna"), where it is converted to standard AC.

The continuous, intense sunlight in the GSO means that that no energy storage is needed, and that the solar array is smaller than a similar terrestrial array with the same average output by a factor of 8. The almost-perfect operating environment, in vacuum and free fall, permits high solar concentration without complex sun-tracking mechanisms and avoids maintenance problems caused by wind, dust, rain, snow or hail.

Imagine for a moment, large satellites delivering 2 GW to the utility grid, an output similar to a large nuclear plant. And there is room in the GSO for thousands of them.

Thus generated power is beamed to Earth-based substations via microwave flux, which is invisible to aircraft and birds. The rectenna area is smaller than the terrestrial solar farm that it replaces by a factor of 9 and can be located close to the intended load center. The structure shields the ground underneath from microwaves but is largely transparent to sunlight, so that it can be used for agriculture or other purposes.

The technical feasibility of space-based solar power (SBSP) is—theoretically—justifiable. PV cells have been used in space for decades, and wireless power transmission has been demonstrated repeatedly on Earth and in space.

Several NASA and the DOE sponsored studies of the subject have found no showstoppers, and this result has been confirmed by several major studies since then. Advances in space technology are capable of reducing the installation and operation costs to a competitive level, and a demo project could be done as soon as money becomes available.

And therein lies the biggest problem: the hardware needed for such project is prohibitively expensive. Mass production that is needed for power satellites would reduce these prices to terrestrial levels, but that will take lots of time...and money. The state-of-the-art technology power satellite could be built at a hardware cost of about $8,500/kW. Future advances are expected to reduce the cost in half.

SBSP, however, requires a major expansion of space operations, which although small compared to terrestrial solar arrays of similar output, represents a huge jump in size as compared to anything yet deployed in space.

Spaceflight is also too expensive for justifiable SBSP development, but future development of the space technology could bring space launch contribution to about 2,400/kW of the cost of the system.

Fuel Cells

The U.S. DOE's solid-state energy conversion alliance (SECA) is developing a fuel cell program that is working on successful proof-of-concept fuel cells. Recently a breakthrough for solid oxide fuel cell (SOFC)-based power systems was made, which reflects the potential of this technology for this and many other market applications.

DOE's office of fossil energy established SECA in 2000 to research and develop low-cost, modular, fuel-flexible solid oxide fuel cell systems by 2010. In early 2005, the SECA program was accelerated to deliver megawatt-class fuel cell systems in response to emerging national needs for low-cost carbon capture technologies, more efficient and cost effective use of fuels abundantly available in the U.S., and reduced water use by power plants. The office of fossil energy's National Energy Technology Laboratory manages the SECA program and its projects.

The two technologies developed under the SECA program were:

- SOFC stacks manufactured by Delphi Corporation of Flint, MI
- A specialized blower developed for SECA SOFC systems by R&D Dynamics, Bloomfield, CT, under DOE's small business innovation research program

The blower was used successfully in the test to recycle high-temperature fuel exhaust flows back to the fuel reformer. The proof-of-concept system met the U.S. Navy's targets for system size, power output, and efficiency.

SECA fuel cells make efficient use of plentiful domestic fuel sources and are a clean source of energy. They operate by separating and transferring oxygen across a solid electrolyte membrane, where it reacts with a fuel—such as synthesis gas derived from coal, biofuels, or natural gas—to produce steam and carbon dioxide (CO_2). Condensing the steam results in a pure stream of CO_2 gas that can be readily captured in a central location for storage or other uses.

This feature, coupled with the fact that fuel cell efficiency does not depend on high temperatures, results in near-zero emissions at equivalent or reduced cost-of-electricity compared to today's power generation. Furthermore, SECA systems have low water requirements and high efficiencies relative to conventional technologies.

SECA fuel cells are well-suited to unmanned undersea vehicles because they can operate on logistic fuels (such as jet fuels), tolerate fuel impurities, generate high-quality heat for fuel reforming, and are highly efficient in converting fuel energy into electricity. Use in unmanned undersea vehicles represents a spinoff application of SECA's fuel cell technology.

Spinoffs into a variety of other applications and markets are possible and are encouraged, because they enable increased manufacturing production volume and lower the costs of these technologies.

Promising Solar Materials and Processes

Since all solar devices are made of some type of physical material, their type and quality determines the performance and reliability of the solar cells and modules that are made out of those materials. Garbage in, garbage out, is most appropriate qualifier in this case. We cannot possibly expect great performance from a device made out of poor quality materials.

The situation is not that extreme in most cases, so what we get in many cases instead is something in between, something that may or may not work well. Because of that, the research of existing materials and the development of new ones is an ongoing and very large business.

The work in the area of materials R&D includes:

Hi Purity poly silicon

Metallurgical-grade (MG) silicon, which is usually produced from sand, is about 99% pure. According to generally accepted guidelines regarding silicon purity, electronic grade (EG) material suitable for the semiconductor industry requires at least 99.9999999% pure material (known as "9-nines" purity), which represents impurity concentrations of about 0.0005 ppm.

The rising needs for faster and better operating semiconductor devices, however, have pushed the poly silicon producers of EG materials to routinely achieve 11-nines purity. At present, the purity requirement for the solar grade (SG) poly silicon for the PV market is somewhat less stringent. The prevailing opinion is that silicon with a purity of 99.9999% (6-nines) is the lower limit for a viable solar cell.   Research in the area suggests that the efficiency with which solar cells convert sunlight into electricity is correlated with material purity; therefor, a solar cell made out of 6-nines SG would be less efficient and less reliable than one made out of 7-8-nines. The price goes up according to the level of purity, so a balance needs to be struck by the manufacturers in terms of efficiency and reliability, vs. purity and quality of poly silicon materials.

More CPV companies are pushing for higher-quality material. Substantial R&D is underway throughout the solar industry, intended to validate the correlation between poly silicon purity and PV cell performance. In Japan, for example, the limited space available for solar installations is forcing the use of the most efficient cells and PV modules. This trend will grow with time, as customers start finding out that higher quality materials provide not only higher efficiency, but also a higher long-term reliability.

Going beyond the established and accepted purity limits of the poly silicon materials will play an increasingly important role in the solar installations of the 21st century. Finding new ways to achieve and ensure high purity, thus increasing the efficiency and reliability of the final products, will be on the agenda of all solar cells and PV modules manufacturers for the duration as well.

New Feedstock for FB Process

A development-stage company called Peak Sun Silicon Corp. (Albany, OR) is working on an FB process using tribromosilane (TBS) as the feedstock, rather than either silane or trichlorosilane. While TBS costs more than its brethren, Peak Sun's process uses less, so the feedstock costs are almost even.

The inclusion of massive bromine atoms in the feedstock compound also offers several key advantages, such as a much wider tolerance of temperatures and pressures, which is an advantage over the tight control that needs to be exerted in other processes.

TBS processes operate at lower temperatures, which allows energy savings and additional quality control. It also helps avoid the formation of submicron-diameter amorphous silicon dust through a homogeneous nucleation route, which are significant challenges encountered by silicon reactor operations that use silane or trichlorosilane as the feed gas.

Homogeneous nucleation can occur when materials move from vapor to solid phase and reach a "critical nucleus" of solid-phase material. At certain values of "re" atoms, the thermodynamics of the system favors self-nucleation, rather than deposition on the surface of a seed particle. The phase-change energy barrier is overcome more readily at higher values of n, since surface area-to-volume ratio decreases as particle diameter increases. Silane and trichlorosilane have a natural propensity for self-nucleation when overcoming the phase change energy barrier.

By virtue of its relatively large molecular size, TBS requires a greater n value to achieve critical nucleus, and molecules prefer to transition to a solid phase by nucleating on an existing silicon surface. The result is that TBS

deposition favors growth on the surface of crystalline seed particles over the formation of low-value amorphous silicon dust.

Another advantage to the Peak Sun TBS-FB process is the formation of dense metallic beads with a narrow particle size distribution. Silicon beads formed by the TBS-FB process also tend to have less surface oxidation and less gas molecule inclusions, which gives the silicon better melt properties.

When completed, the Peak Sun project will be the first demonstration of a FB silicon unit using TBS. Peak Sun claims that its process will have lower capital costs and 25% lower operating costs than a Siemens process unit.

Crystallization Technologies

Another key process in the manufacture of high-purity silicon involves a re-crystallization step that converts poly crystalline material to mono crystalline silicon. The process is more important at present for semiconductor-grade silicon, since poly crystalline silicon is suitable for PV cells.

Manufacturers typically use some variation of the so-called Czochralski process, in which a seed crystal is introduced to a silicon melt and slowly withdrawn to generate a long mass of mono crystalline silicon.

An alternative is a modified float-zone process, in which impurities are segregated during a transition that occurs as a mass of poly silicon passes through a radio-frequency heating coil, which creates a localized molten zone from which the pure crystal grows.

This way the purity and the final quality of the product can be tightly controlled and significantly improved.

UMG

One technology approach to poly silicon production that appears to be under consideration for low cost manufacturing of solar cells is upgraded metallurgical grade (UMG) silicon. Melting metallurgical-grade silicon and slowly and directionally recrystallizing it produces UMG. The approach would offer a less expensive route to material, but the 5-nines or 6-nines purity that UMG can achieve wouldn't be viable if the higher-purity methods are cost competitive.

The drive today is for achieving high levels of purity—over and above what UMG can offer—but UMG is a viable alternative for some specialized applications, where low cost silicon can be used. It also might be considered for applications where the PV modules would be used temporarily.

Nevertheless, UMG offers a niche market worth exploring; for use in special cases, and if and when poly silicon prices reach the $500 mark again.

Solar Cleaning Services

New areas for specialized services will be opening in the near future in the solar mega fields. One such service of great importance might be the periodic cleaning of PV modules in utility solar power plants. Contrary to the claims of some companies that their PV modules do not need cleaning, experience shows that the millions of PV modules, parabolic troughs, mirrors and other sunlight reflecting or focusing surfaces installed in large-scale solar power plants do need cleaning.

Some locations are much worse than others, with the deserts being the worst and dirtiest places on Earth. Sand storms, monsoons, and other weather phenomena, in addition to blistering daily sunshine and freezing nights, dominate the desert landscape and the PV modules are stuck in the middle to bear the brunt of it all.

After every monsoon storm, the shiny front glass of the PV modules and the reflective surfaces of parabolic troughs and mirrors get covered with dust and mud spots. Those have to be cleaned immediately, or there would be much less power generated. If the dust and mud are not cleaned quickly, they get hard and baked with time, thus becoming more difficult to remove.

Dirt, sand, water spots, and so objects accumulated on the active surfaces reduce the power generation according to the type and amount of the deposits. In all cases, it amounts to loss of revenue, unless the surfaces are promptly and properly cleaned.

This is where we envision specialized cleaning crews jumping into action and attacking the dirt, mud, and sand on the solar equipment's active surfaces in an organized and efficient way. New cleaning chemicals, processes and technologies would be developed to solve those problems quickly, efficiently and cost-effectively. A niche market would be born, and entire industries might develop around this service as well.

NOTE: The claim of some reputable companies that their PV modules "need no water," or "need cleaning once or twice a year," is a further confirmation of the ignorance surrounding the complex issue of operating solar power equipment in the deserts. Such misinformation, coming from large and reputable companies, is often interpreted as a fact based on scientific research and long-term experience—both of which are far from the truth.

Regular dusting and thorough cleaning are parts of life in the deserts, so the required effort and expense needs to be estimated and included in the power plant design from the very beginning.

Recycling of PV Modules

This is shaping into a great business opportunity for specialized companies. This is because millions of PV modules mounted on steel frames are getting old and will eventually have to be disassembled and disposed of or recycled. As a result, many PV companies and government bodies worldwide are actively looking into the process of recycling and disposal of the PV products, both as manufacturing waste and as end-of-life (EOL) modules.

E.U. companies have proposed a voluntary take-back system capable of meeting the future waste recycling demands. The new recycling process lines need to be capable of processing crystalline silicon and thin-film modules alike. The recycling issues are now at the pilot stage, and reuse of PV material will be timely for the industry.

U.S. companies have been reclaiming solar cells and semiconductor process wafers for many years, so the expertise and equipment are available. Scaling up to accommodate the large demand of the future is a key to success here.

The forecast is that 40,000 MT of PV components will be ready for decommissioning and recycling by 2020. That number will double or triple during the following decade, and includes silicon and thin-film based PV components recycling. The thin-film component will be ~20% by then, with about 8,000 MT CdTe thin-film PV modules the majority of the recycled products in this category.

That number of CdTe PV modules is a lot of modules, which, with an average of 8-9 grams of cadmium in each module, could create a serious hazmat debacle if not handled and processed properly.

As can be clearly seen here, the manufacturer is legally responsible for the safety and proper execution of all steps from the beginning to the end of the useful life of their products. The retailers, installers, and plant operators are also responsible in some stages of the product life.

Overall, all entities who have been involved in the power plant's planning, design, installation, and operation are responsible to one degree or another for the proper execution of the respective steps, including the final decommissioning, recycling, and disposal of the plant components and land cleanup.

Used PV materials and waste are different, because of the long lag time between the production and de-

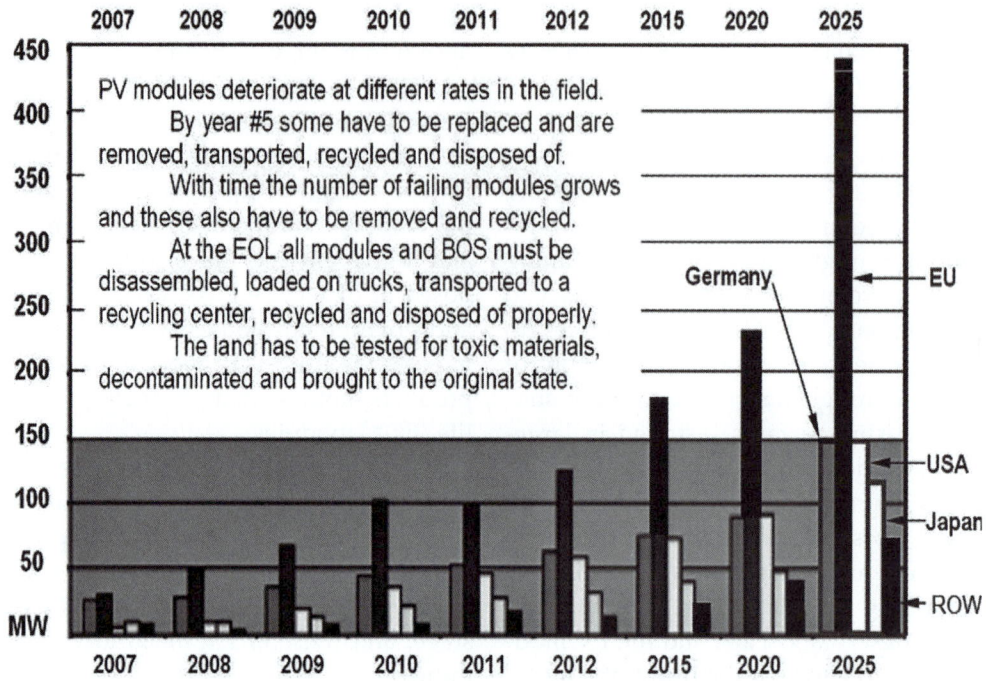

Figure 9-25. Forecast of PV waste recycling in the decades to come

Table 9-15. End-of-life outline of the participants' responsibilities

EOL TREATMENT OF TFPV MODULES	DECISION AND EOL* NOTICE	REMOVAL	TRANSPORT	RECOVERY & DISPOSAL
GENERAL REQUIREMENTS	Notify proper authorities of EOL	Proper and safe procedures use	Authorized Hazmat carrier use	Authorized facilities use
ORGANIZATIONAL RESPONSIBILITY	Plant operator	Manufacturer and operator	Manufacturer	Manufacturer
TECHNICAL RESPONSIBILITY	Plant operator	Manufacturer and operator	Manufacturer	Manufacturer
FINANCIAL RESPONSIBILITY	Plant operator	Manufacturer and operator	Manufacturer	Manufacturer
LEGAL RESPONSIBILITY	Plant operator	Manufacturer and operator	Manufacturer	Manufacturer

commissioning. It is more than a generation, and many things might change during that time.

The amount of waste will vary dramatically after 2030-2040, because different modules and power fields have different life timelines and require different handling. The situation is further complicated by the fact that many PV modules contain hazardous materials such as cadmium, tellurium, lead and selenium.

Cadmium compounds are toxic and are regulated in many countries because of their toxicity to all life forms and humans. In some countries the sale of CdTe-containing PV modules is prohibited because of the poli-cies regulating cadmium in photoelectric semiconductor devices.

Cadmium is associated with numerous human illnesses, such as lung, kidney and bone damage. It is especially dangerous due to its absorption in the body, where it is cumulatively collected and can remain for decades.

Cadmium also accumulates in the environment, which is sometimes caused by leaching from landfills collecting into ground and surface water. It can also contaminate the atmosphere while escaping from incinerator smokestack emissions.

Table 9-16. PV modules recycling steps and methods

RECYCLING OF PV MODULES AT EOL

c-Si MODULES				TFPV MODULES		
RECYCLABLE	kg/m^2	%		RECYCLABLE	kg/m^2	%
Glass	10.0	90		Glass	15.0	90
Aluminum	1.4	100		Aluminum	0	0
Solar cells	0.5	90		Solar cells	0.1	90
EVA, Tedlar	1.4	0		EVA, Tedlar	0	0
Ribbons	0.1	95		Ribbons	0	0
Adhesives	0.2	0		Adhesives	0.2	0

RECYCLING AND DISPOSAL METHODS

Mechanical	Crushing, attrition, density separation, flotation, adsorption, radiation, laser beam, metal separation, and other methods.
Chemical	Acid / base treatment, extraction with solvents, dissolving, precipitation, slagging, and other methods.
Thermal	Incineration, burn-out, pyrolysis, melting, slagging, and other similar methods.
EOL disposal	Recycling into the same product, recycling into another product, recovery of energy from thermal treatment of organic layers, utilization of mineral fractions (e.g., concrete, road material, etc.), and landfill disposal.

Using air pollution control equipment at incinerators could trap cadmium gasses into the ash, which could cause problems later on by leaching from the containment sites.

So, it is of utmost importance to realize that a lot of solar waste is, and will be, created in large quantities during the 21st century, and some of this waste contains hazardous material. It is, therefore, the responsibility of the regulators to anticipate the developments and ensure the safe processing and disposal of these materials.

The major types of PV modules worth recycling are c-Si, a-Si, CdTe and CIGS. A number of other upcoming technologies will change the landscape, but most have long way to go, so we'll address them at a later time.

c-Silicon PV Modules

Silicon based modules consist of glass, aluminum, silicon solar cells, and plastic encapsulants. Recycling these materials is not easy and, due to their low market value, not profitable to recycle, except for removing and reprocessing the glass.

Since the toxicity level in these modules is very low with only some trace amounts of Pb and Sn, dump-ing the majority of the modules' materials in waste disposal sites does not seem to pose much danger, so very little effort is dedicated today to recycling the materials in silicon based PV modules.

In the future, however, when millions upon millions of silicon modules will reach their EOL, their "as is" disposal might become a problem and recycling might be necessary. In any case, recycling would be uneconomical, so plans need to be made even now as to when and how the silicon modules will be handled and recycled at EOL, and by whom.

a-Silicon PV Modules

The semiconductor material in a-Si PV modules is composed of very thin layer of silicon material, which has very low market value and is not considered toxic. Because of that, there is currently little drive to recycle these modules at EOL. It is assumed, therefore, that if needed the a-Si based PV modules recycling and disposal can be done by any of the commonly accepted techniques.

It is clear from work done with a-Si, that the economic benefit from recycling these modules would be negative, even if a good way is found to recycle the top glass with the pre-deposited transparent conducting oxide intact. Finding a good way to do this would significantly improve the economics for all the thin film modules, because the glass is a major part of the overall cost of the finished product.

CdTe PV Modules

The CdTe PV modules fall into a totally different category. As much as the manufacturers and their supporters try to paint them as "green" and environmentally friendly," there is a presence of significant quantities of toxic, carcinogenic, heavy metals that necessitates using proper (and quite expensive) HazMat procedures during their EOL disassembly, transport, recycling and disposal process.

The recycling process involves a chemical stripping of the metals and other materials that have been in contact with them. This is followed by electro-deposition, precipitation, and evaporation of the different compounds as needed to separate and recover the base metals, cadmium and tellurium. The plastic solute can be skimmed from the chemical solution, decontaminated and possibly re-used. The glass and frame can be recovered, decontaminated and reused as well.

The cost of recycling and disposal of CdTe modules is much higher than any of the other types of modules, simply because they contain a substantial amount of cadmium which is a toxic heavy metal that is considered a hazardous material.

Recycling CdTe PV modules is required, and although it might be beneficial for the recycling mandate, the total profitability of recycling CdTe modules is heavily negative. Recycling CdTe modules is not a profitable process, but it is part of the environmentally responsibility of the manufacturers and the related parties.

Handling, processing and disposing of hazardous materials is a complex, dangerous and very expensive process, and as chemicals and labor costs increase, in addition to tightening regulations, so will the cost of the recycling and waste disposal processes.

That is something the investors and owners of large-scale PV power fields using CdTe PV modules need to be well aware of. A good understanding of the situation is a necessity, and a contract, detailing each of the already mentioned EOL procedures, should be signed. This will ensure the proper handling of the hazardous materials in case the manufacturer is no longer in business, or if something happens to the modules in the field.

CIGS PV Modules

CIGS modules contain a number of metals, such as: copper, selenium, indium, and gallium. Some of these are also toxic, albeit in much smaller quantities. Nevertheless, the disassembly, transport, recycling, and waste disposal process of CIGS PV modules is complex and expensive too, due to the presence of toxic materials.

The recycling process involves smelting of the materials, or processing them in acid baths as needed to dissolve and recover the different metals—dirty, dangerous, expensive and heavily regulated processes. With the increase of chemicals and labor costs and tightening regulations, they are getting more and more expensive too.

The top glass is usually processed through thermal decomposition, solvent or acid dissolution to remove any remaining PV layers that could be recovered.

It has been estimated by researchers that the profit from re-using or re-selling the recovered semiconductor material, metals and glass from CIGS PV modules exceeds the cost of recycling. However, the presence of cadmium, tellurium and other toxic materials in most of CIGS modules increases the cost of recycling significantly, which makes re-selling the recovered materials

not an economically feasible proposition.

There is a need to recycle the toxic materials, which, combined with the economic benefits from diverting the dumping of toxics into the landfills, is the way of the future that is being driven by a number of related regulations.

Basically speaking, there is no economic benefit derived from recycling any type of PV modules. So, critical and mandatory recycling is presently looked at as a necessary evil in the case of PV modules containing toxic materials. There is a growing need to modify the existing policies to ensure recycling considering its growing environmental and social benefits, which are presently ignored.

Nevertheless, PV modules recycling will grow from a niche market, which it is now, into a big business by the mid-21st century.

Non-market based approaches to handling recycling are also needed to ensure the environmental sustainability of the EOL dilemma. This could be done via corporate and social responsibility, or through governmental regulations that would ban the disposal of any PV modules without proper treatment and recycling.

Electric Vehicles

Electric vehicles are the transportation solution of our not-so-distant future, or at least this is how the official mantra goes. In just the last couple years, significant cost reductions and improvements in vehicle performance have had a dramatic impact on the U.S. automotive market. Sales of plug-in electric vehicles (PEV) in the U.S. tripled in 2012, with more than 50,000 cars sold. Sales are growing significantly again in 2013. Last year, the Chevy Volt PEV topped *Consumer Reports'* annual owner-satisfaction survey for the second straight year, while the Tesla Model S was awarded the 2013 *Motor Trend* magazine's car of the year.

Nevertheless, electric cars have a spotted history. There were a number of small businesses making electric cars even in the 1970s. None of these cars was reliable or attractive compared with the conventional vehicles, so most of the companies went out of business for those and other reasons.

Case study: GM's EV1

In 1996 General Motors decided to produce and sell their new EV1 electric car for the American market. It was the first mass-produced and purpose-designed electric vehicle at the time from a major automaker. It was also the first mass-produced car ever designed to be an all-electric vehicle from the outset.

EV1 was designed as an improvement of GM's 1990 Impact electric concept car. Anticipating a great potential for success, the California air resources board (CARB) passed a mandate that made the production and sale of zero-emission vehicles a requirement for the seven major automakers to continue selling their vehicles in California.

The EV1 was sold through limited lease-only agreements to residents of Los Angeles, CA, and Phoenix and Tucson, AZ. In reality, the new EV1 owners became willing (or unwilling) participants in a GM "real-world engineering evaluation and market study" into the feasibility of producing and marketing a commuter electric vehicle in the U.S.

EV1 could not be purchased, and could be serviced only at designated dealerships. Later on, similar leasing programs were also launched in San Francisco and Sacramento, CA, and a limited program in GA.

Most customers loved their new, quiet, and economic means of transportation. GM, however, was not sure from the very beginning that this type of car belongs in their line of profitable gas and diesel vehicles.

Figure 9-26. The EV1 graveyard

Not long after that, GM made a decision to cancel all lease agreements and collected all EV1s sold in the U.S.—no exceptions. Loaded on trucks, under furious protests of the owners, all EV1s were taken to a junkyard. GM washed its hands of EV1 and for almost a decade did not even look at electric cars.

To top it off, the major automakers litigated the CARB regulation in court, resulting in a slackening of the ZEV stipulation, permitting the companies to produce super-low-emission vehicles, natural gas vehicles, and hybrid cars in place of pure electrics.

The EV1 program was totally dismantled in 2002, and lessees were not given the option to purchase their cars, due to parts, service, and liability regulations. The repossessed EV1s were crushed, except 40 of them that were delivered to museums and educational institutes with their electric power trains deactivated. The condition was that the cars were not to be reactivated and driven on the road. Of the total, 20 cars were donated to overseas institutions, and the only intact EV1 was donated to the Smithsonian Institution.

The EV1 debacle remains controversial with electric car enthusiasts, environmental interest groups and former EV1 lessees—all accusing GM of self-sabotaging its electric car program to avoid potential losses in spare parts sales. They also blame the oil industry for conspiring to keep electric cars off the road to sell more oil products.

Electric Vehicles Today and Tomorrow

Electric vehicles are receiving wider acceptance by most people and organizations, including environmentalists. Most governments, including the U.S., are also embracing and encouraging this technology.

For example, the U.S. Department of Energy launched the eGallon initiative in the summer of 2013. This is a quick and simple way for consumers to compare the costs of fueling electric vehicles vs. driving with gasoline. Consumers can see gasoline prices posted at the corner gas station, but do not know the cost of fueling their electric vehicle.

The eGallon brings greater transparency to vehicle operating costs, and helps drivers figure out how much they might save on fuel by choosing an electric vehicle. It also shows the low and steady price of fueling with electricity. According to the DOE, electric vehicles save consumers on fuel costs, and reduce our dependence on oil, and also reduce harmful gasses being emitted into the atmosphere.

The eGallon price depends on electricity prices, which historically are very stable, while gasoline prices depend on the global oil market, which can be very unstable and are often influenced by unpredictable international events. The eGallon provides a metric that is easily comparable to the traditional gallon of unleaded fuel.

Calculating how much it would cost to drive an electric vehicle the same distance as a similar conventional vehicle could travel on a gallon of gasoline makes that comparison. For example, if gasoline costs $3.60 per gallon and the eGallon price is $1.20, that means that for $1.20 worth of electricity you can drive the same distance as you could for $3.60 worth of gasoline. The eGallon price varies from state to state based on the price of electricity.

Today's national average eGallon price is about $1.14, meaning that a typical electric vehicle could travel as far on $1.14 worth of electricity as a similar vehicle could travel on a gallon of gasoline.

The Issues

The trend of thought of electric vehicle owners is that electricity is cleaner, greener, and cheaper than gasoline and diesel. While this is true when superficially looking at the final results, a deeper look into the entire process of electric vs. gasoline production reveals a number of discrepancies.

First, to buy an average electric vehicle, the person needs to shed $40-60,000. And the prestigious, award winning Tesla car would cost the average U.S. worker the entire 2-3 years worth of salary. How many people can afford an average electric car, let alone a Tesla?

Secondly, e-vehicles use a ton of batteries—the production, maintenance, and disposal of which is a major, expensive and very polluting process, which is not openly discussed. And then, supposing that the average person has money (or credit) to buy an electric car, the high insurance rates and maintenance costs, including the replacement of the batteries once in a while, would cost another year's salary during the life of the car.

And thirdly, the electricity that the economic electric vehicle is charged with every night comes from a polluting coal-fired plant close by. That $1.14 of electricity that replaces gasoline comes from a long, dirty, and polluting process of mining the coal, transporting it, processing it, burning it, disposing of the solids (after dumping tons of GHG into the atmosphere) and then getting the electricity to the e-vehicle via the national grid. Not exactly clean, green, and cheap process now, is it?

Electric vehicles will become much cleaner and greener in the future, when most of the electric power in the world will be generated by renewable power sources. Until then, however, every time we see an electric car zoom by, we need to also see the long tail of smoke and GHGs it leaves behind.

As a matter of fact, our attitude toward electric vehicles is very similar to our attitude toward the environment, which is focused on doing less harm. While this is good, doing less harm is still doing some harm. Electric vehicles are responsible for half of the emissions of gas cars, which is good to a point, but this is still 100% more than what is needed to reverse the environmental damage: zero emissions.

Combined Cycle Power Plants

Saudi Arabia's Shoaiba power plant is one of the largest oil-fired power plants in the world. Following the completion of stage 1 in 2003, a stage 2 (phases 1 and 2), consisting of a further six 400 MW units was executed, bringing the total output of the plant's stage 1 and 2 to 4400 MW.

Stage 3 was completed recently, adding 1.2 GW of electric power generation, bringing the total power generation to 5.6 GW. The plant uses oil furnaces to burn crude oil and generate steam, which drives the steam turbines and generators to produce electric power.

This plant alone provides over 40% of the western region's current power requirements, and is a record breaker in terms of size for an oil- fired plant in the world. During the construction of stage 2, several records were broken in terms of construction and commissioning time for a steam power plant.

A multi-stage flash distillation water desalination plant was constructed as part of the plant complex. It has desalination capacity of 50 million cubic meters of water per year. A second desalination plant with another capacity of 50 million cubic meters of water per year was constructed later on as well.

The clever feature of this setup is that the waste steam generated in the power plant turbines is sent to the desalination plant to be used to heat sea water. This provides cheap clean water, and, at the same time, cools the steam before reuse, thus reducing the waste heat cooling losses.

Is it smart to burn so much oil is the larger question.

Sequestration Technologies

It is becoming very clear that we are not on track to stay below the U.N. target of 450 ppm of CO_2 levels. This is evidenced by the increased publicity of the recent advancement to 400 ppm, which is making a big splash in the media, technical journals, and into the public consciousness.

There are two possible approaches to addressing the problem of increasing CO_2 content in the atmosphere. The most commonly mentioned is a rapid global conversion to non-fossil fuel energy sources. While this does address the root of the problem, this solution cannot be implemented rapidly enough to solve the climate crisis and also steer clear of other serious problems.

The other approach is massive carbon sequestration, which is basically the removal of CO_2 from the air and the provision for its long-term storage.

There are a number of proposed CO_2 sequestration

methods, all of which have potential shortcomings, as follows:

- *Subterranean Injection* is a method in which CO_2 would be captured from the smoke stacks of power plants and injected into depleted oil and gas wells or other underground formations with available empty volume.

  The drawbacks to this approach are likely to keep it from becoming a viable solution:
  a. It's very expensive to implement
  b. There is no guarantee that the captured CO_2 won't leak out from its subterranean grave
  c. This method is also viable only for point sources of carbon dioxide like a smoke stack, so it cannot not be applied to cars and other dispersed CO_2 sources
  d. There is not enough underground storage space to accommodate the huge volume of CO_2 gas generated from burning fossil fuels

- *Biochar* production is an interesting technology that is garnering increasing attention in progressive media outlets. This process involves heating organic matter (wood and such which would otherwise decompose and release CO_2 back into the atmosphere) to 400-500°C in an oxygen-free atmosphere. During this process, the matter is converted to a charcoal-like material.

  Biochar is slow to oxidize back to CO_2, and can be incorporated into the soil where it improves water retention and nutrient availability. But biochar has a number of shortcomings, such as:
  a. It's most important contribution is preventing the eventual (future) release of carbon dioxide from decomposing plant matter, however
  b. Biochar cannot directly remove CO_2 from the air now. This limits the rate of sequestration available from biochar to an inadequate level, which is too low to make much of a dent in the CO_2 concentration in the air
  c. Biochar production requires complex and expensive, specialized equipment and processes
  d. The high temperatures needed to produce biochar require significant fuel consumption, thus partially offsetting its benefit

- Carbonate chemicals are produced when CO_2 reacts with minerals such as magnesium and calcium to form solid carbonate deposits. This process sequesters the CO_2, but at very slow rates of forma-

tion. So it is impractical unless the reaction is carried out at elevated temperatures. This then makes this approach suffer from the same limitations as the biochar production.

All these process suffer from an important, additional problem that is common to all. They don't allow for the captured carbon to be recycled. This matters because if we bury all the carbon while reducing its production, we might get to a reverse scenario, where the CO_2 levels drop below the minimum of 300 ppm. At that point, the photosynthesis process that keeps vegetation alive might collapse. That might bring another set of calamities to our environment and Earth.

Artificial Photosynthesis

Why not imitate the Earth while looking for solutions to our energy and environmental problems. Developing an artificial, and fully controllable, photosynthesis process seems to be an ideal solution to the present day environmental and climate problems.

This could be done, but not with the present technologies, since such a process needs to operate efficiently at room temperature and pressure and also needs to be more efficient than that of the natural plants.

Plants store about 2-4% of the energy from the sunlight that falls on them in the chemical bonds of the hydrocarbons they form. For artificial photosynthesis to be effective in combating climate change, it would need to have a sunlight-to-hydrocarbon efficiency of at least 10 times greater (or store about 20-40% of the sun energy). This is needed to capture more that the current 10 gigatons of carbon added to the atmosphere each year globally.

Some of the resulting hydrocarbons could be recycled as fuel. The remainder could be converted into long-lived items like plastic building materials, effectively sequestering the carbon in useful infrastructure.

There are already a number of research efforts chasing this Holy Grail. As an example, in 2010 the Department of Energy, under the leadership of President Obama and with collaboration from Cal Tech, opened the joint center for artificial photosynthesis. Although this sounds promising on paper, making it work in practice and on a mass scale is a long shot at best.

Materials that are needed for this process need very high surface-to-volume ratios to provide a sufficient number of sites for the CO_2 to be captured. But there are no such materials on Earth right now, so they have to be developed from scratch.

The materials also need to have unique and quite

impressive chemical and electronic properties to drive a complex photosynthesis-like reaction using only sunlight. Nanotechnology might be one of the solutions, but this is a fairly new and not so well developed field, so we will not hold our breath for a quick solution. Instead, we will keep our fingers crossed for the center of artificial photosynthesis and its success in finding and developing these new materials in the near future.

Nuclear Waste

The evil of the nuclear industry, and #2 barrier to its progress (#1 being the risk of large-scale nuclear accidents) is the lack of permanent storage for thousands of tons of radioactive waste. The U.S. plans to bury nuclear waste in Yucca Mountain died shamefully and unconditionally recently, but now there are real plans to build an enormous bunker for permanent storage of the dangerous radioactive waste.

And it is not in the U.S. It is rather in Finland, where a radical solution is planned. It consists of burying the stuff deep underground, sealing the depository and throwing the key away. Literally. The intent is to keep everyone—including future civilizations—away by hiding the nuclear waste somewhere so unremarkable and unpleasant that nobody would ever think to go there, let alone dig into it.

Located on Olkiluoto Island, just off Finland's southwest coast, the underground facility known as Onkalo will hold all of the country's 5,500 tons of nuclear waste—al that is expected to be produced by the end of the century. It is designed to keep that waste secure for at least 100,000 years, counting on making humans forget that Onkalo was ever there.

Onkalo is intended to store permanently and safely high-level waste (HLW), which consists of spent nuclear fuel and some equally dangerous decay products. This residue emits dangerous types and levels of radiation for tens of thousands of years. Over 300,000 tons of this stuff now exists around the world and about 12,000 more tons are produced annually. It is also expected that those numbers will increase significantly in the years to come.

Presently, the HLW is usually stored in water-filled pools at the nuclear plants, or in temporary offsite storage facilities where the waste is enclosed in borosilicate glass ingots, sealed inside metal canisters. These, however, are temporary and physically insecure solutions to a growing problem.

The permanent storage solution has been the hot potato that the nuclear industry has been holding in its bare hands since the very beginning. The Yucca Mountain depository was to provide the solution, but technical and financial problems put an end to it.

Enter Onkalo. A maze of deep underground bunkers carved from impermeable rock, in geologically stable zones, where the waste can be redundantly sealed and then permanently buried. The U.S. attempt to build such a bunker at Nevada's Yucca Mountain fizzled in a fit of political bickering. But in Finland, Onkalo marches on, with a plan to keep humans out of there long after the entrance is sealed.

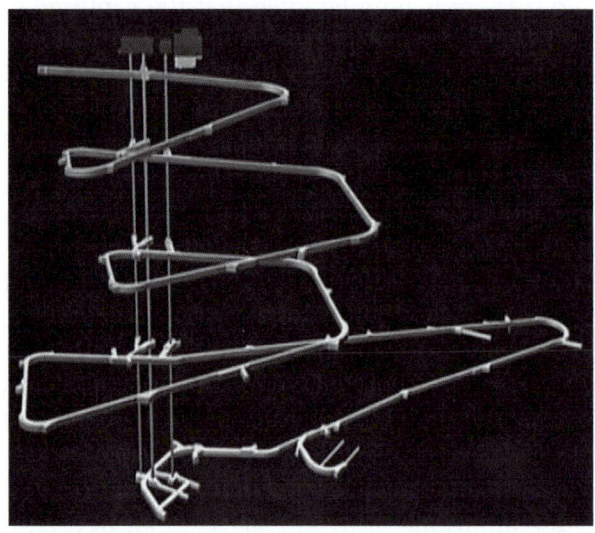

Figure 9-27. Onkalo's maze of underground tunnels

Onkalo's has a maze of access tunnels, vertical ventilation system, and a number of personnel shafts. The tunnels go down to under 1500 feet, and are designed for safety guided by constant hydrologic, geologic, and mechanical tests. The final, lowest, stage of the tunnel consists of hundreds of horizontal burial shafts, arrayed like fish bones along the deepest access tunnels.

The waste materials will be sealed in thick copper containers under argon blankets, with electron beam welded lids. Each copper coffin will be placed in the storage shafts and individually encased in a thick layer of bentonite clay. Bentonite was chosen, because it is natural clay that is almost impermeable to water.

Special, elaborate transportation canisters have been designed to transport the waste containers around the site. These 26-ton capsules with their thick copper walls can withstand extreme impact, temperature, and pressure (earthquakes and such). The canisters' copper tubes in which the waste is enclosed, will be sealed by electron beam welding the lids before burial. This step alone represents the most technically demanding welding project ever attempted.

When the storage shafts in each storage tunnel are filled, the entire tunnel leg will be sealed with a bentonite plug, which will be then covered by a thick ultra-durable concrete layer. At the very end, when the entire site is full to capacity, which is expected to happen around year 2120 after 5500 tons of high-level waste has been safely sealed in permanent coffins and individual graves, the entire site—transport tunnels, vertical shafts, and all—will be completely backfilled with concrete.

This way the dangerous waste materials will be resting forever, away from human contact, under a thick, quarter-mile deep layer of cement and granite.

At a $3 billion price tag thus far, Onkalo will start accepting nuclear waste in 2020, while construction of new tunnels will continue as needed until the facility is shut down and sealed forever.

Crazy? Unreasonable? Or is it the only possible and plausible solution? You be the judge. The future generations will have the last vote...

Tar Sands

Tar sands, also called oil sand, or bituminous sands, are the new crude oil. Technically speaking, this is a type of petroleum deposit that is quite different from the conventional types. It is basically loose sand or partially consolidated sandstone that contains mixtures of sand, clay, and water, saturated with a dense and extremely viscous form of petroleum. This petroleum is bitumen, which looks, feels, and smells like tar.

Such bitumen deposits are reported in many countries, but one of the largest deposits of this type of fuel is the Canadian tar sands in the Canadian Boreal Forest at the eastern foothills of the Rocky Mountains. Preliminary estimates suggest that there are at least 2 trillion barrels of oil, but most likely much more.

The worldwide deposits of oil are more than 3 trillion barrels, including deposits that have not yet been discovered or exploited. The proven reserves of tar sands oil are approximately 100 billion barrels, while the total natural bitumen reserves (including the undiscovered) are estimated at over 250 billion barrels. About 200 billion barrels, or over 70% of the total tar sands oil deposits are in Canada. Kazakhstan and Russia are distant second and third with large tar oil reserves.

Until recently these messy and stinky areas were not even considered worth while exploring, so they were not considered to be part of the world's oil reserves. But now, as oil prices keep rising, and new technology enables profitable extraction and processing of oil from the stinky mess, things are changing.

Bitumen is a thick, sticky form of petroleum hy-drocarbons that are very heavy and viscous. They are locked in their mushy grave and will not flow unless heated or diluted with solvents. With viscosity greater than 10,000 centipoise at room temperature and an API gravity of less than 10° API, their physical behavior is similar to that of molasses.

NOTE: The oil reserves in the Orinoco Belt in Venezuela are non-bituminous, instead they are heavy or extra-heavy conventional crude oil, which are distinguished by their very low viscosity. These oils are, nevertheless, different from natural tar sands bitumen, due to the different degree of degradation from the original conventional oils. The extraction methods are different too.

Oil produced from bitumen sands is often referred to as unconventional oil or crude bitumen, to distinguish it from liquid hydrocarbons produced from traditional oil wells. It is becoming quickly an integral part of the global oil supply plans—especially those of the U.S. oil companies. Oil specialists describe the new oil as petroleum that exists in the semi-solid or solid phase in natural deposits.

Making liquid fuels from oil sands requires a lot of energy (heat) for steam injection into the ground as needed to soften the oil so it can be pumped out. Even more energy (heat and electricity) is needed later on for refining of the bitumen into useful fuels, lubricants, and other petroleum products.

The tar sands, however, require 3-4 times more energy to recover and refine the same amount of conventional crude oil, because of the extra energy requirements. These processes also emit 12-15% more GHGs per barrel of final product than are emitted during extraction of conventional oil.

Canada will not meet its reduction commitments due to the increased greenhouse gas emissions associated with tar sands development. In 2010, for example, Canada's greenhouse gas emissions were estimated to be nearly 35% higher than 1990 levels.

A lot of water is also used during the tar oil extraction process; 3-5 times units of water are used to produce each volume unit of tar oil in an ex-situ mining operation. The estimates show that the Canadian oil sands operations use 350 million cubic meters per annum, or as much twice the amount of water used by an average size city.

Some of the water is recycled, but most it ends up in special storage ponds. Presently, such ponds in Canada cover an area of approximately 20 square miles. There are, however, some very efficient operations, where over 90% of the water is recycled. In this case, only about 0.2 volumes of water is used per volume unit of bitumen produced.

In addition to the potential ground and water table contamination by the ponds, such large quantities of water drawn from the local rivers reduces their flow, depletes the water reservoirs, and changes the local environment. Getting the oil out of the tar sands means disturbing an area larger than the state of Ohio, and destroying a significant part of its environment.

In Canada, the toxic burden on communities near the tar sands is already noticeable. In addition to direct human exposure, oil contamination in the local watershed has led to arsenic in moose meat of up to 33 times acceptable levels. Drinking water has also been contaminated. Processing tar sands oil means more asthma and respiratory diseases, more cancer, and more cardiovascular problems.

The newest controversy is the proposed Keystone XL tar sands pipeline, which is actually the third dedicated tar sands pipeline, sending tar oil in the U.S. and further locking it into a dependence on foreign imports. This case is even worse, because the tar oil is hard to extract, which also causes a destruction of large land areas in Canada and the emission of millions of tons of GHG as well.

Tar sands developments are already wreaking havoc on both people and wildlife in the region, where the mining reduces local water supplies and increases exposure to toxic substances. In addition to the extraction impacts, the proposed pipeline would stretch 2,000 miles from Alberta, Canada to Texas, threatening to contaminate freshwater supplies in America's agricultural heartland on its way down. The new inferior oil will also increase refinery emissions in already polluted communities of the U.S. Gulf Coast.

Many local communities in the U.S. and Canada are opposing the tar mining and pipeline expansions, but one way or another, tar sands oil from Canada will be pumped out and sold to somebody no matter what. It is a done deal. Many U.S. oil refineries are applying for permits to expand their facilities as needed to process heavy crude oil from the tar sands.

And even if the Canadian and U.S. environmentalists manage to somehow stop the tar sand oil from reaching U.S. refineries, then the tar oil will surely be sold to China, India and many other countries. And so, we are getting into another catch 22 situation.

Tire Fuel

Tire (rubber) recycling is the process of recycling vehicles' tires that are no longer suitable for normal use due to wear or irreparable damage. There are millions upon millions of old tires discarded around the world every year, and they have become one of the largest and most problematic sources of waste. Due to the large volume produced and the difficulty in disposing or processing the waste tires, they are stacked in large piles with no place to go.

The rubber in these tires, however, is very resilient; it lasts forever under any conditions and thus can be reused in many products. Tire rubber can be used on basketball courts, for making shoe materials, and to pave roads. Presently, however, the material recovered from waste tires, known as "crumb," is generally used in fairly low volume only as a cheap "filler" material.

A big problem until now has been the space and the associated costs required for storing and transporting scrapped tires. New technologies can resolve this issue for temporary storage by "flat-packing" the tires. The used tires can also be used to build new homes by ramming the tires full of Earth materials and covering

Figure 9-28. Tar sands protests are growing...

Figure 9-29. Used tires dump site

them with concrete.

Whole tires can be reused in a number of other applications, such as in a steel mill to use as a carbon source to replace coal or coke in steel manufacturing. Tires can also be bound together and used as different types of physical barriers such as: collision reduction, erosion control, stopping rainwater runoff, wave action that protects piers and marshes, and sound barriers between roadways and residences.

Pyrolysis is a good candidate process for reprocessing the tires into a number of useful products, such as fuel gas, oils, solid residue (char), and low-grade carbon black. A number of pyrolysis methods have been suggested, some of which can produce (in addition to the above mentioned materials) a variety of valuable consumables such as activated carbon and high-grade carbon black.

In the conventional pyrolysis process, the tires are shredded and heated in a reactor vessel containing oxygen-free atmosphere. The rubber softens after a while, and the polymers in it break down into smaller molecules, eventually vaporizing and exiting from the reactor. Thus produced vapors have a high enough heat value to be burned directly as needed to produce useful heat or electric power. With additional processing, the larger molecules in the vapors can be condensed and converted into fuel.

The minerals that are about 40% of the weight of the tire are removed as a solid and can be used as fillers in different applications. When performed well, a tire pyrolysis process is a very clean operation that has hardly any emissions or waste.

Recent equipment and process developments in devulcanization and other techniques enable reprocessing of large volumes of tires. One of these processes converts tire crumbs into value-added compounds in which the original polymer properties are preserved without generating significant pollution. The process operates at a very high productivity while maintaining low-energy footprint. Thus produced compounds can be blended with virgin rubber materials, maintaining desired performance and reducing the raw material cost.

The U.S. EPA estimates that over 80% of scrap tires can be used or processed for further use. Over 200 million waste tires can be reused or processed annually, which theoretically amounts to approximately 2.5 million tons of products from tires every year.

The potential recycled tire markets could be divided into: tire derived fuel (TDF) using 130 million tires; civil engineering projects using 56 million tires;

ground rubber turned into molded rubber products using 18 million tires; ground rubber turned into rubber-modified asphalt using 12 million tires; exported items using 9 million tires; cut, stamped and punched products using 6.5 million tires; and agricultural and miscellaneous uses of 3 million tires.

Environmental Concerns

Due to the heavy metals and other pollutants in tires, there is a potential risk for toxins to leach into the groundwater when tires are placed in wet soils. This impact on the environment varies according to the pH level and conditions of local water and soil. Research has shown that very little leaching occurs when shredded tires are used as light fill material; however, limitations have been put on use of this material. Each site should be individually assessed to determine if this product is appropriate for the given conditions.

Ecotoxicity may be a bigger problem than some first thought. Studies show that zinc, heavy metals, and a host of vulcanization and rubber chemicals leach into water from tires. Shredded tire pieces leach much more, creating a bigger concern, due to the increased surface area of the shredded pieces. Many organisms are sensitive, and without dilution, contaminated tire water has been shown to kill some organisms.

Off-grid Street Lighting

Today, about 600 million people across Africa have no access to electricity. Even more are living in darkness in other parts of the world. In these places, the darkness remains for 10-12 hours every night and life comes to a halt. This life in darkness is affecting the security, productivity, employment, and quality of life of the locals.

Off-grid street lighting, using PV modules to charge batteries during the day and power LED lights at night, is the most plausible solution. There are a number of such street lighting designs for areas with limited or no access to electricity.

Off-grid street lighting could be designed as a completely sustainable system, offering efficient and brightly lit streets. With addition of light, life in the local communities changes, and safety and quality of life improve dramatically. Road safety for drivers and pedestrians is improved too, and all this creates more attractive conditions for businesses and commercial life, and offers a more secure and comfortable outdoor environment for residents.

The primary advantage of LED street lighting is energy efficiency. The advanced LED technologies offer low power consumption, long lifetimes, more accurate color rendering and fewer electrical losses compared with the conventional and CFC light bulbs.

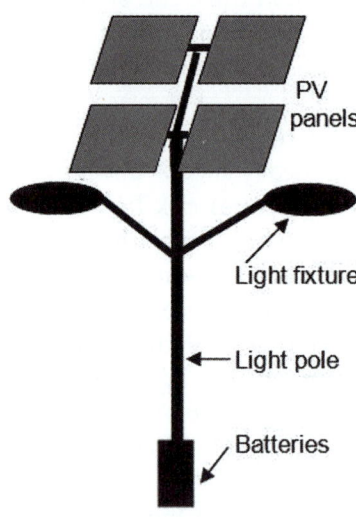

Figure 9-30. Off-grid street light

Case study: Off-grid Streetlights

During the summer of 2013, the author had a chance to participate in a couple of off-grid lighting projects in Asian countries. In one of the cases, the main objective was to provide lighting to urban areas with no access to electricity. In the other case, lighting was the primary goal, but selling power to the local utility was to be considered as well.

The preliminary design looked something like that shown in Table 9-17..

The capital cost of the complete, installed off-grid street lighting project came to about \$1,500-2,500 per light pole system, each complete with PV modules, LED lights, batteries and controllers. The price varies according to the number of PV modules and batteries per pole.

In the case of a grid-connected street lighting system, an additional inverter setup had to be considered, which raised the initial cost much higher, and further complicated things.

The financing structure in both cases was as follows:

- 30% government subsidy
- 20% private finance
- 50% bank finance with 5% interest rate
- FIT is approximately \$0.12/kWh (if needed)

The final design was drawn and approved from technical and logistical points of view, but the capital cost (equipment and construction) in both cases was too high for the investors and banks to get comfortable with. There were also serious concerns with events, such

Table 9-17. Off-grid lighting system (India, 2013)

Local Info		Roadway	
Solar insolation	5.18 kWm²/day	Number of road lanes	2
Daily sunshine, avg.	6.9 hrs	Lane width	10 ft
Daily sunshine, min.	3.6 hrs (Jul)	Median width	6 ft
Daily sunshine, max.	10.2 hrs (Feb)	Pavement type	Asphalt
Daily temperature, max.	30°C	Roadway type	Urban
Daily temperature, min.	0°C	Pedestrian Conflict	Minimal
Solar panels		**Lighting**	
Type of cells	CIGS	Light power (each light)	100W (LED)
Size of panel	50 W	Illumination (each light)	1,200 lumens
Mounting location	top of pole	Light loss factor	1%
Efficiency loss	1 %/year	Arm Tilt (to street level)	45°
Temp coefficient	0.5/°C	Arm length	4 ft
		Light pole height	20 ft
Batteries		Spacing (each pole)	50 ft
Type U2200		Length (each string)	1,000 ft
Charge hold (days)	3 days	Quantity (each string)	20
Control system		**O&M (contracts)**	
Auto on off (light)	yes	Warranty & Insurance	5 years
Auto charge	yes	Monitoring & Maintenance	20 years

as vandalism, theft, storms, floods, etc., that can cause significant damage that cannot be foreseen, prevented, or insured.

Each of these events could cause a major and even irreparable damage, which would bring the project to its knees, technically and financially speaking. The projects are still under consideration, however, and new ways to approach the different issues are under evaluation.

The most important lesson here and what these projects made quite obvious, is the fact that street lighting is no longer considered a luxury that only the few privileged can afford to enjoy. Instead, street lighting is a must—an important part of life for all people, and something that people all over the world are fully aware of and in need of.

It also became obvious that the streets provide ample (and unused) space for the installation of solar modules that could be used for either street lighting or providing power to the grid or both.

Because of the growing needs for street lighting and electric power in general, as well as the increasing versatility of the PV and related technologies, it is only time before many dark streets of the world's developing countries will be lit at night to begin with using off-grid street lighting. Hanging many PV modules on light poles (in tree-branch-like setup) and sending the electricity to the grid is the next step in this process.

NOTE: We don't see off-grid street lighting, or using light poles for hanging PV modules in the future of the U.S. roadways. Nevertheless, there are over 250 million streetlights in this country. Worldwide there might be over a billion lights that light the streets, parks, and many other areas at nighttime in cities and on roadways.

At an average of 100 watts per light, that is 25 billion watts (25 GW) of electricity used for street lighting in the U.S. At an average 10 hrs of use every night, that represents 250 GW/h of wasted electric power in the U.S. alone. It seems that the U.S. is responsible for a quarter of the global electricity wasted on street lighting—a true sign of a rich country, the richest, no doubt if we can waste so much energy every single day, non-stop, 365 days every year.

There is an estimate of 100 billion watts used for street lighting at night worldwide. This is 100 GW of electric power used the average of 10 hours, or 1,000 GW/h of electricity used every single night around the world just to light the streets.

This may not seem like much, compared with the much larger number of over 50,000 GWh electric power used every day world wide (only 1/50th), but it still is a lot of power that simply is wasted. Replacing streetlights with LEDs might help reduce this waste of precious power. They consume 2-3 times less electricity than conventional incandescent lights, or the now preferred high pressure sodium lights, and last several times longer as well.

Dropping the power use from 250 GWh to 75-100 GWh nightly in the U.S., and from 1,000 GWh per night down to 300-400 GWh would be a considerable gain in electric energy and reduction in pollution. It would also spark the development of new technologies and products, and might also bring new companies into existence, thus generating additional jobs in the energy sector. A pipe dream…yes!…for now. These are large numbers and cannot/should not be left out of the overall energy-environment balance sheet. It is time to account for waste and to consider implementing changes, especially when such large energy waste sources still exist.

Future(istic) Concepts

There is no lack of ideas and proposals for solutions and fixes of our energy and environmental problems. Here are some of them, and you can be the judge:

Silver balloons reflecting sunlight back into space is an idea that has been circulating the scientific world for the last decade. This is a technical fix of an environmental problem, by filling the stratosphere with billions of silver balloons to reflect the sun's rays. This method requires flooding the stratosphere with billions of tiny silver metal-coated balloons, making optical chaff as needed to backscatter the sun's rays.

Another plan calls for putting giant mirrors into orbit, ready to be positioned at will by a global climate controller. Reconfigured to reflect solar heating onto the earth, the mirrors could in a future millennium halt the next ice age, said Lowell Wood, of Lawrence Livermore.

A third idea is to float thousands of bubble-making machines across the world's oceans to send huge amounts of salt spray into the atmosphere. The trillions of tiny droplets would make the clouds bigger, whiter, and more reflective, which would be enough, in theory, to shut down several decades' worth of global warming.

There are other, seemingly wacky ideas, like spraying the oceans with iron to make them suck up the gases causing global warming.

Controlling the sun's rays also for the first time offers us the chance to independently manipulate temperatures and CO_2 levels at different parts of the world. Crops, for example, would grow faster in a CO_2-fertilized atmosphere, without the downside of droughts caused by rising temperatures. Millions of people could be better fed that way.

But, of course, there are problems with all these plans and ideas. Even if any of the suggested technologies worked as planned, who would pay for them, and who would be in charge? Who would tilt the solar reflectors or deploy the optical chaff or sprinkle the iron? Who would decide what the optimal global temperature should be, and whether to tilt the mirrors to warm Siberia a bit, or cool New England? The scientists have not agreed on any of these points, so the ideas for now are just that—ideas on a drafting board.

Artificial sky shading has been around for many years as well, albeit one that has never been tried on a large scale. Recently, Harvard engineers announced their intention to spray thousands of tons of particles into the sky to block the sun's rays in an attempt to control global warming. The plan is to launch a large balloon to 80,000 feet over New Mexico and pump tens or hundreds of kilograms of sulfate-based aerosols into the sky. The idea is that the particles will reflect sunlight back into space, helping decrease the temperature of the Earth.

This is actually an attempt to replicate the effects observed as volcanoes spew out similar sulfates into the atmosphere. But can it be done as planned? Nobody's ever done it before, so we don't know what the consequences would be. The objective actually is not to alter the climate, but simply to probe the processes at a micro scale. This makes the direct risk very small and controllable, and any effects can be reversed if needed.

The opposition is from scientists who believe that the experiment could have unpredictable, and possibly negative effects.

Is this a good idea or not? While it is easy and cheap to speculate about how effective geo-engineering projects can be, we will never know without actually putting one into action. So we will keep our fingers crossed for the brave scientists, wishing them the best of luck.

Space flight power is a new idea that Los Alamos engineers are working on. A team of research engineers developed and demonstrated a new concept for a reliable nuclear reactor that could be used on space flights. The process uses a pipe to cool a small nuclear reactor, and the hot liquid in the pipe is then used to power a Stirling engine.

The Flattop Fissions (DUFF) experimental reactor produced 24 watts of electricity. The Flattop allows a water-based heat pipe to extract heat from an uranium fission reaction and transfer the heat to a pair of free-piston Stirling engines manufactured by Sunpower Inc.

The nuclear characteristics and thermal power level of the experiment are remarkably similar to a conventional space reactor flight concept, with the biggest difference between DUFF and a possible flight system being that the Stirling engine input temperature needs to be kept higher to maintain the required efficiency and power output needed for space mission applications.

This experiment illustrates the fact that nuclear energy has some new and exciting possibilities, which can be further developed for efficient flight power generation. This will be then followed by expansion of the technology for terrestrial applications, which might open new possibilities for nuclear power use.

Space power generation is going even further, and it is where Mitsubishi Electric Corporation and IHI Corporation are headed. The two companies are undertaking an ambitious project of about $21 billion. They are aspiring to design and develop a space-based solar farm that would generate 1.0 GW of electric power. This power plant would occupy a four square kilometers area, and consist of rows upon rows of solar panels. This space solar power plant would be installed 25,000 miles above the surface of the Earth and oriented towards the sun. Its advantage is the higher solar insolation falling on the PV modules, which would generate power at a greater efficiency.

There are, however, a number of serious problems too. First, very special solar cells need to be used as needed to generate higher power levels on a non-stop 24/7/365 basis. Secondly, maintenance of such power plants so far in space is a very complicated and expensive challenge, to say the least. We have to envision dozens of maintenance technicians in space suites floating among the modules, testing and tuning the strings, which is not an easy or efficient way to do this type of work.

Thirdly, and most importantly, there is no technology available—even on the design boards—for the wireless transmission of 1.0 GW of power from 25,000 miles away. This just has not been done, and will not be done any time in the near future. So, until then, this power plant is going to sit on the drawing boards until the $21 billion is available.

Nevertheless, the effort to harness space energy is already under consideration and plans for its development are being made on an international level. The national space society and India are working together to create an international organization to harness solar power in to meet the world's ever-surging energy requirements. The organization includes a global platform to share knowledge about the subject, a virtual library, and an international advisory committee.

A clearer plan of action will be presented in 2014 to G8 or G20 nations' meetings. Core members of the international organization will be from nations that are already exploring the idea of harvesting energy from space such as the U.S., India, Japan and the U.K.

This international collaborative mission will act as a catalyst for a livable planet, which will "promote prosperity and peaceful relations within and between nations," the statement said.

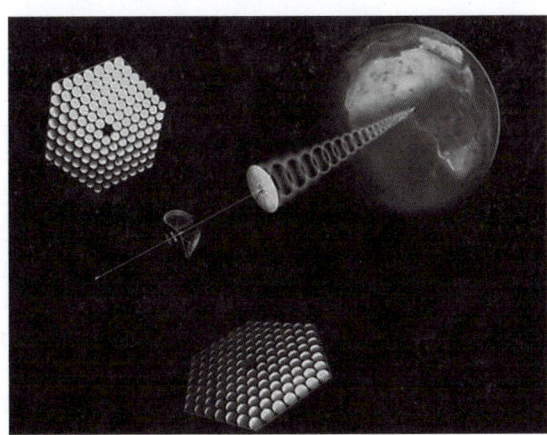

Figure 9-31. An orbital power plant beaming power to Earth

Russia and China have already initiated work on setting up a Space-Based Solar Plant (SBSP). Roscosmos, the Russian space agency, has a working 100 kW SBSP prototype that is yet to be launched, and China plans to put up a 100-kilowatt SBSP by 2025.

Now west coast power utility Pacific Gas and Electric (PG&E) is also looking toward heaven to trap the sources of renewable energy. PG&E is working on getting approval from U.S. regulators to purchase 200 MW worth of solar energy delivered from solar panels located far up in space.

There is nothing new in this proposal, since the Pentagon conducted such a study as far back as 2007. The conclusion then was that satellite-based solar power is feasible but not economical, for it will cost a lot of money for the power consumers.

Things have changed today and power is much more expensive, so PG&E and its partner Solaren (the solar panels manufacturer) might be thinking that this is much more opportune time for such an adventure. They have estimated that their costs will be comparable to rates for other lines of renewable power, but are not disclosing how exactly this would be done.

Solaren claims it has developed a technology that would make it commercially feasible to harvest solar energy from space within the next several years. A while ago Solyndra claimed that its technology was the most efficient and practical too, but Solyndra is no more. The lessons we learned from the latest solar boom-bust cycle are: talk is cheap; doing the impossible is not possible; and everything in between is to be proven feasible and economical for practical use.

Electric catamaran cruisers are the water-navigating cousins of the solar-power electric hybrid vehicles. These are a proven success story on the roads today, so the appearance of solar-electric watercraft is not a great surprise. There is already a hybrid pontoon boat, named Loon, a solar-electric powered watercraft that can seat eight passengers, available on the market. A smaller one, the purely electric Infinyte I4, is the newest addition to the family of solar-powered watercraft. And of course, there are plans for much bigger solar-electric boats in the future.

Flying wind farms look like swarms of kite-like airborne turbines that fly at high altitudes and send power to substations below via nanotube cable. This is what the future looks like, according to NASA. A grant of $100,000 is being offered to develop the high-altitude nanotube wired wind farms. The project is designed to investigate and verify all aspects of wind generation at high altitudes and present the pros and the cons of such endeavors.

Hydrogen generation and storage does not emit GHG pollution like gasoline and other hydrocarbon fuels (see note). Hydrogen generation and use is a good alternative to fossil fuels and many people have been working on improving the processes for almost half a century. Hydrogen, however, has proven difficult to work with mainly because of a lack of storage facilities and issues with large-scale commercial production operations. Once breakthrough technologies are created and developed, hydrogen would have very wide application in transport and commercial applications. Now, for the first time, researchers are working with a newly discovered bacterium that produces twice as much hydrogen gas as the bacteria currently used. The results show how, when, and why the bacterium can perform its excellent work and increase the possibilities of competitive biological production of hydrogen gas.

Italy has the world's first hydrogen power plant. It is situated in Fusina, near Venice in the Veneto region of Italy, and was constructed by Enel, Italy's largest power company with over fifty million power and gas customers. Enel is procuring hydrogen from a petrochemical plant, from where the hydrogen will be brought to the power plant by especially built pipelines. The hydrogen power plant provides power to 20,000 households.

NOTE: Normally, the hydrogen-rich gas (tail gas) is burned in the ethylene plant in the furnaces, where a lot of energy is used and a lot of GHGs are emitted. The hydrogen that is not burned on the spot is sent to the new power plant where it will be used more efficiently, but will still emit some GHGs. Back at the ethylene production plant, they need to burn something else to replace the hydrogen—most likely natural gas. So the GHGs will come out of a different pipe (actually two different pipes in this case), but the environmental advantage is zero, or worse. Something to think about…

Hydrogen fuel from water, a magical method that can split water into hydrogen and oxygen to allow the hydrogen then to be used as fuel, is a quest for green and clean future energy production. While Nature performs this task wonderfully through the process of photosynthesis, man is still facing challenges in duplicating it.

Once we figure out how to split water into oxygen and hydrogen in the presence of sunlight, we will be able to harness the potential of hydrogen as a clean and green fuel. Many trials to date of man-made systems have been quite inefficient, time and money consuming, and often require additional use of chemical agents or other energy sources.

A novel approach of splitting water molecules was developed, where the oxygen molecules are separated and bound in a different molecule. This leaves the hydrogen free to combine with other compounds and to be separated for further processing.

The new approach has three important steps that end in the liberation of hydrogen and oxygen with the help of a special metal catalyst complex, such as ruthenium. This "smart" complex's metal part and organic part help in splitting the water molecules. When water is mixed with this complex, the bonds between the hydrogen and oxygen atoms break. Then one hydrogen atom binds with the organic part of the complex, and the hydrogen and oxygen atoms (OH group) bind to its metal center.

The second stage is known as heat stage. Here the water solution is heated up to 100°C. This releases the hydrogen gas from the complex. Here comes our clean and green source of fuel. Another OH group is added to the metal center.

The magic is in the third light stage, where not only is oxygen gas produced, but the metal complex also reverts back to its original state, so it could be recycled for use in further reactions. During the third stage, light provides the energy for the two OH groups to get together to form hydrogen peroxide (H_2O_2), which quickly breaks up into oxygen and water.

Hydrogen peroxide is considered a relatively unstable molecule, so scientists have always disregarded this step, deeming it implausible, but actual tests have shown otherwise. Another interesting thing in this process is that the bond between the two oxygen atoms is generated within a single molecule. This bond formation doesn't occur between oxygen atoms located on separate molecules, but it comes from a single metal center.

This process is also unique because of the generation of a bond between two oxygen atoms promoted by a man-made metal complex, which is a very unusual event, and it is still a mystery as to how and why it can take place. The greatest achievement of this process has been the development of a mechanism for the formation of hydrogen and oxygen from water, without the need for sacrificial chemical agents.

The splitting has been achieved by using individual steps in the presence of sunlight and a catalyst complex that can be recycled and reused.

Hydrogen from nanotubes is another approach with the same results. Here sunlight and titanium oxide nanotubes are used to transform carbon dioxide into methane. Methane can then be used as an energy source, which is a double benefit of fuel production and reducing the quantity of carbon dioxide released into the atmosphere.

The TiOx nanotubes can be arranged vertically, in a shape similar to that of an empty honeycomb. The top of the nanotubes is covered with a thin, reddish-brown layer of copper oxide. In this stack, copper and titanium oxide operate as catalysts designed to speed up chemical reactions that happen naturally but at much slower pace.

When sunlight strikes the copper oxide, carbon dioxide is transformed into carbon monoxide. When sunlight comes into contact with titanium oxide, water molecules split apart and hydrogen is freed from the water. At the same time, carbon that was released from CO_2, unites again into a different molecule configuration to create methane, and oxygen is released as byproduct.

Reacting more carbon dioxide and more sunlight produces more methane, and the estimates show that focusing sunlight collected from 1,100 square feet onto one of the membranes would generate more than 132 gallons of methane on a sunny day.

The formation of methane by this process is actually a different form of solar power, where instead of storing electricity in batteries, it stores energy chemically.

Hydrogen storage is badly needed to ensure the great potential of hydrogen as a fuel of the future. Hydrogen can be stored relatively safely in metal hydride for possible mobility, but this is expensive and a bulky technology, so, before it becomes a fuel for the masses, we need necessary infrastructure to store it, move it, and dispense it. We will also need fuel cells on an economical scale.

To make hydrogen as a popular alternative fuel some engineers are working on storage of hydrogen fuel by avoiding compressing hydrogen into a tank. Instead, they plan to store hydrogen fuel into large molecules, where it could be stored indefinitely. When needed, the hydrogen could be extracted for use from the molecules. The extraction process would require the use of a catalyst, which is what some researchers are working on and have high hopes of developing for mass use in the near future.

Metallic hydrogen is (theoretically) a new superconductor under development in the never-ending quest for new elements, alloys and substances that can provide clean and green energy and meet our energy demands. Superconductor materials have no electrical resistance, which allows electrons to travel through them freely. They also carry large amounts of electrical current for long periods of time without losing energy as heat. These properties make semiconductors perfect conductors and storage media.

The research opens the exciting possibility that non-traditional combinations of light elements under high pressure can produce metallic hydrogen under experimentally accessible pressures, which can then lead to the discovery of new materials and new states of matter. Scientists are now working with one of these materials—metallic hydrogen—that can just prove to be a high-temperature superconductor. This would bring new opportunities in the energy generation plants and energy storage facilities.

Hydrogen that is used as transport fuel is an exciting alternative, but it has always been a challenge mostly because of no hydrogen fueling stations. The distance vehicles can travel on a full tank and very few places, especially on the East Coast, offer a refueling station. A hydrogen highway is being planned, and when it comes to fruition, it will finally change the way we travel. At that time the East Coast will become the hydrogen highway of the country.

A group of students are planning to travel up the Hudson River, but in a different vehicle. They are using a boat driven by clean and green hydrogen fuel. Their boat is the 22-foot New Clermont, operated by a three-member crew. The boat is fitted with a pair of 2.2-kilowatt fuel cell units.

There are hundreds of documented hydrogen users claiming to be able to run their vehicles on hydrogen. While this might be true, engines need to be retrofitted and specially tuned to run on hydrogen. Even in best of cases, burning hydrogen in conventional car and truck engines causes premature engine failure, because hydrogen burns much hotter than gasoline. This then requires a new engine design and a new fleet of cars and trucks especially designed and built exclusively for hydrogen fuel use. This creates another problem for the hydrogen future, which will take some time to resolve.

Hydrogen from cellulose is an unusual and unique process, since normally these kinds of fuels are derived from high quality starch. Using cellulose instead of starch expands the renewable resource for producing hydrogen to include biomass.

A new process produces hydrogen gas by reacting cellulosic materials, such as switch grass, wood chips, and other materials with the help of 14 enzymes and one coenzyme. The mixture is heated to about 90°F in water, where the low-quality chemical energy from the sugars in the materials is captured and converted into high-quality hydrogen energy.

The benefit of this one-step process is the use of a unique combination of enzymes, which results in hydrogen generation rate that is as fast as natural hydrogen fermentation. Another advantage is that the chemical energy output is greater than the chemical energy stored in sugars, since the maximum hydrogen yield is produced from the cellulosic materials.

Utilizing a small fraction of annual biomass production for cellulose-to-hydrogen fuel cells for transportation can lead transformational fuel independence.

NOTE: to get rid of fossil fuels from transportation, the U.S. needs to convert about 10% of available biomass, or about 1.3 billion tons of usable biomass, for fuel production.

Transport fuel from carbon dioxide is a sci-fi dream, where a car running on the road is consuming carbon dioxide from the air as fuel instead of burning gasoline or diesel. To make the dream reality, researchers are working on a project to do just that—it turns the CO_2 from the air into useful fuel. The car of the future will not only save on fuel, but will also consume excess CO_2, which is one of the root causes of greenhouse effects. Scientists and engineers from many universities have combined their efforts to produce that dream car running on carbon dioxide, led by the University of Bath together with the University of the West of England and members from the University of Bristol.

Methanol from CO_2 is one way to make the mass production of methanol more cost-effective, while also reducing the amount of carbon dioxide released in the earth's atmosphere. A group of scientists have already achieved an unparalleled feat by transforming carbon dioxide into methanol. Methanol is a widely used form of industrial feedstock and clean-burning biofuel.

Their main achievement was treating CO_2 with "organocatalysts" and making the whole process non-toxic to produce the more useful chemical compound, methanol. This is done by reacting carbon dioxide with a stable organocatalyst called N-heterocyclic carbene (NHC) under mild conditions in dry air. NHCs show tremendous potential for activating and fixing carbon dioxide, and can contribute to transforming excess carbon dioxide in the environment into useful products, such as methanol and other organo-chemicals.

A combination of silica and hydrogen known as hydrosilane can be added to the NHC-activated carbon dioxide, to be converted into methanol through hydrolysis processes. Hydrosilane provides hydrogen, which bonds with carbon dioxide in a reduction reaction and the carbon dioxide reduction is efficiently catalyzed by NHCs at room temperature. This makes methane mass production from CO_2 a possibility for the near future, where useful fuel is produced, while reducing CO_2 content in the atmosphere.

Water and CO_2 *fuel* is what researchers are trying to do by duplicating the natural process of photosynthesis. If successful, the "evil" carbon dioxide emitted by power plants and industrial units will be put to very good use. This way, industrial units don't have to establish new subsidiary units for the treatment of carbon dioxide.

Researchers at Sandia National Laboratories have developed a prototype machine that utilizes the sun's energy to convert water and carbon dioxide into the molecular building blocks that can be utilized as transportation fuels. If researchers can make this device produce twice the energy generated by the natural process of photosynthesis, it will do great service to environment. It will pave the way to recycle CO_2.

Researchers from the UCLA Henry Samueli school of engineering and applied science have been working on a cyanobacterium bacteria, which, when successfully modified genetically, is capable of consuming carbon dioxide to generate the liquid fuel isobutanol. The whole process is driven by sunlight, via the bacteria's photosynthesis reactions. Thus produced isobutanol can prove to be of great potential as a gasoline alternative.

Biofuels have been produced for a long time now via various methods as a substitute for fossil fuels, our dependency on them, and eliminating the carbon footprints to ensure a healthier and more eco-friendly future. Corn-produced ethanol has been used for mixing with gasoline but there have been side effects like excess corrosion by the ethanol. Also huge tracts of precious farmlands need to be diverted for corn production. Common algae might be the solution to this problem. New research shows that these tiny organisms can be used successfully and efficiently for biofuel production. This way we can clean algae from the waters, while making bio-fuels.

Microbes are also used in the biofuels production process. The oils, carbohydrates or fats generated by the digestion of plant materials by the microbes are refined to produce biofuel, a green and renewable energy that helps in conserving fossil-fuel usage. A new research effort has led to a discovery of getting the microbes to produce fuel from the proteins instead of utilizing the protein for their own growth. This process also generates ammonia, which is used extensively as a fertilizer. Fertilizing with bio-ammonia products would also save energy and could be as important as the bio-fuels.

Biofuels from tobacco plants is the new energy frontier, where researchers have developed a new method to increase the quantity of oil in tobacco leaves. By increasing the amount per unit plant, the tobacco leaves can be treated and the oil extracted to be used as biofuel when the process is fully developed and mass scaled.

Bio-jet fuel is a dream that might come true. And just on time, because jet fuel is very expensive and is a major GHG emitter. By using the seeds of a humble weed, Camelina sativa, researchers are planning to lower a jet fuel's cradle-to-grave carbon emissions by 84% and reduce its price in half.

Camelina sativa is an oilseed crop that can be processed as a biofuel to fuel in aircrafts in the near future, since it has shown to be one of the more promising alternatives to petroleum jet fuel. Studies of the entire from planting to airplane's tailpipe have determined that Camelina jet fuel exhibits one of the largest greenhouse gas emission reductions of any agricultural feedstock-derived biofuel ever seen. This is the result of the unique attributes of the crop: its low fertilizer requirements; high oil yield; and the availability of its co-products, such as meal and biomass, for other uses.

Heating and cooling from carbon is a very attractive concept, since carbon is a major ingredient of environmental damage. While many scientists are working to decrease the amount of carbon emission in the environment, the researchers at the University of Warwick have been working on a completely different use of carbon. They actually use carbon (and carbon materials) for cooling and heating of cars and homes, thus using carbon for useful purposes in a clean and green way. This process utilizes the heat from a gas flame or engine waste heat to power a closed system containing only active carbon and refrigerant.

The process works, because at room temperature carbon adsorbs the refrigerant and, when heated, the refrigerant is driven out. This is a procedure that alternately heats and cools the carbon, which can be used to remove heat from the outside air and put it into radiators or hot water tanks. The process works in opposite manner for air conditioning cars, by extracting the heat from the inside of the car.

The major problem of this adsorption technology is that it requires over 300 liters for an automobile's air conditioner and much more for a heat pump to heat or cool a house. Good idea…we just have to wait until the scientists find a way to shrink the volume to a reasonable size.

Hybrid power generation, where power is generated by several sources at once, is not a new concept. The problem is that the alternative energy technologies are clean but inefficient, at least compared with their main rival, the fossil fuels. So using different sources of alternative energy to generate power at the same time and place is one of the solutions of increasing their efficiency.

Several large companies are attempting to combine two or more forms of external energy sources, such as light, heat, and vibration to generate power. That generated energy can be collected in different forms for practical use. Fujitsu Laboratories, for example, has been working on such a hybrid energy-harvesting device, which is capable of generating power. The plans call for the new technology to be made commercially available by 2015.

Hybrid organic materials, which are made by special processes and have special properties, can generate power from both photovoltaic and thermoelectric modes. Such devices have been under development also by Fujitsu Laboratories. The organic material can make power both from heat in thermoelectric mode and indoor lighting in photovoltaic mode. That way the device works as a thermoelectric generator or a photovoltaic cell by changing the electrical circuitry connecting P-type and N-type semiconductors. The production cost is very low because of the organic materials and the processing costs are very low.

Solid-oxide fuel cells development is the goal of a team of researchers at the Harvard school of engineering and applied sciences. The new solid-oxide fuel cells are made with plentiful fuel resources and low operating temperatures, along with special, low cost materials. SOFC films used in these cells utilize very thin, tightly packed layers of special ceramic films to reduce electrolytes by hundreds and thousands of times compared with the conventional cells.

The problem is that these cells had to be contained in platinum electrodes, which made them unreliable and costly. Platinum free micro- solid-oxide fuel cells were developed to avoid that problem. These cells are now not only more reliable, but also low in cost. Methane gas is the preferred fuel for solid-oxide fuel cells because it is reliable, cheap, and abundant. It can also be more useful in low temperatures. Scaling to commercial application is a challenge, but once solved, the solid-oxide fuel cells are capable of replacing fossil fuel with pollution-less fuel, so they have a place in our energy future.

Thermo-Chemical Solar Power is on the agenda of several R&D teams that are hoping to capture and release energy from the sun with the help of thermo-chemical technology. That technology has been around since the 1970s, but was aborted due to its high cost and because it was considered impractical. But researchers are now gearing up…again…to develop the thermo-chemical technology that is supposed to convert the heat in solar energy, which is presently wasted, into electrical energy.

Thermo-chemical technology traps and stores the heat contained in sunlight in the molecules of special chemicals. This heat energy can be then converted into electricity and used as needed, which in effect is a "rechargeable heat battery" that can repeatedly store and release heat gathered from sunlight or other sources. Fuel made from chemical compounds like fulvalene diruthenium can be stored and released. The devices operate at 200°C, which is enough to heat a residence or generate electricity.

Carbon nanotubes electric power is another project that researchers at MIT are working on. They have discovered a new phenomenon of carbon nanotubes discharging powerful waves of electricity under certain conditions. The process of creating electron motion— and thereby electricity—by producing heat waves inside a carbon nanotube is an exciting possibility for a large number of applications. Those waves are called thermo-power waves, which are capable of generating enough electricity to be used in electrical appliances and eventually in large-scale power generating applications too. The U.S. Air Force office of scientific research and the U.S. National Science Foundation funded the research.

Wind turbine blades have gone through many changes through the years, which have led to significant increases in the wind turbines' efficiency and safety. A new kind of airflow technology is being developed now, focused on the efficient design of the wind turbine blades under various wind conditions. For example, the overall working scope of the wind turbine can be enlarged by using the flow control on the outboard side of the blade beyond the half radius.

Attempts are being made to increase the rated output power without increasing the level of operating range. An anechoic chamber can be set up to measure and define the effects of flow control on the noise spectrum of the wind turbine. Scientists are also trying to attain a greater efficiency by placing blades at various angles through wind tunnel tests of 2.5 MW turbine airfoil surfaces and computer simulations. The new developments are to be introduced on the global markets shortly.

Solar and wind power are, no doubt, the future of renewable energy. Energy generated from the sun, which is better known as solar power, and energy generated from wind, called wind power, are being considered as the best means of generating power. Though these two sources of energy are growing around the world, they have problems related to their variability: no sun, no

power; no wind, no power. It is that simple, yet complicated at the same time.

So which of the two is a better source to generate power? Instead of choosing, we should consider a third, much more practical and efficient option. It consists of combining solar and wind power to produce enormous, more consistent and reliable types of energy called solar-wind power. Using this combination of the two most widely available and accepted technologies will satisfy all energy requirements of the world.

Waste Heat to electricity is another hope of the rapidly industrialized world. We have seen the development of a number of technologies that generate heat from waste materials, like garbage, agricultural waste and such. Until now, however, this heat has often been treated as a waste, making people wonder if this enormous heat being generated can be transformed into a source of electric power. Now, researchers are finding new ways to harvest energy through heat, and this dream is actually going to become a reality.

Thermoelectricity is the new process that can convert heat directly into electric energy in a device with no moving parts. Although the device is still on the computer desktops, it can be built with the characteristics that are seen in our simulations. When built, this device will use waste heat to generate electric power, which has multiple advantages. It will eliminate ozone-depleting material by increasing the efficiency of cars, power plants, factories, and solar panels, thus making ozone-depleting chlorofluorocarbons, or CFCs, outdated.

The thermoelectric voltage using this design is 100 times higher than that obtained previously. If the design works, it will be a dream come true for all who wanted to catch and make use of energy lost through waste but did not have the required efficient and economical devices to do so.

The new heat-conversion device does not require any kind of machines or ozone-depleting chemicals, as was the case with refrigerators and steam turbines, which were earlier used to convert waste into electric energy. Now, sandwiching a rubber-like polymer between two metals, which acts like electrodes, does the same work. The thermoelectric devices are self-contained, have no moving parts and are easy to manufacture and maintain; however, they are still in the R&D labs and lots of work is still needed to bring them to mass production levels.

Solar electricity at 5-6 cents/kWh is supposed to revolutionize the energy industry with its cheap power, according to the ads from many solar companies. At a cost equal to that from coal and about 1/3 the cost of other solar power, the claim received a broad audience. Nanosolar's mass production of solar power was supposed to become feasible with their differently manufactured solar panels by 2013.

Nanosolar's CIGS semiconductor printed solar panels are composed of copper, gallium, indium and selenium, which perform as well as conventional solar panels in lab conditions according to Nanoslar. An inexpensive printing process makes it ideal for mass production by an automated facility with robots and other hi-tech equipment.

At least this is how the claim went—unfortunately Nanosolar is now all but history, and will not be able to put this claim into practice. Nevertheless, the dream is alive to be taken up by others. You never know...it sounds good on paper.

Solar greenhouses that produce food and electricity at the same time is another dream of the future. Nevertheless, such an experiment is underway in Italy. The companies involved in this project were Solar ReFeel, CeRSAA and solar panel manufacturer Solyndra. The test site was constructed at CeRSAA's Albenga, Italy. The project intends to attain the production of both food and electricity. The research team also wants to validate the crop growth benefits of Solyndra's technology by getting the help of independent testing by a leading agricultural research institution. Unfortunately, Solyndra did not survive the latest solar boom-bust cycle and is no more. The greenhouse project was shut down too, for somebody else to try in the future.

Algae can generate electricity by converting light energy to chemical energy. The chemical energy is then stored in the bonds of the sugars they use for food, where photosynthesis happens inside a chloroplast. Chloroplasts are considered as the cellular powerhouses that make sugars and give leaves and algae a green hue. During photosynthesis, water is split into oxygen, protons and electrons.

When sunrays fall on the leaves and reach the chloroplast, electrons get excited and attain higher energy levels. Proteins catch the excited electrons. The electrons are passed through a series of proteins. These proteins utilize more of the electrons' energy to synthesize sugars until the entire electron's energy is exhausted. If the electrons were intercepted just after they have been excited by light and are at their highest energy levels (and on the way to the proteins), an electric current can be generated and redirected to an outside circuit.

Experiments have been done with gold electrodes inside the chloroplasts of algae cells, which tapped the electrons, thus creating a tiny electrical current. If this process can be brought up to a mass scale, the generated electricity could be in the kW and MW level. This process represents a "high efficiency" bioelectricity, a clean and green source of energy with no carbon dioxide emissions.

• *Battery technologies* are being developed very quickly today and some of the advancements are simply mind-boggling. The latest and most exiting is a battery technology that is very different from everything we know about charging batteries. In this technology, the frame of a device or a vehicle is made out of material that creates its own power.

In the case of portable devices, the entire outer shell would actually be made from this material, which would serve as the charging agent. There would simply never be a need to ever plug the device into a charger again.

Cars, trucks, boats, and other vehicles will have areas such as the roof or the doors made out of material integrated into the body that generates power that can be then routed to the battery of the vehicle for storage and use. Again, electric or hybrid car owners are spared the inconvenience of having to recharge their batteries.

Solar Parking Lots are thing of the future, but some are here today. Industrial designers are dreaming of a solar-powered parking lot, which can light up its own lights, and charge electric vehicles at the same time and place too. There are actually such places in Europe and recently popping up in the U.S., a parking lot was constructed on a half-acre site.

One such place was constructed in the suburbs of Santa Barbara, California, where a newly built solar powered parking area can accommodate 45 parking spaces, powered by 98 solar panels mounted on steel beams close by. The solar panels are charging batteries, which provide power to light the parking lot at night, power the parking meters, and even provide power for charging electric cars (in the future).

The not-so-nice part of this project is its cost: $1.4 million was spent for the property; construction of the parking lot cost $760,000; and the solar addition cost mere $200,000. Nearly $2.4 million for a parking lot of 45 spaces comes to nearly $52,500 per space, of which the solar portion is about $4,500 per space.

Adding the maintenance and replacement costs, on

top of the periodic fog in that location, we assure the city officials that it will take extremely long time to recover the costs of this project...if ever. Aside from thinking that this is not a good way to spend taxpayers' money, we see it as a glimpse into the future of opulent America, where paying $200,000 for 98 solar panels (about $2,000 per panel) is considered proper city planning.

THE UTILITIES

The utilities are crying *"wolf"* today, claiming that the wind turbines, and especially the solar industry, are making their work harder and stealing their profits. A paper issued by the Edison Electric Institute in 2013 raises numerous questions and throws a shadow of a doubt over the future relations between solar industry and the utilities.

The utility industry business is disrupted, the institute report says, which is prompting serious worries about the reliability and stability of power generation and the proper grid operation.

The key challenges the utilities face as a result of the expansion of solar power generation, including the millions of rooftop solar installations (distributed generation), are:

Demand-side Management

The most expensive for fossil-fueled power plants is power generation at the peak hours. Improving efficiency during peak times, and shifting loads away from, makes sense for consumers and the economy—but this is not what the utilities think.

Efficiency gains have reduced the amount of power that customers use, and spending on energy-efficiency programs will increase by as much as 300% by 2025. The estimates call for $10 to $15 billion per year, which will have a serious impact on the utility load, which means additional lost revenue.

And the utilities are just now waking up to this reality, where the biggest threat is from demand-response technologies and curtailment service providers. Those offer voluntary programs to let customers reduce their power consumption at peak times in return for lower, off-peak electricity rates.

Demand response is one of the reasons why power consumption is decreasing overall, which means that utilities aren't able to make as much money on peak power generation, and therefore increase their revenue by building new power generation capacity and generating more power.

Economic Trends

Thanks to the recession, improved efficiency, and distributed generation, electricity demand in recent years has been steadily dropping below acceptable levels. The electric power industry is not growing as it did in the past, so now it needs to deploy capital investment at almost twice the rate of depreciation to enhance the grid and address various regulatory mandates.

Independent owned utilities (IOUs) find themselves in a vicious cycle, where the industry's decline will make it harder to pass on the costs of providing service to the customers, because the rates are tied to time and amount of usage—all of which are unfavorable to the utilities.

Usage is declining, so the costs of new investment needs to be passed on to a shrinking pool of customer demand, which in turn forces per-unit prices higher still. As those prices increase, investment in efficiency and renewables becomes even more cost-effective, which shrinks usage further, a real catch 22 situation.

Ultimately, those dynamics could leave a small number of customers supporting the costs of a large chunk of grid infrastructure, leaving utilities with stranded investments. IOUs are struggling to remain profitable, which is testing the loyalty of investors. Brokerage firms are forecasting healthy profits (and earnings per share of 4-7%) for most IOUs. If, however, the utilities fail to meet these expectations, a wholesale reevaluation of the sector by the investors is in the cards.

That is not a good situation to be in, with the mighty utilities witnessing their power eroding (no pun intended) daily. They need to act quickly and efficiently to save the industry from collapse. And act they do, as we discuss below.

Natural Gas Prices

U.S. shale gas production has increased helped to drive the price of natural gas down from $13/MMBtu in 2008 to $2/MMBtu in 2012. This sudden and significant price reduction of wholesale power hurt the utilities where it hurts most—their profits. Lower gas prices put pressure on power producers that depend heavily on the sale of excess power to subsidize their retail revenue.

In the long run, this scenario promises to accelerate the retirement of coal-fired power plants whose capital costs were recovered long ago, and which made them very profitable. This will ultimately force the utilities to spend significant capital on newer, cleaner natural gas fired plants, which will further reduce their revenues amidst the already relatively low wholesale power revenues.

The Grid Issues

The U.S. power grid is old, largely analog, and suffering badly from decades of deferred maintenance. This is how for-profit companies operate; they have every incentive to maximize their profits by squeezing every last drop of service from their assets.

Although the law requires them to maintain a level of safety and efficiency, they are not required to pro-actively upgrade their equipment to keep up with the times and get it ready for a more robust, security-orient-ed digital upgrades. At this time, most utilities learn of a power failure only when the customers call to complain. Many utilities still use paper maps of their systems that are unreliable and outdated in some cases.

The new market forces, such as the spread of new technologies like distributed generation and smart me-ters, as well as growing regulatory pressure are forcing the utilities to face a large maintenance backlog, the costs of which are going up too, thus creating another revenue loss source.

All this is worrisome to the utilities, because it is eroding their revenues at a time of changes, uncertain-ties, and shrinking sector shares.

Government Incentives

The utility industry also complains about selected technologies, like renewables, efficiency upgrades, and demand response, which are enjoying preferential treatment. This also cuts into their fossil-fueled power generation business and their profits. The utilities, how-ever, forget that that they have been the governments' favorites for almost a century. They forget that the gov-ernments are known to pick winners when selling coal mining, and oil and gas drilling leases on public lands at below fair market value. They also forget that about the 100-year-old percentage depletion allowance, which lets oil and natural gas companies write off a certain percentage of the oil, and gas they extract.

They also seem to forget that "Drill, baby drill" has been, and still is the government's motto. Picking favorites is the government's business, and it never fails to choose the fossils, as is the case today with the natural gas boom in the U.S. and abroad.

Distributed Generation

The cost of power generation from solar PV, wind, geothermal, micro-hydro, and fuel cells running on nat-ural gas has been dropping dramatically lately. Residen-tial and commercial utility customers can now generate some or all of their own power economically instead of drawing it from the grid. The cost of such distributed

generation is set to continue falling as more of it is de-ployed around the world. This in general could directly threaten the centralized utility model, and the utilities are now painfully aware that something has to change.

Distributed generation costs are falling too rapidly for the utilities to adapt to the new business reality. In Germany, which has deployed the most solar power generating capacity, its price has nearly reached grid parity and may exceed it even without subsidies.

In contrast, the German's coal-fired and nuclear power generators are now struggling to remain profit-able under the unexpected competition as their share of the market shrinks and as higher-priced peak hours of the day are increasingly met by solar.

And to top it off, there is the ever-increasing threat that as people generate their own power—they may eventually decide that they don't need the grid at all. The concern here is that the longer-term threat of fully exiting from the grid raises the potential for irreparable damages to revenues. This is also affecting the growth prospects of the utilities, since it is becoming increas-ingly more difficult to recover investment costs over a 20-30-year period, as was the norm in the past.

All these challenges to the traditional private-sector utility model are indeed disruptive to the utilities. They, however, are amazingly and unintentionally do-ing a lot of good to the environment. Energy transition is coming—with or without the utilities' help—and it won't be easy. The battle is just now starting and, as is always the case, there will be losers and winners.

Some utilities will adapt to the transition and continue to operate successfully and profitably. Others will fight to the very end, in which case their chance of survival will be determined by the political winds, the success of the new energy technologies, and the overall economic situation.

The immediate issue before the utilities, how-ever, is the rising threat from the distributed generation sources—rooftop solar systems—popping up on mil-lions of roofs in the U.S., Europe and Asia.

Distributed Energy Resources

There is a growing conflict among the renewables, the national grid, and the utilities, especially in the U.S. energy sector. It boils down to whether green power, grid's stability, and utilities' functionality and profit-ability are compatible. The problem right now is the rapid growth of the distributed energy resources (DER), which basically represent thousands of small-size roof-top solar installations.

Each of these installations by itself is harmless and

an even useful power generator. Put together, however, they represent a sea of independent actors—each doing whatever it and the weather wants. As the DER number grows, the problems the utilities experience (as a result of their unpredictable activities) grows proportionally.

The *Wall Street Journal* published a story in the summer of 2013 describing a rare joint meeting of California grid operators and planners, during which the discussions were focused on the suggestion that the state's aggressive renewable energy mandates could cause a number of issues resulting in grid instability and loss of revenue for the utilities in the coming years.

Those issues are getting more visibility by the day in rapidly growing markets, such as Germany and California, where wind and solar power represent a significant portion of total grid power.

So, just how much distributed energy the grid can handle? And what can be done, technologically and otherwise, to integrate the renewable, but variable, energy sources? The distributed, renewable grid is actually well developed in California, and the utilities are already complaining about the challenge of the growing distributed energy resources (DER), mostly rooftop solar, on their existing operations and profit margins.

Increasing solar penetration causes several specific problems for the utilities, which include difficulties in efficient handling of the two-way power flows on distribution grids, which were built to handle one-way power only from the grid to the consumers. Adding a counter-flow from the consumers to the grid is a new phenomenon, which the outdated grid technology is having problems handling properly and safely.

And then there are the economic issues of solar-using customers, who are in effect converting the economic picture into a two-way money flow. Until recently money flow was uni-directional; from the consumers to the power companies. Now, the money flows two ways, where some consumers with solar power installations are getting money for the power they send into the grid.

This new, two-way economic relationship is also causing a lot of even more serious, problems to the utilities, for it dips into their pockets in a number of ways.

The solar customers:

1. Use less power, due to their awareness

2. Charge the utility for power sent into the grid

3. Use the grid for free, thus creating more maintenance issues and expense for the utilities

4. The utilities know where the DER sources are, but don't know when and know how much power they are generating at any specific time, which is a "shadow load" invisible to the utilities, but affects their operations and bottom lines.

That is a lose-lose situation for the utilities, no doubt. And that is just the beginning; the problems will multiply accordingly as the DER grows in size. The complexities and additional expenses will increase with it. Solar-power generating customers, on the other hand, have the best of both worlds; they can reduce or even eliminate their bills, while actually increasing the use of the grid. This, however, reduces the income of the utilities and increases their O&M expenses.

The utilities in the highest solar DER penetration areas are starting to see a significant erosion of their revenues and the potential for stranded assets, which gets them, the business, and financial communities excited. They are now involved in a new type of movement, geared to figure out and fix this abnormality.

To start with, California's utilities have been taking their cases to state regulators and the courts, claiming that the extra solar-related costs should be included in a new rate structures. So far, the California public utilities commission hasn't agreed to rate increases, and even rejected SDG&E's network use charge rate case in 2012.

Uncontrolled increase of solar power and other distributed renewable energy technologies is capable of damaging the U.S. utilities and even destroying their business models, which has remained virtually unchanged for a century. Change is needed on both sides of the equation.

The battle is not over…actually it has barely started. The utilities have to find a way to cover the losses and the additional costs of maintaining the grid. Without any major changes, this means rate increases for all customers. The inequality here is that solar-equipped customers are forcing the extra costs on non-solar customers.

In Arizona, for example, the wealthiest communities have the most solar and therefore are getting the most benefit from incentives and reduced bills, while the majority that has no solar and get no benefits, is sharing the increased rates equally. Arizona's community solar initiative is a new program that could help that.

Green power backers argue that wind and solar power output can be predicted and managed in ways that the state's grid can handle. It just has to be planned and managed well with the right technologies, and supported properly by regulatory and economic incentives.

New models can also help manage the DER power

generation, distribution and use. The DER challenge calls for new distributed architectures to manage "transactive loads" between generation and demand resources at both macro- and micro-grid scales.

Smart customer power management and smart grid integration, for example, are new concepts under development, geared to manage the growing DER systems. It is, of course, very difficult to balance the mix of economic principles and the laws of physics that are involved in balancing DER power generation and consumption by a set of independent customers in a market where the product is delivered and used at the same time that it is produced.

The grid has to be flexible for new technologies to come of age to be able to make the difference. This is a complex undertaking, but the industry needs to come up with a solution soon. At the top of priorities here are efficiency and reliability. Everything that is planned and implemented in relation to the DER management needs to be totally efficient and reliable. Else, the utilities will fight the DER growth and slow down the solar expansion in the country.

Right now the utilities don't like renewable DERs in general, because they ultimately negatively impact their operations and bottom line. This is the assessment of the utilities themselves. They are afraid that, as the cost of solar and wind power is dropping fast, a day might come when there would be so much DER power generated that the grid will be used for backup only. This could throw the entire sector into a loop of irreparable damages to revenues and in effect eliminating any profit and growth prospects for the utilities.

So, Can the Utilities and DER Solar Coexist?

On one hand, most of the consumers and even the utilities benefit from more DER power. It is good from a number of points of view: it reduces carbon emissions, provides fossil-free power, stimulates the economy by adding new jobs, and ultimately contributes to our energy independence.

On the other hand, the utilities are just now beginning to see the expansion of DER power generation as a growing existential threat. They are worried about their MO and bottom line, but they are still very well organized and powerful, with tons of money and large support networks, including political power. If and when the utilities decide to put their foot down, DER is done with. Period!

So, for now the utilities and the regulators are in a reconnaissance mode; looking for short-term ways to protect the utilities interests. Hoping that time will al-

low the development of a long-term strategy for coping with the expanding distributed energy.

Not surprisingly, however, the short-term recommendations amount to increasing the rates. The utilities want all power bills to include a flat charge for fixed costs, which apply to all grid-connected customers. This amounts to a minimum and equal contribution from all customers, solar and non-solar alike.

In addition, the utilities want the solar customers to be charged additional charges for grid services. Charges include: off-peak services, back-up interruptible service, and the pathway to send electric power into the grid and sell it to the utilities. And then, as an introduction to the long-term solution, the utilities want the net-metering programs to be revised to pay solar customers only the going market rate.

The long-term effect of these measures, however, will contribute to reducing the economic incentives for rooftop solar and will slow solar's DER growth. Maybe this is the utilities' goal to start with…

In any case, while things don't look good for the solar industry, so it needs to proceed cautiously, because the utilities are very powerful and should not be provoked into extreme action. They have slaughtered the fragile solar industry before…several times, and would not hesitate to do it again.

GIS for Utilities

Geographic Information System (GIS) is a method for communicating content and processes in the utility industry, where a better understanding of the context of present and pending change is needed. The utilities need to know what it means, and how they can manage their present and future activities. Better information means better understanding, communication, and collaboration.

As utilities change via mergers and staff reductions, sharing workflows in an automated and systematic way is one way to keep up the competitive edge. The GIS platform could help facilitate collaboration on all levels by unifying the underlying data infrastructure and workflows with other key utility information system (IS) platforms such as: SCADA; enterprise resource planning (ERP); asset, work, and outage management; and field force automation.

GIS is basically used to apply geospatial information to a host of utility applications. As a result, GIS is helping utilities unify by integrating information from internal and external sources into a common framework. By using GIS, utility managers are discovering new insights that they can transform into tangible business results, which in turn could lower costs and expenses, improve the asset utilization, and allow quicker and more efficient customer hookup.

New technology such as Web services, location-based services, geo-processing, loosely connected distributed spatial databases, smart clients, and intelligent GIS unify information for utility executives, managers, and operators. At the same time, decision-making, communication, and asset management can be based on the same information throughout the organization.

The utilities spent millions of dollars on the automated mapping/facilities management (AM/FM) system in the mid-1990s. They converted the old drawings and maps into detailed, clear, and interactive computer-generated computer screen documents. And yet distribution-operating managers cannot interface the new GPS tracking system in their trucks with the existing AM/FM system. This is because the old maps were converted "as is" in the AM/FM system based on the old mapping standards, before GPS was invented.

It would now take a major effort to reconstruct the locations of all facilities to a new, consistent land base. And so, the operating managers would often opt for an independent vehicle tracking system based on a commercially available land data source with no interface or links to the AM/FM system.

The answer to all issues is to develop comprehensive enterprise GIS architecture. The connection of servers, networks, and PCs is certainly part of the architecture. The database management system is a critical component. The application programs, user interfaces, and inter- application interfaces play a role, because the data are critical.

These are all important, and all of the above utilities had these things. Yet the data in many cases is still incomplete or redundant. The applications don't work together, and the workflows are disrupted or disconnected.

One department would end up maintaining similar data as another, which results in redundancies, lost work time and unnecessary expenses. In the end, the utility processes were not unified.

In summary, the architecture for an efficient utility operation needs to have at least the following interrelated components:

- Workflow and process models are needed to identify the master process and sub-processes that drive business for major stakeholders in the utility: the customer, the shareholder, the community, and the employee.

- Data models are needed to describe the data, data relationships, and behaviors that are needed for the workflows in a logical and disciplined way.

- Actual data is needed to detail the utility land base, customer locations, and infrastructure.

- Output products are also needed as tools that people use to make decisions, do work, and communicate.

- Integration framework allows corporate systems to be visualized along with location, often in the form of a map.

- Physical architecture includes all the hardware, operating systems, processes, tools, DBMSs, and networks that make the whole thing work.

- Adaptation to, and interface of the operating equipment and processes with the new smart grid is another requirement that the utilities need to be able to meet in the near future.

Are utilities on top of their game? Are they capable of adapting to the new technologies, and the new way of doing business in the energy sector? These are questions that we will hear more and more as the utilities are pressured from all sides, as needed to compete and face the new challenges.

Grid Parity

Grid parity is a sound bite that we hear every time we talk about solar or wind energy. It is killing, or at the very least complicating, the solar industry's struggle to compete with conventional energy sources. Grid parity makes the uphill battle unfair at best, and this inequality has been used by utilities and others to show how inferior solar and wind are. That unfair treatment has signaled the end of many new careers, accompanied by the loss of talent—the very expertise the solar industry badly needs to continue innovating and growing.

Grid parity is on the agenda of discussions, conferences and contracts, most of which project a positive (albeit wishful and even false) attitude about the solar industry's achievements of late. Most of the interested parties praise the solar industry for its achievements, and predict that is "almost there," or at least at the point where it has figured out how to compete with conventional energy without any help or subsidies. But not as yet…maybe a bit later when the industry can function without any outside help!

But wait! The conventional energy sources have been, and still are, themselves beneficiaries of enormous financial aid and direct and indirect subsidies, most of which are hidden under different names and shoved into different government programs. And this has been going since the early 1900s. Billions upon billions of taxpayers' dollars have been, and still are, going into paying nuclear, coal, gas and oil power generation research, programs and projects.

Low manufacturing costs, high quality, and efficiencies require many years with decades of research and development, and a lot of money. They do not happen overnight. Just like they didn't happen overnight for the conventional energy sources. These are, instead, the result of long hours in the lab, years of pilot-line developments and up-scaling to commercial-scale manufacturing. And then come the even longer and harder years of field operations and proving the product productivity and reliability.

It almost seems—with all this talk of "grid parity" success—that we are trying to ignore all the hard work that is needed to stabilize the fragile solar industry. Instead of focusing on supporting incremental improvements and successes, we are claiming champion achievements, such as higher cell efficiency and such.

Triumphantly waving partial results, and loudly announcing achievements and roadmaps as actual data, we have placed the solar on the slippery slope of empty promises, wishful successes, and unmet expectations. Grid parity rules, and has been accepted as a measuring stick for all the solar industry stands for.

The grid parity motto has been even used as a reason to sacrifice profits, the approach that has been rejected by the capitalist society time after time. Idealism works only in people's imagination—not under the strict rules of the American capitalist system.

To move forward, we need to agree and accept the fact that the solar value chain needs some profit to stay afloat, and a lot of profit to prosper. Ignoring these simple principles of successful capitalist enterprises leads to unrealistic and unsustainable development, examples of which can be seen in the long list of failures of the past several years, as clearly spelled earlier in this text.

For the manufacturers, realizing reasonable profit margins requires a depth of understanding and the acceptance that there are expenses and costs over which the manufacturers have no control. These costs include the price and quality of raw materials, consumables, equipment and labor.

On the other hand, installers, operators and owners of solar installations (especially these of cost-intensive utility-scale installations), need to know well that performance is the most important metric, but that they have no control over the most important factor—the local weather conditions. The costs of unexpected weather events, such as excess cloudy days, snow, hail, extreme sand storms, and other natural (or unnatural) events, need to be thoroughly understood and taken into account by investors and system owners during the design stages—well before the system is installed.

Recently industry supporters have been trying to cover up the misdeeds of sloppy solar product manufacturers and their spectacular failures, blaming lower prices of PV modules as the reasons for the failures. At the same time, these same people tout the lower prices of PV modules as a proof that the industry has already, or is just about to achieve grid parity and will continue to grow despite these losses and failures.

One has to only take a quick look at financial statements from the leading manufacturers (even these in China) to see the unsustainably low prices. One doesn't have to be a specialist to figure out that this is a temporary situation, which won't end up well for all involved.

Other specialists have been claiming lately that the system price is what matters. That it is the most important metric when discussing grid parity and that the cost of the module is not the major point. But—and here is the catch—you'll be hard pressed to build a PV power field without PV modules, while at the same time without the artificially low module prices there would be no talk of grid parity.

And then, unless something changes, solar manufacturers who cannot ensure reasonable profit margins will continue to fail. And without manufacturers, there will be no PV industry.

And finally, while the dropping cost of PV modules has been blamed for the downward price pressure lately, there are significant improvements in their efficiency and durability, which needs to be plugged into the formula. There are also cost and efficiency improvements at the balance-of-system (BOS) level.

In addition, real opportunities for efficiency improvements are yet to be explored at the permitting and installation level. As a matter of fact, while the cost of solar modules and other components fluctuates, it is a variable that we are familiar with and can follow. In contrast, the complex and unclear costs and uncertainties of land permitting, environmental assessment, obtaining PPA and connection rights, as well as other administrative costs artificially raise the system costs and constrain margins for demand-side participants. Grid parity is very far from reality, and often not possible to even get close to, when we consider all the above variables.

This all shows how confused the entire solar

field is—we don't even know how to deal with the PV systems' price fluctuations and other uncertainties, let alone bring solar to an uniform grid parity level.

And so, no! We should not give up the fight for grid parity, but we should get smarter about how we approach it. We know that it will be costly to push toward a change in the energy sources. Any change is costly, so a higher price of electricity will have to be accepted.

That is not an easy thing to do in a capitalist enterprise system, governed by lowest prices. Solar and wind sectors have a difficult road ahead, but they are not going away. The major correction needed is that all levels of the value chain need to have healthy profit margins.

New and improved financing models are not the entire answer. Governments and consumers alike, need to make a final and painful decision that solar and wind are the future—no matter what. That is the only way to survive the current critical period of hesitation and indecision.

And to that end, knowing that solar is not going away, the promises of grid parity should be renegotiated, revised, redefined, or abandoned all together. We know darn well that solar and wind cannot compete with the conventional energy sources—no matter how cheap or efficient they might be.

We know that even the most efficient and cheapest solar and wind installations have serious problem with variability—when sun and wind are unavailable during the day, and we know even better that they do not work at night. Period.

These two factors alone mean clearly that the new renewable energy sources are not even close to competing with the conventional energy sources. At least not now! Maybe in the future, but not at this moment, and in the predictable near future. So why try to make them into something that they are not?

Solar and wind power grid parity is not even close to the conventional energy sources, so there is no point in—and might prove to be detrimental—building an entire global industry on misconstrued premises, empty promises, and unsustainable goals.

Let's call a spade a spade, and stop avoiding the issues at hand.

OUR ENERGY FUTURE

The future is coming fast, and we need to hurry before we have entered into an irreversible catch 22, which would envelope the world in a nightmare of energy deficiencies and irreversible climate changes.

Energy Use by 2050

So, how much renewable energy will the world consume in the coming decades? That depends on whom you ask. As is usual in the capitalist system that operates under the principle of, "let each sheep hang by its own leg:" a) the oil companies with a stake in the continued use of fossil fuels downplay as much as possible the importance or the degree of penetration of the renewables; b) the international organizations with conservative reputations see moderate growth; c) the advocacy organizations actively work to stop the burning of fossil fuels, and project the highest growth of renewables possible. See Figure 9-32.

Not surprisingly, we see a lot of different and sometimes controversial data on these subjects.

NOTE: One of the key objectives of this text is to present a balanced view of the situation, where all parties' points of view are analyzed and presented as accurately and efficiently as possible for the reader to make his/her own conclusions.

The most recent scenarios, published in 2010–2012, could be viewed in three main groups: conservative, moderate, and high renewables, as shown in Figure 9-32 in a report issued by REN 21 in 2013.

Currently, renewables make up 17% of final energy. About 9% of that is from "traditional biomass" and another 8% is from "modern" renewables like wind, solar, geothermal, and biofuels.

The scenarios reflect final energy consumption, or the actual fuel, Btus, and electricity generated by renewable resources. This also reflects assumptions about technology readiness, abundance of fossil fuels, and the work related to addressing climate change.

Of course, the oil companies don't see much growth, predicting that renewables will account for only 15% of final energy between 2030 and 2040.

The international energy agency (IEA), which has historically underestimated the growth of renewables globally, foresees several scenarios. On the lower end, assuming new policies to limit temperature rise to 4°C, it projects 27% renewables by 2035. The higher scenario outlines what it would take to limit global temperature rise at 2°C, and shows global renewables penetration at 41% by 2050.

Greenpeace's predictions of the future of renewables have always been, and still are, the highest. That is because, as an environmental advocacy organization, Greenpeace believes that climate change is and will be the driving force behind global energy policy in the future, which, in turn, will force a higher penetration of renewables.

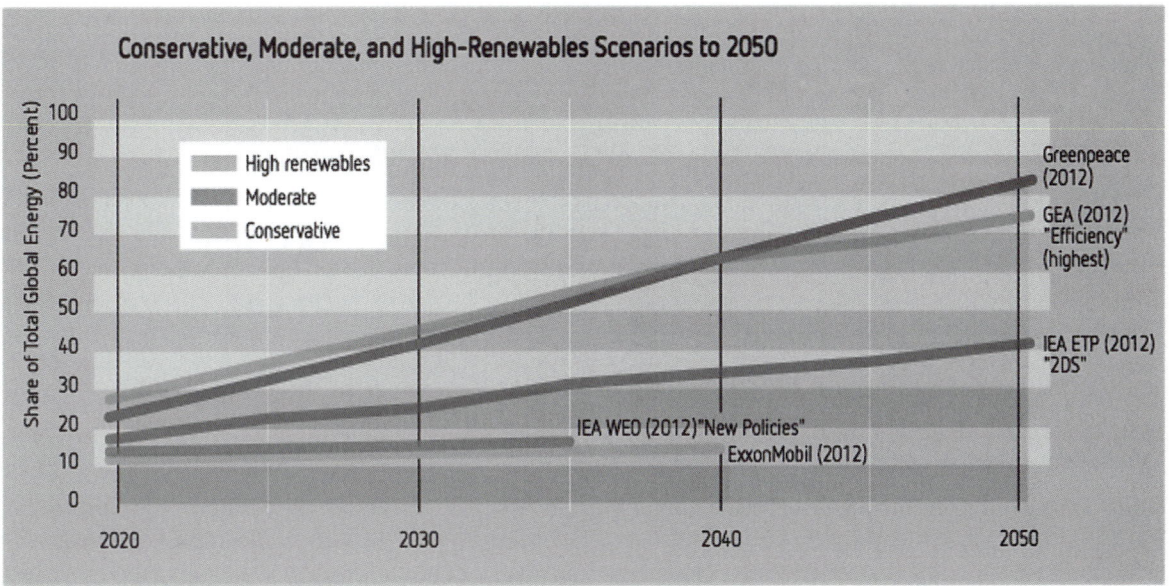

Figure 9-32. Penetration of renewables according to different groups, by 2050

Various countries are expected to contribute different types and amounts of renewables in the future.

As of 2011, renewables accounted for 20% of global electricity production. The REN21 report concludes that a 40-50% electricity share is likely by 2030 in the best of circumstances.

The greatest growth of renewables are expected in the transportation sector:

Biofuels make up only about 3% of fuel consumption globally today, but their share will increase significantly as the targets in the U.S. and Europe drive continued demand. The increases, however, depend on the competitiveness of unconventional biofuels, the scope of political backlash against food-based fuel standards, and above all, the price of oil.

Another key driver of the aggressive global growth scenarios is climate change. Even the most conservative projections show more bullish outlook for renewables because of the need to rapidly lower carbon emissions. So the energy vs. environment battle is on and we are going to be witnesses to some great and exciting things happening in the energy sector—especially in the field of renewables—in the future.

Of course, a lot of time and money is needed to in-

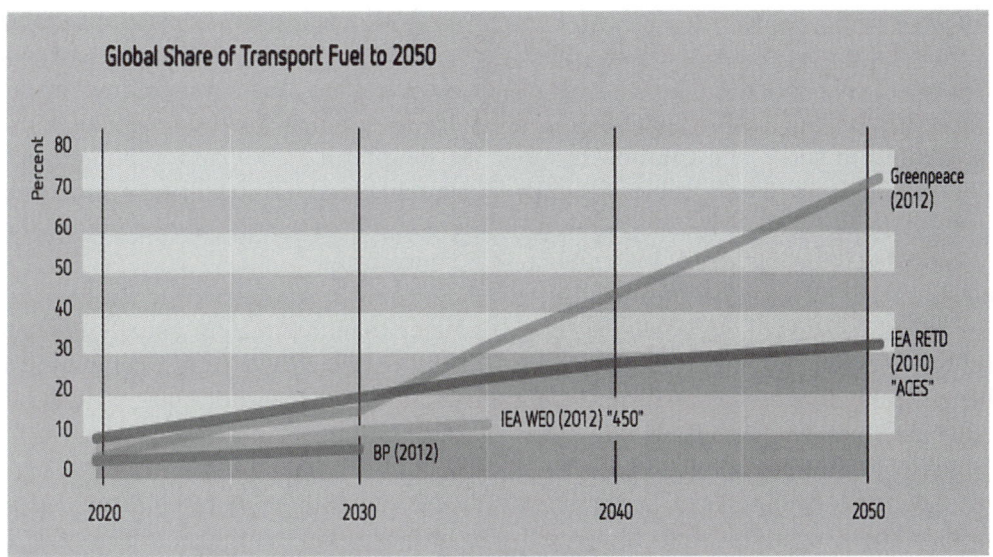

Figure 9-33. Renewables in the transport sector by 2050

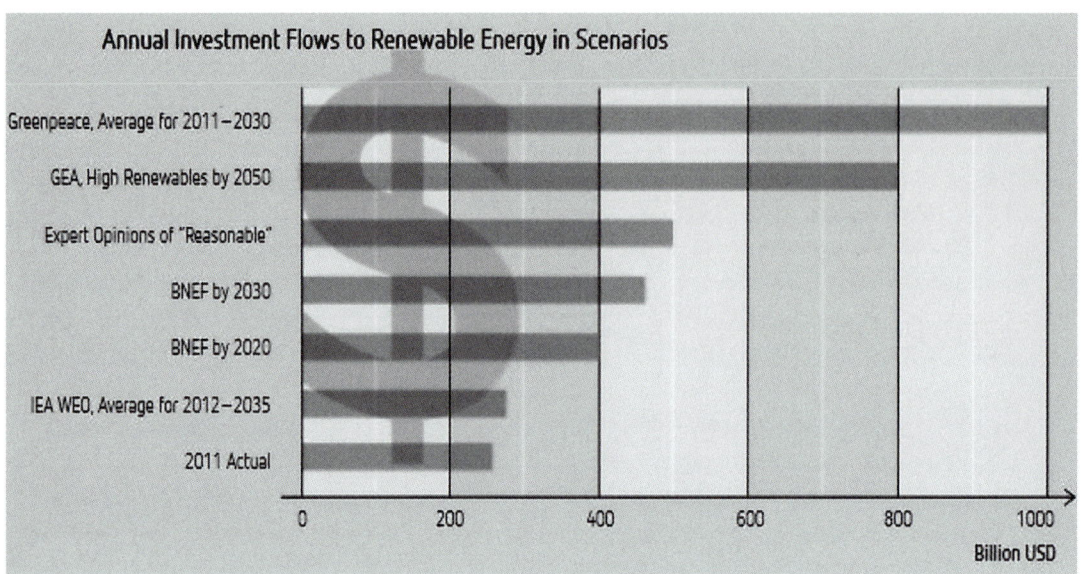

Figure 9-34. Investment in renewables in the future, in $ billions

crease the use of renewables as needed to make a major impact on the energy and environmental issues at hand.

Even the lowest estimates call for several hundred billion dollars in investment. Where is this money going to come from? It is one thing to plan and another to actually get the money, build, and operate the projects. Each step of the process is full of risks and uncertainties, which are hard to predict, let alone eliminate.

So in conclusion, it is undeniable that the future of the renewables looks bright. We don't know exactly how bright it is going to be, and how we are going to get there.

Alas, there are some bright streaks of hope in the future energy and environmental markets. Some of these, in our opinion, are:

Natural Gas Hydrates

Natural gas hydrates (NGH), also called methane hydrates, are, according to some, the solution to our long-term energy and environmental problems, while others think that they are the devil in disguise. The subject is somewhat obscured today by lack of information, and misinformation, but will grow in importance as time goes on.

In any case, this is extremely important, albeit not well known phenomenon, so we will take some more time and space dwelling into it in this text.

Gas hydrates are basically methane gas trapped in ice formation form in marine sediments during millions of years in the past. There are huge areas filled with that stuff under the ocean floor, which represents an immense fuel (fossil gas) reservoir that is considered by

some to be a dominant factor in estimating unconventional energy resources. At the same time, others also carefully assess the role of methane as a "greenhouse" gas. And here is where the line between the "some" and "others" is drawn deeply in the sand.

Gas hydrate is a crystalline solid consisting of gas molecules, usually methane, each surrounded by a cage of water molecules. It looks very much like ice. Methane hydrate is stable in ocean floor sediments at water depths greater than 300 meters, and where it occurs, it is known to cement loose sediments in a surface layer that is several hundred meters thick.

The Formation Process

Methane is part of the natural carbon cycle, but the processes of methane generation are somewhat unclear. Even less clear are its transformations in the sediments, since it is the new kid on the block. Its significance in the long-term global carbon budgets is just now being acknowledged, so it will take time to get all the facts right and take the right decisions as far as its future use is concerned.

Some organic-rich sediments at water depths greater than 500 meters usually contain methane as a clathrate, which is a frozen compound in which methane and other low molecular weight gases are trapped in a water lattice, in a form of a ice cage.

Sub-seabed methane within the continental margin sediments is thought to be produced primarily by: a) microbial; or b) thermogenic processes. In the microbial process, organic debris is decomposed by a complex sequence (methanogenesis) into methane, usually by a specialized bacteria in an anoxic environment.

Organic matter is composed of carbon, hydrogen, and phosphorus in the ratio of 106:16:1, and decomposition results in production of methane, so we can expect to see the following methane producing reaction:

$$106(CH_2O)+16(NH_3)+(H_3PO_4) = 53CO_2 +53CH_4 +16NH_3+H_3PO_4$$

The local acetate fermentation, which is a key stage in the decomposition process, also produces methane:

$$CH_3COOH \rightarrow CH_4 +CO_2$$

And finally, the continuous reduction of carbon dioxide can also produce methane, as follows:

$$CO_2 +4H_2 \rightarrow CH_4 +2H_2O$$

In the thermogenic process, thermal cracking of organically derived materials form petroleum hydrocarbons (including methane). This generally occurs at considerable depth (>2,000 meters) in sedimentary basins where temperatures exceed 273 K. Thermogenic methane may also be derived by thermal degradation of oil at even greater depths, and by the maturation of coal.

Whichever way the methane was formed, it is trapped in its icy cages, awaiting release from the multi-century entombment. But how can we do it?

Extraction of methane from hydrates could provide an enormous energy and petroleum feedstock resource. Additionally, conventional gas resources appear to be trapped beneath methane hydrate layers in ocean sediments.

Because the methane gas is held in a crystal structure, gas molecules are more densely packed than in conventional or other unconventional gas traps. Gas-hydrate-cemented strata also act as seals for trapped free gas. These traps provide potential resources, but they can also represent hazards to drilling, and therefore need to be thoroughly investigated and well understood.

Production of gas from hydrate-sealed traps may be an easy way to extract hydrate gas because the reduction of pressure caused by production can initiate a breakdown of hydrates and a recharging of the trap with gas.

In any case, the NGH are an important addition to our energy arsenal, as we embark in our energy-dubious future, so they do deserve a closer look.

The Nature and Chemistry of NGH (5)

Natural gas hydrates are a curious kind of chemical compound called a clathrate. Clathrates consist of two dissimilar molecules mechanically intermingled but not truly chemically bonded. Instead one molecule forms a framework that traps the other molecule. Natural gas hydrates can be considered modified ice structures enclosing methane and other hydrocarbons, but they can melt at temperatures well above normal ice.

At 30 atmospheres pressure, methane hydrate begins to be stable at temperatures above 0°C and at 100 atmospheres it is stable at 15°C. This behavior has two important practical implications. First, it's a nuisance to the gas company. They have to dehydrate natural gas thoroughly to prevent methane hydrates from forming in high-pressure gas lines. Second, methane hydrates will be stable on the sea floor at depths below a few hundred meters and will be solid within sea floor sediments. Masses of methane hydrate "yellow ice" have been photographed on the sea floor. Chunks occasionally break loose and float to the surface, where they are unstable and effervesce as they decompose.

The stability of methane hydrates on the sea floor has a whole raft of implications. First, they may constitute a huge energy resource. Second, natural disturbances (and man-made ones, if we exploit gas hydrates and aren't careful) might suddenly destabilize sea floor methane hydrates, triggering submarine landslides and huge releases of methane. Finally, methane is a ferociously effective greenhouse gas, and large methane releases may explain sudden episodes of climatic

Figure 9-35. Methane escaping from melting methane hydrate reservoir

warming in the geologic past. The methane would oxidize fairly quickly in the atmosphere, but could cause enough warming that other mechanisms (for example, release of carbon dioxide from carbonate rocks and decaying biomass) could keep the temperatures elevated.

The Different Structure

There are three types of methane hydrate structure. They all include pentagonal dodecahedra of water molecules enclosing methane. This geometry arises from the happy accident that the bond angle in water is fairly close to the 108° angle of a pentagon. Generally, the dodecahedra are slightly distorted so that three dodecahedra can share an edge. This requires a dihedral (inter-face) angle of 120°, whereas the dihedral angle of a true dodecahedron is 116.5°. Between the dodecahedra are other cages of water molecules with different shapes. In practice, not all cages are occupied by hydrocarbons, but occupancy rates of over 90% occur.

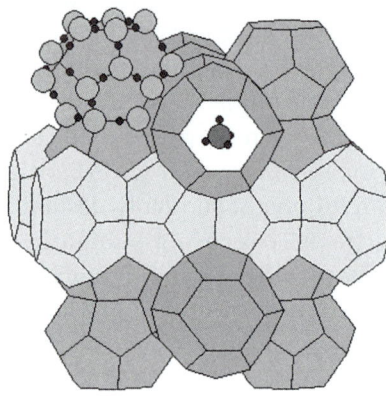

Figure 9-36.a. Basic methane hydrate structure (5)

NOTE: in all the figures, an oxygen atom occupies each vertex and the midpoint of each edge is a hydrogen atom. This atom is attached to oxygen as one part of a water molecule and hydrogen bonded to the other.

Structure I

Structure I is cubic. A dodecahedral cage is centered at the corners of the unit cell and a rotated dodecahedron is in the center of the cell. 14-faced cages that consist of hexagonal ends and 12 pentagons link the dodecahedra. In Figure 9-36b, the central rotated dodecahedron is hidden, but its counterpart in the next unit cell above is shown at the top.

Structure II

Structure II is also cubic. 16-faced cages consisting

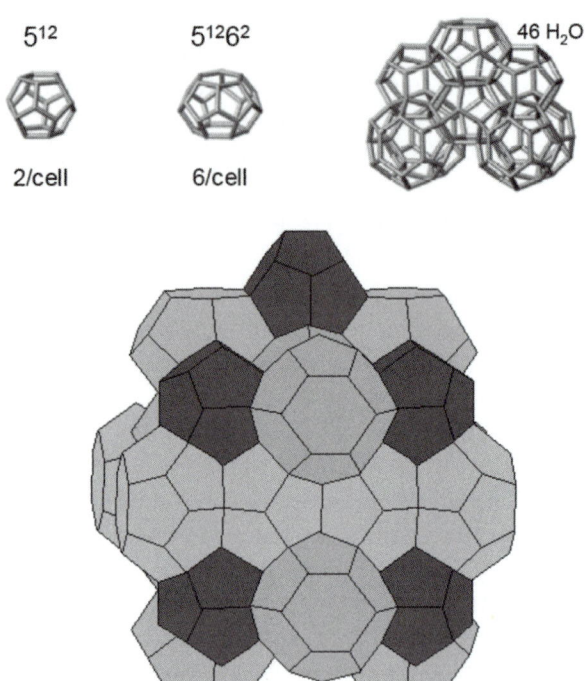

Figure 9-36.b. Structure I

of 12 pentagons and 4 hexagons are arranged tetrahedrally (left side of figure). The interstices are filled by dodecahedral cages (right side of figure).

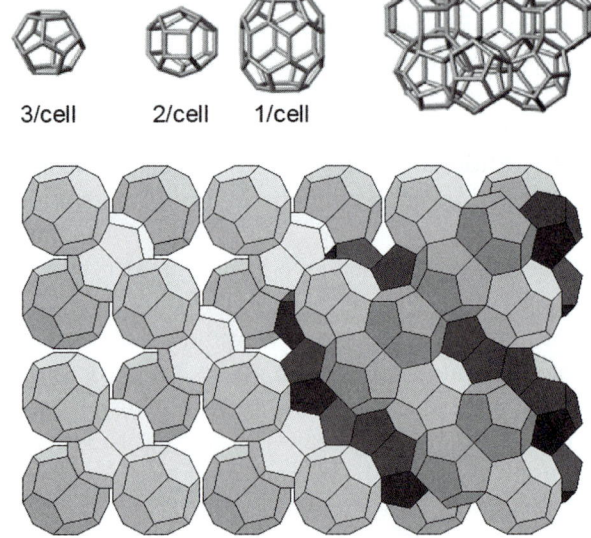

Figure 9-36.c. Structure II

Structure III-H Structure

The H (for hexagonal) structure consists of three cages: dodecahedra; cages with 4, 5 and 6-sided faces; and "barrels" consisting of 12 pentagonal and 8 hexagonal faces. The "barrels" can hold large hydrocarbon molecules. They are surrounded by a hexagonal net of the 4-5-6 cages and layers of these cages alternate with hexagonal nets of dodecahedra.

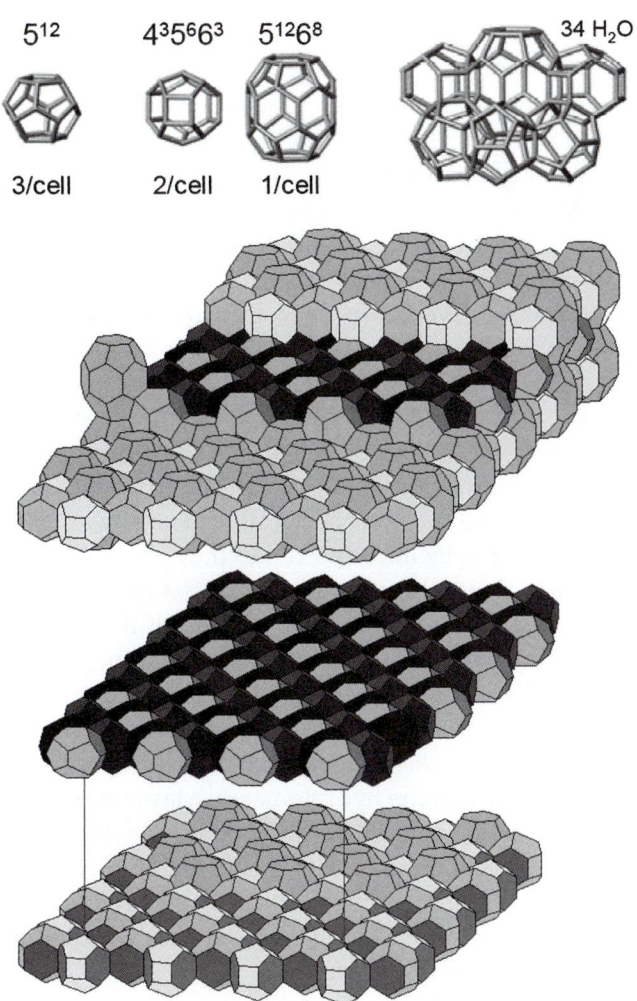

Figure 9-36.d. H-Structure

The Extraction of NGH

This is the hard part…taking the useless ice blocks out of the depth of the oceans and converting them into useful methane gas is a truly overwhelming technological, logistical and financial undertaking. If all goes well, and we have all the luck we need, the natural gas hydrates (NGH) might be the solution of all our problems. If not done right, and if our luck runs out, it might just kill us all.

A pair of relatively small areas, each about the size of the state of Rhode Island, shows intense concentrations of gas hydrates. USGS scientists estimate that these areas contain more than 1,300 trillion cubic feet of methane gas, an amount representing more than 70 times the 1989 gas consumption of the U.S. Bacteria in the sediments formed some of the gas, but some may be derived

from deep strata of the Carolina Trough. The Carolina Trough is a significant offshore oil and gas frontier area where no wells have been drilled. It is a very large basin, about the size of the state of South Carolina, that has accumulated a great thickness of sediment, perhaps more than 13 kilometers. Salt diapirs, reefs, and faults, in addition to hydrate gas, may provide greater potential for conventional oil and gas traps than is present in other east coast basins.

Seafloor slopes of 5° and less should be stable on the Atlantic continental margin, yet many landslide scars are present. The depth of the top of these scars is near the top of the hydrate zone, and seismic profiles indicate less hydrate in the sediment beneath slide scars. Evidence available suggests a link between hydrate instability and the occurrence of landslides on the continental margin. A likely mechanism for initiation of landslides involves a breakdown of hydrates at the base of the hydrate layer. The effect would be a change from a semi-cemented zone to one that is gas-charged and has little strength, thus facilitating sliding. The cause of the breakdown might be a reduction in pressure on the hydrates due to a sea-level drop, such as that which occurred during glacial periods when ocean water became isolated on land in great ice sheets.

Methane bound in hydrates amounts to approximately 3,000 times the volume of methane in the atmosphere. There is insufficient information to judge what geological processes might most affect the stability of hydrates in sediments and the possible release of methane into the atmosphere. Methane released as a result of landslides caused by a sea-level fall would warm the Earth, as would methane released from gas hydrates in Arctic sediments as they become warmed during a sea-level rise. This global warming might counteract cooling trends and thereby stabilize climatic fluctuation, or it could exacerbate climatic warming and thereby destabilize the climate.

The velocity of sound in hydrate is very high; therefore, the velocity of sound in the surface layer of hydrate-cemented sediments also is high. Specific acoustic characteristics of hydrate-cemented sediments are not well known and require further study. Such information has significant implications in the use of sonar devices for defense, seismic exploration, and research.

At this stage, it is important for USGS scientists to learn how the hydrates form, evolve, and break down, how they affect sediments, and what factors control their concentration at certain locations, as well as to explore for new hydrate accumulations. Cooperation with other Federal agencies, such as the National Oceanic and Atmospheric

NOTE: NGH are large—the largest—deposit(s) of fossils ever. Much larger than all fossils we know of combined. Huge amounts of methane gas are trapped under the ocean floor, waiting for their day under the sun. Literally. When that day comes, after we figure out what it is that we are dealing with and how to deal with it, the enormous amount of gas will flood the planet to abundantly power our lives.

But it can also eliminate all life forms from the face of the Earth by increasing the greenhouse gasses, thus boiling the atmosphere in case of a uncontrolled slow release, or suffocating us in a case of uncontrolled rapid release of mass quantities.

Anyway, we will continue trying to find the right way…what choice do we have? There is a lot of money to be made, a lot of power to be generated, and a lot of GHG saved from replacing coal-fired power.

The Production Process

Methods of dissociation of hydrates are based on shifting the thermodynamic equilibrium of the three-phase water-hydrate-gas system, thus releasing the methane gas from the hydrate suspension. Awaking the giant from its multi-million year slumber can be done either by changing the pressure and temperature of the hydrate bearing media, or by injection of inhibitors (chemicals).

There are presently three main methods for producing gas from hydrates. These are:

1. Depressurization
2. Thermal stimulation
3. Inhibitor addition

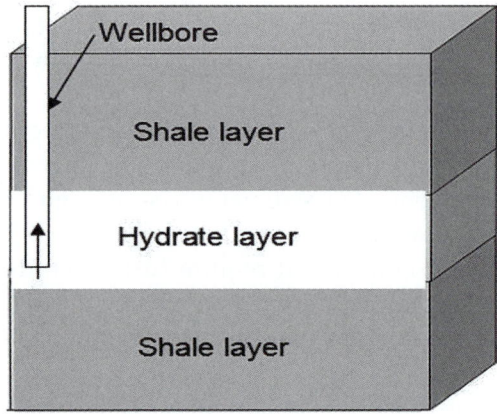

Figure 9-37. NGH extraction

Depressurization is a technique where the pressure is reduced below the equilibrium value at a fixed temperature; in thermal stimulation, the temperature is increased to shift equilibrium and bring about hydrate dissociation, and adding inhibitors shifts the pressure temperature equilibrium.

Due to its simplicity, it is considered to be the method—when fully developed—that is most likely to be economic for commercial production of gas hydrates. Here a well is drilled into the hydrate reservoir, similar to regular gas or oil wells, and a pressure difference is created between the wellbore and the NGH reservoir, which frees the methane molecules from the hydrate entrapment.

Thus removed associated free gas and formation water in the reservoir force the hydrate to dissociate into gas and water molecules. The gas migrates towards the surface via the wellbore and is collected for processing.

There are different models for hydrate decomposition in the porous media, but in all cases this method is likely to be the most economically feasible, as there is no extra heat to be introduced into the system. The heat needed to drive the endothermic dissociation process is supplied by the in situ sensible heat of the reservoir induced by the pressure reduction, which (the pressure reduction) is created by simply pumping out excess gasses and water from the NGH reservoir.

Thermal Injection is a method that uses heat, which is introduced into the hydrate-bearing layer through an injector well. The injection wells require high-pressure pumps to inject hot water or steam into the reservoir. That raises the temperature of the hydrate layer, causing hydrate dissociation. Methane gases mix with the hot water and return to the surface.

Since hydrate-bearing layers are generally found in permafrost and in oceans at a depth of 150 m and 600 m respectively, heat loses to the surroundings during the injection would be enormous. A lot of energy would be wasted to provide heat to the hydrate layer, so it is not feasible to produce gas from this method at a profit. The net energy balance is negative, for the energy needed to release the gas is greater than that produced by it after processing. No go…

Addition of chemical Inhibitors, such as different salts, alcohols and glycols, is the third process used to release the NGH from its icy entombment. An inhibitor such as methanol (a glycol) can be added to hydrate formations to shift the pressure-temperature (P-T), which in turn would shift the chemical equilibrium of the hydrate mixture. If done right, this process enables hydrate dissociation without changing the pressure or temperature of the hydrate layer. At that point, the methane is released from the multi-centuries' icy embrace of Earth and flows to the surface via the wellbore.

There is a catch here, however. In order for the reaction to proceed smoothly and in controlled manner, a) proper inhibitor needs to be used, and b) the inhibitor needs to be added to the hydrate layer uniformly. If improper chemicals or ratios are used, the results might release methane gas either too slowly, or too fast. In the latter case, the well might explode, destroying the wellbore, causing further damage to the layer and the surface.

A large explosion at the wrong time and place could cause a chain reaction in the entire layer, thus releasing its potential energy at once, blowing up the upper layers and erupting like a volcano. That is not very likely? Maybe so, but let's not try it, please, and proceed carefully.

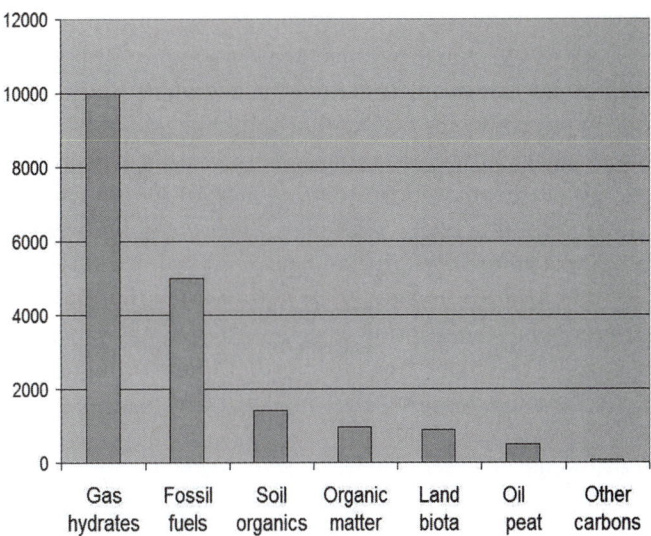

Figure 9-38. Worldwide organic carbon deposits (in gigatons)

Summary

Realizing the importance of methane hydrates in marine sediments, a number of scientific organizations are focused on the investigation and exploration of NGH deposits. There are selected areas where hydrates are known to be common, and where the influences of hydrates on energy resources, climate, and seafloor stability can be analyzed.

The results of recent investigations indicate that methane hydrates possess unique acoustic properties, which could facilitate their exploration and make their exploitation easier.

NGH contain immense amounts of methane, with major implications for energy resources and climate, but the natural controls on hydrates and their impacts on the environment are very poorly understood. The worldwide amount of carbon bound in gas hydrates is conservatively estimated to total twice the amount of carbon to be found in all known fossil fuels on Earth.

Processing the released methane gas is similar to that of processing natural gas coming from the wellbores of today.

NGH Global Supply

This is where the enormous importance of this (future) fuel comes to play. Speaking of disruptive technologies; this one of great importance, due to its immense size and potential benefits and damages.

Note the enormous supply of natural gas hydrates—more than twice the amount of ALL other carbon deposits on Earth. So maybe future generations will not miss the readily available coal, oil, and natural gas that we will burn completely by the end of the 21st century. If they are smarter and more ingenious than we are,

they will be able to figure out a way to extract, process and use the huge NGH deposits and live happily thereafter for another century or two.

Who knows…by then other energy sources might be available and the world will continue on without energy shortages and environmental problems. Let's hope…for their sake. But until then, we have a lot of issues to resolve. Just consider the following.

Environmental Impact of NGH Extraction and Use

Here is where things get sticky. Very sticky! The immense volumes of gas and the richness of the deposits make NGH deposits a strong candidate for development as an abundant energy resource. But they contain enormous amount of methane, a "greenhouse" gas, which is 10 times more effective than carbon dioxide in causing climate warming.

Recent investigations indicate that some NGH deposits are unstable mechanically, and may cause landslides on the continental slope, if carelessly disturbed. A large NGH "avalanche" could result in an immense amount of methane being released very quickly. What would be the consequences of such "explosions" of GHG into the atmosphere?

Mining these deposits is impossible to accomplish, as the depths and freezing temperatures would require special and expensive production, transportation, and storage equipment and facilities. In all cases, the transition to NGH won't be an easy, quick, or cheap process.

These and many other issues need to be addressed and resolved first, and before any large-scale work can be undertaken reliably and safely.

Hydrogen Power

Sunlight can turn water into hydrogen. If the process could scale up, it could make hydrogen a major power source in the U.S. and around the world. It could also be used as energy storage by converting excess electric power generated by solar and wind into hydrogen for use when needed. That way we could solve several problems at once.

Generating hydrogen via the conventional fossil power makes no economic or environmental sense, so hydrogen produced by solar power is one of the best, if not only, ways to move into the hydrogen future.

Background

Over the last century, our technological revolution has been developing at amazingly fast pace, and the global population has been keeping pace with it. Global population has increased from about 1.0 billion persons in 1800 to 3.0 billion in 1960 and peaking at over 6.0 billion at the beginning of the 21st century. With it, the demand for energy has also increased proportionally in most places and ridiculously un-proportionally in others—such as the U.S.—where people use several times more energy than they need just because they can, and because the electricity is always there.

We have been for the last century, and still are, relying mostly on fossil fuels—coal, oil, and natural gas—that are not renewable natural resources, and the global demand for energy is increasing by the day, expected to double by the middle of this century. By then, the world's oil resources will be exhausted, while gas and coal reserves will be substantially depleted.

That means that we live in a time warp, where 3-4 generations (present company included) consumed natural reserves that took over 100 million years to generate. Some of us are quite aware of this unreasonable reality and are doing something about it, while most of us are totally oblivious and live like there is no tomorrow. What are we doing? What would the future generations say about us?

We live in a vicious, wealth-depleting circle where we burn fossil fuels equivalent to 9.0 billion gallons of oil per day. Every day, the Earth contains less and less coal, oil, and natural gas, while the environment bears the scars of our race to eliminate the natural resources. This means that we (the entire humanity) lives on borrowed time as far as natural resources are concerned.

We eventually have to pay the fiddler, but it will be the following generations who will pay. Forget about using oil to burn, future generations! You'll be lucky to have oil to make the necessities of life, which we take for grant-ed today, such as cheap plastics, clothing, medications, and cosmetics. And the only benefit from this would be a significant decrease in pollution. We can't help but wonder if the future generations will thank us for that?

But just imagine…yes, scientists are allowed to imagine. Not surprisingly the most imaginative genre of literature and movie making is called "science fiction." One can argue that science does not mix with fiction, but let's imagine, nevertheless, life in year 2095. Crude oil deposits are long gone, coal and natural gas are near depletion, and so are rare and exotic minerals and materials. What would life look like in this natural resources depleted society? Let's look at two extreme cases:

Best Case Scenario

The new generations have found a way to eliminate or bypass the use of oil and all other natural resources, replacing them with new man-made, abundant and cheap materials. As a consequence, there is no danger of shortages, prices are low, and the environment is clean. Life is better than ever. I don't believe that anyone today can foresee how this could happen, but it could happen if the new generations are smarter and more capable than we are.

One way they could do that is to stop the indiscriminant use of natural resources for producing energy and other, not absolutely necessary, activities and things. They could maximize the use of solar and wind energy, hydropower, ocean wave and tidal power. They could be smart enough to prioritize and compartmentalize the use of scarce natural resources for manufacturing only most important items and life-supporting medications, while relying on other materials and processes for everything else.

Worst Case Scenario

Wow! We can paint a very bleak picture here. But keeping it within reason, we still see a society wrapped in darkness and misery. Things have gone bad during the last 70-80 years. Solar and wind energy sources have not been as good as promised and are not producing enough energy. And now there is no money for optimization of the existing energy sources, or R&D and implementation of new energy sources. Energy is at high demand, it is largely unavailable, and is extremely expensive.

Because of the indiscriminant use of natural resources during the century, the environment is badly contaminated, and the climate has changed drastically. People live in extreme conditions—boiling summers and freezing winters make life miserable, and take many lives. Many coastal communities are under water and the deserts have taken thousands of acres of formerly productive agricultural lands.

Plastic bags would cost $1,000 each. Medications and cosmetics would be astronomically high and unavailable as well. Who wants to live in such a place? And yet, this is what we are promising our children and grandchildren.

Solar Hydrogen (Most Possible) Future

Mass hydrogen production is one of the sure ways to reduce the use of natural resources and to stop the rampant air, water and soil pollution. Hydrogen is a nontoxic, clean-burning fuel that can be produced from water and sunlight, producing "solar hydrogen," which can be then used in every application where the conventional fuels are used today.

Solar hydrogen is hydrogen produced when using solar energy (as a primary energy source) or one of its derivative, renewable forms (secondary energy source), such as wind, ocean waves, falling water, and biomass. As a bonus, by replacing fossil fuels with solar hydrogen, we can move from an unsustainable, wealth-depleting economy to a wealth-enhancing one.

Solar energy, although abundant in many areas of the world, is inconveniently remote and inaccessible in large quantities. Thus, to produce, store, transport, and use it requires extensive installations and procedures. Generating hydrogen, by splitting water as primary energy source, is one of the most promising solutions.

Hydrogen is an efficient fuel; it is carbon-free and is converted back into water during the combustion process. This means that we start with water, use the sunlight to split it and generate hydrogen during the day, store it, and then burn the hydrogen at night to generate heat and electricity, which produces water...again.

That is an almost perfect closed-loop system, a type of a perpetuum mobile, using only the sun's energy to assist in the never-ending and very efficient conversion process, with little energy and water lost.

The water-to-hydrogen-to-heat-to-electricity process goes something like this:

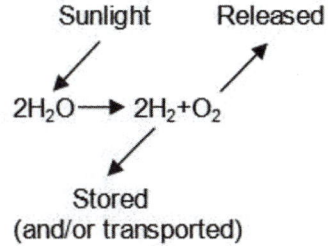

1. During the day:

Sunlight   Released

$$2H_2O \longrightarrow 2H_2 + O_2$$

Stored
(and/or transported)

2. During the night:

$$2H_2 + O_2 \longrightarrow 2H_2O + heat$$

$$heat \longrightarrow electricity$$

Hydrogen is generated from sunlight to be used immediately, or stored for later use. The generated water, together with the sunlight used for splitting it, are sources of clean and abundant energy in a carbon-free, natural and renewable cycle. Hydrogen can be also liquefied and transported over long distances and in any imaginable direction to areas that need it most. Hydrogen also can be stored underground or in containers to be used as needed by industrial enterprises, in households, power stations, vehicles and aviation.

Upon combustion, hydrogen produces heat and clean water. Two pounds of hydrogen release about 120,000 Btu heat, or as much as one gallon of gasoline. Or, 10 million tons of hydrogen per year can fuel 25-30 million hydrogen-fueled cars, or provide enough energy to power 6-8 million homes.

That's not bad, keeping in mind that 10 million tons of hydrogen could be easily generated in the Arizona or Nevada deserts, where sunlight is as abundant as the sand on the ground. Waste heat energy from different sources can be converted into valuable energy source that could solve the energy and environmental fiascos we live in.

NOTE: The production and use of 10 million tons of hydrogen annually would require:

- 250,000 small neighborhood-based hydrogen electrolysis generators to fuel cars and provide the power needs
- 16,000-hydrogen vehicle refueling stations, or about one tenth of the current gasoline stations
- 35 coal/biomass gasification plants, similar to today's large coal fired plants
- 25 large nuclear plants making only hydrogen
- 5 medium-size plants that use oil and natural gas in multi-fuel gasifiers and reformers

So how do we generate hydrogen using solar power?

Hydrogen is the most abundant element in the universe, for it is in the molecules of most organic and some inorganic materials. It, however, does not exist naturally as gas or liquid in large quantities or high concentrations. Hydrogen, therefore, needs to be produced from other compounds such as water, biomass, or fossil fuels. Various methods of production have unique needs in terms of energy sources (e.g., heat, light, electricity), all of which generate unique by-products and emissions.

Hydrogen Generation Methods

Conventional hydrogen generation methods under consideration and development today include:

1. Hydrogen generation by steam methane reforming constitutes 95% of the hydrogen produced in the U.S. today. This is a process of reacting natural gas or other light hydrocarbons catalytically with steam to produce a mixture of hydrogen and carbon dioxide. The mixture is then separated to produce high-purity hydrogen. This method is the most energy-efficient commercialized technology currently available, and is most cost-effective when applied to large, constant loads. It, however, uses ever more expensive and depleting natural resources, and produces large quantity of carbon dioxide, which has to be sequestered, or otherwise taken care of somehow.

2. Partial oxidation of fossil fuels in large gasifiers is another method of thermal hydrogen production. It is done by the reaction of conventional fuels with a limited supply of oxygen to produce a hydrogen mixture, which is then purified. This process can be applied to a wide range of hydrocarbon fuels including natural gas, heavy oils, solid biomass, and coal. Large amounts of carbon dioxide are produced as well.

3. Using electricity in electrolyzers can extract hydrogen from water. We call this process "splitting water." This method is not as efficient or cost effective as using fossil fuels in steam methane reforming and partial oxidation, but it is most promising for the near future due to a number of factors already discussed. It also allows more distributed hydrogen generation and use, and open possibilities for using electricity made from renewable resources. The primary by-products of this process are oxygen and small amount of carbon dioxide (as a by-product from electricity generation).

Methods for producing hydrogen without using natural resources are most interesting, due to the obvious avoidance of depleted natural resources and with little environmental contamination. Some of these methods (solar power mostly) are our best hope for efficient and safe 21st century power generation. Although components of these systems are still in development phases, we do hope and pray that proper attention will be focused on these technologies, because hydrogen generated by solar energy (thermal or electrical) induced water splitting is capable of replacing fossil fuels, thus ultimately bringing us energy independence and a cleaner environment.

The fossil-free solar hydrogen generation approaches include:

1. Splitting (electrolysis) of water using electricity generated from solar energy or other energy sources (wind, hydro etc.)
2. Thermochemical reactions that release hydrogen from water or biomass
3. Thermal dissociation of water using concentrated solar energy
4. Microbial activity that releases hydrogen from organic compounds and biomass

In general, when exposed to special conditions, hydrogen readily reacts with oxygen in a highly exothermic reaction (energy is released—heat in this case), producing pure water as a result of the reaction and as unique by-product, which could be used in a number of applications, including re-use in the hydrogen generation process:

$$2H_2(gas)+O_2(gas)=2H_2O(liquid)+572 \text{ kJ(heat)}$$

In reality, fuel cells use air rather than pure oxygen, and, as a consequence, small amounts of nitrogen oxides are formed as exhaust products as well. PEM and SOFC (high temperature) fuel cells, the most efficient H_2 technologies today, emit trace amounts of nitrogen oxide (NO_x) gasses, while others might emit more.

Hydrogen needs to be generated by extracting it from hydrogen sources, and unfortunately today most of the commercially produced H_2 gas comes from fossils, which process contributes to the overall CO_2 emissions and to global warming.

Once available, however, H_2 is an excellent fuel that can replace hydrocarbons with numerous advantages, including a specific heat capacity three times higher than that of our best fossil fuel (natural gas, or methane).

NOTE: Fossil fuels have high-energy content, and the power densities (the rate of energy production per unit of the earth's area these come from) are approximately $102 \text{ W}/\text{m}^2$, while in contrast, the energy production is well below $1.0 \text{ W}/\text{m}^2$. At the same time, densities of electricity produced by PV generation are over $40 \text{ W}/\text{m}^2$ at peak power when using some highly efficient PV technologies (i.e. HCPV trackers).

One of the big problems of the PV technologies is their variability, such as no sunlight at night or rainy days, thus there is no electricity generation during that time. Also, when a cloud covers the sky, the PV power is drastically reduced, and all this contributes to the increase of reluctance on part of users to rely on solar power.

The best solution, in our humble opinion, is H_2 energy storage. H_2 is an excellent storage option for storing the excess energy during the day for use during the nighttime and cloudy days. There are several methods that rely on the two main solar energy technologies, namely photovoltaics (PV) and concentrated solar power (CSP).

Water Electrolysis

This is the water electrolysis using electrical current generated by a number of different power generators, including solar or wind as most economical and environmentally friendly power sources, where:

$$H_2O + 2F = H_2 + \frac{1}{2}O_2$$

Where:

F is the Faraday constant, measuring 1 mol of electricity.

Once available in gaseous or liquid form, H_2 can be used to generate electricity by the reverse of reaction:

$$H_2 + \frac{1}{2}O_2 = H_2O + 2F \text{ (energy)}$$

This is the process that occurs in an H_2–O_2 fuel cell, which can work as a fuel cell, or as an electrolyzer, depending on the operating conditions.

The water hydrolysis process is able to create any amount of hydrogen, as needed to power a house or commercial building. Hydrogen can also be used to power cars and boats with internal combustion engines, providing similar power density with added safety.

NOTE: Although hydrogen is highly flammable, it is 14.4 times lighter than air, rising at $20\,\text{m}/\text{s}^{-1}$ rate, so if ignited, the flame tends to shoot up vertically, while gasoline and diesel are heavy and tend to run and accumulate under the vehicles, where they can explode or spread and feed a fire.

The energy needed for the electrolysis can be provided by a number of sources, such as from the grid, solar panels or wind turbines. Presently concentrated solar power (CSP) is the energy of choice for generating large quantities of H_2 from water. The preferred process includes catalytic thermo-chemical processes that make use of the intense heat or electricity generated by the solar radiation to create a large surplus of hydrogen suitable for storage and later use. The entire process is entirely renewable, using abundant energy sources and raw materials, solar energy and water, respectively, without the generation of any appreciable CO_2 emissions.

Theoretically speaking, the product yield of the water-splitting reaction is 100% efficient, since no electrical energy is wasted. And since the cost of water is negligible, it is quite cheap too. The economics of the process is driven mostly by the cost of electricity.

Small amounts of electrolyte (usually KOH) are dissolved in water to enhance conductivity and thus the overall rate of the process of water electrolysis. A 30% KOH solution at 80°C (alkaline electrolysis) is used, and the electrolyte can be recovered and re-used time after time. Such electrolysis systems make use of a ceramic micro porous separator, whereas the electrodes are usually made of nickel, with Pt coated cathode and MgO_2 coated anode.

The reactions during electrolysis are:

$$2H_2O + 2e = H_2 + 2OH \text{ (cathode)}$$
$$2OH = \frac{1}{2}O_2 + H_2O + 2e \text{ (anode)}$$

Typically, a commercial alkaline electrolyzer produces H_2 by consuming $4.49\,\text{kW h}/\text{m}^3$ of electricity with a current yield and hydrogen purity both close to 100%. The fuel cell makes it possible to use the solar power made available as H_2 when the (weather) conditions are optimal, and to store the excess power so that it can be made available for later use as required.

Extracted from water using PV and electrolysis, H_2 is oxidized in the fuel cell and the only emission is clean water, completing a zero-emission energy production cycle.

The necessary investment for the hydrogen infrastructure gains more economic profitability with an increasing number of cells.

Today, when solar panels generate more electricity

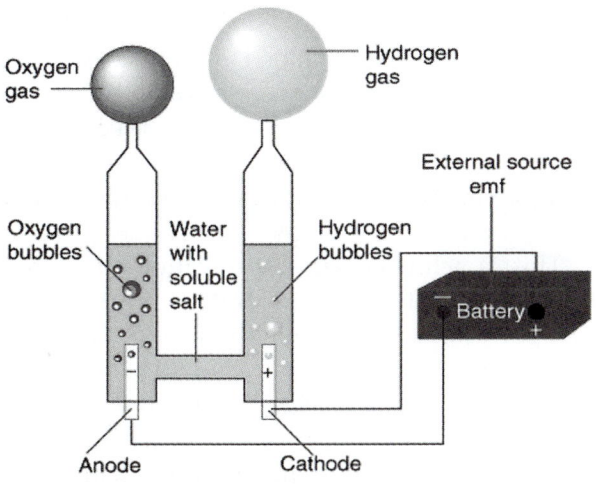

Figure 9-39. Water hydrolysis

than a home is using, the excess is simply fed back into the grid, essentially subtracting from the homeowner's utility bill. In an off-grid application, the excess is put into batteries. But fuel cells are more versatile and their price is rapidly declining.

Existing electrolyzers are costly; hence, the challenge is devising a system that is efficient enough to make energy inexpensively. In general, however, PV electricity should be used as such, for electricity is the highest quality energy available, but this will require the introduction of new generation batteries able to recharge rapidly with large amounts of energy.

Yet, the idea is plausible to use the PV energy to crack water molecules into hydrogen and oxygen to be used later in a fuel cell to make electricity when the sun is not shining. The concept is a closed-loop system in which hydrogen oxidized with air in the fuel cell creates water, which is captured and used again.

Thermo-chemical Water Splitting

Achieving our energy independence will require large-scale alternative energy generation, where solar-based H_2O splitting could play a deciding role. This process requires practical technology in terms of quantity and cost, which the thermo-chemical redox-cycle process using simple and robust materials is capable of.

This process is a thermal reaction that requires an energy input in a multichannel ceramic honeycomb reactor resembling the familiar catalytic converter of automobiles, coated with active water-splitting materials. The system is heated by concentrated solar radiation using a set of mirrors to concentrate the solar energy, increasing the temperature in the reactor.

In the first step of water splitting, the activated redox reagent (usually the reduced state of a metal oxide) is oxidized by taking oxygen from water. With the help of high temperature heat, the process produces hydrogen, according to the reaction:

$$MOx \text{ (reduced)} + H_2O \longrightarrow MOx \text{ (oxidized} + H_2$$

During the second step, the oxidized state of the reagent is reduced, to be used again (regeneration), delivering some of the oxygen of its lattice according to reaction:

$$MOx \text{ (oxidized)} \longrightarrow / MOx \text{ (reduced)} + O_2$$

The metal oxide (such as mixed iron oxide) in this case acts as redox system, which is fixed on the surface of a porous absorber. At the beginning, the metal oxide

is present in a reduced form. By adding water vapor at 800°C, oxygen is abstracted from the water molecules and hydrogen is produced. When the metal oxide system is saturated, or fully oxidized, it is heated for regeneration at 1100°C-1200°C in an oxygen-lean atmosphere.

Oxygen is exhausted from the redox system using nitrogen as a flushing gas. The product gas passes through heat exchangers and is cooled down before residual water is separated.

The receiver surface is divided into several square apertures; two apertures make up one receiver pair. One aperture is applied for the dissociation of the water vapor, while the other one is used for the regeneration of the redox system.

Thus, hydrogen can be produced continuously by alternating the reaction steps.

One advantage is the production of pure hydrogen and the removal of oxygen in separate steps, avoiding the need for high temperature separation and the chance of an explosive mixture formation. The active redox material is capable of water splitting and regeneration, so that complete operation (water splitting and redox material regeneration) is achieved in a closed solar reactor.

Iodine–sulfur Thermo-chemical Water Splitting

Another promising approach for hydrogen production is the iodine–sulfur (IS) thermo-chemical water splitting cycle. Here, high temperature is needed to start and maintain the reaction, which consists of three sections:

1. Bunsen
2. Hydrogen–Iodide (HI)
3. Sulfuric acid

This complex process is initiated in the Bunsen section, where under the effects of high heat influx, assisted by the action of sulfur dioxide (SO_2) and iodine (I_2), excess water and heat are added to keep the exothermic and spontaneous character of the reaction.

Once started, the reaction needs to be kept exothermic, and when it is stabilized, excess iodine is added to help the mixture split into two immiscible aqueous phases.

This is achieved via the so-called spontaneous liquid–liquid (L–L) phase separation process, during which sulfuric acid and poly-hydroiodic acid (HIx) phases are obtained.

The lighter sulfuric acid phase is fed to the sulfuric acid (H_2SO_4) decomposition section, where it is concentrated, while at the same time it is thermally decomposed to sulfur trioxide (SO_3) and water (H_2O).

Increasing the temperature dissociates the sulfur trioxide, which is readily divided into oxygen (O_2) and sulfur dioxide (SO_2).

Thus obtained O_2 can be used as a by-product of the reaction if and when needed, while the SO_2 and H_2 have to be re-cooled and recycled back to the Bunsen section and stored for further use.

At the same time, the heavier HIx phase is sent to the HI decomposition section, where the hydrogen iodide (HI) is separated from the mixture and is exposed to high heat, where it is thermally decomposed into H_2 and I_2. The resulting H_2 gas is the final product of this process, and is stored for future use.

The accompanying I_2 and H_2 are also cooled and recycled.

NOTE: Using the waste heat from solar (CSP) installations to maintain the H_2 generation reaction have been proposed. We see this as one way to do both: provide very much needed cooling for the CSP plant steam, while at the same time providing heat as needed to maintain the exothermic nature of the H_2 generation reaction.

One problem with this approach is that the volume and heat content of the CSP plant's steam varies with the weather conditions. Inconsistent steam volume or heat content would hinder the proper maintenance of the H_2 generating reaction. CSP plants with energy storage, however, might be able to resolve this problem and provide constant quality steam using the stored heat as a source.

Photo-electrochemical H_2 Gas Generation

Hydrogen generation is a big business, which will increase in importance in the near future.

Presently hydrogen is generated by several commercial methods:

1. Steam reforming uses *natural gas*, or methane mixed with steam, where the mixture is exposed to very high temperatures (700–1100°C) to react and release *syngas* (mixture of hydrogen and carbon monoxide).

2. Partial oxidation is a process that occurs when a *sub-stoichiometric* fuel-air mixture is partially *combusted* in a reformer, creating a hydrogen-rich *syngas*. There are thermal partial oxidations, and catalytic partial oxidations, different types of processes that produce the same syngas mixture.

3. Plasma reforming is a high-power plasma method conducted in a plasma reactor. It is used for the production of hydrogen and *carbon black* from crude oil.

4. Coal gasification and carbonization are processes that convert coal into *syngas* and *methane* via low and high temperature processes.

One of the most practical—and for now most useful—ways to use photo electrochemical devices is the generation of hydrogen gas. Hydrogen gas obtained that way can be used for energy production or stored for later use. The method we describe in the following uses special photo-electro-chemical cells (PECs) to convert water into hydrogen, using solar energy for a power source.

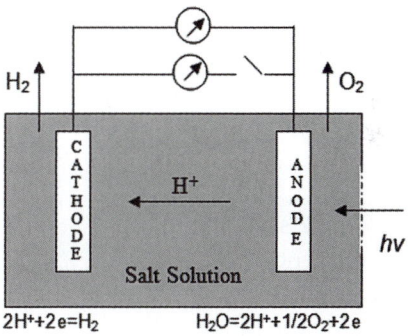

Figure 9-40. Photo-electrochemical cell

The photo-electrochemical (PEC) principle of power generation (involving water decomposition) is based on the conversion of sunlight energy into electricity by a cell consisting of two electrodes immersed in a liquid (usually water) electrolyte.

One of these electrodes is usually a semiconductor material, which when exposed to sunlight is able to absorb part of it as needed to generate electricity.

In theory, there are three options for the arrangement of photo-electrodes in the PEC assembly:

1. Photo-anode made of n-type semiconductor and cathode made of metal

2. Photo-anode made of n-type semiconductor and photo-cathode made of p-type semiconductor

3. Photo-cathode made of p-type semiconductor and anode made of metal

PEC reactions involve several processes within photo-electrodes and at the photo-electrode/electrolyte interface, including:

1. Semiconductor material (photo-anode) partici-

pates into a light-induced intrinsic ionization, forming electronic charge carriers (quasi-free electrons and electron holes)

2. Water at the photo-anode by electron holes is oxidized

3. Transport of H+ ions from the photo-anode to the cathode through the electrolyte and transport of electrons from photo-anode to the cathode through the external circuit

4. Reduction of hydrogen ions at the cathode by electrons. Light results in intrinsic ionization of n-type semiconducting materials over the band gap, leading to the formation of electrons in the conduction band and electron holes in the valence band:

The reactions can be summarized and described as follows:

$$2hv \longrightarrow 2e + 2h_o$$

where:

h is the Planck's constant
v is the frequency
e is the electrons
h_O is the electron hole

This reaction may take place when the energy of photons (hv) is equal to or larger than the band gap. An electric field at the electrode/electrolyte interface is required to avoid recombination of these charge carriers. This may be achieved through modification of the potential at the electrode/electrolyte interface.

The light-induced electron holes result in the splitting of water molecules into gaseous oxygen and hydrogen ions:

$$2h_o + H_2O(liquid) \longrightarrow 1/2O_2(gas) + 2H^+$$

This process takes place at the photo-anode/electrolyte interface. Gaseous oxygen evolves at the photo-anode and the hydrogen ions migrate to the cathode through the internal circuit (aqueous electrolyte).

Simultaneously, the electrons, generated as a result of the initial reaction at the photo-anode, are transferred over the external circuit to the cathode, resulting in the reduction of hydrogen ions into gaseous hydrogen:

$$2H^+ 2e \longrightarrow H_2 (gas)$$

Accordingly, the overall reaction of the PEC may be expressed in the form:

$$2hv + H_2O (liquid) \longrightarrow 1/2O_2 (gas) + H_2 (gas)$$

The above reaction takes place when the energy of the photons absorbed by the photo-anode is equal to or larger than Ei, the threshold energy:

$$Ei = G° (H_2O)/2N_a = hv = 1.23eV$$

where:

$G° (H_2O)$ is the standard free enthalpy of water
N_a is Avogadro's number = $6:022 \times 1023$ mol^{-1}

Hence, the electrochemical decomposition of water is possible when the electromotive force of the cell (EMF) is equal to or larger than 1.23 V. The most frequently studied material for the photo-anode is TiO_2.

Despite its high band gap of 3 eV, it is the favored material owing to its high corrosion resistance. The maximal value obtained for the photo-voltage of a PEC equipped with a photo-anode of TiO_2 is ~ 0.7–0.9 V.

The application of TiO_2 as a photo-electrode requires an electrical bias to decompose water through external or internal bias voltage (through the use of different concentrations of hydrogen ions, or a hybrid electrode).

A typical cell involves both a photo-anode (made of an oxide material) and cathode (made of Pt) immersed in an aqueous solution of a salt (electrolyte). The process results in oxygen and hydrogen evolution at the photo-anode and cathode, respectively.

The related charge transport involves the migration of hydrogen ions in the electrolyte and the transport of electrons in the external circuit.

Photo-catalytic Water Decomposition

The principle of photo-catalytic water decomposition is similar to that of photo-electrochemical water decomposition, except for the difference in the location of the sites of their respective reactions: a) at the photo-anode and cathode in case of photo-electrochemical process, and b) on the surface of the photo-catalyst in the photo-catalytic process.

Thus, the practical difference between these processes is that: a) the photo-electrochemical water decomposition results in the generation of separate oxygen and hydrogen gas streams, while b) in the photo-catalytic process the gasses are mixed.

Progress in R&D

The intensity of research on materials for photo-assisted water decomposition, aiming at the development of PEC technology, is increasing rapidly. To achieve success, the focal points are likely to remain as materials selection, types of electrolytes, and the structure of the PEC units.

The end products need to address the following requirements:

1. The photo-electrodes need to exhibit high-energy conversion efficiencies

2. The PEC units need to be durable and require low maintenance

3. The costs of manufacturing of the PEC units need to be low

PEC cells have reached 10% efficiency in the lab lately, with the main problem being the corrosion of the materials that are in direct contact with liquids, which leads to premature failure of the devices.

In addition, the liquids tend to evaporate and crystallize under long-term exposure to extreme temperatures, which means that the locations of their use need to be carefully selected.

A service life of a minimum of 10,000 hours is needed to meet DOE goals and to provide reliability and cost efficiency to this technology, so the effort is just now starting to address the critical area of reliability.

The Challenges

Despite the advantages, water electrolysis and hydrogen/oxygen fuel cell technologies still face challenges. For instance, the electrodes used in water electrolysis are currently coated with platinum, which is expensive and not a sustainable resource.

Researchers are currently investigating the employment of nano materials with a large reduction on the amount of precious metal needed. Indeed, the main advantage of these materials used as catalysts that splits the water molecules using cobalt phosphate is that it is far cheaper and more abundant compared to expensive metals such as platinum.

Another problem is the intermittent nature of PV electricity (or heat), due to interruptions, like nighttime, clouds, etc., as discussed previously in more detail in this text.

These anomalies create several problems for the H2 generation process, mostly expressed as: 1) the process activity would decrease in time of cloud activity, and 2) A shutdown of H_2 generation process is unacceptable, with numerous consequences. For instance, Ni dissolution at the cathode is initiated, since it is driven to more positive potentials by short-circuit with the anode.

Using stored heat or electricity as energy sources can alleviate these shortcomings. In case of the Ni cathodes, they could be activated, by coating them with a thin layer of different, more active and more stable materials.

The Hydrosol Project

The Hydrosol project was designed and proposed by a group of E.U. scientists and has won a number of prestigious awards as a practical way to generate large amounts of clean energy, including energy storage (for nighttime use) and transport of energy (hydrogen) to remote locations.

The Hydrosol process consists of innovative solar thermo-chemical reactors for the production of hydrogen from water splitting, resembling the familiar catalytic converter of automobiles.

The reactor contains no moving parts and is constructed from special ceramic multi-channeled monoliths that absorb solar radiation. The monolith channels are coated with active water-splitting nano materials capable of splitting water vapor passing through the reactor by trapping its oxygen and leaving as product pure hydrogen in the effluent gas stream.

In a next step, the oxygen-trapping material is solar-aided regenerated (i.e. releases the oxygen absorbed) and a cyclic operation is established on a single, closed reactor/receiver system. The integration of solar energy concentration systems with systems capable to split water will have an immense impact on energy economics worldwide, as it is a promising route to provide affordable, renewable solar hydrogen with virtually zero CO_2 emissions.

The uniqueness of the hydrosol approach is based on coating nano materials with very high water-splitting activity and regenerability (produced by novel routes such as aerosol & combustion synthesis) on special ceramic reactors with high capacity for solar heat absorption. The production of solar hydrogen will offer opportunities to many poor regions of the world, which have a huge solar potential. Producing solar hydrogen will create new opportunities for countries of Southern Europe that can become local producers of energy.

Hydrosol is a new approach, paving a way to new age in energy generation, storage, transport and use in the 21st century.

With traditional energy sources diminishing, interest in alternative energy supplies is increasing. Hydrogen is considered by many to be the next link in the evolution of energy, after nuclear energy.

Hydrogen Economy

1. Hydrogen promises a smooth transition from the existing dirty, inefficient, and unsustainable energy systems of power generation, storage and transport, to clean, efficient, renewable energy.

2. Hydrogen energy generation, storage and transport systems are fully developed today, do not need special materials or processes and can be implemented immediately.

3. The use of hydrogen as energy source is ecologically safe, because there is virtually no pollution generated in the process, unlike most of the conventional energy generators and their supply chains.

4. Solar hydrogen generated power could be quite cheap, around 8-10 cents/kWh.

5. Hydrogen is a convenient, renewable energy source that can be distributed all over the world, including Third World countries, where such implementation is badly needed.

Hydrogen can be cost competitive with gasoline. This estimate is based on the use of solar thermal energy to generate hydrogen, the mass production of the necessary equipment, and subsidies equivalent to those provided to the oil, coal, and utility industries. Large-scale production could deliver hydrogen at under $1 per GGE. Likewise, given the low cost of producing electrical power from existing hydroelectric dams, the use of this electricity to produce hydrogen by electrolysis would cost less than gasoline.

Hydrogen holds the world's record for burning faster than any other fuel and at leaner (lower) fuel-to-air ratios than the ratios for hydrocarbon fuels. These characteristics allow engines that burn hydrogen to operate more efficiently than those that depend on other fuels.

Virtually every existing engine application from lawn mowers to automobiles and locomotives can be fueled with hydrogen, and benefits include more power and longer engine life. But perhaps the most astonishing benefit of burning hydrogen in a conventional engine is what we might call minus emissions—that is, the exhaust pipe releases cleaner air than that which enters the engine. Atmospheric levels of carbon monoxide, tire particles, hydrocarbons, pollen, and diesel soot are reduced as the hydrogen flame cleans air. The pollutants are substantially converted into harmless gases.

Kits for high-efficiency combustion of hydrogen

can be retrofitted on most engines in the global fleet of motor vehicles. Ordinary engines that have been converted to operate on hydrogen show no sign of metal embrittlement or other degradation after decades of pollution-free service. Engine oil stays clean, spark plugs last much longer, and degradation as measured by corrosion and wear on piston rings and bearings is greatly reduced. These vehicles can therefore last longer, run better, and clean the air. And this transition will facilitate the distribution of hydrogen for the advent of fuel cells on a commercial scale [see "The Fuel Cell Future," *The World & I*, April 1994, p. 192].

Solar hydrogen can make any country energy-independent and pollution-free as far into the future as the sun will shine. Illustratively, just a small portion of North America can produce enough solar hydrogen to supply all the energy needs of the whole continent. Currently, Canada, Germany, Japan, Saudi Arabia, and Russia lead the world in developing plans to employ solar hydrogen. And several major auto manufacturers have experimental fleets of hydrogen-powered vehicles.

In this manner, if solar hydrogen is used to provide energy-intensive goods and services to the world's population, it will facilitate wealth addition as opposed to wealth depletion that results from burning fossil resources. The harder that we work in the solar-hydrogen economy, the more goods and security everyone can have, resulting in a lower rate of inflation and less reason for conflicts and strife. These circumstances can create a global incentive to work for higher sustainable living standards for both present and future generations.

Practical Hydrogen Economy

A quote in the media from an unknown source: "With most hydrogen today being produced from hydrocarbons, the cost per unit of energy delivered through hydrogen is higher than the cost of the same unit of energy from the hydrocarbon itself." Duh!

Energy economy powered by solar hydrogen requires complete control of the production, storage, distribution, and utilization of hydrogen and the production of electricity from renewable energy sources. This could happen by:

1. Establishing renewable power fields, where generators convert solar energy and its derivatives, such as wind, falling water, wave motion, and biomass resources into electricity and hydrogen to be used as storage of energy or for transport to be used at remote locations.

2. Surplus hydrogen, and that for night power gen-

eration, could be stored in depleted natural gas and oil wells and similar geological formations.

3. Existing infrastructure of electricity grids, natural gas pipelines, highways, and rails to distribute hydrogen and electricity from renewable resources could be used without much modification and expense.

4. Installation of kits that enable the current internal combustion engines of motor vehicles to operate with directly injected hydrogen, landfill gas, or gasoline. A vehicle converted to operate on hydrogen cleans the air through which it travels.

5. Introduction of automobiles that run on hydrogen-based fuel cells, to replace the wasteful and dirty internal combustion engines.

6. Installation of reversible electrolyzers and fuel cells in homes and businesses, where these could produce electricity during off-peak hours to be converted to storable hydrogen. Thus stored hydrogen can be used to make electricity at peak hours.

DOE Hydrogen Roadmap

The U.S. Department of Energy (DOE) has fully appreciated and evaluated the need for a new hydrogen-based economy, and has made some attempts to outline and implement the steps. Some of the conclusions and decisions—albeit focusing on the generation, storage and transport of hydrogen for fueling cars—follow herein: (2)

Hydrogen Production, Challenges

Multiple challenges need to be overcome to achieve the vision of secure, abundant, inexpensive, and clean hydrogen production with low carbon emissions.

The DOE roadmap established in 2002 is as follows: (11)

Hydrogen production costs are high relative to conventional fuels. With most hydrogen currently produced from hydrocarbons, the cost per unit of energy delivered through hydrogen is higher than the cost of the same unit of energy from the hydrocarbon itself. This is especially the case when the comparison is made at the point of sale to the customer, as delivery costs for hydrogen are also higher than for hydrocarbons.

The large-scale, well-developed production and delivery infrastructures for natural gas, oil, coal, and electricity keep energy prices low and set a tough price point for hydrogen to meet.

Low demand inhibits development of production capacity. Although there is a healthy, growing market for hydrogen in refineries and chemical plants, there is little demand for hydrogen as an energy carrier. Demand growth will depend on the development and implementation of hydrogen storage and conversion devices, and on demand from products such as hydrogen-powered cars and electric generators. Without demand for high-quality hydrogen in the merchant energy carrier market, there is little incentive for industry to completely develop, optimize, and implement existing and new technologies.

Table 9-18. Hydrogen production issues and cost

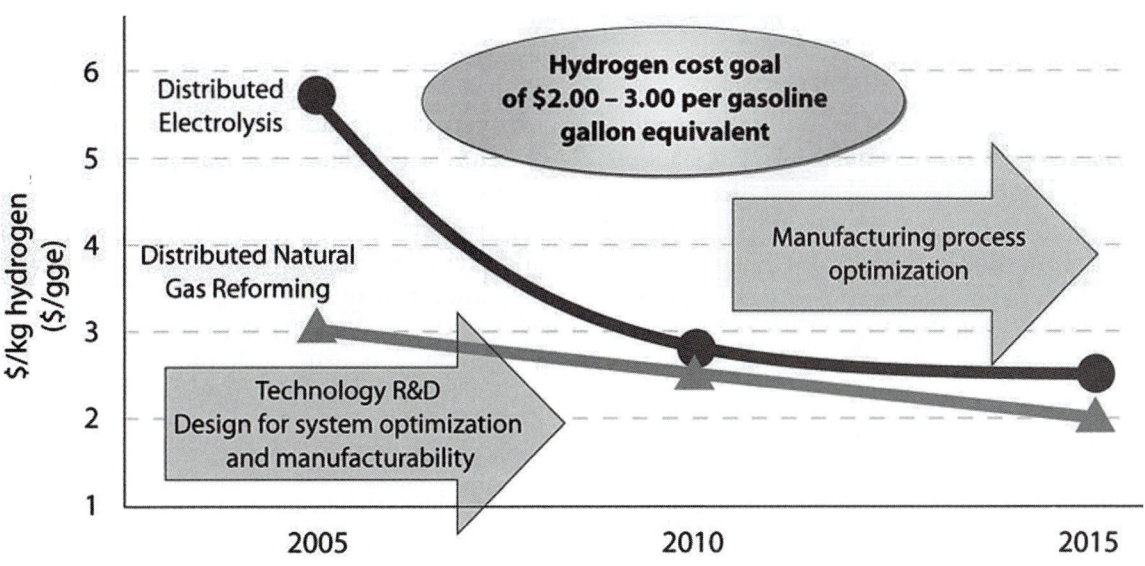

Current technologies produce large quantities of carbon dioxide and aren't optimized for making hydrogen as an energy carrier. Existing production technologies can produce vast amounts of hydrogen from hydrocarbons, but they emit large amounts of carbon dioxide into the atmosphere. Existing commercial production methods (such as steam methane reformation, multi-fuel gasification, and electrolysis) require technical improvements to reduce costs, improve efficiencies, and produce inexpensive, high-purity hydrogen with little or no carbon emissions.

Advanced hydrogen production methods need development. While wind, solar, and geothermal resources can produce hydrogen electrolytically, and biomass can produce hydrogen directly, other advanced methods for producing hydrogen from renewable and sustainable energy sources without generating carbon dioxide are still in early research and development phases. Processes such as nuclear thermo-chemical water splitting, photo-electrochemical electrolysis, and biological methods require long-term, focused efforts to move toward commercial readiness. If hydrogen production is to be more cost-competitive using renewable technologies such as solar, wind, and geothermal, they will need further development.

Public-private production demonstrations are essential. Stakeholders need a basic understanding of the different sources of hydrogen production before they will be willing to embrace the concepts. Demonstrations are the best way to gain the needed confidence. The large scale of some production processes, however, makes them particularly difficult and expensive to demonstrate.

H_2 Generation

The most developed technologies for alternative electricity generation are photovoltaic, thermal and wind energy conversion. All these technologies are today sufficiently developed and field-tested, so they are becoming household terms. They are also becoming technologically and economically feasible. For example, a 100 MWp photovoltaic power plant installed in a desert area with yearly insolation of 2300 kWh/m, and 15% efficiency of conversion into hydrogen would have a collector surface of about 1/2 km^2 and would produce yearly 0.5×10^9 m^3 of hydrogen.

New, more efficient solar technologies, like multi-junction solar cells and efficient CSP receivers, are capable of bringing the sunlight-to-AC power efficiencies to 30% today, and over 50% in the near future. This will also reduce land and labor costs, and material and land requirements.

The E.U. electricity consumption could be met with the European yearly insolation of about 1000 kWh/mZ/y and 15% conversion efficiency, using less than 1% of Europe's land surface. This is, actually, how much surface is actually used for the E.U. roads (2.5×10^6 km length). It, however, doesn't make much sense to use the population-dense and cloud-covered Europe for such mass energy production. A better alternative is using the deserts in Africa, especially those in North Africa, which could produce all the energy that Europe needs, and much more if and when needed.

That is a grand undertaking, but it also represents a smart investment in the future, which will benefit not only the European nations, but will provide the inhabitants of the African countries with opportunities that they presently do not have and desperately need. This might bring much needed peace in the entire region as well.

The yearly insolation in Africa's deserts is approximately 2000 kWh/m^2, so a surface area of less than 0.035% of Africa's land mass would be required by the collector field to meet Europe's entire electricity consumption.

It is easy to see underwater cables crossing the Mediterranean Sea to deliver high voltage DC power to sub-stations in France, Spain, Germany, and Italy for conversion to AC and distribution to the other E.U. nations.

Some of the energy produced by the solar fields in Africa (approximately 1/4) can be converted to LH$_2$ and delivered in conventional transport vehicles to power stations to those already mentioned E.U. countries for conversion into electricity and distribution in the E.U. power network.

Far fetched? Not really. Where are the Europeans of the 21st century going to get their energy—from the unreliable and unfriendly Russian gas deliveries? From the almost depleted Saudi Arabian oil wells? The E.U. nations have very few choices, and sooner they realize that, sooner they would be able to start this monumental task. It seems to be the only choice Europe has for long-term energy independence, like it or not.

The continental U.S. has similar problems, although the situation here is somewhat different. We (and Canada) have a lot of oil and gas deposits and could go much longer down the path of unsustainable, wasteful and dirty carbon economy, but would be the most selfish people on Earth to do that. We need to wake up and realize that the on-going exploitation of Earth and the environment cannot continue indefinitely, so smarter and more sustainable ways need to be found. Solar hydrogen production comes to the rescue as the most efficient, versatile, and cost-effective alternative energy technology available today.

Storage and Distribution

Once generated, hydrogen can be stored in its gaseous form, but it is more convenient to convert it into a liquid form. In this state, hydrogen can be transported, stored and burned either as free hydrogen or linked to other molecules like ammonia (NH_3), methanol (CH_3OH), methylcyclohexane (C_7H_{14}), or in a solid, such as a metal hydride.

Although liquid hydrogen (LH_2) has the highest energy density, it is disadvantaged by the energy required (approximately 30% of its combustion energy) for conversion into liquid and to keep it at a very low temperature of 20 K. Although large quantities of LH_2 is a relatively new process, experience from the space sector, and transport of liquid natural gas (LNG) is directly applicable, since the storage techniques of hydrogen as a gas are similar to those of natural gas. It can be stored in tanks, underground in confined aquifers, or in abandoned natural gas reservoirs. The losses from underground reservoirs are in the order of 2- 30 per year. Most rock formations are sealed by water in their capillary pores, so that the nature and properties of the contained gas have no effect on the overall leakage.

Transportation and distribution of LH_2 can be done also, and most conveniently by pipelines and in pressurized or cryogenic containers. A gaseous hydrogen pipeline system of some hundred kilometers and a vacuum-jacketed LH2-System of some hundred meters are in operation today, including the U.S. Kennedy Space Center.

Another method is to convert (combine) LH_2 into Methylcyclohexane, which is liquid at ambient pressure and temperature, so it can in its "as is" state (its consistence and specific weight are similar to diesel fuel) to be stored and transported in normal oil product carriers. This is important for a smooth energy-system infrastructure transition from crude oil to hydrogen.

And yet another form LH_2 that lends itself for storage and transport is solids. Solid, rechargeable metal hydrides, for example, offer favorable volumetric hydrogen packing, although the weight of the non-saturated compounds needed for storage of hydrogen is rather high. In a transition period, hydrogen could be mixed with natural gas; the "town gas" we knew in the past contained up to 60% hydrogen.

End use of Hydrogen

Hydrogen is a carbon-free fuel with excellent combustion properties. This makes it a clean, universal fuel for use in industry, households, power stations, road vehicles and aviation.

The specific properties of hydrogen induce new end use techniques, such as:

Fuel Cells

The key element of an efficient, future electricity generation is the fuel cell, for which hydrogen is the best fuel. Since these are devices that transform chemical energy directly into electric energy, hydrogen generation is not subjected to Carnot cycle limitations. It is also done silently without moving parts and with high efficiency.

Efficiencies of future fuel cells like molten carbonate cells operating at 600-800°C with total energy efficiencies of 60-80% with waste heat at 600°C make the fuel cell concept a potential candidate for use in power stations, road and space vehicles.

Advances in catalyst and electrode technology and cost reductions will have to be made, however, before fuel cells can seriously be considered for general use.

Notwithstanding, several power plants have already been built around the world.

Catalytic burners

Hydrogen, having lower ignition energy than some conventional fuels, including natural gas, burns smokeless when in contact with a suitable catalytic surface. Its burning temperature is quite low too—between 100-400°C. This then makes it a preferred technology for generating low-temperature heat in residential space heaters, cooking devices and industrial dryers and heaters.

Catalytic combustion has the advantages of higher safety level and very high efficiency of up to 99% with negligible emissions of nitrogen oxides.

Liquid hydrogen technologies:

Super/hypersonic aviation and direct use in jet engines at super/hypersonic speeds could be advantageously—if not necessarily—powered with liquid hydrogen because it has:

a. Higher (three-fold) gravimetric heating value compared with kerosene

b. Cooling capacity, which can be used to cool critical parts (turbine inlet rim, wing leading edges, passenger cabins, etc.), since the LH_2 cryogenic storage temperature is approximately -252°C

In addition, and as an added benefit, cooling of the wing skin induces laminar flow and therefore reduces drag considerably, theoretically by up to 30% ("laminar flow control").

Automotive vehicles

The main problem of hydrogen utilization in vehicles is storage, due to the low volumetric energy content of hydrogen, which is about one-third that of gasoline. Even liquid hydrogen is far less dense than hydrocarbon fuels. Three different storage technologies are actually available and more or less mature: gaseous hydrogen in pressure vessels, cryogenic liquid hydrogen and hydrogen chemically bonded in metal and liquid hydrides (methylcyclohexane).

The low ignition energy of hydrogen and its wide ignition range of hydrogen/air mixtures make gas turbines as well as piston engines well adaptable for hydrogen combustion. The ignition within a wide range of non-stoichiometric air/fuel mixture permits combustion with high amounts of excess air and thus full and load operations with low nitrogen oxides emission.

Many vehicles with hydride storage have been built and operated by Daimler Benz and others through the years, although the operation of the necessary infrastructure, refueling and service are other issues to be solved.

A number of liquid hydrogen cars have been built and operated by BMW and DFVLR (Deutsche Forschungs-und Versuchsanstalt fur Luft-und Raumfahrt). And trucks with the methylcyclohexane technology have been built and operated by the Paul Scherrer Institute in Switzerland.

It should be emphasized that the problems of the necessary infrastructure development are at least as significant as the development of the different components.

Hydrogen Homesteads

In a transition period, gaseous hydrogen can be utilized in the existing natural gas pipelines of natural gas fueled appliances in home areas and in industry, bearing in mind, however, that such a pipe-system would not be optimized for the use of hydrogen. Hydrogen has a volumetric heating value of approximately 1/3 of that of natural gas, it requires a three times higher flow rate and compressor power at given pipe diameter and energy flow to keep the system under pressure (50-70 bar).

Practical Examples

There is a lot of work underway in this area of the energy industry. For example, Enel, Italy started operation of a 12 MW H2-powered electricity plant in Venice recently. Hydrogen by-products from local petrochemical industries fuel the plant. The turbines were specially designed to resist embrittlement from hydrogen, but in any case the only emission of hydrogen combustion is water.

In the last ten years, much hype has been associated with the topic of hydrogen, which has raised several questions, such as the claim that hydrogen is an economically viable fuel for transportation because of the cost and greenhouse gases generated during production, the low energy content per volume and weight of the container, the cost of the fuel cells, and the cost of the infrastructure.

The price of solar electricity in the last three years has fallen to such an extent, and the pace of innovation in both fields of solar energy has been so intense, that a number of unexpected practical hydrogen-based applications have emerged.

One application is commercial boat engines, such as the commercial electric boat powered by an H_2–O_2 fuel cell.

In 2009, the Austrian companies Fronius, Bitter and Frauscher successfully presented Riviera 600, the first electric boat powered by solar hydrogen fuel cells. The concept is that of a self-contained energy supply provided by hydrogen simply obtained by photovoltaic electrolysis of water.

The team Future Project Hydrogen has created budget calculations for the generation of hydrogen on site by the use of PVs under the premises of 10 boats for commercial use, for example, boat rentals. With a range of 80 kilometers with a full hydrogen tank, the boat is 6 m long, 2.2 m wide and weighs 1400 kg. It was awarded a safety certificate by Germany's T€ UV. Its 4 kW continuous power electric motor has twice the range of conventional battery-powered boats. The 47% efficiency of the noise-free fuel cell engine should be compared to the 18–20% efficiency of a conventional (steel) internal combustion engine.

The main economic advantage of those, compared with conventional electric boats, is the fact that no time has to be spent charging the batteries. For conventional electric boats, 6–8 h of charging gives just 4–6 h of use. The hydrogen-powered electric boat requires only the time that it takes to change the cartridge—5 min. The boat's fueling system consists of a 20 kg cartridge that can be charged with up to 0.7 kg of hydrogen kept at 350 bar. Refueling is done using standard filler coupling or a simple exchange of an empty cartridge for a full one.

For example, all three companies involved in the "Future Project Hydrogen" are based in Austria, very close to each other. The Technical University of Graz provided scientific and technical advice, whereas the project was realized with support of the European Union regional programs and further funding from one of Austria's regions. The first 600 Riviera boat is commercialized at 150 000 V; the first exemplars were to be delivered to customers in early 2010.

The energy filling ("Clean Power") station makes use of PV modules integrated in a 250 m² flat roof, and further connected to an electrolytic cell. Even at Austria's cold latitudes, the station is capable of affording an annual yield of 823 kg of hydrogen, equivalent to 1100 cartridges with a 27,200 kW h energy content, namely enough hydrogen to run a boat for 80,000 km. Its installation is simple thanks to the "container construction" design that can be carried out simply and quickly to many different locations. The station is comprised of an electricity power charger, hydrogen, and payment units (Fig. 8). By comparison, storing power in batteries over long periods of time is linked to huge losses due to self-discharge (5–10% per month), while the energy density is a fraction of that for hydrogen, which means that by storing energy in the summer in a battery of the same capacity, one would have no more energy available in the winter.

Another example that shows that photovoltaic renewable hydrogen is far from being solely a research topic is given by the world's first underground pipeline supplying H2 to customers in the Italian city of Arezzo.

The pipeline serves 4 companies and the Hydro-LAb with a main channel of around 600 m where the whole network is around 1 km. Four goldsmith companies use it for industrial and energy needs, using four 5 kW fuel cells and two 1 kW fuel cells at the HydroLAb, the laboratory for hydrogen and renewable energies.

The aim was to set up a completely off-grid testing lab for technologies in the renewable energy sector, collecting data to test solar energy technologies linked with hydrogen production and use. Hence, solar panels provide electricity, solar thermal vacuum tube panels provide space heat heating and feed a 5 kW solar cooling machine for zero emission air conditioning in summer.

Wastewater is completely recycled through a special remediation dry technique and rain is collected and stored. The technologies implemented are continuously monitored, with the aim of further optimization in view of widespread commercial application in the building industry.

Fuel cells are the best use for hydrogen as fuel. Hydrogen generated by solar or wind power could also serve as an efficient energy storage medium in the future. Presently, however, its use in fuel cells is the focus.

Fuel Cells

During his 2003 State of the Union address, then President Bush announced the hydrogen fuel initiative (HFI), which supported by legislation in the energy policy act of 2005 (EPACT 2005) and the advanced energy initiative of 2006 was aimed to develop hydrogen, fuel cell and infrastructure technologies to make fuel-cell vehicles practical and cost-effective by 2020.

During the last decade, the U.S. alone has dedicated more than $1.0 billion to hydrogen and fuel cell research and development. Why the push? The general thinking is that fuel cells generate electrical power quietly and efficiently, without pollution. Unlike power sources that use fossil fuels, the by-products from an operating fuel cell are heat and water. But how does it do this, and what is the catch? There is always a catch…

A fuel cell is an electrochemical energy conversion device. In a fuel cell the chemical elements hydrogen and oxygen are reacted to create water, which also produces electricity.

$$2H_2 + O_2 = 2H_2O + \text{electric energy}$$

This process is similar to that of the common battery, which has all its chemicals stored inside and is capable of converting them into electricity when needed. Once the chemicals are used, the battery "goes dead" and has to be recharged. The fuel cell, on the other hand, has chemicals supplied constantly from the outside, so it is operational as long as the chemicals flow into it. Most fuel cells in use today use hydrogen and oxygen as the precursors that are used in water and energy generation by the cell.

There are several different types of fuel cells, distinguished mostly by the different chemical processes, operating temperature and the type of electrolyte they use. Some fuel cells are used in large stationary power generation plants, while others are more practical for

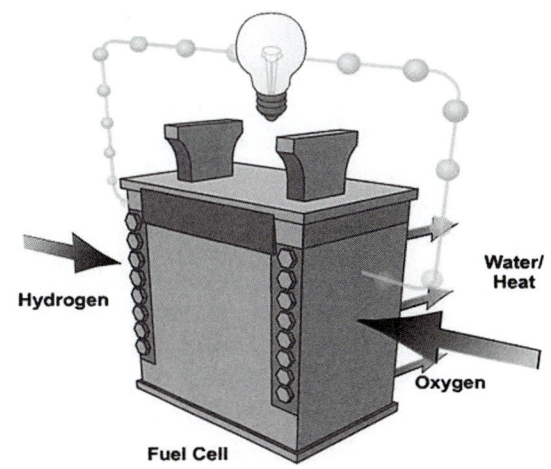

Figure 9-41. Fuel cell operation

use in smaller, portable applications, including powering cars and trucks.

The main types of fuel cells are:

Alkaline fuel cell (AFC)

AFC is one of the oldest fuel cells, a version of which was used in the U.S.'s space program in the 1960s. The AFC, however, is very expensive and susceptible to contamination, so it requires very pure hydrogen and oxygen. That makes it unlikely to be commercialized.

Direct-methano Fuel Cell (DMFC)

DMFC operate at relatively low temperatures, but are not very efficient. DMFC also requires a large amount of platinum catalyst, which makes these fuel cells expensive, and therefore not likely to be used in general commercial applications.

Molten-carbonate Fuel Cell (MCFC)

MCFC are best suited for large stationary power generators, since they operate at 600°C to make steam that can be used to generate more power. Since they have lower operating temperatures than the solid oxide fuel cells, no exotic materials are needed for their fabrication, thus their cost is lower.

Phosphoric-acid Fuel Cell (PAFC)

PAFCs operate at a higher temperature than polymer exchange membrane fuel cells, so they have a longer warm-up time, which makes them unsuitable for use in cars. They can be successfully used in small, stationary power-generation systems.

Solid oxide Fuel Cell (SOFC)

SOFCs are also best suited for large-scale stationary power generators, since they operate at very high temperatures, in the 700-1,000°C range, which is suitable for steam turbine operation. The high temperatures, however, create reliability problems, since parts of the fuel cell can break down after cycling on and off repeatedly. SOFCs are very stable under continuous operation, and have demonstrated the longest operating life of any fuel cell under normal operating conditions.

Polymer (proton) Exchange Membrane Fuel Cell (PEMFC)

PEMFC is considered the most practical fuel cell by the U.S. DOE, which is focused on developing this technology for transportation applications.

It consists of a proton-conducting membrane, such as a perfluorosulphonic acid polymer as the electrolyte that has good proton conducting properties, contained between two platinum-impregnated porous electrodes. The backs of the electrodes are coated with a hydrophobic compound such as TeflonR, thus forming a wet-proof coating which provides a gas diffusion path to the catalyst layer.

Within the cell, H_2 at the anode provides protons and releases electrons, which pass through the external circuit to reach the cathode. The protons dissolve in the water molecules and diffuse through the membrane to the cathode to react with the O_2, while picking up electrons and forming water.

To function properly, the membrane needs to conduct hydrogen ions (protons)—but not electrons—as this would in effect "short circuit" the fuel cell. The membrane needs to also not allow either gas to pass to the other side of the cell, a problem known as gas crossover. Finally, the membrane needs to be resistant to the reducing environment at the cathode as well as the harsh oxidative environment at the anode.

A proton exchange membrane fuel cell is different, in that it transforms the chemical energy liberated during the electrochemical reaction of hydrogen and oxygen to electrical energy, as opposed to the direct combustion of hydrogen and oxygen gases to produce thermal energy.

Hydrogen is delivered to the anode side of the membrane electrode assembly, where it is catalytically split into protons and electrons. The newly formed protons permeate through the polymer electrolyte membrane to the cathode side.

At the same time, the electrons travel along an external load circuit to the cathode side of the MEA, thus creating the current output of the fuel cell, while a stream of oxygen is delivered to the cathode side of the MEA.

At the cathode side, oxygen molecules react with the protons permeating through the polymer electrolyte membrane and the electrons arriving through the external circuit to form water molecules. The reversible reaction causes the reincorporation of the hydrogen protons and electrons together with the oxygen molecule and the formation of one water molecule.

PEMFCs have very high power density and operate at relatively low temperature in the range of 140-175°F. This low operating temperature allows the cell to warm up quickly and begin to generate electricity almost immediately. These factors make it most suitable for powering cars and trucks.

Fuel Cells Efficiency and Use

Efficiency is the practical measure of the usefulness

of an energy system or device that converts energy. It is measured by the ratio of the amount of useful energy put out by the system ("output energy") to the total amount of energy that is put in ("input energy"). It can be also expressed as the useful output energy in percentage of the total input energy.

The useful output energy of fuel cells is measured in terms of total electrical energy produced by the system. The input energy is the energy stored in the fuel used by the cell, and according to the U.S. DOE, fuel cells are 40–60% efficient. This means that 40-60% of the total (100%) incoming energy is converted into useful electricity, vs. 25% efficiency (58% theoretical efficiency) of a car engine.

In some combined heat and power systems, the heat produced by the fuel cell is captured and put to use, increasing the efficiency of the system to up to 90%. Solid oxide fuel cells or molten carbonate fuel cells) can be also combined with gas turbines to allow stationary fuel cells efficiency to get closer to the theoretical limit.

A gas turbine would capture heat from the fuel cell and turn it into mechanical energy to increase the fuel cell's operational efficiency. This solution has been predicted to increase total efficiency to as much as 70%. In practice, the tank-to-wheel efficiency of a fuel cell vehicle is greater than 45% at low loads and about 36% at higher loads.

Fuel cell vehicles running on compressed hydrogen may have an overall power-plant-to-wheel efficiency of 22% if the hydrogen is stored as high-pressure gas, but only 17% if it is stored as liquid hydrogen, due to the high energy used at the plant.

Fuel cells also cannot store energy like a battery, but in some stand-alone solar or wind power plants they are combined with electrolyzers and storage systems to form an energy storage system that generates hydrogen. Presently, however, steam methane reforming produces most hydrogen, and so it is a carbon dioxide polluter.

The overall efficiency (electricity to hydrogen and back to electricity) of such plants (known as round-trip efficiency), using pure hydrogen and pure oxygen can be in the 35-50% range, depending on gas density and other conditions. The electrolyzer/fuel cell system has an advantage in that it can store indefinite quantities of hydrogen; therefore, it is better suited for long-term storage.

Solid-oxide fuel cells produce exothermic heat from the recombination of the oxygen and hydrogen. The ceramic can run as hot as 800°C. This heat can be captured and used to heat water in a micro combined heat and power (m-CHP) application. When the heat is captured, total efficiency can reach 80–90% at the unit, but that does not consider production and distribution losses. CHP units are being developed today for the European home market.

We can conclude that fuel cells are efficient relative to combustion engines, but are not as efficient as batteries, which is due primarily to the inefficiency of the oxygen reduction reaction and the oxygen evolution reaction, when the hydrogen be formed by electrolysis of water.

The fuel cells also make sense for solo-operation (disconnected from the grid), or when fuel can be provided continuously. For applications that require frequent and relatively rapid start-ups, or where zero emissions are a requirement, as the enclosed spaces in warehouses, where hydrogen is unacceptable fuel, or if changing or charging batteries is inconvenient, then a PEM fuel cell is an attractive choice.

Fuel cells can also be used with low-quality gas from landfills or wastewater treatment plants to generate power and lower methane emissions.

Although there are currently no fuel cell electric vehicles available for commercial sale, there have been over 20 FCEV prototypes and demonstration cars since 2009. Honda FCX Clarity, Toyota FCHV-adv, and Mercedes-Benz F-Cell are some examples of the most promising prototypes. Demonstration fuel cell vehicles have a 250 mi range between refueling stops. They can be refueled in less than 5 minutes at properly equipped fueling stations.

At the Paris auto show in September 2012, Hyundai announced that it plans to begin producing a commercial production fuel cell model (based on the ix35) and hopes to deliver 1,000 of them by 2015. Other manufacturers planning to sell fuel cell electric vehicles commercially by 2016 or earlier include General Motors, Honda, and Nissan.

In 2003, U.S. President George W. Bush proposed the hydrogen fuel initiative (HFI). This aimed at further developing hydrogen fuel cells and infrastructure technologies with the goal of producing commercial fuel cell vehicles. By 2008, the U.S. had contributed $1 billion to this project. The Obama administration sought to reduce funding for the development of fuel cell vehicles, concluding that other vehicle technologies will lead to quicker reduction in emissions in a shorter time. Steven Chu, the U.S. Secretary of Energy, stated in 2009 that hydrogen vehicles "will not be practical over the next 10-20 years."

In 2012, however, Chu stated that he sees fuel cell cars as more economically feasible as natural gas prices

Table 9-19. U.S. DOE fuel cell program

FUEL CELL TECHNOLOGIES PROGRAM

Comparison of Fuel Cell Technologies

Fuel Cell Type	Common Electrolyte	Operating Temperature	Typical Stack Size	Efficiency	Applications	Advantages	Disadvantages
Polymer Electrolyte Membrane (PEM)	Perfluoro sulfonic acid	50-100°C 122-212° typically 80°C	< 1kW-100kW	60% transportation 35% stationary	• Backup power • Portable power • Distributed generation • Transporation • Specialty vehicles	• Solid electrolyte reduces corrosion & electrolyte management problems • Low temperature • Quick start-up	• Expensive catalysts • Sensitive to fuel impurities • Low temperature waste heat
Alkaline (AFC)	Aqueous solution of potassium hydroxide soaked in a matrix	90-100°C 194-212°F	10-100 kW	60%	• Military • Space	• Cathode reaction faster in alkaline electrolyte, leads to high performance • Low cost components	• Sensitive to CO$_2$ in fuel and air • Electrolyte management
Phosphoric Acid (PAFC)	Phosphoric acid soaked in a matrix	150-200°C 302-392°F	400 kW 100 kW module	40%	• Distributed generation	• Higher temperature enables CHP • Increased tolerance to fuel impurities	• Pt catalyst • Long start up time • Low current and power
Molten Carbonate (MCFC)	Solution of lithium, sodium, and/ or potassium carbonates, soaked in a matrix	600-700°C 1112-1292°F	300 kW-3 MW 300 kW module	45-50%	• Electric utility • Distributed generation	• High efficiency • Fuel flexibility • Can use a variety of catalysts • Suitable for CHP	• High temperature corrosion and breakdown of cell components • Long start up time • Low power density
Solid Oxide (SOFC)	Yttria stabilized zirconia	700-1000°C 1202-1832°F	1 kW-2 MW	60%	• Auxiliary power • Electric utility • Distributed generation	• High efficiency • Fuel flexibility • Can use a variety of catalysts • Solid electrolyte • Suitable for CHP & CHHP • Hybrid/GT cycle	• High temperature corrosion and breakdown of cell components • High temperature operation requires long start up time and limits

have fallen and hydrogen- reforming technologies have improved. And so, the battle continues…

DC Power Transmission

High-voltage direct current (HVDC) electric power transmission lines use direct current (DC) for bulk transmission of electrical power, while the presently used alternating current (AC) power transmission lines use AC power. DC power has different characteristics than AC power, and for long-distance transmission, HVDC systems may be more suitable, less expensive and may suffer lower electrical losses.

HVDC is much better and more economical for uninterrupted large distance transport, as well as for underwater power lines, since it avoids the heavy currents required by the AC line capacitance.

HVDC also allows power transmission between unsynchronized AC distribution systems, and can increase system stability and reliability by preventing cascading failures from propagating from one part of a wider power transmission grid to another.

The controllability of current-flow through HVDC rectifiers and inverters, their application in connecting

unsynchronized networks, and their applications in efficient submarine cables mean that HVDC cables are often used at national boundaries for the exchange of power. As an example, HVDC connections divide much of Canada and the U.S. into several electrical regions that cross national borders, although the purpose of these connections is still to connect unsynchronized AC grids to each other.

AC transmission lines can interconnect only synchronized AC networks (these that oscillate at the same frequency and in the same phase). Many areas, however, share power but have unsynchronized networks. For example: the U.K., Northern Europe and continental Europe are not synchronized, while Japan uses dual (50 Hz and 60 Hz) power transmission networks.

Continental North America is operating at 60 Hz throughout, but is subdivided into regions, which are unsynchronized: East, West, Texas, Quebec, and Alaska. South America's Brazil and Paraguay share the enormous Itaipu Dam hydroelectric plant, but operate at different frequencies (60 Hz and 50 Hz respectively.)

And lately the growing number of offshore wind farms requires undersea cables, but their turbines are

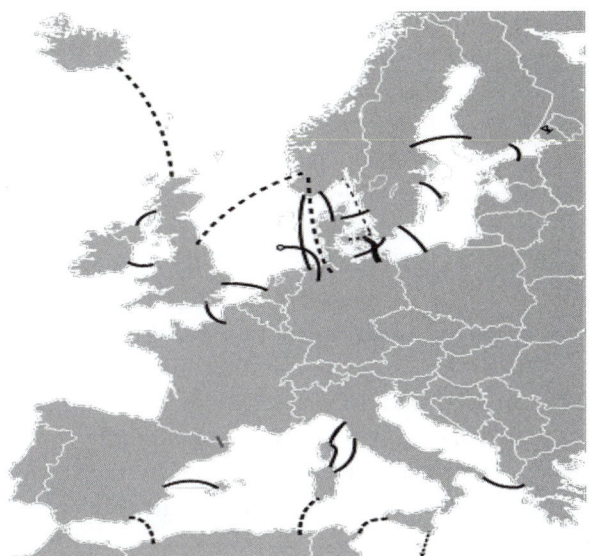

Figure 9-42. Existing and planned DC lines in Europe

unsynchronized, so they require complex and expensive equipment to transmit and synchronize the produced power before plugging it into the national grid.

By using HVDC transmission, all these different networks and systems can be uniformly interconnected, and as an added big bonus, the resulting voltage and re-active power flow can be precisely controlled and made much more stable than by using AC power lines.

And with the increased power generation by alter-native power sources, HVDC may become the preferred transmission current, and could provide the needed sta-bility and efficiency to the grid of the 21st century. The best way to do this is to start with the conversion of the local networks, and working up into the national and international power grids.

In the near future, the installation of DC transmis-sion lines could be easily converted from a niche market into a large-scale effort on national level, to convert the grid to DC power. This undertaking could bring thou-sands of jobs, and more efficient power transport and distribution.

Internet Data Centers Cooling

The Internet is hot, no doubt. And the hotter it is, the better, right? Not so, although most of us never thought that the Internet needs cooling; it does—a lot of it. Cooling is not for the ever-increasing use and applica-tions; it is cooling of the hardware used to provide those applications.

Cooling of the servers and the related hardware is an important part of ensuring the efficiency and reliabil-ity of the Internet providers. This is the Internet's hidden

cost. A data center with efficient cooling design cost 50% less energy to run than an inefficient one on the average, depending on location and operational specifics.

Today power and cooling costs outpace the cost of the actual equipment in some places, like Phoenix, Arizona, where the summer temperatures are in the mid 110s. This is because companies are paying not only for the power that is necessary to run equipment, but also for power to cool it during hot days. A lot of power is needed to keep the hot running computers and super-computers cool, and within the operating specs.

Imagine a 110°F day in Phoenix in a room full of computers belonging to a local Internet provider. The ambient temperature by 2:00 PM would approach the outside air temperature, and the operating equipment is adding even more heat. If the equipment in the room is left unattended with no cooling, by 6:00 PM it will reach critical temperature levels, and overheating super-computers is not a good thing.

Most CPUs are equipped with over-heating protec-tion interlocks, so it is very likely that the computers in that room without cooling in Phoenix, Arizona, will start shutting down one by one. Those without overheating protection will continue operation until something inside melts and they go blank. In either case, around 6:15 PM that day, the local Internet provider will have no comput-ers to provide Internet services. No more Internet services means no more profits, so the coolers and air conditioners are absolutely necessary, and they are quite busy.

Cold climate countries have seized the opportuni-ty to market their environmentally friendly (for Internet servers) lands as a cheap solution to this cooling issue, which would also bring jobs to their citizens and reduce the energy bottom line of web-focused businesses, a win-win situation. Facebook and other major players have been contemplating this idea, and some are plan-ning to move their data centers abroad to cooler places.

Environmentalists have been criticizing Facebook for using energy derived from coal, and this new solu-tion is one more step in the company's campaign to change a perception of social irresponsibility in energy.

The best way to keep your data center cool is to use the cool, ambient air of your natural surroundings. But if your company doesn't have the luxury of locating the data center near the moderate Oregon coast, like Face-book, or near the fjords of Norway, the cost of cooling data can be significant.

Data center efficiency is big business today, so startups like Power Assure are getting into the busi-ness along with power engineering giants IBM, General Electric and HP. And another company, SM Group International (SMi), an international engineering firm based in Montreal, is tackling the cooling methods, claiming savings of up to 50%.

SMi's patent-pending technology isn't actually new technology at all, but rather a paradigm shift in how to cool computers. The key is to pressurize the space and blow cool air into the area directly over the servers before the heat builds up. Using traditional pre-cooling of the equipment helps too. But in hot areas like Phoenix, AZ, pre-cooling doesn't help much during the day hours, and only a little during the night.

Amazingly enough, data centers account for about 2% of the total electricity used in the U.S. today, and that figure is increasing with the increase of Internet use in the country. Who knew?

While SMi was working on optimizing the pre-cooling process, they also started looking into putting the computers in a wind tunnel. This way avoids the turbulence of pushing cold air in a systematic way instead of into a chaotically organized square room, where cooling cannot be efficiently controlled. The basic direction of moving air efficiently, and in controlled way, in a pressurized environment could theoretically cut the energy use by up to 50%.

The average data center has a power use effectiveness (PUE) ratio of about 2-3. Facebook's latest Oregon data center sports a PUE of 1.07 and consumes 38% less power than the average setup, thanks to a new server design. GE's new, ultra-efficient data center scores 1.63.

SMi's cooling approach could cut the PUE to as low as 1.1 for a newly designed facility. Retrofits results would vary, but if a data center had a PUE of 2, it could be brought down to about 1.3.

Cooling, of course, is just one aspect of data center power use. Other ideas for curbing power usage have included: weather mapping inside data centers computer rooms, application shifting, improved AC controls, switching from AC to DC power, swapping disks for flash memory, better power conversion, and smaller and more energy-efficient servers.

All this helps to reduce power use in the ever-increasing use of the Internet. And since this (the Internet) is one thing that will continue growing disproportionally during the 21st century, as we depend more and more on it, we need to improve the ways the data centers are operating—including switching to power-efficient equipment and cost-saving cooling methods.

This, somewhat hidden and obscure niche market, promises to grow to great proportions as time goes by. What we learn from these efforts could be then applied in other industries as well.

Military Micro-grids

Traditionally, if the power goes out at a military base, each building within the base will switch to a backup energy source, most often provided by a diesel generator. The military isn't crazy about this setup, in part because this is an expensive solution, and also because generators can fail to start—especially bad news for base hospitals and other critical operations. And if a building's backup power system doesn't start, there is no way to use power from another building's generator.

In addition, most generators are oversized and use a lot of dirty and increasingly expensive fuel. So the military is working on ways to change that by connecting clean energy sources like solar and wind in micro-grids that can function when commercial power service is interrupted.

A new $30 million initiative could transform the way U.S. military bases deal with power failures. Termed SPIDERS—short for smart power infrastructure demonstration for energy reliability and security—the three-phase project will focus on building smarter, more secure micro-grids on military bases and other facilities that make use of renewable energy sources. Sandia Labs has been (very appropriately so) chosen as the lead designer and technical support for the SPIDERS project.

Diesel generators are used all the time to provide emergency power to buildings, but they are usually not interconnected with alternative energy sources like solar, hydrogen fuel cells, etc., as needed for a stable and significant energy source. It's a real integration challenge, according Sandia's engineers working on the SPIDERS program. So, Sandia will work to set up a smart, cyber-secure micro-grid that will allow renewable energy sources to stay connected and run in coordination with diesel generators, which can all be brought online as needed. The new system is expected to not only make the military's power more reliable, it will also lessen the need for diesel fuel and reduce its carbon footprint.

The project is being funded and managed through the Defense Department's joint capability technology demonstration with the support of the U.S. Department of Energy.

Some day soon, the departments hope to use the SPIDERS plan for civilian facilities like local hospitals and others as well.

The Pentagon

The U.S. Department of Defense (DoD) has awarded $7 billion of contracts to 22 companies for the right to develop and sell solar energy to the U.S. Army. The winning companies include Gehrlicher U.S., Siemens and Sunpower.

Once projects are developed it is understood that the winning companies will bid against each other to supply solar power with the remainder of the ring-fenced $7 billion available for purchasing.

The "multiple-vendor, indefinite-delivery/indefinite-quantity, firm-fixed-price, non-option, non-multi-year contracts" are specifically to be used for solar power.

The projects will be developed on land owned or under the jurisdiction of the DoD, and 114 bids were received for the original tender.

The 22 firms selected thus far are:
- Acciona Energy North America Corp
- Apex Wind Energy Holdings
- Borrego Solar
- Cobra Industrial Services
- Dominion Energy
- Element Power U.S.
- Emerald Infrastructure
- Enel Green Power North America
- Energy Matters
- Gehrlicher Solar America Corporation
- Johnson Controls Government Systems
- Lend Lease
- LTC Federal
- New Generation Power
- NRG Energy
- Photon Finance
- Siemens Government Technologies
- Silverado Power
- Solar Power Ventures
- Standard Solar
- Sunpower Corporation
- Washington Gas Energy Systems

In the fall of 2013, the U.S. Army issued $600 million of contracts to 11 companies to assist with its clean energy project development. The Army Corps of Engineers' engineering and support center awarded the contracts for the design and construction to various U.S. technology and engineering companies, including AMEC and Balfour Beatty.

The shared-capacity contractors will support the U.S. Army Corps with energy support and energy conservation globally. The projects span generating renewable energy from wind turbines, geothermal heating and solar power plants as well as energy efficiency improvements. Services have been contracted for one base year, and then four option years for all design, construction and construction related work.

That is in addition to the already mentioned $7 billion recently awarded to 22 companies specifically for solar development. The additional 11 companies contracted are:

- AMEC Environment & Infrastructure, Inc., Plymouth Meeting, PA
- Ameresco, Inc., Framingham, MA
- Balfour Beatty Energy Solutions, Fairfax, VA
- CH2M Hill Constructors, Englewood, CO
- Eaton Corp., Raleigh, NC
- ECC Energy Conservation, LLC (ECC-EC), Burlingame, CA
- Perini Management Services, Inc. (PMSI), Framingham, MA
- Science Applications International Corporation (SAIC), McLean, VA
- Shaw Environmental & Infrastructure, Austin, Texas
- URS Group, Inc., Washington, DC
- Weston Solutions, Inc., West Chester, PA

The contracts follow the news that the public will be able to invest in solar energy projects for military housing. Solar project crowd-funder, Mosaic, is offering investors in California the option to back a 12.3 MW PV installation for 547 houses at the New Jersey, Joint Base McGuire-Dix-Lakehurst. The base houses military employees and their families.

Once completed, the installation hopes to supply 30% of electricity and to save approximately $1.3 million in energy costs. The U.S. Department of Energy awarded Mosaic a $2 million grant, part of $27 million in grants that were awarded to various solar energy projects as part of the national sunshot initiative to bring down the cost of solar.

The Smart Grid

The term "smart grid" is a fairly new concept, with growing importance. It is a common denominator for a wide range of developments that make power generation and the related medium- and low-voltage grids, as well as the use of electric power, much more intelligent and flexible than they are presently.

Communications among, and control of, the key elements will allow them to be managed more efficiently and much easier. The main motive for smart grid initiatives is that such developments improve reliability of supply and support the trend towards a more sustainable energy supply.

Presently, most medium- and low-voltage networks cannot be remotely observed and controlled, so, when fully developed, smart grid components will eventually solve that problem. Or at least this is the goal and hope of the industry specialists and the companies involved.

Various companies are already developing a variety of technologies that are aimed at creating and supporting different smart grid network segments. However, some of those developments are either futuristic or are based on technological possibilities, rather than being conducted with a sound problem analysis and a coordinated, structured smart grid approach.

The major players in the U.S. and Asia are: ABB, Accenture, BPL Global, Echelon, Freescale, GE, Holley Metering, Moxa, RuggedCom, Siemens, State Grid Corporation of China, Wasion, XD Electric, and the XJ Group.

Many other, not so major, companies all over the world are working feverishly on developing new components for the smart grid technologies, which is leading to new inventions and concepts that will prove to be helpful in the future.

In the recent past, a great variety of sensors, protocols, communication equipment and the like have been designed to support the move toward smart grids. However, because of differences of opinion and a lack of standardization, most of them have not found wide application. This can also be at least partly attributed to the fact that they simply do not provide significant enough solutions to the existing problems at hand.

In other words, there is too much technology push and too little market pull, comparatively speaking. There are cases where manufacturers of unsuccessful technologies blame network operators for being conservative instead of improving the price performance ratio of their products, which reflects the anomaly and further hampers a real takeoff of smart grid concepts.

In the longer term, smart grid technologies will play an important role in maintaining the reliability of supply and improving sustainability. The complexity of electricity distribution increases, as new PV plants are connected into the grid, and the number of wind turbines and solar power plants increases as well. This also applies to small generators, such as roof top PV installations, where smart grids support these developments by continuously monitoring and controlling the grid and the generators.

The smart grid vision is becoming clearer over time, and increasing efforts will be spent on developing appropriate and necessary smart grid technologies in cooperation with commercial energy companies, other grid operators, and suppliers. These efforts will also help to increasingly focus discussions between regulators and the government on the future energy supply and the role of smart grids in it. The energy future looks bright, and smart grids will play a significant part in it.

The Smart Grid Markets

The smart grid, although a fairly new development, is finding enthusiastic support in many developed and developing countries. It is a technically complex and expensive financial undertaking, and yet there are takers, as follows:

The U.S.

In December 2007, Congress passed and the President approved Title XIII of the Energy Independence and Security Act of 2007 (EISA). EISA provided the legislative support for DOE's smart grid activities and reinforced its role in leading and coordinating national grid modernization efforts. Key provisions of Title XIII include:

- Section 1303 establishes at DOE the smart grid advisory committee and federal smart grid task force.

- Section 1304 authorizes DOE to develop a "smart grid regional demonstration initiative."

- Section 1305 directs the National Institute of Standards and Technology (NIST), with DOE and others, to develop a smart grid interoperability framework.

- Section 1306 authorizes DOE to develop a "federal matching fund for smart grid investment costs."

The office of electricity (OE) is the national leader, partnered with key stakeholders from industry, academia, and state governments to modernize the nation's electricity delivery system. OE and its partners identify research and development (R&D) priorities that address challenges and accelerate transformation to a smarter grid, supporting the demonstration of not only smart grid technologies, but also new business models, policies, and societal benefits.

OE has demonstrated leadership in advancing this transformation through cooperative efforts with the National Science and Technology Council (NSTC) subcommittee on smart grid and the federal smart grid task force.

"The National Science and Technology Council subcommittee on smart grid, chaired by the assistant secretary for OE and the national director for smart grid at NIST, the subcommittee is promulgating a vision for a smarter grid including the core priorities and opportunities it presents; facilitating a strong, coordinated effort across federal agencies to develop smart grid policy; and developing a policy framework for the 21st century grid which describes four goals the Obama administration will pursue to ensure that all Americans benefit from investments in the nation's electric infrastructure: better alignment of economic incentives to boost development and deployment of smart-grid technologies; a greater focus on standards and interoperability to enable greater innovation; empowerment of consumers with enhanced information to save energy, ensure privacy, and shrink bills; and improved grid security and resilience."

The above is a long and winding statement, which, in our opinion, reflects the long and winding road in front of the U.S. smart grid. Please note that the statement is calling for a "smarter" grid, while what we need is a totally "smart grid." This might mean that the government bureaucrats are thinking of implementing a "smarter" grid first, before jumping to the "smart" grid version, which only makes the road even longer and more winding.

We saw similarly long, winding, confused and even misdirected statements in the 1970s, when solar energy was hailed as the "savior" of the American dream, and where the U.S. government was taking charge of its development. Solar was hailed as the only way to a sustainable energy future, and so lots of money was thrown at solar companies then (some of it at the wind, as it happened today)...until the government changed, and things went downhill from there on.

Solar energy has been brought out of and shoved back into the closet several times since then, and that is where it was until recently, when it was taken out, dusted off, and hailed again as the only way to energy independence...until the new government takes power and solar is shoved back in the closet...again. That may not be so easy or fast this time around, but the signs unequivocally point in that direction.

Is the same fate awaiting the U.S. smart grid? Nobody knows, but due to the great amount of effort and money involved, and judging from the lessons of the past, we cannot, and should not, count on the government bureaucrats—self-proclaimed "smarter" grid saviors—to lead the smart grid effort to a successful end.

Interfering personal interests, changing political winds and everything else that is awkward with politics and politicians today, makes us believe that the government should stay out. Instead, we should let the U.S. capitalist system take over and dictate the rules and the

effort. Keeping the government bureaucrats in a subserving role, where they belong, and where they can be controlled, is the best, if not the only, way to manage this, and any other, serious effort.

One example of ill-conceived (albeit good intentioned) intervention of the government is the Department of Energy's smart grid investment grant program. Grants ranging from $500,000-$200 million are to be issued for deployment of smart grid technologies, most of the recipients of which seem to be working on smart metering solutions (since it is the easiest, and most accepted by the public, smart grid-related technology).

In addition, IRS issued guidance in 2010 that provided a safe harbor, under which the $3.4 billion of federal smart grid investment grants (SGIGs) issued under the American recovery and reinvestment act of 2009 (ARRA) will not be taxable to corporate recipients.

That was great news, right? But here is the catch: energy conservation, derived from the full implementation of smart meters (as encouraged by the government grant and tax programs) means lost revenue to utilities at a time when the utilities are in the midst of expensive changes and are not ready for additional revenue losses. The lost revenue, forced by the government programs, is simply untimely and is not aligned with the objectives of most utilities and their shareholders.

In addition, long-established regulations have favored supply-side resources over energy conversation, so utilities have been encouraged to add new generation because they earn a rate of return on investments on their assets, mainly the power generation, transmission and distribution infrastructure. And now, without proper warning and preparation, the utilities need to abandon the profitable business model and gear for energy conservation, which translates to loss of revenue.

This misalignment might cause delays and even failure of some energy-efficient technologies and services in the U.S. and it reflects disconnect and fragmentation in the sector. Some of the disconnect is caused by the inadequacy of the government bureaucrats, who talk the talk, but seem more interested in their own agendas than anything else. This anomaly is fueled by the ignorance of the regulators as well, which completes the circle of incompetency, and which will make the smart grid implementation that much harder.

The bureaucrats do not take into account the fact that the technologies that promote energy conservation have evolved much faster than the regulations that govern utilities and other suppliers. This creates an imbalance, which will continue until new regulations, promoting the implementation of demand response and other energy conservation programs are implemented. To cross the divide seamlessly, appropriate and timely regulations and other policies should be properly structured to justify and encourage full utility participation and investments in demand response.

Table 9-20. Smart grid investment

Country	Total	
China	$7,500	million
USA	7,000	"
Japan	850	"
S. Korea	850	"
Spain	800	"
Germany	400	"
Australia	360	"
UK	300	"
France	260	"
Brazil	200	"

The work has started, no doubt, but it is full of gaps, fragmentation and misdirection, but to coordinate and encourage the activities, new legislation need to be approved, and regulation needs to be implemented to create incentives for utilities to reconsider investing in generation, transmission, and distribution assets and promote energy conservation and demand response instead. There needs to be a balance between the approaches, and the utilities need to be encouraged to use demand response as part of the generation portfolio and modus operandi.

There should be also some type of shared-savings program that allows utilities to participate in the savings customers receive from reducing their energy usage. This will persuade them to promote energy conservation because they will benefit, as well. In addition, there should be a penalty if a utility does not encourage customers to reduce their energy usage.

Another way to encourage utility participation would be that a utility gets compensated for a portion of its avoided supply costs obtained through demand response and other related programs.

The future of the smart grid in the U.S. is not clear; nobody knows what exactly will happen and when, so we can only guess. Looking at the history lessons of the past shows that solar was the hope for energy independence in the early 1970s. It is still the hope...albeit still in embryonic state and hesitant, at best. After 40 years, we know what solar can do, but we still don't know what to expect from it.

Smart grid technologies are headed in the same direction. Right now they are changing at an exponential pace—ten years ago we didn't even have smart phones, and the term "social media" was still in the making. Today, these are everywhere and we cannot even imagine life without them.

So how could we—stuck in the beginning of an era—even imagine where, or what, "smart" might be in 2015...2020...2050 and beyond. It is not possible, but we can say with certainty that there will be progress, with a heavy component of customer service, partially virtual.

The utilities are well aware of the demographic changes and the pending changes. They see the new generation of informed and active young customers, as well as the large retiring workforce, where by 2020 half of the utility workforce will be retired as well. And they know too much, so nothing can be kept hidden.

Customers are accepting new technologies quickly as evidenced by the fact that, according to some statistics, the volume of text messages now exceeds that of phone calls. But just think. Five years ago, text messaging did not even exit. So, information is the foundation, customer acceptance is the route, and integration is the vehicle.

The existing data are enormous, and growing exponentially, and all participating systems need to be integrated in parallel to receive and process the data for maximum efficiency and lowest possible cost.

No matter how you look at it, at least the direction is clear; the smart grid and its smarter virtual applications are here to stay. Some things haven't even been invented yet, but whatever is coming in the area of smart grids will have a large virtual component with a high level of self-sufficiency and reliability. The utilities need to be given a chance to get ready for the new order of things.

Our fully implemented and integrated, smart grid based "green" energy future seems attractive, but we cannot even guess how and when it will arrive. We just have to go step by careful baby step toward its proper and complete development.

Europe

Europe's smart energy collective is a sector-transcending cooperation involving a wide range of companies working for smart energy and smart grid implementation. Members include: ABB, Alliander, APX Endex, BAM, DELTA, DNV KEMA Energy & Sustainability, Efficient Home Energy, Eaton, Eneco, Enexis, Essent, GEN, Gemalto, Heijmans, IBM, ICT Automatisering, Imtech, KPN, Nedap, NXP Semiconductors, Philips,

Priva, Siemens, Smart Dutch, Stedin and TenneT.—Eco-Seed Staff.

In May 2012, members of the smart energy collective in Europe have approved the second phase of the smart grid initiative, which involves the development of five large-scale smart grid demonstration projects in the Netherlands.

Schiphol Airport, ABB, and Siemens offices, and several residential districts were the chosen sites for smart grid implementation and tests. To make this possible, an intelligent energy system was designed that uses a combination of innovative technologies and services. It will enable the owners to keep the costs of energy low, with a comparably high level of reliability.

This effort could be an important step towards standardization, in addition to testing the smart grid operation in actual use. A survey during the first phase showed that there are more than 6,000 relevant standards that play a role in the new technologies that, according to the group, will be introduced to the market over the coming years.

Working groups have been established for standardization, market mechanisms, services and business cases, smart grids, privacy and security, and ICT infrastructure, to establish a solid foundation for the design of the five demonstration projects, as well as for future projects.

Asia

Asia is quickly becoming a major player, and the center of global smart grid activity. The combined smart grid market in China, Japan and South Korea is estimated at over $10.0 billion, with estimated increases to over $30.0 billion by 2020, according to industry specialists.

As Asian countries are irreversibly becoming the predominant smart grid markets, the competition and the positioning of different vendors is increasing as well. Lack of clear understanding of the energy scenarios (present and future) in the major Asian countries (China, Japan, and South Korea) is an obstacle that needs to be resolved first.

It is widely expected that the smart grid markets in Asia will move forward at a breakneck pace during the next decade or two. The developed countries are already positioned for the race with over $45 billion in funding, earmarked by the respective governments and utilities across China, Japan and South Korea. The majority of funding and related opportunities, of course, are located in China with its booming energy market.

A level of uncertainty is still distorting the smart grid vision, so determining the trends and establishing a clear path of energy policies and currents will allow much faster implementation of smart grid technologies in these countries. Once the uncertainties of today are lifted, the meaningful entry in the Asian smart grid markets will proceed very fast.

China

The growth of the smart grid market is characterized by the special needs of each country's energy demands, as well as the local utilities' and existing grids' specifics. For example, the smart grid investment in China is focused on transmission and distribution automation, as needed to support the plans for a planned new power grid and planned robust renewable energy.

China is aiming to become a world leader in smart grid technologies in the next decade. The "Strong and Smart Grid," an 11-year plan revealed in 2009, outlines the ambitious steps to get there. It involves all aspects of the power grid, including: increase of power generation capacity; implementation of smart meter programs; emphasis on large-scale renewable energy; and large transmission lines and substation build-out.

Today, the plan is still alive and well. The State Grid Corporation of China, which is actually one of the largest utilities in the world, and the executor of China's smart grid plans, is already in phase two of the three-phase program. It is the construction phase, which is scheduled for completion in 2015.

New transmission lines are a major focus for State Grid in the construction phase, which is struggling to meet the growing energy demands of the rising middle class in the East and South. Most coal, hydro, wind, and solar load sources are over 1,000 kilometers away from the populous east and south. High voltage (HV, under 300 kilovolts), extra-high voltage (EHV, 300 kilovolts to 765 kilovolts), and ultra-high voltage (UHV, 765 kilovolts and up) lines are being installed currently, with at least one 1,000-kilovolt UHV AC or DC line installed annually until 2015. Overall transmission line investments for 2015 are approximately $269 billion, equivalent to the combined market cap of ABB, GE, and Schneider Electric as of May 21, 2012.

China is adding so much new transmission capacity and so many power lines that it could build three quarters the length of a new American transmission grid in just five years. When the dust settles, there will be over 200,000 kilometers of new 330-kilovolts-and-up transmission lines built, for a total of 900,000 kilometers of transmission lines, compared to 257,500 kilometers of transmission lines presently in the U.S.

At a cost of $1.05 million per mile for UHV transmission line and equipment, each UHV line requires billions of dollars to build, and State Grid put in a staggering $80 billion investment into 40,000 kilometer of UHV lines for the 2011 to 2015 construction phase. The business case is readily apparent: a 2,000-kilometer, 800-kilovolt UHV DC line has an incredibly low 3.5% line loss rate per 1,000 kilometer and a high 6.4-gigawatt transmission capacity, all the while being 30% cheaper than a 500-kilovolt EHV DC or 800-kilovolt UHV AC line of the same length. By 2020, UHV lines will have 300 gigawatts of transmission capacity, roughly split to 60% AC and 40% DC.

The competitive business environment seen in the transmission grid build-out is indicative of the rest of the smart grid market in China—high-quality goods, competitive costs, and a well-built relationship with State Grid all go a long way toward winning a contract. Fierce vendor competition exists, due in part to State Grid's competitive construction procurement process. All projects costing over $300,000 to build are required to go through an open bidding process that aims to enforce fairness and transparency, but State Grid still holds the reins tightly on choosing project developers. In the process, State Grid has the final say and does a rough 45/45/10 split when evaluating meters, based on quality, cost, and bankability of the company.

With the promise of power shortages disappearing and a stable energy supply base, the build-out of the transmission grid is ushering in the next era of smart grid opportunities in China. Smart meters and renewable integration are already big businesses, and new substation infrastructure has brought with it a vibrant and growing substation automation market. The need for better monitoring equipment has risen as China is keen on decreasing its system average interruption duration index (SAIDI) and improving power quality to its customers.

State Grid has earmarked over $40 billion toward these smart grid technologies from 2011-2016, with smart meters alone being a $2.5 billion-$3 billion annual market. State Grid has paid special attention to substation automation technologies, and plans on installing 74 new digital substations for 63 kilovolts-500 kilovolts by 2015.

While this number is small compared to the existing 40,000 plus substation base, State Grid has stated that it intends to include digital technology in all new substations built. Companies such as BPL Global have been expanding their substation operations in China, which have been met with stiff domestic competition. The substation market offers promising growth over the next 10 years.

The transmission grid build-out also has an impact on technologies at the distribution level and downward. China is building 36 million new urban homes from 2011-2015, and modern building automation and smart meter technologies will be utilized. The coming years promise to create a new and vibrant building automation market, but for the time being, the market continues to focus on meeting demand shortfalls and other key infrastructure challenges.

Expect to see an exciting shift toward technologies at the distribution level and downward in the next 5-10 years, as China solidifies its transmission grid and generation sources. If the past three years have been any indication of future progress, expect to see China become a leading smart grid market for the next 5-10 years. The distribution grid build-out and digitization will be the next major indicator of China's smart grid prowess.

The Rest…

In Japan, the shutdown of many nuclear plants created a need for demand response, energy management, and smart meter deployments. A smart grid is on the agenda. Money is available, the need is there, and the customers are willing, so only time separates Japan from the full implementation of efficient smart grid concepts.

We would not be surprised if Japan leads the world in this area in the near future, and even becomes the first country to claim complete smart grid deployment.

The South Korean market is quite different. The country with the most reliable grid in the world, South Korea is looking into developing the next-gen smart grid technologies and components (hardware and software) across all segments, but primarily for global export.

So, in summary, the global smart grid future is bright. It has the potential to develop into one of the most important parts of the world's energy markets, thus bringing us closer to the overall goals of achieving energy independence and cleaning the environment.

The 21st century will bring a lot of developments in this area, and the Asian countries will be the first to claim smart grid implementation and use.

Smart Grid Cyber-security

Smart grid activities are shaping as some of the most promising as far as ensuring the future grid functionality is concerned. From a technical standpoint this is a doable, exciting, and profitable effort—but there is a big problem—the new smart grid opens the power grid to cyber-attacks. Since the smart grid will grow no matter what, ensuring its security is going to be a very big business.

Unfortunately, this big business will not make money for the utilities that will end up buying it. Nope, the majority of cyber-security investments will go mostly to meet regulations and make the investors happy. The major effort and money will go into trying to justify the extra costs for preventing grid attacks, and the related failures, accidents and incidents.

There are estimates that the $120 million spent on cyber-security products and services in 2011 will double by 2015. This number will grow to over $6 billion spent mostly by the utilities and the U.S. government by 2020 to secure the grid and avert the consequences of a successful cyber-intrusion. Worldwide, this number could grow to $80 billion for the same time frame. These figures exceed the total amount of money allocated for spending on the smart grid itself, so it is truly big business that is taken very seriously by all involved.

Nevertheless, it is a very risky business, since the grid needs to be protected from any eventuality, such as minor data theft to taking over grid assets, causing blackouts, or damaging substations and power plants' equipment. A lot of research and trials will go into making sure that this is done right.

A number of cyber-attacks and hacks at major U.S. organizations and installations have elevated the issue at the White House level. As a consequence, the Obama administration has issued an executive order demanding that all industries involved in the smart grid and power generation come up with a plan to deal with the threats.

How far and how fast this effort will develop remains to be seen, but it will not be a transparent process, since one of the key tenets of cyber-security is that cyber-security is most secure when nobody knows how secure it is. We surely will not learn much about the specifics of discovering, isolating, and eliminating and new intrusions and attacks. And since the methods of the intruders change daily, there will be a lot of changes and adjustments done to the cyber-security infrastructure as well.

The utilities are interested in, and required, to secure their infrastructure by all means available and necessary. The effort will spread on all levels from installing fences and locking gates and doors to ensuring the safety of the smart meters and computer networks, and to implementing the latest cyber-intrusion detection software and schemes. All this will require new products and support services, similar in size and form to what the banking and telecommunications industries have been doing for the last 20 or more years.

The cyber-security spending in North America is controlled by the North American Electric Reliability Corporation (NERC)'s critical infrastructure protection (CIP) requirements. In the U.S. and Canada, these rules are implemented and enforced by stiff fines. There are cases of up to $1 million per day fines for utilities and other entities that do not meet the security guidelines.

The Department of Energy is dangling a $4.5 billion carrot in front of the cyber-security principals and wanna-be companies. The DOE stimulus grants for a number of projects require cyber-security compliance, as outlined and coordinated by the U.S. National Institute of Standards and Technology.

Around the world, governments are working on their own regulations for ensuring the safety of their respective power grids. The European Union's cyber-security agency, ENISA, for example, is building a framework that is focused on a risk-based approach with a certain degree of freedom for the utilities and all companies involved, to do their job more promptly and efficiently.

Securing the new IT infrastructure of the power grid against cyber-attack is going to be big business, but that's not because it makes money for the utilities that are buying it. Instead, today's smart grid cyber security investments are mostly about meeting regulations, satisfying shareholders, and trying to justify the costs based on what it's trying to prevent.

Putting a dollar figure on averting the consequences of a successful cyber-intrusion is a risky business, of course. Utilities have to worry about everything from data theft to a full-blown attempt to take over grid assets to cause blackouts or overload generators.

Reports of cyber-attacks on U.S. infrastructure by foreign actors, as well as hacks at the Defense Department and Department of Energy, have brought the issue into focus this year, and the Obama administration has issued an executive order demanding that the industries involved come up with a plan to deal with the threats.

Recent research forecasts that the trends can lead to market opportunity at a pretty big chunk of change. U.S. utilities are expected to spend a cumulative $7.25 billion in security from now until 2020, with distribution automation assets as the core focus.

Other estimates reach $14 billion through 2020, with about 63% of that spending aimed at the industrial control systems and SCADA networks used to control today's grid assets. Even wilder claims exist of an exuberant $80-90 billion global market by 2020, which exceeds total smart grid spending figures in most of the world.

North America accounts for over 40% of the global

market presently, with Europe at 30% and Asia-Pacific at 17%. China is expected to overtake the U.S. as the largest market by 2020, leaving the Asia-Pacific region with 35% of the market. China, Japan, South Korea, and Russia will see growth rates of 40% and up in the next decade.

How far along the industry is toward that vision is hard to say, since one of the key tenets of cyber-security is that it is secretive and you just don't talk about cyber-security. And even less we know about the specifics of how the principals are discovering, isolating, eliminating and building new protections against new intrusions and attacks that change from day to day.

In North America, much of that spending is being driven by the North American Electric Reliability Corporation (NERC)'s Critical Infrastructure Protection (CIP) requirements. Covering the U.S. and Canada, these rules come with stiff fines of up to $1 million per day for utilities that can't prove they're meeting security guidelines, and newer versions add a lot more serial-connected smart grid assets to their purview.

The Department of Energy's $4.5 billion in stimulus grants also came with cyber-security strings attached, as outlined by the ongoing government-industry work being coordinated by the U.S. National Institute of Standards and Technology, or NIST.

Other parts of the world have their own regulations in place for how to secure the grid. The European Union's cyber security agency, ENISA, is building a framework that, in "contrast to the U.S. " strict regulatory path," is aimed at a risk-based approach that allows "a certain degree of "freedom" to the utilities and technology partners involved.

California Edison's Smart Grid Roadmap

Southern California Edison (SCE), which serves about 13 million people in the Golden State, is expected to make more changes to the grid and its overall power infrastructure in the next ten years than in the previous century. It is a good example of a big investor-owned utility that's taken a leading role in the smart grid.

There is already an impressive list of smart grid accomplishments, which mark the beginning of a transformation that is going to bring many changes. That, however, comes with a long list of projects to be undertaken as needed to meet the myriad challenges in the coming years.

The Issues

One of the top concerns of the California utilities is how to manage the growing share of intermittent renewables (solar and wind) powering its grid. The recent

increases in distributed energy resources (solar roof systems) have complicated the situation even further.

State mandates call for utilities to get 20% of their power from green energy today, and that figure is set to grow to 33% by 2020. Some of that power comes from stable sources like geothermal or small hydro- power, but an increasing share is coming from solar and wind power. And much more renewable power is to be added during the next 2-3 decades.

The variable power sources are creating problems for the utilities that have traditionally delivered power from central generation plants to end-customers in a number of ways.

The present-day issues and solutions can be summarized as follows:

* Solar and wind power are different from the base load sources (fossil power plants) because they cannot be dispatched when needed. Instead they force the utilities to react to the whims of Nature that drives the solar and wind power generation.

* Many of the generation resources are connected directly to the distribution networks, thus bypassing the transmission lines all together. The distribution network, however, was not designed to handle two-way power flow. This prevents the central grid control structure from managing this extra power, so a new system control needs to be developed and implemented.

* Plug-in electric vehicles are another headache for the utilities. As their number grows, they still use enough power when plugged, which at the grid looks like an entire household's power use.

* Millions of new smart meters deployed recently represent another disrupting factor, because they force the utilities to collect and process more data than usual. The new meters also enable customers to sign up for time-of-use rates, instead of the old way of paying flat fees for power used. That is forcing the utilities to base the energy use on real-time feedback from home energy management platforms.

* The traditional customers are now sophisticated "transactive energy" players, who generate electricity and a) either send it into the energy markets, or b) shift energy use to take advantage of price fluctuations.

* Customers now have a chance to make energy decisions based on economic choices. This brings

a new level of unpredictability into the utilities equation. And as the renewables increase in number, so will the utilities' headaches.

- Battery-based, grid-scale energy storage is presently on the drawing boards as one way of balancing the grid. Two Department of Energy smart grid stimulus grant-funded projects are fueling the drive. The energy storage effort is focused simultaneously on the large-scale and small-scale energy storage systems.

- On the large scale: SCE is working with A123 Systems on an 8-megawatt, 32-megawatt-hour lithium-ion battery storage option in the Tehachapi mountains. The goal is to stabilize and integrate large-scale wind power generation into the grid. For that purpose, SCE has undertaken a number of projects, including a California Energy Commission (CEC)-funded partnership with GRIDiant and New Power Associates, which analyzes transmission and distribution systems for a grid serving about 275,000 customers. SCE is also a leading player in a DOE stimulus grant-funded project to deploy synchrophasors, which are devices that monitor transmission lines by collecting data in sub-second intervals, across the entire western U.S.

- On the small scale: SCE is also integrating four different configurations of batteries, ranging from a 2-megawatt substation battery to smaller residential energy storage units (RESUs), into its smart grid demonstration project in Irvine, California. This is an $80 million, Department of Energy grant-funded project designed to test the interplay of energy-smart homes, solar panels, grid batteries, plug-in car chargers, grid voltage management, self-healing circuits, and communications and controls networks in a one single neighborhood. The list of partners, and potential designers and manufacturers of the related equipment includes: Boeing, General Electric, SunPower and Space-Time Insight, to name a few.

SCE is also testing a variety of "smart inverters" and other devices that could help integrate the roof solar power into the grid by allowing each rooftop solar system to better manage its interaction with the grid. This has been tried successfully in Germany, where solar inverter regulations and requirements were put in place recently to manage the massive share of distributed solar power and the grid interactions.

Ultimately, using digital devices on the grid can help record and even manage the variable flow of distributed energy resources and customers' energy use. The challenges, however, are great, from hooking up smart meters to distribution management systems, to integrating transmission grid measurement units into the utility's operations.

- The future role of energy storage is undeniable, but the type and size of the systems will depend on the respective economics, reliability, and efficiency factors. CPUC recently decided that it would require at least 50 megawatts of energy storage for the Los Angeles region power mix by 2020. This may or may not happen, but if it is not done right it might distort the market without solving the energy storage problems.

- At the same time, the utilities are spending a lot of effort and money on keeping the old grid humming. Replacing old power poles and wires, transformers and other components of the crumbling electric infrastructure cost SCE over $3-billion-per-year in capital investment. The number is tripled when the efforts of the other California utilities is added. Utilities in other states are in the same situation, and like it or not need to dedicate a lot of effort and money to fixing the old grid and its components. This alone makes any investment in smart grid initiatives involving the old grid imprudent.

With all this considered, we need to conclude that:

- The U.S. power grid is not ready for smart grid additions and improvements.

- The most advanced and most promising smart grid technologies are not be ready for mass-deployment.

- Most of the smart grid technologies that are commercially ready and available are not approved by the California Public Utilities Commission, since they requires a lot of testing and verification of the cost-benefit equations involved with deploying them.

And so, the smart grid is a great idea and could work miracles for the grid, the utilities, and their customers, but it its full implementation is still in the distant future. Partial additions and improvements are underway, so we have to wait and see how these work out and how they affect the overall energy situation in the country.

Energy Storage

Energy storage is the key to serious development of solar and wind power in the U.S. It is badly needed to eliminate the variability and reliability of these technologies, as well as for use at night. Energy storage technologies are now on the design boards and many companies are working towards their commercialization.

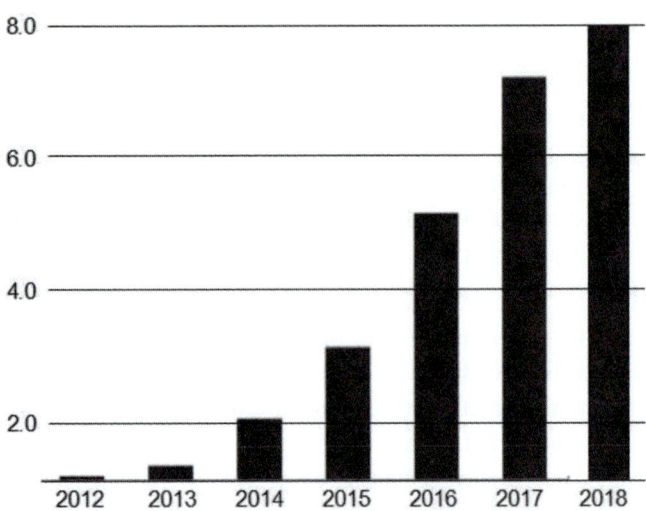

Figure 9-43. PV energy storage (in GW)

Energy storage can be done using different technologies, but none has proven cost-effective and reliable to date. There are efforts to develop and prove some of the existing technologies, as well as developing new ones, but those are far behind the estimates.

While there are some successes with demo equipment and small energy storage sites, the success is far from proven. This is especially true for large-scale energy storage. There is a lot of equipment needed to store 10 MW of electricity, and even more is needed to store 100 MW.

In our estimates, large-scale, cost-effective and reliable energy storage technology will not be available for the next several decades, so we will have to assume that we will have to proceed without solar back up. This, however, won't be easy, because the utilities simply cannot handle the variability and intermittency of solar power without energy back up.

And of course, there are other barriers and unresolved issues in solar's future.

Grid Energy Storage

There is an emerging market in the U.S. for *grid energy storage* devices, processes, and procedures. This might be a shot in the arm for the old and tired U.S.

grid and its owners—the utilities. It might provide the frustrated utility operators with a new opportunity for increased profits and much-needed recognition.

NOTE: This is a good time and place to express our gratitude to the thousands of utilities and grid operators, managers and employees, who are often on the short end of the stick and are being blamed for things for which they are not personally responsible.

They all, as tireless servants of the old and outdated national grid, are doing their best to keep it going even under the unfavorable circumstances of late. That is not an easy with the ever-changing demand, supply, and regulations, so we need to give them due credit for their hard work now and in the future.

The need for new grid energy storage technologies and approaches has created a number of separate and specific market niches, which are expected to grow and develop during the next few years. These new opportunities will help the industry development and will quickly make way for more substantive market developments that may exceed $100 billion in the future.

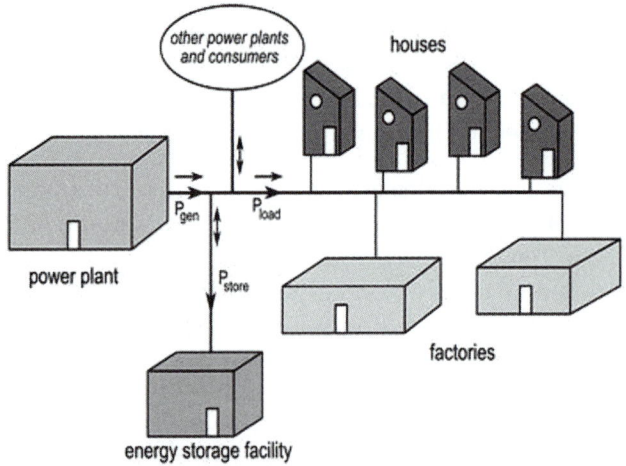

Figure 9-44. Energy storage scheme (the dream)

Sounds easy and elegant, no? Excess electricity is sent into some sort of a storage facility and is kept there until needed. The problem is that while water, air, or dirt can be stored in pools, tanks, or piles, electricity does not lend itself to storage at least not easily or cheaply.

The grid power storage schemes of the future can be built to have a single function or to provide a combination of services. They can consist of a number of electrical storage hardware, such as batteries, or pressurized air, which can be released at will. For now, however, due to the high cost of such facilities, grid storage will have to use some more indirect ways and schemes that simulate energy storage.

Those could be commercial and industrial energy management systems, which can provide commercial and industrial customers with a method to reduce electricity costs incurred by time-of-use pricing, or by demand changes. At the same time, this system can also be set up to provide distribution benefits by providing distribution grid support and peak-load management.

Industry insiders, forecasting the adoption rates, feasibility and overall volume of installations for facilities that provide either single or combined applications, predict the near-term grid storage market to grow by 50% by 2020. This upsurge in installation will be primarily driven by storage facilities and schemes able to perform multiple applications.

More than 90% of all operating grid storage facilities at that time will be able to serve more than one application. This is so because it all ultimately boils down to financial considerations. Facilities providing combined solutions will produce the best economic results in the short-to-medium term by increasing the opportunities for revenue and value, thereby maximizing their inherent financial viability. That will be critical for early adoption, as economic feasibility is currently the most significant barrier to the development of grid storage projects.

While the installation of facilities providing multiple applications will experience the most growth, we see a number of limited, long-term opportunities in multi-application installations. These are mostly niche markets that are expected to reach saturation by 2020.

The gradual decline in installation potential for combined application facilities in association with further decreases in technological and economic barriers will provide ideal conditions for an increase in the installation of facilities optimized for individual applications.

Collectively, the market size for individual and combined application grid storage facilities will range between $70-90 billion by 2020. Participants will need a solid understanding of the technologies and the market forces at play to position themselves to take full advantage of the vast potential in this nascent sector.

In all cases, the solutions won't be as simple as constructing a new building and stuffing it with equipment. Much more sophistication and imagination is needed to bring energy storage (and conservation) to fruition. There are already such attempts underway in California and other U.S. states, which are watched carefully by other states and countries.

In addition to energy storage, we need to focus on different ways to co-produce energy. Solar and wind power plants can be combined with coal and gas power generation to supplement their daily output in peak hours and as needed or possible.

But the most successful combination in power co-production is combining large-scale solar and wind power generators, where these two power sources take turns and complement each other to provide a more stable power output.

Combined Wind and Solar

The future of the renewable energies is not clear, mostly because of capital investment uncertainties, but even more importantly by their variability. As already discussed, the utilities are concerned with the variability problem (solar and wind in particular) and a lot of work and money will go into finding solutions.

One of the immediate solutions might be seen in combining wind and solar operation. One example is the wind and solar plant by Element Power in New Mexico. According to the insiders, it happened almost by an accident. Or rather, it was like an unplanned pregnancy, which produced a beautiful, healthy baby.

There were plans for two different projects—wind and PV—that were developed separately. The demand for renewables in that part of the country is immense, and it just so happened that it is a place where both solar and wind can be operated at maximum capacity. The synergy is not just in sharing land and resources, but in conveniently spread out peak time power generation, which provides much more power than what wind or solar can produce by themselves.

The wind power plant is composed of 28 Vestas V100 turbines, 1.8 MW each, which were installed with labor, services and materials from the local community. This cooperation always brings prosperity to the locals, which helps build the trust between the parties, which is a very important element in the success of any project.

The solar plant is a 50-megawatt PV installation, using conventional solar modules. The solar plant also has a PPA with the local utilities, so the power produced by both plants will be pumped into the local power grid, via a near-by substation, which was built for this purpose.

The fact that there is excellent solar radiation, and good winds at the right times, enables both; wind and solar, to be cost-competitive sources of energy for the local utilities. Combining these two power-generating sources is a big plus as well, which brings more profit and contributes further to the success of the project.

Transmission system operators are always concerned with managing wind and solar variability, but since these two plants are near to each other, it makes the task somewhat simpler. Since wind and solar generate at different times, there is alternating of the generated power. I.e., wind feeds the transmission lines 30-40% of the time, but is usually weak during the mid-day hours. Solar kicks in exactly during those hours, thus generating power when is most needed—during the noon peak hours.

In general, the combination of wind and solar power generation reduces the variability, these power sources experience when operating separately, which is a good news and welcomed by the grid operators.

Solar energy generation could be combined with other energy sources when constant output is the goal. Addition of solar power to conventional power sources (power plants) is one approach. Using energy storage devices (batteries or water storage) is another.

A more natural and most efficient way, however, is combining PV power with wind at certain locations especially chosen for this purpose. At such locations PV power is complementary to the output of wind generation, since it is usually produced during the peak load hours when wind energy production may not be available. Variability around the average demand values for the individual characteristic wind and solar resources can fluctuate significantly on a daily basis.

However, as illustrated by Figure 9-45, solar and wind plant profiles—when considered in aggregate—can be a good match to the load profile and hence improve the resulting composite capacity value for variable generation.

In this example, the average load (upper line) is closely followed during the day by the average output from the combined wind and solar generators (the sec-

ond from top line) during the same time. This average is created regardless, and because, of the fluctuations of the individual wind and solar power generators. This is a marriage made in heaven, and this combined power generating combination will work quite well if wind and solar power outputs can be matched as closely as this one.

Although there are areas in the U.S. and abroad that match this wind and solar profile, the combined effort is usually hard to execute, because the best places for wind and solar are at different locations, often miles apart, and also because of lack of infrastructure at the most suitable locations.

Because of that, it will require a great and very expensive effort to implement large-scale "wind-solar load matching" schemes anytime soon with existing technologies.

Nevertheless, having as a goal matching wind and solar power outputs will force us to look for and find the most suitable locations and appropriate technologies for this match. This is not going to happen overnight, but if we approach this solution seriously and intelligently, we will have a large-scale power output—nationally—that matches the grid power loads.

Solar and wind combinations are not uncommon in residential and small commercial applications. The combo solar panels and small wind turbines can maximize local resources, provide power for remote locations, pump water, and run appliances.

On a larger scale, China's biggest power network operator, State Grid Corp, installed and is operating a 140-megawatt combined wind-solar hybrid project, where 100 megawatts of wind and 40 megawatts of PV solar are installed and operating side-by-side since January 2012.

This is the largest, but not the last, online utility-scale solar-wind hybrid project in the world. It also has a 20-megawatt battery storage capability, which provides even more stability to the hybrid power generation.

A smaller example is the Western Wind's fully integrated 10.5-megawatt hybrid system in Arizona, which consists of five 2.0 MW Gamesa turbines and a 500 kWp c-Si PV array. There are a number of plans to develop similar projects, either new installations or retrofitting existing solar with wind power generation capabilities as needed to reduce the harmful variability issue.

Presently enXco's Pacific Wind/Catalina Solar undertaking is the largest in the US.

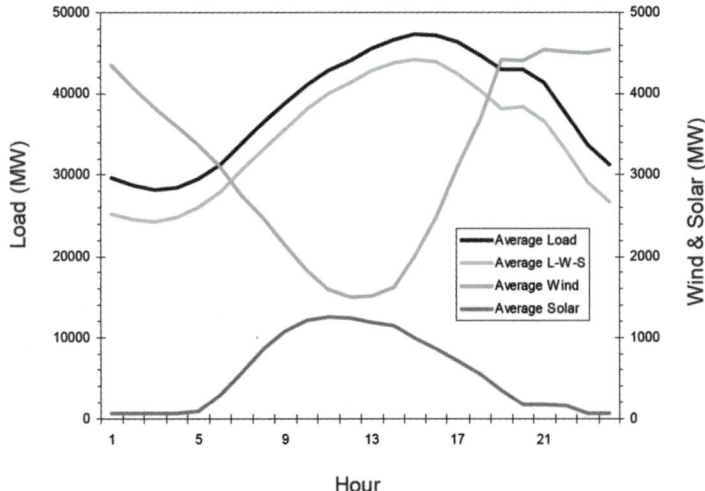

Figure 9-45. Simultaneous wind and solar generation

It has 70 2. MW REPower turbines, combined with the largest Solar Frontier CIGS solar field in the world. It will be used to test the effectiveness of feeding the grid with both resources.

We do foresee the wind-solar hybrid generation to be one of the most reliable and widely spread alternatives energy generators in the 21st century. The combined action of these two power sources, with added energy storage, will eliminate (or reduce significantly) the generated power variability, which is one of the major barriers to the development of large-scale power fields today. The wind-solar hybrid is also the surest way to compete successfully with the conventional energy sources in the near future.

FiT-less Solar Power

Here is the new trend of solar power development in the 21st century that will find wider use in the future:

Solaria Energía y Medio Ambiente, S.A. are leading the way into a new era of solar power development and use—without FiT, they are going head-to-head with the big guys.

The new 60-MW photovoltaic plant in Spain will not receive a FiT, due to the Spanish government's renewable energy moratorium on subsidies imposed in 2011.

And so, the new solar plant will feed the generated electricity into the Spanish grid at the going market rate of electrical power. It will be, therefore, competing directly with the local energy sources. Gutsy move, yes!

The company will manage the design and the EPC services, using its own PV modules to build the project at a cost of around $65 million.

Solaria is the first solar company in the world to put its neck on the line. That shows real commitment to and confidence in the Spanish energy market. And sure enough, the grid parity is becoming a reality in Spain, and PV generation is a mature technology, which dares to compete with the conventional energy sources.

Another company, Gehrlicher Solar, is planning a 250 MW photovoltaic plant in Spain on the same principal—without any FiT and any economic incentives. Go solar! If everything goes well, the new PV plant will to start construction in 2013 and be completed in 2015.

NOTE: In 2011 the Spanish government suspended all subsidies and incentives for renewable energy, due mostly to its poor financial health. There are no indications as of when the moratorium will end, if ever. This, of course, had an immediate negative impact on the photovoltaics' industry, ending with the cancellation of several PV projects in the country.

Industry insiders estimate the new policy will halt many more installations for the duration. Nevertheless, an increase of up to 4,177 MW is possible by 2013, compared with 3,985 MW in 2011. But then the solar industry will stop growing at least until 2015-2016, unless the FiT-less projects succeed, at which point the Spanish solar industry will take on a life on its own. If this happens, then it will signal the beginning of a new era of grid parity, and the Spaniards will lead the world again in new installations.

Presently, solar electricity can be produced for $0.06-0.07 per kWh. If the PV modules are purchased at $0.55-0.65/Wp, then this becomes an attractive ROI of approximately 5-6%.

But there are risks.

The electricity market price in Spain is wildly fluctuating, which makes it impossible to predict what will happen next year, let alone 20-25 years down the line.

Green electricity certificates, sold for clean energy credits, are one of the hopes for additional income, but the market for these is now developing and its future is not secure.

The biggest problem we see, however, in Spain's solar future is the fact that there is not much sun in most of the country. And the desert-like areas available for large-scale installations are of limited size.

On top of that, those areas are far away from large populated and industrial centers where the power is needed, which will require improvements to, or adding new, transmission lines and substations. It is not clear who will pay for these, so this issue has to be resolved before the work on the large-scale power fields is started.

Nevertheless, the pioneering development toward grid parity prices in Spain is an incredibly positive development. It has captured the attention of investors, developers, and potential customers alike. A number of planned PV projects are looking into the FiT-less system of operation. And since they don't have any other choice, they are forced to find the way. Maybe this is what is needed to push the solar industry into overdrive to jump over the barriers.

We foresee the FiT-less model as the best, if not only, way to implement large numbers of large-scale PV power fields in the 21st century, so we wish the Spaniards good luck in this undertaking. We, and all PV-related companies, will be watching very closely.

As a confirmation of the legitimacy of the FiT-less concept (as temporary as it might be for now, driven by artificially low prices), the Asian Development Bank (ADB) has been reviewing options to support solar projects without the need for feed-in-tariffs. Discussions within the bank's renewable energy group are currently centered on supporting solar development programs specifically without any subsidies or FiT.

ADB has penciled an initial $100-million credit facility to be considered by interested solar power developers and owners, and expects "fierce competition" on capital access for clean energy projects, including those on renewable energy (RE) developments.

The Manila, Philippines bank touts its own solar rooftop-installed power system, showing that the technology can be utilized viably without subsidies. Hm-mmm…we wonder where did ADB learned about solar, and how long did it take to come to those conclusions?

Presently the energy regulatory commission (ERC) prepares a ruling on the FiTs for various renewable energy developments, regulators are cautioned on subsidy impositions for solar especially with reports that the technology is already at grid parity in various jurisdictions.

In fact, sources from the National Renewable Energy Board's (NREB) technical working group have announced that the initial high FiT calculations were not supported by the data presented by the prospective developers. So ADB is willing to extend technical assistance to the Department of Energy (DoE) for a study can be undertaken to assess the viability of solar installations in the Philippines, primarily for rooftop solar. This option might be extended later on to industries and businesses.

The bank is convinced that rooftop-installed solar facilities are now economically feasible for higher-demand customers—even without subsidies and FiTs.

There is only one problem, most people in the Philippines have a hard time getting a job and feeding their families, let alone spending money (they don't have) on solar installations. Bringing down the cost to the level of the low-to-medium class residential end-users is the key, but it is not there yet—even with today's unsustainably low PV module prices. And it will take a long time to get there, if ever.

At the same time, the bank's Asia Solar Energy Initiative (ASEI) is targeting solar capacity installations of up to 3,000 megawatts within Asia and the Pacific over three years, ending in 2013. The ADB is looking into financing up to $2.25 billion worth of projects under its ASEI program, and shall also leverage an additional $6.75 billion in solar investments, using instruments such as London interbank offered rate (LIBOR)-based loans, donor contributions, grant funds, innovative risk mitigation mechanisms, carbon market support measures, and direct support for its solar lending program.

This initiative might be more doable, but we still question the availability of money, appropriate land, infrastructure etc. needed to undertake such a large program. It could happen, but a lot of other things need to happen first before it can be called a success.

With other words, talk is cheap, and plans are good for building investor's confidence. Building large-scale PV plants in that part of the world, where the sun is a precious commodity, however, is not that easy, so let's hope that they know something we don't.

Taking this plunge into uncharted waters of solar energy is a major step that most people are hesitant of taking today, so we will be watching the developments closely, hoping that the Asian banks and initiatives know what they are doing.

Mandatory Time-of-use Program

Sign of the times…PG&E (one of California's largest power generator, including solar and wind power) introduced a new energy saving program, designed to help its small and medium sized customers to prepare for a mandatory shift to time-of-use pricing of the power they use.

The CPUC mandated switch will not affect residential customers, but is designed to help customers save money while easing the strain on the power. Large commercial and industrial customers have been already moved to time-of-use pricing, so only smaller businesses and enterprises will be affected by the new program, and PG&E is trying to make the process as transparent and painless as possible.

PG&E, being sensitive to its customers' needs and wants is in the process of asking state regulators to consider an opt-out option for customers who wish to remain under the current pricing model for a while longer.

According to PG&E analysis, 60% of the customers would benefit from the new pricing structure, since the rates would increase only to about 2% of the affected customers.

PG&E thinks that conserving even a small amount of energy during afternoon peak demand can lower costs to everyone. It also helps the environment by reducing the need for utilities to buy power from fossil-fueled power plants and increases the reliability of the state's electric grid. SCE and SDG&E are working on similar programs and estimate switching to time-of-use pricing by March 2013.

This is one of the ways to save energy without adding energy generating sources. And we will surely see a lot of such programs in the near future, although not everyone can benefit from them.

R&D Efforts

Obama's climate action plan pumped billions of dollars in investment and changing policies intended to put solar energy in the energy mix of the country. As many U.S. companies jumped full bound into dominating solar, many foreign solar companies jumped at the chance too. A flurry of activities followed, ending with the embargo of Chinese made solar products.

Now the U.S companies have to find a way to dominate the U.S. and global markets. A number of events recently suggest that one way for the U.S. to take a lead in the sphere of solar power is through advanced research and academia.

Texas A&M University revealed in the summer of 2013 plans for establishing the world's largest solar research institute. This is the new off-campus $600 million Center for Solar Energy (CSE). Then, the State University of New York (SUNY) announced plans for a $100 million new PV manufacturing and development research center to be initiated by 2014.

CSE is planning to bring practical solar to academia, by offering a side-by-side comparison for installation approaches. CSE is also helping promote and advertise solar to the general public, as the "population is more likely to embrace solar if it is from a university." CSE plans to provide independent verifications and breakdowns of solar products to make it clear what has been proven and what is viable in solar energy.

CSE will also run a solar entrepreneurship program lasting two years aimed at amateurs and established solar professionals. Students are promised the chance to work with cutting edge technology teams and to learn how to start and run a global solar company.

There are also ten scholarships offered per company, with participants given the chance to live in CSE, refine their technology, train in solar business, acquire additional talent and hit the ground at a full run ready for an advanced venture capital investment—leaving the inventors and entrepreneurs in charge of their company, and the technology.

The CSE grandiose project is impressive. In its promotional CSE emphasized on the reality that the U.S. controls only 7% of the global solar market, down from 50% in 1995 and allowing 90% of solar products to come from abroad. This signifies the loss of over 2,000 jobs at a time when some countries are spending 500 times more on solar than the US. CSE insists that the U.S. is left behind, and that a lot of work is needed for it to regain its rightful place in the solar energy field through innovation and leadership.

The message is clear: America is in a war and needs to win the international solar leadership battle and CSE is ready and willing to answer that call.

CSE is offering the biggest and best of everything: the largest pure solar PV research facility in the world; the only utility-scale test site in the world; the largest exclusively solar PV innovation lab globally; the most technologies deployed anywhere. CSE also pledges to generate 100% of the campus' energy from its own 50 MW solar plant.

The new $600 million CSE venture is majority funded by venture philanthropists and government subsidies. The first venture partner is in the bag, but the project is far from being fully funded. And so, CSE is looking for corporate groups, financial institutions, venture capitalists, and philanthropists to help it finance its dream. CSE plans to sell spare electricity from the 50 MW plant to the national grid to finance its plans and provide Texans with clean, green, cheap energy.

But the competition in this area is quite tough. In order for CSE to compete it has to reach and exceed the level of other qualified and established centers such as America's National Renewable Energy Laboratory, or Germany's Fraunhofer Institute.

And what about CSE's ambition of America's becoming a world leader in solar again? That is not very likely, because overtaking China in solar production would require dozens of CSEs and many more billions of dollars. Nevertheless, CSE ambitions are contagious, and so is its vision of becoming the biggest and best solar research institute in the world.

We can only wish CSE best of luck, hoping that they would be able to complete at least part of their vision in the near future.

OUR Renewables' Future

Conventional economic comparisons (circa 2012-2013) are typically made on the basis of leveled cost (LCOE), or cents per kWh electricity production. This includes direct investment costs, fuel costs, O&M expenses, as well as the related insurance and capital repayment rates. There are, however a number of serious deficiencies of the conventional approach, which does not account for some factors.

The key factors, not fully accounted for in the conventional economic approach, are:

Fuel and Technology Subsidies

Fossil fuel subsidies, direct and indirect, "tilt the playing field" toward fossil fuels and amount to large public expenditures. The 2012 estimate is that that global subsidies to fossil fuels in 2011 exceeded $520 billion, compared to roughly $90 billion in policy support for renewable energy.

Some experts call for elimination of fossil fuel subsidies, or justified equivalent subsidies to renewable energy, and also point to significant public subsidies to nuclear power, both direct and indirect (i.e. Fukushima-like accident liability). The existing subsidies for coal, gas, and nuclear will be greatly reduced by 2020, which will provide a more leveled playing field.

Environmental Costs

Most environmental costs associated with fossil fuels and nuclear are not included (or internalized) in conventional economic comparisons. Many emissions regulations targeting conventional power plants are an attempt to partly internalize environmental costs, but the existing regulations just don't go far enough.

A full assessment of the input-output variables of all energy technologies needs to be developed and agreed upon by all parties to level the environmental costs field.

Fossil Fuel Price Risk

The risks of future fossil fuel price swings is not properly accounted for, calculated and incorporated into economic comparisons. Nor is it clear who is responsible and who bears the related risks. Analyses have been done on the "hedging premium" necessary to account for natural gas price volatility and uncertainty; for example, one estimate is that between 2 and 3 cents/kWh generated power needs to be added to the cost of power from natural gas to account for a hedging premium.

By 2020 there will be real competition in the energy markets for wind and solar power in Europe and the U.S., because by then the investors will be fully familiarized and exposed to the reality of increased fuel prices risks and the related carbon costs.

Solar Conflicts

This is another big problem for solar—especially large-scale solar power projects. Conflicts with conservationists and environmentalists have proven a serious obstacle in the U.S. 's large-scale solar development. Placards and angry slogans, and stormy town meetings proclaim that the enemy—solar project developers—are destroying land and hurting endangered species. SunPower, NextEra, Brightsource, and other large developers have been at the receiving end of protests and law suites over the impact of their solar projects in California.

The Mojave Desert in California has at least twice the sunlight of other regions of the country, and many times more that of countries like Germany, the UK, and all Scandinavian countries put together. The desert, however, is a dynamic system; not a wasteland as portrayed by some developers. It is home to tortoises, coyotes, rattlesnakes, and hawks, and many other species, which are vulnerable to careless intrusion by solar developers

Figure 9-46. NIMBY movement

Public resistance has brought regulations and developers to the front lines of the battle to protect the desert and the locals. Huge solar installations cause extreme changes in the landscape, thus some control and regulations are needed to limit the negative impact on people and the environment.

The Department of the Interior has come up with a solution to avert conflicts between solar development and the interests of conservation by dividing 115,335 hectares of public land into 17 Solar Energy Zones (SEZs). This way different development zones with fewest resource conflicts are made available to solar developers.

Large-scale installations on this land could generate nearly 24 GW of electricity, which could power around 7 million homes. The SEZ program also considers solar projects on a case-by-case basis inside the zones, as well as around 19 million acres in additional "variance" areas. The SEZ program excludes nearly 80 millions acres of desert land, which has been deemed inappropriate for solar development.

All interested parties are in favor of the program, but one of the major problems remains: project approval from the Bureau of Land Management and the California Energy Commission takes a very long time. For example, a large solar installation of over 50 MW needs several years to pass during the permitting stages. In one case, applying for a 250 MW solar project under a power purchase agreement took over 3 years.

The developers have to work closely with the local community, environmental groups, biologists, and a number of local, state and federal agencies to deliver a design that would be agreed by all parties as needed to minimize or eliminate impacts to sensitive biological resources.

The conservation and environmental protection groups insist that rooftop solar is less controversial and if fully developed the need for large-scale solar projects will go away and with it the clash between with the solar industry. But the problem with rooftop solar is the economy of scale; it is a proven fact that initial and O&M costs come down dramatically at larger scales. A roof top solar system is about three times more expensive to install and operate than any large-scale ground mounted solar power plant.

Large-scale power plants can compete with gas-fired power plants at the wholesale level, and even beats them in some cases—something that roof-top solar cannot even get close to. This makes a huge difference in the penetration of solar as a renewable in the long run.

The solar industry needs to find a way to work with the utilities, the local population, and the environmentalists before it can spread its wings over the U.S. deserts.

Counterfeit

While dealing with the complex and sophisticated problems of energy and environment, we need to also address the more mundane internal problems of cheating and counterfeiting. Cheating usually involves tax evasion and numbers fixing, and the authorities are on top of it. Counterfeiting, however, is growing out of control and is becoming one of the world's largest industries.

China is responsible for over 3/4 of the entire global volume of counterfeited goods and services presently. Counterfeiting steals revenue from legitimate companies and their brands. And even worse, some counterfeit products expose innocent customers to danger.

That brings us into the area of energy counterfeiting. Gasoline, oil, diesel and any other fuels can be counterfeit. Those fuels can be made with inferior materials, contain harmful substances, may not perform as expected, and may cause severe damage to the vehicles that can lead to breakdowns and accidents. Human lives could be put in immediate and unpreventable danger when using such fuels.

Fuel counterfeiting and smuggling is a reality in many parts of the world today. As fuel prices increase, the counterfeiting becomes more profitable, which leads to increase in counterfeit activity. We see a big surge in fuel counterfeiting as oil prices continue to rise.

Fuel counterfeiting and smuggling is most prominent in Europe where fuel prices are the highest due to high taxes, which are getting even higher as the global prices are getting close to the European price levels.

Fuel Counterfeiting in Ukraine

The Kyiv Motorist Club reports that in the summer of 2013, one out of every three liters of fuel sold in Ukraine are counterfeit and of substandard quality. About 30% of the gas sold at many major gas stations does not meet Ukraine and the E.U. quality and performance standards.

Over 75% of the petrol sold at filling stations that are not part of major chains is counterfeit fuel containing spirits and other additives. In some areas the indicator reached 90%.

While until recently the spirit trail was seen only in cheap fuels, now it is expanding to all fuels, thus creating a mass lack of correspondence in spirit content for Euro A-95 petroleum fuels. Tests of A-95 fuels conducted in a certified laboratory show irregularities of many samples.

The test results of fuels from random gas stations show that the standards for benzene content have been exceeded by almost 11 times, and those for sulfur content by almost 80 times. In the extremes, one gas company in Kharkiv sold fuels containing over 60% spirits.

Earlier mainly benzene was used in the production of counterfeit fuel; now we see a trend toward spirits. Along with ethanol, methanol is used, and it is a poison, and it seems like the pace of the usage of spirits in counterfeit fuel is growing.

All that is contributing to increase the failure rates of cars and trucks on the roads, accompanied by accidents. Along with the vehicle breakdowns, the public health has been affected as well. The large quantity of counterfeit fuel and its consequences is amounting to large losses for the national budget as well.

A comparison of the replenishment of the market and consumption shows that at least 20% of the petroleum fuels market is conducted amidst shadowy companies with similarly shadowy business practices. The state is trying to remove of this growing practice to prevent the problems and losses from non-payment of excise duties and value added tax, which costing the country over half a billion dollars in 2013 alone.

Fuel Counterfeiting in UK

United Kingdom authorities reported nearly 400 occasions of illegal sales of fuels to motorists. The number of incidents reported during the 2012-2013-time period was almost 50% higher than those during 2009-2010. Northern Ireland authorities reported 128 detections of illegal fuel sites, with 260 sites being in the rest of the UK.

The known criminal activities amount to nearly $1 billion lost in fuel tax revenue from illegal fuel smuggling and sales. This, however, might be just the tip of the iceberg, because nearly 90% of the illegal fuel sales activities are not discovered or reported.

The other problem is that the cheap fuel often is contaminated with unauthorized additives, making it of substandard quality and lower performance.

In the U.K., fuel that's meant off-road vehicles is dyed red for identification and taxed at a much lower rate than regular gasoline. The rest is sold at regular—much higher—prices. The criminals have figured out a way to buy the cheap red diesel and remove the red dye to sell it at much higher price, thus making huge profit on the difference.

One criminal factory in Northern Ireland that specialized in removing the red color had cost the government an estimated $10 million annually in lost tax revenue alone.

In the first half of 2013, environmental officials in Ireland recovered 400 tons of waste that was illegally dumped by organized crime groups in Ireland. The waste was used to create white fuel that was used by drivers, and it included ingredients such as sulfuric acid, cat litter, charcoal, and sand. In 2012, officials seized 445 tons of such waste.

Across the country, police discovered 11 illegal oil and fuel producing plants in 2012. The fuel smuggling operations were estimated to have cost the government up to $130 million in tax revenues.

The Extreme Cases

Coal emissions are limited by quota and cost-reduction can't help much, in part because it is already too late. The half-life of atmospheric carbon dioxide is roughly one hundred years, and some of it remains in the atmosphere for thousands of years. So even if humans immediately stopped burning all fossil fuel, the existing carbon dioxide would remain in the atmosphere for several generations.

Even if the U.S. and Europe miraculously converted overnight and became zero-carbon societies, and even if they persuaded China and perhaps India (not very likely) to demolish every coal-burning power plant and diesel truck on their territory. Even then, as far as atmospheric carbon dioxide is concerned, it might not matter all that much. And the zero-carbon society we have been dreamily thinking about is way too optimistic.

In addition, lots of things we take for granted need clarification. For example, solar cells are thought of as "good things" and to an extent they are, but they are designed to absorb light from the sun, and only about 12% gets turned into electricity. The rest is reradiated in the surrounding air as heat, which in turn contributes to global warming.

While this may not be a big deal for one single solar cell or PV module, there are millions of them spread over thousands of acres around the globe. So with time, these countless black surface modules will start heating the surrounding air more than before adding significantly to climate warming.

In addition, the energy consumed by manufacturing the millions of solar modules and thousands of new solar plants as necessary to replace coal-burning and other power plants would create a huge long-term "warming" debt. Some day we will have a great carbon-free energy infrastructure, but that will be only after making emissions and global warming worse every year until we're done building out the solar plants, which could take thirty, or fifty years, or more.

A widespread conversion to solar power seems appealing to all involved presently. The reality, however, is much more complicated and even tricky. This doesn't mean that the energy problem should be dismissed, which is why thousands of scientists and inventors all over the world are working toward the Holy Grail: cheaper and cleaner forms of energy.

But from an atmospheric perspective, energy represents what might be called the input dilemma. How about the output dilemma? What if the greenhouse gases we've already emitted do produce an ecological disaster? How would we do about a collapse of massive ice sheets in Greenland or Antarctica, or a release of huge amounts of methane caused by the melting of Arctic permafrost? Or how about a breakdown of the thermohaline circulation system in the North Atlantic that would put an end to the Gulf Stream, which in turn would produce serious climate and physical changes. What if the Moon or Sun shift orbits enough to affect the Earth's fragile environment. What if...?

We can go on and on with endless IFs and BUTs, and although life is not worth living in fear, we need to always keep in mind that things could eventually go as bad as the doomsayers say they will? And leaving the extremes aside, what if the Earth is already too dangerously warm to save it, whether because of our fossil-fuel profligacy or because of some natural climate cycle? Are we on the right direction with all measures in place and those planned? What else can be done to ensure energy and environmental future for the next generations…?

And speaking of extreme cases, one that exemplifies things to come is in China…

China's Virtual Reality

There is a new reality in China, where municipalities and private developers are constructing large, well-designed "ghost cities" that are ready to be populated, but have been sitting completely devoid of people for years now. A giant new Chinese-built city was also built in Africa in the outskirts of Angola's capital Luanda.

Do the Chinese know something we don't? Are they preparing for the Apocalypse, or is this a new way to put their money in a safe place for use in the future?

One of the ghost cities, Nova Cidade de Kilamba, was designed to hold up to a half million people and features 750 eight-story apartment buildings, 12 schools and more than 100 retail units. It covers 12,355 acres. State-owned China International Trust and Investment Corporation took less than three years to build the city at a cost of $3.5 billion. But…the city's buildings are completely empty.

Amazingly, these "ghost cities" have a life of their own—without any people—after countless billions of dollars have been spent on the towns' design and construction. Block after block of empty houses and apartment buildings, glamorous public buildings, magnificent public parks and sports complexes, even art museums, remain entirely empty.

Just like a giant movie sets prepared to film an apocalyptic event or a bizarre natural disaster has eliminated people from the face of the Earth while leaving the skyscrapers, sports stadiums, parks and roads perfectly intact. One of China's ghost cities is actually built in the middle of a desert in Inner Mongolia. There are no cars on the city streets except for 100 cars parked in empty lots clustered around a government building, while some pictures show a beautiful wetland park with people added using Photoshop.

At one time, China had an estimated inventory of 64 million vacant homes and was building up to 20 new ghost cities a year. Obviously, for awhile at least, it seemed as if the Chinese needed to put their money somewhere, so developers have decided to build, as a place to store the wealth. This, even if the Chinese building these cities do not intend to live in them and there is no prospect that they can find buyers or renters.

It also seems that this is a remnant of the old communist system, which provided incentives to build new buildings to show growth. Building new cities is the easiest way to achieve growth, so they build.

In reality, these cities have sprung up as a result of China's drive to increase the national GDP, since manufacturing has actually decreased some lately. Chinese officials have been attempting to span the GDP gap with new construction projects larger than life and as useless as a dead horse.

The new cities will remain ghostly cities, because the speculators have purchased many of the units not to live in but to rent. The speculators have driven the price of condos up into the $200,000-$300,000 range, but since the average Chinese worker only makes approximately $6,000 per year the newly constructed condos and houses will remain vacant for a long time…and maybe forever. This is an ominous plan…and ominously bad at that. Useless, impractical, deceiving, and even stupid in its naiveté; it is a full fledged reminder of the old communist ideas of building a new and more perfect society…without even taking into account the basics of human needs and wants.

One good thing about these new cities is that they are emission free. Yes, there are near-zero emissions coming from all these new developments. No people, no economic activities, no pollution…

Figure 9-47. China ghost city

China's Present Reality

To the people living in and having activities around packed Beijing and other major Chinese cities, it is like living in a cigar lounge, or worse. Although China is racking up all the top spots in the global energy market, recently it overtook the U.S. as the world's biggest emitter of carbon dioxide. In 2010, it became the world's largest car market, with car emissions increasing daily.

In 2011, China came close to burning as much coal as all the countries in the world combined, and at the same time emitting more GHGs than any country. The Chinese people are, however, paying a price for these distinctions. The 2010 data on disease-related deaths show that 1.2 million Chinese died from outdoor air pollution that year alone. China now holds another record: 40% of global deaths from air pollution.

That data also show an increase of mortality from just a few years before, where in 2007 roughly 650,000 Chinese had been killed by air pollution. This is just how bad things are in Chinese cities. Turns out, that living in Beijing is *worse* than living in a cigar lounge.

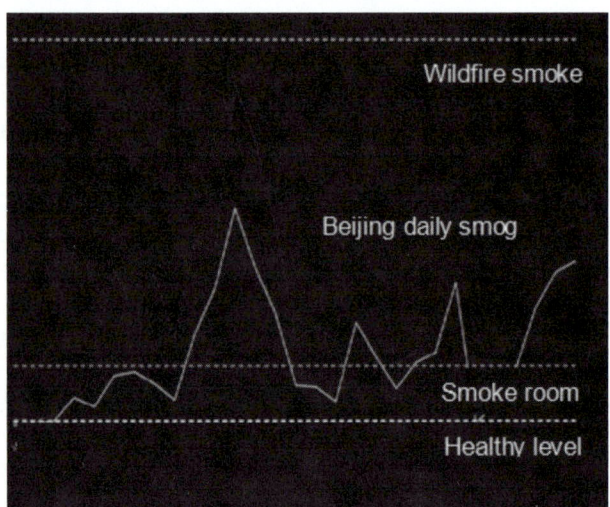

Figure 9-48. Beijing's killer smog levels

The world organizations' estimates are that less than 1% of Chinese who are living in large cities are breathing healthy air. And things seem to be getting worse, as China is planning to build hundreds upon hundreds of new coal-fired power plants. While these will provide a lot of the much-needed electric power, they will also add a lot of additional toxic gasses in the air people breathe.

The Plans

On the positive side of things, the Chinese government has been trying to address the air pollution prob-

lem by better reporting requirements, stronger pollution controls on power plants and automobiles, limiting coal consumption, and promoting hydro, solar and wind power.

China has been a leader in solar panels' manufacturing, which has not helped China that much, but has contributed to bringing cheap solar power to the world. China also received another positive distinction in 2012 by becoming the world's largest wind market. The plans are to also become a world leader in solar power generation, so we are now witnessing a race in China. It is a race between record pollution deaths and record expansion of clean energy resources. What is going to win?

China's central government seems to be awakening to the grim reality, so in 2013 it leapfrogged the U.S. in GHG policy designs and implementation and now is taking the lead on carbon legislation. China also surpassed the U.S. in renewable energy and efficiency investment in 2011 and 2012. China averages approximately $65 billion per year of clean tech investments, compared to the $45 billion invested by the U.S.

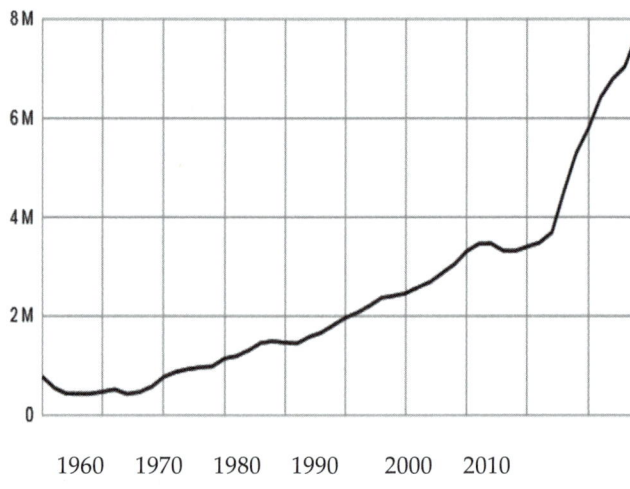

Figure 9-49. China GHG emissions, 1960-2010

China's pollution is approaching apocalyptic levels, so the government is taking some decisive actions. The plan is for China to introduce a set of new taxation policies designed to preserve the environment, including a tax on carbon dioxide emissions. The government will collect the new environmental protection tax instead of pollutant discharge fees, as well as levy a tax on carbon dioxide emissions.

In more detail:

- The tax will be collected by the local taxation authority, rather than the environmental protection department.

- The government will tax energy-intensive products such as batteries, as well as luxury goods such as aircraft, yachts, SUVs, and other such large vehicles that are not used for public transportation.

- The government will also push forward resource tax reforms by taxing coal based on price instead of sales volume, as well as raising coal taxes, to protect and conserve natural resources.

- There are also plans to levy resource taxation on water use especially by energy generators and other large water consumers.

China is a major source of carbon emissions, so the move to implement a carbon tax is good news for the environment. It is also good news for the clean tech industry, which China is already becoming a leader of by investing billions and billions of dollars. Solar, wind, and clean transportation development, in addition to a carbon tax, will drive more demand and more innovation.

If and when the new China environmental policies become reality, we will see more activity by U.S. clean tech companies in China, a trend that is already underway. Pricing carbon will have ripple effects across the world and will raise the bar for the energy policies of the U.S. and the E.U. and other nations.

At this time it is difficult to foresee what market or political forces could drive U.S. politicians to act on effective carbon legislation, but the fact that President Obama charged the EPA to enforce the carbon policy of the U.S. is a good step in the right direction.

CLIMATE VS. POWER GENERATION

We live in an era of increasing socio-political complexities. Developing nations are demanding more energy and fuels for their economies and personal comfort. Burning fossils is one of the ways they can achieve both, and the developed nations dare not stop them, since this is how they, themselves, became developed.

In the end, fossil burning is one of the greatest evils of today, and a crime against the environment; however, it is a profitable business for the big energy companies and is generally accepted by the public as the evil we cannot live without.

Environmental protection is alive in theory, but with very little to show in practice. It is not profitable enough to be taken seriously by big business, so it's limping along propped partially by government subsidies and partially by good-will measures.

It appears unlikely now that we will see any great changes until someone figures a way to make lots of money by protecting the environment. Then, and only then, will we see any serious improvements in the quality of our environment. Until then, we will be talking and writing about what can or should be done, and what was not done.

The Energy Picture

There are a lot of attempts in the U.S. and around the world geared to introduce policies to stop global warming and allow for world ecological improvements. Many international conferences outlined the issues and decided on goals and targets, but implementing these changes is a different story. Most countries have abandoned promises and changed their policies as needed to support their economic growth. Even Germany, which is considered as one of the leaders in the renewables revolution, is going back on its promises and is converting many gas-fired plants to coal and oil.

The future of our energy supply can follow three scenarios as shown in Table 9-21.

At the present time we are following the "balance scenario." Energy prices are rising, and there is no commitment to global environmental policies. We are faced with technical development, which makes it probable that we will choose the scenario that provides us with growth in the oil and gas sector combined with increased nuclear power production.

In the U.S. and Canada, large amounts of oil sands have been found, which are exploited through fracking processes. China is, to a certain extent, using renewable energies, which is just not sufficient to keep up with its population and industry growth. So China is planning expansion in the energy sector via coal, gas, and oil fuels. There are also plans to build a significant number of nuclear power plants.

Amazingly enough, Germany and other developed and environmentally responsible countries have also decided to ramp up their coal-fired power plants. The result of this action will be a further increase of GHG in the next decade. This will very likely keep us in the "balance" scenario for a while longer.

The new power sources will generate a lot of GHGs and also come with a lot of other risks and problem, such as nuclear accidents and having to figure out what to do with nuclear waste.

There are simply no solid plans today for switching to the "emergence scenario," which is the only one that could lead to a long-term, sustainable future. Economic

Table 9-21. The three possible future energy and environment scenarios

BALANCE	EMERGENCE	RENAISSANCE
• Climate policies have been addressed in some countries by promotion of renewables, carbon tax and other initiatives. • Most countries are going back on their pledges, thus adding more uncertainties. • Without enforceable global agreement, only minimum policies are maintained. • Business-as-usual prevails, energy prices rise and not much improvement of the environment is achieved.	• Europe exceeds the 20% target in 2020, followed by the U.S. and other developed countries. • Developing countries meet their Copenhagen pledges, and contribute to further reduction of GHG emissions. • But most importantly, a new international agreement is achieved, where the key polluter countries pledge to reduce the GHG emissions by additional 50 percent by 2050.	• A lot of effort and money is poured into the production of new and unconventional oil, natural gas, and methane hydrates. • A new and much larger wave of fossil fuel resources is overtaking the world, at which point the global energy dilemma is solved for a century or more. • New actors appear in the energy sector, and the emphasis now is on controlling the environmental issues.

interests and short-term political actions are, at the present time, hindering the development of our sustainable future. Not stopping these developments will lead us to a bleak future. We are on the way to destroying the environment of our planet and harming all living things on it—including us all—in the process.

Climate Effects vs. Power Generation

One way or another, the Earth's environment and climate are changing. The final results of our crimes against the environment are yet to be seen, but we all agree that some changes are undeniable and inevitable, and some are surprising and even beneficial.

Some of the expected and unexpected changes would be:

• A rise in global temperatures will most likely reduce the heating demand, but at the same time will increase the cooling (air conditioning) demand, which is more energy-hungry. The inter-annual variability of energy supply-demand cycle won't be affected much by the changes, while seasonal energy demands will force power generators to respond and adapt to users' needs for energy. Extreme seasonal and periodic temperature tolerances will affect the energy infrastructure, forcing additional O&M effort and expense.

• The permafrost will be affected by the rising temperatures eventually too. The problem is that there

is nothing we can do to reverse the permafrost's melting in case of extreme temperature rise. In case of significant melting of the methane hydrates in the permafrost, methane gas (and there is a lot of it in the permafrost) thus released in the water and atmosphere might accelerate further the global warming process.

• Flooding and droughts will increase also. There are many areas that are very sensitive to these weather phenomena, and we are taking measures to reduce the negative effect and disasters caused by these. Risk management is the key here, even if there are guarantees that either or both will occur at any location. Impacts on energy infrastructure, including silting of nuclear plants and water reservoirs need to be considered during design and construction.

• The production of biomass and biofuels will be impacted by the rising temperature and increased frequency of floods and droughts as well. Because of that, appropriate measures need to be taken to prevent major loss of crops due to the climate and weather pattern changes related events.

• Sea level is rising measurably and is expected to accelerate with time, and with that the risk of damage to low-lying coastal energy infrastructure and storm damage is increasing as well. Risks of damage due to rising sea level and extreme events, like hurricanes and storm surges, to offshore energy-producing infrastructures (wind turbines, oil platforms, wave and tidal generators) is real and in need of protection measures.

- The frequency of storm activities and their increased intensities at tropical and extra-tropical latitudes, bring increased flooding and additional offshore risks, accompanied by structural damage due to increased wind speeds.

- Climate change may impact the generation cycle efficiency and disrupt cooling water operations of fossil, nuclear, and biomass power plants, thus increasing their O&M costs.

- The renewables' energy generators will be no doubt affected too, but we can only guess that hydro-, solar-, biofuels-, and ocean power sources will benefit, or suffer, at different times, depending on the changes in temperature, storms, and rainfall frequency and intensity.

- Water availability is a critical issue that has to be coordinated through the different sectors. In all cases it will become more difficult to maintain adequate water supplies in the new era of rising demand by new technologies that require more water, sometimes in areas of reduced water availability.

Concentrated solar power (CSP) plants are installed in the world's deserts and need a lot of water for cooling. The water table goes lower with time, and the energy needed to pump it up increases until there is no more water. This is a good example of unsustainable energy generation.

So we are looking at a brand new set of climate-imposed and man-aggravated conditions that dictate a new approach to design, installation and operation of energy equipment and natural resources.

Which is Affecting What

Until now we discussed the effects of power generation on the environment. But how do the environment and the changing climate affect power generation? One of the most recent, and possibly best examples of these effects, is the earthquake-tsunami effect on the Fukushima nuclear power pant in Japan in 2012. No doubt, the effect was tremendously disruptive and ultimately destructive to the locals.

Hurricane Sandy in the fall of 2013 unleashed a

Figure 9-50. The iconic image of hurricane Sandy's fury

powerful blow on the U.S. East Coast. It was also as a result of the whims of Earth, and very likely provoked by man-made activities that caused climate changes. In both cases, the aftermath of the disasters was felt most by the locals, but the effects resounded hundreds and thousands of miles away as well.

Those are just two recent examples of the forces we are faced with, and how unprepared we are to deal with what Nature can do in a fury. It will not hesitate to teach us to be more respectful. So, we better listen and learn.

All man-made equipment and activities—no matter how sophisticated they might seem to us—are but a child's toy when compared with Nature's power. We should have learned by now that we cannot fight with Nature. History offers a number of lessons of Nature's wins; every time we try to face off with Nature, we lose. Instead, we should've learned that working with and along Nature is the best, if not the only successful approach.

We should've also learned by now that building larger and more powerful power plants, dams and other power generating facilities does no change the equation in our favor. Nature is in control no matter what we do or plan to do. Ask the people who lived around the Fukushima; they will tell you how helpless they felt after the earthquake and the nuclear plant's failure.

There is a great lesson in this, and most other accidents with man-made equipment, which we need to study and learn. It is that, no matter how big and complicated our equipment and installations are, they are no matches for Nature's might. As a matter of fact, the bigger and more complicated projects we build, greater the risks and less in control of our environment and destiny we are.

Energy and Environment Timeline

Energy and the environment are tied together in an awkward dance, which is looking more like a fight with every passing day. It is a fight where there are no winners. The more energy we use, the less of it we have left and the more pollution that is emitted. So while the fossil fuel reservoirs are getting emptied, the atmosphere is getting filled with poisonous gases.

Figure 9-51 clearly shows that in the year 2000 we had lots of fossils and relatively modest energy use, which was accompanied by a small amount of environmental problems. As we continue, and even accelerate the use of fossils for energy generation and transport, we see the fossil reserves shrink by 2050, and slowly go away by 2100. At the same time the environmental issues grow proportionally.

That is a picture of unsustainable resource management. In fact, this is not management at all; it is exploitation and abuse of Nature at its highest levels.

So what can we expect, and what can be done to improve our power generation infrastructure, while protecting the environment?

The Environment and Power Generation

We've discussed some of the key observed and projected climate changes in the future. We explored the trends, extremes, and the hotspots in different geographic and technological areas, some of which are destined to see major changes. We also predicted unforeseeable variability in the key parameters such as temperature, runoff, and sea level rise, as well as the impacts of these changes on the environment and the people living in it.

We also discussed the contribution of power generation to the environmental effects and climate change, as well as the related damages. But as these damages occur, they also affect the power generators. That is similar to an accident caused by a drunk driver, where he slams into a wall, destroying the building and killing people in it, but is also hurt when the wall falls on him and his car catches on fire.

This is a catch 22 situation; you do damage, and the damage does you. The Fukushima disaster is a good example of such a catch 22, where environmental changes affecting the Earth's balance cause damaging and long-lasting counter-effects. The energy resources, infrastructure, and transportation systems are, and will be, seriously affected by these counter-effects, and so we need to pay attention and take appropriate measures.

Some technologies and services are more vulnerable than others, and in some cases urgent action is needed for near-term planning. Regional issues are also factors to be considered. For example, coastal installations would be affected differently that those in the mountains. In all cases, open discussions with energy sector officials to disaggregate climate impacts to regional and local settings, and to improve the knowledge base are badly needed.

A summary of the key issues, as related to awareness and mitigation of climate change effects, impacting the power generating industry, are:

The power generation infrastructure will be increasingly affected by climate change. We see increasingly signs of unpredictable changes in the weather trends, climate variability, greater temperature extremes, and large

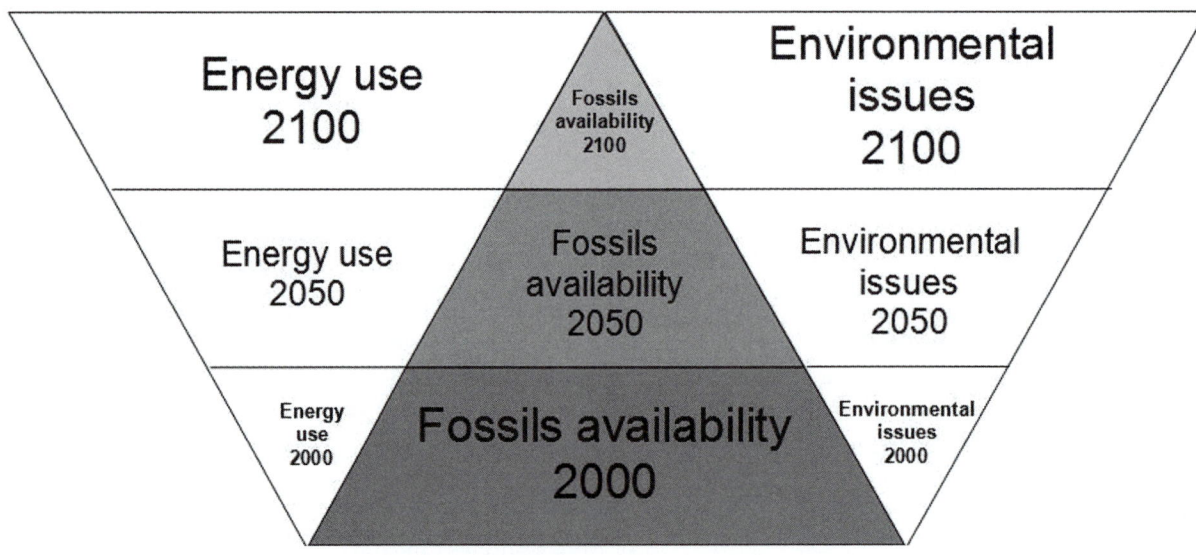

Figure 9-51. Energy vs. fossils, vs. environment, 2000-2100

inter-annual variations in climate parameters around the globe. Though potential climate impacts have been recognized strongly within the energy sector, the focus has mainly been on the responsibility for greenhouse gas mitigation rather than on the management of energy infrastructure.

The climate-related issues are very complex from technical and socio-economic points of view. The environmental and climate change processes consist of hundreds, if not thousands, of different issues. Chemistry, physics, geology, biology, climatology, metrology, among other sciences are involved in the entire process. A myriad of complex phenomena, trends, and reactions take place for a time, until they eventually result in observable events. And then, when the event occurs, some places and groups of people are affected more than others, which further complicate the picture.

Climate changes impact the entire energy supply and demand chain. Accepting the fact that there are environmental and climate changes is one thing. Accepting that some of these changes are due to power generation is another. Accepting that the climate changes can affect the power generation sector is yet another. That adds a new dimension to the already complex interaction between climate change and power generation. What can we expect as a result of the new climate change energy picture:

Impact on the energy infrastructure. When we do pay attention to the climate effects, we focus on the immediate impact on the energy supply and demand chain, since power disruption and power lines damage are most obvious and most frequent consequences. In the process, however, we ignore the direct effects on the energy infrastructure, as illustrated by Fukushima disaster.

Impact on the local and national economy. In most disaster cases much less attention is paid to the damaging effects of the event to the local and national economies. Usually, these are left on the back burner until the emergency is taken care of. Often, however, this neglect becomes a major problem during the recovery process, when it becomes a priority. It is then that the key economic sectors, such as water supply and agriculture receive the needed attention, but sometimes it is too late. Fukushima is again a principal example of a case where the local economy and people were caught totally unprepared and paid dearly for neglecting to plan ahead.

Awareness is needed to acknowledge the fact that there is a problem. There is not yet full and unquestionable awareness of the risks associated with climate change, especially its effects on the power sector. Even after the Fukushima and Sandy disasters, the connection between what happened and the climate change is lost to most people. Climate change, as a destructive force to anything that happens to be in its way—including power infrastructure—is not well understood, and therefore it is not taken seriously. Actually, it has been simply ignored (until now) by the power generation sector.

Understanding the changes is the first step toward efficient risk mitigation. The existing energy infrastructure, and any future modifications and additions to it, need to consider the changing climate conditions. This knowledge needs to be then used in proper design, construction, and O&M planning and procedures. Some energy systems operators are aware of the climate risks, and already take some of into account during their daily work, but deeper understanding and coordinated adaptation measures are needed to reduce the vulnerability to environmental change to the minimum. Building the knowledge base and improving information exchange for more efficient decision making and climate risk management can do this.

There is a lack of reliable research, and timely observations and predictions. The scarcity of climate change related data, accompanied by limited experience in dealing with climate associated uncertainties, limits the energy sector's understanding, acceptance, and adaptation to the present and coming changes—some of which would be spectacular, and might bring other Fukushima-like disasters in the near future. The situation is even worse in developing countries, where there is lack of historical hydro-meteorological data, limited climate-related services, and overall indifference to the upcoming climate events.

Taking special actions is needed to increase the energy systems' resilience. There is no doubt that unplanned variations in climate conditions are on the way. This requires, in addition to thorough knowledge, special planning and action to protect the energy systems, regardless of the type and level of global climate change. In many cases, small adaptations can be implemented at relatively low cost, thus bringing great benefits to the energy system and the public.

Coordinated risk-assessment-and-mitigation planning is critical to address the possible impacts. Coordination and harmonization of the actions across sectors is a key of success. This is absolutely needed, to avoid misusing the old and unsustainable practices of the past. Long-term planning for climate mitigation need to account for the possible energy sector climate impacts, and implement adaptation strategies to optimize energy and natural resource management.

Adapting to variations in energy demand. The variations in energy demand are unavoidable, and are caused by a number of internal and external factors. Adapting to these variations involves reducing energy demand, especially for increased cooling demand cycles, and compensating for any capacity-reducing impacts that coincide with peak demand. Energy storage technologies are one plausible option to level electricity consumption, avoid peak hour disruptions, and store excess electricity in low-demand hours.

The smart grid solution. Energy efficiency gains are not restricted to only compensating for increased energy demand, as offered by the energy storage option. The smart grid is another solution to this problem. Malta's smart grid solution is an example of an electricity / water saving alternative, achieved by building a smart grid to control water use and electricity generation.

The thus designed smart grid watches constantly for abnormalities, such as theft, leakage, defective meters, unusual parameters, and alerts the operators or automatically takes preventative measures. The overall result is complete control of the resources, which improves the system's efficiency and promotes conservation.

The only problem is that we don't have a smart grid right now. It will also take a long time before we figure out how to do it, find the money for it, and finally get it done. This entire process will take at least half a century.

OUR ENVIRONMENTAL FUTURE

"The era of procrastination, of half measures, of soothing and baffling expedience of delays, is coming to its close. In its place we are entering a period of consequences. We cannot avoid this period; we are in it now," said Winston Churchill on November 12, 1936.

Although this was said almost 80 years ago, it sounds as relevant as if it were said today. Was Mr. Churchill clairvoyant, or is this problem so obvious for all to see—even those almost three-quarters of a century ago?

Whatever the case might've been, it is more than clear now that we are in such a period of half measures, and procrastination. The fossil energy resources are being depleted very quickly and our environment is getting dirtier by the day. Although there are talks on all levels, the situation is only getting worse...

But this was not supposed to be so! According to the Kyoto Protocol, an official commitment of 7% decrease of GHGs was agreed upon to happen by now; alas, something went wrong and things are just not going as planned. The Kyoto Protocol is an official international agreement on the environment linked to the United Nations framework convention on climate change. It was agreed to by a number of countries, was adopted in Kyoto, Japan on December 11, 1997, and entered into force on February 16, 2005.

The detailed rules for the implementation of the protocol were adopted at COP 7 in Marrakesh, Morocco, in 2001, and are referred to as the "Marrakesh Accords." Its first commitment period started in 2008 and ended in 2012.

All parties committed to setting internationally binding emission reduction targets, recognizing that the developed countries are principally responsible for the current high levels of GHG emissions in the atmosphere. Since the developed countries have benefited from over 100 years of unrestricted industrial activity, the Kyoto Protocol places a heavier burden on the developed nations under the principle of "common but differentiated responsibilities."

In December 2012, the "Doha Amendment to the Kyoto Protocol" was adopted In Doha, Qatar. It includes:

- New commitments for Annex I parties to the Kyoto Protocol who agreed to take on commitments in a second commitment period from January 1, 2013 to December 31, 2020

- A revised list of greenhouse gases (GHG) to be reported on by Parties in the second commitment period

- Amendments to several articles of the Kyoto Protocol, which specifically referenced issues pertaining to the first commitment period and which needed to be updated for the second commitment period

During the first commitment period, 37 industrialized countries and the European Community committed to reduce GHG emissions to an average of 5% against 1990 levels. During the second commitment period, parties committed to reduce GHG emissions by at least 18%

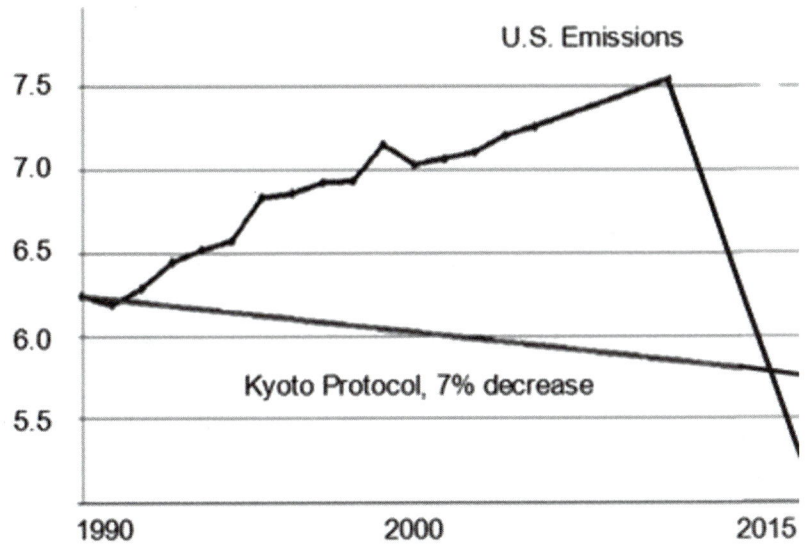

Figure 9-52. U.S. GHG emissions in gigatons of CO_2 equivalent

The reduction in GHG emissions in the U.S. is due mostly to the decrease of coal for power generation, as well as reduction of use of crude oil for transportation. Further decrease in emissions from these fossil sources is expected in the near future for similar reasons.

But how much good all this does to the world as a whole, if China, India and a number of other developing countries continue to increase their CO_2 emissions in their attempt to develop their industries and provide better life to their citizens? As a matter of fact, China now leads the world with about 10.0 billion tons of annual GHG emissions and that is increasing by the addition of new coal-fired plants, millions of vehicles, and so forth. The U.S. is second, with slightly over 5.0 billion tons, or half as much as China, and dropping.

below 1990 levels in the eight-year period from 2013 to 2020; however, the composition of parties in the second commitment period is different from the first.

The U.S. refused to be part of this agreement for a number of reasons. We, however, should take credit for the fact that today our GHG emissions—Kyoto or no Kyoto—have been reduced significantly.

In 2012, the U.S. industrial complex emitted about 5.5 billion tons of CO_2, while the Kyoto target puts the cap on U.S. emissions at 5.8 billion tons annually. This unexpected (and we dare say unplanned) environmental compliance makes the U.S. the first major industrialized nation in the world to meet the United Nation's original Kyoto Protocol 2012 target for CO_2 reductions. And we didn't even sign the darn thing...

What can we say? Don't the developing countries deserve the lifestyle that we here in the West enjoy after a century of unrestricted fossils exploitation and use? Do we have a right to put limits on their CO_2 emissions and industrial development? Maybe not...even if it jeopardizes the global climate and our own wellbeing and health.

OK. By now we know all that there is to know about energy (or at least most of it), and how it affects our environment. The overwhelming fact is that we use fossils more than any other fuel, while at the same time we blame them for most of our energy and environmental problems. It might do us some good to take a quick glimpse at what life would be without fossil fuels. Let's try to imagine life after all crude oil, coal, and natural gas has been pumped out and otherwise extracted from the ground.

Let's take an imaginary walk in the distant fossil-less future.

The year is 2525.

It is not very hard to imagine that by then—over five centuries away—people would have figured out how to live without fossils. Otherwise there would be no humans on Earth, since they all would've been killed by hunger and the confusion that would ultimately result in wars for survival.

This, however, is not a likely scenario, because humans are smarter than that, so instead, we are looking at things that are hard to imagine today. There are flying cars in the skies, people moving on conveyor belts in the cities, and—stop my heart—the air is clean and fresh

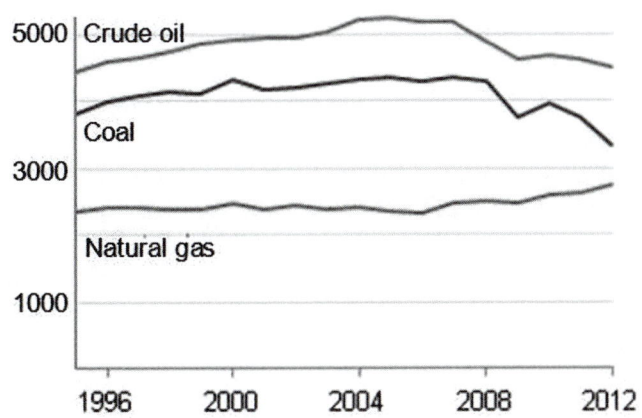

Figure 9-53. U.S. Fossil GHG emissions (in millions of tons per year)

even in the middle of a hot and muggy August day in downtown Los Angeles.

This is the easy and pleasant part of our walk in the future. The hard part is during the previous several decades, during the hard years of transition from fossils to non-fossils. That was the time when we reached the oil peak, which is when natural resources (and fossils in particular) became too difficult and too expensive to extract, at which point they had to be replaced by something cheaper, better and more plentiful.

That was the time for hard, sometimes life-changing, decisions.

Amazingly enough, after all the years of talks on the subject, our sophisticated and advanced society woke up one day with no substitutes for coal, oil, and natural gas. And what is even more amazing is that we were not even putting much effort into it, thus the humanity was faced with jumping down the proverbial fossil-less energy cliff.

And so, in the beginning of the 21st century, oil peaked at just over 74 million barrels per day (mbpd) and has remained at that level ever since. There was some additional oil that brought the total to about 84 mbpd in 2012, but it is not the conventional crude we are so used to; it was rather a number of unconventional hydrocarbons, such as natural gas and coal derivatives, "extra heavy" oil, synthetic oil from Canadian tar sands, biofuels, and some renewables.

Crude oil production went downhill after that, mostly because the large and most productive world oil fields were getting depleted quickly and new deposits have been progressively smaller, of lesser quality, and much harder (and expensive) to exploit. And the decline rate accelerated over 10% per year as of 2025. By 2050, crude oil was on the list of endangered species.

Natural gas was hailed as the energy problem solver (albeit temporary), but it peaked around 2025, and started a sharp decline by 2050. It was a short-lived glory that brought with it a number of environmental disasters, human suffering and death.

Coal was more plentiful and its use has been decreasing (while the production of cheaper natural gas was increasing), but even then, coal was also depleted shortly after year 2100.

Figure 9-54 depicts our vision of the global energy future, where the depletion of oil, gas, and coal will be complete by the end of the 21st century.

So, in summary, and everything else considered:

a.   With the crude oil happy days gone mid-21st century, gasoline would be at \$100/gal by the year 2075, and no natural gas would be available at all

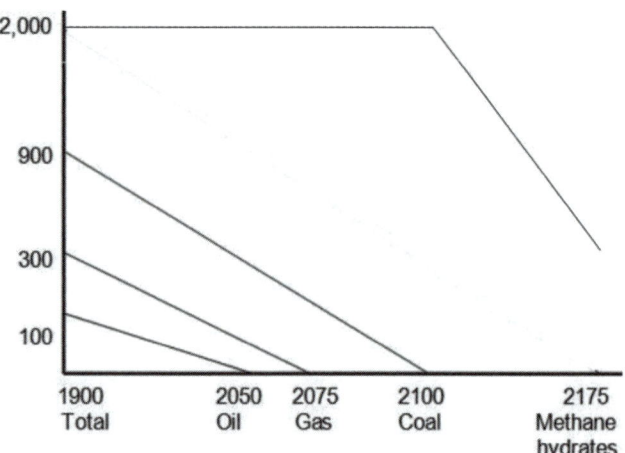

Figure 9-54. Fossil reserves; in billions of tons vs. depletion time

by the year 2100, due to unreasonably fast increase of population around the world.

b.   Natural gas was the king for a while, but its kingdom ended around 2075, with the price increasing dramatically by 2100, and then there was no more natural gas at all by the year 2150.

c.   Coal experienced a short decline and renaissance in the middle of the 21st century, but lasted the longest of its fossil cousins. It was the sole fossil energy source by the end of the 21st century, and then started the eminent decline people have been talking about for a long time, until it was completely depleted by mid-22nd century, again due to unreasonably quick increase of its use globally.

The transition to non-fossil fuels is slow and painful. As oil gets harder to pump out, and its quality deteriorates with time, by 2050 oil, gasoline, diesel, and jet fuel prices go sky high. With prices at levels unheard of and unimagined before and continuing to go up steadily, things on the ground and in the air change—some drastically.

Cruise ships are no longer able to zigzag and run in circles in the world's oceans, while trying to entertain their passengers and offer them an alternative, albeit short-lived, happiness at the expense of thousands of gallons of diesel fuel. Airplane tickets and large gasoline cars are now luxury that only very few can afford, and even they have a hard time getting enough fuel to go long distances. Small electric cars are humming everywhere. The American dream is now downsized and trimmed to the max. Later on, by the end of the century, even those luxuries were no longer available.

Around that time the technology for extracting

methane hydrates from the permafrost was fully developed, together with other sources (advanced peat, shale, etc. new fossils production) so the world now had another type of fossils for another century. People had enough electricity, and were able to drive electric cars, recharged by electricity from the new methane hydrate power plants. Cruise ships engines were modified to use the new methane gas from the new deposits and started zigzagging the world's oceans with the happy-wanna-be people on board.

But even that energy source was exhausted by the end of the 22nd century. There was just no way around it; this is a hungry world that needs to be fed, clothed, and transported every day. And since only today matters, we are not used to worry about tomorrow, not really. We talk about it and find ways to make money on the subject, but we do not like to sacrifice for sake of tomorrow.

So, by the year 2225, all fossils on Earth are gone. A real transition from fossils to non-fossil types of energy finally became an absolute and unavoidable reality. Little was done in terms of preventing major energy transition disasters until then, so the work finally started at that time.

Governments and companies were forced to look into the different ways to jump over the energy cliff, and with oil, gas and coal in the rear view mirror, the stark reality hit hard. But amazingly enough, and as many times before, great things happen during times of extreme duress.

The world's economies were forced (as never before) to live within shrinking, instead of expanding, energy budgets. Having gone through the cycle of commodity price spikes several times, all indications pointed to economic destruction, leading to supply destruction, leading back to price spikes, and on the cycle goes. The entire world economy was in a free fall and spiraling down for a long while.

The first consequence was the end of globalization as we know it today. The days of shipping raw materials to Asia and shipping back ready-to-use gadgets were gone, so people had to re-learn how to make things with their own hands—just like our predecessors did a long time ago—and live within the local boundaries. All countries were left on their own.

Americans are less than 5% of the world population, but are used to consuming 25% of its energy and goods, so they were hit the hardest. The American dream was reduced to a daily fight for survival. Production of any and all goods was localized, and having food and other goods travel an average 1,000 miles before reaching the markets was no longer feasible. Foods needed to now come from nearby fields.

High prices and the lack of fertilizers forced the use of organic crops and alternative growing methods. The good old days of using 10-15 calories of fossil fuel inputs (diesel fuel and fertilizers) for every calorie of food were gone too.

Bedroom communities, 50 miles from the industrial centers were converted in self-sustaining independent entities with specialized local economies. The long daily drive, and sitting in idling cars was seen only in the old movies. Instead mass transport and moving walkways were the new transportation methods of choice (or necessity.)

The signs of an increasing global devastation are quite obvious today:

- The national electric grid is mostly gone and in need of rebuilding.

- The national highway and railway systems are mostly gone and in need of rebuilding.

- The large cities infrastructure (streets, bridges, sewers) is mostly gone and in need of rebuilding.

In the near future, we will see much more of that and some new negative events taking place, such as ocean levels rising, where Venice, the Maldeves, the Florida coastline, parts of Lousiana and the Netherlands are flooded and remain under water. Unprecedented droughts and killer floods hit other parts of the world. Even worse, excess methane hydrate exploitation accelerates the global warming when ocean drilling of those enormous but unpredictable fossil reserves expands.

Transitions are usually hard and very often tragic events. The fossil-less energy transition would be the most serious global crisis ever. The consequences will be dramatic and even tragic, but it could eventually have a very positive outcome too. It all depends on which path the governments chose. Solar, wind, geothermal and ocean resources could provide the total energy the world consumes every day, if and when the 22nd century people learn how to harvest them, and their 25th century descendants follow through.

They could build energy efficient, carbon-free economies, put an end to climate change and avert resource wars. They would have healthier food and a safer, more resilient and equitable, world where all nations and peoples live in peace and harmony. This is a dream after all...so dream with us...

The Mirage...

The worst part of any transition, including the pending fossil-less transition, is that some people just don't understand, nor believe, that a drastic change to their usual way of life can occur. Ever! And even if it does occur, it will not affect them personally.

It is built in the human psyche, and especially in that of most Americans, that we deserve what we have, and that life only can get better, not worse. Other people, like the Arabian prince have come up with solutions to the new oil-less world that is devoid of reason. His idea is to build a large vacationland type of infrastructure that would support him and his people when their and all-global fossil reserves ran out.

His vision consists of luxury vacation villas, event venues, sports clubs, and other luxuries, designed for the world's richest people to play in and enjoy from time to time, thus bringing badly needed income to the oil-less Arab Peninsula when it is most needed.

A large part of the global village functionality, however, and personal transport especially, depend exclusively on fossils, so how does the Prince think (when oil runs out) the owners of the thousands of vacation villas and venues he is creating, are going to get there from the U.S. or Canada? Or even from Europe, when the oil guzzling jet liners are parked for good in the Arizona desert junkyards?

There is no known substitute for jet fuel. None! And jumbo jets cannot fly on batteries, solar, or any other fuel, in that matter. Without precious jet fuel, every jet plane will be sent to the junkyard, where there are already thousands of these machines standing in lined up in neat rows, baking in the rust-free heat of the Arizona desert. Some are quite new, some not so, but they are all mothballed—a reminder of the things to come. They are all sitting there awaiting supposed fuel price reductions and an explosion in passenger numbers, but the reality even today is that most will never fly again. And the junk pile keeps getting larger.

The Prince's vision is so full of folly that we are wondering what world he lives in. Tourism and vacationing, as we know them, will not exist in the new jet-less world, so the only way for him to fill the thousands of villas is to convince the owners to come visit and live in his kingdom or move there. But much more than a vacation villa will be needed to make most people move.

And with the crude oil resources gone, the national GDP of the kingdom will drop to nearly zero, since there is nothing in its sand dunes that can sustain a decent economy without the vast oil revenues. And then, the artificial islands that need constant refurbishment and propping up with vast quantities of expensively dredged sand will start melting into the sea. The reality will sink in slowly, which will give the oil sheikhs, deprived of their precious commodity and only real income, enough time to watch their beautiful concrete dreams—including the thousands of vacation villas—slowly crumbling and sinking into the sand.

And even worse, this could happen much sooner than anticipated, for the oil table is getting depleted quickly and nobody can provide assurances about how long the oil reserves will last anywhere else in the world.

The real problem, however, is how long can we hide our heads in the sand, and ignore the upcoming reality without taking even the basic, realistic and so much needed, precautions.

Figure 9-55. "We are working on the fossil problem..."

People of this world, including princes and princesses, beware! Once the fossil-less transition starts, it will be too late to stop, *let alone reverse it*. We have been kept in our comfort zone by "specialists" and oil-interests telling us day after day that crude oil, gas and coal reserves will last a long time, as new reserves are discovered daily. So not to worry!

These calculations, however, are made mostly by interested parties, using today's demand levels and with today's level of production, which are easy to manipulate. But global demand is growing, outstripping the supply as the multi-billion people economies of China and India mature and grow, and as other nations are starting to climb the ladder of civilized prosperity and westernization—all of which require a lot of fossils. And the new discoveries, no matter how significant, cannot keep up with the demand. As a matter of fact, they only give us the wrong idea that things can go this way for much longer. So not to worry!

Independent industry specialists claim that major oil company producers like BP, Shell, and the others have already seen their production peak, and that new discoveries are only helping them to keep the present levels of production. So while the demand is growing, even the best and most powerful oil companies won't be able to supply our needs. This will only lead to a faster depletion of the fossils, and when the fossil bucket, which we have been told is bottomless, finally is empty, it cannot be refilled and will stay empty forever! Then what?!

"The Age of Stupid"

In the movie "The Age of Stupid" the producers paint a clear and quite frightening picture of the total devastation on our Earth and all life on it as a result of serious pollution and climate change. The film begins in the year 2055 shortly after the world has been ravaged by catastrophic climate change. London is flooded, Sydney is burning, Las Vegas has been swallowed up by desert, the Amazon rainforest has burnt up, snow has vanished from the Alps and nuclear war has laid waste to India.

Figure 9-56. The only man left on Earth in 2055 ("The Age of Stupid")

Only one man is left alive and is entrusted with the safekeeping of the only thing left on Earth—the world's archives. He reviews archive footage from way back "when we could have saved ourselves," trying to discern where it all went wrong.

Amid news reports of the gathering effects of climate change and global civilization teetering towards destruction, he tells the stories of several individuals who lived in the early 21st century in an attempt to illustrate some of the key aspects of the impending climate-caused disaster.

These stories are actually documentary segments reflecting the lives of real people in early 21st century. The actions of individuals and groups of individuals are what we witness today, so what follows—albeit very scary—makes a lot of sense.

We see and hear a lot of discussions on these subjects today, with most people agreeing that the resolution of critical energy and environmental issues is paramount, and yet the actions do not match the verbal intercourse. So, although we don't think that such large devastation can happen by year 2055, we think it is quite possible to occur by year 2155.

So let's try imagining life in year 2155—the key year of the 22nd century when fossils are officially pronounced dead and finished. We are walking downtown Los Angeles. Thousands of people on bicycles pedal down the streets, going to work, or to visit the civic center or Bunker Hill. Thousands of others are riding the sidewalk conveyors, while others are being whisked away by the Metro or the electric trolleys.

Electricity is abundant, but fossils are gone, and with them the large, muscle cars are history too. Without those monsters on wheels, the long-distance, hour-long, daily ride from the suburbs is also in the history books. Instead, gutless electric cars, with enough space to barely squeeze two people, are now the only means of personal transportation. Their range is still only 20-30 miles, so not many of those are seen downtown. They are used for occasional trips to the store or the local movie theater.

One striking difference now is the absence of smog and sewer smell in the air, which was the standard for downtown LA in the past. The air is fresh, and walking, which in the past was a health hazard, is now an easy, healthy exercise. Life goes on, and it is not as bad as some thought it might be.

But getting here was rough. Getting used to a life without gas- powered cars, plastics and cheap medications took a while and many battles were fought on different fronts and levels. Finally the end of fossils came as predicted, and without anyone being able to stop it. The American dream shrunk to the basics, is no longer a goal, but rather a dream of the days past.

Around the world things are even worse. As a result of the crude oil termination, the Saudi Arabian sheikhs are now back in their tents in the Sahara desert, riding camels to their farms, where they grow whatever grows in the desert sands. The Russians are focused on growing their trees in Siberia, which is now their only source of fuel.

The oil companies are still around, but with new, slick names, like Exxo-renewables (providing 30% of the solar and wind energy in the U.S.), Tex-alcohols (providing 30% of the grain alcohol in the U.S.), and Chev-nuclear-is-us (providing 30% of U.S. nuclear energy).

The electric energy that powers life today comes from millions of acres covered with solar panels in the

Arizona's and Nevada's deserts, the wind power plants built in the end of the 21st century in the Midwest and the off-shore plants in the oceans and the Gulf of Mexico—replacing the large oil rigs that once provided so much oil and created so many environmental problems.

Organic (synthetic fertilizers are no longer available) cornfields stretch as far as the eye can see in Kansas and other Midwestern states. New underground nuclear power stations, located hundreds of miles away from populated centers, provide half of the country's energy.

Manufacturing operations in the U.S. are booming, because the Chinese communist party fell during the energy bust by the end of the 21st century. The resulting political chaos destroyed the fragile manufacturing sector in China and many Asian countries. Lacking the generous government subsidies, and deprived of the easy gains from enormous exports to the West, China is now a shrinking giant. Shrinking in economic terms and in population, since a century of restrictions to "one-baby per family" and aborting girls resulted in reduced population and a weak society.

Russia is now also a dying giant. After all the crude oil was pumped out of the ground, the Putin regime (which, through Putin's children and relatives ruled Russia throughout the 21st century) was finally brought down as a result of the energy bust. With the energy sources gone, the Russian economy is running on wood from the large Siberian woods. After 50-60 years of indiscriminate woodcutting, the forests are decimated, and now Russia is entering a hibernation period, where the economy and agriculture are shrinking to pre-revolution (1918) levels.

The European Union was dissolved a long time ago, but the major powers—Germany, France and the U.K.—have found ways to keep up with the fossil depletion. Newly built solar power plants in the North African deserts and wind farms in the costal regions are providing abundant electric power that keeps their economies running.

The transformation from fossil to non-fossil economy is now complete. The smart and innovative have found a way to replace the fossils and can breathe easier in the clean air too. The rest of the world is still going through the pains of the energy transformation and is looking for ways to survive.

The Green Game

There is a trend for oil companies to hide behind their alleged interest and modest investment in renewable technologies. Royal Dutch Shell, for example, has been criticized and praised for its green investment initia-

tive, or lack thereof. There is no doubt that venture capital at Shell is focused on serving the oil and gas business first and foremost. But in the summer of 2013, Shell Technology Ventures (STV) announced that it intents to invest hundreds of millions of dollars into emerging technology and companies through its second venture fund.

Most of the money is aimed at industry-specific power fields like oil and gas exploration, sub-surface visualization, well construction and automation, as well as wastewater and drilling fluid treatment and disposal.

About one-quarter of the fund will be directed at future energies, which include advanced biofuels, solar-assisted enhanced oil recovery, and other renewable technologies.

Shell Technology Ventures' first investment was in a form of its share of a $26 million Series B round for Glass Point Solar, Fremont, California. Glass Point Solar is a startup, working on technology to convert the sun's heat to create steam for use in California's Central Valley oil fields. This is actually one of several similar solar thermal power projects seeking to use renewable energy to the oil industry's advantage.

In general, STV is looking to finance technologies that are capable of solving challenges, and open opportunities for, renewable energy and efficiency in the oil and gas fields. STV is also looking for new ways to get insights from the massive amounts of data that oil companies collect in the process of turning geological survey data into new discoveries of oil. For that purpose it is in active talks with startups and venture connections in the Silicon Valley that deal with data collection and processing.

This is the second fund for Shell Technology Ventures, which launched in 1997. Ten years later, in 2007 it sold its first fund to Kenda Capital. Since then it has seen some portfolio companies testing products that could be rolled out by Shell in the near future, which makes sense, since some of them were Shell spinoff technologies to begin with.

Shell Technology Ventures Fund II is actually quite different, since it invests directly into third-party technology companies that are thought of as having an exciting strategic fit with Shell technologies, where all parties involved would benefit from the partnership.

It is not clear how much exactly the fund is planning to raise, since it depends in part on how much investment opportunity the firm discovers and would be interested in. The core purpose remains to invest in technologies that Shell can use, at first in test runs at its sites, which then can be used for broader commercial adoption.

It is also now clear which companies the fund is considering investing in on the future energy front, though carbon capture and storage was one area of the major of interest. Other areas of interest are ways to integrate renewables into the company's energy operations. Biofuels are not of particular interest of the new fund, although Shell has billions of dollars invested in that sector already. This is because biofuels are freestanding and already under consideration.

Shell is also avoiding investing in startups with business plans that include challenging industry giants with new forms of hardware or processes, such as solar modules. Nevertheless, any technology that is capable of integrating renewable power generation into Shell's day-to-day operations would be considered.

Looking back in history, however, we see that Shell sold off its investments in wind and solar power in 2009 to concentrate on biofuels and carbon capture and storage (CCS) technologies. Getting out of PV manufacturing then seems like a wise move now, since Shell would not have been able to compete with the Chinese influx of cheap PV cells and modules.

Most oil companies have a spotty record in the solar business, Shell included. After 20-30 years in the solar field it dropped the ball, and never looked back. BP followed Shell's example by abandoning its long-term reputation and achievements in the solar business.

Some of the other major oil companies, like Chevron and its Chevron Energy Solutions are working with Saudi Aramco on developing solar projects in the Middle East and North Africa. The French oil giant, Total, bought SunPower in 2011. Its long-term goal is to transition from selling modules to selling energy, which is nothing new, just another way of making money using solar's reputation and capabilities.

Global Warming and the Fossils

Energy generation through current technologies (i.e., burning coal, gas, and oil with the excess release of CO_2 into the atmosphere) pollutes the atmosphere and worsens the global climate prospects. Alternatives to fossil fuel combustion, e.g. nuclear energy, hydrologic energy, and wind and solar energy supply about 10% of the world's electricity.

Other sources of energy are under development or headed into mass production:

GHGs and Global Warming

Green house gasses (GHGs) have been blamed for a newly observed phenomenon named global warming (or climate warming). It refers to the increase of globally averaged ground-level air temperature since the beginning of the industrial revolution. It has many known and postulated environmental impacts including severe weather, sea level rise, the spread of diseases, and the extinction of species due to changing habitats. It also has many indirect impacts on society and economies.

The current consensus of the cause of global warming is the enhanced atmospheric greenhouse (warming) effect due to increased concentrations of greenhouse gases (GHGs) such as water vapor, carbon dioxide (CO_2), methane (CH_4), nitrous oxide (N_2O), and chlorofluorocarbons (CFCs). At present, most of the long-term warming of the atmosphere comes from the ever-rising annual mean concentration of CO_2 and CH_4. This is due to their non-precipitation, relative abundance and strong radiation forced to the atmosphere—the greenhouse effect.

The Earth's climate has fluctuated wildly over its long history well before humans evolved. Paleoclimate records derived from carbon and oxygen isotope analyses of gas bubbles trapped in worldwide ice core samples show roughly synchronized saw-tooth-pattern fluctuations (the rise and fall) among atmospheric temperature, CO_2 and CH_4 concentrations.

Due to the limitations in accuracy of isotope dating methods, it is impossible to determine from these records the sequence of closely sequenced events. Therefore, it is impossible to determine whether the increase of atmospheric CO_2 concentration is the cause or rather an effect of global warming.

Recently a new hypothesis, called "Clathrate gun hypothesis," proposes that dissociation of marine sedimentary methane hydrates likely induced episodes of rapid climate warming at various times in the geologic

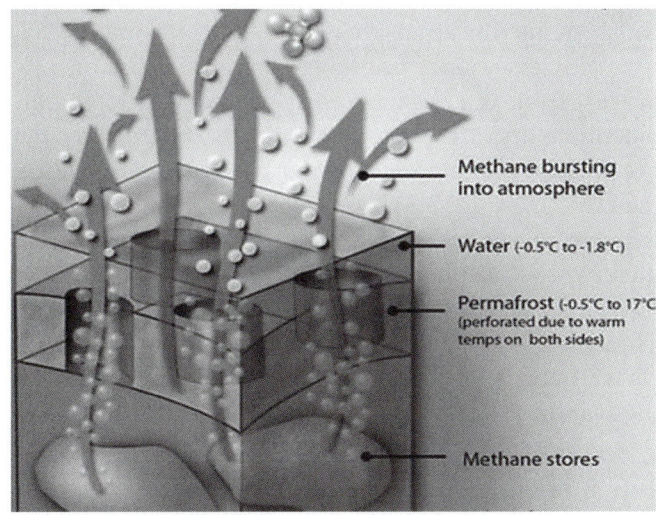

Figure 9-57. The "clathrate gun" in action…

past. The huge fields of clathrate deposits emit methane gas as they warm up, which then increases the greenhouse effect.

Atmospheric CH_4 concentrations have increased from 800-parts-per-billion-by-volume (ppbv) in the year 1800 to 1750 ppbv in year 2000. Even though the atmospheric concentrations of CO_2 and CH_4 have both shown the same monotonically increasing pattern, the atmospheric concentration of CH_4 is only 0.3-0.4% of that of CO_2. Furthermore, the annual mean globally averaged surface air temperature did not monotonically increase over this period as expected.

For example, the time series of five-year running-means of global average surface air temperature shows that, following the steady rise from 1905-1940 there was a period of (almost) constant air temperature between 1940-1975. After 1975, the temperature rose again.

Several explanations have been offered to explain the conflicting and puzzling correlation between air temperature and GHG concentrations. Among them are variations of solar irradiance, atmospheric aerosols due to volcanic eruptions, other natural events, and large-scale biomass burning in developing countries.

Ocean Warming

Global warming is not caused by increased atmospheric green house gasses (GHGs) concentrations alone. The world emits ~5.5 gigatons of carbon (Gt-C) per year emission of CO_2 from power plants and automobiles into the atmosphere. There is another estimated ~1.5 Gt-C emission due to changes in land use (deforestation, and so forth). Thus, the total anthropogenic contribution is ~7.0 Gt-C per year. The net uptake of carbon by terrestrial vegetation changes in land use and the oceans constitute a 3.5 Gt-C per year reduction of the emission into the atmosphere.

However, since both the estimated emission rate of CO_2 from the oceans and the biosphere to the atmosphere and the rate of absorption/fixation by the oceans/biosphere are one order of magnitude greater than the "missing" 3.5 Gt-C in CO_2, it cannot be asserted whether or not anthropogenic CO_2 is the sole cause of increased atmospheric CO_2 concentrations. There is a possibility that the climate system itself is producing even more CO_2 than humans do.

Analysis of ocean sediment cores supported by the National Science Foundation's ocean deep-drilling program has provided strong evidence for the existence of microscopic methane bubbles in ocean water. These methane bubbles provide a nutrient for the methane oxidation bacteria that in turn become food for the

"methane-ice worm" which in turn becomes a foundation of the deep-sea food chain.

These processes not only transform chemical energy into heat that increases water temperature in situ but also produce CO_2 that might either dissolve in water again or escape into the atmosphere.

There are several key points to be noted about the ocean and atmospheric warming phenomena:

- The total and the annual variation of the oceans' heat content are much greater than those of the atmosphere. The volume of ocean observation records has been increasing rapidly since the 1950s. Using these temperature vs. depth profiles, a 1955–1995 history of the deviation (from the mean) of the heat content of each ocean basin and the total for world oceans has been estimated. It reveals that the variations lie between -10 and $+10^{23}$ joules. The fastest growth of heat content of world's oceans happened after 1988.

Similar estimates have been calculated for the atmosphere, resulting in a variation range of -5 to $+5^{19}$ joules. So, the majority of heat driving the climate system is stored in oceans.

- In both the North Atlantic and North Pacific Ocean basins, there is a distinct maximum warming layer between 350-450 meter depth range since 1955. That indicates the possibility of a heat source within the ocean water column. On the other hand, the average of results from six climate models, including atmospheric, ocean and land-biosphere components, presents a maximum warming at the ocean surface in each of the basins. That is an obvious result, because in each of the models the air-sea heat flux is from the atmosphere.

Traditionally, climate scientists have focused on the pathway and transfer of external thermal forcing (e.g. solar radiation) to the atmosphere and the fluxes across the land-ocean-atmosphere boundaries. Climate researchers have traditionally believed that the climate system's internal thermal forcing, if any, is insufficient to affect the balance of the energy budget. However, a mere 1.2 W/m^2 increase in net heating to the atmosphere due to increased GHGs (heating effect) and aerosols (cooling effect) is enough to cause the observed 1.0°C atmospheric warming since industrialization.

This 1.2 W/m^2 residual is slightly smaller than the resolution of the sensor on the satellite currently carrying out the Earth radiation budget experiment observations.

- The heat required to cause thinning of the Arctic sea ice cover over last four decades matches the heat generated by oxidation of methane in the North Atlantic during the same period. The average thickness of the Arctic Sea ice cover has decreased by ~1.3 meter between 1958 and 1997. Also, there has been an average depletion of dissolved oxygen by 20%, ~2 ml of oxygen per liter of ocean water, at 400 meters depth along that segment of the Gulf Stream that flows over the Blake Ridge.

The area of the Arctic Sea ice cover is ~8.7^6 km^2. The heat required to melt this 1.3 meters thick of sea ice is ~0.81^{21} calories. Two competing mechanisms that could lead to this phenomenon are: 1) increased atmospheric heat fluxes; or 2) increased volume fluxes of warm Atlantic waters feeding the Arctic.

The first mechanism seems to be intuitive and may contribute some of the energy needed to melt part of the Arctic ice. But, the satellite remote-sensing data have not indicated a significant warming of the Arctic air temperature that would support an enhanced heat flux from the atmosphere to Arctic Ocean.

The growth of atmospheric heat content, to some extent, should have contributed to the melting of sea-ice cover, but that is not big enough to become the main factor. Several studies have presented evidence of the warming of Atlantic water that is feeding the Arctic Ocean.

Arctic ice thinning has been accelerating since the early 1990s. That matches an increased presence of Atlantic origin warmer ocean currents in the Arctic Basin since 1990. The heat storage for the North Atlantic for 1988–1992 minus 1970–1974 showed an obvious increase between surface and 300-m depths along the Gulf Stream.

Microbes easily oxidize the methane gas released from ocean sediments and hydrothermal vents before it reaches the ocean surface. Assuming that all the depleted oxygen contained within the Gulf Stream has been consumed by biochemical processes (bacteria and other organisms) to oxide that methane which has escaped from MH, then the additional heat content (other than radiation and thermodynamic processes) is ~8.7 calories per liter of sea water.

The average Gulf Stream transport near the Grand Banks of Newfoundland is ~60^6 m^3/s. This leads to a total of ~0.64^{21} calories of heat that is biochemically generated and being carried northward by the Gulf Stream into high latitudes (and eventually into the Arctic Ocean) over the 1958–1997 period.

That amount of heat alone is very close to that required to thin the Arctic sea ice by 1.3 meters. Note that the oxidation of methane in ocean takes time. The energy (heat) from oxidizing methane is released step-by-step following the chemical reactions and transferred from one organism to another throughout the food chain.

As long as the final products are water and CO_2, the total heat to be generated will be conserved in the water mass no matter what processes take place. Bacteria will likely mediate the oxidation processes. So, the energy density might be low due to diffusion, but the total yield remains the same. Thus, the slightly warmed "water mass" can actually be carried along by deep ocean currents into Arctic basin after forming a deep (slightly) warmed layer by thermocline-capped convective mixing (rather like the atmospheric tropopause).

Once this water arrives in the Arctic Ocean, it becomes buoyant in the cold water and rises to the bottom of sea ice and accelerates the ice melting.

The Pecan Project

Pecan Street Inc. is a University of Texas-based research organization working on a research trial designed to save energy and reduce carbon footprint by introducing "smart" solutions in the ways we generate, distribute and use electricity.

In 1999, the City of Austin, Texas, closed its Mueller municipal airport, and the community decided to redevelop the site into a ground-breaking-mixed-use, sustainable urban neighborhood. A decade later, the Mueller community is a bustling mini-city, home to the world's first leadership in energy and environmental design (LEED) hospital, dozens of green-built office buildings and stores and over 1,000 residents who call themselves "pioneers."

Austin Energy, the nation's largest seller of green power and the first utility in the world to create a green building code (which became the basis of the LEED rating system), together with Pecan Street Inc., are the coordinators of the project.

The team is dedicated to installing and test energy systems and solutions systems in up to 1,000 residences in and around the Mueller community that include:
— distributed clean energy (solar installations)
— energy storage technologies (batteries)
— smart grid water and smart grid irrigation systems

— smart appliances
— plug-in electric vehicles
— advanced meters and home energy management systems
— green building
— new electricity pricing models

It's an ambitious effort intended to not only "smarten" up the utility's grid, but also to find true benefits that energy customers want. It is geared to understand how best to lower the collective carbon impact, which starts with understanding how energy is being used by the different homeowners.

Figure 9-58. The Pecan Street project, Austin, TX

With the help of a $10 million from the U.S. DOE, the Pecan project gives the well-to-do individuals in the chosen neighborhood the tools that they need to use and control their energy use efficiently–above and beyond what can be done with the monthly utility bill. This will help collect data to understand what homeowners need to manage their energy use.

This is all good, no doubt, and it is how we'd like to envision our future. But to get there we need to get all Americans in Mueller-types of well-to-do neighborhoods. For that to happen they all need to be well educated and hold well paying jobs with six-figure salaries. Then they need to be able to afford property values, which are also in the high six figures, and mortgage payments well above average person's monthly salary.

In addition to paying $15,000-25,000 for a solar installation and the related smart meters and appliances, they will need a new $40-50,000 electric car. And finally, they all need an engineering degree to be able to operate and maintain all the energy generating and using devices, and the related controlling systems (remote and otherwise).

Not a bad dream and it might happen some day,

but how many people in the U.S.—let alone other countries—can afford the Pecan Street-type benefits today? Plus, how many neighborhoods have adequate sunlight and other conditions necessary for proper implementation of the smart grid dream? Where do we start is the $64,000 question.

Nope, for now we have to deal with our economic problems, our "dumb" power grid, less-than-smart appliances, and "dumb" home energy controls, while most of us live in our much-less-than six figure homes, go to our much-less-than-six-figure jobs in our much-less-than $40,000-50,000 used cars. And most of us just don't have extra $15-25,000 to spend on shiny solar panels and digital gadgets, since paying the rent and mortgage is challenging enough.

And even more importantly, to implement the Pecan Project on a large scale, we need to fix our "dumb" and crumbling national grid first. That alone is going to cost many billions of dollars. Converting it into a "smart" one will cost another large sum of money, which is just not available for now, nor is it on anyone's agenda. And so, the Pecan Project dream, no matter how good it sounds, is not very likely to happen any time soon.

The Pecan Project is the model for the future, granted; more power to the participants, and we wish them best of luck in this undertaking. But the big question of how to get there on a large scale still remains. The answer is not simple, since lots of time and money are needed to get even close to that level of sophistication and opulence.

On the list of national priorities, we'd put it well below fixing the crumbling infrastructure, including our national power grid—all of which will cost billions upon billions of dollars and will take many, many years to complete.

Climate Change or Not?
First, let's clarify some of the most used environmental terms: "global warming" and "climate change." Some claim that both mean the same and that the names have been changed from time to time for unknown reason and purpose. In reality, the two terms mean two completely different (albeit related) things that have been used for decades.

Both, *global warming and climate change* are used frequently in the scientific literature, because they refer to two different physical phenomena. As the name suggests, *"global warming"* refers to the long-term trend of a rising average global temperature, which has been documented and only a few doubt today (although the reasons and trends are still locked in a heated debate).

Climate change, on the other hand, is a more broad term that refers to the changes in the global climate, which result from a number of factors, including increase of average global temperature. For example, changes in precipitation patterns, increased prevalence of droughts, heat waves, and other extreme weather, etc. generally speaking are different forms of *climate change*. These changes might or might not have been brought up upon us by increase of global temperature, therefore *global warming* is just one of the factors in the broader *climate change* category.

And so, while those physical phenomena are causally related, they are not the same thing. Greenhouse gas emissions, for example, are causing *global warming*, which in turn is causing climate change. However, because the terms are causally related, they are often used interchangeably in normal daily communications.

Now that we have cleared the terminology, is the climate really and measurably changing? Well, some people think so—and some don't. Without taking sides, we can clearly identify the pros and cons of each side of the issue.

Climate Change is Real

Let's start with the defense of climate change and global warming.

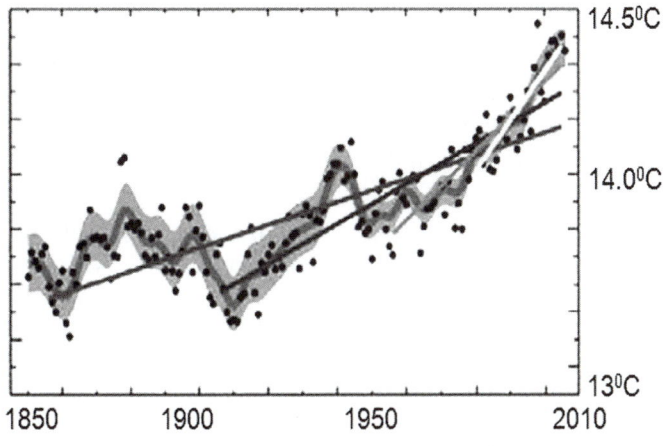

Figure 9-59. Average global warming measurements

The measurements in Figure 9-59 are reliable, to our knowledge, since similar charts have been issued by a number of world organizations. They are quite convincingly and clearly pointing to the fact that the global warming trend has been accelerating during the last 50 years. A certain increase has been observed and recorded since 1900 (the only question is exactly how much).

On the other hand, there have been other warm-cool periods in the distant past—all of which are attributed to natural events, since man was not part of the environmental picture in those days.

So, what do we know for sure? We know without a shadow of a doubt that:

- Greenhouse gases (GHGs) levels in the atmosphere are increasing, mostly because of human activities and mainly due to increased fossil fuels use during the last century

- GHGs absorb and re-radiate Sun's infrared radiation quite efficiently, thus heating the planet directly.

- GHGs have been emitted by humanity for many centuries, in the form of firewood burning and other activities. Thus emitted GHGs remain in the atmosphere for long periods of time—up to centuries.

- Decrease in ozone levels in the lower stratosphere, and increase in sulfate particles, produce a cooling effect, although the results are insufficiently understood and quantified.

- Increase of man-made CO_2 emissions, and unrelated ozone decrease in the stratosphere, have resulted in a 1.0°C global average cooling there.

- There is a good chance that the stratosphere will continue to cool significantly as the CO_2 levels increase. And if the ozone levels continue to decrease, then the cooling will be magnified. We have no way to prevent the cooling of the stratosphere under these scenarios.

- Increase of atmospheric CO_2 concentration by 1.0% equivalent per year, means that we will see CO_2 levels doubling after 70 years and quadrupling after 140 years. Considering the long residence time of CO_2 at such high concentrations, this increase is plausible, but cannot be used as prediction of changing social events, because there are a number of other factors that play roles in these events.

- Further increases in atmospheric CO_2 will lead to a global warming in the range of 2.5-4.5°C during the next 100 years. The wide range is due mostly to uncertainty of natural variations, such as the radiative feedbacks of clouds, changing amounts of water vapor in the upper troposphere, the ocean currents, and the effects of melting ice.

- Since the 1900s, the Earth's surface has warmed by

about 0.5°C.

- The natural variability of climate, which could be quite significant at times, adds a level of complexity and confuses the effort to estimate the human-induced climate changes in the long run.

- A number of uncertainties, brought by the weather pattern and other natural and man-made activities, change the picture on daily basis, and since reduction of these uncertainties is not expected any time soon, the short-term predictions are also flawed.

- The response of clouds, water vapor, ice, ocean currents, and specific geographic regions to increased GHG levels are important factors, some of which are well understood, while others are not. The gaps in understanding, and the complexity of the interaction among these factors and the resulting effects, are too complex to use as reliable predictions of future events and developments.

- Tropical storms will tend to become more intense in the warmer ocean, where weather and geographical conditions permit.

- The amount of water vapor in the lower troposphere will increase at roughly 6% per each 1.0°C of increase in warming. At the same time, the average relative humidity around the globe will change less as compared to the total water vapor concentration.

- As the climate warms, the rate of evaporation will increase too, which will lead to increase in precipitations in the range of about 2% per each 1.0°C increase in global surface temperature.

- Decrease in soil moisture is expected in response to increases in surface temperatures during different seasons in some areas.

- Increase in precipitation, ice melting, and seawater thermal expansion (due to temperature increase) will contribute to ocean level rise of over a foot by the end of this century. The sea level could rise over 3 ft during the next several centuries.

- The global climate has considerable thermal inertia, mainly due high heat capacity of the world's oceans. Changes in this and other radiative bodies offset the warming effect of the increased greenhouse gases' release, thus making the picture even more complex.

Climate…What?

OK, that is what the glass looks like when it's mostly full, so let's see now how it looks through the eyes of those who see it as mostly empty:

NOTE: We, as most engineers, see the environmental issues as works in progress, which allows us to remain impartial and only analyze and present the issues from a scientific and engineering points of view.

There are a number of people and groups that do not believe in the man-made effects on the environment. Their views are as follows:

Climate change is part of the natural change. The Earth's climate has gone through drastic changes many times throughout its long history. There is evidence of frozen and boiling climate in ancient times, which of course were caused by natural events, but things are different now—how different is debatable.

The natural events on Earth are much more powerful than man-made ones. There are some immense forces acting upon the Earth, such as the Earth's gravity and rotation, solar and spacial energies, and the related phenomena. Each of these forces is capable of drastically changing and even destroying life on. Just imagine a solar burst arriving at Earth with 10,000°C cosmic winds and evaporating the killing humankind within hours. Just imagine a momentary change of the Earth's gravity or rotation. Like in the movies, we will see trains flying and airplanes crashing not being able to stay airborne. Compared with these immense powers, human activities are insignificant and affect climate change much more than anything man can do.

Scientists are not sure. Although an overwhelming majority of scientists agree that human activity is largely responsible for recent warming, there is no complete consensus among scientists. Just like there is no consensus on the Big Bang, or the Earth's gravity.

Scientists are exaggerating claims of environmental changes. There is a lot of talk today about glaciers melting, ocean levels rising, excess floods and droughts, etc. anomalies. While these are real, they have been around since day one. Just look back at the great volcanoes eruptions, huge floods, and sea level rises in the past. Some have been many times more serious than what we have today.

The Earth is going through a natural warming period. Temperature records clearly show that the global temperature has steadily, albeit slightly, risen during the last century. That much is true, but what is the reason? Why did the Earth go through the Ice Age? Why did so many other serious changes and disasters have happened many years before the industrial revolution, which is now blamed for all evil on Earth.

Global warming periods in the distant past were not carbon dioxide related. The role of CO_2 in the planet's history is reasonably well understood, and there is a consensus that CO_2 levels are not the only force at work on the climate—now and in the past. Past climate change cannot be blamed on increase of CO_2 levels, because there were none. There were other forces in play, which we do not understand completely, and so we blame it all on CO_2, because it is an easy target.

There have always been droughts, heat waves, floods, and wildfire weather around the world. These natural phenomena have been around since the beginning of time, and are too many and too complex for us to put into perspective, understand, and link to climate change. Droughts, heat waves, floods, and large wild fires are normal in many areas of the world where there are no human activities so many other factors need to be considered as well when discussing climate change.

The Sun is partially(or fully) responsible for the climate change. The Sun obviously has a big influence on the Earth and we have seen many serious changes in its activities lately. Although the Sun's overall output has somewhat diminished in recent decades, there have been observations of huge solar flares that eject immense amounts of heat particles, some of which reach the Earth, and could be causing some of the climate changes.

Volcanoes emit more carbon dioxide than humans possibly could. Although it is a fact that volcanoes on the average emit much less CO_2 than humans, the effects of large volcano eruptions are catastrophic for the environment and life in the affected areas. These damages in turn have a huge effect on the global environment, including large increase in GHG and particles emissions.

Carbon dioxide is a pollutant, but it is natural and absolutely essential for life. Carbon dioxide is needed to maintain life on Earth. Slight increases in CO_2 emissions cannot result in catastrophic climate change. Other factors need to be considered to get a complete picture of the issues at hand and the resulting damages. There are

a lot of theories on the matter, but it has not been proven beyond the shadow of a doubt what level of increase of CO_2 levels is harmful and what to expect at each level.

Global warming is a problem that we can turn into a benefit. Global warming has its benefits, which could be used to help humanity, and especially the world's poor who need most help. For example a degree or two of temperature rise would reduce the heating requirements in northern countries. It also would lengthen the crops growing season, so that more crops can be grown and harvested.

Climate-related Decisions

Figure 9-60 shows the never-ending cycle of evaluating, mitigating, and monitoring climate-related problems. This cycle involves, and is valid for, any and all climate-related decisions.

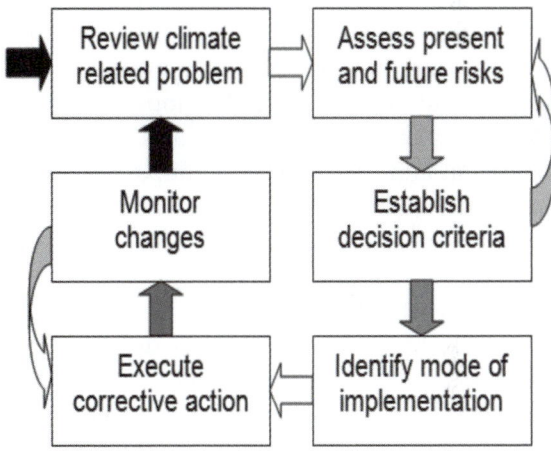

Figure 9-60. Climate decision-making cycle

• It starts with the decisions each of us makes every day, several times a day: how far to drive, how low to set the thermostat, and so forth.

• The decision-making cycle is even more pertinent to large companies, that make decisions involving the use of large quantities of energy, such as how much energy can be saved by better heating and cooling management, weatherizing the buildings, and other choices.

• But the greatest impact of proper decision making process comes from governmental policies. Decisions to subsidize a certain fuel type, setting the fuel prices, and other such decisions affect the climate profoundly. For example, the decision of the Obama administration to reduce renewable energy subsidies and to encourage oil and natural gas fracking will have a profound effect on the local environments and will affect the global climate significantly.

Whether this is the right decision or not remains to be seen. There are a number of very complex factors involved in the day-to-day operations, so only time will tell if the climate is hurt as a consequence, and how much if so. At the very least, the government regulators and the companies that are involved need to use the decision-making cycle daily to figure out and resolve the issues at hand.

The corrective action process starts now with assessing the effects of *large-scale fracking* on the environment and global climate, establishing decision criteria, and outlining and executing corrective actions. This is a national and global emergency that needs to be properly handled instead of being ignored as it is presently.

Construction of long oil and gas pipelines, such as the more than thousand-mile long Keystone pipeline across several central U.S. states, is another example of a decision of great importance and serious long-term impact. Proper assessment of all factors and variables, with environmental and climate change impacts in mind, is necessary, so we can only hope that this is diligently done by the responsible parties.

The Environmental Players

Presently the environmental issues, and the responsibilities for these, are well defined. Also quite well defined is the list of responsible groups and their activities, as follows:

Government Officials

This group is the smallest, but has the most power. These are the people who make the decisions. Within it there are different entities and decision power responsibilities, but the trend usually follows the government line of action, or lack thereof.

Presently—under the Obama administration during 2012-2016—we are looking forward to middle-of-the-road approach. Yes, there are energy and environmental problems, and the solution is to increase the coal, oil and gas production, while trying to minimize the environmental damage.

Although this is not good enough, it is many times better than the approach Mr. Mitt Romney and his cronies would've taken, and might still take if they get into the White House. Their approach is full deployment of fossils and nuclear power regardless of the short and long-term environmental damages. So, yes, we need to

be thankful for the little benefits we get from the present administration, because things could be many times worse.

Blaming politicians and regulators for the decisions they make is useless and even unfair. We, the people, chose them. We, the people, put them in their places, so we now have no right to complain. Plus, we have no say so in the matter, for they speak for us. And fighting with them won't change things, since they follow a power line that is hard to impossible to change… until the next election.

Coal Mine and Oil Field Operators

No doubt, owners and operators of mines, and oil and gas fields are concerned with the profit margin first and utmost, just as any of us in the capitalist society are concerned with the success of our business. Production efficiency, plant safety, and other technical issues affecting the daily operations are their primary concern. The environment…yea, it is important too, but we need to dig the coal and pump the oil first, to put bread on the table at home first.

We should not blame this group for what they do and how they do it, because everything they do is legal and useful to us all. We all benefit from their efforts, and should be thankful for their efforts and self-sacrifice. If we don't do this right, we might just end up in total darkness with empty gas tanks. Reckless actions are not advisable, and half-baked decisions on the parts of different environmental groups could only make things worse.

Power Plant Operators

This group is in a similar situation as the previous and is part of the utilities network. They have a complex business to run, and talking about environmental concerns is done only if and when forced by regulations and laws. Everyday issues are related to quality of coal and oil, equipment performance and maintenance and such. The environment is not their problem. So, while it is still legal to produce electric power by burning coal, oil and gas, they will do it. And they will do the best they can to do it properly, efficiently and safely. But that is where they draw the line.

Blaming these people for our environmental problems is also useless and unfair. All their actions are within the framework of the law and the local, state and federal regulations. Making electricity is what they are concerned about and focused on. The rest is not on their agenda, unless it is forced upon them, and we cannot expect it to be any other way any time soon.

Utilities

Utility operators are a group of companies and people, a mixture of specialists in different disciplines. They are the ones responsible for bringing power, heat, and cool air to our homes and businesses. Public opinion is noticed, documented, and handled by one of the sub-groups on ad-hoc basis, but it is not a priority for the entity. Regulatory changes, infrastructure issues, and daily technical problems are where the attention is focused, and where most of the daily effort is spent. The utilities know their place in the U.S. economy, and are fully aware of their importance, so self-preservation at all cost—regardless of everything else—is to be expected now and for a long time to come.

Environmentalists

Here we have a group of professionals that has made protecting the environment the center of their careers, and very often their entire existence. To them the glass is always empty.

The General Public

This is the largest, the loudest, most influential, and yet the most ignorant group of them all. Most representatives of this group would not know, or care about, the difference between coal and gas energy generation, nor would they be able to distinguish between the issues of solar vs. wind power generation.

Nevertheless, this group is divided, for different reasons, into:

Pro-environmental segment, which blindly defends any and all measures proposed and taken to protect the environment, no matter what the reasons or how much the cost. They are usually found among the 1.0% in developed countries. Here we most often see people driving Prius hybrid cars and other such contraptions, thinking that they are helping the environment with clean engines. What they don't consider is where the electricity they charge their clean mobiles with comes from.

They are like the proverbial ostrich, with their head buried into the proverbial environmental save-haven. They do not see the miners headed into the coal mine for 10 hours of dirt and coal digging, enduring roof collapses, so that they can deliver coal to the coal burning power plant several hundreds miles away. They don't see the billowing smoke from the coal power plants that are making the electricity that charges their shiny Prius. They also don't see the steel foundries, or stinky chemical plants that gobble gigawatts of electric

energy to shape the steel and batteries of their shiny, super-efficient cars.

All they see is that they get 45 miles per gallon, which is actually equivalent to less than 6 miles per gallon when all technical and monetary actors are entered in the cradle-to-grave lifetime economic and environmental calculations of their shiny electric or hybrid cars, including their driving habits (which are a subject for another discussion).

NOTE: Have you noticed lately how many little Prius and *Volt* cars pass you on the highways, and how many cut you off on the city streets? This is a new trend. A new phenomenon, where the owners of these little buzzers think that they are entitled to special privileges and benefits for driving small, awkward looking cars that save on gas (if and only if driven normally).

The skeptics, those holding a *skeptical view of the environmental changes,* are people who look at the world through rosy-tinted glasses. They are the lucky ones. They are the ones who are not affected by the energy and environmental problems, no matter what the facts tell them.

Those who don't care about the environmental issues. These are usually people who are too busy with other things that they simply have no opinion and don't want to be bothered by these issues. It could be the very poor segment of some countries, where the daily bread is the only preoccupation, or the very rich in developed countries, which are mostly concerned with the best way of spending their money today to worry about the future.

Extraordinary Events

Since we are on the subject of energy and environment, we cannot ignore the possibility of encountering

Figure 9-61. What environment...?

some extraordinary high levels of energy-related events in the future that might alter life on Earth. Imagine the Moon changing its orbit for some reason. That would immediately change the gravity pull between these great bodies.

The first and immediately noticeable effect would be changes in the tides. Higher tides would cause serious flooding of low-lying coastal land areas, inundating many familiar places on Earth. The gravity pull change would also affect the fixed axis of the Earth, which would cause serious climate change in different geographic areas.

The Earth orbit might be changed as well, which could cause additional climate changes and a more pronounced rise and fall of global temperatures. More natural disasters, such as hurricanes, tornadoes, and tsunamis, would be expected to occur as well.

But there are other equally devastating events that the world has not seen before (at least not for a long time), most of which we are unprepared to handle. Imagine a huge solar flare reaching the Earth's surface like a giant fireball. Where are we going to hide? The damage following such an attack would be unimaginable, and the aftermath even more difficult to describe.

The 2013 TV miniseries *Cat.8* gives a good, albeit unsettling, account of what a large solar explosion can do to Earth. And not surprisingly, when faced with the ominous threat, the earthlings were helpless. All they can do is sit and wait for the world around them to collapse and take them with it.

Another good example of how not to do things that the *Cat.8* miniseries offers is of scientists trying things before they are fully tested and proven, and even worse, doing it in large-scale experiments. We have a number of such examples today, too—some of which have been discussed in detail in this and other books on the subject.

Now imagine a large asteroid colliding with the Earth. What if 2012 DA14 hit the Earth? How much energy could it release if it crashed into our planet? The kinetic energy of a 50-meter-wide asteroid with a density of 2.6 grams per cubic centimeter and a speed of 12.7 kilometers per second hitting Earth at a 45°angle, which is the scenario of 2012 DA14, could result in over 3.0 Megatons of kinetic energy at entry. This is an airburst energy of 2.9 Megatons at about 8.5 kilometers from the surface.

What these numbers mean is that an asteroid like this would likely explode in the air, releasing the energy equivalent of about 138 atomic bombs like the one that the Super fortress Enola Gay dropped over Hiroshima on August 6, 1945. This is also equivalent to the energy of nine W87 nuclear warheads like the ones carried by the American Minuteman III intercontinental ballistic missiles.

The magnitude of such an explosion is hard to imagine, and the effects depend on many other factors, such as angle of entry, and the impacted area, but in all cases, this is a major event that we are powerless to avoid.

In many cases, we will have plenty of warning, but even then what can we do? Hide where? Do what? In some cases there would be no warning, because some of the asteroids are hard to follow. In such a case we will hear a loud thump, and be thankful that we were not in the direct path…until the next time.

And what if the asteroid is as big as the Earth? Well, then the Earth might just end as a bunch of small rocks floating in space. Fortunately, the chance of that happening any time soon is very small, but increasing as time goes on. The cosmic roulette keeps on turning, leaving us with a lot of unanswered questions…

The Quantum Leap in Energy and Environment

While we are looking very closely at, and are getting familiar with the natural events, we need to keep an eye on the not-so-natural events. These are more difficult to understand and explain, let alone manage, and yet they are very important and we cannot ignore them.

A closer look at a new dimension of energy generation and environmental control is in order here. It is part of Quantum Mechanics (QM), which is part of modern physics. Physicists and chemists live and work in the realm of the classical mechanics (CM). In it they have a complete understanding, and are in complete control, of all aspects of life on Earth. They can easily figure out and calculate the different units of the three-dimensional world around us.

One major and very important aspect of the modern science and technology they have not mastered yet is the realm of QM. Even Albert Einstein died thinking that QM is one-quarter CM, one-quarter illusion, and the rest incomplete sets of thoughts and theories. Actually some of the suppositions of QM did not jibe with his theories, so he was readily willing to dismiss it as a real possibility.

Fast forward to today's state of the art. QM is a subject of much talk and some work today, and although there are some practical achievements, we are still mostly in the fog as far as understanding and putting its principles to work for us.

This situation reminds us of what Guglielmo

Marconi was dealing in the beginning of the 20th century, when he decided to dedicate his life to developing wireless telecommunications. He had no special education and very limited understanding of the principles involved in wireless transmission. Through hard work, and endless trial and error, he built crude transmitter and receiver stations all over the world. Finally, he was able to prove the concept and introduce the radiotelegraph on the world markets.

Similarly so, today we have a very limited understanding of the principles of QM, and in particular the principle of *quantum entanglement*, where pairs of particles can be created as "entangled twins." These unusual types of particles exhibit what Einstein called "spooky action at a distance," mimicking each other even when at a great distance and no physical connection between them that could account for these correlations.

Classical physics consider these states of matter to be random, since it is the logical thing to assume. But QM claims that there is nothing random in this behavior, and that it is a property built into small particles that could be very useful once completely understood and applied in practice.

Teleportation of objects and humans is one activity that the entangled particles might allow in the near future, but we won't go that far. Instead, we'd limit our fantasy walk in the world of tomorrow's QM to teleportation of energy. Just like Marconi, today we are only guessing what QM is and are trying to get some results that would prove its usefulness. And just like Marconi, we will succeed some day and will use the effects of QM for the good of humanity.

And just as we are now laughing at Marconi's ignorance, the future generations will be laughing at us. Just think of the crude means of collecting and using energy today. We dig out, transport, and burn up millions of tons of coal, oil, and natural gas, all of which are dirty and getting depleted quickly. We also build and install millions of solar modules under the cloudy skies of Germany, or Maine. How ridiculous is that?

Imagine instead, a large energy teleportation plant in the Arizona desert, where photons and other electromagnetic particles are efficiently teleported from the environment above and converted into useful energy without silicon materials' use. At the very least, there will be new, more efficient and inexpensive materials for solid oxide fuel cells, photovoltaic, and photo-catalytic electrodes. Already various observations have identified the key metrics needed for determining the utility of a given material, which can be accurately calculated by using QM principles.

Or equally important application for the new level of energy use would be its large quantity storage. Large amount of energy could be teleported into small containers and stored until needed. This achievement alone would revolutionize the energy sector.

And how about the environment? There are billions of tons of different GHG particles floating in the atmosphere now, and their number is increasing daily. Could it be that a century or two down the road QM would provide a way to teleport these particles into space, or deposit in one place on Earth? Why not?

Using all advantages offered by QM might turn out to be the new frontier for energy generation, storage, and use. There is no doubt that the future generations will put a lot of effort in it, and it might be the best way of ensuring their energy independence and clean environment.

Earth Observation Satellites

Providing a lot of information about the unknown and invisible events around us, and putting our fears into perspective is the main role of our smart companions high up in space. Earth observation satellites are a special type of satellites specifically designed to observe Earth from orbit. They function like spy satellites but are intended for non-military uses, such as environmental monitoring, meteorology, and map making. Most Earth observation satellites operate at altitudes above 500 kilometers to reduce the significant air-drag that is present at low altitudes, which forces frequent orbit maneuvers.

Earth observation satellites vary according to: the type of orbit they have; the payload they carry; and, from the point of view of imaging instruments, the spatial resolution; spectral characteristics; and swath width of the sensors. All these parameters are designed at the beginning of the mission depending on the application the satellite mission is targeting.

To monitor the weather at large scales and high frequency, it is convenient for a satellite to be in a geostationary orbit. In such an orbit a satellite is able to continuously view almost an entire hemisphere. However, as the orbit is very high (approximately 36,000 km above the Earth) a high spatial resolution is difficult to attain. But for such applications as the tracking of clouds over continents, a high spatial resolution is not necessary.

For applications requiring high resolution imaging of a very specific area, such as the monitoring of a glacier lake, or the mapping of buildings destroyed by an earthquake, a high-resolution sensor would be required. Such a sensor would generally have a narrow swath and be on a satellite at a low earth orbit, called LEO (such as

600 km above the Earth in the case of the QuickBird satellite). In such an orbit, it is not possible to continuously monitor the same area, because of the relative movement of the satellite with respect to the Earth. Images can only be acquired continually over a given area when the satellite passes over it.

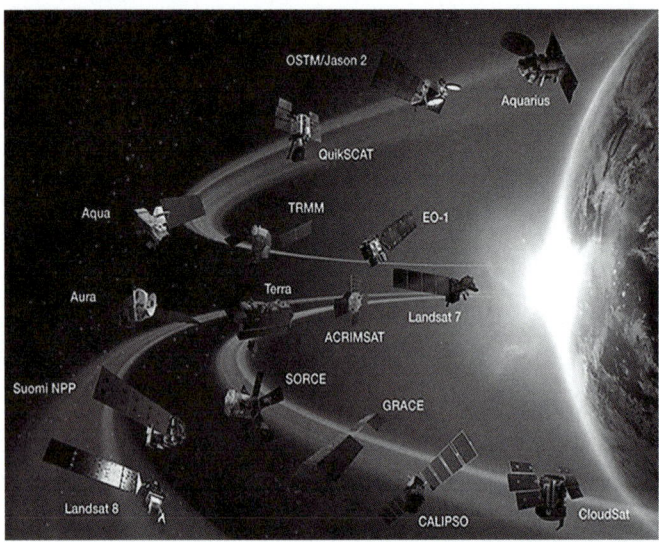

Figure 9-62. NASA's Earth observation satellites

NASA's Earth observing system (EOS) is a coordinated series of polar-orbiting and low inclination satellites for long-term global observations of the land surface, biosphere, solid Earth, atmosphere, and oceans. As a major component of the earth science division of NASA's science mission directorate, EOS enables an improved understanding of the Earth as an integrated system.

The EOS project science office (EOSPSO) is committed to bringing program information and resources to the Earth science research community and the general public alike, and is funded through the Earth science division of NASA's science mission directorate.

.   Many of NASA's Earth-observing satellite missions are joint efforts with other nations and agencies, along with other elements of NASA's Earth science program.

The Earth observation satellites ERS-1, ERS-2 and Envisat of European space agency as well as the MetOp spacecraft of the European organization for the exploitation of meteorological satellites are all operated at altitudes of about 800 km. The Proba-1, Proba-2 and SMOS spacecraft of European space agency are observing the Earth from an altitude of about 700 km.

These groups of satellites play a major, if not critical, role in following the changes on the Earth's surface and its atmosphere. They transmit a lot of data to the scientists in the different countries, to be analyzed and converted into weather maps, natural events warning signals, and other information that is critical for conducting normal daily operations.

These satellites also constantly follow the changes on Earth and its atmosphere, which allows the scientists to make accurate real-time measurements and predictions of future events. They will play an even more important role in the future as we enter into a period of uncertainties caused by increased GHG levels, air and ground pollution, and climate warming.

In addition to watching for weather patterns, the satellites assist environmental monitoring by detecting changes in the Earth's vegetation, atmospheric trace gas content, sea state, ocean color, and ice fields. By monitoring vegetation changes over time, droughts can be monitored by comparing the current vegetation state to its long-term average. Anthropogenic emissions can be monitored by evaluating data of tropospheric NO_2 and SO_2 as well.

These types of satellites are almost always in Sun synchronous and "frozen" orbits. The Sun synchronous orbit is in general sufficiently close to polar to get the desired global coverage while the relatively constant geometry to the Sun mostly is an advantage for the instruments. The "frozen" orbit is selected because that is the closest to a circular orbit that is possible in the gravitational field of the Earth.

The problem is that while the satellites see everything, they cannot do anything about it. We, the people who live on this Earth, are responsible for taking the information that these never-tiring observers send us and take the appropriate actions based on it. Thus far, there is a great discrepancy between the alarming data we receive every day and the overwhelming lack of activities in correcting the problems at hand.

The satellites tell us that the CO_2 levels are rising, air pollution in major cities is increasing, glaciers are melting at unprecedented speed, deforestation is growing, and the global temperature is rising. These are major and very obvious events, which we all agree are pushing life on Earth to the limits, and yet we continue doing exactly what brought us into this situation.

It is becoming overwhelmingly clear that the future won't change the direction we have taken; the satellites will continue sending alarming signals and we will continue selfishly to do whatever we are doing today without any regard for the consequences of our activities (or inactivity) in the future.

ENVIRONMENTAL CHALLENGES *TODAY*

The world is faced with a dilemma, to believe or not in the upcoming major climate changes and their consequences. We will only expose some of the facts as agreed by many scientists for people to decide on their own.

Table 9-22 gives us a glimpse into what to expect as we continue to pump up, dig out, and burn millions of tons of fossils. We are filling the bucket of our environment with amazingly large amounts of poisons, gasses and solids, all of which contribute to deteriorating air and water quality. The final result of all this is property damage, human health deterioration, and deaths.

In addition to the polluted air effects, which we already discussed in detail above, there are other effects that are less noticeable, and yet with equally important significance to the environment and the health of living things. Some of these events are shown in Table 9-22.

Ocean Acidification

Fundamental changes in seawater chemistry are occurring throughout the world's oceans. Since the beginning of the industrial revolution, the release of carbon dioxide (CO_2) from humankind's industrial and agricultural activities has increased the amount of CO_2 in the atmosphere.

The world's oceans absorb about a quarter of the CO_2 we release into the atmosphere every year, so as

Table 9-22. Possible future scenarios due to global temperature rise

IMPACT	Temperature rise of 1^0C could cause:	Temperature rise of 3^0C could cause:	Temperature rise of 5^0C could cause:
Fresh water supplies	• Glaciers in the Andes and other areas around the globe shrink and disappear. • Over 50 million people are left without fresh water. • Water supplies decrease 30% in Southern Africa and Mediterranean countries.	• Serious draughts occur in Southern Europe every 10 years of even more often. • 2-4 billion people worldwide are left without water. • Water supplies decrease 50% in Southern Africa and Mediterranean countries.	• Large glaciers in the Himalayas disappear all together. • Quarter of the population in China, and surrounding countries, is left without fresh water supplies. • Disease and death increase.
Food and agriculture	• A modest increase in crop yields is possible in some temperature regions. • Crop yields in the tropics decrease significantly. • 5-10% crop decrease in Africa.	• Crop yields increase at higher altitudes. • Half a billion people are at risk of hunger. • 20-30% crop yield decrease in Africa.	• Significant increase of ocean acidity and toxicity is blamed for reducing fish stocks. • Warmer ocean waters change fish population habits and reduce fishing.
Human Health	• Reduction in mortality in high latitude countries. • Quarter million die yearly from climate-related disease • 50-60 million more people in Africans are exposed to malaria and other diseases.	• 5-6 million more people world-wide suffer from malnutrition, and 2-3 million more die from it. • 80 million more people are exposed to malaria in Africa and many die from it.	• The number of climate-related diseases and death increase, putting additional burden on the health care and services systems, especially in the world's poorest countries and regions.
Coastal areas	• Increased damage from flooding in coastal areas. • Flooding and inundation of low-lying counties, and permanent change of coastal areas. • Forced evacuations of 10-20 million people from coastal areas.	• 200 million people subject to forced evacuation from low-lying coastal areas • The numbers of people getting sick due to changing climate and living conditions increases.	• Ocean level rise is threatening major population centers in the U.S. and the West. • New York, Tokyo, London, and others are on the evacuation list.
Ecosystems	• 10-15% of land species are facing extinction. • 20-30% of all species face some change, or extinction • Wild life risk is increased significantly.	• 40-50% of all wild life species face extinction. • Half of the Arctic tundra is lost. • Amazon forest collapse. • Significant coral reefs loss.	• Uncontrolled world-wide wild-life extinction, coral reefs and glaciers loss. • The entire human race is threatened by irreversible negative changes.

atmospheric CO_2 levels increase, so do the levels in the ocean. Initially, many scientists focused on the benefits of the ocean's removing this greenhouse gas from the atmosphere. However, decades of ocean observations now show that there is also a downside; the CO_2 absorbed by the ocean is changing the chemistry of the seawater in a process called ocean acidification.

When CO_2 is absorbed by seawater, chemical reactions occur that reduce the seawater pH, carbonate ion concentration, and saturation states of biologically important calcium carbonate minerals. These chemical reactions are termed "ocean acidification" or "OA" for short. Calcium carbonate minerals are the building blocks for the skeletons and shells of many marine organisms. In areas where most life now congregates in the ocean, the seawater is supersaturated with respect to calcium carbonate minerals. This means there are abundant building blocks for calcifying organisms to build their skeletons and shells. However, continued ocean acidification is causing many parts of the ocean to become under saturated with these minerals, which is likely to affect the ability of some organisms to produce and maintain their shells.

Since the beginning of the Industrial Revolution, the pH of surface ocean waters has fallen by 0.1 pH units. Since the pH scale, like the Richter scale, is logarithmic, this change represents approximately a 30% increase in acidity. Future predictions indicate that the oceans will continue to absorb carbon dioxide and become even more acidic. Estimates of future carbon dioxide levels, based on business as usual emission scenarios, indicate that by the end of this century the surface waters of the ocean could be nearly 150% more acidic, resulting in a pH that the oceans haven't experienced for more than 20 million years.

Ocean acidification is expected to impact ocean species to varying degrees. Photosynthetic algae and sea grasses may benefit from higher CO_2 conditions in the ocean, as they require CO_2 to live just like plants on land. On the other hand, studies have shown that a more acidic environment has a dramatic effect on some calcifying species, including oysters, clams, sea urchins, shallow water corals, deep sea corals, and calcareous plankton. When shelled organisms are at risk, the entire food web may also be at risk. Today, more than a billion people worldwide rely on food from the ocean as their primary source of protein. Many jobs and economies in the U.S. and around the world depend on the fish and shellfish in our oceans.

In recent years, there have been near total failures of developing oysters in both aquaculture facilities and natural ecosystems on the West Coast. These larval oyster failures appear to be correlated with naturally occurring upwelling events that bring low pH waters under saturated in aragonite as well as other water quality changes to near shore environments.

Lower pH values occur naturally on the West Coast during upwelling events, but recent observations indicate that anthropogenic CO_2 is contributing to seasonal under saturation. Low pH may be a factor in the current oyster reproductive failure; however, more research is needed to disentangle potential acidification effects from other risk factors, such as episodic freshwater inflow, pathogen increases, or low dissolved oxygen. It is premature to conclude that acidification is responsible for the recent oyster failures, but acidification is a potential factor in the current crisis to this $100 million a year industry, prompting new collaborations and accelerated research on ocean acidification and potential biological impacts.

Increasing CO_2 levels and decreasing pH in seawater negatively impact many marine organisms that produce calcium carbonate shells or skeletons. For example, increasing ocean acidification has been shown to significantly reduce the ability of reef-building corals to produce their skeletons.

In a recent article, coral biologists reported that ocean acidification could compromise the successful fertilization, larval settlement and survivorship of Elkhorn coral, an endangered species. These research results suggest that ocean acidification could severely impact the ability of coral reefs to recover from disturbances. Other research indicates that, by the end of this century, coral reefs may erode faster than they can be rebuilt. This could compromise the long-term viability of these ecosystems and perhaps impact the estimated one million species that depend on coral reef habitats. For more information on the impact of ocean acidification on coral, see NOAA's Coral Reef Watch website.

Ocean acidification is an emerging and quite serious global problem. Over the last decade, there has been much focus in the ocean science community on studying the potential impacts of ocean acidification. Since sustained efforts to monitor ocean acidification worldwide are only beginning, it is currently impossible to predict exactly how ocean acidification impacts will cascade throughout the marine food chain and affect the overall structure of marine ecosystems.   With the pace of ocean acidification accelerating, scientists, resource managers, and policymakers recognize the urgent need to strengthen the science as a basis for sound decisions and action.

Floods

Climate change is causing more frequent deviations and fluctuations in weather, such as an increase in storms or droughts, and is predicted to affect weather conditions adversely throughout the globe. The changes are quite obvious in a place like Cockermouth in Britain, which suffered some of the worst floods in a century last year, are now experiencing nearly record-low river levels.

Among the 12 countries listed by the World Bank as most vulnerable to the adverse effects of climate extremes are: Bangladesh which is most susceptible to floods, Malawi to droughts, the Philippines to storms, and low lying island countries like Vietnam, to rising sea levels.

Figure 9-63. Periodic flood in Bangladesh

Bangladesh is well known as being the world's most flood-prone country, with monsoon floods and cyclones being almost an annual event, and severe flooding occurring every four to five years. Annual floods have wreaked havoc in Bangladesh throughout history.

During the last 50 years, at least seven mega floods have occurred, affecting about 35-75% of the land area. Major flooding recorded in recent years occurred in 1987, 1988, and 1998, 2004 and 2007. A historical overview of floods since 1954 indicates that the frequency, magnitude, and duration of floods have increased substantially, probably due to climate change.

All major floods, some covering more than 30% of the country, occurred after 1974. Four floods of such great magnitude (1974, 1987, 1988, and 1998) took place during the last 25 years, averaging one in every six years.

There are a number of reasons for this. One is the Ganges-Brahmaputra Delta, the flood plain formed by four major rivers: the Brahmaputra, Meghna, Ganges,

and Wang rivers, which converge into Bangladesh, creating the world's largest river delta. There is a labyrinth of smaller rivers in the area as well, and all eventually empty out into the Bay of Bengal, which often sees the wrath of nature in the form of cyclones and floods.

Bangladesh is a very low-lying country, with 70% of its land area merely 1-2 meters above sea level, with a monsoon climate that brings torrential rains, where the volume of the annual torrential downpours often exceed the combined river capacity.

Thawing snow from the Himalayas in springtime further increases the flood risks as torrents of melt water enter the rivers at their source. The thawing process is also accelerated by global warming, thus consistently exacerbating the excess river discharge.

The annual floods are also caused by the deforestation of the upstream regions in India and Nepal, which has increased soil erosion, resulting in large amount of silt deposition at the river beds, which reduces their channel capacity and increases significantly the likelihood of flooding the low lying areas along the river banks.

Global warming is a major force behind the floods, which arise due to increased rainfall and sea level rise as a result of the warmer climate. The floods have seriously affected the country's economy, agriculture, water & food security, and human health. Population displacement and shelter scarcity are big problems in Bangladesh, and the estimates are that in the coming decades the rising sea level alone will create more than 25 million climate refugees.

Bangladesh is one of the countries most vulnerable, and least able to adapt, to the effects of climate change.

Water Wars

On the other extreme, fresh and safe to drink water is scarce in Bangladesh and many other areas of the world. Mark Twain once remarked that, "whisky is for drinking; water is for fighting over," as if he knew that the fight for water would become a global reality.

And now, the U.S. Director of National Intelligence said recently that the risk of conflict would grow as fresh water demand is set to outstrip sustainable current supplies by 40% by 2030.

Of all the water on earth, 97% is salt water and the remaining 3% is fresh, with less than 1.0% of the planet's drinkable water readily accessible for direct human uses. Scarcity is defined as each person in an area having access to less than 1,000 m^3 of water a year.

The scarcity of water in some regions of the world

have led to "water wars" starting about 4,500 years ago, when the city-states of Lagash and Umma went to war in the Tigris-Euphrates basin.

More recently, according to Israel's Ariel Sharon, the reason for going to war against the Arab states in 1967 was for access to fresh water. Analysts believe that Israel continues to occupy the Golan Heights, seized from Syria in 1967, to control issues related to water use.

Senegal and Mauritania also fought a war starting in 1989 over grazing rights on the River Senegal. And Syria and Iraq have fought minor skirmishes over the Euphrates River. The Nile is another potential flash point. In 1989, former Egyptian president Hosni Mubarak threatened to send demolition squads to a dam project in Ethiopia. The Egyptian army still has jungle warfare brigades, even though they have no jungle. Today we are witnessing serious problems with water access in India and its neighbors, which is leading to social unrest and political frictions.

To make things worse, the areas where water scarcity is the biggest problems are some of the same places where political conflicts are rife, leading to potentially explosive situations.

Presently 780 million people around the world lack direct access to safe drinking water, and by 2030, nearly half of the world's population will be living in areas of high water stress. Rapid population growth and increased industrial demand are causing increases in water withdrawals, which have tripled over the last 50 years, and have left many water reservoirs empty.

There were 20 nations with limited or no access to fresh water in 1990. Now the UN predicts that 30 nations will be water scarce in 2025, and 18 of them are in the Middle East and North Africa. These include Egypt, Israel, Somalia, Libya and Yemen. A water war between south and north Yemen is shaping up as the scene of the next regional water war, with other countries in the region following suit if the situation is not improved.

Water scarcity is a serious issue exacerbated by demographic pressures, climate changes and pollution. The world's water supplies just are not abundant enough to guarantee enough water to the increasing population as needed for their personal needs and for the growing economies.

Wars of the future will be fought over the "blue gold," as the conflict among thirsty people, opportunistic politicians and powerful corporations increases, and the battle for dwindling resources intensifies.

Social awareness and unrest in many countries that are threatened by water shortages are leading to organized protests that seem to be intensifying.

Bolivia, South Africa, India, Botswana, Mexico, and even parts of the U.S. have seen vigorous water-related protests. The fight over water privatization in Cochobamba, Bolivia turned into a bit of a water war and the army was called in. In Botswana, the government smashed bore holes in an effort to remove indigenous Bushmen from the Kalahari Desert. Mexico City has been forcibly taking water from the countryside, confiscating water sources from other areas, and building fortresses around it like it's a gold mine. In India, Coca Cola gets water contracts and then builds fortresses around the water sources, thus forcibly taking drinking and irrigation water away from the locals.

Even some of the richest countries are not immune to water shortages. The U.A.E., which until recently had the highest per capita consumption of water in the world now is implementing water conservation measures.

And well they should, because their luxurious cities are built in the middle of a desert, where during the past thirty years the water table has been dropping about a meter every year. At this rate, the U.A.E. will deplete its natural freshwater resources in about fifty years.

As a matter of fact, water scarcity in Jordan is forcing Amman's citizens to get their water delivered once a week. The water comes from Sunday night until Monday morning, and is supposed to last the entire week. So many people have constructed wells or fill water tanks for their weekly water needs. This water is unsuitable to drink, so most people buy additional bottled water for drinking and cooking.

Figure 9-64. Watering hole in African village

Some large cities in the wealthiest region of the world have run completely out of water as a result of overuse, and now depend solely on water delivered from distant water sources. In an average morning one can see a long caravan of water trucks going out of the city empty and returning later on full of water. The water is delivered to homes and companies or is sold on the street.

The water situation is approaching a critical state in other countries in the region too, so now desalination is the name of the game there. About 70% of the world's desalination plants are located in this area, and mostly in Saudi Arabia, the United Arab Emirates, Kuwait and Bahrain.

While the desalination plants produce water needed for the arid region, they also create problems for health and the environment. The seawater used most in desalination plants has high amounts of boron and bromide, and the process can also remove essential minerals like calcium.

At the end of the day, millions of tons of concentrated sea salt are dumped back into oceans where the increased salinity affects the ocean's environment with time. The plants harm local wildlife and add pollutants to the region's climate.

Desalination is also a high energy-consumption process, which uses more energy to produce a gallon of fresh water than is needed to produce a gallon of gasoline. The high use of energy results in raised energy prices and higher prices on water produced, which ultimately hurts the poorest in the societies.

Thus produced water can substitute the lack of natural freshwater, but some of the countries in the M.E.N.A. region have tendencies towards the overuse of their natural resources, which is not going to change any time soon. This then brings serious concerns with the large amount of desalination plants in the Middle East with the focus on the improper dependency that will cause, instead of encouraging alternate forms of water and energy and conserving freshwater.

As the renewables (solar, wind, and biofuels in particular) are becoming very popular, we need to take a look at their contribution to the energy vs. environment conundrum.

The Renewables

All renewable energy facilities located in desert and non-desert locations face environmental issues, depending on the technology, location, and size. The desert locations are more affected, because they are usually very large—thousands of acres containing mil-

lions upon millions of PV modules and BOS equipment, working day and night under excruciatingly adverse conditions.

All power-generating facilities have some adverse effect. Solar PV facilities can cause a number of problems, including potential glare and glint hazards to aircraft, trains, and highway traffic, and can impact agricultural lands and open space/habitat lands.

Depending on their location, technology, and site design, wind farms have the potential for killing migrating or foraging raptors and bats, adversely affecting the visual landscape, creating aviation hazards, and causing noise problems if located near urban areas.

Geothermal facilities can affect rare and endangered plant and animal species, cultural resources, the quantity and quality of local water supplies, and visual landscapes. Geothermal projects can also cause or contribute to local and regional air quality problems through the emission of moderate amounts of regulated air pollutants, although they are required to use the best available emissions control technology and provide emission offsets to comply with local air district regulations.

Biomass plants can cause regional increases in criteria pollutants and particulate matter, post ash disposal, local land use concerns, and increased water use (if a facility uses water cooling towers or employs "wet scrubbers" to reduce hydrochloric acid emissions).

For renewable facilities in the desert, the primary environmental concerns are impacts on biological and cultural resources, water supply, visual impacts, transportation-related visual hazards, and land use, which will be discussed. Depending on the project, there may also be air quality, hazardous materials, noise, public safety, and local community concerns.

Here is a brief list of the different negative impacts, most frequently associated with renewable energy installations:

Biological Resource Impacts

Proposed desert locations for utility-scale solar and wind energy projects often provide habitat for sensitive species like raptors, bats, desert tortoises, kit foxes, various reptiles and amphibians, Mohave ground squirrels, and sensitive plants. Solar PV and solar thermal parabolic trough projects generally cause greater habitat loss than wind farms and solar thermal heliostat and power tower projects because the sites often need to be leveled to accommodate a linear design, which typically cannot be altered to avoid sensitive areas.

Heliostat and power tower projects do not necessarily require that a site be leveled, so habitat impacts can be less. The site topography can be maintained and some vegetation left intact since that technology has far greater flexibility regarding where the mirrors are located and do not always need to be in a line.

Wind energy projects, if located in key migration routes or foraging areas, can affect bird and bat species through collisions with turbine blades and through barotraumas (tissue damage and lung failure) caused by rapid air pressure reduction when bats and some birds get too close to moving turbine blades.

Wind farms generally cause less absolute habitat loss within a project footprint than utility scale solar facilities, because habitat for plant and wildlife species remains between turbines. Indirect impacts to wildlife outside the turbine footprint can result from roads, vehicles, and noise—possibly rendering a site generally unusable by wildlife depending on usage on the site and density of turbines. It may be easier to protect rare plant populations on a wind energy site. In addition to habitat loss, most large, renewable generation projects (both solar and wind) can potentially affect wildlife movement patterns, particularly if they are proposed in or near migration corridors or if they impede the connections between sensitive species populations, which can be critical to the species' local and regional health and survival.

Water Supply Impacts

Water is limited in the desert, and groundwater basins are often already in an overdraft condition. Fresh water is an increasingly critical resource, not only in the desert regions, but also throughout California. Increasingly, power plants may be competing with other local users for diminishing water supplies. As California's population and water demand continue to grow, the department of water resources anticipates that the state will experience water supply shortfalls of more than several million-acre feet within the next 10 years.

In the desert region, the majority of proposed utility-scale renewable energy facilities use either wind or solar technologies. The solar technologies are further categorized as either solar thermal or PV. Wind and solar facilities require large areas of open desert land to take advantage of higher wind speeds or to maximize the collection of solar radiation, but their water use can vary significantly.

Solar thermal facilities, which use steam turbine generators, need to dissipate waste heat. The preferred technology for heat dissipation (cooling) is evaporative cooling. Use of this technology requires a sizable volume of water during operation.

Wind technologies and PV do not require thermal cooling equipment, resulting in significantly less water use. Activities such as grading and dust control for construction of both PV and solar thermal projects may require significant water use.

Mirror washing throughout the life of a project may also contribute to significant water use. Water needs for PV panel washing are estimated as one-tenth of the requirements for solar thermal power mirror washing values.

Renewable energy facilities can take advantage of different strategies to reduce their water consumption. Solar thermal facilities can also use alternative approaches, such as dry cooling (air cooled condensers) and hybrid cooling, which are available and commercially viable. This can reduce a project's water demand by up to 90%, and simplify the analysis involved in the permitting process. Rather than using fresh water, renewable projects can use degraded water, also known as non-potable water, which can be treated and reused for power plant process water.

Surface Water Impacts

Federal and state regulations protect many of the ephemeral and intermittent streams in the desert region because they are important sources of sediment, water, nutrients, seeds, and organic matter for downstream ecosystems and also provide habitat for many species. Unlike other streams, in the desert streams typically have relatively long periods where no flow occurs, punctuated by episodic flows of relatively short duration and high intensity.

Site design needs to also be modified where important biological resources are identified and site drainage would have an impact. Diversion of high velocity flows through and around a site can be difficult where potential impacts up and downstream of a project site need to be decreased and there is a need to mimic natural conditions. Temporary erosion and sediment protection measures should be installed to control soils disturbed by construction.

Visual Impacts

Utility scale solar thermal power plants or wind farms can cover many square miles, including the power block facilities, access roads and transmission lines, and cause major visual changes in non-industrialized desert or mountainous landscapes with scenic values. The steam plumes produced by the wet cooling towers of solar thermal power plants may also change the view of the landscape.

Geothermal power plants, including well pads, steam pipelines, power generation facilities, access roads and transmission lines, may occupy as much as 350 acres, and power plant wet cooling towers can produce steam plumes—all potentially causing similar visual impacts on undeveloped desert or mountainous terrain.

Cultural Resources Impacts

State laws define cultural resources as buildings, sites, structures, objects, and historic districts. There are three kinds of cultural resources: prehistoric (related to prehistoric human occupation and use of an area); historical (associated with Euro-American exploration and settlement of an area); and ethnographic (materials important to the heritage of a particular ethnic or cultural group, such as Native Americans).

A major challenge to the development of lands, especially in the southern desert, is the lack of comprehensive information regarding the locations and significance of cultural resources. While some archaeological sites are small and well defined, historic and prehistoric landscapes can stretch for miles.

Many of the elements within these and other areas of historical significance have not been identified or evaluated. Information on both historical and archaeological sites is scattered among city, county, state, and private archives, multiple information centers, and state and federal agencies, such as the California office of historic preservation, national register of historic places, and the California register of historic resources.

Scarce and fragmented information, along with confidentiality requirements limiting access to cultural resource information, can make it difficult for developers to select sites that will avoid significant cultural resources. That can cause delays or inaccuracies in the resource analysis during the licensing process and create the need for more extensive site surveys, especially in remote desert areas.

Much of the land under consideration for solar and wind development includes Native American ancestral lands that contain artifacts, burial sites, historical villages, trails, plants, animals, landscapes, and vistas with cultural and spiritual significance. The spiritual value of these areas and artifacts is separate from the archaeological and historical value of these or other cultural resources and, from a Native American perspective; the loss of the use of these lands or their spiritual context within the landscape cannot be mitigated. Only tribal elders or tribal historic preservation officers often know information regarding landmarks and other areas of significance to Native Americans.

Another significant challenge to avoiding or mitigating cultural resource impacts, especially under the California environmental quality act (CEQA), is the lack of flexibility in site location and design once a project reaches the application phase. Developers frequently fail to adequately consider the potential cultural sensitivity of a site through appropriate resource studies and discussions with knowledgeable technical specialists and Native American tribal representatives before settling on a final location. To avoid cultural resources, staff and tribal representatives need to have the opportunity to identify resources before site finalization.

Land Use Impacts

Most desert lands are owned by the federal government and managed for multiple uses by the BLM and National Park Service. The Department of Defense also owns and manages large tracts of desert land for military purposes. Siting renewable energy facilities on BLM and National Park Service lands can affect existing and future multiple uses such as recreation, wildlife habitat, livestock grazing, and open space.

For example, solar thermal facilities within the BLM's California desert conservation area plan have significantly impacted or restricted other uses of the land. Similarly, siting renewable energy facilities on or near Department of Defense lands may affect military operations and related programs.

If located in productive agricultural areas, solar thermal or PV projects that require grading of many acres may result in the permanent loss of crop and grazing lands. In contrast, wind energy projects are generally compatible with agricultural land uses and may even help farmers preserve their farms with supplemental income received from leasing land to wind developers.

The average wind farm requires 5.5 acres of land to produce 1 MW of electricity, allowing land outside the turbine footprint to remain available for planting and grazing. However, wind projects can affect agricultural resources through soil disturbance during construction and the loss of agricultural land from installing access roads, wind turbine towers, and transmission lines.

Geothermal facilities are usually land intensive and can result in the permanent loss of productive agricultural land due to geothermal steam well field development, steam pipeline installation, construction of the power plant facilities and transmission lines, and permanent access roads to develop and maintain all of the steam field and power plant facilities.

Transportation-related Visual Hazards

Solar thermal, PV, wind, and geothermal technologies present significant hazards to general aviation and military flight activities, as well as to motorists on the nation's roads and highways, and railroad crews on their normal runs.

Solar thermal and PV plants, with their huge number of mirrors and collectors, can emit glint and glare that can pose a nuisance to pilots. They can even cause flash blindness, which is especially dangerous during takeoff and landing, so solar plants located near airports could be considered especially dangerous.

Wind turbines cause turbulence, which can affect low flying aircraft (light planes and helicopters) due to upward airflow disruption. Wind turbines are also being blamed for interrupting birds flight paths and even killing them due to collision with the turning blades, and disorienting them by means of the heavy airflow disruption in the field.

The evaporative and dry cooling towers of some solar thermal plants and cooling towers of geothermal plants may emit high velocity, hot air plumes, disrupting airflow and potentially causing severe turbulence to low flying aircraft as well.

The Department of Defense has also raised concerns about thermal plumes from power plants located near military flight areas and their effect on radar operations. All very tall structures, including wind turbines and solar power towers, have the potential to interfere with low-flying aircraft and with military flight zones that have structure height restrictions.

Renewables Planning

The importance of streamlining renewable permitting processes is widely recognized; therefore, a number of efforts are either completed or underway to help promote the development of utility-scale renewable electricity generating facilities especially in California.

Some of these efforts and initiatives in this area are:

Renewable Energy Transmission Initiative

In 2007, the renewable energy transmission initiative (RETI) was initiated as a joint statewide effort combining land use and transmission planning factors among the CPUC, the energy commission, the California ISO, and investor-owned and publicly owned utilities.

The primary goals of RETI were to:

1. Help identify the transmission projects needed to accommodate California's renewable energy goals

2. Ease the designation of corridors for future transmission line development

3. facilitate transmission line and renewable generation siting and permitting

The stakeholder-driven process identified competitive renewable energy zones throughout the state with the greatest potential for cost-effective and environmentally responsible renewable energy development.

Renewable Energy Action Team

To address challenges with permitting renewable projects in sensitive California desert regions, the renewable energy action team (REAT) was formed in 2008 to streamline and expedite the permitting processes for renewable energy projects, while conserving endangered species and natural communities at the ecosystem scale. Based in part on recommendations from the RETI process, the REAT is developing a desert renewable energy conservation plan (DRECP) for the Mojave and Colorado Desert regions.

The REAT also published the multidisciplinary *Best Management Practices and Guidance Manual: Desert Renewable Energy Projects* in December 2010 to help project developers design projects that minimize environmental impacts for desert renewable projects. The manual provides guidance on initiating permitting processes, conducting land-use assessments and surveys, decision making on water use and quality, roadway planning, avoiding conflicts with aviation, and grid interconnection issues.

Desert Renewable Energy Conservation Plan

In conjunction with other federal, state, and local agencies and stakeholder groups, the REAT is developing the DRECP to identify areas in the Mojave and Colorado Desert regions suitable for renewable energy project development and areas that will contribute to the conservation of sensitive species and natural communities. The DRECP encompasses about 22 million acres in Kern, Inyo, Los Angeles, San Bernardino, Riverside, San Diego, and Imperial counties. It will promote development of solar thermal, utility-scale solar PV, wind, and other forms of renewable energy along with associated infrastructure like transmission lines.

The DRECP will be a natural community conservation plan (NCCP) and will serve as the basis for one or more habitat conservation plans (HCP).145 As required by state and federal law, the environmental impact of the DRECP will be analyzed in a joint environmental impact report and statement anticipated to be completed by December 2012, along with the NCCP.

Solar Energy Development Programmatic Environmental Impact Statement

At the federal level, the U.S. Department of Energy, energy efficiency and renewable energy program, and the U.S. Department of the Interior, BLM, are preparing a solar energy development programmatic environmental impact statement (PEIS) to assess environmental impacts from programs intended to promote environmentally responsible utility-scale solar energy in six Western states.

The draft PEIS was issued Dec. 16, 2010, and in May 2011 the Energy Commission and the California Department of Fish and Game (DFG) submitted joint comments on the draft with the following recommendations:

a.   Abandon further consideration of the Iron Mountain solar energy zone (SEZ).

b.   Consider designating and studying additional SEZs on previously disturbed lands in the western Mojave Desert.

c.   Delay final PEIS-triggered amendments to the affected land use management plans until the DRECP process is complete in 2012.

d.   Fully consider and address all Energy Commission and DFG comments made previous to and in response to the publication of the draft PEIS. A supplement to the draft PEIS was released in the fall of 2011.

Cross-agency Coordination

State and federal agencies are working to streamline the permitting of renewable energy projects in California by increasing cross-agency cooperation and coordination, with several multi-agency agreements already in place:

In 2007, the Energy Commission, the U.S. Department of the Interior, and the BLM signed a memorandum of understanding (MOU) on agency roles, responsibilities, and procedures for joint environmental review of solar thermal projects proposed on federal land.

In 2009, the Energy Commission entered into an MOU with the California state lands commission to ensure timely and effective coordination during the Energy Commission's thermal power plant review process.

In 2010, the State of California and FERC signed an MOU to coordinate and share information for reviewing offshore wave and tidal energy projects.

In 2010, the Energy Commission and the departments of general services, corrections and rehabilitation, transportation, water resources, and fish and game all signed an MOU to promote the development of renewable energy projects on state buildings, properties, and rights-of-way. The state lands commission and the University of California subsequently joined the MOU.

Transmission Infrastructure Issues

In addition to the environmental, planning, and permitting issues already identified, California also faces challenges to the planning and permitting of power lines and other transmission infrastructures needed to bring electricity generated by large-scale renewable facilities to consumers. Governor Brown's clean energy jobs plan states that the Energy Commission "should 'fast-track' projects based on their anticipated ability to deliver clean energy to market. The permitting time for these projects—which now can take six to eight years—should be dramatically reduced, and in no case be longer than three years." Furthermore, the plan states, "As Governor, I will ensure that all agencies involved work together with a sense of urgency to permit the new transmission lines without delay."

We are still waiting...and although we even saw some progress, lately the Governor seems busy with other projects...

Packaging

It has been estimated that one third of the weight of all products shipped around the world is in the packaging materials. About 15%-20% of household garbage in developed countries is packaging—plastic, paper, Styrofoam, and many other materials are used to protect consumer goods to the point of consumption or use. Approximately 150-200 million tons of packaging is disposed in landfills every year.

There are many types of materials used for packaging, but the most common types are paper, fiberboard, plastic, glass, steel and aluminum.

•   Paper is the most widely used packaging materials, particularly corrugated cardboard used for transport packaging. The current recycling rate for paper and board packaging waste is 49%.

•   Glass is the most common form of packaging waste. Glass can be returned and reused or recycled easily and a well-established recovery and recycling system exists in the U.S.

•   Aluminum is used in many packaging applications such as beverage cans, foil, and laminates. It has a high value as a scrap metal and can be recycled economically.

- Steel is also used for packaging material for food, paint, and beverages and aerosols. Recycling steel brings significant resource and energy savings.

- Plastic offers several advantages over other packaging materials in its sturdiness and low weight. Some plastic types can be recycled and an effort is underway in the U.S. And yet, only 5-10% of all plastic materials are recycled, with the remainder either land filled or incinerated, which wastes more energy and emits more GHGs into the atmosphere.

- Mixed materials packaging can sometimes have the benefits of being more resource and energy efficient than single material packaging, but combining materials makes recycling difficult. Recycling these materials is hindered by the lack of facilities and technology necessary to separate materials to avoid contamination.

Most packaging materials can be reprocessed into other products such as road paving, floor coverings, shoe soles and car mats, or incinerated to produce energy or land fill.

Take a bottle of Coca Cola, for example, and think what it took to make it: how much raw materials and energy were used in the process, how much it weighs, and where it is going after the drink has been consumed. The same goes for the elaborate plastic packaging materials, which come with all gadgets—small or large. Millions of tons of packaging materials are discarded or recycled around the world every year.

And then think of what happens to the piles of plastic, glass, and other materials in the dumpsites. They are buried deep under ground, where they stay unchanged for hundreds and thousands of years, interfering with the natural soil processes. Recycling is much better, and yet it is also a huge energy consumer and pollution emitter.

U.S. consumers throw away 60 million plastic bottles every day, and less than 3% are recycled. In the U.K., 15 million plastic bottles are used every day and much less than 3% gets recycled. Less than 1% of the billions of plastic bags used each year are recycled and the majority of the bags are used only once.

There are now attempts to pass laws in Europe to recover 50% of all of the packaging and to recycle at least 25% once. However, educating the public and offering some compliance incentives are better ways to succeed

Figure 9-65. Excessive packaging awareness

in a mass packaging materials recycling campaign.

Regardless of the success of the different initiatives, packaging is a huge business that consumes a lot of energy and creates a lot of pollution from the beginning to the end

Emissions Trading

Emissions trading seems to be one of the most effective tools in putting some measure of control in the battle of power generation vs. the environment. In 1990, the U.S. Congress decided that a 50% reduction in SO_2 emissions from power plants and a significant reduction in NOx emissions from power plants were necessary first steps to address the acid rain problem. The resulting 1990 Clean Air Act Amendments created the U.S. Acid Rain Program, which made a wholesale change in the way SO_2 emissions were regulated. Rather than relying on command-and-control, it set a strict emissions cap for power plants and, in return, provided them with unprecedented flexibility in determining how to meet that cap.

The Acid Rain Program set the cap at 8.95 million tons of SO_2 per year. The program is implemented in two phases. In Phase I, which began in January 1995, the largest, highest emitting electric utility generating units were required to reduce emissions.

In Phase II, which will begin in 2000, virtually all the electric utility units will be required to reduce their emissions to roughly one-half of 1980 levels or the 8.95 million ton cap. Under the program, sources are required to hold allowances equal to each year's emissions. Participants are free to choose how they want to comply, but at the end of each year they have to surrender enough allowances to the EPA to cover their actual emissions. Failure to comply with this provision results in automatic penalties, which are enforced by EPA.

An effective tool for harnessing the power of the open market was found in a cap and trade system. Many view it as a model for other environmental programs. Under the acid rain program, the "cap" was firmly set and reduced emissions to levels that were roughly half of those in 1980. Looked at another way, the cap reduced the level of SO_2 emissions utilities were allowed to emit by 50%.

The cap was denominated in allowances, which were provided to all affected sources. Strictly speaking, an allowance authorizes a unit within a utility to emit one ton of SO_2 during a given year. Allowances are standardized and issued by vintage years, or the first year in which the allowance can be surrendered to the EPA to cover a source's actual emissions for that year.

Allowances are also bankable, meaning unused allowances can be used in future years. Most importantly, allowances are tradable, and any individual can open an account to buy or sell them. These attributes make allowances both an asset and a rationed commodity, empowering the involvement of financial markets.

Although at its core the SO_2 market is a part of a regulatory program, it has many attributes of a financial market as well. For example, market institutions such as brokerage houses and law firms specializing in contracts have emerged with the market. Allowances are transferred and traded among parties, creating an efficient market mechanism.

Utilities can chose among a host of options with which to reduce emissions, including switching from high-sulfur fuels (primarily coal) to lower sulfur fuels (low-sulfur coal or natural gas) or installing pollution control equipment. Trading allows the market to redistribute the rights to emit SO_2, thereby determining a more efficient and economic source of reductions.

Sources are required to execute allowance transactions through the EPA's allowance tracking system (ATS). The ATS allows the public to review all transactions as well as the accounts of all market participants. Improvements in the ATS have also allowed the EPA to reduce the time and cost of completing transactions to minutes.

At the end of each year, each unit needs to hold a number of allowances at least equal to its actual annual emissions. Utilities not in compliance face severe penalties and find no reprieve from their responsibilities to reduce overall emissions. The penalties include a $2,000-per-ton fine adjusted for inflation. And the offending source needs to supply offsetting allowances

in the next year through reduced allocations or an emission reduction proposal submitted to EPA.

The Results Today

Since the program began in 1995, there has been 100% compliance with SO_2 requirements. The incentives created by banking opportunities have led the sector as a whole to reduce and bank roughly 30% more emissions reductions through 1998 than was required under law. Market observers projected banked emissions reductions would reach between 10-11 million tons by the year 2000.

Just as importantly, the cost of protecting the environment through the U.S. acid rain program has fallen softer on the economy than originally anticipated. The economic efficiencies gained through compliance flexibility and the trading and banking provisions are thought to be primarily responsible for the cost savings. Reductions were projected to cost utilities between $4-$8 billion annually when the program was fully implemented in 2010. However, more recent projections indicate that the program will cost around $1 billion annually when it is fully implemented.

Today, electric utilities have a host of pollution control options before them and choosing the mix of options that best fits from both an economic and environmental perspective can be a difficult task. A utility's planning process is complex and must factor in demand for power and the emissions associated with generating it. From there, the utility needs to assess its pollution control options, including participation in allowance trades.

These variables are influenced by a large number of factors, which give rise to an astounding range of permutations in compliance planning. However, breaking the decision process down into its core components, applying time-honored economic techniques, and using computer technology can assist in mapping a course for compliance. The experience of a few utilities can be helpful and their perspectives are provided.

The Long-term Strategy

Because internal compliance planning brings together so many varying disciplines, many utilities have formed cross-functional teams, which span the company to assemble the expertise necessary to make the best decisions on pollution control. For instance, Potomac Electric Power Company (Pepco), a major utility in the mid-Atlantic region, pulls individuals from the generation group, engineering and power marketing, business planning, fuel procurement, environmental management, and emissions trading operations to assist in compliance planning.

No matter how the compliance planning team is assembled, it is essential that the team set in place a comprehensive long-term strategy that spans several years, yet is flexible enough to be fine tuned on a weekly or even daily basis. Aside from making fundamental infrastructure decisions, emissions control is essentially a function of making changes to the way a utility generates power. Because power plants represent massive capital expenditures that can take up to 10 years to design, permit, and construct, a compliance plan needs to take a long view on how these resources will be used.

For its part, Pepco operates with a ten-year compliance plan. The long-range plan is compiled by the entire compliance planning team, including the emissions trading practitioner, who provides insight on market supply and demand for allowances. The trader adds value to the long-term compliance planning process by outlining emissions trading strategies that can assist in managing compliance cost risks.

Emissions Reduction Measures

If the utility is in a long position, it may "bank" the allowance surplus, or it may sell or trade excess allowances in the emissions market. The emissions trading practitioner will be instrumental in this decision, providing emissions trading market data on allowance availability and prices.

If the utility is in a short position, it has to decide whether to cut emissions in the coming months to bring them in line with allowance holdings or to purchase allowances in the market. Again, the cross-functional team will analyze base-case scenarios using sensitivity analysis to explore the emissions performance and costs associated with a variety of pollution control options, and the emissions trading practitioner plays an important role in this process.

The emissions trading practitioner informs the compliance planning team of the current trading prospects and prices in the marketplace, as well as supply and demand trends for allowances. The team then compares these figures, which are compiled from a variety of market sources including published indexes and figures quoted by other market participants, with the other strategies available in the compliance plan.

In the current environmental market there are several emission reduction strategies available:

Fuel Choice. This is probably the most pollution control mechanism most often used. Utilities can switch from high-sulfur fuels to low-sulfur fuels, such as low-sulfur coal and natural gas, and sometimes achieve dramatic reductions in SO_2 emissions. Furthermore, with improved access to low-sulfur coal supplies in the West, this has become an attractive and economic option for many utilities.

Purchased Power/Power Markets: There are cases where utilities can purchase power that is cleaner than its own power to supply its customer base. The sources from which the utility purchases power will, however, have to have allowances to cover any emissions that would result from this generation. Therefore, the integrity of the cap will be preserved.

Electric Power Dispatch: The U.S. acid rain program provides strong incentives for electric utilities to factor the environmental "cost" of SO_2 emissions control into the economics of running each generating station. This "cost" of SO_2 emissions is sometimes referred to as the "environmental dispatch adder." Conceptually, by adding this SO_2 "cost" to the dispatch equation, it accomplishes two things. One, it sends the right signal for the lower-emitting units to run first, assuming all other things are equal. Secondly, it attempts to reflect the "true" cost of generation by units regulated under Phase I of the acid rain program are subject to rules regarding utilization, thus reflecting the cost of environmental compliance in the price of energy that is sold into the market. Hence, environmental dispatch should send the proper signal to reach optimization at the lowest emission level and at the lowest overall cost the customers.

Pollution Control Technology: This is perhaps the most direct, and the most expensive, method of controlling emissions. Certain technologies can be applied to a unit to clean up emissions as the pollutants move through the smoke stack. However, most pollution control device decisions are long-term rather large capital investments. Therefore, they afford little flexibility to adapt to changes in short-term market conditions.

Carbon tax is a tax levied on the carbon content of fuels in a form of carbon pricing. Carbon in coal, petroleum, and natural gas and is released as CO_2 when they are burned. Since GHG emissions caused by the combustion of fossil fuels are closely related to the carbon content of the respective fuels, a tax on these emissions can be levied by taxing the carbon content of fossil fuels at any point in the product cycle of the fuel.

The concept is quite elegant and easy to understand, but difficult to implement on global scale. Nevertheless, many countries have adapted some sort of a carbon tax. The future will force more countries to levy carbon taxes, and the entire concept will undergo many changes, successes, and failures.

Table 9-23. Comparative carbon tax values

Tons of carbon per unit of fuel	COAL	OIL	GAS
	0.574/ton	0.102/barrel	0.015/Mcf
Average price	$25.16/ton	$88.79/barrel	$5.90/Mcf
Carbon tax amount per unit of fuel, IF the carbon tax is:			
$10/ton of carbon	$5.74/ton	$1.02/barrel	$0.15/Mcf
$100/ton of carbon	$57.42/ton	$10.15/barrel	$1.49/Mcf
$200/ton of carbon	$114.85/ton	$20.31/barrel	$2.98/Mcf
Carbon tax as a percentage of fuel price If the carbon tax is:			
$10/ton of carbon	23%	1%	3%
$100/ton of carbon	228%	11%	25%
$200/ton of carbon	456%	23%	51%

Over-the-counter Market is one of the basic markets for emissions allowance trading is the over-the-counter market. Over-the-counter trading directly matches buyers and sellers, rather than moving trades through a centralized system. By contrast, trades for exchange-listed stocks are done through specialists that ensure the efficient movement of each listing. Emissions trading markets move with the participation of buyers, sellers, brokers, market makers, and traders—each using a direct link to purchase or sell allowances.

The prices for buying or selling emissions are fluid and determined with each individual trade. Because of the over-the-counter format, there is no central recording structure for current allowance bids and asks. Price information is readily available from market sources, such as brokers, traders, and indexes published by trade journals.

The buyers and sellers in emissions trading are individuals, organizations, or corporations that have a position in the market. Their motivations vary. Some trade to achieve regulatory compliance, others to retire allowances, or still others simply to turn a profit. Each buyer and seller has a publicly identified representative. This allows the buyer or seller to do due diligence and ensure its trade is legitimate.

There are three ways to participate in the over-the-counter emissions trading market, including bilateral transactions, trades transacted through a broker, and allowances purchases in the annual allowance auction:

1. *Bilateral Trades* is the direct point of entry into over-the-counter emissions trading markets by contacting participants directly and arranging bilateral deals. There is no intermediary exchange for the emissions trading market; therefore, all transactions are made on a direct, one-to-one basis. The ATS allowance account information found on the Internet enables participants to find other participants with whom to transact allowance trades.

Active market players who have extensive experience—and contacts—in the marketplace, however, usually employ this relationship-based approach. Unless you possess this type of market presence, it is difficult to fully assess trading options without some assistance. One set of market participants that has this market presence is:

2. *Traders* are likely to be counterparties with the emissions trading practitioner in bilateral trades, but often their market profile differs from the practitioner. Traders put their own money at risk in the market. Their motivation for participation in emissions markets is much like their motivation would be for entering stock markets or commodities markets: profit. Seldom do traders make decisions based on the need for compliance.

Because traders are willing to take positions in either direction of the market, they assist in generating liquidity. Their ability to generate a flow of deals makes some traders "market makers," in which they play a role similar to that of a stock specialist on an equity exchange. Liquidity refers to a volume of trading in the market that allows buyers to find sellers at prices reasonable to both. Without sustained liquidity, the market would have improper pricing information discouraging any type of emissions trading practitioner from participating.

Traders operate under a long-term view that looks to profit from the market's movement—up or down. Traders profit from arbitrage opportunities by buying and selling allowances to capture the value between spreads. This can be executed, for example, through the simple standard of buying low and selling high, working the price spreads to turn a profit.

3. Brokers serve emissions trading practitioners who do not wish to transact bilateral trades themselves.

Brokers do not take a position in the market, but rather facilitate transactions for counterparties. Just as importantly, brokers are a valuable source of market information, which market participants use to get an accurate sense of the current prices, as well as market volume.

Another aspect of the broker's responsibility is to maintain the anonymity of counterparties. Being unknown to the marketplace gives a buyer or a seller the luxury to test the waters for a perspective transaction without tipping their identity or strategy. This element of confidentiality is vital when shopping for the best possible price. Only after the transaction is confirmed are the counterparties' identities revealed to each other.

The hands-on-role of the broker also enables it to engage in structured transactions, which can be more time consuming than a normal cash settlement or option transactions. Deals involving complex swaps of vintage years, cross-pollutant trading, or cross-commodity trading are likely to involve a broker who can provide expertise to the transaction as well as the manpower to shepherd a deal to completion. Brokers profit from the market through commissions charged on brokered transactions.

Annual Allowance Auction is the creation of the U.S. acid rain program, where there was some uncertainty among lawmakers as to the future robustness of the emissions trading market and the availability of allowances for new sources of generation that were not in service during the baseline allocation period of 1985-1997. Of course, a case for an active trading market could be made on paper. But if the economics did not coalesce around allowance trading as anticipated, it was going to be tough to ascertain with certainty whether trading would be able to perform its pivotal role in compliance.

Therefore, the clean air act amendments set up an auction system designed to ensure a measure of allowance market liquidity and provide valuable price information. The auction is held annually on the last day of March and is run by the Chicago board of trade. To supply the auctions with allowances, the EPA set aside a special allowance reserve of approximately 2.8% of the total allowances allocated to all units. During Phase I, when the allocated allowances total 5.7 million allowances annually, 150,000 allowances are available each year for auctions. During Phase II, when allowance allocations total 8.95 million allowances annually, 250,000 allowances are earmarked annually for auctions.

The sale starts with the highest-priced bid and continues until all allowances have been sold or the bids are exhausted. Credits purchased in the advance auction

cannot be used until seven years after purchase. The EPA may not set a minimum price for allowances used in the auction. The EPA on its Web site posts the end results.

And speaking of the EPA...

EPA

One critical area of the environment vs. power generation debacle where the EPA plays a decisive role is in controlling the GHG emissions of power plants and other fuel producing and using facilities. The EPA's role in the environmental cleanup, however, is still stuck somewhere among fully responsible, not-sure-what-to-do, and looking-the-other-way. There are some good things coming from the EPA, but many are either half-baked, or baked on the wrong side. There are a number of examples to justify such a statement, but it will take too much space here, so we'll give the EPA due credit in trying to do the right thing as efficiently as possible.

Figure 9-66. The EPA controversies

Some people blame the EPA for not doing enough, thus allowing a number of environmental and health problems in the U.S. Others think that the EPA is interfering with business-as-usual and should stay out of mandating regulations that hurt business enterprises.

Who is right? We see some of the bad things of the past, but there is not much that can be done now, so looking forward we see one good thing that is still in the works; it is EPA-452/R-12-001 rule, stating:

"The proposed EGU GHG NSPS will limit greenhouse gas emissions (GHG) from new fossil fuel fired electric generating units (EGU) constructed in the U.S. in the future....This proposal requires that all new fossil-fuel fired units that exceed 25 MW in capacity be able to meet an emission rate standard of 1,000 pounds of CO_2 per megawatt hour (lbs CO_2/MWh) calculated over a rolling 12-month period. It also proposes an alternative compliance option that would allow units to meet the 1,000 lbs CO_2/MWh standard using a 30-year averaging period. These standards could be met either by natural gas combined cycle (NGCC) generation with no additional GHG control, or coal-fired generation using CCS."

Great, right? Maybe so, if the rule were not so generous and so open-ended, so that the end result is:

- Presently coal-fired power plants emit approximately 1,500 lbs. CO_2/MWh, so dropping this to 1,000 lbs. CO_2/MWh is significant, but still far from enough. A 500 MW coal power plant is actually emitting 500,000 lbs of CO_2 in the atmosphere every hour, and 12,000,000 lbs CO_2 every single day.

- Presently a 500 MW coal-fired power plant will emit 6.6 billion lbs of CO_2 per annum. With the new rule, this amount will be reduced (in the very distant future, because only newly built plants are affected) to 4.4 billion lbs of CO_2 per annum. Not bad as far as progress is concerned, but it is still 4.4 billion of CO_2 toxic gasses pumped in the atmosphere every year by just one plant.

- There are 594 coal-fired power plants in the U.S. (2009 count) with approximately 330,000 MW of combined power generation. Several dozens of new coal-fired power plants are in the making, so the number will grow significantly with time. This is 2,890,800,000,000 lbs. (2.9 trillion lbs), or 1.3 billion tons of CO_2 being pumped into the atmosphere every year by the U.S. power plants alone.

Multiplying this ever increasing number by the lbs of CO_2 per MW generated worldwide (by thousands of dirty coal-fired plants) produces a number with too many zeroes to even count.

- The 30 years "averaging period" opens a large loop hole where many, if not most plant operators will squeeze through, delaying the CO_2 sequestration for as long as possible.

In all cases, the EPA rule is a good step in the right direction, although it won't provide much environmental protection from large CO_2 emissions in the U.S. for a long time…if ever! And this is only the tip of the iceberg, because most of the several thousand coal-fired power plants around the world are totally unregulated

and spew as much poisons in the air as, and when, they wish. EPA, or no EPA…

China, for example, generates 2 billion MWh/annum by its 2,000 coal-fired power plants (almost 10 times the U.S. numbers discussed above), and also burns that much coal for other domestic and industrial purposes. How many zeroes of lbs of CO_2 and other toxic gasses does this represent? As a matter of fact, it is expected that China will add several hundred additional coal-fired plants to its arsenal, and as a result of that expansion, emit as much poisonous gas as the total of the rest of the entire world by 2030. Great neighbor, eh?

So, the immense cloud of stinky, poisonous gasses containing many stinky, poisonous chemicals—some of which are many times more dangerous to the environment and human health than CO_2—are dumped into the atmosphere every day where they produce the negative effects we all know and fear.

With this large-scale, ongoing debacle, the big question remains: "How long is Nature going to be able to keep its balance with this large cloud of toxic gasses thrown at it?" Won't we choke and cough out of existence one of these days?

Comparing conventional energy sources with the solar technologies of today is not a straightforward process, and although there is no line that can be drawn between them, there are definite differences—a number of plus and minuses that can be identified and quantified.

Although our objective is not to compare different technologies from an environmental point of view, we will discuss the characteristics and draw some conclusions to open the subject to an honest discussion. This may not happen any time soon, for obvious reasons, but it will happen eventually, make no mistake about it!

The excess use of fossils (coal, oil, and natural gas) has been blamed for most of the climate changes—including temperature rise—and most of us have accepted this theory as the truth. Because of that we do dedicate a lot of time and space in this text on this subject.

THE SOLUTION(S)

But wait. Maybe there is a solution or a number of solutions, that, if implemented on time, could bring us closer to energy independence and clean environment.

Here are some examples:

Coal Sequestration

OK, we fully understand that coal is not going away. We also know that it is not clean, but that we need it nevertheless, so we need to deal with it. But is it possible to clean it a little bit, so that it stops killing us with those noxious fumes emitted at high volume.

The clean coal technology is here, and it is just a matter of implementing it. Yes, it might be somewhat more expensive, but it is important that we stop, or at least reduce, the CO_2 and other GHG gasses produced during coal burning from killing the environment and all life in it.

A good example for this technology is the new GreenGen power station near Beijing, China. It is a 400 MW coal burning plant that is using a coal-to-gas conversion and gas burning process, which is much cleaner than solid-coal burning. The plant is also equipped with efficient gas sequestration equipment, which ensures that the gasses that are released into the atmosphere are 90-95% clean. Thus generated CO_2, which is the major component in the waste gasses, is trapped, segregated, purified and stored. It is then sold for the bottling of soft drinks and other commercial needs.

GreenGen demonstrates multiple integrated gasification combined cycle (IGCC) technologies that can be scaled to simultaneously address several environmental challenges in response to climate change and energy security concerns.

The $1.0 billion GreenGen plant features pre-combustion technology that will strip pollutants such as SO_2 and particulates from the coal-burning process.

The second phase will implement fuel cell power generation and carbon capture and sequestration (CCS)

technology for nearly zero-emission power generation.

The third phase of the project is planned for completion by 2016, when the plant would produce a total of 650 MW and 3,500 tons of syngas per day.

When completed and optimized, this model will be duplicated in many such IGCC-CCS plants. And with China continuing to build about 30 power plants a year, these technologies could have a significant impact on the air quality and greenhouse gas emissions not only in China but also all around the world.

Figure 9-67 looks so good that we wonder what is stopping us? The answer is money. Lots of money is needed, as well as some more work on the technologies as a whole.

In any case, even if and when this all works well, it is not the solution to all our problems. Nevertheless, we have to agree that during this energy transitional period, which is upon us already, we need to look into any and all possible solutions, no matter how expensive or temporary they might be. Little by little, we might just be able to add another drop to the bucket of emergency environmental solutions. Any measure that reduces environmental pollution needs to be taken seriously and implemented immediately—it is our priority at this point and time.

Grain Alcohol

Another great example of energy generation diversification is the massive use of alcohol to power cars and commercial enterprises in Brazil. Starting in the mid-

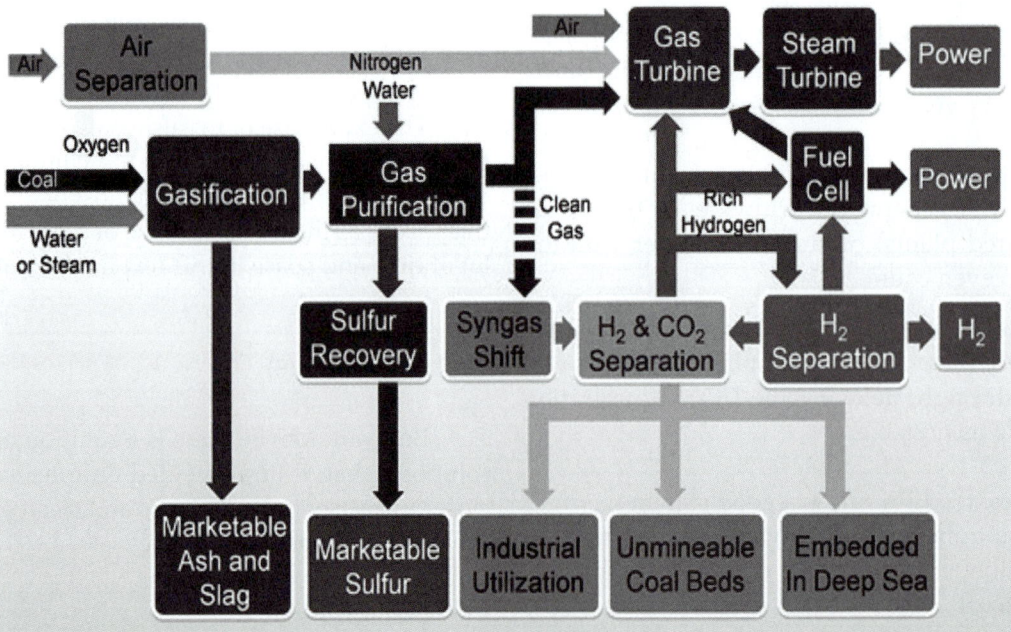

Figure 9-67. Green Gen function

1970s, Brazil initiated a large modification of its energy infrastructure by cultivating millions of acres sugar cane for the production of alcohol. Cars in Brazil can run on gas or alcohol and any mixture of those.

The U.S. and most other countries cannot grow sugarcane for climatic and economic reasons, but they all can produce a lot of grain and other alcohols. The American alcohol experiment of the mid-2000, however, failed for a number of not-so-good reasons, and grain alcohol is now a dirty word in the US. Whether that was a sloppy error or an intentional murder of a good idea, we'll never know.

What we know for sure is that grain alcohol will not be a primary fuel source any time soon here. It is still used for mixing in gasoline during certain times of the year, and this is as far as it will go for now. But we foresee it making a great comeback in the future…the distant future. It could be the fuel of choice for all personal and public transportation vehicles.

That is one of the ways to get away from crude oil imports and to gain true energy independence.

Energy Conservation

This is a new concept, especially in the U.S., where conservation of anything is contrary to the free spirit of all Americans and one of the killers of the American dream. The amazing fact, however, is that by just implementing moderate efficient energy saving measures in homes and commercial buildings, the U.S. could save over 25% of its energy demand immediately. Today! Who knew…?

This, however, won't happen any time soon, because pursuing the American dream does not allow many, if any, personal sacrifices. This includes preserving the extreme home, work, and transportation comforts, etc. necessities of the "American" lifestyle we are so comfortable living in.

PV Installations on Contaminated Land Sites

Identifying and using land located in areas with high quality, renewable energy resources will be an essential component of developing electricity from renewable energy sources. As the number of large PV projects increases, the demand for large pieces of land will increase as well. Land that has been previously used for activities such as mining and waste disposal will become increasingly important for this application.

The U.S. (EPA) estimates that there are approximately 490,000 sites and almost 15 million acres of potentially contaminated properties across the U.S. tracked by the EPA. This estimate includes superfund, resource conservation and recovery act (RCRA), brownfields, and abandoned mine lands.

Cleanup goals have been achieved and controls put in place to ensure long-term protection for more than 917,000 acres. Through coordination and partnerships among federal, state, tribal, and other government agencies, as well as utilities, communities, and the private sector, many new renewable energy facilities can be developed on those contaminated properties.

The EPA office of solid waste and emergency response (OSWER) center for program analysis (CPA) is seeking opportunities to facilitate the reuse of contaminated properties and active and abandoned mine sites for renewable energy generation.

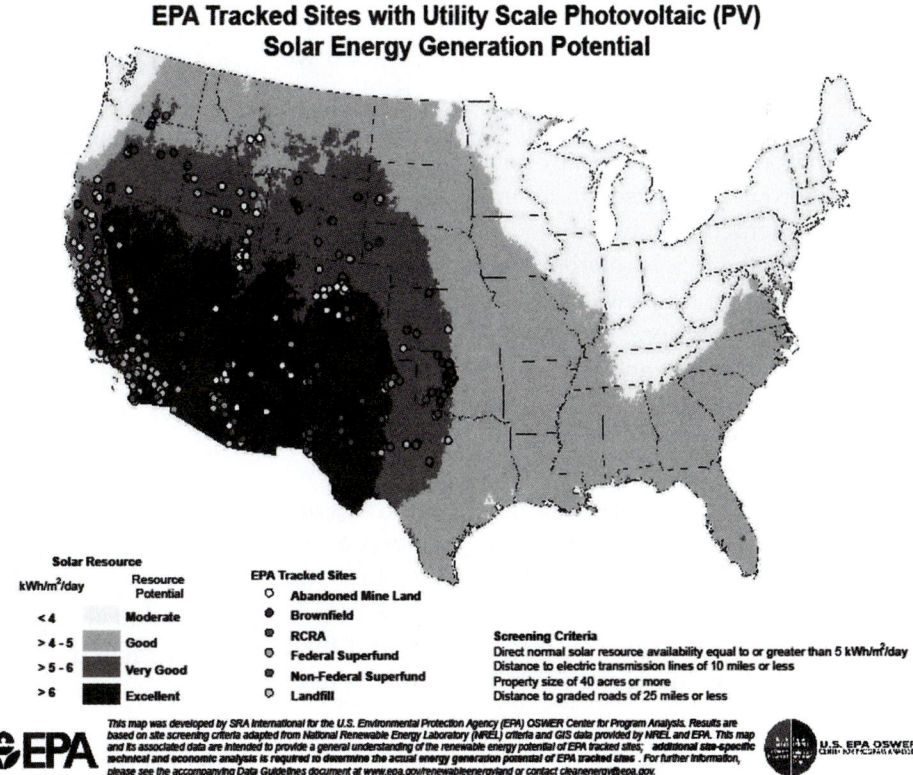

Figure 9-68. The EPA tracked landfills and other contaminated areas for potential solar sites

Those lands are environmentally and economically beneficial for siting renewable energy facilities because they:

1. Offer thousands of acres of land with few site owners

2. Often have critical infrastructure in place, including electric transmission lines, roads, and on-site water, and they are adequately zoned for such development

3. Provide an economically viable reuse for sites with significant cleanup costs or low real estate development demand

4. Take the stress off undeveloped lands for construction of new energy facilities, preserving the land carbon sink.

5. Provide job opportunities in urban and rural communities.

6. Advance cleaner and more cost effective energy technologies, reducing the environmental impacts of energy systems (e.g., reduce greenhouse gas emissions).

What are the advantages and disadvantages of installing PV power plants on contaminated land? Are there risks associated with such a move? How do we separate the past, present, and future issues, be they environmental, health, etc.? Who is ultimately responsible for the environmental and health safety of those potentially dangerous fields, used in an untested, unproven, and unprecedented manner?

What are the U.S. regulators and politicians saying on the matter? Are they aware of this development, or did it slip their attention? This is another set of important questions awaiting an answer, demonstrating again how young and immature the PV industry is.

We have a number of options to address the energy crisis, as already pointed out. As with any new thing, we need to protect it from abuse and misuse, which is our goal herein—to bring the issues to the attention of the U.S. public, the scientific community, the regulators, and politicians. Which solution(s) we chose will determine our energy future, and that of our children and their children. Let's be wise and unselfish in making the right choices.

Energy Storage Update

Energy storage is one of the conditions to ramping up wind and solar installations. Without it, these power sources would be considered variable and therefore unreliable. By storing the generated power, however, and using it when needed, they can generate power more consistently and reliably.

California is taking the first large steps in this area by proposing a 1.325 GW target for energy storage by 2020 that could boost solar adoption rates in the state. This is in response to the utilities' concerns that wind and solar have the potential to create some problems with intermittency. Energy storage can certainly help alleviate some of those concerns and boost the renewables in the state and the country.

The proposed framework from the California public utilities commission (CPUC) outlines specific, year-by-year energy storage procurement targets for Southern California Edison, San Diego Gas & Electric, and Pacific Gas & Electric. It also breaks down targets into three categories: transmission, distribution, and customer-sited storage.

Utilities will be allowed to employ energy storage for a variety of functions, such as capacity, ancillary services, and peak shaving. Utilities may own some energy storage systems, and will procure at least 50% from independent developers across all segments of the grid. The first solicitation for new energy storage capacity will be required to occur no later than December 1, 2014.

This is the moment the wind and solar industries have been waiting for, and this decision provides a critically needed market signal to realize the many benefits energy storage can bring to California's ratepayers. If successful, this effort will be followed by other states and countries.

California is on track to achieve the state mandate for 33% renewables by 2020, but there is some increasing push back from utilities that will be required by law to procure energy storage. This resistance to energy storage legislation resulted in a mandate for the CPUC to consider setting standards and the proposed decision will pave the way to doing that.

Nevertheless, there are still concerns on part of the utilities about the technical issues and the cost of implementing any such mandate and the resistance to doing that will not decrease much. However, there is a good chance that this proposed decision will be adopted in some form or another and California will have a energy storage mandate in the near future.

Battery Power Storage

California has witnessed a number of rolling blackouts through the years, so the talk of power storage for backup has been, and still is, on the agenda of politicians and utilities. And yet, when some people installed solar electric systems with battery backup, Southern California Edison (SCE) rejected them for grid connection under their net metering program. Soon all homeowners with solar electric systems with battery backup in California could be affected by similar actions.

The grid connection was denied because the batteries used to store energy for emergency backup power when the grid went down were considered "power generators" and not energy storage devices. As such, they did not qualify for the net metering program because the utility could not distinguish between power produced by the solar panels and power produced by the batteries, which it considers a nonrenewable source of power. According to SCE, their policy had not changed; it was the equipment that had changed.

Thus, many Californians now have thousands of dollars of PV systems on their roofs that cannot be used. The utility is also worried that homeowners will charge batteries during off-peak hours and then sell excess power back to the grid during peak hours (buy low/sell high). And, although each battery bank is small, thousands of those used that way could put a dent in SCE's pocketbook.

SCE is also issuing an order for all battery backup systems to undergo a review. Homeowners with battery backup solar electric systems are being asked to pay $800 as part of that review. SCE is claiming that the solar manufacturers are to blame for the debacle, because they have changed the equipment at will.

This review process, however, is the same process used for the large commercial megawatt systems, so it is apparent that SCE and other utilities are jumping on the bandwagon and plan to remove credits from all homeowners with backup systems.

Complaints filed with the California public utility commission on the matter have been rejected. There is no science to support SCE's claims, so it seems that they are operating on the old capitalist principle of protecting their pocketbook, which is been threatened by the new technologies. At the same time, customers who have invested $10,000-20,000 in their roof solar systems cannot use them. How these disputes will be resolved is anyone's guess.

Climate Management

The connection between volcanoes and climate is hardly a new idea. Benjamin Franklin, who wrote the first scientific paper on the topic in "Meteorological Imaginations and Conjectures," published in 1784, suggested that recent volcanic eruptions in Iceland had caused a particularly harsh winter and a cool summer with "constant fog over all Europe, and great part of North America."

In 1815, the gargantuan eruption of Mount Tambora in Indonesia produced "The Year Without a Summer," a worldwide disaster that killed crops, prompted widespread starvation and food riots, and brought snow to New England as late as June of the same year.

No doubt, all large volcanoes have some climate effects, but what is not clear is what exactly these effects are. Volcanoes erupt all the time, all over the world, but the truly big ones are rare. If there were more of them, the global warming discussion would be on a different subject.

Some anthropologists argue that a volcanic explosion at Lake Toba on Sumatra, roughly seventy thousand years ago, blocked the sun so badly that it triggered an ice age that nearly wiped out Homo sapiens of the time. What matters in huge volcano explosions is not just the volume, but where the ejected smoke, dust, and ashes go. The typical volcano sends sulfur dioxide into the troposphere, the atmospheric layer closest to the earth's surface. This is similar to what a coal-burning power plant does with its sulfur emissions. In both cases, the gas stays in the sky only a week or so before falling back to the ground as acid rain, generally within a few hundred miles of its origin.

But a big volcano shoots sulfur dioxide far higher, into the stratosphere; the layer at about seven miles above the earth's surface, or six miles at the poles. Above that threshold altitude, there is a drastic change in a variety of atmospheric phenomena. The sulfur dioxide, rather than quickly returning to the earth's surface absorbs stratospheric water vapor and forms an aerosol cloud that circulates rapidly, blanketing most of the globe. In the stratosphere, sulfur dioxide can linger for a year or more, and will thereby affect the global climate.

According to the scientists, this is what happened in 1991 when Mount Pinatubo erupted in the Philippines. The eruption was so large that it made Mount St. Helens look like a hiccup. The volcano spit more sulfur dioxide into the stratosphere than any volcano since Krafcatoa, more than a century earlier. The atmospheric aftereffects of Pinatubo were undeniable; there was a measurable decrease in ozone, more diffuse sunlight, and a sustained drop in global temperature.

A 900-page report from the National Academy of Sciences (NAS), called "Policy Implications of Greenhouse Warming," includes a chapter on geo-engineering, which the NAS defined as "large-scale engineering of our environment to combat or counteract the effects of changes in atmospheric chemistry.

What this means is that if human activity is warming up the planet, human ingenuity could cool it down. That is not a new revelation, since people have been trying to manipulate the weather since day one. But the efforts have increased in intensity and ingenuity in recent decades.

The 1992 NAS report gave a credibility boost to geo-engineering, which until then had largely been seen as the province of crackpots and rogue governments. Still, some of the NAS proposals would have seemed outlandish even in a Vonnegut novel. A "multiple balloon screen" is one of the proposals intended to deflect sunlight by launching billions of aluminized balloons into the sky. Another scheme, named "space mirror," called for fifty-five thousand reflective "sails" to orbit high above the earth.

The NAS report also raised the possibility of intentionally spreading sulfur dioxide in the stratosphere. The idea was attributed to a Belarus Ian climate scientist named Mikhail Budyko. The Pinatubo explosion proved that stratospheric sulfur dioxide can cool the Earth to a degree. But relying on volcanoes to do the job is impossible, so we could pump tons of SO_2 high up in the stratosphere and by controlling the amount we could control the greenhouse effect. Or can we?

Case Study: Mount Pinatubo

This is a story of one of the unlikeliest positive externalities (and a useful scientific lesson) on record, cloaked in a natural disaster. In 1991, an eroded, wooded mountain on the Philippine island of Luzon began to rumble and spew sulfuric ash. It turned out that beloved old Mount Pinatubo was a dormant volcano. The nearby farmers and townspeople were reluctant to evacuate, but the geologists, seismologists, and volcanologists who rushed in ultimately persuaded most of them to leave.

It was a good thing, too; on June 15, Pinatubo erupted for nine furious hours. The explosions were so massive that the top of the mountain caved in on itself, forming what is known as a caldera, a huge bowl-shaped crater, its new peak 850 feet lower than the original mountaintop. Worse yet, the region was simultaneously being lashed by a typhoon.

According to one account, the sky poured down "heavy rain and ash with pumice lumps the size of golf balls." Around 250 people died, mainly from collapsed roofs, and more died in the following days from mudslides. Still, thanks to the scientists' warnings, the death toll was relatively small.

Mount Pinatubo was the most powerful volcanic eruption in nearly one hundred years. Within two hours of the main blast, sulfuric ash had reached twenty-two miles into the sky. By the time it was done, Pinatubo had discharged more than 20 million tons of sulfur dioxide into the stratosphere. What effect did that have on the environment?

Figure 9-69. 1991 explosion of Mt. Pinatubo

As it turned out, the stratospheric haze of sulfur dioxide acted like a layer of sunscreen, reducing the amount of solar radiation reaching the earth. For the next two years, as the haze was settling out, the Earth cooled off by an average of nearly 1.0°F, or .5°C. A single volcanic eruption practically reversed, albeit temporarily, the cumulative global warming of the previous hundred years.

Pinatubo created some other positive externalities too. Forests around the world grew more vigorously because trees prefer their sunlight a bit diffused. And all that sulfur dioxide in the stratosphere created some of the prettiest sunsets that people had ever seen.

Of course it was the global cooling that got scientists' attention. A paper in *Science* concluded that a Pinatubo-size eruption every few years would "offset much of the anthropogenic warming expected over the next century." Many scientists conceded the point that our environment could be saved by an unexpected event such as a series of huge volcanic eruptions severe enough to block out sunlight that would cool the Earth. But we cannot possibly bet our lives on such poor odds.

Sure enough, only a fool would believe that many volcanoes could be persuaded to spew their protective effluvia into the sky at the right time and place. But what if humans could duplicate these events? And so, here we go again with the theory of pumping large amounts of SO_2 high up in the atmosphere.

We don't have the technology for such an experiment, but even if we did there would be a huge fight among the scientists and politicians on whom, how, and where to do it. In other words, we will leave this project to the future generations to design, build, and execute.

In more detail:

The Sky Tube

The preliminary plans for a sky tube capable of spreading tons of SO_2 in the upper atmosphere are just that—plans—for now. The plan calls for a base station where sulfur would be burned into sulfur dioxide and then liquefied. Such technology exists, because early in the twentieth century sulfur dioxide was the major refrigerant gas, but it is still expensive and energy consuming.

A hose would be stretched from the base station to about 18 miles into the stratosphere. The hose with 2" diameter would be very light and suspended in the air by a number of helium-filled balloons. The balloons range in diameter from 25 feet near the ground to 100 feet near the top. The liquefied sulfur dioxide would be pumped upward by a series of very light pumps, attached to the balloons.

The advantage of using many small pumps rather than one large pump at the base station is that the large pump would create very high pressure, which would require a heavier hose. Also, even if one or more of the small pumps failed, the pumping would continue. Plus, using smaller standard units would keep costs down.

At the end of the hose, there would be a cluster of nozzles, spraying a fine mist of colorless liquid SO_2 in the stratosphere. Two hoses—one in the South and one in the North hemisphere—would spray enough SO_2 to do the job; the stratospheric winds would do the rest. At 100 miles-per- hour, they would carry the spray around the earth. Within 10 days, the estimate goes, the Earth would be wrapped up in Budyko's Blanket.

Stratospheric winds naturally spiral toward the poles, and since the Arctic regions are more vulnerable to global warming, the high-latitude spraying would be most beneficial and fast acting.

Budyko's Blanket seems like a simple plan that could work, but when including other complex elements of our climate, and how much we don't know about it, we need to start small and monitor the results for a long while. That would not be a permanent or irreversible process, so no great damage could be done in worst of cases.

The entire project would cost about $500 million and could be set up in just two years. There is also an annual operating cost of about $10 million. And if cooling the poles alone is not enough, then several additional base stations could be added with two or three hoses at each site. This way the amount of SO_2 pumped up into the stratosphere would be increased or decreased as needed and when needed.

Didn't we just spent billions of dollars to clean coal-fired power plants' smoke from SO_2? Wouldn't it be easier, faster, and cheaper to just junk all the expensive SO_2 separation equipment and let the emitted SO_2 fly into the stratosphere?

Clouds Seeding

Similar to volcanic eruptions, clouds also produce a cooling effect, albeit via different mechanism. Clouds in the sky are responsible for the climate changes, and without them the Earth surface would be a lot hotter than it is now. Man-made clouds—the contrails from a jet plane, for instance—have a significant cooling effect too. This was especially evident after the terrorist attack on September 11, 2001. For several days after the incident all commercial flights in the U.S. were grounded.

The sky was totally empty from flying man-made objects and their exhausts. Data from more than four thousand weather stations across the country show that the sudden absence of jet contrails accounted for a subsequent rise in ground temperature of nearly 2°F.

There are three essential ingredients for the formation of clouds: ascending air, water vapor, and solid particles known as cloud condensation nuclei. When planes fly, particles in the exhaust plume serve as the nuclei. Over landmasses, dust particles do the job. But there are far fewer cloud-friendly nuclei over the world's oceans, so the clouds contain fewer droplets so are less reflective. As a result, more sunlight reaches the earth's surface. The ocean, because it is dark, is particularly good at absorbing the sun's heat.

An increase of just 10% or 12% of the reflectivity of oceanic clouds would cool the Earth enough to counteract even a doubling of current greenhouse gas levels. So one solution is to use the ocean itself to make more clouds. The salt-rich spray from seawater can be used for this purpose, since it creates excellent nuclei for cloud formation. So how do we get the spray into the air several yards above the ocean's surface, covering hundreds of square miles? If we can achieve this, the "seeded" hot water vapor will rise upward to the altitude where clouds form and presto—an abundant source of clouds is created.

Cloud seeding is not a new concept, but most attempts have failed thus far. And yet, there are a variety of ways to make this happen, in addition to the Indian rain dance. The most elegant and promising idea is a fleet of wind-powered fiberglass boats with underwater turbines speeding on the ocean's surface along planned routes.

Their propulsion is especially designed to produce enough thrust and to kick up a steady stream of spray high in the air. By managing the boats number and speed, one could control the volume of spray, thus adjusting the cloud reflectivity. The clouds usually stay over the ocean and will not travel overland, where sunshine is needed for agricultural activities.

It is obvious by now that we will not be able to reduce the global climate warming by reducing CO_2 emissions alone, so other methods are needed, and adding cloud to cool the oceans might be one very efficient approach to solving a global problem. But $50 million is needed for the first prototypes and then many billions dollars for a fleet of vessels large enough to offset the projected warming cycle. Where would the money come from?

The Future...

Gore said it best, "If we don't know enough to stop putting 70 million tons of global-warming pollution into the atmosphere every day, how in God's name can we know enough to precisely counteract that?" Geo-engineering provides many solutions to the global climate problems, but cold-blooded economists do not agree with warmhearted humanists, and so to them, Gore's reasoning doesn't make sense. We know how to stop polluting the atmosphere. We just cannot agree on the methods. And even more importantly, we are not willing to pay the price.

At present, the rewards for limiting consumption are non-existent (or weak at best), and so are the penalties for over-consuming. Gore and other environmentalists are pleading for humankind to consume less and therefore pollute less, and that is a noble invitation. But as incentives go, it's not a very strong one.

At least for now new, more decisive methods for energy generation, use, and environmental protection need to be agreed upon and implemented. Judging from the developments in the recent past, it is not very likely that this will happen soon. Maybe during the next decade or two, things will drift toward the positive side of the equation.

The Conflict

Although we don't know the answers to any of the major questions of our future, we know for sure that we are on the crossroads of economic development vs. environmental objectives. These two concepts are in a serious conflict, but in most cases the economic concerns win over environmental issues.

That is because most environmental regulations thus far have resulted in unacceptable job and economic losses. So the conflicts usually result in a choice between improved environmental quality and a robust economy, which wins most of the time.

It is that simple...on the surface. While protecting the environment clearly involves some costs, including job losses in some sectors, the focus usually is on whether the benefits justify these costs. Environmental regulations, however, could also create jobs in some other sectors. Environmental restrictions on coal plants, for example, lead to expansion of gas, solar, and wind power production. As these industries grow, they lead to net job gains and economic prosperity for the local areas.

There are also suggestions lately that a well-designed response to current environmental and energy challenges can actually be the engine for future economic growth and jobs creation. Companies that make the investments necessary to create a low-environmental-impact society may gain a competitive advantage over those that continue to pursue business as usual and disregard the environment. Although the latter might be more successful in the short term, its long-term future is plagued with problems.

On global level, excessive rates of natural capital degradation can reduce economic productivity, measured in traditional terms as a reduction in GDP, or in broader terms. Thus maintaining natural capital may be a critical factor to ensure future economic growth.

The Green Economy

The ultimate goal at this time, and for the near future, is to create a new *"green economy"* that embodies the concept of sustainable development, as defined by the United Nations environment program (UNEP). According to UNEP, green economy is one that results in improved human health and social equity, while significantly reducing environmental risks and ecological scarcities.

In its simplest expression, a *green economy* can be thought of as one, which is low carbon, resource efficient and socially inclusive. In a green economy, public drives the growth in income and employment and private investments that reduce carbon emissions and pollution, enhance energy and resource efficiency, and prevent the loss of biodiversity and ecosystem services.

Those investments need to be catalyzed and supported by targeted public expenditure, policy reforms and regulation changes. This development path should maintain, enhance and, where necessary, rebuild natural capital as a critical economic asset and source of public benefits, especially for poor people whose livelihoods and security depend largely on nature.

The concept of a *green economy* does not necessarily reject economic growth, but instead seeks to foster growth that is compatible with sustainability. It, however, explicitly rejects the standard jobs vs. the environmental choices.

The most widespread myth in this area is that there is an inescapable trade-off between environmental sustainability and economic progress. While this might have been true in the past, there is now substantial evidence that the "greening" of economies neither inhibits wealth creation nor employment opportunities. As a matter of fact, there are many green sectors that show significant opportunities for investment and related growth in wealth and jobs.

In addition to environmental sustainability, the green economy promotes social equity, so the properly understood and implemented green economy concept rejects the notion that sustainability needs to limit the economic development of any one group of people, including the world's poorest.

And yet, *green economy* is still just a concept. There is no country in this world that is even close green economy. Nor is any country getting close to achieving it. Looking realistically at the developments around the world lately, we doubt that any country will achieve a *green economy* status during this decade, and the next, and the next…

As a matter of fact, we will be lucky to keep the situation from getting worse. The present day environmental movement and our general attitude towards the environment are focused on doing less harm. But even less harm is still a lot of harm if done daily. In a cumulative way it is making things worse with time.

SUMMARY

We live in an exciting time of amazing technological achievements, which contributed to improving lifestyles of the people in developed countries, and promise to do the same for the billions living in the developing world.

Availability of energy is a key to continuing this trend, but the more energy we use, the more polluted our environment gets. It appears that we are faced with a problem: how to get abundant energy and keep the environment clean at the same time.

Presently we are doing a lot to make sure that we have abundant energy, but are doing very little to protect our environment. As a result, there are dangerous signs of serious changes, including global warming. These signs are felt by millions of people in the poorest areas of the world.

Tuvalu, Maldives, Bangladesh, and Indonesia are the first victims of the environmental changes as a result of man-made activities—mostly due to the use of fossil fuels for transport and power generation. The changes in those areas of the world are not imaginary; they are a true-to-life reality.

There have been severe storms in those areas in recent years that have killed or otherwise affected thousands. And worst of all, some of those places are simply disappearing as the ocean level rises.

This is happening today, and other even worse events are predicted for the future. We, the people of this world, need to take a much closer look at the events around us and start thinking of a transition to fossil-less society. We need to act now, because several decades of inactivity might be too late.

We know what needs to be done to achieve our energy independence and clean the environment. We can do it if we want to, but instead we live in a state of stupidity, selfishness, wastefulness, and greed. This state of stupor will continue for a generation or two, when things will suddenly change. Lack of cheap energy and ruined environment will force the future generations to use their **IMAGINATION, INGENUITY, AND PERSEVERANCE** to solve their urgent problems with energy availability and environmental disasters.

We could've, should've, but we did not!

The energy problem in the U.S. is not energy deficiency, but energy use inefficiency. Enough energy is available at all times, and will be available for a long time. The problem now is that energy is inefficiently used, overused, abused, and simply wasted…just because we can. The use and overuse of energy creates more pollution, which in turn creates a lot of problems for the environment, the people, and all living things in it.

We waste energy every second of our waking hours in our homes and work places. We are so used to this parasitic lifestyle, and are so insensitive to the issues at hand, that we are missing the main point: there is impending doom awaiting us and the future generations if we don't change our ways. Depletion of the fossils and total collapse of our environment are not figments of somebody's imagination. Nope, they are facts of life. Facts that cannot be changed unless we change the way we do things.

Some examples of the gross energy wastes and great environmental polluters in the U.S. are:

- Excessive and inefficient packaging and packaging waste control
- Junk mail proliferation and its inefficient disposal
- Excess military energy use; military bases and activities
- Suburb zoning issues related to excess energy use and long- distance driving
- Limited biking and walking facilities in major cities
- Limited public transport and car sharing around the country
- Lack of adequate regulations and incentives for efficient building energy use
- Lack of efficient and enforceable carbon taxes
- Lack of excess energy use tax in addition to a carbon tax
- Lack of energy saving incentives in all sectors of the economy
- Unfair energy and money coupling schemes
- Lack of efficient energy education
- Misinformation about energy availability and use
- Lack of sufficient environmental education
- Misguided and extreme environmentalism
- Inadequate government intervention in energy and environmental projects

Well, we could write another book on the issues in the above list, but for now we will leave the esteemed reader with the thought that power generation, its use, and the environment are interrelated, and intimately engaged in a life and death dance, which at times resembles a battle.

The problem is that there will be no winners in this battle. If it continues uncontrolled, it might bring the world to its knees in a state of energy deficiency and environmental collapse. What can be done? All involved needs lots of things, but a complete understanding and agreement on the issues. This is not going to be quick, or easy, so we just have to do our best to facilitate the work at hand.

The End Days...

Immediately after those times of distress, the sun will be darkened, the moon will not shed her light, the stars will fall from the firmament, and the forces which control the heavens will be disordered and disturbed.

—Matthew 24:29

The Bible goes on describing a drastic change that will be taking place at the end times, when the Earth takes a new shape and a new heavenly order is established. To those who believe in the Bible, there is no doubt that end times are coming some day, just like St. Mark describes it. It is the foundation of the Christian faith, so the only unknowns are when and how. The rest is quite clear. It is a done deal and we are awaiting the arrival of the good news.

For those of us who don't believe in the Bible, however, and for the myriad of scientists trying to formulate the future, and the possible end of life on the Earth as we know it, things are more complicated. These people have to go through tons of materials and dig into thousands of pieces of information in an attempt to foresee the future.

None of them have been successful thus far, and we don't think that it is possible to know what will happen 100 years, 10 years, 1 year, or even one day in the future. This is because there are so many factors that play major roles in our lives on Earth that just one of them that goes astray could play a decisive role in changing or even terminating life here as we know it.

Whichever camp we are in, however, we cannot deny that life on Earth will one day end. Be it slowly from natural events, such as gradual cooling of the Earth's core, or suddenly from a cataclysmic natural disaster, like darkening of the sun, thus freezing people to death in either case, life on Earth will sooner or later come to an end.

The laws of physics and chemistry dictate and describe the unavoidable occurrence of slow changes, winding down and eventual extinction of life on Earth in the distant future. They, however, cannot dictate, or even predict the occurrence of a life-ending disaster, which could be brought upon us at any moment. Just think of a large meteor colliding with our small rock, called Earth. Only small pieces of the rock and lots of dust, floating in space for eternity, will remain as a reminder of our once prosperous humanity.

There is not much we can do about these events, because some of them are too powerful for humans to stop them. What we need to concentrate on, instead, is to do everything possible to not accelerate nor aggravate the natural events with man-made problems.

We, the people in the present generation, are on a critical point of human history, where we can, and should, make a difference by raising our collective awareness and act more responsibly towards the Earth's environment. Failure to do so will surely bring hardship to the future generations, and might even bring the end of the world much sooner.

Do we care? Yes, we do! So let's not forget to turn the lights off, and the thermostat down, when leaving the house. Let's not take unnecessary trips in the gas guzzling cars, planes, and boats, and avoid generating hazardous waste. And basically speaking, let's consider the environment in everything we do, and every step we take, for the sake and well being of the future generations.

Yes, this is much easier to say than to do, but let's start with the first step of the recovery process: awareness. Let us be aware of all that we do, and be fully conscious of the consequences of every step we take—be it turning the lights off, or introducing a major environmental law. Let us be remembered as honorable citizens of Earth, and defenders of Earth's environmental rights.

Notes and References

1. GHG reporting http://media.saic.com/audio/evolution-mandatory-greehouse-gas-reporting
2. Green House Regs http://www.martindale.com/appellate-practice-law/article_Barnes-Thornburg-3. LLP_1545124.htm
3. http://www.oilfracking.com/
4. Counter-claims http://www.fool-me-once.com/
5. *Natural Gas Hydrates: Overview*, Steven Dutch.
6. Most Polluted http://www.worstpolluted.org/
7. REN21, 2013 Report. http://www.ren21.net/Portals/0/REN21_GFR_2013_print.pdf
8. http://www.greentechmedia.com/articles/read/27-Gigawatts-of-Coal-Fired-Capacity-to-Retire-Over-Next-Five-Years-EIA/
9. http://www.fiercesmartgrid.com/story/could-us-utilities-be-next-say-if-only/2012-08-06
10. http://www.greentechmedia.com/articles/read/Will-Regulators-Put-the-San-Onofre-Nuclear-Plant-Back-Online/
11. http://www.hydrogen.energy.gov/pdfs/national_h2_roadmap.pdf
12. http://science.howstuffworks.com/environmental/earth/geophysics/question473.htm
13. http://www.chestertontribune.com/Environment/nasa_strange_and_sudden_massive.htm Haboobs.
14. http://www.beyondcoal.org/dirty-truth
15. http://wiki.answers.com/Q/Does_coal_release_less_toxins_than_natural_gas
16. http://articles.latimes.com/2011/dec/21/local/la-me-gs-epa-issues-mercury-arsenic-rules-20111219
17. http://www.greenamerica.org/programs/climate/dirtyenergy/coal/whydirty.cfm
18. http://www.sourcewatch.org/index.php?title=Coal_waste
19. http://www.ccag.org.au/images/stories/pdfs/coal%20is%20toxic.pdf
20. Electrofuels, DOE. http://arpae.energy.gov/ProgramsProjects/Electrofuels.aspx
21. Li, H., et al. 2012. Integrated electromicrobial conversion of CO_2 to higher alcohols. *Science* 335:1596.
22. Peralta-Yahya, P. P., et al. 2012. Microbial engineering for the production of advanced biofuels. *Nature* 488:320-328.
23. Shapouri, H.G.P.W., W. Nefstead, R. Schwartz, S. Noe, and R. Conway. 2008. Energy balance for the corn-ethanol industry. In *Agricultural Economic Report 2010*, U.S. Department of Agriculture, Washington, D.C. 64 Microbe—Volume 8, Number 2, 2013.
24. *Photovoltaics for Commercial and Utilities Power Generation*, Anco S, Blazev. The Fairmont Press, 2011.
25. *Solar Technologies for the 21st Century*, Anco S Blazev. The Fairmont Press, 2013.

Appendices

Abbreviations

A

a Acceleration

ABE acetone-butanol-ethanol (process used in the production of butanol)

ACCS Assured Combinable Crop Scheme

AD anaerobic digestion

AEZ agro-ecological zoning

Ag Silver

ALCC Life Cycle Cost Annualized

AO Arctic Oscillation

AAO Antarctic Oscillation

ACC Arizona Corporations Commission

ADB Asian Development Bank

AFRETEP African Renewable Energy Technology Platform

AOGCM Atmosphere-Ocean General Circulation Model

ARAR Applicable or Relevant and Appropriate Requirements

AR4 Fourth Assessment Report (of the IPCC)

Ar Argon

As Arsenic

Au Gold

AU$ Australian dollars

B

B Boron

Be Beryllium

BIG Biomass integrated gasifier

BLM Bureau of Land Management (USA)

Bio-SG bio synthetic gas (also referred to as bio synthetic natural gas)

BOE Barrels of oil equivalent

Br Bromine

BTL biomass-to-liquids

Btu British thermal units

C

c Speed of light (300 million meters per second)

C carbon

Celsius (degrees)

Ca Calcium

CAFE Corporate average fuel economy

CARB California Air Resources Board

CCl_4 Carbon tetrachloride

CCS Carbon capture and storage

CCSM Community climate system model

Cd Cadmium

CdTe Cadmium telluride

CDD Consecutive dry days

CDM Clean development mechanism

CDP Carbon Disclosure Project

CEC California Energy Commission

CER Certified emission reduction

CFC Chlorofluorocarbons

CFE National electric utility, Mexico

CFL Compact fluorescent light

CEQA California Environmental Quality Act.

CERCLA Comprehensive Environmental Response, Compensation and Liability Act of 1980

CH_2Cl_2 Methylene chloride

CH_3Br Methyl bromide

CH_4 Methane

CMIP3 Coupled Model Inter-comparison Project 3

CNG Compressed natural gas

Co Cobalt

CO_2 Carbon dioxide

CO_2e Carbon dioxide equivalent

COP Conference of Parties

CPUC California Public Utilities Commission

CPV Concentrating photovoltaics (solar PV)

Cr Chromium

CRA Climate risk assessment

CRM Climate risk management

Cs Cesium

CSIRO Commonwealth Scientific and Industrial Research Organization

CSP Concentrating solar power (thermal solar)

Cu Copper

D

DBCP Dibromochloropropane

DCB Dichlorobenzene

DDGS dried distiller's grains with solubles

DDT An environmentally-persistent insecticide

banned for most uses by the U.S. EPA in 1972.

DESERTEC DESERTEC Foundation "Clean Power from Deserts"

DHHS Department of Health and Human Services (USA)

DHS Department of Homeland Security (USA)

DI Deionized water

DJF December, January, February

DME dimethylether

DOI Department of Interior (USA)

DOC Department of Commerce (USA)

DOE Department of Energy (USA)

DOT Department of Transportation (USA)

DOJ Department of Justice (USA)

DRE Destruction and removal efficiency

DTSC Department of Toxic Substances Control

E

E Energy

EACC Economics of adaptation to climate change

ECMWF European Centre for Medium-Range Weather Forecasts

EDF Électricitè De France

EIA Environmental impacts assessment

EJ exajoule

ENSO El Niño-Southern Oscillation

EPA Environmental Protection Agency (USA)

EPCRA Emergency Planning and Community Right-to-Know Act

ERA-40 ECMWF 45-year analysis of the global atmosphere and surface conditions 1957-2002

ESMAP Energy Sector Management Assistance Program

ESCO Energy service company

ETP Energy Technology Perspectives

EUMETNET European National Meteorological services

EV Electric vehicle

F

F Fluorine

°F Fahrenheit(degrees)

FAME fatty acid methyl ester

FAO Food and Agricultural Organization

FDA Food and Drugs Administration

Fe Iron

FFV Flex-fuel vehicle (multi-fuel use)

FT Fischer-Tropsch

G

Ga Gallium (semiconductor)

GaAs Gallium Arsenide (semiconductor)

GAC Granular activated carbon

GBEP Global Bioenergy Partnership

GCM General Circulation Model

GCOS Global climate observing system

GDP Gross domestic product

Ge Germanium

GEF Global Environment Facility

GET-CCA Global Expert Team on Climate Change Adaptation (of the World Bank)

GFCS Global Framework for Climate Services

GHG Green house gas (effect)

GNP Gross national product

GPI Genesis Potential index

GT gigatonne

$GTCO_2eq$ Giga tons of carbon dioxide equivalent

GTS Global Telecommunication System

GW Gigawatt

GWP Global warming potential

H

H Enthalpy as in pH, measure of strength of acidic or basic aqueous solution.

H_2 Hydrogen

H_2O Water

H_2SO_4 Sulfuric acid

HCL Hydrochloric acid

HDD Heating degree days

HDI Human development index

HEAT Hands-on Energy Adaptation Toolkit

HF Hydrofluoric acid

HFC Hydrofluorocarbons

Hg Mercury

HHV Gross calorific value

HP Horse power

hr Hour

HVO hydrotreated vegetable oil

I

I current (in Amps)

I Iodine

IAEA International Atomic Energy Agency

IATA International Air Transport Association

IBEP International Bio-energy Platform

ICAO International Civil Aviation Organization

ICBM Intercontinental Ballistic Missile

ICPD International Conference on Population and Development.

IEA International Energy Agency

IEO International Energy Outlook

IFAD International Fund for Agricultural Development

IFC International Finance Corporation
IFES Integrated Food and Energy Systems
IFRC International Federation of Red Cross
IGCC Integrated combined cycle plant
IGO international government organisations
IIASA International Institute for Applied Systems Analysis
ILUC indirect land-use change
IPCC Intergovernmental Panel on Climate Change
IPPF International Planned Parenthood Federation
IRENA International Renewable Energy Association
IRR Internal rate of return
ISCC International Sustainability and Carbon Certification System

J

J Joule
JJA June, July, August

K

K Potassium
kcal Kilocalories
km Kilometer
km² Square kilometers
kW Kilowatt

L

LCA life-cycle assessment
LCC Life cycle cost
LDCF Least Developed Countries Fund
LDE liter of diesel equivalent (energy content 36.1 MJ/litre)
LGE liter gasoline equivalent (energy content 33.5 MJ/litre)
LHPP Large hydropower
LHV Lower heating value, or net calorific value
LPG Liquefied natural gas (Propane)
lt Long ton
LUC land-use change
LULUCF land use, land use change and forestry

M

m Mass
m Meter
mm/yr Millimeter per year
m/s Meters per second
m³/year Cubic meters per year
mi² Miles square

MCL Maximum contaminant level
MEA Multilateral Environmental Agreement
MEK Methyl ethyl ketone
Mg Magnesium
mg/g Microgram per gram
mg/kg Microgram per kilogram
mg/l Microgram per liter
MHA million hectares
min. Minute
MJ megajoule
MMA March, April, May
Mo Molybdenum
MRI Meteorological Research Institute, Japan
MW Megawatt
mt metric ton
MTOE million tons of oil equivalent
mW milliwatt
MW Megawatt

N

Na Sodium
NAO North Atlantic Oscillation
NAM Northern Annular Mode
NAPA National adaptation plan of action
NATO North Atlantic Treaty Organization
NCEP/NCAR 40-year reanalysis project, NOAA
NCS National Climate Service
NGO Nongovernmental organization
NGV natural gas vehicle
NMHS National Meteorological and Hydrological Services
NNI Net national income
NNP Net national product
NO_x Nitrogen oxides
NOOA National Oceanic and Atmospheric Administration
NPDES National Pollutant Discharge Elimination System
NPL National Priorities List
NPP Net Primary Production
NSW New South Wales
nW nanowatt

O

O_2 Oxygen
O_3 Ozone
O&M Operation and maintenance
OECD Organization for Economic Co-operation and Development
OPEC Organization of Petroleum Exporting Countries

P

P   Phosphorous
   Power (as in Watts)
   Pressure (as in lbs/in^2)
PAH   (or PNA) Polynuclear Aromatic Hydrocarbons,
Pb   Lead
PCB   Polychlorinated biphenyls
PCE   Perchloroethylene
PCP   Pentachlorophenol
PM10   Particulate matter less than 10 microns in diameter.
PNA   Pacific North American Pattern
PRECIS   Regional climate modeling system, UK Met Office
POP   Persistent organic pollutants
ppb   Parts per billion
ppm   Parts per million
PPP   Purchasing power parity
Proalcool   Brazilian ethanol fuel program
PRP   Potentially Responsible Party
Pu   Plutonium
PV   Photovoltaic
PVC   Polyvinyl chloride
pW   Picowatt
PW   Petawatt
Q   Heat (BTU, calories)

R

R   Resistance (in Ohms)
R&D   Research and development
RAP   Remedial Action Plan
RCM   Regional climate model
RCOF   Regional Climate Outlook Forum
RCRA   Resource Conservation and Recovery Act
RD&D   research, development and demonstration
RDD&D   research, development, demonstration and deployment
RED   Renewable Energy Directive
RFF-PI   Resources for the Future—Policy Instruments
RI/FS   Remedial Investigation/Feasibility Study
ROI   Return on investment
RPS   Renewable portfolio standards
RRSO   Roundtable on Responsible Soy Oil
RSA   Insurance Group, Munich
RSB   Roundtable for Sustainable Biofuel
RSPO   Roundtable on Sustainable Palm Oil
RX5D   Yearly maximum precipitation in five consecutive days
RWQCB   Regional Water Quality Control Board

S

S   Sulphur
SAL   State action level
SAM   Southern Annular Mode
SARA   Superfund Amendments and Reauthorization Act of 1986.
SARA Title III—Emergency Planning and Community Right-to-Know Act of 1986
SBS   Sick building syndrome
SCCF   Special Climate Change Fund
sec.   Second
SERP   Super Efficient Refrigerator Program
SHPP   Small hydropower
Si   Silicon
SiO$_2$ Silicon dioxide (sand)
SIP   State Implementation Plan
SLBM   Submarine Launched Ballistic Missile
SNARL   Suggested No Adverse Response Level
SO$_2$ Sulfur dioxide
SON   September, October, November
SREC   Solar renewable energy credits
SRES   Special report on emissions scenarios, IPCC
st   Short ton
STLC   Soluble Threshold Limit Concentration
SWMU   Solid waste management unit

T

t   Time
T   Temperature
TAR   Third Assessment Report (of the IPCC)
TCE   Tetrachloroethylene
   Tons of coal equivalent
TCLP   Toxicity Characteristic Leaching Procedure.
TCP   Tetrachlorophenol
TFR   Total fertility rate
TLV   Threshold Limit Value
TNT   Equivalent A measure of energy released during nuclear explosion
TOC   Total organic content
toe   Tons of oil equivalent
TSCA   Toxic Substances Control Act
TTLC   Total Threshold Limit Concentration
TW   Terawatt

U

U   Internal energy (molecular level)
U   Uranium
UFRJ   Federal University of Rio de Janeiro
UK   United Kingdom
UKCIP   United Kingdom Climate Impacts Programme

UN   United Nations
UNCCO UN Convention on Combating Desertification
UNDP United Nations Development Programme
UNEP United Nations Environment Programme
UNESCO United Nations Educational, Scientific and Cultural Organization
UNFCCC UN Framework Convention on Climate Change
UNIDO United Nations Industrial Development Organization
US   United States
USA   United States of America
US$ United States Dollar
UNWTO World Tourism Organization

V

V   Potential (in Volts)
VOC Volatile organic compounds

W

W   Watt
W   Work
WBG   World Bank Group
WCC-3 World Climate Conference—3
WCRP World Climate Research Programme
WCSS World Climate Services Systems
WFP   World Food Program
WHO   World Health Organization
Wm-2 Watts per square meter
WMO   World Meteorological Organization
WRMA Weather Risk Management Association
WRMF Weather Risk Management Facility
WU   Wage units

Glossary of Terms

A

Acceptable intake (as related to sub-chronic and chronic exposure). Numbers which describe how toxic a chemical is. The numbers are derived from animal studies of the relationship between dose and non-cancer effects. There are two types of acceptable exposure values: one for acute (relatively short-term) and one for chronic (longer-term) exposure.

Accumulation: the build up of a particular pollutant over time

Acetone. A widely used, highly volatile solvent. It is readily absorbed by breathing, ingestion or contact with the skin. Workers who have inhaled acetone have reported respiratory problems.

Acids. A class of compounds that can be corrosive when concentrated. Weak acids, such as vinegar and citric acid, are common in foods. Strong acids, such as muriatic (or hydrochloric), sulfuric and nitric acid have many industrial uses, and can be dangerous to those not familiar to handling them. Acids are chemical "opposites" to bases, in that they can neutralize each other.

Acid Rain: term applied to acid precipitation formed when emissions of sulfur dioxide (SO_2) and oxides of nitrogen (NO_x) react in the atmosphere with water and other compounds

Acid Rain Program: created under the Clean Air Act to reduce acid rain; employs a cap and trade framework to achieve SO_2 reductions. Specifically means the limited authorization to emit one ton of SO_2 during a given year.

Act. In the legislative sense, a bill or measure passed by both houses of Congress; a law.

Action level. A guideline established by environmental protection agencies to identify the concentration of a substance in a particular medium (water, soil, etc.) that may present a health risk when exceeded. If contaminants are found at concentrations above their action levels, measures must be taken to decrease the contamination.

Activated sludge. A term used to describe sludge that contains microorganisms that break down organic contaminants (e.g., benzene) in liquid waste streams to simpler substances such as water and carbon dioxide. It is also the product formed when raw sewage is mixed with bacteria-laden sludge, then stirred and aerated to destroy organic matter.

Activity (of a radioactive isotope). The number of particles or photons ejected from a radioactive substance per unit time.

Active solar. Using solar energy with the assistance of external power.

Acute hazards. Hazards associated with short-term exposure to relatively large amounts of toxic substances.

Acute Loading: a term that applies to the short-term build up of a pollutant and which suggests that, in the short-term, significant amounts of a pollutant can accumulate

Adjournment. The end of a legislative day or session.

Adverse health effects. Effects of chemicals or other materials that impair one's health. They can range from relatively mild temporary conditions such as minor eye or throat irritation, shortness of breath or headaches to permanent and serious conditions such as cancer, birth defects or damage to organs.

Advisory level. The level above which an environmental protection agency suggests it is potentially harmful to be exposed to a contaminant, although no action is mandated.

Aeration. Passing air through a solid or liquid, especially a process that promotes breakdown or movement of contaminants in soil or water by exposing them to air.

Aerosol. A suspension of small liquid or solid particles in gas.

Air pollution. Toxic or radioactive gases or particulate matter introduced into the atmosphere, usually as a result of human activity.

Air stripping tower. Air stripping removes volatile organic chemicals (such as solvents) from contaminated water by causing them to evaporate. Polluted water is sprayed downward through a tower filled with packing materials while air is blown upwards through the tower. The contaminants evaporate into the air, leaving significantly-reduced pollutant levels in the water. The air is treated before it is released into the atmosphere.

Alkaline (synonym basic, caustic). Having the properties of a base, a pH greater than 7. Usually used as an adjective, i.e. "alkaline soil."

Allowance: the term generally used to refer to the emission reduction unit traded in emissions trading programs; in the Allowance Loan: transaction wherein an owner of allowances, the lender, allows another party, the borrower, to use the allowances. The borrower customarily promises to return the allowances after a specified period of time with payment for their use, called interest. The allowances returned are not necessarily the exact ones loaned, but are allowances of similar vintage years

Allowance Loan Rate: payment for the lending of allow-

ances over a specified period of time, calculated including the cost-of-carry charge

Allowance Tracking System (ATS): a computerized system administered by EPA and used to track the allowances and allowance transactions by all market participants

Allowance Transfer Form (ATF): official form used to report allowance transfers to the ATS. The ATF lists the serial numbers of the allowances to be transferred and includes the account information of both the transferor and the transferee

Alluvial deposit. An area of sand, clay or other similar material that has been gradually deposited by moving water, such as along a river bed or shore of a lake.

Alpha particle. A positively-charged particle emitted by radioactive atoms. Alpha particles travel less than one inch in the air and a thin sheet of paper will stop them. The main danger from alpha particles lies in ingesting the atoms which emit them. Body cells next to the atom can then be irradiated over an extended period of time, which may be prolonged if the atoms are taken up in bone, for instance.

Alternative energy. Energy that is not popularly used and is usually environmentally sound, such as solar or wind energy (as opposed to fossil fuels).

Alternative fibers. Fibers produced from non-wood sources for use in paper making.

Alternative fuels. Transportation fuels other than gasoline or diesel. Includes natural gas, methanol, and electricity.

Alternative transportation modes. Travel other than private cars, such as walking, bicycling, rollerblading, carpooling and transit.

Ambient air. Refers to the surrounding air. Generally, ambient air refers to air outside and surrounding an air pollution source location. Often used interchangeably with "outdoor air."

Amendment. A change or addition to an existing law or rule.

Ancient forest. A forest that is typically older than 200 years with large trees, dense canopies and an abundance of diverse wildlife.

Applicable or Relevant and Appropriate Requirements (ARARs). Federal or state laws, regulations, standards, criteria or requirements which would apply to the cleanup of hazardous substances at a particular site.

Apportionment. The process through which legislative seats are allocated to different regions.

Appropriation. The setting aside of funds for a designated purpose (e.g., there is an appropriation of $7 billion to build 5 new submarines).

Aquaculture. The controlled rearing of fish or shellfish by people or corporations who own the harvestable product, often involving the capture of the eggs or young of a species from wild sources, followed by rearing more intensively than possible in nature.

Aqueous. Water-based.

Aquifer. A water-bearing layer of rock or sediment that is capable of yielding useable amounts of water. Drinking water and irrigation wells draw water from the underlying aquifer.

Arms control. Coordinated action based on agreements to limit, regulate, or reduce weapon systems by the parties involved.

Arsenic. A gray, brittle and highly poisonous metal. It is used as an alloy for metals, especially lead and copper, and is used in insecticides and weed killers. In its inorganic form, it is listed as a cancer-causing chemical under Proposition 65.

Artesian well. A well that flows up like a fountain because of the internal pressure of the aquifer.

Asbestos. A general name given a family of naturally occurring fibrous silicate minerals. Asbestos fibers were used mainly for insulation and as a fire retardant material in ship and building construction and other industries, and in brake shoes and pads for automobiles. Inhaling asbestos fibers has been shown to result in lung disease (asbestosis) and in lung cancer (mesothelioma). The risk of developing mesothelioma is significantly enhanced in smokers.

Ash. Incombustible residue left over after incineration or other thermal processes.

Ask: the price a prospective seller is willing to accept (a.k.a. "offer")

Asthma. A condition marked by labored breathing, constriction of the chest, coughing and gasping usually brought on by allergies.

Atmosphere. The 500 km thick layer of air surrounding the earth which supports the existence of all flora and fauna.

Atomic energy. Energy released in nuclear reactions. When a neutron splits an atom's nucleus into smaller pieces it is called fission. When two nuclei are joined together under millions of degrees of heat it is called fusion.

Average Weighted Price: calculation used to determine price taking into account the quantity of allowances sold.

B

Backfill. The word is used in two contexts; a.) to refill an excavated area with uncontaminated soils; and b.) the material used to refill an excavated area.

Background concentration. Represents the average amount of toxic chemicals in the air, water or soil to which people are routinely exposed. More than half of the background concentration of toxic air in metropolitan areas comes from automobiles, trucks and other vehicles. The rest comes from industry and business, agricultural, and from the use of paints, solvents and chemicals in the home.

Bases. A class of compounds that are "opposite" to acids, in that they neutralize acids. Weak bases are used in cooking (baking soda) and cleaners. Strong bases can be corrosive, or "caustic." Examples of strong bases that are common around the house are drain cleaners, oven cleaners and other heavy duty cleaning products. Strong bases can be very dangerous to tissue, especially the eyes and mouth.

Beach closure. The closing of a beach to swimming, usually because of pollution.

Bear Market: prolonged period of falling allowance prices.

Benzene. A petroleum derivative widely used in the chemical industry. A few uses are: synthesis of rubber, nylon, polystyrene, and pesticides; and production of gasoline. Benzene is a highly volatile chemical readily absorbed by breathing, ingestion or contact with the skin. Short-term exposures to high concentrations of benzene may result in death following depression of the central nervous system or fatal disturbances of heart rhythm. Long-term, low-level exposures to benzene can result in blood disorders such as aplastic anemia and leukemia. Benzene is listed as a cancer-causing chemical under Proposition 65.

Berm. A curb, ledge, wall or mound used to prevent the spread of contaminants. It can be made of various materials, even earth in certain circumstances.

Beta particles. Very high-energy particle identical to an electron, emitted by some radioactive elements. Depending on their energy, they penetrate a few centimeters of tissue.

Bid: price a prospective buyer is willing to pay

Bill. A proposed law, to be debated and voted on.

Billfish. Pelagic fish with long, spear-like protrusions at their snouts, such as swordfish and marlin.

Biodegradable. Waste material composed primarily of naturally-occurring constituent parts, able to be broken down and absorbed into the ecosystem.

Wood, for example, is biodegradable, for example, while plastics are not.

Bioaccumulation. The process by which the concentrations of some toxic chemicals gradually increase in living tissue, such as in plants, fish, or people as they breathe contaminated air, drink contaminated water, or eat contaminated food.

Biodiversity. A large number and wide range of species of animals, plants, fungi, and microorganisms. Ecologically, wide biodiversity is conducive to the development of all species.

Biomass. Two meanings: a.) the amount of living matter in an area, including plants, large animals and insects; and b.) plant materials and animal waste used as fuel.

Bioremediation. A process that uses microorganisms to change toxic compounds into non-toxic ones.

Biosolids. Residue generated by the treatment of sewage, petroleum refining waste and industrial chemical manufacturing wastewater with activated sludge.

Biosphere. Two meanings; a.) the part of the earth and its atmosphere in which living organisms exist or that is capable of supporting life; and, b.) the living organisms and their environment composing the biosphere.

Biosphere Reserve. A part of an international network of preserved areas designated by the United Nations Educational, Scientific and Cultural Organization (UNESCO). Biosphere Reserves are vital centers of biodiversity where research and monitoring activities are conducted, with the participation of local communities, to protect and preserve healthy natural systems threatened by development. The global system currently includes 324 reserves in 83 countries.

Biota. The animal and plant life of a particular region.

Biotic. Of or relating to life.

Birth control. Preventing birth or reducing frequency of birth, primarily by preventing conception.

Biotransformation. Transformation of one chemical to others by populations of microorganisms in the soil.

Birth defects. Unhealthy defects found in newborns, often caused by the mother's exposure to environmental hazards or the intake of drugs or alcohol during pregnancy.

Birth rate. The number of babies born annually per 1,000 women of reproductive age in any given set of people.

Bloc. A group of people with the same interest or goal (usually used to describe a voting bloc, a group of representatives intending to vote the same way).

Blood lead levels. The amount of lead in the blood. Human exposure to lead in blood can cause brain damage, especially in children.

Boring. Usually, a vertical hole drilled into the ground from which soil samples can be collected and analyzed to determine the presence of chemicals and the physical characteristics of the soil.

Borrow pit. An area where soil, sand or gravel has been dug up for use elsewhere.

Bottled water. Purchased water sold in bottles.

Broker: person who acts as an intermediary between a buyer and a seller, usually charging a commission

Brownfields. Abandoned, idled, or under-used industrial and commercial facilities where expansion or redevelopment is complicated by real or perceived environmental contamination.

Bubble: a regulatory term which applies to the situation when a company combines a number of its sources in order to control pollution in aggregate; under a bubble facility operators are allowed to choose which sources to control as long as the total amount of emissions from the combined sources is less than the amount each source would have emitted under the conventional requirement

Budget. A formal projection of spending and income for an upcoming period of time, traditionally submitted by the President or Executive for consideration and approval.

Budget reconciliation. Legislation making changes to existing law (such as entitlements under Social Security or Medicare) so that it conforms to numbers in the budget resolution.

Budget resolution. The first step in the annual budget process. This resolution must be agreed to by the House and Senate. It is not signed by the President and does not have the effect of law, but instead sets out the targets and assumptions that will guide Congress as it passes the annual appropriations and other budget bills.

Bull Market: prolonged rise in the price of allowances. Bull markets usually last at least a few months and are characterized by high trading volume

Bycatch. Fish and/or other marine life that are incidentally caught with the targeted species. Most of the time bycatch is discarded at sea.

Bycatch reduction device (bdr). A device used to cut bycatch while fishing. These gear modifications are most commonly used with shrimp trawls. They are also called "finfish excluder devices" (feds) or, when specifically designed to exclude sea turtles, they are called "turtle excluder devices" (teds).

C

Cadmium. Cadmium is a natural element in the earth's crust, usually found as a mineral combined with other elements such as oxygen. Because all soils and rocks have some cadmium in them, it is extracted during the production of other metals like zinc, lead and copper. Cadmium does not corrode easily and has many uses. In industry and consumer products, it is used for batteries, pigments, metal coatings, and plastics. It is used also to make solar cells and panels. Cadmium salts are toxic in higher concentrations.

Cairo Plan. Recommendations for stabilizing world population agreed upon at the U.N. International Conference on Population and Development, held in Cairo in September 1994. The plan calls for improved health care and family planning services for women, children and families throughout the world, and also emphasizes the importance of education for girls as a factor in the shift to smaller families.

Calendar. In the legislative sense, a group of bills or proposals to be discussed or considered in a legislative committee or on the floor of the House or Senate.

California Environmental Quality Act (CEQA). First enacted in 1970 to provide long-term environmental protection, the law requires that governmental decision-makers and public agencies study the significant environmental effects of proposed activities, and that significant avoidable damage be avoided or reduced where feasible. CEQA also requires that the public be told why the lead public agency approved the project as it did, and gives the public a way to challenge the decisions of the agency.

Call Option: a contract that grants the right to buy, at a specified price, a specific number of allowances by a certain date

Cancer. Unregulated growth of changed cells; a group of changed, growing cells (tumor).

Cancer risk. A number, generally expressed in exponential form (i.e., 1×10^{-6}, which means one in one million), which describes the increased possibility of an individual developing cancer from exposure to toxic materials. Calculations producing cancer risk numbers are complex and typically include a number of assumptions that tend to cause the final estimated risk number to be conservative.

Cap. A layer, such as clay or a synthetic material, used to prevent rainwater from penetrating the soil and spreading contamination.

Carbamates. A group of insecticides related to carbamic acid. They are primarily used on corn, alfalfa, tobacco, cotton, soybeans, fruits and ornamental plants.

Carbon adsorption. A treatment system in which organic contaminants are removed from groundwater and surface water by forcing it through tanks containing activated carbon, a specially-treated material that retains such compounds. Activated carbon is also used to purify contaminated air by adsorbing the contaminants as the air passes through it.

Carbon monoxide (CO). A very poisonous, colorless and odorless gas formed when carbon-containing matter burns incompletely, as in automobile engines or in charcoal grills used indoors without proper ventilation.

Carbon dioxide (CO_2). A naturally occurring greenhouse gas in the atmosphere, concentrations of which have increased (from 280 parts per million in preindustrial times to over 350 parts per million today) as a result of humans' burning of coal, oil, natural gas and organic matter (e.g., wood and crop wastes).

Carbon tax. A charge on fossil fuels (coal, oil, natural gas) based on their carbon content. When burned, the carbon in these fuels becomes carbon dioxide in the atmosphere, the chief greenhouse gas.

Carbon tetrachloride (CCl_4). A colorless, nonflammable toxic liquid that was widely used as a solvent in dry-cleaning and in fire extinguishers. It is listed as a cancer-causing chemical under Proposition 65.

Carcinogens. Substances that cause cancer, such as tar.

Carpooling. Sharing a car to a destination to reduce fuel use, pollution and travel costs.

Catalyst. A substance that accelerates chemical change yet is not permanently affected by the reaction (e.g., platinum in an automobile catalytic converter helps change carbon monoxide to carbon dioxide).

Catalytic Cracker Unit. In a petroleum refinery, the catalytic cracker unit breaks long petroleum molecules apart, or "cracks" them, during the petroleum refining process. These smaller pieces then come together to form more desirable molecules for gasoline or other products.

Caucus. A meeting of a political party, usually to appoint representatives to party positions.

Caustic. The common name for sodium hydroxide, a strong base. Also used as an adjective to describe highly corrosive bases.

Caustic scrubber. An air pollution control device in

which acid gases are neutralized by contact with an alkaline solution.

Chlorinated herbicides. A group of plant-killing chemicals which contain chlorine, used mainly for weed control and defoliation.

Chlorination byproducts. Cancer-causing chemicals created when chlorine used for water disinfection combines with dirt and organic matter in water.

Chlorine. A highly reactive halogen element, used most often in the form of a pungent gas to disinfect drinking water.

Chlorofluorocarbons (CFCs). Stable, artificially-created chemical compounds containing carbon,

Chlorine, fluorine and sometimes hydrogen. Chloro-fluorocarbons, used primarily to facilitate

cooling in refrigerators and air conditioners, have been found to damage the stratospheric ozone layer which protects the earth and its inhabitants from excessive ultraviolet radiation.

Chlorobenzene. A volatile organic compound that is often used as a solvent and in the production of other chemicals. It is a colorless liquid with an almond-like odor. It is toxic.

Chloroform. Chloroform was once commonly used as a general anesthetic and as a flavoring agent in toothpastes, mouth wastes and cough syrups. It is listed as a cancer-causing chemical under Proposition 65.

Chromated copper arsenate. An insecticide and herbicide containing three metals: copper, chromium and arsenic. This salt is used extensively as a wood preservative in pressure-treating operations. It is highly toxic and dissolves in water, making it a relatively mobile contaminant in the environment.

Chromium. A hard, brittle, grayish heavy metal used in tanning, in paint formulation, and in plating metal for corrosion protection. It is toxic at certain levels and, in its hexavalent (versus trivalent) form, chromium is listed as a cancer-causing agent under Proposition 65.

Chronic exposure. Repeated contact with a chemical over a period of time, often involving small amounts of toxic substance.

Class I landfill. A landfill permitted to accept hazardous wastes.

Clayoquot Sound. One of the last remaining unlogged watersheds on the west coast of Canada's Vancouver Island.

Clean Air Act Amendments of 1990: reauthorization of the Clean Air Act; passed by the U.S. Congress; strengthened ability of EPA to set and enforce pollution control programs aimed at protecting human health and the environment; included provisions for Acid Rain Program

Clean Air Act. A federal law passed in 1955 and extensively modified in 1970. It is enforced by the California Air Resources Board and the local air quality management or air pollution control districts, as well as by U.S. EPA nationally.

Clean fuel. Fuels which have lower emissions than conventional gasoline and diesel. Refers to alternative fuels as well as to reformulated gasoline and diesel.

Cleanup. Treatment, remediation, or destruction of contaminated material.

Clear cutting. A logging technique in which all trees are removed from an area, typically 20 acres or larger, with little regard for long-term forest health.

Clean Water Act. A federal law of 1977 enforced by U.S. EPA. A key provision is that "any person responsible for the discharge of a pollutant or pollutants into any waters of the United States from any point source must apply for and obtain a permit." This is reflected by the National Pollutant Discharge Elimination System (NPDES), through which the permits are issued by Regional Water Quality Control Boards. Permits are now being required for storm water runoff from cities and other locations.

Cleanup process. A comprehensive program for the clean-up (remediation) of a contaminated site. It involves investigation, analysis, development of a cleanup plan and implementation of that plan.

Clearing Price: price at which a buyer and seller agree to transact a trade

Climate change. A regional change in temperature and weather patterns. Current science indicates a discernible link between climate change over the last century and human activity, specifically the burning of fossil fuels.

Cloture. The formal end to a debate or filibuster in the Senate requiring a three-fifths vote.

Coastal pelagic. Fish that live in the open ocean at or near the water's surface but remain relatively close to the coast. Mackerel, anchovies, and sardines are examples of coastal pelagic fish. commercial extinction—the depletion of a population to the point where fisherman cannot catch enough to be economically worthwhile.

Collar/Zero-cost Collar: set of contracts used to hedge against the risk of prices moving in both directions; involves purchasing a call option and selling a put option. Option premiums in a collar that cancel each other out are "zero-cost" collars

Communities of color. Hispanic, black or Asian people or groups living together or connected in some way.

Community right-to-know. Public accessibility to information about toxic pollution.

Compact fluorescent light (CFL). Fluorescent light bulbs small enough to fit into standard light sockets, which are much more energy-efficient than standard incandescent bulbs.

Compost. Process whereby organic wastes, including food wastes, paper, and yard wastes, decompose naturally, resulting in a product rich in minerals and ideal for gardening and farming as a soil conditioners, mulch, resurfacing material, or landfill cover.

Combustion gases. Gases produced by burning. The composition will depend on, among other things, the fuel; the temperature of burning; and whether air, oxygen or another oxidizer is used. In simple cases the combustion gases are carbon dioxide and water. In some other cases, nitrogen and sulfur oxides may be produced as well. Incinerators must be controlled carefully to be sure that they do not emit more than the allowable amounts of more complex, hazardous compounds. This often requires use of emission-control devices.

Combustible vapor mixture. The composition range over which air containing vapor of an organic compound will burn or even explode when set off by a flame or spark. Outside that range the reaction does not occur, but the mixture may nevertheless be hazardous because it does not contain enough oxygen to support life, or because the vapor is toxic.

Comprehensive Environmental Response, Compensation and Liability Act of 1980 (CERCLA). Also known as Superfund, authorizes EPA to respond directly to releases of hazardous substances that may endanger public health or the environment.

Congressional Record. A document published by the government printing office recording all debates, votes and discussions taking place in the Congress; available for free inspection at all government document repositories, as well as in some major libraries.

Consent decree. A legal document, approved and issued by a judge, formalizing an agreement between DTSC and the parties potentially responsible for site contamination.

Confirmation Sheet: formal memorandum from a broker to a client giving details of an allowance transaction

Containment. Enclosing or containing hazardous substances in a structure to prevent the migration of contaminants into the environment.

Contamination. Pollution.

Contraceptive. Preventing conception and pregnancy.

Copper. Distinctively-colored metal used for electric wiring, plumbing, heating and roof and building construction, and in automobile brake linings. It is known to be toxic at certain levels.

Corrosivity. A characteristic of acidic and basic hazardous wastes.

The characteristic is defined by a waste's pH and its ability to corrode steel. A waste is corrosive if it has a pH less than or equal to 2.0 or greater than or equal to 12.5.

Cost-of-carry: out-of-pocket costs incurred while an allowance holder retains allowances for future transfer

Counterparty: the party opposite the buyer or seller in a transaction

Credit Risk: the financial risk that an obligation will not be paid and a loss will result

Creek. A watercourse smaller than, and often tributary to, a river.

Creosotes. Chemicals used in wood preserving operations that are produced by distilling coal-tar. They contain polycyclic aromatic hydrocarbons and polynuclear aromatic hydrocarbons (PAHs and PNAs) and so high-level, short-term exposures may cause skin ulcerations. Creosotes are listed as cancer-causing agents under Proposition 65.

Criteria pollutants. Air pollutants for which standards for safe levels of exposure have been set under the Clean Air Act. Current criteria pollutants are sulfur dioxide, particulate matter, carbon monoxide, nitrogen oxides, ozone and lead.

Critical mass. The minimum mass of fissionable material that will support a sustaining chain reaction.

Crop dusting. The application of pesticides to plants by a low-flying plane.

Cryptosporidium. A protozoan (single-celled organism) that can infect humans, usually as a result of exposure to contaminated drinking water.

Cumulative impact. The term cumulative impact is used in several ways: as the effect of exposure to more than one compound; as the effect of exposure to emissions from more than one facility; the combined effects of a facility and surrounding facilities or projects on the environment; or some combination of these.

Cyanide. A highly toxic chemical often used in metal finishing or in extraction of precious metal from ore.

D

Deferred Swap: a trade of one allowance for another in order to exchange the vintage years of the allowances; settlement occurs after more than 180 days

Degrease. To remove grease from machinery, tools, etc., usually using solvents. Aqueous (water-based) cleaners are becoming popular and are required in some parts of the state.

Deionized water. Water which has been specifically treated to remove minerals.

Demand Side Management (DSM). An attempt by utilities to reduce customers' demand for electricity or energy by encouraging efficiency. A term referring to the need (or demand) for power generation among a utility's customers.

Demersal. Fish that live on or near the ocean bottom. They are often called benthic fish, groundfish, or bottom fish.

De minimis risk. A level of risk that the scientific and regulatory community asserts is too insignificant to regulate.

Department of Toxic Substances Control (DTSC). A department within the California Environmental Protection Agency charged with the regulation of hazardous waste from generation to final disposal, and for overseeing the investigation and clean-up of hazardous waste sites.

Designated Representative: for a unit account, the individual who represents the owners and operators of that unit and performs allowance transfer requests and all correspondence with EPA concerning compliance with the Acid Rain Destruction and removal efficiency (DRE). A percentage that represents the number of molecules of compound removed or destroyed in an incinerator relative to the number of molecules that entered the incinerator system. A DRE of 99.99 percent means that 9,999 molecules of a compound are destroyed for every 10,000 molecules that enter the system. For some compounds a DRE of 99.9999 is required.

Development. a.) developed tract of land (with houses or structures); b.) the act, process or result of developing.

Dewater. To remove water from wastes, soils or chemicals.

Diazinon. An organophosphate insecticide. It is used in agriculture, and for home, lawn and commercial uses.

Dibromochloropropane (DBCP). An amber-colored liquid used in a agriculture to kill pests in the soil. Inhalation of high concentrations of DBCP causes nausea and irritation of the respiratory tract. Chronic exposure results in sterility in males. Although not in use as a pesticide in this country since 1979 (until 1985 in Hawaii), it is found as a contaminant at many hazardous substances sites. DBCP is listed as a cancer-causing agent under Proposition 65.

Dichlorobenzene (DCB). A volatile organic compound often used as a deodorizer, and as a moth, mold and mildew killer. It is a white solid with a strong odor of mothballs. It is toxic and is listed as a cancer-causing agent under Proposition 65.

1,1-Dichloroethane. A colorless, oily liquid having an ether-like odor. It is used to make other chemicals and to dissolve other substances such as paint and varnish, and to remove grease. In the past, this chemical was used as a surgical anesthetic, but it is no longer used for this purpose. Because it evaporates easily into air, it is usually present in the environment as a vapor rather than a liquid.

Dieldrin. An insecticide that was used on crops like corn and cotton. U.S. EPA banned its use in 1987. It is listed as a cancer-causing chemical under Proposition 65.

Diesel. A petroleum-based fuel which is burned in engines ignited by compression rather than spark; commonly used for heavy duty engines including buses and trucks.

Diesel engine. An internal combustion engine that uses diesel as fuel, producing harmful fumes.

Dioxins. A group of generally toxic organic compounds that may be formed as a result of incomplete combustion (as may occur in incineration of compounds containing chlorine). RCRA regulations require a higher destruction and removal efficiency (DRE) for dioxins and related furans (99.9999 percent) burned in incinerators than the DRE required for most other organic compounds (99.99 percent). They are rapidly absorbed through the skin and gastrointestinal tract and are listed as cancer-causing chemicals under Proposition 65.

Dispatch: the ordered use of generation facilities by an electric power utility including which units will operate, when they will operate, and at what capacity

Double hulled tankers. Large transport ships with two hulls with space between them, protecting the cargo (in most cases, oil) from spilling in case of a collision.

Downgradient. The direction in which groundwater flows.

Dredge. A fishing method that utilizes a bag dragged behind a vessel that scrapes the ocean bottom, usually to catch shellfish. Dredges are often equipped with metal spikes in order to dig up the catch.

Driftnet. A huge net stretching across many miles that drifts in the water; used primarily for large-scale commercial fishing.

Dump sites. Waste disposal grounds.

E

Ecologist. A scientist concerned with the interrelationship of organisms and their environment.

Ecology. A branch of science concerned with the interrelationship of organisms and their environment.

Ecosystem. An interconnected and symbiotic grouping of animals, plants, fungi, and microorganisms.

Edge cities. Cities bounded by water, usually with eroding or polluted waterfront areas.

Effluent. Wastewater, treated or untreated, that flows out of a treatment plant, sewer or industrial outfall. Generally refers to wastes discharged into surface waters.

Electric vehicles (EV). Vehicles which use electricity (usually derived from batteries recharged from electrical outlets) as their power source.

Electrostatic precipitator. An air pollution control device that uses electrical charges to remove particulate matter from emission gases.

Emulsifiers. Substances that help in mixing liquids that don't normally mix; e.g., oil and water.

Emissions cap. A limit on the amount of greenhouse gases that a company or country can legally emit.

Endangered species. Species of wild life in danger of extinction throughout all or a significant part of its range.

Endocrine disruptors. Substances that stop the production or block the transmission of hormones in the body. energy conservation—using energy efficiently or prudently; saving energy.

Endosulfan. An insecticide used on vegetable crops, fruits and nuts.

Energy efficiency. Technologies and measures that reduce the amount of electricity and/or fuel required to do the same work, such as powering homes, offices and industries.

Enrolled bill. The final, certified bill sent to the President; House and Senate versions of a bill must match exactly in order to be enrolled.

Equity. In the environmental sense, the planned dispersement of toxic or waste facilities in regions throughout the socioeconomic strata.

Estuary. Areas where fresh water from rivers mixes with salt water from nearshore ocean. They include bays, mouths of rivers, salt marshes and lagoons. These brackish water ecosystems shelter and feed marine life, birds and wildlife.

Ethylene glycol. Used in the manufacture of a wide variety of industrial compounds and in certain cosmetics. It is used most commonly as an automobile antifreeze. It is toxic.

Eugenics. The study of hereditary improvement of the human race by controlled selective breeding.

Everglades. Large and biologically diverse wetland ecosystem in South Florida.

Executive session. A congressional meeting closed to the public (and the media).

Exercise Date (or Expiration Date): last day on which an option can be exercised

Exposure pathways. Existing or hypothetical routes by which chemicals in soil, water or other media can come in contact with humans, animals or plants.

Extraction wells. Wells that are used primarily to remove contaminated groundwater from the ground. Water level measurements and water samples can also be collected from extraction wells.

Exurbia. a.) the area of suburbs; b.) the region outside a city and its suburbs where wealthier families live.

F

Factory farming. Large-scale, industrialized agriculture.

Factory ships. Industrial-style ships used for the large-scale collection and processing of fish.

Fallout. The radioactive dust particles that settle to earth after the denotation of a nuclear device. It is also used to describe dust particles settling from smoke, etc.

Family planning. A system of limiting family size and the frequency of childbearing by the appropriate use of contraceptive techniques.

Fauna. The total animal population that inhabits an area.

Federal land. Land owned and administered by the federal government, including national parks and national forests.

Feasibility study. An evaluation of the alternatives for remediating any identified soil or groundwater contamination.

Feedlots. A plot of ground used to feed farm animals.

Fertility. The ability to reproduce; in humans, the ability to bear children.

Fertility rates. Average number of live births per woman during her reproductive years, among a given set of people.

Filibuster. A tactic used to delay or stop a vote on a bill by making long floor speeches and debates.

Fiscal year. A financial term referring to any twelve-month period, usually to set a budget. The federal government's fiscal year begins October 1.

Filter cake. A mixture of sediments that results from filtering and dewatering of treated wastewater.

Fisheries. An established area where fish species are cultivated and caught.

Fissile material. Material fissionable by slow neutrons. The fission process and the fissile isotopes are the source of energy in nuclear weapons and nuclear reactors.

Fission. The process whereby the nucleus of a particular heavy element splits into (generally) two nuclei of lighter elements, with the release of substantial amounts of energy.

Flammables. A class of compounds that ignite easily and burn rapidly. The Department of Transportation requires that Vehicles transporting flammables must have special markings (placards).

Flash point. The lowest temperature at which a liquid generates enough vapor to ignite in air. If a waste has a flash point of less than 140° F, then it is an ignitable hazardous waste.

Flora. The total vegetation assemblage that inhabits an area.

Florida Bay. A bay at southern tip of Florida which is bounded by the Florida Keys.

Fly ash. Non-combustible residue that results from burning fuels in an incinerator, boiler or furnace. It can include metal oxides, silicates and sulfur compounds, as well as many other chemical pollutants. It is fine ash carried along by flue gases that must be captured by some means before it reaches the mouth of the chimney.

Footprint. The outline of an area within which hazardous substances are suspected or known to exist.

Forest certification. A process of labeling wood that has been harvested from a well-managed forest.

Forests. Lands on which trees are the principal plant life, usually conducive to wide biodiversity.

Formaldehyde. A water-soluble gas used widely in the chemical industry and in the construction and building industries, largely in wood products and in foam insulation. It is also used in some deodorizing preparations, in fumigants and as a tissue preservative in laboratories. Formaldehyde is listed as a cancer-causing agent under Proposition 65.

Fossil fuel. A fuel, such as coal, oil, and natural gas, produced by the decomposition of ancient (fossilized) plants and animals; compare to alternative energy.

Fresh Kills. New York City's only operating landfill, located in Staten Island. Infamous as the largest landfill in the world.

French drain system. A pit or trench filled with crushed rock and used to collect and divert stormwater or wastewater. Most often, perforated piping at the bottom provides easy drainage.

Fugitive emissions. Releases of pollutants to the atmosphere that occur when vapors are vented from containers or tanks where materials are stored. They can also be caused by spillage during the unloading of vehicles, leaks from pipes and valves, and through equipment operation.

G

Gamma radiation. A high-energy photon (ray) emitted from the nucleus of certain radioactive atoms. Gamma rays are the most penetrating of the three common types of radiation (the other two are alpha particles and beta particles) and are best stopped by dense materials such as lead.,

Gas. Natural gas, used as fuel.

Gasoline. Petroleum fuel, used to power cars, trucks, lawn mowers, etc.

General Accounts: accounts in the SO_2 or NO_x ATSs which were created after the initial allocation; general accounts can be opened by any individual and they are not automatically adjusted for compliance

Geophysical logging. A general term that encompasses all techniques for determining whether a subsurface geological formation may be sufficiently porous or permeable to serve as an aquifer. These techniques typically involve lowering a sensing device into a borehole to measure properties of the subsurface formation.

Geothermal. Literally, heat from the earth; energy obtained from the hot areas under the surface of the earth.

Gigawatt (GW). One thousand megawatts, or one billion watts.

Gigawatt hour (GW/h). One thousand MW generated or used in one hour

Gillnets. Walls of netting that are usually staked to the sea floor. Fish become entangled or caught by their gills.

Global Climate Change: change in the earth's climate; caused by increasing greenhouse gas (GHG) concentrations in the atmosphere; human activities considered to be major new source of

GHGs

Global warming. Increase in the average temperature of the earth's surface.

Golden Carrot. An incentive program that is designed to transform the market to produce much

Greater energy efficiency. The term is a trademark of the Consortium for Energy Efficiency.

Granular activated carbon (GAC). A form of crushed and hardened charcoal. GAC has a strong potential to attract and absorb volatile organic compounds from extracted groundwater and gases.

Grassroots. Local or person-to-person. A typical grassroots effort might include a door-to-door education and survey campaign.

Grazing. The use of grasses and other plants to feed wild or domestic herbivores such as deer, sheep and cows.

Green design. A design, usually architectural, conforming to environmentally sound principles of building, material and energy use. A green building, for example, might make use of solar panels, skylights, and recycled building materials.

Greenhouse. A building made with translucent (light transparent, usually glass or fiberglass) walls conducive to plant growth.

Greenhouse effect. The process that raises the temperature of air in the lower atmosphere due to heat trapped by greenhouse gases, such as carbon dioxide, methane, nitrous oxide, chlorofluorocarbons, and ozone.

Greenhouse gas. A gas involved in the greenhouse effect. A variety of gases including carbon dioxide, methane, and nitrous oxide; the buildup of these gases in the atmosphere prevents energy from the sun to escape back out into space, creating the "greenhouse effect"

Greenway. Undeveloped land usually in cities, set aside or used for recreation or conservation.

Groundfish. A general term referring to fish that live on or near the sea floor. Groundfish are also called bottom fish or demersal fish.

Ground-level Ozone: the occurrence in the troposphere (at ground level) of a gas that consists of 3 atoms of oxygen (03); formed through a chemical reaction involving oxides of nitrogen (NO_x), volatile organic compounds (VOC), heat and light; At ground level, ozone is an air pollutant that damages human health, vegetation, and many common materials and is a key ingredient of urban smog.

Groundwater. Water beneath the earth's surface that flows through soil and rock openings, aquifers, and often serves as a primary source of drinking water.

Growth overfishing. The process of catching fish before they are fully grown resulting in a decrease in the average size of the fish population.

H

Habitat. the natural home of an animal or plant; or the sum of the environmental conditions that determine the existence of a community in a specific place.

Half-life. The amount of time that is required for a radioactive substance to lose one-half its activity. Each radioactive substance has a unique half-life. It is also used to describe:

the time for a pollutant to lose one half of its concentration, as through biological action; and the time for elimination of one half a total dose of a drug from a body.

Halogens. The family of elements that includes fluorine, chlorine, bromine and iodine. Halogens are very reactive and have many industrial uses. They are also commonly used in disinfectants and insecticides. Many hazardous organic chemicals—such as polychlorinated biphenyls (PCBs), some volatile compounds (VOCs) and dioxins contain halogens, especially chlorine.

Harpooning. A surface method of fishing that requires considerable effort in locating and chasing individual fish. Harpoons are hand-held or fired from a harpoon gun and aimed at high-value fish, such as giant tuna and swordfish.

Hazardous waste. Waste substances which can pose a substantial or potential hazard to human health or the environment when improperly managed. Hazardous waste possesses at least one of these four characteristics: ignitability, corrosivity, reactivity or toxicity; or appears on special U.S. EPA lists.

Haze. An atmospheric condition marked by a slight reduction in atmospheric visibility, resulting from the formation of photochemical smog, radiation of heat from the ground surface on hot days, or the development of a thin mist.

Health-based remediation targets and levels to which hazardous substances on the site will be cleaned up. These target levels are health-based, meaning that exposure to the hazardous substances at or below the target is not expected to present a significant health risk.

Health risk/endangerment assessment. A study prepared to assess health and environmental risks due to potential exposure to Hazardous substances.

Hearings. Testimony (sworn statements like those given in court) given before a Congressional committee.

Heavy metals. A group of elements (such as chromium, cadmium, lead, copper and zinc) that can be toxic at relatively low concentrations and tend to accumulate in the food chain..

Hedge: strategy used to offset investment risk. A perfect hedge is one eliminating the possibility of future gain or loss

Heptachlor. An organochloride insecticide once widely used on food crops, especially corn, but has not been in use since 1988. It is listed as a cancer-causing chemical under Proposition 65.

High seas. International ocean water under no single country's legal jurisdiction.

Highly migratory fish. Fish that travel over great areas.

Horizontal wells. Extraction and monitoring wells are typically drilled vertically. A horizontal well has the advantage of providing a large area of groundwater capture for a lower overall cost.

Hot spot criteria. Cleanup levels for small areas on the site that have particularly high concentrations of hazardous substances.

Household hazards. Dangerous substances or conditions in human dwellings.

Hydrochloric acid (HCl). Clear, colorless and acidic solution of hydrogen chloride in water often used in metal cleaning and electroplating. Many hazardous wastes contain chlorine compounds which create small amounts of hydrogen chloride when they are burned. This can contribute to the formation of acid rain. Regulations require that air pollution control equipment remove either 99% of the hydrochloric acid, or that the emissions contain less than four pounds per hour.

Hydroelectric. Relating to electric energy produced by moving water.

Hydrofluorocarbons (HFC). Chemicals used as solvents and cleaners in the semiconductor industry, among others; experts say that they possess global warming potentials that are thousands of times greater than CO2.

Hydrogeology. The geology of groundwater, with particular emphasis on the chemistry and movement of water.

Hydropower. Energy or power produced by moving water.

Hypoxia. The depletion of dissolved oxygen in water, a condition resulting from an overabundance of nutrients of human or natural origin that stimulates the growth of algae, which in turn die and require large amounts of oxygen as the algae decompose. It was the most frequently cited direct cause of fishkills in the U.S. from 1980 to 1989.

I

Ignitability. A characteristic of hazardous waste. If a liquid (containing less than 24% alcohol) has a flash point less than 140° F, it is a hazardous waste in the United States.

Immediate Settlement: conclusion of an allowance trade in which a party pays for allowances within days of the confirmation of the transaction

Immediate Vintage Year Swap: an trade of one allowance for another in order to exchange the vintage years of the allowances; settlement occurs within days (or at least less than 180 days)

Impoundment. A body of water or sludge confined by a dam, dike, floodgate or other barrier.

In-situ soil aeration. Applying a vacuum to vapor extraction wells to draw air through the soil so that chemicals in the soil are brought to the surface where they can be treated.

Incinerators. Disposal systems that burn solid waste or other materials and reduce volume of waste. Air pollution and toxic ash are problems associated with incineration.

Incompatible wastes. Wastes which create a hazard of some form when mixed together. This could be intense heat or toxic gases, for example.

Indicator chemicals. Chemicals selected from the group of chemicals found at the site and used for a public health evaluation. They are selected on the basis of toxicity, mobility and persistence, and are thought to be the chemicals of the greatest potential risk.

Industrialized countries. Nations whose economies are based on industrial production and the conversion of raw materials into products and services, mainly with the use of machinery and artificial energy (fossil fuels and nuclear fission); generally located in the northern and western hemispheres (e.g., U.S., Japan, the countries of Europe).

Insecticides. Substances used to kill insects and prevent infestation.

Interim remedial actions (IRAs). Also known as Interim Remedial Measures—Cleanup actions taken to protect public health and the environment while long-term solutions are being developed.

International Conference on Population and Development. A conference sponsored by the United Nations to discuss global dimensions of population growth and change in Cairo, Egypt in September 1994. The conference is generally considered to mark the achievement of a new consensus on effective ways to slow population growth and improve quality of life by addressing root causes of unwanted fertility.

International Planned Parenthood Federation (IPPF). An international organization made up of national level affiliates representing every region of the world. IPPF receives and distributes funds from international donor nations to its affiliates, who in turn provide services (prenatal care, contraceptive counseling and service provision, and other reproductive health services) within a country. Some national level organizations provide abortion services, others do not.   IPPF sets and supports policies encouraging governmental provision of comprehensive reproductive health care.

Irritant. A chemical that can cause temporary irritation at the site of contact.

J
Joule; unit of energy measurement

K
Kilowatt (kW). One thousand watts of electric energy

Kilowatt hour (kW/h). 1000 Watts generated or used in one hour

Kyoto Protocol: an agreement under the UNFCC signed by 84 nations; establishes greenhouse gas targets ("budgets") and framework for implementation; the Protocol has been agreed to and signed by the U.S. and now awaits ratification by the U.S. Senate

L
Landfill. Disposal area where garbage is piled up and eventually covered with dirt and topsoil.

Landings. The amount of fish brought back to the docks and marketed. Landings can describe the kept catch of one vessel, of an entire fishery, or of several fisheries combined.

Land use. The way in which land is used, especially in farming and city planning.

Law. An act or bill which has become part of the legal code through passage by Congress and approval by the President (or via Congressional override).

Leachate. Typically, water that has come in contact with hazardous wastes. For example:

Water from rain or other sources that has percolated

through a landfill and dissolved or carries various chemicals, and thus could spread contamination. Current landfills have systems to collect leachate before that can happen.

Lead. A heavy metal present in small amounts everywhere in the human environment. Lead can get into the body from drinking contaminated water, eating vegetables grown in contaminated soil, or breathing dust when children play or adults work in lead-contaminated areas or eating lead-based paint. It can cause damage to the nervous system or blood cells. Children are at highest risk because their bodies are still developing. Lead and its compounds are listed as a reproductive toxic substance for women and men, and a cancer-causing substance under Proposition 65.

Lead agency. A public agency which has the principal responsibility for ordering and overseeing site investigation and cleanup.

Lead poisoning. Damaging the body (specifically the brain) by absorbing lead through the skin or by swallowing.

Least-cost planning. A process for satisfying consumers' demands for energy services at the lowest societal cost.

Leukemia. A form of bone marrow cancer marked by an increase in white blood cells.

Life cycle assessment. Methodology developed to assess a product's full environmental costs, from raw material to final disposal.

Light pollution. Environmental pollution consisting of harmful or annoying light.

Lindane. Lindane (gamma hexachlorocyclohexane) is an insecticide, once used on fruit and vegetable crops. It is still used to treat head and body lice, and scabies. It is highly toxic to humans, freshwater fish and aquatic life. It is listed as a cancer-causing chemical under Proposition 65.

Litter. Waste material which is discarded on the ground or otherwise disposed of improperly or thoughtlessly.

Logging. Cutting down trees for commodity use.

Long: a market position in which a party records (or anticipates recording) emissions less than its yearly emissions allocation, thus it has surplus allowances

Longlines. Fishing lines stretching for dozens of miles and baited with hundreds of hooks. longlines are indiscriminate and unintentionally catch and kill immature fish along with a wide variety of other animals in the Atlantic including tunas, sharks, marlins, sailfish, sea turtles and occasionally pilot whales and dolphins.

Long-term Forward purchase or sale of a specific quantity of allowances, with delivery and settlement scheduled for a specified future date, usually more than one year out

Low-emission vehicles. Vehicles which emit little air pollution compared to conventional internal combustion engines.

Low-impact camping. Camping that does not damage or change the land, where campers leave no sign that they were on the land.

Lumber. Wood or wood products used for construction.

Lung diseases. Any disease or damaging conditions in the lung or bronchia such as cancer or emphysema.

Lymphoma. A tumor marked by swelling in the lymph nodes.

M

Magnesium oxide. Also known as magnesia, magnesium oxide is used medicinally ("Milk of Magnesia"), industrially and in agricultural soil supplements. It is also used to enhance biological processes and to cleanup groundwater.

Magnesium. This light metal and its derivatives are used in aerospace alloys, in incendiary devices such as flares, and elsewhere. When scrap magnesium is thinly shaved or powdered, it is considered to be a hazardous waste, as it ignites easily and burns with an intense, white flame. It is also a nutritionally essential trace metal.

Majority leader. The leader of the majority party in either the House or the Senate.

Malthusian—based on the theories of British economist Thomas Robert Malthus (1766-1834), who argued that population tends to increase faster than food supply, with inevitably disastrous results, unless the increase in population is checked by moral restraints or by war, famine, and disease.

Malathion. Insecticide that, at high doses, affects the human nervous system.

Mammal. An animal that feeds its young with milk secreted from mammary glands and has hair on its skin.

Managed growth. Growth or expansion that is controlled so as not to be harmful.

Manatee. A plant-eating aquatic mammal found in the waters of Florida, the Caribbean, and off the coast of West Africa.

Marbled murrelet. A rare and imperiled bird that nests in ancient forests on the west coast of the U.S.

Marine mammal. A mammal that lives in the ocean, such as a whale.

Market Maker: an individual or company that maintains firm bid and offer prices in allowances by standing ready to buy or sell allowances at market prices

Mark-up. Action by a Congressional committee to amend and/or approve a bill; following mark-up the bill is "reported" out of committee and is ready for consideration by the entire House or Senate. marsh—wetland, swamp, or bog.

Mass transit. Public transportation.

Maximum contaminant level (MCL). A contaminant level for drinking water, established by the California Department of Health Services, Division of Drinking Water and Environmental Management, or by the U.S. Environmental Protection Agency. These levels are legally-enforceable standards based on health risk (primary standards) or non-health concerns such as odor or taste (secondary standards).

Medfly. The Mediterranean fruit fly, a flying insect.

Megalopolis. A large city expanding so fast that city government cannot adjust to provide services (such as garbage disposal).

Megawatt (MW). One million watts.

Megawatt hour (MW/h). One million watts generated or used in one hour

Mercury. Also known as "quicksilver," this metal is used in the paper pulp and chemical industries, in the manufacture of thermometers, and thermostats, and in fungicides. Mercury exists in three biologically important forms, elemental, inorganic and organic. It is highly toxic and affects the nervous system, kidneys and other organs. It also accumulates in animals that are high in the food chain (predators). Organic mercury compounds are the most toxic, and transformations between the three forms of mercury do occur in nature.

Methane (CH_4). An odorless, colorless, flammable gas that is the major constituent of natural gas. It can be formed from rotting organic matter (i.e., trash in a landfill), and seep up through soils or migrate through underground piping to the surface. It also seeps up through the ground in areas that have shallow petroleum deposits or improperly abandoned oil wells, such as certain areas of the Los Angeles Basin. If it collects in a closed space and reaches certain concentrations, a spark can cause an explosion. It can also displace air and cause a suffocation hazard in low, enclosed spaces. This is one of the reasons landfill gas is collected and burned, sometimes for generation of electricity.

Methyl bromide (CH_3Br). The gaseous compound is used primarily as an insect fumigant; found to be harmful to the stratospheric ozone layer which protects life on earth from excessive ultraviolet radiation.

Methyl ethyl ketone (MEK). MEK is a flammable solvent that has many industrial uses, primarily in the plastic industry as a solvent. MEK is also used in the synthetic rubber industry, in the production of paraffin wax, and in household products such as lacquer and varnishes, paint remover, and glues.

Methylene chloride. A colorless liquid that evaporates easily. It has been used as a metal cleaner, paint thinner, in wood stains, spot removers, fabric protectors, shoe polish and aerosol propellants. Mild exposure can cause skin and eye irritation

Microgram per gram (mg/g). A measurable unit of concentration for a solid. A mercury level of 1.0 mg/g means that one microgram (one millionth of a gram) of mercury was detected in one gram of sample. It is equivalent to one part per million.

Migration. The movement of chemical contaminants through soils or groundwater.

Milligram per cubic meter (mg/m3). A unit of concentration for air contaminants. A mercury vapor level of 1.0 mg/m3 means that one milligram (one thousandth of a gram) of mercury vapor was detected in each cubic meter of sampled air.

Milligram per kilogram (mg/kg). A unit of concentration for a solid. A mercury level of 1.0 mg/kg in fish means that one milligram (one thousandth of a gram) of mercury was found in each kilogram of sampled fish. (A kilogram is 1,000 grams or approximately 2.2 pounds). Also equals one part per million.

Mining. The removal of minerals (like coal, gold, or silver) from the ground.

Minority leader. The leader of the minority party in either the House or the Senate.

Minuteman. An American-made ICBM; 500 Minuteman III ICBMs are deployed currently in the United States.

Mitigation. Actions taken to improve site conditions by limiting, reducing or controlling hazards and contamination sources.

Monitoring wells. Specially-constructed wells used exclusively for testing water quality.

Moratorium. Legislative action which prevents a federal agency from taking a specific action or implementing a specific law.

Mulch. Leaves, straw or compost used to cover growing plants to protect them from the wind or cold.

N

National Ambient Air Quality Standards (NAAQS): health-based standards for a variety of pollutants set by EPA that must be met by states across the country.

National Pollutant Discharge Elimination System (NPDES). A system under the federal Clean Water Act that requires a permit for the discharge of pollutants to surface waters of the United States. In California, NPDES permits are obtained from the Regional Water Quality Control Board.

National Priorities List (NPL). U.S. EPA's list of the top priority hazardous waste sites in the country that are subject to the Superfund program.

Natural long: a party whose allowance allocation is greater than its actual emissions.

Natural short: a party whose allowance allocation is less than its actual emissions.

National Recreation Areas. Areas of federal land that have been set aside by Congress for recreational use by members of the public.

Negative Declaration. A California Environmental Quality Act document issued by the lead regulatory agency when the initial environmental study reveals no substantial evidence that the proposed project will have a significant adverse effect on the environment, or when any significant effects would be avoided or mitigated by revisions agreed to by the applicant.

Neutrals. Organic compounds that have a relatively neutral pH (are neither acid nor base), complex structure and, due to their carbon bases, are easily absorbed into the environment. Naphthalene, pyrene and trichlorobenzene are examples of neutrals.

Nickel. A metal used in alloys to provide corrosion and heat resistance for products in the iron, steel and aerospace industries. Nickel is used as a catalyst in the chemical industry. It is toxic and, in some forms, is listed as a cancer-causing agent under Proposition 65.

Nitrate. Formed when ammonia is degraded by microorganisms in soil or groundwater. This compound is usually associated with fertilizers.

Nitroaromatics. Common components of explosive materials, which will explode if activated by very high temperatures or shocks. 2,4,6-trinitrotoluene (TNT) is a nitroaromatic. Some are listed as cancer-causing chemicals under Proposition 65.

Nitrogen oxides (NO$_x$). Harmful gases (which contribute to acid rain and global warming) emitted as a byproduct of fossil fuel combustion. Gases produced during combustion of fossil fuels in motor vehicles, power plants and industrial furnaces and other sources; is a precursor to acid rain and ground-level ozone

Nitrogen oxides (NO$_x$) Budget Program: a NO$_x$ cap and trade program adopted by 13 jurisdictions in the Northeast to address ozone transport in that region

Noise pollution. Environmental pollution made up of harmful or annoying noise.

Non-attainment pollutants. See "Criteria pollutants." If any of the criteria pollutants exceed established health-based levels in a given air basin, they are identified as "non-attainment pollutants."

Nuclear energy. Energy or power produced by nuclear reactions (fusion or fission). Alsop called nuclear power.

Nuclear reactor. An apparatus in which nuclear fission may be initiated, maintained, and controlled to produce energy, conduct research, or produce fissile material for nuclear explosives.

Nuclear tests. Government tests carried out to supply information required for the design and improvement of nuclear weapons, and to study the phenomena and effects associated with Nuclear explosions.

O

Offers: price at which someone who owns an allowance is willing to sell (a.k.a. "Ask")

Oil. A black, sticky substance used to produce fuel (petroleum) and materials (plastics).

Oil spills. The harmful release of oil into the environment, usually in the water, sometimes killing area flora and fauna. Oil spills are very difficult to clean up.

Old growth forests. See ancient forests.

Omnibus spending bill. A bill combining the appropriations for several federal agencies.

Operation Plan. A document submitted to DTSC that gives details about how a permitted hazardous waste facility is built, a detailed description of the hazardous waste operations, the plan to be used in case of emergency, and other plans. A DTSC facility permit requires that the reviewed and approved Operations Plan be followed. It is sometimes referred to as the "Part B" of the hazardous waste facility permit.

Option: a contractual right to buy or sell allowances at an agreed price; the option buyer pays a premium for this right. If the option is not exercised after a specified period it expires Option Premium: amount per share paid by an option buyer to an option seller for the option Out-of-the-money Call Option: term used to describe an call option whose strike price for an allowance is higher than the current market value

Organochlorides. A group of organic (carbon-containing) insecticides that also contain chlorine. These chemicals tend not to break down easily in the environment. DDT, Toxaphene and Endosulfan are all organochlorides.

Organophosphate. A group of organic (carbon-containing) insecticides that also contain phosphorus. Although they do not have a long life, some can be very toxic when first applied. Malathion and Parathion are organophosphates. Malathion is mildly toxic, and parathion is extremely toxic.

Out-of-the-money Put Option: term used to describe a put option whose strike price for an allowance is lower than the current market value

Over-development. Expansion or development of land to the point of damage.

Over-fishing. Fishing beyond the capacity of a population to replace itself through natural reproduction.

Over-grazing. Grazing livestock to the point of damage- Overpacking. Process used for isolating waste by jacketing or encapsulating waste-holding containers to prevent further spread or leakage of contaminating materials. Leaking drums may be contained within oversized ones as an interim measure prior to removal and final disposal.

Over-the-counter Market: Market in which allowance transactions are conducted through the direction interaction of counterparties rather than on the floor of an exchange

Oxidizers. A group of chemicals that are very reactive, often but not always supplying oxygen to a reaction. Some oxidation reactions can release large amounts of heat and gases, and, under the right conditions, cause an explosion. Others can cause rapid corrosion of metal, damage to tissue, burns and other serious effects. Examples of oxidizers include chlorine gas, nitric acid, sodium perchlorate, and ammonium nitrate.

Ozonation. Ozone reacts with volatile organic compounds (VOCs) to change them into chemicals which pose no potential threat to human health, by breaking them down to form carbon dioxide and water. This is done with an ozonation unit.

Ozone. A naturally occurring, highly reactive gas comprising triatomic oxygen (O_3) formed by recombination of oxygen in the presence of ultraviolet radiation. This naturally occurring gas builds up in the lower atmosphere as smog pollution, while in the upper atmosphere it forms a protective layer which shields the earth and its inhabitants from excessive exposure to damaging ultraviolet radiation.

Ozone depletion. The reduction of the protective layer of ozone in the upper atmosphere by chemical pollution.

Ozone hole. A hole or gap in the protective layer of ozone in the upper atmosphere.

Ozone Transport Assessment Group (OTAG): a multi-stakeholder workgroup convened to address problems associated with the long-range transport of ozone and its precursors; encompassed stakeholders in 37 jurisdictions

P

Paper. Thin sheet of material made of cellulose pulp, derived mainly from wood, but also from rags and certain grasses, and processed into flexible leaves or rolls. Used primarily for writing, printing, drawing, wrapping, and covering walls.

Paper mills. Mills (factories) that produce paper from wood pulp.

Paper products. Materials such as paper and cardboard, produced from trees.

Parathion and Methylparathion. Toxic insecticides.

Particulates. Small solid or liquid particles, especially those in the emission gases of incinerators, boilers, industrial furnaces or in exhaust from diesel and gasoline engines. Particles below 10 microns (10 one-millionths of a meter, 0.0004 inch) in diameter are considered potential health risks because, when inhaled, they are taken deep into the lungs. Regulations require that an incinerator emit no more than 180 milligrams of total particulates per dry standard cubic meter per minute.

Particulate pollution. Pollution made up of small liquid or solid particles suspended in the atmosphere or water supply.

Parts per million (ppm). A measuring unit for the concentration of one material in another. When looking at contamination of water and soil, the toxins are often measured in parts per million. One part per million is equal to one thousandth of a gram of substance in one thousand grams of material. One part per million would be equivalent to one drop of water in twenty gallons.

Parts per billion (ppb). A unit of measure used to describe levels or concentrations of contamination. A measure of concentration, equaling 0.0000001 percent. For example, One part per billion is the equivalent of one drop of impurity in 500 barrels of water. Most drinking water standards are ppb concentrations.

Passive solar. Using or capturing solar energy (usually to heat water) without any external power.

Pelagic species. Fish that live at or near the water's surface. Examples of large pelagic species include swordfish, tuna, and many species of sharks. Small pelagics include anchovies and sardines.

Pentachlorophenol (PCP). A petroleum-based chemical that is used as a wood preservative because it kills fungus and termites. It is toxic listed as a cancer-causing chemical under Proposition 65.

Perched groundwater. Water that accumulates beneath the earth's surface but above the main water bearing zone (aquifer). Typically, perched groundwater occurs when a limited zone (or lens) of harder, less permeable soil is "perched" in otherwise porous soils. Rainwater moving downward through the soil stops at the lens, flows along it, then seeps downward toward the aquifer.

Perchloroethylene (PCE). A volatile organic compound used primarily as a dry-cleaning agent. It is often referred to as "perc." It is toxic and listed as a cancer-causing chemical under Proposition 65.

Percolation. The downward flow or filtering of water or other liquids through subsurface rock or soil layers, usually continuing to groundwater.

Pesticide. A general term for insecticides, herbicides and fungicides. Insecticides kill or prevent the growth of insects. Herbicides control or destroy plants. Fungicides control or destroy fungi. Some pesticides can accumulate in the food chain and contaminate the environment.

Petrex Method. A method for collecting vapor samples from surface soil.

Petrochemicals. Chemical substances produced from petroleum in refinery operations. Many are hazardous.

Phenols. Organic compounds used in plastics manufacturing, tanning, and textile, dye and resin manufacturing. They are by-products of petroleum refining. In general, they are highly toxic.

Piezometers. Small-diameter wells used to measure groundwater levels.

Pilot study. A study of a possible cleanup alternative

during the Feasibility Study for a specific site. It is used to gather data necessary for the final selection of the cleanup method.

Plastics. Durable and flexible synthetic-based products, some of which are difficult to recycle and Pose problems with toxic properties, especially PVC plastic.

Plume. A body of contaminated groundwater flowing from a specific source. The movement of the groundwater is influenced by such factors as local groundwater flow patterns, the character of the aquifer in which the groundwater is contained, and the density of contaminants. A plume may also be a cloud of smoke or vapor. It defines the area where exposure would be dangerous.

Plutonium. A heavy, radioactive, man-made, metallic element (atomic number 94) used in the production of nuclear energy and the explosion of nuclear weapons; its most important isotope is fissile plutonium-239, produced by neutron irradiation of uranium-238.

Poison. A chemical that adversely affects health by causing injury, illness, or death.

Poison runoff. See polluted runoff.

Polluted runoff. Precipitation that captures pollution from agricultural lands, urban streets, parking lots and suburban lawns, and transports it to rivers, lakes or oceans.

Pollution prevention. Techniques that eliminate waste prior to treatment, such as by changing ingredients in a chemical reaction.

Polychlorinated biphenyls (PCBs). A group of toxic chemicals used for a variety of purposes including electrical applications, carbonless copy paper, adhesives, hydraulic fluids, and caulking compounds. PCBs do not breakdown easily and are listed as cancer-causing agents under Proposition 65.

Polynuclear aromatic hydrocarbons (PAHs or PNAs). PNAs or Polynuclear Aromatic Hydrocarbons, are natural constituents of crude oil, and also may be formed when organic materials such as coal, oil, fuel, wood or even foods are not completely burned. PNAs are also found in lampblack, a by-product of the historic gas manufacturing process. PNAs are found in a wide variety of other materials, including diesel exhaust, roofing tars, asphalt, fireplace smoke and soot, cigarettes, petroleum products, some foods, and even some shampoos. PNAs tend to stick to soil and do not easily dissolve in water, and generally do not move in

the environment. The test method used to analyze for PNAs detects seventeen different compounds. Of the seventeen, seven are suspected of causing cancer in humans.

Polyvinyl chloride (PVC). A plastic made from the gaseous chemical vinyl chloride. PVC is used to make pipes, records, raincoats and floor titles. It produces hydrochloric acid when burned. Health risks from high concentrations of vinyl chloride (not the polymer) include liver cancer and lung cancer, as well as cancer of the lymphatic and nervous systems. Vinyl chloride (not the polymer) is listed as a cancer-causing chemical under Proposition 65.

Population. Two meanings: a.) the whole number of inhabitants in a country, region or area; b.) a set of individuals having a quality or characteristic in common.

Post consumer waste. Waste collected after the consumer has used and disposed of it (e.g., the wrapper from an eaten candy bar).

Potentially Responsible Party (PRP). An individual, company or government body identified as potentially liable for a release of hazardous substances to the environment. By federal law, such parties may include generators, transporters, storers and disposers of hazardous waste, as well as present and past site owners and operators.

Power plants. Facilities (plants) that produce energy.

Power Pool: a situation where output from different power plants are "pooled" together, scheduled according to increasing marginal cost, technical and contractual characteristics (so-called must-runs), and dispatched according to this "merit order" to meet demand

Pretreatment unit. A wastewater treatment unit that is designed to treat wastewater that does not meet the sewage discharge standards so that it meets or exceeds those standards. Pretreatment units usually require a permit from a local agency.

Principal organic hazardous constituents (POHCs). Specific hazardous compounds monitored during an incinerator, boiler or industrial furnace trial burn. They are selected on the basis of their high concentration in the waste feed and the difficulty of burning them.

Proprietary information (trade secret). The Department will classify information as proprietary provided the owner demonstrates the following: the business has asserted a business confidentiality claim; the business has shown it has taken reasonable measures to protect the confidentiality of the information both within the company and from outside entities; the information is not, and has not been reasonably obtainable without the business' consent; no statute specifically requires disclosure of the information ; and either the business has shown that disclosure of the information is likely to cause substantial harm to its competitive position, or the information is voluntarily submitted and its disclosure would likely impair the government's ability to obtain necessary information in the future.

Public estate. Area or plot of public land owned by community or government.

Public health. The health or physical well-being of a whole community.

Public land. Land owned in common by all, represented by the government (town, county, state, or federal).

Public participation plan. A document approved by DTSC that is designed to determine a community's informational needs and to provide a program for public involvement during facility permitting, site investigation and cleanup, or other similar activities.

Public transportation. Various forms of shared-ride services, including buses, vans, trolleys, and subways, which are intended for conveying the public.

Pulp. Raw material made from trees used in producing paper products.

Pump test. A field test by which a well is pumped for a period of time and data are collected for use in assessing characteristics of subsurface water-bearing zones, or aquifers.

Put Option: a contract that grants the right to sell, at a specified price, a specific number of allowances by a certain date

Q

Quench tower. A gas cooling and pollution control device in which heated gases are showered with water. Gases are cooled and particulates "drop out" of the gases. They can generate a waste called "quench tower drop-out."

R

Radiation. The process of emitting energy in the form of energetic particles (such as alpha particles or gamma radiation), light or heat. It also refers to that which is emitted.

Radioactive. Of or characterized by radioactivity.

Radioactive waste. The byproduct of nuclear reactions that gives off (usually harmful) radiation.

Radioactivity. The spontaneous emission of matter or energy from the nucleus of an unstable atom (the emitted matter or energy is usually in the form of alpha or beta particles, gamma rays, or neutrons).

Radionuclides. Radioactive elements, which may be naturally-occurring or synthetic. They emit various types of energetic radiation — alpha and beta particles and gamma radiation. Their half-lives range from a minute fraction of a second to many thousand years. Certain radionuclides have valuable medical and industrial uses. One is used in home smoke detectors at an amount that can cause no harmful effects.

Radium. A radioactive element with a half-life of 1,600 years that emits alpha particles as it is transformed into radon. In the past, radium was mixed with special paints to make watch faces and instrument dials glow in the dark.

Radon. A gaseous, radioactive alpha particle-emitting element with a half-life of about four days. Radon exists naturally in many locations, and may present a serious health risk when it accumulates in basements or crawl spaces beneath homes. A cancer-causing radioactive gas found in many communities' ground water.

Rainforest. A large, dense forest in a hot, humid region (tropical or subtropical). Rainforests have an abundance of diverse plant and animal life, much of which is still uncatalogued by the scientific community.

Ranking member. The lead member of a Congressional committee from the minority party, usually chosen on the basis of seniority.

Reactive. A class of compounds which are normally unstable and readily undergo violent change, react violently with water, can produce toxic gases with water, or possess other similar properties. Reactivity is one characteristic that can make a waste hazardous.

Recess. Ending a legislative session with a set time to reconvene.

Recycling. System of collecting, sorting, and reprocessing old material into usable raw materials.

Reduce. Act of purchasing or consuming less to begin with, so as not to have to reuse or recycle later.

Refrigerants. Cooling substances, many of which contain CFCs and are harmful to the earth's ozone layer.

Regional Clean Air Incentives Market (RECLAIM): initiated in 1993; a set of market initiatives designed address air pollution in the Greater Los Angeles area of California; includes cap and trade programs for NO_x and SO_x.

Regional Water Quality Control Board (RWQCB). Agencies that maintain water quality standards for areas within their jurisdictions and enforce state water quality laws.

Remedial Action Plan (RAP). A plan that outlines a specific program leading to the remediation of a contaminated site. Once the Draft Remedial Action Plan is prepared, and approved by DTSC a public meeting is held and comments from the public are solicited for a period of not less then 30 days. After the public comment period has ended and the comments have been responded to in writing, DTSC may modify the Draft Plan on the basis of those comments before it approves the final remedy for the site (the Final RAP).

Remedial Investigation/Feasibility Study (RI/FS). A series of investigations and studies to identify the types and extent of chemicals of concern at the site and to determine cleanup criteria (Remedial Investigation), and to provide an evaluation of the alternatives for remediating any identified soil or groundwater problems (Feasibility Study).

Remediation. Cleanup of a site to levels determined to be health-protective for its intended use.

Resource Conservation and Recovery Act (RCRA)

Renewable energy. Energy resources such as wind power or solar energy that can keep producing indefinitely without being depleted.

Reservoir. An artificial lake created and used for the storage of water.

Responsible party. An individual or corporate entity considered legally liable for contamination found at a property and, therefore, responsible for cleanup of the site.

Resolution. A formal statement from Congress.

Retire (Allowances): to remove a portion of allowances from the market

Reuse. Cleaning and/or refurbishing an old product to be used again.

Rider. Usually unrelated provisions tacked onto an existing Congressional bill. Since bills must pass or fail in their entirety, riders containing otherwise unpopular language are often added to popular bills.

Riparian. Located alongside a watercourse, typically a river.

Risk assessment. A risk assessment looks at the chemicals detected at a site, the frequency and concentration of detected chemicals, the toxicity of the chemicals and how people can be exposed, and for how long. Routes of exposure to people are generally through ingestion, such as eating, contact with the skin, or inhalation. The most significant potential routes of exposure are trough ingestion and contact with the skin. Based on the standard risk assessment guidelines established for use nationwide by U.S. EPA, exposures for an on-site resident are generally assumed to e daily contact over a 30-year period starting with children ages 0-6, and continuing from 6-30 years.

Rotary kiln. An incinerator with a rotating combustion chamber. The rotation helps mix the wastes and promotes more complete burning. They can accept gases, liquids, sludges, tars and solids, either separately or together, in bulk or in containers.

Run-off. Precipitation that the ground does not absorb and that ultimately reaches rivers, lakes or oceans.

S

Sagebrush Rebellion. A movement started by ranchers and miners during the late 1970s in response to efforts of the Bureau of Land Management (B.L.M.) to improve management of federal lands. While its announced goal was to give the lands "back" to the western states, its real goal—and the one it achieved—was to force the B.L.M. to abandon its new approach to public land management.

Salvage logging. The logging of dead or diseased trees in order to improve overall forest health; used by timber companies as a rationalization to log otherwise protected areas.

Sanitary landfill. A landfill which does not take hazardous waste, often called a "garbage dump." It must be covered with dirt each day to maintain sanitary conditions. The Integrated Waste Management Board regulates these facilities.

SARA Title III. Or the Emergency Planning and Community Right-to-Know Act of 1986. It requires each state to have an emergency response plan as described, and any company that produces, uses or stores more than certain amounts of listed chemicals must meet emergency planning requirements, including release reporting.

Scrubber: a pollution control technology utilized in power plants to remove pollutants from plant emissions

Secondary containment. A structure designed to capture spills or leaks, as from a container or tank. For containers and aboveground tanks, it is usually a bermed area of coated concrete. For underground tanks, it may be a second, outer, wall or a vault. Construction of such containment must meet certain requirements, and periodic inspections are required.

Second-growth forests. Forests that have grown back after being logged.

Sediment. The soil, sand and minerals at the bottom of surface waters, such as streams, lakes and rivers. Sediments capture or adsorb contaminants. The term may also refer to solids that settle out of any liquid.

Seismic stability. The likelihood that soils will stay in place during an earthquake.

Selenium. This metal is a nutritionally essential trace element that is toxic at higher doses. High levels of selenium have been shown to cause reproductive failure and birth defects in birds.

Semi-volatile organic compounds. Compounds that evaporate slowly at normal temperatures.

Short: a market position in which a party records (or anticipates recording) emissions in excess of its yearly emissions allocation, thus it has a deficit of allowances

Short-term Forward: purchase or sale of a specific quantity of allowances at the current or spot price, with delivery and settlement at a specified future date, usually within one year

Sick building syndrome. A human health condition where infections linger, caused by exposure to contaminants within a building as a result of poor ventilation.

Silos. Fixed vertical underground structures made of steel and concrete that house an ICBM and its launch support equipment.

Silver. Silver is a metal used in the manufacture of photographic plates, cutlery and jewelry. Silver nitrate is used in an array of industrial chemical processes. It is toxic.

Silvex. A chlorinated herbicide.

Sinkhole. A depression formed when the surface collapses into a cavern.

Site mitigation process. The regulatory and technical process by which hazardous waste sites are identified and investigated, and cleanup alternatives are developed, analyzed, decided upon and applied.

Slurry wall. Barriers used to contain the flow of contaminated groundwater or subsurface liquids. Slurry walls are constructed by digging a trench around a contaminated area and filling the trench with a material that tends not to allow water to pass through it. The groundwater or contaminated

liquids trapped within the area surrounded by the slurry wall can be extracted and treated.

Smog. A dense, discolored radiation fog containing large quantities of soot, ash, and gaseous pollutants such as sulfur dioxide and carbon dioxide, responsible for human respiratory ailments. Originally meaning a combination of smoke and fog, smog now generally refers to air pollution; ground level ozone is a major constituent of smog. Most industrialized nations have implemented legislation to promote the use of smokeless fuel and reduce emission of toxic gases into the atmosphere.

SO_2 Allowance Auction: provided for in the Clean Air Act, the SO_2 auction is held annually by the US EPA; the auctions help to send the market an allowance price signal, as well as furnish utilities with an additional avenue for purchasing needed allowances

Soil borings. Soil samples taken by drilling a hole in the ground.

Soil gas survey. Soil gas or (soil vapor) is air existing in void spaces in the soil between the groundwater and the ground surface. These gases may include vapor of hazardous chemicals as well as air and water vapor. A soil-gas survey involves collecting and analyzing soil-gas samples to determine the presence of chemicals and to help map the spread of contaminants within soil.

Soil vapor extraction. A process in which chemical vapors are extracted from the soil by applying a vacuum to wells.

Solar energy. Energy derived from sunlight.

Solid waste. Non-liquid, non gaseous category of waste from non-toxic household and commercial sources.

Solid waste management units (SWMUs). Any unit at a hazardous waste facility from which hazardous chemicals might migrate, whether or not they were intended for waste management. They include such things as containers, tanks, landfills among others.

Solidification. Mixing additives, such as fly ash or cement, with soil containing hazardous chemicals, especially metals, to make it more stable. This process lessens the risk of exposure to the hazardous chemicals by making it less likely that those chemicals will move into and through surface or groundwater.

Soluble Threshold Limit Concentration (STLC). The limit concentration for toxic materials in a sample that has been subjected to the California Waste Extraction Test (WET), a state test for the toxicity characteristic that is designed to subject a waste sample to simulated conditions of a municipal waste landfill. If the concentration of a toxic substance in the special extract of the waste exceeds this value, the waste is classified as hazardous in California. This is distinct from the Total Threshold Limit Concentration (TTLC). The California Waste Extraction Test procedure is more stringent than the federal Toxicity Characteristic Leaching Procedure (TCLP).

Solvent. A liquid capable of dissolving another substance to form a solution. Water is sometimes called "the universal solvent" because it dissolves so many things, although often to only a very small extent. Organic solvents are used in paints, varnishes, lacquers, industrial cleaners and printing inks, for example. The use of such solvents in coatings and cleaners has declined over the last several years, because the most common ones are toxic, contribute to air pollution and may be fire hazards.

Soot. A fine, sticky powder, comprised mostly of carbon, formed by the burning of fossil fuels.

Speaker. The leader of the House of Representatives, who controls debate and the order of discussion; chosen by vote of the majority party.

Special Allowance Reserve: roughly 2.8 percent dangerous anthropogenic interference with the of the cap set aside each year to supply the climate system; established a framework for annual allowance auction agreeing to specific actions

Spotted owl. Reclusive bird, found in the American West, requiring old-growth forest habitat to survive.

South Coast Air Quality Management District (SCAQMD): the air pollution control agency for the four-county region including Los Angeles and Orange counties and parts of Riverside and San Bernardino counties

Sprawl. The area taken up by a large or expanding development or city.

Stabilization. Changing active organic matter in sludge into inert, harmless material. The term also refers to physical activities such as compacting and capping at sites that limits the further spread of contamination without actual reduction of toxicity.

State action level (SAL). The maximum concentration of a contaminant in drinking water that The California Department of Health Services considers to be safe to drink. Drinking Water Action Levels (ALs) are health-based advisory levels established by the Department of Health Services (DHS) for

chemicals for which primary maximum contaminant levels (MCLs) have not been adopted. There are currently 36 ALs. ALs are usually expressed in parts per billion (ppb) or parts per million (ppm). Drinking water with concentrations of impurities greater than the state action level must be treated to reduce or remove the impurities.

State Implementation Plan (SIP). Mandate for achieving health-based air quality standards. The plan that each state must develop and have approved by the US EPA which indicates how the state will comply with the requirements in the Clean Air Vintage Year: represents the first year in which Act; each State's SIP is amended as they address the allowance can be used for compliance specific or new requirements such as the NO_x reductions required in the NO_x SIP.

State land. Land owned and administered by the state in which it is located.

State parks. Parks and recreation areas owned and administered by the state in which they are located.

Static stability. The likelihood that soils at rest will remain at rest.

Still bottoms. Residues left over from the process of recovering spent solvents in a distillation unit.

Stockpile. Nuclear weapons and components under custody of the U.S. Department of Defense.

Straddling stocks. Fish populations that straddle a boundary between domestic and international waters.

Strangle: sale or purchase of a put option and a call option on the same underlying instrument, with the same expiration, but at strike prices X equally out of the money.

Stratosphere. The upper portion of the atmosphere (approximately 11 km to 50 km above the surface of the Earth).

Strike Price (or Exercise Price): price at which Y the allowance underlying a call or put option can be purchased (call) or sold (put) over the specified period. Z

Strip mining. Mining technique in which the land and vegetation covering the mineral being sought are stripped away by huge machines, usually damaging the land severely and limiting subsequent uses.

Submarine Launched Ballistic Missile (SLBM). A ballistic missile carried by and launched from a submarine.

Subsidence. Sinking or settling of soils so that the surface is disrupted, creating a shallow hole.

Suggested No Adverse Response Level (SNARL). Drinking water standards established by the U.S. EPA, but not enforceable by law. SNARLs suggest the level of a containment in drinking water at which adverse health effects would not be anticipated (with a margin of safety).

Sulfur dioxide (SO₂). A heavy, smelly gas which can be condensed into a clear liquid; used to make sulfuric acid, bleaching agents, preservatives and refrigerants; a major source of air pollution in industrial areas. A gaseous pollutant which is primarily released into the atmosphere when as a by-product of fossil fuel combustion; the largest sources of SO₂ tend to be power plants that burn coal and oil to make electricity

Sump. A pit or tank that catches liquid runoff for drainage or disposal.

Super Efficient Refrigerator Program (SERP). An organization of 24 U.S. utilities that developed a $30 million competition to produce a refrigerator at least 25% lower in energy use and 85% lower in ozone depletion than projected 1994 models. The winning product, produced by Whirlpool, cut energy use by 40% in 1995.

Superfund Comprehensive Environmental Response, Compensation and Liability Act of 1980 (CERCLA).

Supply-side: a term referring to the generation (or supply) of power by a utility

Surge tanks. A tank used to absorb irregularities in flow of liquids, including liquid waste materials, so that the flow out of the tank is constant.

Sustainable communities. Communities capable of maintaining their present levels of growth without damaging effects.

Swap: an exchange of one allowance for another to exchange the vintage years of the allowances held in accounts Surface water. Water located above ground (e.g., rivers, lakes).

T

Table. In the legislative sense, an action taken to halt debate on a bill.

Tailings or Mine Tailings. Crushed waste rock deposited on the ground during mining and ore processing, including some of the rock in which the ore is found. Unless they are handled carefully, they frequently release contaminants. As they age under the effects of air, rainfall and bacteria, some oxidize to produce new toxic materials, such as sulfuric acid, that can leach out and poison streams, rivers and lakes.

Tap water. Drinking water monitored (and often filtered) for protection against contamination and available for public consumption from sources within the home.

Tax shift. Replacing one kind of taxes with another, without changing the total amount of money collected. For example, replacing a portion of income taxes with carbon tax or other pollution taxes.

Telecommuting. Working with others via telecommunications technologies (e.g., telephones, modems, faxes) without physically travelling to an office.

Tetrachloroethylene (TCE). Volatile organic compound that is commonly used as an industrial degreasing solvent. TCE affects the central nervous system and is listed as a cancer-causing chemical under Proposition 65.

Tetrachlorophenol (TCP). Tetrachlorophenol is a toxic fungicide.

Thermonuclear. The application of high heat, obtained via a fission explosion, to bring about fusion of light nuclei.

Threatened species. Species of flora or fauna likely to become endangered within the foreseeable future.

Three Gorges. A project along the Yangtze river in China to build the largest hydroelectric dam in the world.

Threshold Limit Value (TLV). Public health exposure level set by the National Institute for Occupational Safety and Health for worker safety. It is the level above which a worker should not be exposed for the course of an eight-hour day, due to possible adverse health effects.

Timber. Logged wood sold as a commodity.

Time Weighting: an investment strategy in which allowance purchases and sales are transacted over an extended period of time and in small increments, thereby eliminating risk associated with highs and lows in the market

TNT Equivalent. A measure of the energy released in the detonation of a nuclear weapon, expressed in terms of the quantity of TNT which would release the same amount of energy.

Toluene. A toxic volatile organic compound often used as an industrial solvent.

Tongass. A national forest in southeast Alaska comprising one of the United States' last remaining temperate rainforests.

Total Threshold Limit Concentration (TTLC). A test for the toxicity characteristic: If the total concentration of a toxic substance in a waste is greater than this value, the waste is classified as hazardous in California. This is distinct from the Soluble Threshold

Limit Concentration, or STLC, which is concerned with only the soluble concentration.

Toxaphene. A chlorinated pesticide insecticide that was widely used to control pests on cotton and other crops until 1982, when it was banned for most uses. (In 1990, banned for all uses.) It was also used to kill unwanted fish in lakes. It is toxic to fresh-water and marine aquatic life and is listed as a cancer-causing chemical under Proposition 65.

Toxic. Poisonous.

Toxic emissions. Poisonous chemicals discharged to air, water, or land.

Toxic sites. Land contaminated with toxic pollution, usually unsuitable for human habitation.

Toxicity. Ability to harm human health or environment, such as injury, death or cancer. One of the criteria that is used to determine whether a waste is a hazardous waste (the "Toxicity Characteristic").

Toxicity Characteristic Leaching Procedure (TCLP). A federal test for the Toxicity Characteristic (TC). If the concentration of a toxic substance in a special extract of a waste exceeds the TC value, the waste is classified as hazardous in the United States (a "RCRA waste"). The extraction procedure is different from that of the California Waste Extraction Test (WET).

Toxic Substances Control Act (TSCA). A federal law of 1976 to regulate chemical substances or mixtures that may present an unreasonable risk of injury to health or the environment.

Toxic waste. Garbage or waste that can injure, poison, or harm living things, and is sometimes life-threatening.

Toxification. Poisoning.

Traffic calming. Designing streets to reduce automobile speed and to enhance walking and bicycling.

Trader: anyone who buys or sells allowances with the intention of making a profit

Transit. See public transportation.

Transportation. Any means of conveying goods and people.

Transportation planning. Systems to improve the efficiency of the transportation system in order to enhance human access to goods and services.

Trash. Waste material that cannot be recycled and reused (synonymous with garbage).

Trawls. Nets with a wide mouth tapering to a small, pointed end, usually called the "cod end."

Trawls are towed behind a vessel at any depth in the water column.

Trial burn. A test of incinerators or boilers and industrial furnaces in which emissions are monitored for the presence of specific substances, such as organic compounds, particulates, metals and hydrogen chloride (all specified by agency permits).

Trichloroethane. 1,1,1-TCA, or methylchloroform is used as a cleaning agent for metals and plastics. It is toxic.

Trichloroethylene (TCE). A volatile organic compound that is often used an industrial degreasing solvent. It is toxic and is listed as a cancer-causing chemical under Proposition 65.

Trip reduction. Reducing the total numbers of vehicle trips, by sharing rides or consolidating trips with diverse goals into fewer trips.

Tritium. A radioactive form of hydrogen with a half-life of 12 years. It emits beta particles. It is used to mark chemical compounds so that the structure or chemical activity can be determined. Also used in nuclear weapons research and construction. Small amounts of tritium occur naturally, and some exists as a by-product of previous nuclear testing and nuclear reactor operations.

Trolling. A method of fishing using several lines, each hooked and baited, which are slowly dragged behind the vessel.

Turtle excluder device (TED). A gear modification used on shrimp trawls that enables incidentally caught sea turtles to escape from the nets.

U

Unit Accounts: accounts in the SO_2 or NO_x ATSs which hold allowances initially allocated to those sources required to participate in either the acid rain or OTC NO_x programs; EPA adjusts these accounts for compliance each year

United Nations Framework Convention on Climate Change(UNFCC): a treaty signed in 1992 by 165 countries and ratified by 160 countries (including the U.S.); took effect in March 1994; set a target of stabilizing greenhouse gas concentrations in the atmosphere to a level that would prevent further increase of global climate warming.

Unsaturated zone. Underground soil and gravel that could contain groundwater, but lies above the aquifer. This is in contrast to a saturated zone, where the space between soil particles is filled with water.

Up-gradient. The direction from which water flows in an aquifer. In particular, areas that are higher than contaminated areas and, therefore, are not prone to contamination by the movement of polluted groundwater.

Urban planning. The science of managing and directing city growth.

Uranium (U). A heavy, radioactive metal (atomic number 92) used in the explosion of nuclear weapons (especially one isotope, U-235).

Urban parks. Parks in cities and areas of high population concentration.

Utilities. Companies (usually power distributors) permitted by a government agency to provide important public services (such as energy or water) to a region; as utilities are provided with a local monopoly, their prices are regulated by the permitting government agency.

V

Vanadium. A toxic metal that is both mined and is a by-product of petroleum refining. Compounds of vanadium are used in the steel industry, as a catalyst in the chemical industry, in photography and in insecticides.

Veto. A Presidential action rejecting a bill as passed by the U.S. Congress. The President can also effect a "pocket veto" by holding an unsigned bill past the signing period.

Video logging. A method for close-up inspection of the interior of a well or pipe by means of a color camera that can view the well casing and screen at 90 degrees to the well's axis.

Vinyl chloride. Vinyl chloride is widely used in the plastics industry in creating polyvinyl chloride (PVC). It is listed as a cancer-causing agent under Proposition 65.

Virgin forest. A forest never logged.

Viscosity. A measure of the ease with which a liquid can be poured or stirred. The higher the viscosity, the less easily a liquid pours.

Voice vote. A vote where members vote by saying either "yes" or "no" together; individual member's votes are not placed on record.

Void space. The space in a tank between the top of a tank and the liquid level. If the tank is used to store combustible liquids that easily evaporate, this space can fill with vapors which may reach explosive levels.

Volatile. Describes substances that readily evaporate at normal temperatures and pressures.

Volatile organic compounds (VOCs). Organic liquids, including many common solvents, which readily evaporate at temperatures normally found at ground surface and at shallow depths. They take

part in atmospheric photochemical (sun-driven) reactions to produce smog.

Volatilization rate. The rate at which a chemical changes from a liquid to gas. It is also known as "air flux."

W

Warhead. The part of a missile which contains the nuclear explosive.

Waste. Garbage, trash.

Waste feed. The flow of wastes into an incinerator, boiler or industrial furnace. The waste feed can vary from continuous to intermittent (batch) flows.

Waste site. Waste dumping ground.

Waste stream. Overall waste disposal cycle for a given population.

Waterborne contaminants. Unhealthy chemicals, micro-organisms (like bacteria) or radiation, found in tap water.

Water filters. Substances (such as charcoal) or fine membrane structures used to remove impurities from water.

Water quality. The level of purity of water; the safety or purity of drinking water.

Water quality testing. Monitoring water for various contaminants to make sure it is safe for fish protection, drinking, and swimming.

Watershed. A region or area over which water flows into a particular lake, reservoir, stream, or river.

Water table. In a shallow aquifer, a water table is the depth at which free water is first encountered in a monitoring well.

Well. A dug or drilled hole used to get water from the earth.

Wetland. An area that is regularly saturated by surface or groundwater and, under normal circumstances, capable of supporting vegetation typically adapted for life in saturated soil conditions; they are critical to sustaining many species of fish and wildlife, including native and migratory birds. They include swamps, marshes, and bogs, and may be either coastal or inland. Coastal wetlands are brackish (have a certain mixture of salt).

Wilderness area. A wild area that Congress has preserved by including it in the National Wilderness Preservation System.

Wildlife. Animals living in the wilderness without human intervention.

Wildlife refuges. Land set aside to protect certain species of fish or wildlife (administered at the federal level in the U.S. by the Fish and Wildlife Service).

Windpower. Power or energy derived from the wind

(via windmills, sails, etc.).

Wise use movement. A loosely-affiliated network of people and organizations throughout the U.S. in favor of widespread privatization and opposed to environmental regulation, often funded by corporate dollars.

Woods Hole. A town on Cape Cod where several important ocean research institutes are located.

Work plan. The site work plan describes the technical activities to be conducted during the various phases of a remediation project.

X

x—the horizontal axis in a plot or a chart

x—8-12 GHz frequency band

X-ray; a form of electromagnetic radiation with a wavelength in the range of 0.01 to 10 nanometers, and energies in the range 0.1 to 100 keV, which is shorter than the wavelength of UV radiation but longer than that of gamma rays.

Xylene. An aromatic hydrocarbon used in gasoline, paints, lacquers, pesticides, gums, resins and adhesives. It is toxic and flammable.

x-y tracking; frames with PV cells or modules tracking the sun in the x and y directions all day long

Y

y—often used to denote year (i.e., 100 kWh/y means 100 kWh generated yearly)

y—the vertical axis in a plot or a chart

y—yard

Z

Zoning. The arrangement or partitioning of land areas for various types of usage in cities, boroughs or townships.

Zinc. A metal used for auto parts, for galvanizing, and in production of brasses and dry cell batteries. It is nutritionally essential but toxic at higher levels.

Often Used Environmental Terms

acid mine drainage
acid rain
air pollution
air quality
algal bloom
anoxic waters
arsenic poisoning
asbestos poisoning
asthma
bioaccumulation
biomagnification
birth defects
blast fishing
bottom trawling
burial problems
bycatch
cadmium poisoning
carbon monoxide
carbon oxide
chlorofluorocarbons, CFC
clear-cutting
climate change
coal mining
conservation

consumer capitalism
consumerism
conventional energy sources
coral bleaching
coral reefs extinction
cyanide fishing
dam impacts
DDT
deforestation
desertification
dioxin
earth quakes
efficient energy use
electromagnetic fields
electromagnetic radiation
endangered species
endocrine disruptors
energy conservation
environmental degradation
environmental effects of meat production
environmental health dependency
eonoculture
eutrophication

e-waste
exploitation of natural resources
fish kill
floods
forest fires
forest depletion
fossil fuels
fracking soil pollution
genetic engineering
genetic pollution
genetically modified crops
genetically-modified foods
ghost nets
global dimming
global warming
Great Pacific Garbage Patch
greenhouse gasses
habitat destruction
habitat modification
habitat fragmentation
heat pollution
herbicides
holocene extinction
hurricanes

Illegal fishing
Illegal logging
indoor air quality
intensive farming
invasive species
irrigation-water pollution
island flooding
land degradation
land misuse
land pollution
landfill
leach rate
lead poisoning
light pollution
littering
logging
marine debris
marine pollution
medical waste
mercury in fish
mining
mountaintop removal mining
nanopollution
nanotechnology
nanotoxicology
natural gas fracking
nitrogen oxides
noise pollution
nonpoint source pollution
nuclear fallout
nuclear issues
nuclear meltdown
nuclear power
nuclear waste
obesity
ocean acidification
ocean level increase

ocean warming
ocean deoxygenation
ocean dumping
ocean pollution
oil drilling
oil spills
organic chemicals
organic pollution
over irrigation
over-consumption
overdrafting
overfishing
overgrazing
overpopulation
overpopulation in companion animals
ozone depletion
particulate matter
PCB
pesticide drift
pesticides
planned obsolescence
plasticides
plasticulture
poaching
point source pollution
pollinator decline
pouching
radiation
radioactive waste
rain water pollution
recycling, incineration
renewable energy
renewable energy commercialization.
resource depletion
rise in sea level
shark finning

ship pollution
shutdown of thermohaline circulation
sick building syndrome
slash and burn
slurry impoundments
smog
soil conservation
soil contamination
soil erosion
soil salination
species extinction
sulphur oxide
thermal pollution
tornadoes
tsunamis
toxic heavy metals
toxic waste
toxins
tragedy of the commons
tropospheric ozone
unreported and unregulated fishing
urban runoff
urban sprawl
visual pollution
volatile organic compounds, VOC
waste
waste disposal incidents
wastewater contamination
water crisis
water depletion
water level increase
water pollution
water table pollution
water warming
whaling
wind-mill damage to the land

Index